VIRTUAL BIOLOGY LABOROATORY 3.0

FROM LAB MATERIALS TO PRINT AND AUDIO TO[illegible] RESOURCES THAT HELP YOU SUCCEED

This online tool includes 14 modules with 130 activities that give you virtual experience gathering data and performing experiments through engaging simulations. Change parameters to see what happens in each simulation, generate your own data, and write up results. Each experiment includes a general introduction followed by a series of interactive laboratory activities, each with its own set of questions. With an easy-to-use design and unparalleled flexibility, **Virtual Biology Laboratory 3.0** will make you feel like you're in a real lab!

The following experimental modules are available for purchase at academic.cengage.com/biology:

Choose from the following lab modules:

- Biochemistry
- Cell Chemistry
- Cell Division
- Cell Membranes
- Cell Respiration
- Cell Structure
- Ecology
- Evolution
- Genetics
- Microscopy
- Molecular Biology
- Pedigree Analysis
- Photosynthesis
- Population Biology

ALSO AVAILABLE

Study Guide
This interactive workbook pairs text-specific concepts with questions, illustrations, and exercises that promote active learning, as well as topic maps, study strategies, and case studies to help you study more efficiently.

Just What You Need to Know and Do NOW!

CengageNOW is an online teaching and learning resource that provides you more control in less time and delivers better student outcomes—NOW!

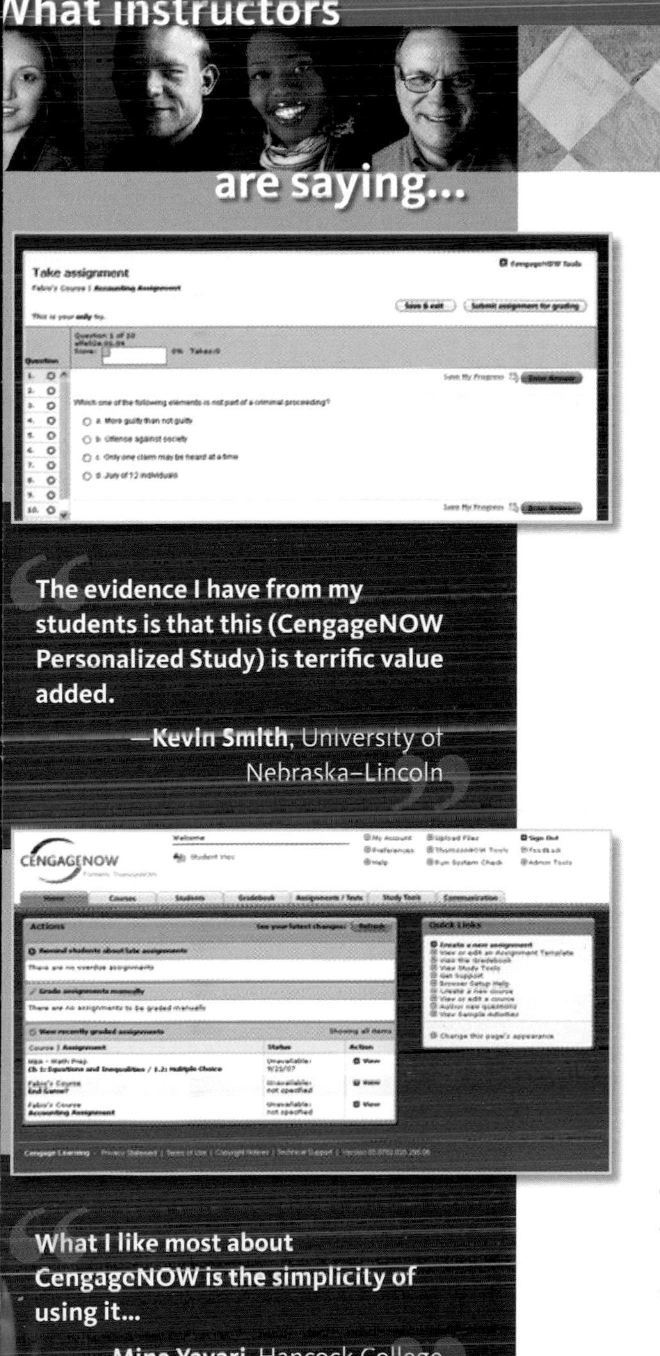

CENGAGENOW IS AN ONLINE TEACHING AND LEARNING RESOURCE.

CengageNOW offers all of your teaching and learning resources in one intuitive program organized around the essential activities you perform for class - lecturing, creating assignments, grading, quizzing, and tracking student progress and performance. CengageNOW's intuitive "tabbed" design allows you to navigate to all key functions with a single click and a unique homepage tell you just what needs to be done and when. CengageNOW, in most cases, provides students access to an integrated eBook, interactive tutorials, videos, animations, games, and other multimedia tools to help them get the most out of your course.

CENGAGENOW PROVIDES MORE CONTROL IN LESS TIME

CengageNOW's flexible assignment and grade book options provides you more control while saving you valuable time in planning and managing your course assignments. With CengageNOW, you can automatically grade all assignments, weigh grades, choose points or percentages and set the number of attempts and due dates per problem to best suit your overall course plan.

CENGAGENOW DELIVERS BETTER STUDENT OUTCOMES

CengageNOW Personalized Study; a diagnostic tool (featuring a chapter specific Pre-test, Study Plan, and Post-test) empowers students to master concepts, prepare for exams, and be more involved in class. It's easy to assign and if you want, results will automatically post to your grade book. Results to Personalize Study provide immediate and ongoing feedback regarding what students are mastering and why they're not - to both you and the student. In most cases, Personalized Study links to an integrated eBook so students can easily review topics.

academic.cengage.com/now

CengageNOW MAKES IT EASIER TO DO WHAT YOU ALREADY DO.

Designed by instructors for instructors, CengageNOW mirrors your natural workflow and provides time-saving, performance-enhancing tools for you and your students—all in one program!

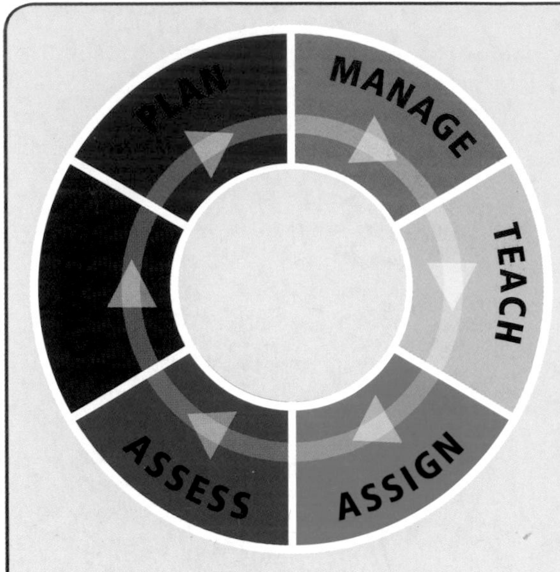

YOU CAN USE **CENGAGENOW** TO...

- **Plan** your curriculum;
- **Manage** your course and communicate with students;
- **Teach** with more freedom;
- **Assign** practice or homework to reinforce key concepts;
- **Assess** student performance outcomes;
- **Grade** with efficiency and control to get the results you want.

STUDENTS CAN USE **CENGAGENOW** TO...

- **Manage** their time;
- **Prepare** for class;
- **Practice & Reinforce** key concepts learned in class;
- **Study** for exams more effectively;
- **Get the Grade** they want.

The flexibility of CengageNOW allows you to use a single aspect of the program, or for maximum power and effectiveness, to use all of the teaching and learning resources to create and customize your own material to match your course objectives.

CENGAGENOW SEAMLESSLY INTEGRATES WITH POPULAR COURSE MANAGEMENT PROGRAMS

eCollege™

CengageNOW on Blackboard, WebCT, and eCollege provides students with seamless single sign-on access to CengageNOW through the school's course management system (CMS). After entering a simple access code just once at the beginning of the term, students get seamless access to both their CMS and CengageNOW textbook specific assignments and activities, with results flowing to your Blackboard, WebCT, or eCollege gradebook. Rich content, seamless integration with CengageNOW functionality, and only one gradebook to manage.

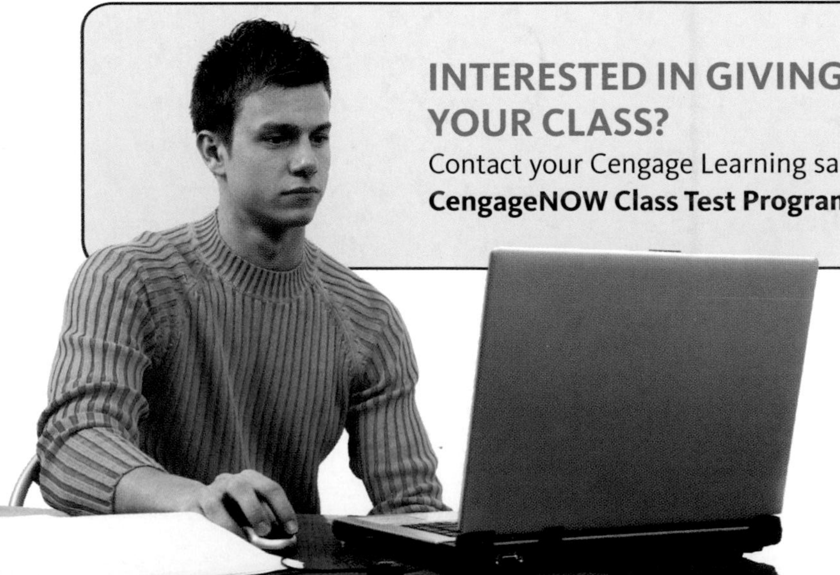

INTERESTED IN GIVING **CENGAGENOW** A TEST DRIVE IN YOUR CLASS?

Contact your Cengage Learning sales representative for more information about the **CengageNOW Class Test Program**.

academic.cengage.com/now

BIOLOGY

Exploring the Diversity of Life

First Canadian Edition

Peter J. Russell

Stephen L. Wolfe

Paul E. Hertz

Cecie Starr

M. Brock Fenton
University of Western Ontario

Heather Addy
University of Calgary

Denis Maxwell
University of Western Ontario

Tom Haffie
University of Western Ontario

Ken Davey
York University (Emeritus)

NELSON EDUCATION

Biology: Exploring the Diversity of Life, First Canadian Edition

by Peter J. Russell, Stephen L. Wolfe, Paul E. Hertz, Cecie Starr, M. Brock Fenton, Heather Addy, Denis Maxwell, Tom Haffie, Ken Davey

Vice President, Editorial Director:
Evelyn Veitch

Editor-in-Chief, Higher Education:
Anne Williams

Executive Editor:
Paul Fam

Senior Marketing Manager:
Sean Chamberland

Managing Editor, Development:
Alwynn Pinard

Photo Researcher:
Indu Arora

Permissions Coordinator:
Indu Arora

Content Production Manager:
Christine Gilbert

Production Service:
PrePress PMG

Copy Editor:
Holly Dickinson

Proofreader:
Martha Ghent

Indexer:
Cindy Coan

Production Coordinator:
Ferial Suleman

Design Director:
Ken Phipps

Managing Designer:
Franca Amore

Interior Design:
Dianna Little

Cover Design:
Johanna Liburd, Cover Concept;
Jennifer Leung, Cover Design

Cover Image:
Main image (bat): Photo courtesy of M. Brock Fenton

Background image (DNA double helix): Grant Faint/Stone/Getty Images

Compositor:
PrePress PMG

Printer:
Courier

Printed and bound in the United States of America
2 3 4 5 12 11 10 09

For more information contact Nelson Education Ltd., 1120-Birchmount Road, Toronto, Ontario, M1K 5G4. Or you can visit our Internet site at http://www.nelson.com

Library and Archives Canada Cataloguing in Publication

Biology : exploring the diversity of life / Peter J. Russell ... [et al.]. — 1st Canadian ed.

Includes index.

ISBN 978-0-17-644094-7

1. Biology—Textbooks. I. Russell, Peter J.

QH308.2.B57 2009 570
C2008-907353-3

ISBN-13: 978-0-17-644094-7
ISBN-10: 0-17-644094-1

About the Cover: A flying little brown bat frozen in mid-wing stroke moves through the blackness of an underground passage. Echolocation allows the bat to collect information about its surroundings or to locate flying insects. In the background is the elegantly sinuous double helix of DNA, a widely recognized vernacular icon for life itself. The blurred DNA connotes the generative activity inherent in the molecule that carries the genetic code of all life into the future.

For, and because of, our generations of students.

About the Canadian Authors

M.B. (Brock) Fenton received his Ph.D. from the University of Toronto in 1969. Since then, he has been a faculty member in biology at Carleton University, then at York University, and then at The University of Western Ontario. In addition to teaching parts of first-year biology, he has also taught vertebrate biology, animal biology, and conservation biology, as well as field courses in the biology and behaviour of bats. He has received awards for his teaching (Carleton University Faculty of Science Teaching Award, Ontario Confederation of University Faculty Associations Teaching Award, and a 3M Teaching Fellowship, Society for Teaching and Learning in Higher Education) in addition to recognition of his work on public awareness of science (Gordin Kaplan Award from the Canadian Federation of Biological Societies; Honourary Life Membership, Science North, Sudbury, Ontario; Canadian Council of University Biology Chairs Distinguished Canadian Biologist Award; The McNeil Medal for the Public Awareness of Science of the Royal Society of Canada; and the Sir Sanford Fleming Medal for public awareness of Science, the Royal Canadian Institute). He also received the C. Hart Merriam Award from the American Society of Mammalogists for excellence in scientific research. Bats and their biology, behaviour, evolution, and echolocation are the topic of his research, which has been funded by the Natural Sciences and Engineering Research Council of Canada (NSERC).

Heather Addy is a graduate of the University of Alberta and received her Ph.D. in plant–soil relationships from the University of Guelph in 1995. During this training and in a subsequent postdoctoral fellowship focusing on mycorrhizas and other plant–fungus symbioses at the University of Alberta, she discovered a love of teaching. In 1998, she joined the Department of Biological Sciences at the University of Calgary in a faculty position that places emphasis on teaching and teaching-related scholarship. In addition to teaching introductory biology classes and an upper-level mycology class, she has led the development of investigative labs for introductory biology courses and the introduction of peer-assisted learning groups in large biology and chemistry classes. She received the Faculty of Science Award for Excellence in Teaching in 2005 and an Honourable Mention for the Student's Union Teaching Excellence Award in 2008.

Denis Maxwell received his Ph.D. from the University of Western Ontario in 1995. His thesis under the supervision of Norm Hüner focused on the role of the redox state of photosynthetic electron transport in photoacclimation in green algae. Following his doctorate, he was awarded an NSERC postdoctoral fellowship. He undertook postdoctoral training at the Department of Energy Plant Research Laboratory at Michigan State University, where he studied the function of the mitochondrial alternative oxidase. After taking up a faculty position at the University of New Brunswick in 2000, he moved in 2003 to the Department of Biology at The University of Western Ontario. His research program, which is supported by NSERC, is focused on understanding the role of the mitochondrion in intracellular stress sensing and signalling. In addition to research, he is passionate about teaching biology and science to first-year university students.

Tom Haffie is a graduate of the University of Guelph and the University of Saskatchewan in the area of microbial genetics. Currently the learning development coordinator for the Faculty of Science at the University of Western Ontario, Tom has devoted his 20-year career to teaching large biology classes in lecture, laboratory, and tutorial settings. He led the development of the innovative core laboratory course in the biology program, was an early adopter of computer animation in lectures and, most recently, has coordinated the implementation of personal response technology across campus. He holds a UWO Pleva Award for Excellence in Teaching, a UWO Fellowship in Teaching Innovation, a Province of Ontario Award for Leadership in Faculty Teaching (LIFT), and a national 3M Fellowship for Excellence in Teaching.

Ken Davey is a graduate of the University of Western Ontario and received his Ph.D. from Cambridge University. He is an emeritus professor of biology at York University and has by preference taught elementary courses in zoology at McGill and York and more advanced courses in invertebrate physiology, parasitology, and endocrinology. He has held a number of academic administrative positions at York. His research interests include invertebrate physiology and the endocrinology of insects and parasitic worms, supported by NSERC. Ken has accumulated a number of academic awards, including the Canadian Council of University Biology Chairs Distinguished Canadian Biologist Award and the Wigglesworth Award for Service to Entomology of the Royal Entomological Society. He is a Fellow of the Royal Society of Canada and an Officer of the Order of Canada.

About the U.S. Authors

Peter J. Russell received a B.Sc. in Biology from the University of Sussex, England, in 1968 and a Ph.D. in Genetics from Cornell University in 1972. He has been a member of the Biology faculty of Reed College since 1972; he is currently a Professor of Biology. He teaches a section of the introductory biology course, a genetics course, an advanced molecular genetics course, and a research literature course on molecular virology. In 1987 he received the Burlington Northern Faculty Achievement Award from Reed College in recognition of his excellence in teaching. Since 1986, he has been the author of a successful genetics textbook; current editions are *iGenetics: A Mendelian Approach*, *iGenetics: A Molecular Approach*, and *Essential iGenetics*. He wrote nine of the BioCoach Activities for The Biology Place. Peter Russell's research is in the area of molecular genetics, with a specific interest in characterizing the role of host genes in pathogenic RNA plant virus gene expression; yeast is used as the model host. His research has been funded by agencies including the National Institutes of Health, the National Science Foundation, and the American Cancer Society. He has published his research results in a variety of journals, including *Genetics, Journal of Bacteriology, Molecular and General Genetics, Nucleic Acids Research, Plasmid,* and *Molecular and Cellular Biology*. He has a long history of encouraging faculty research involving undergraduates, including cofounding the biology division of the Council on Undergraduate Research (CUR) in 1985. He was Principal Investigator/Program Director of an NSF Award for the Integration of Research and Education (AIRE) to Reed College, 1998–2002.

Stephen L. Wolfe received his Ph.D. from Johns Hopkins University and taught general biology and cell biology for many years at the University of California, Davis. He has a remarkable list of successful textbooks, including multiple editions of *Biology of the Cell, Biology: The Foundations, Cell Ultrastructure, Molecular and Cellular Biology*, and *Introduction to Cell and Molecular Biology*.

Paul E. Hertz was born and raised in New York City. He received a bachelor's degree in Biology at Stanford University in 1972, a master's degree in Biology at Harvard University in 1973, and a doctorate in Biology at Harvard University in 1977. While completing field research for the doctorate, he served on the Biology faculty of the University of Puerto Rico at Rio Piedras. After spending 2 years as an Isaac Walton Killam Postdoctoral Fellow at Dalhousie University, Hertz accepted a teaching position at Barnard College, where he has taught since 1979. He was named Ann Whitney Olin Professor of Biology in 2000, and he received The Barnard Award for Excellence in Teaching in 2007. In addition to his service on numerous college committees, Professor Hertz was Chair of Barnard's Biology Department for 8 years. He has also been the Program Director of the Hughes Science Pipeline Project at Barnard, an undergraduate curriculum and research program funded by the Howard Hughes Medical Institute, since its inception in 1992. The Pipleline Project includes the Intercollegiate Partnership, a program for local community college students that facilitates their transfer to 4-year colleges and universities. He teaches one semester of the introductory sequence for Biology majors and preprofessional students as well as lecture and laboratory courses in vertebrate zoology and ecology. Professor Hertz is an animal physiological ecologist with a specific research interest in the thermal biology of lizards. He has conducted fieldwork in the West Indies since the mid-1970s, most recently focusing on the lizards of Cuba. His work has been funded by the National Science Foundation, and he has published his research in such prestigious journals as *The American Naturalist, Ecology, Nature,* and *Oecologia*.

Cecie Starr is the author of best-selling biology textbooks. Her books include multiple editions of *Unity and Diversity of Life, Biology: Concepts and Applications,* and *Biology Today and Tomorrow*. Her original dream was to be an architect. She may not be building houses, but with the same care and attention to detail, she builds incredible books: *"I invite students into a chapter through an intriguing story. Once inside, they get the great windows that biologists construct on the world of life. Biology is not just another house. It is a conceptual mansion. I hope to do it justice."*

Beverly McMillan has been a science writer for more than 20 years and is coauthor of a college text in human biology, now in its seventh edition. She has worked extensively in educational and commercial publishing, including 8 years in editorial management positions in the college divisions of Random House and McGraw-Hill. In a multifaceted freelance career, Bev also has written or coauthored six trade books and numerous magazine and newspaper articles, as well as story panels for exhibitions at the Science Museum of Virginia and the San Francisco Exploratorium. She has worked as a radio producer and speechwriter for the University of California system and as a media relations advisor for the College of William and Mary. She holds undergraduate and graduate degrees from the University of California, Berkeley.

Preface

Welcome to an exploration of the diversity of life. The main goal of this text is to guide you on a journey of discovery about life's diversity across levels ranging from molecules to genes, cells to organs, and species to ecosystems. Along the way, we will explore many questions about the mechanisms underlying diversity as well as the consequences of diversity for our own species and for others.

At first glance, the riot of life that animates the biosphere overwhelms the minds of many who try to understand it. One way to begin to make sense of this diversity is to divide it into manageable sections on the basis of differences. In this book, we highlight the divisions between plants and animals, prokaryotes and eukaryotes, protostomes and deuterostomes, but we also consider features found in all life forms. We examine how different organisms solve the common problems of finding nutrients, energy, and mates on the third rock from our Sun. What basic evolutionary principles inform the relationships among life forms regardless of their different body plans, habitats, or life histories? Unlike many other first-year biology texts, this book has chapters integrating basic concepts such as genetic recombination, the effects of light, nutrition, and domestication across the breadth of life from microbes to mistletoe to moose. As you read this book, you will be referred frequently to other chapters for linked information that expands the ideas further.

Evolution provides a powerful conceptual lens for viewing and understanding the roots and history of diversity. We will demonstrate how knowledge of evolution helps us appreciate the changes we observe in organisms. Whether the focus is the conversion of free-living prokaryotes into mitochondria and chloroplasts or the steps involved in the domestication of rice, selection for particular traits over time can explain the current condition.

We hope that Canadian students will find the subject of biology as it is presented here accessible and engaging because it is presented in familiar contexts. We have highlighted the work of Canadian scientists, used examples of Canadian species, and referred to Canadian regulations and institutions, as well as discoveries made by Canadians.

Although many textbooks use the first few chapters to introduce and/or review background information, we have used the first chapters to convey the excitement and interest of biology itself. Within the centre of the book, we have placed important background information about biology and chemistry in the reference section entitled *The Chemical and Physical Foundations of Biology*. These pages are distinct and easy to find with their purple edges and have become affectionately known as the "Purple Pages." These pages enable information to be readily identifiable and accessible to students as they move through the textbook rather than information that is tied to a particular chapter. The purple background makes the pages easy to find when you need to check a topic. This section keeps background information out of the mainstream of the text, allowing you to focus on bigger pictures.

The Organization of Matter

Any substance in the universe that has mass and occupies space is defined as **matter.** The basic scientific concepts that explain how matter is organized in biological systems are no different from those for nonliving forms of matter. Living organisms are built from the same chemistry building blocks as nonliving systems and abide by the same laws of chemistry. Because of this, a basic understanding of these chemistry principles is important for our understanding of how biological systems operate.

Elements and Compounds

All matter in the universe—anything that occupies space and has mass—is composed of elements. An element is a pure substance that cannot be broken down into simpler substances by ordinary chemical or physical techniques. Ninety-two different elements occur naturally on Earth, and more than 15 artificial elements have been synthesized in the laboratory.

Living organisms are composed of about 25 elements, with only 4—carbon, hydrogen, oxygen, and nitrogen—accounting for more than 96% of the weight of living organisms. Seven other elements—calcium, phosphorus, potassium, sulphur, sodium, chlorine, and magnesium—contribute most of the remaining 4%. Nine additional elements occur in organisms in quantities so small (<0.01%) that they are known as trace elements. The proportions by mass of different elements differ markedly in seawater, the human body, a fruit, and Earth's crust.

Molecules whose component atoms are different (such as carbon dioxide) are called compounds. The chemical and physical properties of compounds are typically distinct from those of their atoms or elements. For example, we all know that water is a liquid at room temperature. We also know that water does not burn. However, the properties of the individual elements of water—hydrogen and oxygen—are quite different. Hydrogen and oxygen are gases at room temperature, and both are highly reactive.

Atoms combined chemically in fixed numbers and ratios form the molecules of living and nonliving matter. For example, the oxygen we breathe is a molecule formed from the chemical combination of two oxygen atoms; a molecule of the carbon dioxide that we exhale contains one carbon atom and two oxygen atoms. Because carbon dioxide is a molecule consisting of different elements, it is referred to as a compound.

Percentage Composition

Seawater	
Oxygen	88.3
Hydrogen	11.0
Chlorine	1.9
Sodium	1.1
Magnesium	0.1
Sulphur	0.09
Potassium	0.04
Calcium	0.04
Carbon	0.003
Silicon	0.0029
Nitrogen	0.0015
Strontium	0.0008

Human	
Oxygen	65.0
Carbon	18.5
Hydrogen	9.5
Nitrogen	3.3
Calcium	2.0
Phosphorus	1.1
Potassium	0.35
Sulphur	0.25
Sodium	0.15
Chlorine	0.15
Magnesium	0.05
Iron	0.004
Iodine	0.0004

Pumpkin	
Oxygen	85.0
Hydrogen	10.7
Carbon	3.3
Potassium	0.34
Nitrogen	0.16
Phosphorus	0.05
Calcium	0.02
Magnesium	0.01
Iron	0.008
Sodium	0.001
Zinc	0.0002
Copper	0.0001

Earth's crust	
Oxygen	46.6
Silicon	27.7
Aluminum	8.1
Iron	5.0
Calcium	3.6
Sodium	2.8
Potassium	2.6
Magnesium	2.1
Other elements	1.5

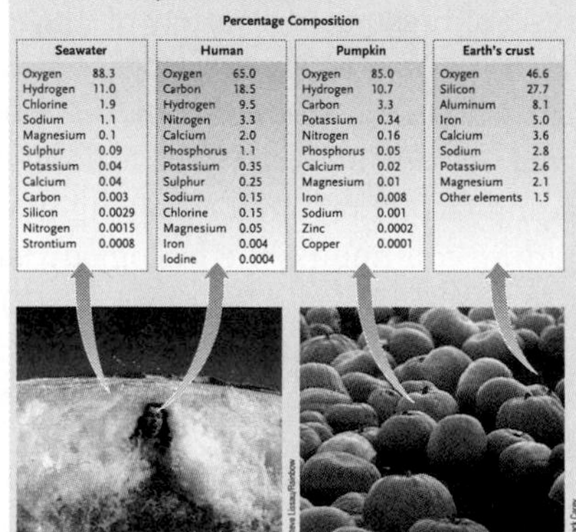

In addition to presenting material about biology, this book also makes a point of highlighting particular people, important molecules, interesting contexts, and examples of life in extreme conditions. Science that appears in textbooks is the product of people who have made careful and systematic observations, which led them to formulate hypotheses about these observations and, where appropriate, design and execute experiments to test these hypotheses. We illustrate this in each chapter with boxed stories about how particular people have used their ingenuity and creativity to expand our knowledge of biology. We have endeavoured to show not just the science itself but also the process behind the science.

Although biology is not simply chemistry, specific chemicals and their interactions can have dramatic effects on biological systems. From water to progesterone, amanitin, and DDT, each chapter features the activity of a relevant chemical.

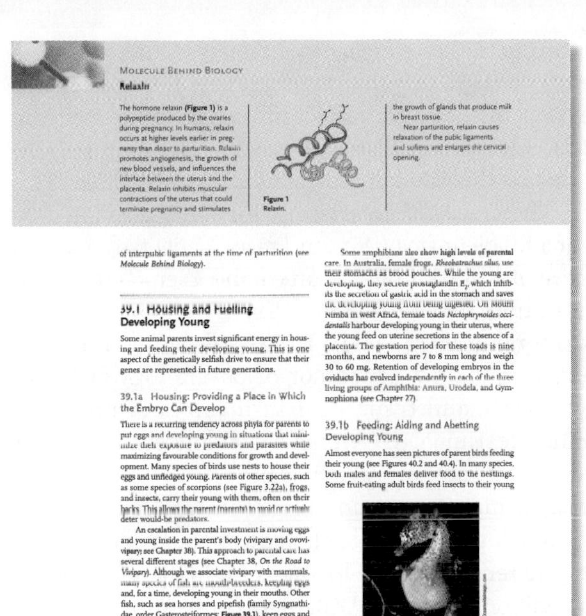
MOLECULE BEHIND BIOLOGY

Relaxin

The hormone relaxin **(Figure 1)** is a polypeptide produced by the ovaries during pregnancy. In humans, relaxin occurs at higher levels earlier in pregnancy than closer to parturition. Relaxin promotes angiogenesis, the growth of new blood vessels, and influences the interface between the uterus and the placenta. Relaxin inhibits muscular contractions of the uterus that could terminate pregnancy and stimulates the growth of glands that produce milk in breast tissue.

Near parturition, relaxin causes relaxation of the pubic ligaments and softens and enlarges the cervical opening.

Figure 1
Relaxin.

of interpubic ligaments at the time of parturition (see *Molecule Behind Biology*).

39.1 Housing and Fuelling Developing Young

Some animal parents invest significant energy in housing and feeding their developing young. This is one aspect of the genetically selfish drive to ensure that their genes are represented in future generations.

39.1a Housing: Providing a Place in Which the Embryo Can Develop

There is a recurring tendency across phyla for parents to put eggs and developing young in situations that minimize their exposure to predators and parasites while maximizing favourable conditions for growth and development. Many species of birds use nests to house their eggs and unfledged young. Parents of other species, such as some species of scorpions (see Figure 3.22a), frogs, and insects, carry their young with them, often on their backs. This allows the parent (parents) to avoid or actively deter would-be predators.

An escalation in parental investment is moving eggs and young inside the parent's body (vivipary and ovovivipary; see Chapter 38). This approach to parental care has several different stages (see Chapter 38, *On the Road to Vivipary*). Although we associate vivipary with mammals, many species of fish are mouthbreeders, keeping eggs and, for a time, developing young in their mouths. Other fish, such as sea horses and pipefish (family Syngnathidae, order Gasterosteiformes; **Figure 39.1**), keep eggs and developing young in specialized incubation areas, called brood pouches, located on the tail or trunk of the male. "Pregnancy" in male sea horses represents an increase in parental investment. It also allows males to be confident about the paternity of the young they raise.

Some amphibians also show **high levels of parental care**. In Australia, female frogs, *Rheobatrachus silus*, use their stomachs as brood pouches. While the young are developing, they secrete prostaglandin E_2, which inhibits the secretion of gastric acid in the stomach and saves the developing young from being digested. On Mount Nimba in west Africa, female toads *Nectophrynoides occidentalis* harbour developing young in their uterus, where the young feed on uterine secretions in the absence of a placenta. The gestation period for these toads is nine months, and newborns are 7 to 8 mm long and weigh 30 to 60 mg. Retention of developing embryos in the oviducts has evolved independently in each of the three living groups of Amphibia: Anura, Urodela, and Gymnophiona (see Chapter 27).

39.1b Feeding: Aiding and Abetting Developing Young

Almost everyone has seen pictures of parent birds feeding their young (see Figures 40.2 and 40.4). In many species, both males and females deliver food to the nestlings. Some fruit-eating adult birds feed insects to their young

Figure 39.1
A male sea horse gives birth.

To help frame the material with an engaging context, we begin each chapter with a section called "Why It Matters." In addition, several chapters include boxed accounts of organisms thriving "on the edge" at unusual temperatures, pressures, radiation dosages, salt concentrations, etc. These brief articles explain how our understanding of "normal" can be increased through study of the "extreme."

Examining how biological systems work is another theme pervading this text and underlying the idea of diversity. We have intentionally tried to include examples that will tax your imagination, from sea slugs that steal chloroplasts for use as solar panels, to hummingbirds fuelling their hovering flight, to adaptive radiation of viruses. In each situation, we examine how biologists have explored and assessed the inner workings of organisms from gene regulation to the challenges of digesting cellulose.

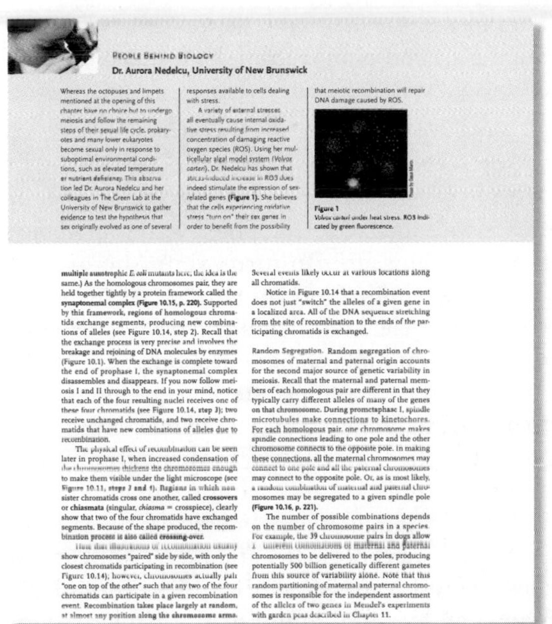
PEOPLE BEHIND BIOLOGY

Dr. Aurora Nedelcu, University of New Brunswick

Whereas the octopuses and limpets mentioned at the opening of this chapter have no choice but to undergo meiosis and follow the remaining steps of their sexual life cycle, prokaryotes and many lower eukaryotes become sexual only in response to suboptimal environmental conditions, such as elevated temperature or nutrient deficiency. This observation led Dr. Aurora Nedelcu and her colleagues in The Green Lab at the University of New Brunswick to gather evidence to test the hypothesis that sex originally evolved as one of several responses available to cells dealing with stress.

A variety of external stresses all eventually cause internal oxidative stress resulting from increased concentration of damaging reactive oxygen species (ROS). Using her multicellular algal model system (*Volvox carteri*), Dr. Nedelcu has shown that stress-induced increase in ROS does indeed stimulate the expression of sex-related genes **(Figure 1)**. She believes that the cells experiencing oxidative stress "turn on" their sex genes in order to benefit from the possibility that meiotic recombination will repair DNA damage caused by ROS.

Figure 1
Volvox carteri under heat stress. ROS indicated by green fluorescence.

multiple auxotrophic *E. coli* mutants here, the idea is the same.) As the homologous chromosomes pair, they are held together tightly by a protein framework called the **synaptonemal complex (Figure 10.15, p. 220)**. Supported by this framework, regions of homologous chromatids exchange segments, producing new combinations of alleles (see Figure 10.14, step 2). Recall that the exchange process is very precise and involves the breakage and rejoining of DNA molecules by enzymes (Figure 10.1). When the exchange is complete toward the end of prophase I, the synaptonemal complex disassembles and disappears. If you now follow meiosis I and II through to the end in your mind, notice that each of the four resulting nuclei receives one of these four chromatids (see Figure 10.14, step 3); two receive unchanged chromatids, and two receive chromatids that have new combinations of alleles due to recombination.

The physical effect of recombination can be seen later in prophase I, when increased condensation of the chromosomes thickens the chromosomes enough to make them visible under the light microscope (see Figure 10.11, steps 3 and 4). Regions in which nonsister chromatids cross one another, called **crossovers** or **chiasmata** (singular, *chiasma* = crosspiece), clearly show that two of the four chromatids have exchanged segments. Because of the shape produced, the recombination process is also called **crossing-over**.

Note that illustrations of recombination usually show chromosomes "paired" side by side, with only the closest chromatids participating in recombination (see Figure 10.14); however, chromosomes actually pair "one on top of the other" such that any two of the four chromatids can participate in a given recombination event. Recombination takes place largely at random, at almost any position along the chromosome arms. Several events likely occur at various locations along all chromatids.

Notice in Figure 10.14 that a recombination event does not just "switch" the alleles of a given gene in a localized area. All of the DNA sequence stretching from the site of recombination to the ends of the participating chromatids is exchanged.

Random Segregation. Random segregation of chromosomes of maternal and paternal origin accounts for the second major source of genetic variability in meiosis. Recall that the maternal and paternal members of each homologous pair are different in that they typically carry different alleles of many of the genes on that chromosome. During prometaphase I, spindle microtubules make connections to kinetochores. For each homologous pair, one chromosome makes spindle connections leading to one pole and the other chromosome connects to the opposite pole. In making these connections, all the maternal chromosomes may connect to one pole and all the paternal chromosomes may connect to the opposite pole. Or, as is most likely, a random combination of maternal and paternal chromosomes may be segregated to a given spindle pole **(Figure 10.16, p. 221)**.

The number of possible combinations depends on the number of chromosome pairs in a species. For example, the 39 chromosome pairs in dogs allow [illegible] different combinations of maternal and paternal chromosomes to be delivered to the poles, producing potentially 500 billion genetically different gametes from this source of variability alone. Note that this random partitioning of maternal and paternal chromosomes is responsible for the independent assortment of the alleles of two genes in Mendel's experiments with garden peas described in Chapter 11.

Solving problems is another theme that runs through the book. Whether the topic is gene therapy to treat a disease in people, increasing crop production, or conserving endangered species, both the problem and the solution lie in biology. We will explore large problems facing planet Earth and the social implications that arise from them.

Science is by its nature a progressive enterprise in which answers to questions open new questions for consideration. Each chapter presents unanswered questions as well as questions for discussion to emphasize that biologists still have a lot to learn—topics for you to tackle should you decide to pursue a career in research.

"Study Breaks" occur after each section in the chapters. They contain questions written by students to identify some of the important features of the section. The answers are embedded in the "Review" section at the end of each chapter. Also included at the end of each chapter is a group of multiple-choice self-test questions, the answers to which can be found at the end of the book. "Questions for Discussion" at the end of each chapter challenge you to think more broadly about biology. You are encouraged to use these in discussions with other students and to explore potential answers by using the resources of the electronic library.

To maximize the chances of producing a useful text that draws in students (and instructors), we sought the advice of colleagues who teach biology (members of the Editorial Advisory Board). We also asked students (members of the Student Advisory Boards) for their advice and comments. Both groups read draft chapters and provided valuable feedback, but any mistakes are ours. The members of the Student Advisory Boards also wrote the Study Break questions found throughout the text.

We hope that you are as captivated by the biological world as we are and are drawn from one chapter to another. But don't stop there—use electronic resources to broaden your search for understanding.

LIFE ON THE EDGE

Rate of Evolutionary Change

How quickly can evolution occur? The role of the fossil record in our knowledge and understanding of evolution can leave the impression that evolution occurs over millions of years, or at least millions of generations. But this is not always true.

In 1971, five adult pairs of Italian wall lizards (*Podarcis sicula*) were introduced to Pod Kopište a 0.09 km² islet in the South Adriatic, and five other pairs to the nearby Pod Mrčaru (0.03 km²). In 1971, another lacertid lizard, *Podarcis melisellensis*, occurred on Pod Mrčaru, but they had vanished by 2007. In 2007, densities of *P. sicula* on Pod Mrčaru were significantly greater than those on Pod Kopište. Female Italian wall lizards may lay several clutches of eggs in one season, translating into a short generation time and high values of R, the intrinsic rate of population increase (see Chapter 45).

In 36 years, *P. sicula* established viable populations on both islets. In 2007, the *P. sicula* on both islets were genetically indistinguishable from the mainland source population. However, their populations had changed in morphology. Specifically, introduced lizards differed both from source populations and from one another in head morphology, bite strength, and digestive tracts. On Pod Mrčaru, *P. sicula* have longer, wider, and taller heads than those on Pod Kopište, corresponding with a difference in diet. *P. sicula* on Pod Mrčaru ate more plant material than those on Pod Kopište.

The changes in morphology and performance of *P. sicula* after introduction to the islets are similar to those documented among other species and families of lizards. Italian wall lizards on small islands demonstrate adaptability, a foundation for evolution. Italian wall lizards have also been introduced to Long Island, New York, where they have thrived. The situation reminds us how introduced species may adapt to and thrive in new settings. However, we will see how such introductions can pose significant problems for conservation (see Chapter 48). Adapting to life on the edge can be a recipe for success.

But some F_1 hybrids are healthy, vigorous, and fully fertile and can breed with other hybrids and with both parental species. Sometimes the F_2 generation, produced by matings between F_1 hybrids, or between F_1 hybrids and either parental species, may exhibit reduced survival or fertility, a phenomenon known as **hybrid breakdown**. Experimental crosses between fruit fly (*Drosophila*) species may produce functional interspecific hybrids, but their offspring experience a high rate of chromosomal abnormalities and harmful types of **genetic recombination**. Thus, reproductive isolation is maintained between the species because there is little long-term mixing of their gene pools.

STUDY BREAK

1. What is a reproductive isolating mechanism? Distinguish between two major types of reproductive isolating mechanisms.
2. Define five types of prezygotic isolating mechanisms that can prevent interspecific mating.
3. Prezygotic isolating mechanisms prevent gene pools of two species from mixing, so why do postzygotic isolating mechanisms exist? Distinguish between three types of postzygotic isolating mechanisms.

18.8 Geography of Speciation

Geography has a huge impact on whether gene pools have the opportunity to mix. Biologists define three modes of speciation based on the geographic relationship of populations as they become reproductively isolated: allopatric speciation (*allo* = different; *patria* = homeland), parapatric speciation (*para* = beside), and sympatric speciation (*sym* = together).

18.8a Allopatric Speciation: New Species Develop from Isolated Populations

Allopatric speciation can occur when a physical barrier subdivides a large population or when a small population becomes separated from a species' main geographic distribution. Allopatric speciation, probably the most common mode of speciation in large animals, occurs in two stages. First, two populations become *geographically* separated, preventing gene flow between them. Then, as the populations experience distinct mutations as well as different patterns of natural selection and genetic drift, they may accumulate genetic differences that isolate them *reproductively*.

Geographic separation sometimes occurs when a barrier divides a large population into two or more

Supplementary Materials

An extensive array of supplemental materials is available to accompany this text. These supplements are designed to make teaching and learning more effective. For more information on any of these resources, please contact your local Nelson Education sales representative or call Nelson Education Limited Customer Support at 1-800-268-2222.

Instructor Resources

These resources are available to qualified adopters. Please consult your local Nelson Education sales representative for details.

Instructor's Resource DVD

The *Instructor's Resource DVD* contains the following resources:

Instructor's Resource Manual

The *Instructor's Resource Manual* for this First Canadian Edition has been dramatically revised by Tanya Noel, Tamara Kelly, and Julie Clark from York University to include tips on teaching using cases as well as suggestions on how to present material and use technology and other resources effectively, integrating the other supplements available to both students and instructors. This manual doesn't simply reinvent what's currently in the text; it helps the instructor make the material relevant and engaging to students.

ExamView® Computerized Test Bank

Create, deliver, and customize tests (both print and online) in minutes with this easy-to-use assessment and tutorial system. ExamView® offers both a Quick Test Wizard and an Online Test Wizard that guide you step-by-step through the process of creating tests, while its "what you see is what you get" capability allows you to see the test you are creating on the screen exactly as it will print or display online. You can build tests of up to 250 questions using up to 12 question types. Using *ExamView's* complete word-processing capabilities, you can enter an unlimited number of new questions or edit existing questions.

Nelson Education Testing Advantage

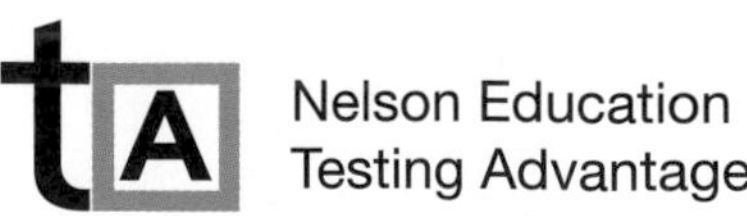

In most postsecondary courses, a large percentage of student assessment is based on multiple-choice testing. Many instructors use multiple-choice testing reluctantly, believing that it is a methodology best used for testing what a student ***remembers*** rather than what she or he has ***learned.***

Nelson Education Ltd. understands that a good-quality multiple-choice test bank can provide the means to measure ***higher level thinking*** skills as well as recall. Recognizing the importance of multiple-choice testing in today's classroom, we have created the Nelson Education Testing Advantage program (NETA) to ensure the value of our high-quality test banks.

The *Test Bank* to accompany *Biology*, adapted by Ivona Mladenovic of Simon Fraser University and Ian Dawe of Selkirk College, offers the Premium Nelson Education Testing Advantage. NETA was created in partnership with David DiBattista, a 3M National Teaching Fellow, professor of psychology at Brock University, and researcher in the area of multiple-choice testing. NETA ensures that subject-matter experts who author test banks have had training in two areas: avoiding common errors in test construction and developing multiple-choice test questions that "get beyond remembering" to assess higher level thinking. In addition, Professor DiBattista confirms the subject-matter expert's understanding of and adherence to the NETA principles through a review.

All Premium NETA test banks include David DiBattista's guide for instructors, "Multiple Choice Tests: Getting Beyond Remembering." This guide has been designed to assist you in using Nelson test banks to achieve your desired outcomes in your course.

Customers who adopt a Premium Nelson Education Testing Advantage title may also qualify for additional faculty training opportunities in multiple-choice testing and assessment. Please contact your local Nelson Education sales and editorial representative for more details about our Premium NETA.

Microsoft PowerPoint® Slides This one-stop lecture tool makes it easy to assemble, edit, publish, and present custom lectures. Adapted by Jane Young of the University of Northern British Columbia, this resource brings together text-specific lecture outlines, art, video, and animations, culminating in a powerful, personalized, PowerPoint® presentation.

Also included on the *Instructor's Resource DVD* are Word files of the *Test Bank*, as well as a full *Image Bank* of the art and photos from the text book. ISBN: 978-0-17-647529-1.

JoinIn™ on TurningPoint®

Transform your lecture into an interactive student experience with JoinIn™. Combined with your choice of keypad systems, JoinIn turns your Microsoft® PowerPoint® application into audience response software. With a click on a handheld device, students can respond to multiple-choice questions, short polls, interactive exercises, and peer-review questions. You can also take attendance, check student comprehension of concepts, collect student demographics to better assess student needs, and even administer quizzes. In addition, there are interactive text-specific slide sets that you can modify and merge with any of your own PowerPoint® lecture slides. These have been adapted by Jane Young of the University of

Northern British Columbia and contain poll slides and pre- and post-test slides for each chapter in the text. This tool is available to qualified adopters at **http://www.turningtechnologies.com/**.

Student Resources

Study Guide

The ***Study Guide*** for the First Canadian Edition has been adapted by Colin Montpetit of the University of Ottawa, Julie Smit of the University of Windsor, and Wendy J. Keenleyside of the University of Guelph. The ***Study Guide*** contains unique case studies to integrate the concepts within the text, study strategies, interactive exercises, self-test questions, and more. ISBN: 978-0-17-647474-4.

CengageNOW™ CENGAGENOW™

CengageNOW *Personalized Study* is a diagnostic tool (featuring a chapter-specific Pretest, Study Plan, and Post-test) that empowers students to master concepts, prepare for exams, and be more involved in class. Results to *Personalized Study* provide immediate and ongoing feedback regarding what students are mastering and why they're not to both the instructor and the student. *CengageNOW Personalized Study* links to an integrated eBook so that students can easily review topics and also contains animations, links to websites, videos, and more as part of their Study Plan. *CengageNOW* has been adapted by Dora Cavallo-Medved, University of Windsor; Todd Nickle, Mount Royal College; and Edward Andrews, Sir Wilfred Grenfell College. Each copy of the First Canadian Edition of *Biology* contains a two semester single-sign-on access card to ***CengageNOW***.

CengageNOW with Premium eBook

Want to take your biology experience to the next level? Our *Premium eBook* allows students access to an integrated, interactive learning environment with advanced learning tools and a user interface that gives students control over their learning experience. *CengageNOW Personalized Study* is included with the Premium eBook for the ultimate online study experience.

Students and Instructors

Visit the website to accompany *Biology: Exploring the Diversity of Life*, First Canadian Edition, at **http://biologyedl.nelson.com**. This website contains quizzes, flashcards, weblinks, and more.

Prospering in Biology

Using This Book

The following are things you will need to know in order to use this text and prosper in Biology.

Names

What's in a name? People are very attached to names—their own names, the names of other people, the names of flowers and food and cars, and so on. It is not surprising that biologists would also be concerned about names. Take, for example, our use of scientific names. Scientific names are always italicized and Latinized.

Castor canadensis Kuhl is the scientific name of the Canadian beaver. *Castor* is the genus name; canadensis is the specific epithet. Together they make up the name of the species, which was first described by a person called Kuhl. "Beaver" by itself is not enough because there is a European beaver, *Castor fiber*, and an extinct giant beaver, *Castoides ohioensis*. Furthermore, common names can vary from place to place (*Myotis lucifugus* is sometimes known as the "little brown bat" or the "little brown myotis").

Biologists prefer scientific names because the name (Latinized) tells you about the organism. There are strict rules about the derivation and use of scientific names. Common names are not so restricted, so they are not precise. For example, in *Myotis lucifugus*, *Myotis* means mouse-eared and *lucifugus* means flees the light; hence, this species is a mouse-eared bat that flees the light.

Birds can be an exception. There are accepted "standard" common names for birds. The American robin is *Turdus migratorius*. The common names for birds are usually capitalized because of the standardization. However, the common names of mammals are not capitalized, except for geographic names or patronyms (*geographic* = named after a country; *patronym* = named after someone; e.g., Canadian beaver or Ord's kangaroo rat, respectively).

Although a few plants that have very broad distributions may have accepted standard common names (e.g., white spruce, *Picea glauca*), most plants have many common names. Furthermore, the same common name is often used for more than one species. Several species in the genus *Taraxacum* are referred to as "dandelion." It is important to use the scientific names of plants to be sure that it is clear exactly which plant we mean. The scientific names of plants also tell us something about the plant. The scientific name for the weed quack grass, *Elymus repens*, tells us that this is a type of wild rye (*Elymus*) and that this particular species spreads or creeps (*repens* = creeping). Anyone who has tried to eliminate this plant from their garden or yard knows how it creeps! Unlike for animals, plant-naming rules forbid the use of the same word for both genus and species names for a plant; thus, although *Bison bison* is an acceptable scientific name for buffalo, such a name would never be accepted for a plant.

In this book, we present the scientific names of organisms when we mention them. We follow standard abbreviations; for example, although the full name of an organism is used the first time it is mentioned (e.g., *Castor canadensis*), subsequent references to that same organism abbreviate the genus name and provide the full species name (e.g., *C. canadensis*).

In some areas of biology, the standard representation is of the genus, for example, *Chlamydomonas*. In other cases, names are so commonly used that only the abbreviation may be used (e.g., *E. coli* for *Escherichia coli*).

Units

The units of measure used by biologists are standardized (metric or SI) units, used throughout the world in science.

Definitions

The science of biology is replete with specialized terms (sometimes referred to as "jargon") used to communicate specific information. It follows that, as with scientific names, specialized terms increase the precision with which biologists communicate among themselves and with others. Be cautious about the use of terms because jargon can be a veneer of precision. When we encounter a "slippery" term (such as species or gene), we explain why one definition for all situations is not feasible.

Time

In this book, we use C.E. (Common Era) to refer to the years since year 1 and B.C.E. (Before the Common Era) to refer to years before that.

Geologists think of time over very long periods. A geologic time scale (**see Table 1.1 on page xii**) shows that the age of Earth could be measured in years, but it's challenging to think of billions of years expressed in days (or hours, etc.). With the advent of using the decay rates of radioisotopes to measure the age of rocks, geologists adopted 1950 as the baseline, the "Present," and the past is referred to as B.P. ("Before Present"). A notation of 30 000 years B.P. (^{14}C) indicates 30 000 years before 1950 using the ^{14}C method of dating.

Other dating systems are also used. Some archaeologists use PPNA (PrePottery Neolithic A, where A is the horizon or stratum). In deposits along the Euphrates River, 11 000 PPNA appears to be the same as 11 000 B.P. In this book, we use B.C.E. or B.P. as the time units, except when referring to events or species from more than 100 000 years ago. For those dates, we refer you to the geologic time scale (see Table 1.1 on page xii).

Sources

Where does the information presented in a text or in class come from? What is the difference between what you read in a textbook or an encyclopedia and the material you see in a newspaper or tabloid? When the topic relates to science, the information should be based on material that has been published in a scholarly journal. In this context, "scholarly" refers to the process of review. Scholars submit their manuscripts reporting their research findings to the editor (or editorial board) of a journal. The editor, in turn, sends the manuscript out for comment and review by recognized authorities in the field. The process is designed to ensure that what is published is as accurate and appropriate as possible. The review process sets the scholarly journal apart from the tabloid.

There are literally thousands of scholarly journals, which, together, publish millions of articles each year. Some journals are more influential than others, for example, *Science* and *Nature*. These two journals are published weekly and invariably contain new information of interest to biologists.

To collect information for this text, we have drawn on published works that have gone through the process of scholarly review. Specific references (citations) are provided, usually in the electronic resources designed to complement the book.

A citation is intended to make the information accessible. Although there are many different formats for citations, the important elements include (in some order) the name(s) of the author(s), the date of publication, the title, and the publisher. When the source is published in a scholarly journal, the journal name, its volume number, and the pages are also provided. With the citation information, you can visit a library and locate the original source. This is true for both electronic (virtual) and real libraries.

Students of biology benefit by making it a habit to look at the most recent issues of their favourite scholarly journals and use them to keep abreast of new developments.

M. Brock Fenton
Heather Addy
Denis Maxwell
Tom Haffie
Ken Davey

London, Calgary and Toronto
February 2009

Table 1.1 The Geological Time Scale and Major Evolutionary Events

Eons (Duration drawn to scale)	Eon	Era	Period	Epoch	Millions of Years Ago	Major Evolutionary Events
Phanerozoic: Cenozoic	Phanerozoic	Cenozoic	Quaternary	Holocene	0.01	
Phanerozoic: Mesozoic				Pleistocene	1.7	Origin of humans; major glaciations
Phanerozoic: Paleozoic			Tertiary	Pliocene	5.2	Origin of ape-like human ancestors
Proterozoic				Miocene	23	Angiosperms and mammals further diversify and dominate terrestrial habitats
				Oligocene	33.4	Divergence of primates; origin of apes
				Eocene	55	Angiosperms and insects diversify; modern orders of mammals differentiate
				Paleocene	65	Grasslands and deciduous woodlands spread; modern birds and mammals diversify; continents approach current positions
		Mesozoic	Cretaceous		144	Many lineages diversify: angiosperms, insects, marine invertebrates, fishes, dinosaurs; asteroid impact causes mass extinction at end of period, eliminating dinosaurs and many other groups
			Jurassic		206	Gymnosperms abundant in terrestrial habitats; first angiosperms; modern fishes diversify; dinosaurs diversify and dominate terrestrial habitats; frogs, salamanders, lizards, and birds appear; continents continue to separate
			Triassic		251	Predatory fishes and reptiles dominate oceans; gymnosperms dominate terrestrial habitats; radiation of dinosaurs; origin of mammals; Pangaea starts to break up; mass extinction at end of period

Archaean	Phanerozoic (continued)	Paleozoic	Permian		Insects, amphibians, and reptiles abundant and diverse in swamp forests; some reptiles colonize oceans; fishes colonize freshwater habitats; continents coalesce into Pangaea, causing glaciation and decline in sea level; mass extinction at end of period eliminates 85% of species
				290	
			Carboniferous		Vascular plants form large swamp forests; first seed plants and flying insects; amphibians diversify; first reptiles appear
				354	
			Devonian		Terrestrial vascular plants diversify; fungi and invertebrates colonize land; first insects appear; first amphibians colonize land; major glaciation at end of period causes mass extinction, mostly of marine life
				417	
			Silurian		Jawless fishes diversify; first jawed fishes; first vascular plants on land
				443	
			Ordovician		Major radiations of marine invertebrates and fishes; major glaciation at end of period causes mass extinction of marine life
				490	
			Cambrian		Diverse radiation of modern animal phyla (Cambrian explosion); simple marine communities
				543	
	Proterozoic				High concentration of oxygen in atmosphere; origin of aerobic metabolism; origin of eukaryotic cells; evolution and diversification of protists, fungi, soft-bodied animals
				2500	
	Archaean				Evolution of prokaryotes, including anaerobic bacteria and photosynthetic bacteria; oxygen starts to accumulate in atmosphere
				3800	
					Formation of Earth at start of era; Earth's crust, atmosphere, and oceans form; origin of life at end of era
				4600	

Acknowledgements

We thank the many people who have worked with us on the production of this text, particularly Paul Fam, Executive Editor, whose foresight brought the idea to us and whose persistence saw the project through. Thanks go to those who reviewed the U.S. text to provide us with feedback for the Canadian edition including Logan Donaldson, York University; Robert Holmberg, Athabasca University; and Thomas H. MacRae, Dalhousie University. We also are grateful to the members of the Editorial Advisory Board and the Student Advisory Board, who provided us with valuable feedback and alternate perspectives (special acknowledgements to these individuals are listed below). We also thank Richard Walker at the University of Calgary, who began this journey with us but who was unable to continue. We thank Carl Lowenberger for contributing Chapter 44 (on defences). We are especially grateful to Alwynn Pinard, Managing Developmental Editor, and James Polley, who kept us moving through the chapters at an efficient pace, along with Tracy Duff, Project Manager, and Christine Gilbert, Content Production Manager. We thank Rosemary Tanner, who provided a thoughtful substantive edit of the entire manuscript, Holly Dickinson for her careful copy editing, and Sandra Peters, who did a cold read as a further check on our presentation. Finally, we thank Sean Chamberland, Senior Marketing Manager, for making us look good.

Brock Fenton would like to thank Allan Noon, who offered much advice about taking pictures; Laura Barclay, Jeremy McNeil, Tony Percival-Smith, C.S. (Rufus) Churcher, and David and Meg Cumming for the use of their images; and Karen Campbell for providing a critical read on the domestication chapter.

It is never easy to be in the family of an academic scientist. We are especially grateful to our families for their sustained support over the course of our careers, particularly during those times when our attentions were fully captivated by bacteria, algae, fungi, parasites, or bats. Saying "yes" to a textbook project means saying "no" to a variety of other pursuits. We appreciate the patience and understanding of those closest to us that enabled the temporary reallocation of considerable time from other endeavours and relationships.

Many of our colleagues have contributed to our development as teachers and scholars by acting as mentors, collaborators, and, on occasion, "worthy opponents." Like all teachers, we owe particular gratitude to our students. They have gathered with us around the discipline of biology, sharing their potent blend of enthusiasm and curiosity that leaves us energized and optimistic for the future.

Editorial and Student Advisory Boards

We were very fortunate to have the assistance of some extraordinary students and instructors of biology across Canada who provided us with feedback that helped shape this textbook into what you see before you. As such, we would like to say a very special thank you to the following people:

Editorial Advisory Board

Mark Brigham, University of Regina
Dion Durnford, University of New Brunswick
Wendy Keenleyside, University of Guelph
Marty Leonard, Dalhousie University
Cindy Paszkowski, University of Alberta
Carol Pollock, University of British Columbia
Kevin Scott, University of Manitoba
Paula Wilson, York University

Student Advisory Boards

University of Western Ontario (pictured above)

Rachael Danielson
Dalal Dharouj
Yvonne Dzal
Liam McGuire
Aimee McMillan
Errin Pfeiffer
Max Rachinsky
Nina Veselka
Ivana Vilimonovic
Marisol Wilcox

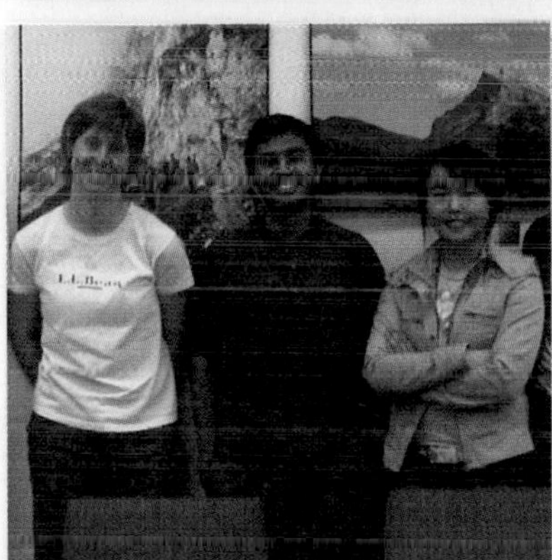

University of Calgary (pictured above)
Kristina Birkholz
Jobran Chebib
Liam Cummings
Aravind Ganesh
Shaista Hashem
Colleen Michael
Simon Sun
Camilla Tapp
Anita Tieu
Sahar Zaidi

University of New Brunswick
Maria Correia
Kelvin Gilliland
Jonathon Neilson
Allison Ritcey
Faith Shannon
Brittany Timberlake
Coleman Ward
Corey Willis

Thanks go as well to the high school students who participated, Meghan Harris and Lindsay Patton. Anne Duguay, a teacher from Queen Elizabeth High School in Calgary, and her student, Saskia, also participated. They provided a unique perspective on what entering students would expect from a text for an introductory course in biology. Finally, we wish to thank the student review boards from the University of Victoria, University of Toronto, Erindale Campus, Ryerson University, Sir Wilfred Grenfell College, and the University of Windsor. High school students, university students, and university instructors together provided us with an amazingly diverse array of feedback that allowed us to understand our audience and create a resource best suited to their needs.

Brief Contents

Contents

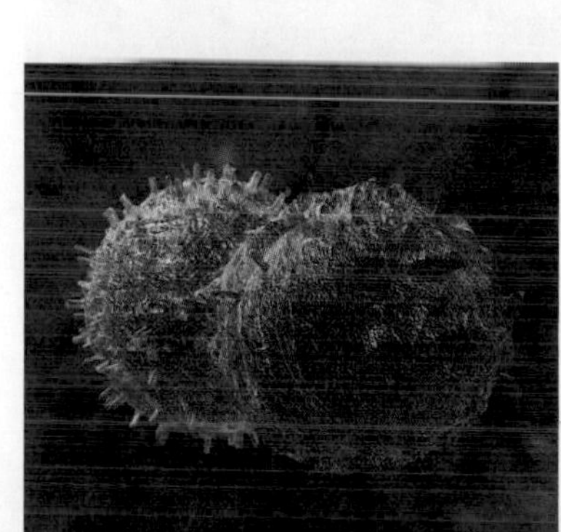
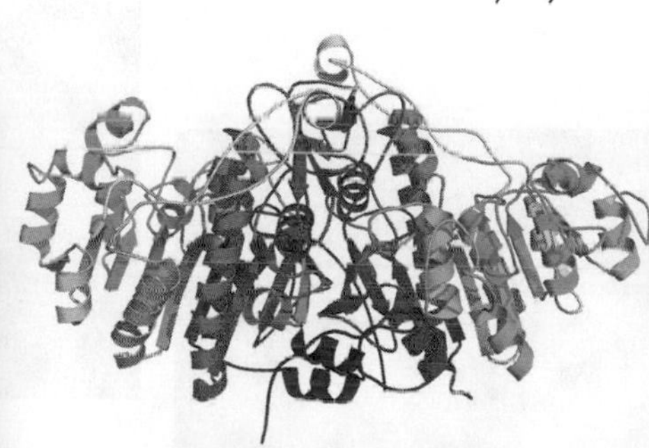
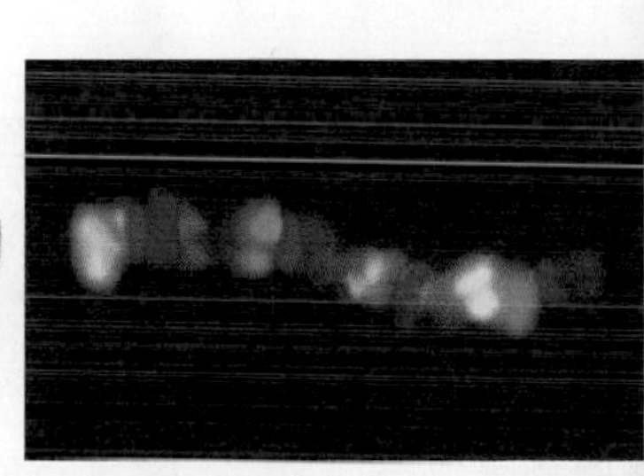
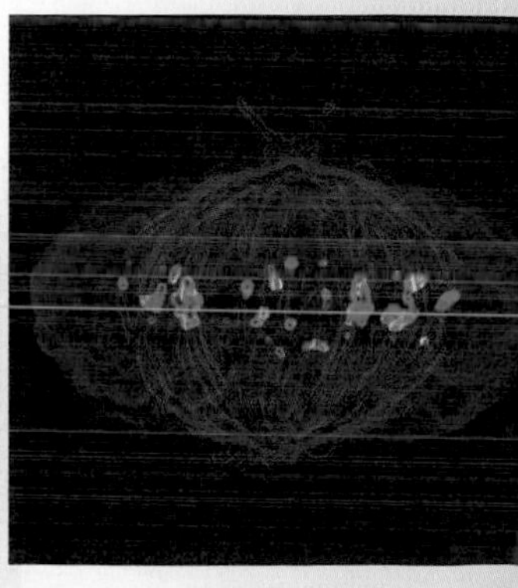

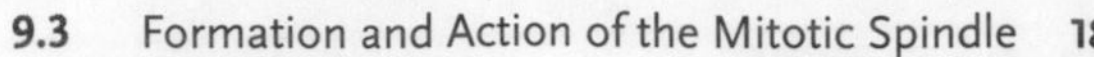

Unit Four DNA and Gene Expression 271

Unit Five Evolution and Classification 373

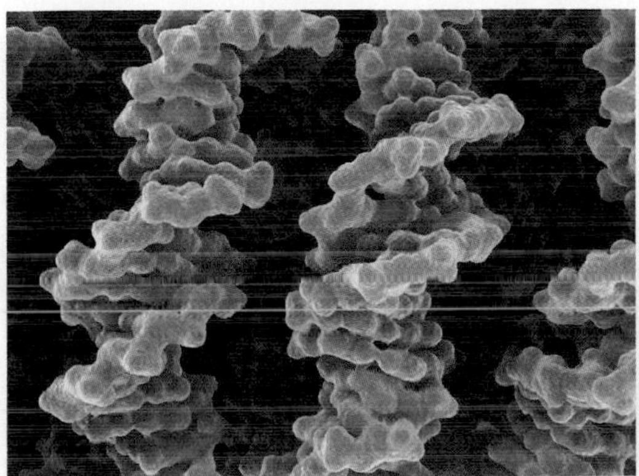

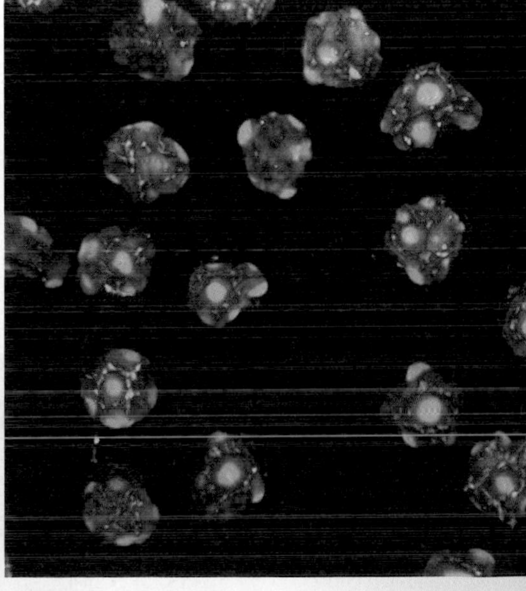

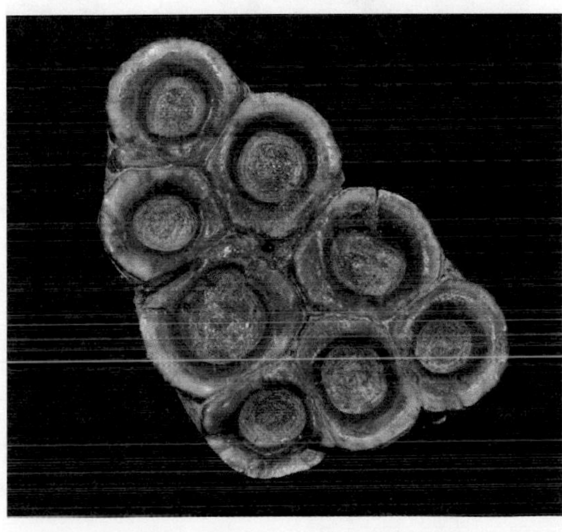

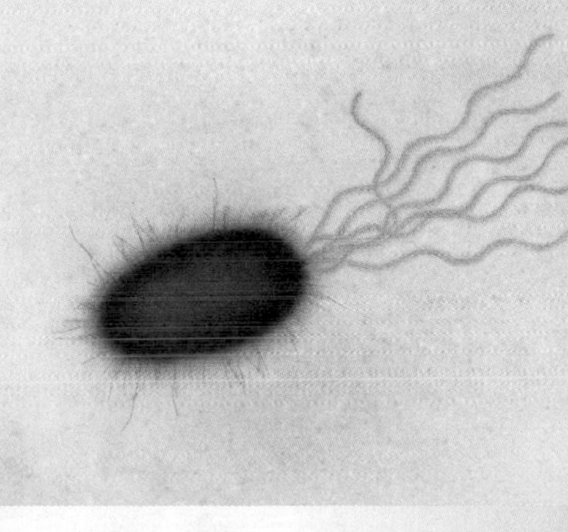

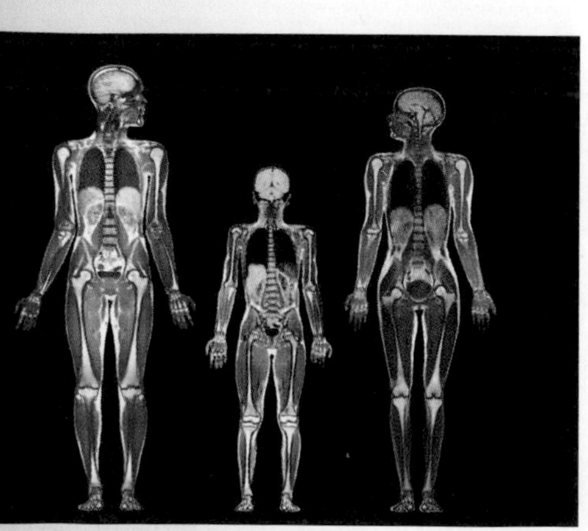

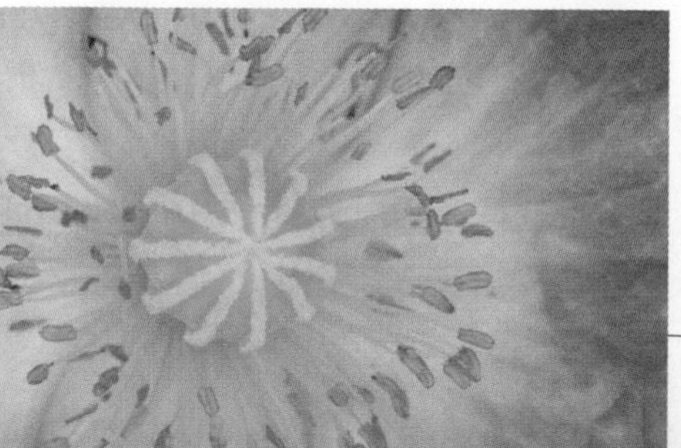

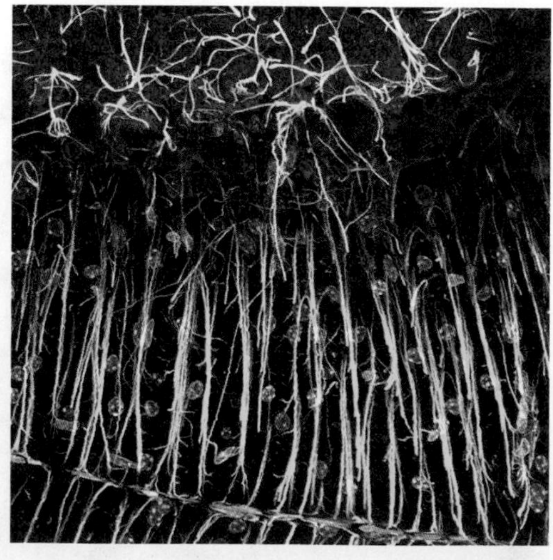

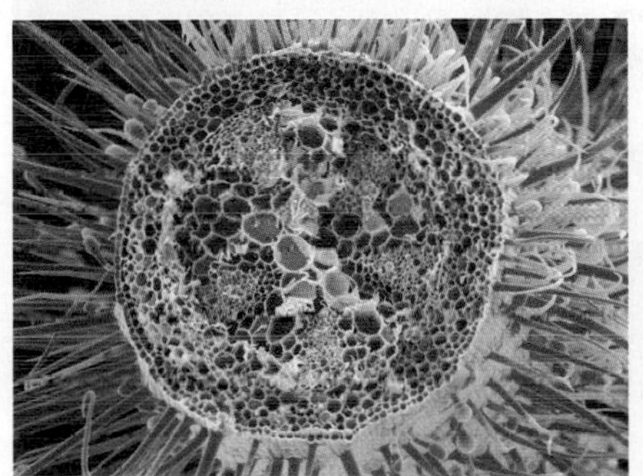

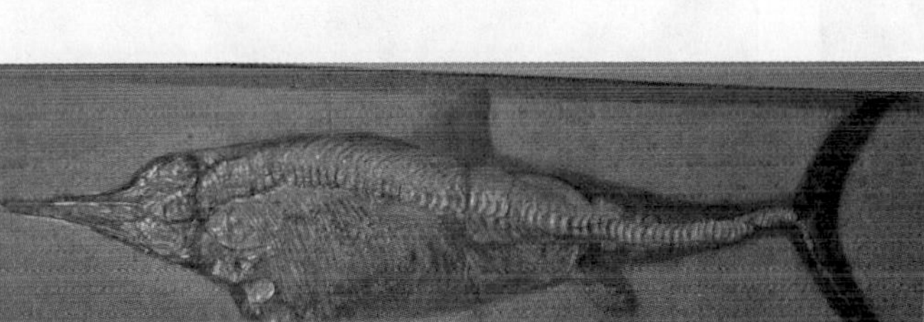

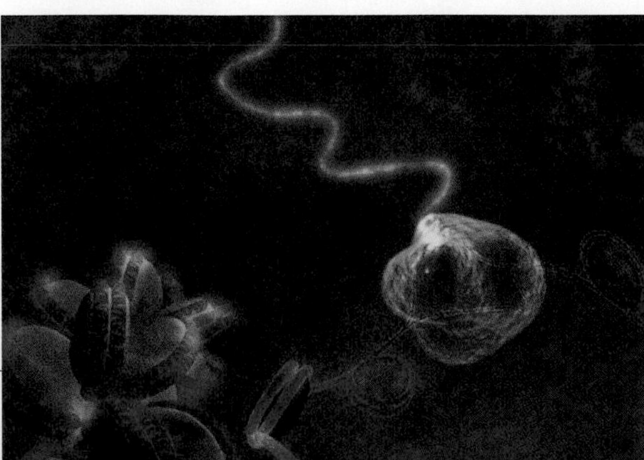

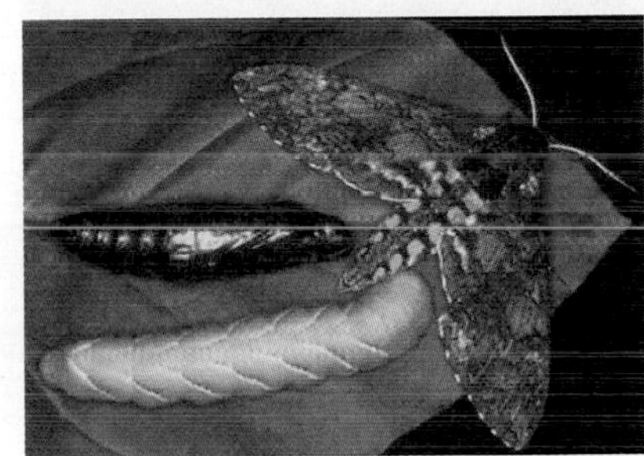

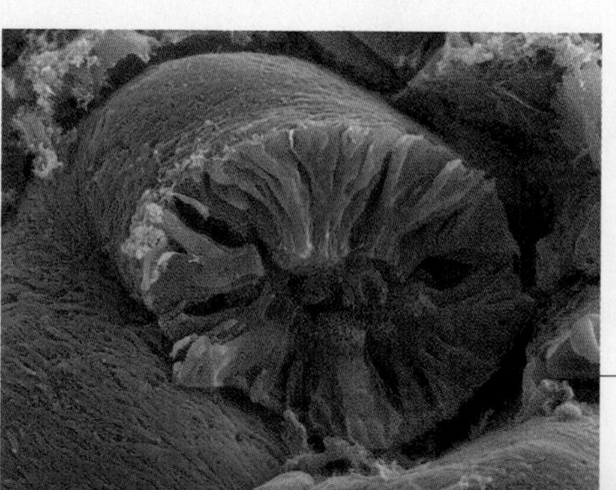

a.

b.

Paintings by Claude Monet (1840-1926). Compared to his early works including The water-lily pond **(a)** his later paintings including the Japanese footbridge **(b)** bordered on the abstract with almost complete loss of light-blue. Monet suffered from vision degenerative disease cataracts which was diagnosed in 1912.

1 Light and Life

Study Plan

Why It Matters

Claude Monet (1840–1926), a French painter, is considered by many to be the master of the impressionist form that rose to prominence in the late nineteenth century. Other well-known impressionists include Edgar Degas and Paul Cézanne. Impressionism as an art movement was characterized by the use of small visible brush strokes that emphasized light and colour, rather than lines, to define an object. The artists used pure, unmixed colour, not smoothly blended, as was the custom at the time. For example, instead of physically mixing yellow and blue paint, they placed unmixed yellow paint on the canvas next to unmixed blue paint so that the colours would mingle in the eye of the viewer to create the "impression" of green. The Impressionists found that they could capture the momentary and transient effects of sunlight and changing colour of a scene by painting *en plein air*, in the open air, outside of the studio, where they could more accurately paint the reflected light of an immediate scene.

Interestingly, compared with his early works, which included the Water Lily Pond (1899), Monet's later paintings verge on the abstract, with colours bleeding into each other and a lack of rational shape and perspective. For example, "The Japanese Footbridge" is an explosion of orange, yellow, and red hues, with heavy, broad brush strokes, leaving the viewer barely able to discern the vague shape of the arched bridge. In many of Monet's later works, the colours in his paintings became more muted, far less vibrant and bright, with a pronounced colour shift from blue-green to red-yellow and an almost total absence of light blues. The sense of atmosphere and light that he was famous for in his earlier works disappeared.

Although the change in Monet's paintings could easily be explained by an intentional change in style or perhaps an age-related change in manual dexterity, Monet himself realized that it was not his style or dexterity that had changed but, rather, it was his ability to see. Monet suffered from cataracts, the vision-deteriorating disease that was diagnosed in both eyes by a Parisian ophthalmologist in 1912 when Monet was 72. A cataract is a change in the lens of the eye, making it more opaque. The underlying cause is a progressive denaturation of one of the proteins that make up the lens. The increased opaqueness of the lens absorbs certain wavelengths of light, decreasing the transmittance of blue light. Thus, to a cataract sufferer such as Monet, the world appears more yellow.

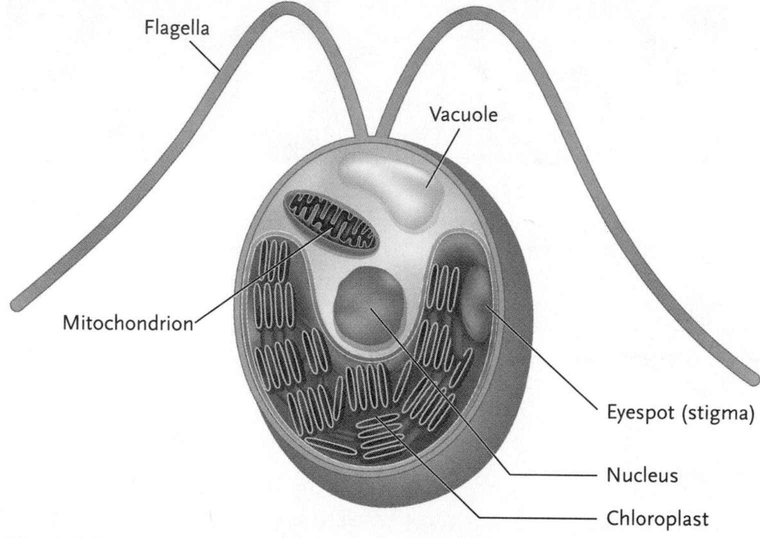

Figure 1.1
Chlamydomonas reinhardtii. A drawing of *Chlamydomonas reinhardtii*, a green alga. Each cell contains a single chloroplast used for photosynthesis as well as an eyespot for sensing light in the environment.

1.1 The Physical Nature of Light

Light serves two important functions for life on Earth: First it is a source of energy that sustains all life. Second, light provides organisms with information about the physical world. An excellent example of an organism that uses light for both energy and information is the green alga *Chlamydomonas reinhardtii* **(Figure 1.1)**. *C. reinhardtii* is a single-celled photosynthetic eukaryote that is commonly found in ponds and lakes. Each cell contains a single large chloroplast that harvests light energy and uses it to make energy-rich molecules through the process of photosynthesis. In addition, each cell contains a light sensor called an *eyespot* that allows it to sense both light direction and light intensity.

Regardless of whether the light is used as a source of energy or information about the environment, both rely on the same fundamental properties of light and require the light energy to be captured by the organism.

1.1a What Is Light?

The reason there is life on Earth and, as far as we know, nowhere else in our solar system has to do with distance—specifically, the distance of 150 000 000 km separating Earth from the Sun **(Figure 1.2)**. By converting hydrogen into helium at the staggering rate of some 3.4×10^{38} hydrogen nuclei per second, the Sun converts over 4 million tonnes of matter into energy every second. This energy is given off as electromagnetic radiation, which travels at the speed of light (1 079 252 848 km/h) and reaches the Earth in just over 8 minutes. Electromagnetic radiation moves in the form of two waves, one electrical and one magnetic, which are oriented at 90° to each other **(Figure 1.3)**. Scientists often distinguish electromagnetic

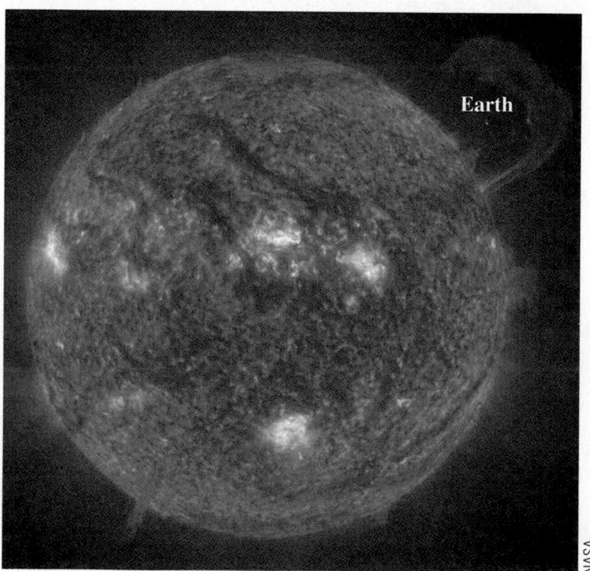

Figure 1.2
The Sun. The sun is a star with a surface temperature of approximately 5000°C. It generates electromagnetic radiation by the nuclear fusion of hydrogen nuclei into helium. Note the superimposed image of the Earth used to illustrate the relative size.

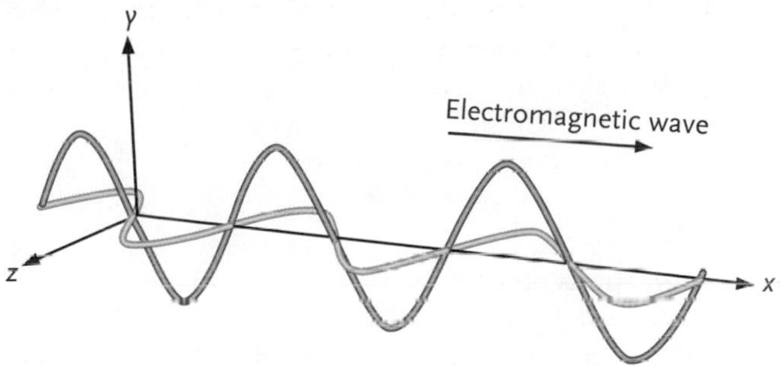

Figure 1.3
Electromagnetic radiation. Electromagnetic radiation can be considered as self-propagating waves which consist of both electrical and magnetic waves which are oriented at 90° to each other. A wave consists of discrete packets of energy called photons.

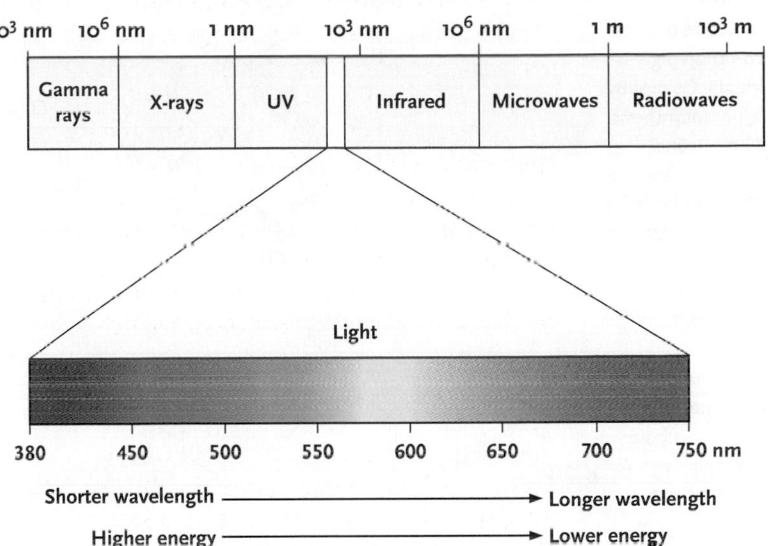

Figure 1.4
The electromagnetic spectrum. Is the grouping of all types of electromagnetic radiation according to wavelength. It ranges from very short wavelengths characteristic of gamma rays to the long wavelengths associated with radio waves. The shorter the wavelength of the electromagnetic radiation the higher the energy of each photon it contains. Light represents only a small portion of the total electromagnetic spectrum.

radiation by its **wavelength**, the distance between two successive peaks. The wavelength of electromagnetic radiation ranges from less than one picometre (10^{-12} m) for cosmic rays to more than a kilometre (10^6 m) for radio waves.

Okay, but what is light? **Light** can be defined as the portion of the electromagnetic spectrum **(Figure 1.4)** that humans can detect with their eyes. Light, or visible radiation, is a narrow band of the electromagnetic spectrum spanning the wavelengths in nanometres (1 nm = 10^{-9} m) from 400 nm (blue light) to about 700 nm (red light). To avoid confusion, wavelengths just outside this range should not be referred to as light but rather as ultraviolet and infrared *radiation*.

One reason that light is a bit of an enigma and hard to characterize is that although it can be described as a wave, it also behaves as a stream of energy particles. These discrete particles or packets of energy are referred to as **photons**. Unlike atoms, photons have no mass, but each contains a precise amount of energy. The amount of energy in a photon is inversely related to its wavelength. Looking just at visible light (see Figure 1.4), this means that blue light, with a shorter wavelength, consists of photons that have higher energy than longer wavelength red light. It is important to realize that although one photon contains a very small amount of energy (red light: 3.01×10^{-19} joules/photon; blue light: 4.56×10^{-19} joules/photon), on a clear summer's day, approximately 10^{21} photons hit each square metre of Earth each second.

1.1b Light Interacts with Matter

Although light has no mass, it is able to interact with and change matter. These changes allow light to be used by living things. When photons of light hit an object, the photons have three possible fates. They can be (1) reflected off the object, (2) transmitted through the object, or (3) absorbed by the object **(Figure 1.5)**. For most objects exposed to sunlight, all three of these processes come into play.

Although light can be reflected or transmitted by an object, to be used by an organism the photons of light must be absorbed. A molecule that can absorb photons of light is called a **pigment**, and individual pigments differ in the wavelengths of light they can absorb. For example, some pigments absorb only blue light and others only green light, whereas others absorb light of a number of different wavelengths. There is a large diversity of pigments **(Figure 1.6, p. 4)**, including chlorophyll *a*, which is involved in photosynthesis; retinal, which is involved in vision; and indigo, which is used to dye jeans their distinctive blue colour.

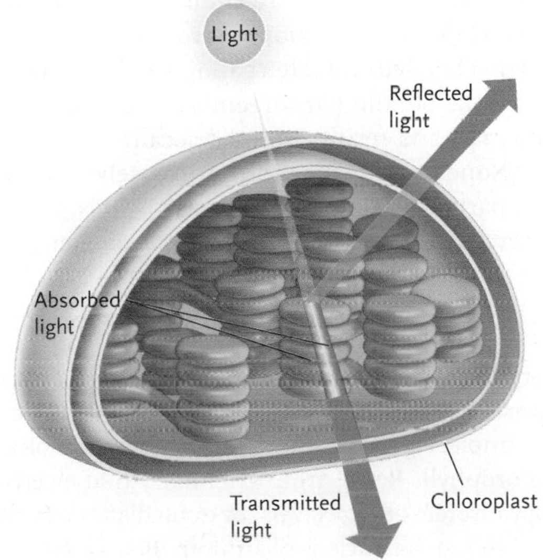

Figure 1.5
Light interacting with matter. When photons of light interact with matter the light energy has three possible fates. It can be reflected by the matter, transmitted through the matter or the energy may be absorbed by the matter.

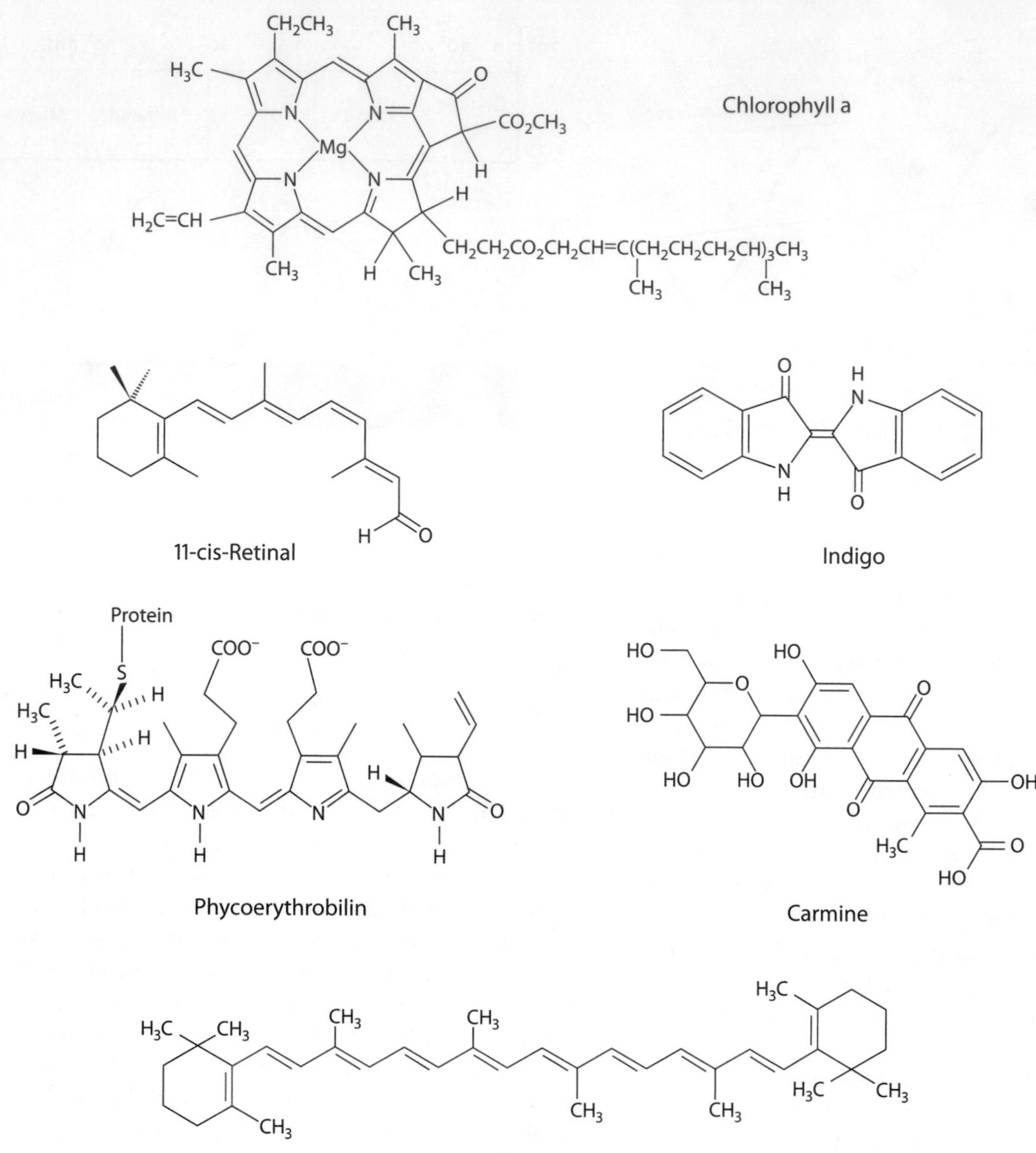

Figure 1.6 Structure of some common pigments. Chlorophyll *a*, photosynthesis. **11-cis-Retinal,** vision: **Indigo,** dye: **Phycoerythrobilin,** red photosynthetic pigment found in red algae: **Carmine,** scale pigment found in some insects. **Beta carotene,** an orange accessory photosynthetic pigment. A common feature of all these pigments that is critical for light absorption is the presence of a conjugated system (shown in red for Beta-carotene) of double/single carbon bonds. The conjugated system is the actual portion of the pigment involved in light absorption.

What is it about pigments that enable them to capture light? At first glance, the pigments shown in Figure 1.6 seem to be very different from each other structurally; however, they all share a common feature critical to light absorption: a region where carbon atoms are covalently bonded with alternating single and double bonds. This bonding arrangement is called a *conjugated system* and results in the delocalization of electrons. None of these electrons are closely associated with a particular atom, and because of this, they are more available to interact with a photon of light.

1.1c Why Chlorophyll Is Green

Absorption of light occurs when the energy of a photon is transferred to an electron of the pigment molecule. For example, **Figure 1.7** shows this in a single molecule of chlorophyll. Recall from chemistry that electrons occupy discrete energy levels, or excited states, in their orbits around the nucleus of an atom. Before absorbing a photon of light, an electron exists in the ground state, which we can designate as 0. Upon absorption of a photon of light, the energy is transferred to the electron, moving it from the ground state to a higher energy, excited state. For a chlorophyll molecule, the electron involved in photon capture can exist in two, and only two, excited states (see Figure 1.7). The lower excited state, designated as 1, is reached by chlorophyll absorbing a photon of red light. The higher excited state, designated as 2, is reached by the absorption of a photon of blue light. Absorption of blue light excites an electron to a higher energy state than absorption of red light because blue photons contain more energy.

Two important principles must be kept in mind when thinking about light absorption by pigments: first, a single photon results in the excitation of one, and only one, electron in a pigment molecule. Second, the energy of the photon must match the energy *difference* between the ground state and one of the excited states in order for the photon to be absorbed. If the energies do not match,

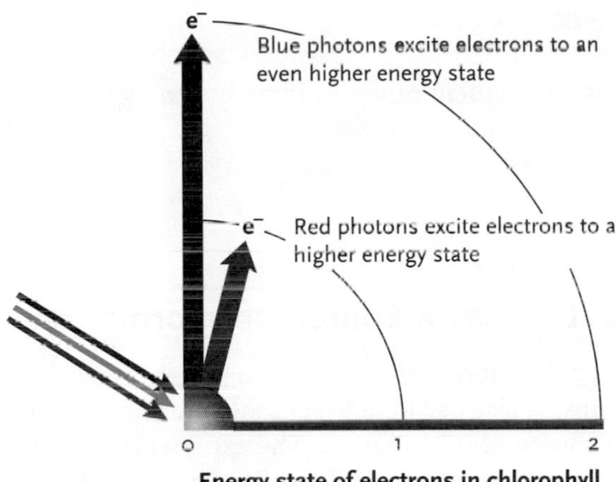

Figure 1.7
Absorption of light by chlorophyll a. Absorption of a photon by a chlorophyll a molecule results in transfer of energy to an electron raising it to a higher energy level. Blue photons raise electrons to a higher energy level because they contain more energy than red photons. Green photons cannot be absorbed since the molecule does not have an energy state which matches the energy contained in a green photon. Because of this, green photons get transmitted through the pigment or reflected by the pigment molecule giving chlorophyll its green colour.

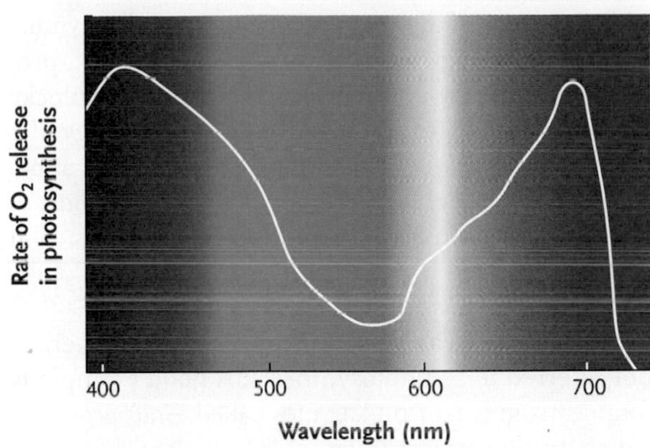

Figure 1.8
Action spectrum shows the relative effectiveness of different wavelengths of light on photosynthesis. The characteristics of the action spectrum reflect the fact that the major photosynthetic pigment, chlorophyll a preferentially absorbs blue and red photons of light.

the photon is not absorbed. In the chlorophyll molecule, the energy of a blue photon or a red photon matches perfectly with the energy required for an electron to reach either the first or the second excited state.

So why is chlorophyll green in colour? The colour of a pigment is determined by the wavelengths of light it *cannot* absorb. Chlorophyll is green because although it can trap photons of blue light and red light, it cannot absorb photons of green light. As shown in Figure 1.7, a chlorophyll molecule cannot absorb a photon of green light because it does not have an energy level matching that of a green photon. Whereas red and blue photons are captured, green photons are reflected or transmitted, giving chlorophyll (and plants) its distinctive green colour.

Because pigments do not absorb all wavelengths of light equally, the effectiveness of light in driving processes that use the absorbed light, such as photosynthesis or vision, varies depending on the wavelength of the light. A plot of the effectiveness of different wavelengths of light on a biological process is called an **action spectrum. Figure 1.8** illustrates the action spectrum for photosynthesis in the leaf of a plant.

Figure 1.8 shows that red and blue wavelengths of light are more effective at driving photosynthesis than green wavelengths are. This fits well with what we know about the wavelengths of light that are absorbed by chlorophyll. You may notice in Figure 1.8 that some photosynthesis still occurs under green light. This is because photosynthesis involves a number of accessory pigments that can absorb wavelengths of light between the red and blue wavelengths used by chlorophyll.

Study Break

1. What form does light take?
2. What do the structures of all pigment molecules have in common?

1.2 Light as a Source of Energy

We have already seen that after a photon of light is absorbed, an electron within a pigment molecule is raised to a higher excited state. This excited state electron is a source of potential energy that can be used to do work. As we will see in Chapter 7, this potential energy is used in photosynthetic electron transport to synthesize energy-rich compounds NADPH (the reduced form of nicotinamide adenine dinucleotide phosphate) and adenosine triphosphate (ATP), which are used to convert carbon dioxide into carbohydrates **(Figure 1.9).** In

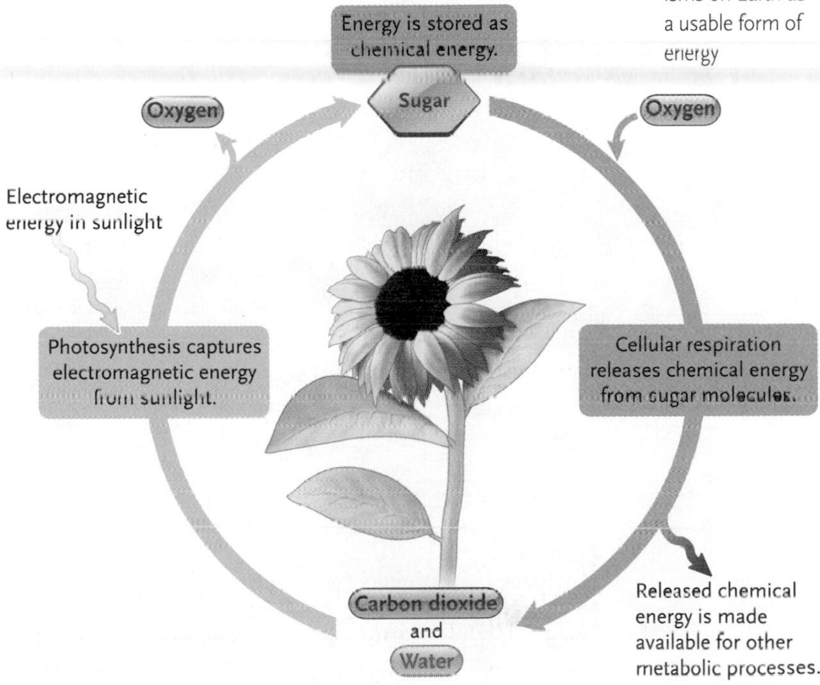

Figure 1.9
Photosynthesis sustains almost all life. Photosynthesis uses the energy in sunlight to build sugar molecules from carbon dioxide and water, releasing oxygen as a by-product. The products of photosynthesis not only sustain photosynthetic organisms but through the process of cellular respiration are used by the vast majority of organisms on Earth as a usable form of energy

addition, some of the chemical energy is used to synthesize other biological molecules, such as lipids, proteins, and nucleic acids, from simple building blocks found in the environment. Although the energy of a single photon is very small, the photosynthetic apparatus within the chloroplast of a single *C. reinhardtii* cell, for example, absorbs millions of photons each second.

Organisms use light as a source of energy in other processes, but to avoid confusion, these are generally not referred to as photosynthesis. A good example is found in a group of prokaryotes called *Halobacterium*, which live in some of the most extreme environments on Earth **(Figure 1.10)**. *Halobacterium* contains a protein complex called bacteriorhodopsin, which functions as a light-dependent proton pump.

Study Break

How do pigment molecules trap the energy of light?

1.3 Light as a Source of Information

As the deterioration of Monet's eyesight illustrates, organisms also use light to sense their environment—as a source of information. The experience of trying to perform even the simplest of tasks in a dark room makes one quickly realize how important the ability to sense light has become for many forms of life.

a. *Halobacterium salinarium*

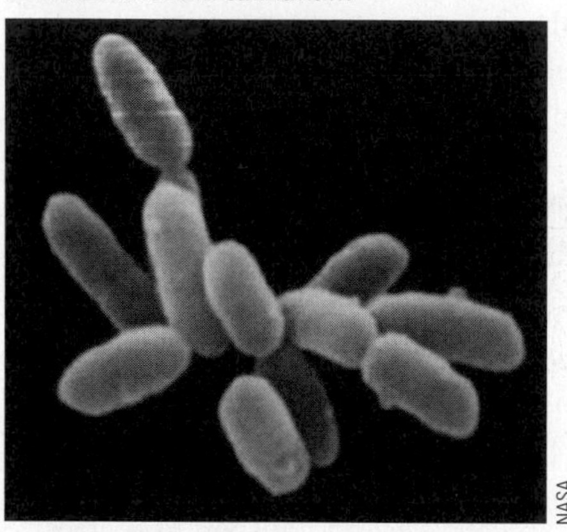

b. Hutt Lagoon, Western Australia

c. A model of bacteriorhodopsin

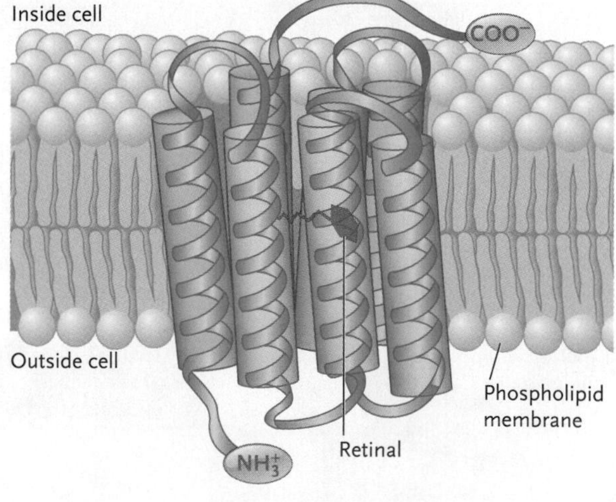

d. Bacteriorhodopsin-driven ATP formation

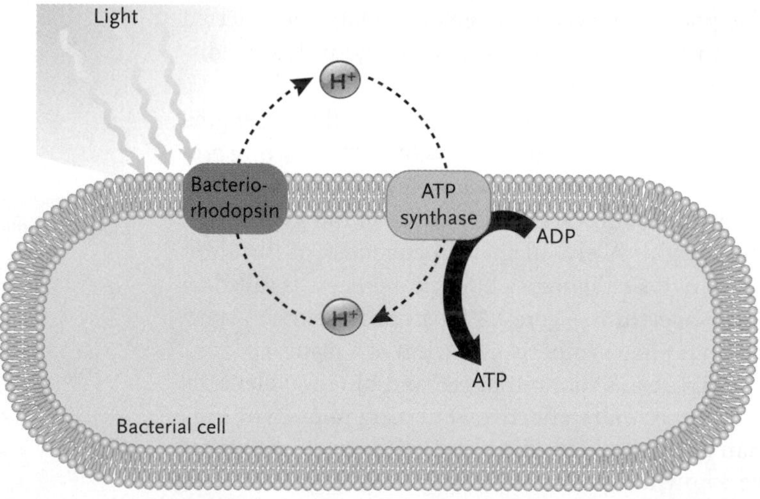

Figure 1.10
Halobacteria are a group of prokaryotes that contain bacteriorhodopsin. **(a)** Electron micrograph of a colony of cells. **(b)** Halobacteria are extremophiles and are found in hypersaline environments like Hutt Lagoon in Australia. The pink colour is due to the presence of bacteriorhodopsin. **(c)** model of bacteriorhodopsin which is composed of the protein, bacteriorhodopsin, and the bound pigment, retinal. **(d)** Bacteriorhodopsin functions as a light-driven proton pump, the proton gradient being used to synthesis ATP.

The change in Monet's eyesight also demonstrates that not every person, and certainly not every species, sees the world in the same way.

1.3a Rhodopsin, a Highly Conserved Photoreceptor

The basic light sensing system, found almost universally in all organisms, is the photoreceptor. By far the most common photoreceptor in nature is rhodopsin **(Figure 1.11)**, which is not only the basis of vision in animals but also the photoreceptor used by many other organisms, including *C. reinhardtii*, where it serves as the light-sensing unit of the eyespot. Each rhodopsin molecule consists of a protein called opsin that binds a single pigment molecule called retinal. Opsins are membrane proteins that span a membrane multiple times and form a complex with the retinal molecule at the centre (see Figure 1.11). As the name implies, rhodopsin is very similar to the bacteriorhodopsin found in *Halobacterium* and other prokaryotes. As shown in Figure 1.11, absorption of a photon of light causes the retinal pigment molecule to change shape. This change triggers alterations to the opsin protein, which, in turn, triggers downstream events, including alterations in intracellular ion concentrations and electrical signals. As we will see in Chapter 34, in the case of vision, these electrical signals are sent to the visual centres of the brain. In humans, capturing of light by the eye involves about 125 million photoreceptor cells (rods and cones) that line the retina. Each photoreceptor cell contains thousands of individual rhodopsin molecules.

Rhodopsin is the most common photoreceptor found in nature, but it is not the only one. Both plants and animals have a range of other photoreceptors that absorb light of particular wavelengths. It remains a mystery why rhodopsin became the most common photoreceptor. Perhaps its widespread occurrence is the result of it developing very early in the evolution of life. Interestingly, whereas vision and smell (olfaction; see Chapter 34) are different senses, proteins very similar to opsins are used in olfaction, suggesting that specific aspects of opsin proteins are particularly useful for sensory perception.

1.3b Sensing Light Without Eyes

When we think about sensing light, we automatically think about our ability to see with our eyes. However, many organisms can sense the light in their surroundings even though they lack eyes. This includes plants, algae, invertebrates, and even some prokaryotes. As an example, let's take a closer look at the eyespot of *C. reinhardtii*. The eyespot, a structure approximately 1 μm in diameter, is located within the chloroplast of a C. reinhardtii cell, in a region closely associated with the cell membrane **(Figure 1.12)**. Although it is in the chloroplast, the eyespot does not play a role in photosynthesis, instead the photoreceptors of the eyespot allow the cell to sense light direction and intensity. Using a pair of flagella, *C. reinhardtii* cells can respond to light by swimming toward or away

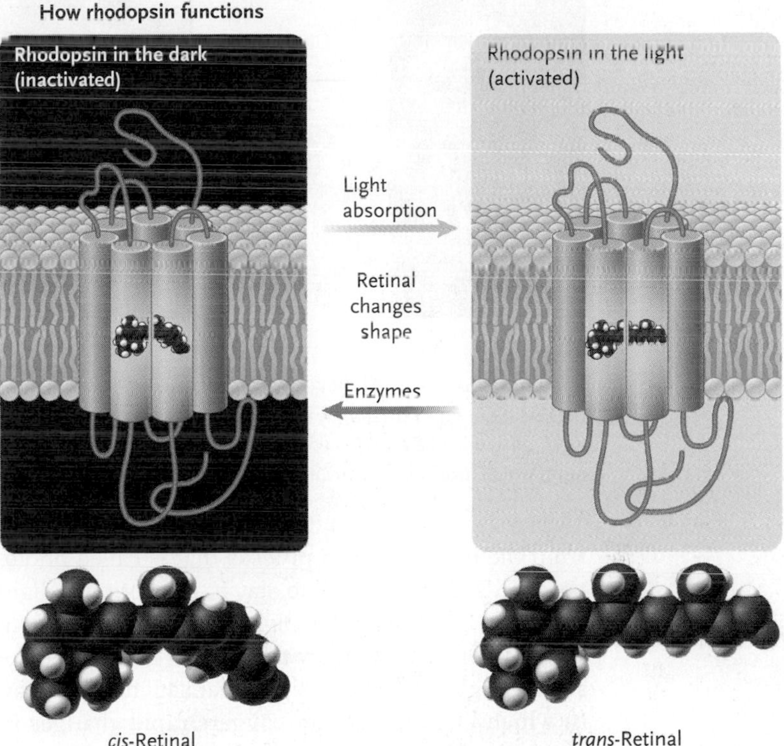

Figure 1.11
Model of the photoreceptor rhodopsin. Rhodopsin consists of a protein (opsin) which binds a pigment molecule (retinal). Upon absorption of a photon of light retinal changes shape which triggers changes to the opsin molecule. These changes trigger signalling events which allow the organism to respond to the light.

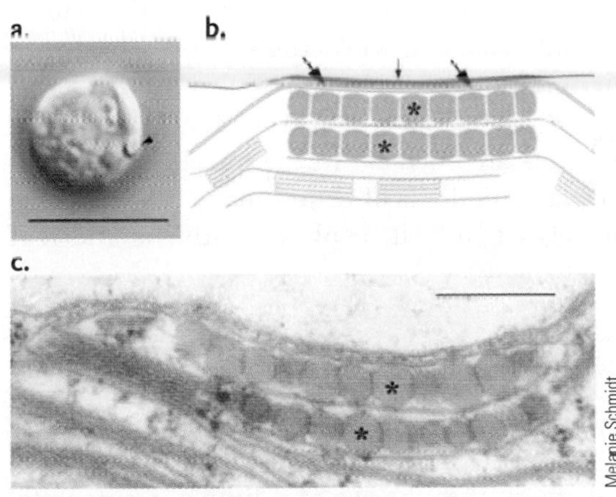

Figure 1.12
An eyespot. Schematic representation of the eyespot found in *Chlamydomonas*. The cell **(a)** is about 10 μM in diameter, **(b)** Drawing of the eyespot apparatus with the asterisks indicating the orange pigment-rich globule layers which are found inside the chloroplast outermembrane (indicated by large arrow). The plasma membrane is indicated by the small arrow. **(c)** Transmission electron micrograph of same area drawn in B.

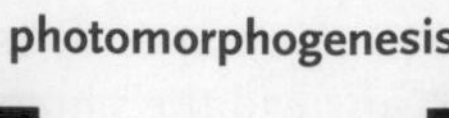

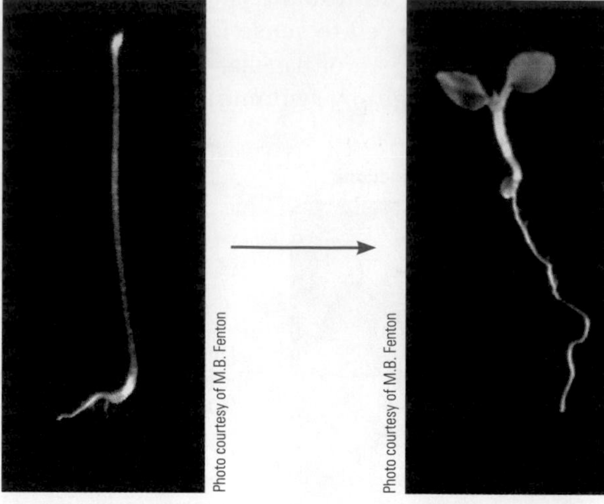

Figure 1.13
Photomorphogenesis. Shifting seedlings from darkness to light triggers a developmental program called photomorphogenesis. Light sensed by the photoreceptor phytochrome initiates the program which involves the activation of hundreds of genes.

from the light source, a process that is called phototaxis. This allows the cell to stay in the optimum light environment to maximize light capture for photosynthesis. Light absorption by the eyespot is linked to the swimming response by a signal transduction pathway, in which light absorption triggers rapid changes in the concentrations of ions, including potassium and calcium, which generate a cascade of electrical events. These, in turn, change the beating pattern of the flagella used for locomotion.

In plants, a different photoreceptor, called phytochrome, senses the light environment and is critical for photomorphogenesis, the normal developmental process activated when seedlings are exposed to light **(Figure 1.13)**. Phytochrome is present in the cytosol of all plant cells, and when the plant is exposed to wavelengths of red light, phytochrome becomes active and initiates a signal transduction pathway that reaches the nucleus. In the nucleus, these signals activate hundreds of genes, many of which code for proteins involved in photosynthesis and leaf development.

1.3c The Eye

The **eye** can be defined as the organ animals use to sense light. It is described in detail in Chapter 34. What distinguishes the eye of a simple invertebrate, for example, from the eyespot of *C. reinhardtii* is vision. The process of vision not only requires an eye but it also requires a brain or at least a simple nervous system that interprets signals sent from the eye. The eye and brain are thought to have co-evolved because detailed visual processing occurs in the brain rather than in the eye. Essentially, we "see" not with our eyes but, rather, with our brain.

The simplest eye is the ocellus (plural, ocelli), which consists of up to 100 photoreceptor cells lining a cup or pit. In planarians, for example, photoreceptor cells in a cuplike depression below the epidermis are connected by bundles of nerves to the cerebral ganglion **(Figure 1.14)**. Each ocellus is covered on one side by a layer of pigment cells that blocks most of the light rays arriving from the opposite side of the animal. As a result, most of the light received by the pigment cells enters the ocellus from the side it faces. Through integration of information transmitted to the cerebral ganglion from the eyecups, planarians orient themselves so that the amount of light falling on the two ocelli is equal and diminishes as they swim. This reaction carries them directly away from the source of the light and toward darker areas, where the risk of predation is smaller. Ocelli occur in a variety of animals, including a number of insects, arthropods, and molluscs.

In many ways, the eye of a planaria is not much more advanced than the eyespot of *C. reinhardtii*. In both cases, the eye is used to sense light intensity and direction to a light source but little else. The greatest advance in vision came with more sophisticated eyes that produced an actual image of the lighted environment for discerning objects and shapes. These "image-forming eyes" are found in two distinctly different types: compound eyes and single-lens eyes.

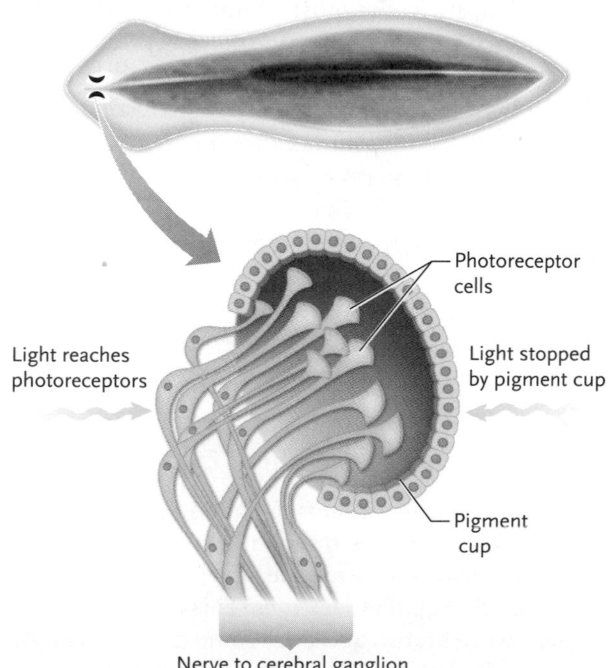

Figure 1.14
The ocellus of *Planaria*, a flatworm, and the arrangement of photoreceptors cells on which its orientation response is based.

Compound eyes are common in arthropods such as insects and crustaceans, and each contains hundreds to thousands of ommatidia (*omma* = eye), units fitted closely together **(Figure 1.15)**. Each ommatidium samples only a small part of the visual field as light entering an ommatidium is focused onto a bundle of photoreceptor cells. From these signals, the brain receives a mosaic image of the world. Because even the slightest motion is detected simultaneously by many ommatidia, compound eyes are extraordinarily adept at detecting movement, a lesson soon learned by fly-swatting humans.

Some invertebrates and most vertebrates have eyes with single lenses, "camera eyes" **(Figure 1.16)**. Light enters this eye through the transparent cornea, a lens concentrates the light, and a layer of photoreceptors at the back of the eye, the retina, records the image. We will learn more about the structural and functional aspects of eyes in Chapter 34.

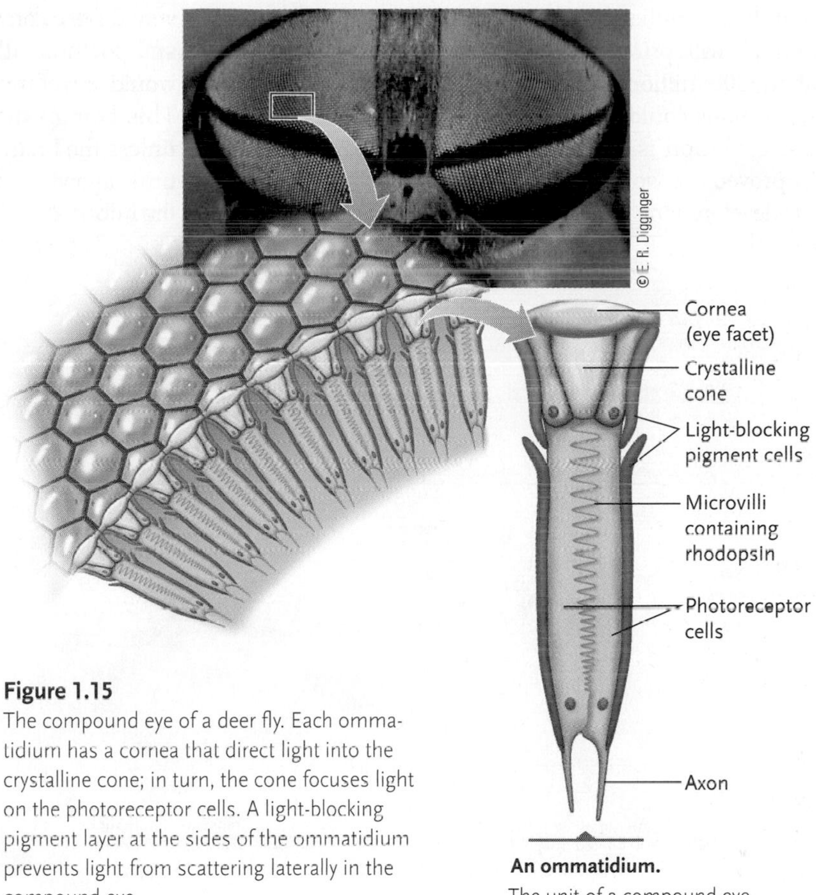

Figure 1.15
The compound eye of a deer fly. Each ommatidium has a cornea that direct light into the crystalline cone; in turn, the cone focuses light on the photoreceptor cells. A light-blocking pigment layer at the sides of the ommatidium prevents light from scattering laterally in the compound eye.

1.3d Darwin and the Evolution of the Eye

When Charles Darwin presented his theory of evolution by natural selection in *On the Origin of Species by Means of Natural Selection* (1859), he recognized that "organs of extreme perfection," such as the eye, would present a problem:

> To suppose that the eye, with all its inimitable contrivances for adjusting the focus to different distances, for admitting different amounts of light, and for the correction of spherical and chromatic aberration, could have been formed by natural selection, seems, I freely confess, absurd in the highest possible degree. Yet reason tells me, that if numerous gradations from a perfect and complex eye to one very imperfect and simple, each grade being useful to its possessor, can be shown to exist; if further, the eye does vary ever so slightly, and the variations be inherited, which is certainly the case; and if any variation or modification in the organ be ever useful to an animal under changing conditions of life, then the difficulty of believing that a perfect and complex eye could be formed by natural selection, though insuperable by our imagination, can hardly be considered real.

Darwin found a way out of this dilemma by proposing that the eye as it exists in humans and other animals did not appear suddenly but evolved by variation (mutation) and natural selection over time from a simple, primitive eye.

How long would it take for an eye to evolve? Starting with a patch of light-sensitive cells on the skin, a recent study predicted that about 2000 small improvements over time would gradually yield a camera-type eye in less

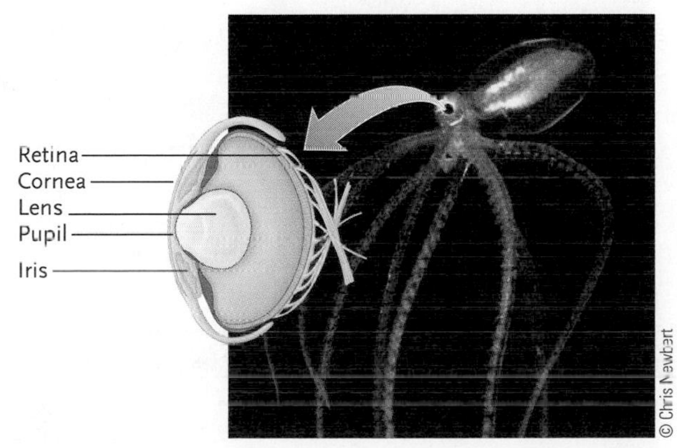

Figure 1.16
The eye of a cephalopod mollusc (an octopus).

than half a million years (**Figure 1.17**). Considering that animals with primitive eyes appeared in the fossil record about 500 million years ago, the camera-type eye found in humans could have evolved more than 1000 times. Eye evolution is explained by the huge advantage an improved eye would give to an organism. For example, the development of heightened visual ability in a predator would force comparable eye improvements in both prey and potential other predators. Rapid eye development would therefore be critical to survival (see Chapter 34). This being said, an optically refined eye is no good unless the brain of the organism improves at the same time, allowing for more advanced neural processing of the information being sent by the optic nerve.

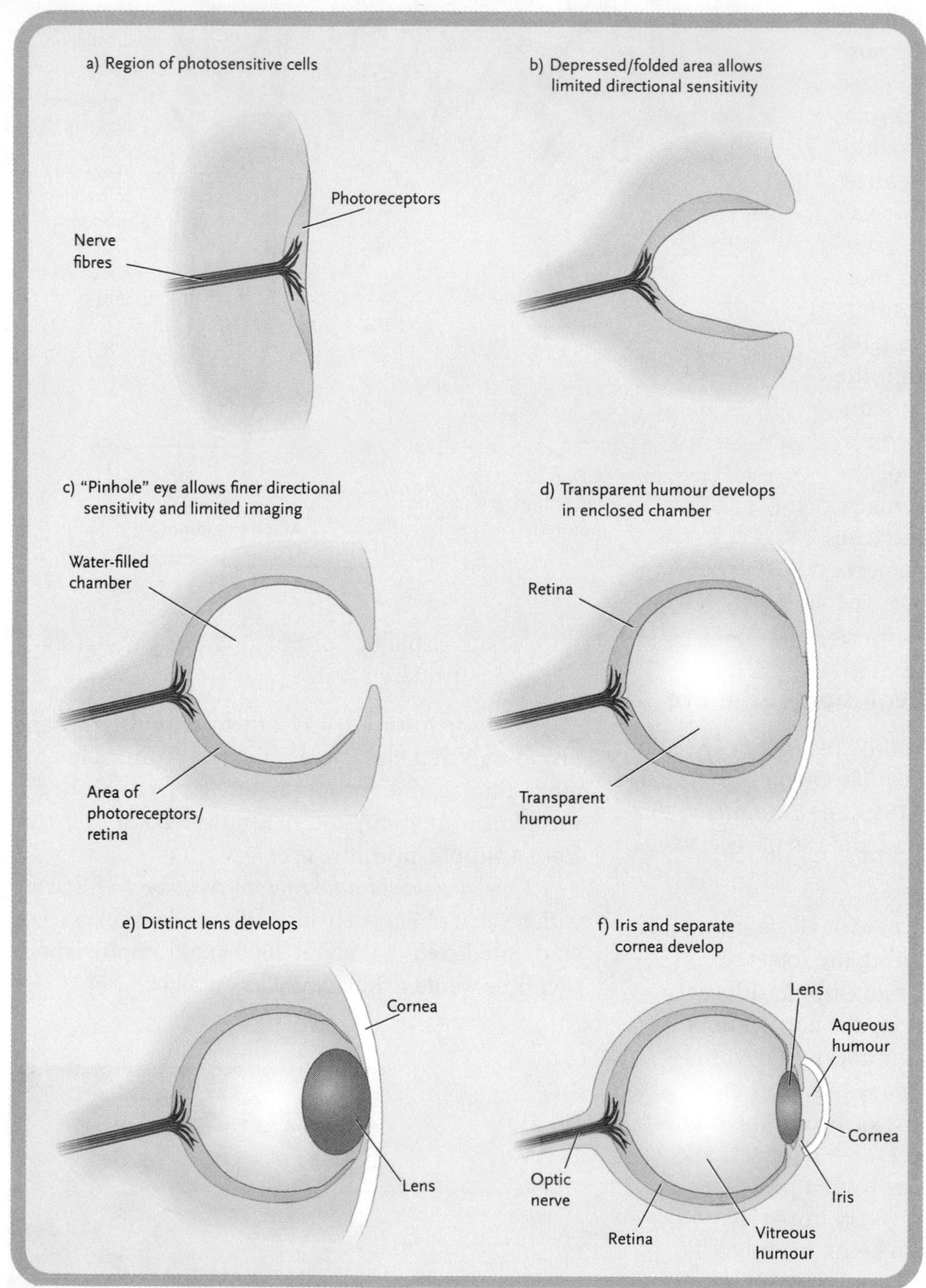

Figure 1.17
The evolution of the eye. Starting with a layer of light-sensitive cells, recent research suggests that a camera eye could evolve in less than 500 million years. The evolution of a more sophisticated eye can be explained by the huge advantage improved eye sight would give an organism.

Study Break

1. What is a photoreceptor?
2. Why, historically, has the eye posed a problem for evolutionary biologists?

1.4 Light Can Damage Biological Molecules

Light is a very small portion of the total electromagnetic spectrum (look back at Figure 1.4), yet this small portion of the spectrum is essential to life on Earth. These wavelengths, from about 400 to 700 nm, are the only wavelengths used for photosynthesis, vision, phototaxis, navigation, and many other light-driven processes.

Is it just a coincidence that all of these processes depend on such a narrow band of the electromagnetic spectrum? According to the Harvard physiologist and Nobel laureate George Wald (1906–1997), it is not a coincidence at all. Wald reasoned that light is used by organisms because it is the most dominant form of electromagnetic radiation reaching Earth's surface **(Figure 1.18).** Shorter wavelengths of electromagnetic radiation are absorbed by the ozone layer high in the atmosphere, whereas wavelengths longer than those in the visible spectrum are absorbed by water vapour and carbon dioxide in the atmosphere.

Another reason life uses light and not other wavelengths of electromagnetic radiation has to do with the energy it contains. Remember that living things are made up of molecules held together by chemical bonds. Radiation of shorter wavelengths than light contains enough energy to destroy these bonds. Absorption of high energy photons wouldn't just excite electrons within a pigment but actually oxidize the molecule producing ions. Because of this, shorter wavelengths of electromagnetic radiation are often refered to as ionizing radiation.

Alternatively, wavelengths longer than those comprising light would not supply enough energy to excite the electrons necessary for photochemistry. Furthermore, longer wavelengths are readily absorbed by water, which is the bulk of all living things. Even if life evolved on some other planet, Wald suggests, it would still use the same narrow range of electromagnetic wavelengths it uses on Earth.

1.4a Damage by Light: Direct Effects

Although not as energetic as some forms of electromagnetic radiation, light is still a form of energy, with the potential to damage biological molecules, both directly and indirectly. However, regardless of how the damage is caused, all organisms that are exposed to sunlight have developed mechanisms either to help prevent light-induced damage or to repair it quickly if damage occurs.

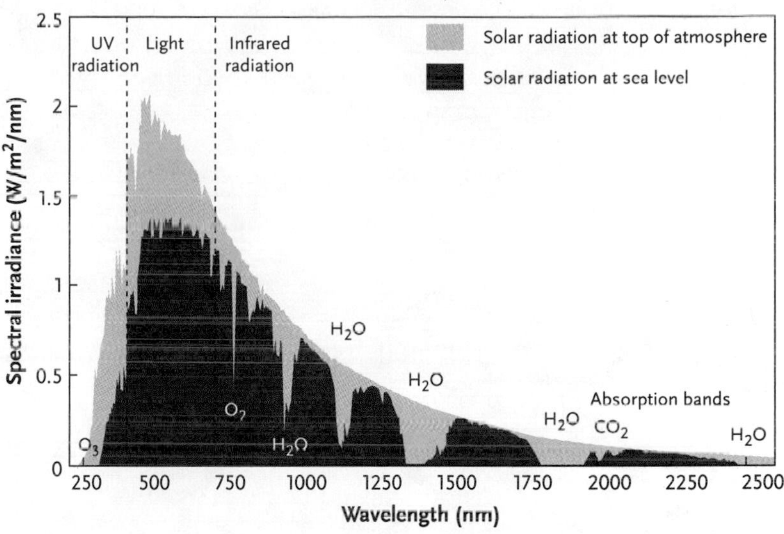

Figure 1.18
Electromagnetic radiation reaching the Earth's surface. Compared to the electromagnetic radiation that reaches the outer atmosphere, the radiation reaching the earths surface is reduced in both short wavelengths and long wavelengths of the electromagnetic spectrum.

A good example of the direct damaging effects of light on a biological process is found with photosynthesis. As we will see in Chapter 7, the photosynthetic apparatus is composed of photosystems **(Figure 1.19),** pigment–protein complexes that trap the energy of light and convert it to chemical energy. Normal chloroplasts contain hundreds of photosystems, each trapping the energy of approximately

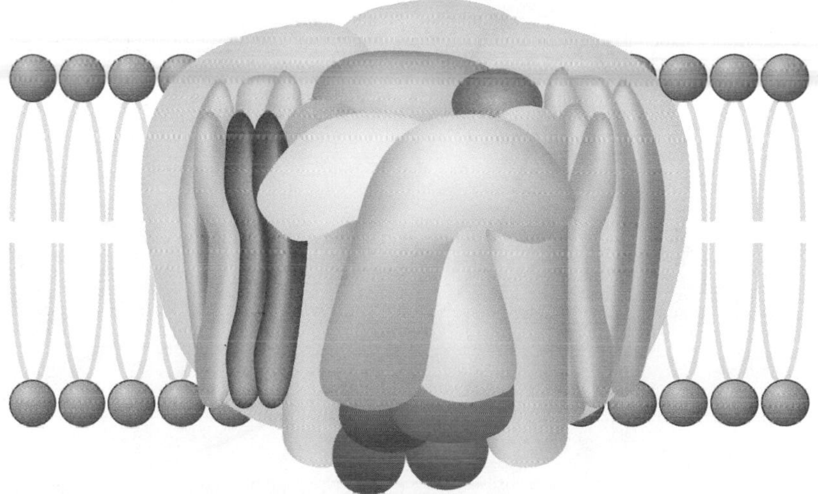

Figure 1.19
Photosystem II is constantly being damaged by light. A single Photosystem II complex involved in the light reactions of photosynthesis can absorb approximately 10,000 photons of light each second. The energetic nature of this results in photosystem II complex constantly being inactivated by light-induced damage to specific proteins. Overall, high rates of photosynthesis are maintained by the presence of a very efficient repair system for damaged photosystems.

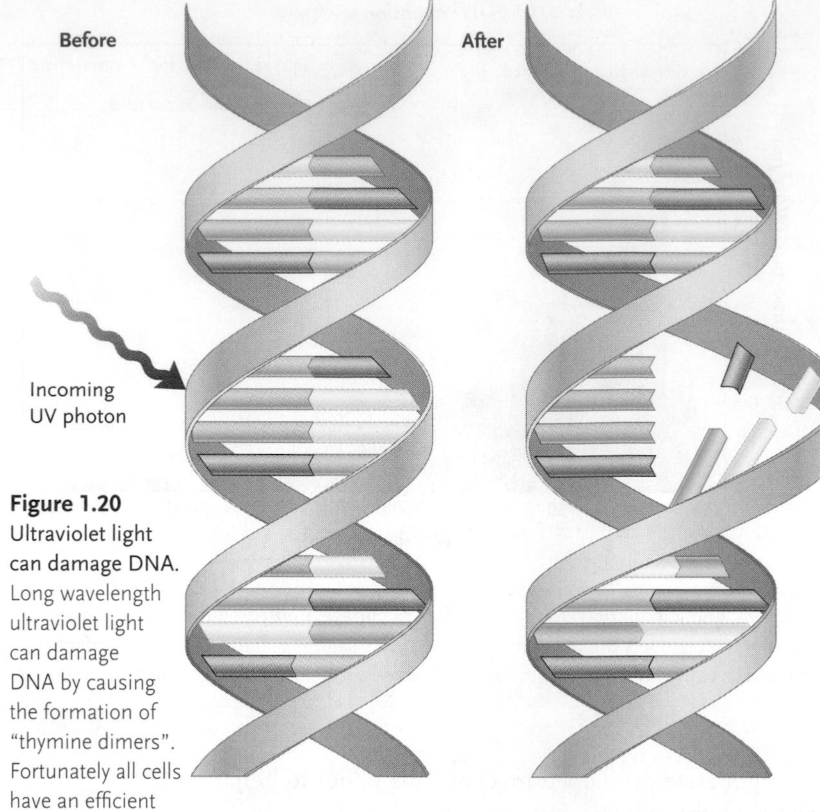

Figure 1.20
Ultraviolet light can damage DNA. Long wavelength ultraviolet light can damage DNA by causing the formation of "thymine dimers". Fortunately all cells have an efficient mechanism to repair damage to DNA.

10 000 photons of light each second. Although a photosystem is very efficient at converting light energy into chemical energy, the high-energy environment within its core often results in damage to its protein components. Although damage to photosystems is unavoidable, rapid repair of damaged photosystems developed early during the evolution of life so that the rate of photosynthesis can be maintained even under high light conditions.

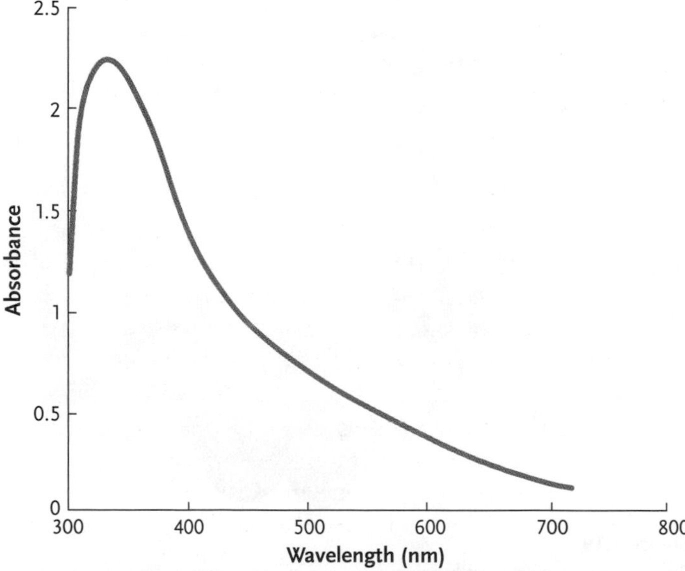

Figure 1.21
Absorption spectrum of melanin. The skin pigment melanin strongly absorbs photons of electromagnetic radiation which are in the ultraviolet region of the spectrum.

Besides an active repair system, all photosynthetic organisms have carotenoids, accessory pigments that can protect the photosynthetic apparatus from high light levels by absorbing excess light and safely dissipating the energy as heat. Although carotenoids are not nearly as abundant as chlorophyll, they are absolutely required to protect the photosynthetic apparatus. Plants unable to synthesize carotenoids turn white when exposed to sunlight because their chlorophyll becomes oxidized and its light-harvesting capabilities destroyed.

1.4b Damage by Light: Indirect Effects

Light from the sun is potentially harmful to life indirectly because of the ultraviolet radiation that accompanies it. This is the electromagnetic radiation between blue light and x-rays, consisting of wavelengths between 200 and 400 nm. Life on Earth is protected from the most damaging form of ultraviolet light, UV-C, by the atmosphere's ozone layer. However, longer wavelengths of harmful ultraviolet radiation, including UV-B and UV-A, do reach Earth's surface.

Because of its high energy, ultraviolet radiation can randomly ionize the atoms in a range of molecules, including pigment molecules and proteins. However, the structural integrity of deoxyribonucleic acid (DNA) is particularly vulnerable to damage **(Figure 1.20).** The interaction of ultraviolet light with nucleotide bases that make up DNA can result in the formation of a "dimer" when two neighbouring bases become covalently linked. Dimers can change the shape of the double-helix structure of DNA and prevent its replication, as well as hinder gene expression (see Chapter 12). Although cells have evolved elaborate mechanisms to repair this damage, dimer formation can give rise to genetic mutations, some of them harmful.

For most organisms, exposure to sunlight and therefore the damaging effects of ultraviolet radiation is unavoidable. Therefore, organisms use a range of behavioural, physiological, and biochemical mechanisms to protect themselves. Animals may avoid intense sunlight and/or shield their skin with fur or feathers. However, organisms with naked skin, such as humans, rely on producing melanin as an important protective mechanism.

Melanin is a pigment that absorbs ultraviolet radiation. This is shown by an absorption spectrum of pure melanin in solution **(Figure 1.21).** An **absorption spectrum** is a plot of the amount of light a pigment absorbs in relation to the wavelength of light. (We discuss absorption spectra related to photosynthesis in Chapter 7.) Figure 1.21 shows that melanin preferentially absorbs photons of electromagnetic radiation in the ultraviolet region of the spectrum. Humans synthesize melanin in specialized skin cells called

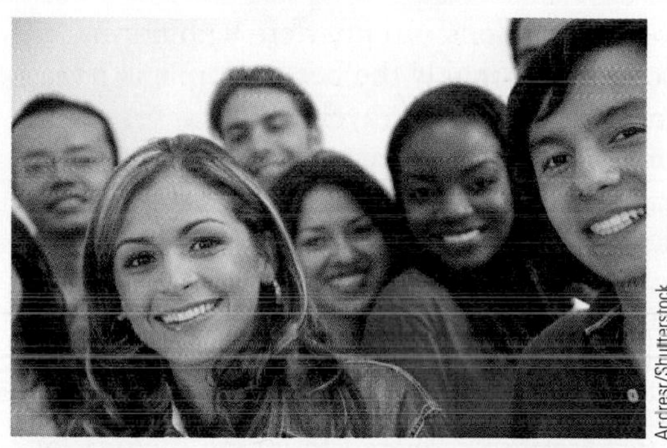

Figure 1.22
Human populations vary in regards to the amount of melanin.

melanocytes. In general, people from countries receiving a lot of sunlight (equatorial regions), such as Uganda, have more melanin in their skin than people from regions receiving less direct sunlight, such as Sweden **(Figure 1.22).** The presence of melanin prevents the DNA damage in skin cells that is linked to the development of skin cancer. Melanin prevents ultraviolet radiation from penetrating the skin and destroying the essential B vitamin folate.

Since melanin protects us from ultraviolet light, *why don't all humans have high melanin levels?* Although melanin filters out damaging ultraviolet wavelengths, humans require some ultraviolet radiation to synthesize vitamin D, which is critical for normal bone development. People with high melanin levels who live in regions that do not receive abundant sunlight are susceptible to vitamin D deficiency, such as someone of African descent living in Sweden. In much of the developed world, inadequate vitamin D intake is rare because many foods, such as milk, yogurt, and grain products (cereals and bread), are fortified with vitamin D. Interestingly, Inuit who are native to the Arctic have retained their relatively dark skin even though they inhabit a sun-poor environment. This can be explained by the fact that their traditional diet is dominated by fish and other marine life that is naturally high in vitamin D.

Study Break

1. What biological molecule is particularly susceptible to damage by ultraviolet radiation?
2. What wavelengths of electromagnetic radiation does melanin absorb?

1.5 Role of Light in Ecology and Behaviour

Nature provides a great range of light environments, ranging from the total darkness of caves or the ocean depths to the stark brightness of deserts and snowscapes. Differences in the intensity and spectral composition of the light coincide with organisms' adaptations to the specific light environment of particular habitats. For photosynthetic organisms, this means adjustments in light-harvesting properties of photosynthetic pigments. For many animals, it leads to unique colourations that may serve to attract members of the same species while making them potentially less visible to potential predators.

1.5a Using Light to Tell Time: Circadian Rhythms

Because Earth rotates on its axis once every 24 hours, life has evolved under a constant rhythmic cycle of light and dark. Many physiological and behavioural phenomena possess 24-hour rhythmicity: they vary depending on the time of day. Such phenomena include sleep-wake cycles, body temperature, locomotion, metabolic processes, cell division, and the behaviours associated with foraging for food and mating (see Chapters 40 and 41).

Many physiological and behavioural responses geared to Earth's day-night cycle are called **circadian rhythms** (*circa* = "around"; *diem* = "day") because they oscillate with a period of approximately 24 hours **(Figure 1.23, p. 14).** A defining characteristic of circadian rhythms is that they are NOT direct responses to changes in the external light environment but instead are controlled by an internal (endogenous), organism-based clock. This "biological clock" is set by the external light environment, but it can run a long time without any input from outside the organism. That circadian rhythms can be "free running" without daily input from the sun was first discovered in 1729 by the French astronomer Jean-Jacques d'Ortous de Mairan. He found that the daily rhythmic movements of certain plant leaves continued when he placed the plants in complete darkness. In humans, daily fluctuations in hormone levels, for example, are controlled by a circadian clock and will occur even if a subject is placed in conditions of constant light or darkness.

The importance of being able to predict the daily fluctuations of light is shown by the fact that circadian rhythms are found in all forms of life, from single-celled bacteria to plants and animals. Being able to keep track of day and night allows organisms to anticipate when a process occurs most efficiently during the 24-hour day and prepare accordingly. For example, in photosynthetic organisms, many proteins needed for photosynthesis are synthesized before dawn. This allows photosynthesis to occur at maximum efficiency during the daylight. It is thought that circadian rhythms originated to protect replicating DNA from damaging ultraviolet radiation during the day. As a result, the process of DNA replication is under circadian control and in many organisms occurs only at night.

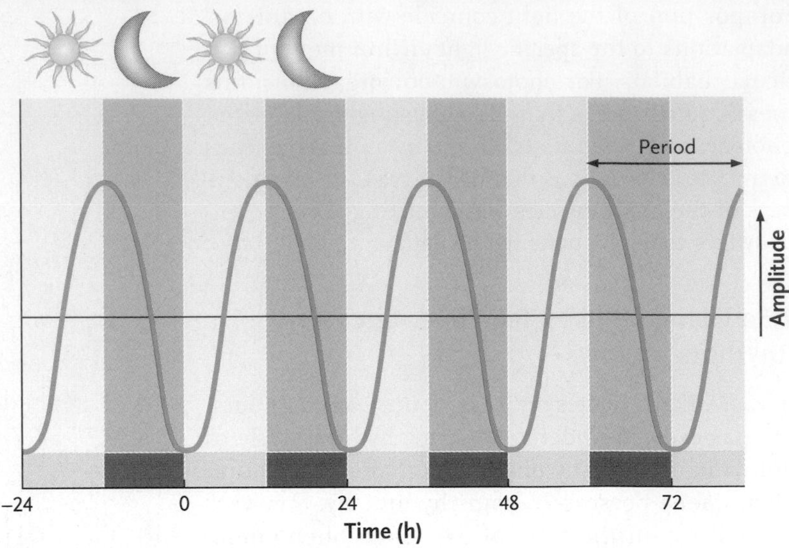

Figure 1.23
Circadian rhythms are oscillations in behaviour and physiology which have a period of approximately 24 hours. These rhythms are controlled by an endogenous biological clock.

In most animals, the central biological clock controlling many circadian rhythms is found within the suprachiasmatic nucleus, a region of the brain within the hypothalamus **(Figure 1.24).** The suprachiasmatic nucleus receives light inputs directly from the eye via the optic nerve, which it uses to set the biological clock. This clock, in turn, regulates a wide range of bodily functions, including the secretion of melatonin, a hormone, from the pineal gland. Melatonin is thought to have a role in controlling our sleep-wake cycles as its synthesis is active at nighttime but inhibited during the day (see Chapters 40 and 41).

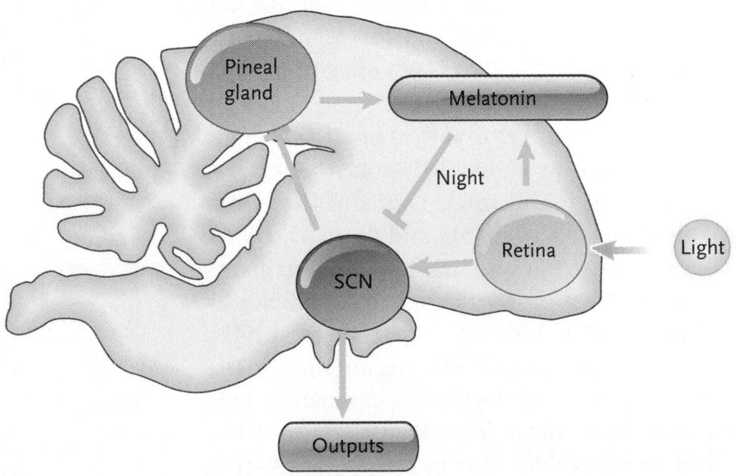

Figure 1.24
In humans circadian rhythms are controlled by a central biological clock which is found in the superchiasmatic nucleus of the brain. Changes in physiology and/or behaviour are linked to the central clock through changes in the levels of the hormone melatonin.

Several conditions can interfere with normal circadian cycling. Probably the best example is jet lag, which occurs when you travel rapidly across many time zones, putting your circadian clock out of synchronization with the external light environment. For example, if you take a five hour flight from Halifax to Vancouver starting at 6 P.M. when you arrive in Vancouver the local time is 7 P.M. The feeling of jet lag occurs because while it is only 7 P.M. your biological clock is telling you to go to bed because it thinks it is 11 P.M. Symptoms related to jet lag include lack of appetite, fatigue, insomnia, and mild depression. The physiological consequences of jet lag clearly indicate the number of processes that are linked to circadian time keeping. They also show that the circadian clock cannot be automatically reset to the new light conditions but may take a few days to become readjusted or entrained.

Many plants and animals show cycles of seasonal activities as well as daily cycles. In plants, this includes the timing of flowering and dormancy. In animals, this includes migration or hibernation (see Chapter 40). In some parts of the world, changes in day length (photoperiod) herald changes in seasons. Plants and animals in these regions mainly depend on the photoperiod to prepare for changes in their seasonal activities. What better way to measure the relative length of day and night than by enlisting the machinery by which circadian rhythms are entrained?

1.5b Avoiding Detection: Camouflage

Camouflage works when one animal fails to distinguish another from the background. Pattern and behaviour play central roles in camouflage. The female duck sitting on her nest is hard to distinguish from the background because of the pattern of colour in her feathers and because she does not move **(Figure 1.25).**

The importance of background in camouflage is demonstrated by the case of the peppered moth, *Biston betularia.* Prior to the Industrial Revolution in England, light-coloured peppered moths were considered "typical" and dark-coloured individuals were exceptions prized by moth collectors. Light colour made the moths inconspicuous when resting on lichen-covered tree trunks during the day **(Figure 1.26a).** The situation changed after the Industrial Revolution, when many tree trunks became dark-coloured from deposits of soot and because air pollution killed the lichens. In this setting, light-coloured moths were easily detected by hunting birds and dark-coloured individuals quickly became the most common form **(Figure 1.26b).** Today, as a result of clean air legislation and reduced air pollution, the ratio

Figure 1.25
From a distance, **(a)** it is easy to overlook the duck (*Anas* spp.) sitting on her nest in an urban graveyard. Up close **(b)**, the pattern on her feathers breaks up her body outline, making her difficult to see, particularly when she does not move. As usual, looking for eyes can be a good way to see animals you otherwise might have overlooked, such as the Scops Owl **(c)** (*Otus scops*).

Figure 1.26
An example of camouflage in the peppered moth, *Biston betularia*. The moth is found in one of two forms: lightly-coloured or darkly-coloured. During the industrial revolution pollution darkened the bark of trees **(a)** that were part of the moth's habitat. This resulted in increased predation of the light-coloured moth. Following anti-pollution measures, trees returned to being lightly coloured **(b)** which resulted in an increase in the numbers of the moths that are similarly coloured.

of light to dark coloured moths has returned to the pre–Industrial Revolution norm in some areas. The case of the peppered moth is clear and has become an often-cited example of evolution by natural selection (see Chapters 3 and 18).

1.5c Using Colour as Signals

Animals often use bright colours to signal that they are distasteful and/or armed and dangerous. As animals that make extensive use of vision, we humans are familiar with colourful warning signals **(Figure 1.27, p. 16)**. To be effective, a signal must be received, so if the signal receiver is blind to colour **(Figure 1.28, p. 16)**, the signal is of no use. But animals use other media, and most North Americans are familiar with the odour of a skunk or the buzz of a bee, not to mention the rattle of a rattlesnake. Monarch butterflies (*Danaus plexippus*) use a distinct red and black pattern to warn of their bad taste **(Figure 1.29, p. 16)** (see Chapter 47). Bees and wasps, with their black and yellow stripes as warning signals, are other examples of dangerous animals. Some animals mimic the warning signals of others (see Figures 47.6 and 47.10 and Chapter 47).

Figure 1.27
The red signal on a traffic light sends an unmistakable signal **(a)** that is completely lost on a species or individual that is blind to colour **(b)**.

M.B. Fenton

a.

M.B. Fenton

b.

Figure 1.28
Comparing a colour **(a)** and grey scale **(b)** view of a chart designed to assess colour vision in humans is one way to demonstrate the impact of colour blindness.

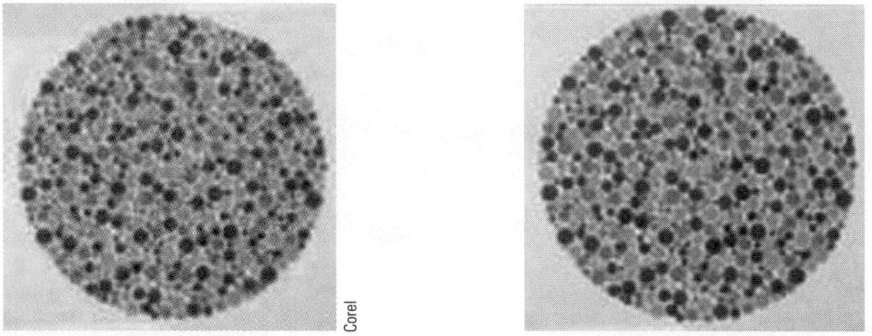

Corel

a.

Corel

b.

M.B. Fenton

a.

M.B. Fenton

b.

M.B. Fenton

c.

M.B. Fenton

d.

M.B. Fenton

e.

M.B. Fenton

f.

Figure 1.29
The colourful warning signal of a bee **(a)** or a monarch butterfly **(b)** loses its impact when viewed in greyscale (**c** and **d**). The situation is further complicated by their predators. Whereas a Bluejay **(e)** has excellent colour vision, a hedgehog **(f)** does not.

Although humans marvel at the diversity of colours and patterns of flowers, biologists correctly conclude that such displays were not designed to please humans but rather to attract animal pollinators (see Chapter 30). Pollination involves the movement of pollen from the anthers (male parts) of one flower to the stigma (female parts) of the same or other flowers to effect fertilization and production of seeds (see Chapters 30 and 47). Pollinators obtain sugar-rich nectars and protein-rich pollen at flowers.

Plants that use animals as pollinators must attract the correct candidates to ensure that they are pollinated and do not waste pollen and nectar. The characteristics of flowers (shape, colour, smell) make them more attractive to specific groups of potential pollinators, reflecting differences in pollinator behaviour. Potential pollinators differ in their perception of light of different wavelengths, so they are attracted by flowers of specific colours. Birds such as hummingbirds are attracted to red flowers, whereas bees are attracted primarily to blue and yellow flowers (see Figure 18.18). Bees are important pollinators that also perceive ultraviolet light and are attracted to flowers with ultraviolet-reflecting pigments **(Figure 1.30)**.

a.

b.

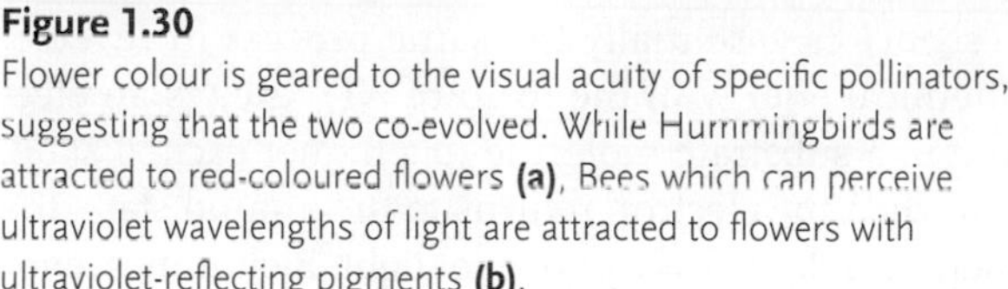

Carel

Carel

Figure 1.30
Flower colour is geared to the visual acuity of specific pollinators, suggesting that the two co-evolved. While Hummingbirds are attracted to red-coloured flowers **(a)**, Bees which can perceive ultraviolet wavelengths of light are attracted to flowers with ultraviolet-reflecting pigments **(b)**.

1.5d Light in Aquatic Habitats

Water attenuates light rapidly, and almost no light penetrates below about 150 metres. Furthermore, water selectively scatters and absorbs longer wavelengths of light more effectively than shorter wavelengths, so below about 30 metres, light is essentially monochromatic, consisting solely of blue wavelengths. Red algae **(Figure 1.31)** thrive at a greater depth in the oceans than many other photosynthetic organisms because they have phytoerythrin, an accessory photosynthetic pigment not found in land plants. Phytoerythrin preferentially absorbs blue wavelengths of light, giving red algae their distinctive colour.

Fish living in shallow marine waters tend to be brilliantly coloured, whereas species that live deeper tend to have black backs and silver underbodies, making them less conspicuous when viewed from both above and below.

1.5e Ecological Light Pollution

The electric light bulb is considered one of the greatest inventions because it allowed people to carry on pursuits at night that otherwise would not have been possible. However, rapid proliferation of artificial lighting that illuminates public buildings, streets, and signs has resulted in "light pollution," which has transformed the nighttime environment over significant portions of Earth's surface. In the United States, only about 40% of people live where it truly gets dark at night **(Figure 1.32, p. 18)**.

Ecologists have begun to study the sometimes devastating consequences of light pollution on natural populations. The presence of artificial light disrupts orientation in nocturnal animals otherwise accustomed to operating in the dark. For example, newly hatched sea turtles emerge from nests on sandy beaches and orient themselves and move toward the ocean because it is

Image collection of the University of Wisconsin-La Crosse. Image used with permission.

Figure 1.31
Why are red algae....red? Red algae preferentially absorb shorter wavelength blue light-red photons are reflected. Blue light is the dominant wavelengths of light that reach deep in the water column where red algae are found.

Thomas Hawk

Figure 1.32
An example of light pollution.

Figure 1.33
The blind mole rat (*Spalax* sp.) is subterranean rarely venturing above ground. They are functionally blind.

brighter than the silhouette of dark dunes. However, with increased beachfront lighting, hatchlings become disoriented, head inland, and die. The nocturnal lives of many species of frogs and salamanders have been disrupted by light pollution. We know that artificial lighting has a negative effect on migrating birds. Hundreds of thousands of migrating birds are killed each year when they collide with lighted buildings and towers.

Other animals, such as bats and geckos, benefit from night lights that attract insects, effectively concentrating their prey.

Study Break

1. What is a circadian rhythm?
2. How does water affect the properties of light?

1.6 Life in the Dark

Humans see very well by day, but our visual powers quickly falter at night, when light levels may be 100 million times dimmer than daylight. With decreasing light levels, we first lose our ability to see colour, followed by our ability to distinguish shapes. Animals that are nocturnal, such as moths, fish, bats, and frogs, see very well under dim light.

In some environments, such as caves and ocean deeps, animals live in complete darkness. Many of these animals cannot see even though their ancestors had functional eyes. The blind mole rat spends all of its life in underground darkness, only rarely venturing above ground **(Figure 1.33)**. Twenty-five million years of adaptation to life in the dark has resulted in the natural degeneration of the blind mole rat's visual system to the point at which the mole rat is effectively blind. Their eyes are not only small (less than 1 mm in diameter) but also are covered by several layers of tissue. Behavioural and physiological studies have shown that the photoreceptors of the eye remain functional even though the image-forming part of the brain is dramatically reduced. *So what purpose do these functional photoreceptors have?* Since individual mole rats are exposed to brief periods of natural light, the photoreceptors allow entrainment or setting of their biological clocks and control of their circadian rhythms. Although the image-producing portion of the brain in these mole rats is greatly reduced, the suprachiasmatic nucleus is well developed and receives information from the eyes.

Another good example of the degeneration of the eye over time is found in the Mexican cavefish, which occurs as two morphological types: a surface-water form that has eyes and skin pigment **(Figure 1.34a)** and a cave-dwelling form that lacks eyes and pigment **(Figure 1.34b)**. The ancestors of the cavefish lived on the surface, and both eyes and pigment have been lost over approximately 10 000 years.

Study Break

Do the eyes of the blind mole rat have a function?

1.7 Organisms Making Their Own Light: Bioluminescence

Many organisms, including certain bacteria, algae, fungi, insects, squid, and fish, are bioluminescent: they produce light **(Figure 1.35)**. Bioluminescence has developed many times during evolution but always involves the same basic biochemical reaction. Recall that in the process of light absorption by a pigment, the energy of a photon is transferred to an electron, raising it from the ground state to an excited state. Bioluminescence is essentially the same process in reverse. Chemical energy in the form of ATP excites an electron in a substrate molecule to a higher excited state, and when the electron returns to the ground state, the energy is released as a photon of light. Bioluminescence

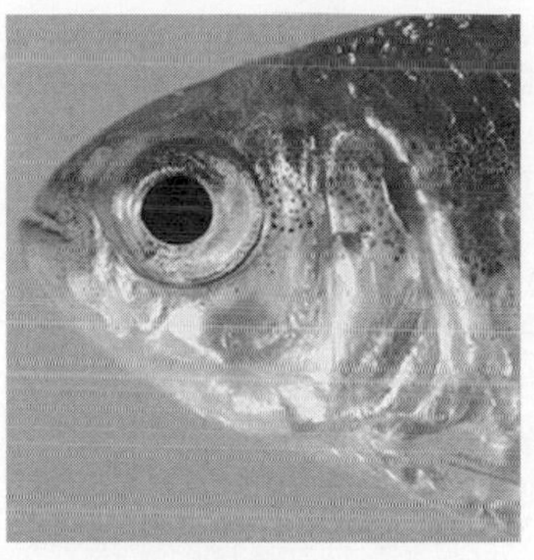

a.

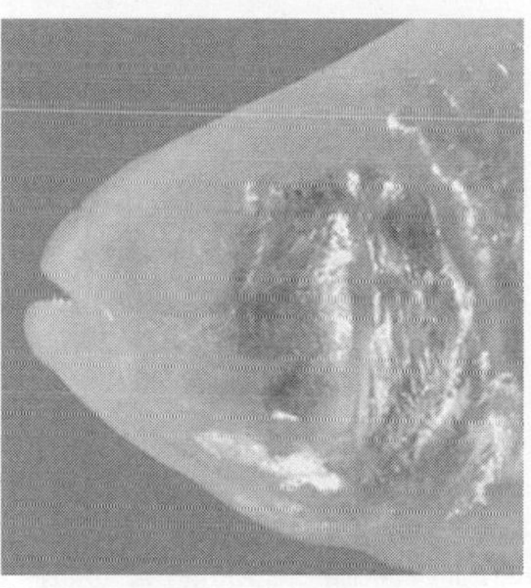

b.

Figure 1.34
If you don't use it you lose it. An example of eye degeneration in the Mexican cave fish, *Astyanax mexicanus.* The single species exists as a surface-dwelling form (left) and a blind cave-dwelling form (right).

W. R. Jeffery, "Adaptive Evolution of Eye Degeneration in the Mexican Blind Cavefish", The Journal of Heredity, 2004, vol. 96, issue number 3, pp. 186 by permission of Oxford University Press.

a. b. c. Steve Miller/Naval Research Lab; Photo: Steven Haddock; Cas Liber

d.

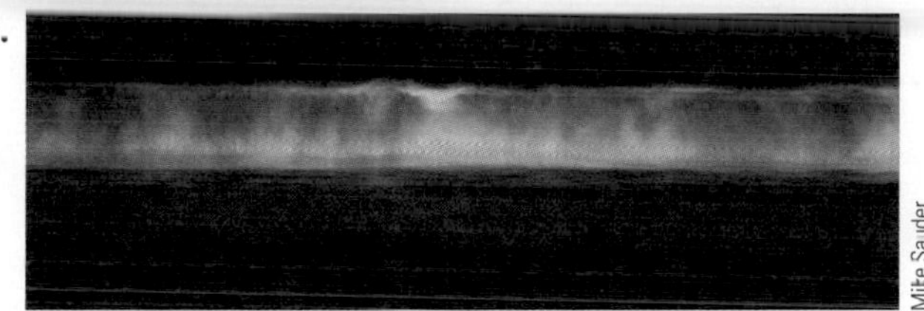

Mike Sauder

Figure 1.35
Examples of bioluminescence. **(a)** Satellite image of a "milky sea" a bloom of bioluminescent bacteria off the east coast of Africa. **(b)** bioluminescent octopus. **(c)** A type of fungus in the light (top) and dark (bottom) showing bioluminescence **(d)** A beach in California showing a wave of bioluminescence caused by the presence of billions of cells of a group of unicellular algae called dinoflagellates.

reactions are remarkably efficient. Although up to 95% of the energy of a light bulb is lost as heat, less than 5% of the energy used for bioluminescence is given off as heat. This extraordinary efficiency is essential because high heat production would be incompatible with life.

Why do bioluminescent organisms invest so much energy in light production? Bioluminescent organisms use light to attract a mate, for camouflage, to attract prey, or to communicate. Dinoflagellates are unicellular algae that use bioluminescence as an "alarm bell" to scare off potential predators. In these tiny organisms, bioluminescence is triggered simply by disturbance of the water surrounding them. When a predator such as a small fish swims close to a dinoflagellate at night, the resulting burst of light produced by all the dinoflagellates in the vicinity lights up the water around the fish. This defensive behaviour makes the fish clearly visible to its own predators.

Some marine bacteria use bioluminescence in a type of communication called quorum sensing. Individual bacteria often release compounds into their environment at concentrations too low to elicit a response from their neighbours. However, as a bacterial population grows its size reaches a threshold, a quorum, whereby the concentration of compounds is high enough to elicit a physiological response in all members of the population. The response results in the activation of certain genes, including those that encode for proteins required for bioluminescence. Quorum sensing is now believed to be the basis for what are termed "milky seas" (see Figure 1.35). This strange phenomenon of luminescence from the surface of the ocean has been reported many times over the past several hundred years by sailors, including a mention in Jules Verne's classic book *Twenty Thousand Leagues under the Sea.*

If you have ever walked through a forest at night, you may have seen glowing light here and there on the forest floor. This light, known as "foxfire," is part of many ghost stories and folktales, but it is produced by bioluminescent fungi growing in rotten wood. Unlike bioluminescence in other organisms, we do not yet understand how fungi produce light or what role bioluminescence plays in their lives. One suggestion is that the fungi produce light to attract insects that will disperse spores, but this cannot always be the case as at least some bioluminescent fungi use wind to disperse their spores. In many bioluminescent fungi, the vegetative body produces light, not the spore-producing structure. Fungal bioluminescence remains a mystery (see Chapter 24).

Bioluminescent light must be perceived by another organism in order to be useful to the organism producing it. Therefore, organisms that use bioluminescent signals must have light-sensing organs. We presume, perhaps correctly, that bioluminescence evolved later than light sensing.

Most bioluminescent organisms are marine and are most abundant below 800 metres, a depth to which sunlight does not penetrate. Bioluminescence has not been reported in land plants or higher vertebrates. Why is bioluminescence absent in these organisms? We do not yet have the answers to this or other questions about bioluminescence, reminding us how much there is still to discover about life on Earth.

In closing, this introductory chapter discussed one phenomenon, light, and how it impinges on the biology of Earth. From absorption of a single photon by a pigment molecule in a single cell to affecting the composition of entire ecosystems, the influence of light spans all levels of biological organization. This chapter touched on many topics, from physics and chemistry, photosynthesis, genes and proteins, evolution and natural selection to ecology and behaviour. As you work through the remaining chapters of this texbook, you will learn much more about these topics and many others.

Study Break

1. What is bioluminescence?
2. Bioluminescence is found in many organisms found in which habitat?

Unanswered Questions

Is there any hope for the development of a "bionic eye"?

For most of us, having good vision throughout our lives is something we take for granted. However, a number of diseases result in diminished vision and often progressively lead to blindness. These include retinitis pigmentosa and age-related macular degeneration, two diseases that have genetic links for which there is no foreseeable cure. Recent data indicate that about one-third of people between 55 and 74 years of age will develop age-related macular degeneration.

Both age-related macular degeneration and retinitis pigmentosa lead to a loss of vision because they both result in degeneration of the photoreceptor cells (rods and cones) found in the retina at the back of the eye. We will learn much more about eye structure and function in Chapter 34. The rods and cones convert light into electrical impulses, which are carried by the optic nerve to the brain, where images are formed.

For years, the development of an artificial "bionic eye" that could restore at least some vision to people who are otherwise blind has been the realm of science fiction—an unattainable dream for both scientists and those with vision degeneration. However, a great deal of research has been carried out in recent years, specifically in the development of an artificial retina since this is the part of the optic system that is damaged in many forms of vision degeneration. The most significant advances have come with the production of a functional artificial retina through research carried out by Mark Humayun, professor of ophthalmology and biomedical engineering, and his associates at the Doheny Eye Institute at the University of Southern California.

Current versions of the artificial retina, which has been successfully implanted in a number of patients, consist of a flexible, wafer-thin, square grid of 16 electrodes surgically attached in the back of the eye. The system also consists of a miniature camera mounted on a pair of sunglasses. The retina and camera are interfaced by a small external wallet-size computer that converts the information from the camera into electrical signals, which are then sent wirelessly to the artificial retina. From there, the current passes through the optic nerve to the brain. The implant has allowed patients to regain some rudimentary vision, including the ability to detect motion and to distinguish between dark and light.

Given the tremendous technological and engineering hurdles that have been overcome to develop this artificial retina, the results for vision may seem relatively primitive. These problems reflect the highly impressive ability of the vision system to process information. Human vision is remarkably sensitive to a wide range of wavelengths and light intensities and can differentiate subtleties in colour, shading, and depth. There are roughly 1.2 million fibres in the optic nerve, each connected to a neuron, which can fire 200 pulses per second. A single eye can send the brain up to 200 million bits of information per second. Although the current technology does not come close to the staggeringly fast rate of information transfer, the current system is rapidly improving. Advancements include reducing the size and power demands on the camera such that it can be placed within the eye itself. Researchers have also successfully moved from implanting a 16-electrode retina to a more advanced 60-electrode device. Researchers are currently developing a 1000-electrode implant that should allow recipients of the retina to gain facial recognition capabilities.

Review

Go to CENGAGENOW™ at http://hed.nelson.com/ to access quizzing, animations, exercises, articles, and personalized homework help.

1.1 The Physical Nature of Light

- For organisms, light serves as a source of energy and as a source of information.
- Light can be defined as electromagnetic radiation that humans can detect with their eyes.
- Light can be thought of as a wave of discrete particles called photons.
- To be used, light energy must be absorbed by molecules called pigments.
- Colour is the result of wavelengths of light that are not absorbed by a pigment.

1.2 Light as a Source of Energy

- The absorption of light by a pigment results in electrons becoming excited. This represents a source of potential energy.
- Photosynthesis is the dominant process on Earth that uses pigments to capture light energy and uses it to convert carbon dioxide into energy-rich carbohydrates.

1.3 Light as a Source of Information

- The basic light-sensing system is called the photoreceptor.
- A photoreceptor (e.g., rhodopsin) consists of a pigment molecule (retinal) bound to a protein (opsin).

- The *C. reinhardtii* eyespot allows the organism to sense both light direction and intensity and respond by swimming toward or away from the light (phototaxis).
- The eye can be defined as the organ animals use to sense light.
- Vision requires a brain to interpret signals sent from the eye.
- The simplest eye is the ocellus found in planarians. It enables the sensing of light direction and intensity.
- Image-forming eyes include compound eyes found in arthropods and single-lens eyes found in some invertebrates and most vertebrates, including humans.
- Because it was thought to be an organ of "extreme perfection," Darwin initially had a difficult time explaining how it could have arisen by evolution.
- The relatively rapid evolution of the eye is explained by the huge advantage an improved eye would give an organism.

1.4 Light Can Damage Biological Molecules

- Photosynthesis, vision, and most other light-driven processes use only a narrow band of the electromagnetic spectrum. This may be because shorter wavelengths are more harmful (higher energy) and longer wavelengths tend not to reach Earth's surface.
- Light is a form of energy; thus, too much light can damage biological molecules.
- The photosynthetic apparatus is constantly being damaged by light and the damage repaired.
- Ultraviolet radiation, because of its high energy, is particularly harmful to biological molecules, particularly DNA.
- Human skin cells are protected by the pigment melanin that absorbs ultraviolet radiation.

1.5 Role of Light in Ecology and Behaviour

- Organisms are adapted to specific light environments from total darkness to bright light.
- Many physiological and behavioural responses are geared to the daily changes in light and darkness and are called circadian rhythms.
- Circadian rhythms are found in all forms of life and evolved to enable organisms to anticipate changes in the light environment.
- Many organisms use colour to attract, warn, or hide from other organisms.
- Aquatic habitats have an altered light environment because water rapidly attenuates longer wavelengths (red) of light. Below 30 m, only blue wavelengths of light penetrate; below about 150 m, there is a total absence of light.
- The widespread use of artificial lighting has been shown to disrupt numerous biological phenomena, including bird migration and the orientation of nocturnal animals.

1.6 Life in the Dark

- Unlike humans, many nocturnal animals (moths, fish, bats, frogs) see very well under dim light conditions.
- Some animals, such as the blind mole rat, are functionally blind yet are descended from ancestors that had functional eyes.

1.7 Organisms Making Their Own Light: Bioluminescence

- A range of organisms can use chemical energy to make light—bioluminescence.
- Bioluminescent organisms use light to attract a mate, for camouflage, to attract prey, or to communicate.

Questions

Self-Test Questions

1. Which of the following statements about light is NOT correct?
   a. Light is a form of electromagnetic radiation.
   b. Organisms use light as a source of energy and information.
   c. Light can be considered a wave composed of packets of energy called photons.
   d. Electromagnetic radiation moves in the form of two waves.
   e. The longer the wavelength, the more energy the photons of light contain.
2. Chlorophyll appears green because it
   a. reflects red light.
   b. absorbs green and blue wavelengths of light.
   c. reflects blue light.
   d. does not absorb green photons.
   e. contains an excited state that matches the energy of a green photon.
3. To be used as a source of information or energy, a photon of light must
   a. have sufficient energy to oxidize a molecule.
   b. first be absorbed by a pigment molecule.
   c. interact with a protein in the plasma membrane.
   d. be reflected off a substance.
   e. None of the above statements are correct.
4. A photoreceptor consists of
   a. a pigment molecule bound to a protein.
   b. a protein that is involved in photosynthesis.
   c. a group of many pigment molecules.
   d. a molecule of chlorophyll.
   e. None of the above is correct
5. Compared to the eyespot of *C. reinhardtii*, the human eye
   a. is composed of photoreceptors.
   b. can detect changes in light intensity.
   c. can activate a signal transduction pathway when it absorbs light.
   d. is not damaged by ultraviolet radiation.
   e. is image forming.
6. Which of the following statements is NOT correct?
   a. Rapid eye evolution is explained by the huge advantage an improved eye would give an organism.
   b. The ocellus is common in a number of insects, arthropods, and molluscs.
   c. "Vision" requires not only eyes but also a brain.
   d. All eyes consist of a single large photoreceptor cell.
   e. The ommatidium of insects is very adept at detecting movement.
7. Light represents only a very narrow region of the electromagnetic spectrum, yet it is used for a diversity of processes, including vision, photosynthesis, phototaxis, and navigation. This is because
   a. light contains the most energy.
   b. light can excite molecules without destroying them.
   c. all other wavelengths of light are too destructive to biological molecules.

d. light is the dominant form of radiation that reaches Earth's surface.
e. Both b and d are correct.

8. Which of the following statements about circadian rhythms is correct?
   a. They have a period of approximately 12 hours.
   b. They stop if an organism is placed in complete darkness.
   c. They are found only in animals and plants.
   d. They enable organisms to anticipate changes to their light environment.
   e. They are not affected by airplane travel.
9. The Mexican cavefish illustrate that
   a. animals can still see in complete darkness.
   b. you don't need eyes for vision.
   c. eyes can still function without photoreceptors.
   d. organs that are no longer of use can degenerate over time.
   e. None of the above is correct.
10. Bioluminescence is
   a. the process whereby organisms capture light and then release it.
   b. the production of light energy from chemical energy.
   c. found only in bacteria.
   d. commonly found in organisms that are found in the deep ocean.
   e. Both b and d are correct.

Questions for Discussion

1. In writing this chapter, the authors found it difficult to define the "eye." Why do you think this was difficult?
2. Are eyes perfect?
3. What is the biochemical basis of circadian rhythms and biological clocks? What are the components of this clock, and how does it work?

Scanning electron microscope image of a portion of the meteorite ALH84001. The elongate structure may represent a fossilized microorganism.

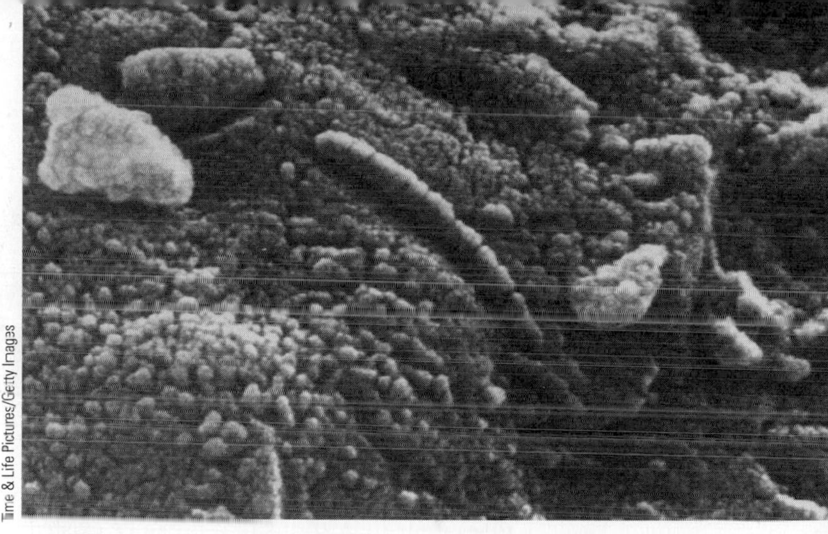
Time & Life Pictures/Getty Images

Study Plan

2 Origins of Life

Why It Matters

In 1984, a group of scientists in the Antarctic discovered a 1.9 kg meteorite that they catalogued as ALH84001. Initial studies of the meteorite showed that it was about 4.5 billion years old, which is about the same age as the solar system. As well, its chemical composition indicated that it had originated from Mars and had impacted Earth approximately 13 000 years ago. The meteorite garnered headlines around the world in 1996 when an article was published in the prestigious journal *Science* with evidence that ALH84001 contained distinct evidence that life had at one time existed on Mars.

Chemical analysis showed that, when on Mars, ALH84001 had at one time been fractured and subsequently infiltrated by liquid water. Using scanning electron microscopy, the coauthors of the article observed very small, elliptical, ropelike, and tubular structures in the fractured surfaces of ALH84001 that look very similar to fossilized prokaryotes. Furthermore, the scientists found microscopic mineral "globules," which bear strong resemblance to mineral alterations caused by primitive prokaryotes on Earth. One last piece of evidence is that the meteorite contains an abundance of polycyclic aromatic hydrocarbons (PAHs). These compounds are commonly formed when microorganisms die and break down.

Figure 2.1
Red-eyed treefrog on a rock.

Art Wolfe/Stone/Getty Images

Analysis of ALH84001 continues as it remains controversial as to whether the evidence presented gives clear indications that life once existed on Mars. However, taken together, the PAHs, unusual mineral deposits, and bacteria-like structures were all located within a few micrometres of one another, suggesting a relationship that may be due to life.

2.1 What Is Life?

Picture a frog sitting on a rock, slowly shifting its head to follow the movements of insects flying nearby **(Figure 2.1)**. You know instinctively that the frog is alive and that the rock is not. However, if you examine both at the molecular level, you will find that the differences between them blur. The types of atoms and molecules found in living things are no different from those found in nonliving forms of matter. Furthermore, living cells obey the same fundamental laws of chemistry and physics as does the abiotic (nonliving) world. For example, the biochemical reactions that take place within living cells, although seemingly remarkably complex, are only modifications of reactions that take place in the abiotic world.

2.1a Seven Characteristics that All Forms of Life Share

Although life seems relatively easy to recognize, it is not easy to define using only a single sentence. Instead, all forms of life share a set of attributes that collectively differentiate them from nonliving things. The seven fundamental characteristics that are common to all forms of life are listed below and shown in **Figure 2.2.**

Figure 2.2
The seven characteristics of life.

harmeet/StockXchng

a. Display order: All forms of life including this flower are arranged in a highly ordered manner, with the cell being the fundamental unit of life.

© Visuals Unlimited/Corbis

b. Harness and utilize energy: Like this hummingbird, all forms of life acquire energy from the environment and use it to maintain their highly ordered state.

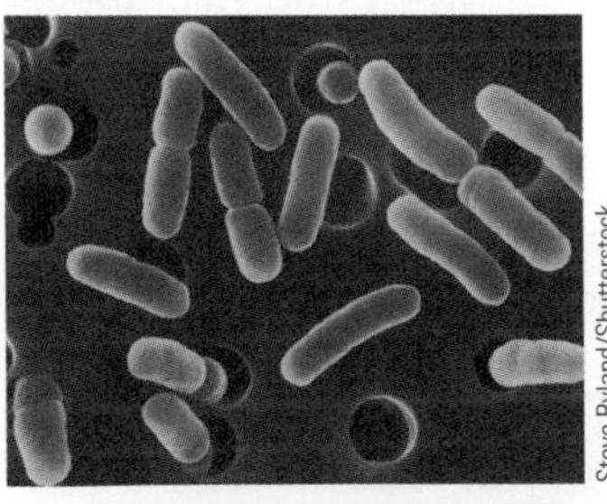

Steve Byland/Shutterstock

c. Reproduce: All organisms have the ability to make more of their own kind. Here, some of the bacteria can be seen having just divided into two daughter cells.

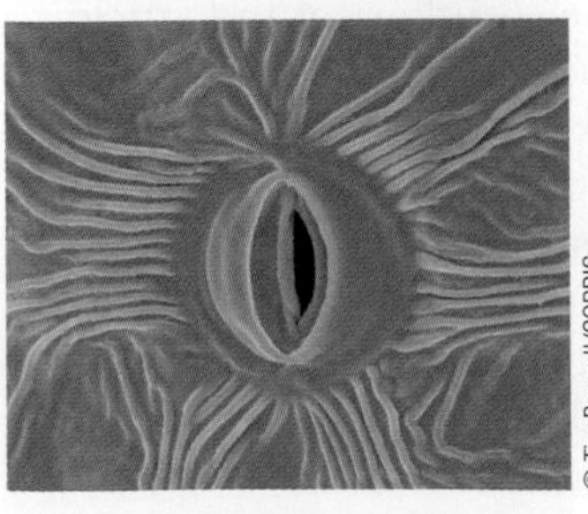

© Tim Pannell/CORBIS

d. Respond to stimuli: Organisms can make adjustments to their structure, function, and behaviour in response to changes to the external environment. A plant can adjust the size of the pore on the surface of a leaf (a stomata) to regulate gas exchange.

© PHOTOTAKE Inc./Alamy

e. Exhibit homeostasis: Organisms are able to regulate their internal environment such that conditions remain relatively constant. Sweating is one way in which the body attempts to remove heat and thereby maintain a constant temperature.

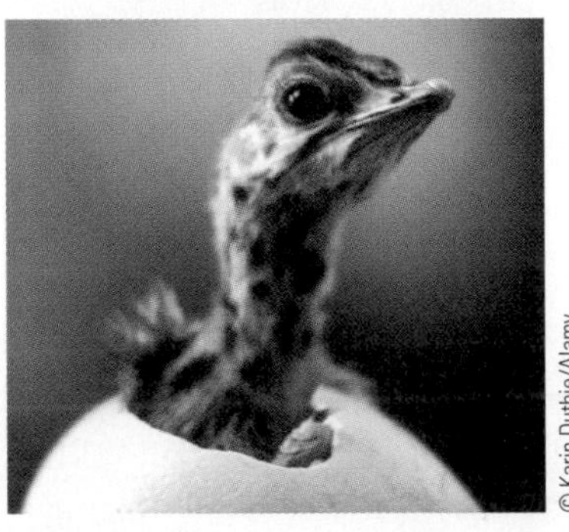

© Karin Duthie/Alamy

f. Growth and development: All organisms increase their size by increasing the size and/or number of cells. Many organisms also change overtime.

Art Wolfe/Stone/Getty Images

g. Evolve: Populations of living organisms change over the course of generations to become better adapted to their environment. This snowy owl illustrates this perfectly.

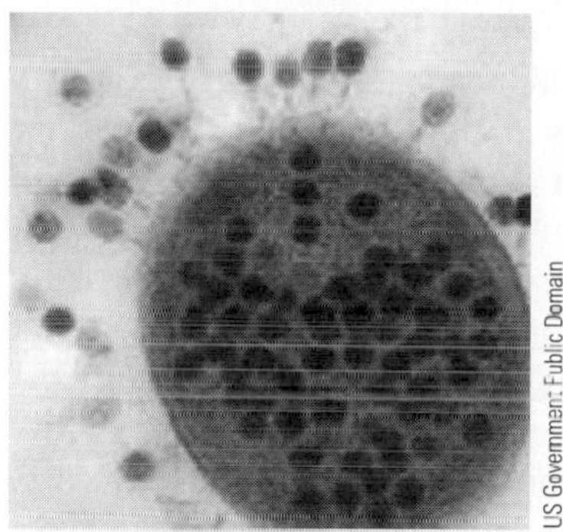

US Government Public Domain

Figure 2.3
Bacteriophage (a type of virus) infecting a bacterium. A virus is not considered to be alive.

Is a virus alive? A handful of biological entities straddle the definition of life, and the best example of these is a virus **(Figure 2.3)**. Viruses seemingly display many of the properties of life, including the ability to reproduce and evolve over time. However, the characteristics of life that a virus possesses are based on its ability to infect living cells. Although viruses contain nucleic acids, they lack the cellular machinery to synthesize their own proteins. They essentially highjack the machinery and metabolism of a living cell in order to reproduce. For this reason, most scientists do not consider a virus alive.

2.1b The Fundamental Unit of Life Is the Cell

By the middle of the nineteenth century, observations by biologists using light microscopy (see *The Chemical and Physical Foundations of Biology* pages) yielded three profound generalizations about the organization of living organisms. Together, these have become known as the three tenets of the **cell theory**:

1. **All organisms are composed of one or more cells.** Some types of organisms, such as prokaryotes, are composed of only a single cell. In these unicellular organisms, the one cell is a functionally independent organism capable of carrying out all life activities. In more complex multicellular organisms, including plants and animals, major life activities are divided among varying numbers of specialized cells. Individual cells of multicellular organisms are potentially capable of surviving by themselves if placed in a chemical medium that can sustain them.
2. **The cell is the smallest unit that has the properties of life.** If cells are broken open, the property of life is lost: they are unable to grow, reproduce, or respond to outside stimuli in a coordinated, potentially independent fashion. Scientists can learn a lot about how a cell functions by doing experiments on disrupted cells, examining only a single component of the cell.
3. **Cells arise only from the growth and division of preexisting cells.** Although deoxyribonucleic acid (DNA) and ribonucleic acid (RNA) contain the information required to manufacture a vast array of biological molecules, they cannot orchestrate the formation of an entire cell. New cells can arise only from the division of preexisting cells.

As shown by the examples in **Figure 2.4,** there are many different kinds of cells.

Study Break

Why are viruses not considered a form of life?

2.2 The Chemical Origins of Life

Recall that the third tenet of the cell theory states that cells arise only from the growth and division of preexisting cells. This tenet has probably been true for hundreds of millions of years, yet there must have been a time when this was not the case. There must have been a time when no cells existed, when there was no life. Over the course of hundreds of millions of years, cells with the characteristics of life arose out of a mixture of molecules that existed on the primordial Earth. In the next few sections, we discuss how life arose on Earth. For parts of this discussion, the theories have been firmly supported by experimentation; for other parts, all we have are vague hypotheses.

a. Bacterium

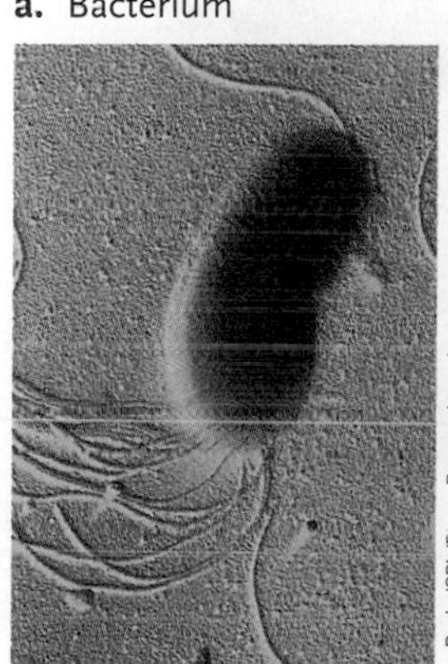

Tony Brain/SPL/Photo Researchers, Inc.

b. Protozoan

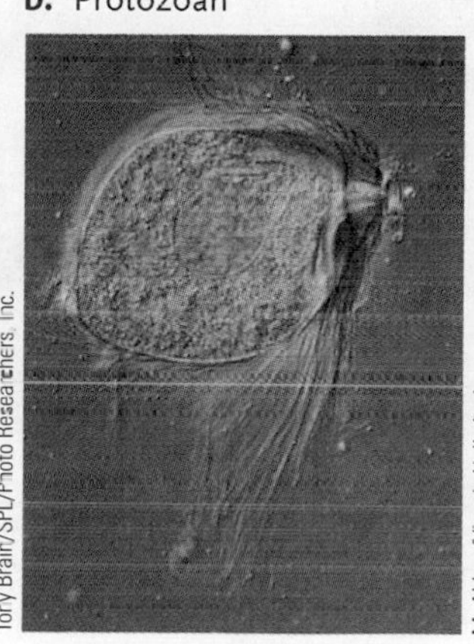

M. Abbey/Visuals Unlimited

c. Algae

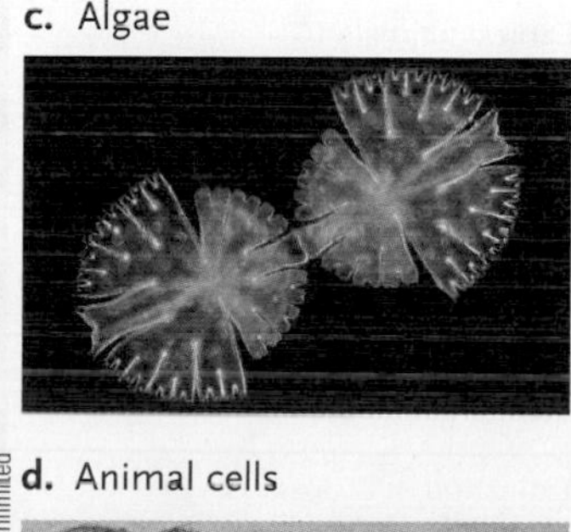

Wim van Egmond/Visuals Unlimited

d. Animal cells

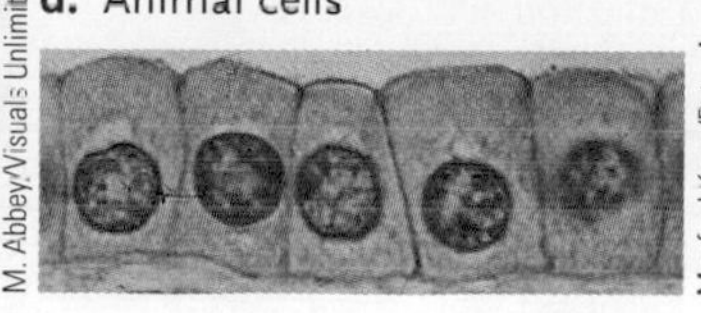

Manfred Kage/Peter Arnold

e. Plant cells

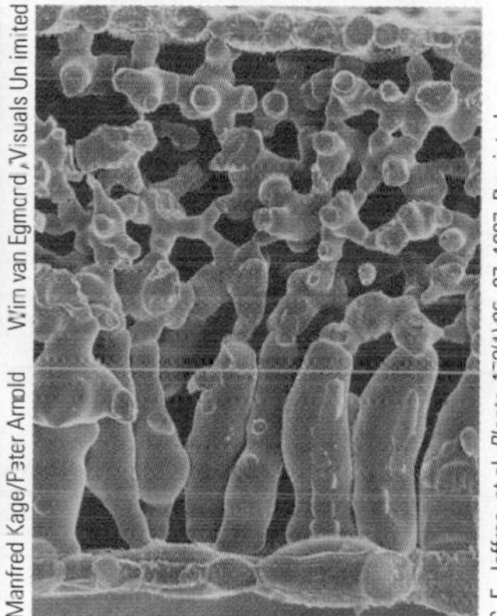

C. E. Jeffree, et al, *Planta*, 172(1):20–37, 1987. Reprinted.

Figure 2.4
Examples of cells.

2.2a 4.6 Billion Years Condensed into 1

Earth is approximately 4.6 billion or 4 600 000 000 years old. To give us some sense of this immense length of time and the relative timing of some major events in the history of life on Earth, **Figure 2.5** condenses the entire history of Earth into a unit of time that we are familiar with—one year. By condensing 4.6 billion years into a single year, each day represents an interval of 12.6 million years.

According to this analogy, Earth was formed on January 1 at 12:00 A.M., however, the earliest chemical evidence of life doesn't occur until mid-March, with the first fossil evidence of prokaryotic life appearing in late March. It is not until early July, however, that the first eukaryotic cells appear. Animals do not make an appearance until mid-October and land plants until the following month. Using our calendar, the extinction of dinosaurs, which we discuss in Chapter 20, does not occur until late December. What about humans? We may think humans, *Homo sapiens*, have been around a long time, but relative to other forms of life, the roughly 150 000 years that modern humans have existed is a very short period of time. Using our year analogy, modern humans have existed only since December 31—more precisely, December 31 at 11:42 P.M.

January	1	2	3	4	5	6	7	← Earth forms
	8	9	10	11	12	13	14	
	15	16	17	18	19	20	21	
	22	23	24	25	26	27	28	
	29	30	31	1	2	3	4	
February	5	6	7	8	9	10	11	
	12	13	14	15	16	17	18	
	19	20	21	22	23	24	25	
	26	27	28	1	2	3	4	
March	5	6	7	8	9	10	11	
	12	13	14	15	16	17	18	
	19	20	21	22	23	24	25	← Earliest prokaryotes
	26	27	28	29	30	31	1	
April	2	3	4	5	6	7	8	
	9	10	11	12	13	14	15	
	16	17	18	19	20	21	22	
	23	24	25	26	27	28	29	
	30	1	2	3	4	5	6	
May	7	8	9	10	11	12	13	← Oxygen increases in atmosphere
	14	15	16	17	18	19	20	
	21	22	23	24	25	26	27	
	28	29	30	31	1	2	3	
June	4	5	6	7	8	9	10	
	11	12	13	14	15	16	17	
	18	19	20	21	22	23	24	
	25	26	27	28	29	30	1	
July	2	3	4	5	6	7	8	← Earliest eukaryotes
	9	10	11	12	13	14	15	
	16	17	18	19	20	21	22	
	23	24	25	26	27	28	29	
	30	31	1	2	3	4	5	
August	6	7	8	9	10	11	12	
	13	14	15	16	17	18	19	
	20	21	22	23	24	25	26	
	27	28	29	30	31	1	2	
September	3	4	5	6	7	8	9	
	10	11	12	13	14	15	16	
	17	18	19	20	21	22	23	
	24	25	26	27	28	29	30	
October	1	2	3	4	5	6	7	
	8	9	10	11	12	13	14	← Earliest animals
	15	16	17	18	19	20	21	
	22	23	24	25	26	27	28	
	29	30	31	1	2	3	4	← Earliest land plants
November	5	6	7	8	9	10	11	
	12	13	14	15	16	17	18	
	19	20	21	22	23	24	25	
	26	27	28	29	30	1	2	
December	3	4	5	6	7	8	9	
	10	11	12	13	14	15	16	
	17	18	19	20	21	22	23	← Extinction of Dinosaurs
	24	25	26	27	28	29	30	
	31							← Earliest humans (Dec. 31st at 11:43 pm)

1 day = 12.6 million years
1 second = 143 years

Figure 2.5 The history of Earth condensed into one year.

2.2b Conditions on Primordial Earth

Evidence using a range of dating methods has firmly established that Earth, the Sun, and the other planets of the solar system all formed at about the same time. According to the most widely accepted hypothesis, the solar system was formed by the gravitational condensation of matter present in a molecular cloud, which initially consisted mostly of hydrogen. Intense heat and pressure generated in the central region of the cloud formed the Sun, whereas the remainder of the spiralling dust and gas condensed into the planets. Astronomers agree that this series of events is typical for the vast majority of the estimated 400 millions stars in our galaxy, the Milky Way, and that since planet formation is a natural consequence of the condensation of interstellar gas, which leads to the formation of stars **(Figure 2.6)**, our galaxy most likely contains many millions of planets.

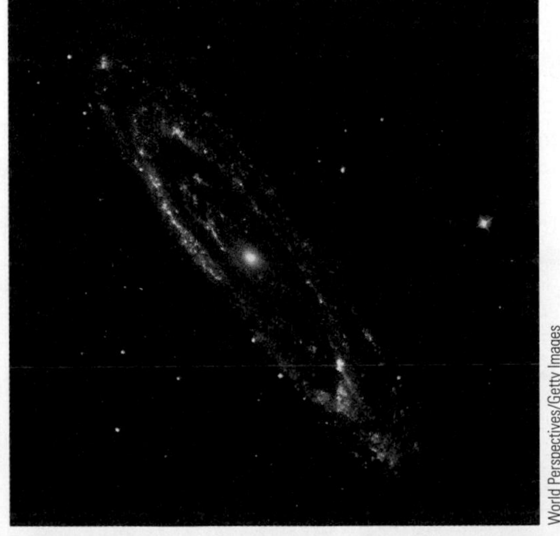

World Perspectives/Getty Images

Figure 2.6
A galaxy. Andromeda (M31) is similar to the Milky Way in being a spiral galaxy. Andromeda is estimated to contain about 1 trillion stars.

Once Earth was formed, its early history was marked by bombardment of rock from the still-forming solar system and extensive volcanic and seismic activity **(Figure 2.7)**. Over time, Earth radiated away some of its heat and surface layers cooled and solidified into the rocks of the crust. Because of its size, Earth's gravitational pull was strong enough to hold an atmosphere around the planet. The atmosphere was derived partly from the original dust cloud and partly from gases released from the planet's interior as it cooled. It is estimated that it took approximately 500 million years for Earth to cool to temperatures that could nurture the development of life.

The atmosphere of 4 billion years ago was vastly different from the one today. The primordial atmosphere probably contained an abundance of water vapour from the evaporation of water at the surface, as well as large quantities of hydrogen sulphide (H_2S), carbon dioxide (CO_2), ammonia (NH_3), and methane (CH_4). Some of these compounds were formed spontaneously by reactions in the atmosphere, whereas others were the result of volcanic eruptions. From these basic building blocks, the molecules essential to the formation of life are thought to have formed.

In the 1920s, two scientists, Aleksander Oparin and John Haldane, independently proposed that organic molecules essential to the formation of life—including amino acids, sugars, and the nucleotide bases that form DNA and RNA—could have been made in the absence of life (abiotic synthesis), given the conditions and simple molecules thought to be present on primordial Earth.

A critical aspect of what is known as the Oparin–Haldane hypothesis is that the early atmosphere was a *reducing atmosphere* because of the presence of large concentrations of molecules such as hydrogen (H_2), methane, and ammonia. These molecules contain the maximum possible number of electrons and hydrogen and are said to be fully reduced (see *The Chemical and Physical Foundations of Biology* pages). A rich source of electrons that can be easily donated makes reactions possible that lead to the building up, or synthesis, of large and complex organic molecules. By comparison, today's atmosphere, which contains 21% O_2, is an *oxidizing atmosphere*. The presence of O_2 prevents complex, electron-rich molecules from being formed because oxygen is a strong oxidizing molecule.

Figure 2.7
An artist's depiction of Earth during its early cooling stage.

2.2c The Miller–Urey Experiment

The lack of oxygen in the primordial atmosphere meant that there was no ozone (O_3) layer to partially block the Sun's energetic ultraviolet light from reaching Earth's surface. Oparin and Haldane hypothesized that the ultraviolet light, along with abundant lightning, provided the energy that, combined with the reducing conditions present in the atmosphere, would lead to the accumulation of the simple "building blocks" required for life.

Experimental evidence in support of the Oparin–Haldane hypothesis came in 1953 when Stanley Miller, a graduate student of Harold Urey at the University of Chicago, created a laboratory simulation of the reducing atmosphere believed to have existed on early Earth. Miller placed components of a reducing atmosphere—hydrogen, methane, ammonia, and water vapour—in a closed apparatus and exposed the gases to an energy source in the form of continuously sparking electrodes **(Figure 2.8)**. Water vapour was added to the "atmosphere" in one part of the apparatus and subsequently condensed back into water by cooling in another part. After running the experiment for only a week, Miller found a large assortment of organic compounds in the water, including urea, amino acids, and lactic, formic, and acetic acids. In fact, as much as 15% of the carbon that was originally in the methane (CH_4) was now in the form of organic compounds.

Other chemicals have been tested in the Miller–Urey apparatus, including hydrogen cyanide (HCN) and formaldehyde (CH_2O), which are considered likely

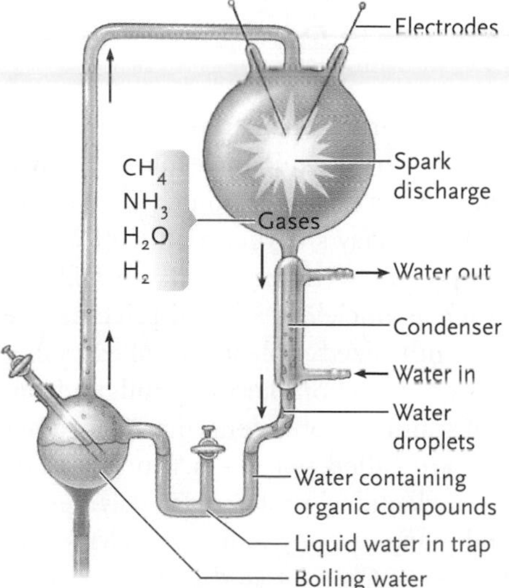

Figure 2.8
The Miller–Urey apparatus demonstrating that organic molecules can be synthesized spontaneously under conditions simulating primordial Earth. Operation for 1 week converted 15% of the carbon in the "atmosphere" inside the apparatus into a surprising variety of organic compounds.

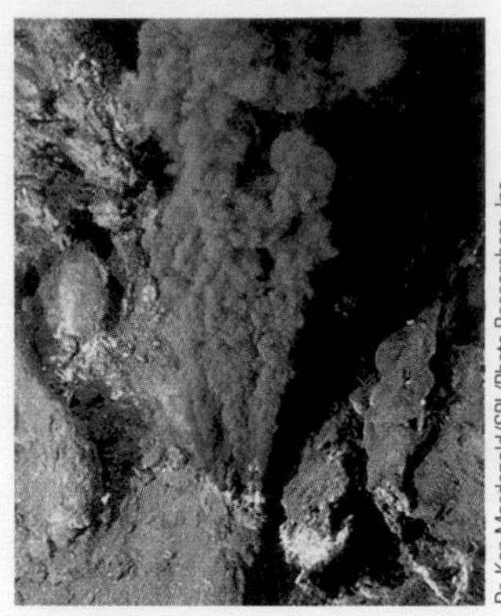
Dr. Ken Macdonald/SPL/Photo Researchers, Inc.

Figure 2.9
Deep sea vent.

to have been among the earliest substances formed in the primitive atmosphere. When HCN and CH_2O molecules were added to the simulated primitive atmosphere in Miller's apparatus, all the building blocks of complex biological molecules were produced—amino acids; fatty acids; the purine and pyrimidine building blocks of nucleic acids; sugars such as glyceraldehyde, ribose, glucose, and fructose; and phospholipids, which form the lipid bilayers of biological membranes.

Considerable debate exists in the scientific community as to whether the atmosphere of primitive Earth contained enough methane and ammonia to provide the reducing characteristics necessary to yield the results found with Miller–Urey experiments. However, besides the primordial atmosphere, highly reducing conditions would have been found near volcanoes and near the hydrothermal vents found on the ocean floor **(Figure 2.9)**. Today, the areas around these vents support a wide range of organisms that are of tremendous scientific interest because of their ability to thrive under extreme conditions of pressure and the total absence of light. Besides releasing geothermally heated water, the vents also release methane and ammonia, which could have led to the formation of the building blocks of life on primitive Earth.

Regardless of the specifics, the significance of the Miller–Urey experiment cannot be overstated. It showed that molecules critical to life, such as amino acids (the building blocks of proteins), as well as many other biologically important molecules, could be produced abiotically, and that they could be produced relatively simply. At the time, this finding was remarkable and laid the groundwork for further research into the origins of life.

2.2d The Synthesis of Polymers from Monomers

Given that primordial Earth contained very little oxygen, it is thought that after the organic molecules were synthesized, they could have existed for much longer than would be possible in today's oxygen-rich world. That being said, it is important to realize that the key building blocks of life, such as nucleic acids and proteins, are not individually synthesized molecules, called monomers. Instead they are macromolecules, built up from large numbers of subunit monomers coming together to produce what are called polymers. Nucleic acids are polymers of nucleotides, proteins are polymers of amino acids, and many carbohydrates are polymers of simple sugars (see *The Chemical and Physical Foundations of Biology* pages). Today, the synthesis of proteins and nucleic acids, for example, requires protein-based catalysts called enzymes and results in macromolecules, which are very large, often consisting of hundreds to many thousands of monomers linked together.

So how do you make the polymers that are required for life without sophisticated enzymes? Given that the earliest forms of life were probably nowhere near as elaborate as even the simplest prokaryote, scientists hypothesize that a polymer that consists of even 50 monomers may have been of sufficient length to impart a specific function (like a protein) or store sufficient information (like a nucleic acid) to make their formation advantageous to an organism. It is, however, doubtful that polymerization could have occurred in the aqueous environment of primordial Earth as macromolecules would have been quickly broken down or hydrolyzed. An alternative hypothesis is that solid surfaces, especially clays, would have provided a unique environment for polymerization to occur. In fact, numerous experiments have demonstrated the formation of short nucleic acid chains and polypeptides on the surface of clay. Clay would have been present in evaporating tidal pools, for example, on early Earth. Clays consist of very thin layers of minerals separated by layers of water only a few nanometres thick. The layered structure readily absorbs ions and organic molecules and promotes their interactions, including condensations and other assembly reactions. Clays can also store potential energy and therefore could have channelled some of that energy into reactions taking place in them.

2.2e Protobionts: The First Cells

The next key factor we need to consider on the way to life is the development of a boundary that would separate the polymers required for life from the external environment. A **protobiont (Figure 2.10)** is the term given to a group of abiotically produced organic molecules that are surrounded by a membrane or membrane-like structure. The development of protobionts was important because it allowed for an internal environment to develop that was distinctly different from the external environment: the concentration of key

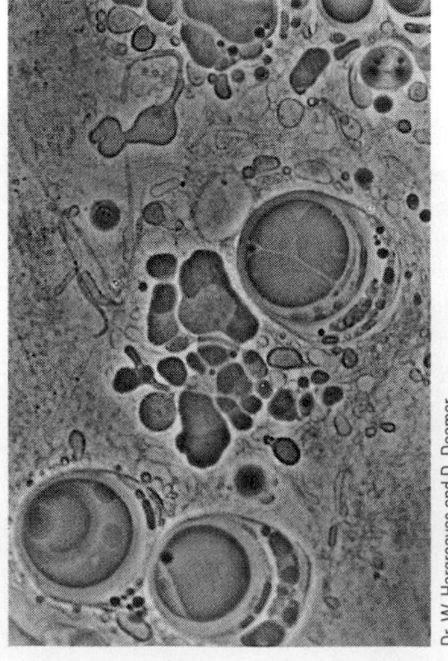
Dr. W. Hargreaves and D. Deamer

Figure 2.10
An electron micrograph of vesicles of various sizes and shapes assembled from phospholipids synthesized under simulated primordial conditions. Such molecules may have been the precursor protobionts of living cells.

molecules could be higher, and molecules could attain more order in a closed space. Laboratory experiments have shown that protobionts could have formed spontaneously, given the conditions of primordial Earth. For example, liposomes, which are small membrane-bound spheres, can be formed when lipid molecules accumulate in an aqueous environment. Lipid molecules are hydrophobic and consequently can spontaneously aggregate into spheres in which the lipid molecules form a bilayer very similar to cell membranes. Liposomes are also selectively permeable, allowing some molecules to move in and out. As well, liposomes can swell and contract depending on the osmotic conditions of their environment.

Study Break

In trying to understand the origin of life, what was the significance of the Miller–Urey experiment?

2.3 The Origins of Information and Metabolism

Of the several critical events necessary for the development of life, two stand out: the development of a system for the storage, replication, and translation of information for protein synthesis and the development of metabolic pathways that would capture and harness energy for metabolism.

2.3a The Origin of the Information System

All organisms contain **deoxyribonucleic acid (DNA).** DNA is a large, double-stranded, helical molecule that contains a unique alphabet that provides the instructions for assembling many of the important components of a cell organism from simpler molecules. DNA functions similarly in all organisms—the information in DNA is copied onto molecules of a related substance, **ribonucleic acid (RNA)**, which then directs the production of protein molecules **(Figure 2.11).** Even the simplest of cells contains thousands of proteins, each coded for by a unique DNA sequence. This flow of information from DNA to RNA to protein is common to all forms of life (see Figure 2.11). Enzymes are required to catalyze the replication of DNA, the transcription of DNA into RNA, and, subsequently, the translation of the RNA into protein. This information pathway is preserved from generation to generation by the ability of DNA to direct its own replication so that offspring receive the same basic molecular instructions as their parents have. Changes in the DNA, regardless of how they are brought about, are what contribute to evolutionary change over generations.

2.3b Ribozymes Are Biological Catalysts that Are Not Proteins

A fundamental question about the flow of information from DNA to RNA to protein is *how did such a system evolve when the products of the process, proteins, are required to catalyze each step of the process?* For years, scientists struggled to come up with a reasonable hypothesis for how this system could have evolved. A breakthrough in our thinking came in 1979, Thomas Czech and his coworkers discovered a group of RNA molecules that could themselves act as catalysts. This group of RNA molecules, called **ribozymes**, can catalyze reactions on the precursor RNA molecules that lead to their own synthesis, as well as on unrelated RNA molecules **(Figure 2.12, p. 30).** The property of RNA that makes some able to act as catalysts is that they are single-stranded molecules that can fold into very specific shapes. Ribozyme function depends on how it is folded, similar to protein function, which is achieved only after the amino acid chain acquires a precise three-dimensional shape (see *The Chemical and Physical Foundations of Biology* pages).

The discovery of ribozymes revolutionized thinking about the origin of life. Instead of the contemporary system that requires all three molecules—DNA, RNA, and protein—early life may have existed in an "RNA world," where a single type of molecule could serve as both a carrier of information (in its

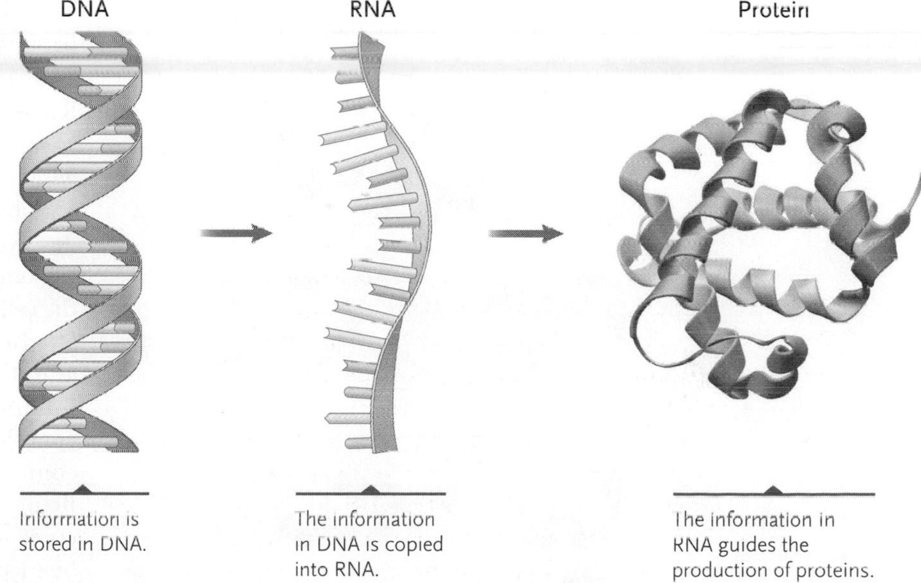

DNA
RNA
Protein
Information is stored in DNA.
The information in DNA is copied into RNA.
The information in RNA guides the production of proteins.

Figure 2.11
The pathway of information flow in living organisms. Information stored in DNA is copied into RNA which then directs the construction of protein molecules.

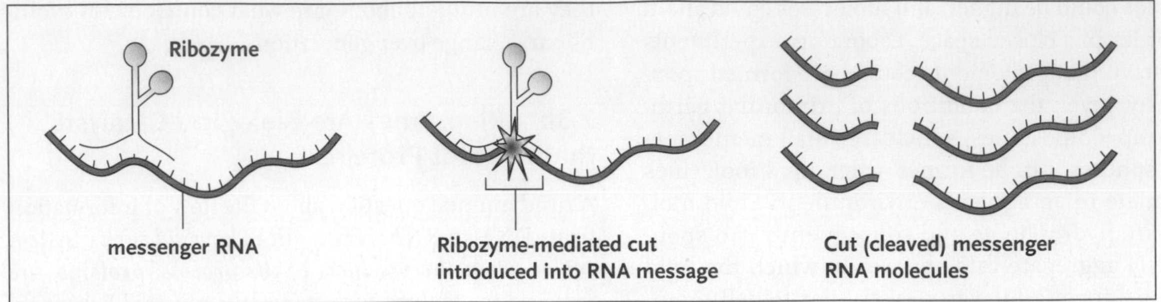

Figure 2.12
An example of a ribozyme binding to a RNA molecule and catalyzing its breakage. WIthin a cell such a reaction may help control gene expression by altering the abundance of functional messenger RNA molecules.

nucleotide sequence) and a catalyst (due to its ability to form unique three-dimensional shapes). Prior to the discovery of ribozymes, enzymes, which are proteins, were the only known biological catalysts. Chapter 4 is devoted to this very important group of molecules.

2.3c The Evolution of Proteins and DNA

If life developed in an "RNA world" and RNA served as both an information carrier and a catalyst, why is life today dominated by DNA and proteins? The simple answer, which we discuss further below, is that they do the respective jobs of information storage (DNA) and catalysis (protein) far better than RNA does by itself; thus, the evolution of these molecules would have given organisms that had them a distinct advantage over others that used only RNA.

A possible scenario for the development of today's system of information transfer is shown in **Figure 2.13.** The first cells may have contained only RNA, which was self-replicating and could catalyze a small number of reactions critical for survival. It is hypothesized that, subsequently, a small population of RNA molecules evolved that could catalyze the formation of very simple proteins, independent of the ribosome (the organelle in contemporary organisms required for protein synthesis). It is interesting to note that the modern ribosome, which plays a key role as an intermediate between RNA and protein, is composed of about two-thirds RNA and one-third protein. Interestingly, it has recently been shown that the RNA of the ribosome, not the protein, actually catalyzes the incorporation of amino acids onto a growing peptide chain. Thus, the ribosome may be considered a type of ribozyme.

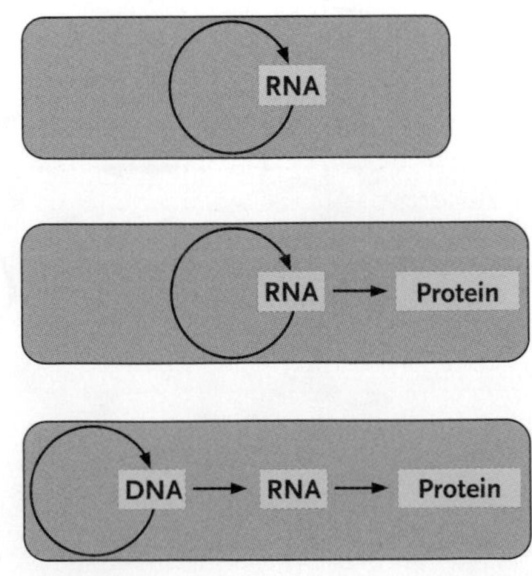

Figure 2.13
Possible scenario for the evolution of the flow of information from DNA to RNA to protein.

RNA molecules that developed the ability to synthesize even small proteins would be at a tremendous advantage because proteins are far more versatile than RNA molecules, for two main reasons. First, the catalytic power of most enymes is greater than that of any known ribozyme. That is, a typical enzyme can catalyze the same reaction using a pool of substrate molecules many hundreds and even thousands of times a second. Second, proteins are much more diverse compared with ribozymes. Twenty different kinds of amino acids can be incorporated into a protein, whereas an RNA molecule is composed of only four nucleotide bases. As well, amino acids can interact chemically with other amino acids in bonding arrangements not possible between nucleotides. Because of the tremendous diversity in the structure of proteins, they are the dominant structural and functional molecule in the cell.

In the RNA world, DNA would have developed after the development of proteins (see Figure 2.13). Compared with RNA, molecules of DNA are more complex. Not only is DNA double stranded, it also contains the sugar deoxyribose, which is more difficult to synthesize than the ribose found in molecules of RNA. At first, DNA nucleotides may have been produced by random removal of an oxygen atom from the ribose subunits of the RNA nucleotides. At some point, the DNA nucleotides paired with the RNA informational molecules and were

Molecule Behind Biology

L1 Ligase Ribozyme

RNA molecules may have been critical in the development of life on Earth since it is thought that they not only could store information but also could act as biological catalysts prior to the evolution of DNA and proteins. However, to replicate RNA, individual nucleotide triphosphate monomers need to be joined, or ligated, together to form an RNA polymer.

Today, this ligation reaction, carried out by a group of protein enzymes called polymerases, can result in RNA strands being many thousands of nucleotides in length. How this polymerization reaction would have been catalyzed in an RNA-only world stumped scientists for years.

Using what is called *in vitro* evolution and selection, scientists recently produced a range of synthetic ribozymes that do not currently exist in nature. One of these synthetic ribozymes is called the L1 ligase ribozyme, and it has been shown to catalzye the joining of two RNA monomers together. This finding clearly suggests that, although not currently found in nature, a ribozyme capable of ligating nucleotides together may have existed on primitive Earth.

assembled into complementary copies of the RNA sequences. Some modern-day viruses carry out this RNA-to-DNA reaction using the enzyme reverse transcriptase (see Chapter 22). Once the DNA copies were made, selection may have favoured DNA as it is a much better way to store information than RNA, for three main reasons:

- Each strand of DNA is chemically more stable than a strand of RNA. This is due to the presence of the sugar deoxyribose instead of ribose.
- The base uracil found in RNA is not found in DNA; it has been replaced by thymine. It is thought that the reason for this is that a common mutation in DNA is the conversion of cytosine into uracil. By utilizing thymine in DNA, any uracil is easily recognized as a damaged cytosine and can be repaired.
- DNA is double stranded, so in the case of a mutation, the complementary strand can be used to repair the damaged strand.

The stability of DNA makes it an excellent molecule to store and preserve genetic information. This is reflected by the fact that, using the polymerase chain reaction, intact DNA can be successfully extracted and amplified from tissue that is many thousands of years old.

Many unanswered questions remain concerning the origin of life and how the first cells came about. A wide range of theories exist, with different degrees of experimental support. What is indeed frustrating is that we simply do not know the specifics of what happened because we lack evidence—both fossil evidence and otherwise. Sifting through the various models and theories, we can perhaps agree that there were some basic steps:

1. the abiotic (nonliving) synthesis of organic molecules such as amino acids
2. the assembly of complex organic molecules from simple molecules, including protein, RNA, or both
3. the aggregation of complex organic molecules inside membrane-bound protobionts

2.3d The Development of Energy-Harnessing Reaction Pathways

Oxidation–reduction reactions were probably among the first energy-releasing reactions of the primitive cells. In our cells, we *oxidize* food molecules (e.g., sugars) and use some of the liberated energy (electrons) to *reduce* other molecules, for example, those needed to synthesize proteins. In primitive cells, the electrons removed in an oxidation would have been transferred directly to the substances being reduced, in a one-step process. This, however, is not very efficient and leads to a lot of wasted energy. Over time, multistep processes would have evolved, whereby the energy from an oxidation is slowly released. A good example of this is cellular respiration, which is discussed in Chapter 6. The greater efficiency of stepwise energy release would have favoured development of intermediate carriers and opened the way for primitive electron transport chains.

As part of the energy-harnessing reactions, adenosine triphosphate (ATP) became established as the coupling agent that links energy-releasing reactions to those requiring energy. ATP may first have entered early cells as one of many organic molecules absorbed from the primitive environment. Initially, it was probably simply hydrolyzed into adenosine diphosphate (ADP) and inorganic phosphate, resulting in the release of energy. Later, as cells developed, some of the energy released during electron transfer was probably used to synthesize ATP directly from ADP and inorganic phosphate. Because of the efficiency and versatility of energy transfer by ATP, it gradually became the primary substance connecting energy-releasing and energy-requiring reactions in early cells.

Study Break

1. What are ribozymes, and what is their significance in our understanding of the origins of life?
2. In what ways was DNA better than RNA as a means of storing genetic information?

2.4 Early Life

2.4a Earliest Evidence of Life

The earliest conclusive evidence of life is found in the fossilized remains of structures called stromatolites, which have been dated to about 3.5 billion years ago. **Stromatolites** are a type of layered rock that is formed when microorganisms bind particles of sediment together, forming thin sheets **(Figure 2.14).** Confidence that fossil stromatolites were formed by microbial activity comes from the fact that modern-day stromatolites although rare, do exist in habitats characterized by warm shallow water, and do harbour microbial life (see Figure 2.14).

Modern-day stromatolites are formed by the action of a group of photosynthetic prokaryotes called cyanobacteria. As we discuss in a later section, cyanobacteria possess a sophisticated metabolism that suggests that earlier life forms must have preceded their evolution. Indirect (nonfossil) evidence of life existing as early as 3.9 billion years ago comes from research looking at the carbon composition of ancient rocks. Early organisms would have required the ability to take CO_2 from the atmosphere and "fix it" by incorporating it into various organic forms (sugars, amino acids, etc.). Interestingly, organisms preferentially incorporate the carbon-12 isotope over other isotopes, see *The Chemical and Physical Foundations of Biology*, such as carbon-13. Researchers have discovered sedimentary rocks, originating from the ocean floor, that contain deposits that are depleted in ^{13}C. This finding suggests that the deposits are remnants of ancient microbes.

2.4b Could Life Have Come to Earth from Space?

It is a well-regarded hypothesis that life on Earth could have had an extraterrestrial origin. Panspermia is the name given to the hypothesis that very simple forms of life are present in outer space and may have seeded early Earth. Two points of discussion support the extraterrestrial origin of life on Earth:

- Although life seems very complex, it arose relatively quickly after the formation of Earth. The Earth formed 4.6 billion years ago, and we have clear fossil evidence of life dated to about 3.5 billion years ago and chemical evidence to about 3.9 billion years ago. Given that primordial Earth had to cool after being formed, many scientists argue that this window for the development of life is very narrow.
- Research in the past decade has shown that life is far more resilient than previously thought and could possibly survive for years in space. Extremophiles, which are mostly prokaryotes, can thrive under very harsh conditions of temperature, pressure, and nutrients and might be able to survive in a dormant state in interstellar space. Prolonged dormancy is a property of the spores of a range of organisms, including a number of prokaryotes and simple eukaryotes. Spores are highly resistant to changes in the external environment and can be restored to active growth after exposure to high levels of radiation, water deficiency, and/or exposure to extreme temperatures. Given this, one cannot discount the possibility that simple life forms came to Earth about 4 billion years ago and initiated the evolution of life as we know it.

2.4c Prokaryotes Have Properties Common to All Cells

All forms of life are based on two fundamentally distinct types of cells: prokaryotic and eukaryotic. The earliest forms of life, including those found in stromatolites, are the simplest organisms known, prokaryotes **(Figure 2.15).** As we discuss in Chapter 21,

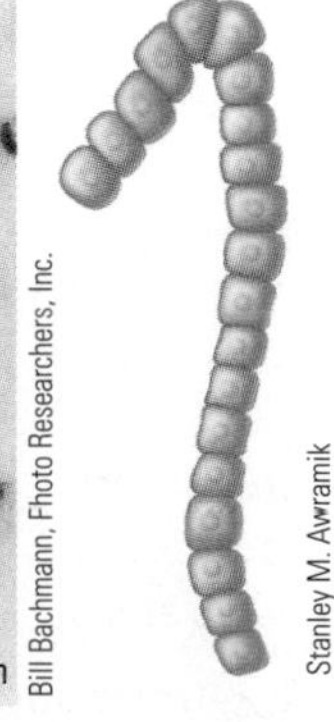

Figure 2.14
(a) Stromatolites exposed at low tide in Western Australia's Shark Bay. These mounds, which consist of mineral deposits made by photosynthetic cyanobacteria, are about 2000 years old; they are highly similar in structure to fossil stromatolites that formed more than 3 billion years ago. As a result of photosynthesis by cyanobacteria, oxygen began to accumulate in the atmosphere. **(b)** Structures that are believed to be a strand of fossil prokaryote cells in a rock sample 3.5 billion years old.

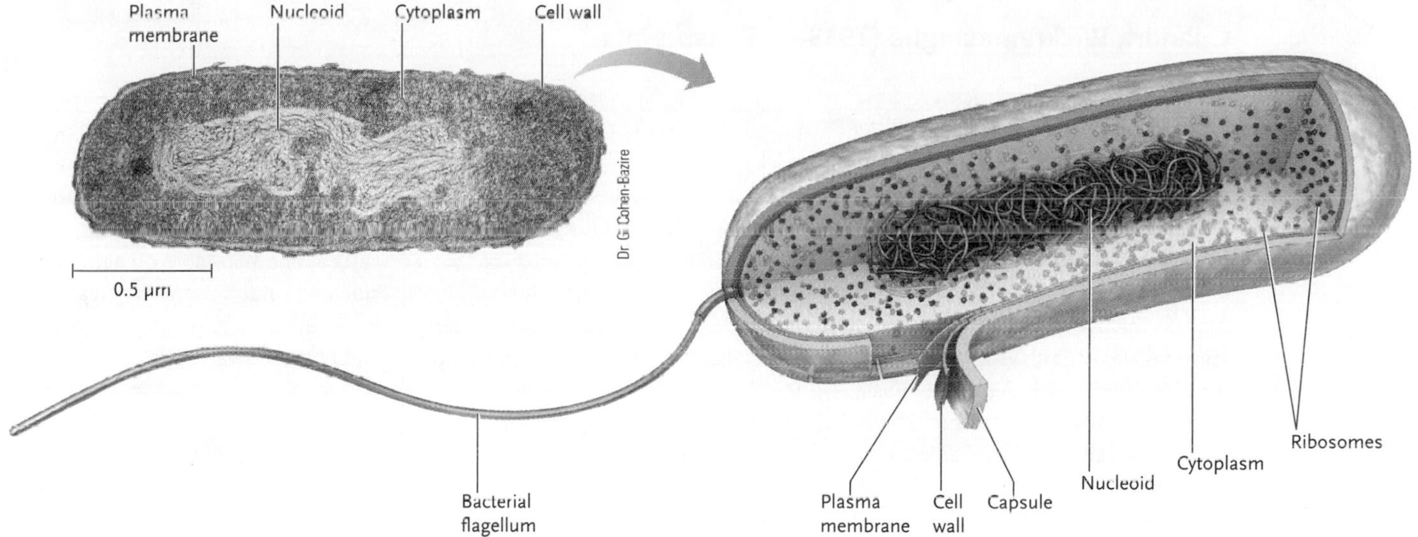

Figure 2.15
Prokaryotic cell structure. An electron micrograph (left) and a diagram (right) of the bacterium *Escherichia coli.*

prokaryotic organisms are found in two domains of life: the bacteria and the Archaea. Although the lack of a nucleus makes prokaryotes distinctly different from eukaryotic cells, it is important to realize that all cells share many fundamental features. All cells possess a selectively permeable *plasma membrane,* which separates the external environment from the **cytoplasm** of the cell. The cytoplasm consists of the **cytosol,** which is mostly water, salts, and various organic molecules, along with the various structural features within the cell, including organelles. The plasma membrane contains protein complexes that allow the controlled transport of materials into and out of the cells. In addition, the prokaryotic plasma membrane also contains protein complexes that form electron transport chains, used to link the oxidation of various molecules to the synthesis of ATP. In photosynthetic prokaryotes, the plasma membrane, or internal membranes derived from the plasma membrane, are the sites of photosynthetic electron transport chains, which harvest light energy for the synthesis of energy-rich molecules, including ATP. We will see that in eukaryotes, energy transduction machinery is found in organelles called mitochondria and chloroplasts.

The DNA of both prokaryotic and eukaryotic cells is organized into *chromosomes.* However, as you will learn in subsequent chapters, the structure of the chromosome is distinctly different between prokaryotes and eukaryotes. Lacking a nucleus, the DNA of a prokaryote is found localized in a central region of the cell called a **nucleoid.** The processes of transcription and translation, which are discussed in detail in Chapter 14, are also fundamentally similar in prokaryotes and eukaryotes relying on ribosomes for the synthesis of proteins from an RNA template.

2.4d Prokaryotes Display Remarkable Diversity

Prokaryotic cells are usually not much more than a few micrometres in length and a micrometre or less in diameter, which makes them about 10 times smaller than a typical eukaryotic cell. Also, prokaryotes have much less internal membrane organization, compared to eukaryotic cells. Although prokaryotic cells appear to be relatively simple, their simplicity is deceptive. As we discuss further in Chapter 21, prokaryotes display remarkable metabolic flexibility, being able to use a variety of substances as energy and carbon sources and to synthesize almost all of their required organic molecules from simple inorganic raw materials. In many respects, prokaryotes are biochemically more versatile than eukaryotes. Their small size and metabolic versatility are reflected in their abundance; prokaryotes vastly outnumber all other types of organisms and live successfully in almost all regions of Earth's surface, from the Antarctic to hot springs. Chapter 21 outlines the diversity of prokaryotes and extends the discussion of the prokaryotic structure.

2.4e Oxygenic Photosynthesis and the Rise of Atmospheric Oxygen

Geologic evidence indicates that the earliest prokaryotic cells relied on anaerobic metabolism as the atmosphere of Earth lacked molecular oxygen. Evidence for an increase in atmospheric O_2 starting about 2.5 billion years ago is found by the presence of a type of sedimentary rock called banded iron. It is thought that this type of rock was formed in the sediments of lakes and oceans as dissolved oxygen reacted

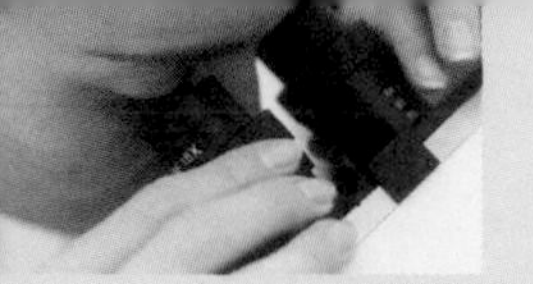

People Behind Biology

Chandra Wickramasinghe (1939–): Panspermia

A professor of applied mathematics and astronomy at Cardiff University in the United Kingdom, Dr. Chandra Wickramasinghe is currently the director of the Cardiff Centre for Astrobiology. Along with Sir Fred Hoyle, Wickramasinghe is credited with the modern theory of panspermia—the idea that life on Earth was seeded by microbes from space. Although initially rejected as absurd, the concept of panspermia has come to be regarded as a plausible hypothesis for the starting of life on Earth.

Professor Wickramasinghe was born in Sri Lanka and educated at Royal College, Colombo, and later the University of Ceylon. He received his Ph.D. from the University of Cambridge in the United Kingdom, under the supervision of the late Sir Fred Hoyle. In 1964, he was appointed as a staff member of the Institute of Astronomy at the University of Cambridge, where he started his pioneering work on the nature of interstellar dust. In 1974, he first proposed the theory that dust in interstellar space and in comets was largely organic, a theory that has now been confirmed.

Through his research, Wickramasinghe is credited with developing the field of astrobiology as a serious academic program that includes biology, astronomy, and geology in the study of the origin, evolution, distribution, and future of life in the universe. This multidisciplinary field encompasses the search for habitable environments in our solar system and habitable planets outside our solar system, the search for evidence of prebiotic chemistry and life on Mars and other bodies in our solar system, laboratory and field research into the origins and early evolution of life on Earth, and studies of the potential for life to adapt to challenges on Earth and in space. Numerous universities around the world now have undergraduate degree programs in astrobiology.

with dissolved iron, which formed the precipitate, iron oxide (rust) **(Figure 2.16).**

An obvious question to ask is *where did the O_2 come from?* The most primitive forms of metabolism probably included anaerobic respiration, fermentation, and photosynthesis. The earliest form of photosynthesis relied on compounds such as H_2S and ferrous iron (Fe^{2+}), which could be easily oxidized by energy trapped from sunlight. The liberated electrons, would in turn, be used to reduce CO_2 into sugars.

However, starting about 3 billion years ago a group of prokaryotes called cyanobacteria appeared that could use something more common than H_2S or ferrous iron as an electron donor for photosynthesis. Cyanobacteria could harness electrons from water **(Figure 2.17).** A consequence of oxidizing water was that besides releasing electrons and protons, the "splitting of water" resulted in the formation of O_2, which was released and over millions of years slowly accumulated in the atmosphere. Because it releases O_2, photosynthesis that relies on the oxidation of water is termed *oxygenic photosynthesis.* As discussed in detail in Chapter 7, the evolution of oxygenic photosynthesis represents a remarkable energetic feat since water is not an easy molecule to oxidize.

Figure 2.16
The rust layers in banded iron formations provide evidence for the rise of atmospheric oxygen.

Yuri Arcurs/Shutterstock

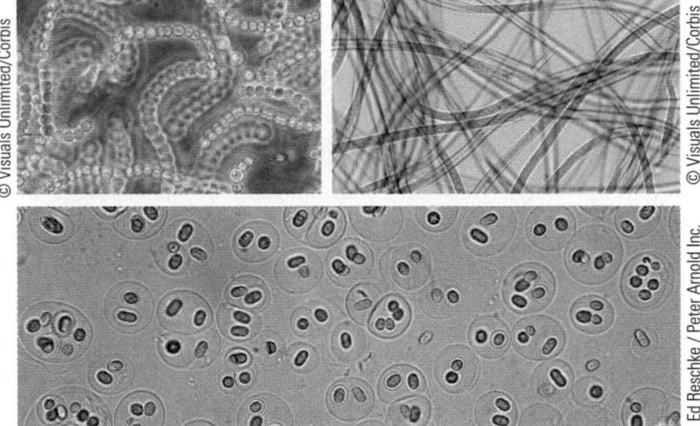
© Visuals Unlimited/Corbis; © Visuals Unlimited/Corbis; Ed Reschke / Peter Arnold Inc.

Figure 2.17
Examples of present-day cyanobacteria. This group of photosynthetic prokaryotes evolved oxygenic photosynthesis.

The huge advantage afforded to cyanobacteria by utilizing oxygenic photosynthesis has, interestingly, nothing to do with oxygen but everything to do with water. Unlike compounds such as H_2S and Fe^{2+}, water was, and remains, far more abundant in the environment. This meant that cyanobacteria could thrive virtually anywhere there was sunlight. As you would expect, the evolution of oxygenic photosynthesis resulted in an explosion of life as cyanobacteria quickly became a dominant life form on early Earth. Although it evolved about 3 billion years ago, oxygenic photosynthesis remains the dominant form of photosynthesis used by all plants and algae, as well as present-day cyanobacteria.

The development of oxygenic photosynthesis was also a critical event in the evolution and diversification of life on Earth because the rise in atmospheric O_2 led quite rapidly to the evolution of prokaryotic cells, which are able to undergo aerobic respiration. We discuss this in detail in Chapter 6, but for now remember that in aerobic respiration, energy is extracted from food molecules, with O_2 acting as the final electron acceptor. Aerobic respiration allowed organisms to extract a much greater amount of energy from food molecules than respiration that does not use O_2 (anaerobic respiration). As you will see in the next few sections, the rise in atmospheric O_2 by the development of oxygenic photosynthesis was a key factor that led to the development of eukaryotic cells.

Study Break

1. What is panspermia?
2. What was the advantage gained by oxygenic photosynthesis?

2.5 Eukaryotic Cells

Figure 2.18 shows a typical eukaryotic cell. All present-day eukaryotic cells have several interrelated characteristics that distinguish them from prokaryotes:

- the separation of DNA and cytoplasm by a nuclear envelope
- the presence in the cytoplasm of membrane-bound compartments with specialized functions: mitochondria, chloroplasts, endoplasmic reticulum (ER), and the Golgi complex, among others
- highly specialized motor (contractile) proteins that move cells and internal cell parts

In this section, we discuss how eukaryotes most probably evolved from associations of prokaryotes.

2.5a The Endomembrane System Is Derived from the Plasma Membrane

Eukaryotic cells are characterized by an **endomembrane system** (*endo* = within), a collection of interrelated internal membranous sacs that divide the cell

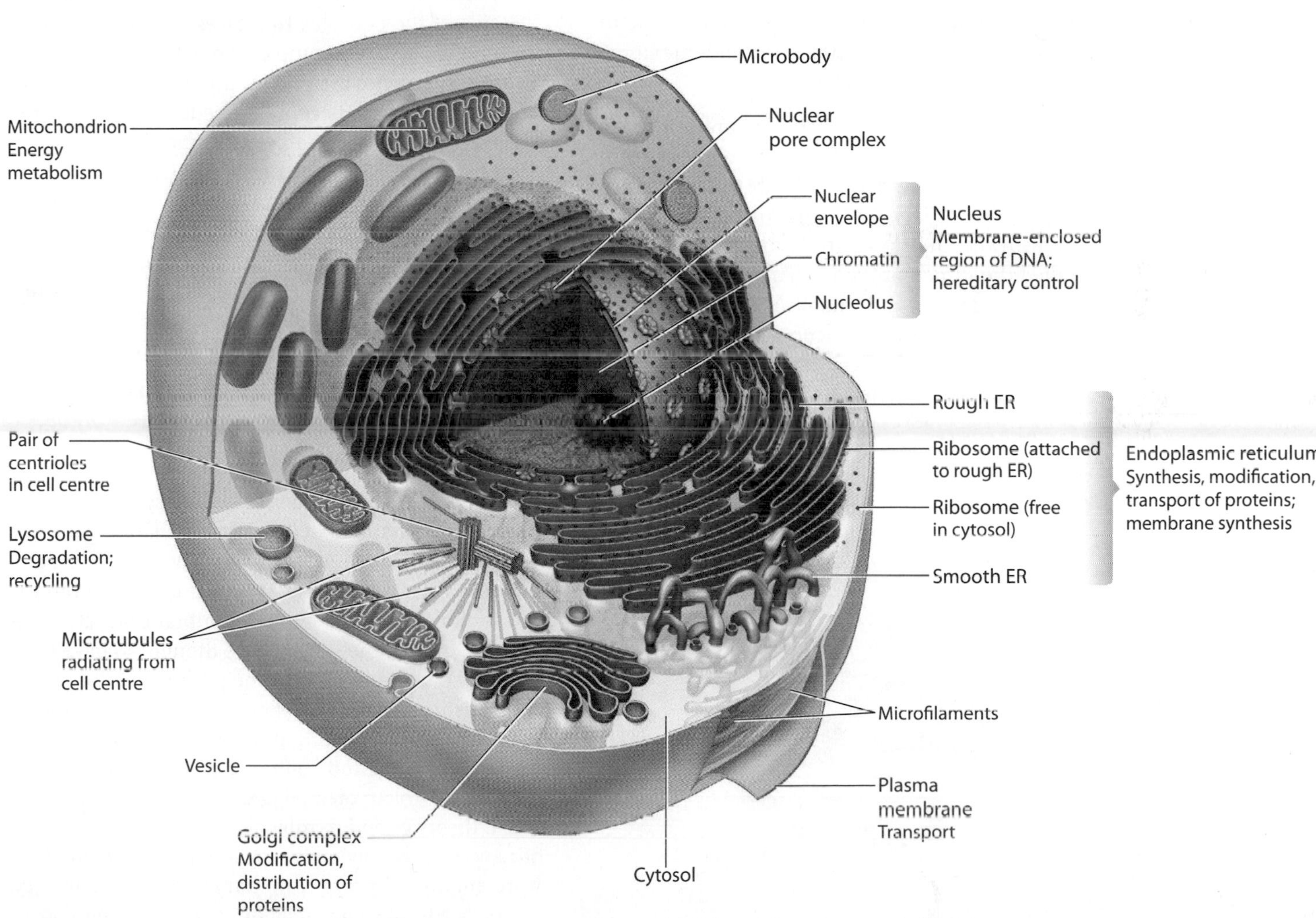

Figure 2.18
Eukaryotic cell.

into functional and structural compartments called organelles. The major membrane components include the nuclear envelope, the ER, and the Golgi complex. Infolding of the plasma membrane is believed to be responsible for the evolution of all of these structures **(Figure 2.19, left illustration)**. Researchers hypothesize that, in cell lines leading from prokaryotes to eukaryotes, pockets of the plasma membrane may have extended inward and surrounded the nuclear region. Some of these membranes fused around the DNA, forming the nuclear envelope and, hence, the nucleus. The remaining membranes formed vesicles in the cytoplasm that gave rise to the ER and the Golgi complex **(Figure 2.19, right illustration)**.

The membranes of the endomembrane system **(Figure 2.20)** are connected either directly, in the physical sense, or indirectly by **vesicles**, which are small membrane-bound compartments that transfer substances between parts of the system. The nuclear envelope controls the movement of both proteins and RNA molecules into and out of the nucleus. The ER and the Golgi complex together serve a variety of functions, including the synthesis and modification of proteins, their transport into membranes or to the outside of the cell, the synthesis of lipids, and the detoxification of harmful compounds. Let's look into the structure and function of these two parts of the endomembrane (see Figure 2.20) in more detail:

1. **Endoplasmic reticulum.** The **endoplasmic reticulum (ER)** is an extensive interconnected network (*reticulum* = little net) of membranous channels and vesicles. Each vesicle is formed by a single membrane that surrounds an enclosed space called the lumen of the ER. The ER occurs in two forms, rough ER and smooth ER, each with a specialized structure and function. The **rough ER** gets its name from the many ribosomes that stud its outer surface. Proteins synthesized on the rough ER are destined for the plasma membrane or for release outside the cell. After being synthesized, these proteins enter the lumen where they fold into their final form. The proteins are then delivered to the cell surface within vesicles that pinch off from the ER and move to join with the Golgi complex. In comparison, the **smooth ER** does not have ribosomes attached to its surface. Instead of protein synthesis, the smooth ER serves various functions, including the synthesis of lipids that become part of cell membranes.

   Proteins made by the ribosomes that are freely suspended in the cytosol remain in the cytosol, pass through the nuclear pores to enter the nucleus, or become parts of mitochondria, chloroplasts, the cytoskeleton, or other cytoplasmic structures.
2. **Golgi complex.** The **Golgi complex** consists of a stack of flattened membranous sacs and is usually located between the rough ER and the plasma membrane. The Golgi complex receives proteins made in the ER and transported to the complex in vesicles. Within the Golgi complex, further chemical modifications of the proteins occur. The modified proteins are then sorted into other vesicles that pinch off from the margins of Golgi sacs on the side of the complex that faces the plasma membrane. The Golgi complex regulates the movement of several types of proteins. Some are secreted from the cell, others become embedded in the plasma membrane, and yet others are placed in lysosomes. For example, proteins secreted from the cell are transported to the plasma membrane by **secretory vesicles**, which release their contents to the exterior by **exocytosis.** Vesicles may also form by the reverse process, called **endocytosis**, which brings molecules into the cell from the exterior.

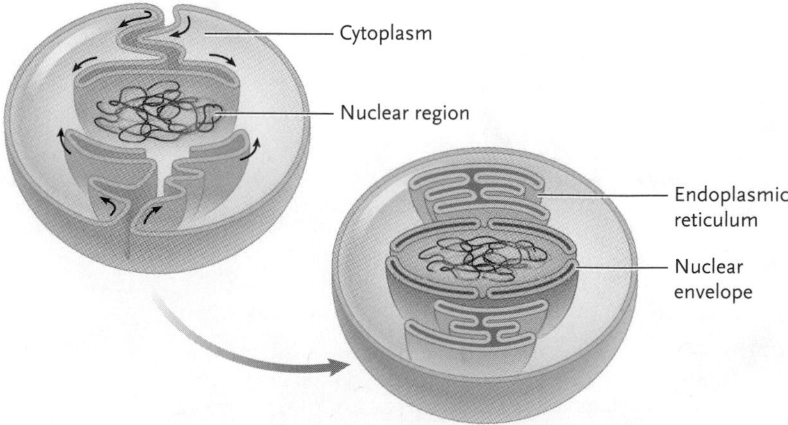

Figure 2.19
A hypothetical route for formation of the nuclear envelope and endoplasmic reticulum, through segments of the plasma membrane that were brought into the cytoplasm by endocytosis.

2.5b The Theory of Endosymbiosis Suggests that Mitochondria and Chloroplasts Evolved from Ingested Prokaryotes

Besides the extensive endomembrane system, another clear characteristic of eukaryotic cells is the presence of energy-transducing organelles: the chloroplast and the mitochondrion (plural = mitochondria). From the last section, recall that all the membrane structures of the endomembrane systems are thought to have been derived from an infolding of the plasma membrane. By comparison, a large body of evidence supports a model of eukaryotic evolution that involves endosymbiosis—the mitochondria and chloroplasts are descendants of free-living prokaryotes **(Figure 2.21, p. 38)**. The established **theory of endosymbiosis** states that the prokaryotic ancestors of modern mitochondria and chloroplasts were engulfed by larger prokaryotic cells, forming a mutually advantageous relationship called a symbiosis, and that slowly, over time, the host cell and the endosymbionts became inseparable parts of the same organism.

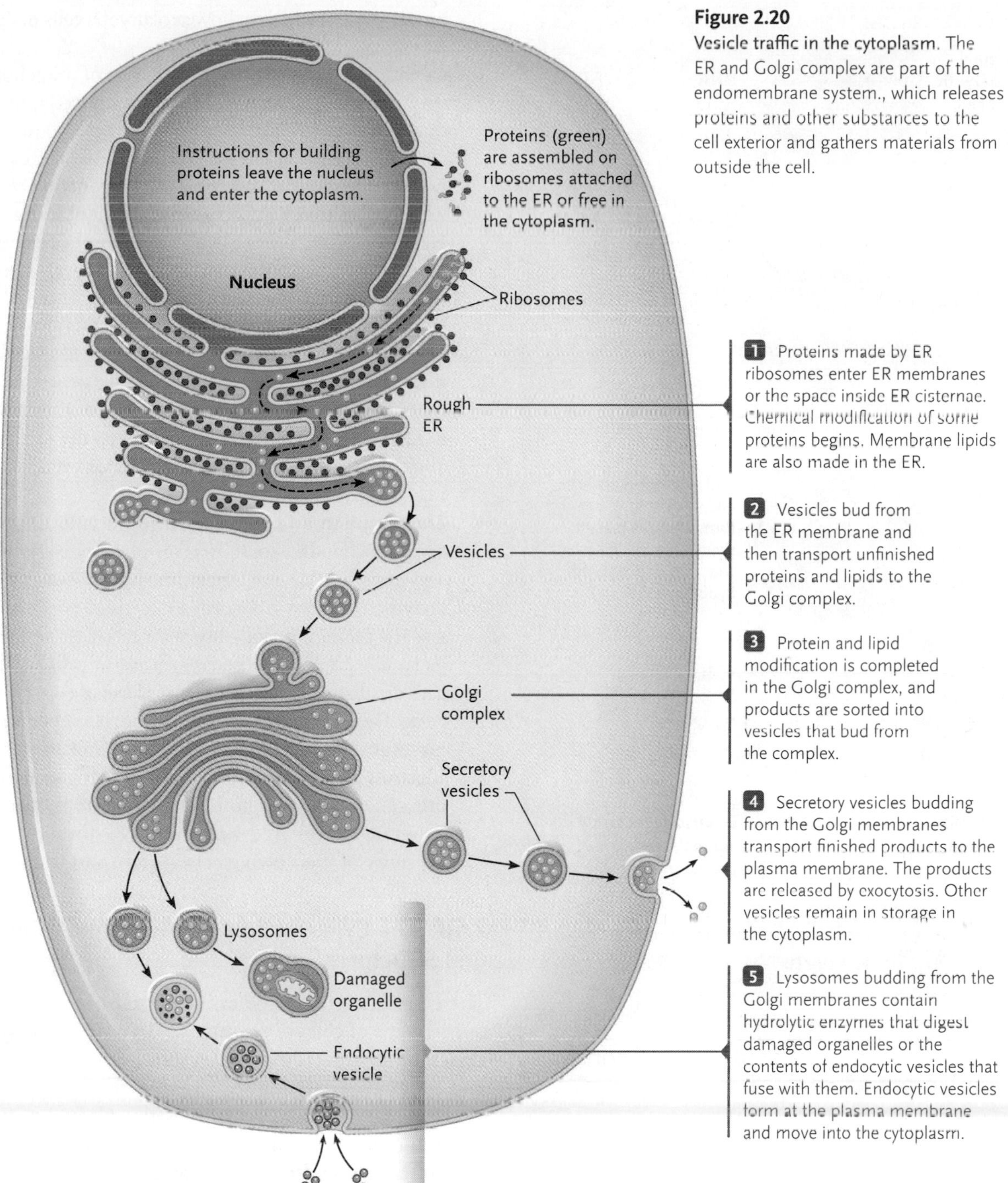

Instructions for building proteins leave the nucleus and enter the cytoplasm.
Proteins (green) are assembled on ribosomes attached to the ER or free in the cytoplasm.
Nucleus
Ribosomes
Rough ER
Vesicles
Golgi complex
Secretory vesicles
Lysosomes
Damaged organelle
Endocytic vesicle
1 Proteins made by ER ribosomes enter ER membranes or the space inside ER cisternae. Chemical modification of some proteins begins. Membrane lipids are also made in the ER.
2 Vesicles bud from the ER membrane and then transport unfinished proteins and lipids to the Golgi complex.
3 Protein and lipid modification is completed in the Golgi complex, and products are sorted into vesicles that bud from the complex.
4 Secretory vesicles budding from the Golgi membranes transport finished products to the plasma membrane. The products are released by exocytosis. Other vesicles remain in storage in the cytoplasm.
5 Lysosomes budding from the Golgi membranes contain hydrolytic enzymes that digest damaged organelles or the contents of endocytic vesicles that fuse with them. Endocytic vesicles form at the plasma membrane and move into the cytoplasm.

Figure 2.20
Vesicle traffic in the cytoplasm. The ER and Golgi complex are part of the endomembrane system., which releases proteins and other substances to the cell exterior and gathers materials from outside the cell.

The rise in atmospheric O_2 is thought to be a key factor in the occurrence of endosymbiosis. Mitochondria carry out aerobic respiration; thus, it is thought their ancestors were free-living aerobic prokaryotic cells. These cells would have been able to generate far more ATP from the same amount of food as a comparable anaerobic cell. Endosymbiosis of these small aerobic cells would give a larger anaerobic cell a distinct energy advantage compared with other anaerobic cells. In the same way, the modern chloroplast is thought to be derived from endosymbiotic events involving cyanobacteria. Because cyanobacteria are photosynthetic, the host cell would be able to utilize sunlight as a source of energy. Additionally, because cyanobacteria carry out *oxygenic* photosynthesis, the host cell could easily supply the water needed to drive photosynthesis.

Whereas virtually all eukaryotic cells contain mitochondria, only plants and algae contain both mitochondria and chloroplasts. This fact indicates that endosymbiosis occurred in stages, with the event leading to the evolution of mitochondria occurring first. Once eukaryotic cells with the ability for aerobic respiration developed, some of these became photosynthetic after taking up cyanobacteria. This lineage developed into the plants and algae of today.

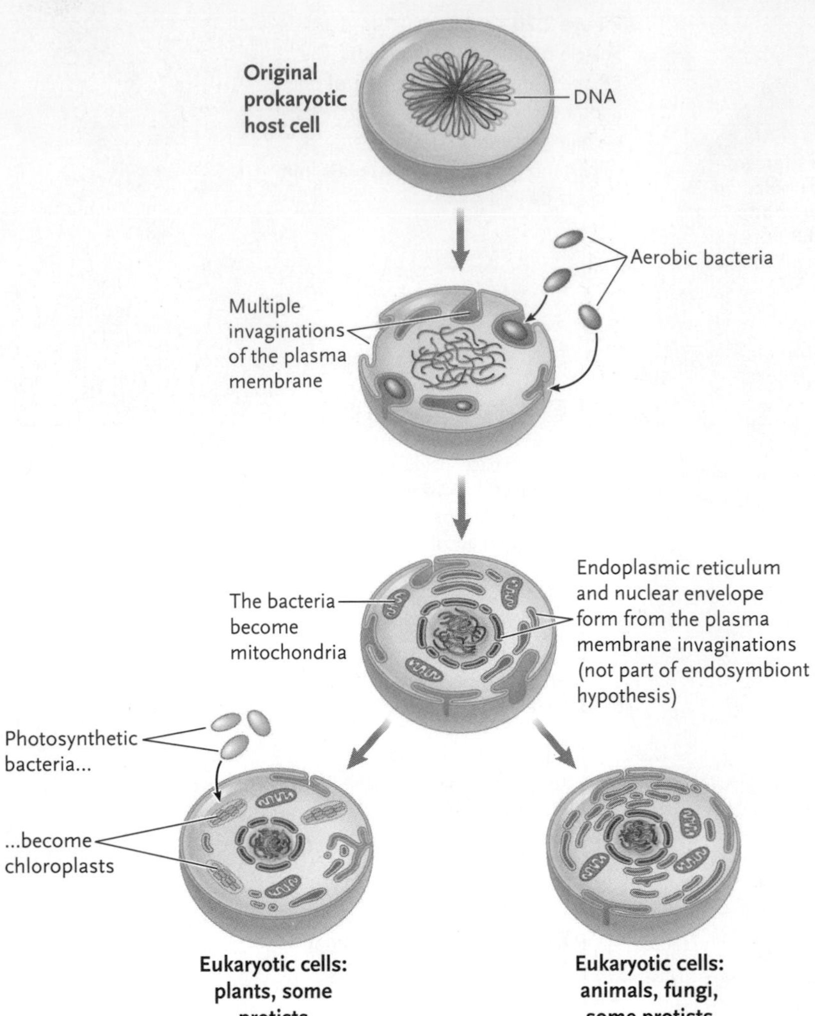

Figure 2.21
The endosymbiont hypothesis. Mitochondria and chloroplasts of eukaryotic cells are thought to have originated from various bacteria that lived as endosymbionts within other cells.

2.5c Several Lines of Evidence Support the Theory of Endosymbiosis

If the endosymbiont theory is correct and both mitochondria and chloroplasts are descendants from prokaryotic cells, then these organelles should share some clear structural and biochemical features with modern prokaryotes. Five lines of evidence suggest that these energy-transducing organelles do have distinctly prokaryotic characteristics that are not found in other eukaryotic cells:

1. **Morphology.** The form or shape (morphology) of both mitochondria and chloroplasts is similar to that of a prokaryotic cell. Mitochondria resemble aerobic prokaryotes, and chloroplasts resemble cyanobacteria.
2. **Reproduction.** A cell cannot make a mitochondrion or a chloroplast. Just like free-living prokaryotic cells, mitochondria or chloroplasts are derived only from preexisting mitochondria or chloroplasts. Both chloroplasts and mitochondria divide by binary fission, which is how prokaryotic cells divide (see Chapter 9).
3. **Genetic information.** If the ancestors of mitochondria and chloroplasts were free-living cells, then one could predict that these organelles should contain their own DNA. This is indeed the case. Both mitochondria and chloroplasts contain DNA, which codes for the proteins essential for the organelle's function. Whereas a free-living bacterium contains a few thousand protein-coding genes, the DNA found in energy-transducing organelles contain less than a hundred. The reason for this is that many of the genes have been relocated to the nucleus. The protein encoded by the gene is still the same, but the movement of some of the genes to the nucleus is thought to have given the nucleus and thus the host cell better control of overall cell function.
4. **Transcription and translation.** Both chloroplasts and mitochondria contain a complete transcription and translational machinery, including a variety of enzymes and the ribosomes necessary to synthesize the proteins encoded by their DNA. As you will learn in Chapter 13, the ribosomes of prokaryotic cells are distinctly different from those of eukaryotic cells. The ribosomes of mitochondria and chloroplasts are similar to the type found in prokaryotes.
5. **Electron transport.** Similar to free-living prokaryotic cells, both mitochondria and chloroplasts can generate energy in the form of ATP through the presence of their own electron transport chains.

2.5d The Cytoskeleton Supports and Moves Cell Structures

The characteristic shape and internal organization of each type of cell are maintained in part by its **cytoskeleton**, the interconnected system of protein fibres and tubes that extends throughout the cytoplasm. The cytoskeleton also reinforces the plasma membrane and functions in movement, both of structures within the cell and of the cell as a whole. The cytoskeleton of animal cells contains three major types of structural elements: microtubules, intermediate filaments, and microfilaments **(Figure 2.22).** Plant cytoskeletons contain only microtubules and microfilaments. As shown in Figure 2.22a, **microtubules** are microscopic hollow tubes. **Intermediate filaments** (see Figure 2.22b) are fibres that occur singly, in parallel bundles, and in interlinked networks, either alone or in combination with microtubules, microfilaments, or both. **Microfilaments** (see Figure 2.22c) are thin fibres that consist of two rows of protein subunits wound around each other in a long spiral.

Eukaryotic cell movements are generated by "motor" proteins that push or pull along microtubules or microfilaments. One end of a motor protein is firmly fixed to a cell structure such as a vesicle, a

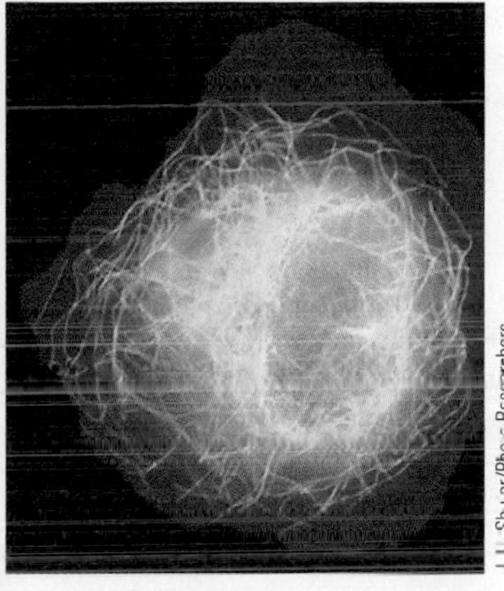

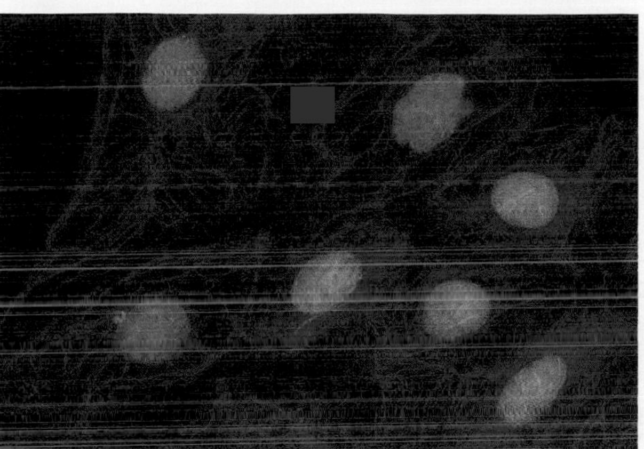

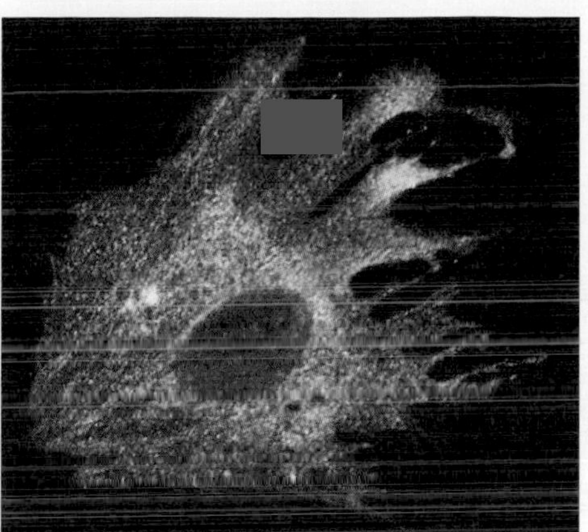

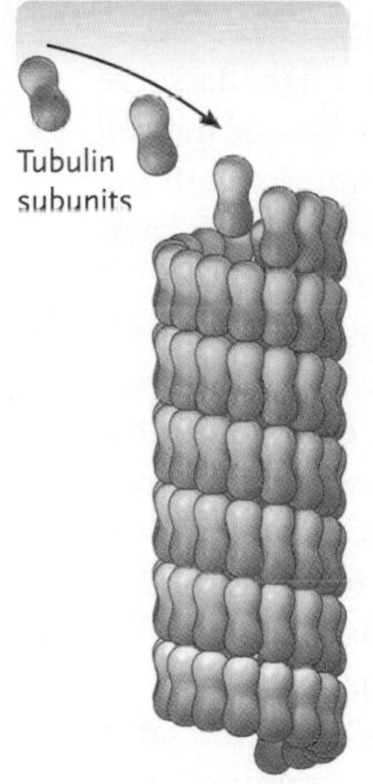

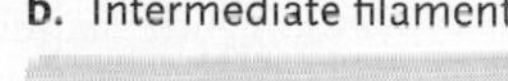

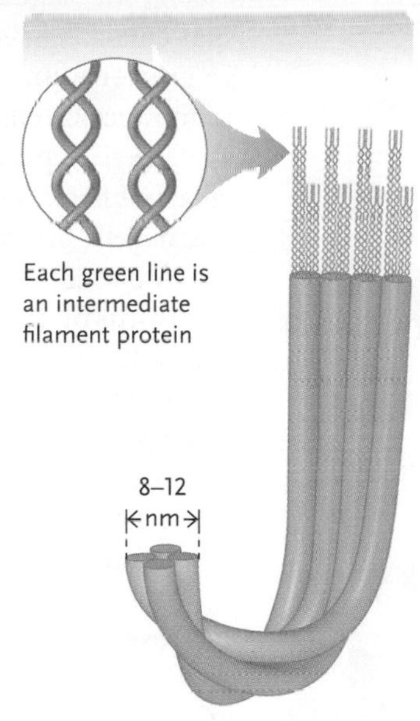

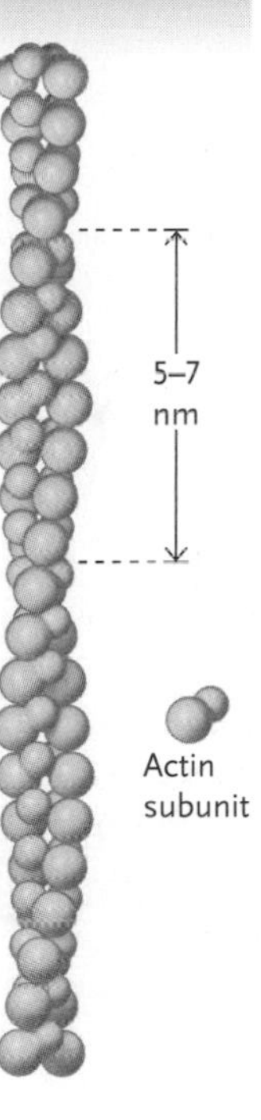

Figure 2.22
The major components of the cytoskeleton as visualized by specific staining and light microscopy (TOP) and molecular models (BOTTOM). **(a)** Microtubules are stained yellow in a pancreatic cell. Microtubules are assembled from individual tubulin subunits. **(b)** Intermediate filaments assembled from keratin proteins in cells of the kangaroo rat. The nucleus is stained blue in these cells. In intermediate filaments eight protein chains wind together to form each subunit shown as a green cylinder. **(c)** Microfilaments (red) in a migrating mammalian cell. A microfilament is assembled from two rows of actin proteins, wound around each other into a double helix.

microtubule, or a microfilament. The other end has reactive groups that "walk" along another microtubule or microfilament by making an attachment, forcefully swivelling a short distance, and then releasing **(Figure 2.23, p. 40)**. ATP supplies the energy for the walking movements.

Some cell movements, such as the whipping motions of sperm tails, depend entirely on microtubules and their motor proteins. Microfilaments are solely responsible for other types of movements, including *amoeboid motion*, the actively flowing motion of cytoplasm called *cytoplasmic streaming*, and the contraction of muscle cells (the roles of myosin and microfilaments in muscle contraction are discussed further in Chapter 36). When animal cells divide, both microtubules and microfilaments are active—the chromosomes are divided and moved by microtubules, and the cytoplasm is divided by microfilaments (see Chapter 11 for further discussion).

2.5e The Flagella of Eukaryotes and Prokaryotes Are Not Evolutionarily Related

Flagella (singular = flagellum) are long, hair-like structures that project from the cell surface and function in cell movement. Flagella are common on single-celled prokaryotes and numerous eukaryotic cells. Although they superficially look the same and serve the same function, the flagella of eukaryotes and prokaryotes are structurally different. A bacterial

a. "Walking" end of a kinesin molecule

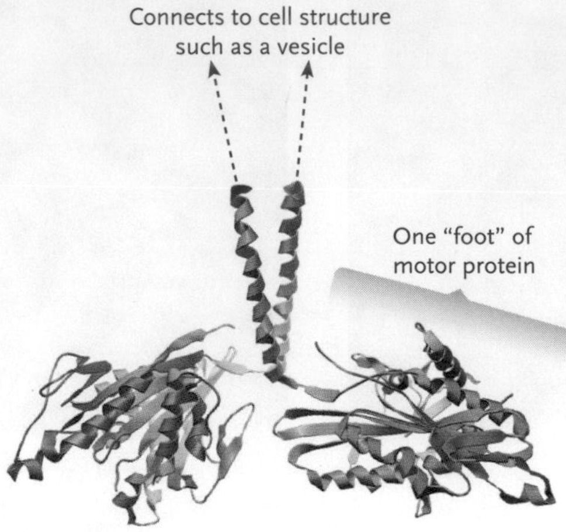

b. How a kinesin molecule "walks"

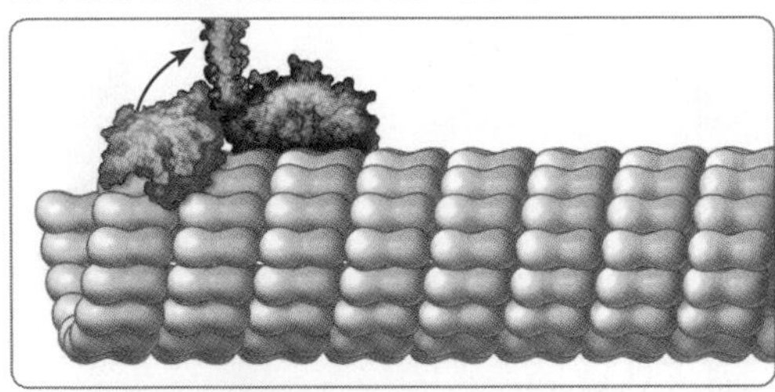

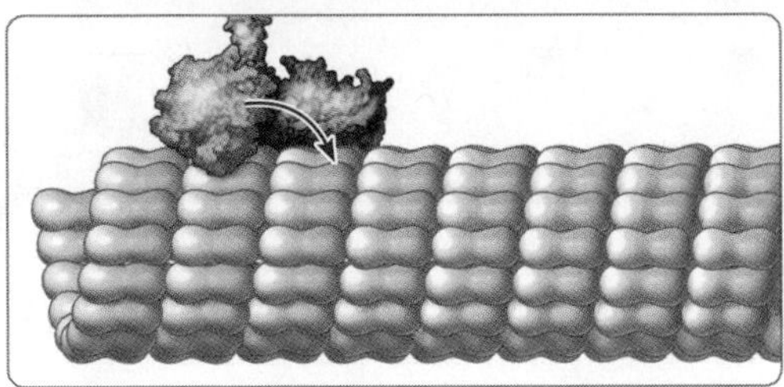

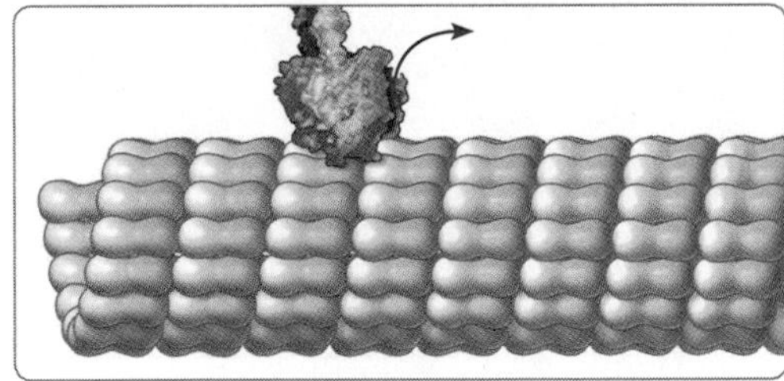

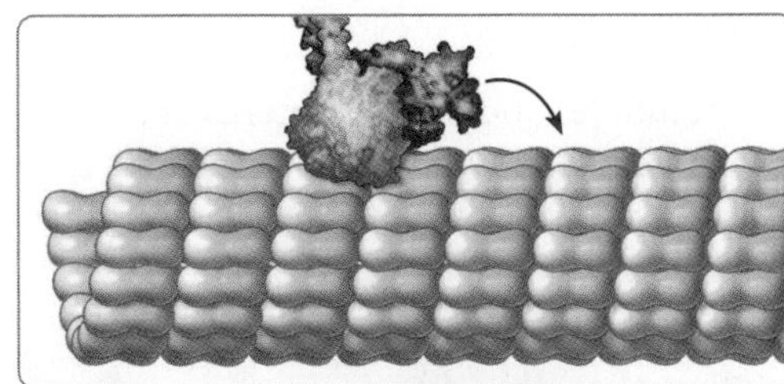

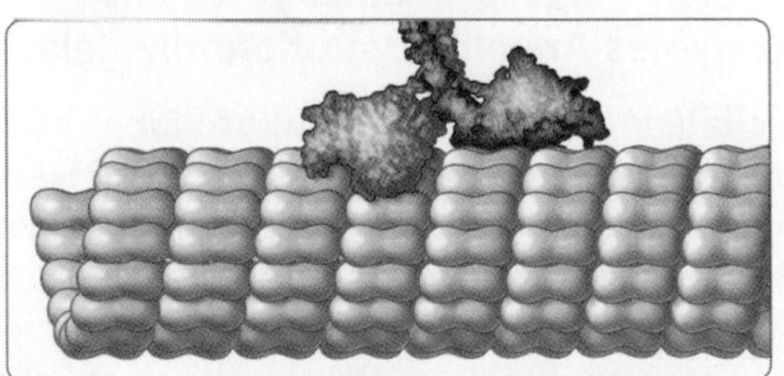

Figure 2.23
The microtubule motor protein kinesin. **(a)** Structure of the end of a kinesin molecule that "walks" along a microtubule, with alpha-helical segments shown as spirals and beta strands as flat ribbons. **(b)** How a kinesin molecule walks along the surface of a molecule by alternately attaching and releasing its "feet."

flagellum **(Figure 2.24)**, which is made of a single protein called flagellin, moves the cell by rotating like the propeller of a boat. In comparison, the flagella of a eukaryote are constructed of microtubules, and their movement is whiplike. The actual flagellum bends in response to the movement of a protein called dynein along one side of each microtubule. The structure of eukaryotic flagella is identical to that of cilia except that cilia are usually shorter than flagella and occur in greater numbers on cells. Whereas flagella serve to move cells, cilia act to move materials over the cell surface. The plasma membrane surrounds both the cilia and flagella of eukaryotic cells, whereas prokaryotic flagella protrude through the membrane.

A bundle of microtubules extends from the base to the tip of a eukaryotic flagellum or cilium **(see Figure 2.25)**. In the bundle, a circle of nine double microtubules surrounds a central pair of single microtubules, forming what is known as the *9 + 2 complex*. Dynein motor proteins slide the microtubules of the 9 + 2 complex over each other to produce the flagellar or ciliar movements **(Figure 2.26, p. 42)**.

Because the flagella of eukaryotes serve the same purpose as the flagella of prokaryotes, combined with the fact that they look similar, you may think that the two are evolutionarily related, that the prokaryotic flagellum was the ancestor of the flagellum of eukaryotes. This, however, is not the case. At the molecular level, there is nothing similar between the two structures. The proteins involved are distinctly different, being encoded by different genes, and as we have seen, they function in distinctly different ways. Structures that perform the same function but do not share a common evolutionary history are said to be analogous structures. Structures that are similar because they *do* share a common evolutionary history are said to be homologous. You will learn much more about analogous and homologous structures in Chapter 10.

2.5f Why Are Eukaryotic Cells Larger than Prokaryotic Cells?

The size of a cell is determined primarily by its *surface area* being able to supply its *volume* with the necessary metabolic requirements for life. The cubes in **Figure 2.27**, p. 42 can be used to represent single cells. Although the overall surface area of a cell increases as the square of its length, the cell's volume increases as the cube of that dimension. So, as a cell gets larger, its volume increases much more rapidly than its surface area does. In other words, its surface area to volume ratio decreases.

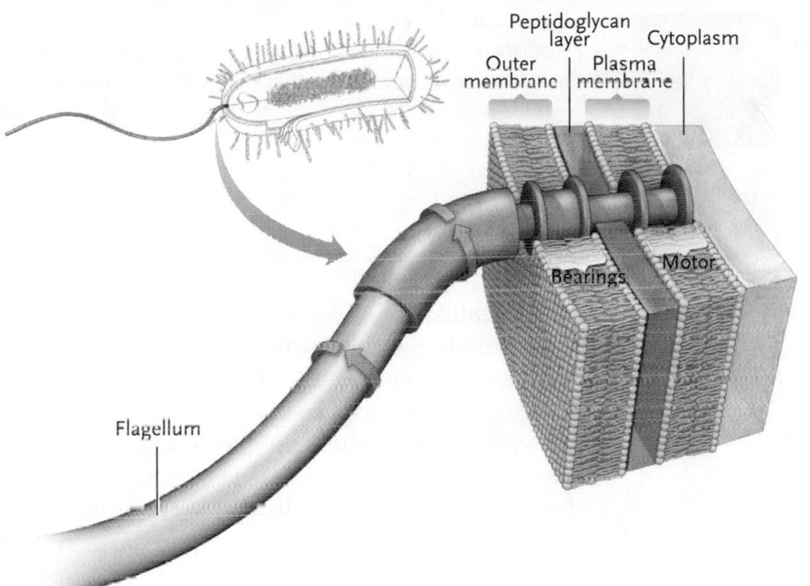

Figure 2.24
A flagellum of a bacterium (prokaryote). The flagellum spins around its axis which causes the cell to move.

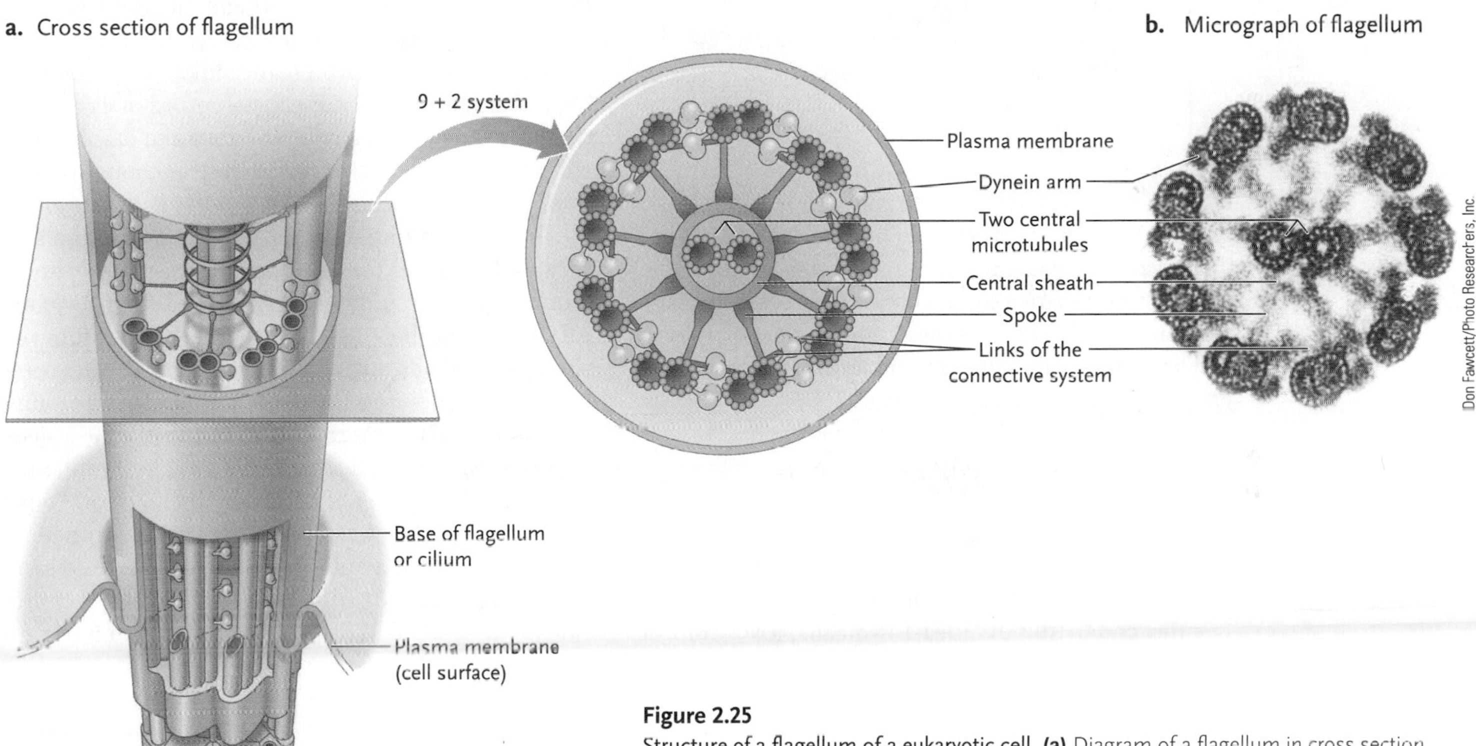

Figure 2.25
Structure of a flagellum of a eukaryotic cell. **(a)** Diagram of a flagellum in cross section, showing the 9 + 2 system of microtubules. The spokes and connecting links hold the system together. **(b)** Electron micrograph of a flagellum in cross section; individual tubulin molecules are visible in the microtubule walls.

Think of the plasma membrane of a prokaryotic cell as the total surface area across which nutrients and waste products move into and out of the cell. It is also the location of the electron transport chains used to make ATP. Now think of the total volume of the cell. This volume needs to be supported by the energy produced by the electron transport chains and the nutrient/waste transport systems of the plasma membrane. As a cell increases in size and its surface area to volume ratio decreases, a point will be reached where the volume is too great to be supported by the processes occurring on the plasma membrane. The plasma membrane can hold only a finite number of transport proteins and only a limited number of electron transport chains.

Figure 2.28, p. 43 shows that the bacterial cells are much smaller than the pink epithelial cells (the lining of the nose). *Why can a eukaryotic cell be larger (and thus have a lower overall surface area to volume ratio) than a prokaryotic cell?* The answer is that a eukaryotic cell has a large area of internal membrane structures with specialized functions

a. Flagella beat in smooth, S-shaped waves that travel from base to tip.

Lennart Nilsson

b. Cilia beat in an oarlike power stroke (dark orange) followed by a recovery stroke (light orange).

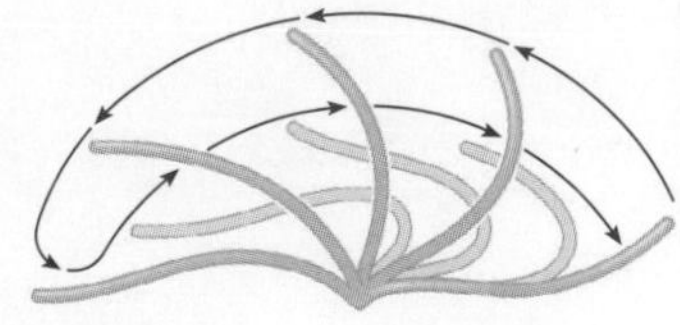

CNRI/SPL/Photo Researchers

c. The waves and bends are produced by dynein motor proteins, which slide the microtubule doublets over each other. An examination of the tip of a bent cilium or flagellum shows that the doublets extend farther toward the tip on the side toward the bend, confirming that the doublets actually slide as the shaft of the cilium or flagellum bends.

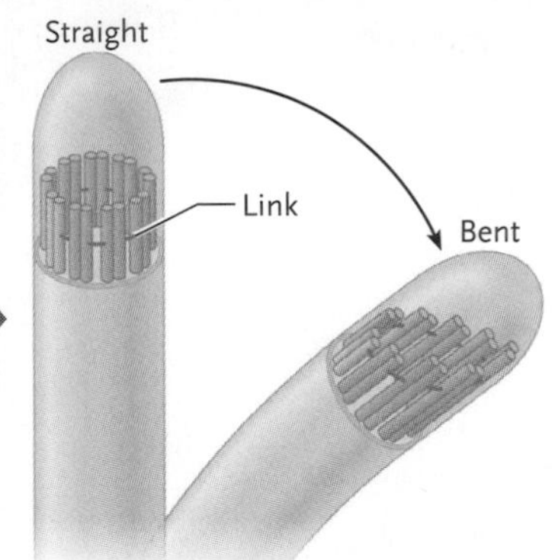

Figure 2.26
Flagellar and ciliary beating patterns. The micrographs show a few human sperm, each with a flagellum (top), and cilia from the lining of an airway in the lungs (bottom).

that can support the larger cell volume. For example, a typical animal cell may contain hundreds of mitochondria, each one producing ATP to support the needs of the cell. As well, eukaryotic cells contain the endomembrane system, which allows the efficient movement of proteins and lipids throughout the cell and provides various compartments for synthesis and storage.

2.5g The Evolution of Multicellular Eukaryotes

One of the most profound transitions in the history of life was the evolution of multicellular eukaryotes. Besides consisting of at least two cells, a key trait of a multicellular organism is that a "division of labour" exists among the cells of the organism. That is, the cells are not identical in structure and/or function. Some cells may specialize in harvesting energy, for example, whereas others may serve a specific role in the motility of the organism. The evolution of multicellularity meant that cells no longer needed to be autonomous (independent). In a multicellular system, the cells cooperate with one another for the benefit of the entire organism. Over evolutionary time, this specialization of cell function led to the development of the specialized tissues and organs that are so clearly evident in modern eukaryotes.

Like early prokaryotes and eukaryotes, there is little, if any, evidence in the fossil record of early multicellular organisms. How they arose and developed is still an area of intensive research. It is thought, however, that multicellularity arose independently along the lineages leading to fungi, plants, and animals. A very useful model for the study of multicellularity is found in a group of green algae called the volvocine. All of the members of this group are evolutionarily closely related and span the full range of size and complexity from the unicellular *Chlamydomonas*, through various colonial genera, to the multicellular *Volvox* **(Figure 2.29).** Unlike a true multicellular organism, a cell colony is a group of cells that are all of one type; there is no specialization in cell structure or function. *Volvox* consists of a sphere of two to three thousand small, flagellated, *Chlamydomonas*-like cells that provide the individual *Volvox* with the ability to move. In

x $2x$ $3x$ $4x$

Total surface area	$\mathbf{6x^2}$	$6\,(2x)^2 = \mathbf{24x^2}$	$6\,(3x)^2 = \mathbf{54x^2}$	$6\,(4x)^2 = \mathbf{96x^2}$
Total volume	$\mathbf{x^3}$	$(2x)^3 = \mathbf{8x^3}$	$(3x)^3 = \mathbf{27x^3}$	$(4x)^3 = \mathbf{64x^3}$
Surface area/ volume ratio	**6:1**	**3:1**	**2:1**	**1.5:1**

Figure 2.27
Relationship between surface area and volume. The surface area of an object increases as a square of the linear dimension, whereas the volume increases as a cube of that dimension.

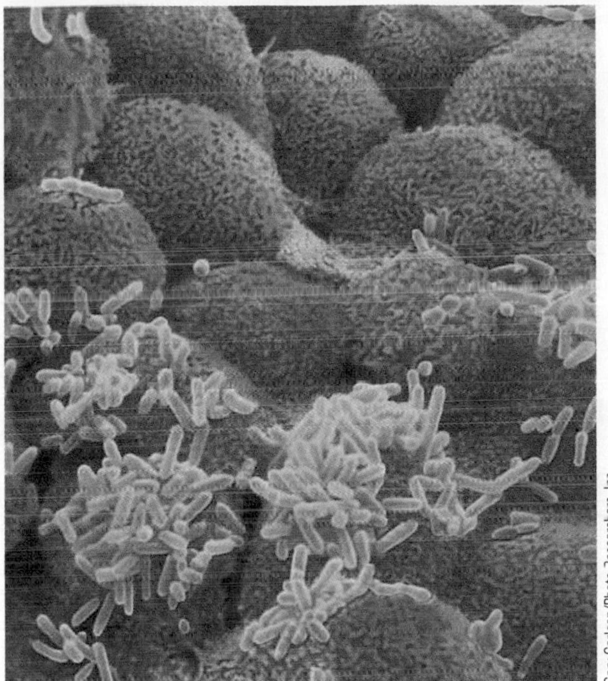

Figure 2.28
The yellow rods are bacteria covering the surface of skin cells lining the interior of a human nose. Why are the skin cells so large compared to the bacterial cells?

addition, within the sphere lie about 16 large nonmotile cells that serve a specialized role in reproduction.

2.5h Life May Have Been the Inevitable Consequence of the Physical Conditions of Primitive Earth

How long did it take for evolutionary mechanisms to produce fully eukaryotic cells? The oldest known fossil eukaryotes are 2.2 billion years old. If prokaryotic cells first evolved some 3.5 billion years ago, it took up to 1.3 billion years for eukaryotic cells to evolve from prokaryotes (see Figure 24.2). If so, this long interval probably reflects the complexity of the adaptations required as prokaryotic cells evolved to become eukaryotic cells. Of course, it is possible that eukaryotic cells evolved more quickly and we have yet to find the evidence.

Overall, the events outlined in this chapter, leading from Earth's origin to the appearance of eukaryotic cells, may seem improbable. But as scientist and author George Wald of Harvard University put it, given the total time span of these events, more than 3.5 billion years, "the impossible becomes possible, the possible probable, and the probable virtually certain. One has only to wait; time itself performs the miracles." Some researchers go a step further and maintain that the evolution of life on our planet was an inevitable outcome of the initial physical and chemical conditions established by Earth's origin, among them a reducing atmosphere (at least in some locations), a size that generates moderate gravitational forces, and a distance from the Sun that results in average surface temperatures between the freezing and boiling points of water.

Study Break

1. What is the evidence in support of endosymbiosis?
2. What role is served by the cytoskeleton?
3. What are the key traits of a multicellular organism?

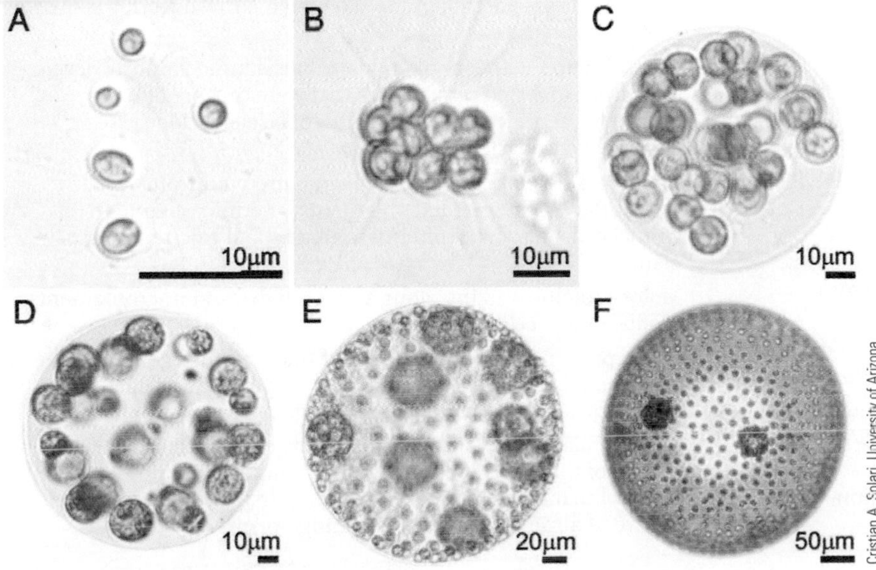

Figure 2.29
Examples of species of the volvocine that differ in cell number, colony size and degree of specialization.
(a) *Chlamydomonas reinhardtii*, a unicell **(b)** *Gonium pectorale*, a group of undifferentiated cells
(c) *Eudorina elegans*, a spherical colony of undifferentiated cells.
(d) *Pleodorina californica*, **(e)** *Volvox carteri* **(f)** *Volvox aureus*. In d.–f. two cell types are present - numerous smaller somatic cells and fewer larger reproductive cells.

Unanswered Questions

1. Does life exist elsewhere in our solar system? In our galaxy?
2. Is it possible to synthesize life in the laboratory?

Review

Go to CENGAGENOW™ at http://hed.nelson.com/ to access quizzing, animations, exercises, articles, and personalized homework help.

2.1 What Is Life?

- All forms of life share seven characteristics: order, energy utilization, homeostasis, response to stimuli, growth, reproduction, and evolution.
- According to the cell theory, (1) all living organisms are composed of cells, (2) cells are the functional units of life, and (3) cells arise only from preexisting cells by a process of division.

2.2 The Chemical Origins of Life

- Earth and the rest of the solar system were formed about 4.6 billion years ago.
- The Oparin–Haldane hypothesis maintains that the organic molecules that formed the building blocks of life, such as amino acids, could have been formed given the conditions that prevailed on primitive Earth, including a reducing atmosphere that lacked oxygen.
- The Miller–Urey experiment demonstrated that abiotic synthesis of biologically important molecules is possible.
- The key macromolecules of life, such as proteins and nucleic acids, are polymers that were not formed by the Miller–Urey experiment. Instead, it is thought that polymerization reactions could have occurred on solid surfaces, such as clay.
- Organic molecules produced by chance in early Earth's environment formed aggregates that became membrane bound in protobionts, primitive cell-like structures with some of the properties of life. Protobionts may have been the precursors of cells.

2.3 The Origins of Information and Metabolism

- Living cells required the development of several critical components, notably energy-harnessing pathways, and a system based on nucleic acids that could store and pass on the information required to make proteins.
- Ribozymes are a group of RNA molecules that can catalyze specific reactions. Because they can store information and drive catalysis, it is thought that RNA was the first molecule from which both DNA and proteins developed.
- Because of their greater diversity and much higher rate of catalysis, proteins became the dominant structural and functional macromolecule of all cells.
- DNA is more stable than RNA and thus evolved as a better repository of genetic information.
- Early metabolism was probably based on simple oxidation–reduction reactions.

2.4 Early Life

- Stromatolites dated to 2.3 billion years ago represent the earliest fossil evidence of life.
- Panspermia is the hypothesis that very simple forms of life are present in space and seeded Earth soon after it cooled.
- Prokaryotic cells lack a nucleus, which is a characteristic of eukaryotic cells.
- Both prokaryotic and eukaryotic cells share common features: plasma membrane, electron transport chains, and transcription–translation machinery that relies on ribosomes.
- Some early cells developed the capacity to carry out photosynthesis using water as an electron donor; the oxygen produced as a by-product accumulated, and the oxidizing character of Earth's atmosphere increased. From this time on, organic molecules produced in the environment were quickly broken down by oxidation, and life could arise only from preexisting life, as in today's world.

2.5 Eukaryotic Cells

- Eukaryotic cells possess an endomembrane system that probably evolved from infolding of the plasma membrane. The endomembrane system consists of the nuclear envelope, the ER, and the Golgi complex.
- The ER occurs in two forms, rough and smooth. The ribosome-studded rough ER makes proteins that become part of cell membranes or are released from the cell. Smooth ER synthesizes lipids and breaks down toxic substances.
- The Golgi complex chemically modifies proteins made in the rough ER and sorts finished proteins to be secreted from the cell or embedded in the plasma membrane.
- The energy-transducing organelles—the chloroplasts and the mitochondria—are thought to have been derived from free-living prokaryotic cells.
- According to the theory of endosymbiosis, mitochondria developed from ingested prokaryotes that were capable of using oxygen for aerobic respiration; chloroplasts developed from ingested cyanobacteria.
- The cytoskeleton is a supportive structure built from microtubules, intermediate filaments, and microfilaments in animal cells but only from microtubules and microfilaments in plants.
- Motor proteins walking along microtubules and microfilaments produce most cell movements.
- Motor protein–controlled sliding of microtubules generates the movements of flagella and cilia of eukaryotes. The flagella of prokaryotes are functionally and structurally very different.
- Multicellular eukaryotes probably evolved by differentiation of cells of the same species that had congregated into colonies. Multicellularity evolved several times, producing lineages of several algae and ancestors of fungi, plants, and animals.

Questions

Self-Test Questions

1. Which of the following is not a characteristic of all living organisms?
   a. Genetic information is used for the synthesis of proteins.
   b. Genetic information is passed to the next generation.
   c. Has DNA that is contained within the nucleus.
   d. Energy is obtained from the surrounding environment.
   e. Populations of organisms change over generations.
2. According to the Oparin–Haldane hypothesis, the atmosphere when life began is thought to have been composed primarily of
   a. H_2O, N_2, and CO_2.
   b. H_2, H_2O, NH_3, and CH_4.
   c. H_2O, N_2, O_2, and CO_2.
   d. O_2 and no H_2.
   e. H_2 only.
3. The O_2 in the atmosphere comes from
   a. aerobic respiration.
   b. a type of photosynthesis that uses oxygen.
   c. a type of photosynthesis that oxidizes water.
   d. anaerobic respiration.
   e. the formation of Earth.
4. The Miller–Urey experiment
   a. used an atmosphere rich in O_2.
   b. demonstrated that abiotic protein synthesis was possible.
   c. did not require a source of energy.
   d. did not require water as a reactant.
   e. demonstrated that abiotic synthesis of amino acids was possible.
5. The hypothesis that life on Earth developed from microbes from space (panspermia) is supported by the fact that
   a. life seemingly developed quickly after Earth was formed.
   b. life on Earth is similar to the forms of life found on Jupiter.
   c. DNA and proteins have been discovered in the tails of comets.
   d. prokaryotic cells have been shown to survive extreme conditions.
   e. Both a and d are correct.
6. Ribozymes may have played a critical role in the evolution of life because they
   a. carry genetic information.
   b. were the first polymers of amino acids.
   c. display catalytic activity.
   d. were double stranded like DNA.
   e. Both a and c are correct.
7. As part of the evolution of eukaryotic cells, infolding of the plasma membrane led to the formation of
   a. chromosomes.
   b. mitochondria.
   c. ribosomes.
   d. the nuclear envelope.
   e. microtubules.
8. Which of the following statements does NOT support the theory of endosymbiosis? Both mitochondria and chloroplasts
   a. are each about the same size and shape of many bacterial cells.
   b. are surrounded by a membrane.
   c. contain ribosomes.
   d. possess electron transport chains.
   e. contain DNA.
9. Compared with prokaryotic cells, eukaryotic cells tend to be larger because they
   a. contain DNA.
   b. contain ribosomes.
   c. contain a nucleus.
   d. grow faster.
   e. have an overall greater membrane surface area.
10. A key trait of multicellular organisms is
   a. different amounts of DNA among cells.
   b. division of labour among cells.
   c. the ability to photosynthesize.
   d. the presence of mitochondria.
   e. the presence of flagellated cells.

Questions for Discussion

1. What evidence supports the idea that life originated through inanimate chemical processes?
2. Most scientists agree that life on Earth can arise only from preexisting life, but also that life could have originated spontaneously on primordial Earth. Can you reconcile these seemingly contradictory statements?
3. What conditions would likely be necessary for a planet located elsewhere in the universe to evolve life similar to that on Earth?
4. What drove the evolution of the eukaryotic cell?

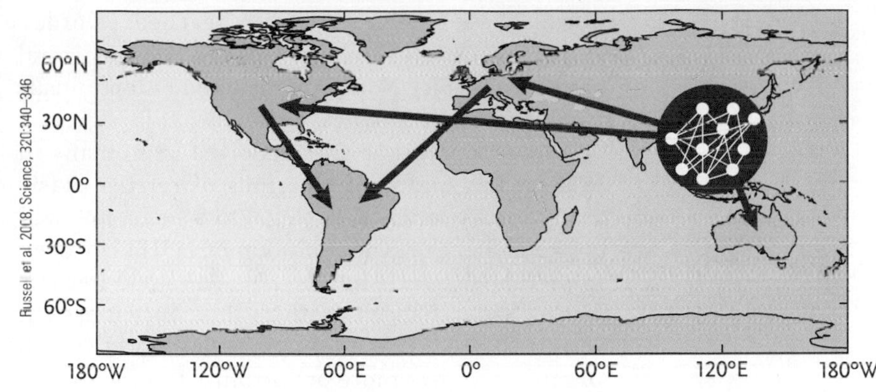

The symbols and arrows show how seasonal influenza A (H3N2) moves out from an area of overlapping epidemics in East and Southeast Asia.

3 Selection, Biodiversity, and Biosphere

Study Plan

3.1 Biodiversity

3.2 Selection

3.2a Case 1, Syphilis: Migration and Emergence of a Disease

3.2b Case 2, Evolution of Whales: A Change from Hoofed Mammal to Whale

3.2c Case 3, Climbing Plants: Reaching for the Light

3.3 Evolution

3.3a Adaptive Radiation: Diversification of Lineages of Life

3.3b Islands: Showcases of Evolution

3.3c Land: Organisms Conquer a New Frontier

3.3d Other Breakthroughs Underlying Adaptive Radiations

3.4 The Biosphere

3.4a Solar Radiation: Energy from the Sun

3.4b Seasonality: Weather through the Year

3.4c Air Circulation: Wind Patterns

3.4d Precipitation: Water

3.4e Ocean Currents: Rivers within the Oceans

3.4f Regional and Local Effects: Local Conditions for Life

3.4g The Effects of Topography: The Ups and Downs of Weather and Life

3.4h Microclimate: Very Local Conditions of Temperature, Humidity, and Air Movement

3.5 Biotic Factors

3.5a Trophic Interactions: Movements of Energy, Biomass, and Numbers

3.6 Cumulative Impact on Biotic and Abiotic Factors

Why It Matters

Imagine yourself sitting in a crowded airplane bound from London, England, to Vancouver, Canada. The person sitting beside you has a runny nose, is sneezing and sucking on cough candies, and appears to have a fever. Your fellow passenger periodically dozes and does not eat anything during the flight. Recognizing that your seat mate is exhibiting many of the symptoms of influenza A, you hope that some of the other symptoms, such as vomiting and diarrhea, do not appear until after you have left the aircraft. You have just seen how influenza ("the flu") can affect people and how air travel can help it spread around the world.

At any given time, 5 to 15% of the global population of people exhibit the symptoms of influenza A. Every year, this strain of the influenza virus kills about 500 000 people. To study the spread of influenza A, Colin A. Russell and his colleagues analyzed about 13 000 human influenza A (H3N2) viruses, collecting viral material from infected people on six continents between 2002 and 2007. Their analysis revealed almost continuous circulation of H3N2 in East and Southeast Asia. This regional network of overlapping epidemics appeared to be the source of influenza outbreaks elsewhere in the world. These epidemics usually reached, in order, Oceania (Australia and other islands in the central and south Pacific), North America, and Europe, finally arriving in South America.

Since H3N2 was first reported in humans in 1968, it has undergone periods of relative stasis (evolutionary stability) lasting 3 to 8 years, followed by rapid changes. The evolution of H3N2 has been "punctuated" (see Chapter 20). The good news is that the virus changes relatively little once it has left Southeast Asia. This means that the World Health Organization has more opportunity to monitor the situation in East and Southeast Asia, allowing vaccines to be developed against the most threatening strains of H3N2. These vaccines offer us some protection from the illness.

This anecdote demonstrates evolutionary change in a virus, its dispersal around the world, and its impact on humans. Biology in action! Have you had your flu shot this year?

3.1 Biodiversity

The astonishing diversity of life in the biosphere is an array of riches. Measured as the number of species of organisms, biodiversity reflects the reality that life on Earth exists from the ocean floor to well into the atmosphere. The study of biology focuses on the levels of life, from molecules to organelles, cells, organisms, ecosystems, and the biosphere **(Figure 3.1)** (see Chapter 1). Exploring and understanding this reality can be one of the most rewarding challenges for humans in general and for biologists in particular.

In Chapter 1, we saw how access to light and energy are organizing factors for life on Earth. Now, examine the photographs in **Figure 3.2.** What organisms or parts of organisms appear in each photograph? What can these pictures tell us about the diversity of life? How can you relate them to the themes of light and energy? Speculate about which of these organisms are most closely related to one another. Look for more information about the members of this gallery as you proceed through this book.

How many different types of organisms live on Earth? There are different ways to answer this question, depending on how we define "type" of organism. If we take a taxonomic definition (see Chapter 18), we can consider the number of organisms in each

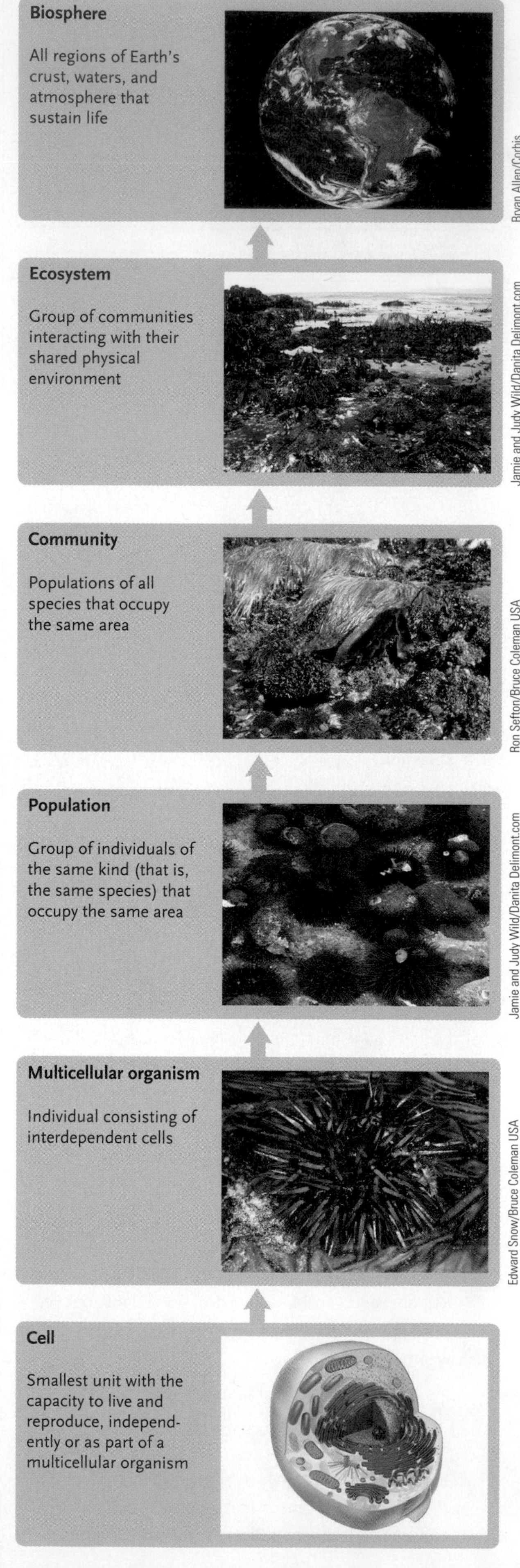

Biosphere
All regions of Earth's crust, waters, and atmosphere that sustain life
Bryan Allen/Corbis
Ecosystem
Group of communities interacting with their shared physical environment
Jamie and Judy Wild/Danita Delimont.com
Community
Populations of all species that occupy the same area
Ron Sefton/Bruce Coleman USA
Population
Group of individuals of the same kind (that is, the same species) that occupy the same area
Jamie and Judy Wild/Danita Delimont.com
Multicellular organism
Individual consisting of interdependent cells
Edward Snow/Bruce Coleman USA
Cell
Smallest unit with the capacity to live and reproduce, independently or as part of a multicellular organism

Figure 3.1
The hierarchy of life. Each level in the hierarchy of life exhibits emergent properties that do not exist at lower levels. The middle four photos depict a rocky intertidal zone on the coast of Washington State.

Figure 3.2
(a) Mushroom orchid **(b)** Scales of pangolin **(c)** Bird's nest fungus **(d)** Zombie worm **(e)** Fern sporangia **(f)** Sea anenome **(g)** Barnacles **(h)** Insects caught by *Pinguicula*.

kingdom. Although these numbers are easier to determine for certain kinds of organisms than for others, we can determine an overview of life on Earth by group of organisms **(Figure 3.3, p. 50).** We have quite accurate information about the numbers of species of large, easily observed organisms such as mammals, birds, and flowering plants. We do not have accurate information about the numbers of species of microscopic organisms that live in habitats where they are hard to observe. We have only rough estimates of the numbers of species of soil fungi and aquatic prokaryotes.

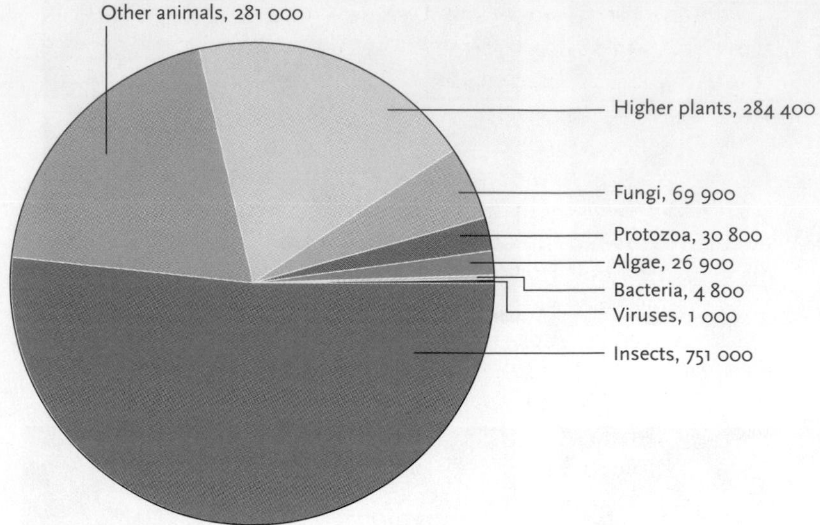

Figure 3.3
Diversity of life. The approximate numbers of species in different groups of organisms.

When we group organisms by factors other than their taxonomic categories, we get a different picture of the diversity of life on Earth. One approach is to consider how organisms obtain carbon because carbon is the "backbone" of all organic molecules synthesized by an organism (see Chapter 47). Most plants are autotrophs (*auto* = self; *troph* = nourishment), which synthesize organic carbon molecules using inorganic carbon (CO_2). (Note that although CO_2 contains a carbon atom, oxides containing carbon are considered inorganic molecules.) All animals are heterotrophs, meaning that they obtain carbon from organic molecules, either from living hosts or from organic molecules in the products, wastes, or remains of dead organisms.

Organisms are also divided according to the source of the energy they use to drive biological activities. Chemotrophs (*chemo* = chemical; *troph* = nourishment) obtain energy by oxidizing inorganic or organic substances, whereas phototrophs obtain energy from light. Combining the carbon and energy sources allows us to group living organisms into four categories **(Table 3.1)**.

Prokaryotes show the greatest diversity in their modes of securing carbon and energy. Note that prokaryotes are the only representatives of two of the categories, chemoautotrophs and photoheterotrophs; see Chapter 21 to find out more about the amazing metabolic diversity that exists among prokaryotes.

Study Break

Describe the differences among heterotrophs, autotrophs, photoautotrophs, and chemoautotrophs. Provide an example of each.

3.2 Selection

Selection occurs when some force or phenomenon affects the survival of individual organisms. An unexpected spring frost can kill many plants in your garden. Only the cold-resistant plants survive the selective force (temperature). When you hear about an outbreak of some disease in a hospital or care facility, you are often seeing an example of the outcome of selection. Bacteria that are resistant to antibiotics, for example, can survive and reproduce, overwhelming the defences of individuals and institutions. The same can be true with the emergence of pests that are resistant to pesticides, whether the targets are weeds, parasites, or insects.

Selection occurs when a large population of individuals is exposed to a lethal factor and only resistant individuals survive to reproduce. If resistance is inherited, then the offspring of survivors will be resistant. If the resistant population is able to reproduce quickly, there is the potential for explosive growth of a population of individuals who are immune to the lethal factor. When the target pests are bacteria, some of which can double their populations in minutes, it does not take long for resistant pests to take over (see Chapter 45). Imagine having 10 million toxic bacteria in your body. You take an antibiotic that kills 99.99% of them. The remaining 1000 bacteria are resistant to the antibiotic.

Table 3.1 **Modes of nutrition among living organisms.**

		Energy source: Oxidation of Molecules*	Energy source: Light
Carbon source	CO_2	**CHEMOAUTOTROPH** Found in some bacteria and archaeans; not found in eukaryotes	**PHOTOAUTOTROPH** Found in some photosynthetic bacteria, in some proteins, and in plants
Carbon source	Organic molecules	**CHEMOHETEROTROPH** Found in some bacteria and archaeans, and also in proteins, fungi, animals, and plants	**PHOTOHETEROTROPH** Found in some photosynthetic bacteria

*Inorganic molecules for chemoautotrophs and organic molecules for chemoheterotrophs.

If their population doubles every 20 minutes, you will have over 10 million (now resistant) bacteria within 5 hours.

The key factors behind selection are a selective force (pressure) and the capacity for explosive population growth. When these factors coincide, we can be overrun by pests, such as antibiotic-resistant bacteria in hospitals or health care facilities, weeds in crop fields, or insect pests. When this happens, the consequences for humans can be deadly.

Selection is the major force responsible for evolution and biodiversity. A recurring theme in selection is genetic variation in the population put to the test by some selection pressure. Here are three examples of selection in action.

3.2a Case 1, Syphilis: Migration and Emergence of a Disease

Treponematoses are diseases caused by bacteria in the genus *Treponema*. *Treponema pallidum pallidum* is the bacterium that causes syphilis, a venereal disease also known as "the pox." Often the first signs of syphilis are small, painless sores (chancres) at the site of contact. This can progress to secondary stages (rash, fever, fatigue) and, if untreated, to tertiary syphilis, with symptoms that can include disfigurement, neurological disorders, and cardiovascular problems. *Treponema pallidum pertenue* causes yaws, a skin disease that usually afflicts people in hot, humid areas. The extinct *Treponema carateum* caused pinta, a skin disease confined to South and Central America. Perhaps also extinct, *Treponema pallidum endemicum* caused bejel, endemic syphilis that was limited to hot, arid climates in the Middle East. Genetic evidence indicates that *T. pallidum pertenue* is an older subspecies of *T. pallidum* than *T. pallidum pallidum* is, meaning that whereas yaws has afflicted people for a long time, syphilis caused by *T. pallidum pallidum* is relatively new. Syphilis and other treponemal diseases, except pinta, leave distinct marks on the skeleton, which have allowed paleoanthropologists to document the incidence of these diseases in human skeletal remains and determine their prehistoric distribution.

The first outbreak of syphilis in Europe occurred in 1495, and since then, it has killed tens of thousands of people. Syphilis has long been thought to have originated in the New World. In 2008, genetic analyses supported the hypothesis that a new strain of *T. pallidum (T. pallidum pallidum)* emerged in Europe in 1495, brought from the New World by members of Columbus's crew.

The history of *T. pallidum* appears to have involved three steps:

- First, *T. pallidum* appeared as a nonvenereal infection and spread with humans throughout the Middle East, Europe, and the New World. At that point, the pathogen caused yaws, which was spread by skin-to-skin contact.
- Second, European explorers brought a strain of *T. pallidum* from the New World to Europe, where it emerged as the progenitor of the modern *T. pallidum pallidum* that caused syphilis. When clothed European explorers, such as Columbus and his crew, met unclothed natives in the New World, yaws (caused by *T. pallidum*) could not readily spread between the two groups of people because of the lack of skin-to-skin contact. But the explorers could be exposed to the lesions of yaws (and *T. pallidum*) during sex.
- Third, although the strains or subspecies of *T. pallidum* that caused yaws were thwarted by clothes, variants that occurred in the genital area could be transferred during sex. This meant success for the bacterium, and syphilis was the result.

The pivotal discovery giving genetic support to the theory that syphilis came from the New World emerged when a Canadian physician (Michael S. Silverman), working in isolated settlements in Guyana (South America), spotted lesions caused by yaws. He obtained samples of bacteria from the lesions and set the genetics side of the story in motion.

The key elements were genetic variation, differences in transmission of the disease-causing agent, and the opportunity for *T. pallidum pallidum* to spread widely due to people's sexual behaviour. In 2008, syphilis became more common, suggesting that the process is still in play.

3.2b Case 2, Evolution of Whales: A Change from Hoofed Mammal to Whale

The first fossil whales were found in rocks in south Asia dated to the Eocene, about 50 million years ago. Paleontologists had presumed that the ancestor of whales lived a hippopotamus-like existence, retreating to the water to avoid predators and going ashore at night to eat vegetation. The fossil evidence also indicated that whales and modern hoofed mammals (ungulates) shared a common ancestor and that hippopotomi are ungulates. But the oldest hippo ancestors are 15 million years old and have been found only in Africa, so timing and location mean that hippos are not close relatives of whales.

In 2007, Hans Thewissen and his colleagues reported evidence of an ungulate ancestor that was closely related to whales. The candidates, raccoon sized species in the genus *Indohyus* (family Raoellidae), were Eocene fossils found in Kashmir (India). Thewissen and his colleagues presented several lines of evidence supporting the proposal that *Indohyus* was aquatic, lived a hippo-like existence, and shared a close ancestor with whales. *Indohyus* had dense bones and high levels of oxygen isotopes (O^{18}), two features indicating an aquatic lifestyle. *Indohyus* had crushing basins in their molar teeth, and the levels of carbon isotopes (C^{13}) suggested that they ate terrestrial plants. Raoellids also shared cochlear structures (see Chapter 34) with whales, notably the presence of a ridge called the "involucrum."

In the Eocene in what is now Kashmir, *Indohyus* lived an amphibious existence, entering the water to avoid predators and going ashore to eat vegetation. At some point, *Indohyus* species started to eat fish, which became the mainstay of their diet; this was also true of the earliest whales but not the living ones. Thewissen's proposal explains the development of an aquatic mammal from a terrestrial one, a herbivore to a piscivore.

Again, genetic variation, survival of individuals that used the water to avoid predation, and selection of strains of individuals that switched their diets to fish were the key elements.

3.2c Case 3, Climbing Plants: Reaching for the Light

Plants such as trees reach for the sun by growing tall, at least as tall as their neighbours. An alternative way for plants to get their share of sunlight is to climb on a physical support. Climbing plants are known as vines or lianas, and those that find suitable support often have biomass and reproductive output that matches or exceeds that of the trees on which they grow. Climbing plants are successful because they grow quickly, depend on reduced biomass of supporting structures (compared with trees), achieve higher leaf biomass, and thus outcompete other plants when it comes to reaching for the sun. At least 130 families of plants include climbing species, and vines represent at least 40% of the plant diversity in tropical forests. Whereas vines such as morning glories (*Ipomoea* spp.) are herbaceous, others, such as grapevines (*Vitus* spp.), are woody. Herbaceous vines grow readily on pioneer species of trees that are rarely robust enough to support woody vines.

In 2004, Ernesto Gianoli compared 48 groups of plants in which there was enough information about evolutionary relationships to assess the relative diversity of climber and nonclimber sister groups. In 38 cases, climbing taxa were more diverse than nonclimbers. Gianoli concluded that climbing was a "key" development in plants because it resulted in a great increase in numbers of species.

The success and diversity of climbing plants are reflected in the variety of structures they use for climbing. Some use tendrils, modified stems or leaves, which coil around supporting structures. Others use modified roots, sometimes holdfasts, to attach to supports. In still others, the stem itself coils clockwise or anticlockwise around the support. Note that Charles Darwin was one of the first to study climbing plants.

STUDY BREAK

Selection is the force responsible for evolution and biodiversity. What key elements aid in the selection and survival of certain individuals and their genetic traits?

3.3 Evolution

Evolution, a gradual change in the characteristics of a population of organisms over time, can be the result of selection. Evolution is a central key to understanding the diversity of life on Earth (see Chapters 17, 18, 19, and 20). Although the theory of evolution is widely accepted today by educated people around the world, the levels of acceptance vary among countries **(Figure 3.4)**, perhaps reflecting variation in the degree to which science has been politicized. Teaching of evolution is not permitted in some educational jurisdictions. In this book, we consider evolution to be an organizing force in life and the foundation of modern biology. Understanding evolution is central to understanding the elements of biodiversity, but it does not mean believing or accepting that humans evolved from apes or from amoebas.

The theory of evolution explains both the unity and the diversity of all life; it tells us that all organisms alive today descended from a common ancestor, which explains why all organisms share features such as the use of adenosine triphosphate (ATP) as a cellular energy source, deoxyribonucleic acid (DNA) as genetic material, and plasma membranes composed of lipid bilayers. But evolution also tells us that species change over time as a result of natural selection. The central ideas of Darwin's theory of evolution by natural selection can be summarized as follows:

- Individual organisms in a population vary in many heritable traits.
- Any population has the potential to produce far more offspring than the environment can support. Competition for limited resources means that only some individuals survive.
- Some individuals in the population have traits that give them an advantage in their local environment; these organisms are more likely to survive and reproduce.

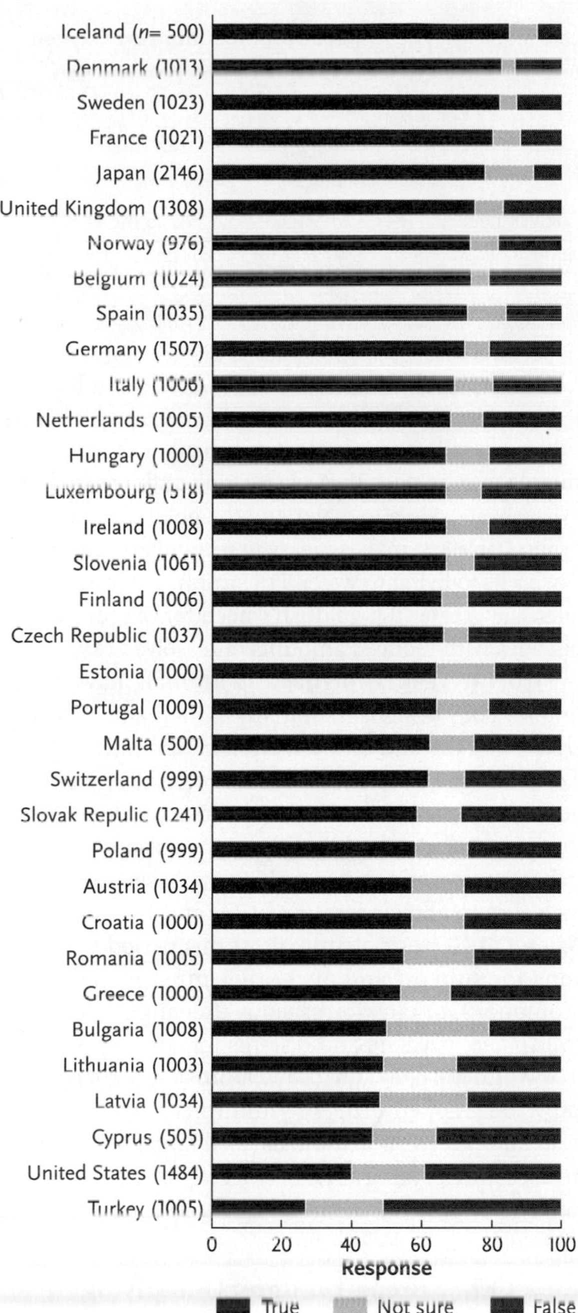

Figure 3.4
Public acceptance of evolution based on surveys of people living in 34 countries. Low acceptance in the United States appears to reflect, in part, the politicization of science and the rise of fundamentalism.

- These organisms pass on favourable traits to their offspring. Over time, the incidence of the trait(s) will change in the population.

Different environments favour different traits. Thus, even though all organisms share a common ancestor, they have diverged over evolutionary time in response to the selection pressures of different environments. The process of adaptive radiation, discussed next, is an example of such divergence.

3.3a Adaptive Radiation: Diversification of Lineages of Life

In the history of life on Earth, organisms have had to overcome fundamental barriers that, once crossed, opened many new opportunities for diversification (for example, the cases above under *Selection*). The development of photosynthesis is another example of such a breakthrough. Organisms with the ability to convert solar energy into usable chemical energy survived and thrived as they exploited the "new" energy source. The appearance of oxygenic photosynthesis increased the concentrations of oxygen (a by-product of the process), which led to aerobic respiration and the ozone layer, which allowed organisms to colonize terrestrial environments by blocking harmful ultraviolet (UV) rays. Together, the changes caused by an increase in atmospheric oxygen triggered an extraordinary diversification of life. There is paleontological evidence of the relative timing of some fundamental changes in life (e.g., evolution of whales), and sometimes we know the underlying factors (again, the whales).

An organism may move into a new adaptive zone after a chance innovation allows it to use the environment in a unique way. The ability of plants to move onto land opened new opportunities for animals. The dehydration-resistant eggs of early reptiles enabled them to complete their life cycle on land, opening terrestrial habitats to them. The evolution of flowers that attract insect pollinators was a key innovation in the history of flowering plants.

An adaptive zone may open up after the demise of a successful group, for example, the replacement of the mammals Multituberculata by Rodentia (see Chapter 48). We know that a rich diversity of soft-bodied organisms thrived in Precambrian seas. But the beginning of the Cambrian, about 600 million years ago, is marked by the disappearance of many of the soft-bodied organisms and the appearance of an extraordinary diversity of life, including many species with skeletons. The change from soft- to hard-bodied is reflected in the fossil record, but the reasons for the switch in body form are not clear.

3.3b Islands: Showcases of Evolution

Adaptive radiations, therefore, occur when an evolutionary breakthrough allows diversification of life. Adaptive radiations are a recurring theme in the development of biodiversity. At one level, we can see it in the evolution of the fauna and flora of the Hawaiian Islands, arguably the most isolated landmasses in the world. When Captain Cook arrived on the islands in 1778, Hawaii had about 2000 species of higher plants that had arisen from about 275 ancestral stocks. There were also about 6500 species of insects descended from 250 ancestral stocks. There were 600 to 700 species in the genus *Drosophila* alone. Many plants on Hawaii have undergone adaptive radiations. Violets have become shrubs, lobelias are tree-like. These radiations have occurred in the absence of the plants normally filling the shrub and tree life styles. Biologists suspect that one ancestral insect species and one ancestral plant species gained access to Hawaii in each of the 25 000 to 100 000 years that the islands were "islands," that is, above water. Hawaii is a showcase of evolution and adaptive radiation. Recall that a species may arrive several times, so each arrival is not necessarily a new colonization event.

Islands elsewhere are well known as showcases of evolution and adaptive radiation. One celebrated case is the richness of the Galapagos Islands that so impressed Charles Darwin (see Chapter 20). But whether the setting is New Zealand, Madagascar, or Mauritius, the story repeats itself. As we will see in Chapter 48, island populations of animals and plants can be very vulnerable to extinction. Lamentably, Hawaii is also a showcase of the negative impact of humans on biodiversity.

Adaptive radiation on islands reminds us that species can be adapting to new ways of life at the same time in different parts of the world. The result is a mosaic of life, with many examples of parallel and convergent evolution (see Chapters 19 and 20, respectively).

3.3c Land: Organisms Conquer a New Frontier

The movement of organisms onto land presented many challenges (see Chapters 25, 26, and 27), and many "terrestrial" organisms actually live in films of water, so they have not forsaken an aquatic existence. Included on the list of challenges are matters of support, conservation of water, reproduction, and disposal of wastes. Other facts of life are also different for organisms living on land as opposed to in water.

Some of the differences between water and air include density and viscosity, which, in turn, affect rates of diffusion and availability of oxygen **(Table 3.2).** Animals operating in water extract dissolved oxygen, although some photoautotrophs actually break water molecules

Table 3.2. Gases in Water and in Air.

	Water	Air
Viscosity	100x	x
Density	1000y	y
Diffusion rate	Low	High
O_2 mL.L^{-1}	0–10	100–130
CO_2 mL.L^{-1}	0–13	>100
O_2 extraction	<80%	25%
% of energy budget to run pump that drives breathing, whether air or water	20%	1–2%

Table 3.3. The Impact of Temperature on Oxygen Availability for Goldfish (*Carassius Auratus*).

	5° C	35° C
O_2 available	9 mL.L^{-1}	5 mL.L^{-1}
Goldfish need	8 mL.kg.h^{-1}	225 mL.kg.h^{-1}
Ventilation rate	1.3 L.kg.h^{-1}	60 L.kg.h^{-1}

The amount of oxygen available is further reduced in salt water.

in the process of photosynthesis. Animals that breathe air have more ready access to oxygen and spend less of their overall energy budget acquiring it than aquatic animals (see Table 3.2). A closer look at the availability of dissolved oxygen in water and the goldfish's need for oxygen **(Table 3.3)** makes it easy to recognize some of the drawbacks to living in water. Put simply, the warmer the water, the greater the goldfish's need for oxygen, which coincides with reduced amounts of dissolved oxygen.

Truly terrestrial plants and animals have more complex body designs than many of their aquatic counterparts. By the end of the Devonian, terrestrial plants had developed specialized sexual organs, stems with mechanisms for fluid transport, structural elements such as wood to provide mechanical support, roots for anchorage, leaves as sites of photosynthesis, stomata in the leaves to allow passage of CO_2 and O_2, and seeds **(Figure 3.5).** Terrestrial animals of this period had skeletons for support and anchoring muscles (allowing locomotion), organs for gaseous exchange (breathing atmospheric oxygen), and systems for circulating materials within the body. Terrestrial animals and plants also had waterproof coverings to minimize the chances of desiccation. Terrestrial animals used nontoxic excretory products (urea and uric acid), whereas aquatic ones still relied heavily on ammonia.

3.3d Other Breakthroughs Underlying Adaptive Radiations

As you proceed through this book, look for other examples of breakthroughs that appeared to result in a radiation of organisms within a group (e.g., mammals or birds), or where different organisms adopted similar strategies. Examples include the insect traps of carnivorous plants, fungi, and spiders; the wings of bats, birds, insects, and pterosaurs; and the reinvasion of the oceans by reptiles and mammals.

See Chapters 17, 18, 19, and 20 for a more in-depth look at evolution and the ample evidence that has been gathered to support this theory.

Evolution is the idea behind representations of "trees of life" **(Figure 3.6).** Traditional trees of life are designed to illustrate the relationships between organisms over time and may be presented in the context of a geologic time series (see the geologic time table in *The Chemical and Physical Foundations of Biology* pages).

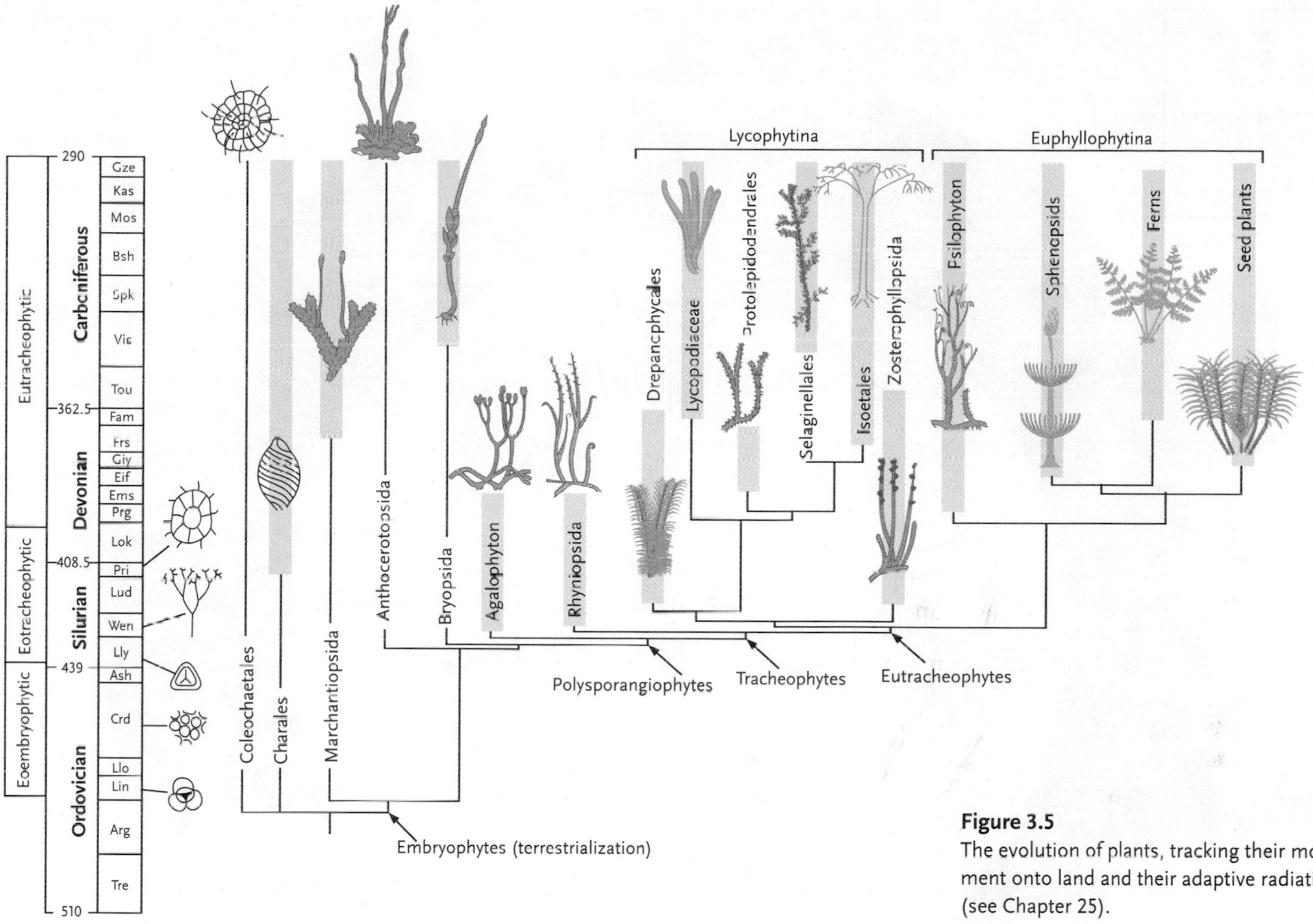

Figure 3.5
The evolution of plants, tracking their movement onto land and their adaptive radiation (see Chapter 25).

With the advent of the tools of molecular genetics (see Chapter 16), biologists have been able to prepare more detailed trees reflecting broader relationships. The example in **Figure 3.7, p. 56** shows that the diversity of life is almost overwhelming because of the broad coverage that can be achieved with genetic data, even though this tree presents only 191 species. One challenge to biologists is putting this diversity in context and appreciating the processes that have produced it.

Study Break

1. How does the theory of evolution explain the unity and diversity of all life?
2. What are the four central ideas of Darwin's theory of evolution by natural selection?
3. List advantages that oxygenic photosynthesis provided organisms living on Earth.

Figure 3.6
The tree of life. Darwin envisioned the history of life as a tree. Branching points represent the origins of new lineages; branches that do not reach the top represent extinct groups.

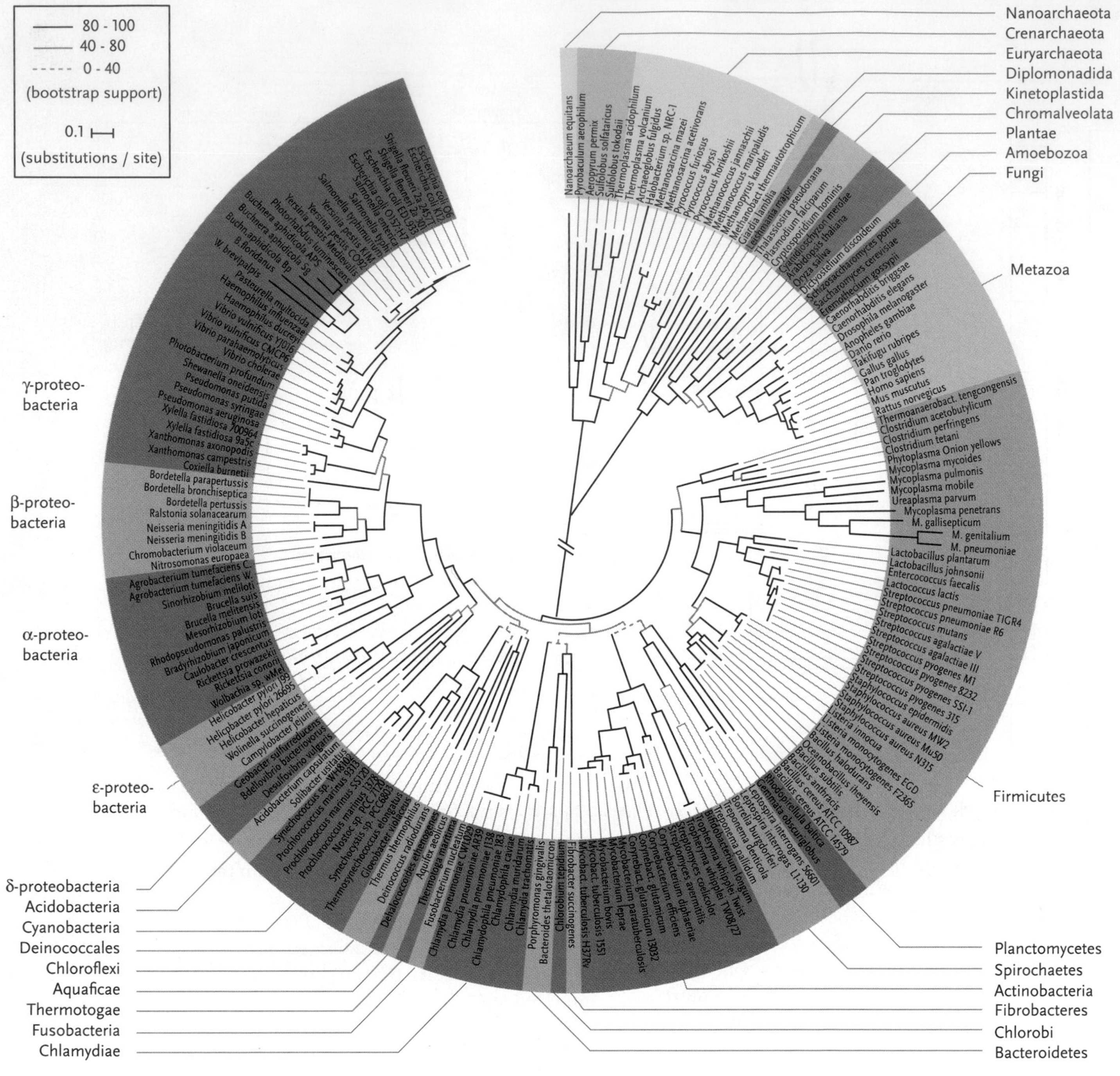

Figure 3.7
Using genetic data, it is possible to generate a global phylogeny or tree of life. This tree is based on 191 species whose genomes have been fully sequenced.

3.4 The Biosphere

The biosphere is the area occupied by life on Earth, from the depths of the ocean to the sky above. The various physical environments of Earth and their different abiotic factors, such as sunlight, temperature, humidity, wind speed, cloud cover, and rainfall, influence the evolution and diversity of organisms. These abiotic factors contribute to a region's **climate,** the weather conditions prevailing over an extended period of time. Climates vary on global, regional, and local scales and undergo seasonal changes almost everywhere.

3.4a Solar Radiation: Energy from the Sun

The global pattern of environmental diversity results from latitudinal variation in incoming solar radiation, Earth's rotation on its axis, and its orbit around the sun **(Figure 3.8).**

Earth's spherical shape causes the intensity of incoming solar radiation to vary from the equator to

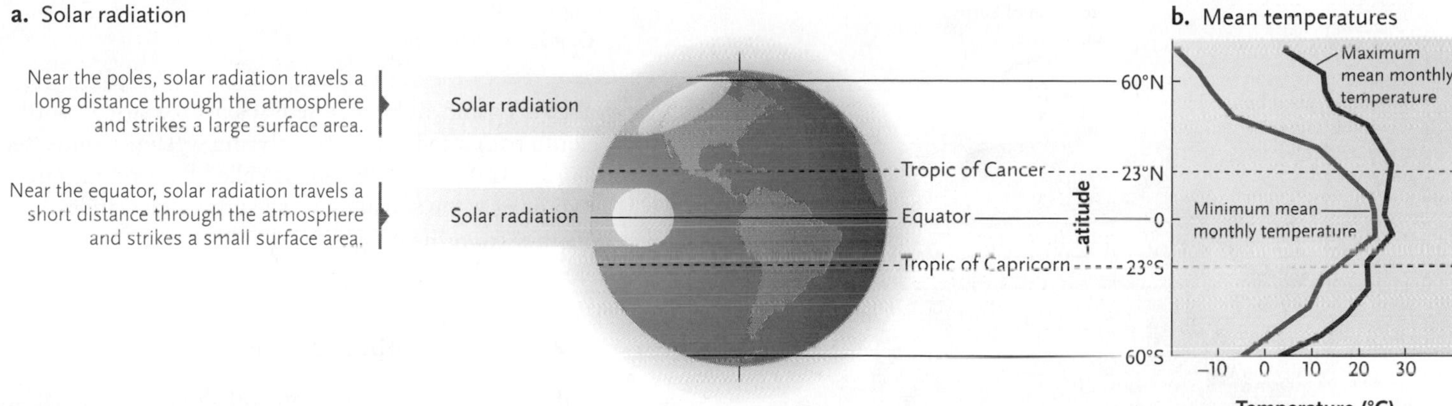

Figure 3.8
Latitudinal variation of solar radiation.

the poles **(Figure 3.9)**. When sunlight strikes Earth directly at a 90° angle, as it does near the equator, it travels the shortest possible distance through the radiation-absorbing atmosphere and falls on the smallest possible surface area. When sunlight arrives at an oblique angle, as it does near the poles, it travels a longer distance through the atmosphere and shines on a larger area. Thus, solar radiation is more concentrated near the equator than it is at higher latitudes, causing latitudinal variation in Earth's temperature (see Figure 3.9).

3.4b Seasonality: Weather Through the Year

Earth is tilted on its axis at a fixed position of 23.5° from the perpendicular to the plane on which it orbits the sun (see Figure 3.9). This tilt produces seasonal variation in the duration and intensity of incoming solar radiation. The Northern Hemisphere receives its maximum illumination, and the Southern Hemisphere its minimum, on the June solstice (around June 21), when the sun shines directly over the Tropic of Cancer (23.5° N latitude). The reverse is true on the December solstice (around December 21), when the sun shines directly over the Tropic of Capricorn (23.5° S latitude). Twice each year, on the vernal and autumnal equinoxes (around March 21 and September 21, respectively), the sun shines directly over the equator.

The Earth's tilt is permanent, and only the **tropics**, the latitudes between the tropics of Cancer and Capricorn, ever receive intense solar radiation from directly overhead. Moreover, the tropics experience only small seasonal changes in temperature and day length: environmental temperature is high, and day length is approximately 12 hours throughout the year. Tropical seasonality is reflected in the alternation of wet and dry periods rather than warm and cold seasons. Seasonal variation in temperature and day length increases steadily toward the poles. Polar winters are long and cold, with periods of continuous darkness, and polar summers are short, with periods of continuous light.

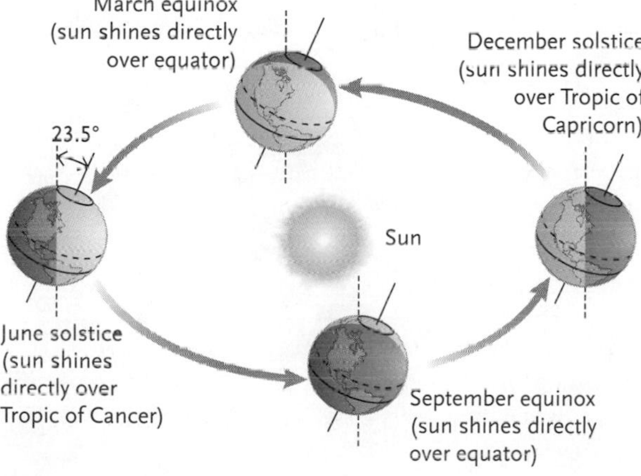

Figure 3.9
Seasonal variation in solar radiation.

3.4c Air Circulation: Wind Patterns

Sunlight warms air masses, causing them to expand, lose pressure, and rise in the atmosphere. The unequal heating of air at different latitudes initiates global air movements, producing three circulation cells in each hemisphere **(Figure 3.10, p. 58)**. Warm equatorial air masses rise to high altitude before spreading north and south. They eventually sink back to Earth at about 30° N and S latitude. At low altitude, some air masses flow back toward the equator, completing low-latitude circulation cells. Others flow toward the poles, rise at 60° latitude, and divide at high altitude. Some of this air flows toward the equator, completing the pair of middle-latitude circulation cells. The rest moves toward the poles, where it descends and flows toward the equator, forming the polar circulation cells.

The flow of air masses at low altitude creates winds near the planet's surface. But the planet's surface rotates beneath the atmosphere, moving rapidly near the equator, where Earth's diameter is greatest, and more slowly near the poles. Latitudinal variation in the speed of Earth's rotation deflects the movement of

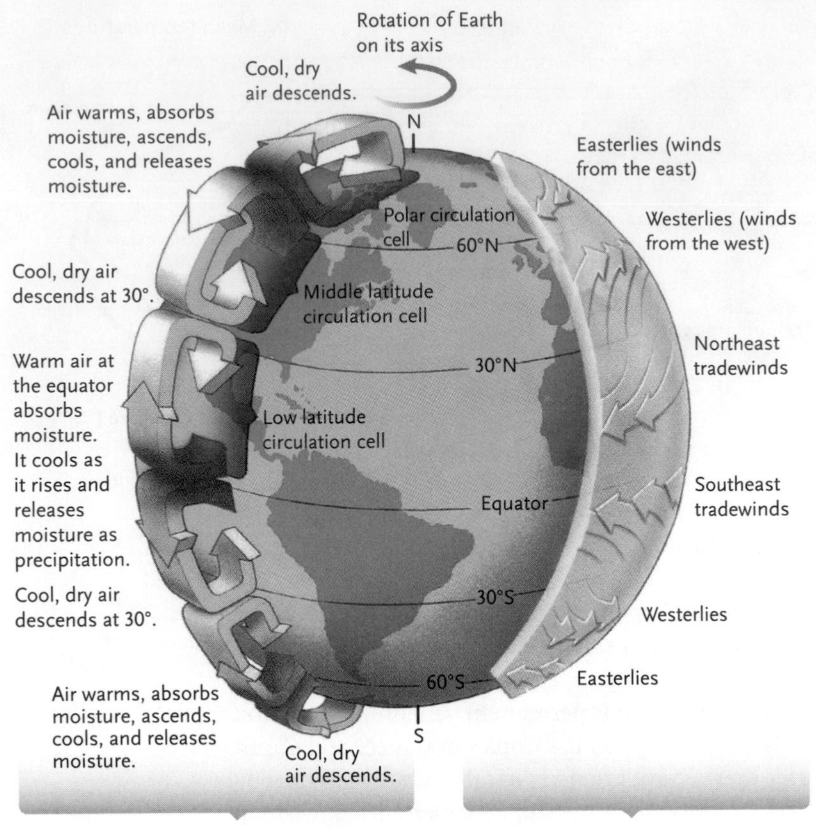

Figure 3.10
Global air circulation.

the rising and sinking air masses from a strictly north–south path into belts of easterly and westerly winds (see Figure 3.10); this deflection is called the Coriolis effect. Winds near the equator are called the trade winds; those further from the equator are the temperate westerlies and easterlies, named for their direction of flow.

3.4d Precipitation: Water

Differences in solar radiation and global air circulation create latitudinal variations in rainfall **(Figure 3.11).** Warm air holds more water vapour than cool air does. As air near the equator heats up, it absorbs water, primarily from the oceans. However, the warm air masses expand as they rise, and their heat energy is distributed over a larger volume, causing their temperature to drop. A decrease in temperature without the actual *loss* of heat energy is called **adiabatic cooling.** After cooling adiabatically, the rising air masses release moisture as rain. Torrential rainfall is characteristic of warm equatorial regions, where rising, moisture-laden air masses cool as they reach high altitude.

As cool, dry air masses descend at 30° latitude, increased air pressure at low altitude compresses them,

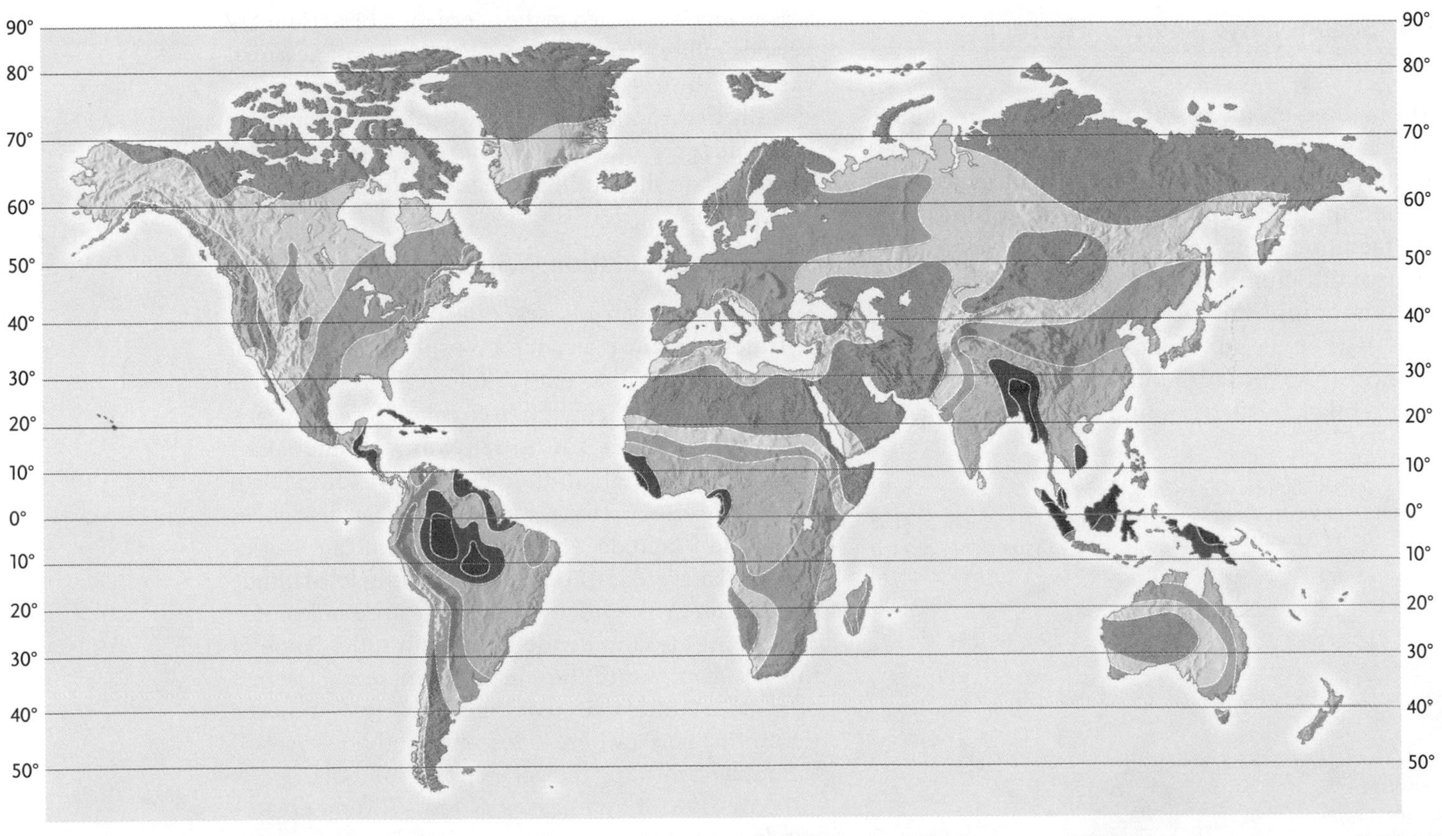

Figure 3.11
Global variation in precipitation.

concentrating their heat energy, raising their temperature, and increasing their capacity to hold moisture. Descending air masses absorb water at these latitudes, which are typically dry. Some air masses continue moving poleward in the lower atmosphere. When they rise at 60° latitude, they cool adiabatically and release precipitation (see Figure 3.11), creating moist habitats in the northern and southern temperate zones.

3.4e Ocean Currents: Rivers within the Oceans

Latitudinal variations in solar radiation also warm the oceans' surface water unevenly. Because the volume of water increases as it warms (= decrease in density), sea level is about 8 cm higher at the equator than at the poles. The volume of water associated with this "slope" is enough to cause surface water to move in response to gravity. The trade winds and temperate westerlies also contribute to the mass flow of water at the ocean surface. Thus, surface water flows in the direction of prevailing winds, forming major currents. The Earth's rotation, the positions of landmasses, and the shapes of ocean basins also influence the movements of these currents.

Oceanic circulation is generally clockwise in the Northern Hemisphere and counterclockwise in the Southern Hemisphere **(Figure 3.12)**. The trade winds push surface water toward the equator and westward until it contacts the eastern edge of a continent. Swift, narrow, and deep currents of warm, nutrient-poor water run toward the poles, parallel to the east coasts of continents. For example, the Gulf Stream flows northward along the east coast of North America, carrying warm water toward northwestern Europe. Cold water returns from the poles toward the equator in slow, broad, and shallow currents, such as the California Current, that parallel the west coasts of continents.

3.4f Regional and Local Effects: Local Conditions for Life

Although global and seasonal patterns determine an area's climate, regional and local effects also influence abiotic conditions.

Currents running along seacoasts exchange heat with air masses flowing above them, moderating the temperature over the nearby land. Breezes often blow from the sea toward the land during the day and in the opposite direction at night **(Figure 3.13, p. 60)**. These local effects sometimes override latitudinal variations in temperature. For example, the climate in London, England, is much milder than that in Winnipeg, Canada, even though Winnipeg is slightly further south. Winnipeg has a **continental climate** that is not moderated by the distant ocean, but London has a **maritime climate**, tempered by winds that cross the nearby North Atlantic Current.

Ocean currents also affect moisture conditions in coastal habitats. For example, the warm Gulf Stream current meets the cold Labrador current off the southeast coast of Newfoundland, in the region known as

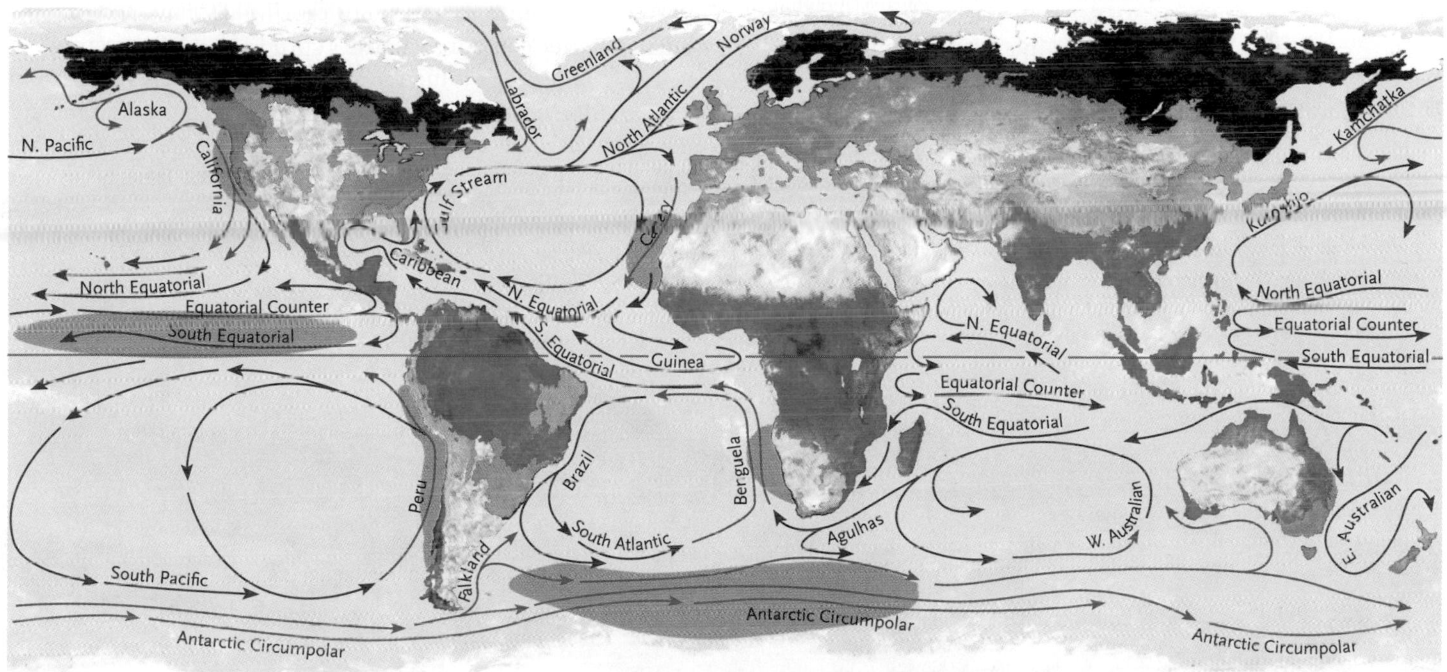

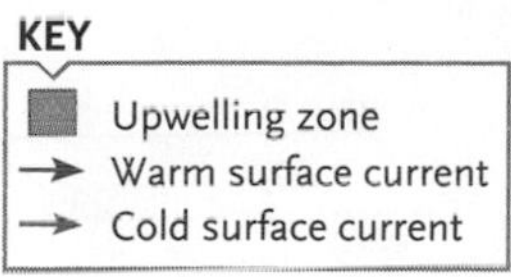

Figure 3.12
Global ocean currents.

a. Daytime: land warmer than sea
1 Warm air ascends.
2 Cool air descends and replaces air over land through onshore flow.

b. Nighttime: sea warmer than land
2 Cool air descends and replaces air over sea through offshore flow.
1 Warm air ascends.

Figure 3.13
Sea breezes and land breezes—daytime and nighttime.

the Grand Banks. As the air above the water cools, its water vapour condenses into heavy fog and rain, making this region one of the foggiest on Earth.

Some regions experience **monsoon cycles** caused by seasonal reversals in wind direction. In the North American southwest, for example, summer heat causes air masses over land to rise, creating a zone of low pressure. Moist air from the nearby Gulf of California flows inland, where it rises and cools adiabatically, releasing substantial precipitation. Summer monsoon rains deliver one-third to one-half of the annual rainfall in Arizona and New Mexico. During the winter, when land is cooler than the nearby ocean, low-pressure systems form over the ocean and winds blow from the land to the sea; thus, winters in the southwest are generally dry. Seasonal monsoon cycles also deliver torrential rainfall to parts of Africa, Asia, and South America.

3.4g The Effects of Topography: The Ups and Downs of Weather and Life

Mountains, valleys, and other topographic features also influence regional climates. In the Northern Hemisphere, south-facing slopes are warmer and drier than north-facing slopes because they receive more solar radiation. In addition, adiabatic cooling causes air temperature to decline 3° to 6°C for every 1000 m increase in elevation.

Mountains also establish regional and local rainfall patterns. For example, after a warm air mass picks up moisture from the Pacific Ocean, it moves inland and reaches the Rocky Mountains. As air rises to cross the mountains, it cools adiabatically and loses moisture, releasing heavy rainfall on the windward side **(Figure 3.14).** After the now-dry air crosses the peaks, it descends and warms, absorbing moisture and forming a **rain shadow.** Habitats on the leeward side of mountains, such as the eastern slopes of the Rockies in Alberta or the Great Basin Desert in western United States, are typically drier than those on the windward side.

3.4h Microclimate: Very Local Changes in Temperature, Humidity, and Air Movements

Although climate influences the overall distributions of organisms, the abiotic conditions that immediately surround them, the **microclimate,** have the greatest effect on survival and reproduction. For example, a fallen log on the forest floor creates a microclimate in the underlying soil that is shadier, cooler, and moister than the surrounding soil that is exposed to sun and wind. Many animals, including some insects, worms, salamanders, and snakes, occupy these sheltered sites and avoid the effects of prolonged exposure to the elements.

1 Winds carry moisture inland from Pacific Ocean.
2 Clouds form and rain falls on windward side of mountain range.
3 Rain shadow forms on leeward side of mountain range.
4000/75
3000/85
2000/50
1800/125
1300/30
Moist habitats
1000/85
15/25

Figure 3.14
Formation of a rain shadow.

Study Break

1. Abiotic factors contribute to a region's climate. List the abiotic factors that affect the diversity of organisms.
2. List three factors affecting the global pattern of environmental diversity.
3. How does Earth's spherical shape cause the intensity of incoming solar radiation to vary from the equator to the poles?

3.5 Biotic Factors

In addition to the influence of the physical environment, the diversity of living organisms is affected by interactions among organisms. A very important type of interaction is competition among organisms for scarce resources. Organisms also exploit each other by consuming each other (see trophic interactions below) and by parasitism, a symbiotic relationship in which one organism benefits at the expense of another. Parasitism is only one type of symbiotic relationship; in the relationship known as mutualism, both organisms benefit (see Chapter 46).

3.5a Trophic Interactions: Movements of Energy, Biomass, and Numbers

In living, most organisms generate opportunities for other organisms. One way to explore these interrelationships is through the trophic roles that organisms play in the global ecosystem. Remember, however, that interactions between species of organisms can be negative, particularly when more than one species depends on the same limited resources (see Chapter 46).

Organisms can be generally classified into three basic trophic roles: producers, consumers, and decomposers. Photoautotrophs, the main producers, are organisms that use photosynthesis to capture and harness the sun's energy. They produce most of their own nutritional needs but serve as food for heterotrophs. Heterotrophs that eat autotrophs are called primary consumers, whereas those that eat other heterotrophs may be referred to as mesopredators (see Chapter 48). Other heterotrophs, such as fungi, are decomposers, breaking down dead organisms and thus making the nutrients available to themselves and other organisms.

Photosynthesis is considered the domain of plants, but in a few exceptional cases, animals capture chloroplasts and use them to capture solar energy through photosynthesis. In a sense, these animals are continuing life's earlier tradition of capturing other organisms and using them to achieve oxygenic photosynthesis and aerobic respiration (see Chapter 5). Co-option of other organisms is a recurring theme and brings with it questions of control because chloroplasts and mitochondria have their own DNA. There are many examples of sequestration of chloroplasts by species from the phyla Protista, Platyhelminthes, Porifera, Cnidaria, Mollusca, and Urochordata.

Some sea slugs (e.g., *Elysia chlorotica*) **(Figure 3.15)** use specialized teeth on their radulae to cut into algal cells so that they can suck out (feed by stenophagy) chloroplasts and other cell contents. In the slug's stomach, chloroplasts are engulfed by phagocytosis and then moved to areas below the epidermis. Slugs such as *E. chlorotica* can live for at least five months on the energy generated by chloroplasts they have obtained, their solar panels. This story is an example of how a heterotrophic organism (the slug) acquires the ability to be autotrophic (engage in photosynthesis). How the slugs control the operations of the chloroplasts remains unanswered. Have slugs also taken over some of the chloroplast or algal genome? At least one species, *Elysia crispata*, has nuclear genes from chloroplasts in its genomic DNA. For more about these slugs, see Chapters 25 and 26.

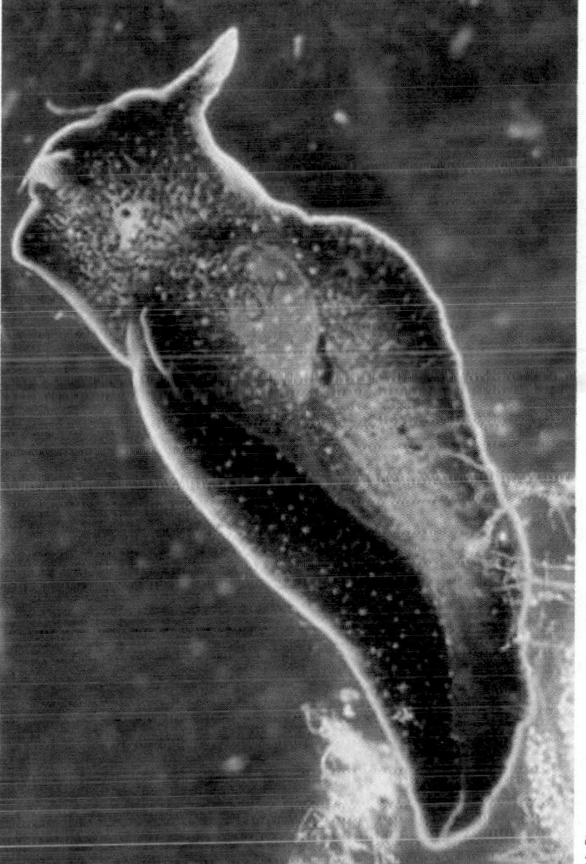

Figure 3.15
The solar-powered sea slug, *Elysia chlorotica*, an animal that extracts chloroplasts from algae and uses them to produce food.

a. *Monotropa unifloris*

M. B. Fenton

b. *Conopholis americana*

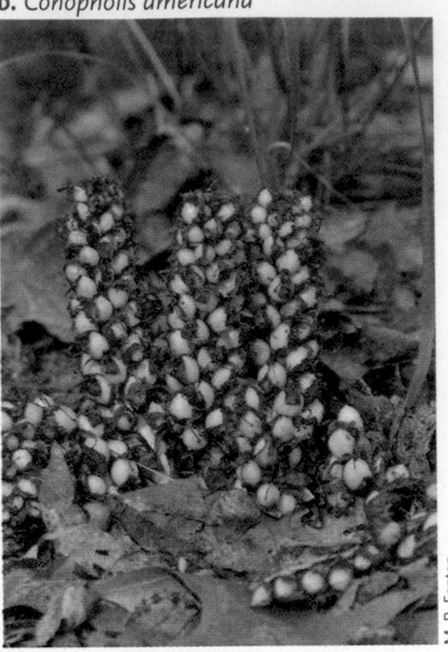

M. B. Fenton

Figure 3.16
Two achlorophyllous plants: **(a)** one (*Monotropa unifloris*) obtains nutrients from other plants via fungi, and **(b)** the other (*Conopholis americana*) is parasitic on the roots of other plants.

So, if animals emulate plants, is the reverse also true? Many species of plants in seven classes and 17 families worldwide appear to lack the ability to perform photosynthesis **(Figure 3.16)**. Some of these "achlorophyllous" species are parasitic on the roots of other plants. Other achlorophyllous plants are mycoheterotrophic, obtaining energy and nutrients from mycorrhizal fungi associated with the roots of neighbouring green plants (see Chapters 24 and 25, respectively). Although plants that cannot photosynthesize are called achlorophyllous, many have trace amounts of chlorophyll *a*, and only one is known to have both chlorophyll *a* and chlorophyll *b*. The evidence demonstrates that some plants whose ancestors were capable of photosynthesis have lost that ability.

If you pause for a moment and think of what you have eaten in the last 24 hours, you will realize that if humans are anything to go by, strict categorization of organisms by the trophic role they fill is probably naive. Setting aside people who only eat plant products (vegetarians), most humans eat a variety of food from organisms in different locations in the food web (see Chapter 46). Many organisms are strict autotrophs, and many are just heterotrophs. Can you think of an animal that never eats plant material? Good examples can be found among animals that feed on blood (see Chapter 46).

Most people are omnivores, and they are in good company. Other omnivorous mammals (see Chapter 27) include bears, pigs, squirrels, and rats. The fact that many animals, as well as fungi and bacteria, live on dung suggests that heterotrophs do not remove all of the energy in the food they consume. Heterotrophs expend energy (kilocalories) to obtain food: the energy of mastication and digestion as well as the cost of catching (or buying) what you eat. Food that passes through the digestive tract with much of its energy intact has not been used efficiently. When food is scarce, many heterotrophs make choices suggesting that they are behaving as efficient predators (see Chapter 41).

Other heterotrophs are more efficient at removing energy from food materials. The most efficient primary consumers (herbivores) are those that use other organisms to help in digestion. A familiar example is a cow (*Bos taurus*), which, like other ruminants, uses fermentation aided by symbiotic organisms (bacteria, protozoa). As we shall see in Chapter 41, fermentation also is used by other mammals, some insects (termites, Isoptera), and even some birds (the Hoatzin, *Opisthocomus hoazin*). But the dung of ruminants is eaten by a wide range of animals and saprotophic fungi, so even they do not extract all the energy available in the food they consume.

Moving up (or down) the food web demonstrates how one species and its activities provide opportunities for others. Parasites are an extension of this reality, whether they live inside the host's body (endoparasites) **(Figure 3.17)**, outside (ectoparasites) **(Figure 3.18)**, or somewhere in between **(Figure 3.19)**. But just the definition of "parasite" is an engaging topic (see Chapter 26).

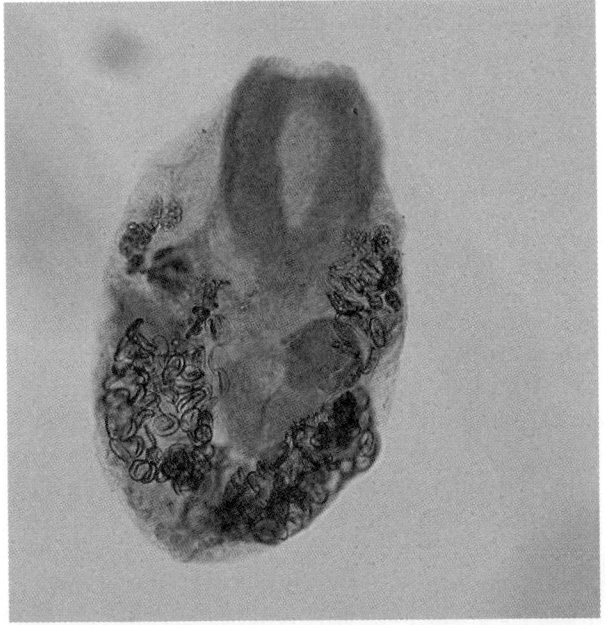

Andy Didyk

Figure 3.17
Paralecithodendrium chilostomum, a 420-micron long endoparasite, was found in the gut of a little brown bat, *Myotis lucifugus*. This species belongs to the class Trematoda, order Plagiorchiida, family Lecithodendriidae.

Life On The Edge

Beetles, Carbon Cycles, and Climate Change

A live tree is a net carbon sink because during photosynthesis, it takes up more carbon as CO_2 than it releases by respiration. The tree's contribution is expressed as $-x$ grams of carbon per year ($-x$ g C yr^{-1}). Autotrophs, organisms capable of photosynthesis, play a vital role in the carbon cycle (see Chapter 48) of Earth.

In south-central British Columbia, 374 000 km^2 of forest dominated by pine (*Pinus* spp.) and spruce (*Picea* spp.) is changing from being a net carbon sink, -15.8 ± 7.9 MtC yr^{-1} (megatonnes of carbon per year), in 2004 to producing an estimated 17.6 MtC yr^{-1} by 2020. Why is this change happening?

The change from carbon sink to carbon produced results from an outbreak of mountain pine beetles (*Dendroctonus ponderosae*) that killed millions of trees in the area. The outbreak of beetles resulted from climate warming because more beetles survived the winter and thus expanded the geographic range of the species. The magnitude of change in carbon is equivalent to approximately 75% of the average direct forest fire emissions from all of Canada between 1959 and 1999.

Insect pests can have a huge impact on our lives. The destruction of millions of trees has economic effects associated with timber supply. Social impacts include the loss of jobs for the people directly and indirectly employed by the forest industry. We have yet to experience the full impact that climate change associated with the carbon cycle can have on our lives and on Earth's biodiversity. Changes in climate can bring many species to the edge of survival.

Figure 3.18
Common vampire bat (*Desmodus rotundus*) with ectoparasites (streblid flies) with their heads tucked into the bat's fur.

M.B. Fenton

3.6 Cumulative Impact on Biotic and Abiotic Factors

For over 3 billion years, our planet has been the stage for interactions between biotic and abiotic factors. Over this time, species have come and gone, reflecting the dynamics of evolution and interactions between species, all under the influence of different climatic conditions. In a sense, the situation in the Hawaiian Islands reflects the richness of the interactions and the products. There the combination of isolation, immigration, and adaptive radiations, in a setting with dramatic climatic variation, produced an impressive diversity of life. One such Hawaiian endemic is a tree in the lily family that grows to a height of 8 metres **(Figure 3.20)**.

Figure 3.19
Schreiber's bent-winged bat (*Miniopterus schreibersii*) with a streblid fly embedded in a tear duct. The adult fly, with wings, entered the tear duct and shed its wings.

M.B. Fenton

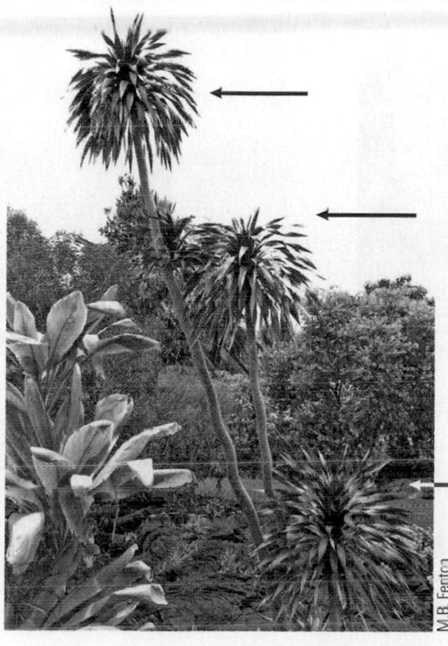

Figure 3.20
In a sense, Hala-pepe *(Dracena aurea)* "trees" growing from an old lava flow epitomize the adaptive radiation that has occurred in Hawaii. This member of the lily family is endemic and can reach 8 m in height. Early Hawaiians used the sap in medicines and the wood for carving images to decorate the altar of the goddess Laka. Laka is the patron of the sacred hula.

M.B. Fenton

Study Break

1. Describe the difference between mutualism and parasitism.
2. Describe three basic trophic roles of organisms and give an example of each.
3. An array of life is shown in **Figure 3.21.** Which organisms or parts of organisms do you recognize?

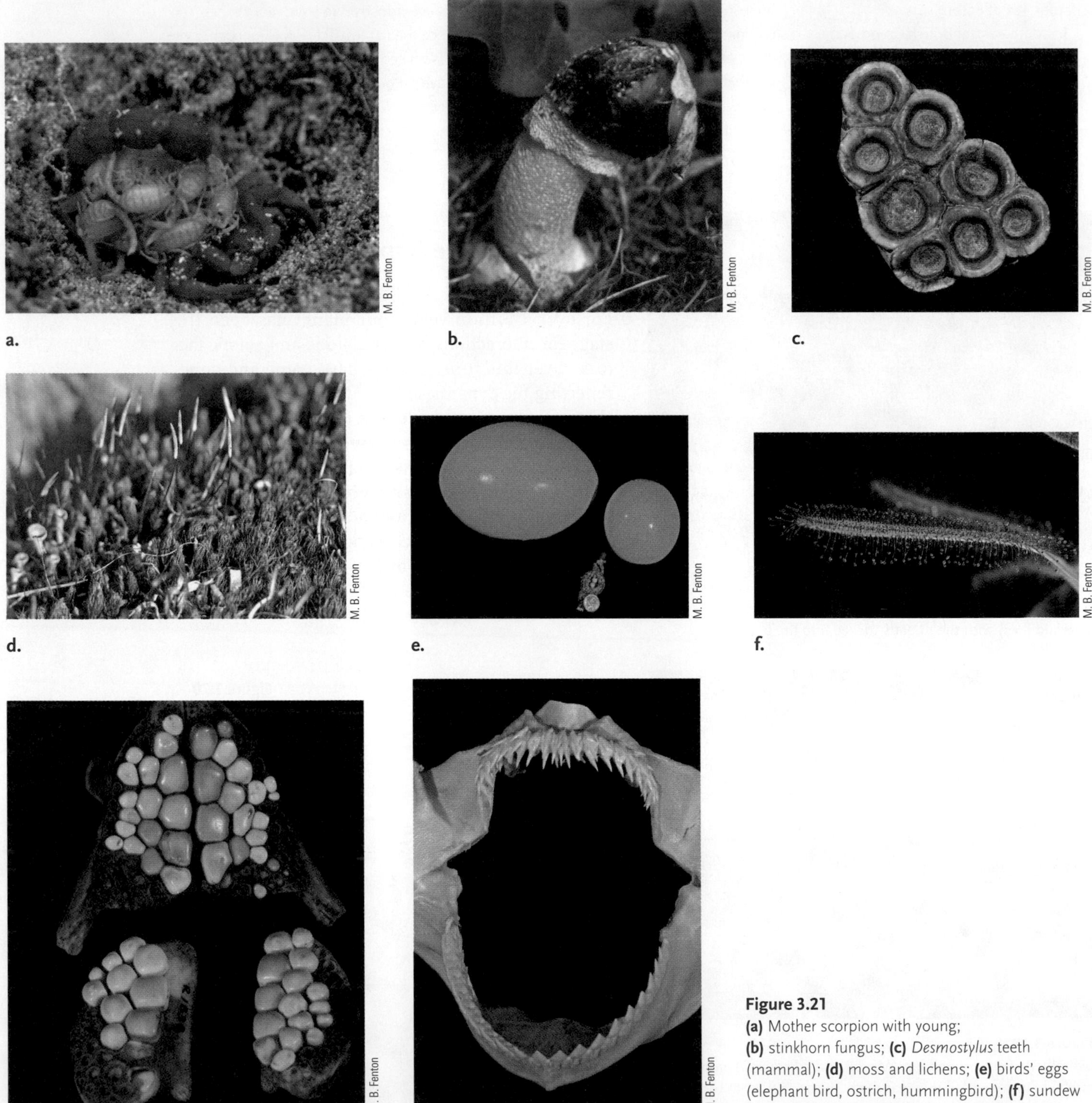

Figure 3.21
(a) Mother scorpion with young; **(b)** stinkhorn fungus; **(c)** *Desmostylus* teeth (mammal); **(d)** moss and lichens; **(e)** birds' eggs (elephant bird, ostrich, hummingbird); **(f)** sundew leaf; **(g)** fish teeth, used for crushing; **(h)** cookie-cutter shark teeth.

Ammonia

Smelling salts are used to revive people who have become disoriented or unconscious after an injury. We most often see smelling salts used on the sidelines at sporting events after a player has been hit. Ammonium carbonate is the active ingredient in smelling salts, which are effective because all animals, including humans, are very averse to the smell of ammonia. This aversion is appropriate and adaptive because ammonia can be very toxic.

In its pure form, ammonia (NH_3) is usually a gas. The polarity of ammonia means that it readily dissolves in water. **(Figure 1)** Except for basic (pH > 9) aqueous environments, ammonia is found as the protonated ion NH_4^+, ammonium.

Directly or indirectly, ammonia is the key building block of almost all nitrogen-containing compounds. In organisms, this includes the amino acids and nucleotides that are the monomers of proteins and nucleic acids, respectively. In the biosphere, ammonia is synthesized through the process of nitrogen fixation by prokaryotes, which converts atmospheric N_2 directly into ammonia using the enzyme nitrogenase. This prokaryotic process makes ammonia available for uptake by microbes and plants that use it to synthesize nitrogen-containing compounds. The enzymes involved in ammonium assimilation are usually abundant within cells. Thus, following import, ammonia is rapidly converted into less toxic forms of nitrogen and does not accumulate within cells.

Ammonia is a major breakdown product of protein and nucleic acid catabolism. Some fungi form fruiting bodies only when ammonia or nitrogenous compounds that release ammonia on breakdown are abundant. These "ammonia" fungi have potential use in forensic science because their fruiting bodies can reveal sites where human remains have been clandestinely buried and can also indicate time since burial.

In aquatic organisms from snails to fish, ammonia is simply excreted across the gills and is rapidly diffused in the surrounding water. Dilution of ammonia by water reduces its danger to the animals that produce it. In land animals, ammonia is converted to uric acid or urea, nontoxic forms that can be excreted without dilution with water. Some amphibious animals, such as snails, excrete ammonia when living in water and urea or uric acid when on land. Some terrestrial animals can live in high concentrations of ammonia. When literally millions of Brazilian free-tailed bats (*Tadarida brasiliensis*) live by day in caves, the levels of ammonia that accumulate are deadly to people. The bats use mucus to protect their respiratory tracts from ammonia.

Several mechanisms are implicated in ammonia toxicity, but all of them relate to the interconversion of ammonia with ammonium. High intracellular concentrations of ammonia may result in a disruption of pH balance within the cell. This is because at physiological pH, ammonia will be converted to ammonium in a process that consumes hydronium ion (H_3O^+), resulting in an increase in pH. Furthermore, high levels of ammonia/ammonium can disrupt the formation of proton gradients across membranes, which are critical for the synthesis of ATP by oxidative phosphorylation and photophosphorylation. Ammonia, despite its toxicity, is vital to life on Earth.

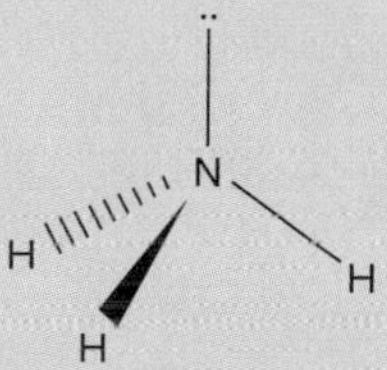

Figure 1
Diagram of ammonia molecule.

People Behind Biology

Elizabeth Lloyd Clare

Beth Clare and others used the barcode approach to examine the bat fauna at different locations in Guyana, South America **(Figure 1).** Working with colleagues from the Royal Ontario Museum (ROM) in Toronto, they collected data from 840 specimens representing 87 species of bats. An important element in the work was the connection between the barcode data and specimens (known as "vouchers" in the ROM collections) so that the genetic data could be associated with known individuals.

Clare and her coauthors predicted and found higher levels of divergence in the *CO1* sequence as they moved within species, to within genera, to within family **(Figure 2).** The tree illustrating their findings **(Figure 3)** demonstrated that whereas 81 species of bats showed one lineage within what is considered to be a species, six others showed larger sequence divergences than expected, suggesting more than one species. The genetic work shows that in some cases, biologists have been correct about the numbers of species, but in other instances, they have underestimated them.

Traditional taxonomic work (see Chapter 19) had suggested that some of the bats currently thought to be one species actually represented several. This use of the barcode approach validated its value to biologists working to document biodiversity and understand the adaptive radiation of bats.

Clare has expanded the use of the barcode approach by looking at the insects eaten by bats. Samples from the mouths of bats that had been feeding produced insect samples that could be analyzed using the barcoding approach. The same was true of insect remains in bat droppings. With a library of barcode data from different insects, bat biologists could use this approach to obtain detailed information about what species of insects bats have eaten.

In 2009, Clare is a Ph.D. student working with Professor Paul Hebert at the Barcode of Life project at the University of Guelph. She completed her honours bachelor of science degree in ecology and evolution at the University of Western Ontario and, as an undergraduate, spent several years studying fish behaviour and genetics.

Figure 1
The general location of Guyana in South America, and specific locations in Guyana from which bat specimens were obtained.

She has a long-standing interest in science and worked as a high school volunteer at a paleontological dig. She also participated in science fairs at both regional and national levels. In addition to her work on bats and barcoding, she is a dedicated photographer.

Study Break

1. How is ammonia toxic to living organisms? Why is it also necessary for life on Earth?

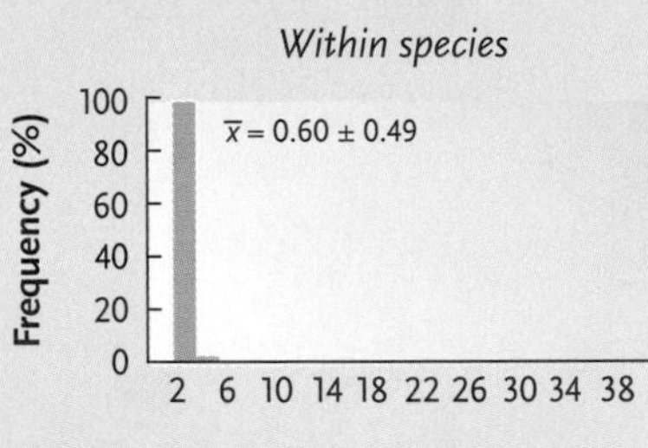

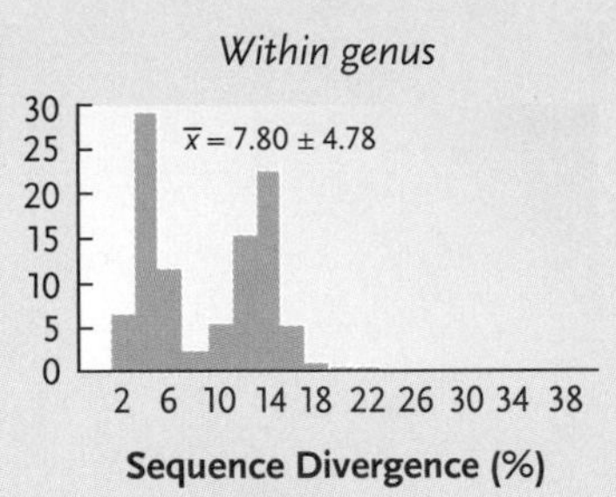

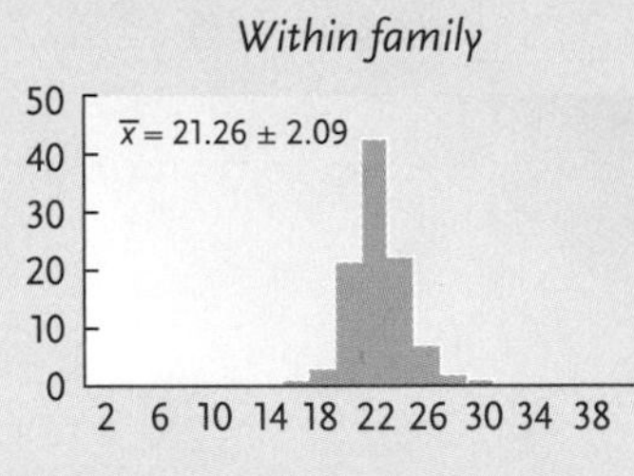

Figure 2
Frequency histograms comparing mean (± standard error) COI sequence divergences at different hierarchical levels: within species, within genus, within family. The data are from 87 species of bats (840 individuals) from Guyana.

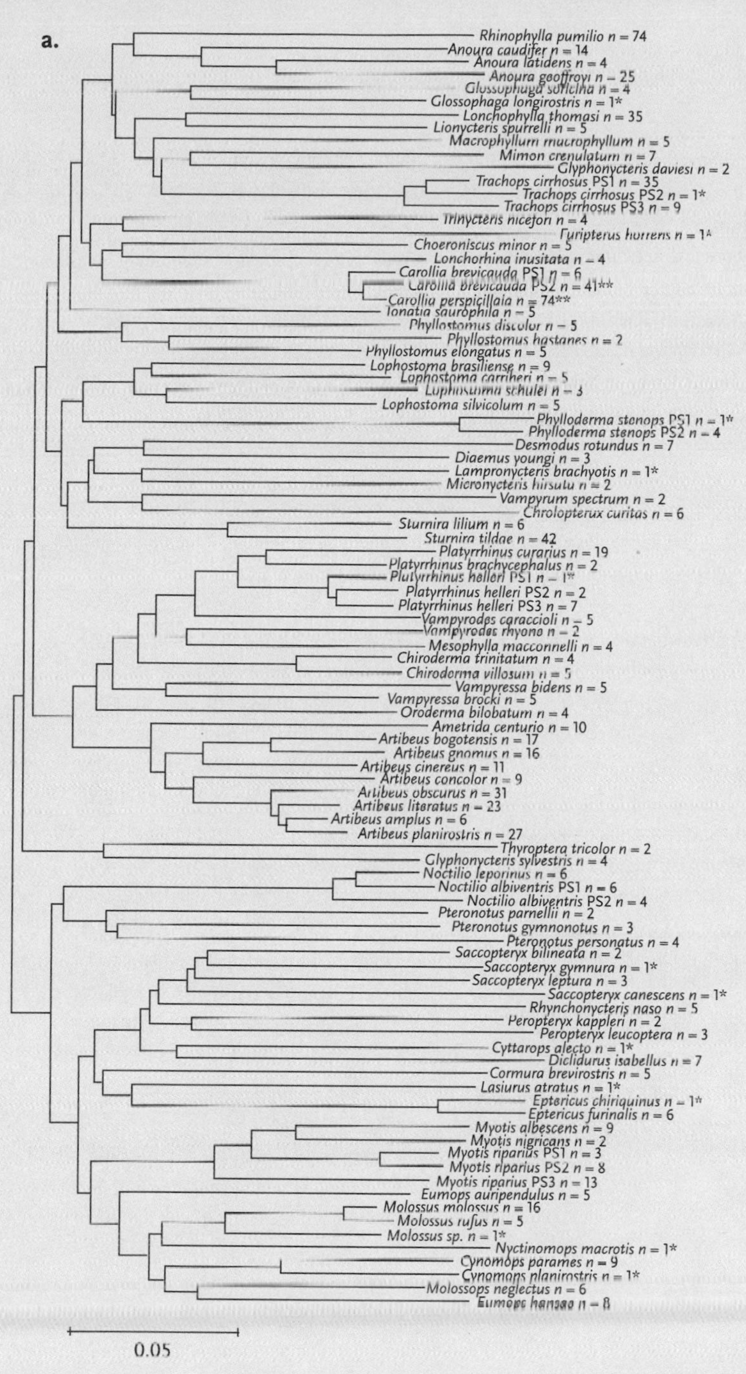

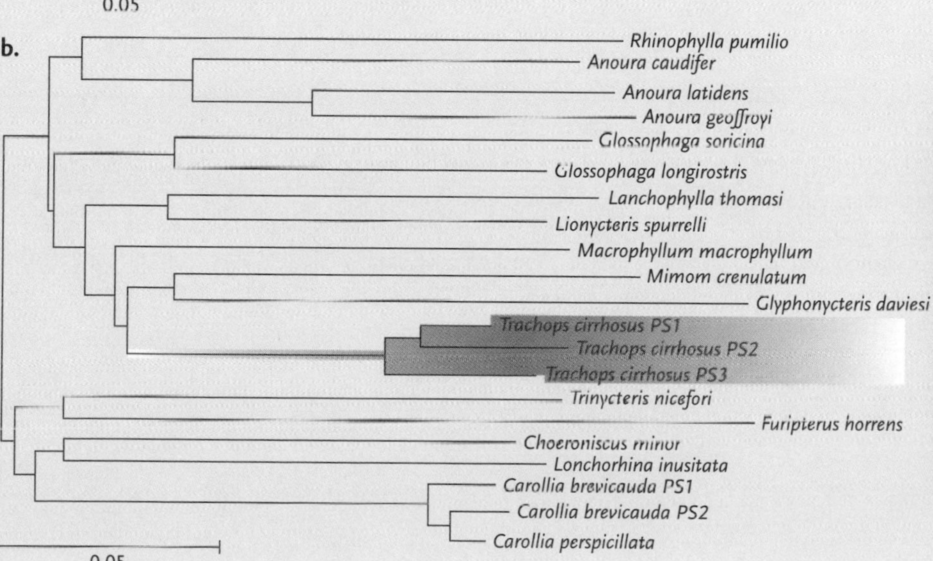

Figure 3
A neighbour-joining tree of COI sequence divergences in 87 species of bats. The * identifies *Trachops cirrhosus*, one of the species showing high sequence divergence suggestive of several different species.

Barcodes of Life

Because the diversity of species is overwhelming, it is difficult to provide a confident estimate of how many species remain undescribed (see Chapter 26). For many groups of organisms, few authorities are available to provide descriptions of "new" species, the ones not yet described and therefore nameless. The Barcode of Life Data Systems, based in Guelph, Ontario, Canada, offers one alternative to the challenge of knowing how many species are in the sample you have just acquired or the origin of a mysterious mouse found in a shipment of frozen chickens from Thailand.

The Barcode of Life project depends on variation in the mitochondrial cytochrome c oxidase 1 (*CO1*) gene, which consists of about 650 nucleotides. This genetic "barcode" is embedded in almost every cell, and it offers biologists a chance to identify a species even if they have only a small sample of feathers or fur, leaf, seed, or caterpillar. Since identification of some species depends on having a whole adult specimen, being able to identify species from an egg, a larva, or a hair offers enormous potential. Identification of organisms with different life stages can be particularly challenging. Using morphology, it can be easy to identify a butterfly or a frog but much more difficult to identify its caterpillar or its tadpole.

The Barcode of Life project is based on polymerase chain reaction (PCR) technology, which allows biologists to process 100 samples every 3 hours. Subsequent advances in genomic technology have increased our capacity for efficient sequencing of DNA. This potential, along with an army of researchers collecting specimens and global positioning technology (GPS) to document locations, means that the Barcode of Life project can deliver accurate (to 97.5%) identifications of specimens in a short time. Further developments could see biologists and naturalists armed with appropriately programmed handheld devices to identify organisms in the field.

One important consequence of this project is that biologists will have a chance to document more fully the diversity of life on Earth. This may mean realizing that the single identified species of a butterfly is actually 10 species, or that what people had thought were several species is, in fact, one. Protecting species through the Convention for Trade in Endangered Species (CITES) means being able to name them so that they can be placed on a protected list. The Barcode of Life project should allow a merchant to be sure that the ivory being sold in her shop is from an extinct mammoth, rather than a living, endangered species (see Chapter 48). The same applies to food species in a market: is that fish really what the label says it is?

But everyone has experience with barcode operations as used in many retail outlets. Scanning barcodes sometimes does not work. These limitations, as well as biological ones associated with genetics of different species, make some organisms more appropriate for Barcode of Life approaches than others.

Figure 1
COI barcode of *Trachops cirrhosus,* the frog-eating bat.

Unanswered Questions

Did life on earth evolve just once (i.e., is it monophyletic)? As you've read in this chapter, there is a tremendous diversity of living organisms but there is an underlying unity at the cellular and molecular level (see Ch. 2). This unity suggests that all organisms alive today share a common ancestor. But what if life arose more than once? Is it possible that descendents of this other lineage could still be alive on Earth, hiding in habitats in which DNA-based life forms can't survive? If life is monophyletic, what does this imply about the diversity of systems we see in living organisms? If life did evolve more than once, how would that affect your perception of diversity? Think about membranes and energy transfer systems.

Review

Go to CENGAGENOW™ at http://hed.nelson.com/ to access quizzing, animations, exercises, articles, and personalized homework help.

3.1 Biodiversity

- Heterotrophs obtain organic carbon and energy by consuming other organisms. Autotrophs, such as plants, are organisms that synthesize organic carbon molecules using inorganic carbon, CO_2. Plants are also photoautotrophs because they use light as the source of energy for photosynthesis. Chemoautotrophs, such as some bacteria, use reduced chemicals rich in electrons as an energy source.
- Key elements in the selection of individuals and their genetic traits are the presence of a selective force (pressure), genetic variation within a population, and the capacity of individuals with the selected trait to survive and reproduce.

3.3 Evolution

- The theory of evolution states that all organisms alive today descended from a common ancestor, which explains why all organisms share certain features (unity). It also tells us that species change over time as a result of natural selection (diversity).
- All organisms use ATP as their cellular energy source, have DNA as their genetic material, and have plasma membranes composed of lipid bilayers.
- The central ideas of Darwin's theory of evolution by natural selection are as follows:
  - Individual organisms in a population vary in many heritable traits.
  - Any population has the potential to produce far more offspring than the environment can support.
  - This situation results in a struggle for existence, and some individuals have traits giving them an advantage in their local environment.
  - These organisms are more likely to survive and reproduce, and surviving organisms pass on favourable traits to their offspring. In this way, the incidence of trait(s) in the population will change.
- Oxygenic photosynthesis generated oxygen, allowed for aerobic respiration, and created the ozone layer that allowed organisms to colonize more terrestrial environments by blocking harmful UV rays. Together, these changes led to diversification of life.
- An organism can move into a new adaptive zone after the chance evolution of a key morphological innovation that allows it to use the environment in a unique way. Thus, adaptive radiations occur when an evolutionary breakthrough leads to diversification of life.
- The challenges facing organisms that moved onto land included support and locomotion, conservation of water, acquisition of oxygen, reproduction, and disposal of wastes.
- The main differences between water and air are density and viscosity, which affect rates of diffusion and oxygen availability. Animals living in water use gills (or gill-like structures) to extract dissolved oxygen, although some photoautotrophs actually break water molecules in the process of photosynthesis. Animals that breathe air have more ready access to oxygen and spend less of their overall energy budget acquiring it than aquatic animals do. Since water is viscous, it provides organisms with support for locomotion, whereas air does not.
- To cope with a lack of support, terrestrial animals have developed more complex body designs for support (skeletons) and anchoring muscles (for locomotion).
- Temperature and the availability of dissolved oxygen in water are inversely related. As the temperature of water increases, the need for oxygen by aquatic organisms increases, which coincides with reduced amounts of dissolved oxygen available.
- By the end of the Devonian period, terrestrial animals had
  - skeletons for support and anchoring muscles (for locomotion),
  - organs for gaseous exchange (breathing atmospheric oxygen),
  - systems for circulating materials within the body,
  - waterproof coverings to minimize the chances of desiccation, and
  - the use of nontoxic excretory products (urea and uric acid).

3.4 The Biosphere

- Sunlight, temperature, humidity, wind speed, cloud cover, and rainfall are abiotic factors affecting the diversity of organisms.
- A global pattern of environmental diversity results from latitudinal variation in incoming solar radiation, Earth's rotation on its axis, and its orbit around the sun.
- Sunlight strikes Earth directly at a 90° angle near the equator, travelling a short distance through the radiation-absorbing atmosphere and shining on a small concentrated area. At the poles, sunlight arrives at an oblique angle, travelling longer distances through the atmosphere and shining on a larger area. Solar radiation is more concentrated near the equator than it is at higher latitudes, causing latitudinal variation in Earth's temperature.
- Earth's fixed tilt of 23.5° on its axis causes the Northern Hemisphere to receive more sunlight in June and the Southern Hemisphere to receive more in December. These differences are reflected in seasonal variation in day length and temperature, which are more pronounced at the poles than at the equator.
- Latitudinal variation in the speed of Earth's rotation deflects movement of rising and sinking air masses from a strictly north–south path into belts of easterly and westerly winds. This deflection is called the Coriolis effect.
- Adiabatic cooling is a decrease in temperature without the actual loss of heat energy. After cooling adiabatically, rising air masses release moisture as rain.
- Prevailing winds, Earth's rotation, gravity, the shape of ocean basins, and the positions of landmasses establish the direction and intensity of surface currents in the oceans. Generally, warm currents flow away from the equator and cold currents flow toward it.
- Monsoons are brought upon by seasonal reversals of wind direction. Usually, summer heat causes air masses over land to rise, creating a zone of low pressure. Moist air from a nearby body of water flows inland, where it rises and cools adiabatically, releasing substantial precipitation.
- Warm air picks up moisture from a body of water. If the warm air moves inland and reaches a range of mountains, it rises to cross the mountains. The air cools adiabatically and loses moisture, releasing heavy rainfall on the windward side. After the now-dry air crosses the peaks, it descends and warms, absorbing moisture and forming a rain shadow.

3.5 Biotic Factors

- Parasitism is a symbiotic relationship in which one organism benefits at the expense of the other. Mutualism is a symbiotic relationship in which both organisms involved benefit.
- The three basic trophic roles are producers, consumers, and decomposers. Photoautotrophs are the main producers because they use photosynthesis to capture and harness the sun's energy.

Heterotrophs are primary consumers when they eat autotrophs and mesopredators if they eat other heterotrophs. Other heterotrophs, such as fungi, are decomposers, breaking down dead organisms.

3.6 Cumulative Impact on Biotic and Abiotic Factors

- Prokaryotes produce ammonia (NH_3) when they reduce atmospheric nitrogen (N_2 gas). The ammonia that results from this process is directly or indirectly the basis for all nitrogenous molecules such as amino acids and nucleotides, as well as proteins and nucleic acids. The conversion of ammonia to these other nitrogenous compounds inside cells is crucial because ammonia is toxic to cells. At physiological pH, ammonia is converted to ammonium (NH_4); this process not only increases cellular pH but can interfere with formation of the proton gradients necessary for ATP synthesis.
- The Barcode of Life project depends on variation in the mitochondrial cytochrome *c* oxidase 1 (*CO1*) gene. This genetic barcode is embedded in almost every cell, offering biologists a chance to identify a species even if they have only a small sample. The Barcode of Life project uses PCR technology, which permits accurate identifications of specimens in a short time.

Questions

Self-Test Questions

1. *Treponema pallidum* can cause diseases such as
   a. acquired immune deficiency syndrome (AIDS).
   b. black death.
   c. syphilis.
   d. tuberculosis.
   e. small pox.
2. Evolution by natural selection depends on
   a. traits of organisms being inherited.
   b. variation in traits.
   c. traits providing advantages to individuals that have them.
   d. individuals competing for resources.
   e. all of the above.
3. Movement of animals onto land first depended on
   a. development of bones.
   b. availability of atmospheric oxygen.
   c. development of muscles.
   d. excretion of urea or uric acid.
   e. development of internal fertilization.
4. Changes in solar radiation reaching Earth are obvious in the differences between
   a. night and day.
   b. spring equinox and summer solstice.
   c. fall equinox and winter solstice.
   d. cloudy and sunny days.
   e. Both a and b are correct.
5. Adiabatic temperature changes involve
   a. warming of air masses.
   b. cooling of air masses.
   c. changes in water content of air masses.
   d. movement of air from the equator to polar regions.
   e. rainfall.
6. Continental climates tend to be ________ than maritime climates.
   a. warmer
   b. colder
   c. wetter
   d. drier
   e. b and c are correct
7. Solar radiation is captured by
   a. respiration.
   b. photosynthesis.
   c. oxygenic photosynthesis only.
   d. decomposition.
   e. all of the above.
8. Plants can be
   a. primary producers.
   b. carnivorous.
   c. achlorophyllous.
   d. terrestrial
   e. all of the above.
9. The Barcode of Life project depends on
   a. DNA fingerprinting.
   b. the cytochrome *c* oxidase 1 gene.
   c. PCR (polymerase chain reaction) technology.
   d. chromosomal variation.
   e. b and c.
10. Fossil evidence reveals that whales evolved from other mammals such as
    a. hippopotami.
    b. rodents.
    c. raoellids.
    d. seals.
    e. elephants.

Questions for Discussion

1. Find an example of a situation in which selection resulted in an adaptive radiation (going from the premise presented for the evolution of syphilis, whales, or climbing plants).
2. Are all ecosystems directly dependent on photosynthesis? If not, give two examples of systems in which primary productivity does not depend on photosynthesis.
3. Find examples of situations in which the Barcode of Life project might not work or might give false information.
4. How long did it take for life to recolonize the island of Krakatoa? Which organisms arrived there first after the explosion in 1883?

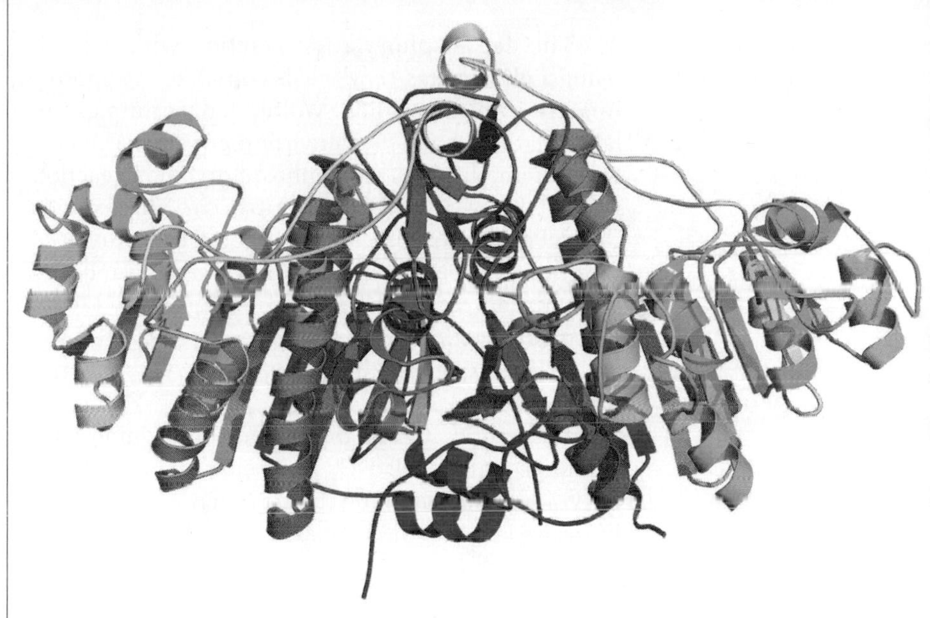

Model of the enzyme alkaline phosphatase

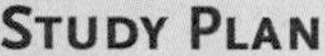

Study Plan

4 Energy and Enzymes

Why It Matters

Earth is a cold place—at least when it comes to chemical reactions. Life cannot survive at the high temperatures routinely used in most laboratories and industrial plants for chemical synthesis. Instead, life relies on a group of catalysts called enzymes that speed up the rates of reaction without the need for an increase in temperature.

Until recently, however, just how good enzymes are at increasing the rate of a reaction was not fully appreciated. Dr. Richard Wolfenden, professor of Chemistry, Biochemistry and Biophysics at the University of North Carolina and his colleagues estimated the rate of the uncatalyzed versus the enzyme-catalyzed reaction for a range of biologically relevant reactions. The prize for the greatest difference between the uncatalyzed rate and the enzyme-catalyzed rate goes to a reaction that simply removes a phosphate group. In the cell, a group of enzymes called phosphatases catalyze the removal of phosphate groups from a range of molecules, including proteins. The rapid reversible phosphorylation of particular proteins is a central mechanism of intracellular communication in almost all cells.

The dephosphorylation reaction within a cell using a phosphatase enzyme is completed in approximately 10 milliseconds. Wolfenden's group calculated that in an aqueous environment such as a cell, without an enzyme, the dephosphorylation reaction would take over 1 trillion years to occur. This exceeds the current estimate for the age of the universe! The difference between the enzyme-catalyzed and uncatalyzed rate is 21 orders of magnitude (10^{21}). For most reactions, the rate difference between the uncatalyzed rate and the catalyzed rate is many millions of times.

It is clear that given the fact that life requires temperatures that are relatively low (below 100°C), without enzymes to speed up the rates of chemical reactions, life as we know it could not exist.

4.1 Energy and the Laws of Thermodynamics

Life, like many chemical and physical activities, is an energy-driven process. Yet, energy cannot be measured or weighed directly. We can detect it only through its ability to do work: to move objects against opposing forces, such as friction, gravity, or pressure, or to push chemical reactions toward completion. Therefore, **energy** is most conveniently defined as the capacity to do work. It takes energy to move a car on a highway, and it takes energy to climb a mountain. It also takes energy to build a protein from a group of amino acids or pump sucrose across a cell membrane.

4.1a Energy Exists in Different Forms and States

Energy can exist in many different forms, including heat, chemical, electrical, and mechanical energy. Electromagnetic radiation, including visible, infrared, and ultraviolet light, is also a type of energy. Although the forms of energy are different, they can be converted readily from one form to another. For example, the chemical energy present in a flashlight battery is converted into electrical energy that passes through the flashlight bulb, where it is transformed into light and heat. Through the process of photosynthesis, the energy of light is converted into chemical energy in the form of complex sugars and other organic molecules.

All forms of energy can be grouped into one of two different states. **Kinetic energy** is the energy possessed by an object because it is in motion. Obvious examples of objects that possess kinetic energy include waves in the ocean, a falling rock, or a kicked football. Less obvious examples include the kinetic energy of electricity, which is a flow of electrons, and heat. Photons of light are also a form of kinetic energy. The movement present in kinetic energy is of use because it can perform work by making other objects move. **Potential energy** is stored energy: the energy an object has because of its location or chemical structure. A boulder at the top of a cliff has potential energy because of its position in the gravitational field of Earth. The arrangement of atoms in a molecule of glucose or gasoline has potential energy stored in the specific arrangement of atoms. This type of energy is often called *chemical potential energy* and is discussed further in Chapter 6.

4.1b The Laws of Thermodynamics Describe the Energy Flow in Natural Systems

The study of energy and its transformations is called **thermodynamics.** When discussing thermodynamics, scientists refer to something called the *system*, which is the object being studied. A system can be anything—a single molecule, one cell, or a planet. Everything outside the system is called the *surroundings*. The *universe*, in this context, is the total of the system and the surroundings. It is important that we distinguish between three different types of systems: isolated, open, and closed. As shown in **Figure 4.1,** an isolated system is one that does not exchange matter or energy with its surroundings. A good example of this would be a perfectly insulated Thermos bottle. A *closed system* can exchange energy but not matter with its surroundings. The Earth can be considered a closed system. It takes in an enormous amount of energy generated by the Sun and releases heat, but, essentially, no matter is exchanged between Earth and the rest of the universe. In an *open system*, both energy and matter can move freely between the system and the surroundings. As we will see later in this chapter, living organisms are open systems.

4.1c The First Law of Thermodynamics

Quantitative research by both physicists and chemists in the nineteenth century regarding energy flow between systems and the surroundings led to the formulation of two fundamental laws of thermodynamics that apply equally to living cells and to stars in galaxies light-years away. According to the **first law of thermodynamics,** *energy can be transformed from one form into another or transferred from one place to another, but it cannot be created or destroyed.* This law is also called the principle of the conservation of energy. The first law of thermodynamics is illustrated by Niagara Falls **(Figure 4.2),** which borders Canada and the United States. Water at the top of the falls has high potential energy because of its location within the Earth's gravitational field. As the water moves over the waterfall, its potential energy is converted into kinetic energy. The higher

a. Isolated system

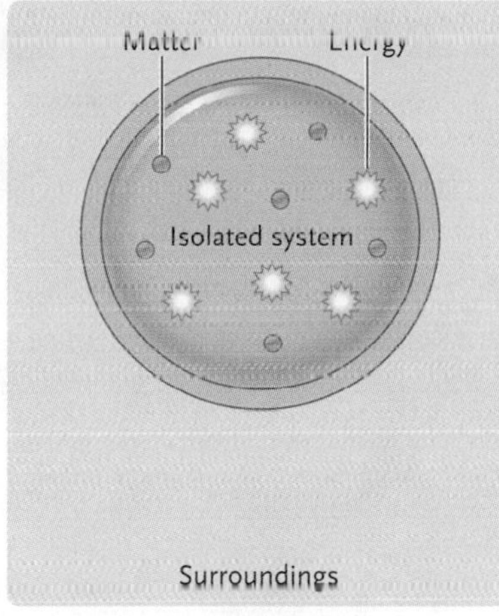

An isolated system does not exchange matter or energy with its surroundings.

b. Closed system

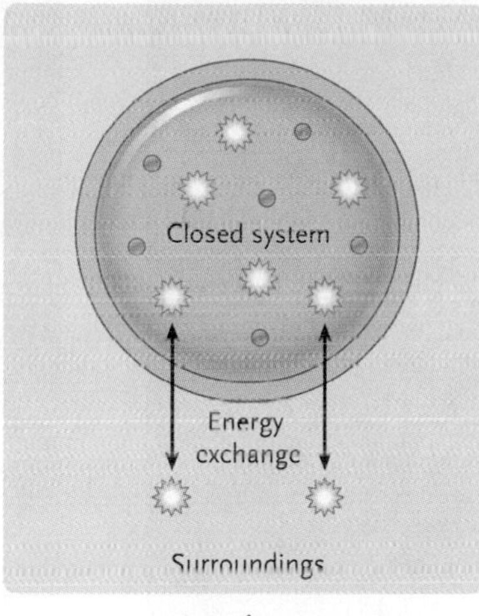

A closed system exchanges energy with its surroundings.

c. Open system

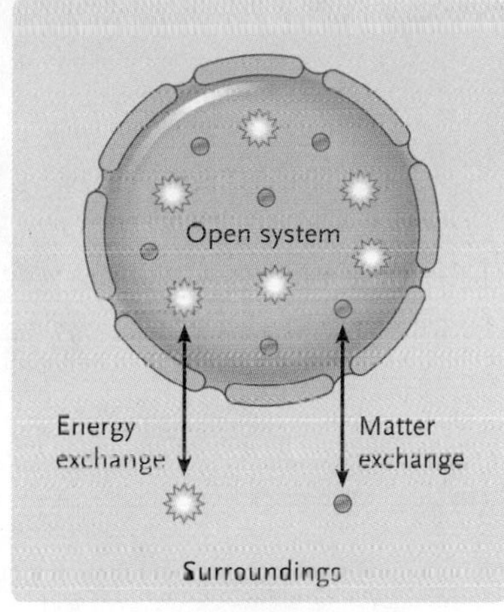

An open system exchanges both energy and matter with its surroundings.

Figure 4.1
Isolated, closed, and open systems in thermodynamics.

the waterfall, the more kinetic energy the water will possess. When it reaches the bottom of the waterfall, the kinetic energy of the water is dissipated into various forms of potential and kinetic energy, including heat, sound, and mechanical energy (causing weathering of the rocks). For thousands of years, the kinetic energy of waterfalls has been used by humans to do work. At Niagara Falls, the kinetic energy of the moving water is converted into electricity through the use of hydroelectric turbines (see Figure 4.2b) and is used to supply electricity to thousands of homes and businesses.

4.1d The Second Law of Thermodynamics

Another important principle of thermodynamics is that each time energy is transformed from one form into another, some of the energy is lost and unavailable to do work. You can think of this as the reason why machines are never 100% efficient. For example, the engine of a car converts only about 25% of the potential energy in gasoline into the kinetic energy that makes the car move

a.

© Corel

b.

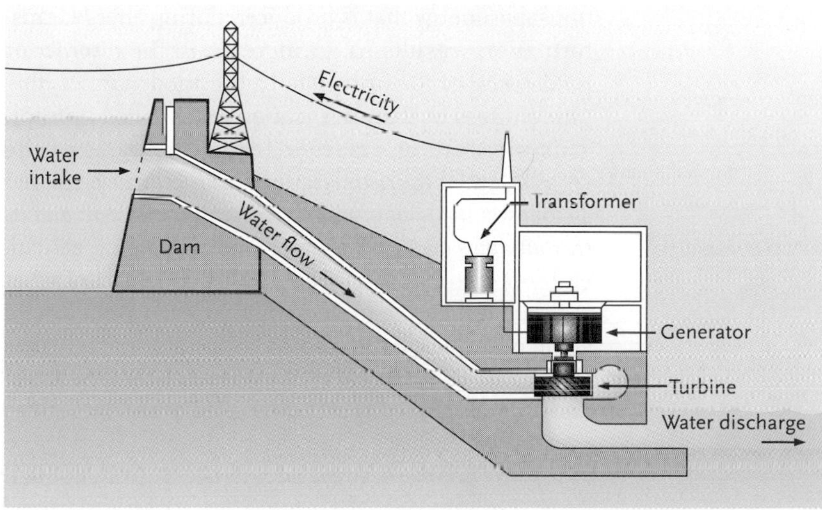

Figure 4.2
Niagara Falls, which borders New York, U.S.A., and Ontario, Canada. **(a)** The potential energy of the water is converted into kinetic energy as it moves over the falls. **(b)** A small portion of this kinetic energy is used to turn hydroelectric turbines, converting the gravitational energy into electrical energy. In accordance with the first law of thermodynamics, energy hasn't been gained or lost but it has changed form. Niagara Falls generates approximately 4.4 gigawatts (a gigawatt is 10^9 watts) of power each year—enough to power thousands of homes and businesses.

a.

b.

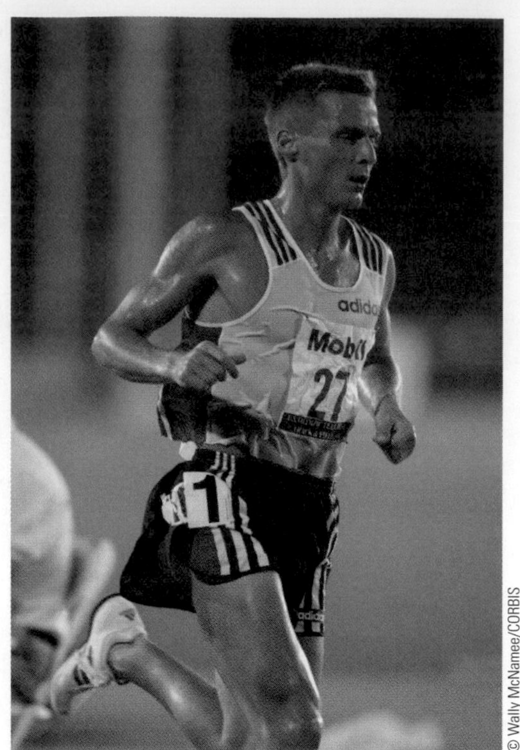

Figure 4.3
Two examples of thermodynamic systems that display the second law of thermodynamics. **(a)** A car engine converts only about 30% of the available energy in gasoline into mechanical energy. **(b)** A runner converts only about 40% of the energy in glucose into ATP, which powers his muscles. In both cases, a significant portion of the energy is unused and is given off as heat, which increases the disorder, or entropy, of the surroundings.

(Figure 4.3). Likewise, only a portion of the energy in a notebook computer battery is used to run the computer. If you touch a car engine that has just been switched off or put a notebook computer on your lap for an extended period of time, it is obvious where the remaining energy is going. It is being lost to the surroundings as *heat*, which is the energy associated with random molecular motion. This concept of energy efficiency also applies to living cells. As we will see in Chapter 6, through the process of cellular respiration, cells are able to convert only about 40% of the potential energy in glucose into a form usable for metabolism; the remainder is lost as heat (see Figure 4.3). In most cases, including living cells, heat cannot be harnessed to do work; instead, it is simply lost to the environment.

Whether it is a car engine or a living cell, the unusable energy that is produced during energy transformations results in an increase in the *disorder* or *randomness* of the universe. In thermodynamics, this randomness or disorder is a quantity called **entropy.** This measure of disorder forms the basis of the **second law of thermodynamics**, which can be stated as follows: *the total disorder (entropy) of a system and its surroundings always increases.* There is no single inclusive way to think of entropy, and that is part of what makes it difficult to understand. So let's work through some examples: a cup of hot coffee gets cold. A new car doesn't stay new; first, it loses its "new car smell," and soon you need new brakes and a tune-up, until, eventually, the passenger door falls off. All of these situations are inevitable and will occur given enough time. The physical disintegration of an organized system is the second law in action. Systems will move spontaneously toward arrangements with greater entropy. Your dorm room or apartment will spontaneously move to a more disordered, higher entropy state **(Figure 4.4)**—essentially, it gets messy. You can reverse it, make things more ordered, but this requires work. It takes energy to maintain low entropy.

4.1e Life and the Second Law of Thermodynamics

But what about life: *does it obey the second law of thermodynamics?* One of the qualities of all life is that it is highly ordered. That is, the molecules and

Figure 4.4
An everyday illustration of the spontaneous move toward disorder. Rooms become messy, disorganized. To make the room more ordered requires an input or energy—it requires work.

structures that define life are very precisely arranged, in a nonrandom manner. Living cells have the ability to create ordered structures out of less ordered starting materials. A molecule of DNA, a protein, and a ribosome are all very ordered structures that living things make out of much simpler building blocks. There is nothing random or disordered about a brain or a flower or photosystem II. These examples suggest that life goes against the second law of thermodynamics: things don't become more random in a living cell, they become more ordered. How is this possible? The answer lies in understanding the statement mentioned at the end of the last section: *it takes energy to maintain low entropy.*

Living cells are not isolated but rather are open systems, exchanging energy and matter with their surroundings. This energy may be in the form of a falafel sandwich or milkshake for you and me or in the form of photons of light and carbon dioxide for a cyanobacterium. Living things bring in energy and matter and use them to generate order out of disorder. It is understandable why elite athletes need to eat a lot of food, but people who don't exercise at all also need to ingest over a thousand kilocalories every day. Although some of this food supplies us with the energy to use our muscles, much of the food energy we ingest is used simply to maintain our cells in their highly ordered state **(Figure 4.5).**

According to the second law of thermodynamics, things are constantly breaking down. For living organisms this means that cell structures become damaged and need to be constantly replaced. New cells need to be made and old ones maintained by the synthesis of a huge array of proteins, carbohydrates, and lipid molecules. In other words, *we eat food to maintain low entropy!*

Figure 4.5
Why do we need to eat? The average person needs to ingest about 1,500 kcal per day. A significant amount of this energy is needed to maintain the order within our cells. We eat food to maintain low entropy.

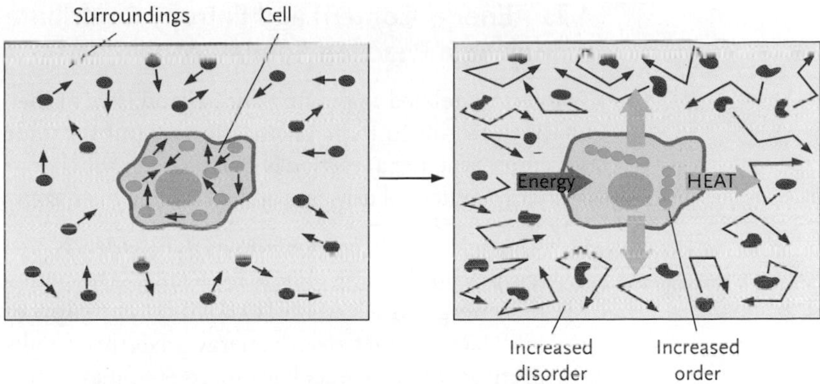

Figure 4.6
A simple thermodynamic example of a living cell. In the diagram on the left, molecules of both the cell and the surroundings are in a relatively disordered state. In the diagram on the right, the cell has taken in energy from the surroundings and used the energy to perform the work required to make molecules more ordered. This energy transformation releases heat, which increases the disorder (or entropy) of the surroundings.

But according to the second law of thermodynamics, the entropy of a system and the surroundings is always supposed to increase. Absolutely—In the course of the thousands of chemical reactions that take place to generate order, living things give off heat and by-products of metabolism such as carbon dioxide that are much less ordered and increase the disorder, or entropy, of the surroundings **(Figure 4.6).** The entropy of a system such as an organism is allowed to decrease as long as the entropy of the universe as a whole increases. Because of this, living organisms can be thought of as islands of low entropy in a sea (the universe) that is constantly becoming more random and disordered.

Study Break

1. Distinguish between kinetic and potential energy.
2. In thermodynamics, what is meant by an

4.2 Free Energy and Spontaneous Reactions

Applying the first and second laws of thermodynamics together allows us to predict whether any particular chemical or physical reaction will occur without an input of energy—what in thermodynamics are called **spontaneous reactions**. In this usage, the word *spontaneous* means only that a reaction will occur—it does not describe the rate of a reaction. Spontaneous reactions may proceed very slowly, such as the formation of rust on a nail, or very quickly, such as a match bursting into flame.

4.2a Energy Content and Entropy Contribute to Making a Reaction Spontaneous

Two factors related to the first and second laws of thermodynamics need to be taken into account for us to determine whether a reaction is spontaneous: the change in energy content of a system and its change in entropy:

1. *Reactions tend to be spontaneous if the products have less potential energy than the reactants.* The potential energy in a system is called its **enthalpy**, or H. Reactions that absorb energy are termed **endothermic**, the products have more potential energy than the reactants. By comparision, those processes that release energy are called **exothermic.** When natural gas burns, methane reacts spontaneously with oxygen to produce carbon dioxide and water:

   $$CH_4 + 2\,O_2 \rightarrow CO_2 + H_2O$$

   The reaction is exothermic, producing a large amount of heat, as the products have less potential energy than the reactants. We discuss the chemical basis for why molecules such as methane have high potential energy in Chapter 6. As a second example, what about the glass of ice water shown in **Figure 4.7?** Why does the ice spontaneously melt at 25°C? The system (the glass of ice water) is absorbing energy from the surroundings and the potential energy of water is greater than that of ice, not less. The process is endothermic, yet the process of the ice melting is it is spontaneous. Clearly, some other factor besides potential energy is at play here.

2. *Reactions tend to be spontaneous when the products are less ordered than the reactants.* Reactions tend to occur spontaneously if the entropy of the products is greater than the entropy of the reactants, that is, if the products are more random than the reactants. In the glass of ice water (see Figure 4.7), it is an increase in entropy that makes the melting of the ice a spontaneous process at 25°C. Molecules of ice are far more ordered (possess lower entropy) than molecules of water that are moving around randomly. In general, phase changes (solid → liquid → gas) result in an increase in entropy.

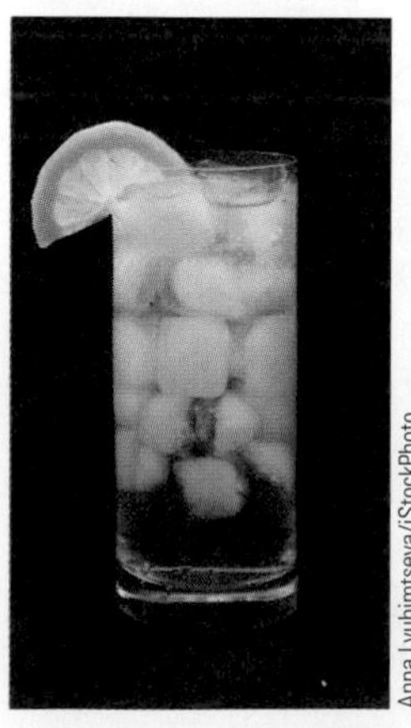

Figure 4.7
The melting of ice at room temperature. This is an example of a spontaneous reaction that is endothermic: the energy content of the product (water) is greater than the reactant (ice). The reaction is spontaneous because the entropy of the system, the disorder, increases.

4.2b The Change in Free Energy Indicates Whether a Reaction Is Spontaneous

Recall from the second law of thermodynamics that energy transformations are not 100% efficient; some of the energy is lost as an increase in entropy. So how much energy is available? The portion of a system's energy that is available to do work is called **free energy**, which is abbreviated by the letter G in recognition of the physicist Josiah Willard Gibbs, who developed the concept. In living organisms, free energy accomplishes the chemical and physical work involved in activities such as the synthesis of molecules, movement, and reproduction. The change in free energy, ΔG ($\Delta G = G_{final\ state} - G_{initial\ state}$), can be calculated for any specific chemical reaction using the formula

$$\Delta G = \Delta H - T\Delta S$$

where ΔH is the change in enthalpy and ΔS is the change in the entropy of the system over the course of the reaction. T is the absolute temperature in kelvin (K, where K = °C + 273.16). The equation says that *the free energy change as a system goes from initial to final states is the sum of the changes in energy content and entropy.*

For a reaction to be spontaneous, the ΔG must be negative. As the above formula tells us, both the entropy and the enthalpy of a reaction can influence the overall ΔG of a reaction. That is, for all chemical and physical processes, there is an interplay of both entropy and enthalpy to determine whether it will occur spontaneously. In some processes, such as the combustion of methane, the large loss of potential energy, negative enthalpy (ΔH), dominates in making a reaction spontaneous. In other reactions, a decrease in order (*ΔS increases*) dominates, such as the melting of ice at 25°C. Once we know what the ΔG for a reaction is, we can determine if the reaction will proceed spontaneously.

It is important not to forget that the ΔG represents the difference between the free energy of the final state compared with the initial state and that a negative ΔG indicates that the products have less free energy than the reactants. Another way to think about free energy has to do with stability **(Figure 4.8).** Systems that have high free energy are less stable than systems that have less free energy. Furthermore, systems will spontaneously change into a more stable state but cannot spontaneously change into being less stable. For example, a molecule of glucose can be considered as unstable and will spontaneously break down into molecules, including carbon dioxide, that have less free energy but that also are more stable. Likewise, a concentration gradient that exists across a membrane is less stable and contains more free energy than after diffusion, when the molecules are equally distributed on both sides of a membrane (see Figure 4.8).

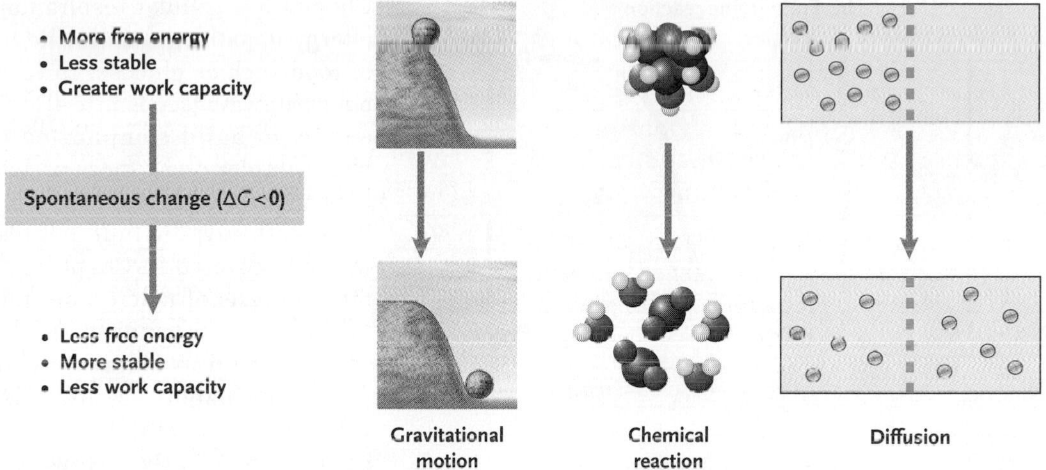

Figure 4.8
The relationship between free energy, stability, and work capacity. The top diagrams represent unstable systems that have high free energy and are unstable. They can spontaneously change into the bottom diagrams releasing free energy resulting in systems that are more stable. The release in free energy may be harnessed to perform work.

4.2c Life and Equilibrium

Another term for maximum stability is *equilibrium*, which is perhaps best explained in the context of the chemical equilibrium that can be achieved in a chemical reaction. Consider a chemical reaction in which glucose 1-phosphate is converted into glucose 6-phosphate **(Figure 4.9).** Starting with 0.02 M glucose 1-phosphate, the reaction will proceed spontaneously until there is 0.019 M of glucose 6-phosphate (product) and 0.001 M of glucose 1-phosphate (reactant) in the solution. In fact, regardless of the amounts of each you start with, the reaction will reach a point at which there is 95% glucose 6-phosphate and 5% glucose 1-phosphate. This is called the point of chemical equilibrium, a state in which the reaction does not stop but rather a state in which the rate of the forward reaction equals the rate of the backward reaction. As a system moves toward equilibrium, the free energy of the system becomes progressively lower and reaches its lowest point and maximum stability when the system is at equilibrium (G is zero). You can think of a reaction as an energy valley, with the equilibrium point being at the bottom. To move away from the equilibrium point requires free energy and thus will not be spontaneous.

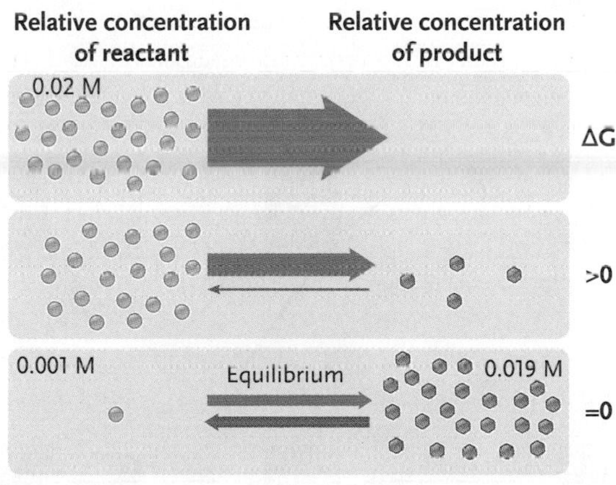

Figure 4.9
Chemical reactions run to equilibrium. No matter what quantities of glucose 1-phosphate and glucose 6-phosphate are dissolved in water, when equilibrium is attained, there will always be 95% glucose 6-phosphate and 5% glucose 1-phosphate. At equilibrium, the number of reactant molecules being converted to products equals the number of product molecules being converted back to reactants. The reaction at the equilibrium point is reversible; it may be made to run to the right (forward) by adding more reactants or to the left (backward) by adding more products.

For each reaction, the point of equilibrium is related to the ΔG for the reaction. The more negative the ΔG, the further toward completion the reaction will move before equilibrium is established. If the reaction shown in Figure 4.9 had a positive ΔG, the reaction would run backward toward glucose 1-phosphate. Many reactions have a ΔG that is near zero and are thus readily reversible by adjusting the concentrations of products and reactants slightly.

The reaction shown in Figure 4.9 represents an isolated system, and, over time, equilibrium is reached, the ΔG becoming zero. However, many individual reactions in living organisms never reach an equilibrium point because living systems are open; thus, the supply of reactants is constant, and as products are formed, they do not accumulate but rather become the reactants of another reaction. In fact, overall, the ΔG of life is always negative as organisms

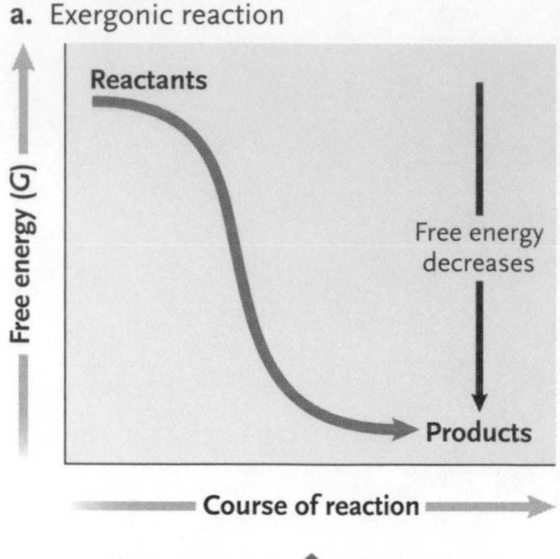

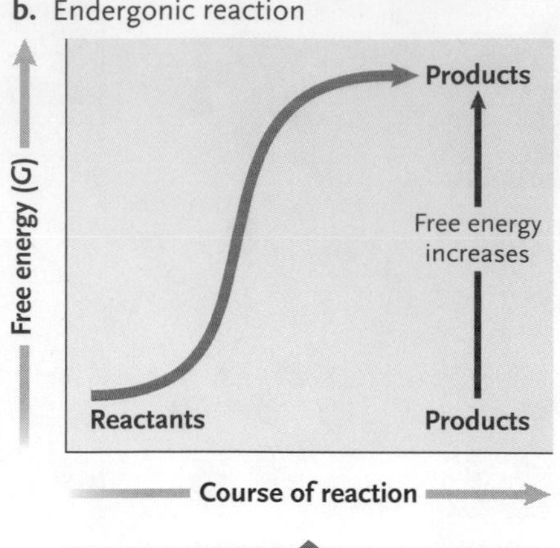

Figure 4.10
Exergonic **(a)** and endergonic **(b)** reactions.

constantly take in energy-rich molecules (or light, if photosynthetic) and use them to do work. Organisms reach equilibrium, $\Delta G = 0$, only when they die.

4.2d Metabolic Pathways Consist of Exergonic and Endergonic Reactions

Based on the free energy of reactants and products, every reaction can be placed into one of two groups. An **exergonic reaction (Figure 4.10a)** is one that releases free energy—the ΔG is negative because the products contain less free energy than the reactants. In an **endergonic reaction (Figure 4.10b)**, the products contain more free energy than the reactants; therefore, the ΔG is positive. The reactants involved in endergonic reactions need to gain free energy from the surroundings to form the products of the reaction.

In metabolism, individual reactions tend to be part of a metabolic pathway, which is a series of sequential reactions in which the products of one reaction are used immediately as the reactants for the next reaction in the series **(Figure 4.11).** In one type of metabolic pathway called a **catabolic pathway** (see Figure 4.11a), energy is released by the breakdown of complex molecules to simpler compounds. An example of a catabolic pathway that we discuss in detail in Chapter 6 is cellular respiration, whereby energy is extracted from the breakdown of food such as glucose. In contrast, **anabolic pathways** (see Figure 4.11b) consume energy to build complicated molecules from simpler ones; these are often called biosynthetic pathways. Examples of anabolic pathways include photosynthesis, which is covered in Chapter 7, as well as the synthesis of macromolecules such as proteins and nucleic acids.

As shown in Figure 4.11, the overall ΔG of an anabolic pathway is positive, whereas the overall ΔG of a catabolic pathway is negative. However, any one pathway may be made up of a number of individual chemical reactions, not all of which need to have the same sign (positive or negative) as the overall ΔG. As we will learn in Chapter 6, cellular respiration is a metabolic pathway made up of many individual reactions, some of which release energy ($-\Delta G$), whereas others require energy ($+\Delta G$). However, when you sum the ΔG of all the reactions, the overall free energy is negative, and the pathway of cellular respiration is thus said to be catabolic.

Study Break

1. What two factors need to be considered to determine if a reaction will proceed spontaneously?
2. Define and distinguish between exergonic and endergonic reactions and anabolic and catabolic pathways.

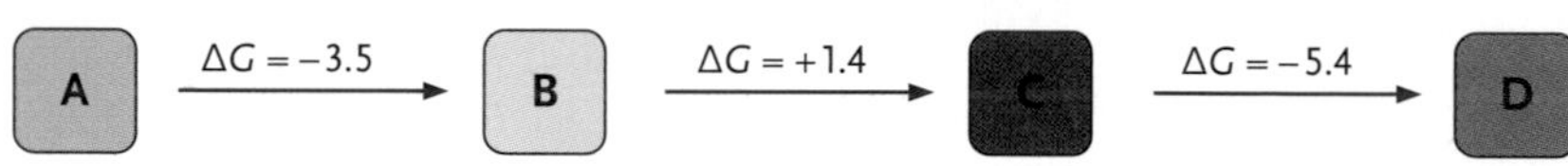

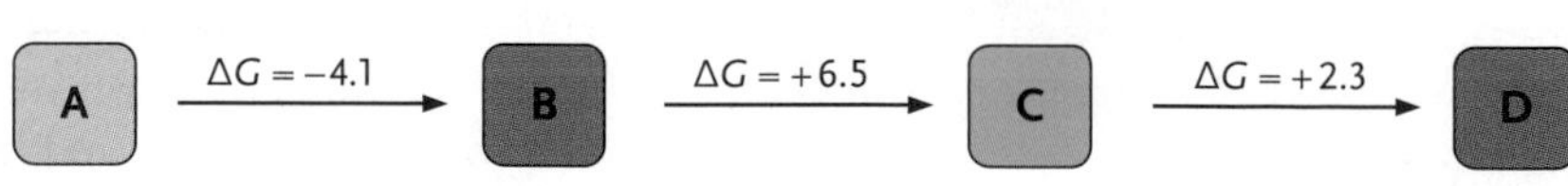

Figure 4.11
Hypothetical examples of the two major types of metabolic pathways. The starting molecule A is converted by a series of enzyme-catalyzed reactions to the product D. In catabolic pathways, the starting molecule A has high amounts of free energy, which is released as it gets converted into D. In anabolic pathways, energy must be provided to convert a molecule with low free energy A to one with higher amounts of free energy D. Although each pathway will have either an overall negative or positive ΔG, individual reactions can have the opposite sign.

4.3 The Energy Currency of the Cell: ATP

A huge array of reactions take place within cells that involve the assembly of complex molecules from more simple components. As we discussed in the last section, these reactions have a positive ΔG and are called endergonic, and they may be part of both catabolic and anabolic pathways. How the cell supplies the energy to drive these endergonic reactions is highly conserved among all forms of life and involves the nucleotide adenosine triphosphate (ATP).

4.3a ATP Hydrolysis Releases Free Energy

ATP is the best example of a group of compounds that contain large amounts of free energy because they possess what are called high-energy phosphate bonds. ATP itself consists of a five-carbon sugar, ribose, linked to the nitrogenous base adenine and a chain of three phosphate groups **(Figure 4.12).** Much of the potential energy of ATP is associated with the arrangement of the three phosphate groups. As shown in Figure 4.12a, each of the phosphate groups is closely associated with each other and their negative charges strongly repel each other, making the bonding arrangements unstable. Removal of one or two of the three phosphate groups is a spontaneous reaction that relieves the repulsion and releases large amounts of free energy. The breakdown of ATP is a *hydrolysis* reaction (see Figure 4.12b) and results in the formation of adenosine diphosphate (ADP) and a molecule of inorganic phosphate (P_i). ADP can be further hydrolyzed to adenosine monophosphate (AMP); however, this releases somewhat less free energy than the hydrolysis of ATP:

$$ATP + H_2O \rightarrow ADP + P_i$$
$$\Delta G = -7.3 \text{ kcal/mol}$$

a. Chemical structure of ATP

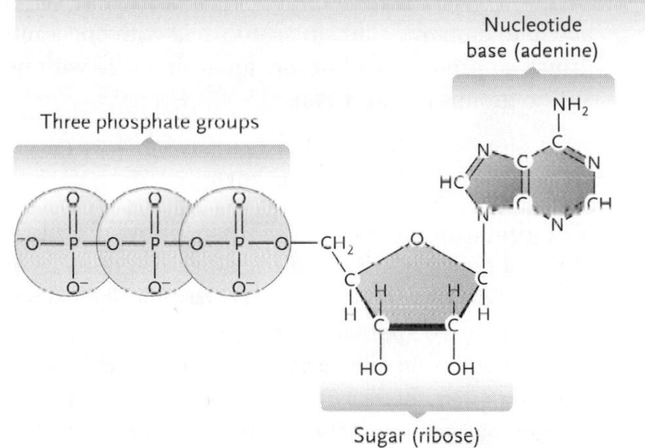

b. Hydrolysis reaction removing a phosphate group from ATP

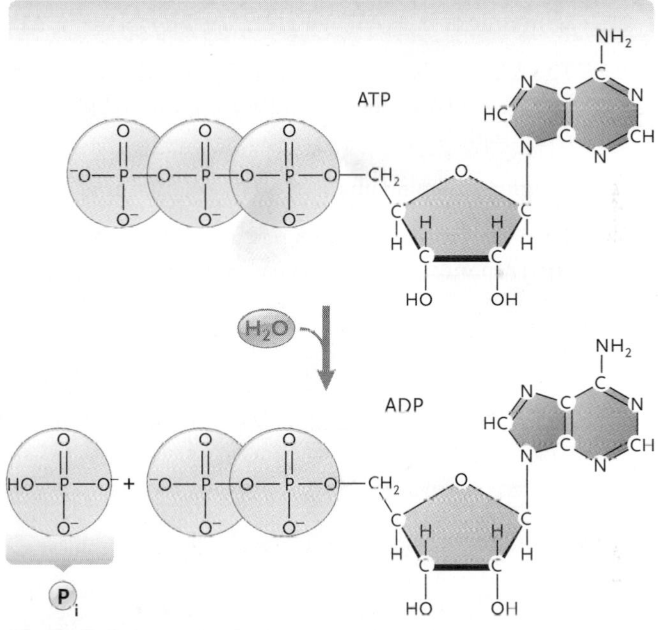

Figure 4.12
ATP, the primary molecule that is used to supply the energy for endergonic reactions. **(a)** Structure of one ATP molecule. **(b)** Reaction of ATP hydrolysis. ATP possesses high free energy because the repulsive forces of the three phosphate groups make the molecule unstable.

4.3b ATP and Energy Coupling

When ATP is dissolved in water in a test tube, the hydrolysis reaction releases free energy that simply warms up the surrounding water. Within cells, the heat produced by the isolated hydrolysis of ATP is rare but does occur during shivering in muscle tissue to maintain body heat. If most ATP was hydrolyzed in this manner, it would be very difficult for the cell to trap the heat produced and use it to do work. In addition, significant heat generation could result in cell death. So, given these two points, how do living cells link or *couple* the hydrolysis of ATP to an endergonic reaction such that energy is not simply wasted as heat?

In a process called **energy coupling,** ATP is brought in close contact with a reactant molecule involved in an endergonic reaction, and when the ATP is hydrolyzed, the terminal phosphate group is transferred to the reactant molecule. The transfer of the phosphate results in the reactant becoming *phosphorylated,* which makes the molecule less stable (more reactive) than when it was present in the unphosphorylated form. Energy coupling requires the action of an enzyme to bring the ATP and reactant molecule(s) into close association. The enzyme has a specific site on it that binds both the ATP and the reactant molecule, allowing for transfer of the phosphate group.

An example of energy coupling that is very common in most cells is the reaction in which ammonia (NH_3) is added to glutamic acid, an amino acid with one amino group, to produce glutamine, an amino acid with two amino groups **(Figure 4.13a)**:

$$\text{glutamic acid} + NH_3 \rightarrow \text{glutamine} + H_2O$$
$$\Delta G = +3.4 \text{ kcal/mol}$$

The glutamine is used in the assembly of proteins and is a donor of nitrogen for other reactions in the cell. The positive value for ΔG shows that the reaction cannot proceed spontaneously.

How, then, do cells carry out this reaction? As shown in **Figure 4.13b,** the reaction proceeds by harnessing the energy released by ATP hydrolysis. As a first step, the phosphate group removed from ATP is transferred to glutamic acid, forming glutamyl phosphate:

$$\text{glutamic acid} + \text{ATP} \rightarrow \text{glutamyl phosphate} + \text{ADP}$$

The ΔG for this reaction is negative, making the reaction spontaneous. In the second step, glutamyl phosphate reacts with NH_3:

$$\text{glutamyl phosphate} + NH_3 \rightarrow \text{glutamine} + P_i$$

This second reaction also has a negative value for ΔG and is spontaneous. Even though the reaction proceeds in two steps, it is usually written for convenience as one reaction, with a combined negative value for ΔG:

$$\text{glutamic acid} + NH_3 + \text{ATP} \rightarrow \text{glutamine} + \text{ADP} + P_i$$
$$\Delta G = -3.9 \text{ kcal/mol}$$

Because ΔG is negative, the coupled reaction is spontaneous and releases energy. The difference between -3.9 kcal/mol and the -7.3 kcal/mol released by hydrolyzing ATP to ADP + P_i represents potential chemical energy transferred to the glutamine molecules produced by the reaction. In effect, the coupling system works by joining an exergonic reaction, the hydrolysis of ATP, to the endergonic biosynthesis reaction, producing an overall reaction that is exergonic. All the endergonic reactions of living organisms, including those of growth, reproduction, movement, and response to stimuli, are made possible by coupling reactions in this way.

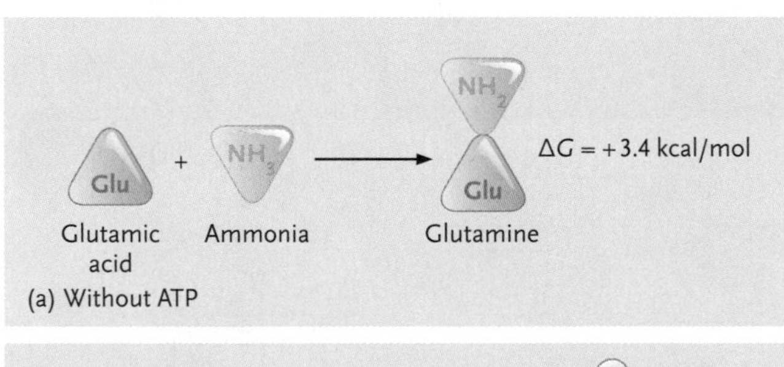

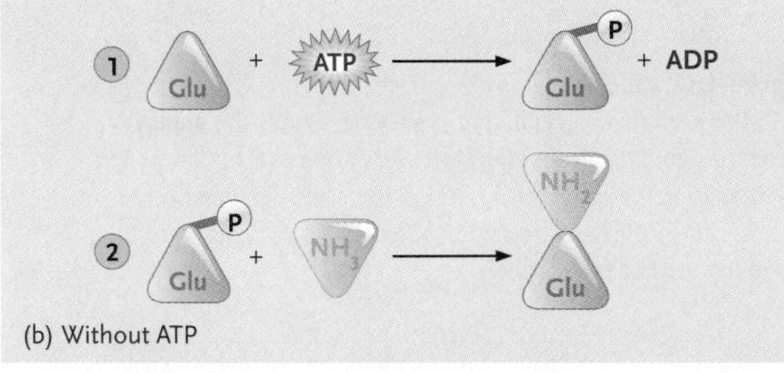

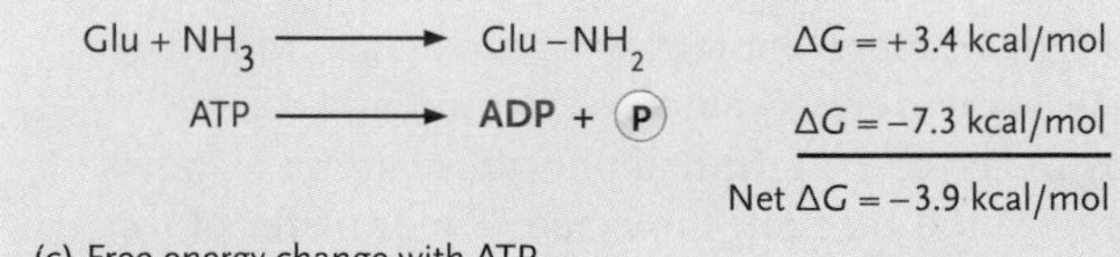

Figure 4.13
Energy coupling using ATP hydrolysis. (a) The synthesis of glutamine from glutamic acid and ammonia is not spontaneous. **(b)** In the presence of ATP hydrolysis, the free energy of the terminal phosphate is transferred to the glutamic acid, making it more unstable. In this form, it spontaneously reacts with ammonia, forming glutamine. **(c)** Adding the ΔG for the amino acid conversion to the ΔG for ATP hydrolysis gives the free energy change for the overall reaction. Because the overall process is exergonic, has a negative ΔG, it occurs spontaneously.

4.3c Regeneration of ATP

We have just seen how the breakdown of ATP into ADP and P_i is an exergonic reaction that can be coupled to make otherwise endergonic reactions proceed spontaneously. These coupling reactions occur continuously in living cells, consuming a tremendous amount of ATP. The question we can now ask is *how do cells generate ATP?* ATP is a renewable resource that is synthesized by recombining ADP and P_i. If ATP hydrolysis is an exergonic process, then ATP synthesis from ADP and P_i is an energy-requiring, endergonic process. The energy for ATP synthesis comes from the exergonic breakdown of complex molecules that contain an abundance of free energy. Essentially, what we are referring to is food, carbohydrates, fats, and proteins—all abundant sources of energy.

The continued breakdown and resynthesis of ATP is called the **ATP cycle (Figure 4.14).** Approximately

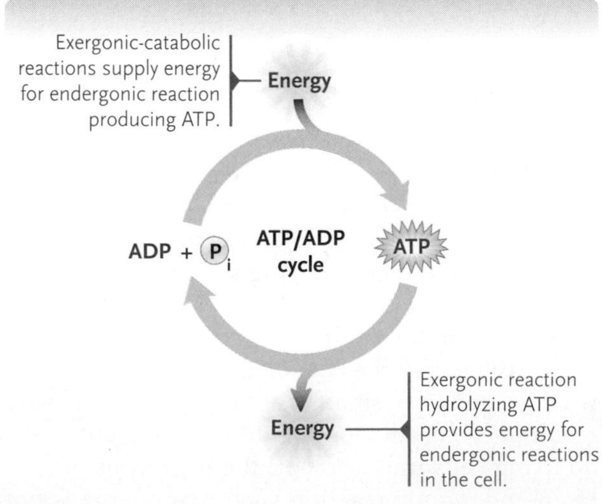

Figure 4.14
The ATP/ADP cycle. This cycle couples reactions that release free energy to reactions that require free energy.

10 million ATP molecules are hydrolyzed and resynthesized each second in a typical cell, illustrating that this cycle operates at an astonishing rate. In fact, if ATP was not regenerated from ADP and P_i, it is estimated that the average human would use an estimated 75 kg of ATP per day. It makes sense that cells should never be limited in their availability of ATP. In fact, a typical cell maintains an ATP concentration that is about 1000 times greater than ADP—very far from equilibrium.

Study Break

1. Explain, given the structure of ATP, why its hydrolysis releases free energy.
2. What is meant by the term *energy coupling*?

4.4 The Role of Enzymes in Biological Reactions

The laws of thermodynamics are useful because they can tell us if a process will occur without an input of energy, or, said another way, if the process is spontaneous. However, the laws do not tell us anything about the speed of a reaction. For example, even though the breakdown of sucrose into glucose and fructose is a spontaneous process with a ΔG of -7 kcal/mol, a solution of sucrose can sit for years without any detectable fructose or glucose being formed. This is an important point that is worth repeating: *that a reaction is spontaneous does not mean it proceeds rapidly.* In the next few sections, we discuss how the speed of a reaction can be altered through the use of a special group of proteins called enzymes.

4.4a The Activation Energy Represents a Kinetic Barrier

In our example above, what is it that prevents sucrose from being rapidly converted into glucose and fructose? Chemical reactions require bonds to break and new bonds to be formed. For bonds to be broken, they must first be strained or otherwise made less stable so that bond breakage can actually occur. To get reacting molecules into a more unstable state requires a small input of energy. Thus, even though a reaction is spontaneous (negative ΔG), the reaction will not actually start unless a relatively small boost of energy is added **(Figure 4.15a)**. This initial energy investment required to start a reaction is called the **activation energy** (E_A). Molecules that gain the necessary activation energy occupy what is called the **transition state**, where bonds are unstable and are ready to be broken.

A rock resting in a depression at the top of a hill provides a physical example of activation energy **(Figure 4.15b)**. The rock will not roll downhill spontaneously, even though its position represents considerable potential energy and the total "reaction"—the downward movement of the rock—is spontaneous and releases free energy. In this example, the activation energy is the effort required to raise the rock over the rim of the depression and start its downhill roll.

What provides the activation energy for chemical reactions? The molecules taking part in chemical reactions are in constant motion (at temperatures above absolute zero), and, periodically, reacting molecules may gain enough energy to reach the transition state. For a solution of sucrose, the number of molecules that reach the transition state at any one time is very small. However, if a significant number of reactant molecules reach the transition state, then the free energy that is released may be enough to get the remaining reactants to the transition state. A good example of this is illustrated by a propane torch **(Figure 4.16, p. 82)**. Propane is a molecule that contains an abundance of free energy and spontaneously decomposes into

a.

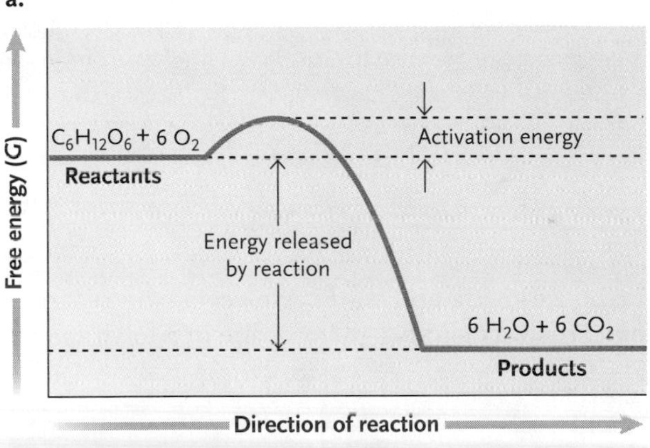

b.

Rock
Activation energy
Hill

Figure 4.15
The concept of activation energy. (a) The activation energy for the oxidation of glucose is an energy barrier over which glucose molecules must be raised before they can react to form H_2O and CO_2. **(b)** In an analogous physical situation, a rock poised in a depression at the top of a hill will not roll downhill unless activating energy is added to raise it over the rim of the depression.

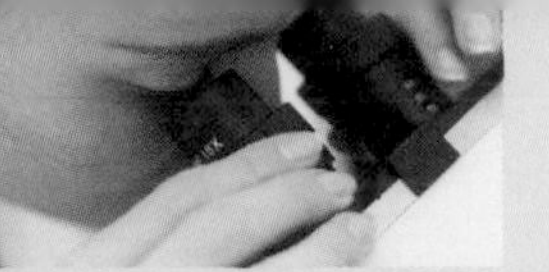

People Behind Biology

Maud Menten (1879–1960)

A fundamental topic covered in almost all introductory biochemistry courses is the Michaelis–Menten equation. First stated in 1913, the equation provides a mathematical description of the kinetics of an enzyme-catalyzed reaction. The equation represents one of the fundamental concepts of biochemistry.

The Menten of the equation refers to Maud Menten, who was born on March 20, 1879, in Port Lambton, Ontario. After completing secondary school, Menten attended the University of Toronto and earned a bachelor of arts degree in 1904, followed by a master's degree in physiology in 1907. In the same year, Menten was appointed a fellow at the Rockefeller Institute for Medical Research in New York City, where she studied the effect of radium bromide on cancerous tumours in rats. Menten and two other scientists published the results of their experiment, producing the institute's first monograph. She returned to Canada and began studies at the University of Toronto a year later. In 1911, she became one of the first Canadian women to receive a doctor of medicine degree.

In 1912, Menten travelled to Germany to work with Leonor Michaelis, a biochemist who shared Menton's interest in understanding enzyme kinetics. After a year of research, the two scientists coauthored a paper that put forward a description of the basis of enzyme-catalyzed chemical kinetics. The paper introduced the Michaelis–Menten equation as a tool for measuring the rates of enzyme reactions. The formula gave scientists a way to record how enzymes worked and is the standard for most enzyme-kinetic measurements. Michaelis and Menten were able to demonstrate that each enzyme, given enough substrate, has its own rate of causing that substrate to undergo chemical change. The Michaelis–Menten equation profoundly changed the study of biochemistry and earned Menten and Michaelis worldwide recognition.

When Menten returned from Berlin, she enrolled at the University of Chicago, where she obtained a Ph.D. in biochemistry in 1916. Unable to find an academic position in her native Canada, in 1918 she joined the medical school faculty at the University of Pittsburgh. While maintaining an active research program, she was also known as an avid mountain climber who went on several expeditions to the Arctic. As well, she spoke numerous languages, loved to paint, and played the clarinet. Over the years, Menten authored more than 70 publications, including discoveries related to blood sugar, hemoglobin, and kidney functions. In so-called retirement, she returned to British Columbia to do research at the British Columbia Medical Research Institute, almost until her death. A plaque commemorating the life and work of Maud Menten is located in the Medical Sciences Building, University of Toronto, Queen's Park.

carbon dioxide and water. However, the reaction proceeds very slowly—the propane in a torch can sit for years and remain unchanged. This is because if left undisturbed, it is a rare event for molecules of propane to acquire the energy needed to reach the transition state. However, if you supply a stream of propane with a spark (see Figure 4.16), then you provide molecules of propane with the energy to reach the transition state, resulting in a tremendous release of free energy into the environment.

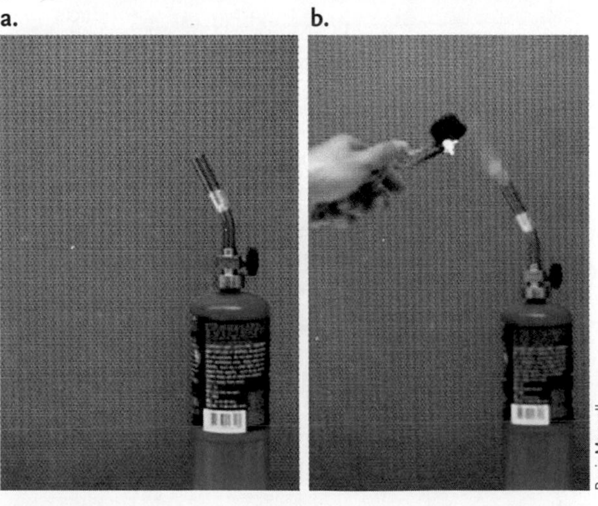

Figure 4.16
Combustion of propane. (a) The combustion of propane is a spontaneous reaction; however, the activation energy is a barrier that makes propane kinetically stable. **(b)** By providing a spark, propane obtains the energy required to attain the transition state.

If you walk through a typical undergraduate chemistry lab, you will often find at least one Bunsen burner that provides the necessary heat to make a range of chemical reactions proceed rapidly. Chemists routinely use heat to provide the energy needed for reactant molecules to get to the transition state and thus speed up the rate of a reaction. In biology, using heat to speed up a reaction is problematic for two reasons: First, high temperatures destroy the structural components of cells, particularly proteins, and can result in cell death. Second, an increase in temperature would speed up all possible chemical reactions in a cell, not just the specific reactions that are part of metabolism.

4.4b Enzymes Accelerate Reactions by Reducing the Activation Energy

So how can you increase the rate of a reaction without raising the temperature? You can use a **catalyst**, which is a chemical agent that speeds up the rate of a reaction without itself taking part in the reaction. The most common biological catalysts is a group of proteins called **enzymes.**

Recall that the activation energy represents a hurdle that a reaction needs to get over in order to proceed spontaneously. This activation energy represents a real *kinetic* barrier that prevents spontaneous reactions from proceeding quickly. The greater the activation energy barrier, the slower the reaction will proceed. Enzymes increase the rate of a reaction by lowering this barrier—by lowering the activation energy of the reaction **(Figure 4.17).** Since the rate of a reaction will be proportional to the number of reactant molecules that can acquire the necessary energy to get to the transition state, enzymes make it possible for a greater proportion of reactant molecules to attain the activation energy.

An important point that is shown in Figure 4.17 is that although enzymes lower the activation energy of a reaction, they do not alter the change in free energy (ΔG) of the reaction. The free energy of the reactants and products is the same; the only difference is the path the reaction takes.

Since it is often a point of confusion, it is important at this juncture to review what enzymes do and do not do with regard to biological reactions. By lowering the activation energy, enzymes DO speed up the rate of spontaneous (exergonic) reactions. However, enzymes DO NOT supply free energy to a reaction. Therefore, enzymes CANNOT make an endergonic reaction proceed spontaneously. ATP hydrolysis can be used to make an endergonic reaction proceed spontaneously, but alone, an enzyme cannot. Lastly, enzymes DO NOT change the ΔG of a reaction.

4.4c Enzymes Combine with Reactants and Are Released Unchanged

In enzymatic reactions, an enzyme combines briefly with reacting molecules and is released unchanged when the reaction is complete. For example, the enzyme in **Figure 4.18,** hexokinase, catalyzes the following reaction:

$$\text{glucose} + \text{ATP} \xrightarrow{\text{hexokinase}} \text{glucose 6-phosphate} + \text{ADP}$$

The reactant that an enzyme acts on is called the enzyme's substrate, or substrates if the enzyme binds two or more molecules. Each type of enzyme catalyzes the reaction of only a single type of molecule or a group of closely related molecules. This *enzyme specificity* explains why a typical cell needs about 4000 different enzymes to function properly. Looking at Figure 4.17, notice that the enzyme is much larger than the size of the substrate. As well, the substrate interacts with only a very small region of the enzyme called the **active site**, the place on the enzyme where catalysis occurs. The active site is usually a pocket or groove that is formed when the newly synthesized enzyme (which is a protein) folds into its correct shape.

In the early twentieth century, biochemists proposed the *lock-and-key hypothesis* to explain the

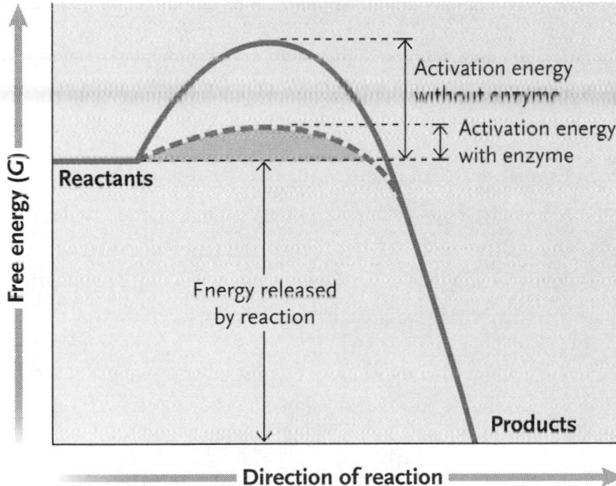

Figure 4.17
Enzymes lower the activation energy of a reaction. The reduction allows biological reactions to proceed rapidly at the relatively low temperatures that can be tolerated by living organisms. As you can see, enzymes do not change the free energy of the reactants or products, and thus do not change the overall ΔG.

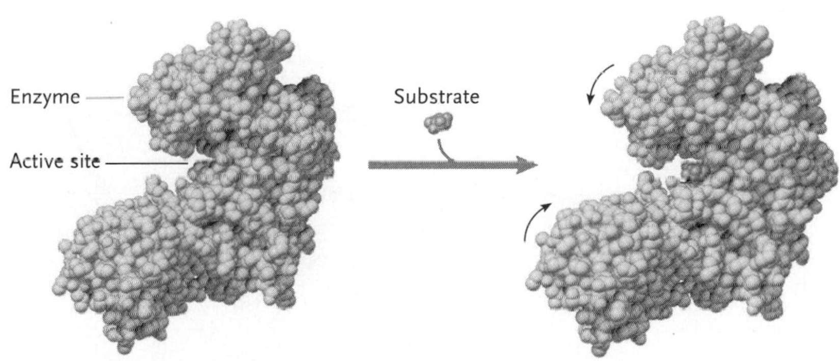

Figure 4.18
Space-filling models showing the combination of an enzyme, hexokinase (in blue), with its substrate, glucose (in yellow). Hexokinase catalyzes the phosphorylation of glucose to form glucose 6-phosphate. The phosphate group that enters the reaction is not shown. Note how the enzyme undergoes a conformational change, closing the active site more tightly as it binds the substrate.

specificity of the substrate–enzyme interaction. The analogy worked well to explain how even somewhat similar substrates (keys) were unable to bind to the same enzyme (lock) to cause catalysis (unlocking of the door). However, more recently, this hypothesis has been superseded by what has become known as the *induced-fit hypothesis*. Research has shown that enzymes are not rigid objects (like locks) but instead are flexible; just prior to substrate binding, the enzyme changes its shape, or what we call its *conformation*, so that the active site becomes even more precise in its ability to bind substrate. This is shown in Figure 4.18 where the conformation of the enzyme changes slightly when it binds to substrate.

As shown in **Figure 4.19,** the enzyme binds to substrate, forming an enzyme–substrate complex. Catalysis occurs when the two are joined, with the action of the enzyme converting the substrate (or substrates) into one or more products. Because enzymes are released unchanged after a reaction, enzyme molecules can rapidly bind to other substrate molecules, catalyzing the same reaction again, repeating what is called the enzyme cycle (see Figure 4.19). The rate at which enzymes catalyze reactions varies depending on the specifics of the enzyme and substrates involved, but typical rates vary between about 100 and 10 million substrate molecules per second.

Many enzymes require a *cofactor*, a nonprotein group that binds very precisely to the enzyme. Cofactors are often metals such as iron, copper, zinc, and manganese. Although your body often needs very small amounts of some of these metals, they are absolutely essential for the catalytic activity of the enzyme to which they bind. Organic cofactors called *coenzymes* play similar roles and are often derived from vitamins.

The disaccharide lactose

Glucose

Galactose

1 The substrate, lactose, binds to the enzyme β-galactosidase, forming an enzyme–substrate complex. Transition state is reached—tightest binding but least stable

β-Galactosidase

Active site

Glucose Galactose

H_2O

3 Enzyme can catalyze another reaction.

2 β-Galactosidase catalyzes the breakage of the bond between the two sugars of lactose, and the products are released.

Figure 4.19
The catalytic cycle of an enzyme. Shown is the enzyme β-galactosidase, which cleaves the sugar lactose to produce glucose and galactose.

4.4d Enzymes Reduce the Activation Energy by Inducing the Transition State

A central question of enzyme function is *how do they actually reduce the activation energy of a reaction?* Recall that substrate molecules need to be in the transition state for catalysis to occur. Enzymes function by increasing the number of reactant molecules that acquire the transition state conformation. Research has shown that enzymes can achieve this through three major mechanisms **(Figure 4.20):**

1. *Bringing the reacting molecules together.* Reacting molecules can assume the transition state only when they collide; binding to an enzyme's active site brings the reactants together in the right orientation for catalysis to occur.

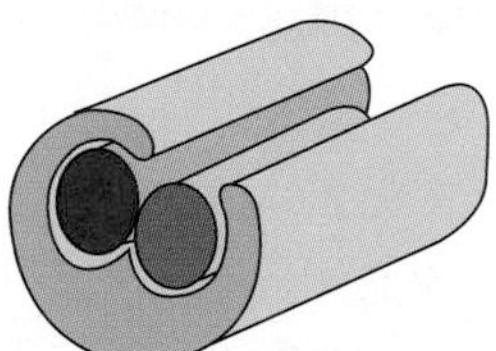

Bring reacting molecules close together

2. *Exposing the reactant molecule to altered charge environments that promote catalysis.* In some systems, the active site of the enzyme may contain ionic groups whose positive or negative charges alter the substrate in a way that favours catalysis.

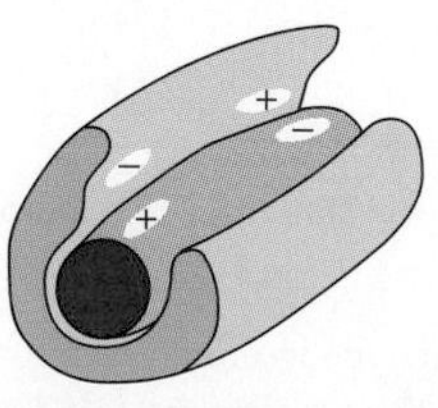

Charge interactions

Figure 4.20
The binding of substrate(s) to an active site results in the substrate acquiring the transition state conformation.

(continued)

3. *Changing the shape of a substrate molecule.* The active site may strain or distort substrate molecules into a conformation that mimics the transition state.

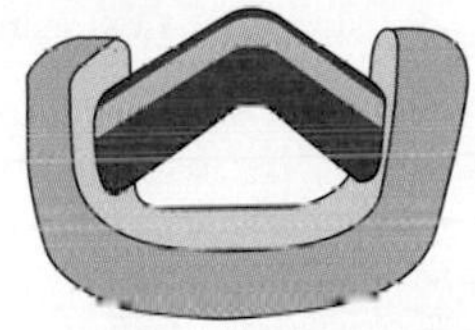

Distort or strain substrate molecules

Regardless of the mechanism, the binding of the substrate to the active site results in the substrate attaining the transition state conformation. Although without the enzyme, substrate molecules do acquire the transition state, this may be a rare event. The inclusion of an enzyme enables many more molecules to reach the transition state more rapidly. This is fundamentally why enzymes speed up the rate of a reaction.

Study Break

1. How do enzymes increase the rate of a chemical reaction?
2. Can enzymes alter the ΔG of a chemical reaction?

4.5 Conditions and Factors that Affect Enzyme Activity

Several conditions can alter enzyme activity, including changes in the concentration of substrate and other molecules that bind to enzymes. In addition, a number of control mechanisms modify enzyme activity, thereby adjusting reaction rates to meet a cell's requirements for chemical products. As well, changes in temperature and pH can have a significant impact on enzyme activity.

4.5a The Influence of Enzyme and Substrate Concentrations on the Rate of Catalysis

Biochemists use a wide range of approaches to study enzymes. These include molecular tools to study the structure and regulation of the gene that encodes the enzyme to using sophisticated computer programs to model the three-dimensional structure of the enzyme itself. The most fundamental and central approach has been to determine the rate of an enzyme catalyzed reaction and how it changes in response to altering certain experimental parameters. This usually requires isolating the enzyme from the remainder of the cell, incubating it in an appropriate buffered solution and supplying the reaction mixture with substrate. With these constituents, one can then determine the rate of catalysis by measuring the rate at which the product of the reaction is formed.

As shown in **Figure 4.21a,** in the presence of excess substrate, the rate of catalysis will be proportional to the amount of enzyme. That is, as enzyme concentration increases, the rate of product formation increases. In this system (see Figure 4.21a), what is limiting the rate of the reaction (the rate-limiting component) is the amount of enzyme in the reaction mixture. Now what happens to the rate of the reaction if we keep the amount of enzyme constant at some intermediate concentration and change the substrate concentration from low to high? As shown in **Figure 4.21b,** at very low concentrations, substrate molecules collide so infrequently with enzyme molecules that the reaction proceeds slowly. As the substrate concentration increases, the reaction rate initially increases as enzyme and substrate molecules collide more frequently. But as the enzyme molecules approach the maximum rate at which they can combine with reactants and release products, increasing substrate concentration has a smaller and smaller effect, and the rate of reaction eventually levels off. When the enzymes are cycling as rapidly as possible, further increases in substrate concentration have no effect on the reaction rate. At this point, the enzymes are said to be *saturated* with substrate.

a.

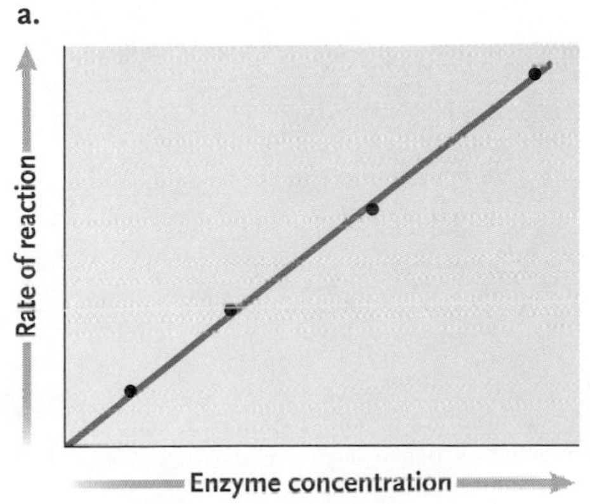

b.

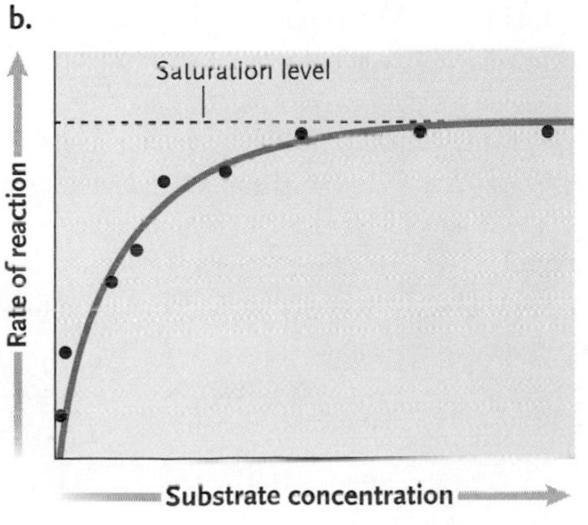

Figure 4.21
Changes in substrate concentration and enzyme concentration alter the rate of reaction. **(a)** The rate of reaction (usually measured as the rate of product formation) as a function of increasing enzyme concentration. The concentration of substrate is kept very high. **(b)** The rate of reaction as a function of increasing substrate concentration. The amount of enzyme is kept constant.

4.5b Enzyme Inhibitors Have Characteristic Effects on Enzyme Activity

The rate at which an enzyme can catalyze a reaction can be lowered by *enzyme inhibitors,* molecules that bind to an enzyme and decrease its activity. Some inhibitors work by binding to the active site of an enzyme, whereas other inhibitors bind to critical sites located elsewhere in the structure of the enzyme.

Inhibitors that combine with the active site have shapes that resemble the normal substrate closely enough to fit into and occupy the active site, thereby blocking access for the normal substrate and slowing the reaction rate. If the concentration of the inhibitor is high enough, the reaction may stop completely. Inhibition of this type is called **competitive inhibition** because the inhibitor *competes* with the normal substrate for access to the active site of the enzyme **(Figure 4.22a).**

In **noncompetitive inhibition,** specific molecules inhibit enzyme activity, but they do not compete with substrate molecules for binding to the active site **(Figure 4.22b).** Instead, noncompetitive inhibitors bind to an enzyme at a location other than the active site. This binding often results in a change to the conformation of the enzyme that reduces the ability of the active site to efficiently bind substrate.

Inhibitors differ with respect to how strongly they bind to enzymes. In reversible inhibition, the binding

a. Competitive inhibition

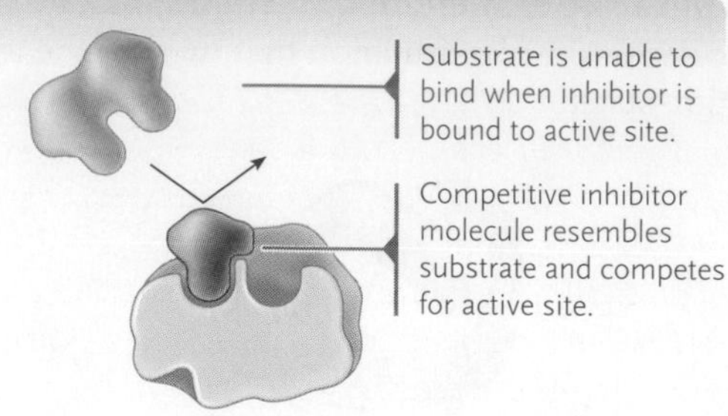

Substrate is unable to bind when inhibitor is bound to active site.
Competitive inhibitor molecule resembles substrate and competes for active site.

b. Noncompetitive inhibition

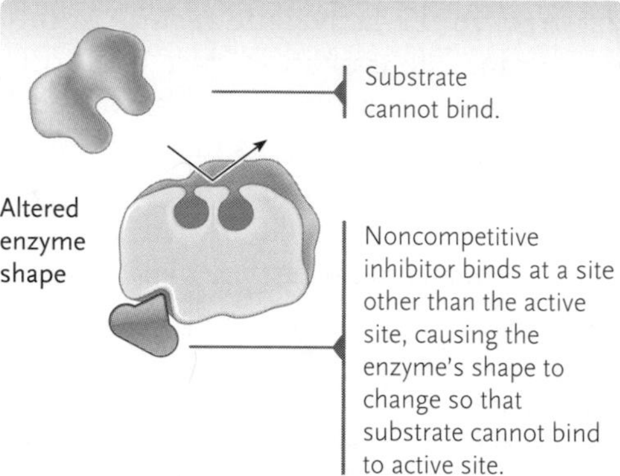

Substrate cannot bind.
Altered enzyme shape
Noncompetitive inhibitor binds at a site other than the active site, causing the enzyme's shape to change so that substrate cannot bind to active site.

Figure 4.22
Actions of **(a)** competitive and **(b)** noncompetitive inhibitors of enzyme activity.

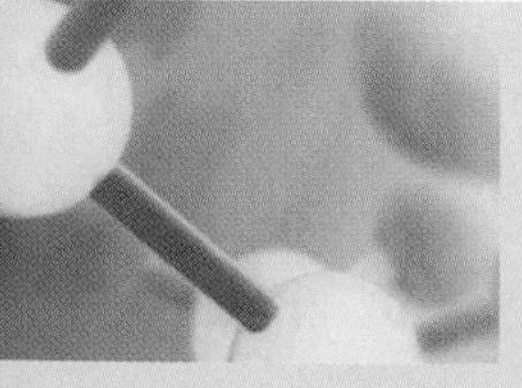

MOLECULE BEHIND BIOLOGY

Penicillin: A Competitive Inhibitor of Enzyme Action

Penicillin is an antibiotic that is used in the treatment of bacterial infections. It was first discovered by Alexander Fleming, who isolated it from the mould *Penicillium* after he accidently found that the presence of the mould inhibited the growth of bacteria on a Petri plate. Following the development of methods for its mass production, penicillin was a true wonder drug as it was effective in treating a wide range of bacterial infections that in the past often led to death.

Penicillin acts by inhibiting the synthesis of peptidoglycan, a key component of the bacterial cell wall. Peptidoglycan is a complex polymer consisting of sugars and amino acids that forms a meshlike structure outside the plasma membrane. As such, peptidoglycan provides structural strength and protects the bacterial cell from osmotic changes that would otherwise cause the cell to burst. If a bacterium is unable to synthesize components necessary for its cell wall, it is unable to grow and divide.

A key factor that is required for the synthesis of peptidoglycan is the enzyme transpeptidase, which catalyzes the formation of a peptide bond between two amino acids, which effectively links two portions of the peptidogylcan together. Penicillin inhibits peptidoglycan synthesis because it is a competitive inhibitor of transpeptidase activity. The structure of penicillin mimics that of the two amino acids, which normally are brought together by the active site. Penicillin binds irreversibly to the active site of transpeptidase, effectively destroying the molecule. Given the concentrations of penicillin usually administered to a patient, this leads to total inhibition of all transpeptidase activity.

Although penicillin was widely employed in the 1950s and 1960s, most infections today involve bacteria that have acquired resistance to the drug. New antibiotics are constantly being developed to try to stop the growing problem of antibiotic-resistant bacteria.

of inhibitors to the enzyme is weak and readily reversible, with the enzyme activity returning to normal following inhibitor release. By contrast, some inhibitors bind so strongly to the enzyme through the formation of covalent bonds that the enzyme is completely disabled. This is called irreversible inhibition. Not surprisingly, many irreversible inhibitors that act on critical enzymes are highly toxic to the cell. This includes a wide variety of drugs and pesticides. Cyanide is a potent poison because it binds strongly to and inhibits cytochrome oxidase, the enzyme that catalyzes the last step of respiratory electron transport. In addition, many antibiotics are toxins that inhibit enzyme activity in bacteria (see *Molecule Behind Biology*). Irreversible inhibition can be overcome only by the cell synthesizing more of the enzyme.

4.5c Allosteric Control of Enzyme Activity

Many cellular metabolites act as reversible inhibitors of enzyme activity and should not be considered detrimental to cell function but rather as an important mechanism of metabolic regulation. A typical cell contains thousands of enzymes, and for many enzymes that synthesize a specific molecule, usually another enzyme exists that catalyzes its breakdown. If both enzymes were active in the same cell compartment at the same time, the result would be what is called futile cycling. A futile cycle occurs when two metabolic pathways run simultaneously in opposite directions and have no overall effect other than wasting energy. To prevent this, the cell is able to regulate enzyme activity in such a way that not all enzymes are active at the same time. Many enzymes are regulated by natural inhibitors, including inhibitors that work either competitively or noncompetitively. Typically, the combination between these inhibitors and the enzyme is fully reversible. If the concentration of the inhibitor increases, it combines with the enzymes in greater numbers, thereby interfering with enzyme activity and decreasing the rate of the reaction. If the concentration of the inhibitor decreases, its combination with enzymes decreases proportionately, and the rate of the reaction increases. Control by the inhibitors changes enzyme activity precisely to meet the needs of the cell for the products of the reaction catalyzed by the enzyme.

In the mechanism of **allosteric regulation (Figure 4.23)**, enzyme activity is controlled by the reversible

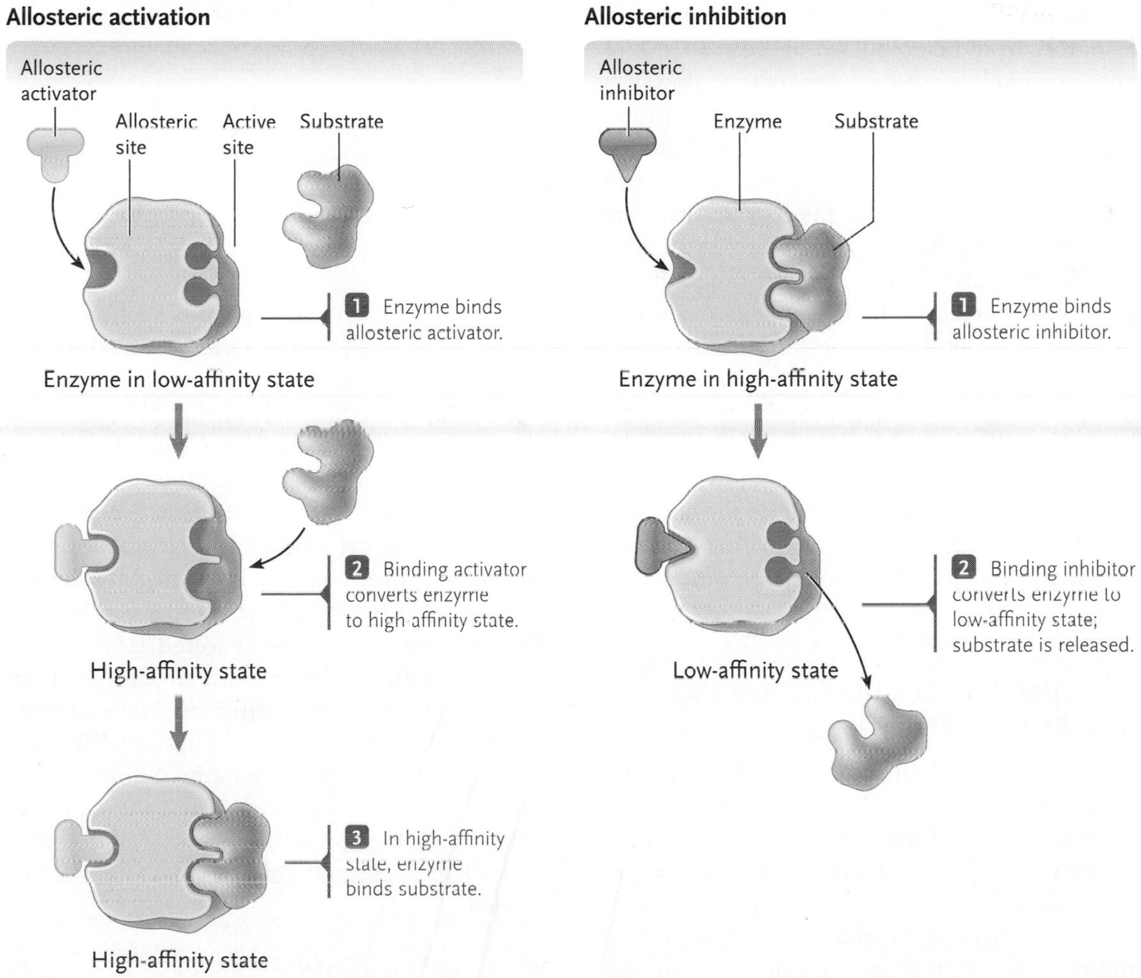

Figure 4.23
Allosteric regulation.

binding of a regulatory molecule to the *allosteric site*, a location on the enzyme outside the active site. The mechanism of control may either increase or decrease enzyme activity. Because allosteric inhibitors work by binding to sites separate from the active site, their action is *noncompetitive*. Enzymes controlled by allosteric regulation typically have two alternate conformations controlled from the allosteric site. In one conformation, called the high-affinity state (the active form), the enzyme binds strongly to its substrate; in the other conformation, the low-affinity state (the inactive form), the enzyme binds the substrate weakly or not at all. Binding with regulatory substances may induce either state: binding an allosteric inhibitor converts an allosteric enzyme from the high- to the low-affinity state, and binding an allosteric activator converts it from the low- to the high-affinity state (see Figure 4.23).

Frequently, allosteric inhibitors are a product of the metabolic pathway that they regulate. If the product accumulates in excess, its effect as an inhibitor automatically slows or stops the enzymatic reaction producing it, typically by inhibiting the enzyme catalyzing the first reaction of the pathway. If the product becomes too scarce, the inhibition is reduced, and its production increases. Regulation of this type, in which the product of a reaction acts as a regulator of the reaction, is termed **feedback inhibition.** Feedback inhibition prevents cellular resources from being wasted in the synthesis of molecules made at intermediate steps of the pathway.

The biochemical pathway that makes the amino acid isoleucine from threonine is an excellent example of feedback inhibition. The pathway proceeds in five steps, each catalyzed by an enzyme **(Figure 4.24).** The end product of the pathway, isoleucine, is an allosteric inhibitor of the first enzyme of the pathway, threonine deaminase. If the cell makes more isoleucine than it needs, isoleucine combines reversibly with threonine deaminase at the allosteric site, converting the enzyme to the low-affinity state and inhibiting its ability to combine with threonine, the substrate for the first reaction in the pathway. If isoleucine levels drop too low, the allosteric site of threonine deaminase is vacated, the enzyme is converted to the high-affinity state, and isoleucine production increases.

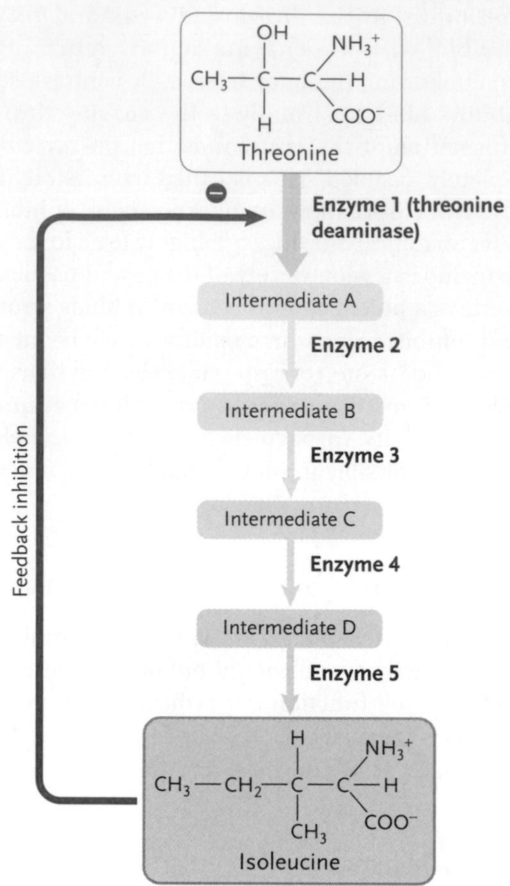

Figure 4.24
Feedback inhibition in the pathway that produces isoleucine from threonine. If the product of the pathway, isoleucine, accumulates in excess, it slows or stops the pathway by acting as an allosteric inhibitor of the enzyme that catalyzes the first step in the pathway.

4.5d Temperature and pH Are Key Factors Affecting Enzyme Activity

The activity of most enzymes is strongly altered by changes in pH and temperature. Characteristically, enzymes reach maximal activity within a narrow range of temperature or pH; at levels outside this range, enzyme activity drops off. These effects produce a typically peaked curve when enzyme activity is plotted, with the peak where temperature or pH produces maximal activity.

Effects of pH Changes. Typically, each enzyme has an optimal pH where it operates at peak efficiency in speeding the rate of its biochemical reaction **(Figure 4.25).** On either side of this pH optimum, the rate of the catalyzed reaction decreases because of the resulting alterations in charged groups. The effects on the structure and function of the active site become more extreme at pH values farther from the optimum, until the rate drops to zero. Most enzymes have a pH optimum near the pH of the cellular contents, about pH 7. Enzymes that are secreted from cells may have pH optima farther from neutrality. An example is pepsin, a protein-digesting enzyme secreted into the stomach. This enzyme's pH optimum is 1.5, close to the acidity of stomach contents. Similarly, trypsin, also a protein-digesting enzyme, has a pH optimum at about pH 8, allowing it to function well in the somewhat alkaline contents of the intestine, where it is secreted.

Effects of Temperature Changes. The effects of temperature changes on enzyme activity reflect two

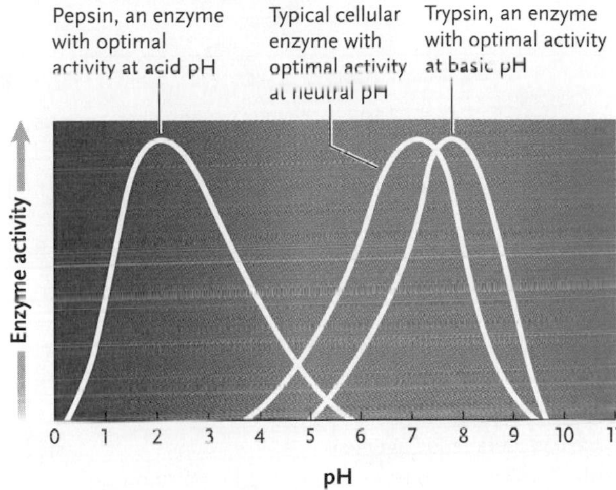

Figure 4.25
Effects of pH on enzyme activity. An enzyme typically has an optimal pH at which it is most active; at pH values above or below the optimum, the rate of enzyme activity drops off. At extreme pH values, the rate drops to zero.

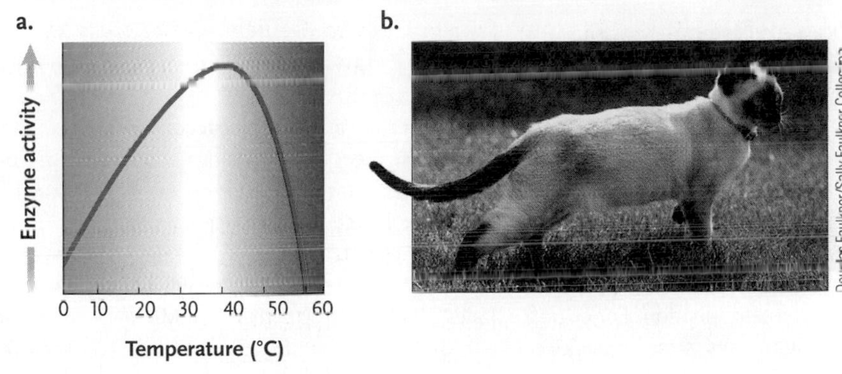

Figure 4.26
Effect of temperature on enzyme activity. **(a)** As the temperature rises, the rate of the catalyzed reaction increases proportionally until the temperature reaches the point at which the enzyme begins to denature. The rate drops off steeply as denaturation progresses and becomes complete. **(b)** Visible effects of environmental temperature on enzyme activity in Siamese cats. The fur on the extremities—ears, nose, paws, and tail—contains more dark brown pigment (melanin) than the rest of the body. A heat-sensitive enzyme controlling melanin production is denatured in warmer body regions, so dark pigment is not produced, but fur colour is.

distinct processes. First, temperature has a general effect on chemical reactions of all kinds. As the temperature rises, the rate of chemical reactions typically increases. This effect reflects increases in the kinetic motion of all molecules, with more frequent and stronger collisions as the temperature rises. Second, temperature has an effect on all proteins, including enzymes. As the temperature rises, the kinetic motions of the amino acid chains of an enzyme increase, along with the strength and frequency of collisions between enzymes and surrounding molecules. At some point, these disturbances become strong enough to denature the enzyme: the hydrogen bonds and other forces that maintain its three-dimensional structure break, making the enzyme unfold and lose its function. The two effects of temperature act in opposition to each other to produce characteristic changes in the rate of enzymatic catalysis **(Figure 4.26)**. In the range of 0° to about 40°C, the reaction rate doubles for every 10°C increase in temperature. Above 40°C, the increasing kinetic motion begins to denature the enzyme, reducing the rate of increase in enzyme activity. At some point, as the temperature rises, the denaturation of the enzyme causes the reaction rate to level off at a peak. Further increases cause such extensive unfolding that the reaction rate decreases rapidly to zero.

For most enzymes, the peak in activity lies between 40° and 50°C; the dropoff becomes steep at 55°C and falls to zero at about 60°C. Thus, the rate of an enzyme-catalyzed reaction peaks at a temperature at which kinetic motion is greatest, but no significant unfolding of the enzyme has occurred. Although most enzymes have a temperature optimum between 40° and 50°C, some have activity peaks below or above this range. For example, the enzymes of maize (corn) pollen function best near 30°C and undergo steep reductions in activity above 32°C. As a result, environmental temperatures above 32°C can seriously inhibit the growth of corn crops. Many animals living in frigid regions have enzymes with much lower temperature optima than average. For example, the enzymes of arctic snow fleas are most active at 10°C. At the other extreme are the enzymes of archaeans that live in hot springs, which are so resistant to denaturation that they remain active at temperatures of 85°C or more.

Study Break

1. Why do enzyme-catalyzed reactions reach a saturation level when substrate concentration is increased?
2. Distinguish between competitive and noncompetitive inhibition.
3. Explain why the activity of an enzyme will eventually decrease to zero as the temperature rises.

Unanswered Questions

Many biological processes rely on enzymes to catalyze key reactions. A complete understanding of those processes requires knowledge about the structure and function of the enzymes involved. Much research continues to be done to elucidate enzyme structure and function.

How does protein structure relate to enzyme function?

Many researchers are studying protein structure and its relation to protein function. For example, Janet Smith at the University of Michigan uses X-ray crystallography to determine the structures of proteins. The patterns of diffraction of X-rays shone at a protein crystal give information about how the protein's atoms are organized. The crystal structure is "solved" once a model for the protein's structure is achieved in this way.

Smith's group uses information about the structure of solved proteins to predict the functions of other proteins. Even though it is possible to solve protein structures rapidly, it is not practical to solve the structures of all proteins involved in important biological processes. Instead, Smith, as well as other researchers, draws on the current understanding of the evolution of proteins. In particular, genes for useful proteins often have been duplicated during evolution and the duplicate copy adapted to a new function. Therefore, proteins can be related in an evolutionary sense. An understanding of the molecular mechanisms of particular enzymes may then be transferrable to other proteins, which is an underlying theme of Smith's research.

How does ribozyme structure relate to function, and how might ribozymes be used as therapeutic agents?

Ribozymes are catalytic ribonucleic acid (RNA) molecules. Various types of ribozymes exist, each type differing in its three-dimensional structure and mechanism of catalysis.

Researcher John Burke at the University of Vermont and his group are studying hairpin ribozymes and hammerhead ribozymes, which are catalytically active once they fold into those two shapes (the hammerhead shape is similar to that of the head of a hammerhead shark). Their research has four directions: determining the molecular structure of ribozymes, characterizing RNA conformational changes during catalysis, elucidating the mechanisms of catalysis, and exploring ways to use ribozymes as therapeutic agents.

For example, Burke's group has shown that the hairpin ribozyme undergoes a dramatic conformational change when the substrate binds to the active site. Furthermore, they have engineered hairpin ribozymes that can inhibit viral replication in mammalian cells. The particular viruses targeted have RNA genomes and include human immunodeficiency virus 1 (HIV-1, the causative agent of acquired immune deficiency syndrome [AIDS]) and hepatitis B virus. To achieve their goal, they had to identify appropriate target sites within the viral RNA molecules and to express the engineered ribozymes efficiently within the cell. Current research focuses on optimizing the inhibition of viral replication by the ribozymes, determining the mechanism of antiviral activity, and extending this technology to develop therapeutic approaches for significant infectious diseases such as AIDS and hepatitis B.

Review

Go to CENGAGENOW™ at http://hed.nelson.com/ to access quizzing, animations, exercises, articles, and personalized homework help.

4.1 Energy and the Laws of Thermodynamics

- Energy is the capacity to do work. Kinetic energy is the energy of motion; potential energy is the energy stored in an object because of its location or chemical structure.
- Thermodynamics is the study of energy flow between a system and its surroundings during chemical and physical reactions. A system that exchanges energy but not matter with its surroundings is a closed system. A system that exchanges both energy and matter with its surroundings is an open system (see Figure 4.1). A system that does not exchange energy or matter with its surroundings is said to be an isolated system.
- The first law of thermodynamics states that the total amount of energy in a system and its surroundings remains constant (see Figure 4.2). The second law states that in any process involving a spontaneous (possible) change from an initial to a final state, the total entropy (disorder) of the system and its surroundings always increases (see Figure 4.3).
- Life is highly ordered, which suggests that it goes against the second law of thermodynamics. However, the high order of living things comes about because organisms are open systems and take in energy from their surroundings. In the process of living, organisms release heat and more simple molecules that increase the disorder of the surroundings (see Figures 4.4 and 4.5).

4.2 Free Energy and Spontaneous Reactions

- A spontaneous reaction is one that will occur without an input of energy from the surroundings. A spontaneous reaction releases free energy—energy that is available to do work.
- The free energy equation, $\Delta G = \Delta H - T\Delta S$, states that the free energy change, ΔG, is influenced by two factors: the changes in energy content and entropy of the system as a reaction goes to completion.
- Systems with high free energy are unstable and will spontaneously move to a more stable state (see Figure 4.8).
- Factors that oppose the completion of spontaneous reactions, such as the relative concentrations of reactants and products, produce an equilibrium point at which reactants are converted to products and products are converted back to reactants, at equal rates (see Figure 4.9).
- Organisms reach equilibrium ($\Delta G = 0$) only when they die.
- Reactions with a negative ΔG are spontaneous; they release free energy and are known as exergonic reactions. Reactions with a positive ΔG require free energy and are known as endergonic reactions (see Figure 4.10).

4.3 The Energy Currency of the Cell: ATP

- The hydrolysis of ATP releases free energy that can be used as a source of energy for the cell (see Figure 4.12).

- A cell can couple the exergonic reaction of ATP hydrolysis to make an otherwise endergonic (anabolic) reaction proceed spontaneously. These coupling reactions require enzymes (see Figure 4.13).
- The ATP used in coupling reactions is replenished by reactions that link ATP synthesis to catabolic reactions. ATP thus cycles between reactions that release free energy and reactions that require free energy (see Figure 4.14).

4.4 The Role of Enzymes in Biological Reactions

- What prevents many exergonic reactions from proceeding rapidly is that they need to overcome an energy barrier (the activation energy) to get to the transition state (see Figure 4.15).
- Enzymes are catalysts that greatly speed the rate at which spontaneous reactions occur because they lower the activation energy (see Figure 4.17).
- Catalysis occurs at the site of substrate binding, which is referred to as the active site of the enzyme (see Figure 4.18). Enzymes usually are specific: they catalyze reactions of only a single type of molecule or a group of closely related molecules.
- The active site of an enzyme combines briefly with the reactants (the substrates); the enzyme is released unchanged when the reaction is complete (see Figure 4.19)
- Many enzymes include a cofactor, which is an inorganic ion or an organic nonprotein group called a coenzyme that is necessary for catalysis to occur.
- Enzymes reduce the activation energy by inducing the transition state of the reaction, from which the reaction can move easily in the direction of either products or reactants.
- Several mechanisms contribute to enzymatic catalysis by helping to induce the transition state. They include bringing the reactant molecules into close proximity, orienting the reactants in positions that favour the transition state, and exposing the reactants to altered environments that promote their interaction (see Figure 4.20).

4.5 Conditions and Factors that Affect Enzyme Activity

- At high substrate concentrations, enzymes become saturated with reactants, and further increases in substrate concentration do not increase the rate of the reaction (see Figure 4.21).
- Enzymes may be inhibited by nonsubstrate molecules. Competitive inhibitors interfere with reaction rates by combining with the active site of an enzyme; noncompetitive inhibitors combine with sites elsewhere on the enzyme (see Figure 4.22).
- Many cellular enzymes are regulated by inhibitors. A special type of regulation, allosteric regulation, resembles noncompetitive inhibition, except that regulatory molecules may either increase or decrease enzyme activity (see Figure 4.23). Allosteric regulation often carries out feedback inhibition, in which a product of an enzyme-catalyzed pathway acts as an allosteric inhibitor of the first enzyme in the pathway (see Figure 4.24).
- Typically, enzymes have optimal activity at a certain temperature and a certain pH; at temperature and pH values above and below the optimum, reaction rates fall off (see Figures 4.25 and 4.26).

Questions

Self-Test Questions

1. Which of the following statements about energy and thermodynamics is correct?
   a. Energy conversions can never be 100% efficient.
   b. All living organisms are open systems.
   c. Earth can be considered a closed system.
   d. The total amount of energy in the universe is constant.
   e. All of the above are correct.
2. Which of the following statements about entropy is NOT correct?
   a. Entropy is a thermodynamic measure of disorder or randomness.
   b. The entropy of a system plus the surroundings always increases.
   c. By consuming food, humans can maintain low entropy.
   d. Entropy increases as a substance changes from a liquid into a solid.
   e. An increase in entropy is the reason why energy transformations are never 100% efficient.
3. For a reaction to be exergonic,
   a. it must also be exothermic.
   b. the entropy of the products must be greater than the reactants.
   c. the products must have less enthalpy than the reactants.
   d. the free energy of the products must be less than the reactants.
   e. the reaction required an input of energy to proceed.
4. Which of the following statements is correct?
   a. Molecules that have high free energy are very stable.
   b. An isolated system will never reach equilibrium.
   c. At equilibrium, the ΔG is negative.
   d. Living organisms are never at equilibrium.
   e. Most biochemical reactions have a ΔG far from zero.
5. Within a cell, the hydrolysis of ATP in a biochemical reaction
   a. produces more heat than if ATP is simply hydrolyzed in a beaker of water.
   b. can occur only in the absence of an enzyme.
   c. is required only for exergonic reactions, which do not proceed spontaneously.
   d. results in transfer of a phosphate group to a substrate, making it unstable.
   e. None of the above are correct.
6. Although propane is thermodynamically unstable, the reason that it is kinetically stable is because
   a. it contains an abundance of oxygen and little hydrogen.
   b. its breakdown is exergonic ($-\Delta G$).
   c. it has a high activation energy (E_A).
   d. it is highly electronegative.
   e. All of the above are correct.
7. An enzyme
   a. is a protein and therefore is encoded by a gene.
   b. can make an endergonic reaction proceed spontaneously.
   c. lowers the ΔG of an endergonic reaction.
   d. increases the probability that reactant molecules will reach the transition state.
   e. Only a and d are correct.
8. Unlike competitive inhibition, the noncompetitive inhibition of an enzyme-catalzyed reaction
   a. inhibits substrate binding to the active site.
   b. is due to molecules that are structurally very similar to molecules of substrate
   c. changes the conformation of the enzyme.
   d. results in the enzyme becoming permanently inactive.
   e. requires the hydrolysis of ATP.

9. Which of the following statements about allosteric enzymes is correct?
   a. The allosteric site of the enzyme binds additional substrate molecules.
   b. An allosteric activator prevents binding at the active site.
   c. An enzyme that possesses allosteric sites does not possess an active site.
   d. Their activity can be finely controlled by metabolites within the cell.
   e. None of the above are correct.
10. What explains the shape of a curve that plots the enzyme activity as a function of temperature?
    a. At high temperatures, the rate of catalysis stays high and constant—it saturates.
    b. As the temperature is low but increasing, the rate of collisions between substrate and enzyme molecules increases.
    c. At high temperatures, the structural integrity of the enzyme breaks down.
    d. As the temperature increases, the rate of all reactions slows down.
    e. Both b and c are correct.

Questions for Discussion

1. Trees become more complex as they develop spontaneously from seeds to adults. Does this process violate the second law of thermodynamics? Why or why not?
2. Trace the flow of energy through your body. What products increase the entropy of you and your surroundings?
3. You have found a molecular substance that accelerates the rate of a particular reaction. What kind of information would you need to demonstrate that this molecular substance is an enzyme?
4. The addition or removal of phosphate groups from ATP is a fully reversible reaction. In what way does this reversibility facilitate the use of ATP as a coupling agent for cellular reactions?
5. Researchers once hypothesized that an enzyme and its substrate fit together like a lock and key but that the products do not fit the enzyme. Criticize this idea with respect to reversible reactions.

The cystic fibrosis transmembrane conductance regulator is a chloride pump. Mutations to the CFTR gene result in the pump being defective, causing cystic fibrosis.

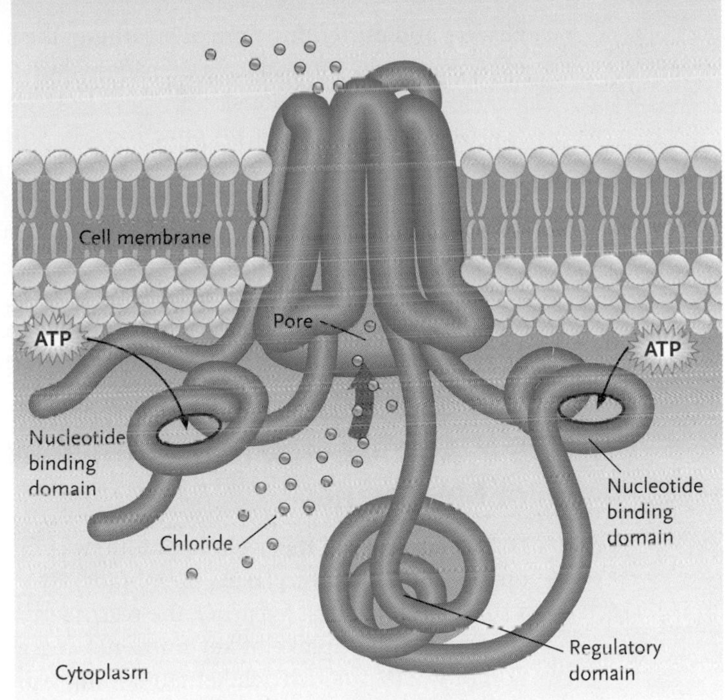

Study Plan

5 Membranes and Transport

Why It Matters

Cystic fibrosis (CF) is one of the most common genetic diseases. It affects approximately 1 in 3900 children born in Canada. People with CF suffer from a progressive impairment of lung and gastrointestinal function. Although the treatment of CF patients is slowly improving, their average life span remains under 40 years.

CF is caused by mutations to a single gene that codes for a protein called the cystic fibrosis transmembrane conductance regulator (CFTR). In normal cells, CFTR acts as a membrane transport protein that pumps chloride (Cl^-, negatively charged) out of the cells that line the lungs and intestinal tract into the covering mucus lining. This results in an electrical gradient across the membrane and leads to the movement of (positively charged) sodium ions in the same direction as the chloride. Because of the high ion concentration (Na^+ and Cl^-), water moves, by osmosis, out into the mucus lining keeping it moist. Keeping the lining of the lungs and intestinal tract wet is critical to their proper functioning. In individuals with CF, the Cl^- channel CFTR does not function properly, which results in water being retained within cells, resulting in a buildup of thick mucus that cannot effectively be removed by coughing. Besides obstructing airways and preventing normal breathing, the buildup of mucus in the lungs makes CF patients very susceptible to bacterial infections.

Currently, there is no cure for CF, with lung transplantation being a common procedure as the disease progresses. Since CF is caused by a defect to a single gene, the greatest hope is in gene therapy (see Chapter 10) that would attempt to insert normal copies of the CFTR gene into affected cells. However, many technical hurdles need to be overcome before gene therapy becomes a viable treatment option.

5.1 An Overview of the Structure of Membranes

One of the keys to the evolution of life was the development of the cell or **plasma membrane.** By acting as a selectively permeable barrier, the plasma membrane allowed for the uptake of key nutrients and elimination of waste products while maintaining a protected environment in which metabolic processes can occur. The subsequent development of internal membranes allowed for compartmentalization of processes and increased complexity. A good example of this is the nuclear envelope, which defines the hallmark of the eukaryotic cell, the nucleus.

5.1a The Fluid Mosaic Model of Membranes

Our current view of membrane structure is based on the **fluid mosaic model (Figure 5.1)**. The model proposes that membranes are not rigid with molecules locked into place but rather consist of fluid lipid molecules in which proteins are embedded and float freely.

The lipid molecules of all biological membranes exist in a double layer, called a bilayer that is less than 10 nanometres (nm) thick. By comparison, this page is approximately 100 000 nm thick. The lipid molecules of the bilayer vibrate, flex back and forth, spin around their long axis, move sideways, and exchange places within the same bilayer half. Only rarely does a lipid molecule flip-flop between the two layers. Exchanging places within a layer occurs millions of times a second, making the lipid molecules in the membrane highly dynamic. As we discuss later, maintaining the membrane in a fluid state is critical to overall membrane function.

The mosaic part of the fluid mosaic model refers to the fact that membranes contain a wide assortment of different types of proteins, each with a specific function. As we discuss in detail later, this includes proteins involved in transport and

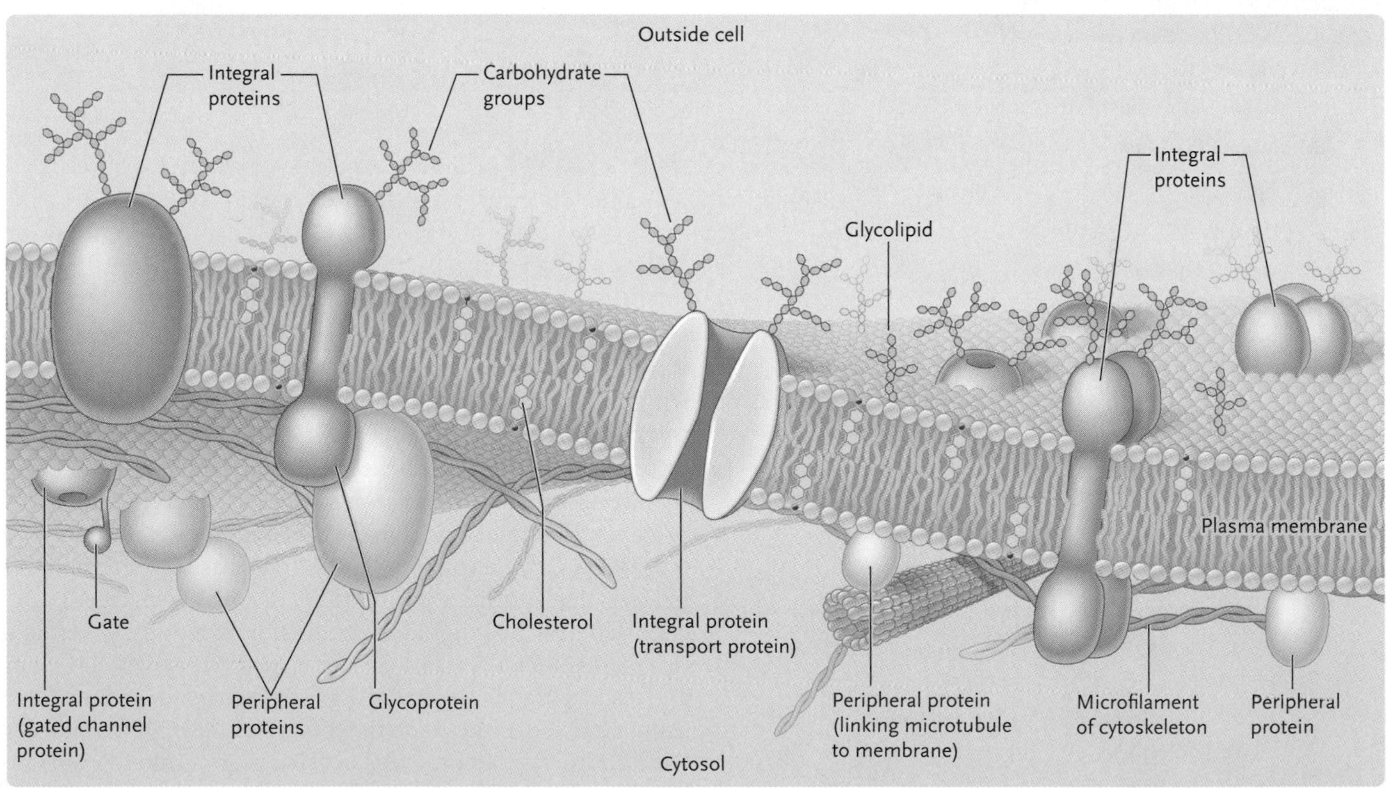

Figure 5.1
Membrane structure according to the fluid mosaic model, in which integral membrane proteins are suspended individually in a fluid lipid bilayer. Peripheral proteins are attached to integral proteins or membrane lipids mostly on the cytoplasmic side of the membrane (shown only on the inner surface in the figure). In the plasma membrane, carbohydrate groups of membrane glycoproteins and glycolipids face the cell exterior.

attachment, as well as a variety of enzymes involved in such processes as electron transport. Because they are larger than lipid molecules, the proteins move more slowly in the fluid environment of the membrane. As well, a small number of membrane proteins anchor cytoskeleton filaments to the membrane and thus do not move (Figure 5.1). As also shown in Figure 5.1, a number of the lipid and protein components of some membranes have carbohydrate groups linked to them, forming glycolipids and glycoproteins.

The relative proportions of lipid and protein within a membrane vary considerably depending on the type of membrane. For example, membranes that contain protein complexes involved in electron transport, such as the inner mitochondrial membrane, contain large amounts of protein (76% protein and only 24% lipid), whereas the plasma membrane contains nearly equal amounts of protein and lipid (49% and 51%, respectively). Myelin, which is a membrane that functions to insulate nerve fibres, is composed mostly of lipids (18% protein and 82% lipid).

An important characteristic of membranes, illustrated in Figure 5.1, is that the proteins and other components of one half of the lipid bilayer are different from those that make up the other half of the bilayer. This is referred to as membrane asymmetry, and it reflects differences in the functions performed by each side of the membrane. For example, a range of glycolipids and carbohydrate groups are attached to proteins on the external side of the membrane, whereas components of the cytoskeleton bind to proteins on the internal side of the membrane. In addition, hormones and growth factors bind to receptor proteins that are found only on the external surface of the plasma membrane. Their binding triggers changes to distinctly different protein components found on the inner surface of the membrane, which lead to signal transduction within the cell (see Chapter 15).

5.1b Experimental Evidence in Support of the Fluid Mosaic Model

The fluid mosaic model of membrane structure is supported by two major pieces of experimental evidence.

Membranes Are Fluid. In a now classic study carried out in 1970, David Frye and Michael A. Edidin grew human cells and mouse cells separately in tissue culture. They were able to tag the human or mouse membrane proteins **(Figure 5.2)** with dye molecules: the human proteins were linked to red dye molecules and the mouse proteins were linked to green. Frye and Edidin then fused the human and mouse cells. Within minutes, they found that the two distinctly coloured proteins began to mix. In less than an hour, the two colours had completely intermixed on the fused cells, indicating that the mouse and human proteins had moved around in the fused membranes.

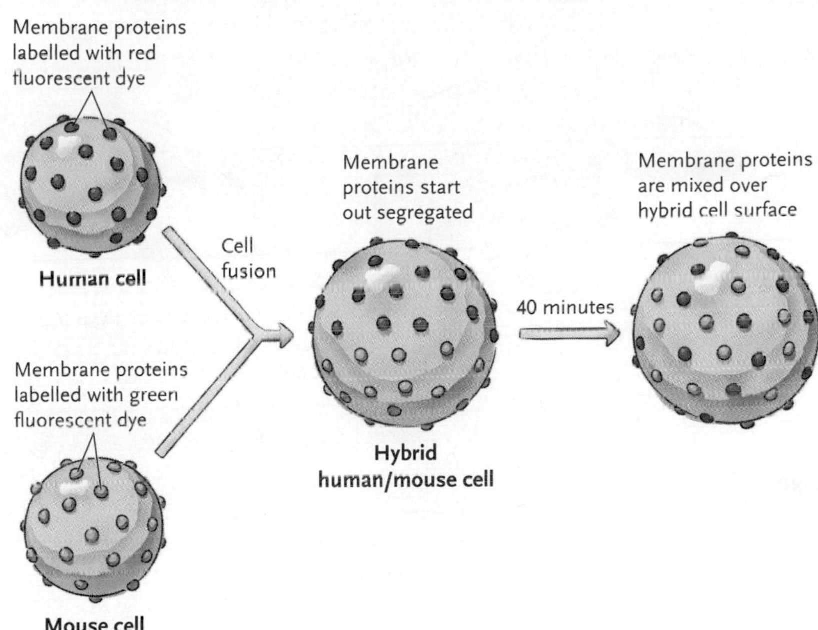

Figure 5.2
The Frye-Edidin experiment provided evidence that the membrane bilayer is fluid. In the experiment, membrane proteins were found to rapidly migrate over the surface of the hybrid cell.

Based on the measured rates at which molecules mix in biological membranes, the membrane bilayer appears to be about as fluid as a light machine oil, like the lubricants you might use around the house to oil a door hinge, the wheels of a skateboard, or a bicycle chain.

Membrane Asymmetry. One of the key experiments revealing membrane asymmetry utilizes the freeze-fracture technique in combination with electron microscopy **(Figure 5.3, p. 96)**. In this technique, a block of cells is rapidly frozen by dipping it in liquid nitrogen (−196°C). Then the block is fractured by hitting it with a microscopically sharp knife edge. Often the fracture splits bilayers into inner and outer halves, exposing the membrane interior. In the electron microscope, the split membranes appear as smooth layers in which individual particles the size of proteins are embedded (shown in Figure 5.3c). From these images, it is clear that the particles on either side of the membrane differ in size, number, and shape, providing evidence that the two sides are distinctly different.

Study Break

1. Describe the fluid mosaic model of membrane structure.
2. What is meant by the term *membrane asymmetry*?

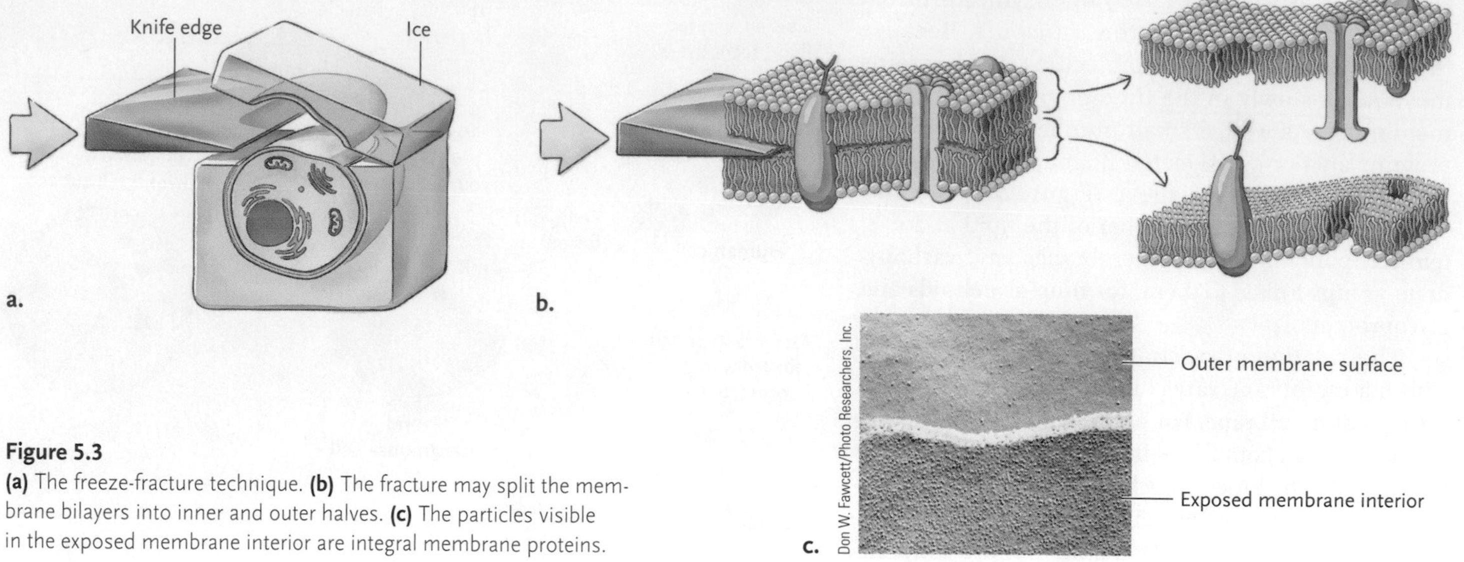

Figure 5.3
(a) The freeze-fracture technique. **(b)** The fracture may split the membrane bilayers into inner and outer halves. **(c)** The particles visible in the exposed membrane interior are integral membrane proteins.

5.2 The Lipid Fabric of a Membrane

The foundation or underlying fabric of all biological membranes is the lipid molecules. As we discuss in this section, keeping membranes in a fluid state is important to membrane function. Many organisms can adjust the types of lipids in the membranes such that membranes do not become too stiff (viscous) or too fluid (liquid). To review the basics of lipid structure, see *The Chemical and Physical Foundations of Biology* pages.

5.2a Phospholipids Are the Dominant Lipids in Membranes

The dominant lipids found in membranes are **phospholipids**, which consist of two fatty acid "tails" linked to one of several types of alcohols or amino acids by a phosphate group **(Figure 5.4a)**. A property that all phospholipids possess, which is critical to the structure and function of membranes, is that they are **amphipathic**. That is, each phospholipid molecule contains a region that is *hydrophobic* and a region that is *hydrophilic*. Whereas the fatty acid chains of a lipid are very hydrophobic (nonpolar), the phosphate-containing head group is charged and hydrophilic (polar). Detergents are excellent at removing oil stains from clothing because they are also amphipathic molecules.

When added to an aqueous solution, phospholipids associate with each other and assemble into a **bilayer**, which is a sheet two lipid molecules thick **(Figure 5.4b)**.

What is required for a bilayer to form? The answer is, absolutely nothing. Both micelles and bilayers form spontaneously in an aqueous environment because of the tendency of the hydrophobic fatty acids to aggregate together while the polar head groups associate with water. These arrangement are favoured because they represent the lowest energy state and are more likely to occur over any other arrangement.

5.2b Membrane Fluidity

The fluidity of the lipid bilayer is dependent on how densely the individual lipid molecules can pack together. This is influenced by two major factors: the composition of the lipid molecules that make up the membrane and the temperature. Fatty acids composed of saturated hydrocarbons, in which each carbon is bound to a maximum number of hydrogen atoms, tend to have a straight shape, which allows the lipids to pack more tightly together **(Figure 5.5a)**. Alternatively, lipid molecules with unsaturated fatty acids are less straight as the double bonds in an unsaturated fatty acid introduce kinks or bends in its structure. This results in lipid molecules packing together less closely **(Figure 5.5b)**.

Membranes remain in a fluid state over a relatively wide range of temperatures. However, if the temperature drops low enough, the phospholipid molecules become closely packed, and the membrane forms a highly viscous semisolid gel. This is exactly what happens when melted butter cools. At any given temperature, the fluidity of a membrane is related to the degree to which the membrane lipids are unsaturated. The more unsaturated a membrane, the lower its gelling temperature is. For most membrane systems, the normal fluid state is achieved by a mixed population of saturated and unsaturated fatty acids. The more carbon–carbon double bonds within the fatty acid tails, the more space will exist between neighbouring lipids, and the more fluid the resulting membrane will be.

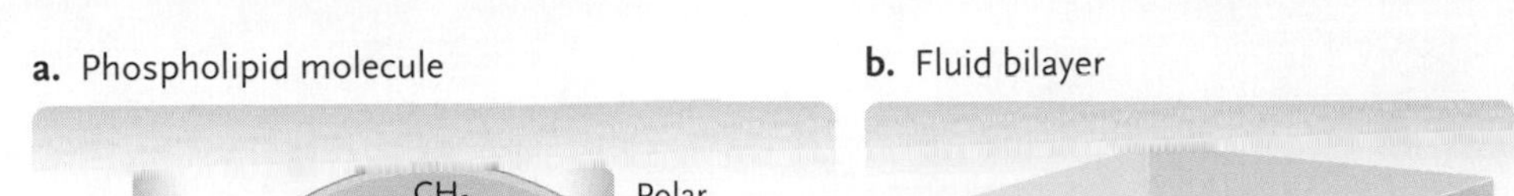

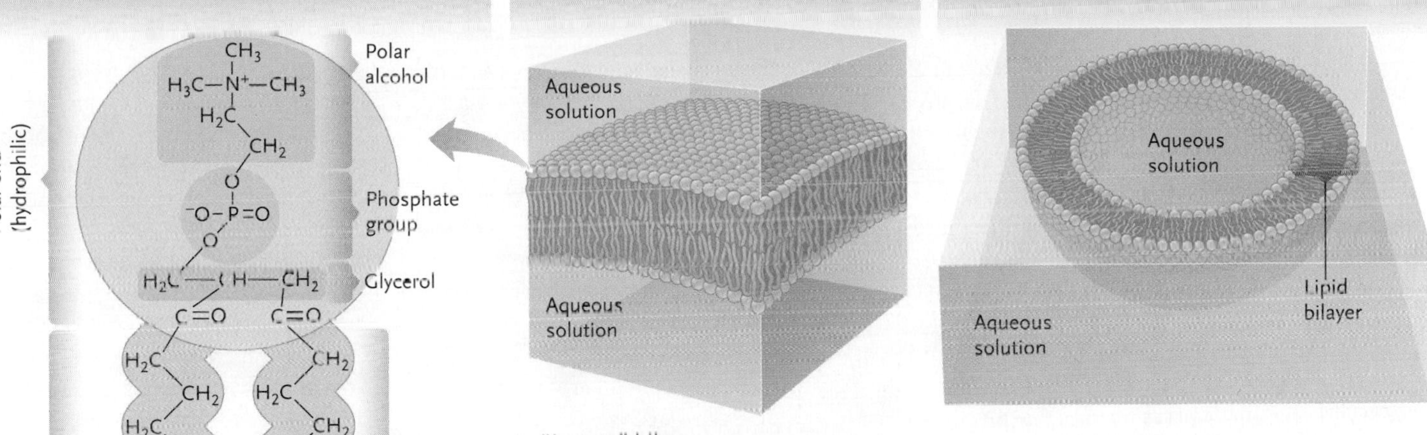

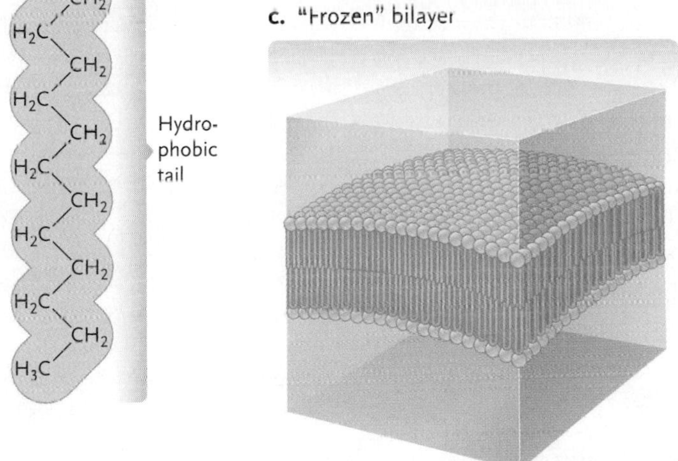

Figure 5.4
Phospholipid bilayers. **(a)** Phospholipid molecule (phosphatidyl choline). Within the circle at the top representing the polar end of the molecule, the polar alcohol (choline) is shown in blue, the phosphate group in orange, and the glycerol unit in pink. **(b)** Phospholipid bilayer in the fluid state, in which individual molecules are free to flex, rotate, and exchange places. **(c)** A bilayer frozen in a semisolid, gellike state; note the close alignment of the hydrophobic tails compared with part **(b).** **(d)** Phospholipid bilayer forming a vesicle.

5.2c Organisms Can Adjust Fatty Acid Composition

The maintenance of membranes in a fluid state is absolutely essential to cell function. Exposure to low temperatures may result in membrane viscosity increasing to the point where normal membrane permeability is inhibited, as well as causing enzymes and other proteins in the membrane to stop functioning. Electron transport chains, for example, require components to move very rapidly within the membrane bilayer. If the membrane solidifies, electron transport ceases to operate. Problems also arise at high temperature. Membranes may become too fluid and liquid due to the increase in molecular motion, which can result in membrane leakage. Ions such as K^+, Na^+, and Ca^{2+} begin to freely diffuse across the membrane, resulting in an irreversible disruption of cellular ion balance that can rapidly lead to cell death.

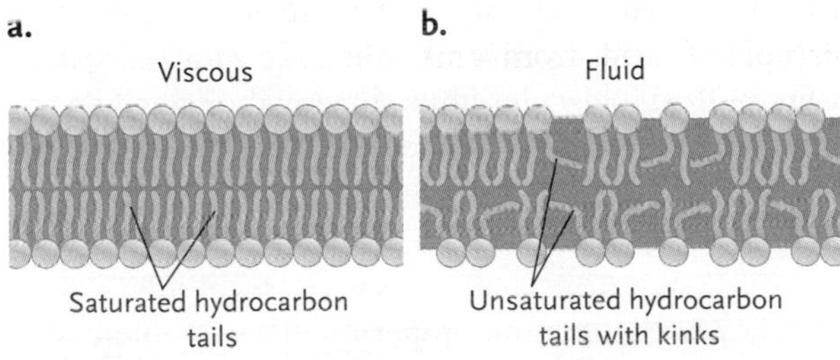

Figure 5.5
Lipid molecules that contain saturated hydrocarbon tails are closely packed, whereas unsaturated hydrocarbon tails have kinks that prevent lipid molecules from packing closely together.

Given this, it is not surprising that most organisms can adjust the fatty acid composition of their membranes such that proper fluidity is maintained over a relatively broad range of temperatures. For example, many prokaryotes, protists, and plants can thrive at temperatures that are far below the temperature at which a typical animal membrane would solidify. Such organisms are able to survive at low temperatures, in part because they are able to increase the relative proportion of unsaturated fatty acids in their membranes.

Unsaturated fatty acids are produced during fatty acid synthesis through the action of a group of enzymes called **desaturases.** All fatty acids are initially synthesized as fully saturated molecules without any double bonds. Desaturases act on these saturated fatty acids by catalyzing a reaction that removes two hydrogen atoms from neighbouring carbon atoms and introduces a double bond **(Figure 5.6a, p. 99).** There are a wide range of desaturase enzymes, each one introducing a double bond at a specific point along the fatty acid. Whereas

Molecule Behind Biology

Trans Fats

In the food industry, the use of fats containing saturated fatty acids is more desirable than the use of oils that contain unsaturated fatty acids. The lack of double bonds means that lipids containing saturated fatty acids are more stable and less prone to oxidation that can decrease shelf life as well as affect the texture and taste of the final product. Moreover, hard fats have a higher melting temperature, which makes them useful in many applications, such as in baking and in the process of deep-frying.

Because animal-based saturated fats such as butter or lard are expensive and susceptible to spoilage, the food industry has, for many decades, used saturated fats produced through the industrial process of hydrogenation. This process removes *cis* double bonds from fatty acids by heating vegetable oil in the presence of hydrogen gas and a catalyst. In the food industry, partial hydrogenation is practised, which results in a product that is still malleable and not too hard. One of the unintended consequences of partial hydrogenation is that the *cis* double bonds that do not become hydrogenated tend to be reconfigured into the *trans* orientation. Although small amounts of *trans* fats are found naturally in the milk and meat of ruminant animals such as cows and sheep, through partial hydrogenation, human consumption of *trans* fats has increased tremendously over the last 70 years.

There is now clear medical evidence that the consumption of *trans* fats is unhealthy. A comprehensive review of research on *trans* fat consumption and health by the *New England Journal of Medicine* in 2006 clearly demonstrated the existence of a strong connection between *trans* fat consumption and elevated risk of coronary heart disease, a leading cause of death in North America. *Trans* fats have also been linked to increased incidence of other health problems as well. The physiological basis for the increased risk to health by increased *trans* fat consumption is not fully understood and remains a very active area of research. The increased risk may be due, in part, to the fact that a major group of enzymes called lipases, which aid in the breakdown of many types of lipids, including *cis* unsaturated fats, do not recognize the *trans* configuration. This leads to *trans* fats staying in the bloodstream longer, which may lead to increased incidence of arterial deposition, which may lead to coronary heart disease.

In response to the overwhelming medical evidence that *trans* fats are harmful, governments around the world are implementing restrictions on the amount of *trans* fats foods can contain. In Canada, the *trans* fat content of vegetable oils and soft margarines is now limited to 2% of the total fat content, whereas the *trans* fat content for all other foods is 5% of the total fat content, including ingredients sold to restaurants. Similar guidelines are in place in many European countries, as well as being implemented in the United States.

In response to these new guidelines, food manufacturers and restaurant chains have reformulated their products to be "*trans* fat free." This has primarily been achieved by simply replacing hydrogenated fats with naturally saturated fats. Many nutritionists argue that these fully saturated alternatives may not offer any health benefit.

some unsaturated fatty acids contain only one carbon–carbon double bond, others may contain two or more.

Changes in the transcription of a gene often result in changes in the abundance of its transcript (mRNA) and resulting protein abundance. **Figure 5.6b** shows that transcript abundance of a desaturase gene increases as the temperature is lowered. This results in an increase in synthesis and overall abundance of the desaturase enzyme. Higher amounts of desaturates would, in turn, result in an increase in the abundance of unsaturated fatty acids. By regulating the amount of desaturase enzyme that is synthesized, a wide range of organisms can closely regulate the amount of unsaturated fatty acids that get incorporated into membranes and thereby maintain membrane fluidity within the optimum range. It is important to realize that *high temperature* and *low temperature* are relative terms. For a typical cyanobacterium, room temperature (20–25°C) is low temperature since its optimum growth temperature is above 35°C.

Besides lipids, a group of compounds called sterols also influence membrane fluidity. The best example of a sterol is cholesterol **(Figure 5.7),** which is found in the membranes of animal cells but not in those of plants or prokaryotes. Sterols act as membrane buffers: at high temperatures, they help restrain the movement of lipid molecules, thus reducing the fluidity of the membrane. However, at lower temperatures, sterols disrupt fatty acids from associating by occupying space between lipid molecules, thus slowing the transition to the nonfluid gel state.

Study Break

1. Why is maintaining proper membrane fluidity important for membrane function?
2. What is the relationship between temperature and desaturase expression?

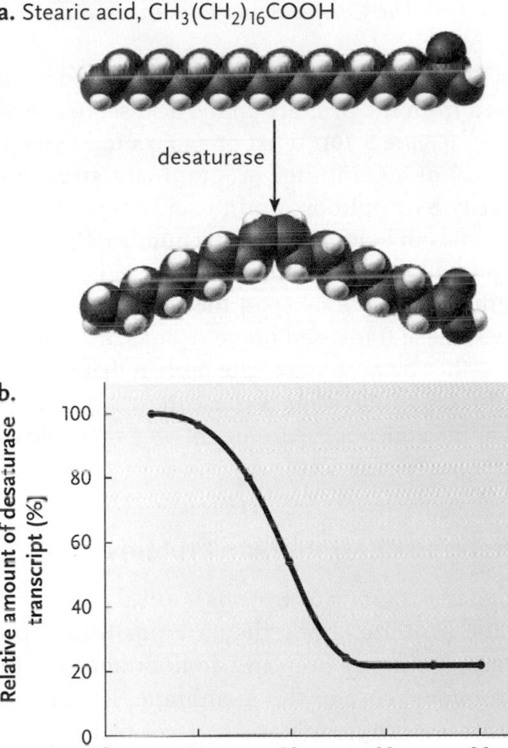

Figure 5.6
Fatty acids become unsaturated **(a)** through the action of a group of enzymes called desaturases that introduce double bonds.
(b) In organisms whose temperature changes with the environment, the expression of desaturase enzymes usually increases as the temperature is lowered.

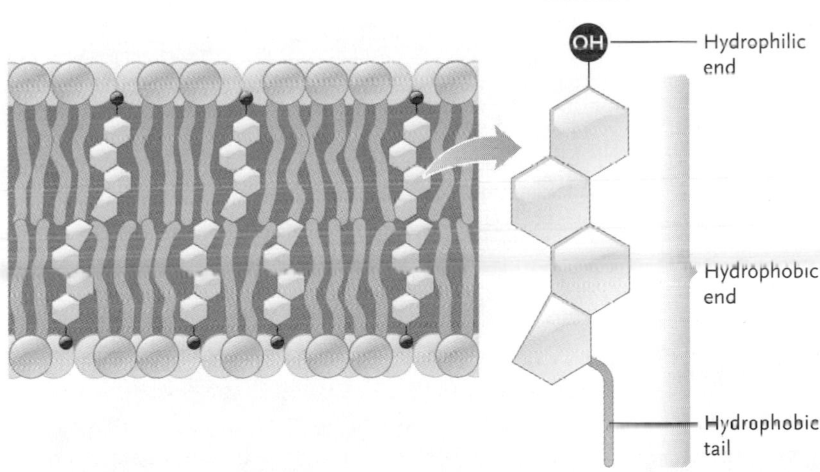

Figure 5.7
The position taken by cholesterol in bilayers. The hydrophilic ↓OH group at one end of the molecule extends into the polar regions of the bilayer; the ring structure extends into the nonpolar membrane interior.

5.3 Membrane Proteins

Although lipid molecules constitute the backbone of a membrane, the unique set of proteins that are associated with the membrane determines its function and makes each membrane unique.

5.3a The Key Functions of Membrane Proteins

Membrane proteins can be separated into four major functional categories as shown in **Figure 5.8, p. 100.** It should be noted that all of these functions may exist in a single membrane and that one protein or protein complex may serve more than one of these functions:

1. ***Transport.*** Many substances cannot freely diffuse through the membrane. Instead, a protein may provide a hydrophilic channel that allows movement of a specific compound. Alternatively, a membrane protein may change its shape and in so doing shuttle specific molecules from one side of a membrane to the other.
2. ***Enzymatic activity.*** A number of enzymes are membrane proteins. The best example of this is the enzymes associated with the respiratory and photosynthetic electron transport chains.
3. ***Signal transduction.*** Membranes often contain receptor proteins on their outer surface that bind to specific chemicals such as hormones. On binding, these receptors trigger changes on the inside surface of the membrane that lead to transduction of the signal through the cell.
4. ***Attachment/recognition.*** Proteins exposed to both the internal and external membrane surfaces act as attachment points for a range of cytoskeleton elements, as well as components involved in cell–cell recognition.

All membrane proteins can be classified into one of two distinct categories, integral and peripheral membrane proteins.

5.3b Integral Membrane Proteins

Membrane proteins that are embedded in the phospholipid bilayer are called **integral membrane proteins**. Although all integral membrane proteins possess at least one region that interacts with the hydrophobic core of the membrane, most integral proteins are *transmembrane proteins,* which span the entire membrane bilayer and therefore have regions that are exposed to the aqueous environment on both sides of the membrane. To be able to interact with the hydrophobic core of a membrane, integral proteins are composed of regions (or domains) that consist of predominantly nonpolar amino acids that are usually coiled into alpha helices

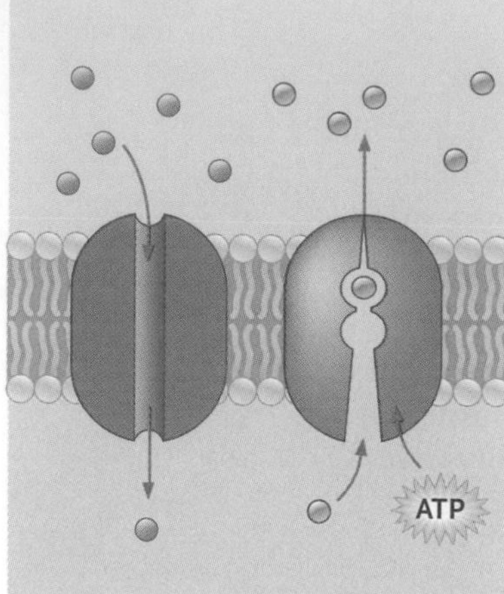

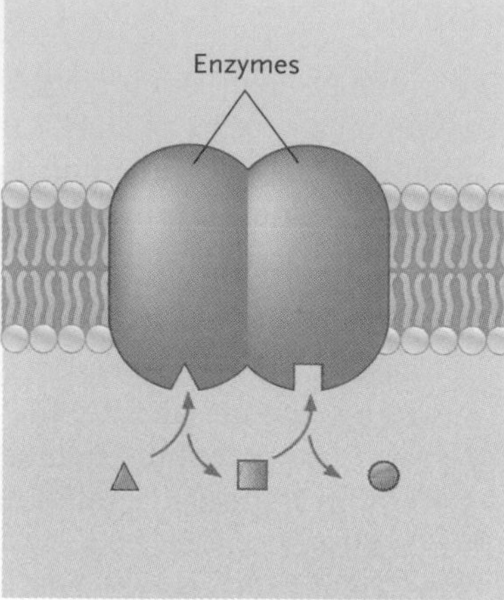

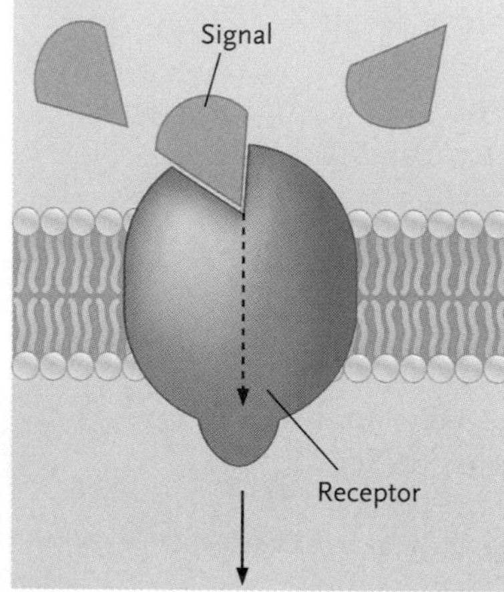

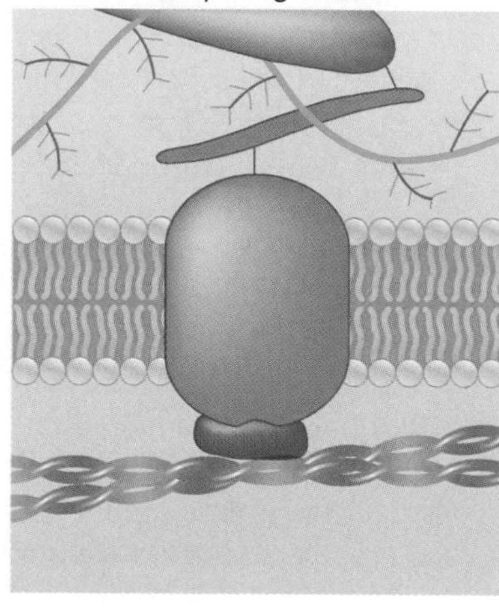

Figure 5.8
The major functions of membrane proteins: **(a)** transport, **(b)** enzymatic activity, **(c)** signal transduction, and **(d)** attachment/recognition.

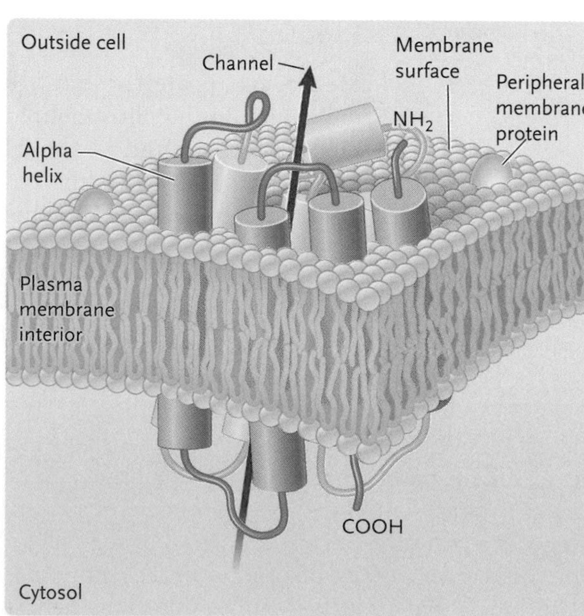

Figure 5.9
The structure of membrane proteins. A typical membrane protein showing the membrane-spanning alpha-helical segments (green cylinders), connected by flexible loops of the amino acid chain at the membrane surfaces.

(Figure 5.9) (see *The Chemical and Physical Foundations of Biology* pages).

That a protein is a transmembrane protein can often be inferred from the primary amino acid sequence of the protein **(Figure 5.10)**. What one looks for, usually with the aid of a computer program, are stretches of primarily hydrophobic amino acids about 17 to 20 amino acids in length. This is the number of amino acids required to span a membrane once. Since many transmembrane proteins span the membrane multiple times, these transmembrane regions are usually linked together by portions of the protein that consist mainly of polar amino acids because these regions are exposed to the aqueous environment on either side of the membrane (Figure 5.10).

5.3c Peripheral Membrane Proteins

The second major group of proteins is called **peripheral membrane proteins** since they are positioned on the surface of a membrane and do not interact with the hydrophobic core of the membrane. Peripheral proteins are held to membrane surfaces by noncovalent bonds—hydrogen bonds and ionic bonds—usually by interacting with the exposed portions of integral proteins as well as directly with membrane lipid molecules. Most peripheral proteins are on the cytoplasmic side of the membrane. Some peripheral proteins are parts of the cytoskeleton, such as microtubules, microfilaments, or intermediate filaments, or proteins

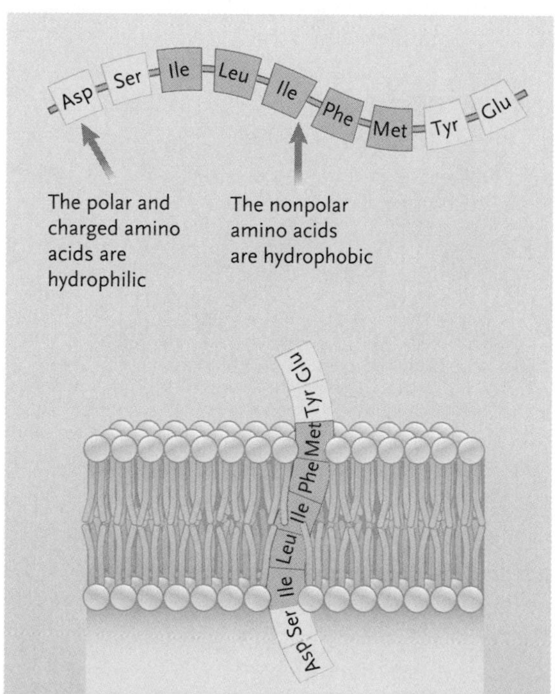

Figure 5.10
Transmembrane proteins can be identified because of the presence of stretches of amino acids that are primarily nonpolar. These regions of the protein interact with the hydrophobic regions of the membrane. Unlike this model that shows five amino acids, usually between 17–20 amino acids are needed to span the membrane once.

that link the cytoskeleton together. These structures hold some integral membrane proteins in place. For example, this anchoring constrains many types of receptors to the sides of cells facing body surfaces, cavities, or tubes. Because peripheral membrane proteins do not interact with the hydrophobic core of the membrane, they are made up of a mixture of polar and nonpolar amino acids like the majority of proteins.

Study Break

1. What are the two major classes of membrane proteins?
2. Give two examples each of integral proteins and peripheral proteins.

5.4 Passive Membrane Transport

Membranes can be considered the cell's "gatekeepers"—they control what gets in and what gets out. The hydrophobic nature of a membrane severely restricts the free movement of many molecules and substances essential for life.

Molecules such as O_2 diffuse very rapidly across membranes, which is important considering the vital role O_2 plays in cellular respiration. However, a range of other molecules, including a huge array of ions and charged molecules, as well as macromolecules such as sugars and proteins, are needed to move between cellular compartments and yet cannot diffuse rapidly across membranes. In the following sections, we address, first, what controls the movement of molecules such as O_2 and CO_2 that can freely move from one side of a membrane to the other and, second, how a cell transports molecules that cannot freely move across a membrane.

5.4a Passive Transport Is Based on Diffusion

Passive transport is defined as the movement of a substance across a membrane without the need to expend chemical energy such as ATP. What drives passive transport is **diffusion**, the net movement of a substance from a region of higher concentration to a region of lower concentration. Diffusion is based on the fact that above absolute zero (−273°C), molecules are in constant motion, and this results in them becoming uniformly distributed in space. Diffusion is the primary mechanism of solute movement within a cell and between cellular compartments separated by a membrane.

The driving force behind diffusion is an increase in entropy. In the initial state, when molecules are more concentrated in one region of a solution or on one side of a membrane, the molecules are highly ordered and in a state of low entropy. As diffusion occurs, the entropy, or disorder, increases until, when the molecules are evenly distributed, entropy reaches its maximum **(Figure 5.11)**. As the distribution proceeds to the state of maximum disorder, the molecules release free energy that can accomplish work (see Section 4.1 for a discussion of entropy and free energy).

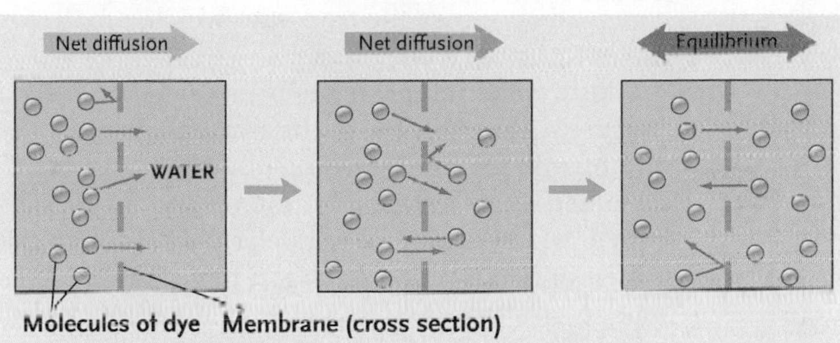

Figure 5.11
Diffusion is an entropy-driven process as molecules move from regions of high concentration to areas of low concentration. Entropy is at its maximum when equilibrium is reached.

The rate of diffusion depends on the concentration difference or concentration gradient that exists between two areas or across a membrane. The bigger the gradient the faster the rate of diffusion. Even after their concentration is the same in all regions, there is still constant movement of molecules or ions from one space to another, but there is no net change in concentration. This condition is an example of a dynamic equilibrium (see Figure 5.11).

5.4b The Two Types of Passive Transport: Simple and Facilitated

There are two types of passive transport: simple diffusion and facilitated diffusion.

Simple Diffusion. As shown in **Figure 5.12,** membranes display selective permeability; whereas some molecules diffuse very rapidly across the membrane, other molecules are essentially unable to transit the membrane. Overall, the interplay of two factors, size and

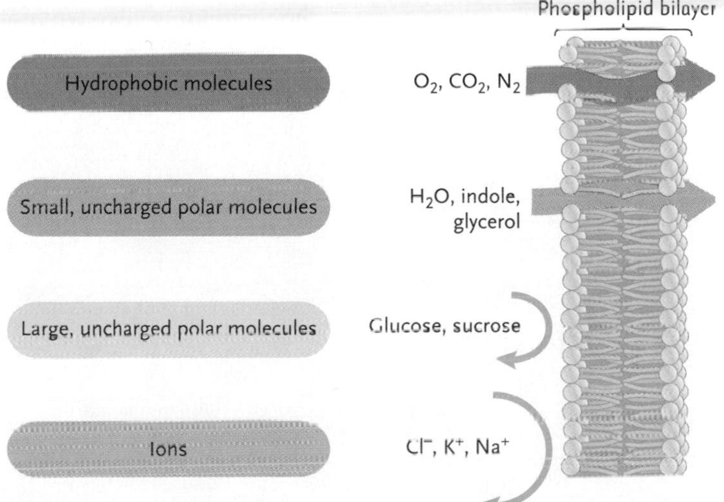

Figure 5.12
The size and charge of a molecule affect the rate of diffusion across a membrane.

charge, determines the ease with which a molecule can move across a membrane.

Very small nonpolar molecules such as O_2 and CO_2 are readily soluble in the hydrophobic interior of a membrane and move rapidly from one side to the other. As well steroid hormones and most drugs both of which tend to be nonpolar can readily transit a membrane. Small uncharged molecules such as water or glycerol, even though they are polar, are still able to move quite rapidly across the membrane (see Figure 5.12). In contrast, however, the membrane is practically impermeable to charged molecules, including ions such as Cl^-, Na^+, and phosphate (PO^{4-}). Compared with the rate of transport of water, transport of small ions is about 10^9 times slower. The presence of a charge and a hydration shell of water surrounding the ion (see *The Chemical and Physical Foundations of Biology* pages) contribute to ions being prevented from entering the hydrophobic core of the membrane.

Facilitated Diffusion. Metabolic processes often have a demand for many polar and charged molecules, such as water, amino acids, sugars, and ions, that cannot be met by the relatively slow rate at which these molecules can diffuse passively across a membrane. To speed up the movement of these compounds, transport can be helped or *facilitated* by protein complexes that span the membrane **(Table 5.1).** Although facilitated diffusion involves specific transporters, what drives the movement of the molecules is still diffusion based on a concentration gradient across the membrane. When the gradient falls to zero, transport stops.

5.4c Two Groups of Transport Proteins Carry Out Facilitated Diffusion

Facilitated diffusion is carried out by integral membrane proteins, called transport proteins, that extend entirely through the membrane. Two types of transport proteins are involved in facilitated diffusion. One type, called **channel proteins**, forms hydrophilic pathways in the membrane through which water and ions can pass **(Figure 5.13a).** The channel aids the diffusion of molecules through the membrane by providing an avenue such that hydrophilic molecules do not have to interact with the hydrophobic portions of the membrane. Other channels facilitate the transport of ions such as Na^+, K^+, Ca^{2+}, and Cl^-. Most of these ion transporters, which occur in all eukaryotes, are **gated channels**; that is, they switch between open, closed, or intermediate states. The gates may be opened or closed by changes in voltage across the membrane, for instance, or by binding signal molecules. In animals, voltage-gated ion channels are used in nerve conduction and the control of muscle contraction.

The second type of transport proteins, called **carrier proteins**, also forms passageways through the lipid bilayer **(Figure 5.13b).** Each carrier protein binds a specific single solute, such as a sugar molecule or an amino acid, and transports it across the lipid bilayer. Because a single solute is transferred in this carrier-mediated fashion, the transfer is called *uniport transport.* In performing the transport step, the carrier protein undergoes conformational changes that progressively move the solute binding site from one side of the membrane to the other, thereby transporting the solute. This property distinguishes carrier protein function from channel protein function.

Many transport proteins display a high degree of substrate specificity, in a way similar to an enzyme. For example, transporters that carry glucose are unable to transport fructose, which is structurally very similar. This specificity allows various cells and cellular compartments to tightly control what gets in and out. The kinds of transport proteins present in the plasma membrane or, for example, on the outer membrane of the mitochondria depend ultimately on the type of cell and growth conditions.

Table 5.1 Characteristics of Transport Mechanisms

	Passive Transport		Active Transport
Characteristic	Simple Diffusion	Facilitated Diffusion	
Membrane component responsible for transport	Lipids	Proteins	Proteins
Binding of transported substance	No	Yes	Yes
Energy source	Concentration gradients	Concentration gradients	ATP hydrolysis or concentration gradients
Direction of transport	With gradient of transported substance	With gradient of transported substance	Against gradient of transported substance
Specificity for molecules or molecular classes	Nonspecific	Specific	Specific
Saturation at high concentrations of transported molecules	No	Yes	Yes

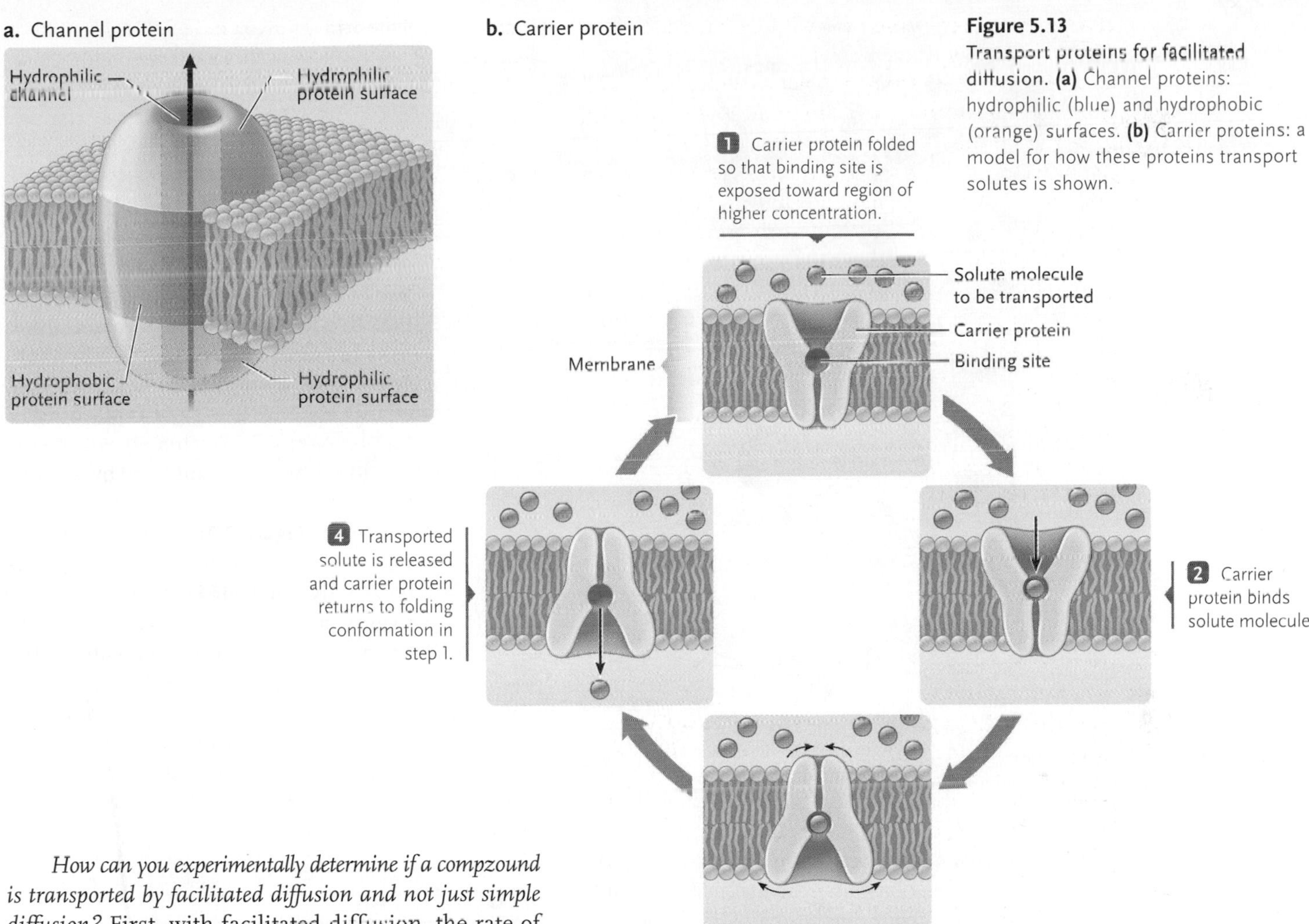
a. Channel protein
Hydrophilic channel
Hydrophilic protein surface
Hydrophobic protein surface
Hydrophilic protein surface
b. Carrier protein
1 Carrier protein folded so that binding site is exposed toward region of higher concentration.
Solute molecule to be transported
Carrier protein
Binding site
Membrane
2 Carrier protein binds solute molecule.
3 In response to binding, carrier protein changes folding conformation so that binding site is exposed to region of lower concentration.
4 Transported solute is released and carrier protein returns to folding conformation in step 1.

Figure 5.13
Transport proteins for facilitated diffusion. (a) Channel proteins: hydrophilic (blue) and hydrophobic (orange) surfaces. **(b)** Carrier proteins: a model for how these proteins transport solutes is shown.

How can you experimentally determine if a compzound is transported by facilitated diffusion and not just simple diffusion? First, with facilitated diffusion, the rate of movement across the membrane is much faster than one would predict based just on the chemical structure of the molecule being transported **(Figure 5.14)**. Second, facilitated diffusion can be *saturated* in a way analogous to an enzyme. A membrane has a limited number of transporters for a particular molecule. If you measure the rate of transport at increasing concentration differences across a membrane, the rate of transport of a particular molecule (the substrate) reaches a plateau that represents a state when all the transporters are occupied. Increasing the concentration further has no effect (see Figure 5.14). By comparison, in simple diffusion, the whole membrane surface is effectively the transporter; thus, the rate of transport, although slower, never reaches a plateau but keeps increasing with increasing concentration gradient.

Rate of transport
Approaches maximum rate when all transporters are occupied
Facilitated transport
Simple diffusion
0
0
Concentration difference across membrane

Figure 5.14
The rate of transport as a function of concentration across the membrane. Compared with simple diffusion, facilitated diffusion leads to higher rates of transport and displays saturation kinetics.

5.4d Osmosis: The Passive Diffusion of Water

Like solutes, water can also move passively across membranes in a process called osmosis. The passive transport of water occurs constantly in living cells. Inward or outward movement of water by osmosis

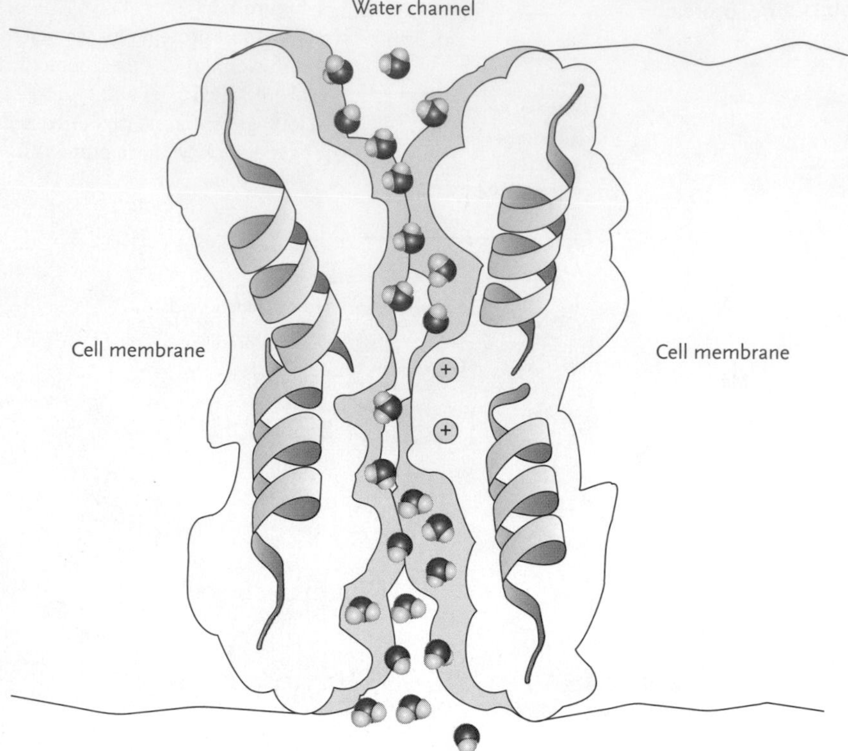

Figure 5.15
A model of aquaporin, a water-specific channel. Positive charges in the centre of the channel prevent the diffusion of protons.

develops forces that can cause cells to swell or shrink. In formal terms, osmosis is *the net movement of water molecules across a selectively permeable membrane by diffusion, from a solution of lesser solute concentration to a solution of greater solute concentration*. For osmosis to take place, the selectively permeable membrane must allow water molecules to pass but not molecules of the solute. Osmosis occurs in cells because they contain a solution of proteins and other molecules that are retained in the cytoplasm by a membrane impermeable to them but freely permeable to water.

Osmosis can occur either by simple diffusion or it can be facilitated by water-specific transport proteins called aquaporins. This group of transporters has been found in organisms as diverse as prokaryotes, plants, and humans. The aquaporin channel is very narrow and allows for the single-file movement of about a billion water molecules every second **(Figure 5.15)**. The channel is also very specific for water and does not allow for the diffusion of ions such as protons. The structural basis of this is explained by recent three-dimensional models of aquaporin-1, which show the presence of positive charges in the centre of the channel that are thought to repel the transport of protons through the channel. For his discovery of aquaporins, Peter Agre was awarded the Nobel Prize for chemistry in 2003.

The movement of water by osmosis is dictated by solute concentration. If the solution surrounding a cell contains dissolved substances at lower concentrations than in the cell, the solution is said to be hypotonic to the cell (*hypo* = under or below; *tonos* = tension or tone). When a cell is in a hypotonic solution, water enters by osmosis, and the cell tends to swell **(Figure 5.16a)**. Animal cells in a hypotonic solution may actually swell to the point of bursting. Organisms that live in surroundings that contain salts or other molecules at higher concentrations than their bodies must constantly expend energy to replace water lost by osmosis. In this situation, the outside solution is said to be hypertonic to the cells (*hyper* = over or above), as shown in **Figure 5.16b.** The concentration of water inside and outside cells is usually equal or isotonic (*iso* = the same), as shown in **Figure 5.16c.** To keep the fluids on either side of the plasma membrane isotonic, animal cells must constantly use energy to pump Na^+ ions from inside to outside by active transport (see Section 5.6); otherwise, water would move inward by osmosis and cause the cells to burst.

Study Break

1. How do the size and charge of a molecule influence its transport across a membrane?
2. What is the difference between passive transport and active transport?
3. Explain how aquaporin functions to transport water.
4. Explain the effect of a hypertonic solution surrounding animal cells.

5.5 Active Membrane Transport

Many substances are pushed across membranes against their concentration gradients by active transport "pumps." Active transport concentrates molecules such as sugars and amino acids inside cells and pushes ions in or out of cells. Passive transport, driven by concentration gradients, accounts for much of the movement of water, ions, and many types of molecules into or out of cells. Often, however, substances need to be moved against a concentration gradient—that is, from a region of low concentration to a region of higher concentration. For example, in muscle cells, a difference in calcium ion concentration between two compartments can be as high as 30 000. Such a huge concentration difference, which is required for normal muscle function, is established and maintained through an energy-dependent mechanism called **active transport.**

5.5a Active Transport Requires Energy

The term "active" in the term active transport means that the cell has to expend energy, which is usually ATP, to pump molecules across a membrane. It is estimated that about 25% of a cell's ATP requirements are for active transport. Active transport concentrates molecules such as sugars and amino acids inside cells and pushes ions in or out of cells.

There are two kinds of active transport. In **primary active transport**, the same protein that transports a substance also hydrolyzes ATP to power the transport directly. In **secondary active transport,** the transport is indirectly driven by ATP hydrolysis. That is, the transport proteins do not break down ATP; instead, the transporters use a favourable concentration gradient of ions, built up by primary active transport, as their energy source for active transport of a different ion or molecule.

Other features of active transport resemble facilitated diffusion (listed in Table 5.1). Both processes depend on membrane transport proteins, both are specific, and both can be saturated. The transport proteins are carrier proteins that change their conformation as they function.

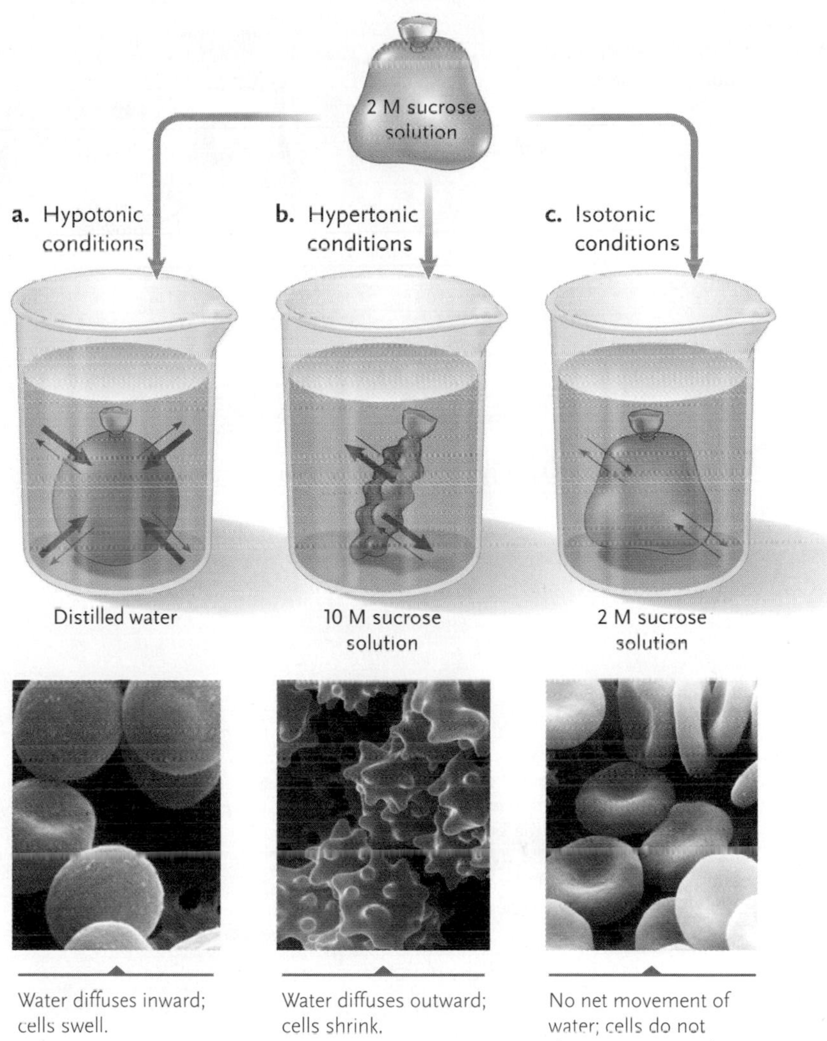

Figure 5.16
Tonicity and osmotic water movement. The diagrams show what happens when a cellophane bag filled with a 2 M sucrose solution is placed in a **(a)** hypotonic, **(b)** hypertonic, or **(c)** isotonic solution. The cellophane is permeable to water but not to sucrose molecules. The width of the arrows shows the amount of water movement. In the first beaker, the distilled water is hypotonic to the solution in the bag; net movement of water is into the bag. In the second beaker, the 10 M solution is hypertonic to the solution in the bag; net movement of water is out of the bag. In the third beaker, the solutions inside and outside the bag are isotonic; there is no net movement of water into or out of the bag. The animal cell micrographs show the corresponding effects on red blood cells placed in hypotonic, hypertonic, or isotonic solutions. (Micrographs, M. Sheetz, R. Painter, and S. Singer. Journal of Cell Biology, 70:493, 1976. By permission of Rockefeller University Press.)

5.5b Primary Active Transport Moves Positively Charged Ions

All primary active transport pumps move positively charged ions—H^+, Ca^{2+}, Na^+, and K^+—across membranes **(Figure 5.17, p. 106).** The gradients of positive ions established by primary active transport pumps underlie functions that are absolutely essential for cellular life.

For example, **H^+ pumps** (also called **proton pumps**) in plasma membranes push hydrogen ions from the cytoplasm to the cell exterior. These pumps (as in Figure 5.17) temporarily bind a phosphate group removed from ATP during the pumping cycle. Proton pumps are not common in animals; although one pump of this type moves H^+ from cells lining the stomach into the gastric juice, making the stomach contents highly acidic.

The **Ca^{2+} pump** (or **calcium pump**) is widely distributed among eukaryotes. It pushes Ca^{2+} from the cytoplasm to the cell exterior and from the cytosol into the vesicles of the endoplasmic reticulum (ER). As a result, Ca^{2+} concentration is typically high outside cells and inside ER vesicles and low in the cytoplasmic solution. This Ca^{2+} gradient is used universally among eukaryotes as a regulatory control of cellular activities as diverse as secretion, microtubule assembly, and muscle contraction. The latter is discussed further in Chapter 41.

The **Na^+/K^+ pump** (or **sodium–potassium pump**), located in the plasma membrane, pushes 3 Na^+ ions out of the cell and 2 K^+ ions into the cell in the same pumping cycle. As a result, positive charges accumulate in excess outside the membrane, and the inside of the cell becomes negatively charged with respect to the outside. Voltage—an electrical potential difference—across the plasma membrane results from this difference in charge as well as from the unequal distribution of ions across the membrane created by passive transport. The voltage across a membrane, called a **membrane potential,** measures

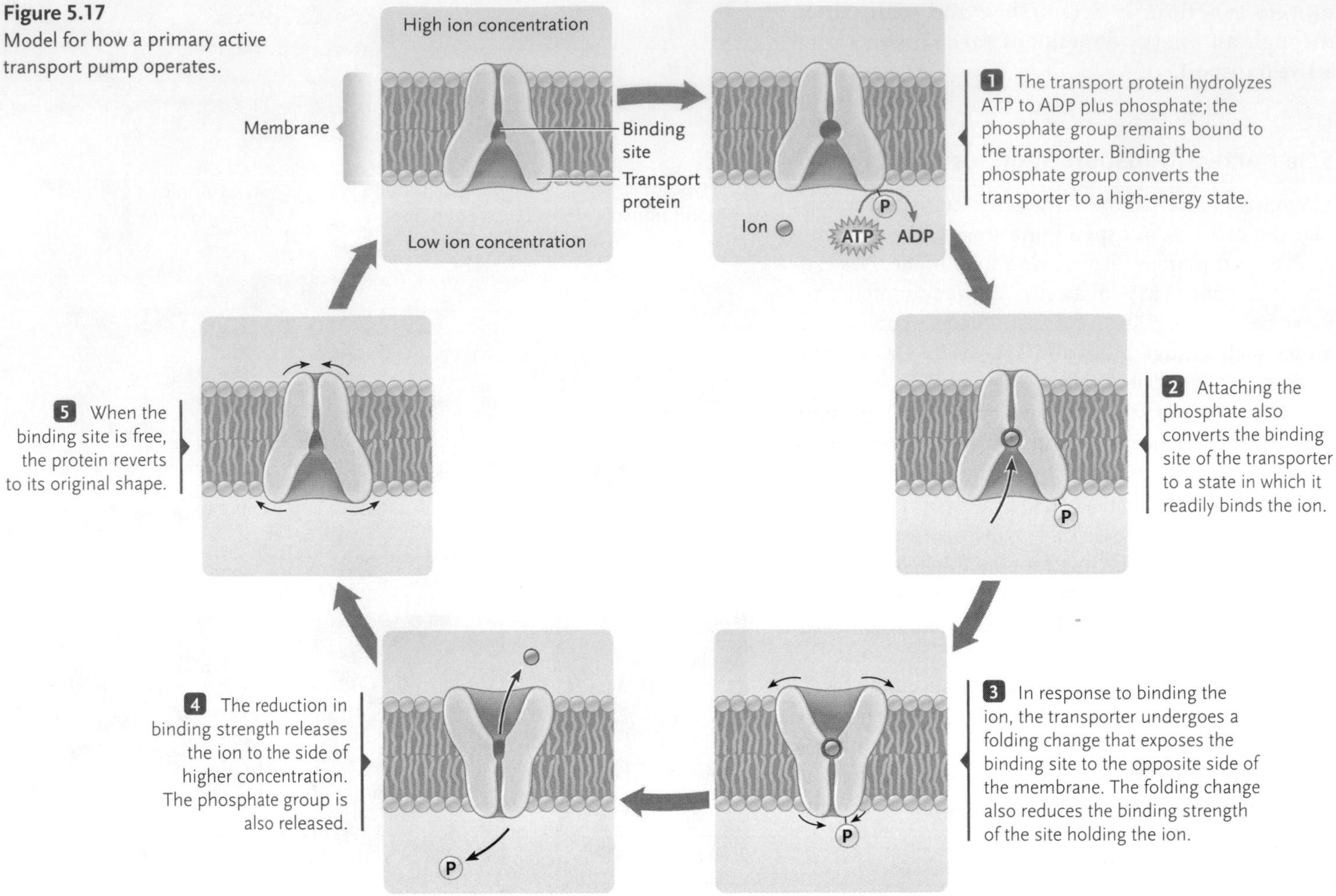

Figure 5.17
Model for how a primary active transport pump operates.

High ion concentration

Membrane

Binding site

Transport protein

Low ion concentration

Ion

ATP ADP

P

1 The transport protein hydrolyzes ATP to ADP plus phosphate; the phosphate group remains bound to the transporter. Binding the phosphate group converts the transporter to a high-energy state.

2 Attaching the phosphate also converts the binding site of the transporter to a state in which it readily binds the ion.

3 In response to binding the ion, the transporter undergoes a folding change that exposes the binding site to the opposite side of the membrane. The folding change also reduces the binding strength of the site holding the ion.

4 The reduction in binding strength releases the ion to the side of higher concentration. The phosphate group is also released.

5 When the binding site is free, the protein reverts to its original shape.

from about –50 to –200 millivolts, with the minus sign indicating that the charge inside the cell is negative versus the outside. In sum, we have both a concentration difference (of the ions) and an electrical charge difference on the two sides of the membrane, constituting what is called an **electrochemical gradient.** Electrochemical gradients store energy that is used for other transport mechanisms. For instance, the electrochemical gradient across the membrane is involved with the movement of ions associated with nerve impulse transmission (described in Chapter 33).

5.5c Secondary Active Transport Moves Both Ions and Organic Molecules

As already noted, secondary active transport pumps use the concentration gradient of an ion established by a primary pump as their energy source. For example, the driving force for most secondary active transport in animal cells is the high outside/low inside Na^+ gradient set up by the sodium–potassium pump. In secondary active transport, the transfer of the solute across the membrane is always coupled with the transfer of the ion supplying the driving force.

Secondary active transport occurs by two mechanisms known as *symport* and *antiport* **(Figure 5.18).** In **symport**, the cotransported solute moves through the membrane channel in the same direction as the driving ion, a phenomenon known as **cotransport.** Sugars such as glucose and amino acids are examples of molecules actively transported into cells by symport. In **antiport**, the driving ion moves through the membrane channel in one direction, providing the energy for the active transport of another molecule in the opposite direction, a phenomenon known as **exchange diffusion.** In many cases, ions are exchanged by antiport. For example, antiport is the mechanism used in red blood cells for the coupled movement of chloride ions and bicarbonate ions through a membrane channel.

Active transport and passive transport move ions and smaller hydrophilic molecules across cellular membranes. Cells can also move much larger molecules or aggregates of molecules from inside to outside, or in the reverse direction, by including them in the cell's inward or outward vesicle traffic. The mechanisms carrying out this movement—exocytosis and endocytosis—are discussed in the next section.

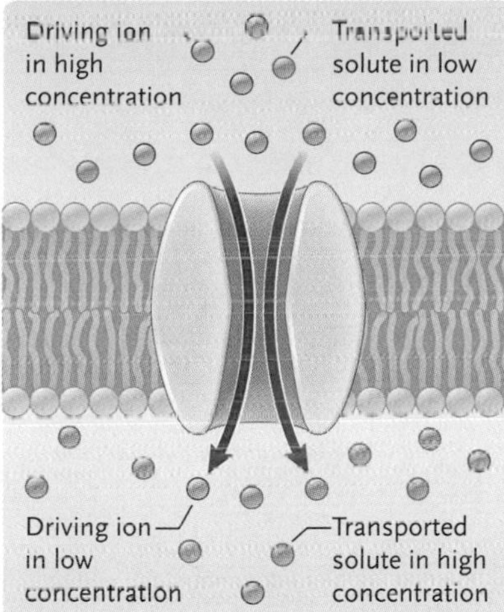

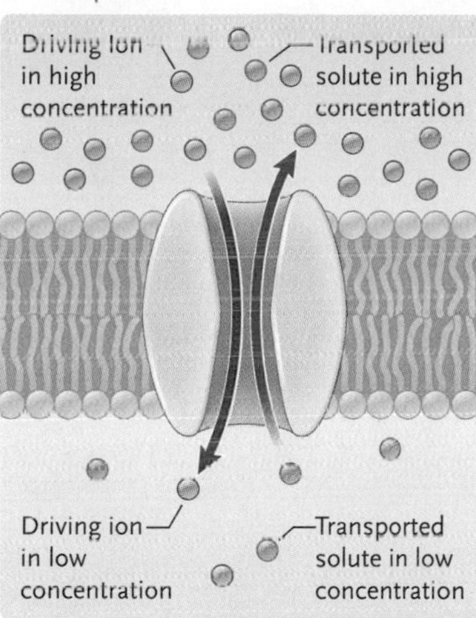

Figure 5.18
Secondary active transport, in which a concentration gradient of an ion is used as the energy source for active transport of a solute. **(a)** In symport, the transported solute moves in the same direction as the gradient of the driving ion. **(b)** In antiport, the transported solute moves in the direction opposite to the gradient of the driving ion.

Study Break

1. What is active transport?
2. What is the difference between primary active transport and secondary active transport?
3. How is a membrane potential generated?

5.6 Exocytosis and Endocytosis

The largest molecules transported through cellular membranes by passive and active transport are about the size of amino acids or monosaccharides such as glucose. Eukaryotic cells import and export larger molecules by endocytosis and exocytosis. The export of materials by exocytosis primarily carries secretory proteins and some waste materials from the cytoplasm to the cell exterior. Import by endocytosis may carry proteins, larger aggregates of molecules, or even whole cells from the outside into the cytoplasm. Exocytosis and endocytosis also contribute to the back-and-forth flow of membranes between the endomembrane system and the plasma membrane. Both exocytosis and endocytosis require energy; thus, both processes stop if a cell's ability to make ATP is inhibited.

5.6a Exocytosis Releases Molecules to the Outside by Means of Secretory Vesicles

In exocytosis, secretory vesicles move through the cytoplasm and contact the plasma membrane **(Figure 5.19, p. 108)**. The vesicle membrane fuses with the plasma membrane, releasing the vesicle's contents to the cell exterior.

All eukaryotic cells secrete materials to the outside through exocytosis. For example, in animals, glandular cells secrete peptide hormones or milk proteins, and cells lining the digestive tract secrete mucus and digestive enzymes. Plant cells secrete carbohydrates by exocytosis to build a strong cell wall.

5.6b Endocytosis Brings Materials into Cells in Endocytic Vesicles

In endocytosis, proteins and other substances are trapped in pitlike depressions that bulge inward from the plasma membrane. The depression then pinches off as an endocytic vesicle. Endocytosis takes place in most eukaryotic cells by one of two distinct but related pathways. In the simplest of these mechanisms, **bulk-phase endocytosis** (sometimes called **pinocytosis**, meaning "cell drinking"), extracellular water is taken in along with any molecules that happen to be in solution in the water **(Figure 5.19b, p. 108)**. No binding by surface receptors takes place.

In the second endocytic pathway, **receptor-mediated endocytosis**, the molecules to be taken in are bound to the outer cell surface by receptor proteins **(Figure 5.19c, d, p. 108)**. The receptors, which are integral proteins of the plasma membrane, recognize and bind only certain molecules—primarily proteins, or other molecules carried by proteins—from the solution surrounding the cell. After binding their target molecules, the receptors collect into a depression in the plasma membrane called a **coated pit** because of the network of proteins (called **clathrin**) that coat and reinforce the cytoplasmic side. With the target molecules attached, the pits deepen and pinch free of the plasma membrane to form endocytic vesicles. Once in the cytoplasm, an endocytic vesicle rapidly loses its clathrin coat and may fuse with a lysosome. The enzymes within the lysosome then digest the contents of the vesicle, breaking them down into smaller molecules useful to the cell. These molecular products—for example, amino acids and monosaccharides—enter the cytoplasm by crossing the vesicle membrane via transport proteins. The membrane proteins are recycled to the plasma membrane.

Mammalian cells take in many substances by receptor-mediated endocytosis, including peptide hormones, antibodies, and blood proteins. The receptors binding these substances to the plasma membrane are present in thousands to hundreds of thousands of copies. For example, a mammalian cell plasma membrane has about 20 000 receptors for low-density lipoprotein

Figure 5.19
Exocytosis and endocytosis. **(a)** Exocytosis. **(b)** Bulk-phase endocytosis. **(c)** Receptor-mediated endocytosis. **(d)** Electron micrographs of receptor-mediated endocytosis.

a. Exocytosis

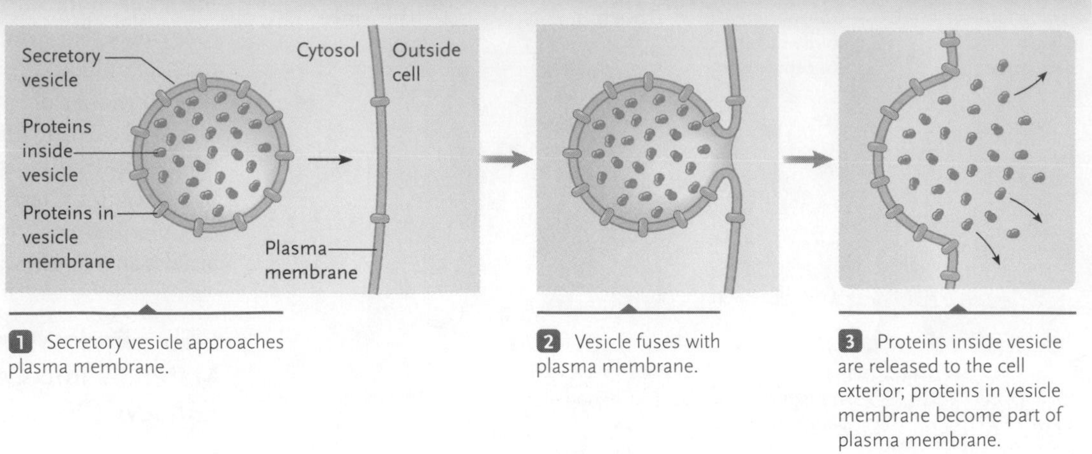

Secretory vesicle
Proteins inside vesicle
Proteins in vesicle membrane
Cytosol
Outside cell
Plasma membrane
1 Secretory vesicle approaches plasma membrane.
2 Vesicle fuses with plasma membrane.
3 Proteins inside vesicle are released to the cell exterior; proteins in vesicle membrane become part of plasma membrane.

b. Bulk-phase endocytosis (pinocytosis)

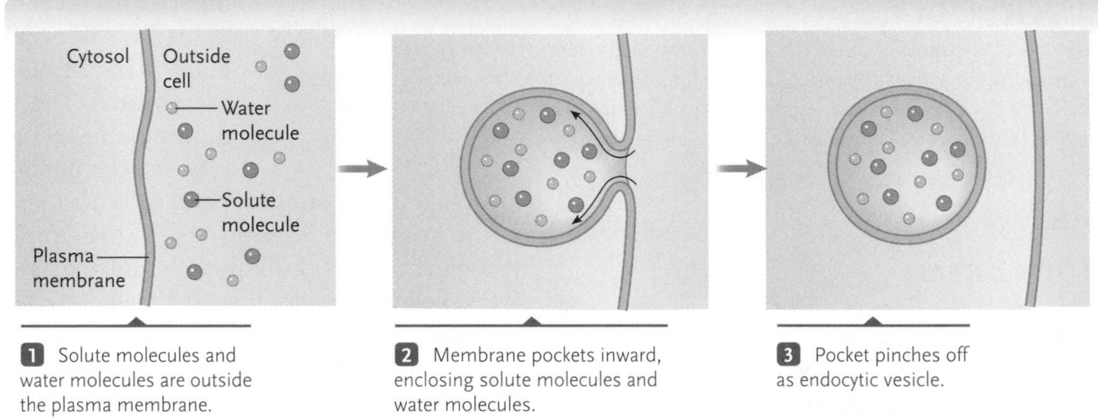

Cytosol
Outside cell
Water molecule
Solute molecule
Plasma membrane
1 Solute molecules and water molecules are outside the plasma membrane.
2 Membrane pockets inward, enclosing solute molecules and water molecules.
3 Pocket pinches off as endocytic vesicle.

c. Receptor-mediated endocytosis

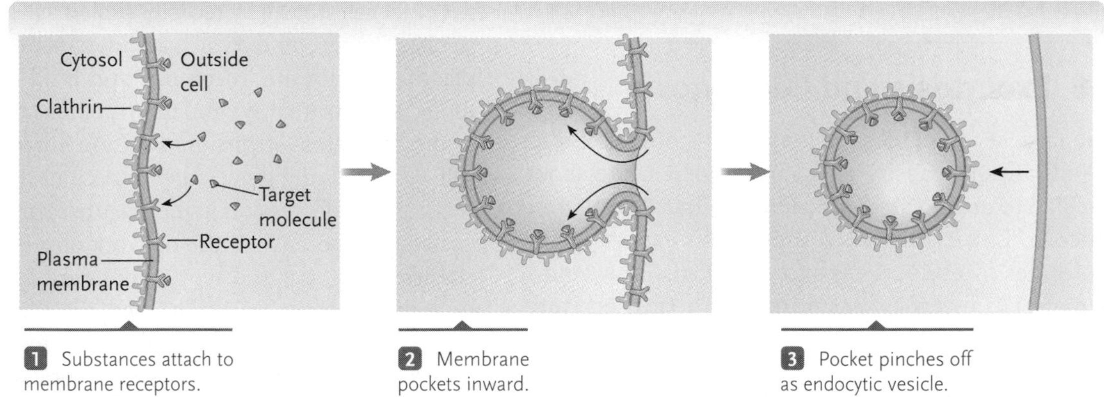

Cytosol
Outside cell
Clathrin
Target molecule
Receptor
Plasma membrane
1 Substances attach to membrane receptors.
2 Membrane pockets inward.
3 Pocket pinches off as endocytic vesicle.

d. Electron micrographs of receptor-mediated endocytosis shown in 5.19c.

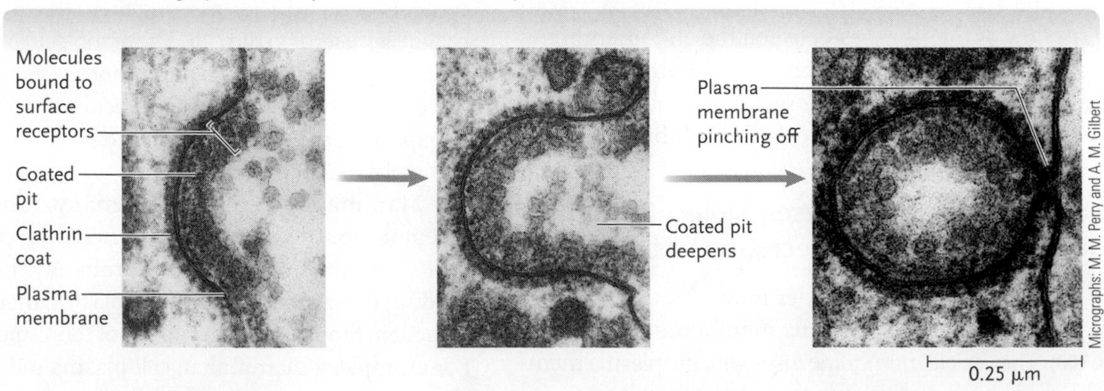

Molecules bound to surface receptors
Coated pit
Clathrin coat
Plasma membrane
Coated pit deepens
Plasma membrane pinching off
0.25 μm
Micrographs: M. M. Perry and A. M. Gilbert

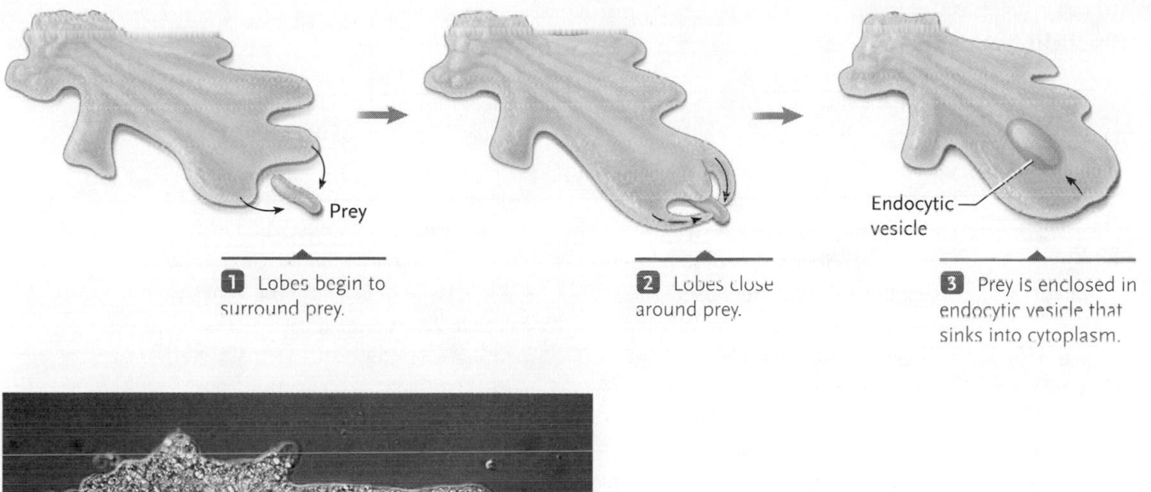
Prey
Endocytic vesicle
1 Lobes begin to surround prey.
2 Lobes close around prey.
3 Prey is enclosed in endocytic vesicle that sinks into cytoplasm.
Mike Abbey/Visuals Unlimited

Figure 5.20
Phagocytosis, in which lobes of the cytoplasm extend outward and surround a cell targeted as prey. The micrograph shows the protistan *Chaos carolinense* preparing to engulf a single-celled alga (*Pandorina*) by phagocytosis; white blood cells called phagocytes carry out a similar process in mammals.

(LDL). LDL, a complex of lipids and proteins, is the way cholesterol moves through the bloodstream. When LDL binds to its receptor on the membrane, it is taken into the cell by receptor-mediated endocytosis. Then, by the steps just described, the LDL is broken down within the cell and cholesterol is released into the cytoplasm.

Some cells, such as certain white blood cells (*phagocytes*) in the bloodstream or protists such as *Amoeba proteus*, can take in large aggregates of molecules, cell parts, or even whole cells by a process related to receptor-mediated endocytosis. The process, called **phagocytosis** (meaning "cell eating"), begins when surface receptors bind molecules on the substances to be taken in **(Figure 5.20)**. Cytoplasmic lobes then extend, surround, and engulf the materials, forming a pit that pinches off and sinks into the cytoplasm as a large endocytic vesicle. The materials are then digested within the cell as in receptor-mediated endocytosis, and any remaining residues are sequestered permanently into storage vesicles or are expelled from cells as waste by exocytosis.

The combined workings of exocytosis and endocytosis constantly cycle membrane segments between the internal cytoplasm and the cell surface. The balance of the two mechanisms maintains the surface area of the plasma membrane at controlled levels.

Thus, through the combined mechanisms of passive transport, active transport, exocytosis, and endocytosis, cells maintain their internal concentrations of ions and molecules and exchange larger molecules such as proteins with their surroundings. The next two chapters on respiration and photosynthesis show another vital role of membranes in cells of all kinds—their participation in the fundamentally important reactions of energy metabolism.

Study Break

1. What is the mechanism of exocytosis?
2. What is the difference between bulk-phase endocytosis and receptor-mediated endocytosis?

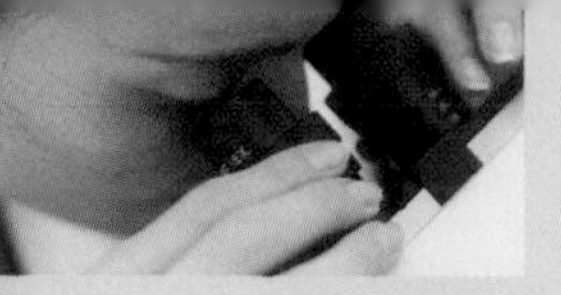

People Behind Biology

Lap-Chee Tsui

Identification of the gene that is defective in patients with cystic fibrosus (CF) (see *Why It Matters*) was a breakthrough in human genetics and was achieved by a research team headed by Lap-Chee Tsui (1950–) of the Department of Genetics at The Hospital for Sick Children in Toronto.

Born in Shanghai, Tsui studied biology at the Chinese University of Hong Kong and was awarded a bachelor of science degree in 1972, which was followed by a master of philosophy degree in 1974. He undertook doctoral research in the United States, completing his Ph.D. at the University of Pittsburgh in 1979. He followed this with postdoctoral training at Oak Ridge National Laboratory in Tennessee before moving in 1981 to the Department of Genetics at The Hospital for Sick Children, where soon after he became a staff member investigating the underlying genetic cause of CF.

Although today reports of gene discovery are commonplace, in the 1980s, the discovery of the gene that is mutated in patients with CF was particularly noteworthy for two major reasons. First, researchers relied on DNA isolated from people with CF to identify genetic markers of the disease. Using these, researchers used the novel method of positional cloning to identify the CF gene without any knowledge of the gene itself or what it did. Second, CF is the most common single-gene disease among Caucasians; thus, much anticipation awaited this particular discovery, with many research teams worldwide trying to be the first to identify the gene.

In 1985, Tsui and his team identified the first DNA marker linked to CF, on chromosome 7. Four years later, Dr. Tsui's team, along with collaborators at the University of Michigan, finally identified the defective gene responsible for CF, defining the principal mutation (Δ*F508). This mutation is the result of a three-nucleotide deletion that results in the loss of the amino acid phenylalanine (F) at the 508th position of the protein. As a result, the protein does not fold normally and is more quickly degraded.

The research was described in three seminal papers in the September 8, 1989, issue of *Science*. The gene was called the cystic fibrosis transmembrane regulator (CFTR). *Science* named Dr. Tsui's achievement "the most refreshing scientific development of 1989," and *Maclean*'s Honour Roll hailed it as one of the "discoveries of hope at the heart of human life" in the same year.

Dr. Tsui has received many honours, including fellow of the Royal Society of Canada, several honorary doctoral degrees, and the Order of Canada. Dr. Tsui is currently the vice-chancellor of the University of Hong Kong, but he remains an active researcher and is still affiliated with The Hospital for Sick Children's Program in Genetics and Genomic Biology.

Unanswered Questions

In this chapter, we have discussed the structure of membranes and the transport of substances across membranes by various mechanisms, and research continues in all of those areas to obtain a more detailed understanding. For instance, research is being done to determine how the assembly of phospholipids and proteins into new membranes occurs. Also, as we will learn later in the book, cells contain a number of signalling pathways in which a signal received at the cell surface is relayed through the cell to the site at which the signal is targeted. How this signalling occurs at the molecular level is an important area of research. And exocytosis is responsible for the secretion of neurotransmitters (chemical messengers that communicate between neurons and between neurons and other cells), hormones, and enzymes. One important area of research is determining the molecular mechanisms for the membrane fusion event of exocytosis. Another is examining how cell-surface receptors control exocytosis.

Let us consider two specific examples of current research, one involving aquaporins and the other endocytosis.

Molecular and Cellular Analysis of Aquaporin Channels

As we discussed in the chapter, aquaporins are specific channels for water transport across cell membranes. Interestingly, problems with aquaporin function are associated with various human diseases, such as congenital cataracts, a form of diabetes, congestive heart failure, and brain edema (fluid-caused swelling). Therefore, having a better understanding of aquaporin function could help facilitate the development of drugs to treat those diseases.

Peter Agre at Johns Hopkins University School of Medicine in Baltimore, Maryland, received a Nobel Prize in 2003 for his discovery of aquaporins. In the chapter, we gave a simple overview of aquaporin channels, but the bigger picture is much more complicated. We know, for instance, that the ability to absorb or release water varies considerably among the cells and tissues of an organism and between organisms. Since Agre's discovery, over 200 different aquaporins have been identified in tissues from mammals, nonmammalian vertebrates, invertebrates, plants, and various microorganisms. Variation in aquaporin structure among these forms is likely responsible for their differences in function. Agre's research group is pursuing this issue by characterizing the structures of various aquaporins from humans, yeast, and bacteria to produce high-resolution models. Such models will be informative for designing experiments to further our understanding of the function of these channel molecules. Agre's group is also studying the regulation of the aquaporin genes to characterize tissue-specific production of aquaporins. The results of this line of investigation will provide a valuable piece of the puzzle concerning the variation in water uptake among tissues mentioned earlier.

Many other research groups are working on aquaporins, so we can expect great strides to be made in this area in the future.

Entry of Nanotubes into Cells by Endocytosis

We learned in this chapter that substances can enter cells by endocytosis. In either bulk-phase endocytosis or receptor-mediated endocytosis, the result is an endocytic vesicle that may then fuse with a lysosome. Using endocytosis to deliver therapeutic agents to diseased cells, such as cancer cells, has been the goal of many research groups. One such group is that of Hongjie Dai, a physical chemist at Stanford University.

There are many possible ways to deliver therapeutic agents to cells. Dai's group has been working with carbon nanotubes, which are cylindrical carbon molecules with a diameter of just a few nanometres (about 50 000 times smaller than the width of a human hair) and up to several centimetres long. In one experiment, Dai's group tagged carbon nanotubes so that they would bind specifically to cancer cells. The carbon nanotubes absorb near-infrared light, whereas normal tissue does not. Therefore, by shining a near-infrared laser on the tagged cells, the researchers could kill just cancer cells without harming normal tissue.

Dai's research team also showed that carbon nanotubes could carry proteins and DNA into cells. This property would be extremely valuable for delivering drugs or therapeutic genes into diseased cells. How were the carbon nanotubes taken into the cells? Knowing the route is important for determining what kinds of chemical bonds will be needed to attach the therapeutic agents to the carbon nanotubes. For example, as described in this chapter, endocytosis produces vesicles that can fuse with lysosomes. Therefore, if carbon nanotubes were taken up by endocytosis, then the drug or DNA being delivered could be attached to the nanotubes by disulfide bonds because those bonds would readily be broken by the acidic environment of the lysosome, thereby releasing the agent.

Dai and his colleagues have obtained evidence that carbon nanotubes are taken into cells by endocytosis. Endocytosis, as opposed to passive mechanisms, requires energy in the form of either ATP or heat. When cell cultures were cooled, or treated with an inhibitor that stopped ATP production, the cells could no longer take in carbon nanotubes. Experiments using specific inhibitors against clathrin provided support for a receptor-mediated endocytosis uptake mechanism.

Future research will turn to using carbon nanotubes to deliver anticancer agents specifically to cancer cells in tissue culture. Undoubtedly, a lot of work will be needed to produce an efficient method for that delivery, as well as an effective way to release and activate the anticancer agent within the cell. If success is forthcoming with tissue culture systems, the protocols would be moved to model organisms for cancer and eventually to humans for clinical trials.

Review

Go to CENGAGENOW™ at http://hed.nelson.com/ to access quizzing, animations, exercises, articles, and personalized homework help.

5.1 An Overview of the Structure of Membranes

- The fluid mosaic model proposes that the membrane consists of a fluid lipid bilayer in which proteins are embedded and float freely.
- Membranes are asymmetrical. The two halves of a membrane are not the same. The membrane proteins found on one half of the bilayer are structurally and functionally distinct from those of the other half.

5.2 The Lipid Fabric of a Membrane

- The lipid bilayer forms the structural framework of membranes and serves as a barrier preventing the passage of most water-soluble molecules.
- The basic part of a membrane is a fluid phospholipid bilayer, in which the polar regions of phospholipid molecules lie at the surfaces of the bilayer and their nonpolar tails associate together in the interior.
- Organisms can adjust the fatty acid composition of membrane lipids to maintain proper fluidity.

5.3 Membrane Proteins

- Proteins embedded in the phospholipid bilayer carry out most membrane functions, including transport of selected hydrophilic substances, enzymatic activity, recognition, and signal reception.
- Integral membrane proteins are embedded deeply in the bilayer and cannot be removed without dispersing the bilayer. Peripheral membrane proteins associate with membrane surfaces.

5.4 Passive Membrane Transport

- Passive transport depends on diffusion, the net movement of molecules from a region of higher concentration to a region of lower concentration. Passive transport does not require cells to expend energy.
- Simple diffusion is the passive transport of substances across the lipid portion of cellular membranes with their concentration gradients.
- Small uncharged molecules can move rapidly across membranes, whereas large or charged molecules may be strongly impeded from transiting a membrane.
- Facilitated diffusion is the passive transport of substances at rates higher than predicted from their lipid solubility. It depends on membrane proteins, follows concentration gradients, is specific for certain substances, and becomes saturated at high concentrations of the transported substance.
- Osmosis is the net diffusion of water molecules across a selectively permeable membrane in response to differences in the concentration of solute molecules.
- Aquaporins are membrane transport proteins that facilitate the diffusion of water.
- Water moves from hypotonic solutions (lower concentrations of solute molecules) to hypertonic solutions (higher concentrations of solute molecules). When the solutions on each side are isotonic, there is no osmotic movement of water in either direction.

5.5 Active Membrane Transport

- Active transport moves substances against their concentration gradients and requires cells to expend energy. Active transport depends on membrane proteins, is specific for certain substances, and becomes saturated at high concentrations of the transported substance.
- Active transport proteins are either primary transport pumps, which directly use ATP as their energy source, or secondary transport pumps, which use favourable concentration gradients of positively charged ions, set up by primary transport pumps, as their energy source for transport.
- Secondary active transport may occur by symport, in which the transported substance moves in the same direction as the concentration gradient used as the energy source, or by antiport, in which the transported substance moves in the direction opposite to the concentration gradient used as the energy source.

5.6 Exocytosis and Endocytosis

- Large molecules and particles are moved out of and into cells by exocytosis and endocytosis. The mechanisms allow substances to leave and enter cells without directly passing through the plasma membrane.
- In exocytosis, a vesicle carrying secreted materials contacts and fuses with the plasma membrane on its cytoplasmic side. The fusion introduces the vesicle membrane into the plasma membrane and releases the vesicle contents to the cell exterior.
- In endocytosis, materials on the cell exterior are enclosed in a segment of the plasma membrane that pockets inward and pinches off on the cytoplasmic side as an endocytic vesicle. Endocytosis occurs in two overall forms, bulk-phase endocytosis (pinocytosis) and receptor-mediated endocytosis. Most of the materials entering cells are digested into molecular subunits small enough to be transported across the vesicle membranes.

Questions

Self-Test Questions

1. In the fluid mosaic model,
   a. the plasma membrane is a rigid association of proteins and lipid molecules.
   b. phospholipids often flip-flop between the inner and outer layers.
   c. the mosaic refers to proteins attached to the underlying cytoskeleton.
   d. the fluid refers to the phospholipid bilayer.
   e. the mosaic refers to the symmetry of the internal membrane proteins and sterols.
2. The freeze-fracture technique demonstrates
   a. that the plasma membrane is a bilayer with individual proteins suspended in it.
   b. that the plasma membrane is fluid.
   c. the different functions of membrane proteins.
   d. that proteins are bound to the cytoplasmic side but not embedded in the lipid bilayer.
   e. the direction of movement of solutes through the membrane.

3. Which of the following statements about desaturase enzymes is correct?
   a. They are expressed specifically in bacteria grown at high temperatures.
   b. They increase the degree of unsaturation of membrane fatty acids.
   c. They increase the number of hydrogens in a fatty acid.
   d. They are essential to keep membranes fluid at low temperatures.
   e. Both b and d are correct.
4. Which of the following statements is correct?
   a. Membrane lipids are polar molecules.
   b. A lipid bilayer requires energy in the form of ATP to form.
   c. The higher the proportion of saturated lipids, the more fluid a membrane will be.
   d. Molecules of cholesterol are found integrated into membranes.
   e. Both a and d are correct.
5. Compared with integral membrane proteins, peripheral membrane proteins
   a. are composed of a greater total number of amino acids.
   b. are involved in the transport of ions across membranes.
   c. tend to be hydrophobic.
   d. are usually composed of a mixture of polar and nonpolar amino acids.
   e. None of the above statements are correct.
6. Which one of the following molecules shows the slowest rate of membrane diffusion?
   a. CO_2
   b. water
   c. O_2
   d. glucose
   e. K^+
7. Unlike simple diffusion, facilitated diffusion
   a. requires a source of chemical energy, such as ATP.
   b. can transport molecules against a concentration gradient.
   c. can be saturated by high substrate concentrations.
   d. is an entropy-driven process.
   e. Both b and c are correct.
8. An ion moving through a membrane channel in one direction gives energy to actively transport another molecule in the opposite direction. This describes
   a. facilitated diffusion.
   b. exchange diffusion.
   c. symport transport
   d. primary active transport pump.
   e. cotransport.
9. Phagocytosis illustrates the phenomenon of
   a. receptor-mediated endocytosis.
   b. bulk-phase endocytosis.
   c. exocytosis.
   d. pinocytosis.
   e. cotransport.
10. Place in order the events of receptor-mediated endocytosis.
    (1) Clathrin coat disappears.
    (2) Receptors collect in a coated pit covered with clathrin on the cytoplasmic side.
    (3) Receptors recognize and bind specific molecules.
    (4) Endocytic vesicle may fuse with lysosome while receptors are recycled to the cell surface.
    (5) Pits deepen and pinch free of plasma membrane to form endocytic vesicles.
    a. 41253
    b. 21354
    c. 32514
    d. 41523
    e. 31245

Questions for Discussion

1. The bacterium *Vibrio cholerae* causes cholera, a disease characterized by severe diarrhea that may cause infected people to lose up to 20 L of fluid in a day. The bacterium enters the body when someone drinks contaminated water. It adheres to the intestinal lining, where it causes the cells of the lining to release sodium and chloride ions. Explain how this release is related to the massive fluid loss.
2. In hospitals, solutions of glucose with a concentration of 0.3 M can be introduced directly into the bloodstream of patients without tissue damage by osmotic water movement. The same is true of NaCl solutions, but these must be adjusted to 0.15 M to be introduced without damage. Can you explain why one is introduced at 0.3 M and the other at 0.15 M?

Mitochondrion (colorized SEM). Mitochondria are the sites of cellular respiration.

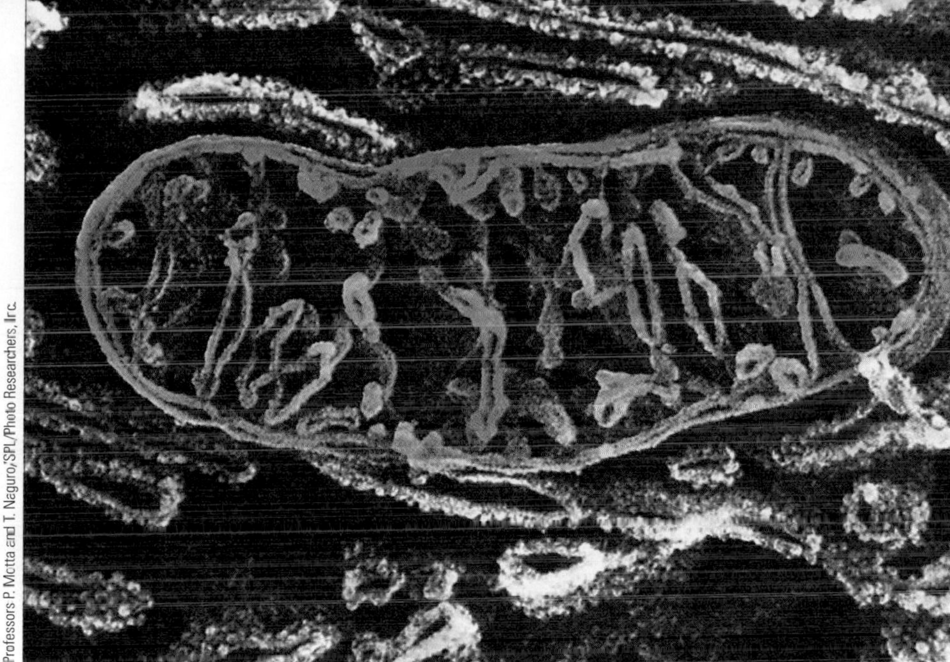
Professors P. Motta and T. Naguro/SPL/Photo Researchers, Inc.

STUDY PLAN

6 Cellular Respiration

WHY IT MATTERS

In the early 1960s, Swedish physician Rolf Luft mulled over some odd symptoms of a patient. The young woman was hot all the time. Even on the coldest winter days, she never stopped perspiring and her skin was always flushed. She also felt weak and was thin, despite a huge appetite.

Luft inferred that his patient's symptoms pointed to a metabolic disorder. Her cells seemed to be active, but much of their activity was being dissipated as metabolic heat. He decided to order tests to measure her metabolic rates. The patient's oxygen consumption was the highest ever recorded!

Luft also examined a tissue sample from the patient's skeletal muscles. Using a microscope, he found that her muscle cells contained many more mitochondria—the adenosine triphosphate (ATP)-producing organelles of the cell—than are normal; also, her mitochondria were abnormally shaped. Other studies showed that the mitochondria were engaged in cellular respiration—their prime function—but little ATP was being generated.

The disorder, now called *Luft syndrome,* was the first disorder to be linked directly to a defective cellular organelle. This syndrome is extremely rare and has now been shown to be due to a defect in one of the complexes of cellular respiration that links electron transport to proton pumping and subsequent ATP generation. With such a disorder, skeletal and heart muscles and the brain, the tissues with the highest energy demands, are affected the most.

More than 100 mitochondrial disorders are now known. Defective mitochondria also contribute to many age-related problems, including type 1 diabetes, atherosclerosis, and amyotrophic lateral sclerosis (ALS, also called Lou Gehrig disease), as well as Parkinson, Alzheimer, and Huntington diseases.

Clearly, human health depends on mitochondria that are structurally sound and functioning properly. More broadly, every animal, plant, and fungus and most protists depend on mitochondria that are functioning correctly to grow and survive.

6.1 The Chemical Basis of Cellular Respiration

The vast majority of energy enters the biosphere through the process of photosynthesis, which we describe in detail in the next chapter. The reactions of photosynthesis trap light energy and use it to convert CO_2 and water into organic molecules such as sugars, which contain an abundance of free energy **(Figure 6.1)**. The focus of this chapter is another fundamental biological process that enables organisms to efficiently extract the energy present in molecules such as sugar: cellular respiration. By slowly oxidizing energy-rich molecules, the reactions of cellular respiration extract the potential energy and convert it into ATP, a form of chemical energy that can readily be used by the cell for the majority of energy-requiring reactions. The complete oxidation of food molecules results in the formation of CO_2, which is released into the environment (see Figure 6.1).

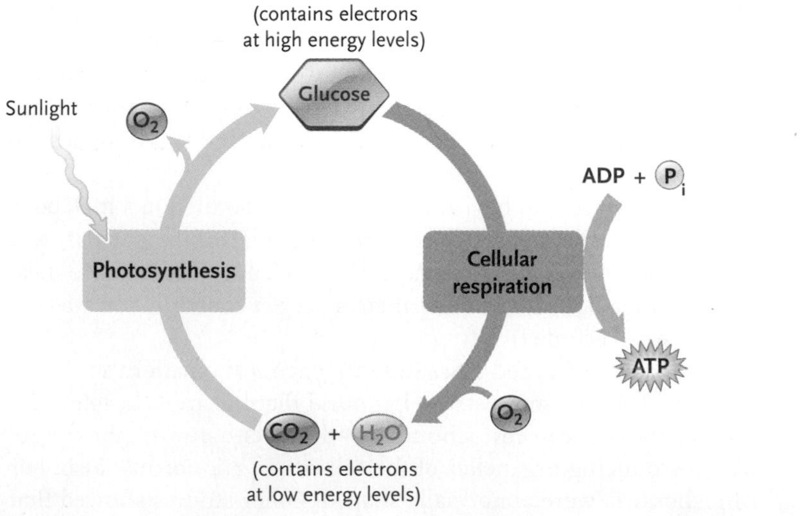

Figure 6.1
Flow of energy from sunlight to ATP. Photosynthesis occurs in plants, many protists, and some prokaryotes. Cellular respiration occurs in all eukaryotes and many prokaryotes.

6.1a Food as Fuel

What is it about the structure of glucose that makes it a source of energy that organisms can use to live? A similar question could be asked about gasoline: what is it about the chemical makeup of gasoline that provides energy to run a car? What glucose and gasoline have in common **(Figure 6.2)** that makes them both good fuel molecules is an abundance of hydrogen in the form of carbon–hydrogen (C–H) bonds.

The chemical basis for why C–H bonds are a source of energy can be explained by **Figure 6.3.** For any atom, an electron that is farther away from the nucleus contains more energy than an electron that is more closely held by the nucleus. As a result, an electron loses energy as it moves closer to the parent nucleus and gains energy as it moves away. The electrons associated with a C–H bond are equidistant from both nuclei. Because of this, they contain high energy and can be easily removed. In contrast, molecules that have an abundance of oxygen contain less potential energy because oxygen is strongly electronegative. The more electronegative an atom is, the greater the force that holds the electrons to that atom, and, therefore, the greater the energy required to remove these electrons. These fundamental principles of chemistry have an everyday relevance; they explain why, for example, compared to proteins (polymers of amino acids) and carbohydrates (groups of sugars), fats contain more calories per unit of weight. A fat is almost entirely C–H bonds (to review the structure of these molecules, see the *The Chemical and Physical Foundations of Biology* pages).

6.1b The Principle of Redox

The potential energy that is contained within fuel molecules is released by their oxidation. The term **oxidation** refers to the loss of electrons (e^-),

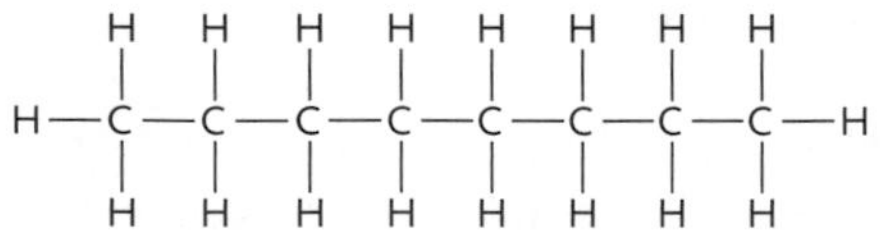

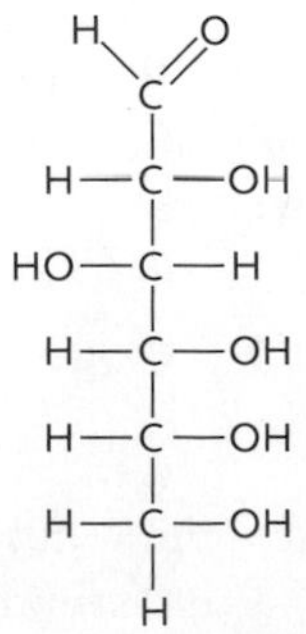

Figure 6.2
Two good fuels: gasoline and glucose. Both are excellent fuels due to the presence of an abundance of easily accessible electrons present in the form of C–H bonds.

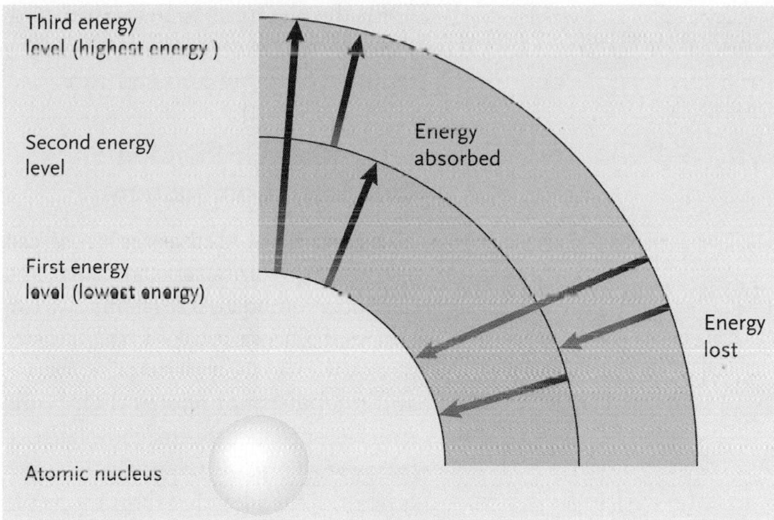

Figure 6.3
Energy levels of electrons of an atom. Electrons can exist only in discrete energy states. Electrons that gain energy move to a higher energy level that is farther away from the nucleus. Electrons that lose energy move closer to the nucleus.

and the molecule afterward is said to be **oxidized.** The oxidation of a molecule is linked to a **reduction** reaction in which another molecule gains the electrons, or becomes **reduced.** Oxidation and reduction reactions are coupled processes; you never have one without the other. A simple mnemonic to remember the direction of electron transfer is OIL RIG—Oxidation Is Loss (of electrons), Reduction Is Gain (of electrons). For short, oxidation–reduction reactions are called redox reactions. A generalized redox reaction can be written like this:

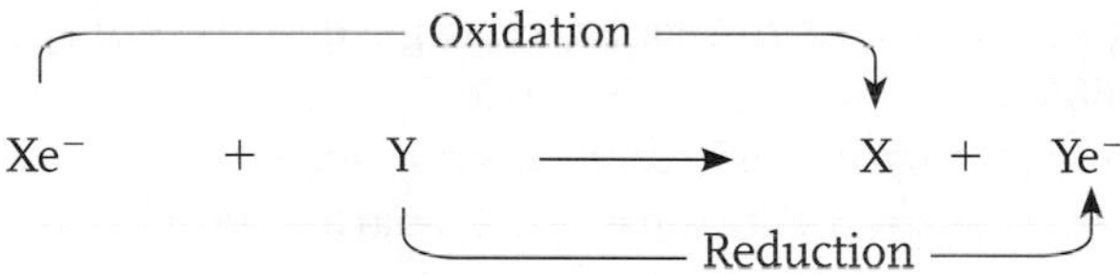

The redox reaction describing the respiratory breakdown of glucose is as follows:

Oxidation

$$C_6H_{12}O_6 + 6O_2 \longrightarrow 6CO_2 + 6H_2O$$

Reduction

The term *oxidation* comes from that fact that many reactions in which electrons are removed from fuel molecules involve oxygen as the atom that accepts the electrons (or, stated in another way, the molecule that gets reduced, or the electron acceptor). The involvement of oxygen is essential for many commonplace oxidation reactions: a car engine requires large amounts of air to be delivered to each piston for combustion to take place; an oil fire on a stove can be rapidly put out by putting a lid on the pot, restricting its supply of air. As we will see later in this chapter, the high affinity of O_2 for electrons, its high electronegativity, makes it ideal as the terminal electron acceptor of cellular respiration.

The concept of redox reactions is made a little more challenging to understand by two points of fact. First, although many oxidation reactions involve oxygen, many others, including many involved in cellular respiration, do not. Second, the gain or loss of an electron in a redox reaction is not always complete. That is, whereas in some redox reactions, electrons are transferred completely from one atom to another, in other redox reactions, what changes is the degree to which electrons are shared between the two atoms. As an example, the reaction between methane and oxygen (the burning of natural gas in air) illustrates a redox reaction in which only the degree of electron sharing changes. The dots in **Figure 6.4** indicate the positions of the electrons involved in the covalent bonds of the reactants and products. Compare the reactant methane with the product CO_2. In methane, the covalent electrons are shared essentially equally between bonded C and H atoms because C and H are almost equally electronegative. In CO_2, electrons are closer to the O atoms than to the C atom because O atoms are highly electronegative. Overall, this means that the C atom has partially "lost" its shared electrons in the reaction. In short, methane has

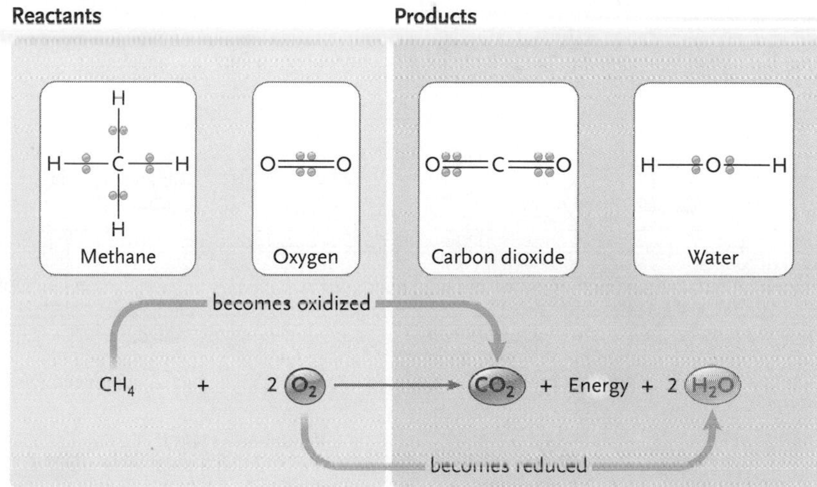

Figure 6.4
Relative loss and gain of electrons in a redox reaction, the burning of methane (natural gas) in oxygen. Compare the positions of the electrons in the covalent bonds of reactants and products. In this redox reaction, methane is oxidized and oxygen is reduced.

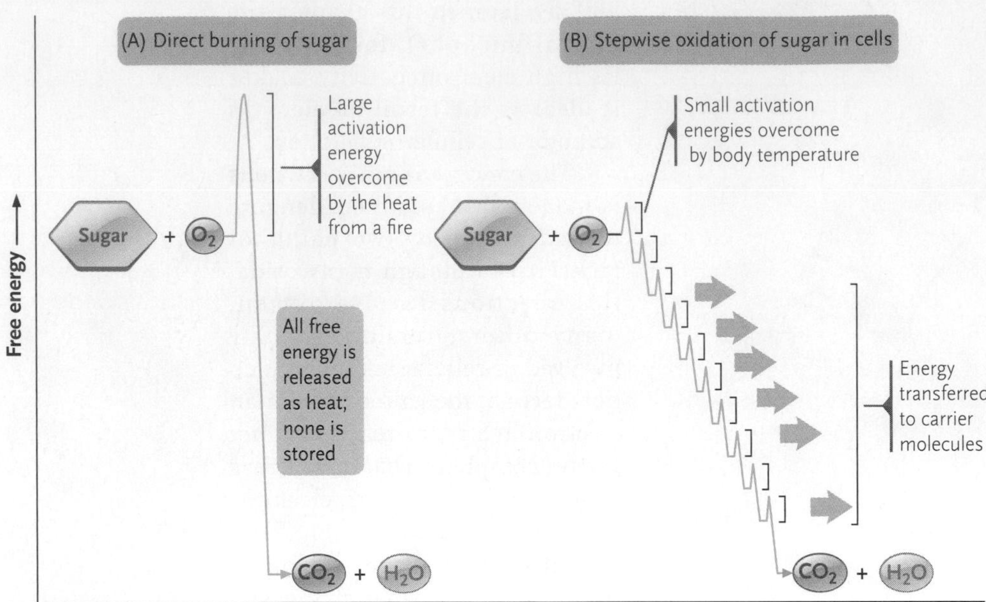

Figure 6.5
A comparison of the oxidation of glucose by direct burning (combustion) with cellular respiration.

been oxidized. Now compare the oxygen reactant with the product water. In the oxygen molecule, the two O atoms share their electrons equally. The oxygen reacts with the hydrogen from methane, producing water, in which the electrons are closer to the O atom than to the H atoms. This means that each O atom has partially "gained" electrons; in short, oxygen has been reduced. Because of this, the reaction between methane and O_2 releases much heat. The energy is released as the electrons in the C–H bonds of methane move closer to the electronegative oxygen atoms that form CO_2. The more electronegative an atom is, the greater the force that holds the electrons to that atom, and, therefore, the greater the energy required to remove an electron.

6.1c Cellular Respiration Is Controlled Combustion

Like gasoline or methane, glucose can also undergo combustion and burn, and like most combustion reactions, the oxidation of glucose results in the transfer of electrons to O_2, yielding CO_2, water, and the release of energy. CO_2 is the common product for the complete oxidation of all organic molecules. Because it is a fully oxidized carbon molecule CO_2 contains no usable energy.

A good way to think of cellular respiration is *controlled* combustion, in which the energy of the C–H bonds is not liberated, suddenly producing heat, but is slowly released in a stepwise fashion, with the energy being transferred to other molecules. If we simply burn some glucose **(Figure 6.5a),** energy would be released as heat, with the initial large energy of activation (see Section 4.4) being overcome by using a spark or flame. In the cell, the oxidation of glucose occurs via a series of enzyme-catalyzed reactions **(Figure 6.5b),** each with a small activation energy. The energy released is transferred to energy-carrying molecules. Thermodynamically speaking, the two processes are identical: they are both exergonic, having the same change in free energy (686 kcal/mol). The difference is that if the energy released by the oxidation of glucose is released as heat, it cannot be harnessed to drive metabolic reactions.

In cellular respiration, the oxidation of food molecules occurs in the presence of a group of enzymes called *dehydrogenases* that facilitate the transfer of electrons from food to a molecule that acts as an energy carrier or shuttle. The most common energy carrier is the coenzyme *nicotinamide adenine dinucleotide* **(Figure 6.6).** During respiration, the dehydrogenases remove two hydrogen atoms from a substrate molecule and transfer the two electrons—but only one of the protons—to NAD^+, resulting in its complete reduction to NADH. The other proton is simply released. The efficiency of energy transfer between food molecules and NAD^+ is high, with very little energy lost as heat. As we will see later, the potential energy carried in NADH is used to synthesize ATP.

Adenine, Ribose, P, P, Ribose, nicotinamide — Oxidized (NAD^+) ⇌ Reduced (NADH)

$NAD^+ + 2e^- + H^+ \rightleftharpoons NADH$ (Reduction of NAD^+ / Oxidation of NADH)

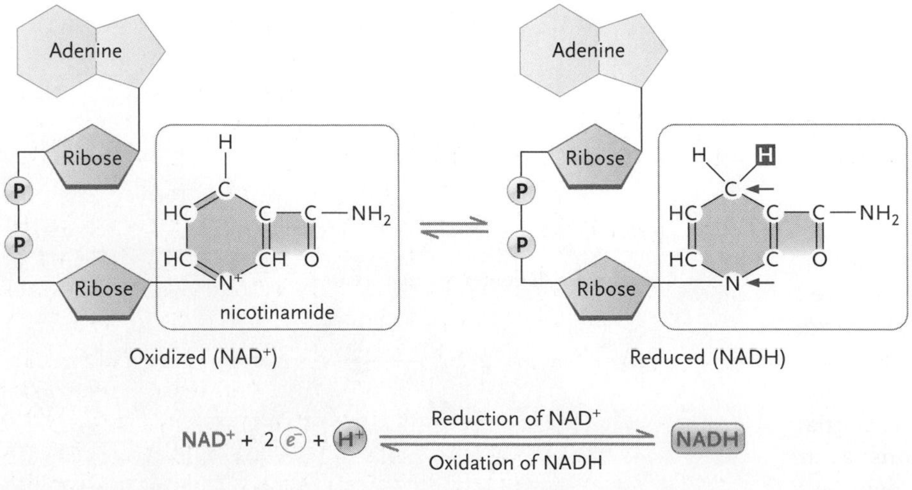

Figure 6.6
Electron carrier NAD^+. As the carrier is reduced to NADH, an electron is added at each of the two positions marked by a red arrow; a proton is also added at the position boxed in red. The nitrogenous base (blue) that adds and releases electrons and protons is nicotinamide, which is derived from the vitamin niacin (nicotinic acid).

Study Break

1. What is it about the structure of gasoline and glucose that makes them both good fuels?
2. In the respiratory breakdown of glucose, what gets oxidized and what gets reduced?

6.2 Cellular Respiration: An Overview

At this point, let's step back and remind ourselves of the primary goal of cellular respiration: it is to transform the potential energy found in food molecules into a form that can be used for metabolic processes, adenosine triphosphate (ATP). We will see later in the chapter that both proteins and lipids can also be oxidized by cellular respiration and their potential energy harnessed. However, because the oxidation of glucose utilizes the entire respiratory pathway, it is the main focus of our discussion.

6.2a The Three Parts of Cellular Respiration

Cellular respiration can be divided into three parts or stages **(Figure 6.7)**:

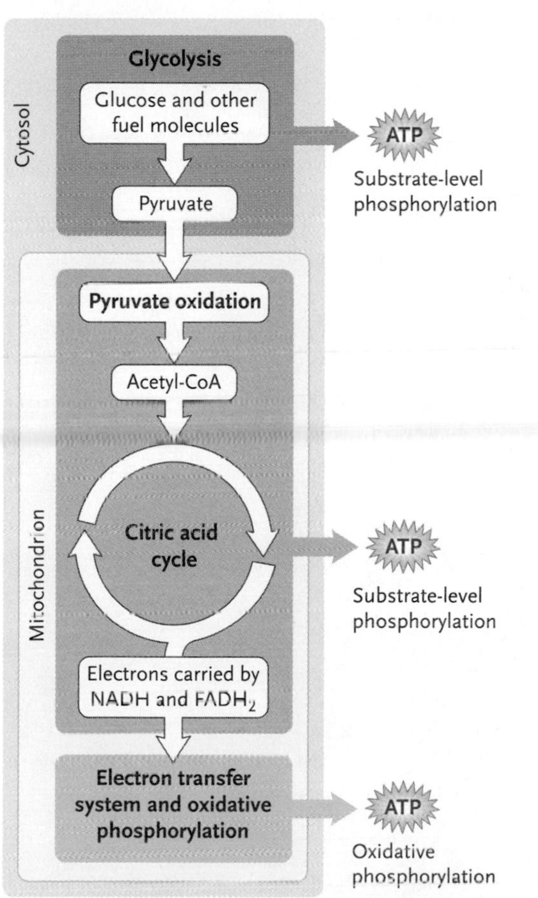

Figure 6.7
The three stages of cellular respiration, glycolysis, pyruvate oxidation, and the citric acid cycle, and the electron transport chain and oxidative phosphorylation.

1. *Glycolysis.* Enzymes break down a molecule of glucose into two molecules of pyruvate. Some ATP and NADH is synthesized.
2. *Citric acid cycle.* Acetyl coenzyme A (acetyl-CoA), which is formed from the oxidation of pyruvate, enters a metabolic cycle, where it is completely oxidized to CO_2. Some ATP and NADH is synthesized.
3. *Electron transport and chemiosmosis.* The NADH synthesized by both glycolysis and the citric acid cycle is oxidized, with the liberated electrons being passed along an electron transport chain until they are transferred to O_2, producing water. The free energy released during electron transport is used to establish a proton gradient across a membrane, and this, in turn, is what synthesizes the remaining ATP.

Although all three stages are required to extract the maximum amount of energy that is biologically possible from a molecule of glucose, not all organisms, and, in fact, not all tissues, possess all three stages.

6.2b The Mitochondrion

In prokaryotes, glycolysis and the citric acid cycle occur in the cytosol of the cell, whereas electron transport occurs on internal membranes that are derived from the plasma membrane. By comparison, in eukaryotic cells, the citric acid cycle and electron transport occur in a specialized organelle called the mitochondrion (plural, mitochondria) **(Figure 6.8)**. This membrane-bound organelle is often referred to as the powerhouse of the cell because as the location of both the citric acid cycle and electron transport, it is the largest generator of ATP in the cell.

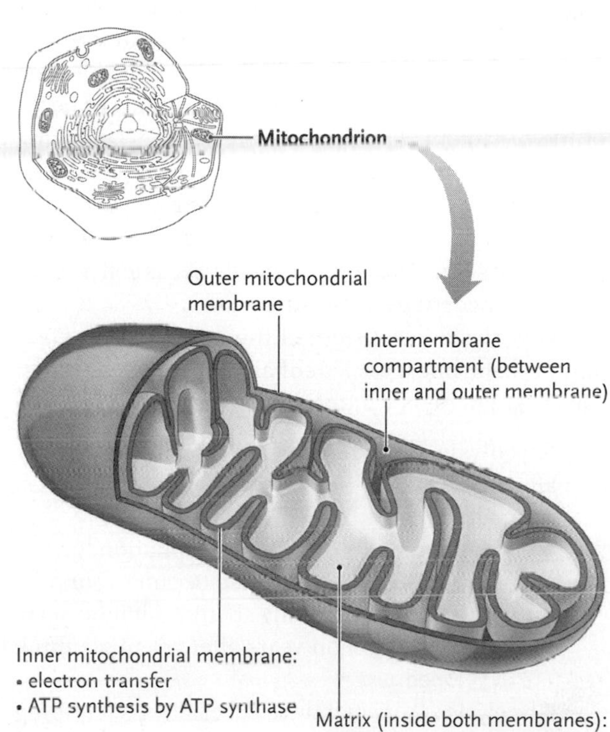

Figure 6.8
Membranes and compartments of mitochondria. Label lines that end in a dot indicate a compartment enclosed by the membranes.

The mitochondrion is composed of two membranes, the outer membrane and the inner membrane, which together define two compartments (see Figure 6.8): the intermembrane space, which is found between the outer and inner membranes, and the matrix, which is the interior aqueous environment of the organelle.

In the description of cellular respiration that follows, we often refer specifically to mitochondria and its various compartments, but it is important to remember that there is nothing uniquely eukaryotic about cellular respiration. Prokaryotes do not have mitochondria, but many do possess the complete complement of reactions that comprise cellular respiration—from glycolysis through electron transport and oxidative phosphorylation.

STUDY BREAK

In eukaryotes, what stages of respiration take place in the mitochondrion?

6.3 Glycolysis

Glycolysis is the first set of reactions that extracts energy from sugar molecules. Glycolysis (*glykys* = sweet; *lysis* = breakdown) consists of 10 sequential enzyme-catalyzed reactions that lead to the oxidation of the six-carbon sugar glucose, producing two molecules of the three-carbon compound pyruvate. The potential energy released in the oxidation leads to the overall synthesis of both NADH and ATP.

6.3a Glycolysis Is an Ancient Pathway

Glycolysis was one of the first metabolic pathways studied and is one of the best understood, in terms of the enzymes involved, their mechanisms of action, and how the pathway is regulated to meet the energy needs of the organism. The first experiments investigating glycolysis took place over 100 years ago and were some of the first to show, using the extracts from yeast cells, that one could study biological reactions in an isolated, cell-free system. These experiments became the foundation of modern biochemistry.

Glycolysis is considered the most fundamental and probably most ancient of all metabolic pathways. This is supported by the following facts:

1. Glycolysis is universal, being found in almost all organisms, both prokaryotes and eukaryotes, from all branches of the tree of life.
2. Unlike other stages of cellular respiration, glycolysis does not require O_2, which became abundant in Earth's atmosphere only about 2.5 billion years ago—about 1.5 billion years after scientists think life developed.
3. Glycolysis occurs in the cytosol of all cells requiring soluble enzymes and therefore does not require more sophisticated electron transport chains or subcellular compartments in order to operate.

6.3b The Reactions of Glycolysis

Figure 6.9 summarizes the major aspects of the glycolytic pathway, whereas **Figure 6.10** provides the details of each step. Looking at both, there are three key points to keep in mind:

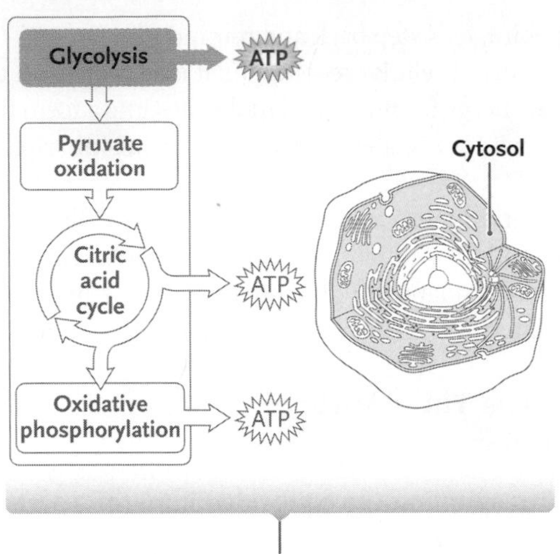

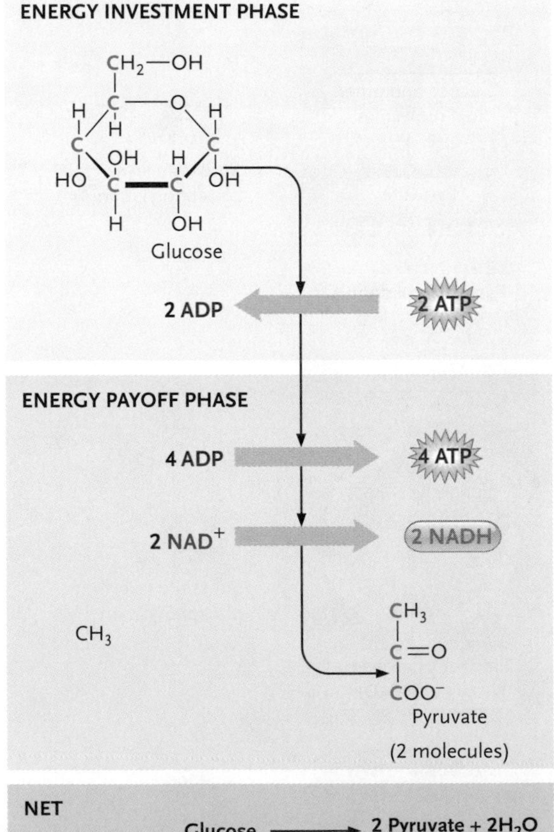

Figure 6.9
Summary of glycolysis showing the energy inputs and outputs.

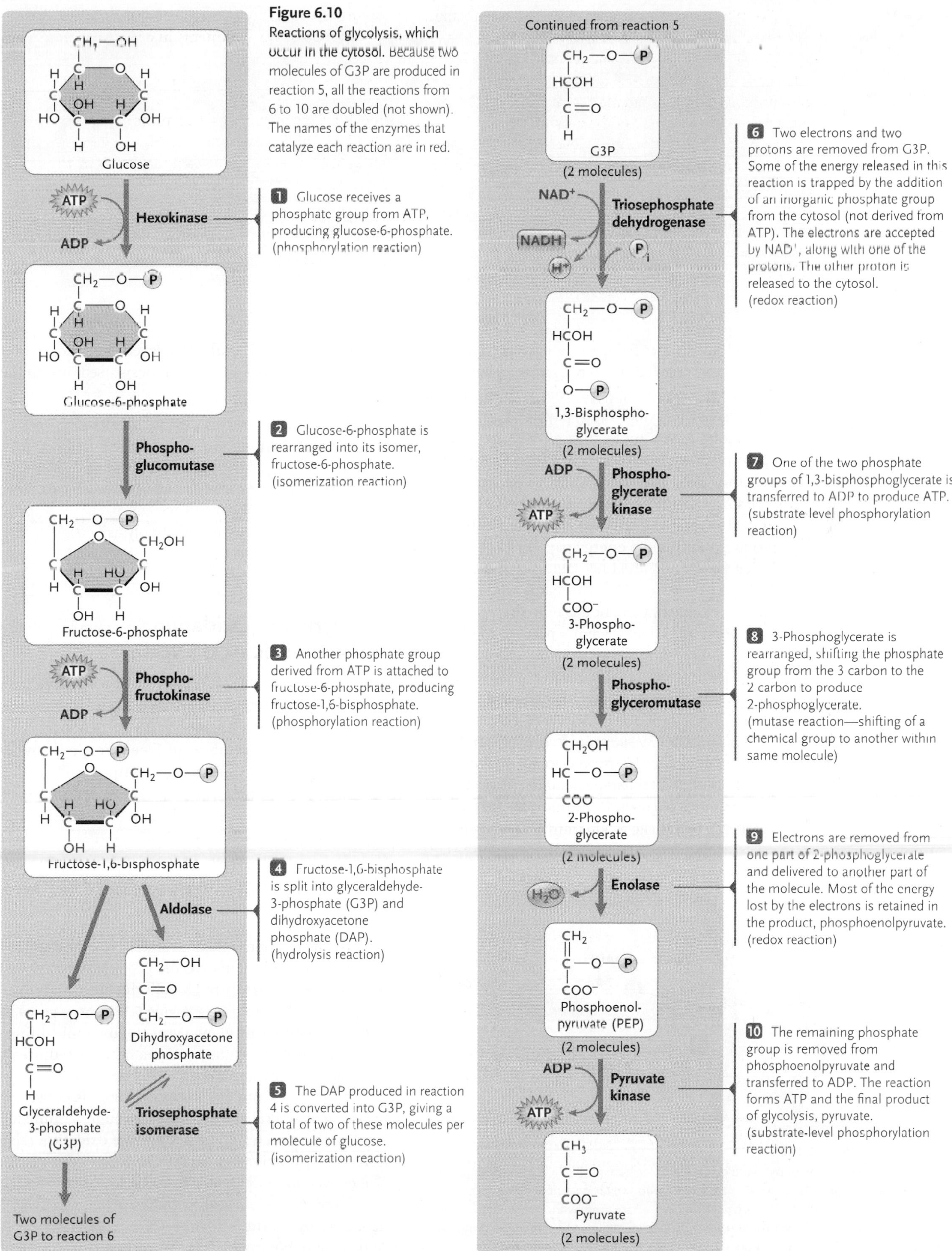

Glucose
ATP
Hexokinase
ADP
1 Glucose receives a phosphate group from ATP, producing glucose-6-phosphate. (phosphorylation reaction)
Glucose-6-phosphate
Phospho-glucomutase
2 Glucose-6-phosphate is rearranged into its isomer, fructose-6-phosphate. (isomerization reaction)
Fructose-6-phosphate
ATP
Phospho-fructokinase
ADP
3 Another phosphate group derived from ATP is attached to fructose-6-phosphate, producing fructose-1,6-bisphosphate. (phosphorylation reaction)
Fructose-1,6-bisphosphate
Aldolase
4 Fructose-1,6-bisphosphate is split into glyceraldehyde-3-phosphate (G3P) and dihydroxyacetone phosphate (DAP). (hydrolysis reaction)
Dihydroxyacetone phosphate
Glyceraldehyde-3-phosphate (G3P)
Triosephosphate isomerase
5 The DAP produced in reaction 4 is converted into G3P, giving a total of two of these molecules per molecule of glucose. (isomerization reaction)
Two molecules of G3P to reaction 6
Continued from reaction 5
G3P
(2 molecules)
NAD+
NADH
H+
Pi
Triosephosphate dehydrogenase
6 Two electrons and two protons are removed from G3P. Some of the energy released in this reaction is trapped by the addition of an inorganic phosphate group from the cytosol (not derived from ATP). The electrons are accepted by NAD+, along with one of the protons. The other proton is released to the cytosol. (redox reaction)
1,3-Bisphospho-glycerate
(2 molecules)
ADP
ATP
Phospho-glycerate kinase
7 One of the two phosphate groups of 1,3-bisphosphoglycerate is transferred to ADP to produce ATP. (substrate level phosphorylation reaction)
3-Phospho-glycerate
(2 molecules)
Phospho-glyceromutase
8 3-Phosphoglycerate is rearranged, shifting the phosphate group from the 3 carbon to the 2 carbon to produce 2-phosphoglycerate. (mutase reaction—shifting of a chemical group to another within same molecule)
2-Phospho-glycerate
(2 molecules)
H2O
Enolase
9 Electrons are removed from one part of 2-phosphoglycerate and delivered to another part of the molecule. Most of the energy lost by the electrons is retained in the product, phosphoenolpyruvate. (redox reaction)
Phosphoenol-pyruvate (PEP)
(2 molecules)
ADP
ATP
Pyruvate kinase
10 The remaining phosphate group is removed from phosphoenolpyruvate and transferred to ADP. The reaction forms ATP and the final product of glycolysis, pyruvate. (substrate-level phosphorylation reaction)
Pyruvate
(2 molecules)

Figure 6.10
Reactions of glycolysis, which occur in the cytosol. Because two molecules of G3P are produced in reaction 5, all the reactions from 6 to 10 are doubled (not shown). The names of the enzymes that catalyze each reaction are in red.

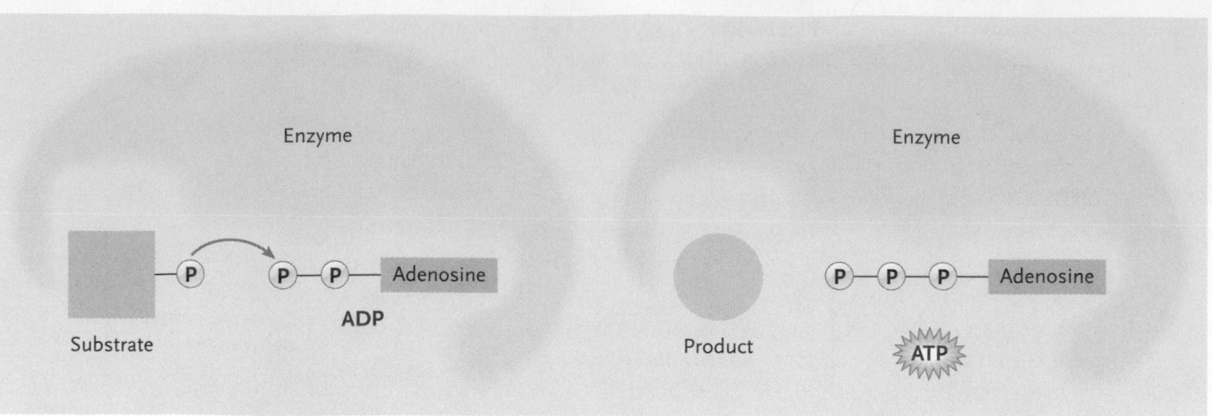

Figure 6.11
Mechanism that synthesizes ATP by substrate-level phosphorylation. A phosphate group is transferred from a high-energy donor directly to ADP, forming ATP.

1. *Energy investment followed by payoff.* Glycolysis can be considered as two distinct phases: an initial five-step energy investment phase followed by a five-step energy payoff phase. Initially in glycolysis, two molecules of ATP are actually consumed as glucose and fructose-6-phosphate become phosphorylated. The investment of two ATP for each glucose molecule leads to an energy reward as four ATP and two NADH molecules are produced during the energy payoff phase.
2. *No carbon is lost.* Besides yielding a net of two ATP and two NADH, for each molecule of glucose oxidized, you should note that no carbon has been lost. All six carbons present in glucose are accounted for in the two molecules of pyruvate. However, since glucose has been oxidized, the potential energy in two molecules of pyruvate is less than that of one molecule of glucose.
3. *ATP is generated by substrate-level phosphorylation.* During glycolysis, ATP is produced using a process called *substrate-level phosphorylation.* This mode of ATP synthesis **(Figure 6.11)** requires an enzyme that transfers a phosphate group from a high-energy substrate molecule to adenosine diphosphate (ADP), producing ATP. Substrate-level phosphorylation is also the mode of ATP synthesis used during the citric acid cycle.

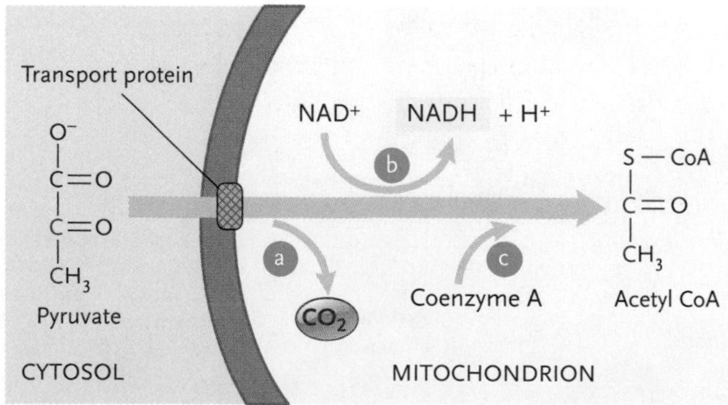

Figure 6.12
Reactions of pyruvate oxidation. After transport into the mitochondrion pyruvate is oxidized to an acetyl group, which is carried to the citric acid cycle by CoA. The reactions which are catalyzed by the *pyruvate dehydrogenase complex* include **(a)** decarboxylation, followed by **(b)** a dehydrogenation and finally **(c)** reaction with coenzyme A producing acetyl CoA.

Study Break

1. What evidence suggests that glycolysis is an ancient metabolic pathway?
2. What are the products of glycolysis?

6.4 Pyruvate Oxidation and the Citric Acid Cycle

The two molecules of pyruvate synthesized by glycolysis still contain approximately 75% of the energy found in one molecule of glucose. The extraction of the remaining free energy in pyruvate and trapping this energy in the form of ATP and electron carriers such as NADH are the overarching goals of the series of reactions described in this section.

6.4a Bridging Glycolysis and the Citric Acid Cycle

Because the reactions of the citric acid cycle are localized to the mitochondrial matrix, the product of glycolysis, pyruvate, must pass through both the outer and inner mitochondrial membranes **(Figure 6.12).** Large pores in the outer membrane allow pyruvate to simply diffuse through, but to cross the inner membrane requires a pyruvate-specific membrane carrier.

Once it gets into the matrix, pyruvate is converted into a molecule called acetyl-CoA through a multistep process that is referred to as **pyruvate oxidation** (also known as **pyruvic acid oxidation**) (see Figure 6.12). The conversion of pyruvate to acetyl-CoA starts with *a decarboxylation reaction* whereby the carboxyl ($-COO^-$) group of pyruvate is lost as CO_2. This reaction is understandable given that the carboxyl group itself contains little potential energy (no C–H bonds and a lot of oxygen). The decarboxylation reaction is followed by oxidation of the remaining two carbon molecules, producing acetate. This *dehydrogenation* reaction leads to transfer of two electrons and a proton to NAD^+, forming NADH. Lastly, the acetyl group reacts with coenzyme A, forming the high-energy intermediate acetyl-CoA.

If you look at the molecule of acetyl-CoA formed in Figure 6.12, you should notice that it still contains three C–H bonds and can be further oxidized to release even more free energy. Extracting this energy is the purpose of the reactions that make up the citric acid cycle.

6.4b The Citric Acid Cycle

The citric acid cycle consists of eight enzyme-catalyzed reactions: seven are soluble enzymes located in the mitochondrial matrix, and one enzyme is bound to the matrix side of the inner mitochondrial membrane. Combined, the reactions result in the oxidization of acetyl groups to CO_2 accompanied by the synthesis of ATP, NADH, and another nucleotide-based molecule, flavin adenine dinucleotide (FAD; the reduced form is $FADH_2$). A summary of the inputs and outputs of the citric acid cycle is shown in **Figure 6.13,** which, to put the cycle in context, also includes the pyruvate to acetyl-CoA step. Looking at the stoichiometry, for each acetyl-CoA that enters the citric acid cycle, three NADH, one $FADH_2$, and a single molecule of ATP, generated by substrate-level phosphorylation, are synthesized. In a complete turn of the cycle, one two-carbon acetyl unit is consumed and two molecules of CO_2 are released, thereby completing the conversion of all the C atoms originally in glucose to CO_2. The CoA molecule that carried the acetyl group to the cycle is released and participates again in pyruvate oxidation to pick up another acetyl group. The net reactants and products of one turn of the citric acid cycle are

$$1\ \text{acetyl-CoA} + 3\ NAD^+ + 1\ FAD + 1\ ADP + 1\ P_i + 2\ H_2O \longrightarrow 2\ CO_2 + 3\ NADH + 1\ FADH_2 + 1\ ATP + 3\ H^+ + 1\ \text{CoA}$$

Because one molecule of glucose is converted to two molecules of pyruvate by glycolysis and each molecule of pyruvate is converted to one acetyl group, all the reactants and products in this equation are doubled when the citric acid cycle is considered as a continuation of glycolysis and pyruvate oxidation. **Figure 6.14 (p. 124)** shows the individual steps of the citric acid cycle.

Study Break

1. What are the steps involved in converting pyruvate into acetyl-CoA?
2. What purpose is served by the citric acid cycle?

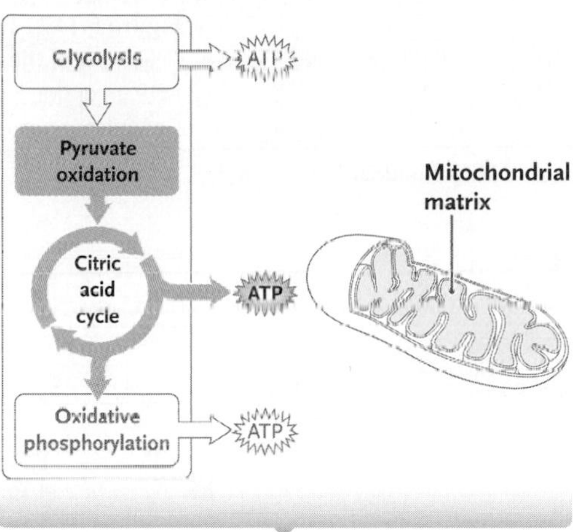

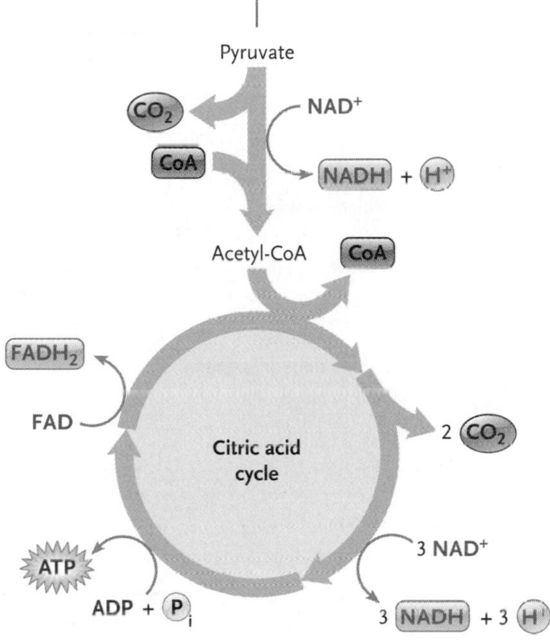

Figure 6.13
Overall reactions of pyruvate oxidation and the Citric acid cycle.
Each turn of the cycle oxidizes an acetyl group of acetyl-CoA to 2 CO_2. Acetyl-CoA, NAD^+, FAD, and ADP enter the cycle; CoA, NADH, $FADH_2$, ATP, and CO_2 are released as products.

6.5 Electron Transport and Chemiosmosis

Following the citric acid cycle, all the carbon present in glucose has been completely oxidized and released as CO_2. As well, besides the formation of ATP by substrate-level phosphorylation, the potential energy originally present in glucose now exists in the form of NADH and $FADH_2$. It is the purpose of the electron transport chain coupled with the process of chemiosmosis to extract the potential energy in these molecules and synthesize additional ATP.

6.5a The Respiratory Electron Transport Chain

The respiratory electron transport chain **(Figure 6.15, p. 125)** comprises a system of components that in eukaryotes is found on the inner mitochondrial membrane. The chain facilitates the transfer of electrons from $NADH_2$ and $FADH_2$ to O_2. The chain consists of four protein complexes: **complex I,** NADH dehydrogenase; **complex II,** succinate dehydrogenase; **complex III,**

Figure 6.14
Reactions of the citric acid cycle; enzyme names are in red. Acetyl-CoA, NAD^+, FAD, and ADP enter the cycle; CoA, NADH, $FADH_2$, ATP, and CO_2 are released as products. The CoA released in reaction 1 can cycle back for another turn of pyruvate oxidation.

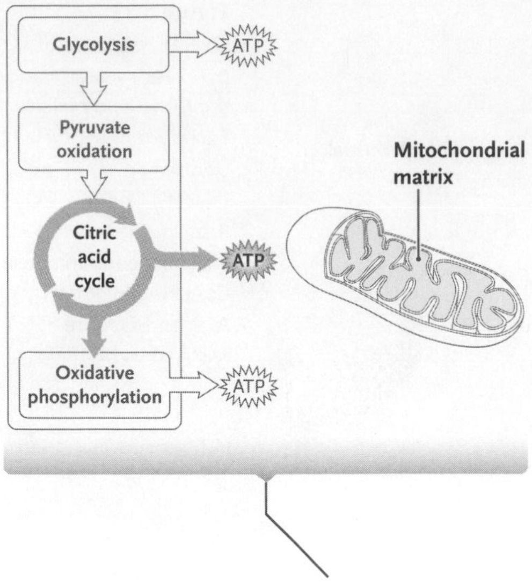

Glycolysis
ATP
Pyruvate oxidation
Citric acid cycle
ATP
Oxidative phosphorylation
ATP
Mitochondrial matrix

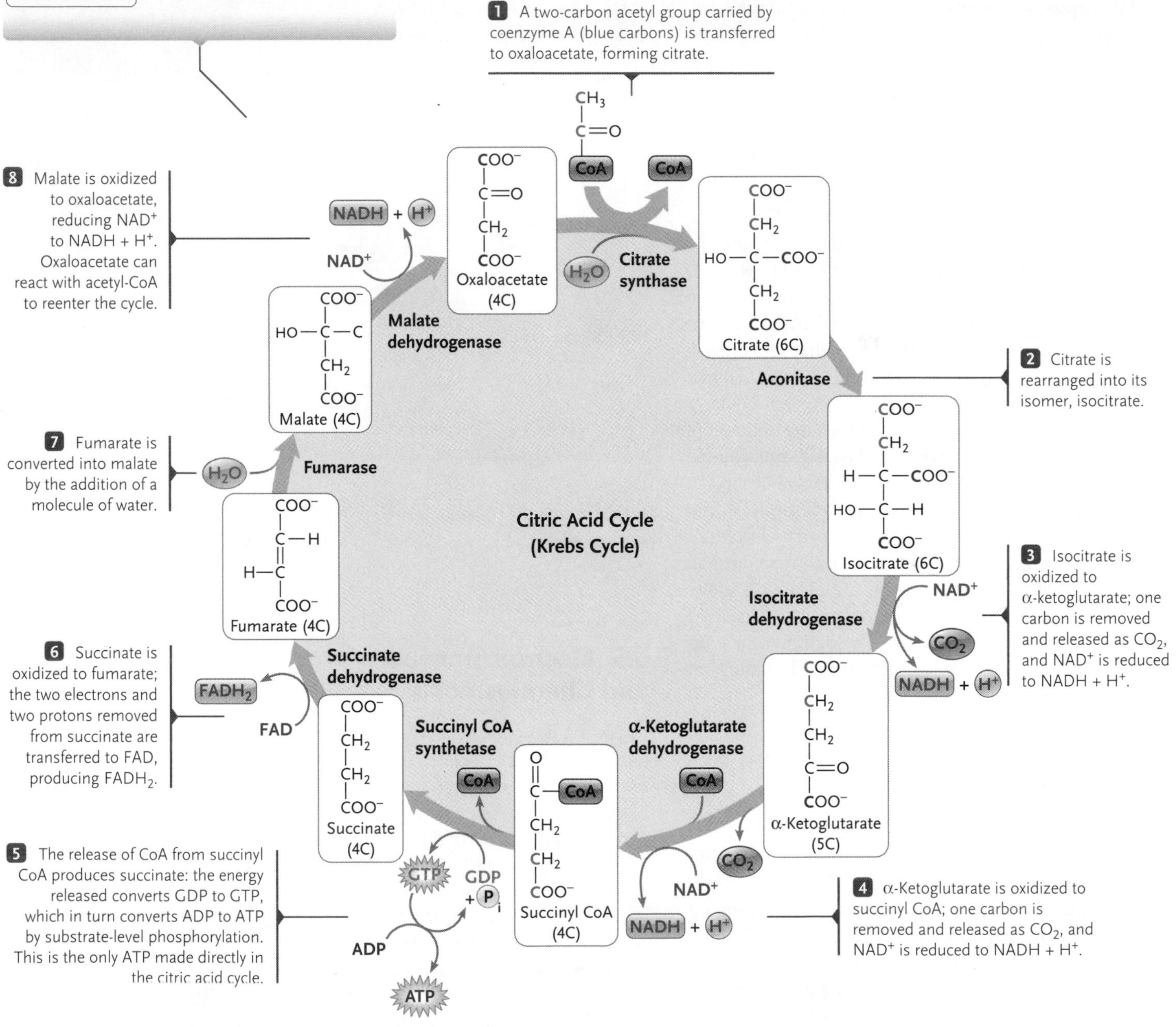

1 A two-carbon acetyl group carried by coenzyme A (blue carbons) is transferred to oxaloacetate, forming citrate.
2 Citrate is rearranged into its isomer, isocitrate.
3 Isocitrate is oxidized to α-ketoglutarate; one carbon is removed and released as CO_2, and NAD^+ is reduced to NADH + H^+.
4 α-Ketoglutarate is oxidized to succinyl CoA; one carbon is removed and released as CO_2, and NAD^+ is reduced to NADH + H^+.
5 The release of CoA from succinyl CoA produces succinate: the energy released converts GDP to GTP, which in turn converts ADP to ATP by substrate-level phosphorylation. This is the only ATP made directly in the citric acid cycle.
6 Succinate is oxidized to fumarate; the two electrons and two protons removed from succinate are transferred to FAD, producing $FADH_2$.
7 Fumarate is converted into malate by the addition of a molecule of water.
8 Malate is oxidized to oxaloacetate, reducing NAD^+ to NADH + H^+. Oxaloacetate can react with acetyl-CoA to reenter the cycle.
Citric Acid Cycle
(Krebs Cycle)
Citrate synthase
Aconitase
Isocitrate dehydrogenase
α-Ketoglutarate dehydrogenase
Succinyl CoA synthetase
Succinate dehydrogenase
Fumarase
Malate dehydrogenase
Oxaloacetate (4C)
Citrate (6C)
Isocitrate (6C)
α-Ketoglutarate (5C)
Succinyl CoA (4C)
Succinate (4C)
Fumarate (4C)
Malate (4C)

cytochrome complex; and **complex IV**, cytochrome oxidase. Whereas complex II is a single peripheral membrane protein, the remaining complexes are composed of multiple proteins. For example, about 40 protein subunits are needed to assemble together to make complex I.

Electron flow from one complex to another is facilitated by two mobile electron shuttles. Ubiquinone, which is a hydrophobic molecule found in the core of the membrane, shuttles electrons from complexes I and II to complex III. A second shuttle, cytochrome *c*, is located on the intermembrane space side of the

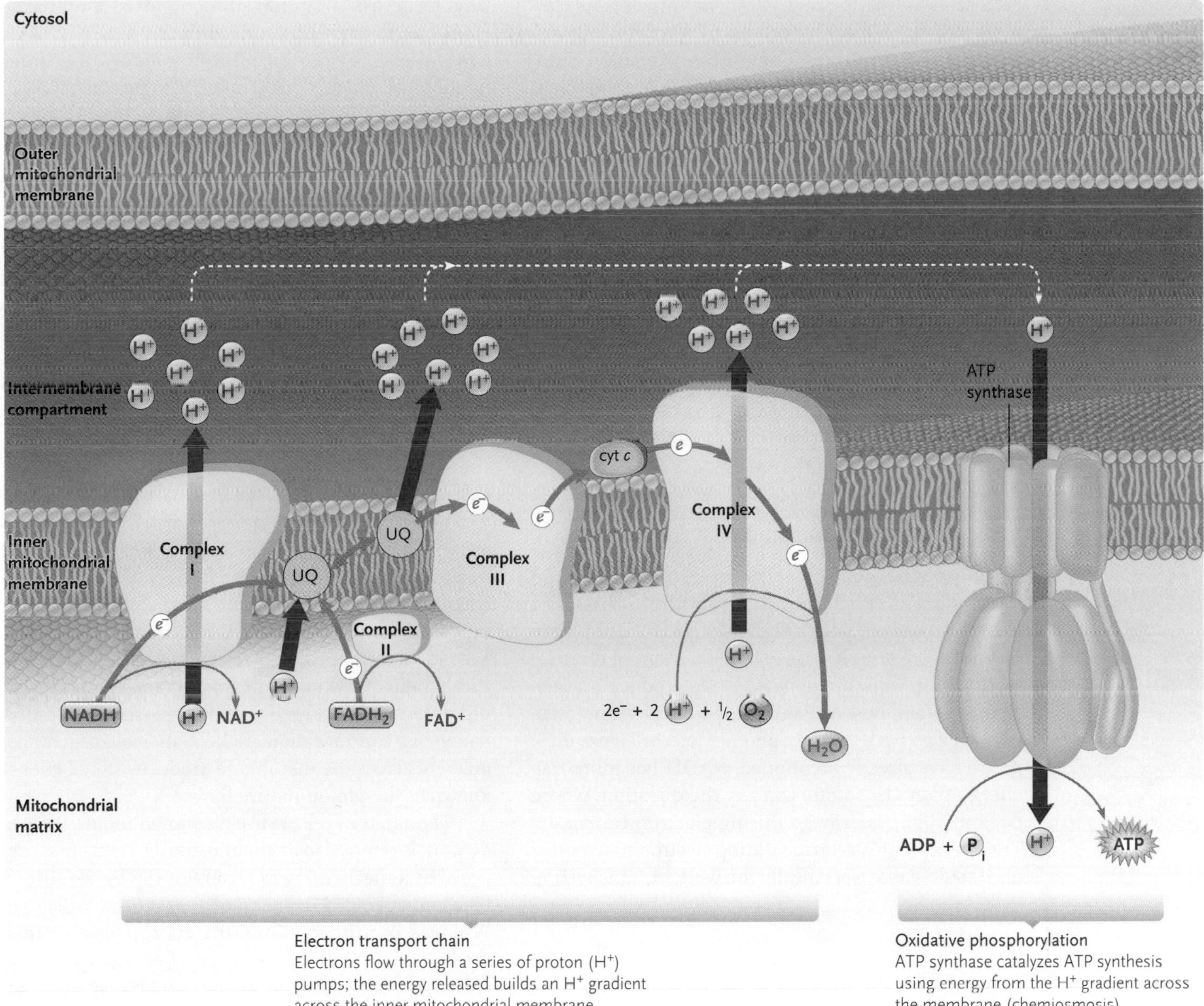

Figure 6.15
Mitochondrial electron transfer system and oxidative phosphorylation. The electron transfer system includes three major complexes, I, III, and IV. Two smaller electron carriers, ubiquinone (UQ) and cytochrome *c* (cyt *c*), act as shuttles between the major complexes, and succinate dehydrogenase (complex II) passes electrons to ubiquinone, bypassing complex I. Blue arrows indicate electron flow; red arrows indicate H^+ movement. H^+ is pumped from the matrix to the intermembrane compartment as electrons pass through complexes I and IV. H^+ are also moved into the matrix by the cyclic reduction/oxidation of ubiquinone. Oxidative phosphorylation involves the ATP synthase–catalyzed synthesis of ATP using the energy of the H^+ gradient across the inner mitochondrial membrane that is, by chemiosmosis.

membrane and transfers electrons from complex III to complex IV, cytochrome oxidase.

6.5b What Is the Driving Force behind Electron Transport?

Each of complexes I, III, and IV has bound to it specific *prosthetic groups* (see **Figure 6.16, p. 126**). These are redox active cofactors that alternate between reduced and oxidized states as they accept electrons from upstream molecules and subsequently donate electrons to downstream molecules. Thus, it is not the proteins themselves that transfer electrons but rather nonprotein groups bound to the proteins of each complex. A common prosthetic group is the molecule heme, which is a component of the cytochromes. Heme is a widely used molecule and is vital to the oxygen-carrying capacity of hemoglobin. The heme group contains a central redox-active iron atom that alternates from Fe^{2+} and Fe^{3+}.

During electron transport, the prosthetic group of complex I, flavin mononucleotide (FMN), is reduced by electron donation from NADH on the matrix side of the inner membrane. FMN then donates an electron to another complex I prosthetic group, the

Fe/S (iron–sulphur) group, which, in turn, donates electrons to ubiquinone. This process of reduction followed by oxidation continues along the entire chain until, finally, the electrons are donated to oxygen, resulting in its reduction to water with the addition of protons, which are abundant in the aqueous environment of the cell.

Why do electrons move down the chain at all? Figure 6.16 shows that the individual electron carriers of the chain are, in fact, organized in a very specific way—from high to low free energy. Any single component is more electronegative (higher affinity for electrons) than the preceding carrier in the chain. Overall, molecules such as NADH contain an abundance of free energy and can be readily oxidized, whereas O_2, the terminal electron acceptor of the chain, is strongly electronegative and can be easily reduced. As a consequence of this organization, electron movement along the chain is spontaneous, releasing free energy.

6.5c Chemiosmosis and ATP Synthesis

Although the goal of cellular respiration is the synthesis of ATP, electron transport from NADH or $FADH_2$ to oxygen does not in itself produce any ATP. Electrons are simply passed along a chain of electron carriers until they are donated to O_2, producing water. To understand how ATP is formed from electron transport, let's go back and take another look at Figure 6.15. As we have already mentioned, NADH has more free energy than O_2, so one can ask the question, where does this free energy go during electron transport? The energy that is released during electron transport is used to do work, specifically the work of transporting protons across the inner mitochondrial membrane from the matrix to the intermembrane space. As a consequence of proton pumping across the inner membrane, which is impermeable to protons, the H^+ concentration becomes much higher (the pH lower) in the intermembrane space compared to the matrix.

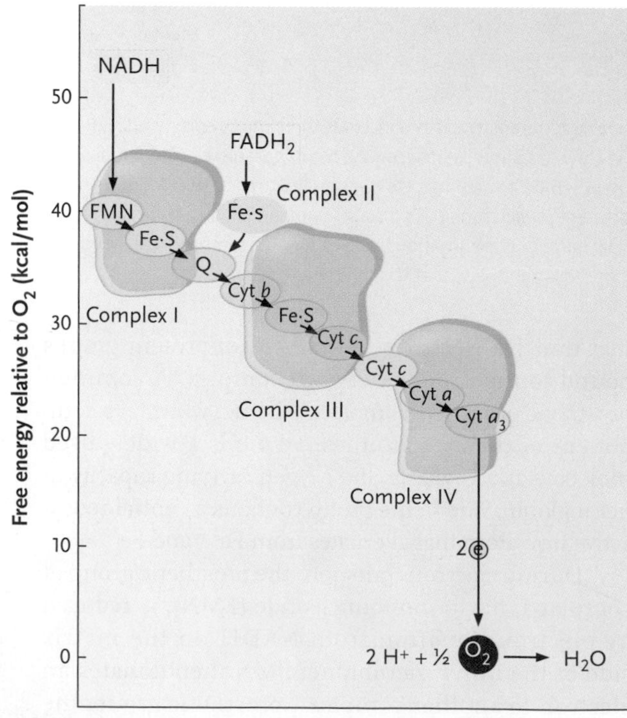

Figure 6.16
Redox components of the electron transport chain are organized from high to low free energy. Electron flow is spontaneous from high to low potential energy as electrons are passed from one redox molecule to the next.

Proton translocation occurs at distinct sites along the electron transport chain (see Figure 6.15). Within complexes I and IV, specific protein components use the energy released from electron transport for proton pumping. In addition, as ubiquinone molecules accept electrons from complexes I and II, they pick up protons from the matrix. After migrating through the membrane and donating electrons to complex III, ubiquinone retains a neutral charge by releasing protons into the intermembrane space.

The situation in which one side of the inner mitochondrial membrane has more protons than the other side represents a source of energy that can be harnessed to do work. The situation is somewhat analogous to water behind a dam. The potential energy possessed by a proton gradient is derived from two factors: first, a chemical gradient exists across the membrane because the concentration of protons is not equal on both sides. Second, because protons are charged, there is an electrical gradient with the intermembrane compartment more positively charged than the matrix. The combination of a concentration gradient and voltage (charge) gradient across the membrane produces stored energy known as the **proton-motive force.**

The ability of cells to use the proton-motive force to do work is referred to as **chemiosmosis.** It was first proposed as a mechanism to generate ATP by the British biochemist Peter Mitchell (see *People Behind Biology*). Whereas in mitochondria, the energy for chemiosmosis comes from the oxidation of energy-rich molecules such as NADPH by the electron transport chain, chemiosmosis also applies to the generation of ATP in chloroplasts, where electron transport is driven by light energy. Chemiosmosis, however, does not only apply to the synthesis of ATP as the proton-motive force is also used to pump substances across membranes. It is also used to drive the rotation of flagella in prokaryotes.

The mode of ATP synthesis that is linked to the oxidation of energy-rich molecules by an electron transport chain is called **oxidative phosphorylation.** Compared with substrate-level phosphorylation that occurs during glycolysis and the citric acid cycle, oxidative phosphorylation relies on the action of a large multiprotein complex that spans the inner mitochondrial membrane called ATP synthase **(Figure 6.17).**

6.5d ATP Synthase Is a Molecular Motor

ATP synthase is a lollipop-shaped structure consisting of a *basal unit,* which is embedded in the inner mitochondrial membrane, connected to a *headpiece* by a *stalk* (see Figure 6.17). The headpiece extends into the

People Behind Biology

Peter Mitchell (1920–1992)

Peter Mitchell was a British biochemist who in 1978 was awarded the Nobel Prize in Chemistry for what the Royal Swedish Academy of Sciences committee stated was "his contribution to the understanding of biological energy transfer through the formulation of the chemiosmotic theory."

Mitchell completed an undergraduate degree and a Ph.D. at Cambridge University, graduating with the latter in 1951. In 1955, he was invited to set up and direct a biochemical research unit in the Department of Zoology, Edinburgh University, where he was a faculty member until 1964. From 1964 onward, he was director of the Glynn Research Institute. Glynn is a mansion that Mitchell renovated and turned into a personal research institute, located near Bodmin in Cornwall, England.

By the 1950s, it was known that both the chloroplast and the mitochondrion contained electron transport chains and made ATP, but a solid theory on how the two were linked was elusive. The dominant theories were based on substrate-level phosphorylation, which was already well understood. It was thought that electron transport chains passed energy to a high-energy chemical intermediate, which, in turn, passed it on to ATP through an ATP synthase that was known to exist in both the chloroplast and the mitochondrion. But, of course, the problem was that no one could find this chemical intermediate. Moreover, the substrate-level phosphorylation idea could not explain troubling findings: Why did so many different reagents act as uncouplers? Why were the enzymes of oxidative phosphorylation associated with the mitochondrial membrane? Why did coupling seem so dependent on the maintenance of membrane structure?

Mitchell proposed the chemiosmotic theory in 1961 in an elegant paper published in *Nature*. It is hard to imagine now how revolutionary the paper was at the time. It contained very little experimental evidence and was opposed by almost the entire biochemical community, which was stuck believing in the high-energy intermediate concept. The paper was based on Mitchell's realization that the movement of ions across an electrochemical membrane potential could provide the energy needed to produce ATP. The basis of chemiosmosis is that the components of the electron transport chain are inserted into a membrane in only one way, which allows for protons to be transported in one direction during electron transport. The protons would flow back through the ATP synthase, causing synthesis of ATP. In Mitchell's model, the proton gradient across the membrane served as the high-energy intermediate and the elusive chemical intermediate could not be found because, of course, it did not exist.

mitochondrial matrix. The basal unit forms a channel through which H^+ can pass freely. The proton-motive force moves protons in the intermembrane space through the channel in the enzyme's basal unit, down their concentration gradient, and into the matrix. The flow of protons powers ATP synthesis by the headpiece. Evidence indicates that the binding of individual protons to sites in the headpiece causes it to rotate in a way that catalyzes the formation of ATP from ADP and P_i. The spinning of the headpiece of ATP synthase represents the smallest molecular rotary motor known in nature.

In Chapter 5, we described active transport pumps that use the energy created by hydrolysis of ATP to ADP and P_i to transport ions across membranes against their concentration gradients (see Figure 5.6). An active transport pump is, in fact, an ATP synthase that is simply operating in reverse. It doesn't synthesize ATP but rather uses the free energy from the hydrolysis of ATP to provide the energy necessary to pump ions (such as protons) across a membrane.

Harnessing the potential energy that is present in a proton gradient to synthesize ATP is fundamental to almost all forms of life and developed early in the evolution of life. This is shown, in part, by the fact that the structure and function of the ATP synthase complex found in mitochondria are essentially identical to those of the ATP synthase complexes found

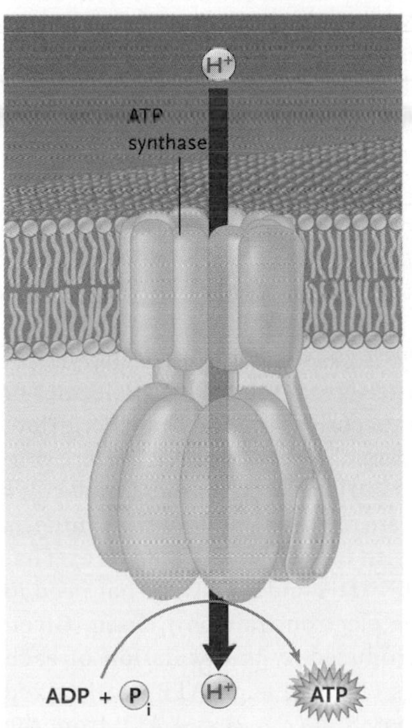

Figure 6.17
Detailed structure of ATP synthase—a molecular motor. The enzyme consists of a *basal unit*, which is embedded in the inner mitochondrial membrane, connected to a *headpiece* by a *stalk*, and with the *stator* bridging the basal unit and headpiece. Protons move through a channel between the basal unit and the stator which makes the stalk and headpiece spin. This results in ATP synthesis.

in the thylakoid membrane of the chloroplast and the plasma membrane of prokaryotic cells.

6.5e Uncoupling Electron Transport and Chemiosmosis

The synthesis of ATP by ATP synthase is linked, or *coupled,* to electron transport by the proton gradient that is established across the inner mitochondrial membrane. A fundamental concept that is important to grasp is that electron transport and the activity of ATP synthase are distinct processes and are not always coupled **(Figure 6.18).** For example, it is possible to have high rates of electron transport without the synthesis of ATP. This *uncoupling* of the two processes can occur by mechanisms that prevent the formation of the proton-motive force by making the inner mitochondrial membrane permeable to protons. A number of chemical compounds called ionophores act as uncouplers because they form channels across membranes through which ions, including protons, can leak. Because these compounds allow for high rates of electron transport but inhibit ATP synthesis, they are all highly toxic. As well, a group of proteins called uncoupling proteins are transmembrane proteins that form channels through which protons can freely flow.

Study Break

1. Why do electrons flow down an electron transport chain?
2. What is the distinction among the terms *proton-motive force, chemiosmosis,* and *oxidative phosphorylation?*
3. What does it mean that electron transport and oxidative phosphorylation are "coupled processes"?

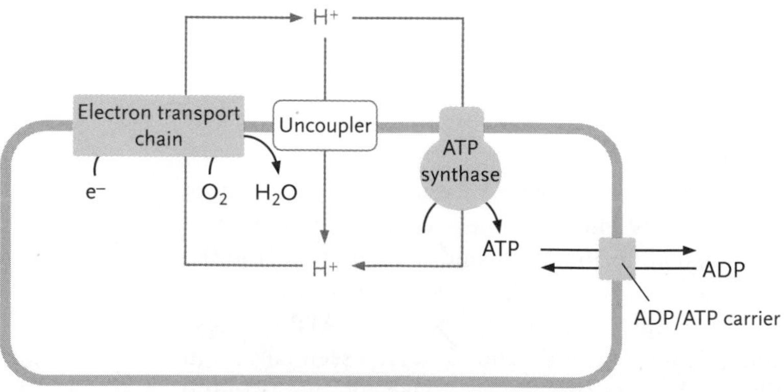

Figure 6.18
Uncoupling of electron transport and ATP synthesis. The respiratory electron transport chain results in the establishment of a proton gradient across the membrane. Usually, this gradient is dissipated by the ATP synthase in the formation of ATP. Uncouplers, which may be specific chemicals or proteins, provide an alternative route for protons to flow back across the membrane. By circumventing the ATP synthase, no ATP is generated.

6.6 The Efficiency and Regulation of Cellular Respiration

In this section, we calculate the efficiency with which cellular respiration extracts the energy from a molecule of glucose. As well, we discuss how this entire multienzyme pathway is regulated such that it remains flexible in the face of changing cellular demands for ATP and changes in food supply.

6.6a How Efficient Is Cellular Respiration?

Determining the total number of ATP molecules synthesized for each molecule of glucose oxidized is an important exercise that forces one to integrate all parts of the respiratory pathway. Before we look at the whole pathway, we oxidative phosphorylation. *How many ATP molecules are produced by oxidative phosphorylation as electrons flow through the mitochondrial electron transport chain?* This is not a straightforward question to answer because electron transport and oxidative phosphorylation, as we have seen, are distinct processes that are not always completely coupled to each other. But research suggests that for each NADH that is oxidized, and thus for each pair of electrons that travels down the electron transport chain, 10 H^+ are pumped into the inner membrane space. (Don't try to figure out how you get 10 protons from 2 electrons—it is not straightforward. Wait to take an advanced biochemistry course.) We also know that somewhere between 3 and 4 H^+ are needed to flow back through the ATP synthase for the synthesis of one molecule of ATP. So that gives about 3 ATP made for every NADH oxidized by the electron transport chain. Because the oxidation of $FADH_2$ bypasses the proton-pumping complex I (look back at Figure 6.15), it does not lead to as many protons being pumped across the membrane. Thus, for each $FADH_2$ oxidized, only about two molecules of ATP are synthesized.

Now we can act as accountants and work out the ATP yield for the entire cellular respiratory pathway given the complete oxidation of glucose to CO_2 and H_2O and assuming that the entire H^+ gradient produced by electron transfer is used for ATP synthesis **(Figure 6.19).**

During glycolysis, substrate-level phosphorylation produces 2 ATP directly and produces 2 molecules of NADH that are transported into the mitochondrion. During the oxidation of pyruvate, 2 NADH are produced. During the citric acid cycle, the 2 molecules of acetyl-CoA that are oxidized result in the synthesis of 2 ATP, along with 6 NADH and 2 $FADH_2$. That gives a total of 10 NADH and 2 $FADH_2$ that need to be oxidized by the electron transport chain. Given that 3 ATP are produced by the oxidation of each NADH, that gives $(10 \times 3) = 30$ ATP synthesized by electron transport and $(2 \times 2) = 4$ ATP from the

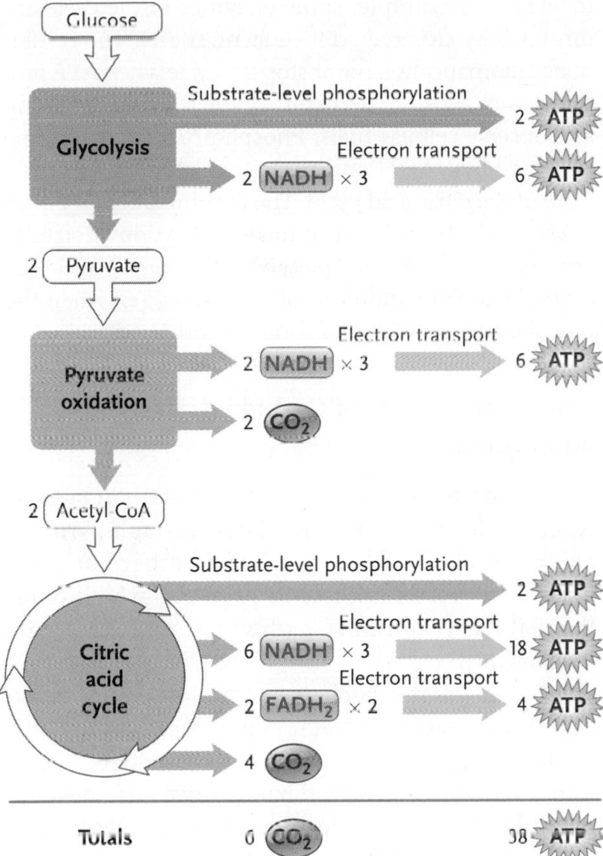

Figure 6.19
Total ATP yield by cellular respiration from the oxidation of one molecule of glucose.

oxidation of the 2 $FADH_2$ molecules. So adding up, 2 ATP from glycolysis, 2 ATP directly from the citric acid cycle, and 34 ATP from electron transport gives a total ATP yield of 38 molecules made from each glucose oxidized.

So how efficient is cellular respiration at extracting the energy from glucose and converting it into ATP? The hydrolysis of ATP to ADP yields about 7.0 kilocalories per mole (kcal/mol). Assuming that complete glucose oxidation produces 32 ATP, the total energy conserved in ATP production would be about 224 kcal/mol. By contrast, glucose contains exactly 686 kcal/mol of energy. On this basis, the efficiency of cellular glucose oxidation would be (224/686 × 100) = about 32%. In other words, 32% of the energy in glucose is converted into ATP. This may not seem amazingly high, but this value is considerably better than that of most devices designed by human engineers—for example, an automobile extracts only about 25% of the energy in the fuel it burns. Recall from Chapter 4 that because of entropy, energy transformations are never 100% efficient.

6.6b The Regulation of Cellular Respiration

Cellular respiration includes a large number of enzymes and transport systems, as well as, in eukaryotes, numerous cellular compartments. The overall rate of cellular respiration, which is often measured as the rate of oxygen consumption, is tightly controlled so that ATP synthesis matches the requirements of the cell for chemical energy. This is often referred to in general terms as the concept of "supply and demand"—the cell does not waste valuable resources, making more of a substance than it needs. Most metabolic pathways are regulated by supply and demand through the process of feedback inhibition: the end products of the pathway inhibit an enzyme early in the pathway (see Section 4.5).

Not surprisingly, the rate of cellular respiration is controlled by key metabolic intermediates. The rate of sugar oxidation by glycolysis is closely regulated by

The physiological importance of uncoupling

During oxidative phosphorylation, the potential energy released by the oxidation of NADH is used to do the work of pumping protons into the intermembrane space and building up the proton-motive force. When electron transport and ATP synthesis are uncoupled, the energy released during electron transport is not conserved but is simply lost as heat. This source of heat is important in mammals and birds in regulating body temperature. One way this is achieved is through regulating the expression of a number of uncoupling proteins. In addition, certain tissues, including brown adipose fat, contain mitochondria in which the expression of uncoupling proteins is particularly high. The heat generated by these tissues is important for the maintenance of body temperature in both hibernating mammals and in very young offspring, including human infants.

several mechanisms to match the cell's need for ATP **(Figure 6.20)**. For example, if excess ATP is present in the cytosol, it binds to *phosphofructokinase*, the enzyme that catalyzes reaction 3 in Figure 6.20, inhibiting its action. The resulting decrease in the concentration of fructose-1,6-bisphosphate slows or stops the subsequent reactions of glycolysis and, as a consequence, the remainder of cellular respiration. Thus, glycolysis does not oxidize fuel substances needlessly when ATP is in adequate supply.

If energy-requiring activities then take place in the cell, ATP concentration would decrease and ADP concentration would rise in the cytosol. As a result, ATP is released from phosphofructokinase, relieving inhibition of the enzyme. In addition, ADP activates the enzyme stimulating cellular respiration. Therefore, the rates of glycolysis and ATP production increase proportionately as cellular activities convert ATP to ADP.

Like glycolysis, the citric acid cycle is regulated at several steps to match its rate to the cell's requirements

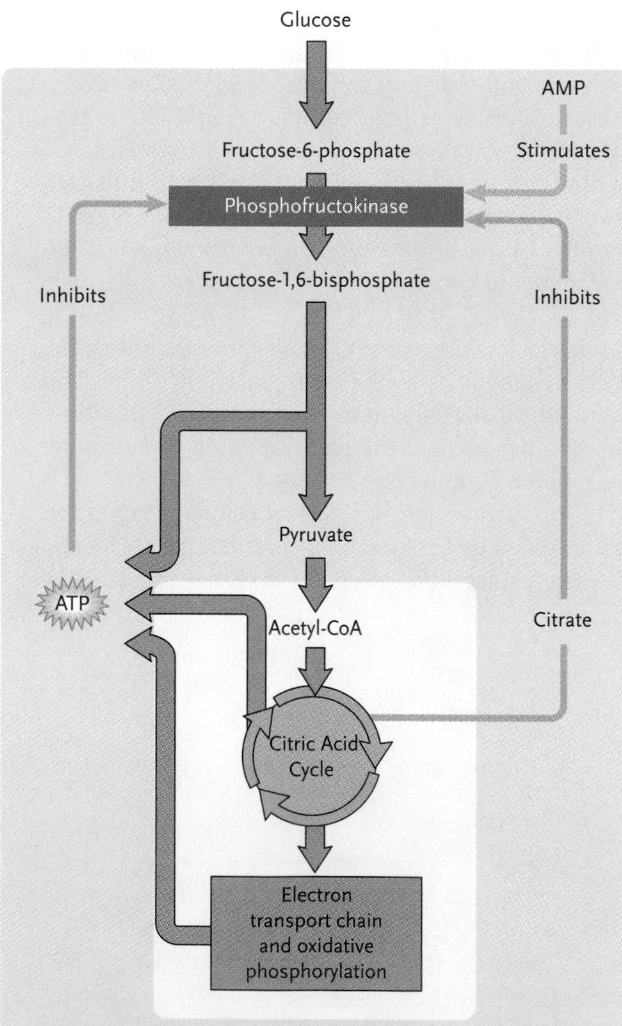

Figure 6.20
The control of cellular respiration. A major mechanism is allosteric control of the activity of the enzyme Phosphofructokinase which is found early in glycolysis. High levels of ATP and the citric acid cycle intermediate citrate allosterically inhibit phosphofructokinase. Alternatively, when ATP concentrations are low the levels of ADP and AMP increase. AMP is an allosteric activator of the enzyme.

for ATP. For example, some enzymes of the cycle are inhibited by elevated ATP concentrations. The inhibitions automatically slow or stop the cycle when ATP production exceeds the demands of the cell and, by doing so, conserve cellular fuels. Phosphofructokinase is also inhibited by NADH and citrate, which is an intermediate of the citric acid cycle. The accumulation of either NADH or citrate is an indication that downstream reactions are moving slowly. This may occur, for example, under conditions of limited oxygen when the rate of oxidative phosphorylation is restricted.

6.6c Catabolism of Carbohydrates, Fats, and Proteins

In addition to glucose and other six-carbon sugars, reactions leading from glycolysis through pyruvate oxidation also oxidize a range of other carbohydrates, as well as lipids and proteins, which enter the cellular respiratory pathway at various points **(Figure 6.21)**.

Carbohydrates such as sucrose and other disaccharides are easily broken into monosaccharides such as glucose and fructose, which enter glycolysis at early steps. Starch is hydrolyzed by digestive enzymes into individual glucose molecules, whereas glycogen, a more complex carbohydrate, is broken down and converted by enzymes into glucose-6-phosphate, an early substrate molecule in glycolysis.

Among the fats, the triglycerides are major sources of electrons for ATP synthesis. Before entering the oxidative reactions, they are hydrolyzed into glycerol and individual fatty acids. The glycerol is converted to glyceraldehyde-3-phosphate before entering glycolysis. The fatty acids—and many other types of lipids—are split into two-carbon fragments, which enter the citric acid cycle as acetyl-CoA.

Proteins are hydrolyzed to amino acids before oxidation. The amino group ($-NH_2$) is removed, and the remainder of the molecule enters the respiratory pathway as either pyruvate, acetyl units carried by coenzyme A, or intermediates of the citric acid cycle (see Figure 6.21). For example, the amino acid alanine is converted into pyruvate; leucine, into acetyl units; and phenylalanine, into fumarate, which enters the citric acid cycle.

6.6d Respiratory Intermediates Are Utilized for Anabolic Reactions

The organic molecules of food are oxidized by cellular respiration to provide ATP for growth and metabolism. In addition, they also supply cells with the carbon skeletons required to synthesize a range of essential molecules that food does not directly provide. The intermediates of glycolysis and the citric acid cycle are routinely diverted and used as the starting substrate for the anabolic pathways required for the synthesis of certain amino acids as well as the pyrimidine and purine bases needed for nucleic acid synthesis. As well, respiratory intermediates supply the carbon backbones for the array of hormones, growth factors, prosthetic groups, and cofactors that are essential to cell function. The huge degree of metabolic flexibility is illustrated by the fact that many reactions illustrated in Figure 6.21 are reversible. For example, whereas fatty acids can be used as a source of energy by being oxidized to acetyl-CoA, excess acetyl-CoA can be removed from the respiration and used to synthesize fatty acids needed for a range of cellular processes.

Study Break

1. What is the maximum yield of ATP from the breakdown of a molecule of ATP? Give an accounting of how each molecule is generated.
2. Explain the various ways cellular respiration can regulate the activity of the enzyme phosphofructokinase.
3. How is cellular respiration used to extract energy from proteins and fats?

6.7 Oxygen and Cellular Respiration

A constant supply of oxygen is required to maintain the high rates of oxidative phosphorylation necessary to supply cells with sufficient ATP. Although humans have an almost constant requirement of oxygen, other organisms and certain tissues can survive in the absence of oxygen. There are two general mechanisms by which certain cells can oxidize fuel molecules and generate ATP in the absence of oxygen: fermentation and anaerobic respiration. The distinction between these two processes is that fermentation does not utilize an electron transport chain, whereas anaerobic respiration uses an electron transport chain that employs a molecule other than oxygen as the terminal electron acceptor.

6.7a Fermentation

Following glycolysis, cellular respiration can continue along one of two distinct pathways depending on whether or not oxygen is present **(Figure 6.22, p. 132)**. When oxygen is plentiful, the pyruvate and two NADH produced by glycolysis are transported into the mitochondrion, where they are oxidized using the citric acid cycle and electron transport chain. If, instead, oxygen is absent or in short supply, the pyruvate remains in the cytosol, where it is reduced, consuming the NADH generated by glycolysis by a series of reactions that are called **fermentation.**

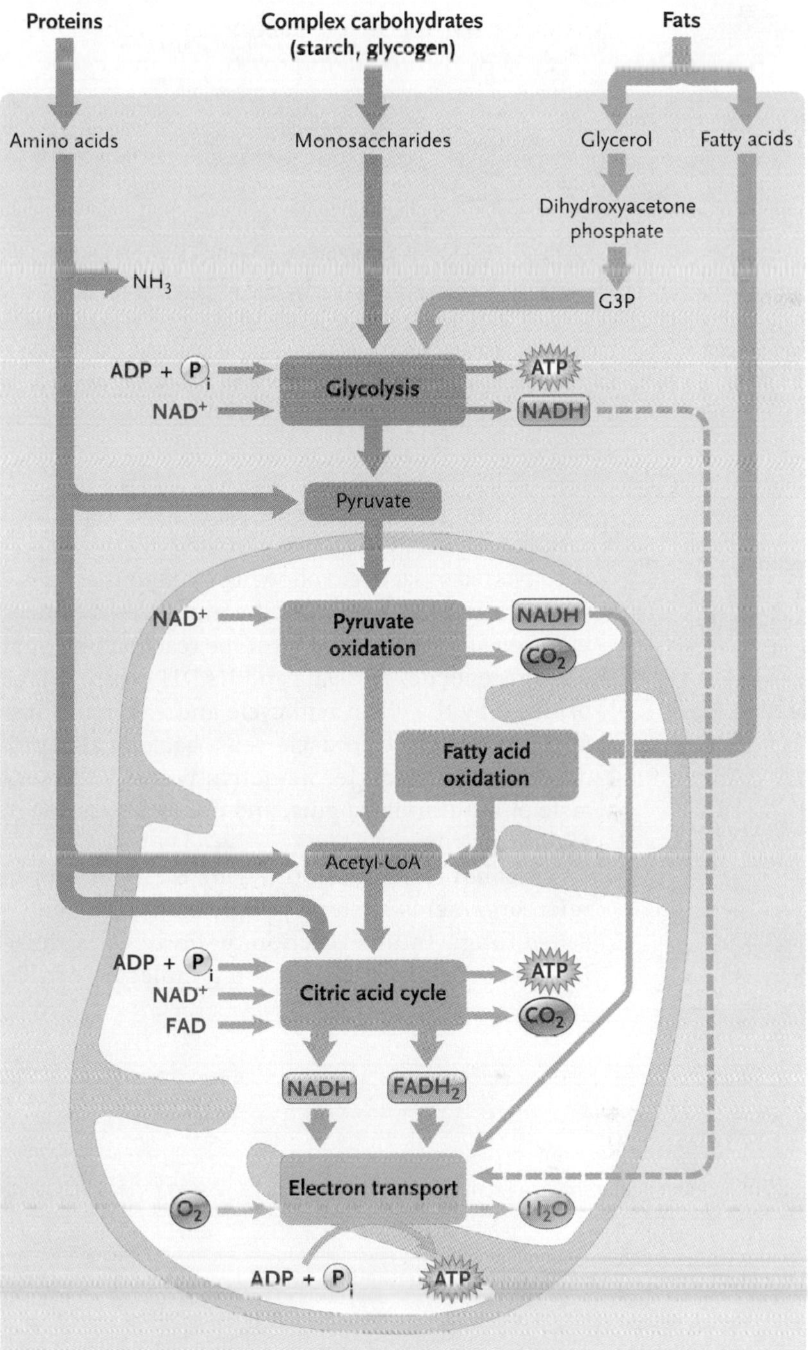

Figure 6.21
Major pathways that oxidize carbohydrates, fats, and proteins. Reactions that occur in the cytosol are shown against a tan background; reactions that occur in mitochondria are shown inside the organelle. CoA funnels the products of many oxidative pathways into the citric acid cycle.

Two types of fermentation reactions exist: lactate fermentation and alcohol fermentation. In **lactate fermentation**, pyruvate is converted into lactate **(Figure 6.23a, p. 132)**. This reaction commonly occurs in the cytosol of muscle cells in animals whenever strenuous activity results in a demand for ATP that exceeds the rate at which O_2 can be supplied to the electron transport chain for oxidative phosphorylation. For example, significant quantities of lactate accumulate in the leg muscles of a sprinter during a 100-metre race. The high rates of O_2 consumption in

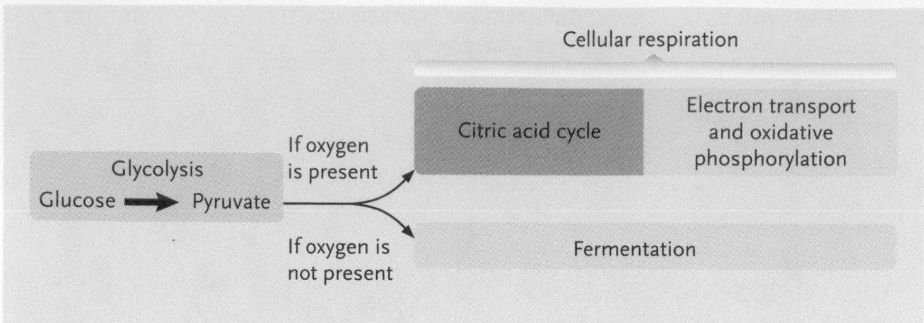

Figure 6.22
The metabolic path of pyruvate oxidation is dependent upon the presence of oxygen.

and a molecule of ethyl alcohol as NADH is converted to NAD^+. Alcoholic fermentation by yeasts has widespread commercial applications. Bakers use the yeast *Saccharomyces cerevisiae* to make bread dough rise. They mix the yeast with a small amount of sugar and blend the mixture into the dough, where oxygen levels are low. As the yeast cells convert the sugar into ethyl alcohol and CO_2, the gaseous CO_2 expands and creates bubbles that cause the dough to rise. Oven heat evaporates the alcohol and causes further expansion of the bubbles, producing a light-textured product. Alcoholic fermentation is also the mainstay of beer and wine brewing. Fruits are a natural home to wild yeasts **(Figure 6.24)**; for example, winemakers rely on a mixture of wild and cultivated yeasts to produce wine. Alcoholic fermentation also occurs naturally in the environment; for example, overripe or rotting fruit frequently will start to ferment, and birds that eat the fruit may become too drunk to fly.

Overall, the reactions of fermentation play a critical role whenever organisms are exposed to conditions in which the oxygen concentration is too low to support oxidative phosphorylation. By consuming the NADH generated by glycolysis, fermentation reactions keep cytosolic NAD^+ levels high, which allows for glycolysis to continue to operate and thereby produce ATP by substrate phosphorylation.

the mitochondria keep the concentration low, which results in pyruvate remaining in the cytosol, where it is converted to lactate. Following strenuous exercise, when the oxygen content of the muscle cells returns to normal levels, the reverse of the reaction in Figure 6.23a regenerates pyruvate and NADH, which can be oxidized by the citric acid cycle and electron transport chain. Besides muscle cells, bacteria also produce lactate as their fermentation product; the sour taste of buttermilk, yogurt, and dill pickles is a sign of their activity.

Alcohol fermentation **(Figure 6.23b)** occurs in microorganisms such as yeasts, which are single-celled fungi. In this reaction, pyruvate is oxidized in two successive reactions to a molecule of CO_2

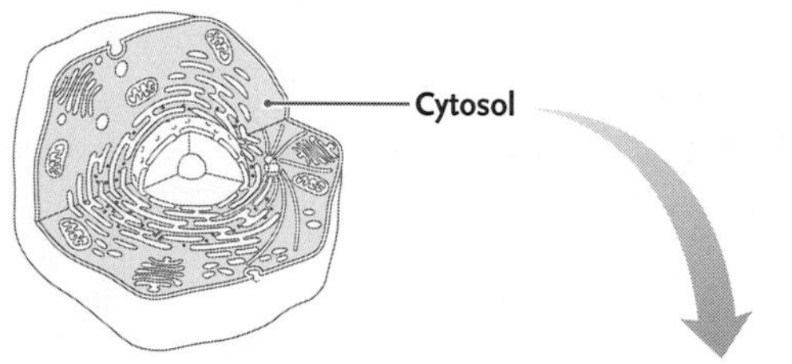

a. Lactate fermentation

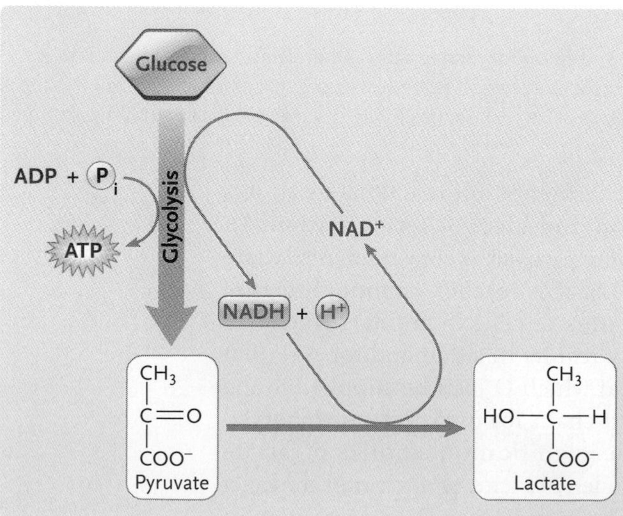

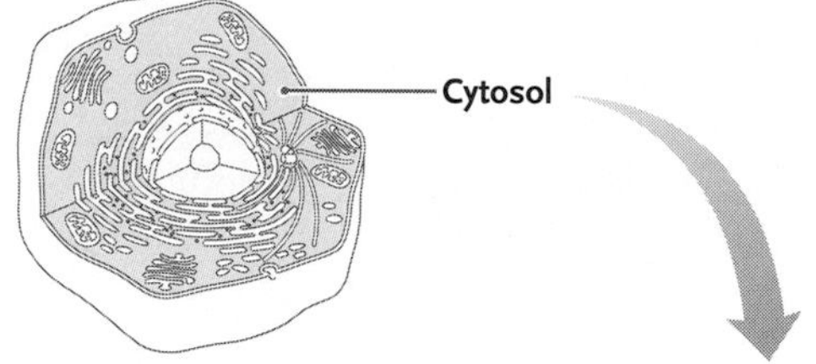

b. Alcoholic fermentation

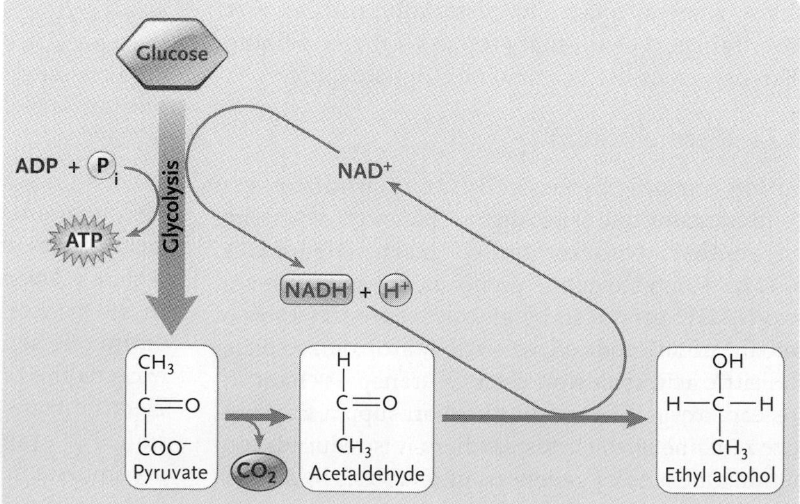

Figure 6.23
Fermentation reactions that produce **(a)** lactate and **(b)** ethyl alcohol. The fermentations, which occur in the cytosol, convert NADH to NAD^+, allowing the electron carrier to cycle back to glycolysis. This process keeps glycolysis running, with continued production of ATP.

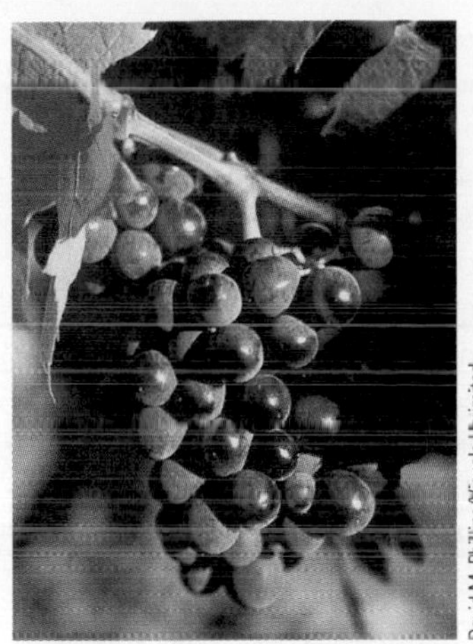

Figure 6.24
Alcoholic fermentation in nature: wild yeast cells, visible as a dustlike coating on grapes.

6.7b Anaerobic Respiration

Although they lack mitochondria, many prokaryotes have respiratory electron transport chains, which are located on internal membrane systems derived from the plasma membrane. Some of these electron transport systems are very similar to those found in the mitochondria of eukaryotes and use O_2 and the terminal electron acceptor. Other prokaryotes, however, have respiratory chains that use a molecule other than O_2 as the terminal electron acceptor and are said to possess anaerobic (*An* = without; *aero* = air) respiration. For example, sulphate (SO_4^{2-}), nitrate (NO_3^-), and the ferric ion (Fe^{3+}) are common electron acceptors used by many groups of prokaryotes that do not use O_2 as the terminal electron acceptor.

Generally, there is a huge diversity of molecules with relatively low potential energy used as electron acceptors; likewise, there are a range of molecules besides glucose that contain high amounts of chemical potential energy that can be used as substrates for cellular respiration. Even though the starting and ending points of cellular respiration may be different, cells are still able to use electron transport chains to create a proton-motive force that drives the synthesis of ATP.

6.7c Lifestyles Dictated by Oxygen

We can differentiate three different lifestyles depending on the ability of an organism to utilize oxygen in cellular respiration. A number of prokaryotes and a few fungi are classified as **strict anaerobes** because they require an oxygen-free environment to survive. Strict anaerobes gain ATP either from fermentation or anaerobic respiration. Among these organisms are the bacteria that cause botulism, tetanus, and some other serious diseases. For example, the bacterium that causes botulism thrives in the oxygen-free environment of canned foods that prevents the growth of most other microorganisms.

Other organisms, called **facultative anaerobes**, can switch between fermentation and full oxidative pathways, depending on the oxygen supply. Facultative anaerobes include *Escherichia coli*, the bacterium that inhabits the digestive tract of humans; the *Lactobacillus* bacteria used to produce buttermilk and yogurt; and *S. cerevisiae*, the yeast used in brewing and baking. Many cell types in higher organisms, including vertebrate muscle cells, are also facultatively anaerobic.

Some prokaryotic and eukaryotic cells are **strict aerobes**—that is, they have an absolute requirement for oxygen to survive and are unable to live solely by fermentation. Vertebrate brain cells are key examples of strictly aerobic cells that need a constant supply of oxygen to function.

6.7d The Paradox of Aerobic Life

Strict anaerobes cannot live in an oxygen environment. But why can't they? Lacking the ability to use O_2 as an electron acceptor is one thing, but actually dying in the presence of O_2? The reason that strict anaerobes die is related to what is often called the *paradox of aerobic life:* although many organisms cannot exist without oxygen because it is required for electron transport, oxygen itself is inherently dangerous to all forms of life.

It takes four electrons to completely reduce a molecule of oxygen to water **(Figure 6.25)**. However, partially reduced forms of O_2 are readily formed when O_2 accepts a fewer number of electrons, producing what are called *reactive oxygen species* (ROS). These molecules, which include the compounds superoxide and hydrogen peroxide (see Figure 6.25), are particularly strong oxidizing agents and can readily remove electrons from proteins, lipids, and DNA, resulting in damage. If ROS levels within a cell are excessive, their strong oxidizing nature can result in destruction of many biological molecules and can lead to cell death. Because most cells contain an abundance of both O_2 and electron-rich molecules (proteins, lipids, DNA), the formation of reactive oxygen molecules is a consequence of aerobic life that cannot be avoided.

To survive in such an unfriendly oxygen environment, all known aerobic organisms have an antioxidant defence system that includes both enzymes and nonenzyme molecules that have the

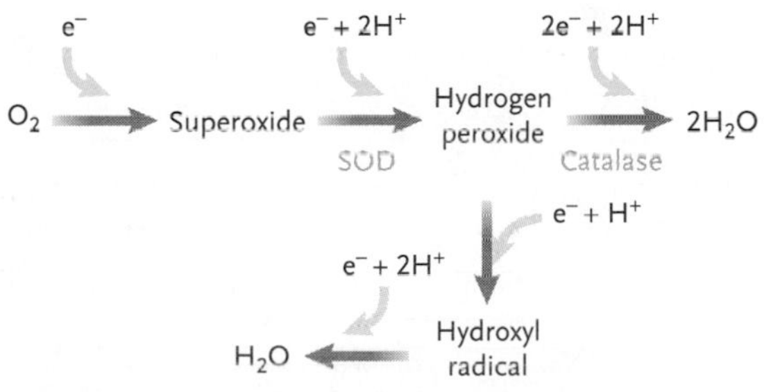

Figure 6.25
The reduction of O_2 to water is a four-electron reduction. If this occurs stepwise, it results in the formation of intermediates called reactive oxygen species (ROS), which are potentially harmful. Aerobic cells contain the enzymes superoxide dismutase (SOD) and catalase, which together quickly convert superoxide and hydrogen peroxide to water.

role of intercepting and inactivating reactive oxygen molecules as they accumulate within cells. Two of the major reactive oxygen scavenging enzymes are superoxide dismutase and catalase (see Figure 6.25). The absence of one or both of these enzymes results in anaerobic cells being unable to live in the presence of oxygen. They die because of high intracellular reactive oxygen levels. In addition to enzymes, many cells have a range of *antioxidants,* including vitamin C and vitamin E, which act as reducing agents, safely and rapidly reducing reactive oxygen compounds to water. Although they are extremely important, the antioxidant enzymes and compounds are not completely effective in preventing oxidative damage. To deal with the damage that does still occur, cells have an elaborate system of damage removal/repair enzymes for proteins, lipids, and DNA.

In recent years, excessive reactive oxygen formation has been implicated in a wide variety of degenerative processes, diseases, and syndromes, including Parkinson disease and Alzheimer dementia, and a wide variety of age-related disorders. It is thought that the buildup of oxidative damage may underlie the aging process itself. This, in part, explains the huge interest in the possible protective value of a wide variety of antioxidant compounds, particularly those from fruits and vegetables.

The huge advantage gained by using oxygen as the terminal electron acceptor is that cells can extract more energy from food molecules. However, the evolution of the aerobic lifestyle required the development of antioxidants and enzymes such as catalase and superoxide dismutase to combat the inevitable formation of ROS. In addition, it required that cytochrome oxidase, the last enzyme of the mitochondrial electron transport chain, develop a remarkable mode of catalysis. Recall that this enzyme complex donates electrons from the electron carrier cytochrome *c* to O_2 (see Figure 6.15). However, it does so in a way that, remarkably, leads to essentially no ROS generation. The enzyme is structurally quite complex, containing four redox centres (two hemes and two copper ions), each of which can store a single electron. When all centres are reduced, the enzyme simultaneously transfers all four electrons to an oxygen molecule, producing two molecules of water. That cytochrome oxidase is the only enzyme that aerobic organisms, from bacterial to human, use as the terminal complex of electron transport indicates the chemical difficulty of carrying out the transfer of electrons to O_2 in a safe and controlled manner. Given that approximately 98% of the oxygen we metabolize is handled by this single enzyme, if the reaction resulted in significant ROS formation, aerobic life as we know it would never have been able to develop.

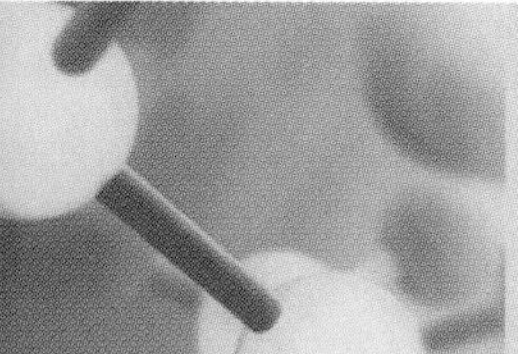

Molecule Behind Biology

Cyanide

Cyanide is an ion that consists of a carbon atom triple-bonded to an atom of nitrogen ($C{\equiv}N^-$). It is a very toxic metabolic poison acting as an irreversible inhibitor of the terminal enzyme of respiratory electron transport, cytochrome oxidase. By binding to the iron atom of the heme prosthetic groups in the enzyme, cyanide prevents electron flow to O_2, essentially inhibiting electron transport and subsequent chemiosmosis. Acute cyanide poisoning can result in death within minutes of exposure.

Cyanide is produced in small amounts by a range of microorganisms and is found in small amounts in apple seeds, almonds, and the pits of fruits such as peaches. In some plants, the production of cyanide in a form bound to sugars is thought to be a deterrent to herbivory. The presence of cyanide in the potato-like root of the cassava plant is of concern because it is a staple food in a number of tropical countries. The presence of cyanide glycosides is diminished by extensive soaking and cooking of the cassava root, but health problems associated with chronic cyanide poisoning remain quite common.

Cyanide has clear applications in a range of industries but especially in electroplating, metallurgy, and mining owing to the high solubility of gold $[Au(CN)_2]^-$ and silver $[Ag(CN)_2]^-$ cyanides in water. For these purposes, approximately 500 000 tons of highly toxic sodium cyanide are produced each year. In gold mining, the addition of a solution of sodium cyanide to ore containing low amounts of gold is effective at extracting the gold by bringing the gold into solution. The resulting formation of huge amounts of cyanide-contaminated water makes this form of gold mining highly controversial, yet it remains a highly effective and cheap method of extraction.

In addition to a respiratory electron transport chain that is inhibited by cyanide, plants contain a pathway of electron transport that is resistant to cyanide. Instead of using cytochrome oxidase, this second pathway of respiration uses a terminal oxidase called the alternative oxidase. This alternative pathway of respiration is not linked to proton pumping like the normal respiratory chain; instead, electron flow simply generates heat. Intestinally, high levels of alternative oxidase in the flowers of some plant species are used to volatilize attractants for pollinators. This includes the aptly named skunk cabbage, which tells you that the attractants for pollinators are not necessarily pleasant.

In addition to being found in all plants, the alternative oxidase has been found in algae, some fungi, and, recently, some animal phyla. The physiological role of cyanide-resistant respiration in these species is being actively investigated by a number of research groups.

Unanswered Questions

Glycolysis and energy metabolism are crucial for the normal functioning of an animal. Research of many kinds is being conducted in this area, such as characterizing the molecular components in detail and determining how the reactions are regulated. The goal is to generate comprehensive models of cellular respiration and its regulation. Following are two specific examples of ongoing research related to human disease caused by defects in cellular respiration.

How do mitochondrial proteins change in patients with Alzheimer disease (AD)?

AD is an age-dependent, irreversible, neurodegenerative disorder in humans. Symptoms include a progressive deterioration of cognitive functions and, in particular, a significant loss of memory. Reduced brain metabolism occurs early in the onset of AD. One of the mechanisms for this physiological change appears to be damage to or reduction of key mitochondrial components, including enzymes of the citric acid cycle and the oxidative phosphorylation system. However, the complete scope of mitochondrial protein changes has not been established, nor have detailed comparisons been made in mitochondrial protein changes among AD patients. Currently, Gail Breen at the University of Texas, Dallas, is performing research to detail qualitatively and quantitatively all mitochondrial proteins and their levels in healthy and AD brains. A mouse model of AD is being used for this research. Breen's group hopes that the information they obtain will provide a better understanding of how mitochondrial dysfunction contributes to AD. With such information in hand, it may be possible to develop interventions to slow or halt the progression of AD in humans.

How are the oxidative phosphorylation complexes in the mitochondrion assembled?

Defects in oxidative phosphorylation may cause disorders in which several systems of the human body are adversely affected. Often these disorders involve the nervous system and the skeletal and cardiac muscles. The enzyme complexes of the oxidative phosphorylation system consist of about 80 different protein subunits, some of which are encoded by nuclear genes and some by mitochondrial genes. The protein subunits are assembled into complexes in the mitochondria. This assembly process requires a large number of accessory proteins, and many important mitochondrial diseases are caused by defects in the assembly protein genes.

Eric Shoubridge of McGill University in Montreal is studying the molecular genetics of assembly of oxidative phosphorylation complexes. His focus is identifying and characterizing the assembly genes, with the long-term goals of understanding how the complexes are assembled and how defects in complex assembly lead to disease. Shoubridge's group has identified mutations in four different assembly genes in infants with a fatal disease caused by cytochrome *c* deficiency (a defect in the assembly of complex IV). They have also identified complex I assembly proteins, and they were the first to show an association between a defect in one of the proteins and a human disease. Unexpectedly, the biochemical deficiencies caused by the mutant assembly proteins tend to be tissue specific, even though the assembly protein genes are expressed in all tissues. As a result, clinical symptoms caused by defective assembly proteins vary based on the extent of the enzyme deficiencies in different tissues. Understanding how the tissue-specific differences occur and how they are regulated will be important in developing therapies for patients with the diseases.

Review

Go to CENGAGENOW™ at http://hed.nelson.com/ to access quizzing, animations, exercises, articles, and personalized homework help.

6.1 The Chemical Basis of Cellular Respiration

- Oxidation–reduction reactions, called redox reactions, partially or completely transfer electrons from donor to acceptor atoms; the donor is oxidized as it releases electrons, and the acceptor is reduced.
- Almost all organisms obtain energy for cellular activities through cellular respiration, the process of transferring electrons from donor organic molecules to a final acceptor molecule such as oxygen; the energy that is released drives ATP synthesis.

6.2 Cellular Respiration: An Overview

- Cellular respiration occurs in three stages: (1) in glycolysis, glucose is converted to two molecules of pyruvate through a series of enzyme-catalyzed reactions; (2) in pyruvate oxidation and the citric acid cycle, pyruvate is converted to an acetyl compound that is oxidized completely to CO_2, and (3) in the electron transfer system and oxidative phosphorylation, high-energy electrons produced from the first two stages pass through the transfer system, with much of their energy being used to establish an H^+ gradient across the membrane that drives the synthesis of ATP.
- Both eukaryotes and prokaryotes may undergo cellular respiration. In eukaryotes, however, most of the reactions of cellular respiration occur in mitochondria.

6.3 Glycolysis

- In glycolysis, which occurs in the cytosol, glucose (six carbons) is oxidized into two molecules of pyruvate (three carbons each). Electrons removed in the oxidation are delivered to NAD^+, producing NADH. The reaction sequence produces a net gain of two ATP, two NADH, and two pyruvate molecules for each molecule of glucose oxidized.
- ATP molecules produced in the energy-releasing steps of glycolysis result from substrate-level phosphorylation, an enzyme-catalyzed reaction that transfers a phosphate group from a substrate to ADP.

6.4 Pyruvate Oxidation and the Citric Acid Cycle

- In pyruvate oxidation, which occurs inside mitochondria, one pyruvate (three carbons) is oxidized to one acetyl group (two carbons) and one CO_2. Electrons removed in the oxidation are accepted by 1 NAD^+ to produce one NADH. The acetyl group is transferred to coenzyme A, which carries it to the citric acid cycle.
- In the citric acid cycle, acetyl groups are oxidized completely to CO_2. Electrons removed in the oxidation are accepted by NAD^+ or FAD, and substrate-level phosphorylation produces ATP. For each acetyl group oxidized by the cycle, two CO_2, one ATP, three NADH, and one $FADH_2$ are produced.

6.5 Electron Transport and Chemiosmosis

- Electrons are passed from NADH and $FADH_2$ to the electron transfer system, which consists of four major protein complexes and two smaller shuttle carriers. As the electrons flow from one carrier to the next through the system, some of their energy is used by the complexes to pump protons across the inner mitochondrial membrane.
- Two major protein complexes (I and IV) and the reduction/oxidation of ubiquinone result in the pumping of protons from the matrix to the intermembrane compartment, generating an H^+ gradient with a high concentration in the intermembrane compartment and a low concentration in the matrix.
- The H^+ gradient produced by the electron transfer system is used by ATP synthase as an energy source for synthesis of ATP from ADP and P_i. The ATP synthase is embedded in the inner mitochondrial membrane together with the electron transfer system.

6.6 The Efficiency and Regulation of Cellular Respiration

- An estimated three ATP are synthesized as each electron pair travels from NADH to oxygen through the mitochondrial electron transfer system; about two ATP are synthesized as each electron pair travels through the system from $FADH_2$ to oxygen.
- In glycolysis, 2 ATP and 2 NADH are synthesized; during the oxidation of pyruvate and the citric acid cycle, 2 ATP, 8 NADH, and 2 $FADH_2$ are produced. That gives a total of 10 NADH and 2 $FADH_2$ that are oxidized by the electron transport chain. This gives a total ATP yield for each glucose oxidized of 38.
- Using these totals gives an efficiency of more than 30% for the utilization of energy released by glucose oxidation if the H^+ gradient is used only for ATP production.

6.7 Oxygen and Cellular Respiration

- Organisms differ in regard to their oxygen requirements.
- Fermentations are reaction pathways that reduce pyruvate in the cytosol by the consumption of NADH. In so doing, NAD^+ is produced, which is required as a substrate for glycolysis. This allows glycolysis to continue to run, producing ATP by substrate-level phosphorylation. The NAD^+ can accept electrons generated by glycolysis, allowing glycolysis to supply ATP by substrate-level phosphorylation.
- Strict anaerobes cannot grow in the presence of oxygen, whereas strict aerobes require oxygen. Facultative aerobes can grow in the presence of oxygen and can grow using fermentative pathways.
- Although oxygen is required for aerobic life, paradoxically, O_2 is toxic to cells. Cells are protected by the toxicity of O_2 by both enzymatic and nonenzymatic antioxidants that detoxify ROS.

Questions

Self-Test Questions

1. What is a common feature of organic molecules that are good fuels?
   a. Easily reduced.
   b. An abundance of oxygen.
   c. Presence of C–H bonds.
   d. High molecular weight.
   e. Low solubility in water.
2. Which of the following general statements about respiration is correct?
   a. The CO_2 produced can be used as an energy source for metabolism.
   b. O_2 is used as an electron donor for the process.
   c. Since bacteria are prokaryotic, they do not respire.
   d. It represents a series of reactions in which a carbon substrate is oxidized.
   e. It is able to extract more energy from glucose than direct burning can.
3. In glycolysis,
   a. all the reactions occur in the mitochondrion.
   b. the carbon products are oxidized further by the electron transport chain.
   c. ATP is generated by substrate-level phosphorylation.
   d. oxygen is required as an electron acceptor.
   e. the two molecules of pyruvate made contain the same amount of potential energy as one molecule of glucose.
4. The proton-motive force associated with chemiosmosis
   a. is only important for ATP synthesis in mitochondria.
   b. needs to be high to synthesize ATP during the citric acid cycle.
   c. requires that membranes are freely permeable to protons.
   d. has an electrical and a concentration component.
   e. Both c and d are correct.
5. You are reading this text while breathing in O_2 and breathing out CO_2. The CO_2 arises from the
   a. oxidation of acetyl-CoA by the citric acid cycle.
   b. conversion of glucose to pyruvate during glycolysis.
   c. conversion of pyruvate to acetyl-CoA.
   d. oxidative phosphorylation.
   e. Both a and c are correct.
6. A key role of fermentation in overall metabolism is to
   a. synthesize extra ATP.
   b. regenerate NAD^+ in the cytosol.
   c. increase O_2 concentration for electron transport.
   d. increase NADH synthesis for oxidative phosphorylation.
   e. produce acetyl-CoA.
7. In cellular respiration, the term *uncoupling* refers to when
   a. the two parts of glycolysis are running independently of each other.
   b. the citric acid cycle is operating but is not generating any ATP.
   c. respiratory electron transport is operating, but chemiosmosis is not.
   d. Substrate-level phosphorylation is inhibited.
   e. None of the above statements are correct.
8. Which of the following statements about phosphofructokinase is *false*?
   a. It is an enzyme found in the cytosol.
   b. It catalyzes a phosphorylation reaction.
   c. It is an enzyme of glycolysis.
   d. It is inhibited by high cytosolic ADP levels.
   e. It is activated by high cytosolic citrate levels.
9. The breakdown of fats release fatty acids which enter the respiratory pathway at the level of
   a. NADH
   b. Glucose
   c. Pyruvate
   d. Acetyl-CoA
   e. Citrate

10. Which of the following statements is correct?
    a. Strict anaerobes can grow either by fermentation, or they can use O_2 in aerobic respiration.
    b. It takes two electrons to fully reduce a molecule of O_2 to water.
    c. Partially reduced forms of O_2 are formed by the action of cytochrome oxidase.
    d. The enzymes superoxide dismutase and catalase are not essential to aerobic life.
    e. Some forms of O_2 can damage macromolecules.

Questions for Discussion

1. Respond to this statement: Respiration occurs in animals but not in plants.
2. In your opinion, are fermentations part of cellular respiration? Why or why not?
3. Why do you think nucleic acids are not oxidized extensively as a cellular energy source?
4. Migrating birds, which fly for long distances without stopping, oxidize fatty acids as an energy source in their flight muscles. Why do you think this would be an advantage to the birds? In the fields below a flock of migrating geese, a rabbit accelerates rapidly to escape a coyote. Which oxidative pathway predominates in the rabbit's leg muscles? Why wouldn't the pathway being used in the flight muscles of the geese benefit the rabbit very much?
5. Recently, a hospital patient was regularly found to be intoxicated. He denied that he was drinking alcoholic beverages. The doctors and nurses made a special point to eliminate the possibility that the patient or his friends were smuggling alcohol into his room, but he was still regularly intoxicated. Then one of the doctors had an idea that turned out to be correct and cured the patient of his intoxication. The idea involved the patient's digestive system and one of the oxidative reactions covered in this chapter. What was the doctor's idea?

False-colour image estimating global marine and terrestrial photoautotroph abundance. Estimates of surface chlorophyll were achieved using data collected by the GeoEye Orb View-2 satellite (SeaWiFS project) and NASA/Goddard Space Flight Centre.

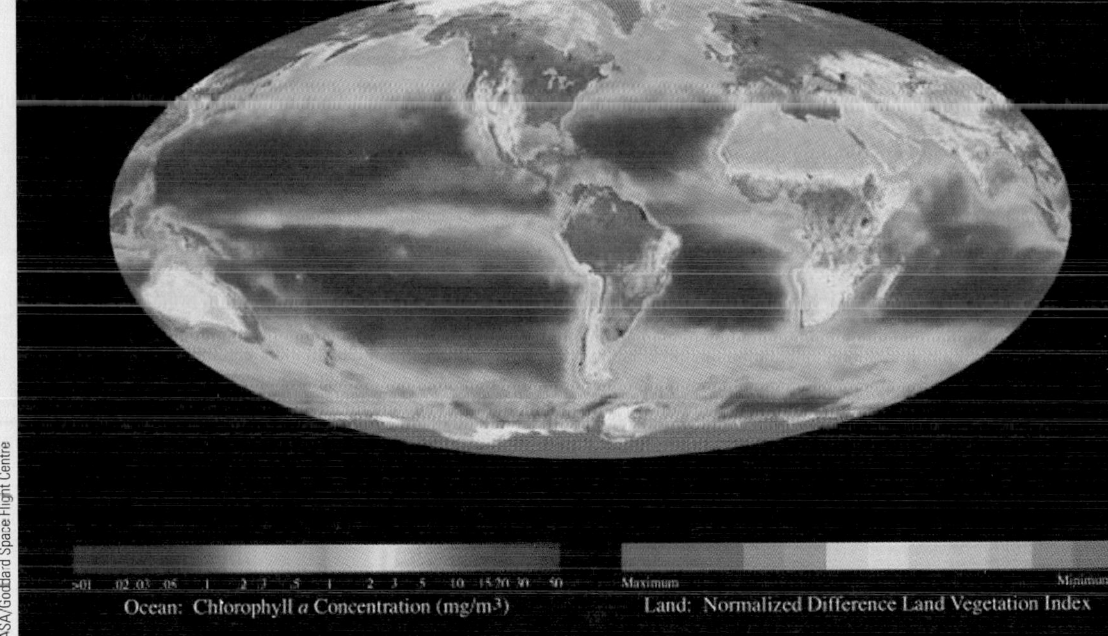

Study Plan

7 Photosynthesis

Why It Matters

The Earth can be considered a giant photoreceptor—a massive harvester of light energy from the sun. Life on Earth is dependent entirely on energy from the Sun, not only to keep the planet at a suitable temperature but also to provide the energy required to sustain life. The energy of the sun is actively captured by chlorophyll and related pigments present in photosynthetic organisms found in both terrestrial and aquatic habitats. The vast majority of energy enters the biosphere through the process of photosynthesis by which the energy of photons is captured by chlorophyll and other pigments founds in photoautotrophs that live in both terrestrial and aquatic habitats. This captured energy is used to convert carbon dioxide into complex energy-rich molecules.

The amount of carbon dioxide that is incorporated into organic form by photosynthetic organisms is staggering—approximately 11×10^{13} kg of carbon per year. And although we often think about photosynthesis in terms of plants and trees, about half of this carbon is fixed by the photosynthetic microorganisms that inhabit marine environments: phytoplankton.

Looking at photosynthesis on a global scale (see opening figure), you may notice that surprisingly, the abundance of phytoplankton (as estimated by chlorophyll concentration) is very low in the temperate regions of the Pacific and Atlantic oceans and higher as you move nearer the poles, especially the Arctic. The reason for this is that, although the waters near the equator are warmer, they are very nutrient poor (being especially deficient in iron) and unable to support phytoplankton growth.

7.1 Photosynthesis: An Overview

Photosynthetic organisms are photoautotrophs and are classified as the *primary producers* of Earth **(Figure 7.1).** They convert the energy of sunlight into chemical energy and use it to assemble simple inorganic raw materials into complex organic molecules. Primary producers use some of the organic molecules they make as energy sources for their own activities. But they also serve—directly or indirectly—as food sources for *consumers*, the animals that live by eating plants or other animals. Eventually, the bodies of both primary producers and consumers provide chemical energy for bacteria, fungi, and other *decomposers*.

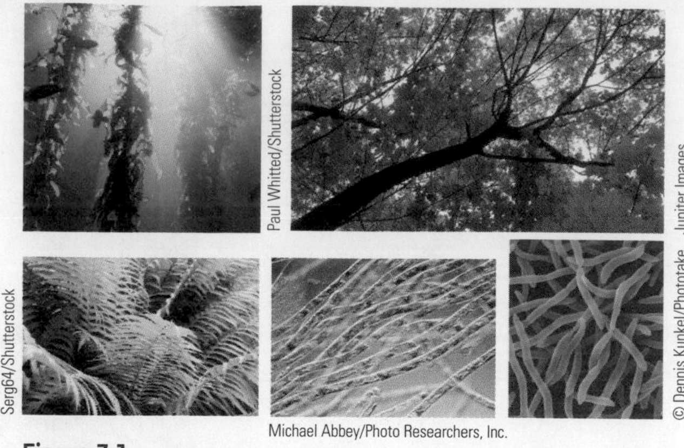

Figure 7.1
Examples of photoautotrophs.

7.1a The Two Parts of Photosynthesis

Photosynthesis can be conceptually divided into two distinct stages **(Figure 7.2):** the light-dependent reactions (sometimes called the light reactions) and the light-independent reactions (called the Calvin cycle). The light reactions involve the capture of light energy by pigment molecules and the utilization of that energy to synthesize both NADPH and ATP. This involves an electron transport chain that in plants, algae, and cyanobacteria utilizes electrons donated from water. Oxygen generated from the splitting of water is released to the environment as a by-product:

$$2H_2O + \text{light energy} \rightarrow 4H^+ + 4\,e^- + O_2$$

In the Calvin cycle, the electrons carried by NADPH and the energy of ATP are used to convert CO_2 from inorganic to organic form, a process called CO_2 fixation. The conversion is a reduction, in which electrons (and protons) are added to CO_2 (reduction and oxidation are discussed in Chapter 6). With the added electrons and protons (H^+), CO_2 is converted to a carbohydrate, with carbon, hydrogen, and oxygen atoms in the ratio 1C:2H:1O. Carbohydrate units are often symbolized as $(CH_2O)n$, with the "n" indicating that different carbohydrates are formed from different multiples of the carbohydrate unit.

$$CO_2 + H^+ + e^- \rightarrow (CH_2O)_n$$

Three-carbon sugars are the major direct product of the Calvin cycle. These can be readily combined to form six-carbon monosaccharides, including glucose.

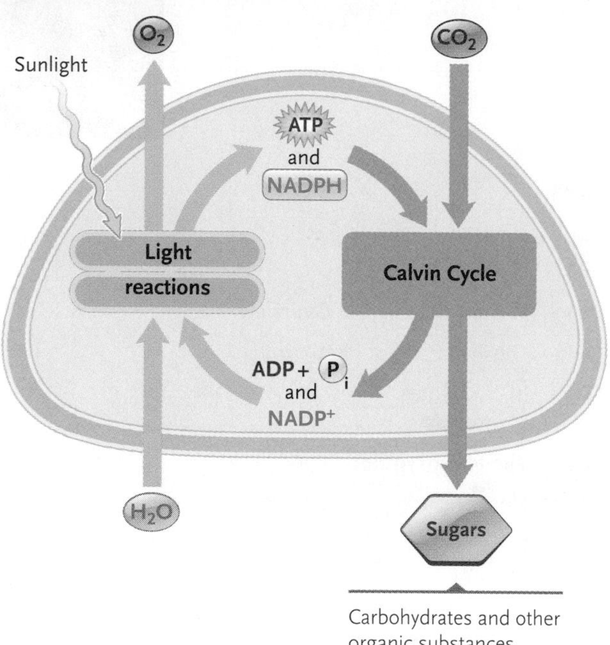

Figure 7.2
Photosynthesis can be conceptually divided into two processes: The light reactions and The Calvin cycle which are linked together by reactants and products. Both processes occur in the chloroplasts of photoautotrophic eukaryotes (plants and algae) as well as in photosynthetic prokaryotes.

Combining the two reactions above, the overall balanced equation for photosynthesis is

$$6CO_2 + 12\,H_2O \rightarrow C_6H_{12}O_6 + 6O_2 + 6H_2O.$$

While sugar (glucose) is the major product of photosynthesis it is important to realize that the reduced carbon produced by photosynthesis is also the source of the carbon back-bone for a huge range of other molecules, including lipids and proteins. In fact, all the organic molecules of plants are assembled as direct or indirect products of photosynthesis.

7.1b In Eukaryotes, Photosynthesis Takes Place in Chloroplasts

In photosynthetic eukaryotes, both the light reactions and the Calvin cycle take place within the chloroplast **(Figure 7.3)**, an organelle that is formed from

Figure 7.3
The membranes and compartments of chloroplasts.

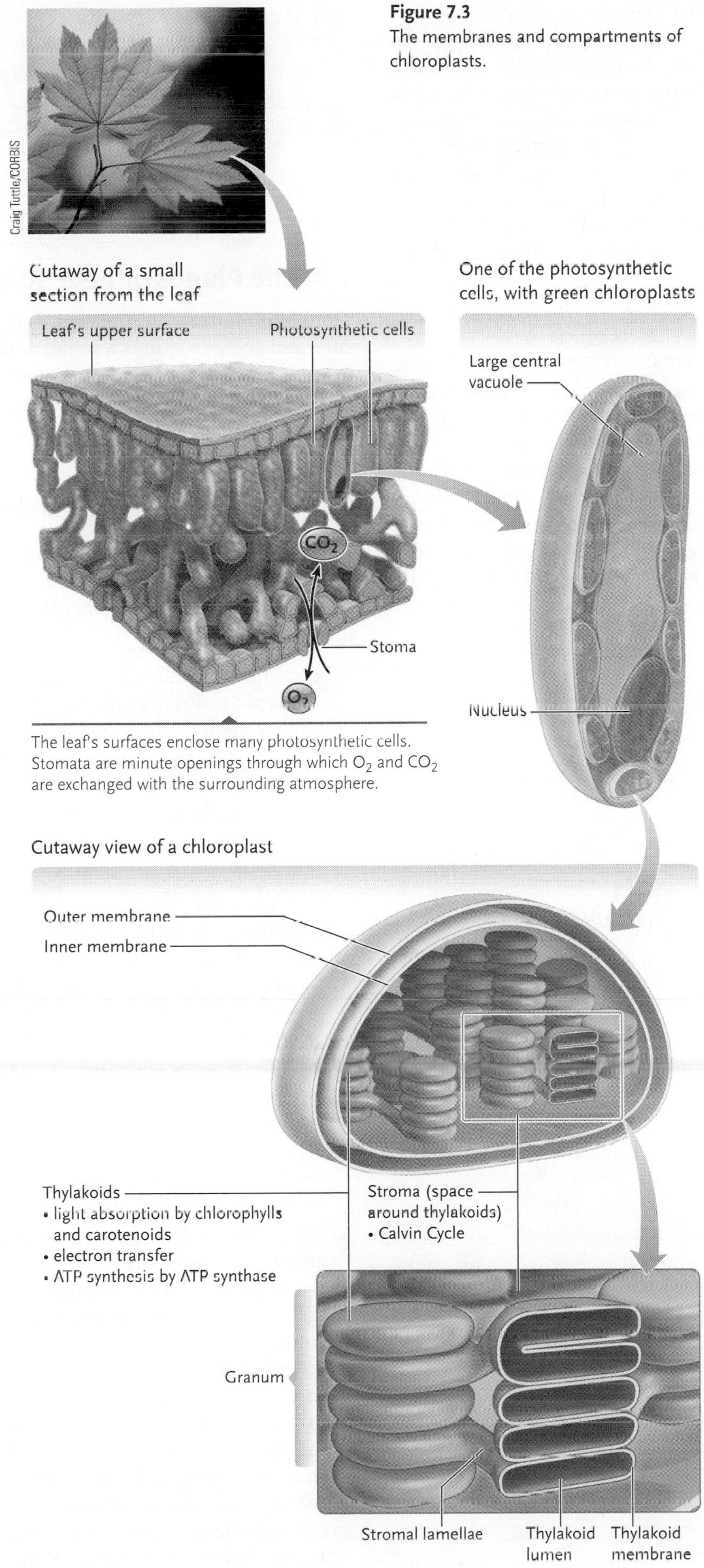
Craig Tuttle/CORBIS
Cutaway of a small section from the leaf
Leaf's upper surface
Photosynthetic cells
CO_2
Stoma
O_2
The leaf's surfaces enclose many photosynthetic cells. Stomata are minute openings through which O_2 and CO_2 are exchanged with the surrounding atmosphere.
One of the photosynthetic cells, with green chloroplasts
Large central vacuole
Nucleus
Cutaway view of a chloroplast
Outer membrane
Inner membrane
Thylakoids
• light absorption by chlorophylls and carotenoids
• electron transfer
• ATP synthesis by ATP synthase
Stroma (space around thylakoids)
• Calvin Cycle
Granum
Stromal lamellae
Thylakoid lumen
Thylakoid membrane

three membranes that define three distinct compartments (see Figure 7.3). An *outer membrane* covers the entire surface of the organelle, whereas an *inner membrane* lies just inside the outer membrane. Between the outer and inner membranes is the *intermembrane compartment*. The aqueous environment within the inner membrane is the *stroma*. Within the stroma is the third membrane system, the *thylakoid membranes*, or thylakoids, which often form flattened, closed sacs. The space enclosed by a thylakoid is called the *thylakoid lumen*.

The thylakoid membrane houses the molecules that carry out the light reactions of photosynthesis, including the pigments, electron transfer carriers, and ATP synthase enzymes for ATP production. The enzymes that catalyze the reactions of the Calvin cycle are found in the stroma of the chloroplast.

In the same way that organisms without mitochondria may still undergo cellular respiration, cells lacking chloroplasts may still be photosynthetic. Many photosynthetic prokaryotes also have thylakoid membranes that are formed from infoldings of the plasma membrane.

Figure 7.4 Three possible fates of an excited-state electron within a pigment molecule.

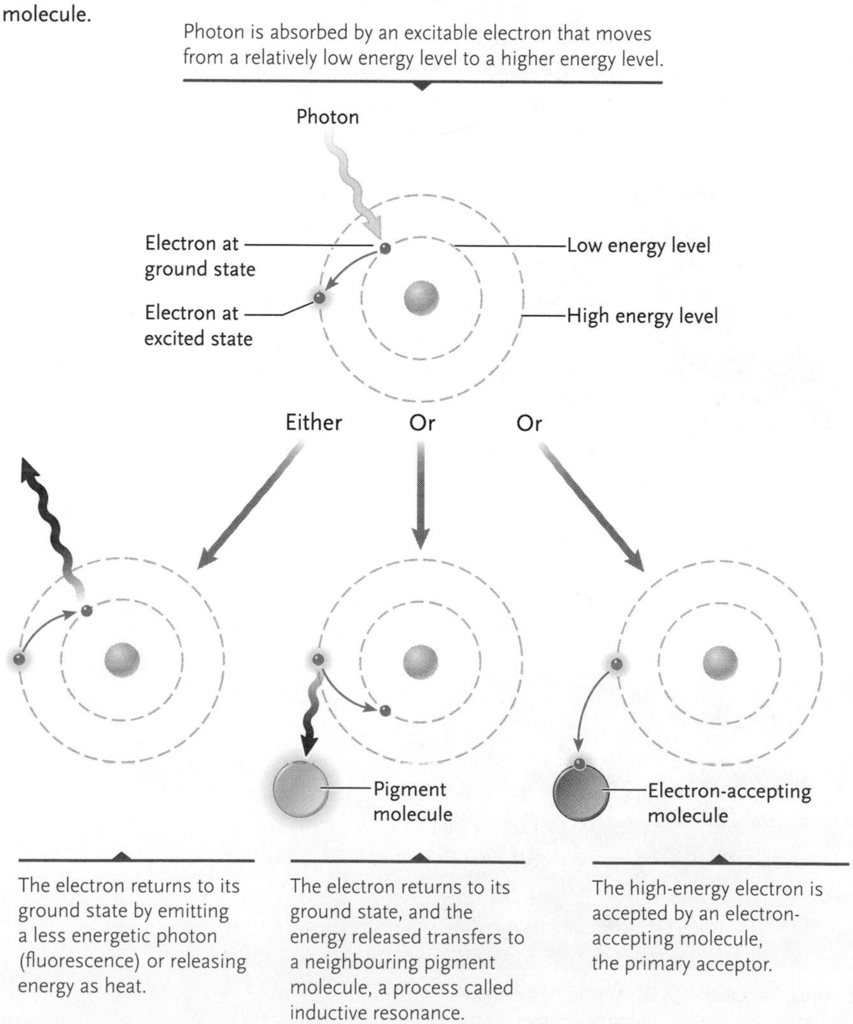

Photon is absorbed by an excitable electron that moves from a relatively low energy level to a higher energy level.
Photon
Electron at ground state
Electron at excited state
Low energy level
High energy level
Either
Or
Or
Pigment molecule
Electron-accepting molecule
The electron returns to its ground state by emitting a less energetic photon (fluorescence) or releasing energy as heat.
The electron returns to its ground state, and the energy released transfers to a neighbouring pigment molecule, a process called inductive resonance.
The high-energy electron is accepted by an electron-accepting molecule, the primary acceptor.

Study Break

1. Why are photoautotrophs considered primary producers?
2. What is CO_2 converted to in the Calvin cycle?

7.2 The Photosynthetic Apparatus

The ability to trap light energy and convert it into chemical energy requires a sophisticated photochemical apparatus that is unique in biology. In this section, we describe the components of the light reactions that are located on the thylakoid membranes.

7.2a Electrons in Pigment Molecules Absorb Light Energy

From our discussion of light in Chapter 1, recall two important points about light and pigment molecules:

1. The absorption of a photon by a pigment molecule excites a single electron, moving it from the ground state to an excited state.
2. The difference in energy level between the ground state and the excited state is equivalent to the energy of the photon of light that was absorbed. If the energies do not match, the photon is not absorbed by the pigment.

As shown in **Figure 7.4,** following light absorption, there are three possible fates of the energy possessed by an excited-state electron within a pigment molecule. The relative probabilities of each event taking place depends on the environment surrounding the pigment molecules, including the presence of other molecules.

In the first mechanism (see Figure 7.4, left), the excited electron may simply return to its ground state, releasing its energy either as heat or as *fluorescence*, which is emission of light of a longer wavelength (lower energy) than the absorbed light. The fluorescence will be of lower energy because a small amount of energy of the photon initially absorbed is always lost as heat (recall from Chapter 4 that energy transformations are never 100% efficient). In the second option (see Figure 7.4, centre), the energy of the excited electron can be transferred to a neighbouring pigment molecule, a process called *inductive resonance*. This transfer of energy excites the pigment molecule, whereas the first molecule returns to its ground state. This requires the two molecules to be very closely and precisely aligned with one another. In the third option (see Figure 7.4, right), the excited-state electron may

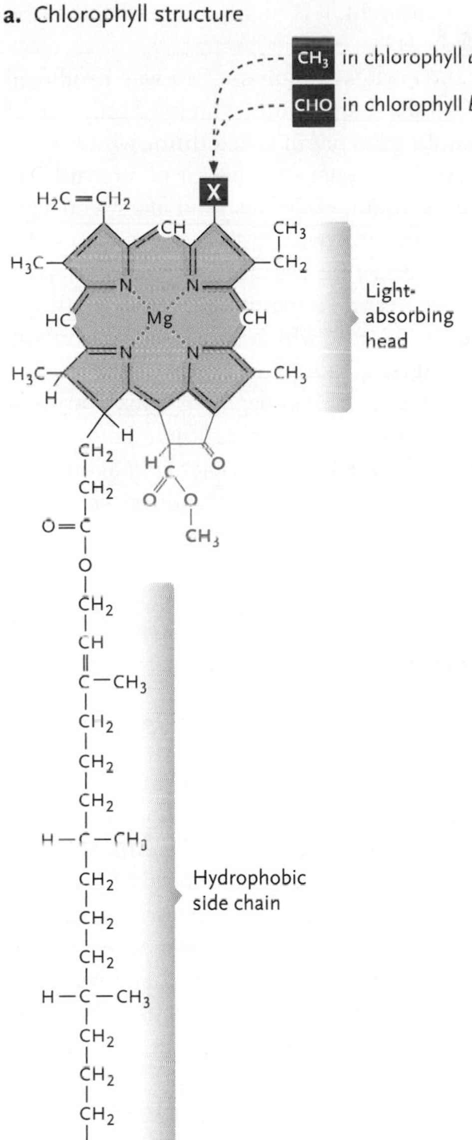

Figure 7.5
Pigment molecules used in photosynthesis.
(a) Chlorophylls *a* and *b*, which differ only in the side group attached at the X. Light-absorbing electrons are distributed among the bonds shaded in red.
(b) Carotenoids. The electrons absorbing light are distributed in a series of alternating double and single bonds in the backbone of these pigments.

itself be transferred to a nearby electron-accepting molecule. In photosynthesis, this molecule is called the primary acceptor.

7.2b Chlorophylls and Carotenoids Cooperate in Light Absorption

Chlorophylls are the major photosynthetic pigments in plants, green algae, and cyanobacteria. Of the chlorophylls, the most dominant types are chlorophyll a and b which are structurally only slightly different **(Figure 7.5)**. Besides the chlorophylls, the closely related molecules, the bacteriochlorophylls, carry out the same functions in groups of photosynthetic prokaryotes other than the cyanobacteria. The second major group of pigments involved in photosynthesis is the carotenoids.

During photosynthesis it is only chlorophyll a that becomes oxidized and donates an electron to the primary electron acceptor. Carrotenoids and chlorophyll b are referred to as accessory pigments because after light absorption they donate excitation energy by indiuctae resonance to molecules of chlorophyll a.

As you may recall from Chapter 1, a pigment molecule does not absorb all wavelengths of light—those wavelengths that are not absorbed give a pigment its distinctive colour. One can precisely determine the wavelengths of light absorbed by a pigment by producing an absorption spectrum for that pigment by using an instrument called a spectrophotometer and a pure sample of a pigment. An **absorption spectrum** is a plot of the absorption of light as a function of wavelength. **Figure 7.6a (p. 144)** shows that chlorophyll *a* absorbs strongly blue and red light but does not absorb green or yellow light. The absorption spectra of the accessory pigments (chlorophyll *b* and carotenoids; see Figure 7.6 a) illustrate that these pigments expand the wavelengths of light that can be effectively captured and used for photosynthesis.

Photosynthesis is dependent on the absorption of light by chlorophylls and carotenoids, acting in combination. This is supported by the **action spectrum** for photosynthesis, which is a plot of the effectiveness of light of particular wavelengths in driving photosynthesis **(Figure 7.6b, p. 144)**. The action spectrum is usually determined by using a suspension of chloroplasts or algal cells and measuring the amount of O_2 released by photosynthesis at different wavelengths of visible light. Whenever an action spectrum for a physiological phenomenon matches the absorption

a. The absorption spectra of chlorophylls *a* and *b* and carotenoids

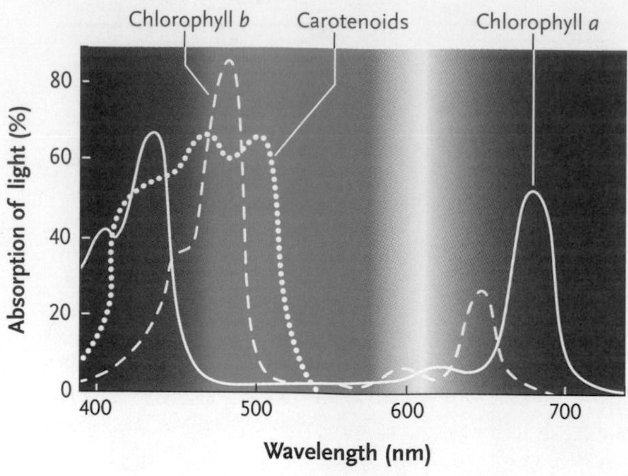

b. The action spectrum in higher plants, representing the combined effects of chlorophylls and carotenoids

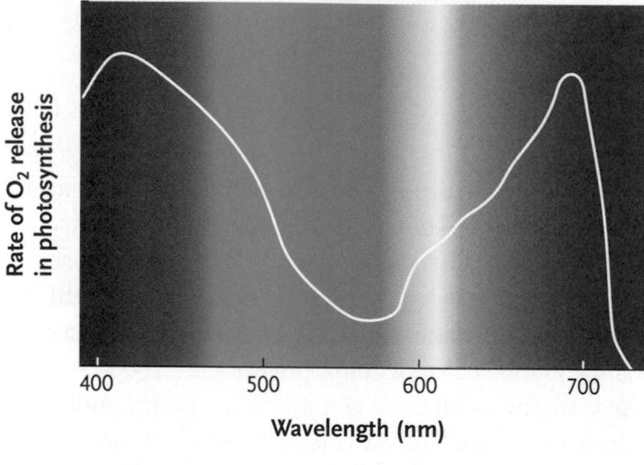

The peaks in the action spectrum are typically broader than those for the individual pigments, reflecting both their combined effects and changes in the absorption spectra of individual pigments by their combination with proteins in chloroplasts.

Figure 7.6
The absorption spectra of the photosynthetic pigments **(a)** and the action spectrum of photosynthesis **(b)**.

spectrum of a pigment, it is highly suggestive that the two are linked.

One of the earliest action spectra was produced in 1883 by Theodor Engelmann, who used only a light microscope and a glass prism to determine which wavelengths of light were most effective for photosynthesis **(Figure 7.7)**. Engelmann placed a strand of a green alga, *Spirogyra*, on a glass microscope slide, along with water containing bacteria that require oxygen to survive. He adjusted the prism so that it split a beam of light into its separate colours, which spread like a rainbow across the strand (see Figure 7.7). After a short time, he noticed that the bacteria had begun to cluster around the algal strand in different locations. The largest clusters were under the blue and violet light at one end of the strand and the red light at the other end. Very few bacteria were found in the green light.

7.2c Photosynthetic Pigments Are Organized into Photosystems

Pigment molecules are not freely floating within the thylakoid membranes but rather are bound very precisely to a number of different proteins. These pigment-proteins are organized into what are called photosystems. Each photosystem is composed of a large *antenna complex* (also called a *light-harvesting complex*) of pigment-proteins that surrounds a central *reaction centre*. The reaction centre of a photosystem comprises a small number of proteins that bind a pair of specialized chlorophyll *a* molecules as well as the primary electron acceptor **(Figure 7.8)**.

There are two distinctly different kinds of photosystems: photosystem I and photosystem II (also called PSI and PSII). The specialized chlorophyll *a* at the reaction centre of photosystem I is called P700 (P = pigment) because it absorbs light optimally at a wavelength of 700 nm, whereas the reaction centre of photosystem II contains a specialized chlorophyll *a*, P680, which absorbs light optimally at a wavelength

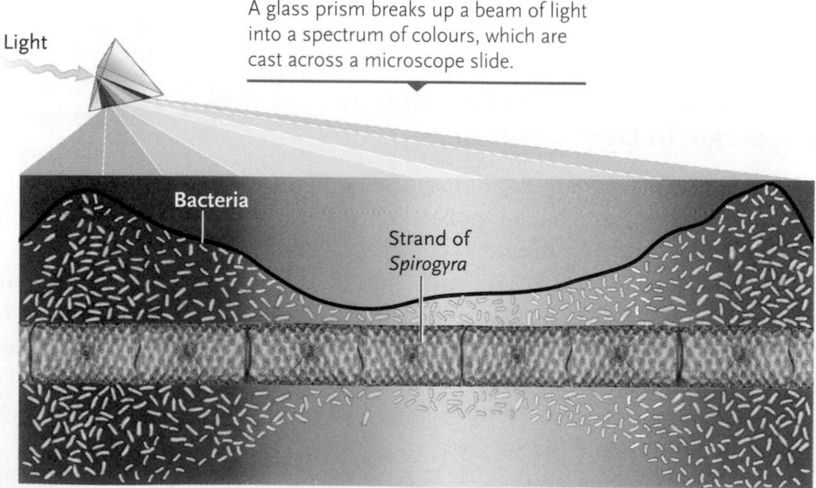

Light
A glass prism breaks up a beam of light into a spectrum of colours, which are cast across a microscope slide.
Bacteria
Strand of *Spirogyra*

Figure 7.7
Engelmann's 1882 experiment revealed the action spectrum of light used in photosynthesis by *Spirogyra*, a green alga. The aerobic bacteria clustered along the algal strand in the regions where oxygen was released in greatest quantity—the regions in which photosynthesis proceeded at the greatest rate. Those regions corresponded to the colours (wavelengths) of light being absorbed most effectively by the alga—in this case, violet and red.

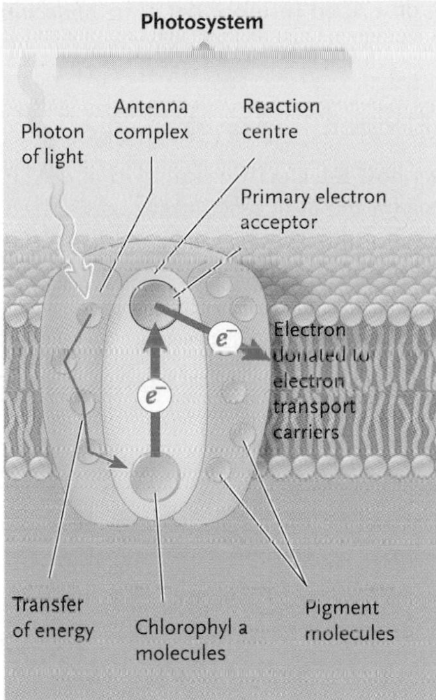

Figure 7.8
A Photosystem: comprised of a light-harvesting antenna complex and a reaction centre. Light energy absorbed by the antenna complex is transferred to specialized chlorophyll molecules in the reaction centre. Light energy is converted to chemical energy as a reaction centre chlorophyll donates an electron to the primary electron acceptor. This electron in turn is passed along an electron transport chain.

of 680 nm. P700 and P680 are structurally identical to other chlorophyll *a* molecules; their specific light absorption patterns result from interactions with particular proteins in the photosystems.

The function of a photosystem is to trap photons of light and use the energy to oxidize a reaction centre chlorophyll, with the electron being transferred to the primary electron acceptor. High rates of oxidation–reduction within the reaction centre are achieved by the large antenna complex of pigments absorbing light of a range of wavelengths and efficiently funnelling the energy to the reaction, through inductive resonance.

Study Break

1. What are the components of a photosystem?
2. What is the difference between an absorption spectrum and an action spectrum?

7.3 Photosynthetic Electron Transport

Photosystem I and photosystem II are the two major light-trapping components involved in photosynthetic electron transport in most photoautotrophs. In this section, we look in detail at how this particular electron transport chain operates and draw some analogies with respiratory electron transport. As in all electron transport systems, the electron carriers of the photosynthetic system consist of nonprotein organic groups that alternate between being oxidized and reduced as electrons move through the system. The carriers include the same types that act in mitochondrial electron transfer—cytochromes, quinones, and iron-sulphur centres.

7.3a The Structure and Function of Photosystem II

In Chapter 2, we discussed the evolutionary significance of the development of oxygenic photosynthesis and how it allowed organisms to use the most abundant substance on Earth—water—as a source of electrons. By splitting water, these organisms released O_2, as a by-product which slowly accumulated in the atmosphere. Oxygenic photosynthesis is the result of the development of photosystem II. The sequence of light harvesting and photochemical events within this very important photosystem (**Figure 7.9**) is as follows.

1. The absorption of photons by the antenna complex and funnelling of energy to the reaction centre results in an electron within P680 being raised from the ground state to an excited state. The excited state is denoted with an asterisk (P680*).
2. Once in the excited state, P680* can be easily oxidized to $P680^+$ by the primary electron acceptor of photosystem II, a molecule called pheophytin

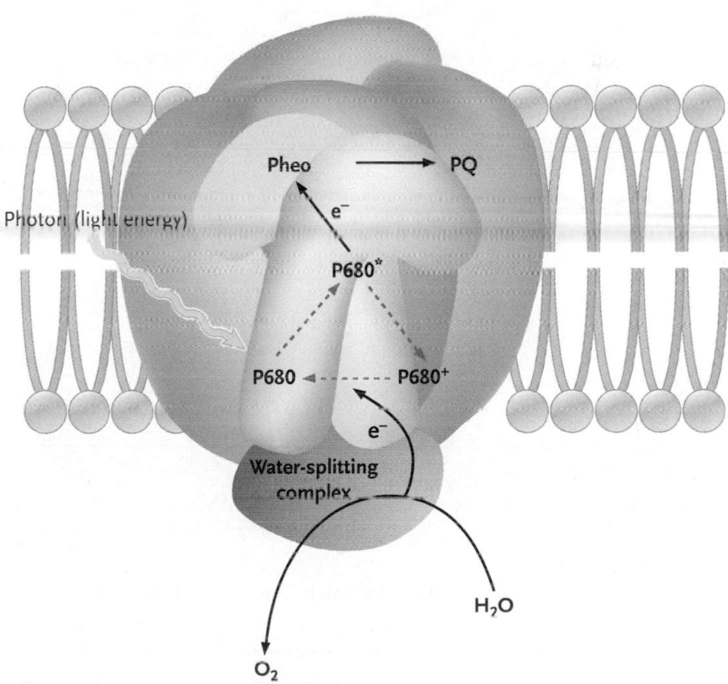

Figure 7.9
A structural model of photosystem II showing the major protein components and pathway of electron flow from water to plastoquinone (PQ). The chlorophyll molecule (P680) remains bound to a reaction centre protein but cycles through three different forms as shown by dashed arrows. See text for full explantation.

(pheo), which initiates electron transport by donation to plastoquinone (PQ) which is analogous to ubiquinone of respiratory electron transport.

3. P680 is re-formed by P680$^+$ gaining an electron by oxidizing water.

P680$^+$ is the strongest oxidant known in biology, and its ability to oxidize water, a very stable molecule, is remarkable. The reduction of P680$^+$ to P680 by electrons from water is facilitated by an enzyme subunit of photosystem II, called the water-splitting complex which is exposed to the thylakoid lumen.

The absorption of energetic photons of light in combination with the formation of such strong oxidants as P680$^+$ and O_2 makes the reaction centre of photosystem II particularly susceptible to damage by reactive oxygen species (see Figure 6.7). In fact, the proteins of the photosystem II reaction centre are constantly being irreversibly damaged. This damage is countered by a very efficient and elaborate system of repair that is described in more detail in *Molecule Behind Biology*.

7.3b Linear Electron Transport

Figure 7.10 shows how the electron transport and ATP synthesis systems for the light reactions are organized in the thylakoid membrane. Let us follow the noncyclic electron pathway using this figure. Don't worry about the stoichiometry of electrons and photons yet.

1. **Oxidation of P680.** Absorption of light energy by photosystem II results in the formation of excited state P680 (P680*). This molecule is rapidly oxidized by the primary electron acceptor pheophytin.
2. **Oxidation–reduction of the plastoquinone pool.** From the primary acceptor, the electrons transfer to *plastoquinone* (PQ), which migrates through the lipid bilayer and acts as an electron transfer

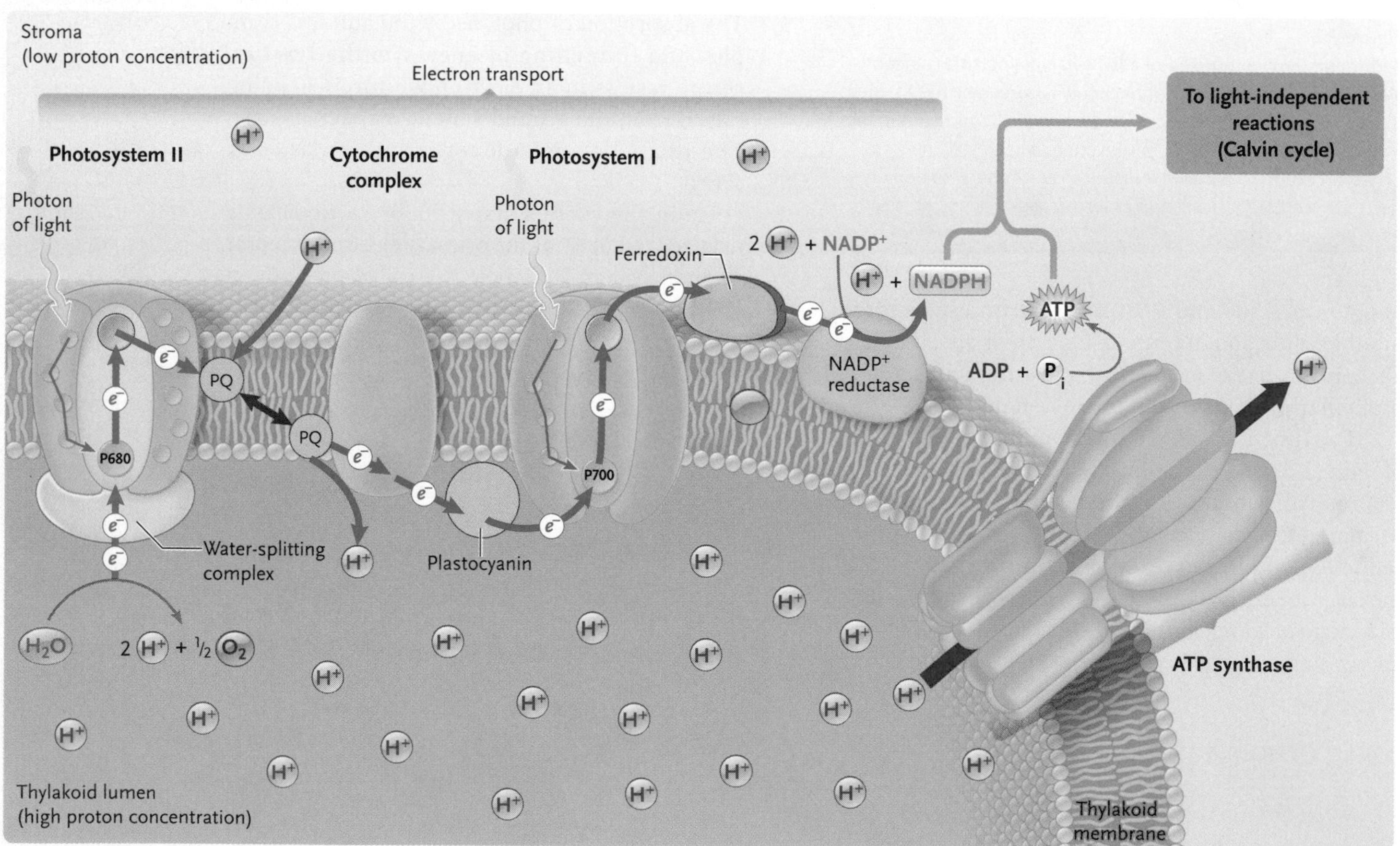

Figure 7.10
A model of the eukaryotic thylakoid membrane illustrating the major protein and redox cofactors required for photosynthetic electron transport and ATP synthesis by chemiosmosis. The four major protein complexes are photosystem II, the cytochrome complex, photosystem I, and ATP synthase. The blue arrow illustrates the pathway of noncyclic (linear) electron transport. As a consequence of electron transport, protons are transported from the stroma into the thylakoid lumen. This occurs during the movement of plastoquinone (PQ) as it alternates from being reduced by photosystem II and then oxidized by the cytochrome complex. The proton gradient is enhanced by the splitting of water on the luminal side of photosystem II and the formation of NADPH on the stromal side of the thylakoid. ATP synthesis occurs by chemiosmosis as protons flow back across the thylakoid membrane through the ATP synthase.

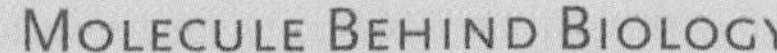

MOLECULE BEHIND BIOLOGY

The D1 Protein Keeps Photosystem II Operating

Photosystem II can be considered the most important development in the evolution of life on Earth. Unlike anything that came before it, organisms that had photosystem II could harvest the energy of the Sun and use it to extract electrons from water. These electrons were used to convert CO_2 from the atmosphere into the organic building blocks of the cell. This ability to use water meant that life could thrive almost anywhere on the planet and led to an explosion in the conversion of CO_2 into organic molecules. By splitting water, photosystem II also produced O_2, which gradually accumulated in the atmosphere and led to the development of aerobic respiration. The process of aerobic respiration extracts 18 times more energy from sugar than the anaerobic pathway that came before it, resulting in an energy bounty that allowed the emergence of complex, multicellular eukaryotic organisms. Because of this, photosystem II is known as "the engine of life."

The splitting of water by photosystem II is the most energetically demanding reaction in all of biology. The reaction is carried out by a molecule, P680, which is found in the core of photosystem II, bound to a protein called D1. When photosystem II absorbs light, P680 is converted into the strongest known biological oxidant, $P680^+$, and this molecule is able to break apart H_2O, releasing electrons, protons, and O_2.

As a consequence of absorbing the energy of about 10 000 photons every second and generating powerful oxidants, photosystem II is constantly being damaged, which results in its inactivation. The major site of damage is the D1 protein, which is found in the core of the complex and binds P680. Over the course of two billion years of evolution, organisms that have photosystem II have been unable to prevent the damage from occurring—but they have developed a highly specialized mechanism to repair it.

It takes only 20 minutes for a newly synthesized photosystem II complex to stop working because of damage to D1. However, damaged complexes are rapidly disassembled, the damaged D1 protein is removed and degraded, a newly synthesized D1 protein is inserted, and a functional photosystem is reassembled. This repair cycle is very efficient and is dependent on a high rate of D1 protein synthesis. It has been estimated that in the absence of this repair system, damage to photosystem II would lower the photosynthetic productivity of the planet by 95%. Thus, life on Earth could not have evolved to present-day levels of both abundance and complexity in the absence of a D1 repair mechanism.

link between PSII and the cytochrome complex. Plastoquinone is analogous in structure and function to ubiquinone of the mitochondrial electron system and exists as a pool within the thylakoid membrane. As plastoquinone accepts electrons from photosystem II, it also gains protons from the lumen. This reduced form migrates through the membrane. When it donates electrons to the cytochrome complex, it also releases protons into the stroma.

3. **Electron transfer from the cytochrome complex and shuttling by plastocyanin.** From the cytochrome complex, electrons pass to the mobile carrier *plastocyanin*, which shuttles electrons between the cytochrome complex and photosystem I.
4. **Oxidation–reduction of P700.** Absorption of a photon of light by photosystem I results in the formation of P700*. This is oxidized to $P700^+$ by the primary electron acceptor of photosystem I. $P700^+$ is reduced back to P700 by electron donation from plastocyanin.
5. **Electron transfer to $NADP^+$ by ferredoxin.** After passage through a short sequence of carriers within photosystem I, the electron from P700 is transferred to *ferredoxin*, an iron–sulphur protein. The ferredoxin transfers the electrons to $NADP^+$, the final acceptor of the noncyclic pathway. $NADP^+$ is reduced to NADPH by the enzyme $NADP^+$ reductase.

7.3c Chemiosmotic Synthesis of ATP

In a way analogous to respiratory electron transport, the flow of electrons along the photosynthetic electron transport chain is coupled to ATP synthesis by the buildup of a proton gradient across the thylakoid membrane. In photosynthetic electron transport, the proton gradient across the thylakoid membrane is derived from three processes. First, protons are translocated into the lumen by the cyclic reduction and oxidation of plastoquinone as it migrates from photosystem II to the cytochrome complex (see Figure 7.10) and back again. Second, the gradient is enhanced by the addition of two protons for each water molecule oxidized on the luminal side of PSII. Third, the removal of one proton from the stroma for each NADPH molecule synthesized further enhances the gradient across the membrane. Recall from Section 6.5 that the proton gradient is a source of energy. The *proton-motive force* (see Section 6.5) established across the thylakoid membrane is utilized to synthesize ATP by chemiosmosis using the chloroplast ATP synthase. This multiprotein complex is identical to the ATP synthase used in oxidative phosphorylation in cellular respiration (see Section 6.5).

7.3d What Light Is Actually Used For

All electron transport chains operate by electrons flowing spontaneously "downhill" from molecules with high-energy electrons (and are thus easily oxidized) to molecules that are progressively more easily reduced (more electronegative). In the case of mitochondrial respiration, flow is "downhill" from NADH to O_2. In photosynthesis, electron transport occurs by the same principle. However, unlike NADH in respiration, the chlorophyll molecules in the reaction centres of PSII and PSI are not readily oxidized. So how does photosynthesis get chlorophyll molecules into a state where they readily give up electrons? By absorbing light! The absorption of light energy and funnelling of this high energy to the reaction centres boost the energy level of the electrons within the reaction centre chlorophylls **(Figure 7.11)**.

By converting P680 into P680*, the absorption of light energy produces a molecule that is easily oxidized by the electron transport chain, and electron flow is downhill from P680* to photosystem I. A second photon of light must be absorbed by photosystem I to form P700*. Only P700* and not P700 can donate electrons to ferredoxin and eventually on to $NADP^+$ (see Figure 7.11).

In respiratory electron transport, electron flow is spontaneous from NADH to O_2, producing water. By comparison, in photosynthetic electron transport, electron flow is essentially opposite, from water to $NADP^+$. Electron flow is made spontaneous through the absorption of light energy. A mechanical analogy of the role of light absorption and the flow of electrons through the electron transport chain is shown in **Figure 7.12.**

7.3e The Stoichiometry of Linear Electron Transport

We have described in detail the structure and function of the photosynthetic apparatus. Now it's time to go over the stoichiometry of the light reactions.

To get a single electron down the electron transport chain from photosystem II (or water; it doesn't matter) to $NADP^+$ takes two photons of light, one photon absorbed by photosystem II and a second by photosystem I. *How many photons need to be absorbed by the photosynthetic apparatus to produce a single molecule of O_2?* First, write out a balanced equation,

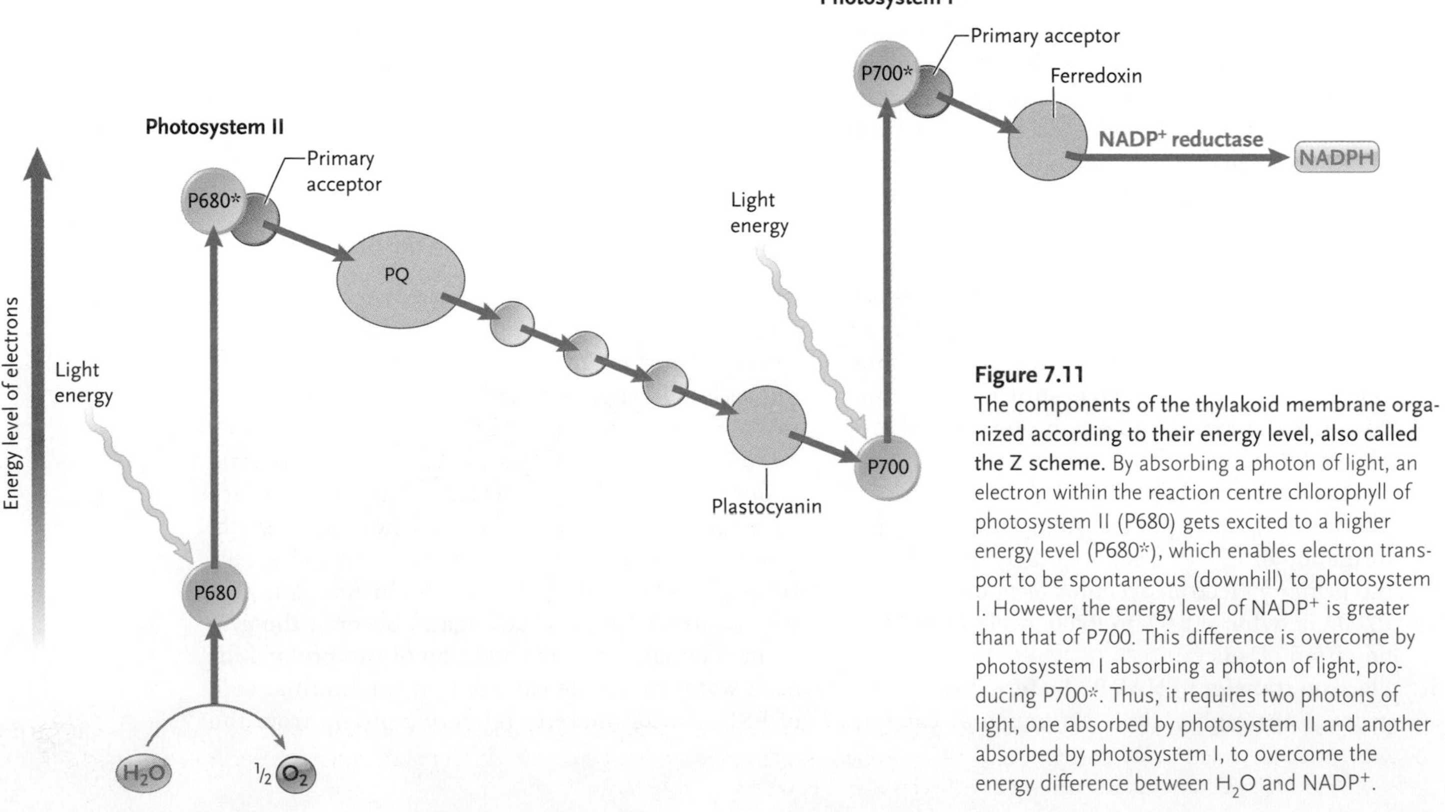

Figure 7.11
The components of the thylakoid membrane organized according to their energy level, also called the Z scheme. By absorbing a photon of light, an electron within the reaction centre chlorophyll of photosystem II (P680) gets excited to a higher energy level (P680*), which enables electron transport to be spontaneous (downhill) to photosystem I. However, the energy level of $NADP^+$ is greater than that of P700. This difference is overcome by photosystem I absorbing a photon of light, producing P700*. Thus, it requires two photons of light, one absorbed by photosystem II and another absorbed by photosystem I, to overcome the energy difference between H_2O and $NADP^+$.

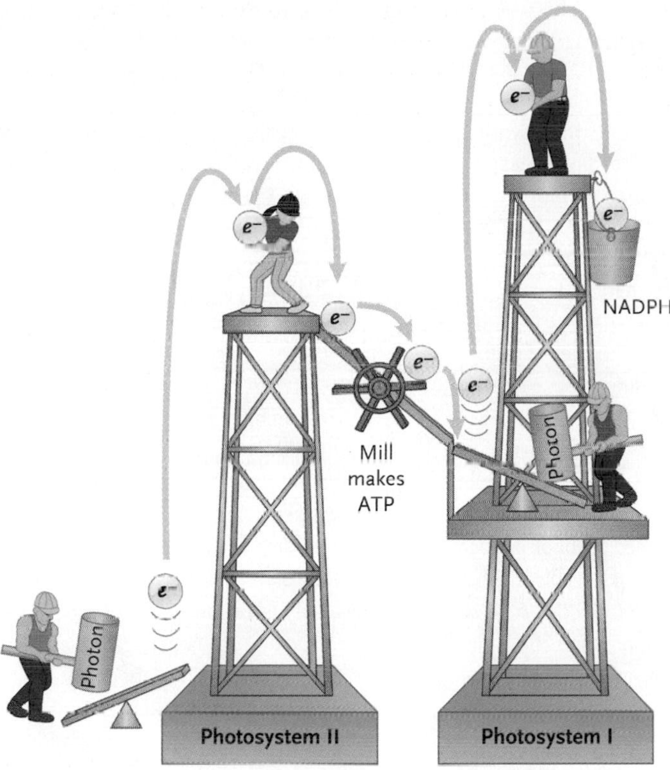

Figure 7.12
A mechanical analogy of the light reactions of photosynthesis.

which shows you need to oxidize two molecules of H_2O which releases 4 electrons

$$2H_2O \rightarrow 4H^+ + 4\,e^- + O_2$$

To move a single electron down the chain requires the absorption of two photons, thus to get four electrons, the photosynthetic apparatus needs to absorb a total of eight photons of light, four by each photosystem.

7.3f Cyclic Electron Transport

Photosystem I can function independently of photosystem II in what is called **cyclic electron transport (Figure 7.13)**. In this process, electron transport from photosystem I to ferredoxin is not followed by electron donation to the $NADP^+$ reductase complex. Instead, reduced ferredoxin donates electrons back to the plastoquinone pool. In this manner, the plastoquinone pool gets continually reduced and oxidized and keeps moving protons across the thylakoid membrane without the involvement of photosystem II. The net result of cyclic electron transport is that the energy absorbed from

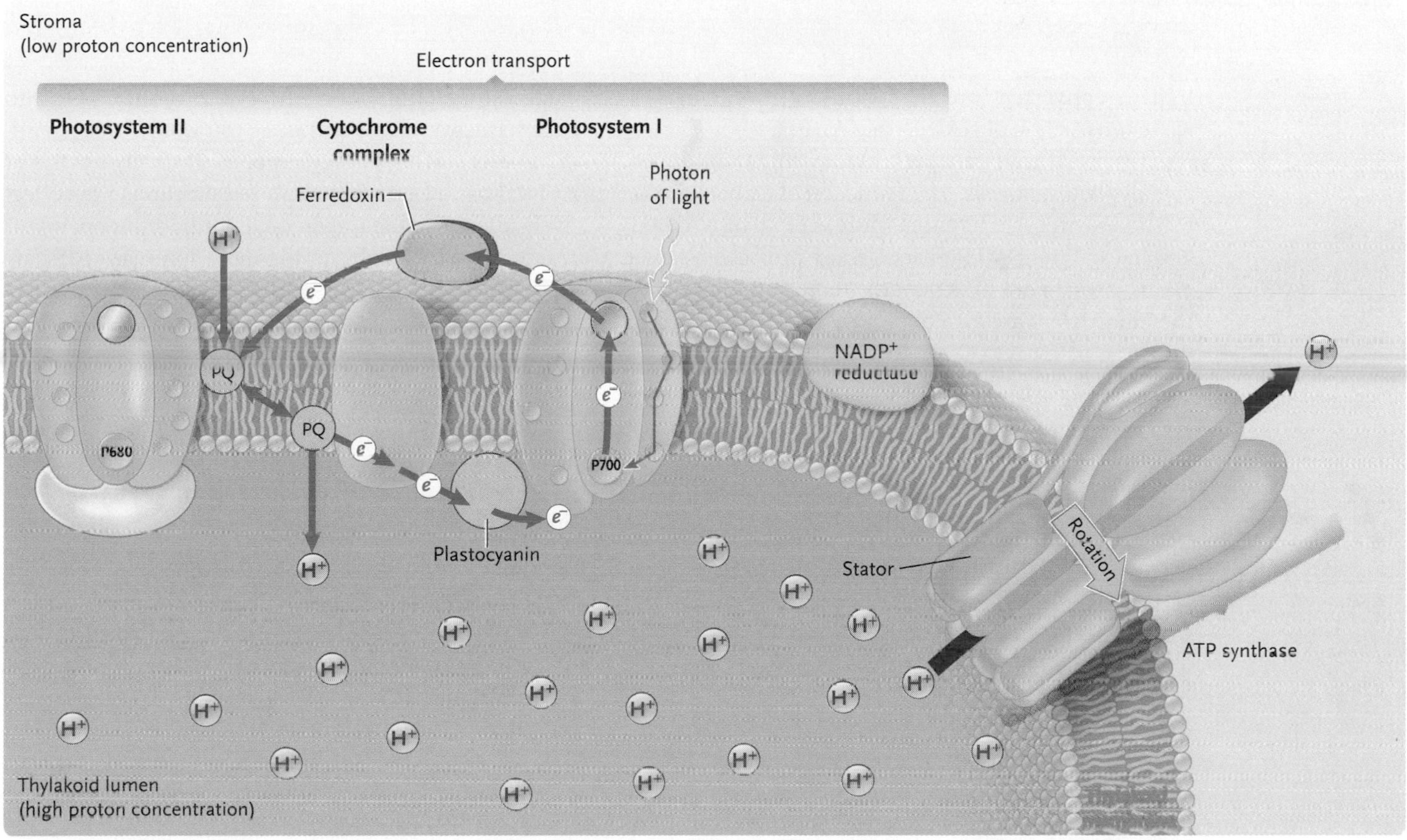

Figure 7.13
Cyclic electron transport. Electrons move in a circular pathway from photosystem I through ferredoxin back to the plastoquinone pool, through the cytochrome complex and plastocyanin and then back to photosystem I. In cyclic electron transport Photosystem II does not operate. The pathway generates proton pumping and thus leads to ATP production but does not result in the synthesis of NADPH.

People Behind Biology

Dr. Norm Hüner

A number of advances into our understanding of the regulation of photosynthesis have been elucidated by the research group of Dr. Norm Hüner, who presently holds a Tier 1 Canada Research Chair in Environmental Stress Biology at the University of Western Ontario in London.

Hüner's research has established that the photosynthetic apparatus has a dual role: not only does it function as the primary energy transformer of the biosphere, it also acts as a sensor of environmental change in all photoautotrophs. Using a range of organisms, including plants, green algae, and cyanobacteria, Hüner's group has discovered that the relative redox state of photosynthetic electron transport acts as a natural sensor of the balance between energy input from the Sun and the demands for that energy by the metabolic processes of the organism.

The redox state of the photosynthetic apparatus can be readily assessed by measuring the "excitation pressure" on photosystem II using a fluorescence-based technique. Hüner's group has shown that changes in excitation pressure are a key trigger that initiates changes to a number of cellular processes, including gene expression, which enable photoautotrophs to readily acclimate to changes in light, temperature, and nutrient availability.

Hüner is the coauthor of an internationally acclaimed textbook entitled *Introduction to Plant Physiology*, which is presently in its fourth edition. As well, he has received more than 25 national and international awards and honours for his research, which include election as a fellow of the Academy of Science, Royal Society of Canada, and as president of the Canadian Society of Plant Physiologists; an honorary degree from the University of Umea, Sweden; and an honorary professorship from Xinjiang University, China.

In recent years, Hüner has been the lead investigator in the establishment of The Biotron Experimental Climate Change Research Centre, an international research facility on the campus of the University of Western Ontario. The research focus of this $30 million facility is the elucidation of the mechanisms by which plants, microbes, and insects sense and adjust to climate change. One of the unique aspects of the Biotron is that it gives researchers the ability to conduct control experiments on a much larger scale than possible in a conventional laboratory. This allows for the study of how changes to temperature, light, nutrients, and carbon dioxide concentrations may impact not only the growth of individual species, but also entire ecosystems.

light is converted into the chemical energy of ATP *without* reduction of $NADP^+$ to NADPH.

Cyclic electron transport plays an important role in overall photosynthesis. The reduction of carbon dioxide by the Calvin cycle requires more ATP than NADPH, and the additional ATP molecules are provided by cyclic electron transport. Other energy-requiring reactions in the chloroplast are also depend on ATP produced by the cyclic pathway.

Study Break

To get one electron down the photosynthetic electron transport chain, how many photons need to be absorbed?

7.4 The Calvin Cycle

Recall from the last chapter that CO_2 is a fully oxidized carbon molecule and thus contains no usable energy. On the other hand, sugar molecules such as glucose and sucrose are highly reduced. They contain many C—H bonds and thus are an abundant source of energy. In the cytosol of prokaryotic photoautotrophs and in the stroma of the chloroplast, a series of 11 enzyme-catalyzed reactions use NADPH to reduce CO_2 into sugar. The overall process is, as you would expect, endergonic, requiring energy supplied by the hydrolysis of ATP. These 11 enzyme-catalyzed reactions are collectively known as the Calvin cycle (or light-independent reactions), which is by far the most dominant pathway on Earth by which CO_2 is *fixed* into carbohydrates.

7.4a The Calvin Cycle Reduces CO_2 to a Carbohydrate

The Calvin cycle is illustrated in **Figure 7.14.** It can be conceptually divided into three distinct phases: fixation, reduction, and regeneration.

Phase 1: carbon fixation. This phase involves the incorporation of a carbon atom from CO_2 into a molecule of ribulose 1,5-bisphosphate (RuBP), a five-carbon sugar, to produce two three-carbon molecules of 3-phosphoglycerate.

Phase 2: reduction. In this phase, each of the two molecules of 3-phosphoglycerate gets an additional phosphate added from the hydrolysis of ATP, producing 1,3-bisphosphoglycerate. This molecule is subsequently reduced by electrons from NADPH, producing glyceraldehyde-3-phosphate (G3P).

The Calvin Cycle.

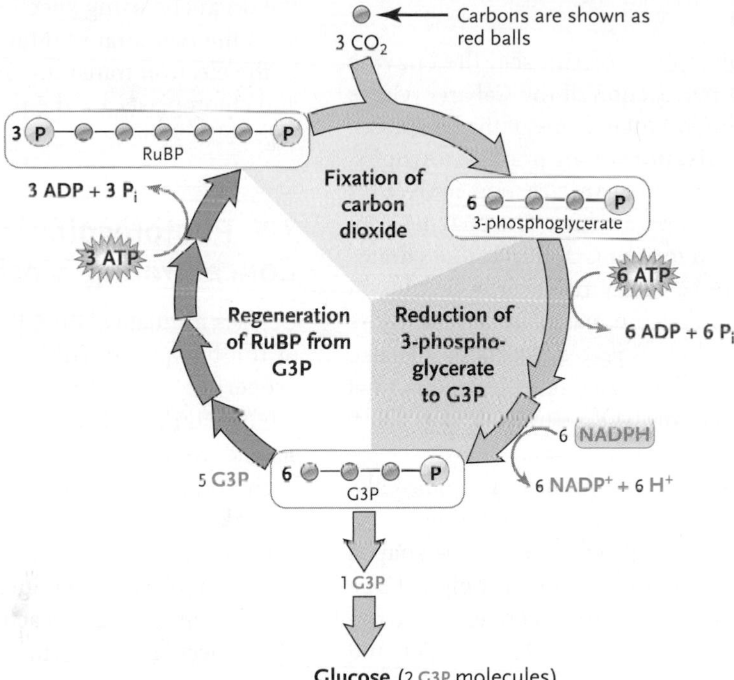

Figure 7.14

Reactions of the Calvin cycle tracking carbon atoms through the cycle. What is shown is the sum of three turns of the cycle (three CO_2 molecules), which produces one extra molecule of a three-carbon sugar G3P.

Phase 3: regeneration. For each turn of the Calvin cycle, two molecules of G3P are produced—a total of six carbon atoms. In a multienzyme-step process, five of these carbons are rearranged to regenerate the single molecule of RuBP required to start the cycle over again.

What we have just described is what takes place during a *single* turn of the Calvin cycle. For each turn, one molecule of CO_2 is converted into one reduced carbon—essentially one (CH_2O) unit of carbohydrate. However, it takes three turns of the cycle to actually produce something the cell can use—one extra molecule of the three-carbon sugar G3P. Because of this, Figure 7.14 actually is a summary of three turns of the cycle as it tracks the fate of three carbon atoms.

Let's work through Figure 7.14—the key is to keep track of the carbons. In three turns of the Calvin cycle, 3 CO_2 (3 carbons) are incorporated into 3 molecules of RuBP (15 carbons), which produces 6 molecules of 3-phosphoglycerate (18 carbons). Three turns of the Calvin cycle produce 6 molecules of G3P (totalling 18 carbons). Of these, 5 molecules of G3P (totalling 15 carbons) are used to regenerate the 3 RuBP molecules (15 carbons) required for three turns of the cycle. Thus, the cycle generate one surplus molecule of G3P (three carbons) after three turns. For the synthesis of this one extra G3P, the Calvin cycle requires a total of nine molecules of ATP and six molecules of NADPH. Both ATP and NADPH are regenerated from ADP and $NADP^+$, respectively, by the light reactions.

7.4b G3P Is the Starting Point for Synthesis of Many Other Organic Molecules

The G3P molecule formed by three turns of the Calvin cycle is the starting point for the production of a wide variety of organic molecules. More complex carbohydrates, such as glucose and other monosaccharides, are made from G3P by reactions that, in effect, reverse the first half of glycolysis. Once produced, the monosaccharides may enter biochemical pathways that make disaccharides such as sucrose, polysaccharides such as starches and cellulose, and other complex carbohydrates. Other pathways manufacture amino acids, fatty acids and lipids, proteins, and nucleic acids. The reactions forming these products occur both within chloroplasts and in the surrounding cytosol and nucleus.

Sucrose, a disaccharide consisting of glucose linked to fructose, is the main form in which the products of photosynthesis circulate from cell to cell in higher plants. Organic nutrients are stored in most higher plants as sucrose, starch, or a combination of the two in proportions that depend on the plant species. Sugar cane and sugar beets, which contain stored sucrose in high concentrations, are the main sources of the sucrose we use as table sugar.

7.4c Rubisco: The Most Abundant Protein on Earth

Rubulose-1,5-bisphosphate or rubisco, the enzyme that catalyzes the first reaction of the Calvin cycle, is arguably the most important enzyme of the biosphere. By catalyzing CO_2 fixation in all photoautotrophs, it provides the source of organic carbon molecules for most of the world's organisms. The enzyme converts about 100 billion tons of CO_2 into carbohydrates annually. There are so many rubisco molecules in chloroplasts that the enzyme makes up 50% or more of the total protein of plant leaves. As such, it is also the world's most abundant protein, estimated to total some 40 million tons worldwide—equivalent to about 10 kg per person on Earth.

Isolation and purification of rubisco from the chloroplast stroma have led to the elucidation of its three-dimensional structure. The molecule is cube shaped and contains eight small subunits and eight large subunits. Each of the large subunits contains an active site, which has defined binding sites for both CO_2 and RuBP. The small subunits do not have a role in catalysis but do serve an important regulatory role, although their exact function remains unknown.

The synthesis of rubisco is quite remarkable as it requires the coordinated expression of genes in two different genomes **(Figure 7.15)**. Whereas the large subunit is encoded by a gene of the chloroplast genome, the small subunit is encoded by a gene that is found in the nucleus. After the small subunit polypeptide is synthesized in the cytosol, it is imported into the chloroplast, where it associates with large subunit monomers to make the functional enzyme.

The vast majority of the proteins found in chloroplasts (and mitochondria) are, in fact, encoded by the nuclear genome and thus are synthesized on ribosomes in the cytosol. They are then imported into the organelle using specific transport complexes that span the membranes. Many of the protein complexes of the electron transport chains of both mitochondria and chloroplasts are the products of both nuclear and organellar genes.

7.5 Photorespiration and CO_2-Concentrating Mechanisms

Besides argulably being the most important enzyme of the biosphere, rubisco has some rather unique properties. First, it is a very slow enzyme catalzying the fixation of only about three molecules of CO_2 per second. Its slow rate of catalysis is countered by it very high abundance within the cell. Second, rubisco is remarkably inefficient at fixing CO_2. This inefficiency is because a Rubsico can also catalyze the incorporation of a molecule of O_2 into RuBP. The product of this so-called oxygenation reaction results in the formation of a molecule that is actually toxic, and its metabolism results in the loss of carbon from the cell and the consumption of ATP (in the form of CO_2). Because O_2 is consumed in this process and CO_2 released at later steps, the entire process is somewhat similar to respiration and is termed **photorespiration.**

Recall from Chapter 4 (Section 4.5b) that a molecule that can compete with the normal substrate for the active site of an enzyme is termed a competitive inhibitor. In this case, O_2 can compete with CO_2 for the active site of rubisco, and is therefore a competitive inhibitor of rubisco. This is surprising because most enzymes have active sites that are very specific for their substrates. Given the importance of rubisco to life on Earth, why would rubisco have evolved an active site that could bind both CO_2 and O_2? The most likely explanation is related to the fact that rubisco is a very ancient enzyme and is found in a range of prokaryotes. Because of this, rubisco developed at a time before oxygenic photosynthesis and, thus, at a time when there was very little O_2 in the atmosphere. Under such conditions of low atmospheric O_2 natural selection would not have favoured an enzyme that had specificity only for CO_2.

In the next few sections, we discuss some of the remarkable adaptations

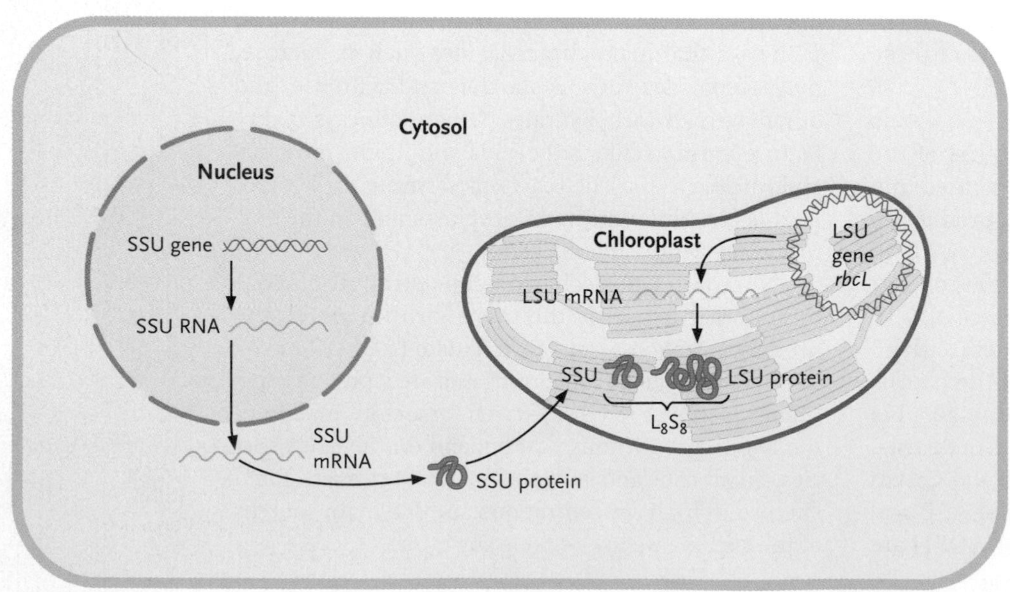

Figure 7.15
Rubisco synthesis. Rubisco is an enzyme that is composed of a total of 16 subunits: 8 large subunits (LSU) and 8 small subunits (SSU). Each LSU is synthesized in the stroma of the chloroplast following the transcription of a gene coded by the chloroplast genome. The gene that encodes the SSU is found in the nucleus with SSU monomers being synthesized by cytosolic ribosomes before being imported into the chloroplast.

plants and algae have made to minimize the competition of O_2 for the active site of rubisco.

7.5a The Oxygenase Activity of Rubisco

When oxygen binds to the active site of rubisco, the enzyme acts as an *oxygenase* instead of a *carboxylase.* A comparison of the products of the carboxylation reaction and the oxygenation reaction of rubisco is shown in **Figure 7.16.** The incorporation of a CO_2 molecule into RuBP leads to a net increase in the carbon of the plant by producing two molecules of 3-phosphoglycerate. As described in the last section, this molecule gets reduced in the Calvin cycle to the three-carbon sugar G3P.

Alternatively, in the oxygenation reaction, the incorporation of O_2 into RuBP produces a single molecule of 3-phosphoglycerate and one molecule of phosphoglycolate. There is no carbon gain—five carbons in and five carbons out. But photoautotrophs cannot use phosphoglycolate. In the process of breaking it down to salvage the carbon, a toxic compound called *glycolate* is produced. The elimination of glycolate results in its oxidation that results in the release of CO_2. Thus, whereas the carboxylation reaction leads to carbon gain, the oxygenation reaction actually results in the cell losing carbon. It is worth remembering that to grow, all organisms must gain carbon.

If one compares the carboxylation and oxygenation reactions of rubisco under laboratory conditions, where we can keep the concentrations of both O_2 and CO_2 equal, then the carboxylation reaction will dominate since the active site of rubisco has a greater affinity for CO_2 than O_2. In fact, the carboxylation reaction will occur about 80 times faster than the oxygenation reaction. However, unlike in the laboratory, the atmosphere does not contain equal amounts of the two gases—it contains approximately 21% O_2 and only about 0.04% CO_2. Under normal atmospheric concentrations and at moderate temperatures, the carboxylation of rubisco will occur about 75% of the time. This means that 25% of the time, the wasteful oxygenation reaction occurs, which is a significant drain on cell resources. It should not come as a surprise that many species have evolved mechanisms to try to decrease the prevalence of the oxygenation reaction. The strategies that we discuss below involve decreasing the extent of photorespiration and the oxygenation reaction using mechanisms that increase the CO_2/O_2 ratio at the site where the Calvin cycle takes place.

7.5b Carbon-Concentrating Mechanisms in Algae

In aquatic environments, the concentration of CO_2 dissolved in the water is usually well below that needed to saturate the active site of rubisco. Yet experimentally, the addition of CO_2 to a culture of phytoplankton does not usually lead to an increase in the rate of photosynthesis.

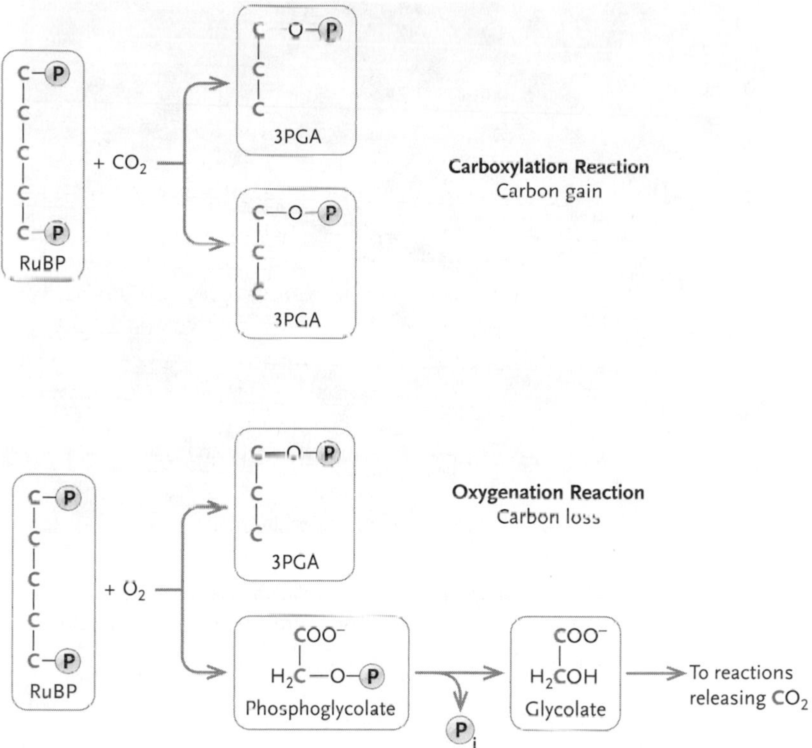

Figure 7.16
The enzyme rubisco possesses both a carboxylase and an oxygenase activity. Compared with the usual carboxylase activity of the Calvin cycle, the oxygenase activity results in a net loss of carbon by the plant. Because oxygenase activity consumes O_2 and releases CO_2, it is also called photorespiration.

These data suggest that aquatic photoautotrophs, including cyanobacteria, phytoplankton, and various other algae, possess a *carbon-concentrating mechanism* whereby inorganic carbon is actively pumped into their cells such that the concentration of CO_2 at the site of rubisco is higher than would otherwise be possible through simple diffusion.

A model for one type of carbon-concentrating mechanism is presented in **Figure 7.17.** In aqueous

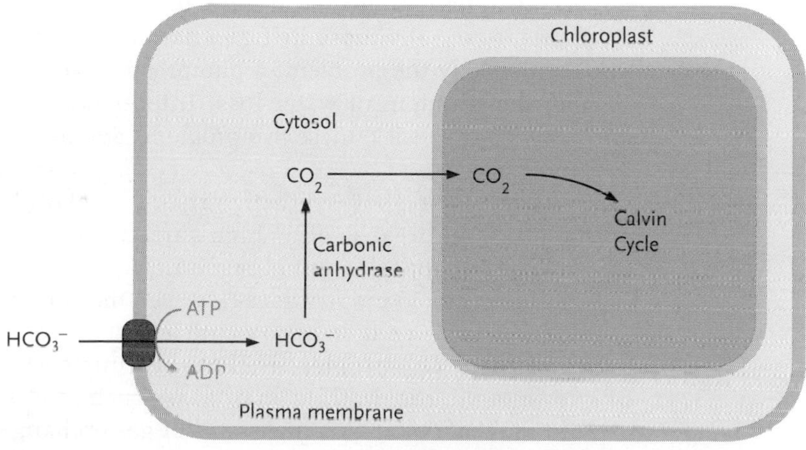

Figure 7.17
Many aquatic photoautotrophs have a CO_2-concentrating mechanism that involves an ATP-dependent bicarbonate (HCO_3) pump on the plasma membrane. The bicarbonate is rapidly converted in the cytosol to CO_2 by the enzyme carbonic anhydrase.

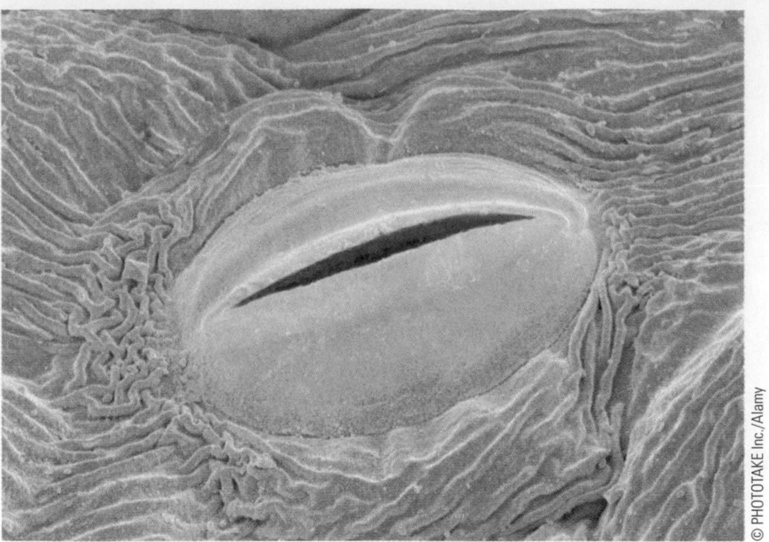

Figure 7.18
Gas exchange and water loss by a plant are controlled by the presence of stomata. Each stoma is formed from two guard cells that control the opening and closing of the pore.

environments of near-neutral pH, the dominant form of inorganic carbon is not CO_2 but rather the bicarbonate anion (HCO_3^-). In the system shown in **Figure 7.18,** an ATP-dependent pump on the plasma membrane transports HCO_3^- into the cell, resulting in a concentration that is higher inside the cell than outside. Within the cytosol, the bicarbonate is rapidly converted into CO_2 by the enzyme carbonic anhydrase. The CO_2 then rapidly diffuses into the chloroplast to the site of rubisco. This system results in a concentration of CO_2 at the site of rubisco that is sufficiently high to essentially outcompete any O_2 that is present for the active site of rubisco.

7.5c Photorespiration and the Problem of Temperature

Unlike aquatic photoautotrophs, many terrestrial plants, especially those living in hot dry climates, face not only the problem of photorespiration but also the problem of water loss. Interestingly, in many plant species, these two problems are inextricably linked.

The major photosynthetic organ of a plant is the leaf, and because of its high surface area, you would think that this would result in high rates of water loss due to evaporation. However, the surface of leaves is covered by a waxy cuticle that prevents water loss. The problem is that the cuticle also prevents the rapid diffusion of gases such as CO_2 into the leaf. To enable high rates of gas exchange (CO_2 in and O_2 out) between the air and the cells within the leaf, the surface of a leaf has small pores, called stomata (singular, stoma) (Figure 7.18). The plant can regulate the size of the stomata from fully closed to fully open to balance the demands for gas exchange with the need to minimize water loss. As you may suspect, plants that are adapted to hot dry climates are faced with a constant dilemma: they need to open their stomata to let CO_2 in for the Calvin cycle, but to conserve water, they need to keep the stomata closed.

The dilemma is even harder to reconcile because photorespiration becomes a bigger problem the warmer the climate. The reason for this relates to the effect of temperature on the solubility of gases in solution (the stroma is an aqueous environment). As shown in **Table 7.1,** the solubility of O_2 and CO_2 decreases as the temperature increases. However, the solubility of CO_2 decreases more rapidly than O_2 as the temperature increases, resulting in a decrease in the CO_2/O_2 ratio. As this ratio decreases, the extent of photorespiration (oxygenation reaction) becomes greater. Under conditions of high temperature, as much as 50% of the plant's energy could be wasted by photorespiration.

7.5d The C_4 Pathway Circumvents Photorespiration

Some plant species that are adapted to hot dry climates have evolved a mode of carbon fixation that minimizes photorespiration. Besides having the Calvin cycle, these plants have a second carbon fixation pathway, called the C_4 cycle **(Figure 7.19).** In this cycle, CO_2 initially combines with a three-carbon molecule, *phosphoenolpyruvate* (PEP), producing the four-carbon intermediate oxaloacetate. Oxaloacetate is then reduced to *malate* by electrons transferred from NADPH. After being transported to the site of the Calvin cycle, the malate gets oxidized to pyruvate, releasing CO_2. To complete the cycle, pyruvate is converted back into PEP in a reaction that consumes ATP. The oxygenation reaction of rubisco is inhibited by the C_4 cycle because the conversion of malate to pyruvate actually generates CO_2, resulting in much higher concentrations at the site of rubisco (see Figure 7.19).

The C_4 cycle gets its name because its first product, oxaloacetate, is a four-carbon molecule rather than the

Table 7.1 **Effect of Temperature on the Solubility of O_2 and CO_2**

Temperature (°C)	$[CO_2]$ (μM in solution)	$[CO_2]$ (μM in solution)	$\frac{[CO_2]}{[O_2]}$
5	21.93	401.2	0.0515
15	15.69	319.8	0.0462
25	11.68	264.6	0.0416
35	9.11	228.2	0.0376

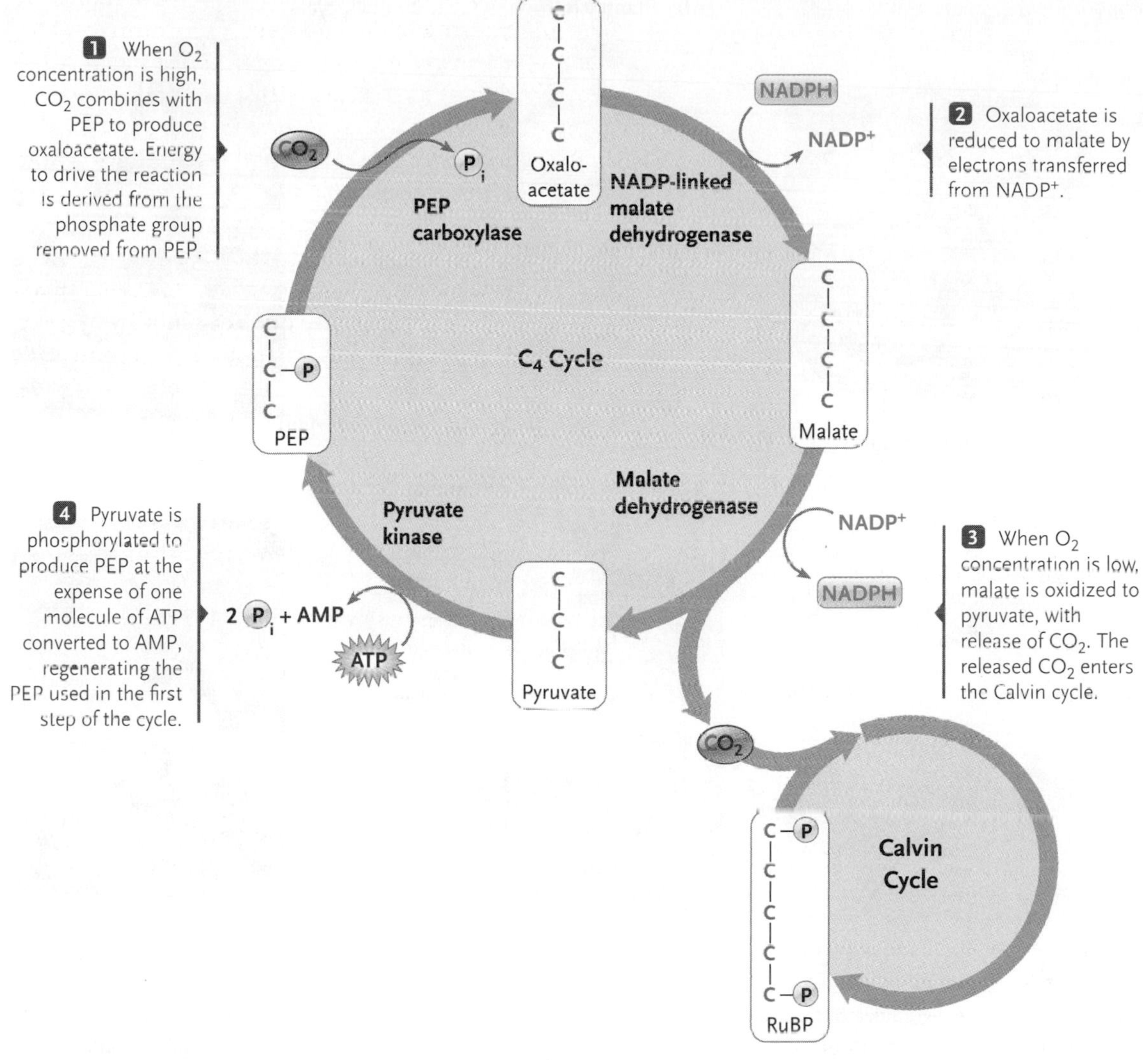

1 When O_2 concentration is high, CO_2 combines with PEP to produce oxaloacetate. Energy to drive the reaction is derived from the phosphate group removed from PEP.
CO_2
P_i
Oxalo-acetate
PEP carboxylase
NADPH
NADP+
NADP-linked malate dehydrogenase
2 Oxaloacetate is reduced to malate by electrons transferred from NADP+.
Malate
C_4 Cycle
PEP
Malate dehydrogenase
Pyruvate kinase
NADP+
NADPH
3 When O_2 concentration is low, malate is oxidized to pyruvate, with release of CO_2. The released CO_2 enters the Calvin cycle.
4 Pyruvate is phosphorylated to produce PEP at the expense of one molecule of ATP converted to AMP, regenerating the PEP used in the first step of the cycle.
2 P_i + AMP
ATP
Pyruvate
CO_2
Calvin Cycle
RuBP

Figure 7.19
The C_4 cycle and its integration with the Calvin cycle. Enzymes are printed in rust. Each turn of the cycle, which delivers one molecule of CO_2 to the Calvin cycle, proceeds at the expense of two phosphate groups removed from ATP.

three-carbon phosphoglycerate, the first product of the Calvin cycle. One often talks in terms of the C_4 versus the C_3 pathways when distinguishing between plants that have the C_4 cycle and those that possess only the Calvin cycle. A key distinction between C_4 and C_3 metabolism concerns the carboxylation reactions. In the C_4 cycle, the initial carboxylation reaction that incorporates CO_2 into phosphoenolpyruvate is catalyzed by the enzyme *PEP carboxylase.* Unlike rubisco, PEP carboxylase has much greater affinity for CO_2 and does not possess any oxygenase activity. It can efficiently catalyze the carboxylation of PEP regardless of the O_2 concentration near the enzyme.

7.5e C_4 Plants

Plants that possess C_4 metabolism include many tropical and several temperate crop species, including corn and sugar cane. In these species, the C_4 cycle occurs in *mesophyll* cells, which lie close to the surface of leaves and stems, where O_2 is abundant **(Figure 7.20a, b, p. 156)**. The malate intermediate of the C_4 cycle diffuses from the mesophyll cells to *bundle sheath cells,* located in deeper tissues, where O_2 is less abundant. In these cells, in which the Calvin cycle operates, the malate enters chloroplasts and is converted to pyruvate and CO_2. Because O_2 concentration is low and CO_2 concentration is high because of its release by malate breakdown, the oxygenase activity of rubisco is inhibited, and the carboxylation reaction runs highly efficiently. The pyruvate produced by malate oxidation returns to the mesophyll cells to enter another turn of the C_4 cycle.

You may ask, *if C_4 metabolism is so good at preventing photorespiration, why don't all plants use it?* Looking back at Figure 7.19, notice that the C_4 pathway has an additional energy requirement. For each turn of the C_4 cycle, the hydrolysis of ATP to AMP is required to regenerate PEP from pyruvate.

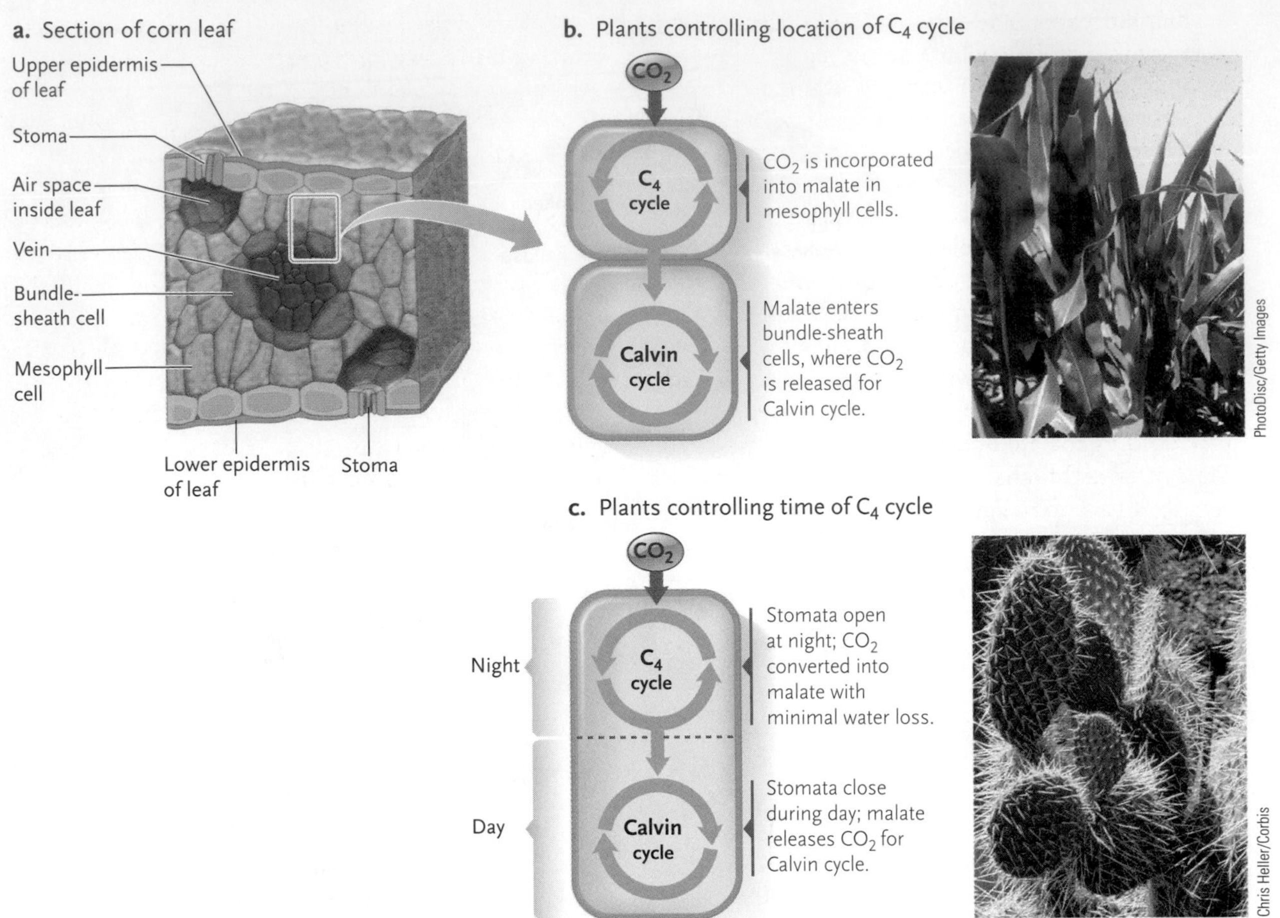

Figure 7.20
Coordination of the C_4 and Calvin cycles to minimize photorespiration. (a) and **(b)** Some C_4 plants separate the two cycles into different locations internally, as in the corn leaf shown in this diagram. The mesophyll cells (lighter green), which are closer to the leaf surfaces, carry out the C_4 cycle in a relatively O_2-rich environment. The bundle sheath cells (darker green), which are cut off from O_2 by the surrounding layer of mesophyll cells, carry out the Calvin cycle. **(c)** Other C_4 plants carry out the two cycles at different times, as in the beavertail cactus (*Opuntia basilaris*) in the photo.

This puts an additional energy requirement equivalent to six ATP molecules for each G3P produced by the Calvin cycle. However, in hot climates, photorespiration can decrease carbon fixation efficiency by over 50%, so the additional ATP requirement is worthwhile. As well, hot climates tend to receive a lot of sunshine; thus, the additional ATP requirement is easily met by increasing the output of the light reactions. In temperate climates, the lower temperatures mean that photorespiration is not as big of a problem (look back at Table 7.1), and the additional ATP requirement is harder to meet given less sunshine. As an example, in Florida, 70% of all native species are C_4 plants compared with 0% in Manitoba.

C_4 plants not only perform better where it is hot, they also perform better where it is dryer. Because PEP carboxylase has a very high affinity only for CO_2, C_4 plants are more efficient at fixing CO_2 than C_3 plants are. As a consequence, they don't have to keep their stomata open for as long as a C_3 plant does under the same conditions. Because this reduces water loss, C_4 plants are much better suited to arid conditions.

7.5f CAM Plants

Instead of running the Calvin and C_4 cycles simultaneously in different locations, some plants, such as pineapple, run the cycles at different times. These plants are known as **CAM plants**, named for **crassulacean acid metabolism**, from the Crassulaceae family in which the adaptation was first observed. The plants in this group include many with thick, succulent leaves or stems, such as the cactus shown in **Figure 7.20c**.

CAM plants typically live in regions that are hot and dry during the day and cool at night. Their fleshy leaves or stems have a low surface-to-volume ratio, and their stomata are reduced in number. Further, the stomata open only at night, when they release O_2 that accumulates from photosynthesis during the day and allow CO_2

to enter the leaves. The entering CO_2 is fixed by the C_4 pathway into malate, which accumulates throughout the night and is stored in large cell vacuoles.

Daylight initiates the second phase of the strategy. As the sun comes up and the temperature rises, the stomata close, reducing water loss and cutting off the exchange of gases with the atmosphere. Malate diffuses from cell vacuoles into the cytosol, where it is oxidized to pyruvate, and CO_2 is released in high concentration. The high CO_2 concentration favours the carboxylase activity of rubisco, allowing the Calvin cycle to proceed at maximum efficiency with little loss of organic carbon from photorespiration. The pyruvate produced by malate breakdown accumulates during the day; as night falls, it enters the C_4 reactions, converting it back to malate. During the night, oxygen is released by the plants, and more CO_2 enters.

Reduction of water loss by closure of the stomata during the hot daylight hours has the added benefit of making CAM plants highly resistant to dehydration. As a result, CAM species can tolerate extreme daytime heat and dryness.

In this chapter, you have seen how photosynthesis supplies the organic molecules used as fuels by almost all the organisms of the world. Photosynthesis is a story of capturing photons of light and using the energy to oxidize water and using the liberated electrons to fix CO_2 into carbohydrates and other fuel molecules. The high-energy electrons are then removed from the fuel molecules by the oxidative reactions of cellular respiration, which use the released energy to power the activities of life. Among the most significant of these activities are cell growth and division, the subjects of the next chapter.

Unanswered Questions

Photosynthesis is considered by many to be the most important biological process on Earth. In particular, directly or indirectly (through herbivorous animals), photosynthesis provides all of our food requirements. Research on photosynthesis therefore is of high importance and is likely to have significant benefit for humankind. For example, a complete understanding of the chemistry of photosynthesis, the regulation of the process, and the genes that encode the components of the process could be applicable to other endeavours of human interest, such as solar energy conversion and the development of therapeutic drugs.

From research on agricultural crops, we have learned that photosynthesis is not a very efficient process. Estimates are that only 1 to 2% of the solar energy that strikes the planet's surface is converted to new photosynthetic products. Research is being done to learn enough about photosynthesis so that crop plants can be engineered to be more efficient. An area of particular relevance here is photorespiration, which reduces the efficiency of energy use in photosynthesis. It is hoped that research will give us a better understanding of the biochemical control of photorespiration and provide clues about breeding new, more energy-efficient plants.

Let us consider two specific avenues of research.

How is the efficiency of photosynthesis regulated?

The laboratory of David Kramer at Washington State University is interested in the energetics and control of photosynthesis, the electron transfer reactions, the coupling of electron transfer reactions to ATP synthesis, and photosynthesis in extreme environments. As you have learned, energy conversion by the chloroplast involves the capture of light energy and the channelling of that energy through an electron transfer system with the eventual synthesis of NADPH and ATP.

At high concentrations, many of the intermediates produced in this energy conversion can potentially destroy the photosynthetic apparatus, a phenomenon called photoinhibition. To prevent such damage, the efficiency of some of the photosystem components is reduced by the release of some of the energy as heat. Increased heat lowers the efficiency of photosynthesis, however. Evidence from a range of studies indicates that the balance between protection against photoinhibition and photosynthetic efficiency is important in enabling plants to acclimate to environmental changes. Kramer's group is doing research to develop an understanding of the structure and function of ATP synthase and the cytochrome complex and the effects of these components on the proton-motive force, which is known to play a pivotal role in balancing photoinhibition and photosynthetic efficiency. The results will illuminate how the specific mechanisms of photosynthesis determine plant growth and survival. In addition, the technology developed as part of the research may lead to applications in plant breeding and farming, providing farmers with a means to assess the physiological states of the plants they are growing and, therefore, to modify the conditions for optimal growth.

How are chloroplast thylakoid membrane–protein complexes assembled?

Research by Andrew Webber's group at Arizona State University is directed at understanding the formation of chloroplast thylakoid membrane–protein complexes. Those complexes are key to the process of photosynthesis, but their assembly is not understood. Using molecular biology and biochemistry techniques, Webber's group is studying how the synthesis of chloroplast proteins, some of which are encoded by genes in the chloroplast and others of which are encoded by genes in the nucleus, is coordinated and regulated. The researchers are also using molecular techniques to change specific amino acids in the chloroplast proteins with the aim of elucidating how those amino acids are involved in the assembly and functioning of the complexes. The results will add more detailed knowledge about the structure and function of components that are key to the process of photosynthesis.

Review

Go to CENGAGENOW™ at http://hed.nelson.com/ to access quizzing, animations, exercises, articles, and personalized homework help.

7.1 Photosynthesis: An Overview

- Photoautotrophs are the primary producers of the planet as they use the energy of sunlight to drive synthesis of organic molecules from simple inorganic raw materials. The organic molecules are used by the photosynthesizers themselves as fuels; they also form the primary energy source for animals, fungi, and other heterotrophs.
- Photosynthesis takes place in two overall stages called the light reactions and the Calvin cycle. In eukaryotes, both stages take place inside chloroplasts.
- Absorption of light energy is used to synthesize NADPH and ATP through photosynthetic electron transport and chemiosmosis, respectively.

7.2 The Photosynthetic Apparatus

- Pigment molecules absorb light of specific wavelengths that result in electrons being raised to an excited state.
- Pigments including chlorophylls and carotenoids are organized into two types of photosystems: photosystem I and photosystem II. Each contains a reaction centre surrounded by an antenna complex.
- Energy trapped by the antenna complex is funnelled to the reaction centre, where it is used to oxidize a chlorophyll and donate an electron to a primary acceptor molecule.

7.3 Photosynthetic Electron Transport

- Photosystem II absorbs light energy that oxidizes the reaction centre chlorophyll P680, producing the powerful oxidant $P680^+$. This molecule oxidizes water, releasing electrons and O_2. The O_2 escapes into the atmosphere.
- Electrons from photosystem II are passed through an electron transfer system. In the first part of the pathway, called noncyclic electron transport, electrons removed from water are excited in photosystem II. The electrons become excited again in photosystem I, and then they are delivered to $NADP^+$ as the final electron acceptor. $NADP^+$ is reduced to NADPH by $NADP^+$ reductase.
- ATP is generated through chemiosmosis by the establishment of a proton gradient across the thylakoid membrane. An ATP synthase in the thylakoid membrane operates in a fashion identical to that seen in cellular respiration.
- Electrons can also flow cyclically around photosystem I, building the H^+ concentration and allowing extra ATP to be produced, but no NADPH.

7.4 The Calvin Cycle

- In the Calvin cycle, CO_2 is reduced and converted into organic substances by the addition of electrons and hydrogen carried by the NADPH produced in the light reactions. ATP, also derived from the light reactions, provides additional energy. The key enzyme of the Calvin cycle is rubisco (RuBP carboxylase/oxygenase), which catalyzes the reaction that combines CO_2 into organic compounds.
- For every three turns of the Calvin cycle, a single molecule of the three-carbon molecule G3P is produced. G3P is the starting point for synthesis of glucose, sucrose, starches, and other organic molecules.
- The Calvin cycle reactions take place in the chloroplast stroma in eukaryotes and in the cytoplasm of photosynthetic bacteria.

7.5 Photorespiration and CO_2-Concentrating Mechanisms

- Oxygen can compete with CO_2 for the active site of rubisco.
- As an oxygenase, rubisco catalyzes the combination of RuBP with O_2 rather than with CO_2, forming toxic products that cannot be used in photosynthesis. The toxic products are eliminated by reactions that release carbon in inorganic form as CO_2, greatly reducing the efficiency of photosynthesis. The entire process is called photorespiration because it uses oxygen and releases CO_2.
- Some plants have evolved the C_4 pathway, a supplemental system that bypasses the oxygenase activity of rubisco. In the pathway, initial fixation of CO_2 is catalyzed by a carboxylase that has no oxygenase activity, in specific locations or at times within the plant when oxygen is overabundant. In later steps, the CO_2 is released at relatively oxygen-free regions or times for final fixation in the reactions using RuBP in the Calvin cycle.

Questions

Self-Test Questions

1. Photosynthesis
   a. results in the breakdown of food molecules releasing energy.
   b. uses the energy of light to oxidize CO_2.
   c. occurs only in eukaryotic cells.
   d. generates ATP by substrate-level phosphorylation.
   e. results in the reduction of CO_2 to energy-rich organic molecules.
2. The light reactions of photosynthesis resemble aerobic respiration as both
   a. synthesize NADPH.
   b. synthesize NADH.
   c. synthesize ATP by chemiosmosis.
   d. require oxygen as the final electron acceptor.
   e. have the same initial energy source.
3. Which one of the following statements is correct?
   a. It takes four photons of light to reduce one molecule of $NADP^+$ to NADPH.
   b. It takes two photons of light to split one molecule of H_2O.
   c. The reaction centre of PSII contains P700.
   d. P680 is easier to oxidize than P680*.
   e. Both a and d are correct.
4. The role of cyclic electron transport is to
   a. produce both ATP and NADPH.
   b. increase the amount of ATP generated by the light reactions.
   c. produce NADH rather than NADPH.
   d. increase the rate of O_2 evolution by the light reactions.
   e. Both b and d are correct.

5. Rubisco
   a. is a catalytically very fast enzyme.
   b. is not very abundant.
   c. is assembled into a functional enzyme in the cytosol.
   d. is encoded by a single gene found in the nucleus.
   e. contains a total of 16 subunits.
6. With regard to rubisco, oxygen
   a. is an allosteric activator of the enzyme.
   b. is a competitive inhibitor.
   c. helps prevent photorespiration.
   d. increases the catalytic efficiency of the carboxylation reaction.
   e. is produced when rubisco "splits" water.
7. In three turns of the Calvin cycle,
   a. one molecule of glucose is synthesized.
   b. six molecules of ATP are hydrolyzed.
   c. six NADPH molecules are oxidized.
   d. one (CH_2O) unit of carbohydrate is formed.
   e. two molecules of phosphoenolpyruvate (PEP) are synthesized.
8. Photorespiration does not occur in C_4 plants because
   a. during the daytime, C_4 plants do not respire.
   b. the active site of rubisco in C_4 plants can only bind CO_2.
   c. C_4 plants lack rubisco.
   d. PEP carboxylase binds O_2.
   e. O_2 concentration in bundle sheath cells is kept very low.
9. Which of the following statements about the C_4 cycle is NOT correct?
   a. CO_2 initially combines with phosphoenolpyruvate.
   b. PEP carboxylase catalyzes a reaction to produce oxaloacetate.
   c. Oxaloacetate transfers electrons from $NADP^+$ and is reduced to malate.
   d. Less ATP is used to run the C_4 cycle than the C_3 cycle.
   e. The cycle runs when O_2 concentration is high.
10. At high temperatures, C_4 plants use less water than C_3 plants because
    a. their leaves are not covered by a waxy cuticle.
    b. they don't have to keep their stomata open as long.
    c. they have a larger root system.
    d. they have smaller leaves.
    e. they can keep their stomata closed at all times.

Questions for Discussion

1. What would be the absorption spectrum of a plant that is purple in colour?
2. Exposing plants to light at low temperatures increases the damage to photosystem II. Why do you think this is the case?
3. If global warming raises the temperature of our climate significantly, will C_3 plants or C_4 plants be favoured by natural selection? How will global warming change the geographic distributions of plants?

A B cell and a T cell communicating by direct contact in the human immune system (computer image). Cell communication coordinates the cellular defence against disease.

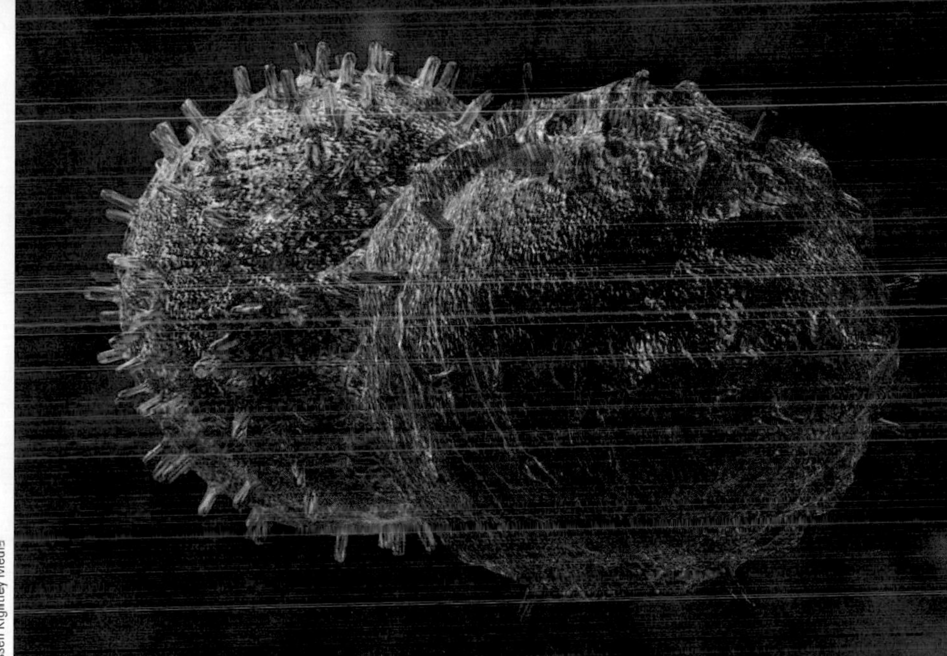

Russell Kightley Media

8 Cell Communication

Study Plan

Why It Matters

Hundreds of aircraft, ranging from small private planes to huge passenger jets, approach and leave airports in Southern California. In addition to the large terminals in Los Angeles and San Diego, dozens of smaller airports are located in the vicinity. The aircraft that approach these airports are travelling at various speeds, entering from all points of the compass, and flying at different altitudes. Airplanes are also leaving the same airports with routes distributed over the same directions, speeds, and altitudes. A wrong turn, ascent, or descent by any one of the hundreds of planes could lead to disaster. Yet disasters are extremely rare. How are all these aircraft kept separate and routed to and from their airports safely and efficiently? The answer lies in a highly organized system of controllers, signals, and receivers.

As the aircraft thread their way along the various approach and departure routes, they follow directions arriving on a radio frequency unique to each aircraft. Instructions arriving on the frequency assigned to Piper 4879Z, a slow-moving two-seater headed for Montgomery Field near San Diego, keep this plane's path separate from that of "five-two heavy," a passenger jet, leaving the main San Diego air terminal. The flow of directing signals, followed individually by each aircraft in the vicinity, keeps the traffic unscrambled and moving safely.

The principle of the air control system is nothing new. An equivalent system of signals and tuned receivers evolved hundreds of millions of years ago as one of the developments that made multicellular life possible. Within a multicellular organism, the activities of individual cells are directed by molecular signals, such as hormones, that are released by controlling cells. Although the controlling cells release many signals, each receiving cell has receptors that are "tuned" to recognize only one or a few of the many signal molecules that circulate in its vicinity; other signals pass by without effect because the cell has no receptors for them.

When a cell binds a signal molecule via a receptor, it modifies its internal activities in accordance with the signal, coordinating its functions with the activities of other cells of the organism. The responses of the receiving cell may include changes in gene activity, protein synthesis, transport of molecules across the plasma membrane, metabolic reactions, secretion, movement, and division. In some cases, the response to a signal may be "suicide" or programmed death of the receiving cell **(Figure 8.1).** As part of its response, a cell may itself become a signaller and thus contribute to the organizational network by releasing signal molecules that modify the activity of other cell types. The total network of signals and responses allows multicellular organisms to grow, develop, reproduce, and compensate for environmental changes in an internally coordinated fashion.

This chapter describes the major pathways that form parts of the cell communication system based on both surface and internal receptors, including the links that tie the different response pathways into fully integrated networks. (Nerve communication in animals is discussed in Chapter 33.) This chapter concentrates primarily on the systems working in animals, particularly in mammals, from which most of our knowledge of cell communication has been developed. Nonetheless, the principles of cell communication illustrated by these pathways apply to most eukaryotic organisms, including plants, protists and fungi. (The plant communication and control systems are described in more detail in Chapter 31.) This discussion begins with a few fundamental principles that underlie the often complex networks of cell communication.

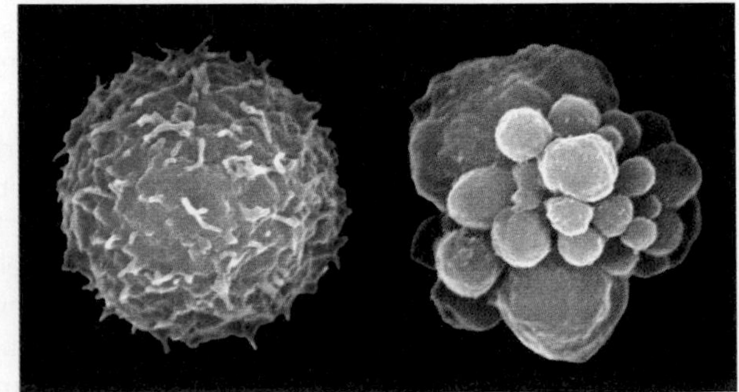

Figure 8.1
A normal cell (left) and a cell undergoing apoptosis (programmed cell death) (right).

Visuals Unlimited

8.1 Cell Communication: An Overview

Communication is critical for the function and survival of cells that compose a multicellular animal. For example, the ability of cells to communicate with one another in a regulated way is responsible for the controlled growth and development of an animal, as well as the integrated activities of its tissues and organs.

Cells communicate with one another in three ways. Adjacent cells use direct channels of communication. In this rapid means of communication, small molecules and ions exchange directly between the two cytoplasms. In animal cells, the direct channels of communication are *gap junctions,* the specialized connections between the cytoplasms of adjacent cells (Chapter 32). The main role of gap junctions is to synchronize metabolic activities or electronic signals between cells in a tissue. For example, gap junctions play a key role in the spread of electrical signals from one cell to the next in cardiac muscle. In plant cells, the direct channels of communication are plasmodesmata (see Chapter 28). Small molecules moving between adjacent cells in plants include plant hormones that regulate growth. In this way, responses triggered by plant hormones are spread to other cells.

Cells also communicate through *specific contact between cells.* Certain cells have molecules on their surfaces that allow them to interact directly with other cells. Some cells use their surface molecules to recognize particular molecules on the surfaces of invading pathogens or parasites that signal them as foreign. The host cell then engulfs the invader. Cells also have on their surfaces *cell adhesion molecules,* integral membrane proteins that allow the cells to bind to other cells or to the extracellular matrix. There are many important functions of cell adhesion molecules, including roles in cell movement and coordinating tissue and organ formation as an embryo develops.

Finally, cells communicate through *intercellular* ("between cell") *chemical messengers.* This method is the most common means of cell communication. Here, one cell, the *controlling cell,* synthesizes a specific molecule that acts as a *signalling molecule* to affect the activity of another cell, the *target cell.* The target cell is not in contact with the cell that synthesizes the signalling molecule; rather, it is either nearby or at a distance away in the organism. For example, in response to stress, cells of the adrenal glands (located on top of the kidneys) secrete the hormone epinephrine into the bloodstream. Among its actions, epinephrine acts on target cells so that the amount of glucose in the blood increases.

Cell communication through intercellular chemical messengers is the focus of this chapter, and the epinephrine example is used to illustrate the principles involved. In the 1950s, Earl Sutherland and his research team at Case Western Reserve University, Cleveland, Ohio, began investigating this cell communication system. Sutherland discovered that the hormone epinephrine acts by activating an enzyme, glycogen phosphorylase, which catalyzes the production of glucose from glycogen. That is, the result of the secretion of epinephrine into the blood by adrenal gland cells is an increase in the amount of glucose in the blood. Sutherland's experiments showed that enzyme activation did not involve epinephrine directly but did require an unknown (at the time) cellular substance. Sutherland called the hormone the *first messenger* in the system and the unknown cellular substance the *second messenger.* He proposed that the following chain of reactions was involved: epinephrine (the first messenger) leads to the formation of the second messenger, which activates the enzyme for conversion of glycogen to glucose.

Sutherland's work was the foundation for research that developed our current understanding of this type of cell communication. In brief, a controlling cell releases a signal molecule that causes a response (affects the function) of target cells. Target cells process the signal in the following three sequential steps **(Figure 8.2)**:

1. **Reception.** Reception is the binding of a signal molecule with a specific receptor of target cells. Target cells have receptors that are specific for the signal molecule, which distinguishes them from cells that do not respond to the signal molecule. The signal molecules are often peptides or steroids, but many other types of molecules, such as amines, can act as chemical signals between cells. Each molecule will have a cellular receptor that is shaped to recognize and bind that molecule specifically **(Figure 8.3)**. Membrane receptors are normally embedded in the plasma membrane with a binding site for the signal molecule on the cell surface (see Figures 8.2 and 8.3a). Epinephrine, the first messenger in Sutherland's research, is an

Outside cell
Signal
Cytoplasmic end of receptor
Activation
Pathway molecule A
Activation
Pathway molecule B
Activation
Molecule that brings about response
Change in cell
Cytosol
1 Reception
2 Transduction through signalling cascade
3 Response

Figure 8.2
The three stages of signal transduction: reception, transduction, and response (shown for a system using a surface receptor).

a. Reception by a cell-surface receptor

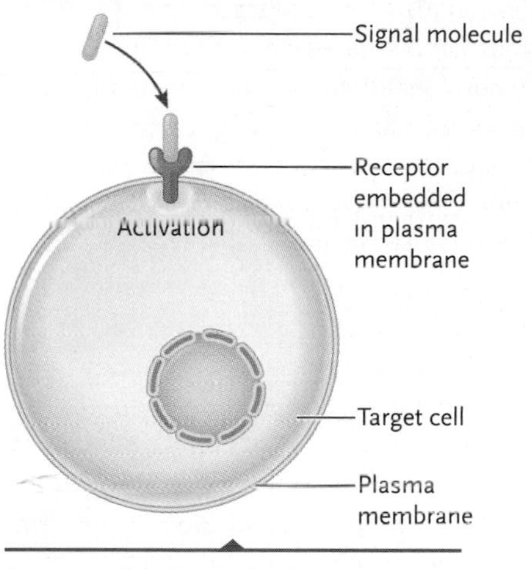

Some signal molecules bind to a receptor on the surface.

b. Reception by a receptor within cell

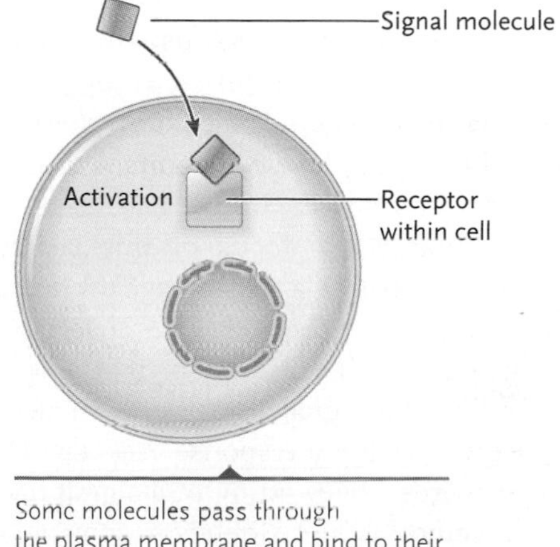

Some molecules pass through the plasma membrane and bind to their receptors in the cell.

Figure 8.3
Reception **(a)** of a signal molecule by a receptor on the cell surface and **(b)** of a signal molecule by a receptor in the cell.

People Behind Biology
Doug Storey

Bacterial cells are also able to communicate with each other via chemical signals, a communication system known as **quorum sensing** (see Chapter 21). In this method of communication, a growing population of bacteria produces signalling molecules (either peptides or lactones, depending on the type of bacterium) that accumulate in the environment around the cells. When the concentration of these signalling molecules reaches a critical threshold, they bind to protein receptors inside the bacterial cells. The complex formed by the signal molecule and the protein receptor then binds to specific regions of the cell's genome, activating certain genes. In this way, cells "know" that their population is large enough to perform some coordinated function and synthesize the proteins necessary to carry out that function. Behaviours that are regulated by quorum sensing include bioluminescence (see Chapter 1) and biofilm formation (see Chapter 21). In addition, quorum sensing also regulates pathogenesis as the bacteria begin to produce virulence factors (molecules that cause disease or create conditions needed for the pathogen to thrive inside the host). This last aspect of quorum sensing has important implications for our understanding of pathogenic bacteria—does quorum sensing occur in pathogenic bacteria infecting humans?

This is a question of great interest to Doug Storey, a microbiologist at the University of Calgary. Storey studies *Pseudomonas aeruginosa*, a bacterium that causes serious lung infections in people with cystic fibrosis (See chapter 5 for a discussion of this disease). Storey's research goal is to understand how *P. aeruginosa* is able to infect the lungs of CF patients and to look for new ways of fighting these infections. Of particular interest to Storey are the virulence factors produced by *P. aeruginosa*—what regulates the production of these factors? Does *P. aeruginosa* use quorum sensing to regulate levels of virulence factors when infecting host lungs? Recent research carried out by Storey and his collaborators indicates that the quorum-sensing system of *P. aeruginosa* does function in the lungs of CF patients and coordinates gene expression. This finding offers the potential for a new way to fight these lung infections: perhaps we can interfere with the bacterium's communication system and so prevent it from synthesizing virulence factors. We need to have a better understanding of the details of quorum sensing, but this is an exciting new tool in the fight against pathogenic infections.

amine that is recognized by a surface receptor on target cells. Receptors for some molecules are located within the cell (see Figure 8.3b). In this case, the signal molecule passes freely through the plasma membrane and interacts with its receptor within the cell. Steroid hormones such as testosterone and estrogen are examples of signal molecules that act on receptors within the cell. Many steroids also have separate actions via membrane receptors. Receptors at the cell surface, *membrane receptors,* usually involve rapid, short-lived events. Internal receptors often act directly on the genome (*nuclear receptors*), activating specific genes. These responses and reactions occur over a longer time.

Although the focus of this chapter is on eukaryotes, bacteria also engage in chemical communication (see *People Behind Biology*).

2. **Transduction.** Transduction is the process of changing the signal into the form necessary to cause the cellular response (see Figure 8.2). In other words, the binding of a signal molecule to its receptor is not directly responsible for the response. Transduction may occur in a single step, although more often it involves a cascade of reactions that include several different molecules, often referred to as a *signalling cascade.* For example, in Sutherland's work, after epinephrine bound to its surface receptor, the signal was transmitted through the plasma membrane into the cell, where transduction by a signalling cascade activated a molecule that triggered a cellular response. This molecule was Sutherland's *second messenger.*
3. **Response.** In the third and last stage, the transduced signal causes a specific cellular response. That response depends on the signal and the receptors on the target cell. In Sutherland's work, the response was the activation of the enzyme glycogen phosphorylase; the active enzyme catalyzed the conversion of stored glycogen to glucose.

The whole series of events from reception to response is called **signal transduction.** As explained in subsequent sections, signal transduction occurs by different mechanisms, depending on the receptor type. Earl Sutherland was awarded a Nobel Prize in 1971 for his research on the mechanisms of action of hormones.

Study Break

What accounts for the specificity of a cellular response in signal transduction?

8.2 Characteristics of Cell Communication Systems with Surface Receptors

Cell communication systems based on surface receptors have three components: (1) the extracellular signal molecules released by controlling cells, (2) the surface receptors on target cells that receive the signals, and (3) the internal response pathways triggered when receptors bind a signal.

8.2a Hormones and Neurotransmitters Are Extracellular Signal Molecules Recognized by Surface Receptors in Animals

Surface receptors in mammals and other vertebrates recognize and bind two major types of extracellular signal molecules: *hormones* and *neurotransmitters*. These signal molecules are released by control cells and enter the fluids that surround cells, including the blood circulation in animals with a circulatory system.

Hormones (see Chapter 35) are molecules, usually peptides or steroids, that are released by specialized gland cells such as the adrenal glands, by specialized nerve cells such as the pituitary, or by cells distributed in organs such as the liver or intestines. A special class of peptides, the growth factors, affects cell growth, division, and differentiation.

Neurotransmitters are molecules released by neurons that trigger activity in other neurons or other cells in the body; they include small peptides, individual amino acids or their derivatives, and other chemical substances. Some neurotransmitters affect only one or a few cells in the immediate vicinity of the neuron that releases the signal molecule, whereas others are released into the body circulation and act essentially as hormones, affecting many types of tissues. (Neurotransmitters are discussed in further detail in Chapter 33.)

Once signal molecules are released into the body's circulation, they remain for only a certain time. They are either broken down at a steady rate by enzymes in their target cells or in organs such as the liver, or they are excreted by the kidneys. The removal process ensures that the signal molecules are active only as long as controlling cells are secreting them.

8.2b Surface Receptors Are Integral Membrane Glycoproteins

The surface receptors that recognize and bind signal molecules are all glycoproteins—proteins with attached carbohydrate chains. They are integral membrane proteins that extend entirely through the plasma membrane **(Figure 8.4)**. The signal-binding site of the receptor, which extends from the outer membrane surface, is folded in a way that closely fits the signal molecule. The fit, similar to the fit of an enzyme to its substrate, is specific, so a particular receptor binds only one type of signal molecule or a closely related group of signal molecules.

A signal molecule brings about specific changes to the receptor and therefore to the cells to which it binds. When a signal molecule binds to a surface receptor, the molecular structure of that receptor is changed so that it transmits the signal through the plasma membrane, activating the cytoplasmic end of the receptor. The activated receptor then initiates the first step in a cascade of molecular events—the signal transduction pathway—that triggers the cellular response (see Figure 8.2).

Animal cells typically have hundreds to thousands of surface receptors that represent many receptor types. Membrane receptors for a specific hormone may number from 500 to as many as 100 000 or more per cell. Different cell types contain distinct combinations of receptors, allowing them to react individually to the hormones and growth factors circulating in the extracellular fluids. The combination of surface receptors on particular cell types is not fixed but rather changes as cells develop. Changes also occur as normal cells are transformed into cancer cells.

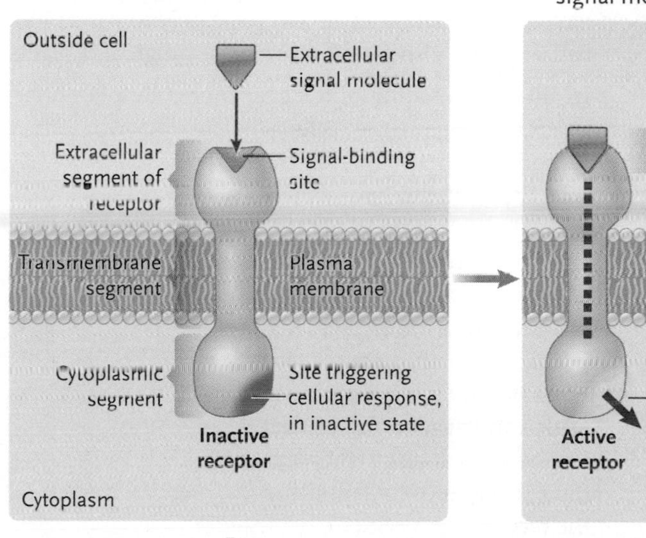

A surface receptor has an extracellular segment with a site that recognizes and binds a particular signal molecule.

When the signal molecule is bound, a conformational change is transmitted through the transmembrane segment that activates a site on the cytoplasmic segment of receptor. The activation triggers a reaction pathway that results in the cellular response.

Figure 8.4
The mechanism by which a surface receptor responds when it binds a signal molecule.

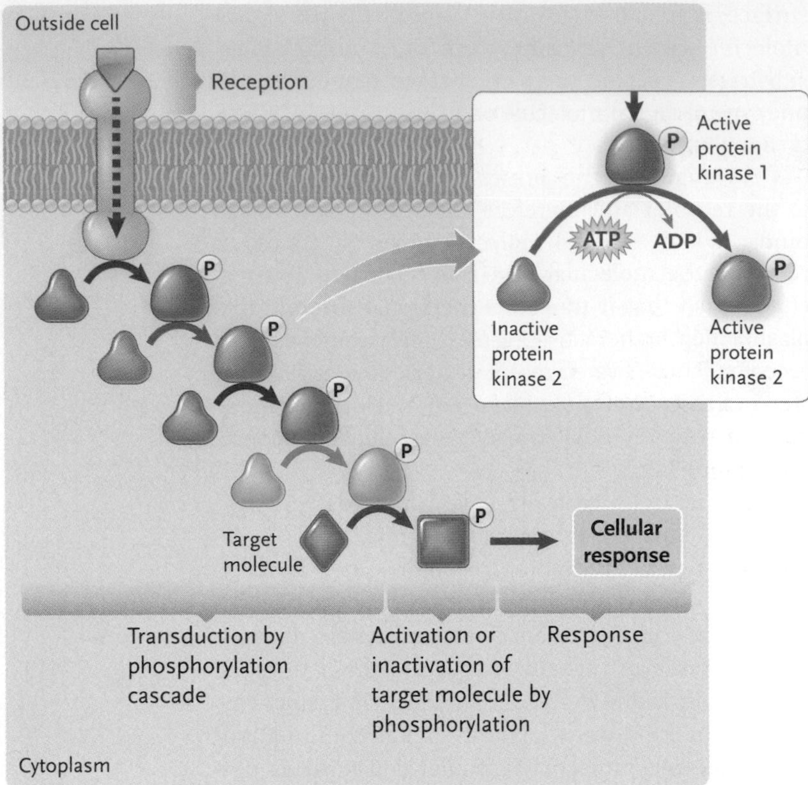

Figure 8.5
Phosphorylation, a key reaction in many signalling pathways.

8.2c The Signalling Molecule Bound by a Surface Receptor Triggers Response Pathways within the Cell

Signal transduction pathways triggered by surface receptors are common to all animal cells. At least parts of the pathways are also found in protists, fungi, and plants. In all cases, binding of a signal molecule to a surface receptor triggers the cellular response without entering the cell. Experiments have shown that (1) a signal molecule produces no response if it is injected directly into the cytoplasm, and (2) unrelated molecules that mimic the structure of the normal extracellular signal molecule can trigger a full cellular response as long as they can bind to the recognition site of the receptor.

A second typical characteristic of signal transduction is that the signal is relayed inside the cell by **protein kinases,** enzymes that transfer a phosphate group from ATP to one or more sites on particular proteins (**Figure 8.5**). These phosphorylated proteins are known as *target proteins* because they are the proteins modified by signalling pathways. The added phosphate groups either stimulate or inhibit the activity of the target proteins; the change in the target proteins' activity leads directly or indirectly to the cellular response. Often protein kinases act in a chain, called a *protein kinase cascade,* to pass along a signal. The first kinase catalyzes phosphorylation of the second, which then becomes active and phosphorylates the third kinase, and so on. The proteins that bring about the cellular response may be parts of the reaction pathways, enzymes of other cellular reactions, end targets of the signal transduction pathways (such as transport proteins), or, at the most fundamental level, proteins that regulate gene transcription.

The effects of protein kinases in the signal transduction pathways are balanced or reversed by another group of enzymes called **protein phosphatases,** which remove phosphate groups from target proteins. Unlike the protein kinases, which are active only when a surface receptor binds a signal molecule, most of the protein phosphatases are continuously active in cells. By continually removing phosphate groups from target proteins, the protein phosphatases quickly shut off a signal transduction pathway if its signal molecule is no longer bound at the cell surface.

A third characteristic of signal transduction pathways involving surface receptors is **amplification**—an increase in the magnitude of each step as a signal transduction pathway proceeds (**Figure 8.6**). Amplification occurs because many of the proteins that carry out individual steps in the pathways, including the protein kinases, are enzymes. Once activated, each enzyme can activate hundreds of proteins, including other enzymes, that enter the next step in the pathway. Generally, the more enzyme-catalyzed steps in a

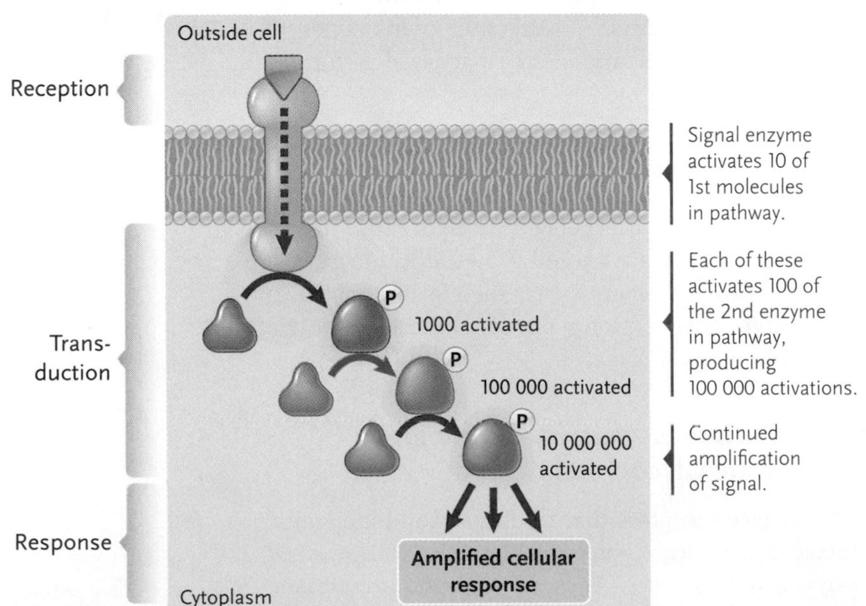

Figure 8.6
Amplification in signal transduction.

response pathway, the greater the amplification. As a result, just a few extracellular signal molecules binding to their receptors can produce a full internal response. For similar reasons, amplification also occurs for signal transduction pathways that involve internal receptors.

As signal transduction runs its course, the receptors and their bound signal molecules are removed from the cell surface by endocytosis. Both the receptor and its bound signal molecule may be degraded in lysosomes after entering the cell. Alternatively, the receptors may be separated from the signal molecules and recycled to the cell surface, whereas only the signal molecules are degraded. Thus, surface receptors participate in an extremely lively cellular "conversation" with moment-to-moment shifts in the information.

The next two sections discuss two large families of surface receptors: the receptor tyrosine kinases and the G protein–coupled receptors.

Study Break

1. What are protein kinases, and how are they involved in signal transduction pathways?
2. How is amplification accomplished in a signal transduction pathway?

8.3 Surface Receptors with Built-in Protein Kinase Activity: Receptor Tyrosine Kinases

In the simplest form of signal transduction, the receptor itself has a protein kinase site at its cytoplasmic end. For this type of receptor, initiation of transduction occurs when two receptor molecules each bind a signal molecule in the reception step, move together in the membrane, and assemble into a pair called a *dimer* **(Figure 8.7)**. Dimer assembly

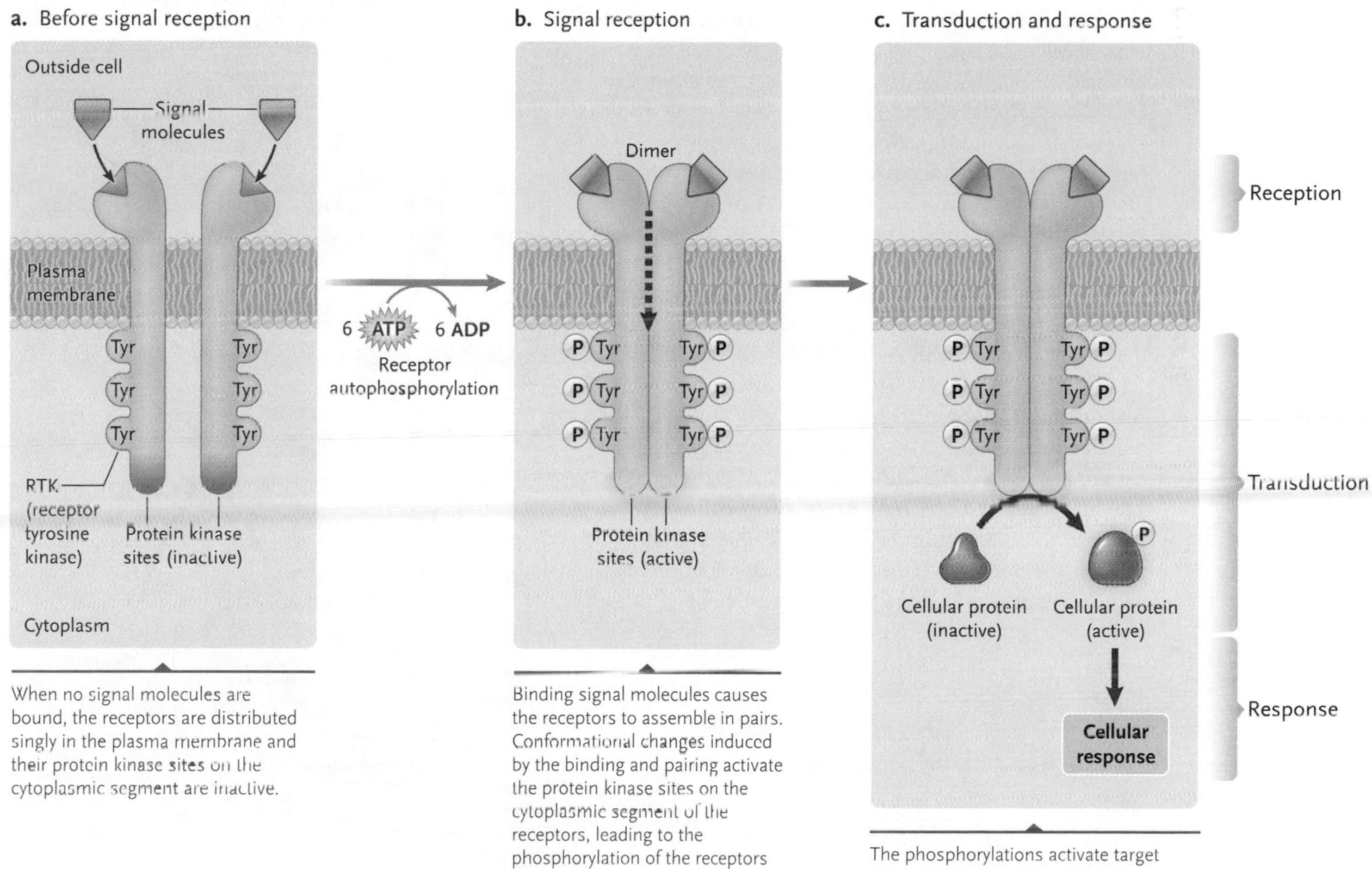

a. Before signal reception
Outside cell
Signal molecules
Plasma membrane
Tyr
RTK (receptor tyrosine kinase)
Protein kinase sites (inactive)
Cytoplasm
When no signal molecules are bound, the receptors are distributed singly in the plasma membrane and their protein kinase sites on the cytoplasmic segment are inactive.
6 ATP
6 ADP
Receptor autophosphorylation
b. Signal reception
Dimer
P
Protein kinase sites (active)
Binding signal molecules causes the receptors to assemble in pairs. Conformational changes induced by the binding and pairing activate the protein kinase sites on the cytoplasmic segment of the receptors, leading to the phosphorylation of the receptors themselves and target proteins.
c. Transduction and response
Cellular protein (inactive)
Cellular protein (active)
Cellular response
Reception
Transduction
Response
The phosphorylations activate target proteins and initiate the cellular response.

Figure 8.7
The action of receptors with built-in protein kinase activity leading to the phosphorylation of the receptors themselves and the subsequent phosphorylation of target proteins. These receptors are called receptor tyrosine kinases because they add phosphate groups to tyrosines in target proteins. These receptors combine into pairs (dimers) when they bind signal molecules; the assembly into a dimer transmits the signal that activates the cytoplasmic end of the receptors.

activates the receptor's protein kinase, which adds phosphate groups to sites on the receptor itself, a process known as *autophosphorylation*. Target proteins recognize and bind to the phosphorylated sites on the receptor and are then activated by being phosphorylated themselves. The total effect of the phosphorylations is to initiate the signal transduction pathway controlled by the receptor.

In autophosphorylation, the phosphate groups are added to tyrosine amino acids on the receptor. The protein kinase activity of the activated receptors also adds phosphate groups to tyrosines in the amino acid chains of target proteins. Because of this specificity of phosphorylation, the receptors in this group are called **receptor tyrosine kinases**. More than 50 receptor tyrosine kinases are known. In mammals, receptor tyrosine kinases fall into 14 different families, all related to one another in structure and amino acid sequence. Relatives of the mammalian receptors have been discovered in yeasts, *Drosophila,* and higher plants, indicating that the origin of the receptor tyrosine kinases is a single ancestral type that must have appeared before the evolutionary splits that led to the fungi, plants, and animals.

The cellular responses triggered by receptor tyrosine kinases are among the most important processes of animal cells. For example, the receptor tyrosine kinases binding the peptide hormone *insulin,* a regulator of carbohydrate metabolism, triggers diverse cellular responses, including effects on glucose uptake, the rates of many metabolic reactions, and cell growth and division. (The insulin receptor is exceptional because it is permanently in the dimer form.) Other receptor tyrosine kinases bind growth factors, including *epidermal growth factor, platelet-derived growth factor,* and *nerve growth factor,* which are all important peptide hormones that regulate cell growth and division in higher animals.

Hereditary defects in the insulin receptor are responsible for some forms of *diabetes,* a disease in which glucose accumulates in the blood because it cannot be absorbed in sufficient quantity by body cells. The inherited defects may impair the ability of the receptor to bind insulin or block its ability to trigger a cellular response. In either case, the cell is unresponsive to insulin and does not add sufficient glucose transporters to take up glucose.

Study Break

How does a receptor tyrosine kinase become activated?

8.4 G Protein–Coupled Receptors

A second large family of surface receptors, known as the **G protein–coupled receptors**, respond to a signal by activating an inner membrane protein called a G protein, which is closely associated with the cytoplasmic end of the receptor. About 1000 different G protein–coupled receptors have been identified; several hundred types are involved in recognizing and binding odour molecules as part of the sense of smell. Almost all of the receptors of this group are large glycoproteins built up from a single polypeptide chain anchored in the plasma membrane by seven segments of the amino acid chain that zigzag back and forth across the membrane seven times **(Figure 8.8).**

Unlike receptor tyrosine kinases, these receptors lack built-in protein kinase activity.

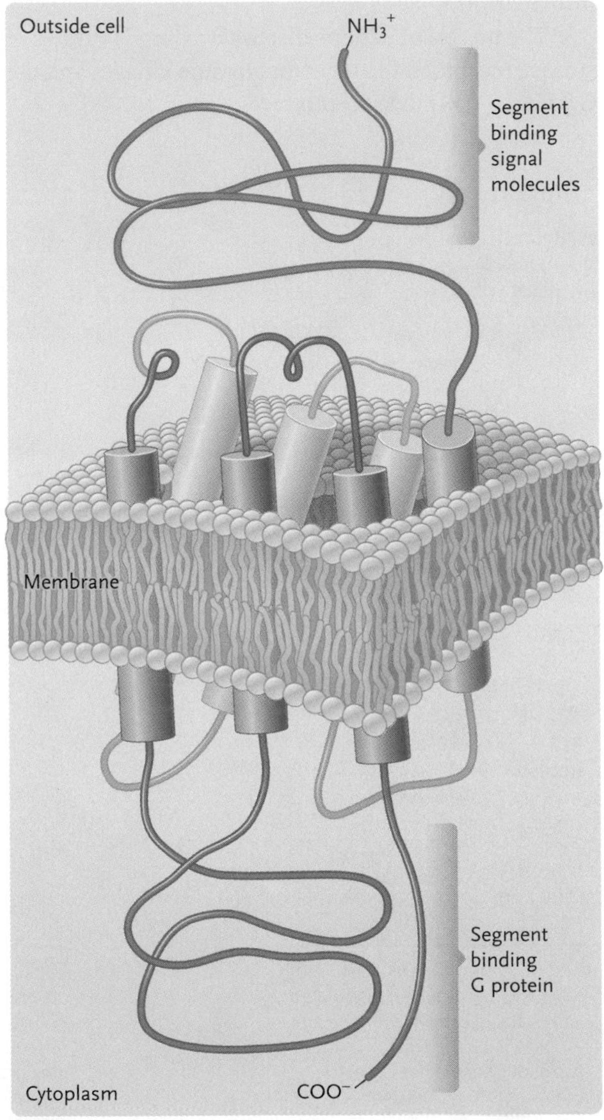

Figure 8.8
Structure of the G protein–coupled receptors, which activate separate protein kinases. These receptors have seven transmembrane α-helical segments (shown as cylinders) that zigzag across the plasma membrane. Binding of a signal molecule at the cell surface, by inducing changes in the positions of some of the helices, activates the cytoplasmic end of the receptor.

8.4a G Proteins Are Key Molecular Switches in Second-Messenger Pathways

The extracellular signal molecule in signal transduction pathways controlled by G protein–coupled receptors is termed the **first messenger.** Binding the first messenger by the receptor activates a site on the cytoplasmic end of the receptor (**Figure 8.9,** step 1). The active site of the receptor then activates the G protein associated with the cytoplasmic tail of the receptor by inducing the G protein to bind GTP, replacing the GDP that was bound to it (step 2). The G protein is an example of a *molecular switch* protein because it changes between inactive and active states. If GDP is bound to the G protein, the G protein is inactive, whereas if GTP is bound, it is active. In fact, G proteins are named because they use GDP and GTP to control their activities. The role of a switched-on G protein is to activate a plasma membrane–associated enzyme called the **effector** (step 3). In turn, the effector generates one or more internal, nonprotein signal molecules called **second messengers** (step 4). The second messengers directly or indirectly activate protein kinases, which elicit the cellular response by adding phosphate groups to specific target proteins (step 5). Thus, the entire control pathway operates through the following sequence:

first messenger → receptor → G proteins → effector → second messenger → protein kinases → target proteins effector

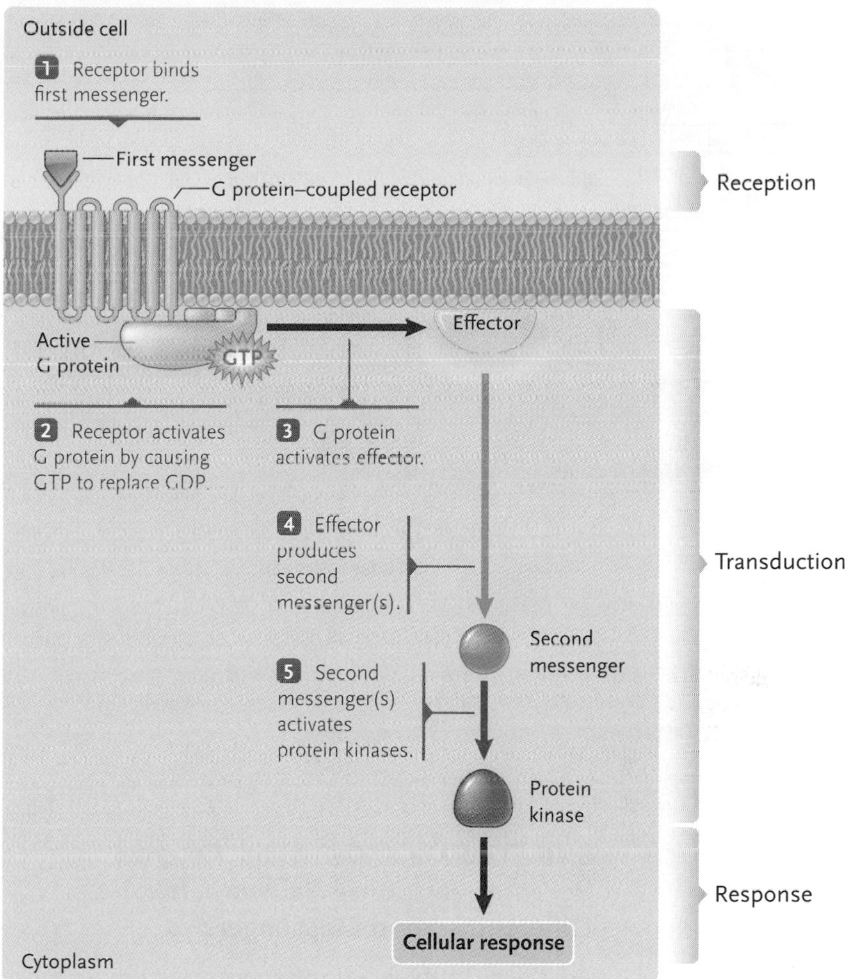

Figure 8.9
Response pathways activated by G protein–coupled receptors, in which protein kinase activity is separate from the receptor. The signal molecule is called the first messenger; the effector is an enzyme that generates one or more internal signal molecules called second messengers. The second messengers directly or indirectly activate the protein kinases of the pathway, leading to the cellular response.

The separate protein kinases of these pathways all add phosphate groups to serine or threonine amino acids in their target proteins, which are typically

- enzymes catalyzing steps in metabolic pathways
- ion channels in the plasma and other membranes
- regulatory proteins that control gene activity and cell division

Cells can make a variety of G proteins, with each type activating a different cellular response. The pathway from first messengers to target proteins is common to all G protein–coupled receptors.

As long as a G protein–coupled receptor is bound to a first messenger, the receptor keeps the G protein active. The activated G protein, in turn, keeps the effector active in generating second messengers. If the first messenger is released from the receptor, or if the receptor is taken into the cell by endocytosis, GTP is hydrolyzed to GDP, which inactivates the G protein. As a result, the effector becomes inactive, turning "off" the response pathway.

The importance of G proteins to cellular metabolism is underscored by the fact that they are targets of toxins released by some infecting bacteria. The cholera toxin produced by *Vibrio cholerae,* the pertussis toxin that causes whooping cough produced by *Bordetella pertussis,* and a toxin produced by a disease-causing form of *Escherichia coli* are all enzymes that modify the G proteins, making them continuously active and keeping their response pathways turned "on" at high levels. For example, the cholera toxin prevents a G protein from hydrolyzing GTP, keeping the G protein switched on and the pathway in a permanently active state. Among other effects, the pathway opens ion channels in intestinal cells, causing severe diarrhea through a massive release of salt and water from the body into the intestinal tract. Unless the resulting dehydration is relieved, death can result quickly. The *E. coli* toxin, which has similar but milder effects, is the cause of many cases of traveller's diarrhea.

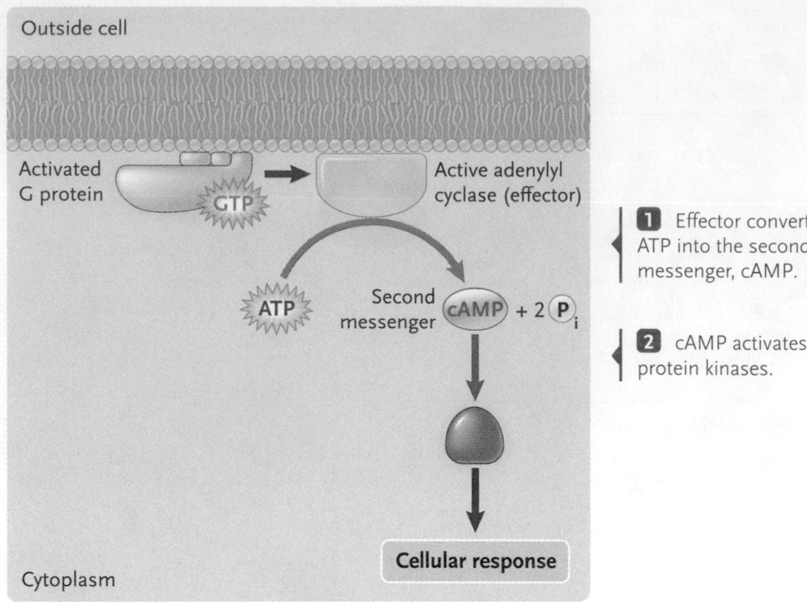

Figure 8.10
The operation of cAMP–response pathways. The second messenger of the pathway, cAMP, activates one or more cAMP-dependent protein kinases, which add phosphate groups to target proteins to initiate the cellular response.

8.4b Two Major G Protein–Coupled Receptor–Response Pathways Involve Different Second Messengers

Activated G proteins bring about a cellular response through two major receptor–response pathways in which different effectors generate different second messengers. One pathway involves the second messenger **cyclic AMP (cAMP)**, a relatively small, water-soluble molecule derived from ATP **(Figure 8.10).** The effector that produces cAMP is the enzyme *adenylyl cyclase,* which converts ATP to cAMP **(Figure 8.11).** cAMP diffuses through the cytoplasm and activates protein kinases that add phosphate groups to target proteins. The other pathway involves two second messengers: **inositol triphosphate (IP_3)** and **diacylglycerol (DAG).** The effector of this pathway, an enzyme called *phospholipase C,* produces both of these second messengers by breaking down a membrane phospholipid **(Figure 8.12).** IP_3 is a small, water-soluble molecule that diffuses rapidly through the cytoplasm. DAG is hydrophobic; it remains and functions in the plasma membrane.

The primary effect of IP_3 in animal cells is to activate transport proteins in the endoplasmic reticulum (ER), which release Ca^{2+} stored in the ER into the cytoplasm. The released Ca^{2+}, either alone or in combination with DAG, activates a protein kinase cascade that brings about the cellular effect.

Both major G protein–coupled receptor–response pathways are balanced by reactions that constantly eliminate their second messengers. cAMP is quickly degraded by *phosphodiesterase,* an enzyme that is continuously active in the cytoplasm (see Figure 8.11). The rapid elimination of the second messengers provides another highly effective off switch for the pathways, ensuring that protein kinases are inactivated quickly if the receptor becomes inactive. Still another off switch is provided by protein phosphatases that remove the phosphate groups added to proteins by the protein kinases.

As in the receptor tyrosine kinase pathways, the activities of the pathways controlled by cAMP and IP_3/DAG second messengers are also stopped by endocytosis of receptors and their bound extracellular signals. As with all cell signalling pathways, cells vary in their response to cAMP or IP_3/DAG pathways depending on the type of G protein–coupled receptors on the cell surface and the kinds of protein kinases present in the cytoplasm.

The cAMP pathway is limited to animals and some fungi. The IP_3/DAG pathway is universally distributed among eukaryotic organisms, including both vertebrate and invertebrate animals, fungi, and plants. The cAMP pathway occurs in animals and fungi, but its presence in plants is uncertain.

Specific Examples of Cyclic AMP Pathways. Many hormones act as first messengers for cAMP pathways in animals. The receptors that bind these hormones control such varied cellular responses as the uptake and oxidation of glucose, glycogen breakdown or synthesis,

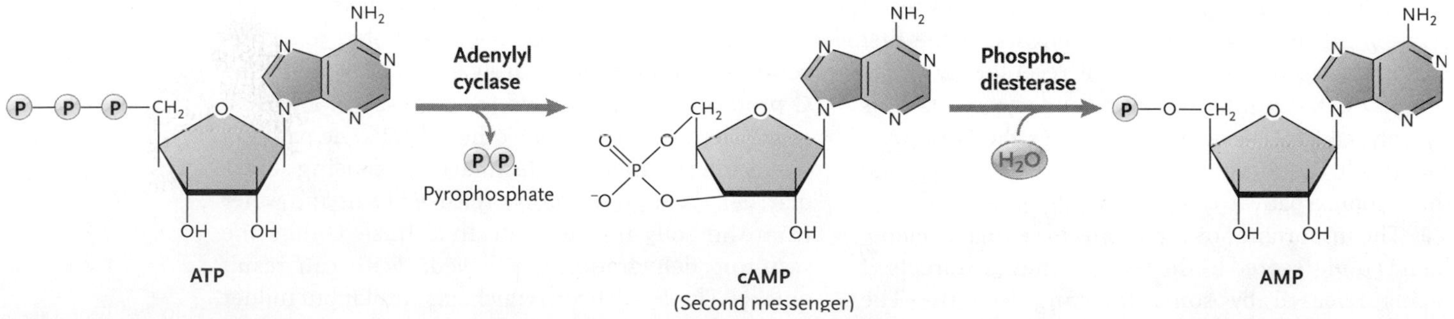

ATP
Adenylyl cyclase
PPi Pyrophosphate
cAMP (Second messenger)
Phosphodiesterase
H_2O
AMP

Figure 8.11
cAMP. The second messenger, cAMP, is made from ATP by adenylyl cyclase and is broken down to AMP by phosphodiesterase.

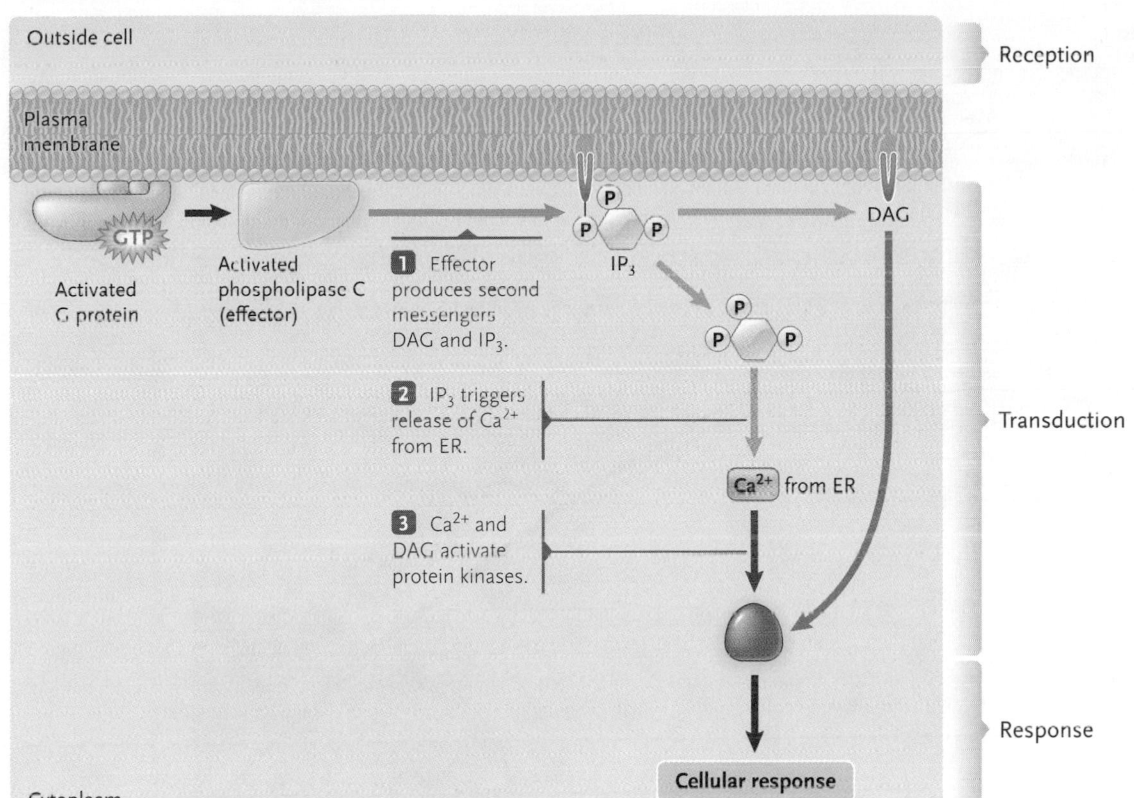

Figure 8.12
The operation of IP_3/DAG receptor–response pathways. Two second messengers, IP_3 and DAG, are produced by the pathway. IP_3 opens Ca^{2+} channels in ER membranes, releasing the ion into the cytoplasm. The Ca^{2+}, with DAG in some cases, directly or indirectly activates the protein kinases of the pathway, which add phosphate groups to target proteins to initiate the cellular response.

ion transport, the transport of amino acids into cells, and cell division.

A cAMP pathway is involved in the regulation of the level of glucose, the fundamental fuel of cells. When the level of blood glucose falls too low in mammals, cells in the pancreas release the peptide hormone glucagon. Binding of the hormone by a G protein–coupled glucagon receptor on the surface of liver cells triggers the cAMP pathway (see Figure 8.10). The cAMP produced activates a protein kinase cascade that amplifies the effects of the pathway at each step. Two enzymes are end targets of the protein kinase cascades. One enzyme is *glycogen phosphorylase,* which catalyzes the breakdown of glycogen into glucose units that pass from the liver cells into the bloodstream and increase the glucose level in the blood; it is activated by the cascades. The other enzyme is *glycogen synthase,* which adds glucose units to glycogen; it is inactivated by the cascades, ensuring that glucose is not converted back into glycogen in the liver cells.

Specific Examples of IP_3/DAG Pathways. The IP_3/DAG-response pathways are also activated by a large number of peptide hormones (including growth factors) and neurotransmitters, leading to responses as varied as sugar and ion transport, glucose oxidation, cell growth and division, and movements such as smooth muscle contraction.

Among the vertebrate hormones that activate the pathways are vasopressin, angiotensin, and norepinephrine. Vasopressin, also known as antidiuretic hormone, helps the body conserve water by reducing the output of urine. Angiotensin helps maintain blood volume and pressure. Norepinephrine, together with epinephrine, brings about the fight-or-flight response in threatening or stressful situations.

Many growth factors operate through IP_3/DAG pathways. Defects in the receptors or other parts of the pathways that lead to higher-than-normal levels of DAG in response to growth factors are often associated with the progression of some forms of cancer. This is because DAG, in turn, causes an overactivity of the protein kinases responsible for stimulating cell growth and division. Also, plant substances in a group called *phorbol esters* resemble DAG so closely that they can promote cancer in animals by activating the same protein kinases.

In plants, IP_3/DAG pathways control responses to conditions such as water loss and changes in light intensity or salinity. Plant hormones—relatively small, nonprotein molecules such as *auxin* (a derivative of the amino acid tryptophan) and the *cytokinins* (derivatives of the nucleotide base adenine)—act as first messengers activating some of the IP_3/DAG pathways of these organisms.

Example of a Signalling Pathway That Combines a Receptor Tyrosine Kinase with a G Protein. Some pathways important in gene regulation link certain receptor tyrosine kinases to a specific type of G protein called Ras. When

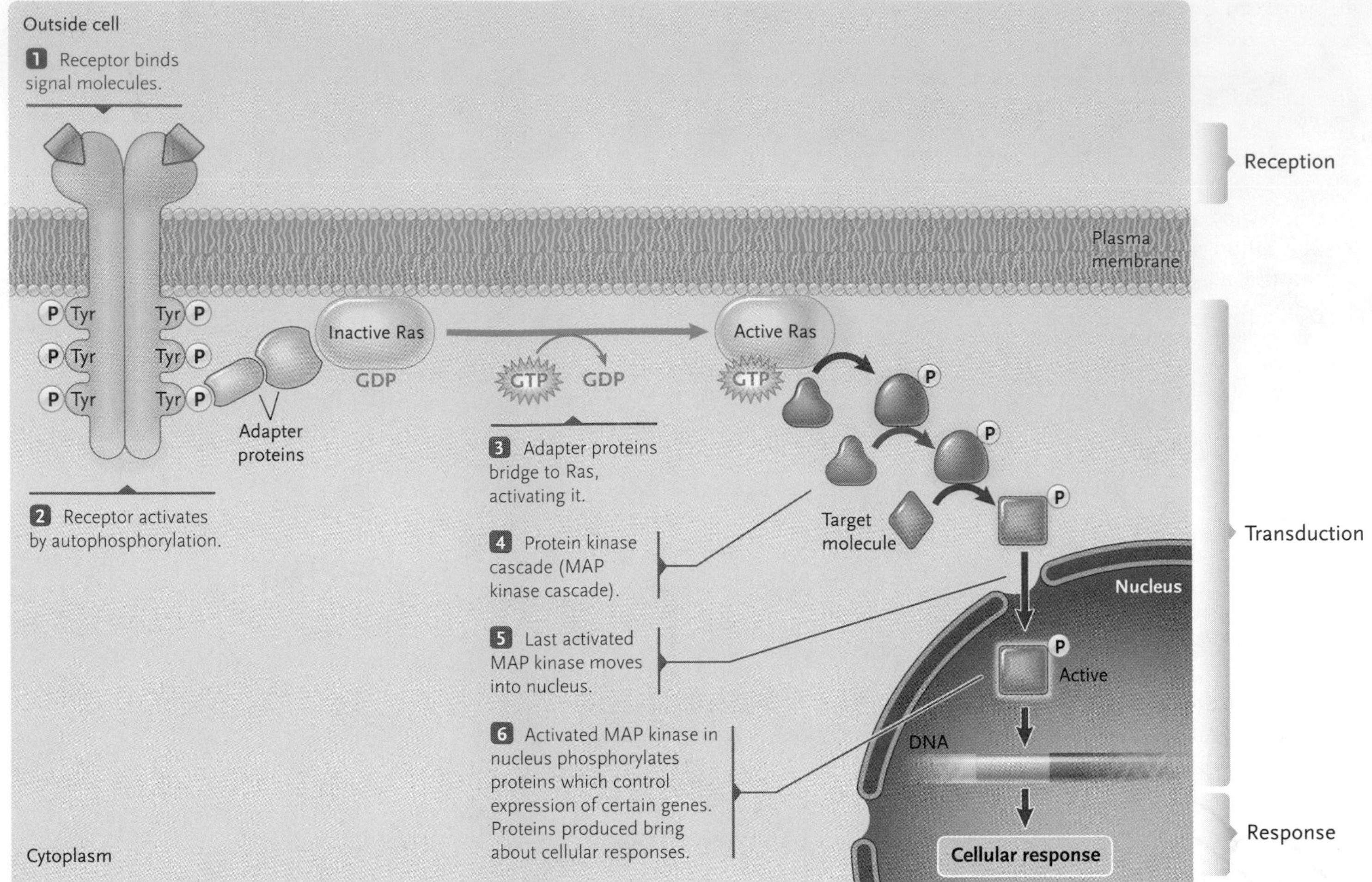

Figure 8.13
The pathway from receptor tyrosine kinases to gene regulation, including the G protein, Ras, and MAP kinase.

the receptor tyrosine kinase receives a signal (**Figure 8.13**, step 1), it activates by autophosphorylation (step 2). Adapter proteins then bind to the phosphorylated receptor and bridge to Ras, stimulating the activation of Ras (step 3). Like other G proteins, Ras is activated by binding GTP. The activated Ras sets in motion a phosphorylation cascade that involves a series of three enzymes known as *mitogen-activated protein kinases* (MAP kinases; step 4). The last MAP kinase in the cascade, when activated, enters the nucleus (step 5) and phosphorylates other proteins, which then change the expression of certain genes, particularly activating those involved in cell division (step 6). (A *mitogen* is a substance that controls cell division, hence the name of the kinases.) Changes in gene expression can have far-reaching effects on the cell, such as determining whether a cell divides or how frequently it divides. The Ras proteins are of major interest to investigators because of their role in linking receptor tyrosine kinases to gene regulation, as well as their major roles in the development of many types of cancer when their function is altered.

In this section, we have surveyed major response pathways linked to surface receptors that bind peptide hormones, growth factors, and neurotransmitters. We now turn to the other major type of signal receptor: the internal receptors binding signal molecules.

Study Break

1. What is the role of the first messenger in a G protein–coupled receptor-controlled pathway?
2. What is the role of the effector?
3. For a cAMP second-messenger pathway, how is the pathway turned off if no more signal molecules are present in the extracellular fluids?

8.5 Pathways Triggered by Internal Receptors: Steroid Hormone Nuclear Receptors

Cells of many types have internal receptors that respond to signals arriving from the cell exterior. Unlike the signal molecules that bind to surface receptors, these signals, primarily, but not exclusively, steroid hormones, penetrate through the plasma membrane and bind to receptors in the cytoplasm. The receptor-hormone complex enters the nucleus and interacts directly with the genome. Although the receptors are often referred to as steroid nuclear receptors, other hormones can act via nuclear receptors. Thyroxine, a nonsteroidal hormone that has many developmental effects, including the control of development from tadpole to frog, acts via nuclear receptors. The internal receptors, called **steroid hormone receptors**, are typically control proteins that turn on specific genes when they are activated by binding a signal molecule.

The same steroid hormones that activate internal receptors may also have different effects when they activate membrane receptors. The membrane receptors may be on different cells or on the same cells.

8.5a Steroid Hormones Have Widely Different Effects That Depend on Relatively Small Chemical Differences

Steroid hormones are relatively small, nonpolar molecules derived from cholesterol, with a chemical structure based on four carbon rings. Steroid hormones combine with hydrophilic carrier proteins that mask their hydrophobic groups and hold them in solution in the blood and extracellular fluids. When a steroid hormone–carrier protein complex collides with the surface of a cell, the hormone is released and penetrates directly through the nonpolar part of the plasma membrane. On the cytoplasmic side, the hormone binds to its internal receptor.

The various steroid hormones differ only in the side groups attached to their carbon rings. Although the differences are small, they are responsible for highly distinctive effects. For example, the male and female sex hormones of mammals, testosterone and estrogen, respectively, which are responsible for many of the structural and behavioural differences between male and female mammals, differ only in minor substitutions in side groups at two positions. The differences cause the hormones to be recognized by different receptors, which activate specific regulatory DNA regions of target genes, leading to development of individuals as males or females.

8.5b The Response of a Cell to Steroid Hormones Depends on Its Internal Receptors and the Genes They Activate

Steroid nuclear hormone receptors are proteins with two major domains **(Figure 8.14)**. One domain recognizes and binds a specific steroid hormone. The other domain

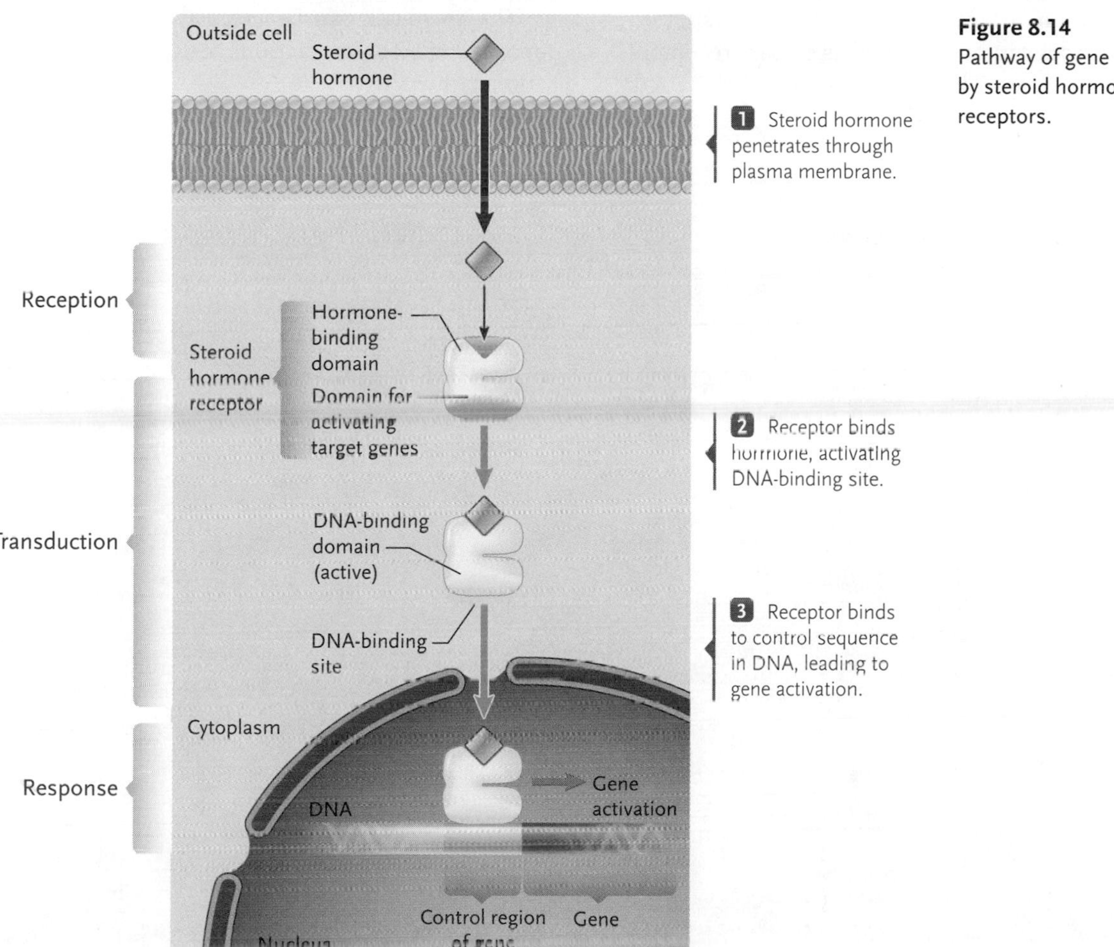

Figure 8.14
Pathway of gene activation by steroid hormone receptors.

interacts with the regions of target genes that control their expression. When a steroid hormone combines with the hormone-binding domain, the gene activation domain changes shape, thus enabling the complex to bind to the DNA control regions of the target genes that the hormone affects. For most steroid hormone receptors, binding of the activated receptor to a gene control region activates that gene, although some may suppress the expression of the target gene.

Steroid hormones, like peptide hormones, are released by cells in one part of an organism and are carried by the organism's circulation to other cells. Whether a cell responds to a steroid hormone depends on whether it has a receptor for the hormone. For responses to steroids mediated by internal receptors, the type of response depends on the genes that are recognized and turned on by an activated receptor. Depending on the receptor type and the particular genes it recognizes, even the same steroid hormone can have highly varied effects on different cells.

Taken together, the various types of receptor tyrosine kinases, G protein–coupled receptors, and steroid hormone nuclear receptors prime cells to respond to a stream of specific signals that continuously fine-tune their function. How are the signals integrated within the cell and organism to produce harmony rather than chaos? The next section shows how the various signal pathways are integrated into a coordinated response. Not all receptors can be classified as surface receptors or internal receptors. The plant hormone ethylene acts via membrane receptors that are inside the cell (see *Molecule Behind Biology*).

Study Break

1. What distinguishes a steroid nuclear receptor from a receptor tyrosine kinase receptor or a G protein–coupled receptor?
2. By what means does a specific steroid hormone result in a specific cellular response?

8.6 Integration of Cell Communication Pathways

Cells are under the continual influence of many simultaneous signal molecules. The cell signalling pathways may communicate with one another to integrate their responses to cellular signals. The interpathway interaction is called **cross-talk**; a conceptual example that involves two second-messenger pathways is shown in **Figure 8.15**. A protein kinase in one pathway might phosphorylate a site on a target protein in another signal transduction pathway, activating or inhibiting that protein, depending on the site of the phosphorylation. The cross-talk can be extensive, resulting in a complex network of interactions between cell communication pathways.

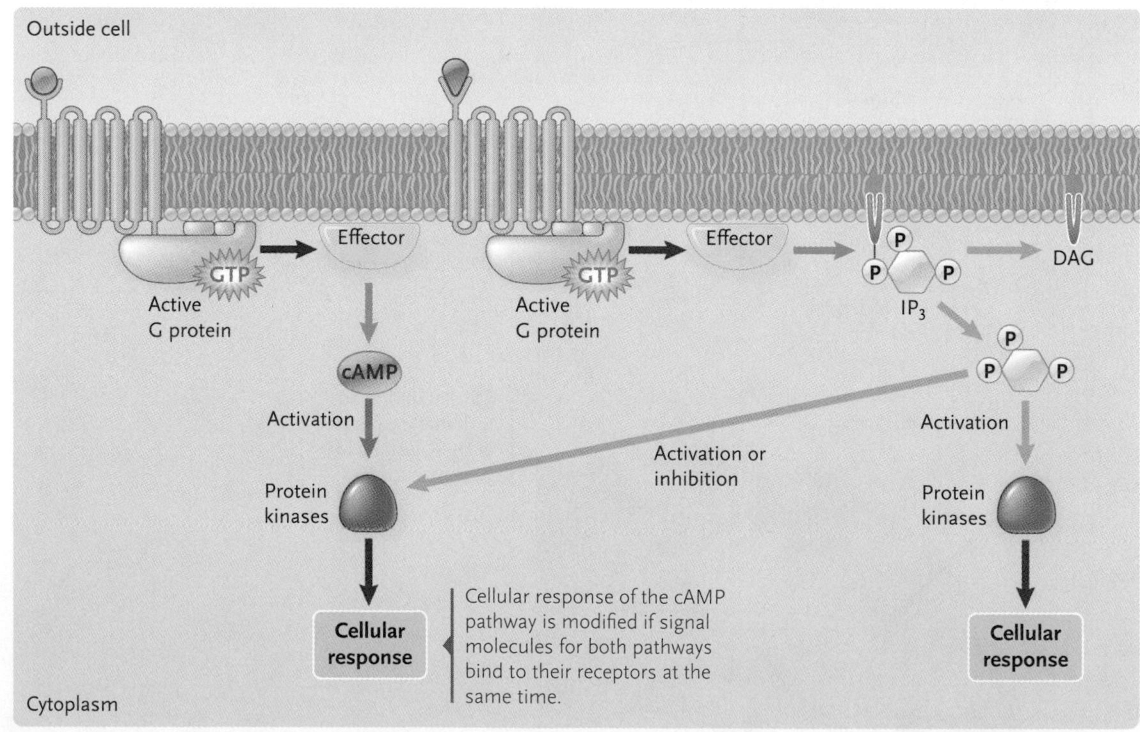

Figure 8.15
Cross-talk, the interaction between cell communication pathways to integrate the responses to signal molecules.

MOLECULE BEHIND BIOLOGY

Ethylene

Ethylene is a structurally simple molecule that has dramatic effects on the physiology of plants throughout their life history. As discussed in Chapter 31, ethylene influences such fundamental physiological processes as seed germination, response to wounding, flowering, fruit ripening, and senescence. Several characteristics of ethylene and its action are interesting in the context of this chapter.

First, this molecule is strikingly simple in structure compared to the peptide or steroid hormones of animals and the auxin or cytokinin hormones of plants. Second, it is one of very few hormones that is a gas at physiological temperature (nitric oxide is another). It is soluble in both water and lipids, and as such, it can readily diffuse to, *and into*, target cells. Third, the receptors for ethylene are a family of membrane-bound proteins found not on the cell surface but within the cell on the ER. Fourth, whereas the membrane receptors discussed in this chapter have binding sites that protrude away from the membrane, the binding site for ethylene is within the transmembrane portion of the receptor protein. That is, ethylene diffuses inside the ER membrane to find its receptor. Fifth, in the absence of ethylene, the cascade of proteins involved in ethylene response is actively repressed and inactive. However, when ethylene binds a receptor, kinase activity and conformational changes activate the pathway, ultimately resulting in production of transcription factors that, in turn, regulate the expression of hundreds of genes.

H H
C=C
H H

Figure 1
Ethylene: a gaseous plant hormone.

Cross-talk often leads to modifications of the cellular responses controlled by the pathways. Such modifications fine-tune the effects of combinations of signal molecules binding to the receptors of a cell. For example, cross-talk between second-messenger pathways is involved in particular types of olfactory (smell) signal transduction in rats and probably in many animals. The two pathways involved are activated upon stimulation with distinct odours. One pathway involves cAMP as the second messenger, and the other involves IP_3. However, the two olfactory second-messenger pathways do not work independently; rather, they operate in an antagonistic way. That is, experimentally blocking key enzymes of one signal transduction cascade inhibits that pathway while simultaneously augmenting the activity of the other pathway. The cross-talk may be a way to refine the animal's olfactory sensory perception by helping discriminate different odour molecules more effectively.

Cross-talk networks may also involve inputs from other cellular response systems, such as those triggered by cell adhesion molecules as a result of specific contact between cells. Cell adhesion molecules are receptor-like glycoproteins in plasma membranes; they link cells together or bind them to molecules of the extracellular matrix. Many of these surface molecules also trigger cellular responses. For example, when the surface molecule *integrin* binds to another cell or to a molecule of the extracellular matrix, such as collagen, it triggers a cellular response, often including cross-talk steps that link the reactions to the cAMP and IP_3/DAG pathways. The responses triggered by the cell adhesion molecules include changes in the rate of cell division and gene activity and alterations in cell motility, development, and differentiation.

Direct channels of communication may also be involved in a cross-talk network. For example, gap junctions between the cytoplasms of adjacent cells admit ions and small molecules, including the Ca^{2+}, cAMP, and IP_3 second messengers released by the receptor–response pathways. Thus, one cell that receives a signal through its surface receptors can transmit the signal to other cells in the same tissue via the connecting gap junctions, thereby coordinating the functions of those cells. For instance, cardiac muscle cells are connected by gap junctions, and the Ca^{2+} flow regulates coordinated muscle fibre contractions.

The entire system integrating cellular response mechanisms, tied together by many avenues of cross-talk between individual pathways, creates a sensitively balanced control mechanism that regulates and coordinates the activities of individual cells into the working unit of the organism.

STUDY BREAK

What cell communication pathways might be integrated in a cross-talk network?

Unanswered Questions

Intercellular signal molecules control many cellular activities; therefore, it is not surprising that many laboratories are extensively researching the mechanisms involved. Experimental goals include determining the molecular details of the receptor structures and how they interact with and change when a signal molecule binds, identifying and characterizing all of the components of the transduction steps, detailing how the final activated component of the transduction steps triggers the cellular responses, and understanding the regulation of signal transduction pathways.

What are the prospects for treating human diseases caused by signal transduction pathway malfunctions?

Receptor tyrosine kinase–mediated signalling is critical for cell growth, division, differentiation, and development. Some human diseases and developmental abnormalities result from mutations in the genes for receptor tyrosine kinases and from overexpression of those genes. Examples are dwarfism, heritable cancer susceptibility, vein malformations, and piebaldism. Researchers are determining the exact nature of the receptor gene mutations in order to explore how the mutations cause the malfunctions of the signal transduction pathways. They have found that some mutations affect the ability of the receptor to form a dimer when the signal molecule binds, and others affect the kinase activity of the cytoplasmic side of the receptor. In fact, there are a surprisingly large number of different mutations that affect receptor tyrosine kinases, meaning that there are many ways that their functions can be affected. In terms of treating human diseases resulting from receptor tyrosine kinase mutations, research is at a relatively early stage. Prospects for therapeutic approaches to treat these diseases include developing anti–tyrosine kinase drugs. Clearly, an increased understanding of receptor tyrosine kinases' signalling and function is crucial for progress to be made in the diagnosis and treatment of human diseases resulting from mutations that cause abnormal regulation of receptor tyrosine kinase function.

Review

Go to CENGAGENOW™ at http://hed.nelson.com/ to access quizzing, animations, exercises, articles, and personalized homework help.

8.1 Cell Communication: An Overview

- Cells communicate with one another through direct channels of communication, specific contact between cells, and intercellular chemical messengers.
- In communication that involves an intercellular chemical messenger, a controlling cell releases a signal molecule that causes a response of target cells. To respond, the target cell must have a receptor for the specific signal molecule. The target cell processes the signal in three steps: reception, transduction, and response. The series of events from reception to response is called signal transduction.

8.2 Characteristics of Cell Communication Systems with Surface Receptors

- Cell communication systems based on surface receptors have three components: (1) extracellular signal molecules, (2) surface receptors that receive the signals, and (3) internal response pathways triggered when receptors bind a signal.
- The systems based on surface receptors respond to hormones and neurotransmitters.
- Hormones include peptides and steroids. A special class of peptide hormones is the growth factors, which affect cell growth, division, and differentiation. Neurotransmitters include small peptides, individual amino acids or their derivatives, and other chemical substances.
- Surface receptors are integral membrane proteins that extend entirely through the plasma membrane. Binding a signal molecule induces a molecular change in the receptor that activates its cytoplasmic end.
- Cellular response pathways operate by activating protein kinases. Phosphate groups added by the protein kinases stimulate or inhibit the activities of the target proteins, thereby accomplishing the cellular response. The response is reversed by protein phosphatases that remove phosphate groups from target proteins. In addition, receptors are removed by endocytosis when signal transduction has run its course.
- Each step of a response pathway catalyzed by an enzyme is amplified because each enzyme can activate hundreds or thousands of proteins that enter the next step in the pathway. Amplification allows a full cellular response when a few signal molecules bind to their receptors.

8.3 Surface Receptors with Built-in Protein Kinase Activity: Receptor Tyrosine Kinases

- When receptor tyrosine kinases bind a signal molecule, it moves together with another protein kinase to form a dimer, activating the kinase. The active dimer adds phosphate groups to tyrosines in the receptor itself and to target proteins. The phosphate groups added to the cytoplasmic end of the receptor are recognition sites for proteins that are activated by binding to the receptor.

8.4 G Protein–Coupled Receptors

- In the pathways activated by G protein-coupled receptors, binding of the extracellular signal molecule (the first messenger) activates a site on the cytoplasmic end of the receptor.
- An activated receptor turns on a G protein, which acts as a molecular switch. The G protein is active when it is bound to GTP and inactive when it is bound to GDP.
- When a G protein is active, it switches on the effector of the pathway, an enzyme that generates small internal signal molecules called second messengers. The second messengers activate the protein kinases of the pathway.
- In one of the two major pathways triggered by G protein–coupled receptors, the effector, adenylyl cyclase, generates

cAMP as second messenger. cAMP activates specific protein kinases.

- In the other major pathway, the activated effector, phospholipase C, generates two second messengers, IP_3 and DAG. IP_3 activates transport proteins in the ER, which release stored Ca^{2+} into the cytoplasm. The released Ca^{2+}, alone or in combination with DAG, activates specific protein kinases that add phosphate groups to their target proteins.
- Both the cAMP and IP_3/DAG pathways are balanced by reactions that constantly eliminate their second messengers. Both pathways are also stopped by protein phosphatases that continually remove phosphate groups from target proteins and by endocytosis of receptors and their bound extracellular signals.
- Some pathways important in gene regulation link certain receptor tyrosine kinases to a specific G protein called Ras. When the receptor binds a signal molecule, it phosphorylates itself, and adapter proteins then bind, bridging to Ras, activating it. Activated Ras turns on the MAP kinase cascade. The last MAP kinase in the cascade, when activated, phosphorylates target proteins in the nucleus, activating them to turn on specific genes. Many of those genes control cell division.

8.5 Pathways Triggered by Internal Receptors: Steroid Hormone Nuclear Receptors

- In addition to their effects on membrane receptors, steroid hormones also penetrate through the plasma membrane to bind to receptors within the cell. The internal receptors are regulatory proteins that turn on specific genes when they are activated by binding a signal molecule, thereby producing the cellular response.
- Steroid hormone nuclear receptors have a domain that recognizes and binds a specific steroid hormone and a domain that interacts with the controlling regions of target genes.
- Steroids may act on membrane and nuclear receptors in the same cells or on different cells. The type of response involving nuclear receptors depends on the genes that are turned on by an activated receptor.

8.6 Integration of Cell Communication Pathways

- In cross-talk, cell signalling pathways such as the cAMP and IP_3 pathways communicate with one another to integrate responses to cellular signals. Cross-talk may result in a complex network of interactions between cell communication pathways.
- Cross-talk often results in modifications of the cellular responses controlled by the pathways, fine-tuning the effects of combinations of signal molecules binding to the receptors of a cell.
- In animals, inputs from other cellular response systems, including cell adhesion molecules, as well as molecules arriving through gap junctions, also can become involved in the cross-talk network.

Questions

Self-Test Questions

1. In signal transduction, which of the following is *not* a target protein?
   a. proteins that regulate gene activity.
   b. hormones that activate the receptor.
   c. enzymes of pathways.
   d. transport proteins.
   e. enzymes of cell reactions.
2. A cell that responds to a signal molecule is distinguished from a cell that does not respond by the fact that it has
   a. a cell adhesion molecule.
   b. cAMP.
   c. a first-messenger molecule.
   d. a receptor.
   e. a protein kinase.
3. In a stepwise pathway activated by a small number of signal molecules binding to their receptors, which of the following enables enzymes to activate thousands of molecules?
   a. autophosphorylation.
   b. second-messenger enhancement.
   c. amplification.
   d. ion channel regulation.
   e. G protein turn-on.
4. Which of the following is *incorrect* about pathways activated by G protein–coupled receptors?
   a. The extracellular signal is the first messenger.
   b. When activated, plasma membrane–bound G protein can switch on an effector.
   c. Second messengers enter the nucleus.
   d. ATP converts to cAMP to activate protein kinases.
   e. Protein kinases phosphorylate molecules to change cellular activity.
5. Which of the following would *not* inhibit signal transduction?
   a. Phosphate groups are removed from proteins.
   b. Endocytosis acts on receptors and their bound signals.
   c. Receptors and signals separate.
   d. Receptors and bound signals enter lysosomes.
   e. Autophosphorylation targets the cytoplasmic portion of the receptor.

Questions for Discussion

1. Describe the possible ways in which a G-protein–coupled receptor pathway could become defective and not trigger any cellular responses.
2. What factors might have contributed to the evolution of two internal mechanisms: one using switching molecules that bind ATP and the other binding GTP?
3. What experiments would you do to determine whether a receptor is located on the cell surface or inside the cell?

A cell in mitosis (fluorescence micrograph). The spindle (red) is separating copies of the cell's chromosomes (green) prior to cell division.

Dr. Paul Andrews University of Dundee/Science Photo Library/Photo Researchers, Inc.

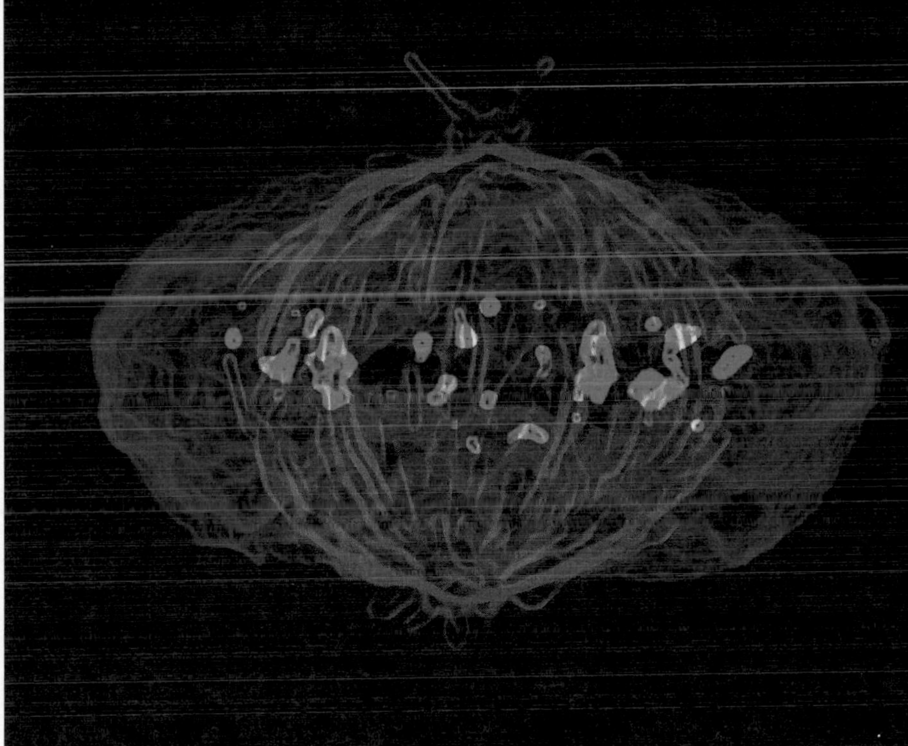

Study Plan

9 Cell Cycles

Why It Matters

As the rainy season recedes in Northern India, rice paddies and other flooded areas begin to dry. These shallow seasonal pools have provided an environment of slow-moving warm water for zebrafish (*Danio rerio*) to spawn **(Figure 9.1, p. 180).** Over the past few months, many millions of cell divisions have fuelled the growth and development of single fertilized eggs into the complex multicellular tissues and organs of these small, boldly striped fish. Most cells in the adults have now stopped dividing and are dedicated to particular functions.

Moving into the fast-running streams that feed the Ganges River, the young zebrafish encounter larger predators, such as knifefish (*Notopterus notopterus*). Imagine for a moment that a zebrafish is attacked by a knifefish; the prey narrowly escapes but not without leaving one of its fins behind in the mouth of the predator. In an amazing feat of cell cycle regulation, the entire zebrafish fin will be regenerated—skin, nerves, muscles, bones, and all—within a week!

As a model system for vertebrate development, the zebrafish has provided a popular tool for researchers to identify the stages of regeneration at the molecular level. (See *The Chemical and Physical Foundations*

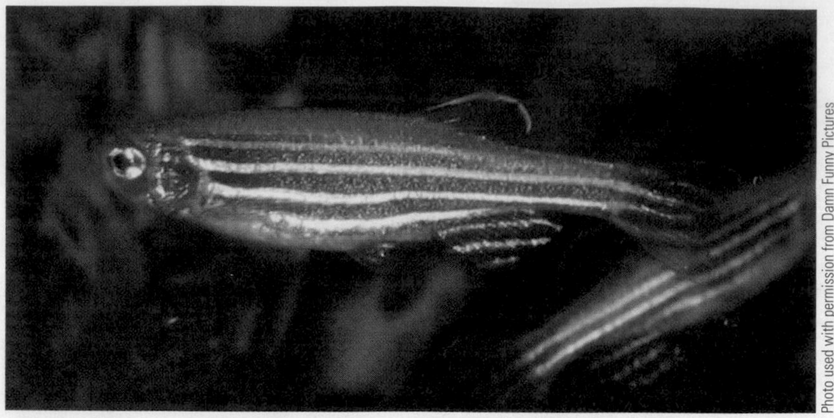

Photo used with permission from Damn Funny Pictures

Figure 9.1
Zebrafish (*Danio rerio*).

of Biology pages for more information about zebrafish as model organisms.) In the first step, existing skin cells migrate to close the wound and prevent bleeding. Then cells just under the new skin transform into "regeneration cells" that form a temporary tissue called a blastema. Blastema cells exhibit two important characteristics: (1) they reenter the cell cycle and divide up to 50 times faster than usual, and (2) they expand their previously restricted range of function. The blastema provides large numbers of daughter cells capable of maturing into new bone, nerve, muscle, and blood vessel cells in response to signal proteins produced by the skin. Once the regenerated fin has reached its normal size and shape, cell cycling returns to its normally quiescent state.

Although regenerating lost fins is dramatic, zebrafish can also regenerate lost heart muscle. Studies are under way to explore the possibility that human hearts could be stimulated to repair themselves following heart attack damage rather than just form scar tissue.

Since multicellular organisms are made (and sometimes remade) almost entirely of cells and their products, understanding organismal development and structure is really a problem of understanding the regulation of cell division and differentiation. Which conditions stimulate cells to divide? Which make them stop? How do cells "learn" their original function, and how do they "relearn" a new one? This chapter is dedicated to helping you better understand the factors that influence and guide cell division. The differentiation of cells for specialized functions in various organisms is discussed in Chapters 14, 20, and 31.

9.1 The Cycle of Cell Growth and Division: An Overview

If we were to show you a living cell and ask, "What does the future hold for this cell?" you would likely reply, "It will grow and divide, grow and divide." You might be correct. If the cell is a prokaryote such as *Escherichia coli* or a single-celled eukaryote such as baker's yeast, then, yes, it would be a safe bet to predict reproduction as frequently as environmental conditions allow. However, if this cell is from inside the cheek of a moose or from a yellow rose petal, the future may hold neither growth nor cell division. In fact, some cells may even be programmed to die immediately!

The increasing size, developmental complexity, and diversity of functioning of multicellular eukaryotic organisms require strict control of cell division that ultimately results in a mature body composed of different subpopulations of cells. Whereas most mature cells divide infrequently, if at all, relatively small populations in the meristem tissues of plants, as well as the stem cells of animals, are actively dividing by the process of mitosis. The new progeny cells are needed for growth (new leaves), asexual reproduction, and replacement of cells lost to wear (shedding skin and gut lining) and tear (wound repair, virus infection) **(Figure 9.2)**. Before dividing, most cells enter a period of growth in which they synthesize proteins, lipids, and carbohydrates and (during one particular stage) replicate their nuclear DNA. After this growth period, the nuclei divide, and, usually, cytokinesis (the division of the cytoplasm; cyto = cell, derived from "hollow vessel"; kinesis = movement) follows, partitioning nuclei to each of two daughter cells. Each daughter nucleus contains a copy of the original DNA. This sequence of events—a period of growth followed by nuclear division and cytokinesis—is known as the **cell cycle**.

a.

© John Cancalosi / Alamy

b.

© M.Brodie / Alamy

Figure 9.2
Actively dividing cells provide for new growth of skin **(a)** and leaves **(b)**.

9.1a The Products of Mitosis Are Genetic Duplicates of the Dividing Cell

As long as eukaryotes require their daughter cells to be exact genetic copies of the parental cell, mitosis serves very well to divide the replicated DNA equally and precisely. This is the result of three elegantly interrelated systems. One component is an elaborate master program of molecular checks and balances that ensures an orderly and timely progression through the cell cycle. Within the overall regulation of the cell cycle, the process of DNA synthesis replicates each DNA chromosome into two copies with almost perfect fidelity (see Section 13.3). The final system is a structural and mechanical web of interwoven "cables" and "motors" of the mitotic cytoskeleton that separates the DNA copies precisely into the daughter cells (see Figure 9.13).

However, at a certain stage of the life cycle of sexually reproducing organisms, some cells are needed that are decidedly *different* from the parent cells. A different type of cell division process is required. **Meiosis** produces the necessary daughter nuclei—different in that they have only half the number of chromosomes as the parental nuclei that began the process. Also, many of the genetic traits carried by these daughter nuclei are in different combinations from those of the parent cell. The cells that are the products of meiosis may function as gametes in animals (fusing with other gametes to make a zygote) and as spores in plants and many fungi (dividing by mitosis).

This chapter concentrates on the mechanical and regulatory aspects of cell division in eukaryotes and prokaryotes; meiosis and its role in eukaryotic sexual reproduction are addressed in the next chapter. We begin our discussion with **chromosomes,** the nuclear units of genetic information that are divided and distributed by mitotic cell division.

9.1b Chromosomes Are the Genetic Units Divided by Mitosis

In all eukaryotes, the hereditary information of the nucleus is distributed among several linear DNA molecules. These DNA molecules are combined with proteins that stabilize the DNA, assist in packaging DNA during cell division, and influence the expression of individual genes. Each chromosome (*chroma* = colour, when stained with dyes used in light microscopy; *soma* = body; **Figure 9.3**) in a cell is composed of one of these linear DNA molecules along with its associated proteins.

Most eukaryotes have two copies of each type of chromosome in their nuclei, and their chromosome complement is said to be **diploid,** or $2n$. For example, humans have 23 different pairs of chromosomes for a diploid number of 46 chromosomes ($2n = 46$). Other eukaryotes, mostly microorganisms, may have only one copy of each type of chromosome in their nucleus, so their chromosome complement is said to be **haploid,** or n. Baker's yeast (*Saccharomyces cerevisiae*) is an example of an organism that can grow as a diploid ($2n = 32$) and as a haploid ($n = 16$). Still others, such as many plant species, have three, four, or even more complete sets of chromosomes in each cell. The number of chromosome sets is called the **ploidy** of a cell or species. See Chapter 18 for a look at the role of ploidy in the formation of new species.

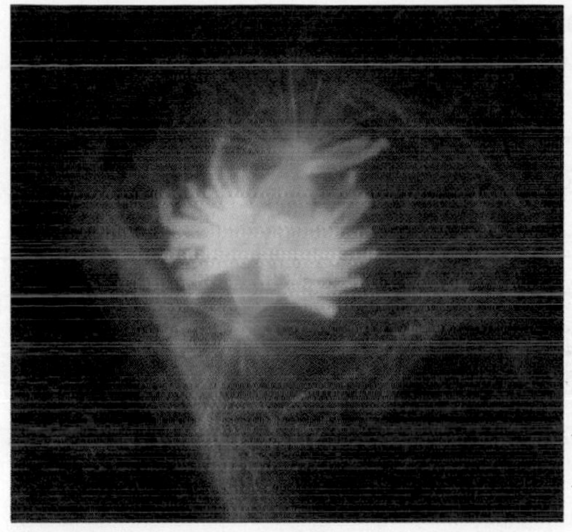

Figure 9.3
Eukaryotic chromosomes (blue).

Replication of the DNA of each individual chromosome creates two identical molecules called **sister chromatids.** Newly formed sister chromatids are held together until mitosis separates them, placing one in each of the two daughter nuclei. As a result of this precise division, each daughter nucleus receives exactly the same number and types of chromosomes, and contains the same genetic information, as the parent cell entering the division. The equal distribution of daughter chromosomes to each of the two cells that result from cell division is called **chromosome segregation.**

The precision of chromosome replication and segregation in the mitotic cell cycle creates a group of cells called a clone. Except for rare chance mutations, all cells of a clone are genetically identical. Since all the diverse cell types of a complex multicellular organism arose by mitosis from a single zygote, they should all contain the same genetic information. Forensic scientists rely on this feature of organisms when, for instance, they match the genetic profile of a small amount of tissue (e.g., cells in dog saliva recovered from a bite victim) with that of a blood sample from the suspected animal.

Study Break

1. What are the three interrelated systems that contribute to the eukaryotic cell cycle?
2. What is a chromosome composed of?

Growing Cell Clones in Culture

How can investigators safely test whether a particular substance is toxic to human cells or whether it can cure or cause cancer? One widely used approach is to work with **cell cultures**—living cells grown in laboratory vessels. Many types of prokaryotic and eukaryotic cells can be grown in this way.

When cell cultures are started from single cells, they form **clones:** barring mutations, all the individuals descending from the original cell are genetically identical. Clones are ideal for experiments in genetics, biochemistry, molecular biology, and medicine because the cells lack genetic differences that could affect the experimental results.

Microorganisms such as yeasts and many bacteria are easy to grow in laboratory cultures. For example, the human intestinal bacterium *E. coli* can be grown in solutions (growth media) that contain only an organic carbon source such as glucose, a nitrogen source, and inorganic salts. Under optimal conditions, the cycle of cell growth and division of *E. coli* cells takes 20 minutes. As a result, large numbers of cells are produced in a short time. The cells may be grown in liquid suspensions or on the surface of a solid growth medium such as an agar gel (agar is a polysaccharide extracted from an alga). Many thousands of bacterial strains are used in a wide variety of experimental studies.

Many types of plant cells can also be cultured as clones in specific growth media. With the addition of plant growth hormones, complete plants can often be grown from single cultured cells. Growing plants from cultured cells is particularly valuable in genetic engineering, in which genes introduced into cultured cells can be tracked in fully developed plants. Plants that have been engineered successfully can then be grown simply by planting their seeds.

Animal cells vary in what is needed to culture them. For many types, the culture medium must contain essential amino acids—that is, the amino acids that the cells cannot make for themselves. In addition, mammalian cells require specific growth factors provided by adding blood serum, the fluid part of the blood left after red and white blood cells are removed.

Even with added serum, many types of normal mammalian cells cannot be grown in long-term cultures. Eventually, the cells stop dividing and die. By contrast, tumour cells often form cultures that grow and divide indefinitely.

The first successful culturing of cancer cells was performed in 1951 in the laboratory of George and Margaret Gey (Johns Hopkins University, Baltimore, MD). Gey and Gey's cultures of normal cells died after a few weeks, but the researchers achieved success with a culture of tumour cells from a cancer patient. The cells in culture continued to grow and divide; in fact, descendants of those cells are still being cultured and used for research today. The cells were given the code name *HeLa,* from the first two letters of the patient's first and last names—Henrietta Lacks. Unfortunately, the tumour cells in Henrietta's body also continued to grow, and she died within two months of her cancer diagnosis.

Other types of human cells have since been grown successfully in culture, derived either from tumour cells or normal cells that have been "immortalized" by inducing genetic changes that transformed them into tumour-like cells.

9.2 The Mitotic Cell Cycle

If cells show a repeating phase of growth and division, they can be thought of as moving through a mitotic cell "cycle." Although the cell cycle is usually a smooth continuum of change in nature, it is helpful to describe discrete "phases" for discussion purposes. If we choose to let the formation of a new daughter cell mark the beginning of the mitotic cell cycle, then the first and longest phase is **interphase.** During interphase, the cell grows and replicates its DNA in preparation for mitosis (also called the *M phase*) and cytokinesis **(Figure 9.4).** Internal regulatory controls trigger each phase, ensuring that the processes of one phase are completed successfully before the next phase can begin. Various internal mechanisms also regulate the overall number of cycles that a cell is allowed. These internal controls may be subject to various "external" influences caused by other cells or viruses as well as signal molecules, including hormones, growth factors, and death factors.

9.2a Interphase Extends from the End of One Mitosis to the Beginning of the Next Mitosis

Interphase begins as a daughter cell from a previous division cycle enters an initial period of cytoplasmic growth. During this initial growth stage, called the **G_1 phase** of the cell cycle, the cell makes various RNAs, proteins, and other types of cellular molecules but not nuclear DNA (the G in G_1 stands for *gap*, referring to the absence of DNA synthesis). Then, if the cell is going to divide, DNA replication begins, initiating the **S phase** of the cell cycle (S stands for *synthesis*, meaning DNA synthesis).

During the S phase, the cell duplicates the chromosomal proteins as well as the DNA and continues the synthesis of other cellular molecules. As the

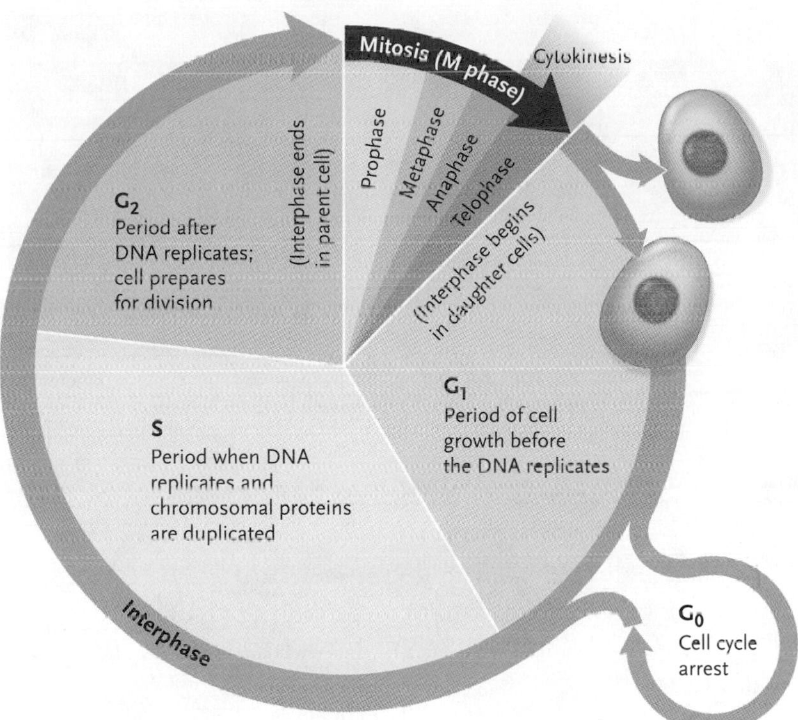

Figure 9.4
The cell cycle. The length of G_1 varies, but for a given cell type, the timing of S phase, G_2 phase, and mitosis is usually relatively uniform. Cytokinesis (red segment) usually begins while mitosis is in progress and reaches completion as mitosis ends. Cells in a state of division arrest are considered to enter a side loop (or shunt) from G_1 phase called G_0 phase.

S phase is completed, the cell enters the **G_2 phase** of the cell cycle (G_2 refers to the second gap during which there is no DNA synthesis). During G_2, the cell continues to synthesize RNAs and proteins, including those required for mitosis, and the cell continues to grow. At the end of G_2, which marks the end of interphase, mitosis begins. During all the steps of interphase, the chromosomes are relatively loose, but organized, in the nucleus **(Figure 9.5)**.

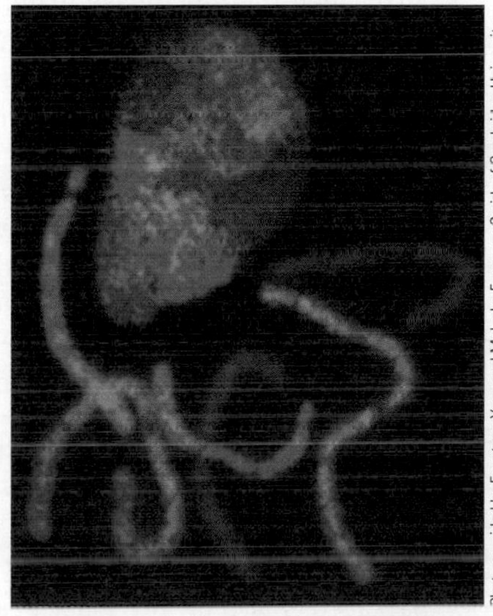

Photo provided by Fengtang Yang and Malcolm Ferguson-Smith of Cambridge University.

Figure 9.5
Chromosomes from the muntjac deer are individually "painted" with fluorescent stain. Note that there are two cells in this picture. The metaphase cell shows six long, condensed chromosomes with homologues stained the same colour. The interphase nucleus shows the homologous DNA organized in close proximity rather than randomly distributed.

Usually, G_1 is the only phase of the cell cycle that varies in length for a given species. Thus, whether cells divide rapidly or slowly primarily depends on the length of G_1. Once DNA replication begins, most mammalian cells take about 10 to 12 hours to proceed through the S phase, about 4 to 6 hours to go through G_2, and about 1 to 4 hours to complete mitosis. G_1 is also the stage in which many cell types stop dividing. This state of division arrest is often designated the **G_0 phase** (see Figure 9.4). For example, in humans, cells of the nervous system normally enter G_0 once they are fully mature.

The events of interphase are an important focus of research, particularly the regulatory controls for the transition from the G_1 phase to the S phase and, with it, the commitment to cell division. Understanding the molecular events that regulate the G_1/S phase transition is important because one of the hallmarks of cancer is the loss of normal control of that transition.

9.2b After Interphase, Mitosis Proceeds in Five Stages

If you watch a cell going through mitosis **(Figures 9.6, p. 184, and 9.7, p. 185)**, you will notice several dramatic changes that signal the progression through different "stages": prophase (*pro* = before), prometaphase (meta = between), metaphase, anaphase (*ana* = back), and telophase (*telo* = end).

Prophase During **prophase**, the greatly extended chromosomes that were replicated during interphase begin to *condense* into compact, rod-like structures (see chromatin packaging in Section 13.5). Each diploid human cell, although, only about 40 to 50 μm in diameter, contains *2 metres* of DNA distributed among 23 pairs of chromosomes. Condensation during prophase packs these long DNA molecules into units small enough to be divided successfully during mitosis. As they condense, the chromosomes appear as thin threads under the light microscope. The word *mitosis* (*mitos* = thread) is derived from this thread-like appearance.

While condensation is in progress, the nucleolus becomes smaller and eventually disappears in most species. The disappearance reflects a shutdown of all types of RNA synthesis, including the ribosomal RNA made in the nucleolus.

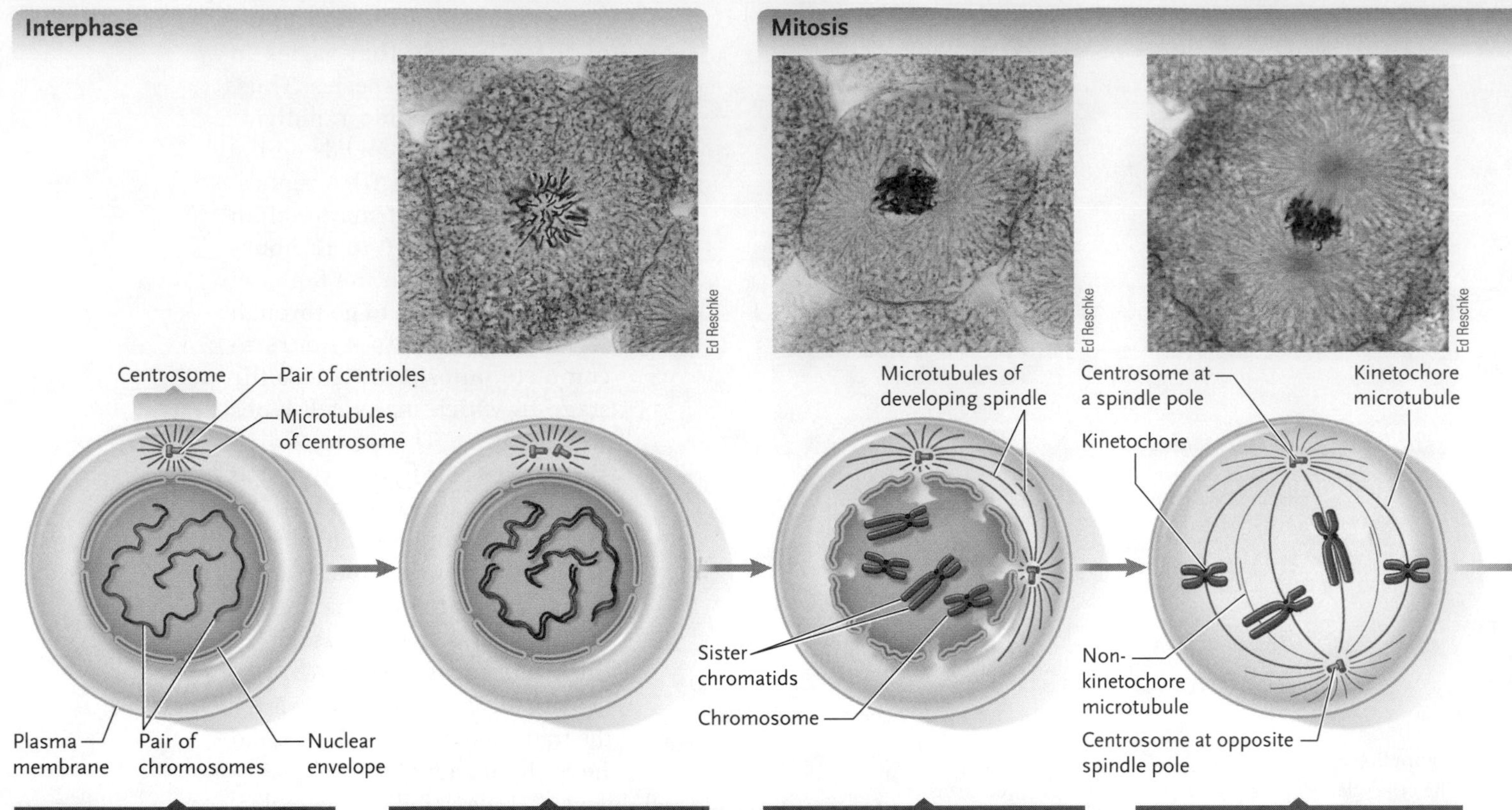
Interphase
Mitosis
Ed Reschke
Ed Reschke
Ed Reschke
Centrosome
Pair of centrioles
Microtubules of centrosome
Plasma membrane
Pair of chromosomes
Nuclear envelope
Microtubules of developing spindle
Sister chromatids
Chromosome
Centrosome at a spindle pole
Kinetochore
Kinetochore microtubule
Non-kinetochore microtubule
Centrosome at opposite spindle pole
G_1 of interphase
The chromosomes are unreplicated and extend throughout the nucleus. For simplicity we show only two pairs of chromosomes. One of each pair was inherited from one parent, and the other was inherited from the other parent.
G_2 of interphase
After replication during the S phase of interphase, each chromosome is double at all points and now consists of two sister chromatids. The centrioles within the centrosome have also doubled into pairs.
Prophase
The chromosomes condense into threads that become visible under the light microscope. Each chromosome is double as a result of replication. The centrosome has divided into two parts, which are generating the spindle as they separate.
Prometaphase
The nuclear envelope has disappeared and the spindle enters the former nuclear area. Microtubules from opposite spindle poles attach to the two kinetochores of each chromosome.

Figure 9.6
The stages of mitosis. Light micrographs show mitosis in an animal cell (whitefish embryo). Diagrams show mitosis in an animal cell with two pairs of chromosomes.

In the cytoplasm, the mitotic **spindle** (**Figure 9.8, p. 186;** see also Figure 9.12) begins to form between the two centrosomes as they start migrating toward the opposite ends of the cell to form the **spindle poles.** The spindle develops as bundles of microtubules that radiate from the spindle poles.

Prometaphase At the end of prophase, the nuclear envelope breaks down, heralding the beginning of **prometaphase.** Bundles of spindle microtubules grow from centrosomes at the opposing spindle poles toward the centre of the cell. Some of the developing spindle enters the former nuclear area and attaches to the chromosomes.

Although seldom visible as a double structure at this point, it is important for you to remember that each chromosome is made up of two identical sister chromatids held together only at their **centromeres.** By this time, a complex of several proteins, a **kinetochore,** has formed on each chromatid at the centromere. Kinetochore microtubules bind to the kinetochores. These connections determine the outcome of mitosis because they attach the sister chromatids of each chromosome to microtubules leading to the opposite spindle poles (see Figure 9.8). Microtubules that do not attach to kinetochores overlap those from the opposite spindle pole.

Metaphase During **metaphase,** the spindle reaches its final form and the spindle microtubules move the chromosomes into alignment at the spindle midpoint, also called the metaphase plate. The chromosomes complete their condensation in this stage and assume their characteristic shape as determined by the location of the centromere and the length and thickness of the chromatid arms.

Only when the chromosomes are all assembled at the spindle midpoint, with the two sister chromatids of each one attached to microtubules leading to opposite spindle poles, can metaphase give way to actual separation of chromatids.

Although chromosomes are generally thought of as "X" shapes, it is important to realize that few chromosomes actually ever look like this. Only chromosomes with their centromere near the middle could appear as an "X." Even so, during most of the cell cycle, such chromosomes would be too loosely packaged to take on any shape at all.

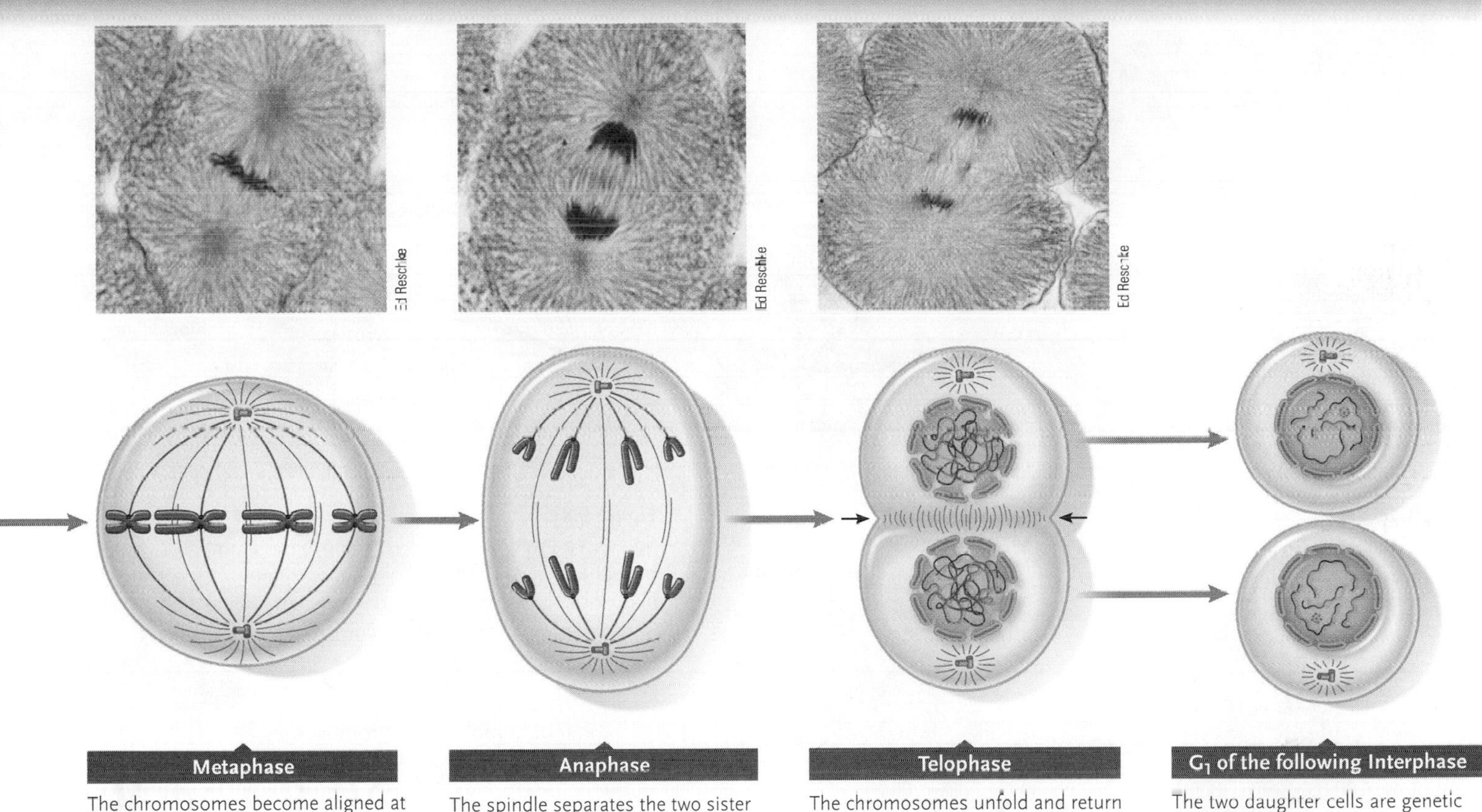

Metaphase The chromosomes become aligned at the spindle midpoint.

Anaphase The spindle separates the two sister chromatids of each chromosome and moves them to opposite spindle poles.

Telophase The chromosomes unfold and return to the interphase state, and new nuclear envelopes form around the daughter nuclei. The cytoplasm is beginning to divide by furrowing at the points marked by arrows.

G_1 of the following Interphase The two daughter cells are genetic duplicates of the parental cell that entered mitotic division.

The complete collection of metaphase chromosomes, arranged according to size and shape, forms the **karyotype** of a given species. In many cases, the karyotype is so distinctive that a species can be identified from this characteristic alone. **Figure 9.9 (p. 186)** shows a human karyotype.

Anaphase During **anaphase**, sister chromatids separate and move to opposite spindle poles. The first signs of chromosome movement can be seen at the centromeres as the kinetochores are the first sections to move toward opposite poles. The movement continues until the separated chromatids, now called daughter chromosomes, have reached the two poles. At this point, chromosome segregation has been completed.

Telophase During **telophase**, the spindle disassembles and the chromosomes at each spindle pole decondense and return to the extended state typical of interphase. As decondensation proceeds, the nucleolus reappears, RNA transcription resumes, and a new nuclear envelope forms around the chromosomes at each pole, producing the two daughter nuclei. At this point, nuclear division is complete, and the cell has two nuclei.

9.2c Cytokinesis Completes Cell Division by Dividing the Cytoplasm between Daughter Cells

Cytokinesis, the division of the cytoplasm, usually follows the nuclear division stage of mitosis and produces two daughter cells, each containing one of the daughter nuclei. In most cells, cytokinesis begins during telophase or even late anaphase. By the time cytokinesis is completed, the daughter nuclei have progressed to the interphase stage and entered the G_1 phase of the next cell cycle.

Cytokinesis proceeds by different pathways in the different kingdoms of eukaryotic organisms. In animals, protists, and many fungi, a groove, the **furrow**, girdles the cell and gradually deepens until it cuts the cytoplasm into two parts. In plants, a new cell wall, called the **cell plate**, forms between the daughter nuclei and grows laterally until it divides the cytoplasm. In both cases, the plane of cytoplasmic division is determined by the layer of microtubules that persist at the former spindle midpoint.

Furrowing In furrowing, the layer of microtubules that remains at the former spindle midpoint expands

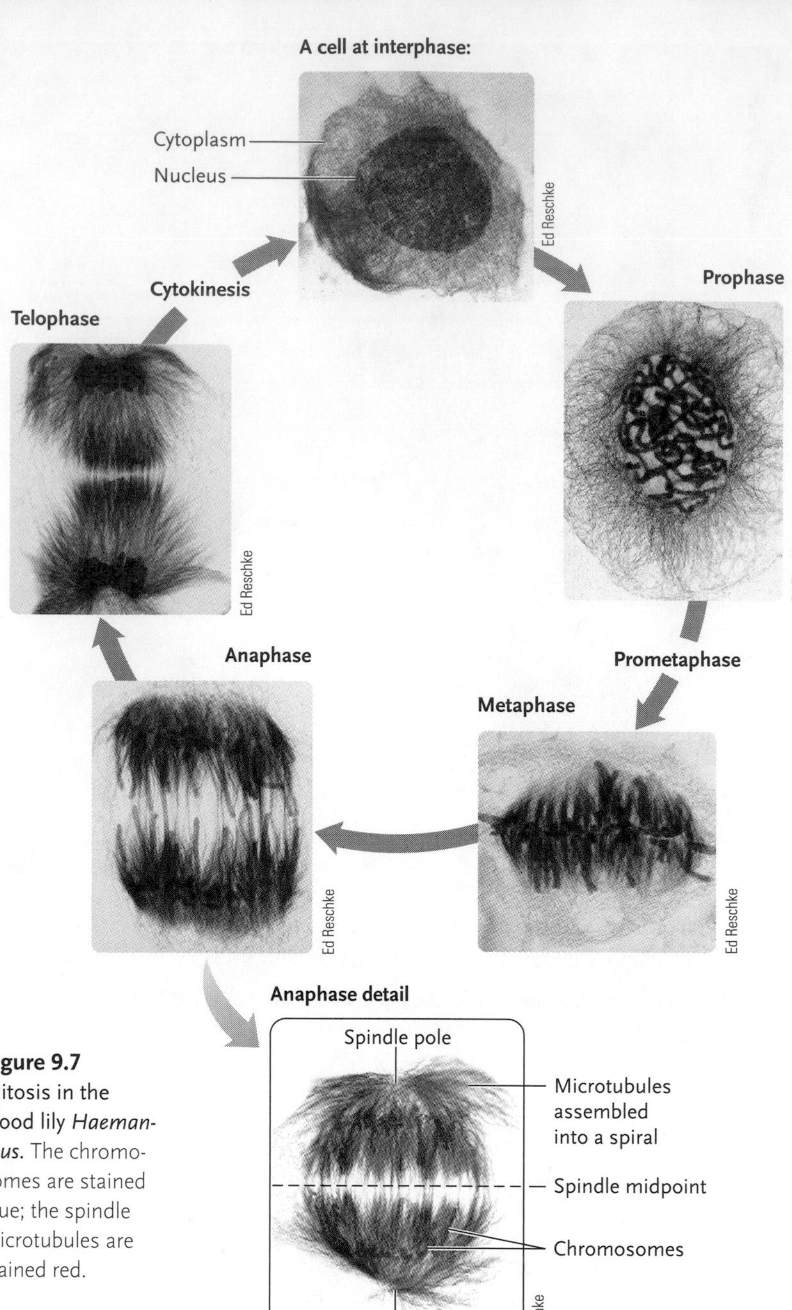

Figure 9.7
Mitosis in the blood lily *Haemanthus*. The chromosomes are stained blue; the spindle microtubules are stained red.

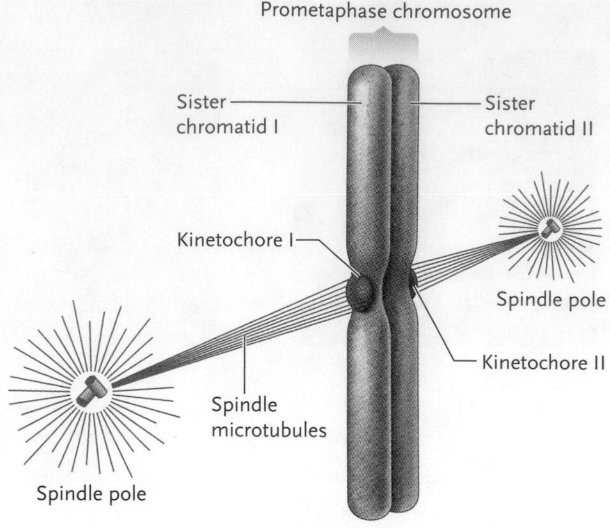

Figure 9.8
Spindle connections made by chromosomes at mitotic prometaphase. The two kinetochores of the chromosome connect to opposite spindle poles, ensuring that the chromatids are separated and moved to opposite spindle poles during anaphase.

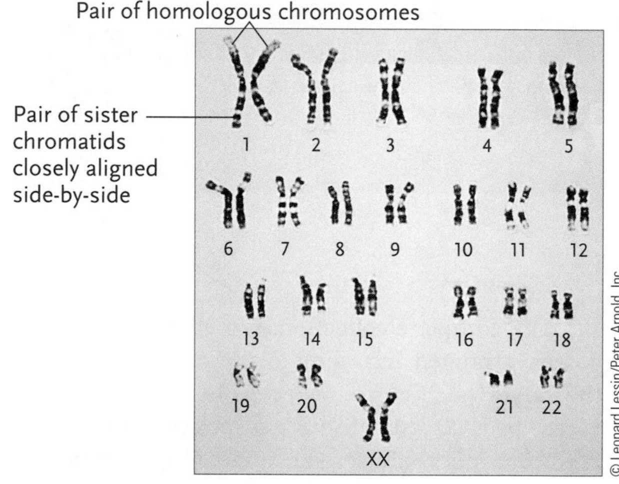

Figure 9.9
Karyotype of a human female. Note the two X chromosomes.

laterally until it stretches entirely across the dividing cell **(Figure 9.10).** As the layer develops, a band of microfilaments forms just inside the plasma membrane, forming a belt that follows the inside boundary of the cell in the plane of the microtubule layer (microfilaments are discussed in Section 2.4). Powered by motor proteins, the microfilaments slide together, tightening the band and constricting the cell. The constriction forms a groove—the furrow—in the plasma membrane. The furrow gradually deepens, much like the tightening of a drawstring, until the daughter cells are completely separated. The cytoplasmic division isolates the daughter nuclei in the two cells and, at the same time, distributes the organelles and other structures (which have also doubled) approximately equally.

Cell Plate Formation In cell plate formation, the layer of microtubules that persists at the former spindle midpoint serves as an organizing site for vesicles produced by the endoplasmic reticulum (ER) and Golgi complex **(Figure 9.11).** As the vesicles collect, the layer expands until it spreads entirely across the dividing cell. During this expansion, the vesicles fuse together and their contents assemble into a new cell wall—the cell plate—stretching completely across the former spindle midpoint. The junction separates the cytoplasm and its organelles into two parts and isolates the daughter nuclei in separate cells. The plasma membranes that line the two surfaces of the cell plate are derived from the vesicle membranes.

Contractile ring of microfilaments

D. M. Phillips/Visuals Unlimited

Figure 9.10
Cytokinesis by furrowing. The micrograph shows a furrow developing in the first division of a fertilized egg cell.

1 The furrow begins as an indentation running completely around the cell in the plane of the former spindle midpoint.

2 The furrow deepens by contraction of the microfilaments, like a drawstring tightening around the cell.

3 Furrowing continues until the daughter nuclei are enclosed in separate cells.

Study Break

1. During which stage(s) of the cell cycle is a chromosome composed of two chromatids?
2. What are the conditions under which a chromosome could appear as an "X" shape under the microscope?
3. How does cytokinesis differ in plant and animal cells?

9.3 Formation and Action of the Mitotic Spindle

The mitotic spindle is central to both mitosis and cytokinesis. The spindle is made up of microtubules and their proteins, and its activities depend on their changing patterns of organization during the cell cycle.

Microtubules form a major part of the interphase cytoskeleton of eukaryotic cells. (Section 2.4 outlines the patterns of microtubule organization in the cytoskeleton.) As mitosis approaches, the microtubules disassemble from their interphase arrangement and reorganize into the spindle, which grows until it fills almost the entire cell. This reorganization follows one of two pathways in different organisms, depending on the presence or absence of a *centrosome* during interphase. However, once organized, the basic function of the spindle is the same, regardless of whether a centrosome is present.

9.3a Animals and Plants Form Spindles in Different Ways

Animal cells and many protists have a **centrosome**, a site near the nucleus from which microtubules radiate outward in all directions (**Figure 9.12, p. 188** step 1).

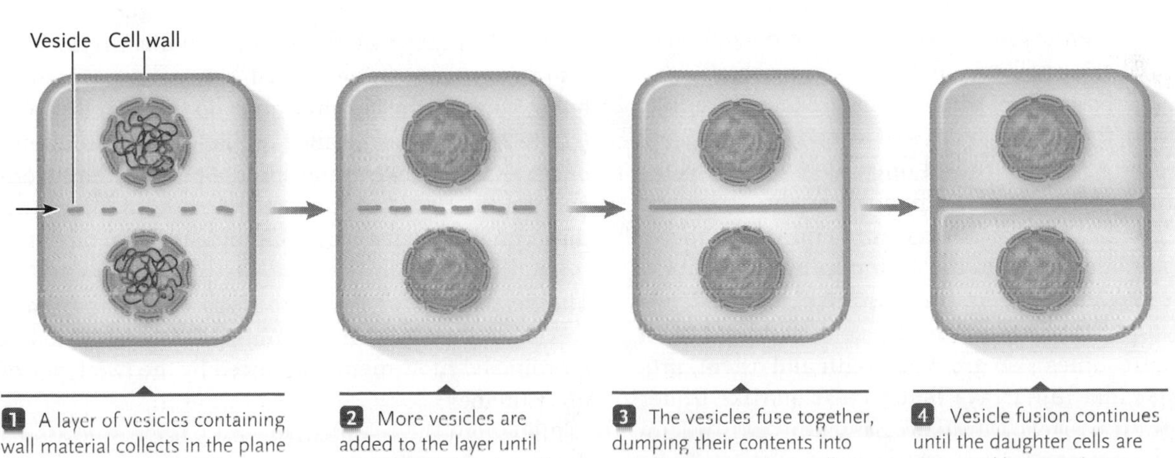

1 A layer of vesicles containing wall material collects in the plane of the former spindle midpoint (arrow).

2 More vesicles are added to the layer until it extends across the cell.

3 The vesicles fuse together, dumping their contents into a gradually expanding wall between the daughter cells.

4 Vesicle fusion continues until the daughter cells are separated by a continuous new wall, the cell plate.

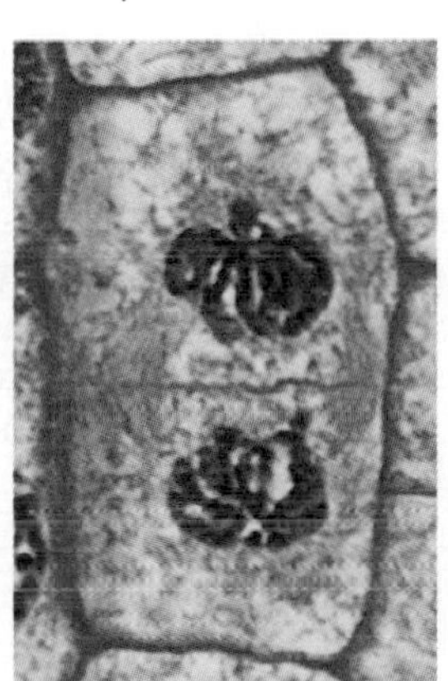

R. Calentine/Visuals Unlimited

Figure 9.11
Cytokinesis by cell plate formation in plant cells.

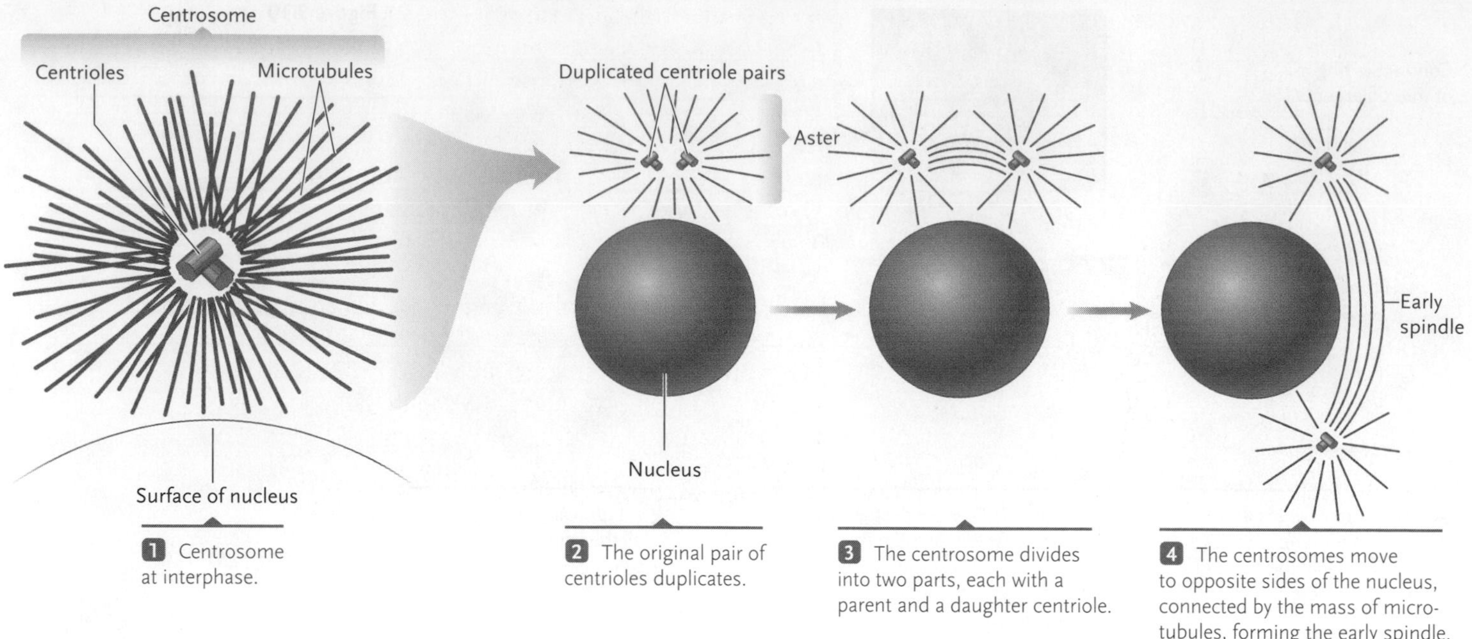

Centrosome
Centrioles
Microtubules
Surface of nucleus
Duplicated centriole pairs
Aster
Nucleus
Early spindle
1 Centrosome at interphase.
2 The original pair of centrioles duplicates.
3 The centrosome divides into two parts, each with a parent and a daughter centriole.
4 The centrosomes move to opposite sides of the nucleus, connected by the mass of microtubules, forming the early spindle.

Figure 9.12
The centrosome and its role in spindle formation.

The centrosome is the main **microtubule organizing centre (MTOC)** of the cell, anchoring the microtubule cytoskeleton during interphase and positioning many of the cytoplasmic organelles. The centrosome contains a pair of **centrioles**, usually arranged at right angles to each other. Although centrioles originally appeared to be important in the construction of the mitotic spindle, it has now been shown that they can be removed with no ill effect. The primary function of centrioles is actually to generate the microtubules needed for flagella or cilia, the whiplike extensions that provide cell motility.

When DNA replicates during the S phase of the cell cycle, the centrioles within the centrosome also duplicate, producing two pairs of centrioles (see Figure 9.12, step 2). As prophase begins in the M phase, the centrosome separates into two parts (step 3). The duplicated centrosomes, with the centrioles inside them, continue to separate until they reach opposite ends of the nucleus (step 4). As centrosomes move apart, the microtubules between them lengthen and increase in number.

By late prophase, when the centrosomes are fully separated, the microtubules that extend between them form a large mass around one side of the nucleus called the early spindle. When the nuclear envelope subsequently breaks down at the end of prophase, the spindle moves into the region formerly occupied by the nucleus and continues growing until it fills the cytoplasm. The microtubules that extend from the centrosomes also grow in length and extent, producing radiating arrays that appear starlike under the light microscope. Initially named by early microscopists, **asters** are the centrosomes at the spindle tips, which form the poles of the spindle. By dividing the duplicated centrioles, the spindle ensures that, when the cytoplasm divides during cytokinesis, the daughter cells each receive a pair of centrioles.

No centrosome or centrioles are present in angiosperms (flowering plants) or in most gymnosperms, such as conifers. Instead, the spindle forms from microtubules that assemble in all directions from multiple MTOCs surrounding the entire nucleus (see prophase in Figure 9.7). When the nuclear envelope breaks down at the end of prophase, the spindle moves into the former nuclear region, as in animals.

9.3b Mitotic Spindles May Move Chromosomes by a Combination of Two Mechanisms

When fully formed at metaphase, the spindle may contain from hundreds to many thousands of microtubules, depending on the species **(Figure 9.13).** In almost all eukaryotes, these microtubules are divided into two groups. Some, called kinetochore microtubules, connect the chromosomes to the spindle poles **(Figure 9.14a).** Others, called nonkinetochore microtubules, extend between the spindle poles without connecting to chromosomes; at the spindle midpoint, these microtubules from one pole overlap with the microtubules from the opposite pole **(Figure 9.14b).** The separation of the chromosomes at anaphase appears to result from a combination of separate but coordinated movements produced by the two types of microtubules.

The exact mechanism by which chromosomes move is still uncertain; at one time, it was believed that microtubules pulled the chromosomes toward the

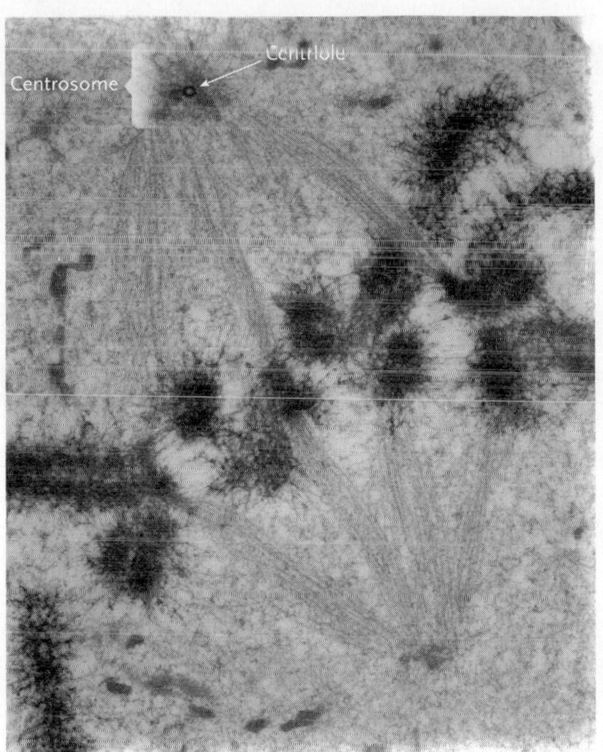

Figure 9.13
A fully developed spindle in a mammalian cell. Only microtubules connected to chromosomes have been caught in the plane of this section. One of the centrioles is visible in cross section in the centrosome at the top of the micrograph (arrow). Original magnification ×14 000.

poles of dividing cells. However, recent data suggest that chromosomes "walk" themselves to the poles along stationary microtubules, using motor proteins in their kinetochores **(Figure 9.15, p. 190)**. The tubulin subunits of the kinetochore microtubules disassemble as the kinetochores pass along them; thus, the microtubules become shorter as the movement progresses (see Figure 9.14a). The movement is similar to pulling yourself, hand over hand, up a rope as it falls apart behind you.

Evidence supporting kinetochore-based movement comes from experiments in which researchers tagged kinetochore microtubules with a microscopic beam of ultraviolet light, producing bleached sites that could be seen in the light microscope **(Figure 9.16, p. 190)**. As the chromosomes moved to the spindle poles, the bleached sites stayed in the same place. This result showed that the kinetochore microtubules do not move much with respect to the poles during the anaphase movement.

In nonkinetochore microtubule–based movement, the entire spindle is lengthened, pushing the poles farther apart (see Figure 9.14b). The pushing movement is presumably produced by microtubules sliding over one another in the zone of overlap, powered by proteins acting as microtubule motors. In many species, the nonkinetochore microtubules also push the poles apart by growing in length as they slide.

Figure 9.14
The two microtubule-based movements of the anaphase spindle.

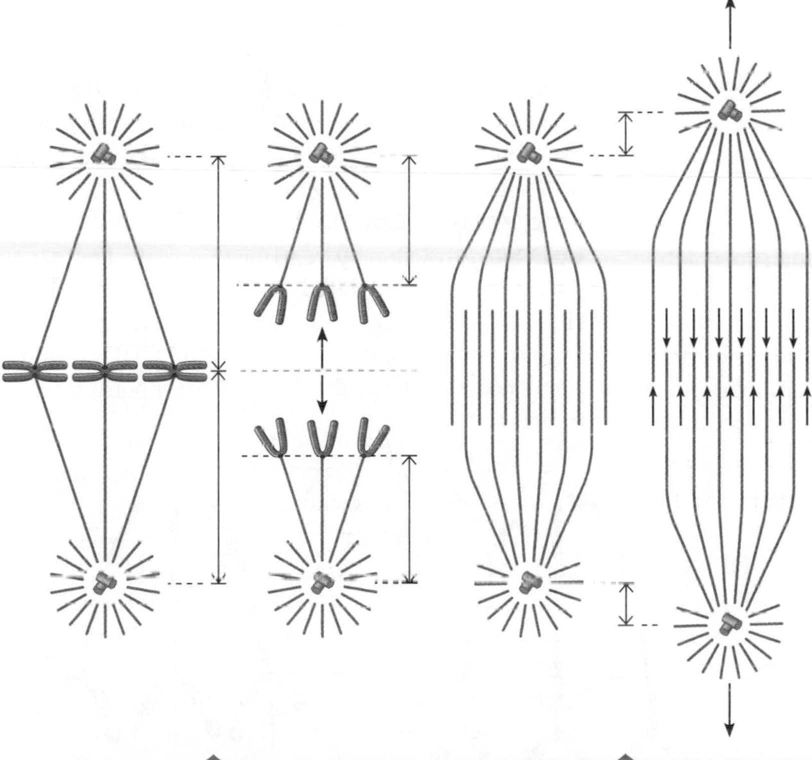

a. The kinetochore microtubules connected to the kinetochores of the chromosomes become shorter, lessening the distance from the chromosomes to the poles.

b. Sliding of the nonkinetochore microtubules in the zone of overlap at the spindle midpoint pushes poles farther apart and increases the total length of the spindle.

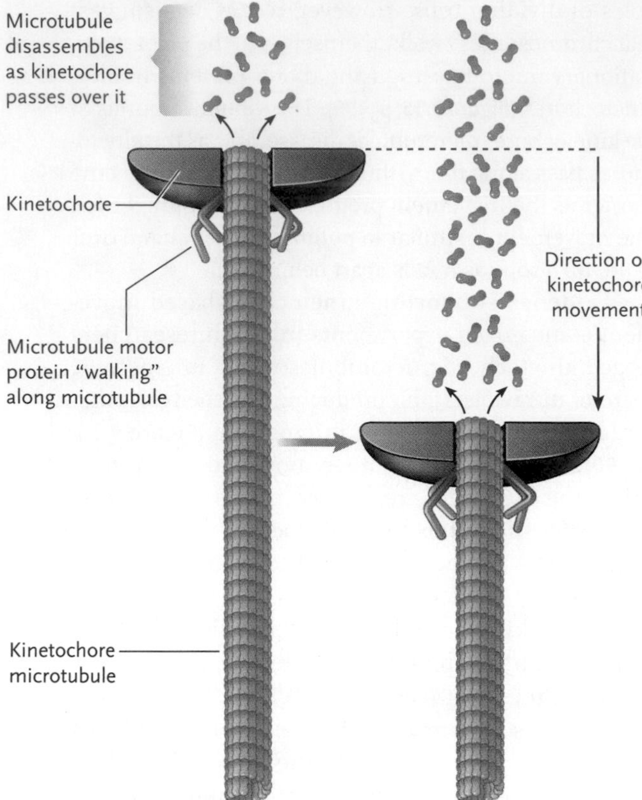

Figure 9.15
Microtubule motor proteins "walking" the kinetochore of a chromosome along a microtubule.

Study Break

1. What is the role of the centrosome?
2. What is the role of the kinetochore?

9.4 Cell Cycle Regulation

We have noted that a number of internal and external regulatory mechanisms control the mitotic cell cycle. As part of the internal controls, the cell cycle has built-in **checkpoints** to prevent critical phases from beginning until the previous phases are completed. Hormones, growth factors, and other external controls coordinate the cell cycle with the needs of an organism by stimulating or inhibiting division. Some key research contributing to our understanding of cell cycle regulation, particularly defining the genes involved and their protein products, was done using yeast. The *Experimental Research Organisms* section describes yeast and its role in research in more detail.

9.4a Cyclins and Cyclin-Dependent Kinases Are the Internal Controls that Directly Regulate Cell Division

Cyclin-dependent kinases (CDK) are major players in the regulation of cell division, directly affecting progression through the cell cycle. CDKs are protein kinases, enzymes that add phosphate groups to target proteins. CDK enzymes are called "cyclin dependent" because they are "switched on" only when combined with another protein called a **cyclin.** Since the concentration of the cyclins rises and falls during the cell cycle, so does the enzyme activity of the CDKs (even though the concentration of CDK proteins remains constant). The name *cyclin* reflects these cyclic fluctuations in its concentration. R. Timothy Hunt, of the Imperial Cancer Research Fund in London, UK, received a Nobel Prize in 2001 for discovering cyclins.

Several different cyclin:CDK combinations regulate cell cycle transitions at different "checkpoints." For example, the cyclin:CDK combination that controls the cell cycle at the G_1-to-S checkpoint is shown in **Figure 9.17.** At the G_1-to-S checkpoint, cyclin E has reached a concentration high enough to form a complex with CDK2 and activate it. The CDK2 then phosphorylates a number of cell-cycle control target proteins, which trigger the cell to make the transition into the S phase. After the transition is made, the cyclin E is degraded, less is available for binding to CDK2, and therefore kinase activity decreases. CDK2 becomes activated again when cyclin E levels rise at the next G_1-to-S checkpoint, after mitosis. Similar events, with a different cyclin:CDK combination, occur to release the G_2-to-M checkpoint referred to below.

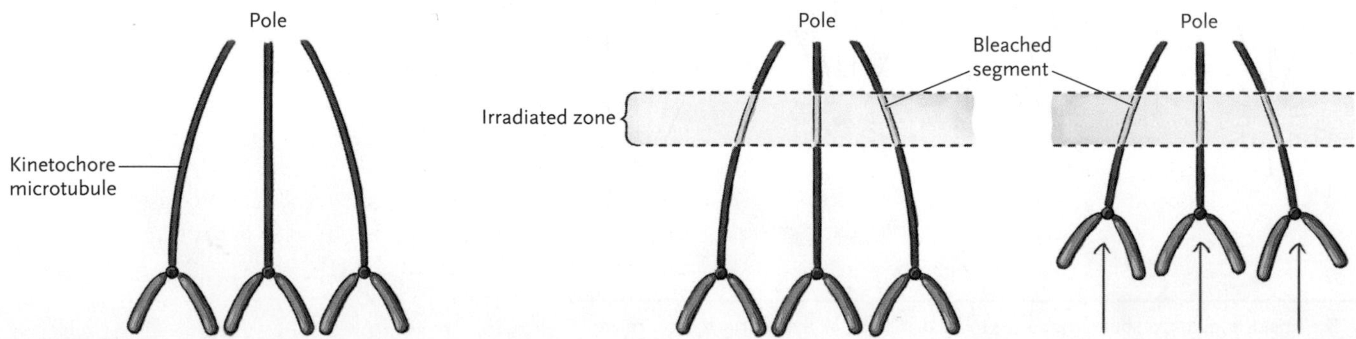

Figure 9.16
Experiment demonstrating that kinetochore microtubules remain stationary as chromosomes move during anaphase.

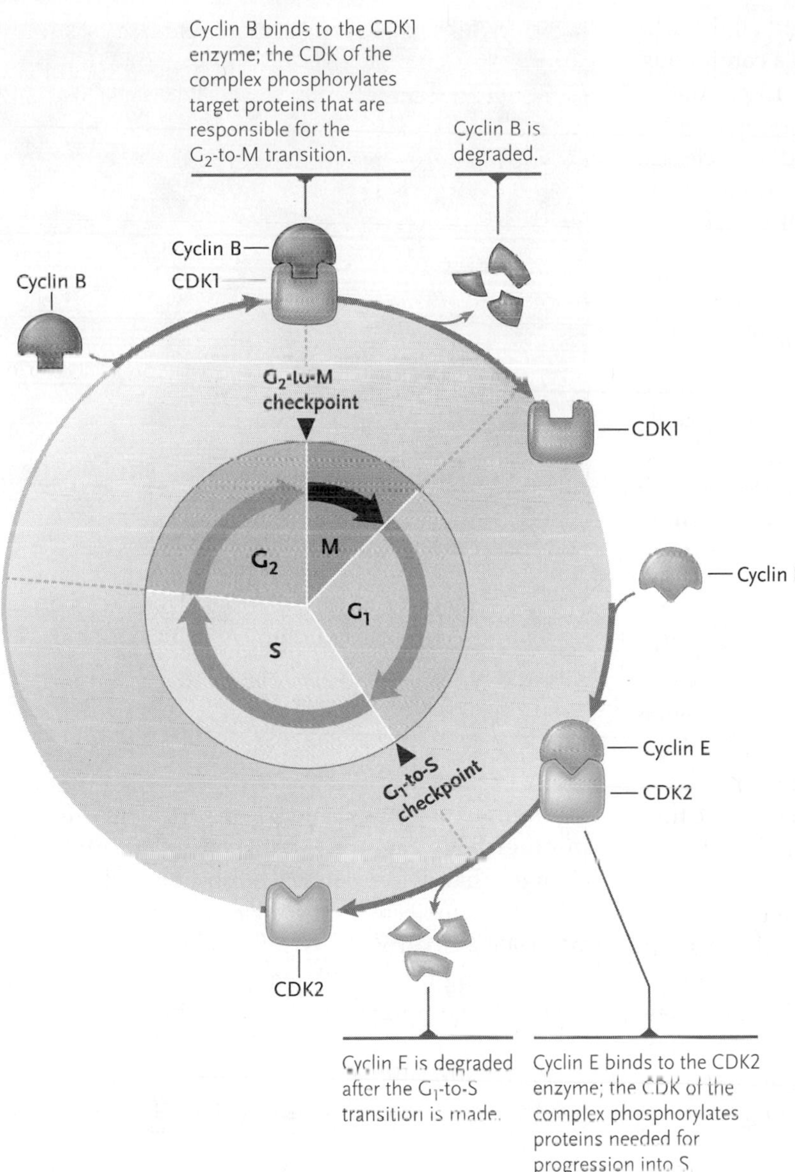
Cyclin B binds to the CDK1 enzyme; the CDK of the complex phosphorylates target proteins that are responsible for the G2-to-M transition.
Cyclin B is degraded.
Cyclin B
Cyclin B
CDK1
G2-to-M checkpoint
CDK1
M
G2
G1
S
Cyclin E
Cyclin E
CDK2
G1-to-S checkpoint
CDK2
Cyclin E is degraded after the G1-to-S transition is made.
Cyclin E binds to the CDK2 enzyme; the CDK of the complex phosphorylates proteins needed for progression into S.

Figure 9.17
Cyclin:CDK control of the G_1-to-S and G_2-to-M transitions of the cell cycle.

9.4b Internal Checkpoints Stop the Cell Cycle if Stages Are Incomplete

The cyclin:CDK combinations directly control the cell cycle, but other factors within the cell act as indirect controls by altering the activity of the cyclin:CDK complexes. At each key checkpoint, regulatory events block the cyclin:CDK complex from triggering the associated cell cycle transition until the actions of a previous phase are successfully completed. For example, the cyclin B:CDK1 complex stimulates the cell to enter the M phase out of the G_2 phase. However, until the cell is ready to enter mitosis, phosphorylation of a site on CDK1 keeps it inactive even though it is bound to cyclin B. When the cell is ready, a phosphatase removes the inhibitory phosphate, the CDK1 becomes active, and the cell is moved into mitosis.

Control at checkpoints is exerted in many types of circumstances. For instance, if some of the DNA remains unreplicated during the S phase, the cell slows its progress during the G_2 phase to allow more time for replication to be completed. Similarly, if radiation or chemicals damage DNA, inhibitory events prevent the onset of S phase to give the cell an opportunity to repair the damage.

9.4c External Controls Coordinate the Mitotic Cell Cycle of Individual Cells with the Overall Activities of the Organism

The internal controls that regulate the cell cycle are modified by signal molecules that originate from outside the dividing cells. In animals, these signal molecules include the peptide hormones and similar proteins called growth or death factors.

Many of these external factors bind to receptors at the cell surface, which respond by triggering reactions inside the cell. These reactions often include steps that add inhibiting or stimulating phosphate groups to the cyclin:CDK complexes, particularly to the CDKs. The reactions triggered by the activated receptor may also directly affect the same proteins regulated by the cyclin:CDK complexes. The overall effect is to speed, slow, or stop the progress of cell division, depending on the particular hormone or factor and the internal pathway that is stimulated. Some growth factors are even able to break the arrest of cells shunted into the G_0 stage and return them to active division. (Hormones, growth factors, and other signal molecules are part of the cell communication system, as discussed in Chapter 8.)

Cell-surface receptors in animal cells also recognize contact with other cells or with molecules of the extracellular matrix. The contact triggers internal reaction pathways that inhibit division by arresting the cell cycle, usually in the G_1 phase. The response, called **contact inhibition**, stabilizes cell growth in fully developed organs and tissues. As long as the cells of most tissues are in contact with one another or with the extracellular matrix, they are shunted into the G_0 phase and prevented from dividing. If the contacts are broken, the freed cells often enter rounds of division.

Contact inhibition is easily observed in cultured mammalian cells grown on a glass or plastic surface.

In such cultures, division proceeds until all the cells are in contact with their neighbours in a continuous, unbroken, single layer. At this point, division stops. If a researcher then scrapes some of the cells from the surface, cells at the edges of the "wound" are released from inhibition and divide until they form a continuous layer and all the cells are again in contact with their neighbours.

9.4d Cells Cannot Divide Indefinitely

In 1961, Leonard Hayflick and Paul Moorhead reported that normal human skin cells eventually stopped dividing when grown in artificial culture. This loss of proliferative ability over time is called **cellular senescence**, and scientists have been searching for the "Hayflick factors" that are responsible for it. We consider two candidates: DNA damage and telomere shortening.

The progressive accumulation of random damage to a cell's DNA sequence, or its chromosome structure, or even the genes coding for the enzyme machinery needed to repair such damage, is perhaps the most intuitive Hayflick factor. One would expect "older" cells to have diminished function if they have suffered mutations in genes controlling critical activities.

Telomeres are repetitive DNA sequences that are added to the ends of chromosomes by the enzyme telomerase. Since DNA replication machinery is unable to replicate the entire ends of linear chromosomes, telomere sequence is lost at each round of replication (see Figure 13.15). Once telomeres diminish to a certain minimum length, cells stop dividing (senesce) and may die.

You might wonder why we do not just take a pill to stimulate our telomerase, rejuvenate our cells, and extend our life span. It turns out that cellular senescence is an important anti-tumour mechanism. Some researchers have stimulated the telomerase of cultured cells: they become "immortal" and divide out of control. Mice that have been engineered to lack telomerase, and therefore suffer faster senescence, are significantly *resistant* to cancer. It seems that by the time cells are short on telomeres, many of them are also a long way toward cancerous growth, as described below.

9.4e Cell Cycle Controls Are Lost in Cancer

Cancer occurs when cells lose the normal controls that determine when and how often they will divide. Cancer cells divide continuously and uncontrollably, producing a rapidly growing mass called a tumour **(Figure 9.18)**. Cancer cells also typically lose their adhesions to other cells and often become actively mobile. As a result, in a process called metastasis, they tend to break loose from an original tumour, spread throughout the body, and grow into new tumours in other body regions. Metastasis is promoted by changes that defeat contact inhibition and alter the cell-surface molecules that link cells together or to the extracellular matrix.

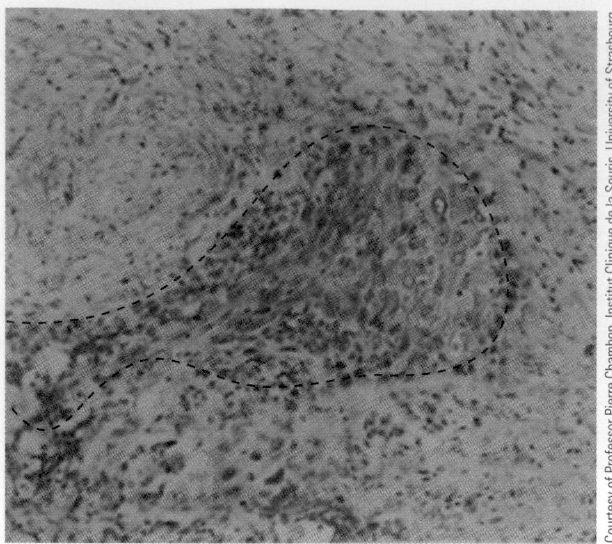

Figure 9.18
A mass of tumour cells (dashed line) embedded in normal tissue. As is typical, the tumour cells appear to be more densely packed because they have less cytoplasmic volume than normal cells. Original magnification ×270.

Growing tumours damage surrounding normal tissues by compressing them and interfering with blood supply and nerve function. Tumours may also break through barriers such as the outer skin, internal cell layers, or the gut wall. The breakthroughs cause bleeding, open the body to infection by microorganisms, and destroy the separation of body compartments necessary for normal function. Both compression and breakthroughs can cause pain that, in advanced cases, may become extreme. As tumours increase in mass, the actively growing and dividing cancer cells may deprive normal cells of their required nutrients, leading to generally impaired body functions, muscular weakness, fatigue, and weight loss.

Cancer cells have typically accumulated mutations in a variety of different genes that promote uncontrolled cell division or metastasis. Before they undergo mutation, many of these genes code for components of the cyclin:CDK system that regulates cell division; others encode proteins that regulate gene expression, form cell surface receptors, or make up elements of the signalling pathways controlled by the receptors. When mutated, the genes, called **oncogenes**, encode altered versions of these products.

For example, a mutation in a gene that codes for a surface receptor might result in a protein that is constantly active even without binding the intended extracellular signal molecule. As a result, the internal

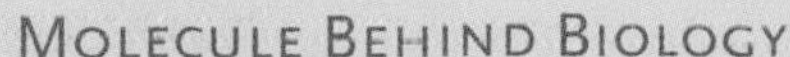

MOLECULE BEHIND BIOLOGY

Roscovitine

Screening of a wide variety of artificially modified adenine molecules has led to the discovery of a group of compounds related to plant cytokinin hormones that selectively inhibit cyclin-dependent kinases by competing for (and blocking) their ATP binding site. The example shown below, roscovitine, has antitumour and antiviral activity resulting from stimulation of apoptosis in affected cells. Note the adenine in each molecule (rectangle).

(a) Roscovitine. **(b)** The plant cytokinin hormone zeatin. **(c)** ATP.

reaction pathways triggered by the receptor, which induce cell division, are continually stimulated. Another mutation, this time in a cyclin gene, could result in increased cyclin:CDK binding that triggers DNA replication and the rest of the cell cycle. Cancer, oncogenes, and the alterations that convert normal genes to oncogenes are discussed in further detail in Chapter 15.

9.4f Some Cells Are Programmed to Die

Normal development of multicellular organisms is a highly regulated balance between cell proliferation and cell death. "Programmed cell death," called **apoptosis**, appears to be a very ancient mechanism common to all multicellular eukaryotes studied so far. Initiation of cell death can result from either internal or external signals. The nematode *Caenorhabditis elegans* is one useful model organism to study this signalling because all adult animals have exactly the same number of cells **(Figure 9.19a)**.

In addition, the fate of each of these cells, from the zygote to the adult, can be tracked with a light microscope. Detailed studies of the 1090 cells that are generated to form an adult reveal that 131 of them not only stop dividing—they stop living.

The apoptosis machinery in *C. elegans* is available in all its cells, waiting in an inactive state for the right trigger. The main "executioner" enzyme is one of a family of normally inactive proteases, called **caspases**, and is coded by the "cell death abnormal" gene, *ced-3* **(Figure 9.19b)**. If a cell is destined to die by apoptosis, the cascade begins when internal developmental cues stimulate expression of a gene called "egg laying deficient," *egl-1*. EGL-1 protein then binds to CED-9 protein, resulting in the release of bound CED-4 protein and the formation

Courtesy of Dr. Sydney Brenner

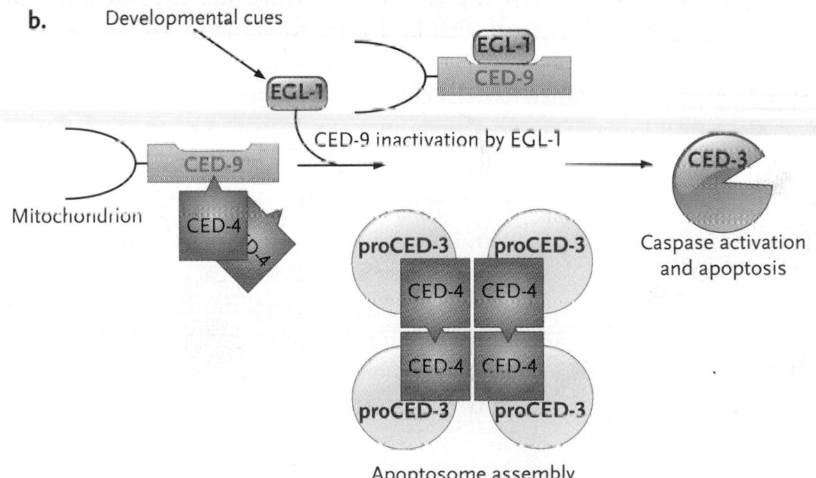

Figure 9.19
(a) The adult nematode "worm" *Caenorhabditis elegans* is about 1 mm long and is composed of 959 living cells. **(b)** The main cascade of programmed cell death in *C. elegans*. Cells destined to die express EGL-1 protein that, by binding to mitochondrial-bound CED-9, releases CED-4 protein. A complex of CED-4 then activates the main "executioner" caspase protease enzyme, CED-3.

of an active apoptosome. CED-3 caspase is thus activated, and cell death ensues. The causes of death are nuclear DNA degradation and disrupted mitochondrial function. The corpses of dead cells are engulfed and eaten by neighbouring cells. The 2002 Nobel Prize in Physiology or Medicine was awarded jointly to Sydney Brenner, Robert Horvitz, and John Sulston for their discoveries concerning "genetic regulation of organ development and programmed cell death" in *C. elegans*. The Experimental Research Organisms (see The Chemical and Physical Foundations of Biology pages) section describes *C. elegans* and its role in research in more detail.

Removing cells that are surplus for development is one function of apoptosis, but why are other cells programmed to die? We hope you will agree that it would be beneficial for an organism to provoke apoptosis in cells suffering severe DNA damage, viral infection, or mutations leading to uncontrolled division. Sometimes perfectly normal and healthy cells die by apoptosis. For instance, the cells that make up xylem elements in the vascular tissue of woody plants actually function as "skeletons." They must die to fulfill their function as hollow, water-conducting pipes.

The overview of the mitotic cell cycle and its regulation presented in this chapter only hints at the complexity of cell growth and division. The likelihood of any given cell dividing is determined by weighing a variety of internal signals in the context of external cues from the environment. If a cell is destined to divide, then the problem of accurately replicating and partitioning its DNA requires a highly regulated, intricately inter-related series of mechanisms. Although male Australian Jack Jumper ants (*Myrmecia pilosula*) have only one chromosome to deal with, think of the problems faced by the fern *Ophioglossum pycnostichum*, which has 1260 chromosomes in each cell!

Study Break

1. Explain how the *activity* of cyclin-dependent kinases can rise and fall with each "turn" of the cell cycle, whereas the *concentration* of these enzymes remains constant.
2. What observation do "Hayflick factors" explain?
3. What is metastasis?

9.5 Cell Division in Prokaryotes

Prokaryotes undergo a cycle of cytoplasmic growth, DNA replication, and cell division, producing two daughter cells from an original parent cell. The entire mechanism of prokaryotic cell division is called **binary fission**—that is, splitting or dividing into two parts. Although binary fission is regulated, the small size of prokaryotic cells makes it particularly difficult to discover just how the chromosomes move. Although actin-like proteins have been found in bacteria, their role in chromosome segregation remains unclear.

9.5a Replication Occupies Most of the Cell Cycle in Rapidly Dividing Prokaryotic Cells

All prokaryotes use DNA as their hereditary information. The vast majority of prokaryotic species have a single, circular DNA molecule known as the **bacterial chromosome** (**Figure 9.20,** step 1). When prokaryotic cells divide at the maximum rate, DNA replication occupies most of the period between cytoplasmic divisions. As soon as replication is complete, the cytoplasm divides to complete the cell cycle. For example, in populations of *E. coli* cells, which can double every 20 minutes, DNA replication occupies 19 minutes of the division cycle.

9.5b Replicated Chromosomes Are Distributed Actively to the Halves of the Prokaryotic Cell

In the 1960s, François Jacob of The Pasteur Institute, Paris, France, proposed a model for the segregation of bacterial chromosomes to the daughter cells in which the two chromosomes attach to the plasma membrane near the middle of the cell and separate as a new plasma membrane is added between the two sites during cell elongation. The essence of this model is that chromosome separation is passive. However, current research indicates that bacterial chromosomes rapidly separate in an active way that is linked to DNA replication events and is independent of cell elongation. The new model is shown in Figure 9.20.

Replication of the bacterial chromosome commences at a specific region called the **origin of replication** (ori). The ori is in the middle of the cell where the enzymes for DNA replication are located. Once the ori has been duplicated, the two origins migrate toward the two ends (poles) of the cell as replication continues for the rest of the chromosome. This active movement distributes the two replicated chromosomes to the two ends of the cell. How this movement occurs is unknown.

Next, cytoplasmic division in prokaryotes occurs through an inward growth of the plasma membrane, along which new cell wall material is assembled to cut the cell into two parts (see Figure 9.20, step 5). The new wall divides the two replicated DNA molecules

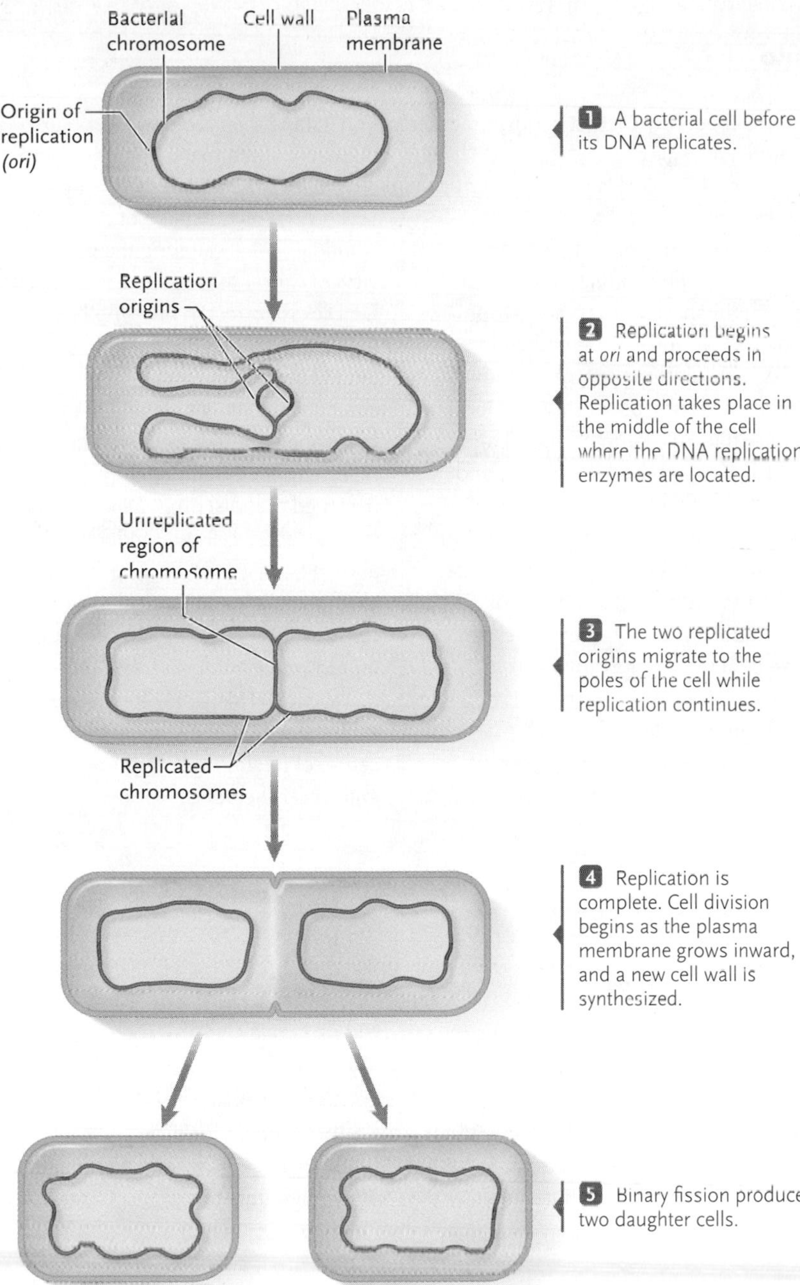

Bacterial chromosome
Cell wall
Plasma membrane
Origin of replication (ori)
1 A bacterial cell before its DNA replicates.
Replication origins
2 Replication begins at ori and proceeds in opposite directions. Replication takes place in the middle of the cell where the DNA replication enzymes are located.
Unreplicated region of chromosome
3 The two replicated origins migrate to the poles of the cell while replication continues.
Replicated chromosomes
4 Replication is complete. Cell division begins as the plasma membrane grows inward, and a new cell wall is synthesized.
5 Binary fission produces two daughter cells.

Figure 9.20
Model for the segregation of replicated bacterial chromosomes to daughter cells.

and the cytoplasmic structures and molecules equally between the daughter cells.

9.5c Mitosis Evolved from Binary Fission

The prokaryotic mechanism works effectively because most prokaryotic cells have only a single chromosome. Thus, if a daughter cell receives at least one copy of the chromosome, its genetic information is complete. By contrast, the genetic information of eukaryotes is divided among several chromosomes, with each chromosome containing a much greater length of DNA than a bacterial chromosome does. If a daughter cell fails to receive a copy of even one chromosome, the effects are usually lethal. The evolution of mitosis solved the mechanical problems associated with distributing long DNA molecules without breakage. Mitosis provided the level of precision required to ensure that each daughter cell receives a complete complement of chromosomes.

Scientists believe that the ancestral division process was binary fission and that mitosis evolved from that process. Variations in the mitotic apparatus in modern-day organisms illuminate possible intermediates in this evolutionary pathway. For example, in many primitive eukaryotes, such as dinoflagellates (a type of single-celled alga), the nuclear envelope remains intact during mitosis, and the chromosomes bind to the inner membrane of the nuclear membrane. When the nucleus divides, the chromosomes are segregated.

A more advanced form of the mitotic apparatus is seen in yeasts and diatoms (another type of single-celled alga). In these organisms, the mitotic spindle forms and chromosomes segregate to daughter nuclei without the disassembly and reassembly of the nuclear envelope. Currently, scientists think that the type of mitosis seen in yeasts and diatoms and the type of mitosis in animals and higher plants evolved separately from a common ancestral type. Mitotic cell division, the subject of this chapter, produces two cells that have the same genetic information as the parental cell entering division. In the next chapter, you will learn about meiosis, a specialized form of cell division that produces cells with half the number of chromosomes as the parent cells that enter into division.

Study Break

What are the three main steps in prokaryotic binary fission?

PEOPLE BEHIND BIOLOGY
Dr. John Dick, University of Toronto

One of the best places to find actively cycling cells in a vertebrate body is in bone marrow. It is here that hematopoietic stem cells divide to produce progeny cells capable of proliferating and differentiating into the various specialized cells needed to maintain the liquid tissue called blood.

One of the best places to try to understand this developmental process, as well as the mechanisms underlying human blood disorders and cancer (leukemia), is the laboratory of Dr. John Dick at the University of Toronto. Dr. Dick is a professor of medical genetics and microbiology, a fellow of the Royal Society of Canada, and Canada Research Chair in Stem Cell Biology. Originally from rural Manitoba, he now heads a team of coworkers and international collaborators from his office in the MaRS Discovery District in downtown Toronto.

One of Dr. Dick's most powerful tools, one that gained him international recognition, is his system for modelling the production of blood by establishing human hematopoietic cells in mice. That is, he creates mice that make human blood instead of their usual mouse blood. Mice that make human blood also show human blood disorders, and Dr. Dick's team has been able to study the initiation and progression of human leukemia entirely in mice. This mouse model system provides an opportunity to better understand the genetic changes involved in leukemia and the effectiveness of emerging therapies.

Dr. Dick's sustained success arises from his ability to locate stem cells and understand their biology. His original discovery of the role of aberrant stem cells at the root of leukemia is now seen as the opening line of a story that is fundamentally altering the prevailing view of cancer and its treatment. If Dr. Dick is correct in his hypothesis that many cancers are initiated and fed by the progeny of relatively slow cycling, genetically aberrant, stem cells (as is suggested by a growing body of research), then traditional therapies designed to indiscriminately kill rapidly cycling cancer cells are understandably "hit and miss." Dr. Dick has been able to identify and sort colon cancer cells into two fractions: those that can reproduce new tumours and those that cannot. This ability to specifically target cancer stem cells will be at the centre of the future development of anticancer therapies.

UNANSWERED QUESTIONS

This chapter has indicated that complex, interacting molecular networks within cells fine-tune the division of each cell in both unicellular and multicellular organisms. Identifying the genes and proteins involved in these networks is crucial both for a complete understanding of cell growth and division and for developing models for diseases caused by cell cycle defects. For example, zebrafish can regenerate damaged heart tissue, but humans cannot. Why might this be?

Review

Go to CENGAGENOW™ at http://hed.nelson.com/ to access quizzing, animations, exercises, articles, and personalized homework help.

9.1 The Cycle of Cell Growth and Division: An Overview

- In mitotic cell division, DNA replication is followed by the equal separation—that is, segregation—of the replicated DNA molecules and their delivery to daughter cells. The process ensures that the two cell products of a division have the same genetic information as the parent cell entering division.
- Mitosis is the basis for growth and maintenance of body mass in multicelled eukaryotes and for the reproduction of many single-celled eukaryotes.
- The chromosomes of eukaryotic cells are individual, linear DNA molecules with associated proteins.
- DNA replication and the duplication of chromosomal proteins convert each chromosome into a structure composed of two exact copies known as sister chromatids.

9.2 The Mitotic Cell Cycle

- Mitosis and interphase constitute the mitotic cell cycle. Mitosis occurs in five stages. In prophase (stage 1), the chromosomes condense into short rods and the spindle forms in the cytoplasm (see Figures 9.4 and 9.6).

- In prometaphase (stage 2), the nuclear envelope breaks down, the spindle enters the former nuclear area, and the sister chromatids of each chromosome make connections to opposite spindle poles. Each chromatid has a kinetochore that attaches to spindle microtubules (see Figures 9.4 and 9.8).
- In metaphase (stage 3), the spindle is fully formed and the chromosomes, moved by the spindle microtubules, become aligned at the metaphase plate (see Figure 9.4).
- In anaphase (stage 4), the spindle separates the sister chromatids and moves them to opposite spindle poles. At this point, chromosome segregation is complete (see Figures 9.4 and 9.6).
- In telophase (stage 5), the chromosomes decondense and return to the extended state typical of interphase. A new nuclear envelope forms around the chromosomes (see Figures 9.4 and 9.6).
- Cytokinesis, the division of the cytoplasm, completes cell division by producing two daughter cells, each containing a daughter nucleus produced by mitosis (see Figures 9.4 and 9.6).
- Cytokinesis in animal cells proceeds by furrowing, in which a band of microfilaments just under the plasma membrane contracts, gradually separating the cytoplasm into two parts (see Figure 9.10).
- In plant cytokinesis, cell wall material is deposited along the plane of the former spindle midpoint; the deposition continues until a continuous new wall, the cell plate, separates the daughter cells (see Figure 9.11)

9.3 Formation and Action of the Mitotic Spindle

- In animal cells, the centrosome divides and the two parts move apart. As they do so, the microtubules of the spindle form between them. In plant cells with no centrosome, the spindle microtubules assemble around the nucleus (see Figure 9.12).
- In the spindle, kinetochore microtubules run from the poles to the kinetochores of the chromosomes, and nonkinetochore microtubules run from the poles to a zone of overlap at the spindle midpoint without connecting to the chromosomes (see Figure 9.14).
- During anaphase, the kinetochores move along the kinetochore microtubules, pulling the chromosomes to the poles. The nonkinetochore microtubules slide over each other, pushing the poles farther apart (see Figures 9.14 and 9.15).

9.4 Cell Cycle Regulation

- The cell cycle is controlled directly by complexes of cyclins and a cyclin-dependent protein kinase (CDK). A CDK is activated when combined with a cyclin and then adds phosphate groups to target proteins, activating them. The activated proteins trigger the cell to progress to the next cell cycle stage. Each major stage of the cell cycle begins with activation of one or more cyclin:CDK complexes and ends with deactivation of the complexes by breakdown of the cyclins (see Figure 9.17).
- Important internal controls create checkpoints to ensure that the reactions of one stage are complete before the cycle proceeds to the next stage.
- External controls are based primarily on surface receptors that recognize and bind signals such as peptide hormones and growth factors, surface groups on other cells, or molecules of the extracellular matrix. The binding triggers internal reactions that speed, slow, or stop cell division.
- Most cells in multicellular eukaryotes progressively lose the ability to divide over time by a process called cellular senescence. Factors that contribute to senescence include accumulating DNA damage and shortening telomeres.
- In cancer, control of cell division is lost and cells divide continuously and uncontrollably, forming a rapidly growing mass of cells that interferes with body functions. Cancer cells also break loose from their original tumour (metastasize) to form additional tumours in other parts of the body.
- Certain cells may undergo programmed cell death called apoptosis. Such a fate would be appropriate for cells that are, for instance, surplus for development, damaged, infected, or functional only after death.

9.5 Cell Division in Prokaryotes

- Replication of the bacterial chromosome begins at a site called the "origin" through reactions catalyzed by enzymes located in the middle of the cell. Once the origin of replication is duplicated, the two origins migrate to the two ends of the cells. Division of the cytoplasm then occurs through a partition of cell wall material that grows inward until the cell is separated into two parts (see Figure 9.20).

Questions

Self-Test Questions

1. During the cell cycle, the DNA mass of a cell
   a. decreases during G_1 phase.
   b. decreases during metaphase.
   c. increases during the S phase.
   d. increases during G_2.
   e. decreases during interphase.
2. Imagine that you are in a job interview for a pharmaceutical company and are asked to suggest a good target for an anticancer drug. You should suggest a drug whose action results in
   a. decreased apoptosis.
   b. decreased binding of cyclin to CDK.
   c. increased CDK activity.
   d. increased telomerase.
   e. decreased caspase.
3. Honeybee eggs that are not fertilized develop into fertile, haploid males called "drones." Fertilized eggs can develop into diploid females, one of which might become a "queen." (Fertilized eggs might also become males, but they are taken out and killed by the drones.)

If the queen has 32 chromosomes in her body cells, how many chromatids would be present in a G_2 drone cell?
a. 8.
b. 16.
c. 24.
d. 32.
e. 64.

4. The major microtubule organizing centre of the animal cell is
a. chromosomes, composed of chromatids.
b. the centrosome, composed of centrioles.
c. the chromatin, composed of chromatids.
d. chromosomes, composed of centromere.
e. centrioles, composed of centrosome.

5. For a given cell, the number of _______ is *higher* at the end of S phase than at the beginning.
a. nuclei.
b. chromatids.
c. chromosomes.
d. CDK2 molecules.
e. Both b and c are correct.

6. Which of the following statements about mitosis is *incorrect*?
a. Microtubules can bind to kinetochores and interact with other microtubules from opposite poles.
b. In anaphase, the spindle separates sister chromatids and pulls them apart.
c. Chromosomes congregate near the centre of the cell during metaphase.
d. Cytokinesis describes the movement of chromosomes.
e. Both the animal cell furrow and the plant cell plate form at their former spindle midpoints.

7. Mitomycin C is an anticancer drug that stops cell division by inserting itself between the strands of DNA and binding them together. You would predict this drug to have its major effect at
a. late G_1 phase, early S phases.
b. late G_2 phase.
c. prophase.
d. metaphase.
e. anaphase.

8. Which of the following statements about cell cycle regulation is *incorrect*?
a. Cyclin is synthesized during the S phase.
b. Caspase is activated by cyclin binding.
c. CDKs combine with cyclin to phosphorylate target proteins.
d. Telomere shortening stops cell cycling.
e. Stem cells divide more often than other somatic cells.

9. Which of the following is *not* characteristic of cancer cells?
a. metastasis.
b. contact inhibition.
c. avoidance of "Hayflick" factors.
d. oncogene overactivation of cyclin.
e. extra growth factor receptors.

10. In bacteria,
a. several chromosomes undergo mitosis.
b. binary fission produces four daughter cells.
c. replication begins at the ori and the DNA strand separates.
d. replication occurs in the same direction off each opposite strand.
e. the daughter cells receive different genetic information from the parent cell.

Questions for Discussion

1. You have a means of measuring the amount of DNA in a single cell. You first measure the amount of DNA during G_1. At what point(s) during the remainder of the cell cycle would you expect the amount of DNA per cell to change?
2. A cell has 38 chromosomes. After mitosis and cell division, 1 daughter cell has 39 chromosomes and the other has 37. What might have caused these abnormal chromosome numbers? What effects do you suppose this might have on cell function? Why?
3. Taxol (Bristol-Myers Squibb, New York), a substance derived from the Pacific yew (*Taxus brevifolia*), is effective in the treatment of breast and ovarian cancers. It works by stabilizing microtubules, thereby preventing them from disassembling. Why would this activity slow or stop the growth of cancer cells?
4. Many chemicals in the food we eat potentially have effects on cancer cells. Chocolate, for example, contains a number of flavonoid compounds, which act as natural antioxidants. Design an experiment to determine whether any of the flavonoids in chocolate inhibit the cell cycle of breast cancer cells growing in culture.
5. The genes and proteins involved in cell cycle regulation are very different in prokaryotes and eukaryotes. However, both types of organisms use similar molecular regulatory reactions to coordinate DNA synthesis with cell division. What does this observation mean from an evolutionary perspective?

Mating octopus.

10 Genetic Recombination

Study Plan

Why It Matters

A couple clearly shows mutual interest. First, he caresses her with one arm, then another—then another, another, and another. She reciprocates. This interaction goes on for hours—a hug here, a squeeze there. At the climactic moment, the male reaches deftly under his mantle and removes a packet of sperm, which he inserts under the mantle of the female. For every one of his sperm that successfully performs its function, a fertilized egg can develop into a new octopus.

For the octopus, sex is an occasional event, preceded by a courtship ritual that involves intermingled tentacles. For another marine animal, the slipper limpet, sex is a lifelong group activity. Slipper limpets are relatives of snails. Like many other animals, a slipper limpet passes through a free-living immature stage before it becomes a sexually mature adult. When the time comes for an immature limpet to transform into an adult, it settles onto a rock or other firm surface. If the limpet settles by itself, it develops into a female. If instead it settles on top of a female, it develops into a male. If another slipper limpet settles down on that male, it, too, becomes a male. Adult slipper limpets almost always live in such piles, with the one on the bottom always being a female. All the male limpets continually contribute sperm that fertilize eggs shed by the female. If the one female dies, the surviving male at the bottom of the pile changes into a female and reproduction continues.

The life history of these octopuses and slipper limpets illustrates a tension in biology between sameness and difference. On the one hand, the growth and repair of their multicellular tissues depend on faithful replication of deoxyribonucleic acid (DNA) during mitotic cell division, as described in the previous chapter. At the level of the organism, it is important that all the individual cells in the body of a slipper limpet, for example, are genetically identical. However, on the other hand, at the level of the population, it is important that the individual limpets are genetically *different*. Evolutionary changes in populations arise from natural selection of particular individuals over others in each generation. Populations must have heritable genetic diversity if they are to evolve.

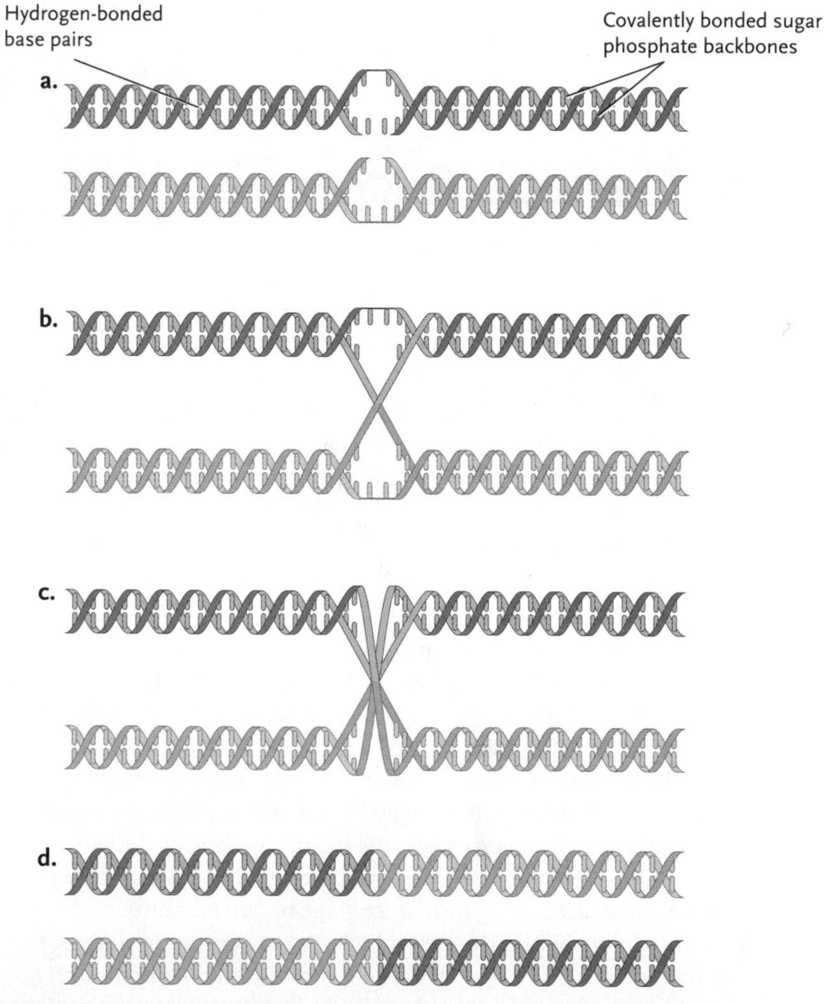

Hydrogen-bonded base pairs

Covalently bonded sugar phosphate backbones

a.

b.

c.

d.

Figure 10.1
A simplified model of genetic recombination. **(a)** Two molecules of DNA with similar sequence are brought into close proximity. **(b)** Enzymes nick the DNA backbones, exchange the ends, and reattach them. **(c and d)** In this case, the final result is two recombined DNA molecules.

The ultimate source of genetic diversity is mutation of the DNA sequence, often resulting from errors during DNA replication. Since mutations are relatively rare, diversity is amplified through various mechanisms that shuffle existing mutations into different combinations. This process, of literally cutting and pasting DNA backbones into new combinations, is called genetic recombination and is very widespread in nature. Genetic recombination allows "jumping genes" to move, inserts some viruses into the chromosome of their hosts, underlies the spread of antibiotic resistance among bacteria, and is at the heart of meiosis in eukaryotes. Genetic recombination puts the "sexual" in sexual reproduction; without genetic recombination, reproduction is "asexual," and offspring are simply identical clones of their parent. We begin this chapter with a look at the basic mechanism of DNA recombination.

10.1 Mechanism of Genetic Recombination

Biologists who study genetic recombination have developed several models to explain precisely how the process proceeds in various situations. In its most general sense, genetic recombination requires the following: two DNA molecules that differ from one another in at least two places, a mechanism for bringing the DNA molecules into close proximity, and a collection of enzymes to "cut," "exchange," and "paste" the DNA back together. **Figure 10.1** conveys a very simple model for recombination that, although lacking the details of more sophisticated models, highlights the basic steps involved.

The elegant double helix of DNA represented in Figure 10.1 is one of the most widely recognized biological molecules, and we expect that you can discern the "backbone" of the helix winding around the interior "steps" of paired bases. The sugar–phosphate backbone is held together by strong covalent bonds, whereas the bases pair with their partners through relatively weak hydrogen bonds. (If these ideas are new to you, see Chapter 13 for a more comprehensive look at DNA structure.) Figure 10.1a shows two similar double helixes lying close together as the first step in recombination. Most of the recombination discussed in this chapter occurs between regions of DNA that are very similar, but not identical, in the sequence of bases. Such regions, which may be as short as a few base pairs or as long as an entire chromosome, are called **homologous.** Homology allows different DNA molecules to line up and recombine precisely. Once homologous regions of DNA are paired, enzymes break a covalent bond in each of the four sugar–phosphate backbones. The free ends of each backbone are then exchanged and reattached to those of the other DNA molecule, as shown in Figure 10.1b and c.

The final result is two recombined molecules in which the originally red DNA is now covalently bound to blue DNA, and vice versa. In this chapter, we consider all the steps shown in Figure 10.1 to comprise a single recombination event. This idea is worth restating: cutting and pasting *four* DNA backbones results in *one* recombination event.

As we move through diverse examples of recombination in this chapter, from plasmids to meiotic crossing-over, to transposons, the characteristics of the participating DNA molecules will be different, the enzymes will change, and the results of recombination will have quite different consequences for the organism in question. However, you can always return to Figure 10.1 to remind yourself of the basic underlying mechanism.

Study Break

What would happen if two circular DNA molecules were involved in a single recombination event?

10.2 Genetic Recombination in Bacteria

Genetic recombination was historically first associated with meiosis in sexually reproducing eukaryotes. Genetic and microscopic research in the early decades of the twentieth century characterized recombination and culminated in the construction of the first genetic maps of chromosomes. However, by the middle of that century, improved techniques for studying the genetics of bacteria and their viruses enabled researchers to look for evidence of genetic recombination even though prokaryotes do not reproduce sexually by meiosis. They found plenty, and we begin our discussion of recombination with a look at prokaryotes. The data showed that, for particular bacteria, there are mechanisms to bring DNA from different cells together and that this DNA recombines to create offspring that are different from either parent cell. Bacteria clearly have a type of sex in their lives. It may be surprising for you to learn that, in some types of bacterial recombination, one of the participating cells is dead. Watch for this.

Escherichia coli, the most extensively studied prokaryote, is named in honour of its discoverer, a Viennese pediatrician named Dr. Theodor Escherich, who isolated it from dirty diapers during an outbreak of diarrhea in 1885. Ready availability and ease of growth in the laboratory have made *E. coli* a workhorse of bacterial genetics that has helped lay the foundations for our understanding of the role of DNA as the genetic material, as well as the molecular structure, expression, and recombination of genes. (See more information about *E. coli* as a model research organism in *The Chemical and Physical Foundations of Biology* pages.)

10.2a Genetic Recombination Occurs in *E. coli*

In 1946, two scientists at Yale University, Joshua Lederberg and Edward L. Tatum, set out to determine if genetic recombination occurs in bacteria, using *E. coli* as their experimental organism. In essence, they were testing whether bacteria had a kind of sexuality in their reproduction process. In order to understand Lederberg and Tatum's work, you first need to know how bacteria are grown in the laboratory.

E. coli and many other bacteria can be grown in a **minimal medium** containing water, an organic carbon source such as glucose, and a selection of inorganic salts, including one, such as ammonium chloride, that provides nitrogen. The growth medium can be in liquid form or in the form of a gel made by adding agar to the liquid medium. (Agar is a polysaccharide material, indigestible by most bacteria, that is extracted from algae.) Since it is not practical to study a single bacterium for most experiments, researchers developed techniques for starting bacterial cultures from a single cell, generating cultures with a large number of genetically identical cells. Cultures of this type are called **clones.** To start bacterial clones, the scientist spreads a drop of a bacterial culture over a sterile agar gel in a culture dish. The culture is diluted enough to ensure that cells will be widely separated on the agar surface. Each cell divides many times to produce a clump of identical cells called a "colony." Cells can be removed from a colony and introduced into liquid media or spread on agar and grown in essentially any quantity.

Now, in order for Lederberg and Tatum to detect genetic recombination, they needed some sort of detectable differences that could be shown to occur in changing combinations. The difference that proved most useful was related to nutrition. Cells require various amino acids for synthesis of proteins. Strains that are able to synthesize the necessary amino acids are called **prototrophs.** Mutant strains that are unable to synthesize amino acids are called **auxotrophs**; they can grow only if the required amino acid is provided for them in the growth medium. A strain that cannot manufacture its own arginine is represented by the genetic shorthand arg^-. In this shorthand, arg refers to the gene that governs a cell's ability to synthesize arginine from simple inorganic molecules. A given strain of bacteria might carry this gene in its normal form, arg^+, or its mutant form, arg^-. These alternative forms of the gene are called alleles and might differ by as little as one base pair in their respective DNA sequence. Prokaryotes typically have one circular chromosome that carries one particular allele for each of their genes.

Using mutagens such as X-rays or ultraviolet light, Lederberg and Tatum isolated two different strains of *E. coli* carrying distinctive combinations of alleles for various metabolic genes. See **Figure 10.2 (p. 202)** to understand how these auxotrophic strains could

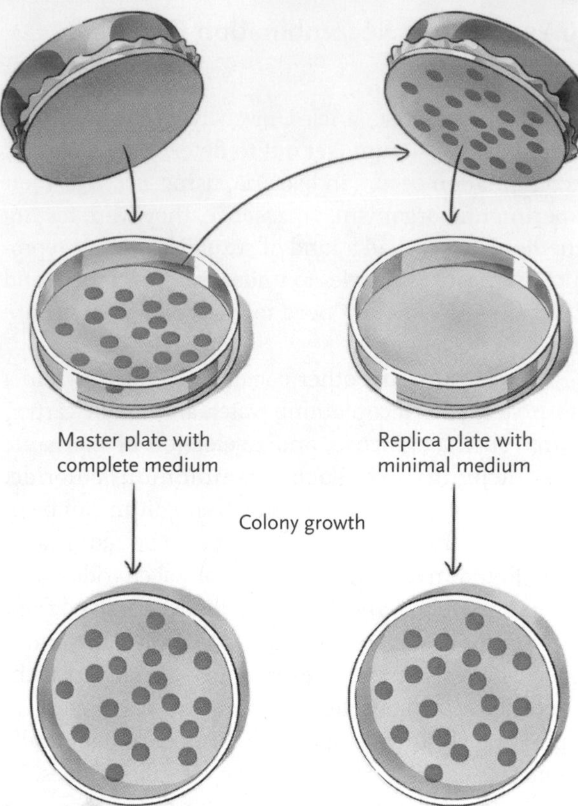

Figure 10.2
Replica plating transfers cells from complete media to minimal media where auxotrophs fail to grow.

be isolated by replica plating. One particular strain could grow only if the vitamin biotin and the amino acid methionine were added to the culture medium. A second mutant strain did not need biotin or methionine but could grow only if the amino acids leucine and threonine were added along with the vitamin thiamine. These two multiple-mutant strains of *E. coli* were represented in genetic notation as

$$\text{bio}^- \ \text{met}^- \ \text{leu}^+ \ \text{thr}^+ \ \text{thi}^+$$

Strain 1

$$\text{bio}^+ \ \text{met}^+ \ \text{leu}^- \ \text{thr}^- \ \text{thi}^-$$

Strain 2

Lederberg and Tatum mixed about 100 million cells of the two mutant strains together and placed them on a minimal medium **(Figure 10.3).** Several hundred colonies grew even though, individually, none of the original cells carried all of the normal alleles needed for growth. You might be thinking, "They are mutants. Maybe some of the originally mutated alleles went back to normal." This possibility was easily discounted by plating large numbers of cells from each original strain onto minimal medium separately. If mutation was responsible for the initial results with mixed cultures, then colonies should also appear when strains were plated separately. There were none. Some form of recombination between the DNA molecules of the two parental types must have produced the necessary combination with normal alleles for each of the five genes:

$$\text{bio}^+ \ \text{met}^+ \ \text{leu}^+ \ \text{thr}^+ \ \text{thi}^+$$

10.2b Bacterial Conjugation Brings DNA of Two Cells into Close Proximity

How was DNA from two different bacterial cells able to recombine? We will see in Section 10.3 that genetic recombination in eukaryotes occurs in diploid cells by an exchange of segments between pairs of chromosomes. However, bacteria are haploid organisms; each cell typically has its own single, circular

Figure 10.3
Experimental evidence for genetic recombination in bacteria.

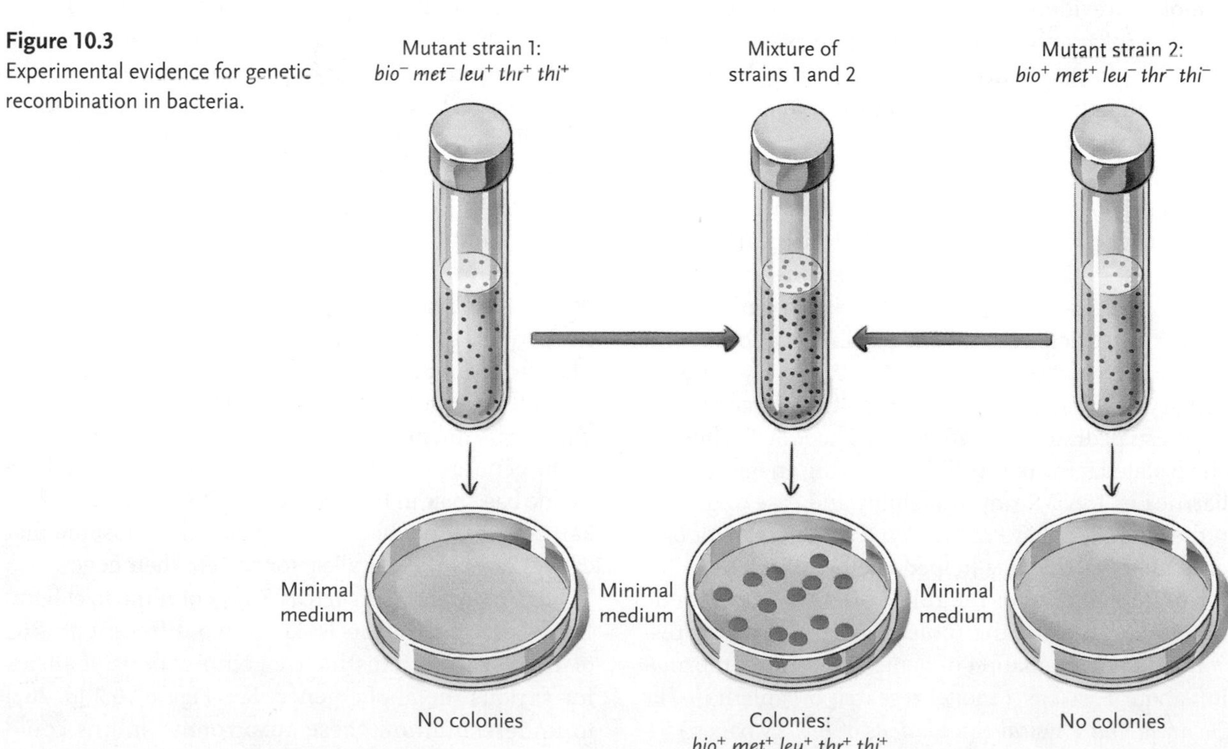

chromosome. So where do the "pairs" of chromosomes come from in bacteria? Although bacterial cells were first thought to bring their DNA together by fusing, it was later established that transfer of genetic information is unidirectional, from one cell to the other. Instead of fusing, bacterial cells *conjugate*. That is, cells contact each other by a long tubular structure called a *sex pilus* and then form a cytoplasmic bridge **(Figure 10.4a, b)**. During **conjugation**, a copy of part of the DNA of one cell moves through the cytoplasmic bridge into the other cell. Once DNA from one cell enters the other, genetic recombination can occur. Through this unidirectional transfer of a part of the chromosome, bacterial conjugation thus facilitates a kind of sexual reproduction in prokaryotes.

The F Factor and Conjugation. Conjugation is initiated by a bacterial cell that contains a small circle of DNA in addition to the main circular chromosomal DNA **(Figures 10.5 and 10.6, p. 204)**. Such small circles are called plasmids, and this particular one is known as the "fertility" plasmid or "the F factor." Like all plasmids, the F factor carries several genes as well as a replication origin that permits a copy to be passed on to each daughter cell during the usual process of bacterial cell division. This is an example of "vertical" inheritance from one generation to the next that you are familiar with. However, during conjugation, the

a. Attachment by sex pilus

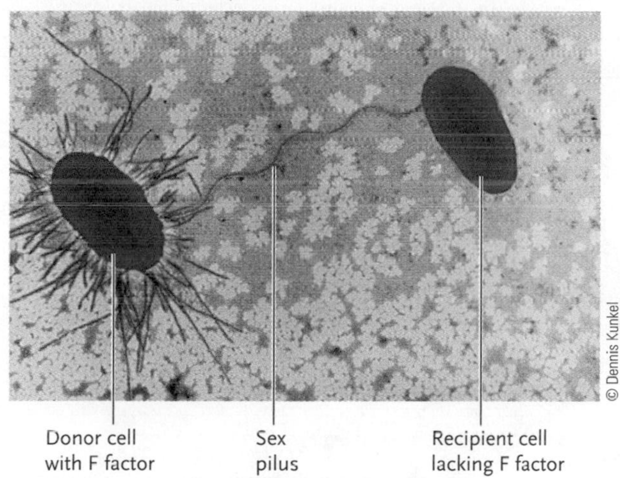

b. Cytoplasmic bridge formed

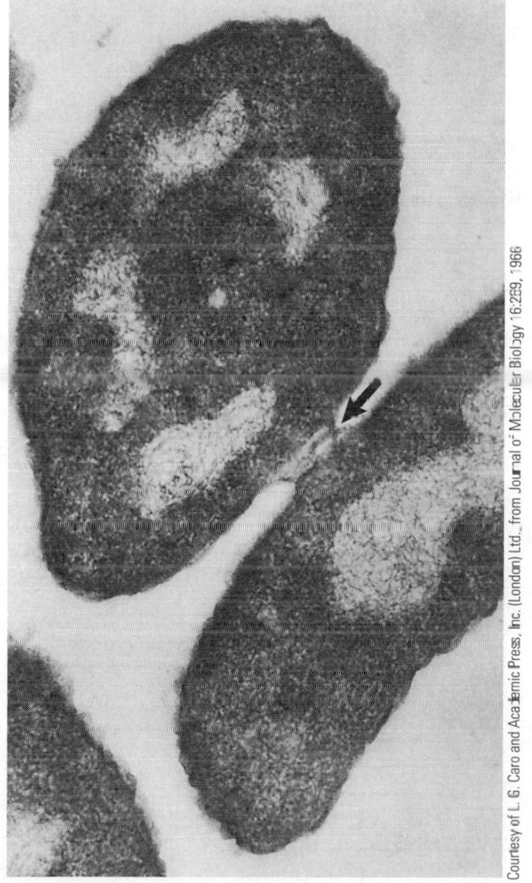

Courtesy of L. G. Caro and Academic Press, Inc. (London) Ltd., from Journal of Molecular Biology 16:269, 1966

Figure 10.4
Conjugating *E. coli* cells. **(a)** Initial attachment of two cells by the sex pilus. **(b)** A cytoplasmic bridge (arrow) has formed between the cells, through which DNA moves from one cell to the other.

a. Bacterial DNA released from cell

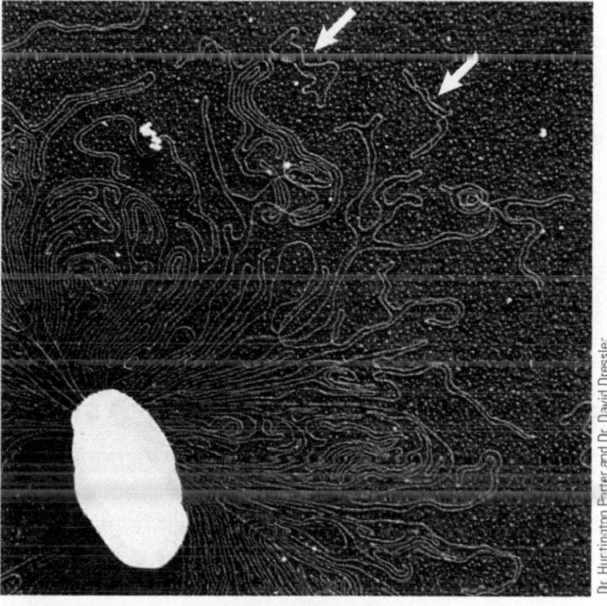

b. Plasmid

Figure 10.5
Electron micrographs of DNA released from a disrupted bacterial cell. **(a)** Plasmids (arrows) near the mass of chromosomal DNA. **(b)** A single plasmid at higher magnification (colourized).

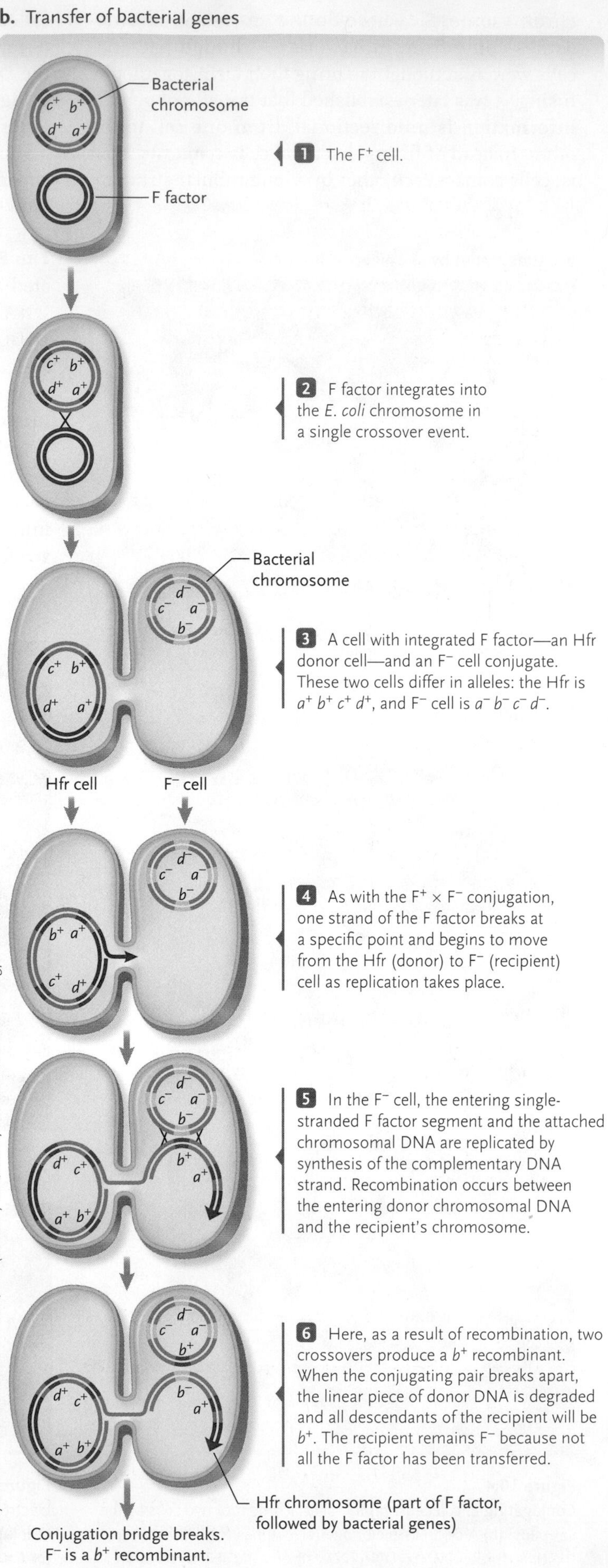

a. Transfer of the F factor
Bacterial chromosome
F factor
1 An F⁺ cell conjugates with an F⁻ cell.
F⁺ cell
F⁻ cell
2 One strand of the F factor breaks at a specific point and begins to move from F⁺ (donor) to F⁻ (recipient) cell as the F factor replicates.
3 DNA replication of the F factor continues in the donor cell, and a complementary strand to the strand entering the recipient cell begins to be synthesized.
4 When transfer of the F factor is complete, replication has produced a copy of the F factor in both the donor and recipient cells; the recipient has become an F⁺. No chromosomal DNA is transferred in this mating.
F⁺ cell
F⁺ cell

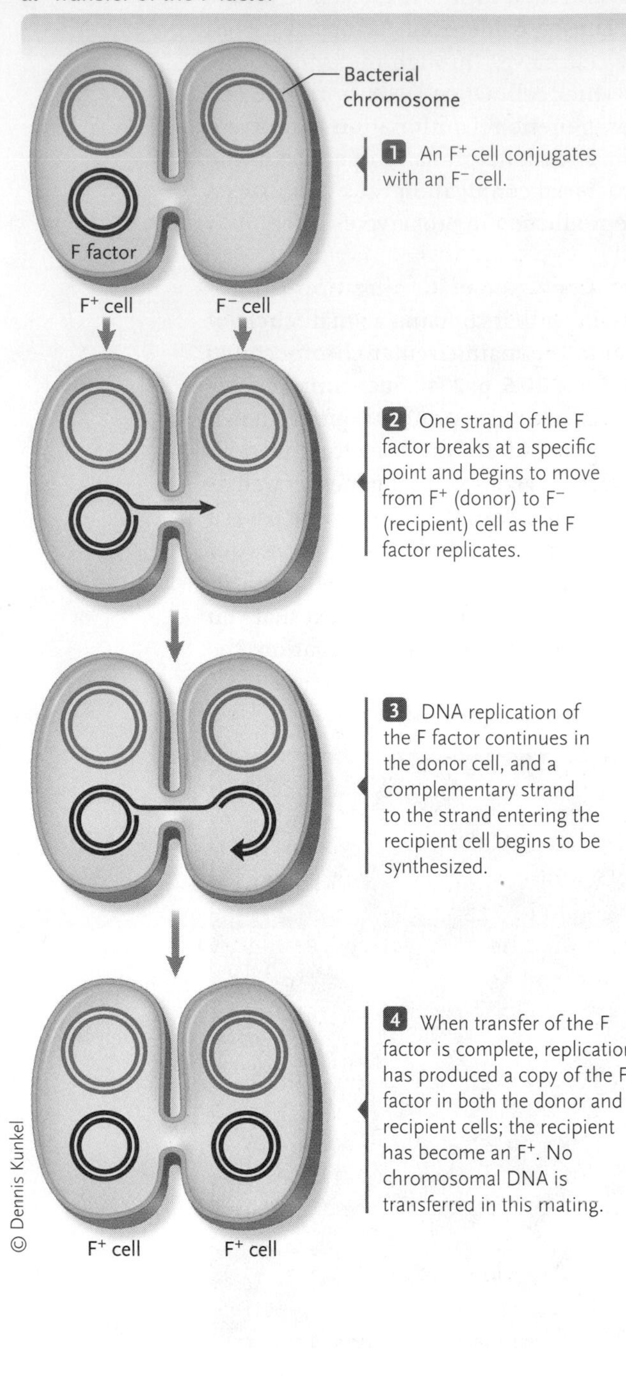

b. Transfer of bacterial genes
Bacterial chromosome
F factor
1 The F⁺ cell.
2 F factor integrates into the *E. coli* chromosome in a single crossover event.
Bacterial chromosome
3 A cell with integrated F factor—an Hfr donor cell—and an F⁻ cell conjugate. These two cells differ in alleles: the Hfr is *a*⁺ *b*⁺ *c*⁺ *d*⁺, and F⁻ cell is *a*⁻ *b*⁻ *c*⁻ *d*⁻.
Hfr cell
F⁻ cell
4 As with the F⁺ × F⁻ conjugation, one strand of the F factor breaks at a specific point and begins to move from the Hfr (donor) to F⁻ (recipient) cell as replication takes place.
5 In the F⁻ cell, the entering single-stranded F factor segment and the attached chromosomal DNA are replicated by synthesis of the complementary DNA strand. Recombination occurs between the entering donor chromosomal DNA and the recipient's chromosome.
6 Here, as a result of recombination, two crossovers produce a *b*⁺ recombinant. When the conjugating pair breaks apart, the linear piece of donor DNA is degraded and all descendants of the recipient will be *b*⁺. The recipient remains F⁻ because not all the F factor has been transferred.
Hfr chromosome (part of F factor, followed by bacterial genes)
Conjugation bridge breaks. F⁻ is a *b*⁺ recombinant.

Figure 10.6
Transfer of genetic material during conjugation between *E. coli* cells. **(a)** Transfer of the F factor during conjugation between F^+ and F^- cells. **(b)** Transfer of bacterial genes and the production of recombinants during conjugation between Hfr and F^- cells.

F factor also has the ability to be copied and passed directly from one cell, called the donor, to another, called the recipient. This is an example of "horizontal" inheritance.

Donor cells are called **F$^+$ cells** because they contain the F factor. They are able to mate with recipient cells but not with other donor cells. Recipient calls lack the F factor and, hence, are called **F$^-$ cells.** The F factor carries about 20 or so genes. Several of them encode proteins of the **sex pilus,** also called the **F pilus** (plural pili) (see Figures 10.4 and 10.6a, step 1).

During conjugation, the F plasmid replicates using a special type of DNA replication called "rolling circle". To understand this mechanism, first picture a site, called the origin of transfer, on the F plasmid. Then imagine a break in just one strand of the double helix at this site. Now, with your imaginary fingers, gently pull the free end of the single strand of DNA away from the F factor, through the cytoplasmic bridge, and into the recipient cell. As the single strand is pulled, the remaining strand—still a circle—"rolls" like the spool on a tape dispenser. DNA synthesis fills in the complementary bases to ensure that the F factor is double-stranded in both the donor and the recipient cells. When the entire F factor strand has transferred and replicated, it circularizes again (see Figure 10.6a, step 4). It is important to understand that although the recipient cell becomes F$^+$, no chromosomal DNA is transferred between cells in this process. *That is, no genetic recombination occurs between the DNA of two different cells in such a mating.*

So why are we including F factor conjugation in this chapter if it does not recombine DNA of different cells? The answer lies in the Hfr cells described in the next section.

Hfr Cells and Genetic Recombination. In some F$^+$ cells, the F factor comes into close proximity with the main chromosome and, lining up in a short region of homology, suffers a recombination event. When two circular DNA molecules recombine, (by the mechanism shown in Figure 10.1) they simply fuse together into one larger circle. In this way, the F factor actually becomes a part of the main bacterial chromosome (see Figure 10.6b, step 2). These special donor cells are known as **Hfr cells** (Hfr = high frequency recombination). It is important not to be confused at this point; although a recombination event integrated the F factor into the host chromosome, this is recombination within one cell, not between the chromosomes of different cells. Hfr cells are called "high frequency recombination" because they can "export" copies of chromosomal genes to another cell, as described below.

When the F factor is integrated into the bacterial chromosome, its genes are still active. Therefore, these Hfr cells make sex pilli and can conjugate with an F$^-$ cell. Figure 10.6b, step 3, shows an Hfr × F$^-$ mating where the two cell types differ in alleles for the genes a, b, c, and d. Note that a segment of the F factor moves through the conjugation bridge into the recipient, bringing the single-stranded chromosomal DNA behind it (see Figure 10.6b, steps 4 and 5). This is, again, rolling circle replication in which both donor and recipient cells restore the DNA to double-strandedness. In this situation, the circle that rolls is the entire Hfr donor chromosome. Although DNA transfer often continues long enough for several genes to be transferred, the conjugation bridge between the mating cells soon breaks. It is rare for the entire donor chromosome to be transferred.

At this point, it is important for you to recall that when the F factor transfers by itself, as described in the previous section, the recipient cells often become F$^+$. However, in Hfr cells, the origin of transfer is near the middle of the integrated F factor. As a result, only half of the F factor DNA is transferred at the front of the chromosomal DNA. (Think of the engine of a train.) The other half of the F factor (the dining car at the end of the train) can follow only after the rest of the entire chromosome (see Figure 10.6b, steps 4 to 6). As a result, it is very unusual for a recipient cell to obtain the entire F factor and become Hfr as well. Most likely, the recipient cell will become a **partial diploid**; it will have two copies of only those genes that came through the conjugation bridge on the donor chromosomal DNA segment.

For our example, the recipient cell in Figure 10.6b, step 5, has become, for the moment, $a^+ b^+/a^- b^-$. Although the DNA carrying + alleles for genes a and b differs slightly from that carrying − alleles, these regions are homologous and can pair for recombination. In fact, Figure 10.6 shows two recombination events, one on either side of the b gene, resulting in the exchange of the donor allele with that of the recipient (see Figure 10.6b, step 5). As a result, the recipient cell has become an $a^- b^+$ recombinant. Since enzymes in the recipient cell degrade the linear Hfr chromosome soon after recombination occurs, any incoming alleles that are not recombined onto the chromosome are lost. Following recombination, the bacterial DNA replicates and the cell divides normally, producing a clone of cells with the new combination of alleles.

In other pairs in the mating population, recombination events at different locations would lead to different recombinant recipients; perhaps the *a* gene could recombine with the homologous recipient gene, or both *a* and *b* genes could recombine to give a^+b^+ recipients. The various genetic recombinants observed in the Lederberg and Tatum experiment described earlier were produced in this general way.

Mapping Genes by Conjugation. The use of conjugation for genetic mapping was discovered by two scientists, François Jacob (the same scientist who proposed the operon model for the regulation of gene expression in bacteria; see Section 14.1) and Elie L. Wollman, at the Pasteur Institute in Paris. They began their experiments by mating Hfr and F cells that differed in a number of alleles. At regular intervals after conjugation commenced, they removed some of the cells and agitated them in a blender to break apart mating pairs. They then cultured the separated cells and analyzed them for recombinants. They found that the longer they allowed cells to conjugate before separation, the greater the number of donor genes that entered the recipient and produced recombinants. By noting the order and time at which genes were transferred, Jacob and Wollman were able to map and assign the relative positions of several genes in the *E. coli* chromosome.

10.2c Transformation and Transduction Provide Additional Sources of DNA for Recombination

The discovery of conjugation and genetic recombination in *E. coli* showed that genetic recombination is not restricted to eukaryotes. Further discoveries demonstrated that DNA can transfer from one bacterial cell to another by two additional mechanisms, transformation and transduction. Like conjugation, these mechanisms transfer DNA in one direction and create partial diploids in which recombination can occur between alleles in the homologous DNA regions. Unlike conjugation, in which both donor and recipient cells are living, transformation and transduction enable recipient cells to recombine with DNA obtained from dead donors.

Transformation. In **transformation,** bacteria simply take up pieces of DNA that are released into the environment as other cells disintegrate. Fred Griffith, a medical officer in the British Ministry of Health, London, discovered this phenomenon in 1928 while trying to understand how bacteria cause pneumonia in mice. Cells of the virulent strains of *Streptococcus pneumoniae* were surrounded by a polysaccharide capsule, whereas the nonvirulent strains were not. Griffith found that a mixture of heat-killed virulent cells plus living nonvirulent cells still caused pneumonia. One interpretation of this observation was that the living nonvirulent cells had been transformed to virulence by something released from the dead cells. In 1944, Oswald Avery and his colleagues at New York University found that the substance derived from the killed virulent cells, the substance capable of transforming nonvirulent bacteria to the virulent form, was DNA (discussed in Section 13.1).

Subsequently, geneticists established that in the transformation of *Streptococcus*, the linear DNA fragments taken up from disrupted virulent cells recombine with the chromosomal DNA of the nonvirulent cells in much the same way as genetic recombination takes place in conjugation. In this case, the recombination introduces the normal allele for capsule formation into the DNA of the nonvirulent cells; expression of that normal allele generates a capsule around the cell and its descendants, making them virulent.

Only some species of bacteria can take up DNA from the surrounding medium by natural mechanisms, and *E. coli* is not one of them. Fortunately for molecular biologists, *E. coli* cells can be induced to take up DNA in the laboratory by a variety of artificial transformation techniques involving exposure to calcium ions and/or pulses of electric current. Artificial transformation is often used to insert recombinant DNA plasmids into *E. coli* cells as part of cloning or genetic engineering techniques. (DNA cloning and genetic engineering are discussed further in Chapter 16.)

Transduction. In **transduction,** DNA is transferred from donor to recipient cells inside the head of an infecting bacterial virus. The infection cycles of viruses that infect bacteria, called **bacteriophage** (or just phage), are described in Chapter 22. For the purposes of this chapter, the basic details of phage infection are shown in **Figures 10.7 and 10.8, p. 208**. In general, transduction begins when new phages assemble in an infected bacterial cell; they sometimes incorporate fragments of the host cell DNA along with, or instead of, the viral DNA. After the host cell is killed, the new phages that are released may then attach to another cell and inject the bacterial DNA (and the viral DNA if it is present) into that recipient cell. The introduction of this DNA, as in conjugation and transformation, makes the recipient cell a partial diploid and allows recombination to take place. Recipients are not killed because they have received bacterial DNA rather than infective viral DNA. Lederberg and his graduate student, Norton Zinder, then at the University of Wisconsin at Madison, discovered transduction in 1952 in experiments with the bacterium *Salmonella typhimurium* and phage P22. Lederberg received a Nobel Prize in 1958 for his discovery of conjugation and transduction in bacteria.

There are two different types of transduction, generalized and specialized, arising from the different infection cycles of the phage involved. **Generalized transduction,** in which all donor genes are equally likely to be transferred, is associated with some **virulent bacteriophages,** which kill their host cells during each cycle of infection (the **lytic cycle**). Notice in Figure 10.7 that, during infection by the virulent phage, the host bacterial chromosome is degraded to provide raw material for synthesis of new phage chromosomes. However, sometimes a fragment of host chromosome avoids degradation and is packed into the head of a new phage *by mistake*. This particular phage now contains a small random sample of bacterial genes *instead of* phage genes. When the host cell

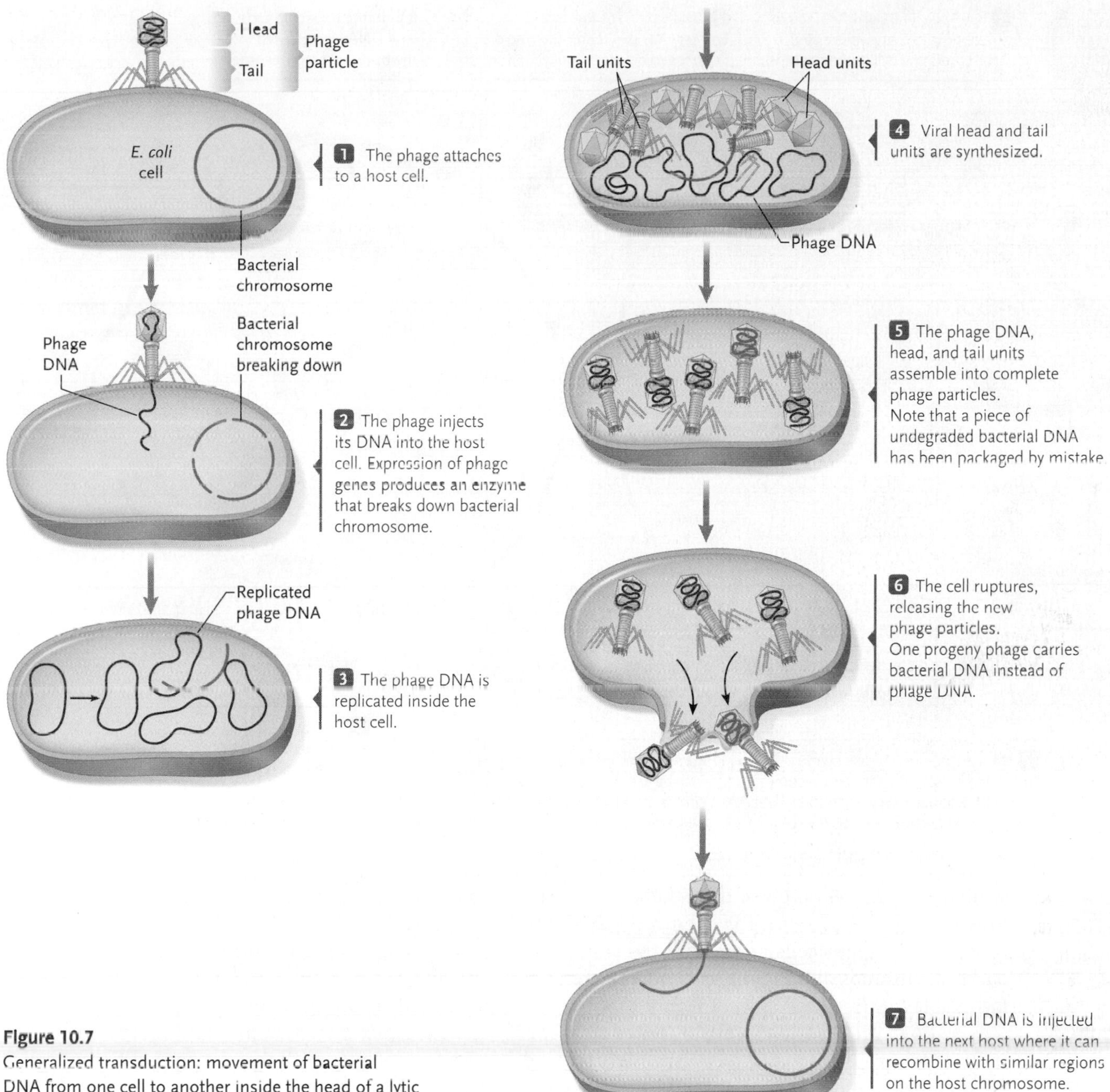

Head
Tail
Phage particle
E. coli cell
1 The phage attaches to a host cell.
Bacterial chromosome
Phage DNA
Bacterial chromosome breaking down
2 The phage injects its DNA into the host cell. Expression of phage genes produces an enzyme that breaks down bacterial chromosome.
Replicated phage DNA
3 The phage DNA is replicated inside the host cell.
Tail units
Head units
4 Viral head and tail units are synthesized.
Phage DNA
5 The phage DNA, head, and tail units assemble into complete phage particles.
Note that a piece of undegraded bacterial DNA has been packaged by mistake.
6 The cell ruptures, releasing the new phage particles.
One progeny phage carries bacterial DNA instead of phage DNA.
7 Bacterial DNA is injected into the next host where it can recombine with similar regions on the host chromosome.

Figure 10.7
Generalized transduction: movement of bacterial DNA from one cell to another inside the head of a lytic bacteriophage.

is burst to release the new phage, this "transducing phage" can mechanically infect a recipient cell. However, it will deliver a linear piece of DNA from the donor cell rather than an infectious phage chromosome. The newly infected (and incredibly lucky) recipient cell will survive; incoming DNA may then pair, and recombine, with homologous regions on the recipient chromosome.

One of the most extensively studied bacteriophages is phage lambda (λ), which infects *E. coli*. Again, a mistake in the infection cycle can result in the transfer of bacterial genes from a donor to a recipient cell. However, in this case, a different type of mistake, in a different infection cycle, gives rise to a different type of transduction: **specialized transduction** (shown in Figure 10.8). Lambda is a **temperate bacteriophage.** That is, when it first infects a new host, it determines whether the host is likely to be a good one. Is it starving? Is it suffering from DNA damage? If the host cell passes this molecular health checkup, then the lambda chromosome lines up with a small region of homology on the bacterial chromosome and a phage-coded enzyme catalyzes a single recombination event. The phage is thus integrated into the host chromosomal DNA and, in this state, is called a **prophage.** (Overall, this mechanism is very

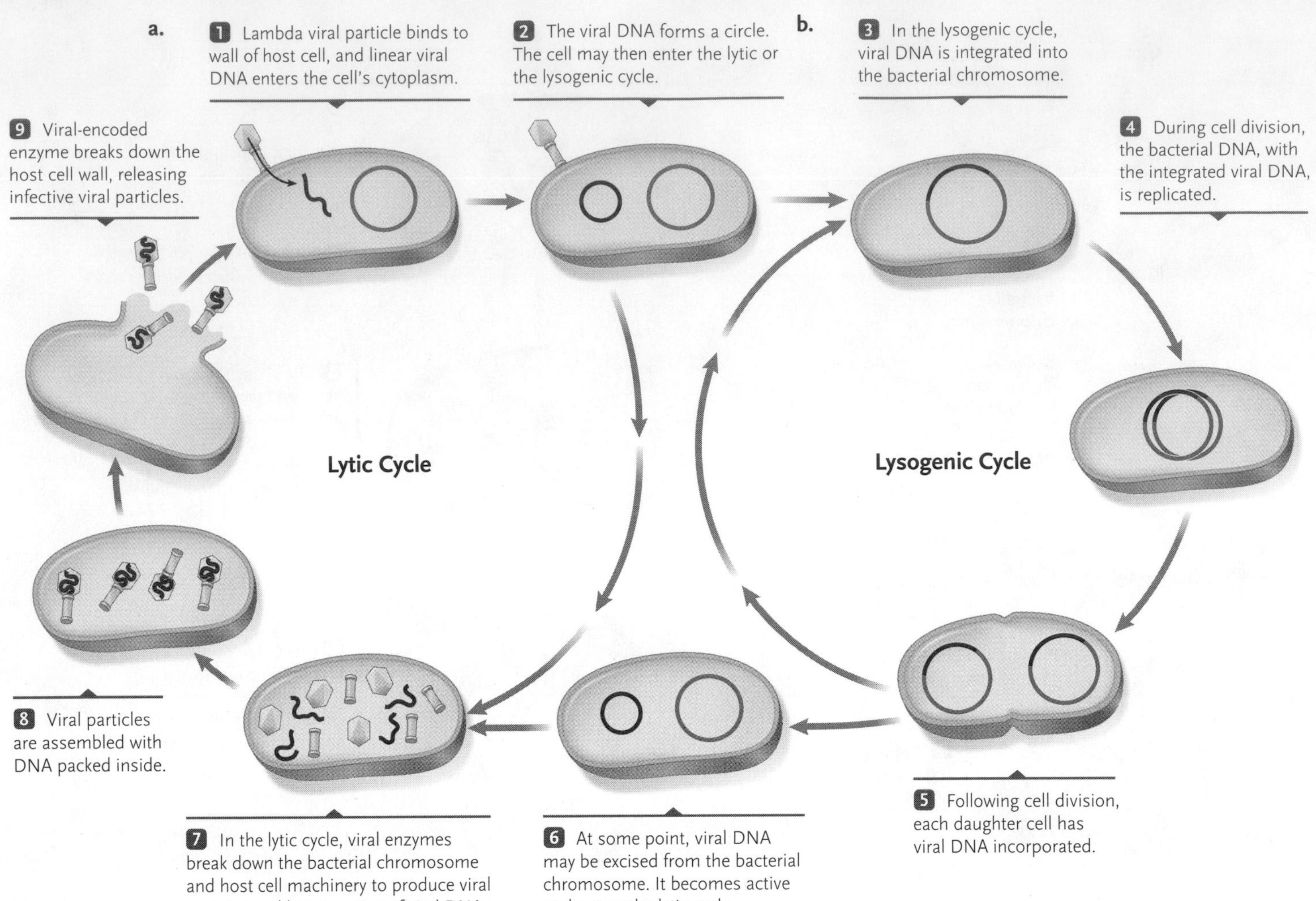

a.
1 Lambda viral particle binds to wall of host cell, and linear viral DNA enters the cell's cytoplasm.
2 The viral DNA forms a circle. The cell may then enter the lytic or the lysogenic cycle.
b.
3 In the lysogenic cycle, viral DNA is integrated into the bacterial chromosome.
4 During cell division, the bacterial DNA, with the integrated viral DNA, is replicated.
5 Following cell division, each daughter cell has viral DNA incorporated.
6 At some point, viral DNA may be excised from the bacterial chromosome. It becomes active and enters the lytic cycle.
7 In the lytic cycle, viral enzymes break down the bacterial chromosome and host cell machinery to produce viral proteins and linear copies of viral DNA.
8 Viral particles are assembled with DNA packed inside.
9 Viral-encoded enzyme breaks down the host cell wall, releasing infective viral particles.
Lytic Cycle
Lysogenic Cycle

Figure 10.8
The infective cycle of lambda, an example of a temperate phage, which can go through the lytic cycle **(a)** or the lysogenic cycle **(b)**.

similar to the integration of the F factor discussed previously.) The prophage is then replicated and passed to daughter cells along with the rest of the bacterial chromosome as long as conditions remain favourable (the **lysogenic cycle** in Figure 10.8).

If, however, the host cell becomes inhospitable (perhaps as a result of ultraviolet-induced DNA damage), the prophage activates several genes, releases itself from the chromosome by a recombination event, and proceeds to manufacture new phage, which are released as the cell bursts as a result of lytic growth.

In specialized transduction, the "mistake" occurs when the prophage is excised from the chromosome. Sometimes this recombination event is imprecise; bacterial DNA is removed from the host chromosome, and some prophage DNA is left behind. As a result, this bacterial DNA is packaged into new phage and carried to recipient cells. Since the transducing phage is defective, having left some of its genes behind in the host, it does not kill its new host. We hope that you can see that in the case of specialized transduction only bacterial genes that are close to the integration site of the phage will ever be incorporated into the phage chromosome by the recombination mistake. Typically, only genes coding for galactose and biotin metabolism are transferred at high frequency by phage lambda.

Conjugation, transformation, and transduction are all ways in which DNA from two different bacterial cells is brought into close proximity. Homologous regions may then pair and recombine to give rise to a recipient cell that carries a different collection of alleles than it had previously. Overall, these processes create more diversity in the DNA sequence among members of a population than would arise by mutation and binary fission alone. More diversity leads to a higher likelihood that at least some individuals will be well suited to survive changes in the environment.

These basic principles also apply to single and multicellular eukaryotes. The next section of this chapter introduces genetic recombination in eukaryotes as it occurs within the overall process of meiosis. Notice how DNA from two different individuals is brought close together in the same cell following fertilization. Also watch for extensive homology that now extends the full length of large linear chromosomes. Finally, notice the genetic recombination at the centre of this process, which generates novel chromosomes with new combinations of alleles.

Study Break

1. Contrast the characteristics of F⁻, F⁺, and Hfr cells.
2. Explain why all genes have an equal likelihood of transfer by generalized transduction but not by specialized transduction.

10.3 Genetic Recombination in Eukaryotes: Meiosis

The octopuses and slipper limpets described at the opening of this chapter are engaged in forms of **sexual reproduction**, the production of offspring through the union of male and female **gametes**—for example, eggs and sperm cells in animals. Sexual reproduction depends on **meiosis**, a specialized process of cell division that recombines DNA sequences and produces cells with half the number of chromosomes present in the **somatic cells** (body cells) of a species. The derivation of the word *meiosis* (*meioun* = to diminish) reflects this reduction. At **fertilization**, the nuclei of an egg and sperm cell fuse, producing a cell called the **zygote**, in which the chromosome number typical of the species is restored. Without the halving of chromosome number by the meiotic divisions, fertilization would double the number of chromosomes in each subsequent generation.

Both meiosis and fertilization also mix genetic information into new combinations; thus, none of the offspring of a mating pair are likely to be genetically identical to either their parents or their siblings. This genetic variability is the raw material for the process of evolution as described in Chapter 19.

The biological foundations of sexual reproduction are the mixing of genetic information into new combinations and the halving of the chromosome number, both of which occur through meiosis, as well as the restoration of the original chromosome number by fertilization. Intermingled tentacles in octopuses, communal sex among limpets, clouds of pollen in the wind, and the courting and mating rituals of humans are nothing more or less than variations of the means for achieving fertilization, thus bringing DNA together for recombination.

10.3a Meiosis Occurs in Different Places in Different Organismal Life Cycles

Although the life cycle of nearly all eukaryotes alternates between a stage with one basic set of chromosomes (haploid) and a stage with two basic sets of chromosomes (diploid), **Figure 10.9** shows that evolution has produced wide variety in the relative timing of mitosis, meiosis, and fertilization among different species. The life cycles of plants, algae, and fungi may be unfamiliar to you and can be better understood by noticing the function of the cells that are the immediate

a. Animal life cycles

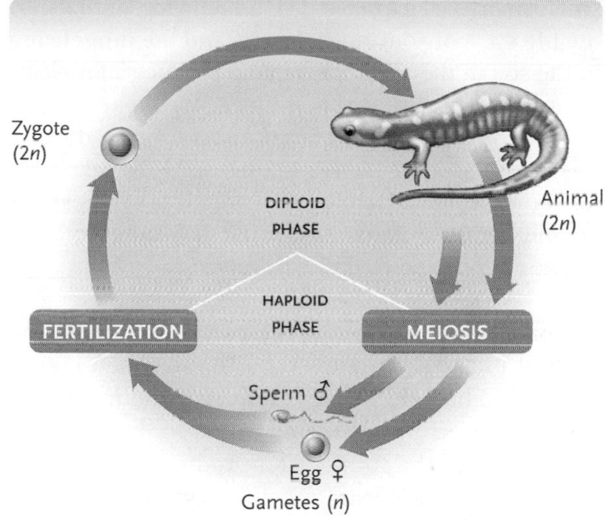

b. All plants and some fungi and algae (fern shown; relative length of the two phases varies widely in plants)

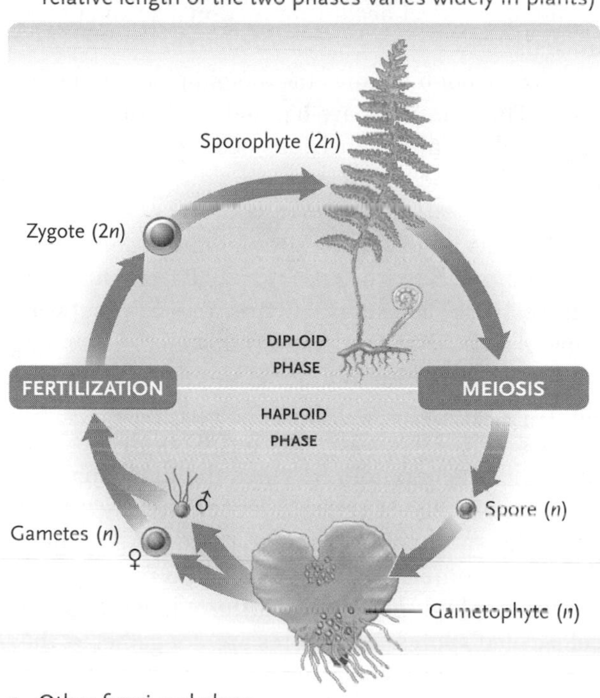

c. Other fungi and algae

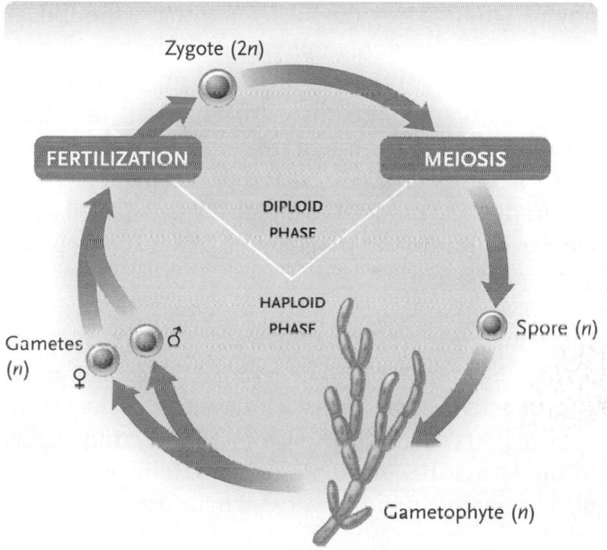

Figure 10.9
Variations in the time and place of meiosis in eukaryotes. The diploid phase of the life cycles is shaded in blue; the haploid phase is shaded in yellow. *n* refers to the haploid number of chromosomes; 2*n* refers to the diploid number. **(a)** Meiosis in animal life cycles. Only zygotes divide by mitosis. **(b)** Meiosis in most plants and some fungi and algae. Spores and zygotes divide by mitosis. **(c)** Meiosis in other fungi and algae. Only spores divide by mitosis.

products of meiosis. Notice that the assumption that "meiosis makes gametes" is true only for animals. In the life cycle of your house plants and the fungi living in the soil in the park, the haploid products of meiosis are spores, not gametes. In animals, the diploid zygote divides by mitosis. However, in some fungi and algae, this is reversed; the haploid spores divide by mitosis to form multicellular haploid gametophytes, whereas the diploid zygote remains unicellular. In plants, both the zygote and the spores divide by mitosis.

Animals. Animals follow the pattern in which the diploid phase dominates the life cycle (see Figure 10.9a), the haploid phase is reduced, and meiosis is followed directly by gamete formation. In male animals, each of the four nuclei produced by meiosis is enclosed in a separate cell by cytoplasmic divisions, and each of the four cells differentiates into a functional sperm cell. In female animals, only one of the four nuclei becomes functional as an egg cell nucleus.

Fertilization restores the diploid phase of the life cycle. Thus, animals are haploids only as sperm or eggs, and no mitotic divisions occur during the haploid phase of the life cycle.

Most Plants and Fungi. Most plants and some algae and fungi follow the life cycle pattern shown in Figure 10.9b. These organisms alternate between haploid and diploid generations in which, depending on the organism, either generation may dominate the life cycle, and mitotic divisions occur in both phases. In these organisms, fertilization produces the diploid generation, in which the individuals are called **sporophytes** (*spora* = seed; *phyta* = plant). After the sporophytes grow to maturity by mitotic divisions, some of their cells undergo meiosis, producing haploid, genetically different, reproductive cells called **spores.** The spores are not gametes; they germinate and grow directly by mitotic divisions into a generation of haploid individuals called **gametophytes** (*gameta* = gamete). At maturity, the nuclei of some cells in gametophytes develop into egg or sperm nuclei. All the egg or sperm nuclei produced by a particular gametophyte are genetically identical because they arise through mitosis; meiosis does not occur in gametophytes. Fusion of a haploid egg and sperm nucleus produces a diploid zygote nucleus that divides by mitosis to produce the diploid sporophyte generation again.

In all plants (except bryophytes), the diploid sporophyte generation is the most visible part of the plant. The gametophyte generation is reduced to an almost microscopic stage that develops in the reproductive parts of the sporophytes—in flowering plants, in the structures of the flower. The female gametophyte remains in the flower; the male gametophyte is released from flowers as microscopic pollen grains. When pollen contacts a flower of the same species, it releases a haploid nucleus that fertilizes a haploid egg cell of a female gametophyte in the flower. The resulting cell reproduces by mitosis to form a sporophyte.

Sphagnum moss (commonly known as "peat moss") is a good example of a plant in which the gametophyte is the most visible and familiar stage of the life cycle. In this case, the sporophyte is reduced and develops from a zygote within the body of the gametophyte. Vast peatlands of *Sphagnum* gametophytes are industrially harvested in many parts of the world for fuel and horticultural use.

Some Fungi. The life cycle of some fungi and algae follows the third life cycle pattern (see Figure 10.9c). In these organisms, the diploid phase is limited to a single cell, the zygote, produced by fertilization. Immediately after fertilization, the diploid zygote undergoes meiosis to produce the haploid phase. Mitotic divisions occur only in the haploid phase.

During fertilization, two haploid gametes, usually designated simply as positive (+) or negative (−) because they are similar in structure, fuse to form a diploid nucleus. This nucleus immediately enters meiosis, producing four haploid cells. These cells develop directly or after one or more mitotic divisions into haploid spores. These spores germinate to produce haploid individuals, the gametophytes, which grow or increase in number by mitotic divisions. Eventually, positive and negative gametes are formed in these individuals by differentiation of some of the cells produced by the mitotic divisions. Because the gametes are produced by mitosis, all the gametes of an individual are genetically identical.

10.3b Meiosis Changes Both Chromosome Number and DNA Sequence

In order to understand the mechanism of meiosis, it is helpful to keep the "big picture" in mind. Chapter 8 made the point that the essence of mitotic cell division is "sameness." That is, chromosomes are replicated and partitioned to ensure that cells produced by the process have the same number of chromosomes, with the same DNA sequence, as the cell that began the process. In this way, somatic cells are produced for most of the requirements of multicellular bodies. However, the essence of meiosis is "difference"—actually two kinds of difference: halved chromosome number and recombined chromosomal DNA sequence. The products of meiosis are not intended to contribute to the body of the organisms that make them. In multicellular animals and plants, you would find that meiosis occurs only in specialized tissues that produce gametes or spores, respectively.

Both types of difference mentioned above arise from the very different behaviour of chromosomes in meiosis relative to mitosis. If you understand the significance of the chromosome pairs in diploid organisms as described below, then the differences in chromosome behaviour in meiosis and mitosis will make sense more easily.

As discussed in Section 8.1, the two representatives of each chromosome in a diploid cell constitute a *homologous pair* they have the same genes, arranged in the same order in the DNA of the chromosomes. One chromosome of each homologous pair, the **paternal chromosome**, is derived from the male parent of the organism, and the other chromosome, the **maternal chromosome**, is derived from its female parent. Although two homologous chromosomes carry the same genes arranged in the same order, different *versions* of these genes, **alleles**, may be present on either chromosome. Recall from the bacterial conjugation material at the beginning of this chapter that different alleles of a given gene have similar, but distinct, DNA sequences. They therefore likely encode variations of the given ribonucleic acid (RNA) or protein gene product, which may then have a different structure, different biochemistry, or both.

For example, all the different breeds of dogs normally have 78 chromosomes in their cells, made up of 39 homologous pairs. However, each individual has a unique combination of the alleles carried by the two chromosomes of each homologous pair. The distinct set of alleles, arising from the mixing mechanisms of meiosis and fertilization in the parents, gives each individual offspring his or her unique combination of inherited traits, including attributes such as size, coat colour, susceptibility to certain diseases and disorders, and aspects of behaviour and intelligence.

One of the more dramatic accomplishments of meiosis in an organism like a dog is the separation of the members of each homologous pair into different cells, thereby reducing the diploid or $2n$ number of chromosomes to the haploid or n number. Each cell produced by meiosis carries only one member of each homologous pair. An egg or sperm cell contains 39 chromosomes, one of each pair. When the egg and sperm combine in sexual reproduction to produce the zygote—the first cell of the new puppy—the diploid number of 78 chromosomes (39 pairs) is regenerated. The processes of DNA replication and mitotic cell division ensure that this diploid number is maintained in the body cells as the zygote divides and develops (see Chapter 8).

The second significant consequence of meiotic cell division is, of course, genetic recombination of the actual DNA sequence on chromosomes. Referring back to Figure 10.1, recall that recombination involves the precise breaking of covalently bonded DNA backbones, exchanging the "ends" with those of the other homologue and reforming the bonds. As a result, each chromosome passed on to offspring is composed of a novel mixture of both maternal and paternal DNA sequence.

The following sections describe how the ability of homologues to find their respective partners, and pair intimately along their length, allows both the partitioning of homologues into separate cells and the process of recombination to occur during the first part of the two-step process of meiosis.

10.3c Meiosis Produces Four Genetically Different Daughter Cells

Cells that are destined to divide by meiosis (called **meiocytes**) move through their last turn of the cell cycle as usual, replicating DNA and making more chromosomal proteins during S phase. (See Chapter 13 for details of DNA replication.) The resulting G_2 cells carry replicated chromosomes, each composed of two identical sister chromatids **(Figure 10.10, p. 212)**. Following this premeiotic interphase, cells enter the first of the two meiotic divisions: meiosis I and meiosis II. During meiosis I, chromosomes behave dramatically differently than they do during mitosis. That is, early in meiosis I, homologous chromosomes find their partners and pair lengthwise, gene for gene, in a process called synapsis. During this intimate pairing, recombination occurs, and chromosomal segments are exchanged. As the meiocyte continues through to the end of the first division, the members of each homologous pair are separated into one or the other of the two daughter cells. These daughter cells still contain replicated chromosomes with two chromatids each; however, the number of such chromosomes is only half that of the original meiocyte. During the second meiotic division, meiosis II, the sister chromatids are separated into different cells. A total of four cells, each with the haploid number of chromosomes and a novel collection of alleles, is the final result of the two meiotic divisions.

For convenience, biologists separate each meiotic division into the same key stages as mitosis: *prophase, prometaphase, metaphase, anaphase,* and *telophase*. The stages are identified as belonging to the two divisions, meiosis I and meiosis II, by a *I* or a *II*, as in *prophase I* and *prophase II*. A brief interphase called **interkinesis** separates the two meiotic divisions, *but no DNA replication occurs during interkinesis.*

Figure 10.10
Production of four haploid nuclei by the two meiotic divisions. For simplicity, just one pair of homologous chromosomes is followed through the divisions.

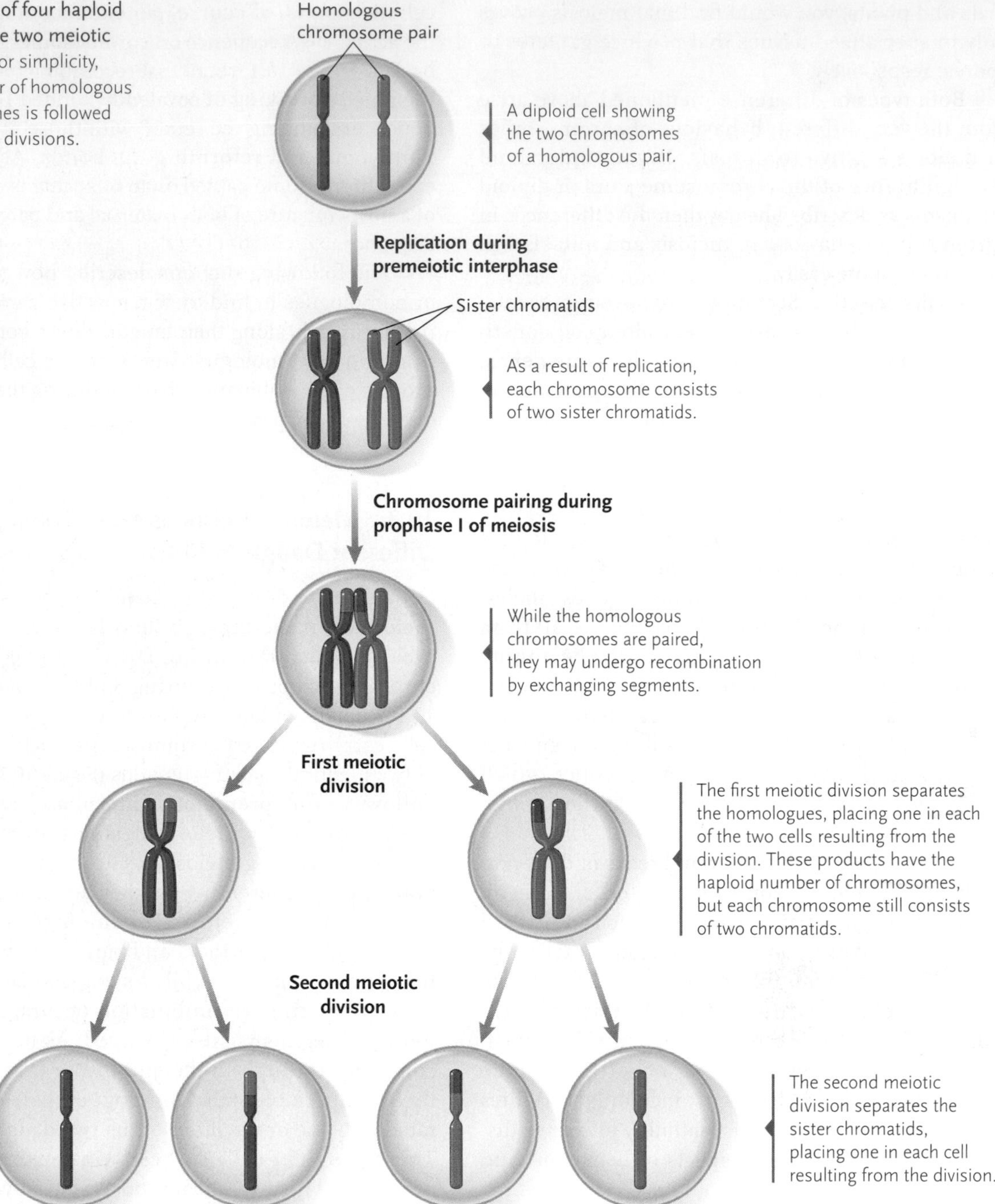

Homologous chromosome pair
A diploid cell showing the two chromosomes of a homologous pair.
Replication during premeiotic interphase
Sister chromatids
As a result of replication, each chromosome consists of two sister chromatids.
Chromosome pairing during prophase I of meiosis
While the homologous chromosomes are paired, they may undergo recombination by exchanging segments.
First meiotic division
The first meiotic division separates the homologues, placing one in each of the two cells resulting from the division. These products have the haploid number of chromosomes, but each chromosome still consists of two chromatids.
Second meiotic division
The second meiotic division separates the sister chromatids, placing one in each cell resulting from the division.

Prophase I. At the beginning of prophase I, the replicated chromosomes, each consisting of two sister chromatids, begin to fold and condense into threadlike structures in the nucleus (**Figure 10.11, p. 214,** step 1). The two chromosomes of each homologous pair then come together and line up side by side in a zipperlike way; this process is called **pairing** or **synapsis** (step 2). The fully paired homologues are called **tetrads**, referring to the fact that each homologous pair consists of four chromatids. Note that chromosomes do not behave like this in mitosis.

While they are paired, the chromatids of homologous chromosomes physically exchange segments (step 3). This physical exchange, genetic recombination, is the step that mixes the alleles of the homologous chromosomes into new combinations and contributes to the generation of variability in sexual reproduction. (This is the process that underlies recombination frequency mapping described in Chapter 12.) As prophase I finishes, a spindle forms in the cytoplasm by the same basic mechanisms described in Chapter 8.

Prometaphase I. In prometaphase I, the nuclear envelope breaks down and the spindle enters the former nuclear area (see Figure 10.11, step 4). The two chromosomes of each pair attach to kinetochore microtubules leading to opposite spindle poles. That is, both sister chromatids of one homologue attach to microtubules leading to one spindle pole, whereas both sister chromatids of the other homologue attach to microtubules leading to the opposite pole. Notice, again, how this is different from the spindle attachments during mitosis.

Metaphase and Anaphase I. At metaphase I, movements of the spindle microtubules have aligned the recombined tetrads on the equatorial plane—the *metaphase plate*—between the two spindle poles (see Figure 10.11, step 5). Then the two chromosomes of each homologous pair separate and move to opposite spindle poles during anaphase I (step 6). The movement segregates homologous pairs, delivering a haploid set of chromosomes to each pole of the spindle. However, all the chromosomes at the poles are still double structures composed of two sister chromatids.

Telophase I and Interkinesis. Telophase I is a brief, transitory stage in which there is little or no change in the chromosomes (see Figure 10.11, step 7). New nuclear envelopes form in some species but not in others. Telophase I is followed by an interkinesis in which the single spindle of the first meiotic division disassembles and the microtubules reassemble into two new spindles for the second division. There is no DNA replication between the first and the second division.

Prophase II, Prometaphase II, and Metaphase II. Although the chromosome behaviour during meiosis II is superficially similar to that in a mitotic division, it is important to remember that these two processes are quite distinct. Meiosis II is not "just like mitosis." Meiosis II occurs only in reproductive tissue, there is no immediately preceding S phase, and the resulting daughter cells are not genetically identical.

During prophase of meiosis II, the chromosomes condense and the spindle begins to form (see Figure 10.11, step 8). During prometaphase II, the nuclear envelope breaks down, the spindle enters the former nuclear area, and spindle microtubules leading to opposite spindle poles attach to the two kinetochores of each chromosome (step 9). At meta-phase II, movements of the chromosomes within the spindle bring them to rest on the metaphase plate (step 10).

Anaphase and Telophase II. Anaphase II begins as the sister chromatids of each chromosome separate from each other and move to opposite spindle poles (see Figure 10.11, step 11). At the completion of anaphase II, the separated chromatids—now called chromosomes—have been segregated to the two poles. During telophase II, the chromatids decondense to the extended interphase state, the spindles disassemble, and new nuclear envelopes form around the masses of chromatin (step 12). The result is four haploid cells, each with a nucleus containing half the number of chromosomes present in a somatic cell of the same species. These chromosomes all carry various new combinations of maternal and paternal alleles.

Nondisjunction. Rarely, chromosome segregation fails at either meiosis I or II. For example, during meiosis I, both chromosomes of a homologous pair may connect to the same spindle pole in anaphase I. In the resulting nondisjunction, as it is called, the spindle fails to separate the homologous chromosomes of the tetrad. As a result, one pole receives both chromosomes of the homologous pair, whereas the other pole has no copies of that chromosome. Meiosis II will proceed to separate the chromatids of the extra chromosome as usual, with the result that gametes will have two copies of this chromosome (instead of one). Zygotes that receive an extra chromosome because of nondisjunction therefore have three copies of a given chromosome instead of two. In humans, most zygotes of this kind do not result in live births. One exception is Down syndrome, which results from three copies of chromosome 21. Down syndrome involves characteristic alterations in body and facial structure, mental retardation, and significantly reduced fertility (see Chapter 12 for a more detailed discussion of Down syndrome).

Sex Chromosomes. In many eukaryotes, including most animals, one or more pairs of chromosomes, called the sex chromosomes, are different in male and female individuals of the same species. For example, in fruit flies, the cells of females contain a pair of sex chromosomes called the *XX* pair. Male flies contain a pair of sex chromosomes that consist of one X chromosome and a smaller chromosome called the Y chromosome. The two X chromosomes in females are fully homologous, whereas the male X and Y chromosomes are homologous only through a short region. The X and Y chromosomes behave as homologues during meiosis in males. As a result of meiosis, a gamete formed in females may receive either member of the X pair. A gamete formed in males receives either an X or a Y chromosome. (See Chapter 12 for a discussion of the inheritance of genes on sex chromosomes.)

First meiotic division

Prophase I

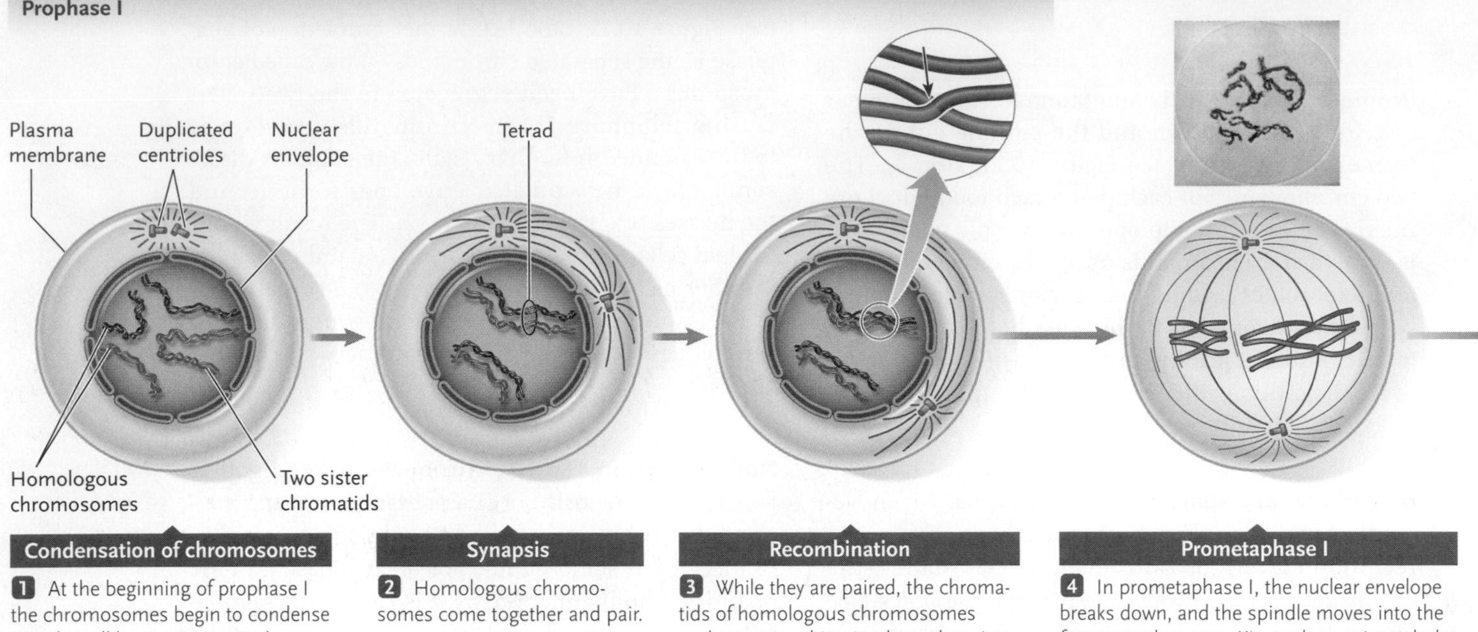

1 At the beginning of prophase I the chromosomes begin to condense into threadlike structures. Each consists of two sister chromatids, as a result of DNA replication during premeiotic interphase. The chromosomes of two homologous pairs, one long and one short, are shown.

2 Homologous chromosomes come together and pair.

3 While they are paired, the chromatids of homologous chromosomes undergo recombination by exchanging segments. The enlarged circle shows a site undergoing recombination (arrow).

4 In prometaphase I, the nuclear envelope breaks down, and the spindle moves into the former nuclear area. Kinetochore microtubules connect to the chromosomes—kinetochore microtubules from one pole attach to both sister kinetochores of one duplicated chromosome, and kinetochore microtubules from the other pole attach to both sister ki-net-o-chores of the other duplicated chromosome.

Figure 10.11
The meiotic divisions. The sequence is shown as it would occur in a two X chromosomes are shown; therefore, female animal also shown are equivalent stages in a plant, the lily (*Lilium* regale). (Two homologous pairs of chromosomes are shown.) Micrographs with thanks to the John Innes Foundation Trustees.

Second meiotic division

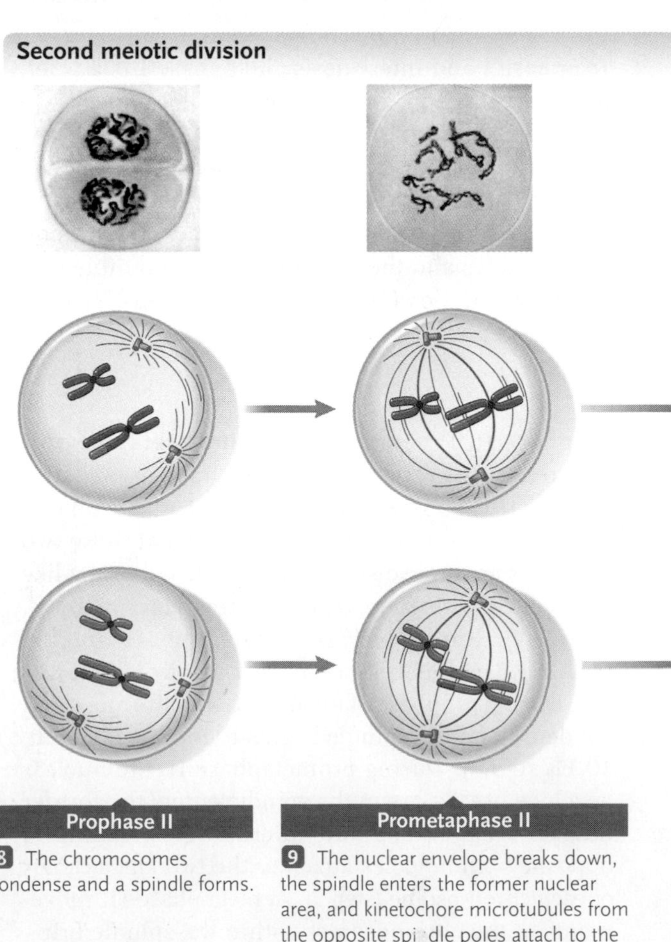

8 The chromosomes condense and a spindle forms.

9 The nuclear envelope breaks down, the spindle enters the former nuclear area, and kinetochore microtubules from the opposite spi dle poles attach to the kinetochores of each chromosome.

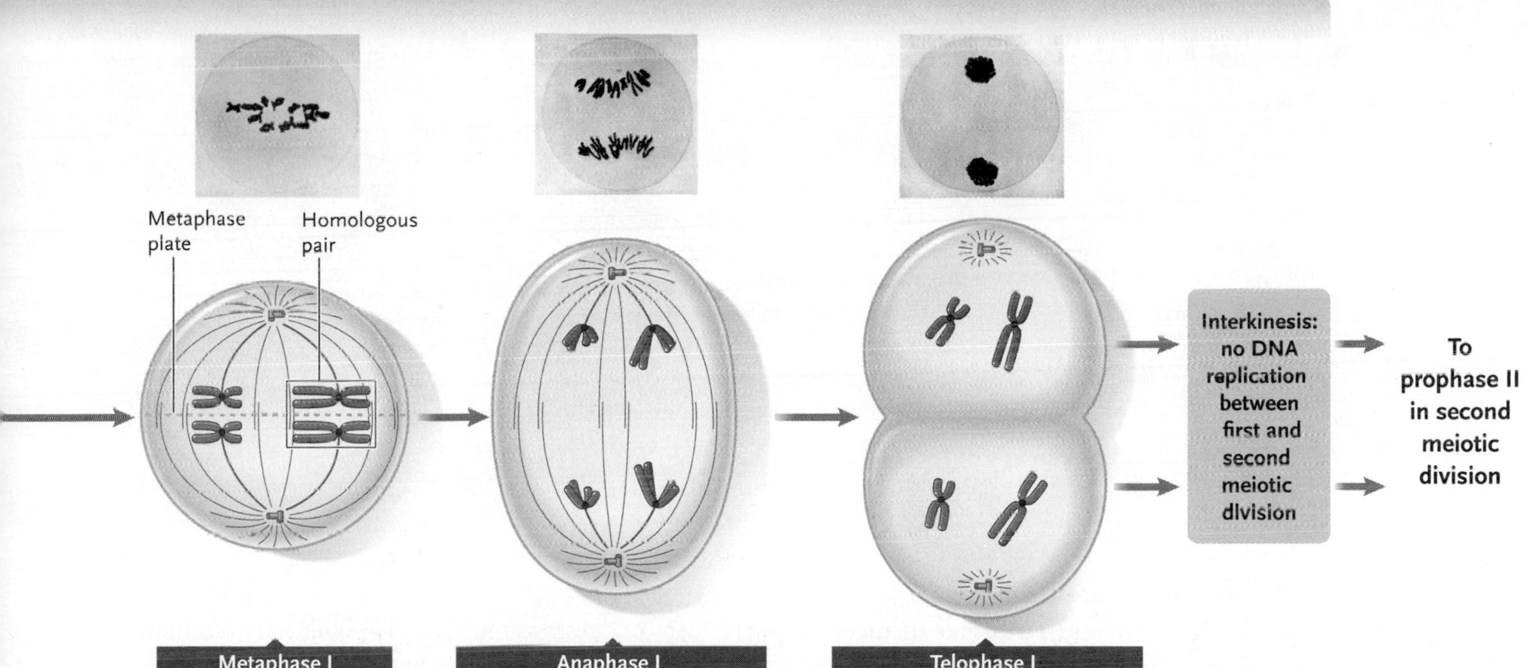

5 Movements of the spindle microtubules align the tetrads in the equatorial plane—metaphase plate—between the two spindle poles.

6 The spindle microtubules separate the two chromosomes of each homologous pair and move them to opposite spindle poles. The poles now contain the haploid number of chromosomes. However, each chromosome at the poles still contains two chromatids.

7 The chromosomes undergo little or no change except for limited decondensation or unfolding in some species. The spindle of the first meiotic division disassembles, and two new spindles form for the second division.

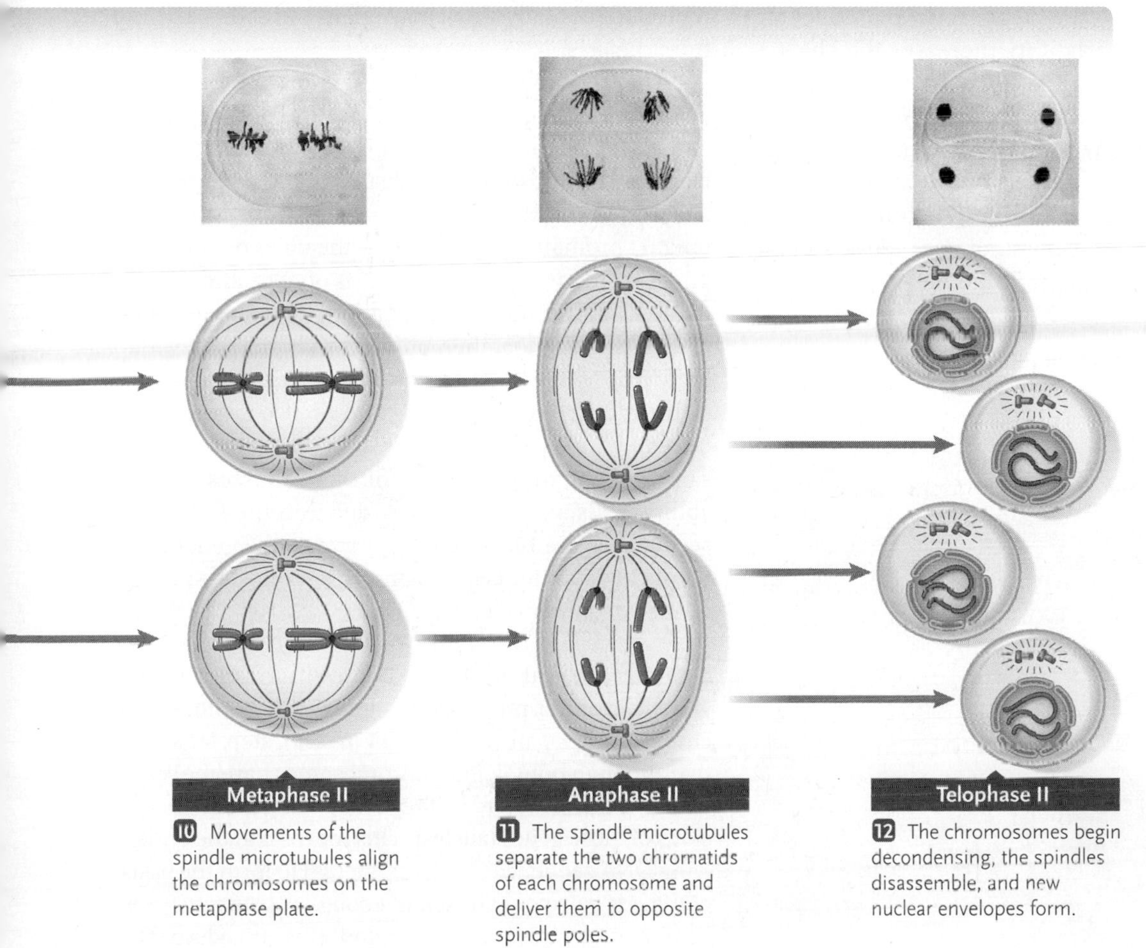

10 Movements of the spindle microtubules align the chromosomes on the metaphase plate.

11 The spindle microtubules separate the two chromatids of each chromosome and deliver them to opposite spindle poles.

12 The chromosomes begin decondensing, the spindles disassemble, and new nuclear envelopes form.

Molecule Behind Biology

Bisphenol A and the Grandmother Effect

Although this chapter documented the role of meiosis in generating genetically diverse offspring, one type of diversity that must be avoided is differences in chromosome number. Cells (or organisms) that have more, or less, than the normal number of chromosomes are called "aneuploid"; agents that promote this problem are known as "aneugens." The formation of gametes by meiosis is under hormonal control in mammals, and it is not surprising to learn that synthetic chemicals influencing the action of reproductive hormones can be aneugenic. Bisphenol A, a chemical monomer used in the manufacture of polycarbonate plastics and resins, binds to estrogen receptors in mice. Exposure to relatively high concentrations has been shown to elevate the incidence of aneuploid gametes and offspring. Since meiosis is active in females before they are born, exposure of pregnant mouse mothers resulted in aneuploid gametes produced by their daughters, which, in turn, gave rise to aneuploid grandchildren.

Figure 1
Bisphenol A

The sequence of steps in the two meiotic divisions accomplishes the major outcomes of meiosis: the generation of genetic variability and the reduction in chromosome number. (Figure 10.13, reviews the two meiotic divisions and compares them with the single division of mitosis.)

10.3d Several Mechanisms Contribute Genetic Diversity

The generation of genetic variability by meiosis is a prime evolutionary advantage of sexual reproduction **(Figure 10.12).** Such variability increases the chance that at least some offspring will have combinations of alleles that will be successful in surviving and reproducing in changing environments. In fact, some scientists argue that meiosis exists not to create just any variability but to generate "repaired" chromosomes to be passed on to the next generation (see *People Behind Biology*). As you work through the ideas in this section, try to envision how you could pass a "perfect" copy of chromosome 6 to your children even though both copies of chromosome 6 you inherited from your parents are damaged (in different places).

Figure 10.12
Genetic variability as shown in the appearance of domestic cats.

Marc Henrie/Dorling Kindersley/Getty Images

Dave King/Dorling Kindersley/Getty Images

Elena Butinova/Shutterstock

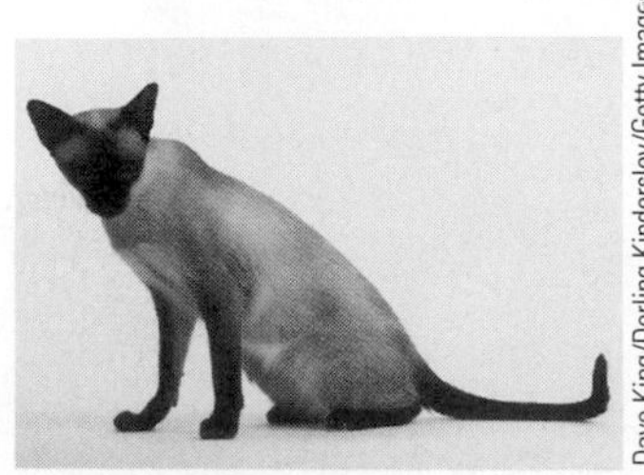
Dave King/Dorling Kindersley/Getty Images

Lexx/Shutterstock

Dave King/Dorling Kindersley/Getty Images

The variability produced by sexual reproduction is apparent all around us, particularly in the human population. Except for identical twins (or identical triplets, identical quadruplets, and so forth), no two humans look alike, act alike, or have identical biochemical and physiological characteristics, even if they are members of the same immediate family. Other species that reproduce sexually show equivalent variability arising from meiosis.

During meiosis and fertilization, genetic variability arises from four sources: (1) genetic recombination, (2) the differing combinations of maternal and paternal chromosomes segregated to the poles during anaphase I, (3) the differing combinations of recombinant chromatids segregated to the poles during anaphase II, and (4) the particular sets of male and female gametes that unite in fertilization. The four mechanisms, working together, produce so much total variability that no two products of meiosis produced by the same or different individuals and no two zygotes produced by union of the gametes are likely to have the same genetic makeup. Each of these sources of variability is discussed in further detail in the following sections. **Figure 10.13 (p. 218),** contrasts the genetically identical daughter cells arising from mitosis with the diverse daughter cells produced by meiosis.

Genetic Recombination. Recombination, the key genetic event of prophase I, starts when homologous chromosomes pair **(Figure 10.14 (p. 220),** step 1). Recall that although homologous chromosomes have the same genes in the same order, they likely carry different versions of those genes (alleles). This means that the underlying DNA sequence is similar enough to form the basis of meiotic pairing yet different enough to generate novel combinations after recombination. (Recall Lederberg's

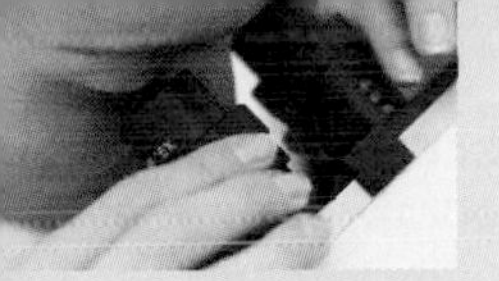

People Behind Biology

Dr. Aurora Nedelcu, University of New Brunswick

Whereas the octopuses and limpets mentioned at the opening of this chapter have no choice but to undergo meiosis and follow the remaining steps of their sexual life cycle, prokaryotes and many lower eukaryotes become sexual only in response to suboptimal environmental conditions, such as elevated temperature or nutrient deficiency. This observation led Dr. Aurora Nedelcu and her colleagues in The Green Lab at the University of New Brunswick to gather evidence to test the hypothesis that sex originally evolved as one of several responses available to cells dealing with stress.

A variety of external stresses all eventually cause internal oxidative stress resulting from increased concentration of damaging reactive oxygen species (ROS). Using her multicellular algal model system (*Volvox carteri*), Dr. Nedelcu has shown that stress-induced increase in ROS does indeed stimulate the expression of sex-related genes **(Figure 1).** She believes that the cells experiencing oxidative stress "turn on" their sex genes in order to benefit from the possibility that meiotic recombination will repair DNA damage caused by ROS.

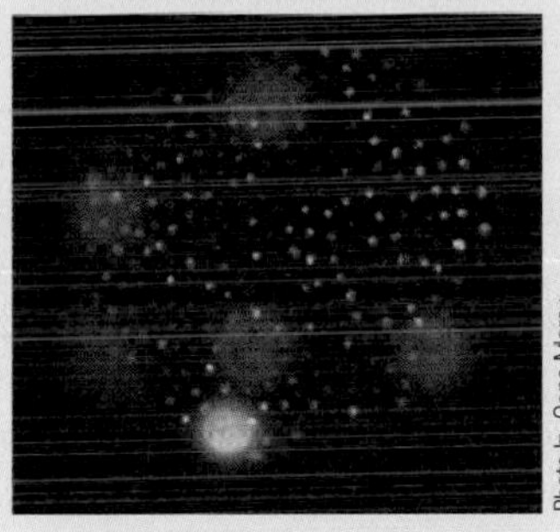

Figure 1
Volvox carteri under heat stress. ROS indicated by green fluorescence.

multiple auxotrophic *E. coli* mutants here; the idea is the same.) As the homologous chromosomes pair, they are held together tightly by a protein framework called the **synaptonemal complex (Figure 10.15, p. 220).** Supported by this framework, regions of homologous chromatids exchange segments, producing new combinations of alleles (see Figure 10.14, step 2). Recall that the exchange process is very precise and involves the breakage and rejoining of DNA molecules by enzymes (Figure 10.1). When the exchange is complete toward the end of prophase I, the synaptonemal complex disassembles and disappears. If you now follow meiosis I and II through to the end in your mind, notice that each of the four resulting nuclei receives one of these four chromatids (see Figure 10.14, step 3); two receive unchanged chromatids, and two receive chromatids that have new combinations of alleles due to recombination.

The physical effect of recombination can be seen later in prophase I, when increased condensation of the chromosomes thickens the chromosomes enough to make them visible under the light microscope (see Figure 10.11, steps 3 and 4). Regions in which nonsister chromatids cross one another, called **crossovers** or **chiasmata** (singular, *chiasma* = crosspiece), clearly show that two of the four chromatids have exchanged segments. Because of the shape produced, the recombination process is also called **crossing-over.**

Note that illustrations of recombination usually show chromosomes "paired" side by side, with only the closest chromatids participating in recombination (see Figure 10.14); however, chromosomes actually pair "one on top of the other" such that any two of the four chromatids can participate in a given recombination event. Recombination takes place largely at random, at almost any position along the chromosome arms. Several events likely occur at various locations along all chromatids.

Notice in Figure 10.14 that a recombination event does not just "switch" the alleles of a given gene in a localized area. All of the DNA sequence stretching from the site of recombination to the ends of the participating chromatids is exchanged.

Random Segregation. Random segregation of chromosomes of maternal and paternal origin accounts for the second major source of genetic variability in meiosis. Recall that the maternal and paternal members of each homologous pair are different in that they typically carry different alleles of many of the genes on that chromosome. During prometaphase I, spindle microtubules make connections to kinetochores. For each homologous pair, one chromosome makes spindle connections leading to one pole and the other chromosome connects to the opposite pole. In making these connections, all the maternal chromosomes may connect to one pole and all the paternal chromosomes may connect to the opposite pole. Or, as is most likely, a random combination of maternal and paternal chromosomes may be segregated to a given spindle pole **(Figure 10.16, p. 221).**

The number of possible combinations depends on the number of chromosome pairs in a species. For example, the 39 chromosome pairs in dogs allow 2^{39} different combinations of maternal and paternal chromosomes to be delivered to the poles, producing potentially 500 billion genetically different gametes from this source of variability alone. Note that this random partitioning of maternal and paternal chromosomes is responsible for the independent assortment of the alleles of two genes in Mendel's experiments with garden peas described in Chapter 11.

Alternative Combinations at Meiosis II. If you look carefully at the cells drawn in metaphase II in Figure 10.13, you will see that the chromosomes are still replicated and, as a result of recombination in prophase I, each chromosome carries one recombinant chromatid and one nonrecombinant chromatid. Notice that, in this case, the chromosomes have aligned at metaphase II with both recombinant chromatids attached to the same spindle pole. However, since the attachment of spindles to kinetochores is random at this stage, we hope that you can see that it is just as likely that these chromosomes *could* have lined up, with the smaller chromosome sending its recombinant chromatid to one pole and the larger chromosome sending its recombinant chromatid to the opposite pole. The resulting daughter cells will be genetically different, depending on how the chromosomes align in metaphase II.

Random Fertilization. The haploid products of meiosis are genetically diverse. The rather random combination of these cells (or their descendants) during fertilization is a matter of chance that amplifies the variability of sexual reproduction. For example, if we consider only the variability available from random separation of homologous chromosomes at meiosis I along with that from random fertilization, the possibility that two children of the same human parents could receive the same combination of maternal and paternal chromosomes is 1 chance out of $(2^{23})^2$ or 1 in 70 368 744 000 000 (~70 trillion), a number that far exceeds the number of humans who have ever lived. The further variability introduced by recombination and shuffling at meiosis II makes it practically impossible for humans and most other sexually reproducing organisms to produce genetically identical gametes or offspring. The only exception is identical twins (or identical triplets, identical quadruplets, and so forth), which arise not from the combination of identical gametes during fertilization but from mitotic division of a single fertilized egg into separate cells that give rise to genetically identical individuals.

We have just seen that meiosis has three outcomes that are vital to sexual reproduction. This process reduces the chromosomes to the haploid number so that they can be brought together with those of another individual without doubling the usual chromosome number during fertilization. Through genetic recombination and random separation of maternal and paternal chromosomes, meiosis produces genetic variability in gametes; further variability is provided by the random combination of gametes in fertilization. These ideas form the "mechanics" that underlie the patterns of inheritance of traits in sexually reproducing organisms discovered by Mendel and described in Chapter 11.

Study Break

1. Which phase (diploid or haploid) dominates the life cycles of animals, plants, and fungi?
2. What are the two functions of meiosis?
3. What are the four sources of genetic variability in sexually reproducing organisms?
4. What is nondisjunction, and how does it occur?

Figure 10.13
Comparison of key steps in meiosis and mitosis. Both diagrams use an animal cell as an example. Maternal chromosomes are shown in red; paternal chromosomes are shown in blue.

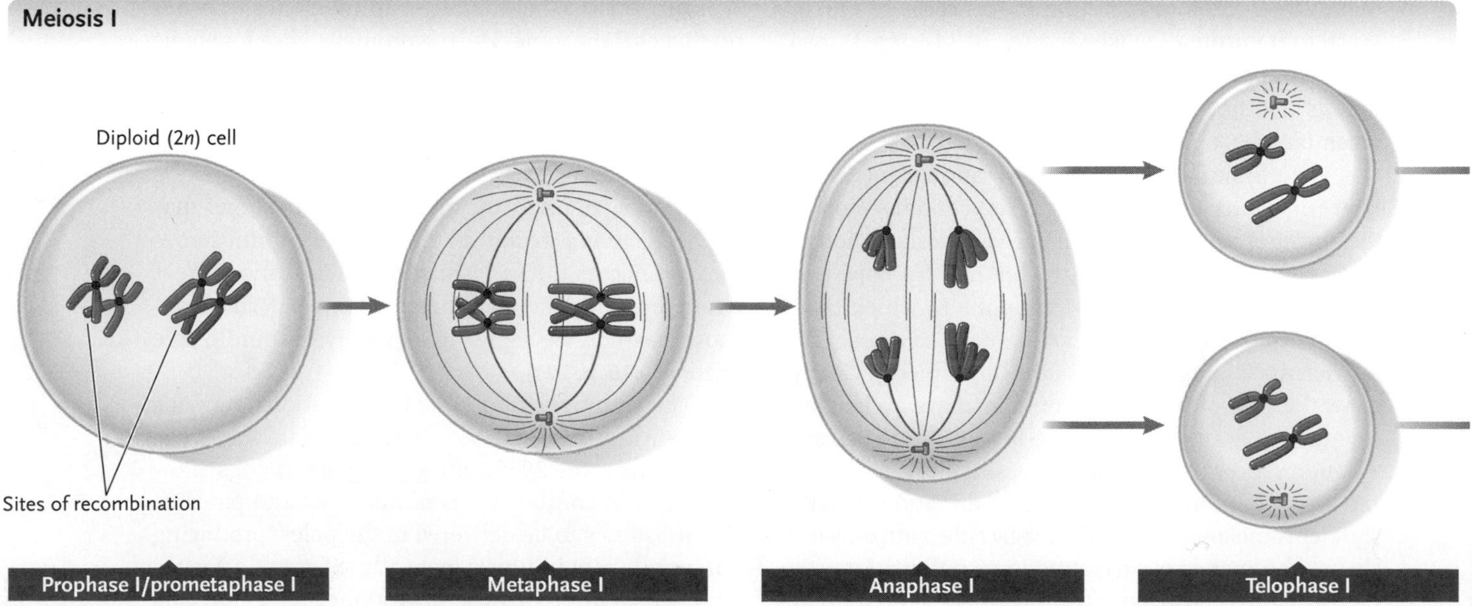

Meiosis I
Diploid (2n) cell
Sites of recombination
Prophase I/prometaphase I
Duplicated chromosomes condense. Homologous chromosomes pair and exchange segments by recombination. Chromosomes attach to spindle in homologous pairs.
Metaphase I
Each maternal chromosome (a pair of sister chromatids) and its paternal homologue align randomly at the spindle midpoint.
Anaphase I
Homologous chromosomes, each as a pair of sister chromatids, separate and move to opposite poles.
Telophase I
Two haploid (n) nuclei form.

10.4 Mobile Elements

Our examples have so far involved two participating DNA molecules that have always been at least partially homologous and that have always originated from two different individuals. However, one of the most interesting examples of genetic recombination in nature shows neither of these characteristics. All organisms appear to contain particular segments of DNA, called **mobile elements,** that can move from one place to another; they cut and paste DNA backbones using a type of recombination that does not require homology. Sometimes called "jumping genes," these elements normally move from place to place *within the genome of a given cell.* The following section describes these fascinating elements in more detail.

10.4a Insertion Sequence Elements and Transposons Are the Two Major Types of Prokaryotic Mobile Elements

Mobile elements are also known by the more specific term **transposable elements (TEs)**, and their mechanism of movement, involving nonhomologous recombination, is called **transposition.** Transposition

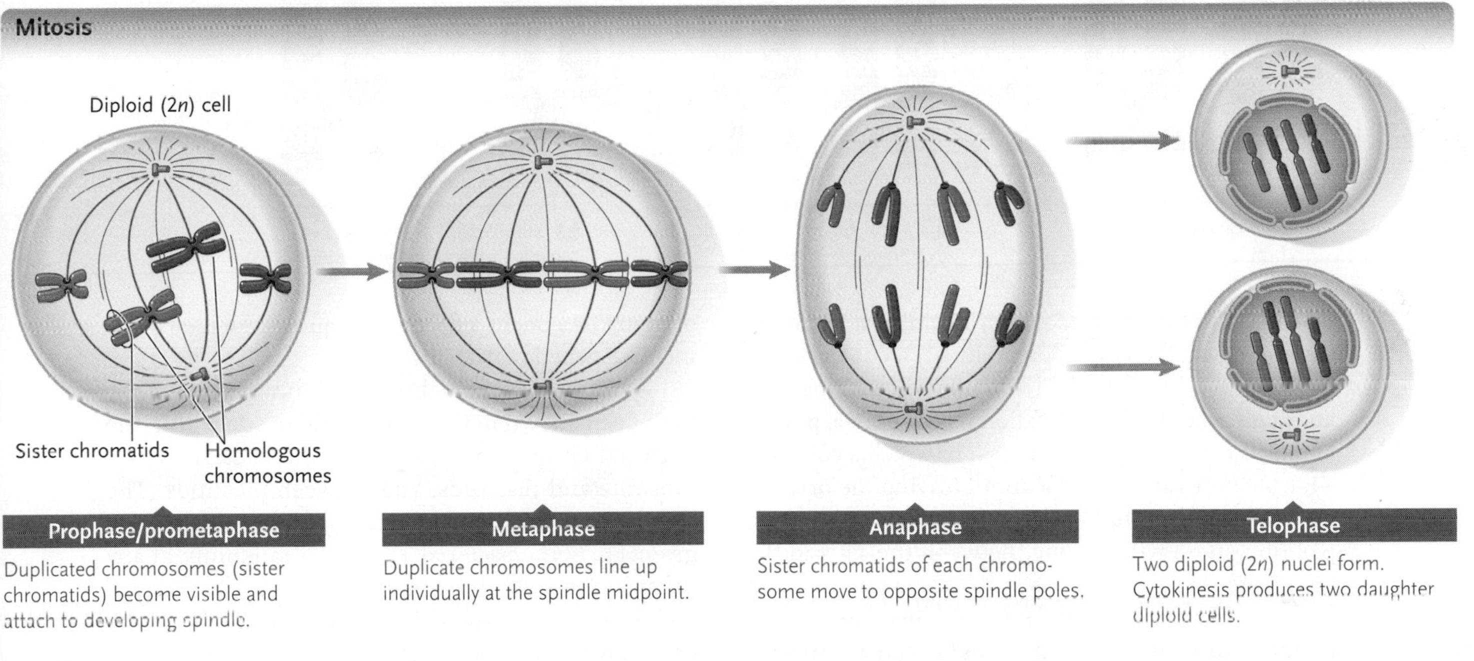

Mitosis
Diploid (2n) cell
Sister chromatids
Homologous chromosomes
Prophase/prometaphase
Duplicated chromosomes (sister chromatids) become visible and attach to developing spindle.
Metaphase
Duplicate chromosomes line up individually at the spindle midpoint.
Anaphase
Sister chromatids of each chromosome move to opposite spindle poles.
Telophase
Two diploid (2n) nuclei form. Cytokinesis produces two daughter diploid cells.

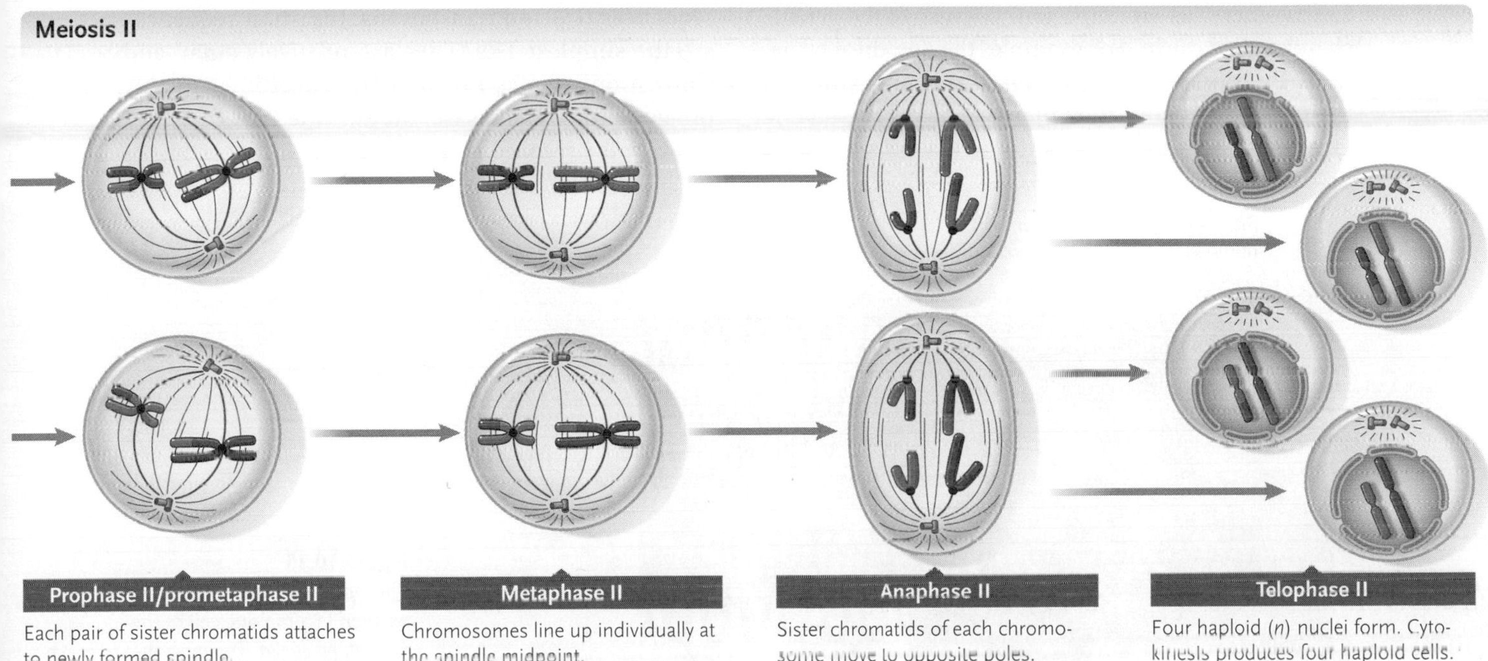

Meiosis II
Prophase II/prometaphase II
Each pair of sister chromatids attaches to newly formed spindle.
Metaphase II
Chromosomes line up individually at the spindle midpoint.
Anaphase II
Sister chromatids of each chromosome move to opposite poles.
Telophase II
Four haploid (n) nuclei form. Cytokinesis produces four haploid cells.

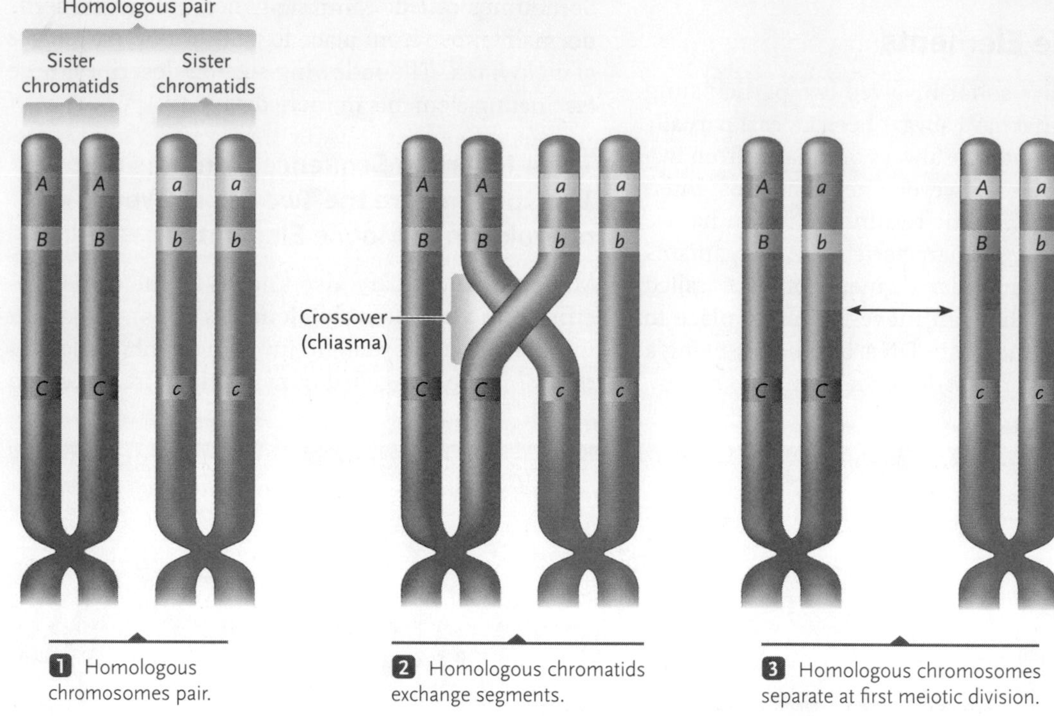

Figure 10.14
Effects of the exchange between chromatids that accomplishes genetic recombination. Although the closest chromatids are shown crossing-over, any pair of nonsister chromatids may recombine. The letters indicate two alleles (e.g., *A and a*) for each of three genes. In the meiocyte, the alleles are in the combination of A – B – C and a – b – c on their respective homologues. As a result of this recombination event, two of the chromatids, the recombinants, have a new combination: a – b – C and A – B – c.

usually occurs at a low frequency in either of two ways, depending on the type of element: (1) a cut-and-paste process, in which the TE leaves its original location and transposes to a new location **(Figure 10.17a, p. 222),** and (2) a copy-and-paste process, in which a copy of a TE transposes to a new location, leaving the original TE behind **(Figure 10.17b, p. 222).** For most TEs, transposition starts with contact between the TE and the target site. This also means that TEs do not exist free of the DNA in which they are integrated; hence, that popular name of "jumping genes" is actually inaccurate. TEs are never "in the air" between one location and another. TEs are important because of the genetic changes they cause. For example, they produce mutations by transposing into genes and knocking out their functions, and they increase or decrease gene expression by transposing into regulatory sequences of genes. As such, TEs are biological mutagens that increase genetic variability.

Bacterial TEs were discovered in the 1960s. They have been shown to move from site to site within the bacterial chromosome, between the bacterial chromosome and plasmids, and between plasmids. The frequency of transposition is low but constant for a given TE. Some bacterial TEs insert randomly, at any point in the DNA, whereas others recognize certain sequences as "hot spots" for insertion and insert preferentially at these locations.

The two major types of bacterial TEs are **insertion sequences** (IS) and **transposons.** Insertion sequences are the simplest TEs. They are relatively small and contain only genes for their transposition, notably the gene for **transposase**, an enzyme that catalyzes some of the recombination reactions for inserting or

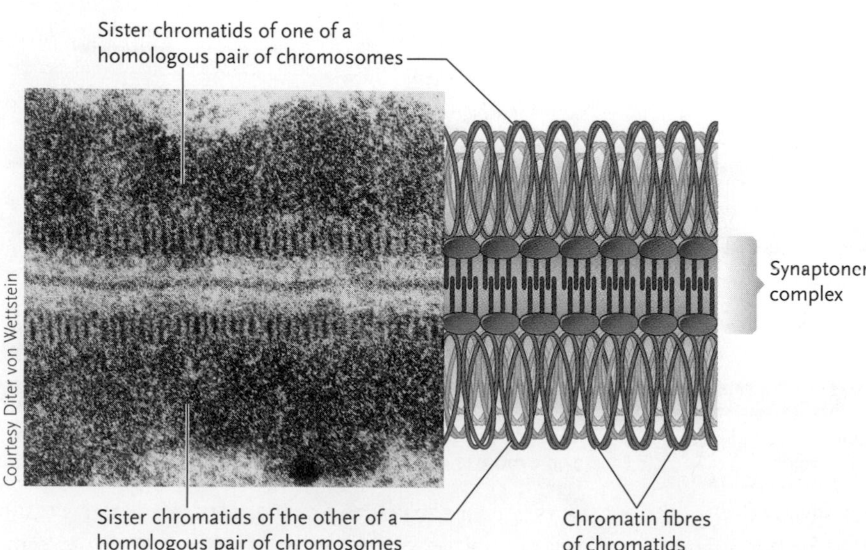

Figure 10.15
The synaptonemal complex as seen in a meiotic cell of the fungus *Neotiella.* The relationship of the complex to the chromatin fibres of the paired chromosomes is shown.

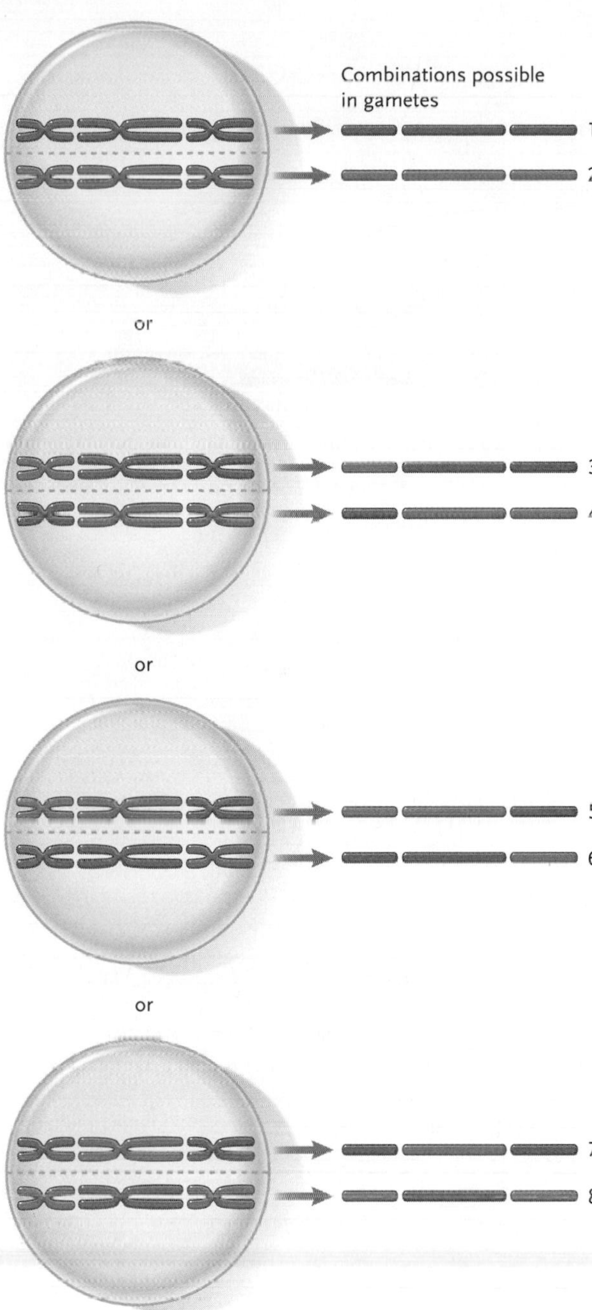

Figure 10.16

Possible outcomes of the random spindle connections of three pairs of chromosomes at metaphase I of meiosis. Maternal chromosomes are red; paternal chromosomes are blue. There are four possible patterns of connections, giving eight possible combinations of maternal and paternal chromosomes in gametes (labelled 1–8).

removing the TE from the DNA **(Figure 10.18, p. 222).** At each of the two ends of an IS is a short **inverted repeat** sequence—the same DNA sequence running in opposite directions (shown by directional arrows in the figure). The inverted repeat sequences enable the transposase enzyme to identify the ends of the TE when it catalyzes transposition. The inverted repeat sequence is an IS element on both the F factor and the bacterial chromosome that provides the homology needed for the creation of the Hfr strains described in Section 10.2.

The second type of bacterial TE, called a transposon, has an inverted repeat sequence at each end enclosing a central region with one or more genes. In a number of bacterial transposons, the inverted repeat sequences are insertion sequences, which provide the transposase for movement of the element (see Figure 10.18). Additional genes in the central region typically code for antibiotic resistance; they originated from the main bacterial DNA circle or from plasmids. These non-IS genes included in transposons are carried along as the TEs move from place to place.

Many antibiotics, such as penicillin, erythromycin, tetracycline, ampicillin, and streptomycin, that were once successful in curing bacterial infections have lost much of their effectiveness because of resistance genes carried in transposons. Movements of the transposons, particularly to plasmids that can be transferred by conjugation within and between bacterial species, greatly increase the spread of genes, providing antibiotic resistance to infecting cells. Resistance genes have made many bacterial diseases difficult or impossible to treat with standard antibiotics.

10.4b Transposable Elements Were First Discovered in Eukaryotes

TEs were first discovered in a eukaryote, maize (corn), in the 1940s by Barbara McClintock, a geneticist working at the Cold Spring Harbor Laboratory in New York. McClintock noted that some mutations affecting kernel and leaf colour appeared and disappeared rapidly under certain conditions. Mapping the alleles by linkage studies produced a surprising result: the map positions changed frequently, indicating that the alleles could move from place to place in the corn chromosomes. Some of the movements were so frequent that changes in their effects could be noticed at different times in a single developing kernel **(Figure 10.19, p. 223).**

When McClintock first reported her results, her findings were regarded as an isolated curiosity, possibly applying only to corn. This was because the then-prevailing opinion among geneticists was that genes are fixed in the chromosomes and do not move to other locations. Her conclusions were widely accepted only after TEs were detected and characterized in bacteria in the 1960s. By the 1970s, further examples of TEs were discovered in other eukaryotes, including yeast and mammals. McClintock was awarded a Nobel Prize in 1983 for her pioneering work, after these discoveries confirmed her early findings that TEs are probably universally distributed among both prokaryotes and eukaryotes.

10.4c Eukaryotic Transposable Elements Are Classified as Transposons or Retrotransposons

Eukaryotic TEs fall into two major classes, transposons and retrotransposons, distinguished by the way the TE sequence moves from place to place in

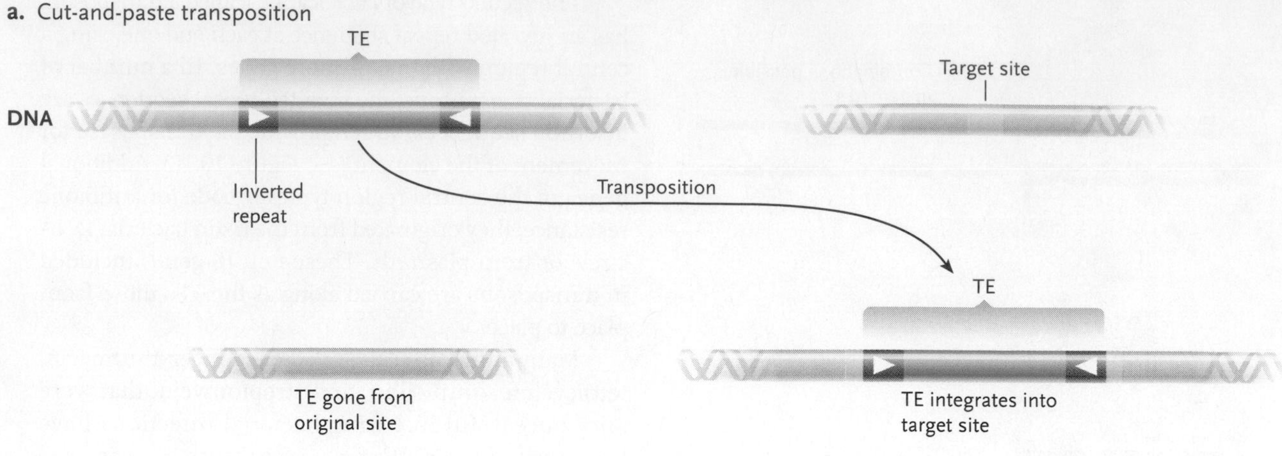

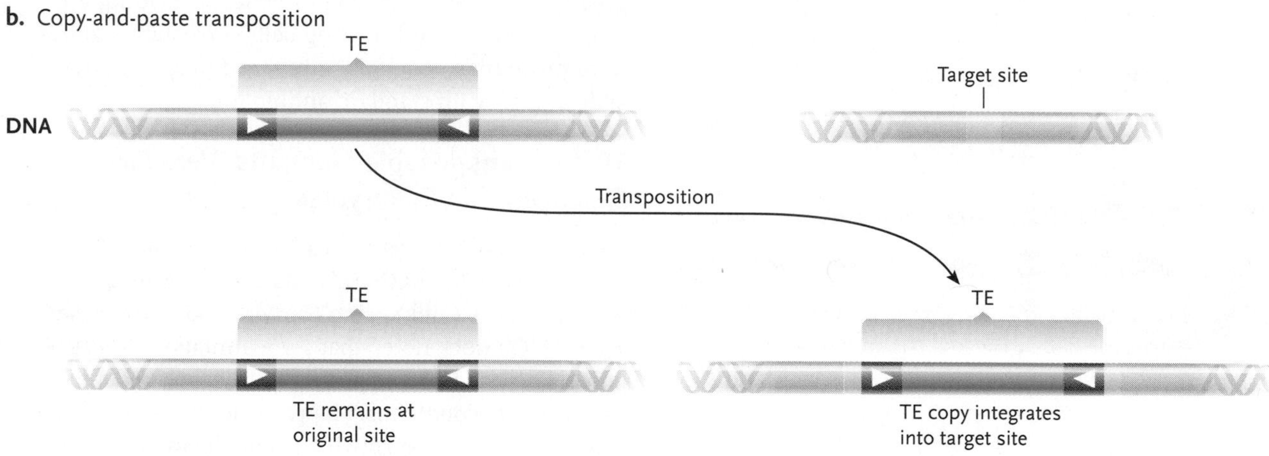

Figure 10.17
Two transposition processes for transposable elements. (a) Cut-and-paste transposition, in which the TE leaves one location in the DNA and moves to a new location. **(b)** Copy-and-paste transposition, in which a copy of the TE moves to a new location, leaving the original TE behind.

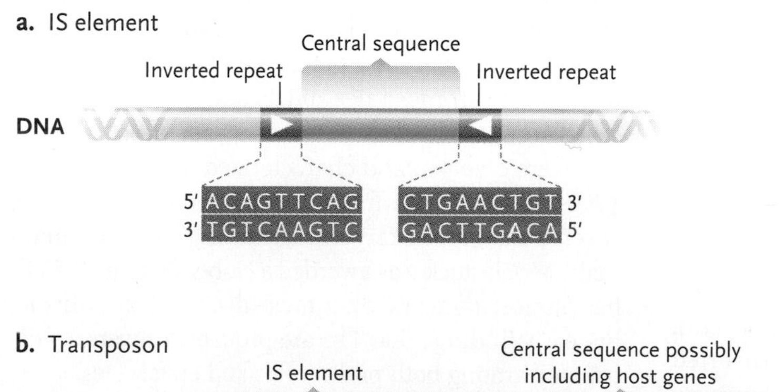

Figure 10.18
Types of bacterial transposable elements. (a) Insertion sequence. **(b)** Transposon.

Figure 10.19
Barbara McClintock and corn kernels showing different colour patterns due to the movement of transposable elements. As TEs move into or out of genes, controlling pigment production in developing kernels, the ability of cells and their descendants to produce the dark pigment is destroyed or restored. The result is random patterns of pigmented and colourless (yellow) segments in individual kernels.

the DNA. Eukaryotic transposons are similar to bacterial transposons in their general structure and in the ways they transpose. However, members of the other class of eukaryotic TEs, the **retrotransposons**, transpose by a copy-and-paste mechanism that is unlike any of the other TEs we have discussed. Retrotransposons have this name because transposition occurs via an intermediate RNA copy of the TE **(Figure 10.20)**. First, the retrotransposon, which is a DNA element integrated into the chromosomal DNA, is transcribed into a complementary RNA copy. Next, an enzyme called **reverse transcriptase**, which is encoded by one of the genes of the retrotransposon, uses the RNA as a template to make a DNA copy of the retrotransposon.

The DNA copy is then inserted into the DNA at a new location, leaving the original in place. This insertion step involves breaking and rejoining DNA backbones, as we have seen several times in this chapter.

Once TEs are inserted into chromosomes, they become more or less permanent residents, duplicated and passed on during cell division along with the rest of the DNA. TEs inserted into the DNA of reproductive cells may be inherited, thereby becoming a permanent

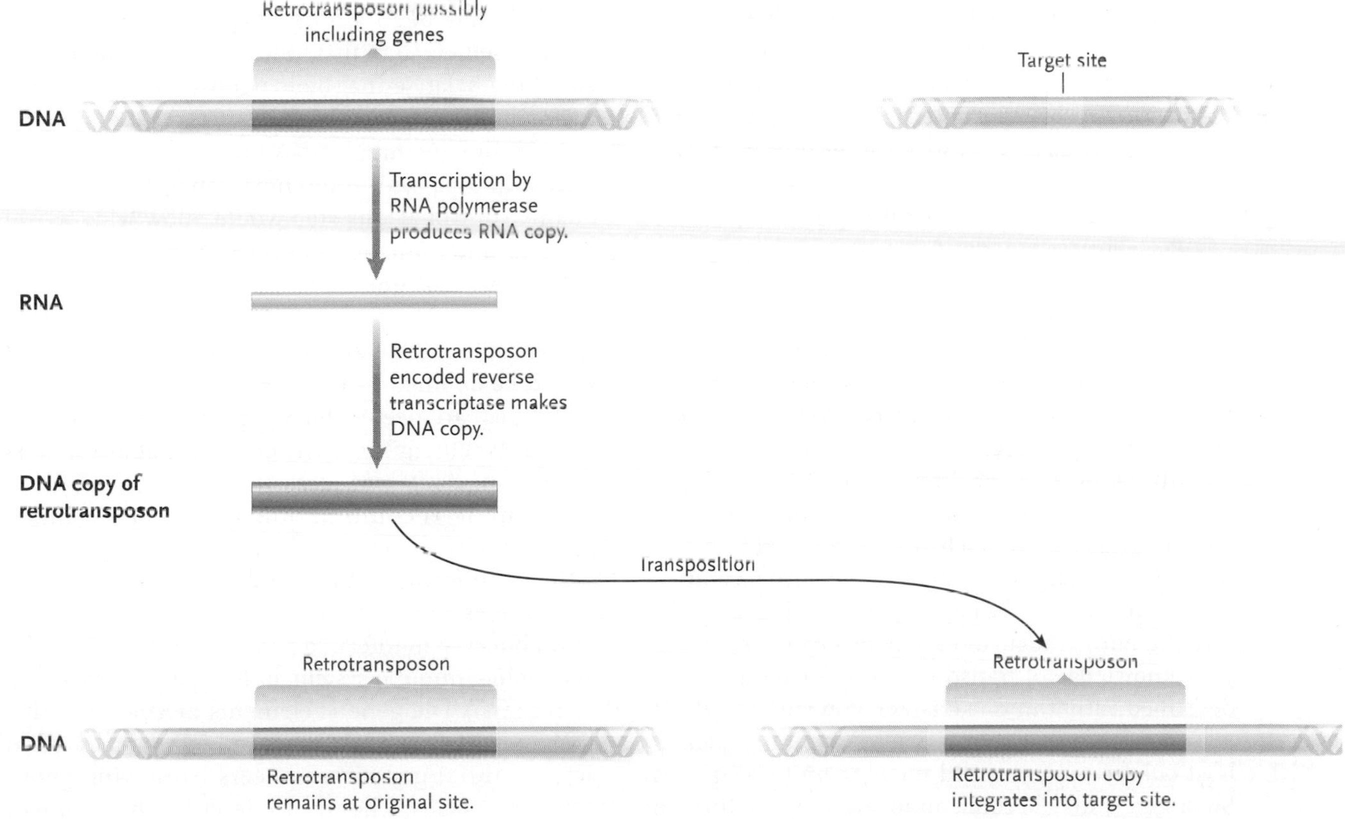

Figure 10.20
Transposition of a eukaryotic retrotransposon to a new location by means of an intermediate RNA copy.

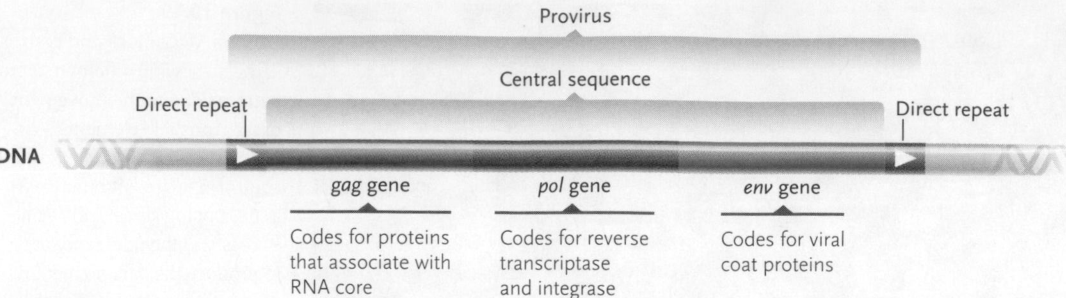

Figure 10.21
A mammalian retrovirus in the provirus form in which it is inserted into chromosomal DNA. The direct repeats at either end contain sequences capable of acting as enhancer, promoter, and termination signals for transcription. The central sequence contains genes coding for proteins, concentrated in the *gag, pol,* and *env* regions. The provirus of human immunodeficiency virus (HIV), the virus that causes acquired immune deficiency syndrome (AIDS), takes this form.

part of the genetic material of a species. Long-standing TEs are subject to mutation along with other sequences in the DNA. Such mutations may accumulate in a TE, gradually altering it into a nonmobile, residual sequence in the DNA. The DNA of many eukaryotes, including humans, contains a surprising amount of nonfunctional TE sequence likely created in this way.

10.4d Retrotransposons Are Similar to Retroviruses

The RNA to DNA reverse transcription associated with retrotransposon movement is strikingly similar to that employed by a class of eukaryotic viruses called **retroviruses.** When a retrovirus infects a host cell, a reverse transcriptase carried in the virus particle is released and copies the single-stranded RNA genome into a double-stranded DNA copy. The viral DNA is then inserted into the host DNA (by genetic recombination), where it is replicated and passed to progeny cells during cell division. Similar to the prophage of bacteria, the inserted viral DNA is known as a **provirus (Figure 10.21).**

Retroviruses are found in a wide range of organisms, with most so far identified in vertebrates. You, as well as most other humans and mammals, probably contain from 1 to as many as 100 or more retroviruses in your genome as proviruses. In total, retrotransposons and retroviruses of all types occupy some 40% of the human genome!

Although many of the retroviruses do not produce infectious virus particles, they sometimes cause DNA rearrangements such as deletions and translocations. Such changes may alter the relative position of DNA sequences on the chromosome and, in turn, disturb the normal regulation of gene expression. Given your knowledge of transduction by bacterial viruses described earlier in this chapter, you will not be surprised to hear that retroviruses sometimes pick up host eukaryotic genes and move them to recipients. Such genes may become abnormally active through the effects of regulatory sequences located in the TE itself or the DNA nearby. Certain forms of cancer have been linked to this type of abnormal activation of genes that are important in regulating cell division (see Section 14.4). In one of the most dramatic examples, a cellular gene is transported to an infected cell by the avian sarcoma retrovirus. The cellular gene is overexpressed in the new environment, resulting in uncontrolled growth of infected cells, leading to tumours in infected birds.

Study Break

Among eukaryotic mobile elements, how do transposons, retrotransposons, and retroviruses differ?

This has been a long chapter. We hope that, taken together, all of these ideas will help you understand the balance that biology must strike between the stability and the plasticity of the genetic material. On the one hand, DNA must be faithfully replicated and passed to the next generation. Lack of quality control at this step would allow widespread random mutations to undermine the selection and preservation of good combinations of alleles. On the other hand, any system that made only perfectly "photocopied" DNA available for the next generation would be doomed as well; a wide variety of diverse "solutions" are needed for a population to survive in constantly changing environments that are impossible to anticipate.

Genetic recombination is central to many processes that contribute changes to the sequence of DNA in all forms of life. (And we did not even discuss interesting examples of developmental genetic recombination in infecting parasites or the cells of the developing immune system, or foreign DNA taken up by rotifers.) The genetic elements discussed in this chapter, particularly plasmids and retroviruses, often act as natural genetic engineers by moving genes between species. Chapter 16 describes how human genetic engineers manipulate and clone DNA and how they analyze genomes at the DNA level.

Unanswered Questions

The overall mechanism and outcomes of meiosis have been known for a long time, since the turn of the twentieth century. However, despite the fundamental importance of meiosis in sexual reproduction, the biochemical, genetic, and molecular mechanisms of meiosis are poorly understood. For example, how do homologous chromosomes recognize their appropriate pairing partners? How do they become aligned in a configuration that allows the formation of crossovers? How is the number of crossover events regulated to ensure that each chromosome pair will have a crossover? Developing a deeper understanding of the molecular mechanisms that regulate meiosis is highly important in human biology because missegregation of chromosomes during meiosis I is a major cause of birth defects and the leading cause of miscarriages.

Review

Go to CENGAGENOW™ at http://hed.nelson.com/ to access quizzing, animations, exercises, articles, and personalized homework help.

10.1 Mechanism of Genetic Recombination

- Genetic recombination requires two DNA molecules that differ from one another in at least two places, a mechanism for bringing the DNA molecules into close proximity and a collection of enzymes to "cut," "exchange," and "paste" the DNA back together.
- Homology allows DNA on different molecules to line up and recombine precisely.
- Enzymatic cutting and pasting of both DNA backbones from each of the two DNA molecules is required for each recombination event.
- Two circular molecules "fuse" together as a result of a single recombination event.

10.2 Genetic Recombination in Bacteria

- Study of bacterial recombination requires detectable genetic differences between strains.
- Lederberg and Tatum created strains that were different in their ability to manufacture certain amino acids and vitamins.
- In bacteria, the DNA of the bacterial chromosome may recombine with DNA brought into close proximity from another cell.
- Three primary mechanisms bring DNA into bacterial cells from the outside: conjugation, transformation, and transduction.
- In conjugation, which is the basis of a kind of sexual reproduction in bacteria, two bacterial cells form a cytoplasmic bridge and part or all of the DNA of one cell moves into the other through the bridge. The donated DNA can then recombine with homologous sequences of the recipient cell's DNA.
- *E. coli* bacteria that are able to act as DNA donors in conjugation have an F plasmid, making them F^+; recipients have no F plasmid and are F^-. In Hfr strains of *E. coli*, the F plasmid is within the main chromosome. As a result, genes of the main chromosome are often transferred into F^- cells along with a portion of the F plasmid DNA. Researchers have mapped genes on the *E. coli* chromosome by noting the order in which they are transferred from Hfr to F^- cells during conjugation.
- In transformation, intact cells of some species absorb pieces of DNA released from cells that have disintegrated. The entering DNA fragments can recombine with the recipient cell's DNA.
- In transduction, DNA is transferred from one cell to another "by mistake" inside the head of an infecting virus.
- Since generalized transduction transfers random fragments of the host chromosome, all host genes are transferred at equal frequency. Specialized transduction only transfers genes lying close to the point of insertion of the prophage.

10.3 Genetic Recombination in Eukaryotes: Meiosis

- The time and place of meiosis follow one of three major pathways in the life cycles of eukaryotes, which reflect the portions of the life cycle spent in the haploid and diploid phases and whether mitotic divisions intervene between meiosis and the formation of gametes.
- In animals, the diploid phase is dominant, and the haploid phase is reduced. Meiosis is followed by gamete formation. Plants and most fungi alternate between haploid and diploid generations, either of which may dominate the life cycle, and both of which will divide by mitosis. The diploid sporophytes are produced by fertilization, and the haploid gametophytes are produced by mitotic divisions of the spores formed by meiosis. In some fungi, the diploid phase is limited to a single cell produced by fertilization, which then immediately undergoes meiosis.
- In animals, the products of meiosis are haploid gametes. The diploid phase of the life cycle is then restored when one gamete fuses with another. In plants, meiosis occurs in some of the cells of the diploid sporophytes and produces a generation of haploid spores. These spores then divide by mitosis to produce multicellular gametophytes.
- The functions of meiosis are to reduce the chromosome number (from diploid to haploid) and to generate genetic diversity in sexually reproducing organisms.
- Meiosis occurs only in eukaryotes that reproduce sexually and only in organisms that are at least diploid—that is, organisms that have at least two representatives of each chromosome.
- DNA replicates and the chromosomal proteins are duplicated during the premeiotic interphase, producing two copies, the sister chromatids, of each chromosome.
- During prophase I of the first meiotic division (meiosis I), the replicated chromosomes condense and come together and pair as the spindle forms in the cytoplasm.
- While they are paired, the chromatids of homologous chromosomes undergo recombination by breaking the covalent bonds of the DNA backbones, exchanging the ends and restoring the bonds.
- During prometaphase I, the nuclear envelope breaks down, the spindle enters the former nuclear area, and kinetochore microtubules leading to opposite spindle poles attach to one kinetochore of each pair of sister chromatids of homologous chromosomes.
- At metaphase I, spindle microtubule movements have aligned the tetrads on the metaphase plate, the equatorial plane between the two spindle poles. The connections of kinetochore microtubules to opposite poles ensure that the homologous pairs

separate and move to opposite spindle poles during anaphase I, reducing the chromosome number to the haploid value. Each chromosome at the poles still contains two chromatids.

- Telophase I and interkinesis are brief and transitory stages; no DNA replication occurs during interkinesis. During these stages, the single spindle of the first meiotic division disassembles and the microtubules reassemble into two new spindles for the second division.
- During prophase II, the chromosomes condense and a spindle forms. During prometaphase II, the nuclear envelope breaks down, the spindle enters the former nuclear area, and spindle microtubules leading to opposite spindle poles attach to the two kinetochores of each chromosome. At metaphase II, the chromosomes become aligned on the metaphase plate. The connections of kinetochore microtubules to opposite spindle poles ensure that during anaphase II, the chromatids of each chromosome are separated and segregate to those opposite spindle poles.
- During telophase II, the chromosomes decondense to their extended interphase state, the spindles disassemble, and new nuclear envelopes form. The result is four haploid cells, each containing half the number of chromosomes present in a G_1 nucleus of the same species.
- Meiosis II differs from mitosis in that meiosis II occurs only in reproductive tissue, is not preceded by an S phase, and results in genetically different daughter cells.
- Nondisjunction occurs when both members of a pair of homologous chromosomes connect to spindles from the same pole. Following anaphase, one pole then receives both copies of the pair, and the other pole receives none. The overall result (following normal meiosis II) is gametes that have two copies of a chromosome. After fertilization, the resulting zygote will therefore have three copies of the chromosome instead of two.
- In many eukaryotes, including most animals, one or more pairs of chromosomes, called the sex chromosomes, are different in male and female individuals of the same species.
- Recombination is the first source of the genetic variability produced by meiosis. During recombination, chromatids generate new combinations of alleles by physically exchanging segments. The exchange process involves precise breakage and joining of DNA molecules. It is catalyzed by enzymes and occurs while the homologous chromosomes are held together tightly by the synaptonemal complex. The crossovers visible between the chromosomes at late prophase I reflect the exchange of chromatid segments that occurred during the molecular steps of genetic recombination.
- The random segregation of homologous chromosomes is the second source of genetic variability produced by meiosis. The homologous pairs separate at anaphase I of meiosis, segregating random combinations of maternal and paternal chromosomes to the spindle poles.
- Random segregation of the chromatids of replicated chromosomes at meiosis II is a third mechanism for generating diversity.
- Random joining of male and female gametes in fertilization is the fourth source of genetic variability.

10.4 Mobile Elements

- Both prokaryotes and eukaryotes contain TEs (transposable elements)—DNA sequences that can move from place to place in the DNA. The TEs may move from one location in the DNA to another or generate duplicated copies that insert in new locations while leaving the "parent" copy in its original location.
- Genes of the host cell DNA may become incorporated into a TE and may be carried with it to a new location. There the genes may become abnormally active when placed near sequences that control the activity of genes within the TE or near the control elements of active host genes.
- Eukaryotic TEs occur as transposons, which release from one location in the DNA and insert at a different site, or as retrotransposons, which move by making an RNA copy, which is then replicated into a DNA copy that is inserted at a new location. The "parent" copy remains at the original location. Like retrotransposons, retroviruses integrate into chromosomal DNA by making a DNA copy of their RNA genome. Retroviruses may have evolved from retrotransposons.
- TE-instigated abnormal activation of genes regulating cell division has been linked to the development of some forms of cancer in humans and other complex animals.

Questions

Self-Test Questions

1. If recombination occurred between bacteria as shown in the figure, the result would be

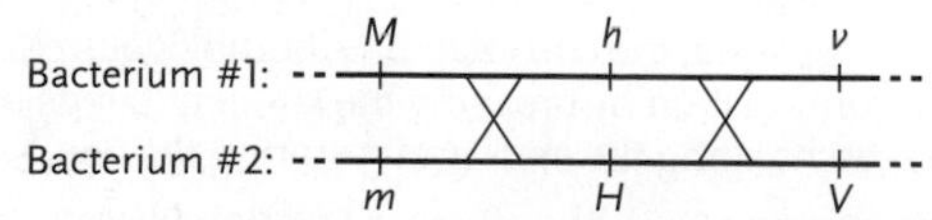

a. MHv and mhV.
b. MHV and mhv.
c. Mhv and mHv.
d. MHV and mhV.
e. mhv and MhV.

2. Which of the following is *not* correct for bacterial conjugation?
a. Both Hfr and F^+ bacteria have the ability to code for a sex pilus.
b. After an F^- cell has conjugated with an F^+, its plasmid holds the F^+ factor.
c. The recipient cell usually becomes Hfr following conjugation.
d. In an Hfr × F^- mating, DNA of the main chromosome moves to a recipient cell.
e. Genes on the F factor encode proteins of the sex pilus.

3. Which of the following is *not* correct for bacterial transformation?
a. Artificial transformation is used in cloning procedures.
b. Avery was able to transform live noninfective bacteria with DNA from dead infective bacteria.
c. The cell wall and plasma membrane must be penetrated for transformation to proceed.

d. A virus is required for the process.
e. Electroporation is a form of artificial transformation used to introduce DNA into cells.

4. Transduction
   a. may allow recombination of newly introduced DNA with host cell DNA.
   b. is the movement of DNA from one bacterial cell to another by means of a plasmid.
   c. can cause the DNA of the donor to change but not the DNA of the recipient.
   d. is the movement of viral DNA but not bacterial DNA into a recipient bacterium.
   e. requires physical contact between two bacterium.
5. A virus in its lysogenic cycle is
   a. lysing the host cell.
   b. transducing a bacterial cell.
   c. assembling viral particles for cell rupture.
   d. damaging the host cell.
   e. embedded in host DNA and is called a prophage.
6. The diploid number of this individual is 6.

   This figure represents
   a. mitotic metaphase.
   b. meiotic metaphase I.
   c. meiotic metaphase II.
   d. a gamete.
   e. six nonhomologous chromosomes.
7. Chiasmata
   a. form during metaphase II of meiosis.
   b. occur between two nonhomologous chromosomes.
   c. represent chromosomes independently assorting.
   d. are sites of DNA exchange between homologous chromatids.
   e. ensure that the resulting cells are identical to the parent cell.
8. If $2n$ is four, the number of possible combinations in the resulting gametes is
   a. 1.
   b. 2.
   c. 4.
   d. 8.
   e. 16.
9. The number of human chromosomes in a cell in prophase I of meiosis is ___ and in telophase II is ___ .
   a. 92; 46
   b. 46; 23
   c. 23; 23
   d. 23; 16
   e. 4; 2
10. The DNA content in a diploid cell in G_2 is X. If that cell goes into meiosis at its metaphase II, the DNA content would be
    a. 0.1X.
    b. 0.5X.
    c. X.
    d. 2X.
    e. 4X.
11. In the human gamete,
    a. there must be one chromosome of each type, except for the sex chromosomes, where both an X chromosome and a Y chromosome are present.
    b. a chromosome must be represented from each parent.
    c. there must be an unequal mixture of chromosomes from both parents.
    d. there must be representation of chromosomes from only one parent.
    e. there is the possibility of 2^{46} different combinations of maternal and paternal chromosomes.
12. Which of the following is *not* correct about transposable elements?
    a. They can be recognized by their ends of inverted transposable elements.
    b. They have an internal portion that can be transcribed.
    c. They encode a transposase enzyme.
    d. They have no harmful effects on cell function.
    e. They move by a cut-and-paste or copy-and-paste mechanism.
13. Which is *not* correct about retroviruses?
    a. They are RNA viruses.
    b. They are believed to be the source of retrotransposons.
    c. They encode an enzyme for their insertion into host cell DNA.
    d. They encode single-stranded viral DNA from viral RNA.
    e. They encode a reverse transcriptase enzyme for RNA to DNA synthesis.

Questions for Discussion

1. You set up an experiment like the one carried out by Lederberg and Tatum, mixing millions of *E. coli* of two strains with the following genetic constitutions.

   Among the bacteria obtained after mixing, you find some

   Strain 1: bio^- met^- thr^+ leu^+

   Strain 2: bio^+ met^+ thr^- leu^-

   cells that do not require threonine, leucine, or biotin to grow but still need methionine. How might you explain this result?
2. You have a technique that allows you to measure the amount of DNA in a cell nucleus. You establish the amount of DNA in a sperm cell of an organism as your baseline. Which multiple of this amount would you expect to find in a nucleus of this organism at G_2 of premeiotic interphase? At telophase I of meiosis? During interkinesis? At telophase II of meiosis?
3. Mutations are changes in DNA sequences that can create new alleles. In which cells of an individual, somatic or meiotic cells, would mutations be of greatest significance to that individual? What about to the species to which the individual belongs?
4. Experimental systems have been developed in which transposable elements can be induced to move under the control of a researcher. Following the induced transposition of a yeast TE element, two mutants were identified with altered activities of enzyme X. One of the mutants lacked enzyme activity completely, whereas the other had five times as much enzyme activity as normal cells did. Both mutants were found to have the TE inserted into the gene for enzyme X. Propose hypotheses for how the two different mutant phenotypes were produced.

Mice, showing genetic variation in coat colour.

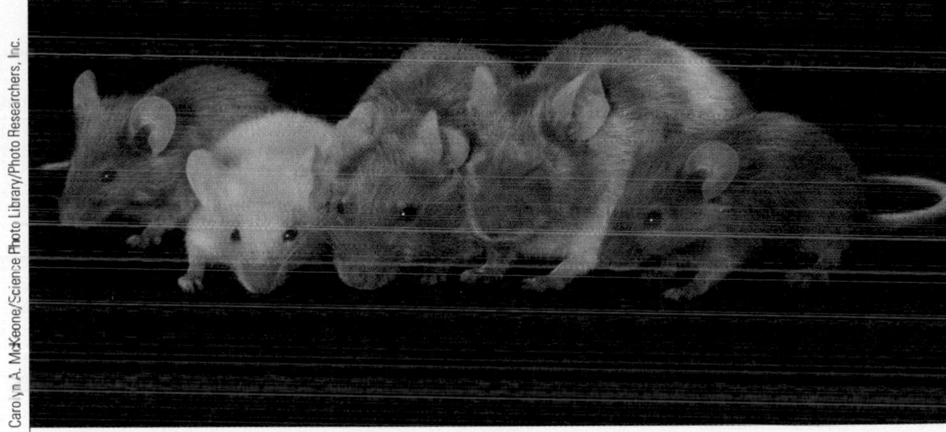

11 Mendel, Genes, and Inheritance

Study Plan

Why It Matters

Parties and champagne were among the last things on Ernest Irons's mind on New Year's Eve, 1904. Irons, a medical intern, was examining a blood specimen from a new patient and was sketching what he saw through his microscope—peculiarly elongated red blood cells **(Figure 11.1, p. 230)**. He and his supervisor, James Herrick, had never seen anything like them. The shape of the cells was reminiscent of a sickle, a cutting tool with a crescent-shaped blade.

The patient had complained of weakness, dizziness, shortness of breath, and pain. His father and two sisters had died from mysterious ailments that had damaged their lungs or kidneys. Did those deceased family members also have sickle-shaped red cells in their blood? Was there a connection between the abnormal cells and the ailments? How did the cells become sickled?

The medical problems that baffled Irons and Herrick killed their patient when he was only 32 years old. The patient's symptoms were characteristic of a genetic disorder now called *sickle cell disease*. This disease develops when a person has received two copies of a gene (one from each parent) that codes for an altered subunit of hemoglobin, the oxygen-transporting protein in red blood cells. When oxygen supplies

a.

b.

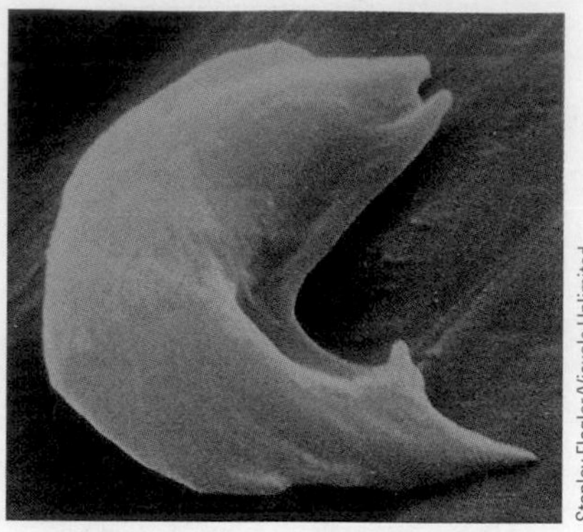

Figure 11.1
Red blood cell shape in sickle cell disease. **(a)** A normal red blood cell. **(b)** A sickled red blood cell.

are low, the altered hemoglobin forms long, fibrous, crystal-like structures that push red blood cells into the sickle shape. The altered protein differs from the normal protein by just a single amino acid.

The sickled red blood cells are too elongated and inflexible to pass through the capillaries, the smallest vessels in the circulatory system. As a result, the cells block the capillaries. The surrounding tissues become starved for oxygen and saturated with metabolic wastes, causing the symptoms experienced by Irons' and Herrick's patient. The problem worsens as oxygen concentration falls in tissues and more red blood cells are pushed into the sickled form. (You will learn more about sickle cell disease in this chapter and in Chapter 12.)

Researchers have studied sickle cell disease in great detail at both the molecular and the clinical levels. You may find it curious, however, that our understanding of sickle cell disease—and all other heritable traits—actually began with studies of pea plants in a monastery garden.

Fifty years before Ernest Irons sketched sickled red blood cells, a scholarly monk named Gregor Mendel **(Figure 11.2)** used garden peas to study patterns of inheritance. To test his hypotheses about inheritance, Mendel bred generation after generation of pea plants and carefully observed the patterns by which parents transmit traits to their offspring. Through his experiments and observations, Mendel discovered the fundamental rules that govern inheritance. His discoveries and conclusions founded the science of genetics and still have the power to explain many of the puzzling and sometimes devastating aspects of inheritance that continue to occupy our attention.

Figure 11.2
Gregor Mendel (1822–1884), the founder of genetics.

11.1 The Beginnings of Genetics: Mendel's Garden Peas

Until about 1900, scientists and the general public believed in the **blending theory of inheritance**, which suggested that hereditary traits blend evenly in offspring through mixing of the parents' blood, much like the effect of mixing coffee and cream. Even today, many people assume that parental characteristics such as skin colour, body size, and facial features blend evenly in their offspring, with the traits of the children appearing about halfway between those of their parents. Yet if blending takes place, why don't extremes, such as very tall and very short individuals, gradually disappear over generations as repeated blending takes place? Also, why do children with blue eyes keep turning up among the offspring of brown-eyed parents?

Gregor Mendel's experiments with garden peas, performed in the 1860s, provided the first answers to these questions and many more. Mendel was an Augustinian monk who lived in a monastery in Brünn, now part of the Czech Republic. But he had an unusual education for a monk in the mid-nineteenth century. He had studied mathematics, chemistry, zoology, and botany at the University of Vienna under some of the foremost scientists of his day. He had also been reared on a farm and was well aware of agricultural principles and their application. He kept abreast of breeding experiments published in scientific journals. Mendel also won several awards for developing improved varieties of fruits and vegetables.

In his work with peas, Mendel studied a variety of heritable characteristics called **characters**, such as flower colour or seed shape. A variation in a character, such as purple or white flower colour, is called a **trait.** Mendel established that characters are passed to offspring in the form of discrete hereditary factors, which now are known as genes. Mendel observed that, rather than blending evenly, many parental traits appear unchanged in offspring, whereas others disappear in one generation to reappear unchanged in the next. Although Mendel did not know it, the inheritance patterns he observed are the result of the segregation of chromosomes, on which the genes are located, to gametes in meiosis (see Chapter 10). Mendel's methods illustrate, perhaps as well as any experiments in the history of science, how rigorous scientific work is conducted: through observation, making hypotheses, and testing the hypotheses with experiments.

11.1a Mendel Chose True-Breeding Garden Peas for His Experiments

Mendel chose the garden pea (*Pisum sativum*) for his research because the plant could be grown easily in the monastery garden, without elaborate equipment. As in other flowering plants, gametes are produced in structures of the flowers (see **Figure 11.3**). The male gametes are sperm nuclei contained in the pollen, which is produced in the *anthers* of the flower. The female gametes are egg cells, produced in the *carpel* of the flowers. Normally, pea plants **self-fertilize** (also known as **self-pollinate**, or more simply, *self*): sperm nuclei in pollen produced by anthers fertilize egg cells housed in the carpel of the same flower. However, for his experiments, Mendel prevented self-fertilization simply by cutting off the anthers. Pollen to fertilize these flowers must then come from a different plant. This technique is called **cross-pollination**, or more simply, a *cross*. This technique allowed Mendel to test the effects of mating pea plants of different parental types.

To begin his experiments, Mendel chose pea plants that were known to be **true-breeding** (also called *pure-breeding*); that is, when self-fertilized, or more simply, *selfed*, they passed traits without change from one generation to the next.

11.1b Mendel First Worked with Single-Character Crosses

Flower colour was among the seven characters Mendel selected for study; one true-breeding variety of peas had purple flowers, and the other true-breeding variety had white flowers (see Figure 11.3). Would these traits blend evenly if plants with purple flowers were cross-pollinated with plants with white flowers?

To answer this question, Mendel took pollen from the anthers of plants with purple flowers and placed it in the flowers of white-flowered plants. He placed the pollen on the *stigma*, the part of the carpel that receives pollen in flowers (see Figure 11.3). He also performed the reciprocal experiment by placing pollen from white-flowered plants on the stigmas of purple-flowered plants. Seeds were the result of the crosses; each seed contains a zygote, or embryo, that will develop into a new pea plant. The plants that develop from the seeds produced by the cross—the first generation of offspring from the cross—are the **F_1 generation** (F stands for *filial; filius* = son). The plants used in the initial cross are called the parental or **P generation.** The plants that grew from the F_1 seeds all formed purple flowers, as if the trait for white flowers had disappeared. The flowers showed no evidence of blending.

Mendel then allowed the purple-flowered F_1 plants to self, producing seeds that represented the **F_2 generation.**

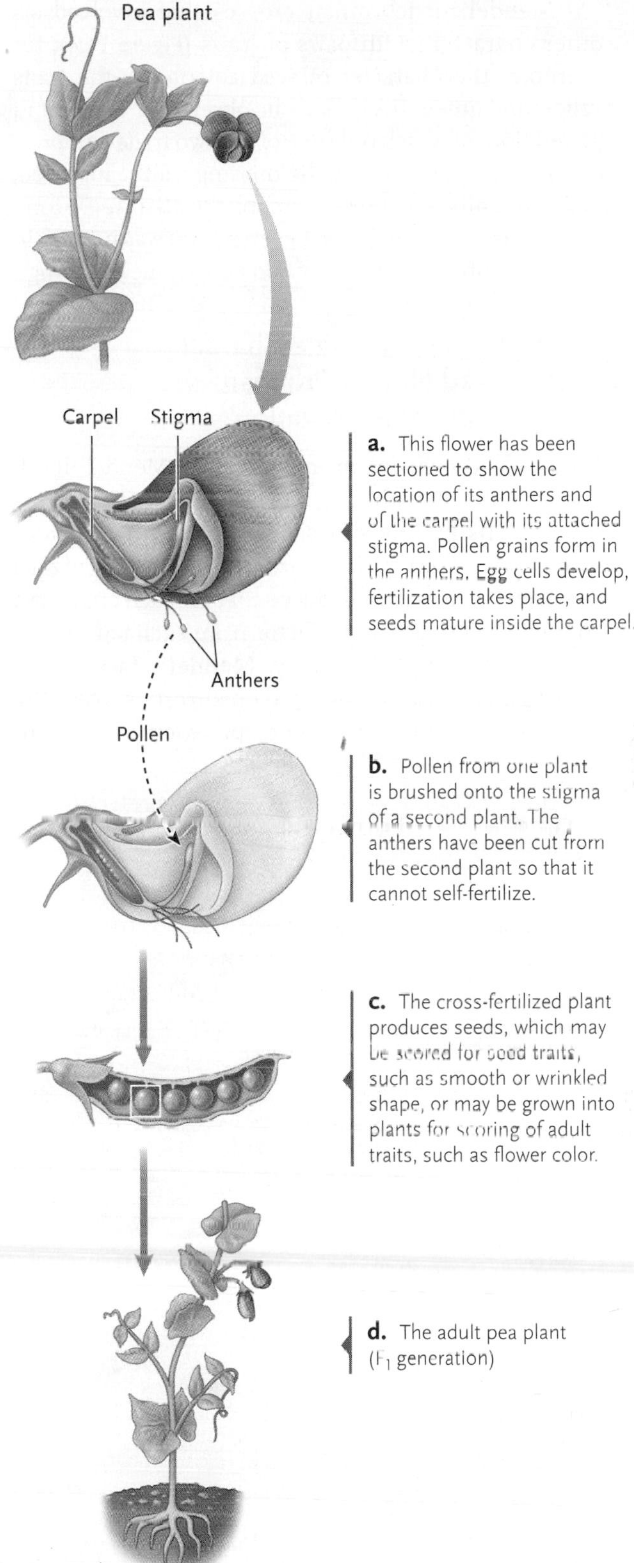

Pea plant
Carpel
Stigma
Anthers
Pollen
a. This flower has been sectioned to show the location of its anthers and of the carpel with its attached stigma. Pollen grains form in the anthers. Egg cells develop, fertilization takes place, and seeds mature inside the carpel.
b. Pollen from one plant is brushed onto the stigma of a second plant. The anthers have been cut from the second plant so that it cannot self-fertilize.
c. The cross-fertilized plant produces seeds, which may be scored for seed traits, such as smooth or wrinkled shape, or may be grown into plants for scoring of adult traits, such as flower color.
d. The adult pea plant (F_1 generation)

Figure 11.3
The garden pea (*Pisum sativum*), the focus of Mendel's experiments.

When he planted the F_2 seeds produced by this cross, the white-flowered trait reappeared: both purple-flowered and white-flowered plants were produced. Mendel counted 705 plants with purple flowers and 224 with white flowers, in a ratio that he noted was close to 3:1, or about 75% purple-flowered plants and 25% white-flowered plants.

Mendel made similar crosses that involved six other characters with pairs of traits (**Figure 11.4**); for example, the character of seed colour has the traits yellow and green. In all cases, he observed a uniform F_1 generation, in which only one of the two traits was present. In the F_2 generation, the missing trait reappeared, and both traits were present among the offspring. Moreover, the trait present in the F_1 generation was present in a definite, predictable proportion among the offspring.

11.1c Mendel's Single-Character Crosses Led Him to Propose the Principle of Segregation

Using his knowledge of mathematics, Mendel developed a set of hypotheses to explain the results of his crosses. His first hypothesis was that *the adult plants carry a pair of factors that govern the inheritance of each character.* He correctly deduced that for each character, an organism inherits one factor from each parent.

In modern terminology, Mendel's factors are called *genes,* which are located on chromosomes; the different versions of a gene, producing different traits of a character, are **alleles** of the gene. Although Mendel did not use the modern terms *genes* and *alleles,* we use them in this chapter in our description of Mendel's work. Thus, there are two alleles of the gene that govern flower colour in garden peas: one allele for purple flower colour and the other allele for white flower colour. Organisms with two copies of each gene are now known as diploids; the two alleles of a gene in a diploid individual may be identical or different.

How can the disappearance of one of the traits, such as white flowers, in the F_1 generation and its reappearance in the F_2 generation be explained? Mendel deduced that the trait that had seemed to "disappear" in the F_1 generation actually was present but was masked in some way by the "stronger" allele. Mendel called the masking effect **dominance.** Accordingly, Mendel's second hypothesis stated that *if an individual's pair of genes consists of different alleles, one allele is dominant over the other.* This hypothesis assumes that one allele is **dominant** and the other allele is **recessive.** When a dominant allele for a trait is paired with a recessive allele for the same trait, the dominant allele is expressed.

Figure 11.4
Mendel's crosses with seven different characters in peas, including his results and the calculated ratios of offspring.

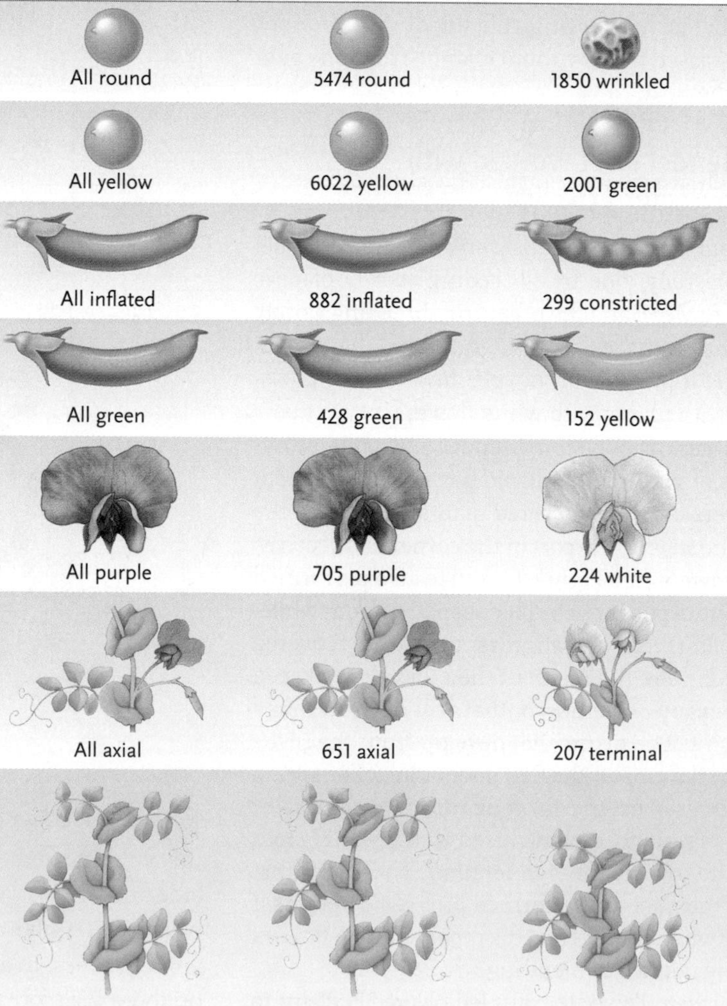

Character	Traits crossed	F_1	F_2		Ratio
Seed shape	round × wrinkled	All round	5474 round	1850 wrinkled	2.96:1
Seed colour	yellow × green	All yellow	6022 yellow	2001 green	3.01:1
Pod shape	inflated × constricted	All inflated	882 inflated	299 constricted	2.95:1
Pod colour	green × yellow	All green	428 green	152 yellow	2.82:1
Flower colour	purple × white	All purple	705 purple	224 white	3.15:1
Flower position	axial (along stems) × terminal (at tips)	All axial	651 axial	207 terminal	3.14:1
Stem length	tall × dwarf	All tall	787 tall	277 dwarf	2.84:1

By contrast, a recessive allele is expressed only when two copies of the allele are present. For example, for flower colour in Mendel's experiments, the allele for purple flowers was dominant and the allele for white flowers was recessive.

As a third hypothesis, Mendel proposed the following: *The pairs of alleles that control a character **segregate** (separate) as gametes are formed; half the gametes carry one allele, and the other half carry the other allele.* This hypothesis is now known as Mendel's **Principle of Segregation.** During fertilization, fusion of the haploid maternal and paternal gametes produces a diploid nucleus called the *zygote nucleus*. The zygote nucleus receives one allele for the character from the male gamete and one allele for the same character from the female gamete, reuniting the pairs.

Mendel's three hypotheses explained the results of the crosses (**Figure 11.5**). Both alleles of the gene that governs flower colour in the original, true-breeding parent plant with purple flowers are the same. The symbol *P* is used here to designate this allele, with the capital letter indicating that it is dominant, which gives this true-breeding parent the *PP* combination of alleles. Such an individual is called a **homozygote** (*homo* = same) and is said to be **homozygous** for the *P* allele. In other words, the individual has two copies of the same allele of the flower colour gene. Therefore, when the individual produces gametes and the paired alleles separate, all the gametes of this individual will receive a *P* allele (see the left side heading in **Figure 11.5a**).

In the original true-breeding parent with white flowers, both alleles of the gene are also the same. The symbol *p* is used here to designate this allele, with the lowercase letter indicating that it is recessive, which gives this true-breeding plant the homozygous *pp* combination of alleles. These alleles also separate during gamete formation, producing gametes with one *p* allele (see the top heading in Figure 11.5a). (Mendel originated the practice of using uppercase and lowercase letters to designate dominant and recessive alleles.)

All the F_1 plants produced by crossing purple-flowered and white-flowered plants—the cross *PP* × *pp*—receive the same combination of alleles, *Pp* (see the cell in Figure 11.5a). An individual of this type, with two different alleles of a gene, is called a **heterozygote** (*hetero* = different) and is said to be **heterozygous** for the trait. Because *P* is dominant over *p*, all the *Pp* plants have purple flowers, even though they also carry the allele for white flowers. An F_1 heterozygote produced from a cross that involves a single character is called a **monohybrid** (*mono* = one; *hybrid* = an offspring of parents with different traits).

According to Mendel's hypotheses, all the *Pp* plants in the F_1 generation produce two kinds of gametes. Because the heterozygous *Pp* pair separates during gamete formation, half of the gametes receive the *P* allele and half receive the *p* allele. **Figure 11.5b** shows how these gametes can combine during selfing of F_1 plants. Generally, a cross between two individuals that are each heterozygous for the same pair of alleles—*Pp* × *Pp* here—is called a **monohybrid cross.** The gametes are entered in both the rows and columns in Figure 11.5b; the cells show the possible combinations. Combining two gametes that both carry the *P* allele produces a *PP* F_2 plant; combining *P* from one parent and *p* from the other produces a *Pp* plant; and combining *p* from both F_1 parents produces a *pp* F_2 plant. The homozygous *PP* and heterozygous *Pp* plants in the F_2 generation have purple flowers, the dominant trait; the homozygous *pp* offspring have white flowers, the recessive trait.

Mendel's hypotheses explain how individuals may differ genetically but still look the same. The *PP* and *Pp* plants, although genetically different, both have purple flowers. In modern terminology, **genotype** refers to the *genetic constitution of an organism*, and **phenotype** (Greek *phainein* = to show) refers to its *outward appearance*. In this case, the two different genotypes *PP* and *Pp* produce the same purple-flower phenotype.

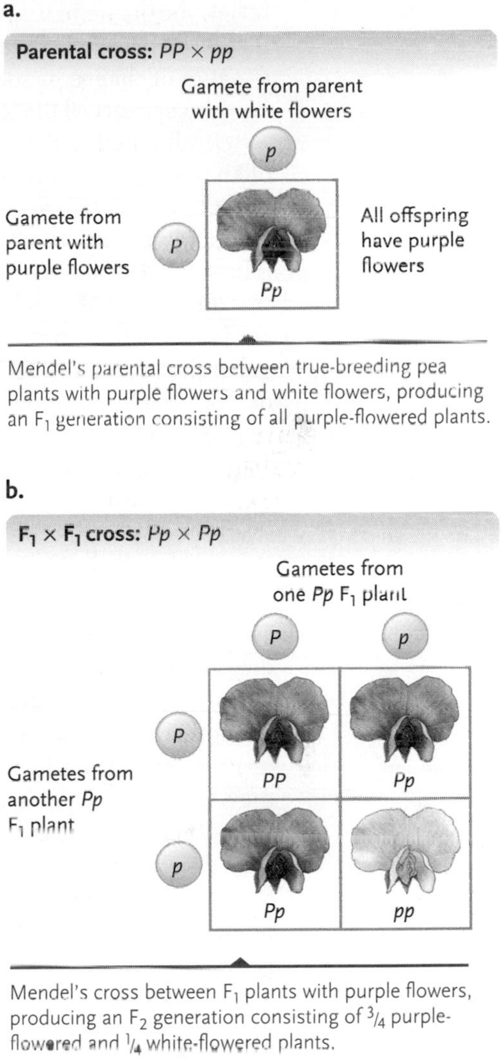

Thus, the results of Mendel's crosses support his three hypotheses:

1. The genes that govern genetic characters occur in pairs in individuals.
2. If different alleles are present in an individual's pair of genes, one allele is dominant over the other.
3. The two alleles of a gene segregate and enter gametes singly.

a.

Mendel's parental cross between true-breeding pea plants with purple flowers and white flowers, producing an F_1 generation consisting of all purple-flowered plants.

b.

Mendel's cross between F_1 plants with purple flowers, producing an F_2 generation consisting of 3/4 purple-flowered and 1/4 white-flowered plants.

Figure 11.5 The principle of segregation in Mendel's crosses studying the inheritance of flower colour in garden peas.

11.1d Mendel Could Predict Both Classes and Proportions of Offspring from His Hypotheses

Mendel could predict both classes and proportions of offspring from his hypotheses. To understand how Mendel's hypotheses allowed him to predict the proportions of offspring resulting from a genetic cross, let's review the mathematical rules that govern **probability**—that is, the possibility that an outcome will occur if it is a matter of chance, as in the random fertilization of an egg by a sperm cell that contains one allele or another.

In the mathematics of probability, the likelihood of an outcome is predicted on a scale of 0 to 1. An outcome that is certain to occur has a probability of 1, and an outcome that cannot possibly happen has a probability of 0. The standard game die, a cube with one of the numbers 1 through 6 on each face, is a familiar model to demonstrate working with probability. In general, we determine the probability of any given outcome (rolling a 4) by dividing that outcome by the total number of possible outcomes. For obtaining 4 in rolling a die, the probability is 1 divided by 6, or 1/6. The likelihood of rolling an even number (2, 4, 6) would be 3/6 = 1/2. The probabilities of all the possible outcomes, when added together, must equal 1.

The Product Rule in Probability. If you were to roll two dice together, what is the chance of rolling double fours? Because the outcome of one die has no effect on the other one, the two rolls are independent. When two or more events are independent, the probability that they will both occur is calculated using the **product rule**—their individual probabilities are multiplied. That is, the probability that events A and B *both* will occur equals the probability of event A *multiplied* by the probability of event B. For example, the probability of getting a 4 on the first die is 1/6; the probability of a 4 on the second die is also 1/6 **(Figure 11.6)**. Because the events are independent, the probability of getting a 4 on both dice is 1/6 × 1/6 = 1/36. Applying this principle to human families, the sex of one child has no effect on the sex of the next child; therefore, the probability of having four girls in a row is the product of their individual probabilities (very close to 1/2 for each birth): 1/2 × 1/2 × 1/2 × 1/2 = 1/16.

a. Likelihood of rolling a double four.

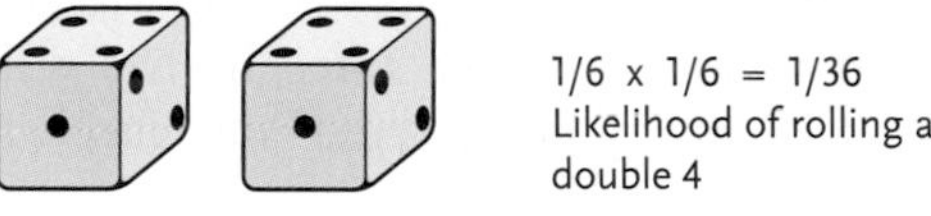

b. Likelihood of rolling a seven in any combination.

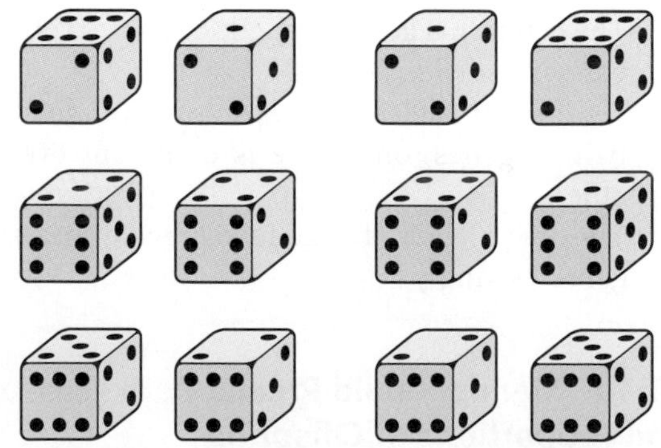

Figure 11.6
Rules of probability. **(a)** For each die, the probability of a 4 is 1/6. Because the outcome of one die is independent of that of the other, the combined probability of rolling a 4 on both dice at the same time is calculated by multiplying the individual probabilities (product rule). **(b)** Since there are six different outcomes, each of which adds up to 7, the total likelihood of rolling a 7 is calculated by adding the individual probabilities (sum rule).

The Sum Rule in Probability. Another relationship, the **sum rule**, applies when several different events all give the same outcome; that is, the probability that *either* event A *or* event B *or* event C will occur equals the probability of event A *plus* the probability of event B *plus* the probability of event C. Returning to the two dice example, what is the probability of rolling a 7? Several different events all give the same total. One could make a total of 7 from a 1 on the first die and a 6 on the second, or a 5 on the first and a 2 on the second, or a 4 on the first and a 3 on the second. Each of these three combinations would be expected to occur at a frequency of 1/6 × 1/6 = 1/36. Hopefully, you can see three more possible combinations that are just the reciprocal of the first three, that is, 6 on the first die and a 1 on the second, and so on, for a total of six different ways to roll "7." That is, there are six ways of obtaining the same outcome. Therefore, for the probability of rolling a 7, we sum the individual probabilities to get the final probability: 1/36 + 1/36 + 1/36 + 1/36 + 1/36 + 1/36 = 6/36 = 1/6. On average, you could expect to roll a combination of numbers totalling 7 once in every six attempts.

Probability in Mendel's Crosses. Since the randomness inherent in meiosis is comparable to the randomness inherent in rolling dice, the same rules of probability just discussed apply to genes carried on chromosomes in Mendel's crosses. For example, in the crosses that involve the purple-flowered and white-flowered traits, half of the gametes of the F_1 generation contain the *P* allele of the gene and half contain the *p* allele (see Figure 11.5b). To produce a *PP* zygote, two *P* gametes must combine. The probability of selecting a *P* gamete from one F_1 parent is 1/2, and the probability of selecting a *P* gamete from the other F_1 parent is also 1/2. Therefore, the probability of producing a *PP* zygote from this monohybrid cross is 1/2 × 1/2 = 1/4. That is, by the product rule, one-fourth of the offspring of the F_1 cross *Pp* × *Pp* are expected to be *PP*, which have purple flowers **(Figure 11.7a)**. By the same line of reasoning, one-fourth of the F_2 offspring are expected to be *pp*, which have white flowers **(Figure 11.7b)**.

What about the production of *Pp* offspring? The cross *Pp* × *Pp* can produce *Pp* in two different ways. A *P* gamete from the first parent can combine with a *p* gamete from the second parent (*Pp*), or a *p* gamete from the first parent can combine with a *P* gamete from the second parent (*pP*) **(Figure 11.7c)**. Because there are two different ways to get the same outcome, we apply the sum rule to obtain the combined probability. Each of the ways to get *Pp* has an individual probability of 1/4; when we add these individual probabilities, we have 1/4 + 1/4 = 1/2.

Therefore, half of the offspring are expected to be *Pp*, which have purple flowers. We could get the same result from the requirement that all of the individual probabilities must add up to 1. If the probability of *PP* is 1/4 and the probability of *pp* is 1/4, then the probability of the remaining possibility, *Pp*, must be 1/2, because the total of the individual probabilities must add up to 1: 1/4 + 1/4 + 1/2 = 1.

What if we want to know the probability of obtaining purple flowers in the cross *Pp* × *Pp*? In this case, the rule of addition applies, because there are two ways to get purple flowers: genotypes *PP* and *Pp*. Adding the individual probabilities of these combinations, 1/4 *PP* + 1/2 *Pp*, gives a total of 3/4, indicating that three-fourths of the F_2 offspring are expected to have purple flowers. Because the total probabilities must add up to 1, the remaining one-fourth of the offspring are expected to have white flowers (1/4 *pp*). These proportions give the ratio 3:1, which is close to the ratio Mendel obtained in his cross.

What we have just stepped through in describing Figure 11.7 is the **Punnett square** method for determining the genotypes of offspring and their expected proportions. To use the Punnett square, write the probability of obtaining gametes with each type of allele from one parent at the top of the diagram and write the chance of obtaining each type of allele from the other parent on the left side. Then fill in the cells by combining the alleles from the top and from the left and multiply their individual probabilities.

11.1e Mendel Used a Testcross to Check the Validity of His Hypotheses

Mendel realized that he could assess the validity of his hypotheses by determining whether they could be used successfully to *predict* the outcome of a cross of a different type than he had tried so far. Accordingly, he crossed an F_1 plant with purple flowers, assumed to have the heterozygous genotype *Pp*, with a true-breeding white-flowered plant, with the homozygous genotype *pp*. In this cross, *Pp* × *pp*, all the gametes of the *pp* plant contain a single *p* allele. Therefore, the probability that a gamete from this parent contains *p* is 1. The gamete and its probability of 1 are entered as the row heading of the Punnett square in **Figure 11.8.** The *Pp* parent produces two types of gametes, half that contain the *P* allele and half that contain the *p* allele. These values, 1/2 *P* and 1/2 *p*, are entered as the column headings. Filling in the possible combinations in the cells gives the two expected classes, *Pp* and *pp*, both with a probability of 1/2. Thus, half the offspring of this cross are expected to have purple flowers and half are expected to have white flowers; the ratio is 1:1. Mendel's actual results in this cross were 85 purple-flowered plants and 81 white-flowered plants, which closely approach the expected 1:1 ratio. Mendel also made the same type of cross with all the other traits used in his study, including those traits affecting seed shape, seed colour, and plant height, and found the same 1:1 ratio.

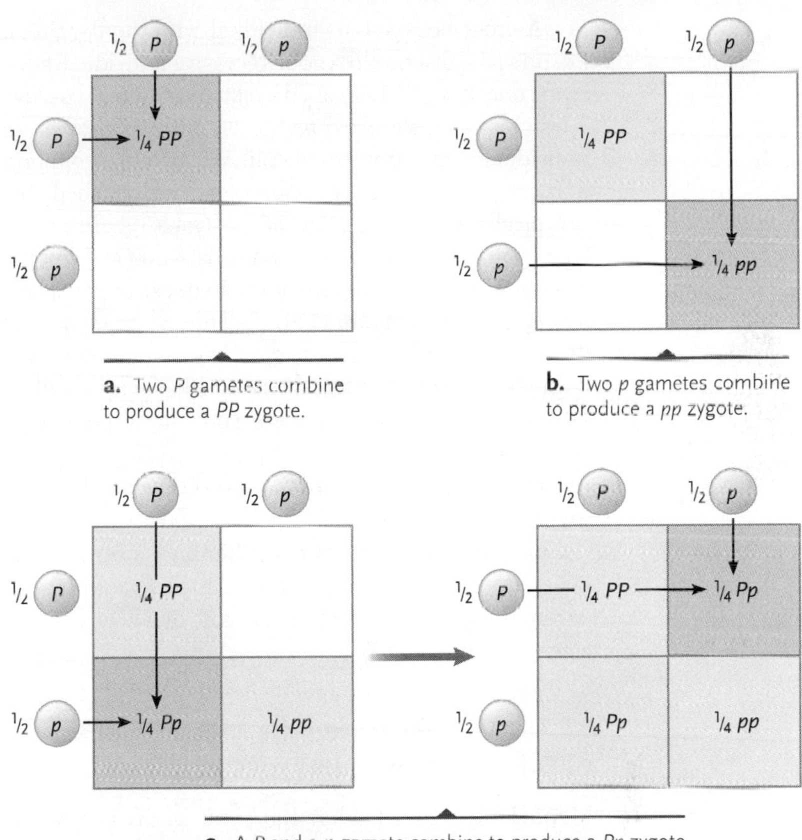

1/2 P
1/2 p
1/4 PP
1/4 Pp
1/4 pp
a. Two P gametes combine to produce a PP zygote.
b. Two p gametes combine to produce a pp zygote.
c. A P and a p gamete combine to produce a Pp zygote in two squares, for a total of 1/4 Pp + 1/4 Pp = 1/2 Pp.

Figure 11.7
Punnett square method for predicting offspring and their ratios in genetic crosses. The example is the F_1 × F_1 cross of purple-flowered plants from Figure 11.5. Each cell shows the genotype and proportion of one type of zygote.

Figure 11.8
Method of predicting the outcome of genetic crosses.

a.

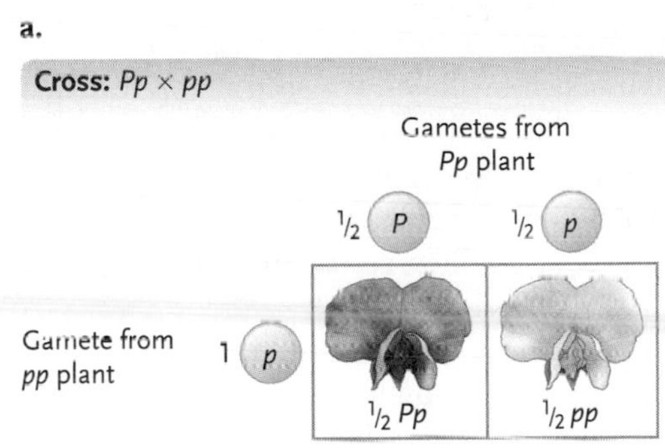

b.

Cross: *PP* × *pp*

Gamete from *pp* plant

1 *p*

Gamete from *PP* plant

1 *P*

1 *Pp*

A cross between an individual with the dominant phenotype and a homozygous recessive individual, such as the one described, is called a **testcross.** Geneticists use a testcross as a standard test to determine whether an individual with a dominant trait is a heterozygote or a homozygote, because these cannot be distinguished phenotypically. If the offspring of the testcross are of two types, with half displaying the dominant trait and half the recessive trait, then the individual in question must be a heterozygote (see Figure 11.8). If all the offspring display the dominant trait, the individual in question must be a homozygote. For example, the cross *PP* × *pp* gives all *Pp* progeny, which show the dominant purple phenotype (see Figure 11.8).

Obviously, the testcross method cannot be used for humans. However, it can be used in reverse by noting the traits present in families over several generations and working backward to deduce whether a parent must have been a homozygote or a heterozygote (see also Chapter 12).

11.1f Mendel Tested the Independence of Different Genes in Crosses

Mendel next asked what happens in crosses when more than one character is involved. Would the alleles of different characters be inherited independently, or would they interact to alter their expected proportions in offspring?

To answer these questions, Mendel crossed parental stocks that had differences in two of the hereditary characters he was studying: seed shape and seed colour. His single-character crosses had shown that each was controlled by a pair of alleles. For seed shape, the *RR* or *Rr* genotypes produce round seeds and the *rr* genotype produces wrinkled seeds. For seed colour, yellow is dominant. The homozygous *YY* and heterozygous *Yy* genotypes produce yellow seeds; the homozygous *yy* genotype produces green seeds.

Mendel crossed plants that bred true for the production of round and yellow seeds (*RR YY*) with plants that bred true for the production of wrinkled and green seeds (*rr yy*) **(Figure 11.9).** The cross, *RR YY* × *rr yy*, yielded an F_1 generation that consisted of all round yellow seeds, with the genotype *Rr Yy*. A zygote produced from a cross that involves two characters is called a **dihybrid** (*di* = two).

Mendel then planted the F_1 seeds, grew the plants to maturity, and selfed them; that is, he crossed the F_1 plants to themselves. A cross between two individuals that are heterozygous for two pairs of alleles—here *Rr Yy* × *Rr Yy*—is called a **dihybrid cross** (see Figure 11.9). The seeds produced by these plants, representing the F_2 generation, included 315 round yellow seeds, 101 wrinkled yellow seeds, 103 round green seeds, and 32 wrinkled green seeds. Mendel noted that these numbers were close to a 9:3:3:1 ratio (3:1 for round: wrinkled, and 3:1 for yellow:green).

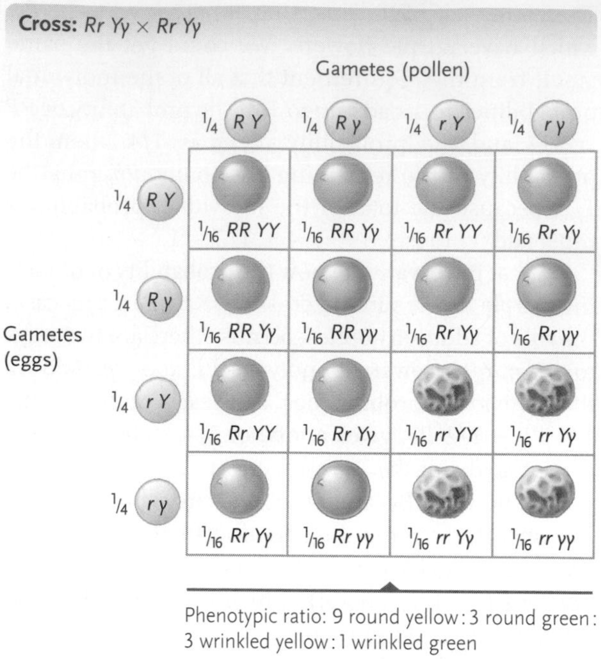

Cross: *Rr Yy* × *Rr Yy*

Gametes (pollen)

Gametes (eggs)	1/4 R Y	1/4 R y	1/4 r Y	1/4 r y
1/4 R Y	1/16 RR YY	1/16 RR Yy	1/16 Rr YY	1/16 Rr Yy
1/4 R y	1/16 RR Yy	1/16 RR yy	1/16 Rr Yy	1/16 Rr yy
1/4 r Y	1/16 Rr YY	1/16 Rr Yy	1/16 rr YY	1/16 rr Yy
1/4 r y	1/16 Rr Yy	1/16 Rr yy	1/16 rr Yy	1/16 rr yy

Phenotypic ratio: 9 round yellow : 3 round green : 3 wrinkled yellow : 1 wrinkled green

Figure 11.9
The Principle of Independent Assortment in Mendel's crosses involving two hereditary characters in garden peas, seed shape, and seed colour.

This 9:3:3:1 ratio was consistent with Mendel's previous findings if he added one further hypothesis: *The alleles of the genes that govern the two characters segregate independently during formation of gametes.* That is, the allele for seed shape that the gamete receives (*R* or *r*) has no influence on which allele for seed colour it receives (*Y* or *y*) and vice versa. The two events are completely independent. Mendel termed this assumption **independent assortment;** it is now known as Mendel's **Principle of Independent Assortment.**

To understand the effect of independent assortment in the cross, assume that the *RR YY* parent produces only *R Y* gametes and the *rr yy* parent produces only *r y* gametes. In the F_1 generation, all possible combinations of these gametes produce only one genotype, *Rr Yy*, in the offspring. As observed, all the F_1 will be round yellow seeds.

If the alleles that control seed shape and seed colour assort independently in gamete formation, each F_1 plant grown from the seeds would produce four types of gametes. The *R* allele for seed shape can be delivered independently to a gamete with either the *Y* or *y* allele for seed colour, and, similarly, the *r* allele can be delivered to a gamete with either the *Y* or *y* allele. Thus, the independent assortment of genes from the *Rr Yy* parents is expected to produce four types of gametes with equal probability: 1/4 *R Y*, 1/4 *R y*, 1/4 *r Y*, and 1/4 *r y*. These gametes and their probabilities are entered as the row and column headings of the Punnett square in Figure 11.9.

Filling in the cells of the diagram (see Figure 11.9) gives 16 combinations of alleles, all with an equal probability of 1 in every 16 offspring. Of these, the genotypes *RR YY*, *RR Yy*, *Rr YY*, and *Rr Yy* all have the same phenotype: round yellow seeds. These combinations occur in 9 of the 16 cells in the diagram, giving a total probability of 9/16. The genotypes *rr YY* and *rr Yy*, which produce the wrinkled yellow seeds, are found in three cells, giving a probability of 3/16 for this phenotype. Similarly, the genotypes *RR yy* and *Rr yy*, which yield round green seeds, occur in three cells, giving a probability of 3/16. Finally, the genotype *rr yy*, which produces wrinkled green seeds, is found in only one cell and therefore has a probability of 1/16.

These probabilities of round yellow seeds, wrinkled yellow seeds, round green seeds, and wrinkled green seeds, in a 9:3:3:1 ratio, closely approximate the actual results of 315:101:108:32 obtained by Mendel. Thus, Mendel's first three hypotheses, with the added hypothesis of independent assortment, explain the observed results of his dihybrid cross. Mendel's testcrosses completely confirmed his hypotheses; for example, the testcross *Rr Yy* × *rr yy* produced 55 round yellow seeds, 51 round green seeds, 49 wrinkled yellow seeds, and 53 wrinkled green seeds. This distribution corresponds well with the expected 1:1:1:1 ratio in the offspring. (Try to set up a Punnett square for this cross and predict the expected classes of offspring and their frequencies.)

Mendel's first three hypotheses provided a coherent explanation of the pattern of inheritance for alternate traits of the same character, such as purple and white for flower colour. His fourth hypothesis, independent assortment, addressed the inheritance of traits for different characters, such as seed shape, seed colour, and flower colour, and showed that, instead of being inherited together, the traits of different characters were distributed independently to offspring.

11.1g Mendel's Research Founded the Field of Genetics

Mendel's techniques and conclusions were so advanced for his time that their significance was not immediately appreciated. Mendel's success was based partly on a good choice of experimental organism. He was also lucky. The characters he chose all segregate independently; that is, none of them are physically near each other on the chromosomes, a condition that would have given ratios other than 9:3:3:1, showing that they do not assort independently. Mendel's findings anticipated in detail the patterns by which genes and chromosomes determine inheritance. Yet, when Mendel first reported his findings, during the nineteenth century, the structure and function of chromosomes and the patterns by which they are separated and distributed to gametes were unknown; meiosis remained to be discovered. In addition, his use of mathematical analysis was a new and radical departure from the usual biological techniques of his day.

Mendel reported his results to a small group of fellow intellectuals in Brünn and presented his results in 1866 in a natural history journal published in the city. His article received little notice outside of Brünn, and those who read it were unable to appreciate the significance of his findings. His work was overlooked until the early 1900s, when three investigators—Hugo de Vries in Holland, Carl Correns in Germany, and Erich von Tschermak in Austria—independently performed a series of breeding experiments similar to Mendel's and reached the same conclusions. These investigators, in searching through previously published scientific articles, discovered to their surprise Mendel's article about his experiments conducted 34 years earlier. Each gave credit to Mendel's discoveries, and the quality and far-reaching implications of his work were at last realized. Mendel died in 1884, 16 years before the rediscovery of his experiments and conclusions; thus, he never received the recognition that he so richly deserved during his lifetime.

Mendel was unable to relate the behaviour of his "factors" (genes) to cell structures because the critical information he required was not obtained until later, through the discovery of meiosis during the 1890s. The next section describes how a genetics student familiar with meiosis was able to make the connection between Mendel's factors and chromosomes.

11.1h Sutton's Chromosome Theory of Inheritance Related Mendel's Genes to Chromosomes

By the time Mendel's results were rediscovered in the early 1900s, critical information from studies of meiosis was available. It was not long before a genetics student, Walter Sutton, recognized the similarities between the inheritance of the genes discovered by Mendel and the behaviour of chromosomes in meiosis and fertilization **(Figure 11.10, p. 238)**.

In a historic article published in 1903, Sutton, then a graduate student at Columbia University in New York, drew all the necessary parallels between genes and chromosomes:

- Chromosomes occur in pairs in sexually reproducing, diploid organisms, as do the alleles of each gene.
- The chromosomes of each pair are separated and delivered singly to gametes, as are the alleles of a gene.
- The separation of any pair of chromosomes in meiosis and gamete formation is independent of the separation of other pairs (see Figure 11.10), as in the independent assortment of the alleles of different genes in Mendel's dihybrid crosses.

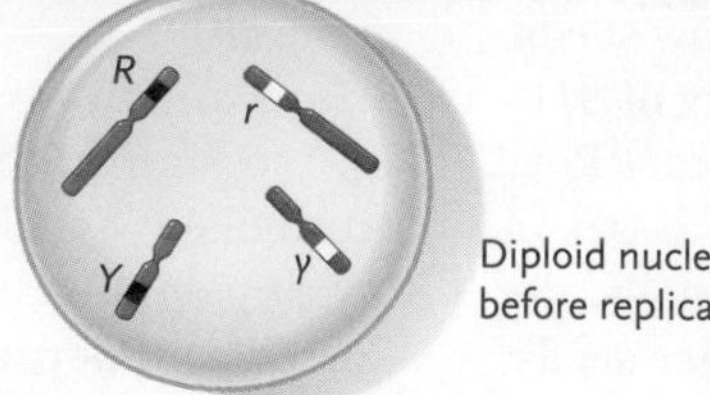

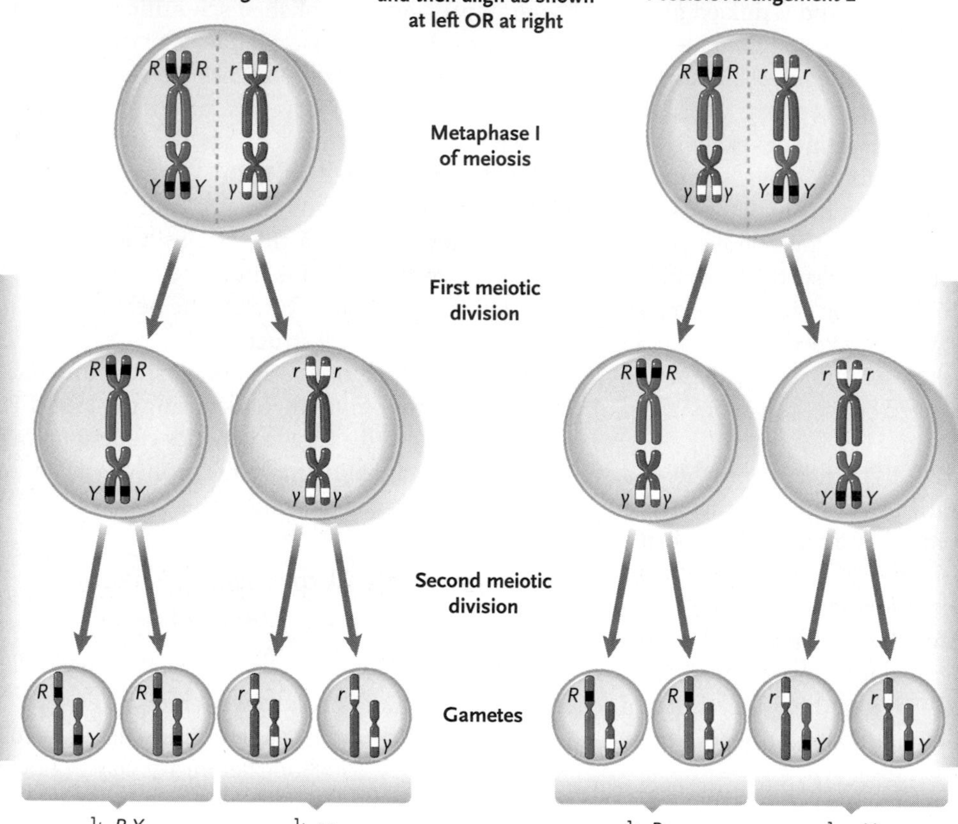

Chromosomes replicate in S phase before meiosis and then align as shown at left OR at right
Possible Arrangement 1
Possible Arrangement 2
Metaphase I of meiosis
First meiotic division
Second meiotic division
Gametes
During chromosome separation, the chromosomes of different pairs segregate independently.
The two meiotic divisions separate chromosome pairs and deliver them singly to gametes.
Principle of segreration:
The two alleles of a gene segregate from each other during gamete formation. (R and r enter gametes singly, as do Y and y.)
Principle of independent assortment:
During the segregation of alleles into gametes, the alleles of different pairs assort independently. (R/r and Y/y alleles give 4 combinations in gametes in equal proportion.)
1/4 R Y
1/4 r y
1/4 R y
1/4 r Y

Figure 11.10
The parallels between the behaviour of chromosomes and genes and alleles in meiosis. The gametes show four different combinations of alleles produced by independent segregation of chromosome pairs.

- Finally, one member of each chromosome pair is derived in fertilization from the male parent, and the other member is derived from the female parent, in an exact parallel with the two alleles of a gene.

From this total coincidence in behaviour, Sutton correctly concluded that genes and their alleles are carried on the chromosomes, a conclusion known today as the **chromosome theory of inheritance.**

The exact parallel between the principles set forth by Mendel, and the behaviour of chromosomes and genes during meiosis, is shown in Figure 11.10 for an *Rr Yy* diploid. For a cross of *Rr Yy* × *Rr Yy*, when the gametes fuse randomly, the progeny will show a phenotypic ratio of 9:3:3:1. This mechanism explains the same ratio of gametes and progeny as the *Rr Yy* × *Ry Yy* cross in Figure 11.9.

The particular site on a chromosome at which a gene is located is called the **locus** (plural, *loci*) of the gene. The locus is a particular DNA sequence that encodes a protein or ribonucleic acid (RNA) product responsible for the phenotype controlled by the gene. A locus for a gene with two alleles, *A* and *a*, on a homologous pair of chromosomes is shown in **Figure 11.11.** At the molecular level, different alleles consist of small differences in the DNA sequence of a gene, which may result in functional differences in the protein or RNA product encoded by the gene. These differences are detected as distinct phenotypes in the offspring of a cross.

All the genetics research conducted since the early 1900s has confirmed Mendel's basic hypotheses about

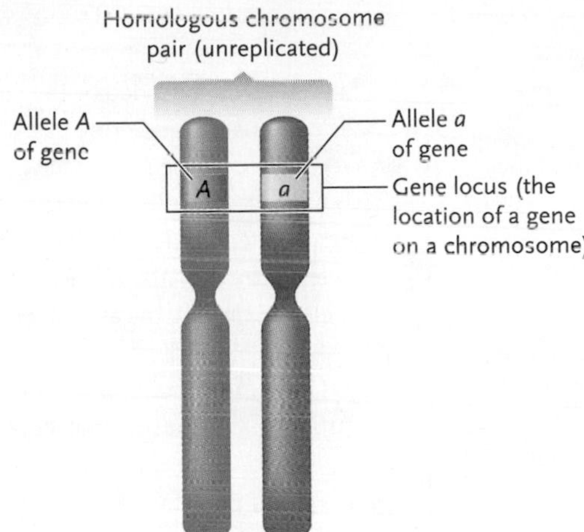

Figure 11.11
A locus, the site occupied by a gene on a pair of homologous chromosomes. Two alleles, *A* and *a*, of the gene are present at this locus in the homologous pair. These alleles have differences in the DNA sequence of the gene.

inheritance. This research has shown that Mendel's conclusions apply to all types of organisms, from yeast and fruit flies to humans, and has led to the rapidly growing field of human genetics. In humans, a number of easily seen traits show inheritance patterns that follow Mendelian principles **(Figure 11.12)**; for example, albinism, the lack of normal skin colour, is recessive to normal skin colour, and fingers with webs between them are recessive to normally separated fingers. Similarly, achondroplasia, the most frequent form of short-limb dwarfism, is a recessive trait that involves abnormal bone growth. Many human disorders that cannot be seen easily also show simple inheritance patterns. For instance, cystic fibrosis, in which a defect in the membrane transport of chloride ions leads to pulmonary and digestive dysfunctions and eventually death, is a recessive trait.

The post-Mendel research has demonstrated additional patterns of inheritance (see the next section) that were not anticipated by Mendel and, in some circumstances, require modifications or additions to his hypotheses.

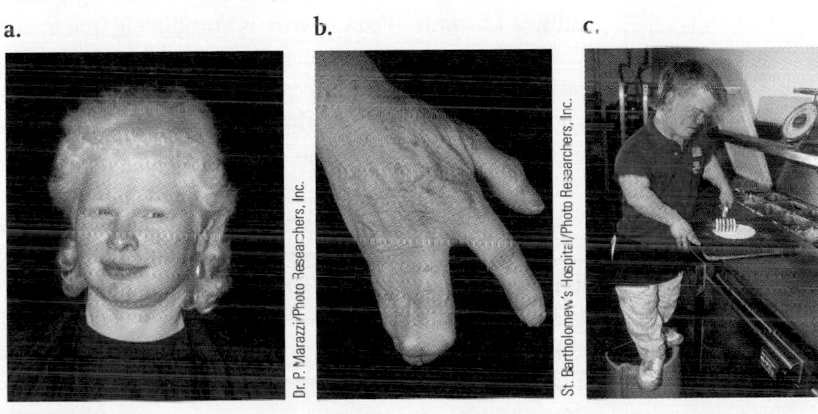

Figure 11.12
Human traits showing inheritance patterns that follow Mendelian principles. **(a)** Lack of normal skin colour (albinism). **(b)** Webbed fingers. **(c)** Achondroplasia, or short-limbed dwarfism.

Study Break

1. What characteristics of the garden pea made this organism a good model system for Mendel?
2. How does independent assortment explain Mendel's dihybrid cross data?
3. How is an allele related to a locus?

11.2 Later Modifications and Additions to Mendel's Hypotheses

The rediscovery of Mendel's research in the early 1900s produced an immediate burst of interest in genetics. The research that followed greatly expanded our understanding of genes and their inheritance. The discovery that the alleles of many genes are neither fully dominant nor fully recessive was among these new findings. Some alleles show incomplete dominance, in which recessive alleles do have some effect on the phenotype of heterozygotes. Other alleles are codominant; that is, they have different and approximately equal effects in heterozygotes.

Further research also demonstrated that more than two alleles of a gene may be present among all the members of a population. This condition, called multiple alleles, is still consistent with Mendel's conclusions because each sexually reproducing, diploid individual in a population has only two alleles of each gene—a pair—which are inherited and passed on according to Mendel's principles.

Geneticists also found that the activity of one gene can influence the activity of a different gene, a phenomenon called epistasis. Furthermore, some characters are explained by polygenic inheritance, in which several different genes each contribute to the phenotype. In addition, alterations in a single gene sometimes affect more than one phenotype in an organism; this phenomenon is called pleiotropy. The following sections discuss each of these so-called extensions of Mendel's fundamental principles.

11.2a In Incomplete Dominance, Dominant Alleles Do Not Completely Mask Recessive Alleles

Incomplete dominance occurs when the effects of recessive alleles can be detected to some extent in heterozygotes. Flower colour in snapdragons shows incomplete dominance

Why Mendel's Dwarf Pea Plants Were So Short

Two independent research teams worked out the molecular basis for one of the seven characters Mendel studied—dwarfing, which is governed by stem length in garden peas. The investigators, including Diane Lester and her colleagues at the University of Tasmania in Australia and David Martin and his coworkers at Oregon State University, were interested in learning the molecular differences in the alleles of the gene that produced tall or dwarf plants. The dominant *T* allele (*T* = tall) of the gene produces plants of normal height; the recessive *t* allele produces dwarf plants with short stems. How can a single gene control the overall height of a plant?

Lester's team discovered that the gene codes for an enzyme that carries out a preliminary step in the synthesis of the plant hormone gibberellin, which, among other effects, causes the stems of plants to elongate. Martin's group cloned the gene and determined its complete DNA sequence. (Cloning techniques and DNA sequencing are described in Sections 16.1 and 16.3.) The sequence showed that the *T* and *t* alleles of the gene encode two versions of the enzyme that catalyzes gibberellin synthesis, which differ by only a single amino acid. Lester's group found that the faulty enzyme encoded by the *t* allele carries out its step (addition of a hydroxyl group to a precursor) much more slowly than the enzyme encoded by the normal *T* allele. As a result, plants with the *t* allele have only about 5% as much gibberellin in their stems as *T* plants. The reduced gibberellin levels limit stem elongation, producing the dwarf plants.

Thus, the methods of molecular biology allowed contemporary researchers to study a gene first discovered in the mid-nineteenth century. The findings leave little doubt that a change in a single amino acid leads to the dwarf phenotype Mendel observed in his monastery garden.

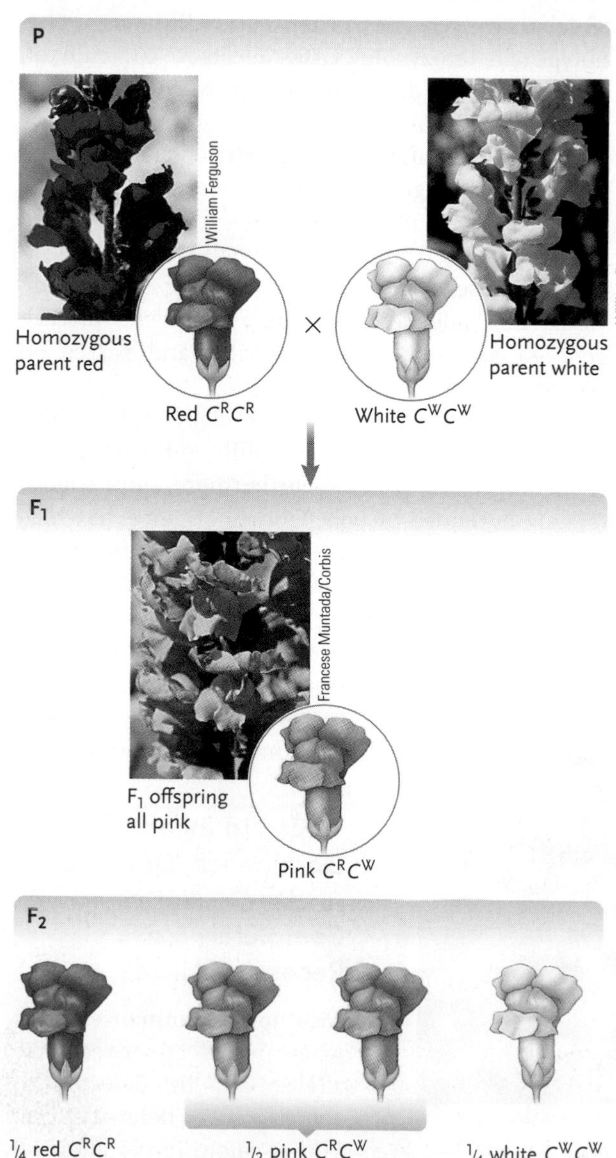

Figure 11.13 Incomplete dominance in the inheritance of flower colour in snapdragons.

(Figure 11.13). If true-breeding, red-flowered and white-flowered snapdragon plants are crossed, all the F_1 offspring have pink flowers (see Figure 11.13). The pink colour might make it appear that the pure red and white colours have blended out and disappeared—mixing red and white makes pink—until two F_1 plants are crossed. The cross demonstrates that the red and white traits both reappear in the F_2 generation, which has red, pink, and white flowers in numbers approximating a 1:2:1 ratio.

This outcome can be explained by incomplete dominance between a C^R allele for red colour and a C^W allele for white colour. When one allele is not completely dominant to the other, we use a superscript to signify the character. In this case, *C* signifies the character for flower colour and the superscripts indicate the alleles (R for red and W for white). Therefore, the initial cross is C^RC^R (red) × C^WC^W (white), which produces C^RC^W F_1 (pink) plants. The C^R allele encodes an enzyme that produces a red pigment, but two alleles (C^RC^R) are necessary to produce enough of the active form of the enzyme to produce fully red flowers. The enzyme is completely inactive in C^WC^W plants, which produce colourless flowers that appear white because of the scattering of light by cell walls and other structures. With their single C^R allele, the C^RC^W heterozygotes of the F_1 generation can produce only enough pigment to give the flowers a pink colour. When the pink C^RC^W F_1 plants are crossed, the fully red and white colours reappear, together with the pink colour, in the F_2 generation, in a ratio of 1/4 C^RC^R (red), 1/2 C^RC^W (pink), and 1/4 C^WC^W (white). This ratio is exactly the same as the ratio of genotypes produced from a cross of two heterozygotes in Mendel's experiments (for example, see Figure 11.7, pp. 233).

Some human disorders show incomplete dominance. For example, sickle cell disease (see the introduction to

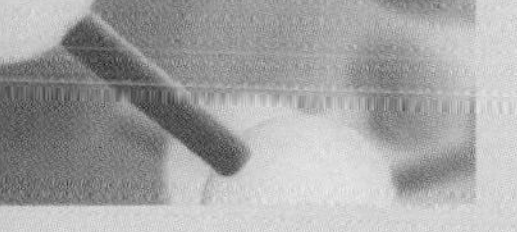

MOLECULE BEHIND BIOLOGY

Phenylthiocarbamide (PTC)

Have you ever sat down to a plate of Brussels sprouts, only to find that they taste unpleasantly bitter? This sensation arises because receptors in the membranes of taste cells on your tongue are binding to compounds such as isothiocyanate (that happens to be toxic to your thyroid in large doses). Much of our understanding of the molecular nature of bitter taste perception has grown out of an accidental observation that a synthetic chemical, phenylthiocarbamide (PTC), tastes intensely bitter to some people and yet is tasteless to others. PTC "nontasters" make up 20 to 30% of almost all populations of humans, chimps, and gorillas studied. Although several genes influence the limits of PTC detection, one particular member of the bitter receptor gene family on human chromosome 7 is mainly responsible for PTC tasting ability. The two most common alleles of this gene, "taster" and "nontaster," show a codominant inheritance pattern in families. Since PTC is not found in nature, it is likely that the two very common alleles detect naturally occurring toxic compounds containing the bitter-tasting thiourea chemical structure shown in the diagram (N − C = S).

Figure 1
The chemical structure of phenylthiocarbamide (PTC). Note the N − C = S component.

this chapter) is characterized by an alteration in the hemoglobin molecule that changes the shape of red blood cells when oxygen levels are low. An individual with sickle cell disease is homozygous for a recessive allele that encodes a defective form of one of the polypeptides of the hemoglobin molecule. Individuals heterozygous for that recessive allele and the normal allele have a condition known as *sickle cell trait,* which is a milder form of the disease because the individuals still produce normal polypeptides from the normal allele.

Familial hypercholesterolemia is another example of incomplete dominance. The gene involved encodes the low-density lipoprotein (LDL) receptor, a cell membrane protein responsible for removing excess cholesterol from the blood (see Section 5.5). Individuals with familial hypercholesterolemia are homozygous for a defective LDL receptor gene, produce no LDL receptors, and have a severe form of the disease. These individuals have six times the normal level of cholesterol in the blood and therefore are very prone to atherosclerosis (hardening of the arteries). Many individuals with familial hypercholesterolemia have heart attacks as children. Heterozygous individuals have half the normal number of receptors, which results in a milder form of the disease. Their symptoms are twice the normal blood cholesterol level, an unusually high risk of atherosclerosis, and a high risk of heart attacks before age 35.

Many alleles that appear to be completely dominant are actually incomplete in their effects when analyzed at the biochemical or molecular level. For example, for pigments that produce fur or flower colours, biochemical studies often show that even though heterozygotes may produce enough pigment to make them look the same externally as homozygous dominants, a difference in the amount of pigment is measurable at the biochemical level. Thus, whether dominance between alleles is complete or incomplete often depends on the level at which the effects of the alleles are examined.

A similar situation occurs in humans who carry the recessive allele that causes Tay–Sachs disease. Children who are homozygous for the recessive allele do not have a functional version of an enzyme that breaks down gangliosides, a type of membrane lipid. As a result, gangliosides accumulate in the brain, leading to mental impairment and eventually to death. Heterozygotes are without symptoms of the disease, even though they have one copy of the recessive allele. However, at the biochemical level, reduced breakdown of gangliosides can be detected in heterozygotes, evidently due to a reduced quantity of the active enzyme.

11.2b In Codominance, the Effects of Different Alleles Are Equally Detectable in Heterozygotes

Codominance occurs when alleles have approximately equal effects in individuals, making the alleles equally detectable in heterozygotes. The inheritance of the human blood types, M, MN, and N, is an example of codominance. These are different blood types from the familiar blood types of the ABO blood group. The L^M and L^N alleles of the MN blood group gene that control this character encode different forms of a glycoprotein molecule located on the surface of red blood cells. If the genotype is L^ML^M, only the M form of the glycoprotein is present and the blood type is M; if it is L^NL^N, only the N form is present and the blood type is N. In heterozygotes with the L^ML^N genotype, both glycoprotein types are present and can be detected, producing the blood type MN. Because each genotype has a different phenotype, the inheritance pattern for the MN blood group alleles is generally the same as for incompletely dominant alleles. That is, you would not be able to distinguish between codominance and incomplete dominance just by comparing the ratio of offspring from crosses.

The MN blood types do not affect blood transfusions and have relatively little medical importance. However, they have been invaluable in tracing human evolution and prehistoric migrations, and they are frequently used in initial tests to determine the paternity of a child. Among their primary advantages in research and paternity determination is that the genotype of all individuals, including heterozygotes, can be detected directly—and inexpensively—from their phenotype, with no requirement for further genetic tests or analysis.

11.2c In Multiple Alleles, More Than Two Alleles of a Gene Are Present in a Population

One of Mendel's major and most fundamental assumptions was that alleles occur in pairs in individuals; in the pairs, the alleles may be the same or different. After the rediscovery of Mendel's principles, it soon became apparent that although alleles do indeed occur in pairs in individuals, **multiple alleles** (more than two different alleles of a gene) may be present if all the individuals of a population are taken into account. For example, for a gene *B*, there could be the normal allele, *B*, and several alleles with alterations in the gene named, for example, b_1, b_2, b_3, and so on. Some individuals in a population may have the *B* and b_1 alleles of a gene; others, the b_2 and b_3 alleles; still others, the b_3 and b_5 alleles; and so on, for all possible combinations. Thus, although any one individual can have only two alleles of the gene, there are more than two alleles in the population as a whole. Genes may certainly occur in many more than the four alleles of the example; for instance, one of the genes that plays a part in the acceptance or rejection of organ transplants in humans has more than 200 different alleles.

The multiple alleles of a gene each contain differences at one or more points in their DNA sequences **(Figure 11.14),** which cause detectable alterations in the structure and function of gene products encoded by the alleles. Multiple alleles present no real difficulty in genetic analysis because each diploid individual still has only two of the alleles, allowing gametes to be predicted and traced through crosses by the usual methods.

Human ABO Blood Group. The human *ABO* blood group provides another interesting example of multiple alleles, in a system that also exhibits both dominance and codominance. The ABO blood group was discovered in 1901 by Karl Landsteiner, an Austrian biochemist who was investigating the sometimes fatal outcome of attempts to transfer whole blood from one person to another. Landsteiner found that only certain combinations of four blood types, designated A, B, AB, and O, can be mixed safely in transfusions **(Table 11.1).**

B allele ...ATGCAGATACCGATTACAGACCATAGG...

b_1 allele ...ATGCAGAGACCGATTACAGACCATAGG...

b_2 allele ...ATGCAGATGCCGATTACAGACCATAGG...

b_3 allele ...ATGCAGATACCGATTACAGGCCATAGG...

Figure 11.14
Multiple alleles. Multiple alleles consist of small differences in the DNA sequence of a gene at one or more points, which result in detectable differences in the structure of the protein encoded by the gene. The *B* allele is the normal allele, which encodes a protein with normal function. The three *b* alleles each have alterations of the normal protein-coding DNA sequence that may adversely affect the function of that protein.

Table 11.1 Blood Types of the Human ABO Blood Group

Blood Type	Antigens	Antibodies	Blood Types Accepted in a Transfusion
A	A	Anti-B	A or O
B	B	Anti-A	B or O
AB	A and B	None	A, B, AB, or O
O	None	Anti-A, anti-B	O

Landsteiner determined that, in the wrong combinations, red blood cells from one blood type are agglutinated or clumped by an agent in the serum of another type (the serum is the fluid in which the blood cells are suspended). The clumping was later found to depend on the action of an antibody in the blood serum. (Antibodies, protein molecules that interact with specific substances called antigens, are discussed in Chapter 44.)

The antigens responsible for the blood types of the ABO blood group are the carbohydrate parts of glycoproteins located on the surfaces of red blood cells (unrelated to the glycoprotein carbohydrates responsible for the blood types of the MN blood group). People with type A blood have *antigen A* on their red blood cells, and people with type B blood have *antigen B* on their red blood cells. At the same time, people with type A blood have antibodies against antigen B, and people with type B blood have antibodies against antigen A. People with type O blood have neither antigen A nor antigen B on their red blood cells, but they have antibodies against both of these antigens. People with type AB blood have neither anti-A nor anti-B antibodies, but they have both the A and B antigens, and their red blood cells are clumped by antibodies in the blood of all the other groups.

The four blood types—A, B, AB, and O—are produced by different combinations of multiple (three) alleles of a single gene *I* **(Figure 11.15).** The three alleles, designated I^A, I^B, and i, produce the following blood types:

I^AI^A = type A blood $\quad$ I^BI^B = type B blood

I^Ai = type A blood $\quad$ I^Bi = type B blood

I^AI^B = type AB blood $\quad$ ii = type O blood

In addition, I^A and I^B are codominant alleles that are each dominant to the i allele.

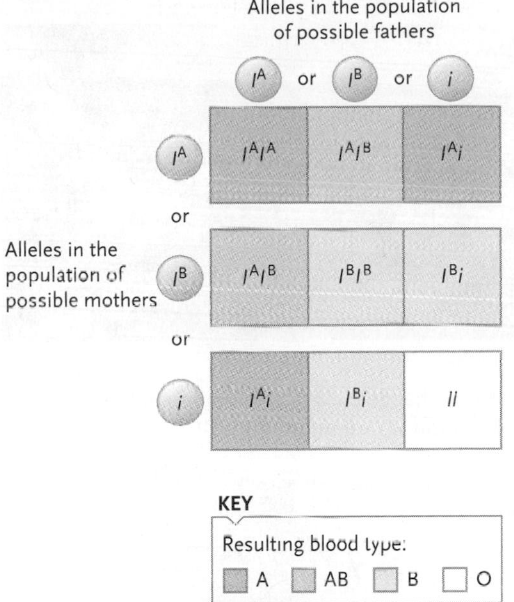

Figure 11.15
Inheritance of the blood types of the human ABO blood group. Note that although there are three possible alleles in the population, each individual parent carries only two.

11.2d In Epistasis, Genes Interact, with the Activity of One Gene Influencing the Activity of Another Gene

The genetic characters discussed so far in this chapter, such as flower colour, seed shape, and the blood types of the ABO group, are all produced by the alleles of single genes, with each gene functioning on its own. This is not the case for every gene. In **epistasis** (*epi* = on or over; *stasis* = standing or stopping), genes interact, with one or more alleles of a gene at one locus inhibiting or masking the effects of one or more alleles of a gene at a different locus. The result of epistasis is that some expected phenotypes do not appear among offspring.

Labrador retrievers (Labs) may have black, chocolate brown, or yellow fur **(Figure 11.16)**. The different colours result from variations in the amount and distribution in hairs of a brownish black pigment called melanin. One gene, coding for an enzyme involved in melanin production, determines how much melanin is produced. The dominant *B* allele of this gene produces black fur colour in *BB* or *Bb* Labs; less pigment is produced in *bb* dogs, which are chocolate brown. However, another gene at a different locus determines whether the black or chocolate colour appears at all, by controlling the deposition of pigment in hairs. A dominant allele *E* of this second gene permits pigment deposition, so that the black colour in *BB* or *Bb* individuals, or the chocolate colour in *bb* individuals, actually appears in the fur. Pigment deposition is almost completely blocked in homozygous recessive *ee* individuals, so the fur lacks melanin and has a yellow colour whether the genotype for the *B* gene is *BB*, *Bb*, or *bb*. Thus, the *E* gene is epistatic to the *B* gene (that is, *E* and *B* interact).

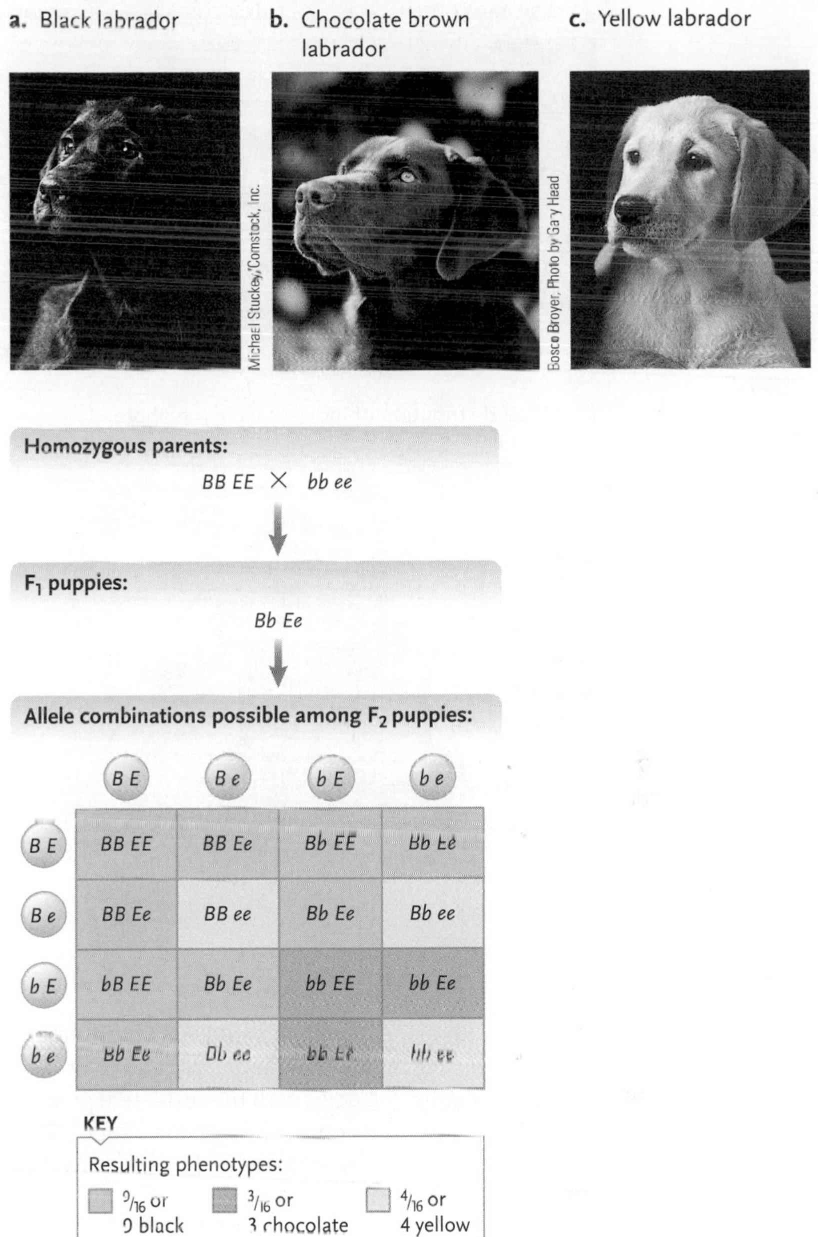

Figure 11.16
An example of epistasis: the inheritance of coat colour in Labrador retrievers.

Epistasis by the *E* gene eliminates some of the expected classes from crosses among Labs. Rather than two separate classes, as would be expected from a dihybrid cross without epistasis, the *BB ee*, *Bb ee*, *bB ee*, and *bb ee* genotypes produce a single yellow phenotype, giving the distribution: 9/16 black, 3/16 chocolate, and 4/16 yellow. That is, the ratio is 9:3:4 instead of the expected 9:3:3:1 ratio. Many other dihybrid crosses that involve epistatic interactions produce distributions that differ from the expected 9:3:3:1 ratio.

In human biology, researchers believe that gene interactions and epistasis are common. The current thinking is that epistasis is an important factor in determining an individual's susceptibility to common human diseases. That is, the different degrees of susceptibility are the result of different gene interactions

a. Students at Brigham Young University, arranged according to height

Dan Fairbanks/Brigham Young University

b. Actual distribution of individuals in the photo according to height

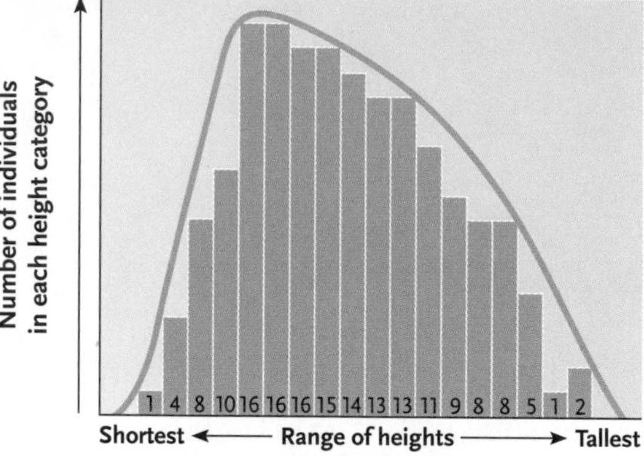

c. Idealized bell-shaped curve for a population that displays continuous variation in a trait

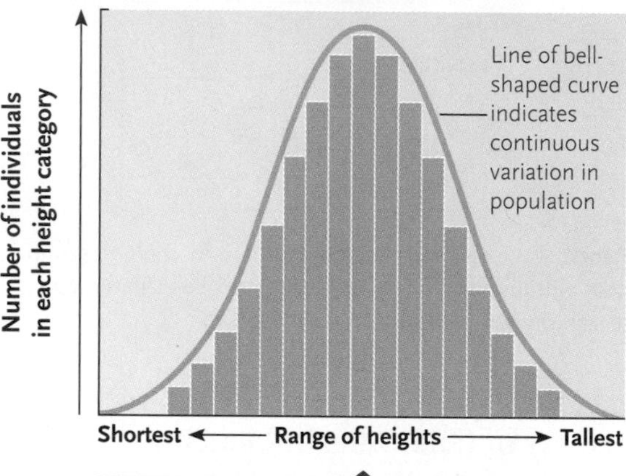

If the sample in the photo included more individuals, the distribution would more closely approach this ideal.

Figure 11.17
Continuous variation in height due to polygenic inheritance.

in the individuals. A specific example is insulin resistance, a disorder in which muscle, fat, and liver cells do not use insulin correctly, with the result that glucose and insulin levels become high in the blood. This disorder is believed to be determined by several genes often interacting with one another.

11.2e In Polygenic Inheritance, a Character Is Controlled by the Common Effects of Several Genes

Some characters follow a pattern of inheritance in which there is a more or less even gradation of types, forming a continuous distribution, rather than "on" or "off" (discontinuous) effects such as the production of purple or white flowers in pea plants. For example, in the human population, people range from short to tall, in a continuous distribution of gradations in height between limits of about 1 and 2 metres. Typically, a continuous distribution of this type is the result of **polygenic inheritance**, in which several to many different genes contribute to the same character. Other characters that undertake a similar continuous distribution include skin colour and body weight in humans, ear length in corn, seed colour in wheat, and colour spotting in mice. These characters are also known as *quantitative traits*.

Polygenic inheritance can be detected by defining classes of a variation, such as human body height of 180 cm in one class, 181 cm in the next class, 182 cm in the next class, and so on. The number of individuals in each class is then plotted as a graph. If the plot produces a bell-shaped curve, with fewer individuals at the extremes and the greatest numbers clustered around the midpoint, it is a good indication that the trait is quantitative **(Figure 11.17).**

Polygenic inheritance is often modified by the environment. For example, height in humans is not the result of genetics alone. Poor nutrition during infancy and childhood is one environmental factor that can limit growth and prevent individuals from reaching the height expected from genetic inheritance; good nutrition can have the opposite effect. Thus, the average young adult in Japan today is several inches taller than the average adult in the 1930s, when nutrition was poorer. Similarly, individuals who live in cloudy, northern or southern climates usually have lighter skin colour than individuals with the same genotype who live in sunny climates.

At first glance, the effects of polygenic inheritance might appear to support the idea that the characteristics of parents are blended in their offspring. Commonly, people believe that the children in a family with one tall and one short parent will be of intermediate

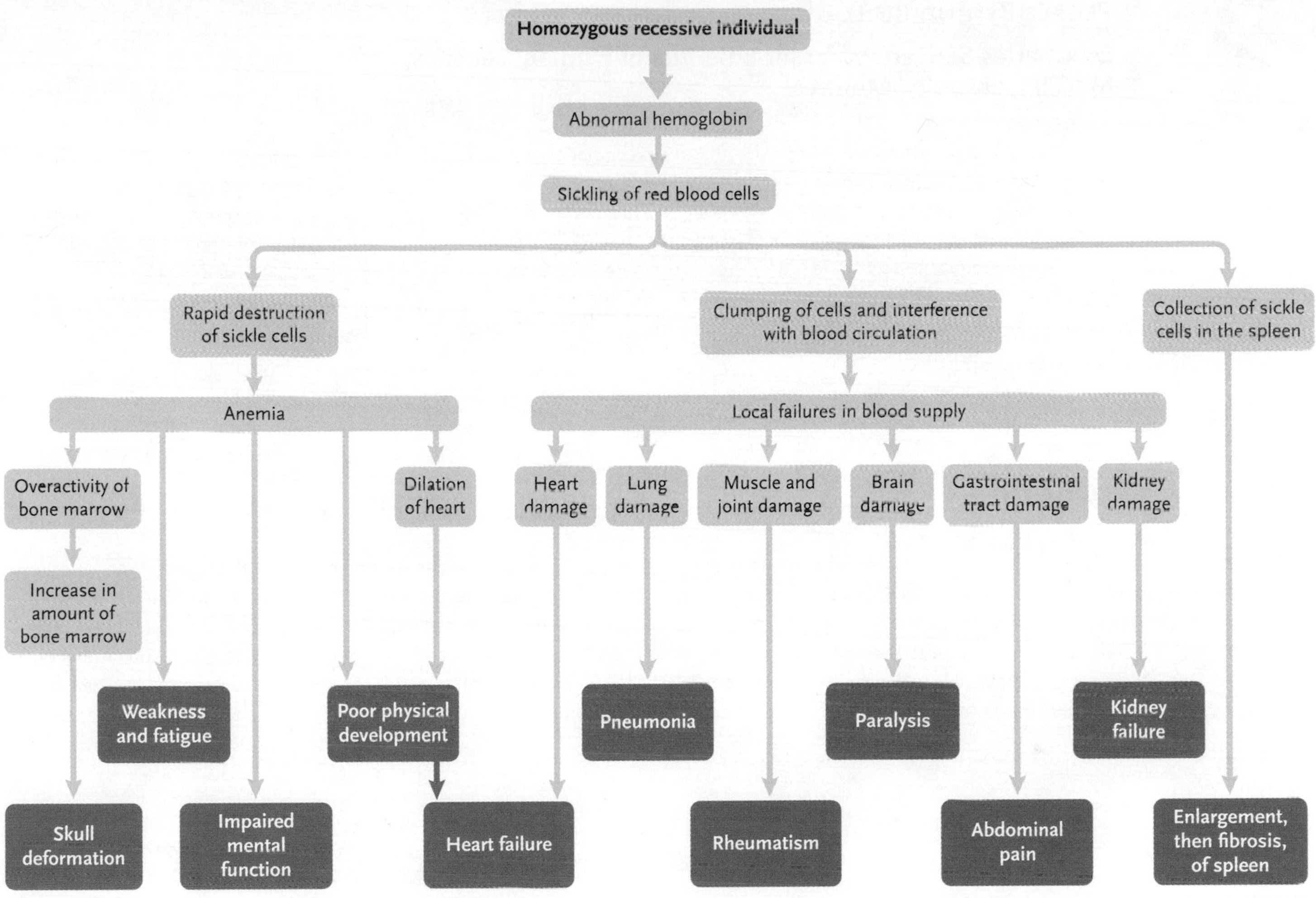

Figure 11.18
Pleiotropy, as demonstrated by the wide-ranging, multiple effects of the single mutant allele responsible for sickle cell disease.

height. Although the children of such parents are most likely to be of intermediate height, careful genetic analysis of many such families shows that their offspring actually range over a continuum from short to tall, forming a typical bell-shaped curve. Careful analysis of the inheritance of skin colour produces the same result: although the skin colour of children is most often intermediate between that of the parents, a typical bell-shaped distribution is obtained in which some children at the extremes are lighter or darker than either parent. Thus, genetic analysis does not support the idea of blending or even mixing of parental traits in polygenic characteristics such as body size or skin colour.

11.2f In Pleiotropy, Two or More Characters Are Affected by a Single Gene

In **pleiotropy**, single genes affect more than one character of an organism. For example, sickle cell disease (see earlier discussion) is caused by a recessive allele of a single gene that affects hemoglobin structure and function. However, the altered hemoglobin, the primary phenotypic change of the sickle cell mutation, leads to blood vessel blockage, which can damage many tissues and organs in the body and affect many body functions, producing such wide-ranging symptoms as fatigue, abdominal pain, heart failure, paralysis, and pneumonia **(Figure 11.18).** Physicians recognize these wide-ranging pleiotropic effects as symptoms of sickle cell disease.

The next chapter describes additional patterns of inheritance that were not anticipated by Mendel, including the effects of recombination during meiosis. These additional patterns also extend, rather than contradict, Mendel's fundamental principles.

Study Break

1. Distinguish between alleles that are incompletely dominant and those that are codominant.
2. How might you know that a trait is polygenic?

People Behind Biology

Dr. Charles Scriver, Professor Emeritus of Human Genetics, McGill University, Montreal

A "paradigm" is a particular way of thinking about a subject, and as Charles Scriver began his career, the way of thinking about genetic disease was beginning to shift. The old paradigm of "nothing can be done" was giving way to an understanding that disease phenotypes have both a genetic *and* an environmental component. Through a combination of basic research, public education, newborn screening programs, and on-line archiving of hundreds of mutations, Dr. Scriver brought this paradigm shift to our understanding of the underlying biology, treatment, and prevention of diseases such as phenylketonuria, vitamin D–deficient rickets, Tay–Sachs disease, and thalassemia.

Unanswered Questions

The determination of genetic principles by Mendel and later geneticists involved crosses of plants and animals with visible traits, that is, phenotypes that could be seen by visual examination. Examples are smooth and wrinkled seeds of garden peas and red and white eyes of fruit flies. Until recently, it was impossible to determine the biochemical or molecular basis for traits. Even now, we do not know the molecular basis for most of the traits mentioned in this chapter, or for many others. For example, the molecular reason for the dwarf (short stem) phenotype of Mendel's peas was determined only as recently as the 1990s. Similar research is ongoing to determine the molecular basis for other visible genetic traits in a wide variety of organisms, including humans.

Review

Go to CENGAGENOW™ at http://hed.nelson.com/ to access quizzing, animations, exercises, articles, and personalized homework help.

11.1 The Beginnings of Genetics: Mendel's Garden Peas

- Mendel made a good choice of experimental organism in that garden peas offered simple cultivation, clearly defined, true-breeding, characters (such as flower colour or seed shape), and an opportunity to make controlled pollinations.
- By analyzing his results quantitatively, Mendel showed that traits are passed from parents to offspring as hereditary factors (now called genes and alleles) in predictable ratios and combinations, disproving the notion of blended inheritance (see Figures 11.3, 11.4, and 11.5).
- Mendel realized that his results with crosses that involve single characters (monohybrid crosses) could be explained if three hypotheses were true: (1) the genes that govern genetic characters occur in pairs in individuals; (2) if different alleles of a gene are present in a pair within an individual, one allele is dominant over the other; and (3) the two alleles of a gene segregate and enter gametes single (see Figures 10.5 and 10.7).
- Mendel confirmed his hypotheses by a testcross between an F1 heterozygote and a homozygous recessive parent. This type of testcross is still used to determine whether an individual is homozygous or heterozygous for a dominant allele (see Figure 11.8).
- To explain the results of his crosses with individuals showing differences in two characters—dihybrid crosses—Mendel added an additional hypothesis: the alleles of the genes that govern the two characters segregate independently during formation of gametes (see Figure 11.9). That is, the dihybrid cross *AaBa* × *AaBa* can be treated as two separate monohybrid crosses: *Aa* × *Aa* and *Bb* × Bb. The monohybrid crosses would give phenotypic ratios of 3/4 *A*__: 1/4 *aa* and 3/4 *B*__: 1/4 *bb*, respectively. The standard dihybrid ratios arise from combinations of these monohybrid ratios. That is, 9/16 *A*__ *B*__ results from 3/4 *A*__ × 3/4 *B*__, 3/16 *aa B*__ results from 1/4 *aa* × 3/4 *B*__, and so on.
- Walter Sutton was the first person to note the similarities between the inheritance of genes and the behaviour of chromosomes in meiosis and fertilization. These parallels made it obvious that genes and alleles are carried on the chromosomes, and are called the chromosome theory of inheritance (see Figure 11.10).
- A locus is the particular site where a given gene is found on the chromosomes of an organism (see Figure 11.11). An allele is just a particular version of the DNA sequence of a gene. Therefore, if an individual is heterozygous for the stem length gene of Mendel's peas, it would have a T allele on one homologue and a t allele on the other. These two alleles would each be located at exactly the same locus on their respective chromosomes.

11.2 Later Modifications and Additions to Mendel's Hypotheses

- Incomplete dominance arises when, in a heterozygote, the activity of one allele is insufficient to compensate for the inactivity of another. Codominance arises when, in a heterozygote, both alleles are equally active. In both cases, the phenotype of heterozygotes is different from that of either homozygote (see Figure 11.13).
- Many genes may have multiple alleles if all the individuals in a population are taken into account. However, any diploid

individual in a population has only two alleles of these genes, which are inherited and passed on according to Mendel's principles (see Figures 11.14 and 11.15).

- In epistasis, genes interact, with one or more alleles of one locus inhibiting or masking the effects of one or more alleles at a different locus. The result is that some expected phenotypes do not appear among offspring (see Figure 11.16).
- A character that is subject to polygenic inheritance shows a more or less continuous variation from one extreme to another. Plotting the distribution of such characters among individuals typically produces a bell-shaped curve (see Figure 11.17).
- In pleiotropy, one gene affects more than one character of an organism (see Figure 11.18).

Questions

Self-Test Questions

1. The dominant *C* allele of a gene that controls colour in corn produces kernels with colour; plants homozygous for a recessive *c* allele of this gene have colourless or white kernels. What kinds of gametes, and in what proportions, would be produced by the plants in the following crosses? What seed colour, and in what proportions, would be expected in the offspring of the crosses?
   a. $CC \times Cc$ b. $Cc \times Cc$ c. $Cc \times cc$
2. In peas, the allele *T* produces tall plants and the allele *t* produces dwarf plants. The *T* allele is dominant to *t*. If a tall plant is crossed with a dwarf, the offspring are distributed about equally between tall and dwarf plants. What are the genotypes of the parents?
3. The ability of humans to taste the bitter chemical phenylthiocarbamide (PTC) is a genetic trait. People with at least one copy of the normal, dominant allele of the *PTC* gene can taste PTC; those who are homozygous for a mutant, recessive allele cannot taste it. Could two parents able to taste PTC have a nontaster child? Could nontaster parents have a child able to taste PTC? A pair of taster parents, both of whom had one parent able to taste PTC and one nontaster parent, are expecting their first child. What is the chance that the child will be able to taste PTC? Unable to taste PTC? Suppose the first child is a nontaster. What is the chance that their second child will also be unable to taste PTC?
4. One gene has the alleles *A* and *a*; another gene has the alleles *B* and *b*. For each of the following genotypes, what types of gametes will be produced, and in what proportions, if the two gene pairs assort independently?
   a. *AA BB* c. *Aa bb*
   b. *Aa BB* d. *Aa Bb*
5. What genotypes, and in what frequencies, will be present in the offspring from the following matings?
   a. $AA\ BB \times aa\ BB$ c. $Aa\ Bb \times aa\ bb$
   b. $Aa\ BB \times AA\ Bb$ d. $Aa\ Bb \times Aa\ Bb$
6. In addition to the two genes in problem 4, assume you now study a third independently assorting gene that has the alleles *C* and *c*. For each of the following genotypes, indicate what types of gametes will be produced:
   a. *AA BB CC* c. *Aa BB Cc*
   b. *Aa BB cc* d. *Aa Bb Cc*
7. A man is homozygous dominant for alleles at 10 different genes that assort independently. How many genotypically different types of sperm cells can he produce? A woman is homozygous recessive for the alleles of 8 of these 10 genes, but she is heterozygous for the other 2 genes. How many genotypically different types of eggs can she produce? What hypothesis can you suggest to describe the relationship between the number of different possible gametes and the number of heterozygous and homozygous genes that are present?
8. In guinea pigs, an allele for rough fur (*R*) is dominant over an allele for smooth fur (*r*); an allele for black coat (*B*) is dominant over that for white (*b*). You have an animal with rough, black fur. What cross would you use to determine whether the animal is homozygous for these traits? What phenotype would you expect in the offspring if the animal is homozygous?
9. You cross a lima bean plant from a variety that breeds true for green pods with another lima bean from a variety that breeds true for yellow pods. You note that all the F_1 plants have green pods. These green-pod F_1 plants, when crossed, yield 675 plants with green pods and 217 with yellow pods. How many genes probably control pod colour in this experiment? Give the alleles letter designations. Which is dominant?
10. Some recessive alleles have such a detrimental effect that they are lethal when present in both chromosomes of a pair. Homozygous recessives cannot survive and die at some point during embryonic development. Suppose that the allele *r* is lethal in the homozygous *rr* condition. What genotypic ratios would you expect among the living offspring of the following crosses?
    a. $RR \times Rr$
    b. $Rr \times Rr$
11. In garden peas, the genotypes *GG* or *Gg* produce green pods and *gg* produces yellow pods; *TT* or *Tt* plants are tall and *tt* plants are dwarfed; *RR* or *Rr* produce round seeds and *rr* produces wrinkled seeds. If a plant of a true-breeding, tall variety with green pods and round seeds is crossed with a plant of a true-breeding, dwarf variety with yellow pods and wrinkled seeds, what phenotypes are expected, and in what ratios, in the F_1 generation? What phenotypes, and in what ratios, are expected if F_1 individuals are crossed?
12. In chickens, feathered legs are produced by a dominant allele *F*. Another allele *f* of the same gene produces featherless legs. The dominant allele *P* of a gene at a different locus produces pea combs; a recessive allele *p* of this gene causes single combs. A breeder makes the following crosses with birds 1, 2, 3, and 4; all parents have feathered legs and pea combs:

Cross	**Offspring**
1×2	all feathered, pea comb
1×3	3/4 feathered; 1/4 featherless, all pea comb
1×4	9/16 feathered, pea comb; 3/16 featherless, pea comb; 3/16 feathered, single comb; 1/16 featherless, single comb

    What are the genotypes of the four birds?
13. A mixup in a hospital ward caused a mother with O and MN blood types to think that a baby given to her really belonged to someone else. Tests in the hospital showed that the doubting mother was able to taste PTC (see problem 3). The baby given to her had O and MN blood types and had no reaction when the bitter PTC chemical was placed on its tongue. The mother had four other children with the following blood types and tasting abilities for PTC:
    a. Type A and MN blood, taster
    b. Type B and N blood, nontaster
    c. Type A and M blood, taster
    d. Type A and N blood, taster

Without knowing the father's blood types and tasting ability, can you determine whether the child is really hers? (Assume that all her children have the same father.)

14. In cats, the genotype *AA* produces tabby fur colour; *Aa* is also a tabby, and *aa* is black. Another gene at a different locus is epistatic to the gene for fur colour. When present in its dominant *W* form (*WW* or *Ww*), this gene blocks the formation of fur colour and all the offspring are white; *ww* individuals develop normal fur colour. What fur colours, and in what proportions, would you expect from the cross *Aa Ww* × *Aa Ww*?

15. Having malformed hands with shortened fingers is a dominant trait controlled by a single gene; people who are homozygous for the recessive allele have normal hands and fingers. Having woolly hair is a dominant trait controlled by a different gene; homozygous recessive individuals have normal, nonwoolly hair. Suppose a woman with normal hands and nonwoolly hair marries a man who has malformed hands and woolly hair. Their first child has normal hands and nonwoolly hair. What are the genotypes of the mother, the father, and the child? If this couple has a second child, what is the probability that it will have normal hands and woolly hair?

Questions for Discussion

1. The eyes of brown-eyed people are not alike but rather vary considerably in shade and pattern. What do you think causes these differences?
2. Explain how individuals of an organism that are phenotypically alike can produce different ratios of progeny phenotypes.
3. ABO blood type tests can be used to exclude paternity. Suppose a defendant who is the alleged father of a child takes a blood type test and the results do not exclude him as the father. Do the results indicate that he is the father? What arguments could a lawyer make based on the test results to exclude the defendant from being the father? (Assume the tests were performed correctly.)

Fluorescent probes bound to specific sequences along human chromosome 10 (light micrograph). New ways of mapping chromosome structure yield insights into the inheritance of normal and abnormal traits.

Study Plan

12 Genes, Chromosomes, and Human Genetics

Why It Matters

Imagine being 10 years old and trapped in a body that each day becomes more shrivelled, frail, and old. You are just tall enough to peer over the top of the kitchen counter, and you weigh less than 16 kilograms. Already you are bald, and you probably have only a few more years to live. But if you are like Mickey Hayes or Fransie Geringer **(Figure 12.1, p. 250),** you still have not lost your courage or your childlike curiosity about life. Like them, you still play, laugh, and celebrate birthdays.

Progeria, the premature aging that afflicts Mickey and Fransie, is caused by a genetic error that occurs once in every 8 million human births. The error is perpetuated each time cells of the embryo—then of the child—duplicate their chromosomes and divide. The outcome of that rare mistake is an acceleration of aging and a greatly reduced life expectancy.

Progeria affects both boys and girls. Usually, symptoms begin to appear before the age of 2. The rate of body growth declines to abnormally low levels. Skin becomes thinner, muscles become flaccid, and limb bones start to degenerate. Children with progeria never reach puberty, and most die in their early teens from a stroke or heart attack

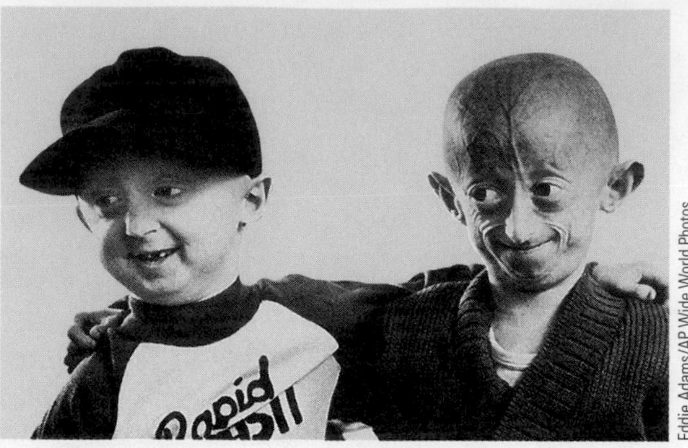

Figure 12.1
Two boys, both younger than 10, who have progeria, a genetic disorder characterized by accelerated aging and extremely reduced life expectancy.

brought on by hardening of the arteries, a condition typical of advanced age.

The plight of Mickey and Fransie provides a telling and tragic example of the dramatic effects that gene defects can have on living organisms. We are the products of our genes, and the characteristics of each individual, from humans to pine trees to protozoa, depend on the combination of genes, alleles, and chromosomes inherited from its parents, as well as on environmental effects. This chapter delves deeply into genes and the role of chromosomes in inheritance.

12.1 Genetic Linkage and Recombination

In his historic experiments, Gregor Mendel carried out crosses with seven different characters in garden peas, controlled by seven different genes. He found that his observations from crosses were consistent with the hypothesis that each of the genes assorted independently of all of the others in the formation of gametes. If Mendel had extended his study to additional characters, he would have found exceptions to this principle. This should not be surprising because an organism has far more genes than chromosomes. Conceptually, then, chromosomes contain many genes, with each gene at a particular locus. Genes located on different chromosomes assort independently in gamete formation because the two chromosomes behave independently of one another during meiosis. Genes located on the same chromosome may be inherited together in genetic crosses—that is, not assort independently—because the chromosome is inherited as a single physical entity in meiosis. Genes on the same chromosome are known as **linked genes**, and the phenomenon is called **linkage**.

12.1a The Principles of Linkage and Recombination Were Determined with *Drosophila*

In the early part of the twentieth century, Thomas H. Morgan and coworkers at Columbia University used the fruit fly, *Drosophila melanogaster,* as a model organism to investigate Mendel's principles in animals. (See more information about Drosophila as a model research organism in The Chemical and Physical Foundations of Biology pages.) Groups of genes that tended to assort together in crosses were believed to be carried on the same chromosome. It was Morgan's group, and an undergraduate student named Alfred Sturtevant working in the lab at the time, who developed the insight that resulted in the construction of the first genetic map showing the relative order of genes on a chromosome as well as a measure of the distance separating them. These brilliant and far-reaching hypotheses were typical of Morgan, who founded genetics research in the United States, developed *Drosophila* as a research organism, and made discoveries that were likely as significant to the development of genetics as those of Mendel.

Although it is tempting to assume that genetic maps could be made simply by looking down a microscope, finding the genes, and measuring the distance between them, the technology to do this was simply not available. Instead, Morgan's group used an indirect measure of "distance." They reasoned that genes sitting relatively far apart on a chromosome would be more likely to be separated from one another during meiotic crossing-over than genes lying closer together. Figure 10.14 illustrates this process of recombination occurring in the space separating two genes as they appear on chromosomes paired during meiosis. Obviously, if recombination is to be used as a measure of distance separating genes, it must be detectable. That is why the organism used in Figure 10.14 is heterozygous for all genes; the chromatids resulting from recombination are then different from the original, nonrecombinant, ones and can be identified. Following meiosis I and II, each of the four different chromatids will become a chromosome in a separate gamete (review the basic mechanisms of meiosis in Figure 10.10). Which chromosome, recombinant or not, is carried by a given gamete is actually revealed only in offspring resulting from fertilization with a homozygous recessive gamete. That is why, in the following cross, which was originally done by Morgan in 1911, you will notice that one parent is heterozygous and the other is homozygous recessive.

To understand the following crosses, you need to learn to work with the genetic symbolism developed by Morgan instead of the *A/a* system used in Chapter 11. Although *Drosophila* notation might appear counterintuitive at first, understanding a few basic principles will help you see the logic behind it. First, note that geneticists working with fruit flies have all agreed on a "normal," or "wild-type," genotype; any change from wild type is, by definition, a mutant. Mutant alleles are named based on the phenotype of the organism that expresses them. The names for dominant mutant alleles are written in uppercase, whereas those for recessive mutant alleles are written in lowercase.

For example, a dominant mutant allele transforming an antenna into a leg is called Antennapedia (Antp), whereas a recessive mutant allele altering eye colour is called vermilion (v). The notation for a wild-type allele is always made by simply adding a superscripted plus (+) sign to the mutant allele notation. You know you understand this system if you agree that $Antp^+$ is a *recessive* allele giving a normal phenotype when homozygous.

Morgan began a specific breeding program using true-breeding fruit flies with normal red eyes and normal wing length, genotype $pr^+pr^+\ vg^+vg^+$, along with a true-breeding fly with the recessive traits of purple eyes and vestigial (that is, short and crumpled) wings, genotype *prpr vgvg* (**Figure 12.2, p. 252,** step 1).

The F_1 (first-generation) offspring were all dihybrid $pr^+pr\ vg^+vg$, and because of the dominance of the wild-type alleles, they had red eyes and normal wings (see Figure 12.2, step 2). Morgan then selected these wild-type F_1 females as the dihybrid parent and mated them to homozygous recessive males (with purple eyes and vestigial wings) as the testcross parent. If the purple and vestigial genes were carried on different chromosomes, Mendel's principle of independent assortment (see Section 11.1) would predict four classes of phenotypes in the offspring, in the approximate 1:1:1:1 ratio of red eyes, normal wings: purple, vestigial: red, vestigial: purple, normal. Given over 2800 offspring from several females, about 700 should have been in each class. However, Morgan observed two types of progeny in which the counts were much higher than 700 (red, normal and purple, vestigial) and two types with counts that were much less (red, vestigial, and purple, normal) (see Figure 12.2, step 4).

Morgan's hypothesis to explain this non-Mendelian distribution is illustrated in **Figure 12.3 (p. 253).** He suggested that the two genes are linked genetically—physically associated on the same chromosome. That is, *pr* and *vg* are linked genes. He further hypothesized that the behaviour of these linked genes is explained by *chromosome recombination* during meiosis. Furthermore, he proposed that the frequency of this recombination is a function of the distance between linked genes.

The $pr^+pr\ vg^+vg$ F_1 dihybrid parents produce four types of gametes (see Figure 12.3, step 1). The two parental gametes, $pr^+\ vg^+$ and *pr vg*, are generated by simple segregation of the chromosomes during meiosis without any crossing-over (recombination) between the genes. The two recombinant gametes, $pr^+\ vg$ and $pr\ vg^+$, result from crossing-over between the homologous chromatids when they are paired in prophase I of meiosis (see Figures 10.10 and 10.14). The offspring of the cross are produced by fusion of each of these four gametes with a *pr vg* gamete produced by the *prpr vgvg* male parent. The phenotypes of the offspring directly reflect the genotypes of the gametes produced by the dihybrid parent. Students of genetics sometimes assume that the wild-type and purple vestigial offspring are called "parental" because they *look like* the parents. However, the term "parental" actually refers to genotype, not phenotype; parental offspring are the ones that inherit chromosomes unchanged from their dihybrid parent. Parental offspring do not always resemble the parents of the cross. Although Morgan could not look down a microscope and measure the distance between genes directly, he could look down a microscope and identify recombinant offspring from dihybrid test-crosses. Thus, the relative frequency of recombinant progeny became his "measure" of the distance separating genes. The example in Figure 12.3 reveals that purple eyes and vestigial wings are on the same chromosome separated by a recombination frequency of 10.7%.

12.1b Recombination Frequency Can Be Used to Map Chromosomes

The recombination frequency of 10.7% for the *pr* and *vg* genes of *Drosophila* means that 10.7% of the gametes originating from the $pr^+pr\ vg^+vg$ parent contained recombined chromosomes. That recombination frequency is characteristic for those two genes. In other crosses that involve linked genes, Morgan found that the recombination frequency was characteristic of the two genes involved, varying from less than 1 to 50% (see the next section).

From these observations, Alfred Sturtevant realized that the variation in recombination frequencies could be used as a means of mapping genes on chromosomes. Sturtevant himself later recalled his light-bulb moment:

> I suddenly realized that the variations in the strength of linkage already attributed by Morgan to difference in the spatial separation of the gene offered the possibility of determining sequence in the linear dimensions of a chromosome. I went home and spent most of the night (to the neglect of my other homework) producing the first chromosome map.

Therefore, recombination frequencies can be used to make a **linkage map** of a chromosome showing the relative locations of genes. For example, assume that the three genes *a, b,* and *c* are carried together on the same chromosome. Crosses reveal a 9.6% recombination frequency for *a* and *b*, an 8% recombination frequency for *a* and *c*, and a 2% recombination frequency for *b* and *c*. These frequencies allow the genes to be arranged in only one sequence on the chromosomes as follows:

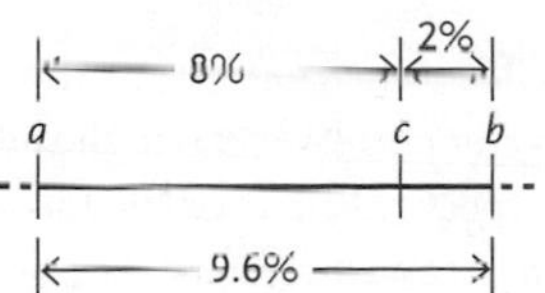

Figure 12.2
Evidence for gene linkage.

QUESTION: Do the purple-eye vestigial-wing genes of *Drosophila* assort independently?

EXPERIMENT: Morgan crossed true-breeding wild-type flies with red eyes and normal wings with purple-eyed, vestigial-winged flies. The F_1 dihybrids were all wild-type in phenotype. Next he crossed the F_1 dihybrid flies with purple-eyed, vestigial-winged flies (this is a testcross) and analyzed the phenotypes of the progeny.

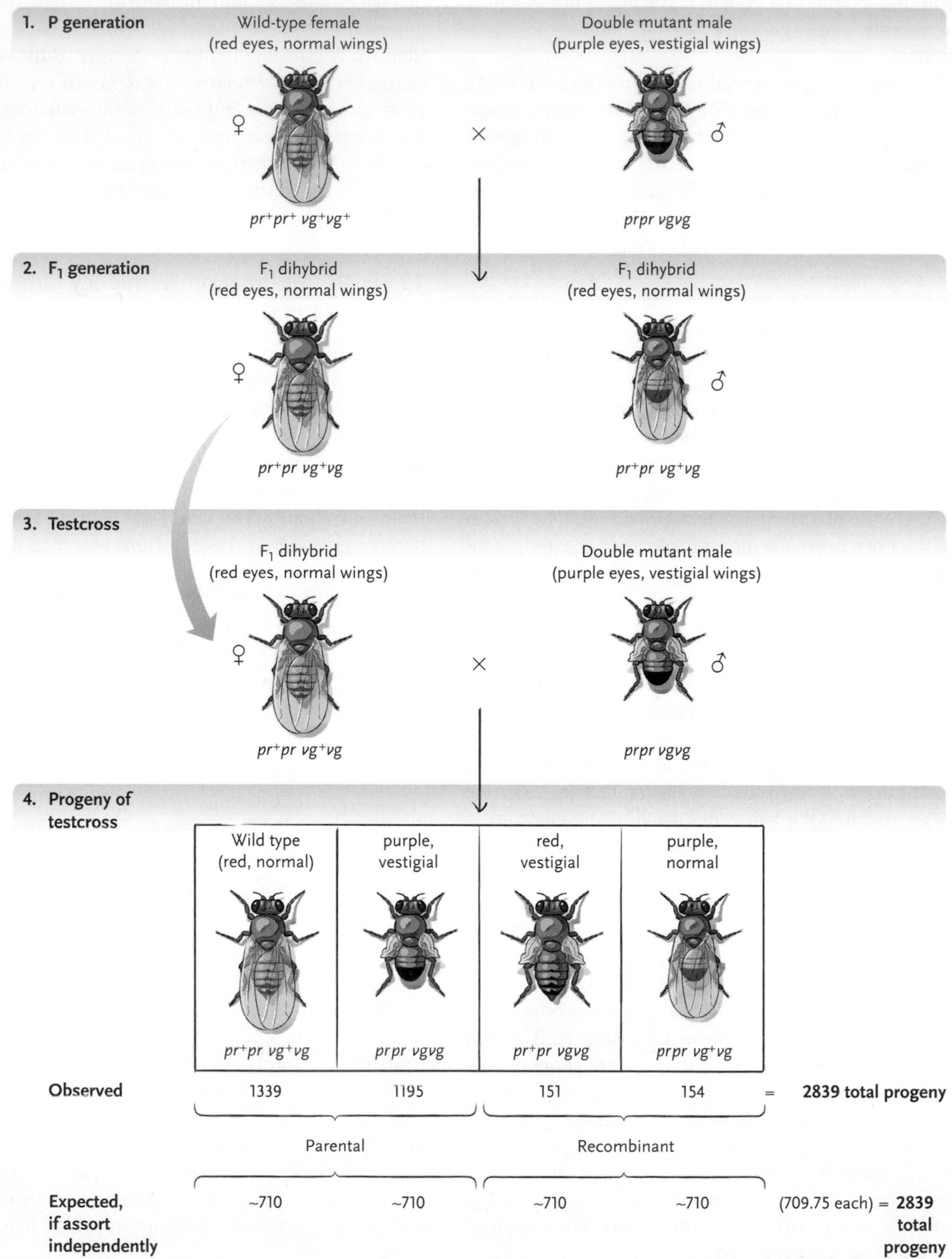

RESULTS: 2534 of the testcross progeny flies were parental, wild-type and purple, vestigial, while 305 of the progeny were recombinant red, vestigial and purple, normal. If the genes assorted independently, the expectation is a 1:1:1:1 ratio for testcross progeny: approximately 1420 of both parental and recombinant progeny.

CONCLUSION: The purple-eye and vestigial-wing genes do not assort independently. The simplest alternative is that the two genes are linked on the same chromosome.

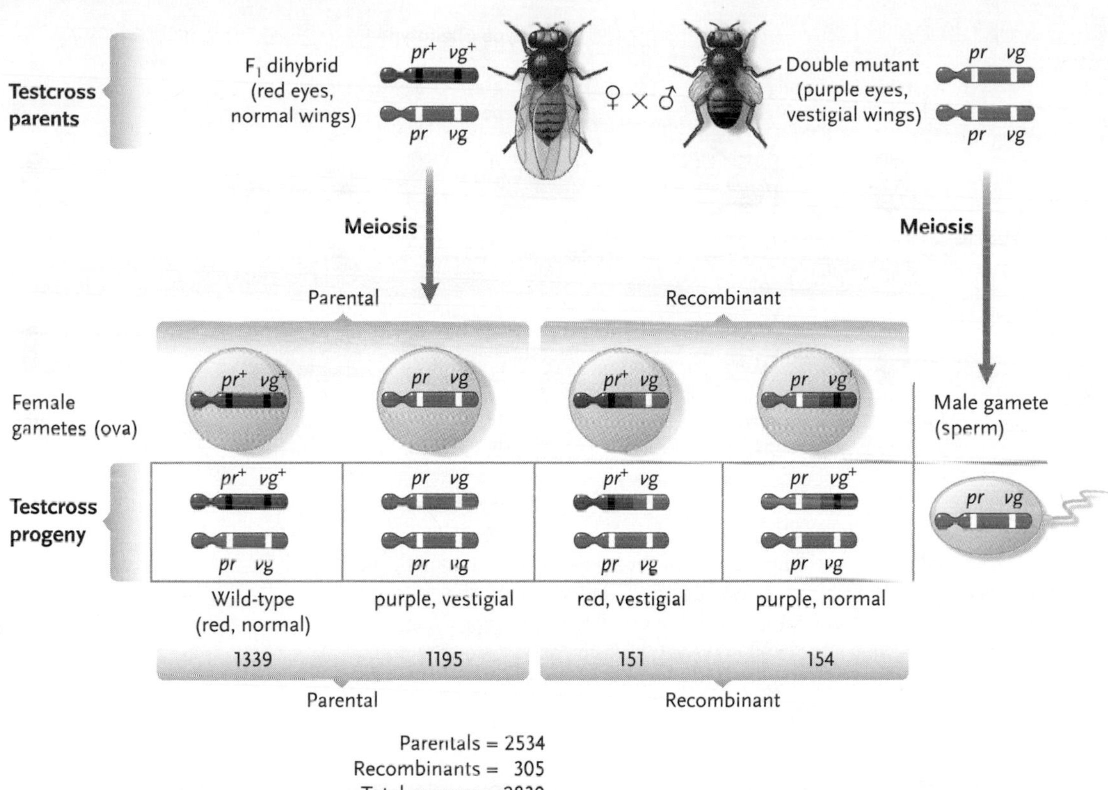

$$\text{Recombination frequency} = \frac{305 \text{ recombinants}}{2839 \text{ total progeny}} \times 100 = 10.7\%$$

Figure 12.3
Recombination, the result of crossing-over between homologous chromosomes. The testcross of Figure 12.2 is redrawn here showing the two linked genes on chromosomes. The two parental homologues are coloured differently to allow us to follow them during the cross. The parental offspring inherit one or the other of the chromosomes unchanged from the dihybrid parent. The recombinant offspring inherit one or the other of the recombined chromosomes from the dihybrid parent.

You will note that the *a–b* recombination frequency does not exactly equal the sum of the *a–c* and *c–b* recombination frequencies. This is because genes farther apart on a chromosome are more likely to have more than one crossover occur between them. Whereas a single crossover between two genes gives recombinants, a double crossover (two single crossovers occurring in the same meiosis) between two genes gives parentals (and is therefore undetectable and would not be counted). You can see this simply by drawing single and double crossovers between two genes on a piece of paper. In our example, the undetectable double crossovers that occur between *a* and *b* have slightly decreased the recombination frequency between these two genes.

Using this method, Sturtevant created the first linkage map showing the arrangement of six genes on the *Drosophila* X chromosome. (A partial linkage map of a *Drosophila* chromosome is shown in **Figure 12.4, p. 254.**)

Since the time of Morgan, many *Drosophila* genes and those of other eukaryotic organisms widely used for genetic research, including *Neurospora* (a fungus), yeast, maize (corn), and the mouse, have been mapped using the same approach. Recombination frequencies, together with the results of other techniques, have been used to create linkage maps of the locations of genes in the DNA of prokaryotes such as the human intestinal bacterium *Escherichia coli*.

The unit of a linkage map, called a **map unit** (abbreviated mu), is equivalent to a recombination frequency of 1%. The map unit is also called the **centimorgan** in honor of Morgan's discoveries of linkage and recombination. Map units are not absolute physical distances in micrometres or nanometres; rather, they are *relative*, showing the positions of genes with respect to each other. One of the reasons that the units are relative and not absolute distances is that the frequency of crossing-over varies to some extent from one position to another on chromosomes.

In recent years, the linkage maps of a number of species have been supplemented by DNA sequencing of whole genomes, which shows the precise physical locations of genes on chromosomes.

12.1c Widely Separated Linked Genes Assort Independently

Genes can be so widely separated on a chromosome that recombination is likely to occur at some point between them in every cell undergoing meiosis. When this is the case, the genes assort independently even though they are on the same chromosome. The map distance separating them will be 50 mu.

To understand why this is, first recall Figure 10.14 showing that a recombination event in a given cell creates 2 recombinant and 2 nonrecombinant chromatids. Next, imagine 100 meiocytes going through meiosis as usual to yield 400 gametes. If a recombination event occurred in the space separating 2 given genes in 10 of those cells, then 20 recombinant chromatids would be produced during prophase I. Twenty gametes would eventually receive recombinant chromosomes, and

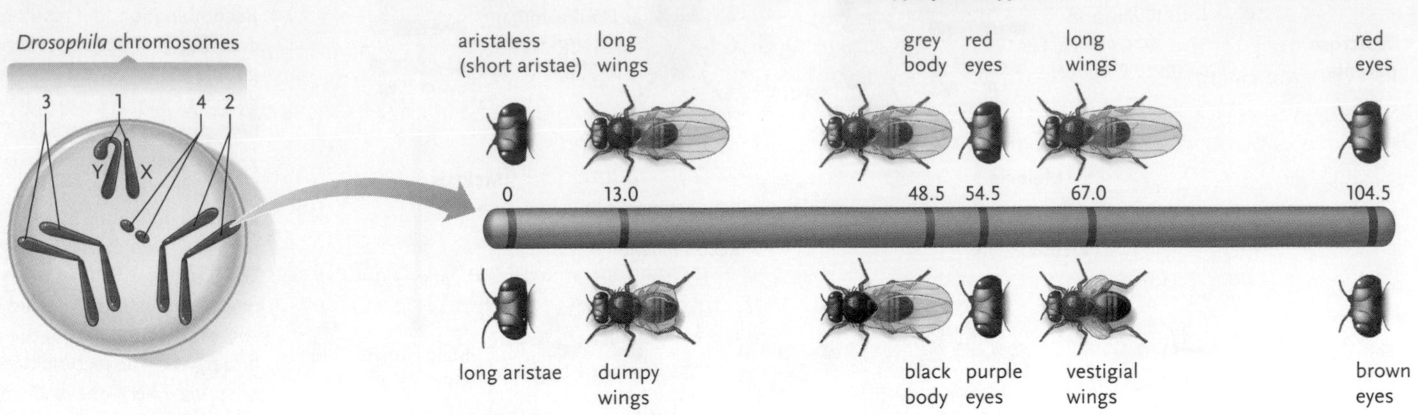

Figure 12.4
Relative map locations of several genes on chromosome 2 of *Drosophila*, as determined by recombination frequencies. For each gene, the diagram shows the normal or "wild-type" phenotype on the top and the mutant phenotype on the bottom. Mutant alleles at two different locations alter wing structure, one producing the dumpy wing and the other the vestigial wing phenotypes; the normal allele at these locations results in normal long-wing structure. Mutant alleles at two different locations also alter eye colour.

20/400 = 5% of the total testcross progeny would be recombinant. We would conclude that these genes are 5 mu apart. Now assume that a recombination event occurs in the space separating two genes in *every one of the 100* cells going through meiosis. Two hundred recombinant offspring would result out of the total of 400; 50% would be recombinants; 50 mu would separate the genes.

Linkage between such widely separated genes can still be detected, however, by testing their linkage to one or more genes that lie between them. For example, the genes *a* and *c* in **Figure 12.5** are located so far apart that they assort independently and show no linkage. However, crosses show that *a* and *b* are 23 mu apart (recombination frequency of 23%), and crosses that show *b* and *c* are 34 mu apart. Therefore, *a* and *c* must also be linked and carried on the same chromosome at 23 + 34 = 57 mu apart. Obviously, we could not see a recombination frequency of 57% in testcross progeny because the maximum frequency of recombinants is 50%.

We now know that some of the genes Mendel studied are actually on the same chromosome. For example, the genes for flower colour and seed colour are located on the same chromosome pair, but they are so far apart that the frequent recombination between them makes them assort independently.

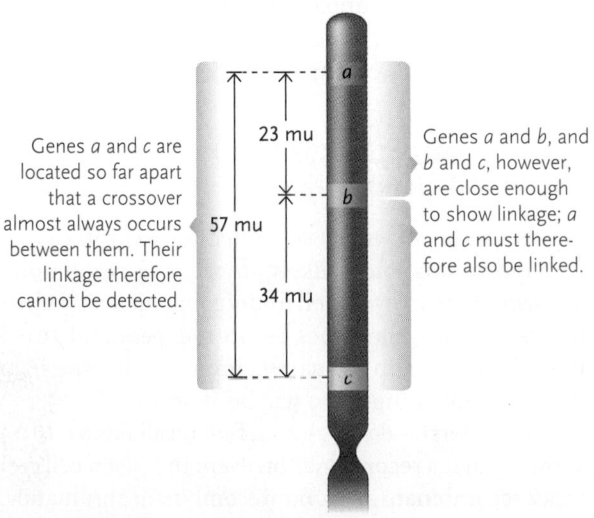

a
b
c
23 mu
57 mu
34 mu
Genes a and c are located so far apart that a crossover almost always occurs between them. Their linkage therefore cannot be detected.
Genes a and b, and b and c, however, are close enough to show linkage; a and c must therefore also be linked.

Figure 12.5
Genes far apart on the same chromosome. Genes *a* and *c* are far apart and will not show linkage, suggesting that they are on different chromosomes. However, linkage between such genes can be established by noting their linkage to another gene or genes located between them—gene *b* here.

Study Break

1. What type of cross can be used to discover whether two genes are linked or not?
2. How can two genes be on the same chromosome yet assort independently as if they were on separate chromosomes?

12.2 Sex-Linked Genes

In many organisms, one or more pairs of chromosomes are different in males and females. Genes located on these chromosomes, the *sex chromosomes*, are called **sex-linked genes**; they are inherited differently in males and females. (Note that the word *linked* in *sex-linked gene* means that the gene is on a sex chromosome, whereas the use of the term *linked* when considering two or more genes means that the genes are on the same chromosome, not necessarily a sex chromosome.) Chromosomes other than the sex chromosomes are called **autosomes**; genes on these chromosomes have the same patterns of inheritance in both sexes. In humans, chromosomes 1 to 22 are the autosomes.

12.2a Females Are XX and Males Are XY in Both Humans and Fruit Flies

In most species with sex chromosomes, females have two copies of a chromosome known as the **X chromosome**, forming a fully homologous XX pair, whereas males have only one X chromosome. Another chromosome, the Y chromosome, occurs in males but not in females. The Y chromosome has a short region of homology with the X chromosome that allows them to pair during meiosis. The XX human chromosome complement is shown in Figure 9.9.

Each normal gamete produced by an XX female carries an X chromosome. Half the gametes produced by an XY male carry an X chromosome and half carry a Y. When a sperm cell carrying an X chromosome fertilizes an X-bearing egg cell, the new individual develops into an XX female. Conversely, when a sperm cell carrying a Y chromosome fertilizes an X-bearing egg cell, the combination produces an XY male. The Punnet square (see **Figure 12.6**) shows that fertilization is expected to produce females and males with an equal frequency of 1/2. This expectation is closely matched in the human and *Drosophila* populations.

Other sex chromosome arrangements have been found, as in some insects with XX females and XO males (the O means there is no Y chromosome). In birds, butterflies, and some reptiles, the situation is reversed: males have a homologous pair of sex chromosomes (ZZ instead of XX), and females have the equivalent of an XY combination (ZW).

12.2b Human Sex Determination Depends on the *SRY* Gene

Although the human X and Y chromosomes are called "sex chromosomes," only a few genes they carry have any influence on sex determination or sexual function. For instance, most of the roughly 2400 known genes on the X chromosome code for phenotypes needed by both sexes, such as colour perception, blood clotting, and DNA replication. However, one gene carried on the Y chromosome, *SRY* (for sex-determining region of the Y), appears to be the "master switch" that directs development toward maleness at an early point in embryonic development.

For the first month or so of embryonic development in humans and other mammals, the rudimentary structures that give rise to reproductive organs and tissues are the same in XX or XY embryos. After 6 to 8 weeks, the *SRY* gene becomes active in XY embryos, producing a protein that regulates the expression of other genes, thereby stimulating part of these structures to develop as testes. As a part of stimulation by hormones secreted in the developing testes and elsewhere, tissues degenerate that would otherwise develop into female structures such as the vagina and oviducts. The remaining structures develop into the penis and scrotum. In XX embryos, which do not have a copy of the *SRY* gene, development proceeds toward female reproductive structures. The rudimentary male structures degenerate in XX embryos because the hormones released by the developing testes in XY embryos are not present. Further details of the *SRY* gene and its role in human sex determination are presented in Chapter 48.

12.2c Sex-Linked Genes Were First Discovered in *Drosophila*

Since males and females have different sets of sex chromosomes, the genes carried on these chromosomes can be inherited in a distinctly non-Mendelian pattern called sex linkage. Sex linkage arises from two differences

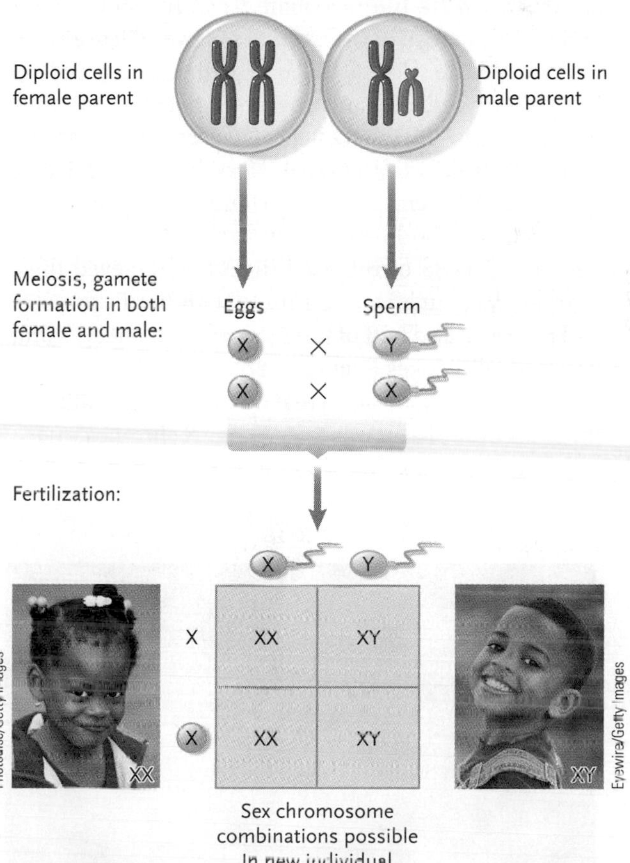

Figure 12.6
Sex chromosomes and the chromosomal basis of sex determination in humans. Females have two X chromosomes and produce gametes (eggs), all of which have the X sex chromosome. Males have one X and one Y chromosome and produce gametes, half with an X chromosome and half with a Y chromosome. Males transmit their Y chromosome to their sons, but not to their daughters. Males receive their X chromosome only from their mother.

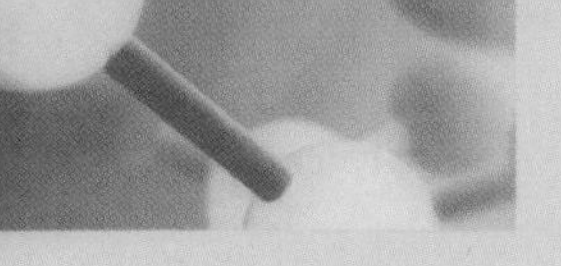

Molecule Behind Biology

Drosopterin

The brick red eyes of wild-type fruit flies owe their colour to a mixture of two types of pigment: bright red drosopterin and brown ommochrome. Drosopterin is the final product of a multistep biochemical pathway beginning with guanine. Mutations that alter the function of enzymes acting at different steps in this pathway result in novel eye colours such as purple, brown, or sepia.

between males and females: (1) males have one X chromosome and therefore one allele for each gene on this chromosome; females have two copies of the X chromosome and therefore two alleles for all genes on the X chromosome; (2) males also have one copy of the Y chromosome and one allele for each gene on this chromosome; females have no Y chromosome and therefore no Y alleles at all. Y chromosomes are present in males but not females.

Morgan discovered sex-linked genes and their pattern of sex linkage in 1910. The story of discovery started when he found a male fly in his stocks with white eyes instead of the normal red eyes **(Figure 12.7).** He crossed the white-eyed male with a true-breeding female with red eyes and observed that all the F_1 flies had red eyes **(Figure 12.8a).** He concluded that the white-eye trait was recessive. Next, he allowed the F_1 flies to interbreed. Based on Mendel's principles, he expected that both male and female F_2 flies would show a 3:1 ratio of red-eyed flies to white-eyed flies. Morgan was surprised to find that all the F_2 females had red eyes, and half of the F_2 males had red eyes and half had white eyes **(Figure 12.8b).**

Morgan hypothesized that the alleles segregating in the cross were of a gene located on the X chromosome—now termed a sex-linked gene. The white-eyed male parent in the cross had the genotype X^wY: an X chromosome with a white (X^w) allele, and no other allele of that gene on the Y chromosome. The red-eyed female parent in the cross had the genotype $X^{w+}X^{w+}$: each X chromosome carries the dominant normal allele for red eyes, X^{w+}.

We can follow the alleles in this cross (see Figure 12.8a). The F_1 flies of a cross $X^{w+}X^{w+} \times X^wY$ are produced as follows. The X chromosome of the males comes from their mother; therefore, their genotype is $X^{w+}Y$, and their phenotype is red eyes. The females receive one X from each parent; therefore, their genotype is $X^{w+}X^w$, and their phenotype is red eyes due to the dominance of the X^{w+} allele.

In the F_2 generation, the females receive an X^{w+} allele from the male F_1 parent and either an X^{w+} or X^w allele from the female F_1 parent; these genotypes result in red eyes (see Figure 12.8a). The males receive their one X chromosome from the female F_1 parent, which has the genotype $X^{w+}X^w$. Therefore, F_2 males are half $X^{w+}Y$ (red eyes) and half X^wY (white eyes).

Morgan also made a *reciprocal cross* of the one just described; that is, the phenotypes were switched between the sexes. The reciprocal cross here was a white-eyed female (X^wX^w) with a red-eyed male ($X^{w+}Y$) (see Figure 12.8b). The F_1 males all had white eyes because they received the X^w-bearing chromosome from the female parent; thus, their genotype is X^wY. The F_1 females have red eyes; therefore, they are all heterozygous $X^{w+}X^w$. This result is clearly different from the cross in Figure 12.8a.

In the F_2 generation of this second cross, both male and female flies showed a 1:1 ratio of red eyes to white eyes (see Figure 12.8b). Again, this result differs markedly from that of the cross in Figure 12.8a.

In summary, Morgan's work showed that there is a distinctive pattern in the phenotypic ratios for reciprocal crosses in which the gene involved is on the X chromosome. A key indicator of this sex linkage is when all male offspring of a cross between a true-breeding mutant female and a wild-type male have the mutant phenotype. As we have seen, this occurs because a male receives his X chromosome from his female parent.

a. **b.**

Figure 12.7
Eye colour phenotypes in *Drosophila.* **(a)** Normal, red wild-type eye colour. **(b)** Mutant white eye colour caused by a recessive allele of a sex-linked gene carried on the X chromosome.

Figure 12.8
Evidence for sex-linked genes.

QUESTION: How is the white eye gene of *Drosophila* inherited?

EXPERIMENT: Morgan crossed a white-eyed male *Drosophila* with a true-breeding female with red eyes and then crossed the F_1 flies to produce the F_2 generation. He also performed the reciprocal cross in which the phenotypes were switched in the parental flies—true-breeding white-eyed female × red-eyed male.

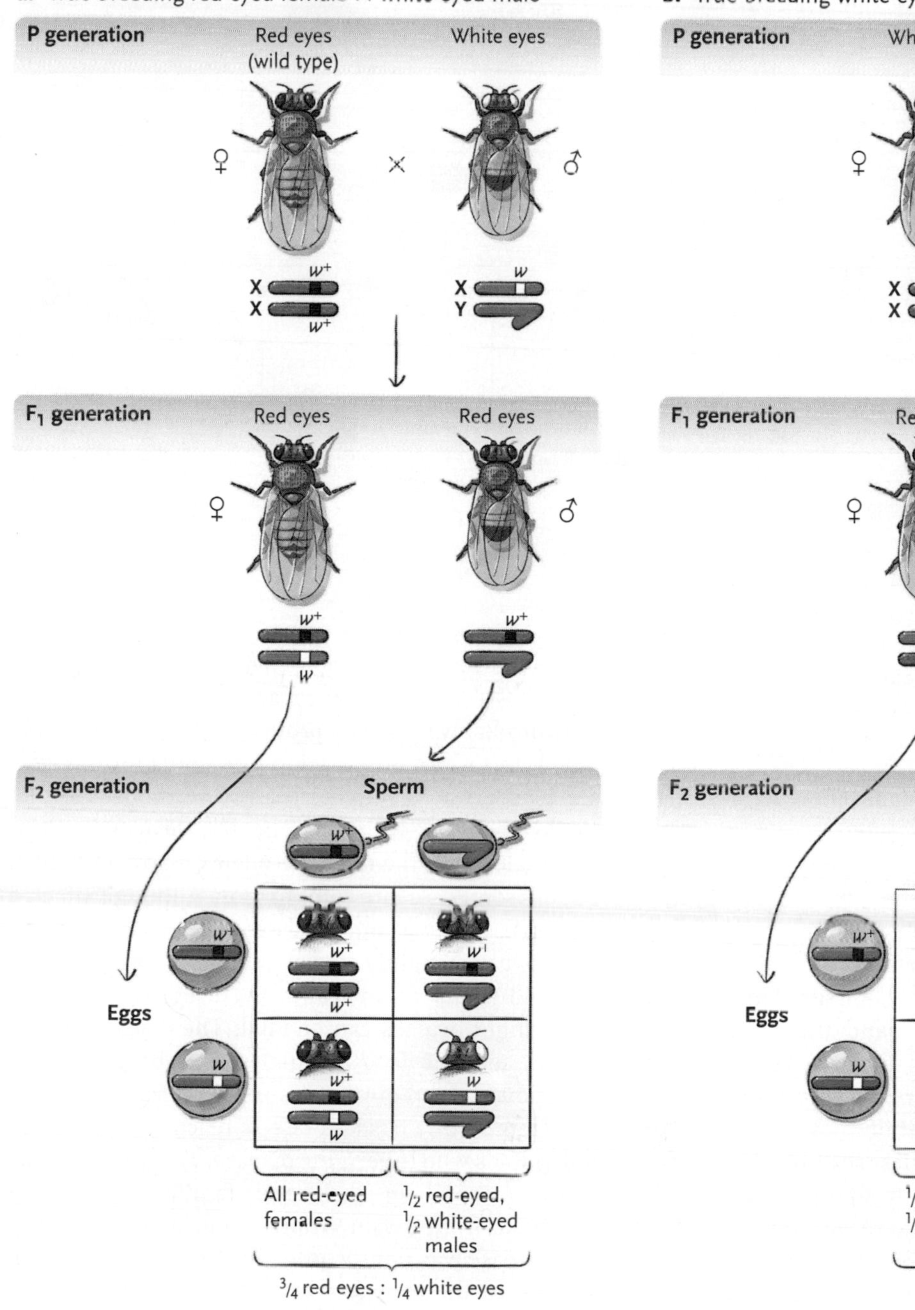

RESULTS: Differences were seen in both the F_1 and F_2 generations for the red ♀ × white ♂ and white ♀ × red ♂ crosses.

CONCLUSION: The segregation pattern for the white eye trait showed that the white eye gene is a sex-linked gene located on the X chromosome.

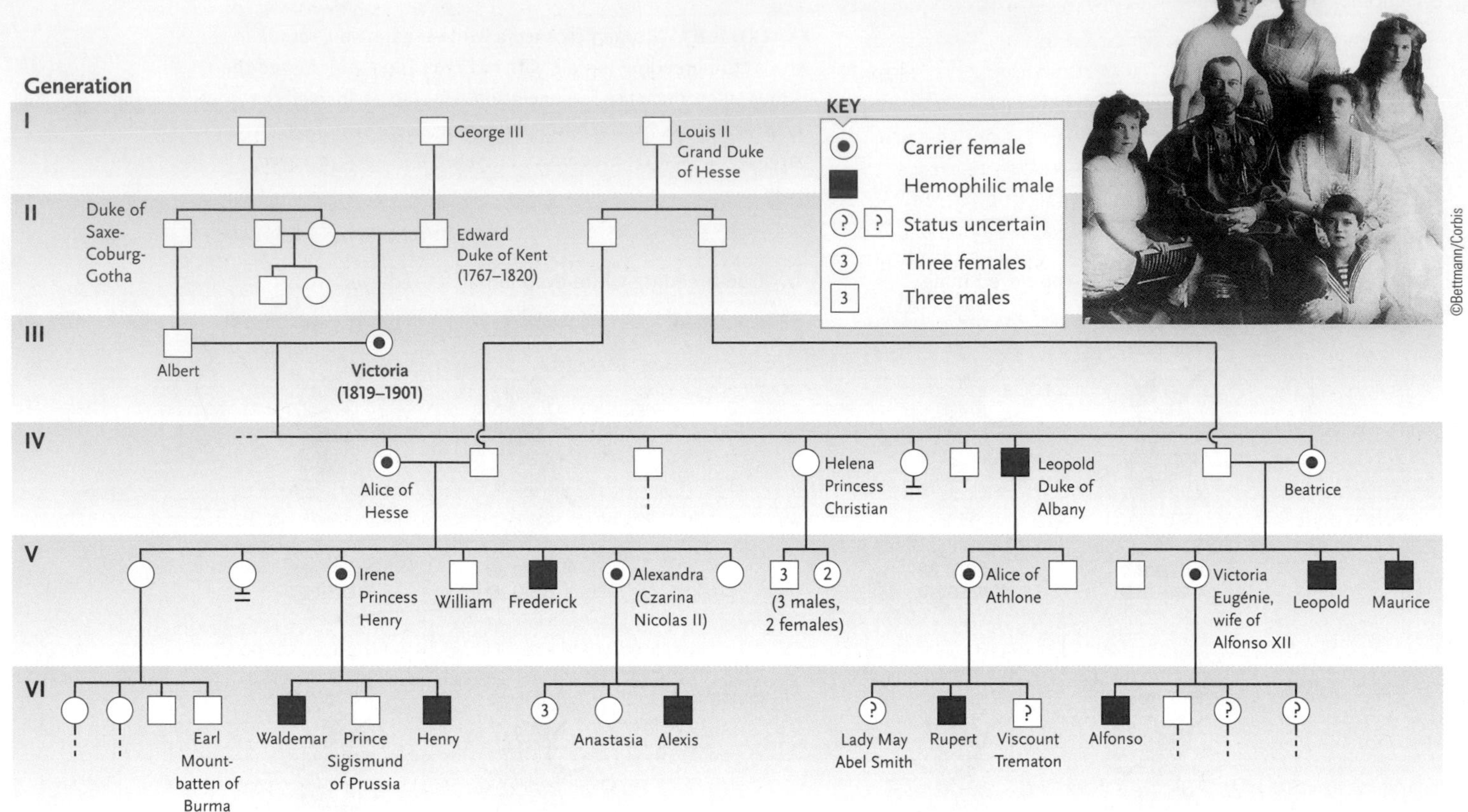

Figure 12.9
Inheritance of hemophilia in descendants of Queen Victoria of England. The photograph shows the Russian royal family in which the son, Crown Prince Alexis, had hemophilia. His mother was a carrier of the mutated gene.

12.2d Sex-Linked Genes in Humans Are Inherited as They Are in *Drosophila*

For obvious reasons, experimental genetic crosses cannot be conducted with humans. However, a similar analysis can be made by interviewing and testing living members of a family and reconstructing the genotypes and phenotypes of past generations from family records. The results are summarized in a chart called a **pedigree,** which shows all parents and offspring for as many generations as possible, the sex of individuals in the different generations, and the presence or absence of the trait of interest. Females are designated by a circle and males by a square; a solid circle or square indicates the presence of the trait.

In humans, as in fruit flies, sex-linked recessive traits appear more frequently among males than females because males need to receive only one copy of the allele on the X chromosome inherited from their mothers to develop the trait. Females must receive two copies of the recessive allele, one from each parent, to express the trait. Two examples of human sex-linked traits are red–green colour blindness, a recessive trait in which the affected individual is unable to distinguish between the colours red and green because of a defect in light-sensing cells in the retina, and hemophilia, a recessive trait in which affected individuals have a defect in blood clotting.

Hemophiliacs—people with hemophilia—are "bleeders"; that is, if they are injured, they bleed uncontrollably because a protein required for forming blood clots is not produced in functional form. Males are bleeders if they receive an X chromosome that carries the recessive allele. The disease also develops in females with the recessive allele on both of their X chromosomes—a rare combination. Although affected persons, with luck and good care, can reach maturity, their lives are tightly circumscribed by the necessity to avoid injury of any kind. Even internal bleeding from slight bruises can be fatal. The disease, which affects about 1 in 7000 males, can be treated by injection of the required clotting protein.

Hemophilia has had effects reaching far beyond individuals who inherit the disease. The most famous cases occurred in the royal families of Europe descended from Queen Victoria of England **(Figure 12.9).** The disease was not recorded in Queen Victoria's ancestors, so the recessive allele for the trait probably appeared as a spontaneous mutation in the queen or one of her parents. Queen Victoria was heterozygous for the recessive hemophilia allele; that is, she was a **carrier,** meaning that she carried the mutant allele and could pass it on to her offspring, but she did not have symptoms of the disease. A carrier is indicated in a pedigree by a male or female symbol with a central dot.

Note in Queen Victoria's pedigree in Figure 12.9 that Leopold, Duke of Albany, had hemophilia, as did his grandson, Rupert, Viscount Trematon. The trait appears in males in alternate generations (i.e., it "skips" a generation) because it passes with the X chromosome from mother to son. Mothers do not express the trait because they are heterozygous carriers. The sons, in turn, pass the X chromosome with the affected allele to their daughters (and the Y chromsome to their sons), as did the Duke of Albany. The appearance of a trait in the males of alternate generations therefore indicates that the allele under study is recessive and carried on the X chromosome.

At one time, 18 of Queen Victoria's 69 descendants were affected males or female carriers. Because so many sons of European royalty were affected, the trait influenced the course of history. In Russia, Crown Prince Alexis was one of Victoria's hemophiliac descendants. His affliction drew together his parents, Czar Nicholas II and Czarina Alexandra (a granddaughter of Victoria and a carrier), and the hypnotic monk Rasputin, who manipulated the family to his advantage by convincing them that only he could control the boy's bleeding. The situation helped trigger the Russian Revolution of 1917, which ended the Russian monarchy and led to the establishment of a Communist government in the former Soviet Union, a significant event in twentieth-century history.

Hemophilia affected only sons in the royal lines but could have affected daughters if a hemophiliac son had married a carrier female. Because the disease is rare in the human population as a whole, the chance of such a mating is so low that only a few unions of this type have been recorded.

12.2e Inactivation of One X Chromosome Evens out Gene Effects

Although mammalian females have twice as many copies of genes carried on the X chromosome as males, it is unlikely that they require twice as much of the products of those genes. Theoretically, products from genes on the X chromosome could be equalized in males and females if (1) expression of genes on the single male X chromosome was doubled, or (2) expression of genes on both female X chromosomes was halved, or (3) one X chromosome was "turned off" in females. All of these dosage compensation mechanisms are known in nature, but mammals use the latter; females with two X chromosomes inactivate most of the genes on one X chromosome or the other in most body cells.

As a result of the equalizing mechanism, the activity of most genes carried on the X chromosome is essentially the same in the cells of males and females. The inactivation occurs by a condensation process that folds and packs the chromatin of one of the two X chromosomes into a tightly coiled state similar to the condensed state of chromosomes during cell division. The inactive, condensed X chromosome can be seen at one side of the nucleus in cells of females as a dense mass of chromatin called the **Barr body.**

The inactivation occurs during embryonic development. Which of the two X chromosomes becomes inactive in a particular embryonic cell line is a random event. But once one of the X chromosomes is inactivated in a cell, that same X is inactivated in all descendants of the cell. Thus, within one female, one of the X chromosomes is active in particular cells and inactive in others and vice versa.

If the two X chromosomes carry different alleles of a gene, one allele will be active in cell lines in which one X chromosome is active, and the other allele will be active in cell lines in which the other X chromosome is active. For many sex-linked alleles, such as the recessive allele that causes hemophilia, random inactivation of either X chromosome has little overall whole-body effect in heterozygous females because the dominant allele is active in enough of the critical cells to produce a normal phenotype. However, for some genes, the inactivation of either X chromosome in heterozygotes produces recognizably different effects in distinct regions of the body.

For example, the orange and black patches of fur in calico cats result from inactivation of one of the two X chromosomes in regions of the skin of heterozygous females **(Figure 12.10).** Males, which get only one of the two alleles, normally have either black or orange fur. Similarly, in humans, females who are heterozygous for an allele on the X chromosome that

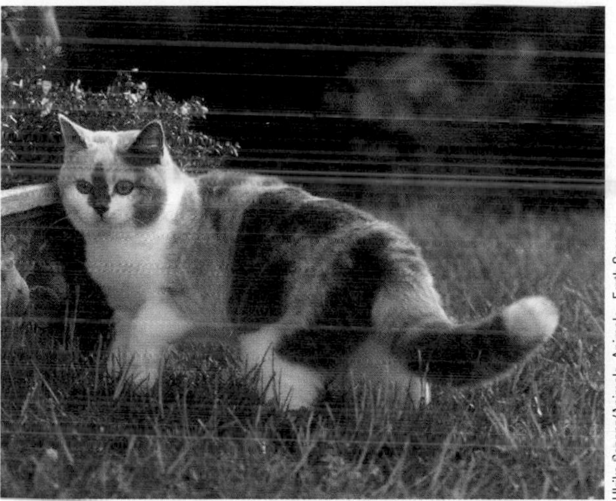

Figure 12.10
A female cat with the calico colour pattern in which patches of orange and black fur are produced by random inactivation of one of the two X chromosomes. Two genes control the black and orange colours: the *O* gene on the X chromosome is for orange fur colour, and the *B* gene on an autosome is for black fur colour. A calico cat has the genotype *Oo BB* (or *Oo Bb*). An orange patch results when the X chromosome carrying the mutant *o* allele is inactivated. In this case, the *O* gene masks the expression of the *B* gene and orange fur is produced. (This example is of epistasis; see Section 11.2.) A black patch results when the X chromosome carrying the *O* allele is inactivated. In this case, the mutant *o* allele cannot mask *B* gene expression and black fur results. The white patches result from interactions with a different, autosomal gene that entirely blocks pigment deposition in the fur.

blocks development of sweat glands may have a patchy distribution of skin areas with and without the glands. Females with the patchy distribution are not seriously affected and may be unaware of the condition.

As we have seen, the discovery of genetic linkage, recombination, and sex-linked genes led to the elaboration and expansion of Mendel's principles of inheritance. Next, we examine what happens when patterns of inheritance are modified by changes in the chromosomes.

Study Break

1. What are the differences in sex chromosomes that underlie sex linkage inheritance patterns?
2. For a given gene, how could you determine if it was sex-linked or not?

12.3 Chromosomal Alterations That Affect Inheritance

Although chromosomes are relatively stable structures, they are sometimes altered by breaks in the DNA, which can be generated by agents such as radiation or certain chemicals or by enzymes encoded in some infecting viruses. The broken chromosome fragments may be lost, or they may reattach to the same or different chromosomes. The resulting changes in chromosome structure may have genetic consequences if alleles are eliminated, mixed in new combinations, duplicated, or placed in new locations by the alterations in cell lines that lead to the formation of gametes.

Genetic changes may also occur through changes in chromosome number, including addition or loss of one or more chromosomes or even entire sets of chromosomes. Both chromosomal alterations and changes in chromosome number can be a source of disease and disability, as well as a source of variability during evolution.

12.3a Deletions, Duplications, Translocations, and Inversions Are the Most Common Chromosomal Alterations

Chromosomal alterations after breakages occur in four major forms **(Figure 12.11)**:

- A **deletion** occurs if a broken segment is lost from a chromosome.
- A **duplication** occurs if a segment is broken from one chromosome and inserted into its homologue. In the receiving homologue, the alleles in the inserted fragment are added to the ones already there.
- A **translocation** occurs if a broken segment is attached to a different, nonhomologous chromosome.
- An **inversion** occurs if a broken segment reattaches to the same chromosome from which it was lost, but in reversed orientation, so that the order of genes is reversed.

To be inherited, chromosomal alterations must occur or be included in cells of the germ line leading to development of eggs or sperm.

Deletions and Duplications. A deletion (see Figure 12.11a) may cause severe problems if the missing segment contains genes that are essential for normal development or cellular functions. For example, one deletion from human chromosome 5 typically leads to severe mental retardation and a malformed larynx. The cries of an affected infant sound more like a meow than a human cry—hence the name of the disorder, *cri-du-chat* (meaning "cat's cry").

A duplication (see Figure 12.11b) may have effects that vary from harmful to beneficial, depending on the genes and alleles contained in the duplicated region. Although most duplications are likely to be detrimental, some have been important sources of evolutionary change. That is, because there are duplicate genes, one copy can mutate into new forms without seriously affecting the basic functions of the organism. For example, mammals have genes that encode several types of hemoglobin that are not present in vertebrates, such as sharks, which evolved earlier; the additional

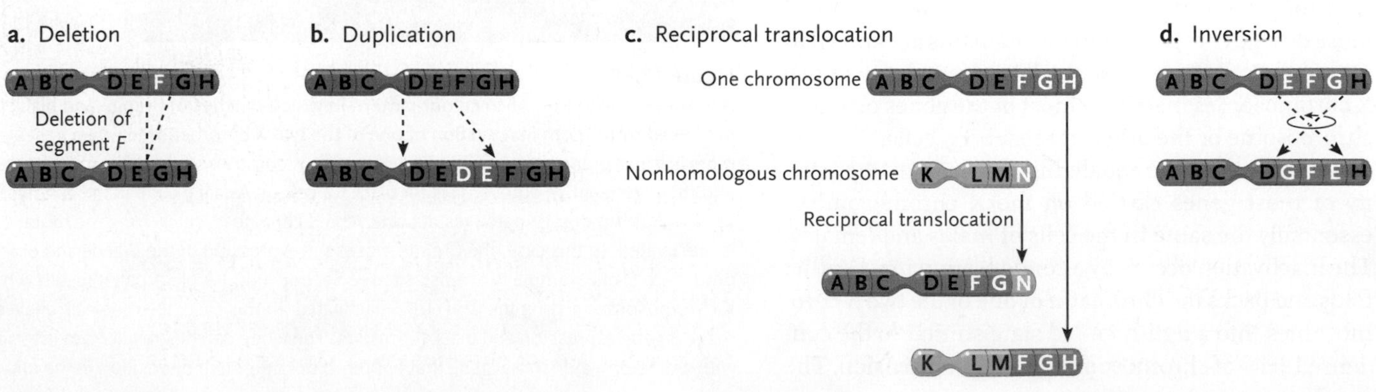

Figure 12.11
Chromosome **(a)** deletion, **(b)** duplication, **(c)** translocation (a reciprocal translocation is shown), and **(d)** inversion.

hemoglobin genes of mammals are believed to have appeared through duplications, followed by mutations in the duplicates that created new and beneficial forms of hemoglobin as further evolution took place. Duplications sometimes arise during recombination in meiosis, if crossing-over occurs unequally, so that a segment is deleted from one chromosome of a homologous pair and inserted in the other.

Translocations and Inversions. In a translocation, a segment breaks from one chromosome and attaches to another, nonhomologous chromosome. In many cases, a translocation is reciprocal, meaning that two nonhomologous chromosomes exchange segments (see Figure 12.11c). Reciprocal translocations resemble genetic recombination, except that the two chromosomes involved in the exchange do not contain the same genes.

For example, a particular cancer of the human immune system, Burkitt lymphoma, is caused by a translocation that moves a segment of human chromosome 8 to the end of chromosome 14. The break does not interrupt any genes required for normal cell function. The translocated segment contains genes that control cell division. These genes are precisely regulated at their normal location but are near the control regions of highly active genes in the new location, causing them to be overactive and leading to uncontrolled cell division and the development of a cancer.

In an inversion, a chromosome segment breaks and then reattaches to the same chromosome, but in reverse order (see Figure 12.11d). Inversions have essentially the same effects as translocations—genes may be broken internally by the inversion, with loss of function, or they may be transferred intact to a new location within the same chromosome, producing effects that range from beneficial to harmful.

Inversions and translocations have been important factors in the evolution of plants and some animals, including insects and primates. For example, five of the chromosome pairs of humans show evidence of translocations and inversions that are not present in one of our nearest primate relatives, gorillas, and therefore must have occurred after the gorilla and human evolutionary lineages split.

12.3b The Number of Entire Chromosomes May Also Change

At times, whole, single chromosomes are lost or gained from cells entering or undergoing meiosis, resulting in a change of chromosome number. Most often, these changes occur through **nondisjunction**, the failure of homologous pairs to separate during the first meiotic division, or through misdivision, the failure of chromatids to separate during the second meiotic division **(Figure 12.12)**. As a result, gametes are produced that lack one or more chromosomes or contain extra copies of the chromosomes. Note that

a.

Nondisjunction

Extra chromosome ($n + 1$)

Extra chromosome ($n + 1$)

Missing chromosome ($n - 1$)

Missing chromosome ($n - 1$)

Meiosis I

Meiosis II

Gametes

Nondisjunction during the first meiotic division causes both chromosomes of one pair to be delivered to the same pole of the spindle. The nondisjunction produces two gametes with an extra chromosome and two with a missing chromosome.

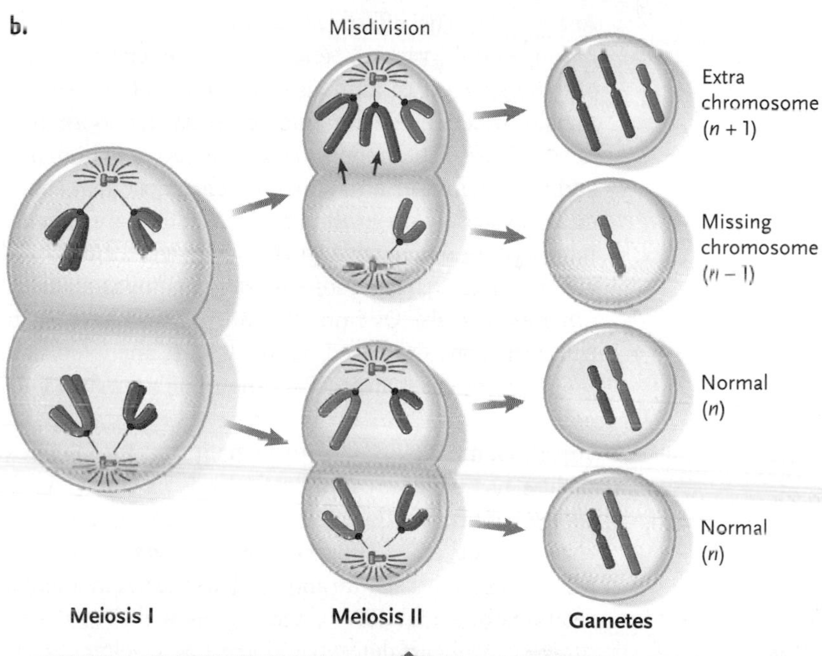

Misdivision during the second meiotic division produces two normal gametes, one gamete with an extra chromosome and one gamete with a missing chromosome.

Figure 12.12
(a) Nondisjunction during the first meiotic division and **(b)** misdivision during the second meiotic division.

chromatids separate normally in meiosis II even if chromosomes do not disjoin properly in meiosis I. Fertilization by these gametes produces an individual with extra or missing chromosomes. Such individuals are called **aneuploids**, whereas individuals with a normal set of chromosomes are called **euploids.**

Changes in chromosome number can also occur through duplication of entire sets, meaning individuals may receive one or more extra copies of the entire haploid complement of chromosomes. Such individuals

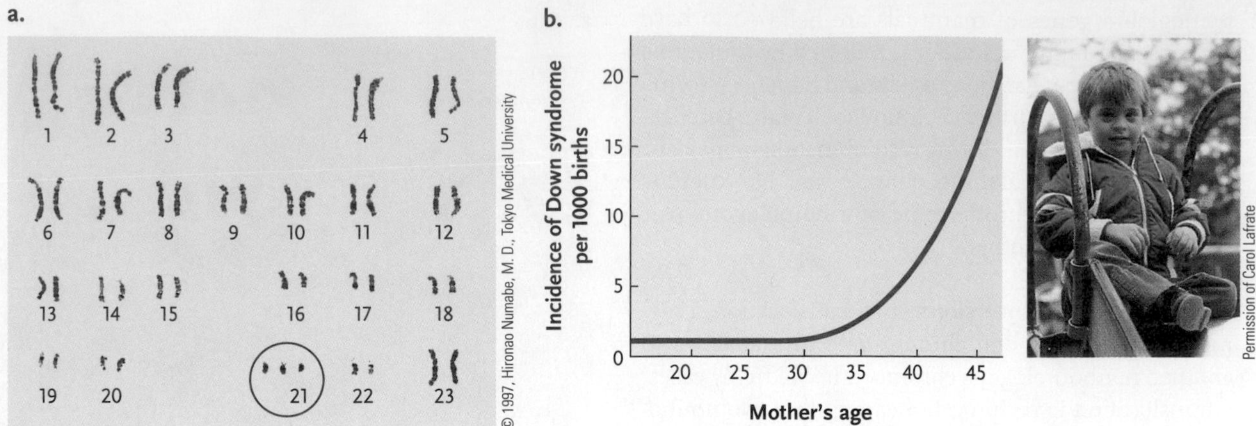

Figure 12.13
Down syndrome. **(a)** The chromosomes of a human female with Down syndrome showing three copies of chromosome 21 (circled in red). **(b)** The increase in the incidence of Down syndrome with increasing age of the mother, from a study conducted in Victoria, Australia, between 1942 and 1957.

are called **polyploids.** *Triploids* have three copies of each chromosome instead of two; *tetraploids* have four copies of each chromosome. Multiples higher than tetraploids also occur.

Aneuploids. The effects of addition or loss of whole chromosomes vary depending on the chromosome and the species. In animals, aneuploidy of autosomes usually produces debilitating or lethal developmental abnormalities. These abnormalities also occur in humans; addition or loss of an autosomal chromosome causes embryos to develop so abnormally that they are aborted naturally. For reasons that are not understood, aneuploidy is as much as 10 times more frequent in humans than in other mammals. Of human embryos that have been miscarried and examined, about 70% are aneuploids.

In some cases, autosomal aneuploids survive. This is the case with humans who receive an extra copy of chromosome 21—one of the smallest chromosomes **(Figure 12.13a).** Many of these individuals survive until young adulthood. The condition produced by the extra chromosome, called *Down syndrome* or *trisomy 21,* is characterized by short stature and moderate to severe mental retardation. About 40% of individuals with Down syndrome have heart defects, and skeletal development is slower than normal. Most do not mature sexually and remain sterile. However, with attentive care and appropriate educational opportunities, individuals with Down syndrome can participate with reasonable success in many activities.

Down syndrome arises from nondisjunction or misdivision of chromosome 21 during meiosis, primarily in women (about 5% of nondisjunctions that lead to Down syndrome occur in men). The nondisjunction occurs more frequently as women age, increasing the chance that a child may be born with the syndrome **(Figure 12.13b).** Around the world, about 1 in every 800 children is born with Down syndrome, making it one of the most common serious human genetic defects.

Aneuploidy of sex chromosomes can also arise by nondisjunction or misdivision during meiosis (**Figure 12.14** and **Table 12.1**). Unlike autosomal aneuploidy, which usually has drastic effects on survival, altered numbers of X and Y chromosomes are often tolerated, producing individuals who progress through embryonic

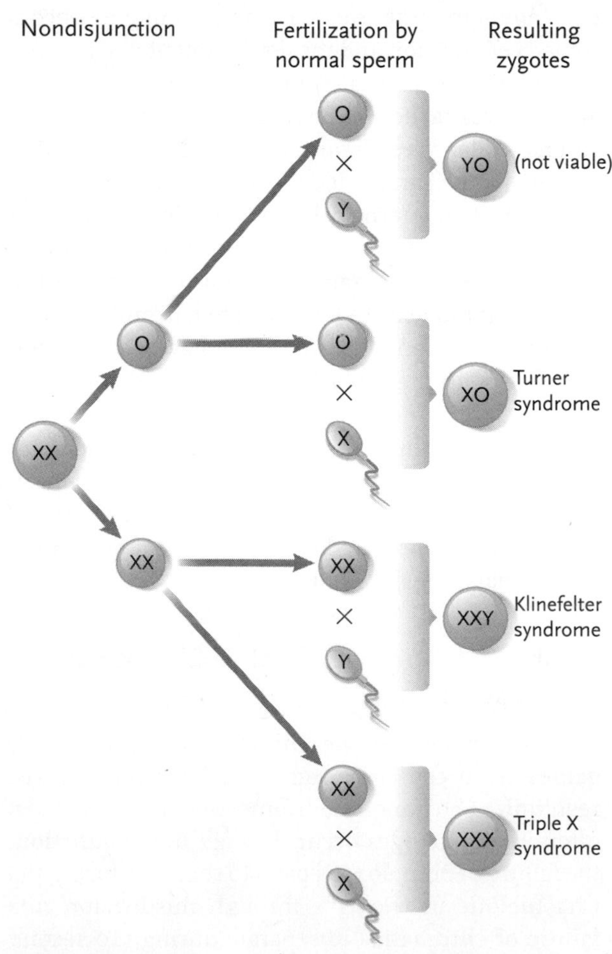

Figure 12.14
Some abnormal combinations of sex chromosomes resulting from nondisjunction of X chromosomes in females.

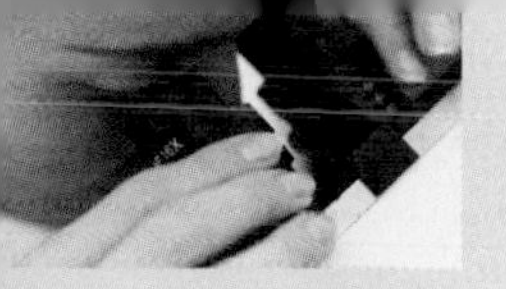

People Behind Biology

Dr. Irene Ayako Uchida, Professor Emeritus, McMaster University

In the early 1940s, the world was at war and Irene Uchida was studying English literature at the University of British Columbia and writing for a student newspaper. On returning home from a visit to Japan, she was prevented from continuing her studies. Fearing a Japanese invasion, and suspecting the Japanese people living on the Pacific coast to be a threat to national security, the Canadian government forced Uchida's family and thousands of other Japanese-Canadians to relocate to internment camps in the interior of British Columbia. During this difficult time, Uchida was head of a school for the children of internees.

She was later able to resume her education, this time at the University of Toronto, where she was encouraged to take up the field of genetics rather than her intended career in social work. Graduating with a Ph.D. in 1951, Uchida became a pioneer in the emerging field of medical cytogenetics and an international authority on the relationship between radiation and trisomies such as 18 and 21 (Down syndrome).

development and grow to adulthood. In the case of multiple X chromosomes, the X-chromosome inactivation mechanism converts all but one of the X chromosomes to a Barr body, so the dosage of active X-chromosome genes is the same as in normal XX females and XY males. However, X chromosomes are not inactivated until about 15 to 16 days after fertilization. Expression of the extra X chromosome genes early in development results in some deleterious effects.

Because sexual development in humans is pushed toward male or female reproductive organs primarily by the presence or absence of the *SRY* gene on the Y chromosome, people with a Y chromosome are externally malelike, no matter how many X chromosomes are present. If no Y chromosome is present, X chromosomes in various numbers give rise to female-like individuals. (Table 12.1 lists the effects of some alterations in sex chromosome number.) Similar abnormal combinations of sex chromosomes also occur in other animals, including *Drosophila,* with varying effects on viability.

Polyploids. Polyploidy often originates from failure of the spindle to function normally during mitosis in cell lines leading to germ-line cells. In these divisions, the spindle fails to separate the duplicated chromosomes, which are incorporated into a single nucleus with twice the usual number of chromosomes. Eventually, meiosis takes place and produces gametes with two copies of each chromosome instead of one. Fusion of one such gamete with a normal haploid gamete produces a triploid, and fusion of two such gametes produces a tetraploid.

The effects of polyploidy vary widely between plants and animals. In plants, polyploids are often hardier and more successful in growth and reproduction than the diploid plants from which they were derived. As a result, polyploidy is common and has been an important source of variability in plant evolution. About half of all flowering plant species are polyploids, including important crop plants such as wheat and other cereals, cotton, strawberries, and bananas.

By contrast, among animals, polyploidy is uncommon because it usually has lethal effects during embryonic development. For example, in humans, all but about 1% of polyploids die before birth, and the few who are born die within a month. The lethality is probably due to disturbance of animal developmental pathways, which are typically much more complex than those of plants.

We now turn to a description of the effects of altered alleles on human health and development.

Study Break

What mechanisms are responsible for (a) duplication of a chromosome segment, (b) generation of a Down syndrome individual, (c) a chromosome translocation, and (d) polyploidy?

Table 12.1 Effects of Unusual Combinations of Sex Chromosomes in Humans

Combination of Sex Chromosomes	Approximate Frequency	Effects
XO	1 in 5000 births	Turner syndrome: females with underdeveloped ovaries; sterile; intelligence and external genitalia are normal; typically, individuals are short in stature with underdeveloped breasts
XXY	1 in 2000 births	Klinefelter syndrome: male external genitalia with very small and underdeveloped testes; sterile; intelligence usually normal; sparse body hair and some development of the breasts; similar characteristics in XXXY and XXXXY individuals
XYY	1 in 1000 births	XYY syndrome: apparently normal males but often taller than average
XXX	1 in 1000 births	Triple-X syndrome: apparently normal female with normal or slightly retarded mental function

12.4 Human Genetics and Genetic Counselling

We have already noted a number of human genetic traits and conditions caused by mutant alleles or chromosomal alterations (see **Table 12.2** for a more detailed list). All of these traits are of interest as examples of patterns of inheritance that amplify and extend Mendel's basic principles. Those with harmful effects are also important because of their impact on human life and society.

Table 12.2 Examples of Human Genetic Traits

Trait	Adverse Health Effects
Autosomal Recessive Inheritance	
Albinism	Absence of pigmentation (melanin)
Attached ear lobes	None
Cystic fibrosis	Excess mucus in lungs and digestive cavities
Sickle cell disease	Severe tissue and organ damage
Galactosemia	Brain, liver, and eye damage
Phenylketonuria	Mental retardation
Tay–Sachs disease	Mental retardation, death
Autosomal Dominant Inheritance	
Free ear lobes	None
Achondroplasia	Defective cartilage formation that causes dwarfism
Early balding in males	None
Campodactyly	Rigid, bent small fingers
Curly hair	None
Huntington disease	Progressive, irreversible degeneration of nervous system
Syndactyly	Webbing between fingers
Polydactyly	Extra digits
Brachydactyly	Short digits
Progeria	Premature aging
X-Linked Inheritance	
Hemophilia A	Deficient blood clotting
Red–green colour blindness	Inability to distinguish red from green
Testicular feminizing syndrome	Absence of male organs, sterility
Changes in Chromosome Structure	
Cri-du-chat	Mental retardation, malformed larynx
Changes in Chromosome Number	
Down syndrome	Mental retardation, heart defects

12.4a In Autosomal Recessive Inheritance, Heterozygotes Are Carriers and Homozygous Recessives Are Affected by the Trait

Sickle cell anemia and cystic fibrosis are examples of human traits caused by recessive alleles on autosomes. Alleles of these particular traits code for defective proteins that function poorly, if at all. Many other human genetic traits follow a similar pattern of inheritance (see Table 12.2). These traits are passed on according to the pattern known as **autosomal recessive inheritance**, in which individuals who are homozygous for the dominant allele are free of symptoms and are not carriers; heterozygotes are usually symptom free but are carriers. People who are homozygous for the recessive allele show the trait.

For sickle cell anemia, between 10% and 15% of African Americans in the United States are carriers—that is, they have sickle cell trait (see Section 11.2). Although carriers make enough normal hemoglobin through the activity of the dominant allele to be essentially unaffected, the mutant, sickle cell form of the hemoglobin molecule is also present in their red blood cells. Carriers can be identified by a simple test for the mutant hemoglobin. In countries where malaria is common, including several countries in Africa, carriers are less susceptible to contraction of the disease, which helps explain the increased proportions of the recessive allele among races that originated in malarial areas.

Cystic fibrosis (CF), one of the most common genetic disorders among persons of Northern European descent, is another autosomal recessive trait **(Figure 12.15).** About

Figure 12.15
A child affected by cystic fibrosis. Daily chest thumps, back thumps, and repositioning dislodge thick mucus that collects in airways to the lungs.

Achondroplastic Dwarfing by a Single Amino Acid Change

Researchers recently found that the gene responsible for achondroplastic dwarfing is on chromosome 4.

The gene codes for a receptor that binds the *fibroblast growth factor (FGF)*, a growth hormone that stimulates a wide range of mammalian cells to grow and divide. This fibroblast growth factor receptor (FGFR) gene is active in chondrocytes—cells that form cartilage and bone.

Arnold Munnich and his colleagues isolated the gene that encodes the FGFR and obtained its DNA sequence. They found two versions of the gene's sequence with a single difference—one version had an adenine–thymine (A-T) base pair and the other had a guanine–cytosine (G-C) base pair at the same position in the DNA sequence. The change substitutes arginine for glycine at one position in the amino acid sequence of the encoded protein. These amino acids have very different chemical properties. The substitution occurs in a segment of the protein that extends across the membrane, connecting a hormone-binding site outside the cell with a site inside the cell that triggers the internal response.

The investigators then looked for the A-T–to–G-C substitution in the mutant form of the gene on chromosome 4 that causes achondroplastic dwarfing. The substitution was present in copies of the gene isolated from 6 families of achondroplastic dwarfs but absent in 120 people who lack the trait. This result supported the hypothesis that a mutant allele of the FGFR on chromosome 4 is responsible for achondroplastic dwarfism.

How does the single amino acid substitution cause dwarfing? The cause is not known exactly. The change may inhibit the transmission of the signal triggered by a hormone binding to the receptor on the outer membrane. As a result, chondrocytes divide improperly and inhibit normal elongation of the limb bones. This helps explain why the achondroplasia mutation is dominant.

Identification of the gene responsible for achondroplastic dwarfing opens the future to finding a cure for the condition, possibly through gene therapy for infants or young children who carry the mutation.

1 in every 25 people from this line of descent is an unaffected carrier with one copy of the recessive allele, and about 1 in 2500 is homozygous for the recessive allele. The homozygous recessives have an altered membrane transport protein that results in excess Cl^- (chloride ions) in the extracellular fluids. Through pathways that are not completely understood, the alteration in chloride transport causes thick, sticky mucus to collect in airways of the lungs, in the ducts of glands such as the pancreas, and in the digestive tract. The accumulated mucus impairs body functions and, in the lungs, promotes pneumonia and other infections. With current management procedures, the life expectancy for a person with cystic fibrosis is about 40 years.

Another autosomal recessive disease, *phenylketonuria* (PKU), appears in about 1 of every 15 000 births. Affected individuals cannot produce an enzyme that converts the amino acid phenylalanine to another amino acid, tyrosine. As a result, phenylalanine builds up in the blood and is converted in the body into other products, including phenylpyruvate. Elevations in both phenylalanine and phenylpyruvate damage brain tissue and can lead to mental retardation. If diagnosed early enough, an affected infant can be placed on a phenylalanine-restricted diet, which can prevent the PKU symptoms. Screening newborns for PKU is routine in the developed world and is becoming more established in the developing world as well.

12.4b In Autosomal Dominant Inheritance, Only Homozygous Recessives Are Unaffected

Some human traits follow a pattern of **autosomal dominant inheritance** (see Table 12.2). In this case, the allele that causes the trait is dominant, and people who are either homozygous or heterozygous for the dominant allele are affected. Individuals homozygous for the recessive normal allele are unaffected.

Achondroplasia, a type of dwarfing that occurs in about 1 in 10 000 people, is caused by an autosomal dominant allele of a gene on chromosome 4. Of individuals with the dominant allele, only heterozygotes survive embryonic development; homozygous dominants are usually stillborn. When limb bones develop in heterozygous children, cartilage formation is defective, leading to disproportionately short arms and legs. The trunk and head, however, are of normal size. Affected adults are usually not much more than 122 centimetres tall. Achondroplastic dwarfs are of normal intelligence, are fertile, and can have children.

12.4c Males Are More Likely to Be Affected by X-Linked Recessive Traits

Red–green colour blindness and hemophilia have already been presented as examples of human traits that demonstrate **X-linked recessive inheritance**, that is, traits due to inheritance of recessive alleles carried on the X chromosome. Another X-linked recessive human disease trait is Duchenne muscular dystrophy. In affected individuals, muscle tissue begins to degenerate late in childhood; by the onset of puberty, most individuals with this disease are unable to walk. Muscular weakness progresses, with later involvement of the heart muscle; the average life expectancy for individuals with Duchenne muscular dystrophy is 25 years.

12.4d Human Genetic Disorders Can Be Predicted, and Many Can Be Treated

Each year, roughly 8 million children around the world are born with a severe disease or disability having a significant genetic component. The rate of such births in middle- and low-income countries is double that for high-income countries. Why might this be? One contributing factor has already been mentioned: in areas where malaria is endemic, the frequency of the sickle cell allele tends to be higher and the incidence of newborn sickle cell anemia is higher. Nutritional deficiencies, consanguinous (blood relative) marriage practices, and higher numbers of children born to older mothers may also elevate birth defect rates in certain societies. In addition to improvements in basic financial, health, and nutritional standards, programs offering genetic counselling, prenatal diagnosis, and genetic screening can help reduce the suffering associated with genetic disorders.

Genetic counselling allows prospective parents to assess the possibility that they might have an affected child. For example, parents may seek counselling if they, a close relative, or one of their existing children has a genetic disorder. Genetic counselling begins with identification of parental genotypes through family pedigrees or direct testing for an altered protein or DNA sequence. With this information in hand, counselors can often predict the chances of having a child with the trait in question. Couples can then make an informed decision about whether to have a child.

Genetic counselling is often combined with techniques of **prenatal diagnosis**, in which cells derived from a developing embryo or its surrounding tissues or fluids are tested for the presence of mutant alleles or chromosomal alterations. In **amniocentesis**, cells are obtained from the amniotic fluid—the watery fluid surrounding the embryo in the mother's uterus. In **chorionic villus sampling**, cells are obtained from portions of the placenta that develop from tissues of the embryo. More than 100 genetic disorders can now be detected by these tests. If prenatal diagnosis detects a serious genetic defect, the prospective parents can reach an informed decision about whether to continue the pregnancy, including religious and moral considerations, as well as genetic and medical advice.

Once a child is born, inherited disorders are identified by **genetic screening**, in which biochemical or molecular tests for disorders are routinely applied to children and adults or to newborn infants in hospitals. The tests can detect inherited disorders early enough to start any available preventive measures before symptoms develop. Worldwide newborn screening for PKU identifies affected children in time for them to avoid the debilitating symptoms of this disease. The first generation of people to ever survive childhood with PKU are now adults.

In addition to the characters and traits described so far in this chapter, some patterns of inheritance depend on genes located not in the cell nucleus, but in mitochondria or chloroplasts in the cytoplasm, as discussed in the following section.

Study Break

1. What inheritance pattern would suggest that a trait is dominant and carried on an autosome?
2. How are inherited disorders detected before symptoms arise?

12.5 Nontraditional Patterns of Inheritance

We consider two examples of nontraditional patterns of inheritance in this section. In **cytoplasmic inheritance**, the pattern of inheritance follows that of genes in the cytoplasmic organelles, mitochondria, or chloroplasts. In **genomic imprinting**, the expression of an allele of a particular nuclear gene is based on whether an individual organism inherits the allele from the male or female parent.

12.5a Cytoplasmic Inheritance Follows the Pattern of Inheritance of Mitochondria or Chloroplasts

Many people believe that offspring inherit half of their DNA from each parent. Although this idea is roughly true for nuclear DNA, recall that both chloroplasts and mitochondria also contain DNA. In many organisms, inheritance of these non-nuclear chromosomes occurs only through the "egg parent." Organelle DNA contains genes and alleles that, like nuclear genes, are also subject to being mutated. Mutant genes in some cases result in altered phenotypes, but the inheritance pattern of these mutant genes is fundamentally different from that of mutant genes carried on chromosomes in the nucleus. The two major differences are as follows: (1) ratios typical of Mendelian segregation are not found because genes are not segregating by meiosis, and (2) genes usually show uniparental inheritance from generation to generation. In *uniparental inheritance,* all progeny (both males and females) inherit the genotype of only one of the parents. For most multicellular eukaryotes, the mother's genotype is passed on, a phenomenon called *maternal inheritance*. Maternal inheritance occurs because the amount of cytoplasm in the female gamete usually far exceeds that in the male gamete. Hence, a zygote receives most of its cytoplasm, including mitochondria and (in plants) chloroplasts, from the female parent and little from the male parent.

In humans, several inherited diseases have been traced to mutations in mitochondrial genes **(Table 12.3)**. Recall that the mitochondrion plays a critical role in synthesizing adenosine triphosphate (ATP), the energy source for many cellular reactions. The mutations producing the diseases in Table 12.3 are in mitochondrial genes that encode components of the ATP-generating system of the organelle. The resulting mitochondrial defects are especially destructive to the organ systems most dependent on mitochondrial reactions for energy: the central nervous system, skeletal and cardiac muscle, the liver, and the kidneys. These inherited diseases show maternal inheritance.

12.5b In Genomic Imprinting, the Allele Inherited from One of the Parents Is Expressed Whereas the Other Allele Is Silent

Genomic imprinting is a phenomenon in which the expression of an allele of a gene is determined by the parent that contributed it. In some cases, the paternally derived allele is expressed; in others, the maternally derived allele is expressed. The silent allele—that which is not expressed—is called the *imprinted allele*. The imprinted allele is not inactivated by mutation.

Table 12.3 Some Human Diseases Caused by Mutations in Mitochondrial Genes

Disease	Symptoms
Kearns–Sayre syndrome	May include muscle weakness, mental deficiencies, abnormal heartbeat, short stature
Leber hereditary optic neuropathy	Vision loss from degeneration of the optic nerve, abnormal heartbeat
Mitochondrial myopathy and encephalomyopathy	May include seizures, strokelike episodes, hearing loss, progressive dementia, abnormal heartbeat, short stature
Myoclonic epilepsy	Vision and hearing loss, uncoordinated movement, jerking of limbs, progressive dementia, heart defects

Rather, it is silenced by chemical modification (methylation) of certain bases in its sequence.

As an example of how imprinting is involved in human disease, Prader–Willi syndrome (PWS) and Angelman syndrome (AS) in humans are each caused by genomic imprinting of a particular gene on a chromosome inherited from one parent, coincident with deletion of the same gene on the homologous chromosome inherited from the other parent. The syndromes differ with respect to the gene imprinted. Both PWS and AS occur in about 1 in 15 000 births and are characterized by serious developmental, mental, and behavioural problems. PWS individuals are compulsive overeaters (leading to obesity), have short stature, have small hands and feet, and show mild to moderate mental retardation. AS individuals are hyperactive, are unable to speak, have seizures, show severe mental retardation, and display a happy disposition with bursts of laughter.

How is genomic imprinting responsible for these two syndromes? PWS is caused when an individual has a normal maternally derived chromosome 15 and a paternally derived chromosome 15 with a deletion of a small region of several genes that includes the PWS gene. The PWS gene is imprinted, and therefore silenced, on maternally derived chromosomes. As a result, when there is no PWS gene on the paternally derived chromosome, there is no PWS gene activity and PWS results. Similarly, AS is caused when an individual has a normal paternally derived chromosome 15 and a maternally derived chromosome 15 with a deletion of the same region; that region also includes the AS gene, the normal function of which is also required for normal development. In this case, genomic imprinting silences the AS gene on the paternally derived chromosome, and because there is no AS gene on the maternally derived chromosome, there is no AS gene activity and AS syndrome develops.

The mechanism of imprinting involves the modification of the DNA in the region that controls the expression of a gene by the addition of methyl ($—CH_3$) groups to cytosine nucleotides. The methylation of the control region of a gene prevents it from being expressed. (Note that there are a few instances of methylation-activating genes.) The regulation of gene expression by methylation of DNA is discussed further in Chapter 15. Genomic imprinting occurs in the gametes where the allele destined to be inactive in the new embryo after fertilization—either the father's or the mother's, depending on the gene—is methylated. That methylated (silenced) state of the gene is passed on as the cells grow and divide to produce the somatic (body) cells of the organism.

A number of cancers are associated with the failure to imprint genes. For instance, the mammalian *Igf2* (insulin growth factor 2) gene encodes a growth factor, a molecule that stimulates cells to grow and divide. *Igf2* is an imprinted gene, with the paternally derived allele on and the maternally derived allele off.

In some cases, the imprinting mechanism for this gene does not work, resulting in both alleles of *Igf2* being active, a phenomenon known as **loss of imprinting.** The resulting double dose of the growth factor disrupts the cell division cycle, contributing to uncontrolled growth and cancer.

In this chapter, you have learned about genes and the role of chromosomes in inheritance. In the next chapter, you will learn about the molecular structure and function of the genetic material and about the molecular mechanism by which DNA is replicated.

STUDY BREAK

What inheritance pattern would suggest that a trait is coded by the mitochondrial genome?

UNANSWERED QUESTIONS

This chapter focused on recombination during meiosis, exchanging sections of homologous chromosomes. Recombination is also known to occur in somatic cells during development of specialized cells of the immune system and in most other cells as a mechanism for repair of chromosome breaks. What remains unclear is the role of recombination in aging and diseases such as cancer.

Influencing the expression of genes in offspring through imprinting by parents has only recently received substantial research attention. Overall, this mechanism provides a way for organisms to regulate gene expression over generations in response to the environment. We are just beginning to understand the implications of this interaction between "nature" and "nurture."

Review

Go to CENGAGENOW™ at http://hed.nelson.com/ to access quizzing, animations, exercises, articles, and personalized homework help.

12.1 Genetic Linkage and Recombination

- Genes, consisting of sequences of nucleotides in DNA, are arranged linearly in chromosomes.
- Genes carried on the same chromosome are linked together in their transmission from parent to offspring. Linked genes are inherited in patterns similar to those of single genes, except for changes in the linkage due to recombination (see Figure 12.2).
- As a result of recombination, the particular collection of alleles linked on any given chromosome is mixed up as a result of exchange with corresponding alleles on the other homologous chromosome. The exchanges occur while homologues pair during prophase I of meiosis.
- The amount of recombination between any two genes located on the same chromosome pair reflects the distance between them on the chromosome. The greater this distance, the greater the chance that chromatids will exchange segments at points between the genes and the greater the recombination frequency.
- The relationship between separation and recombination frequencies is used to produce chromosome maps in which genes are assigned relative locations with respect to each other (see Figure 12.4).
- Dihybrid testcrosses (*AaBb* × *aa bb*) can be used to detect linkage. If all progeny classes are equally frequent, then the genes are not linked.
- Genes carried on the same chromosome may not show genetic linkage (i.e., assort independently) if they are quite far apart.

12.2 Sex-Linked Genes

- Sex linkage is a pattern of inheritance produced by genes carried on sex chromosomes: chromosomes that differ in males and females. Sex-linked inheritance patterns arise because, in humans and fruit flies, females have two copies of the X chromosome and therefore two alleles for each gene. Males have only one copy of the X chromosome and therefore only one allele for each gene. Only males have an allele for genes carried on the Y chromosome.
- Sex linkage is suggested by a particular, non-Mendelian pattern of inheritance when the progeny of reciprocal crosses are different (see Figure 11.8).
- Since males have only one X chromosome, any recessive alleles that they inherit on that X chromosome will be expressed. Females must receive two copies of the recessive allele, one from each parent, to develop the trait (see Figures 12.6–12.8).
- In mammals, inactivation of one of the two X chromosomes in cells of the female makes the dosage of X-linked genes the same in males and females (see Figure 12.10).
- Parents can influence the expression of certain alleles in their offspring through DNA methylation called imprinting.

12.3 Chromosomal Alterations That Affect Inheritance

- Inheritance is influenced by processes that delete, duplicate, or invert segments within chromosomes or translocate segments between chromosomes (see Figure 12.11).
- Chromosomes also change in number by addition or removal of individual chromosomes or entire sets. Changes in single chromosomes usually occur through nondisjunction, in which homologous pairs fail to separate during meiosis I, or sister chromatids fail to separate during meiosis II. As a result, one set of gametes receives an extra copy of a chromosome and the other set is deprived of the chromosome.
- Polyploids have one or more extra copies of the entire chromosome set. Polyploids usually arise when the spindle fails to function during mitosis in cell lines leading to gamete formation, producing gametes that contain double the number of chromosomes typical for the species (see Figures 12.12–12.14).

12.4 Human Genetics and Genetic Counselling

- Three modes of inheritance are most significant in human heredity: autosomal recessive, autosomal dominant, and X-linked recessive inheritance.
- In autosomal recessive inheritance, males or females carry a recessive allele on an autosome. Heterozygotes are carriers that are usually unaffected, but homozygous individuals show symptoms of the trait. Affected children born to unaffected parents would suggest autosomal recessive inheritance.
- In autosomal dominant inheritance, a dominant gene is carried on an autosome. Individuals that are homozygous or heterozygous for the trait show symptoms of the trait; homozygous recessives are normal.
- In X-linked recessive inheritance, a recessive allele for the trait is carried on the X chromosome. Male individuals with the recessive allele on their X chromosome or female individuals with the recessive allele on both X chromosomes show symptoms of the trait. Heterozygous females are carriers but usually show no symptoms of the trait.
- Genetic counselling, based on identification of parental genotypes by constructing family pedigrees and prenatal diagnosis, allows prospective parents to reach an informed decision about whether to have a child or continue a pregnancy.

12.5 Nontraditional Patterns of Inheritance

- Cytoplasmic inheritance depends on genes carried on DNA in mitochondria or chloroplasts. Cytoplasmic inheritance follows the maternal line: it parallels the inheritance of the cytoplasm in fertilization, in which most or all of the cytoplasm of the zygote originates from the egg cell. That is, all of the offspring of affected mothers would be affected; none of the offspring of affected fathers would be affected.
- Genomic imprinting is a phenomenon in which the expression of an allele of a gene is determined by the parent that contributed it. In some cases, the allele inherited from the father is expressed; in others, the allele from the mother is expressed. Commonly, the silencing of the other allele is the result of methylation of the region adjacent to the gene that is responsible for controlling the expression of that gene.

Questions

Self-Test Questions

1. In humans, red–green colour blindness is an X-linked recessive trait. If a man with normal vision and a colour-blind woman have a son, what is the chance that the son will be colour-blind? What is the chance that a daughter will be colour-blind?
2. The following pedigree shows the pattern of inheritance of red green colour blindness in a family. Females are shown as circles and males as squares; the squares or circles of individuals affected by the trait are filled in black.

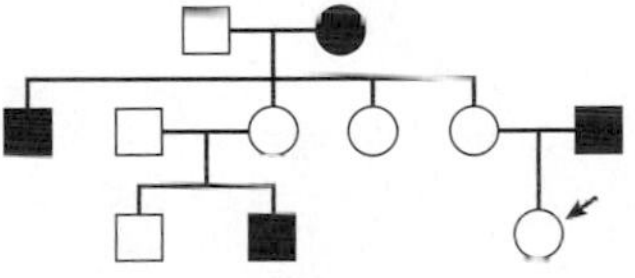

What is the chance that a son of the third-generation female indicated by the arrow will be colour-blind if the father is a normal man? If the father is colour-blind?

3. Individuals affected by a condition known as polydactyly have extra fingers or toes. The following pedigree shows the pattern of inheritance of this trait in one family:

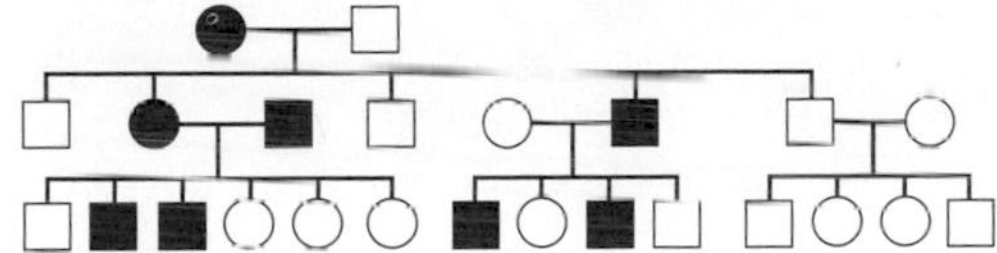

From the pedigree, can you tell if polydactyly comes from a dominant or recessive allele? Is the trait sex-linked? As far as you can determine, what is the genotype of each person in the pedigree with respect to the trait?

4. A number of genes carried on the same chromosome are tested and show the following crossover frequencies. What is their sequence in the map of the chromosome?

Genes	Crossover Frequencies between Them
C and *A*	7%
B and *D*	3%
B and *A*	4%
C and *D*	6%
C and *B*	3%

5. In *Drosophila,* two genes, one for body colour and one for eye colour, are carried on the same chromosome. The wild-type grey body colour is dominant to black body colour, and wild-type red eyes are dominant to purple eyes. You make a cross between a fly with a grey body and red eyes and a fly with a black body and purple eyes. Among the offspring, about half have grey bodies and red eyes and half have black bodies and purple eyes. A small percentage have (a) black bodies and red eyes or (b) grey bodies and purple eyes. What alleles are carried together on the chromosomes in each of the flies used in the cross? What alleles are carried together on the chromosomes of the F_1 flies with black bodies and red eyes, and those with grey bodies and purple eyes?

6. Another gene in *Drosophila* determines wing length. The dominant wild-type allele of this gene produces long wings; a recessive allele produces vestigial (short) wings. A female that is true-breeding for red eyes and long wings is mated with a male that has purple eyes and vestigial wings. F_1 females are then crossed with purple-eyed, vestigial-winged males. From this second cross, a total of 600 offspring are obtained with the following combinations of traits:

   252 with red eyes and long wings
   276 with purple eyes and vestigial wings
   42 with red eyes and vestigial wings
   30 with purple eyes and long wings

   Are the genes linked, unlinked, or sex-linked? If they are linked, how many map units separate them on the chromosome?

Carolina Biological Supply Company

Drosophila with vestigial wings

7. One human gene, which is suspected to be carried on the Y chromosome, controls the length of hair on men's ears. One allele produces nonhairy ears, and another produces hairy ears. If a man with hairy ears has sons, what percentage will also have hairy ears? What percentage of his daughters will have hairy ears?

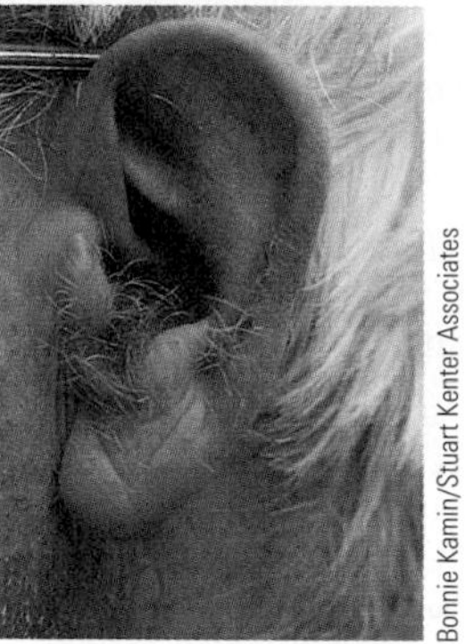

Bonnie Kamin/Stuart Kenter Associates

Male with hairy ears

8. You conduct a cross in *Drosophila* that produces only half as many male as female offspring. What might you suspect as a cause?

Questions for Discussion

1. Can a linkage map be made for a haploid organism that reproduces sexually?
2. Crossing-over does not occur between any pair of homologous chromosomes during meiosis in male *Drosophila*. From what you have learned about meiosis and crossing-over, propose one hypothesis for why this might be the case.
3. Even though X inactivation occurs in XXY (Klinefelter syndrome) humans, they do not have the same phenotype as normal XY males. Similarly, even though X inactivation occurs in XX individuals, they do not have the same phenotype as XO (Turner syndrome) humans. Why might this be the case?
4. All mammals have evolved from a common ancestor. However, the chromosome number varies among mammals. By what mechanism might this have occurred?
5. Assume that genes *a, b, c, d, e,* and *f* are linked. Explain how you would construct a linkage map that shows the order of these six genes and the map units between them.

A digital model of DNA (based on data generated by X-ray crystallography).

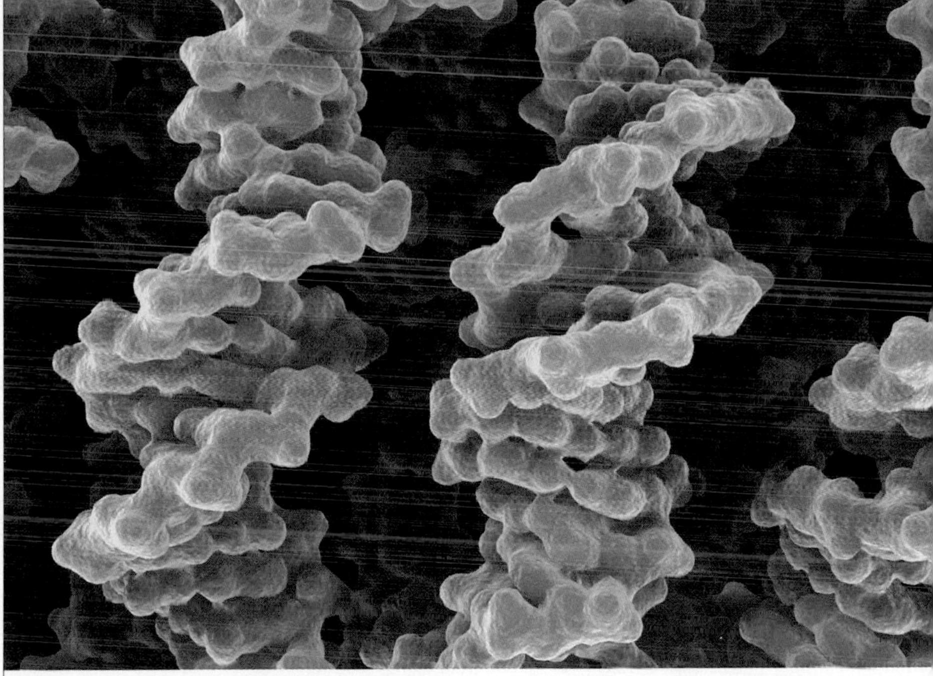

Kenneth Eward/Photo Researchers, Inc.

Study Plan

13 DNA Structure, Replication, and Organization

Why It Matters

Imagine a scene 40 000 years ago in what is now called the Drachenlock Cave in Switzerland. Flickering torchlight reflects from a collection of large bear skulls as a Neanderthal shaman arranges one, then the next, to face toward the entrance to the cave. Now flash-forward to the present to find cave bear bones and teeth once again carefully arranged by human hands, this time on the bench of a modern, ultra-clean, research laboratory. The scientist is completely covered by a protective gown, gloves, and a face mask. The surface of the specimens is bleached and irradiated with high-intensity ultraviolet light. A small drill bores into the interior of a molar tooth, where researchers hope to recover ancient DNA (aDNA) from *Ursus spelaeus,* a long-extinct relative of modern bears.

As much as characterization of aDNA sequences promises to enhance our understanding of the genetic history and composition of modern populations, this field is overshadowed by two significant problems: DNA damage and contamination. The double helix of DNA is subject to breakages in one or both strands in addition to inappropriate cross-linking and chemical modification of individual bases. Living cells very successfully prevent or repair most of this

DNA damage, but postmortem degradation can be extensive after thousands of years. Sustained cold temperatures preserve a DNA relatively well, facilitating successful recovery of sequences from frozen mammoths and bison in permafrost, penguins in ice, and the human "Ice Man" frozen in a glacier. Ancient bacterial DNA sequences have been recovered from 500 000-year-old sections of ice cores.

The natural degradation of DNA over time usually means that aDNA sequences remaining in a given tissue sample are very rare and therefore prone to contamination by DNA from modern or ancient sources—hence the need for ultra-clean laboratories, decontamination procedures, and authentication protocols. Suspicions of contamination have clouded some of the most dramatic reports of aDNA recovery (from specimens 10 to 100 million years old).

As the future brings better techniques for the recovery and characterization of authentic aDNA sequences on Earth, we will undoubtedly turn these skills toward the search for evidence of past or present life on other planets. The Martian polar ice caps are very cold and very persistent, providing ideal conditions for preservation of DNA from any organisms that may have inhabited the Red Planet in the past.

Our current ability to find, characterize, and manipulate DNA arises ultimately from the work of a Swiss physician and physiological chemist, Johann Friedrich Miescher. In 1868, Miescher was engaged in a study of the composition of the cell nucleus. He collected pus cells from discarded bandages and extracted large quantities of an acidic substance with a high phosphorus content. He called the unusual substance "nuclein." Nuclein is now known by its modern name, **deoxyribonucleic acid**, or **DNA**, the molecule that is the genetic material of all living organisms and, as indicated by ancient DNA studies, all extinct organisms as well.

At the time of Miescher's discovery, scientists knew nothing about the molecular basis of heredity and very little about genetics. Although Mendel had already published the results of his genetic experiments with garden peas, the significance of his findings was not widely known or appreciated. It was not known which chemical substance in cells actually carries the instructions for reproducing parental traits in offspring. Not until 1952, more than 80 years after Miescher's discovery, did scientists fully recognize that the hereditary molecule was DNA.

After DNA was established as the hereditary molecule, the focus of research changed to the three-dimensional structure of DNA. Among the scientists striving to work out the structure were James D. Watson, a young American postdoctoral student at Cambridge University in England, and the Englishman Francis H.C. Crick, then a graduate student at the University of Cambridge. Using chemical and physical information about DNA, in particular Rosalind Franklin's analysis of the arrangement of atoms in DNA, the two investigators assembled molecular models from pieces of cardboard and bits of wire. Eventually, they constructed a model for DNA that fit all the known data **(Figure 13.1)**. Their discovery was of momentous importance in biology. The model enabled scientists to understand key processes in cells for the first time in terms of the structure and interaction of molecules. For example, the model immediately made it possible to understand how genetic information is stored in the structure of DNA and how DNA replicates. Unquestionably, the discovery launched a molecular revolution within biology, making it possible for the first time to relate the genetic traits of living organisms to a universal molecular code present in the DNA of every cell. In addition, Watson and Crick's discovery opened the way for numerous advances in fields such as medicine, forensics, pharmacology, and agriculture and eventually gave rise to the current rapid growth of the biotechnology industry.

Figure 13.1
James D. Watson and Francis H.C. Crick demonstrating their 1953 model for DNA structure, which revolutionized the biological sciences.

13.1 Establishing DNA as the Hereditary Molecule

In the first half of the twentieth century, many scientists believed that proteins were the most likely candidates for the hereditary molecules because they appeared to offer greater opportunities for information coding than did nucleic acids. That is, proteins contain 20 types of amino acids, whereas nucleic acids have only 4 different nitrogenous bases available for coding. Other scientists believed that nucleic acids were the hereditary molecules. In this section, we describe the experiments showing that DNA, not protein, is the genetic material.

13.1a Experiments Began When Griffith Found a Substance That Could Genetically Transform Pneumonia Bacteria

In 1928, Frederick Griffith, a British medical officer, observed an interesting phenomenon in his experiments with the bacterium *Streptococcus pneumoniae,* which causes a severe form of pneumonia in mammals. Griffith was trying a make a vaccine to prevent pneumonia infections in the epidemics that occurred after World War I. He used two strains of the bacterium in his attempts. The smooth strain—*S*—has a polysaccharide capsule surrounding each cell and forms colonies that appear smooth and glossy when grown on a culture plate. When he injected the *S* strain into mice, it was virulent (highly infective, or pathogenic), causing pneumonia and killing the mice in a day or two (**Figure 13.2,** step 1). The rough strain—*R*—does not have a polysaccharide capsule and forms colonies with a nonshiny, rough appearance. When Griffith injected the *R* strain into mice, it was avirulent (not infective, or nonpathogenic); the mice lived (step 2). Evidently, the capsule was responsible for the virulence of the *S* strain.

If Griffith killed the *S* bacteria by heating before injecting them into the mice, the mice remained healthy (step 3). However, quite unexpectedly, Griffith found that if he injected living *R* bacteria along with the heat-killed *S* bacteria, many of the mice died (step 4). Also, he was able to isolate living *S* bacteria with polysaccharide capsules from the infected mice. In some way, living *R* bacteria had acquired the ability to make the polysaccharide capsule from the dead *S* bacteria, and they had changed—transformed—into virulent *S* cells. The transformed bacteria were altered permanently; the smooth, infective trait was stably inherited by the descendants of the transformed bacteria. Griffith called the conversion of *R* bacteria to *S* bacteria *transformation* and called the agent responsible the *transforming principle.* What was the nature of the molecule responsible for the transformation? The most likely candidates were proteins or nucleic acids.

Figure 13.2
Griffith's experiment with infective and noninfective strains of *Streptococcus pneumoniae.*

QUESTION: What is the nature of the genetic material?

EXPERIMENT: Frederick Griffith studied the conversion of a nonvirulent (noninfective) *R* form of the bacterium *Streptococcus pneumoniae* to a virulent (infective) *S* form. The *S* form has a capsule surrounding the cell, giving colonies of it on a laboratory dish a smooth, shiny appearance. The *R* form has no capsule, so the colonies have a rough, nonshiny appearance. Griffith injected the bacteria into mice and determined how the mice were infected.

1. Mice injected with live, infective *S* cells (control to show effect of *S* cells)

RESULT: Mice die. Live, infective *S* cells in their blood; shows that *S* cells are virulent.

2. Mice injected with live, noninfective *R* cells (control to show effect of *R* cells)

RESULT: Mice live. No live *R* cells in their blood; shows that *R* cells are nonvirulent.

3. Mice injected with heat-killed *S* cells (control to show effect of dead *S* cells)

RESULT: Mice live. No live *S* cells in their blood; shows that live *S* cells are necessary to be virulent to mice.

4. Mice injected with heat-killed *S* cells plus live *R* cells

RESULT: Mice die. Live *S* cells in their blood; shows that living *R* cells can be converted to virulent *S* cells with some factor from dead *S* cells.

CONCLUSION: Griffith concluded that some molecules released when *S* cells were killed could change living *R* cells genetically to the virulent *S* form. He called the molecule the *transforming principle* and the process of genetic change *transformation.*

13.1b Avery and His Coworkers Identified DNA as the Molecule That Transforms Rough *Streptococcus* to the Infective Form

In the 1940s, Oswald Avery, a physician and medical researcher at the hospital at Rockefeller Institute for Medical Research, and his coworkers Colin MacLeod and Maclyn McCarty performed an experiment designed to identify the chemical nature of the transforming principle that can change *R Streptococcus* bacteria into the *S* infective form. Rather than working with mice, they attempted to reproduce the transformation using bacteria growing in culture tubes. They used heat to kill virulent *S* bacteria and then treated the macromolecules extracted from the cells with enzymes that break down each of the three main candidate molecules for the hereditary material—protein; DNA; or the other nucleic acid, ribonucleic acid (RNA). When they destroyed proteins or RNA, the researchers saw no effect; the extract of *S* bacteria still transformed *R* bacteria into virulent *S* bacteria—the cells had polysaccharide capsules and produced smooth colonies on culture plates. When they destroyed DNA, however, no transformation occurred—no smooth colonies were seen on culture plates.

In 1944, Avery and his colleagues published their discovery that the transforming principle was DNA. At the time, many scientists firmly believed that the genetic material was protein. So although their findings were clearly revolutionary, Avery and his colleagues presented their conclusions in the paper cautiously, offering several interpretations of their results. Some scientists accepted their results almost immediately. However, those who believed that the genetic material was protein argued that it was possible that not all protein was destroyed by their enzyme treatments and, as contaminants in their DNA transformation reaction, these remaining proteins were, in fact, responsible for the transformation. Further experiments were needed to convince all scientists that DNA is the hereditary molecule.

13.1c Hershey and Chase Found the Final Evidence Establishing DNA as the Hereditary Molecule

A final series of experiments conducted in 1952 by bacteriologist Alfred D. Hershey and his laboratory assistant Martha Chase at the Cold Spring Harbor Laboratory removed any remaining doubts that DNA is the hereditary molecule. Hershey and Chase studied the infection of the bacterium *Escherichia coli* by bacteriophage T2. *E. coli* is a bacterium normally found in the intestines of mammals. **Bacteriophages** (or simply **phages**; see Chapter 10) are viruses that infect bacteria. A **virus** is an infectious agent that contains either DNA or RNA surrounded by a protein coat. Viruses cannot reproduce except in a host cell. When a virus infects a cell, it can use the cell's resources to produce more virus particles.

The phage life cycle begins when a phage attaches to the surface of a bacterium. For phages such as T2, the infected cell quickly stops producing its own molecules and instead starts making progeny phages. After about 100 to 200 phages are assembled inside the bacterial cell, a viral enzyme breaks down the cell wall, killing the cell and releasing the new phages. The whole life cycle takes approximately 90 minutes.

The T2 phage that Hershey and Chase studied consists of only a core of DNA surrounded by proteins. Therefore, one of these molecules must be the genetic material that enters the bacterial cell and directs the infective cycle within. But which one? Hershey and Chase prepared two batches of phages, one with the protein tagged with a radioactive label and the other with the DNA tagged with a radioactive label. To obtain labelled phages, they added T2 to *E. coli* growing in the presence of either the radioactive isotope of sulphur (^{35}S) or the radioactive isotope of phosphorus (^{32}P) (**Figure 13.3**, step 1). The progeny phages produced in the ^{35}S medium had labelled proteins and unlabelled DNA because sulphur is a component of proteins but not of DNA. The phages produced in the ^{32}P medium had labelled DNA and unlabelled proteins because phosphorus is a component of DNA but not of proteins.

Hershey and Chase then infected separate cultures of *E. coli* with the two types of labelled phages (step 2). After a short period to allow the genetic material to enter the bacterial cell, they mixed the bacteria in a kitchen blender. They reasoned that only the genetic material was injected into the bacterial cell, leaving the rest of the phage outside. By mixing the cells in a blender, they could shear off the phage parts that did not enter the bacteria and collect them separately for analysis.

When they infected the bacteria with phages that contained labelled protein coats, they found no radioactivity in the bacterial cells but could easily measure it in the material removed by the blender (step 3, top). They also found no radioactivity in the progeny phages (step 4, top). However, if the infecting phages contained radioactive DNA, they found radioactivity inside the infected bacteria but none in the phage coats removed by the blender (step 3, bottom). In addition, radioactivity *was* seen in the progeny phages (step 4, bottom). The results were unequivocal: the genetic material of the phage was DNA, not protein.

When taken together, the experiments of Griffith, Avery and his coworkers, and Hershey and Chase established that DNA, not proteins, carries genetic information. Their research also established the term

Figure 13.3
The Hershey and Chase experiment demonstrating that DNA is the hereditary molecule.

QUESTION: Is DNA or protein the genetic material?

EXPERIMENT: Hershey and Chase performed a definitive experiment to show whether DNA or protein is the genetic material. They used phage T2 for their experiment; it consists only of DNA and protein.

1. They infected *E. coli* growing in the presence of radioactive ^{32}P or ^{35}S with phage T2. The progeny phages were either labelled in their DNA with ^{32}P or in their protein with ^{35}S.

2. Fresh *E. coli* cells were infected with the radioactively labelled phages.

3. After infecting the bacteria, the cells were mixed in a blender to remove the phage coats from the cell surface. The components were analyzed for radioactivity.

4. Progeny phages analyzed for radioactivity.

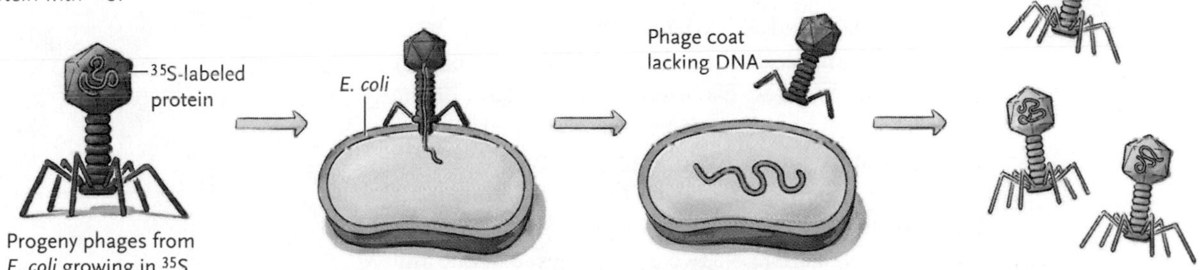

Progeny phages from *E. coli* growing in ^{35}S

RESULT: No radioactivity within cell; ^{35}S in phage coat

RESULT: No radioactivity in progeny phages

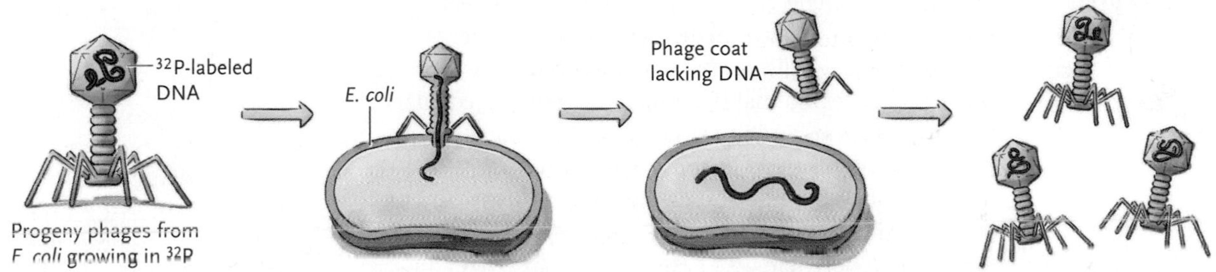

Progeny phages from *E. coli* growing in ^{32}P

RESULT: ^{32}P within cell; not in phage coat

RESULT: ^{32}P in progeny phages

CONCLUSION: ^{32}P, the radioisotope used to label DNA, was found within phage-infected cells and in progeny phages, indicating that DNA is the genetic material. ^{35}S, the radioisotope used to label proteins, was found in phage coats after infection, but was not found in the infected cell or in progeny phages, showing that protein is not the genetic material.

transformation, which is still used in molecular biology. **Transformation** is the conversion of a cell's hereditary type by the uptake of DNA released by the breakdown of another cell, as in the Griffith and Avery experiments. Having identified DNA as the hereditary molecule, scientists turned next to determine its structure.

Study Break

How did Hershey and Chase exploit the life cycle of a phage to gain evidence for DNA as the hereditary material?

13.2 DNA Structure

The experiments that established DNA as the hereditary molecule were followed by a highly competitive scientific race to discover the structure of DNA. The race ended in 1953 when Watson and Crick elucidated the structure of DNA, ushering in a new era of molecular biology.

13.2a Watson and Crick Brought Together Information from Several Sources to Work Out DNA Structure

Before Watson and Crick began their research, other investigators had established that DNA contains four different nucleotides. Each nucleotide consists of the five-carbon sugar *deoxyribose* (carbon atoms on deoxyribose are numbered with primes from 1′ to 5′), a phosphate group, and one of the four nitrogenous bases—adenine (A), guanine (G), thymine (T), or cytosine (C) **(Figure 13.4).** Two of the bases, **adenine** and **guanine**, are *purines,* nitrogenous bases built from a pair of fused rings of carbon and nitrogen atoms. The other two bases, **thymine** and **cytosine**, are *pyrimidines,* built from a single carbon ring. An organic chemist, Erwin Chargaff, measured the amounts of nitrogenous bases in DNA and discovered that they occur in definite ratios. He observed that the amount of purines equals the amount of pyrimidines, but more specifically, the amount of adenine equals the amount of thymine, and the amount of guanine equals the amount of cytosine; these relationships are known as *Chargaff's rules.*

Researchers had also determined that DNA contains nucleotides joined to form a *polynucleotide chain.* In a polynucleotide chain, the deoxyribose sugars are linked by phosphate groups in an alternating sugar–phosphate–sugar–phosphate pattern, forming a **sugar–phosphate backbone** (highlighted in grey in Figure 13.4). Each phosphate group is a "bridge" between the 3′ carbon of one sugar and the 5′ carbon of the next sugar; the entire linkage, including the bridging phosphate group, is called a *phosphodiester bond.*

The polynucleotide chain of DNA has polarity, or directionality. That is, the two ends of the chain are not the same: at one end, a phosphate group is bound to the 5′ carbon of a deoxyribose sugar, whereas at the other end, a hydroxyl group is bonded to the 3′ carbon of a deoxyribose sugar (see Figure 13.4). Consequently, the two ends are called the **5′ end** and **3′ end**, respectively.

Those were the known facts when Watson and Crick began their collaboration in the early 1950s. However, the number of polynucleotide chains in a DNA molecule and the manner in which they fold or twist in DNA were unknown. Watson and Crick themselves did not conduct experiments to study the structure of DNA; instead, they used the research data of others for their analysis, relying heavily on data gathered by physicist Maurice H.F. Wilkins and research associate Rosalind Franklin **(Figure 13.5a),** at King's College, London. These researchers were using X-ray diffraction to study the structure of DNA **(Figure 13.5b).** In **X-ray diffraction**, an X-ray beam is directed at a molecule in the form of a regular solid, ideally in the form of a crystal. Within the crystal, regularly arranged rows and banks of atoms bend

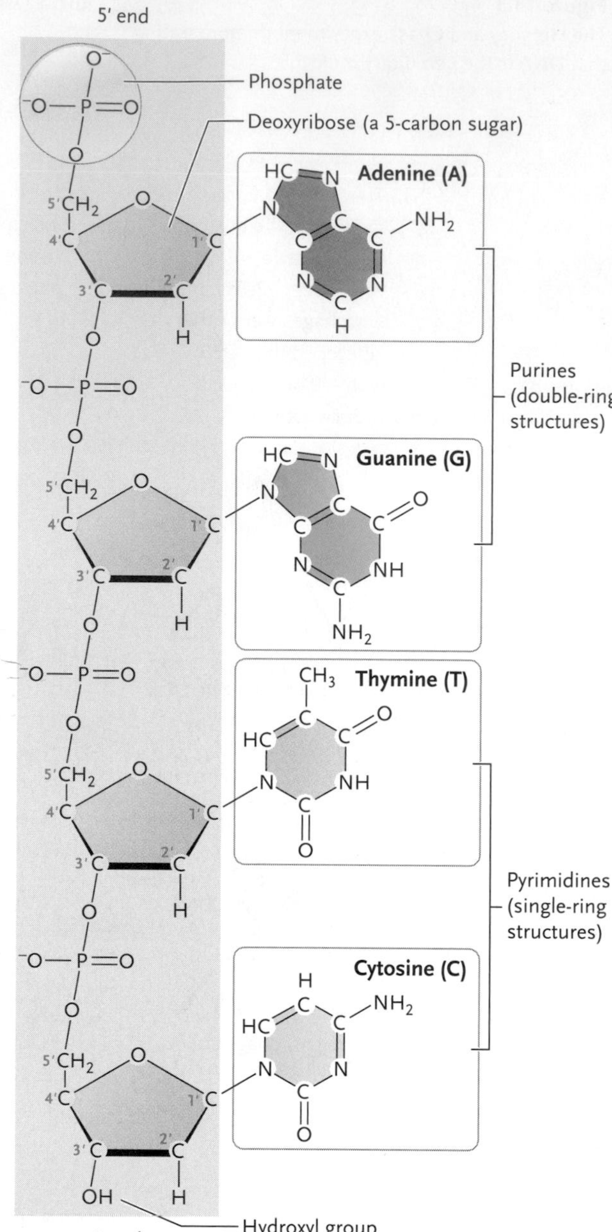

Figure 13.4
The four nucleotide subunits of DNA, linked into a polynucleotide chain. The sugar–phosphate backbone of the chain is highlighted in grey. The connection between adjacent deoxyribose sugars is a phosphodiester bond. The polynucleotide chain has polarity; at one end, the 5′ end, a phosphate group is bound to the 5′ carbon of a deoxyribose sugar, whereas at the other end, the 3′ end, a hydroxyl group is bound to the 3′ carbon of a deoxyribose sugar.

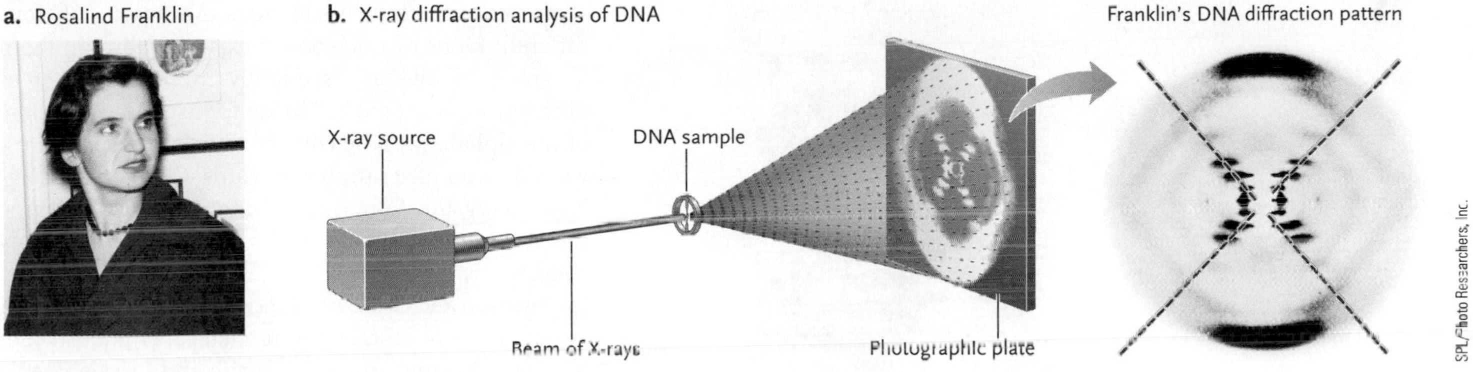

Figure 13.5
X-ray diffraction analysis of DNA. **(a)** Rosalind Franklin. **(b)** The X-ray diffraction method to study DNA and the diffraction pattern Rosalind Franklin obtained. The X-shaped pattern of spots (dashed lines) was correctly interpreted by Franklin to indicate that DNA has a helical structure similar to a spiral staircase.

and reflect the X-rays into smaller beams that exit the crystal at definite angles determined by the arrangement of atoms in the crystal. If a photographic film is placed behind the crystal, the exiting beams produce a pattern of exposed spots. From that pattern, researchers can deduce the positions of the atoms in the crystal.

Wilkins and Franklin did not have DNA crystals with which to work, but they were able to obtain X-ray diffraction patterns from DNA molecules that had been pulled out into a fibre (see Figure 13.5). The patterns indicated that the DNA molecules within the fibre were cylindrical and about 2 nm in diameter. Separations between the spots showed that major patterns of atoms repeat at intervals of 0.34 and 3.4 nm within the DNA. Franklin correctly interpreted an X-shaped distribution of spots in the diffraction pattern (see dashed lines in Figure 13.5) to mean that DNA has a helical structure.

13.2b The New Model Proposed That Two Polynucleotide Chains Wind into a DNA Double Helix

Watson and Crick constructed scale models of the four DNA nucleotides and fitted them together in different ways until they arrived at an arrangement that satisfied both Wilkins' and Franklin's X-ray data and Chargaffs chemical analysis. Watson and Crick's trials led them to a double-stranded model for DNA structure in which two polynucleotide chains twist around each other in a right-handed way, like a double-spiral staircase **(Figure 13.6, p. 278)**. They were the first to propose the famous double-helix model for DNA.

In the **double-helix model**, the two sugar–phosphate backbones are separated from each other by a regular distance. The bases extend into and fill this central space. A purine and a pyrimidine, if paired together, are exactly wide enough to fill the space between the backbone chains in the double helix. However, a purine–purine base pair is too wide to fit the space exactly, and a pyrimidine–pyrimidine pair is too narrow. From Chargaffs data, Watson and Crick proposed that the purine–pyrimidine base pairs in DNA are A-T and G-C pairs. That is, wherever an A occurs in one strand, a T must be opposite it in the other strand; wherever a G occurs in one strand, a C must be opposite it. This feature of DNA is called **complementary base pairing**, and one strand is said to be *complementary* to the other. The base pairs, which fit together like pieces of a jigsaw puzzle, are stabilized by hydrogen bonds—two between A and T and three between G and C (see Figure 13.6; hydrogen bonds are discussed in *The Chemical and Physical Foundations of Biology* pages). The hydrogen bonds between the paired bases, repeated along the double helix, hold the two strands together in the helix.

The base pairs lie in flat planes almost perpendicular to the long axis of the DNA molecule. In this state, each base pair occupies a length of 0.34 nm along the long axis of the double helix (see Figure 13.6). This spacing accounts for the repeating 0.34 nm pattern noted in the X-ray diffraction patterns. The larger 3.4 nm repeat pattern was interpreted to mean that each full turn of the double helix takes up 3.4 nm along the length of the molecule; therefore, 10 base pairs are packed into a full turn.

Watson and Crick also realized that the two strands of a double helix fit together in a stable chemical way only if they are **antiparallel**, that is, only if they run in opposite directions (see Figure 13.6, arrows). In other words, the *3′ end* of one strand is opposite the *5′ end* of the other strand. This antiparallel arrangement is highly significant for the process of replication, which is discussed in the next section.

As hereditary material, DNA must faithfully store and transmit genetic information for the entire life cycle of an organism. Watson and Crick recognized that this information is coded into the DNA by the particular

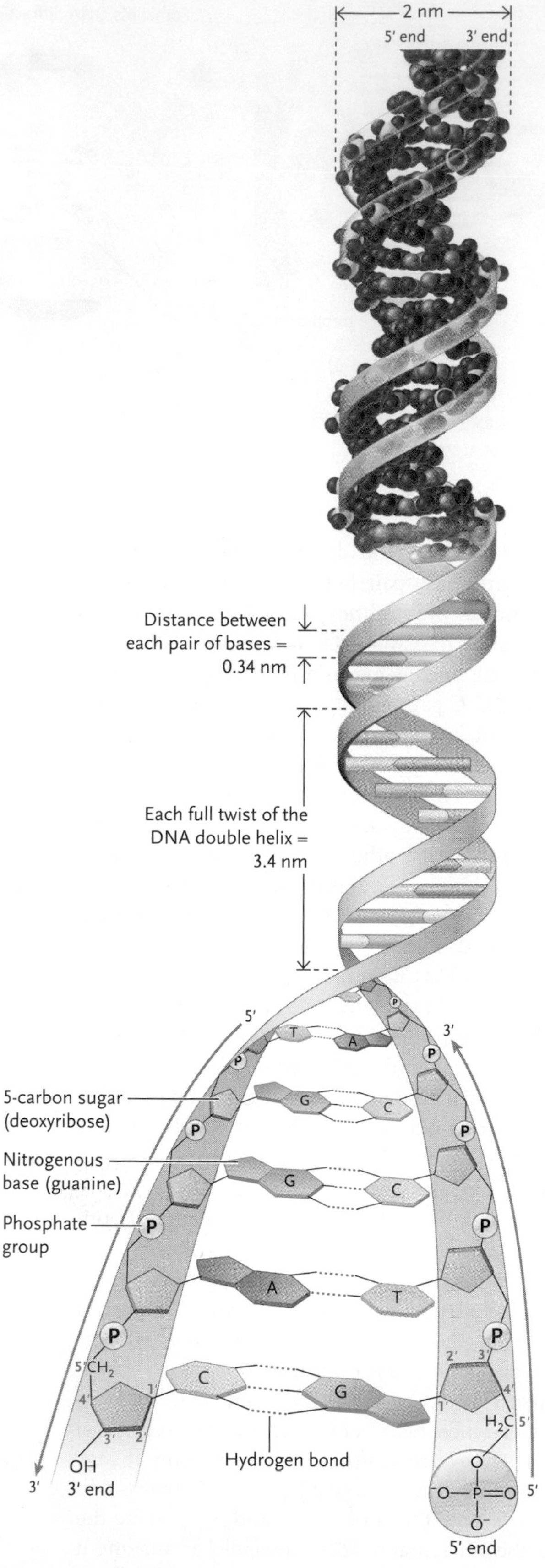

Figure 13.6
DNA double helix. Arrows and labelling of the ends show that the two polynucleotide chains of the double helix are antiparallel—that is, they have opposite polarity in that they run in opposite directions. In the space-filling model at the top, the spaces occupied by atoms are indicated by spheres. There are 10 base pairs per turn of the helix; only 8 base pairs are visible because the other 2 are obscured where the backbones pass over each other.

sequence of the four nucleotides. Although only four different kinds of nucleotides exist, combining them in groups allows an essentially infinite number of different sequences to be "written," just as the 26 letters of the alphabet can be combined in groups to write a virtually unlimited number of words. Chapter 14 shows how taking the four nucleotides in groups of three forms enough words to spell out the structure of any conceivable protein.

Watson and Crick announced their model for DNA structure in a brief but monumental paper published in the journal *Nature* in 1953. Watson and Crick shared a Nobel Prize with Wilkins in 1962 for their discovery of the molecular structure of DNA. Rosalind Franklin might have been a candidate for a Nobel Prize had she not died of cancer at age 38 in 1958. (The Nobel Prize is given only to living investigators.) Unquestionably, Watson and Crick's discovery of DNA structure opened the way to molecular studies of genetics and heredity, leading to our modern understanding of gene structure and action at the molecular level.

Study Break

1. Which bases in DNA are purines? Which are pyrimidines?
2. What bonds form between complementary base pairs? Between a base and the deoxyribose sugar?
3. Which features of the DNA molecule did Watson and Crick describe?

13.3 DNA Replication

Once they had discovered the structure of DNA, Watson and Crick realized immediately that complementary base pairing between the two strands could explain how DNA replicates **(Figure 13.7)**. They imagined that, for replication, the hydrogen bonds between the two strands break, and the two strands unwind and separate. Each strand then acts as a template for the synthesis of its partner strand. When replication is complete, there are two double helices, each of which has one strand derived from the parental DNA molecule base paired with a newly synthesized strand. Most important, each of the two new double helices has the identical base-pair sequence as the parental DNA molecule.

The model of replication Watson and Crick proposed is termed **semiconservative replication (Figure 13.8a, p. 280)**. Other scientists proposed two other models for replication. In the *conservative replication model,* the two strands of the original molecule serve as templates for the two strands of a new

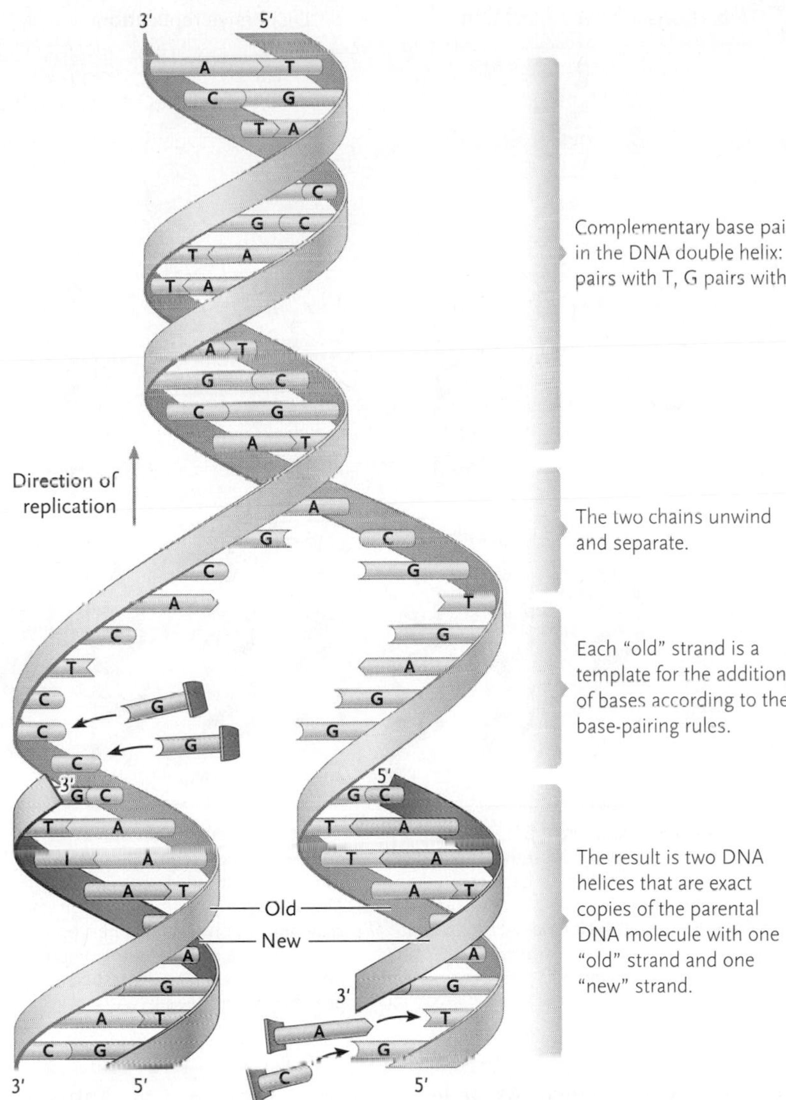

3'
5'
Complementary base pairing in the DNA double helix: A pairs with T, G pairs with C.
Direction of replication
The two chains unwind and separate.
Each "old" strand is a template for the addition of bases according to the base-pairing rules.
The result is two DNA helices that are exact copies of the parental DNA molecule with one "old" strand and one "new" strand.
Old
New

Figure 13.7
Watson and Crick's model for DNA replication. The original DNA molecule is shown in grey. A new polynucleotide chain (red) is assembled on each original chain as the two chains unwind. The template and complementary copy chains remain wound together when replication is complete, producing molecules that are half old and half new. The model is known as the semiconservative model for DNA replication.

DNA molecule and then rewind into an all "old" molecule **(Figure 13.8b)**. After the two complementary copies separate from their templates, they wind together into an all "new" molecule. In the *dispersive replication model*, neither parental strand is conserved, and both chains of each replicated molecule contain old and new segments **(Figure 13.8c)**.

13.3a Meselson and Stahl Showed that DNA Replication Is Semiconservative

A definitive experiment published in 1958 by Matthew Meselson and Franklin Stahl of the California Institute of Technology demonstrated that DNA replication is semiconservative **(Figure 13.9, p. 281)**. In their experiment, Meselson and Stahl had to be able to distinguish parental DNA strands from newly synthesized DNA. To do this, they used a nonradioactive "heavy" nitrogen isotope to tag the parental DNA strands. The heavy isotope, ^{15}N, has one more neutron in its nucleus than the normal ^{13}N isotope. Molecules containing ^{15}N are measurably heavier (denser) than molecules of the same type containing ^{13}N.

As the first step in their experiment, Meselson and Stahl grew the bacterium *E. coli* in a culture medium containing the heavy ^{15}N isotope (see Figure 13.9, step 1). The heavy isotope was incorporated into the nitrogenous bases of DNA, resulting in all the DNA being labelled with ^{15}N. Then they transferred the bacteria to a culture medium containing the light ^{13}N isotope (step 2). All new DNA synthesized after the transfer contained the light isotope. Just before the transfer to the medium with the ^{13}N isotope, and after each round of replication following the transfer, they took a sample of the cells and extracted the DNA (step 3).

Meselson and Stahl then mixed the DNA samples with cesium chloride (CsCl) and centrifuged the mixture at very high speed (step 4). During the centrifugation, the CsCl forms a density gradient and DNA molecules move to a position in the gradient where their density matches that of the CsCl. Therefore, DNA of different densities is separated into bands, with the densest DNA settling closer to the bottom of the tube. In Figure 13.9, "Result" shows the outcome of these experiments, and "Conclusions" shows why the results were compatible with only the semiconservative replication model.

13.3b DNA Polymerases Are the Primary Enzymes of DNA Replication

During replication, complementary nucleotide chains are assembled from individual nucleotides by enzymes known as **DNA polymerases.** More than one kind of DNA polymerase is required for DNA replication in both eukaryotes and prokaryotes. *Nucleoside triphosphates* are substrates for the polymerization reaction catalyzed by

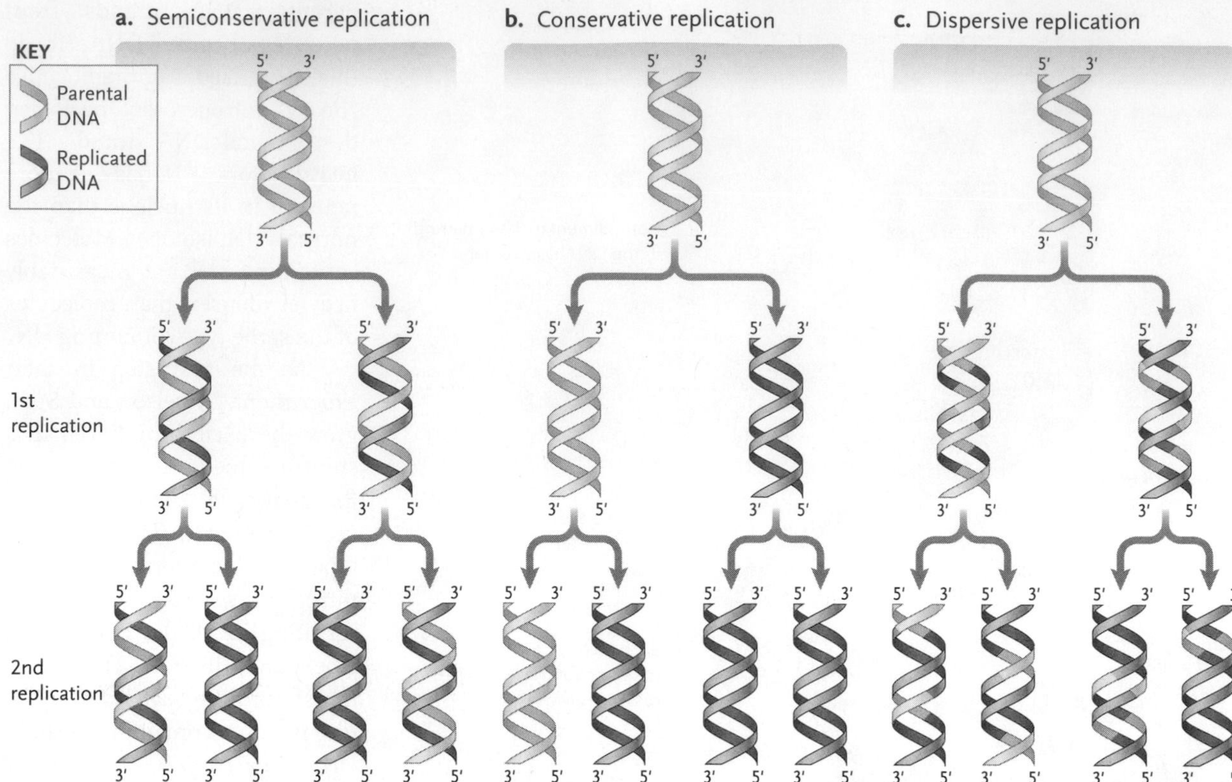

The two parental strands of DNA unwind, and each is a template for synthesis of a new strand. After replication has occurred, each double helix has one old strand paired with one new strand. This model was the one proposed by Watson and Crick themselves.

The parental strands of DNA unwind, and each is a template for synthesis of a new strand. After replication has occurred, the parental strands pair up again. Therefore, the two resulting double helices consist of one with two old strands, and the other with two new strands.

The original double helix splits into double-stranded segments onto which new double-stranded segments form. These newly formed sections somehow assemble into two double helices, both of which are a mixture of the original double-stranded DNA interspersed with new double-stranded DNA.

Figure 13.8
(a) Semiconservative, **(b)** conservative, and **(c)** dispersive models for DNA replication.

DNA polymerases **(Figure 13.10, p. 282)**. A nucleoside triphosphate is a nitrogenous base linked to a sugar, which is linked, in turn, to a chain of three phosphate groups. You have encountered a nucleoside triphosphate before, namely the adenosine triphosphate (ATP) produced in cellular respiration (see Chapter 6). The nucleoside triphosphates used in DNA replication differ from ATP by having the sugar deoxyribose rather than the sugar ribose. Because four different bases are found in DNA—adenine (A), guanine (G), cytosine (C), and thymine (T)—four different nucleoside triphosphates are used for DNA replication. By analogy with the ATP naming, the nucleoside triphosphates for DNA replication are given the short names dATP, dGTP, dCTP, and dTTP, where the "d" stands for "deoxyribose."

Figure 13.10 presents a section of a DNA polynucleotide chain being replicated to show how DNA polymerase catalyzes the assembly of a new DNA strand that is complementary to the template strand. To understand Figure 13.10, remember that the carbons in the deoxyriboses of nucleotides are numbered with primes. Each DNA strand has two distinct ends: the 5′ end has an exposed phosphate group attached to the 5′ carbon of the sugar, and the 3′ end has an exposed hydroxyl group attached to the 3′ carbon of the sugar. As we learned earlier, because of the antiparallel nature of the DNA double helix, the 5′ end of one strand is opposite the 3′ end of the other.

Part of a template strand with two nucleotides of a new strand hydrogen bonded to it by complementary base pairing is shown in step 1 of Figure 13.10. One of the characteristics of DNA polymerase is that it can add a nucleotide *only to the 3′ end of an existing nucleotide chain.* The next template nucleotide has a T base. This means the DNA polymerase will bind a nucleoside triphosphate with an A base (dATP) from the surrounding solution (step 2). The enzyme then catalyzes the formation of the phosphodiester bond involving the 3′—OH group at the end of the existing chain and the innermost of the three phosphate groups of the dATP, releasing the other two phosphates as a pyrophosphate molecule (step 3). Hydrolysis of the bond between the two phosphates provides the energy for the formation of the new bond.

The DNA polymerase then moves to the next base on the DNA template, shown as guanine in step 3, binds a dCTP, and, using the reaction just described, catalyzes the formation of a phosphodiester bond, inserting the C nucleotide to the growing new strand. The process then continues, adding complementary nucleotides one by one to the growing DNA strand.

Figure 13.9
The Meselson and Stahl experiment demonstrating the semiconservative model to be correct.

QUESTION: Does DNA replicate semiconservatively?

EXPERIMENT: Matthew Meselson and Franklin Stahl proved that the semiconservative model of DNA replication is correct and that the conservative and dispersive models are incorrect.

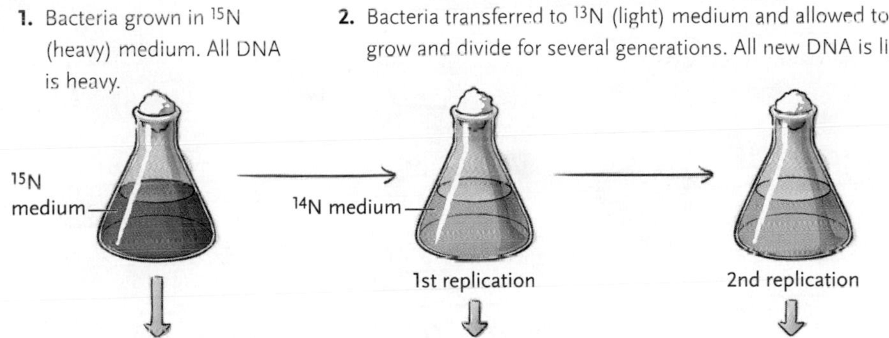

1. Bacteria grown in ^{15}N (heavy) medium. All DNA is heavy.
2. Bacteria transferred to ^{13}N (light) medium and allowed to grow and divide for several generations. All new DNA is light.
^{15}N medium
^{14}N medium
1st replication
2nd replication

3. DNA extracted from bacteria cultured in ^{15}N medium and after each generation in ^{13}N medium.

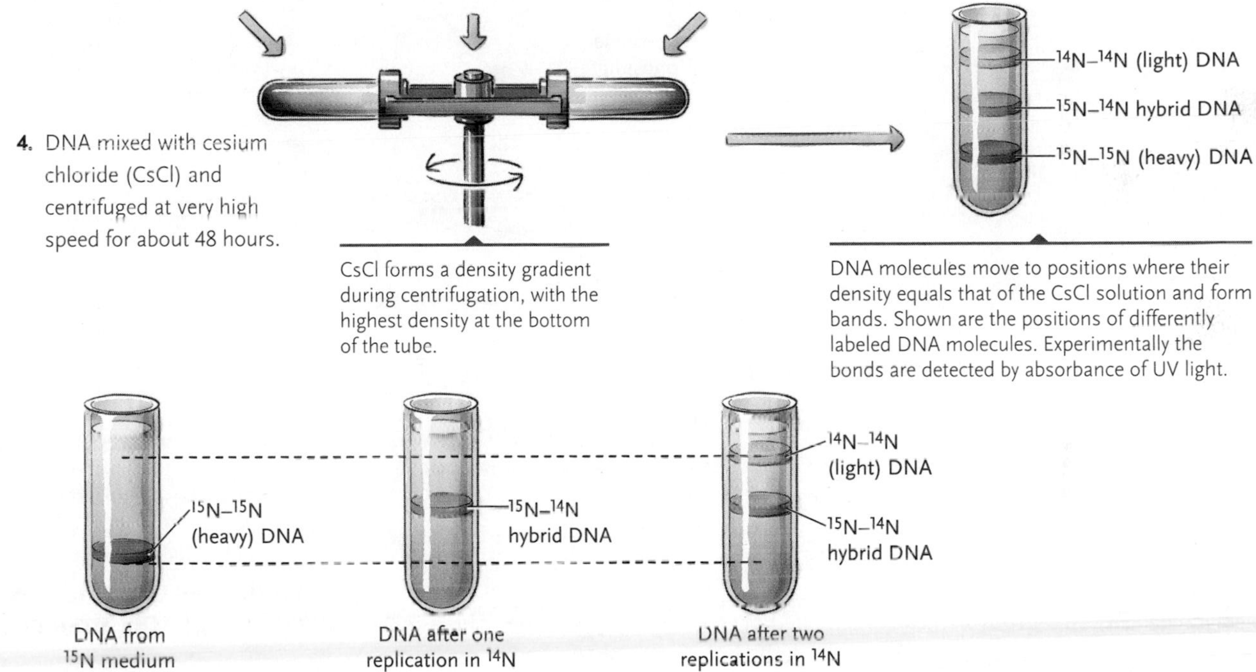

4. DNA mixed with cesium chloride (CsCl) and centrifuged at very high speed for about 48 hours.
CsCl forms a density gradient during centrifugation, with the highest density at the bottom of the tube.
^{14}N–^{14}N (light) DNA
^{15}N–^{14}N hybrid DNA
^{15}N–^{15}N (heavy) DNA
DNA molecules move to positions where their density equals that of the CsCl solution and form bands. Shown are the positions of differently labeled DNA molecules. Experimentally the bonds are detected by absorbance of UV light.
^{15}N–^{15}N (heavy) DNA
^{15}N–^{14}N hybrid DNA
^{14}N–^{14}N (light) DNA
^{15}N–^{14}N hybrid DNA
DNA from ^{15}N medium
DNA after one replication in ^{14}N
DNA after two replications in ^{14}N

RESULT: Meselson and Stahl obtained the following results:

CONCLUSIONS: The predicted DNA banding patterns for the three DNA replication models were.

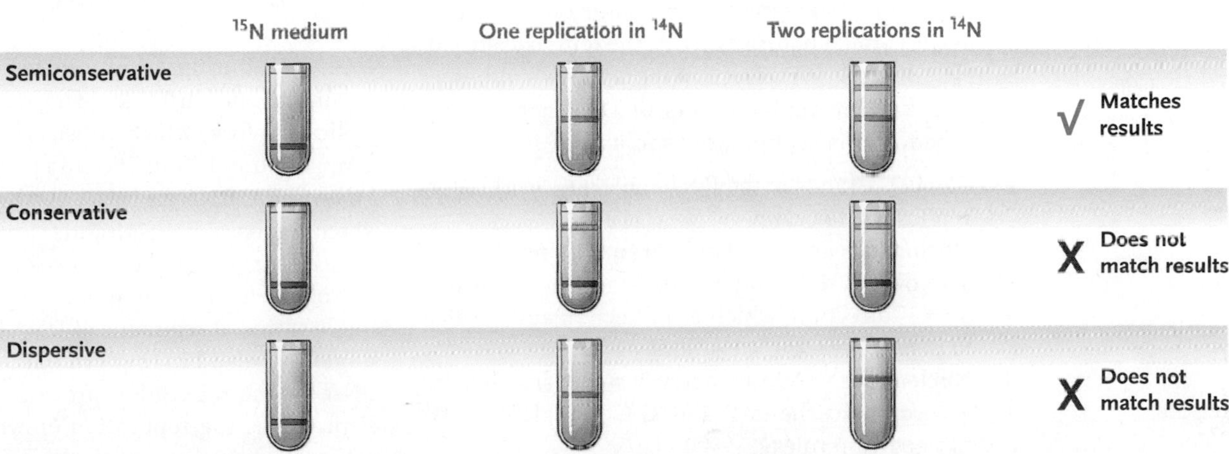

The results support the semiconservative model.

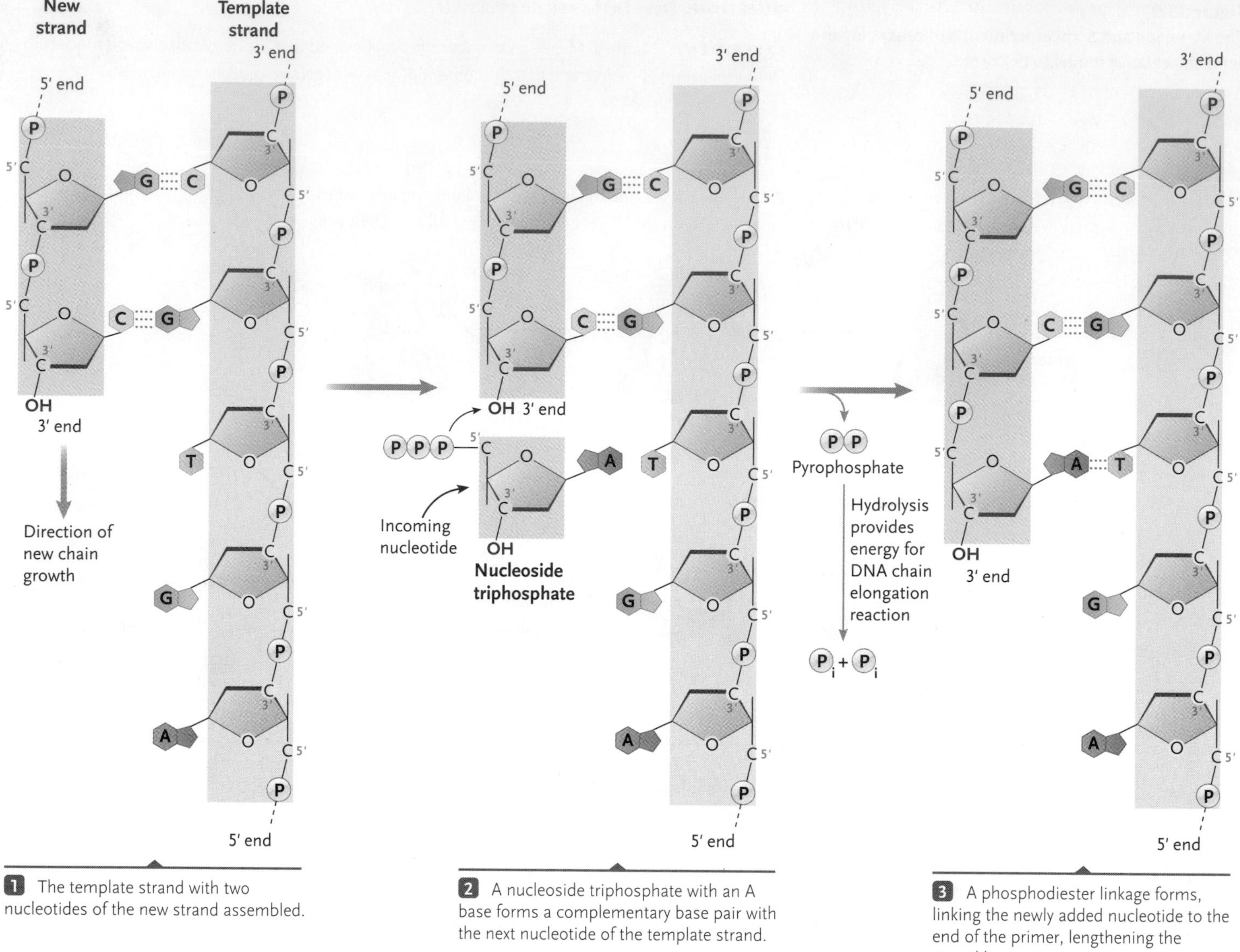
New strand
Template strand
3′ end
5′ end
OH
3′ end
Direction of new chain growth
5′ end
Incoming nucleotide
OH 3′ end
Nucleoside triphosphate
Pyrophosphate
Hydrolysis provides energy for DNA chain elongation reaction
1 The template strand with two nucleotides of the new strand assembled.
2 A nucleoside triphosphate with an A base forms a complementary base pair with the next nucleotide of the template strand.
3 A phosphodiester linkage forms, linking the newly added nucleotide to the end of the primer, lengthening the strand by one.

Figure 13.10 Reactions assembling a complementary chain in the 5′→3′ direction on a template DNA strand, showing the phosphodiester linkage created when the DNA polymerase enzyme adds each nucleotide to the chain.

As a new DNA strand is assembled, a 3′—OH group is always exposed at its "newest" end; the "oldest" end of the new chain has an exposed 5′ triphosphate. DNA polymerases are therefore said to assemble nucleotide chains in the 5′→3′ direction. Because of the antiparallel nature of DNA, the template strand is "read" in the 3′→5′ direction for this new synthesis.

The key molecular events of DNA replication described in this section are as follows:

1. The two strands of the DNA molecule unwind for replication to occur.
2. Nucleotides are added only to an existing chain.
3. The overall direction of new synthesis is in the 5′→3′ direction, which is a direction antiparallel to that of the template strand.
4. Nucleotides enter into a newly synthesized chain according to the A-T and G-C complementary base-pairing rules.

The following sections describe how enzymes and other proteins conduct these molecular events.

13.3c Helicases Unwind DNA to Expose Template Strands for New DNA Synthesis

For replication to be semiconservative, the two strands of the parental DNA molecule must unwind and separate to expose template strands for new DNA synthesis during the replication process. The unwinding produces a Y-shaped structure called a **replication fork**, which consists of the two unwound template strands transitioning to double-helical DNA. An enzyme, **DNA helicase**, catalyzes the unwinding, which exposes both strands for the next steps in replication. The helicase uses the energy of ATP hydrolysis to unwind the DNA helix. The exposed single-stranded segments of DNA become coated with **single-stranded binding proteins**, which stabilize the DNA for the replication process. These proteins are displaced as the replication enzymes make the new polynucleotide chain on the template strands.

Let us consider a possible consequence of the unwinding of DNA by helicases. If the DNA is circular, as is the case for the genomes of most bacteria, unwinding the DNA will eventually cause the still-wound DNA ahead of the unwinding to become knotted. You can visualize this by making a small circular double helix with a pair of shoelaces. Now pick a place and pull apart the laces. You will see that the more you pull, the more the laces become overtwisted and strained on the other side of the circle. In the cell, the overtwisting and strain of DNA ahead of the replication fork during replication are avoided by the action of enzymes known as **topoisomerases**, which remove the overtwisting as it forms.

13.3d RNA Primers Provide the Starting Point for DNA Polymerase to Begin Synthesizing a New DNA Chain

DNA polymerases can add nucleotides only to the 3′ end of an existing strand. How, then, can a new strand begin since there is no existing strand in place? The answer lies in a short nucleotide chain called a **primer**, made of RNA instead of DNA. The primer, assembled by the enzyme **primase**, is laid down as the first series of nucleotides in a new DNA strand. RNA primers are removed and replaced with DNA later in replication.

13.3e One New DNA Strand Is Synthesized Continuously; the Other, Discontinuously

DNA polymerases assemble a new DNA strand on a template strand in the 5′→3′ direction. Because the two strands of a DNA molecule are antiparallel, only one of the template strands runs in a direction that allows DNA polymerase to make a 5′→3′ complementary copy in the direction of unwinding. That is, on this template strand (top strand in **Figure 13.11**), the new DNA strand is synthesized continuously in the direction of unwinding of the double helix. However, the other template strand (bottom strand in Figure 13.11) runs in the opposite direction; this means that DNA polymerase has to copy it in the direction opposite to the unwinding.

How is the new DNA strand made in the opposite direction to the unwinding? The polymerases make this strand in short lengths that are actually synthesized in the direction opposite to that of DNA unwinding (see Figure 13.11). The short lengths produced by this **discontinuous replication** are then covalently linked into a continuous polynucleotide chain. The short lengths are called *Okazaki fragments,* in honour of Reiji Okazaki, the Japanese scientist who first detected them. The new DNA strand assembled in the direction of DNA unwinding is called the **leading strand** of DNA replication; the strand assembled discontinuously in the opposite direction is called the **lagging strand.** The template strand for the leading strand is the *leading strand template,* and the template strand for the lagging strand is the *lagging strand template.*

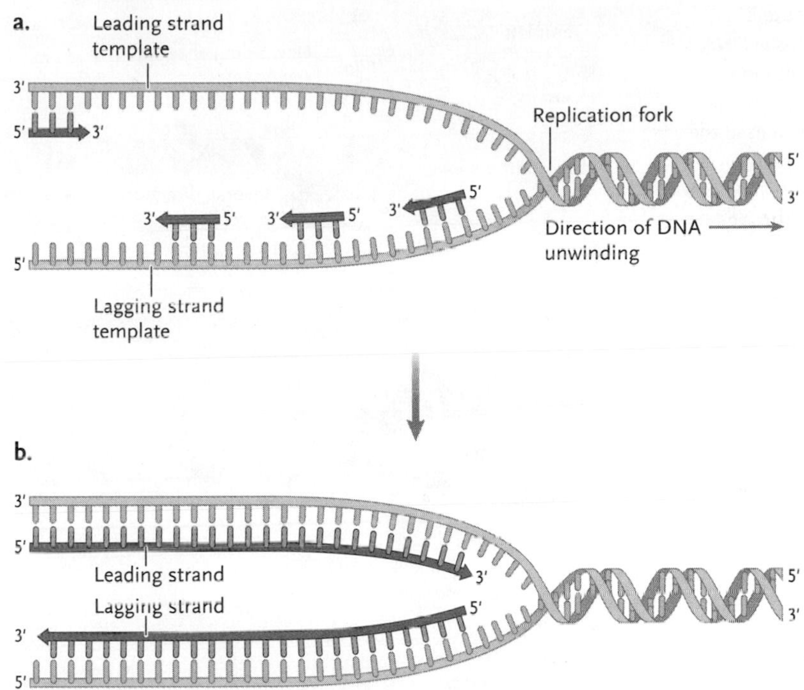

Figure 13.11
How antiparallel template strands are replicated at a fork. The template strand presented to DNA polymerase in the "wrong" 5′→3′ direction—the strand on the bottom in **(a)**—is copied in short lengths that run opposite to the direction of fork movement. The short lengths are then linked into a continuous chain **(b).** The overall effect is synthesis of both strands in the direction of fork movement.

13.3f Multiple Enzymes Coordinate Their Activities in DNA Replication

Helicase, primase, and DNA polymerase coordinate their activities with additional enzymes to replicate DNA. In the first step of the process, a helicase unwinds the template DNA to produce a replication fork (**Figure 13.12, p. 284,** step 1). Just behind the site of unwinding, primases lay down short RNA primers about 10 nucleotides in length. The primers are assembled in the 5′→3′ direction on both template chains—in the direction of unwinding on one chain and in the opposite direction on the other.

DNA polymerase then adds DNA nucleotides to the RNA primers (step 2). Helicase continues to unwind the DNA. Leading strand synthesis continues in the direction of unwinding, whereas on the lagging strand template, primase creates a new RNA primer and DNA polymerase adds DNA nucleotides to the new primer (step 3). When this second fragment reaches the primer of the first fragment, the DNA polymerase leaves and a different type of DNA polymerase binds. This polymerase removes the RNA primer on the first fragment, replacing the RNA nucleotides with DNA nucleotides (step 4). At this point, the two newly synthesized fragments are not covalently joined—they have a "nick" between them (see step 4). Another enzyme, **DNA ligase** (*ligare* = to tie), closes the nick,

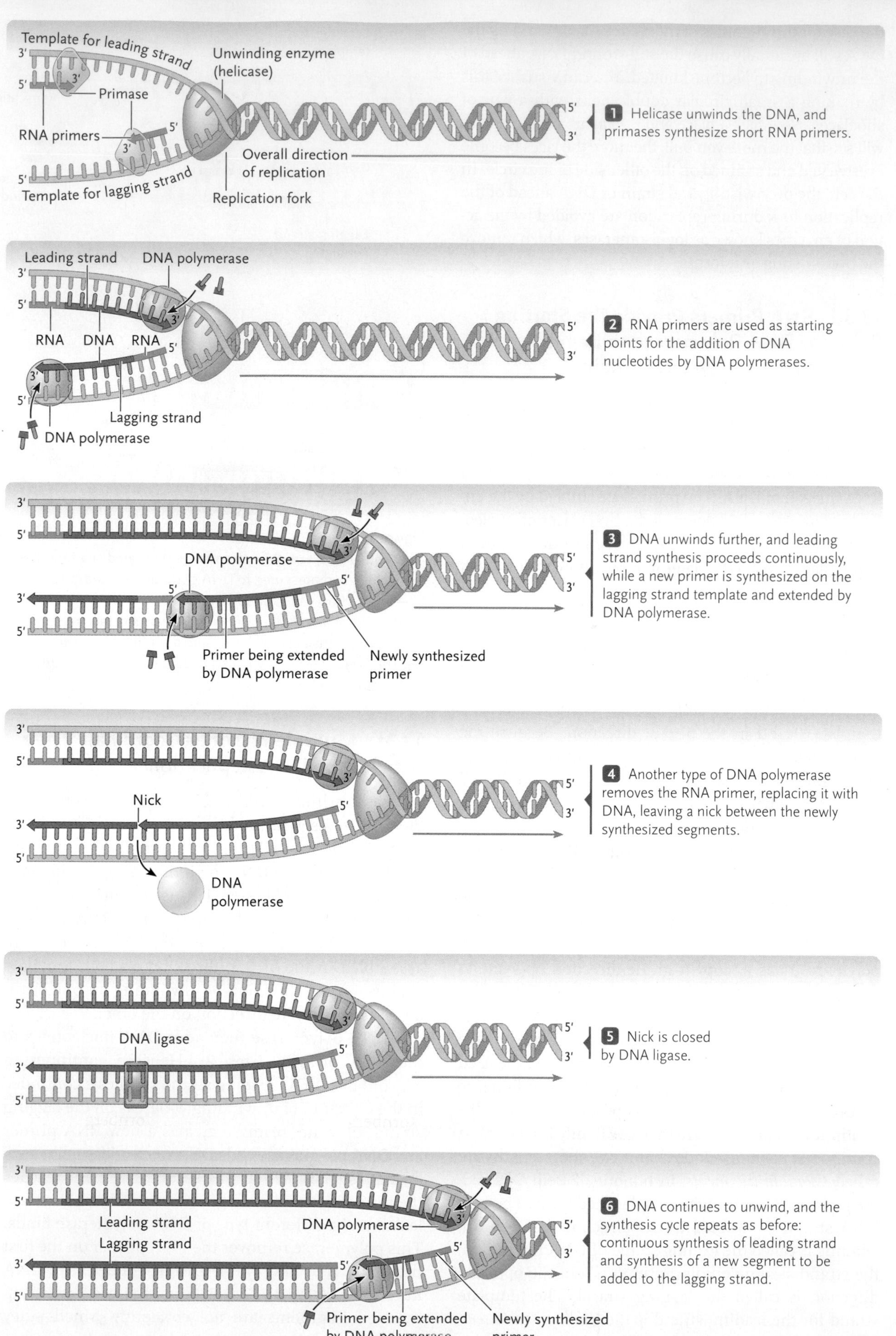
Template for leading strand
3'
5'
3'
Primase
RNA primers
5'
3'
5'
Template for lagging strand
Unwinding enzyme (helicase)
Overall direction of replication
Replication fork
5'
3'
1 Helicase unwinds the DNA, and primases synthesize short RNA primers.
Leading strand
DNA polymerase
RNA
DNA
RNA
Lagging strand
DNA polymerase
2 RNA primers are used as starting points for the addition of DNA nucleotides by DNA polymerases.
DNA polymerase
Primer being extended by DNA polymerase
Newly synthesized primer
3 DNA unwinds further, and leading strand synthesis proceeds continuously, while a new primer is synthesized on the lagging strand template and extended by DNA polymerase.
Nick
DNA polymerase
4 Another type of DNA polymerase removes the RNA primer, replacing it with DNA, leaving a nick between the newly synthesized segments.
DNA ligase
5 Nick is closed by DNA ligase.
Leading strand
Lagging strand
DNA polymerase
Primer being extended by DNA polymerase
Newly synthesized primer
6 DNA continues to unwind, and the synthesis cycle repeats as before: continuous synthesis of leading strand and synthesis of a new segment to be added to the lagging strand.

Figure 13.12
Steps in DNA replication, including the activities of the helicase, primase, DNA polymerases, and DNA ligase taking part in the process. Primer synthesis, removal, gap filling, and nick sealing occur primarily in the lagging strand. The drawings simplify the process. In reality, the enzymes assemble at the fork, replicating both strands from that position as the template strands fold and pass through the assembly.

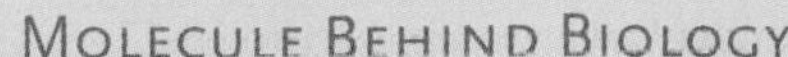

MOLECULE BEHIND BIOLOGY

Acyclic Nucleoside Phosphonates as Antiviral Drugs

Viruses are obligate parasites that exploit the cellular machinery of infected host cells for replication and gene expression. Such intimate association with host biochemistry makes it difficult for scientists to find an exclusively viral "target" for antiviral drug binding.

However, the herpes viruses provide such a target when, once inside the nucleus of an infected cell, they transcribe a gene coding for their own distinctive DNA polymerase. This novel polymerase replicates viral DNA, drawing from the cellular pool of nucleotide triphosphates (see Figure 13.12).

It has been possible to selectively "poison" viral DNA replication with acyclic nucleoside phosphonates such as cidofovir, shown below, because they (1) are converted to their triphosphate form by infected cells, (2) are then selectively incorporated into viral DNA (instead of the normal nucleotides) by viral polymerase, and (3) block further DNA synthesis.

These drugs are part of a large class of compounds called base analogues that are incorporated into DNA by "mistake." Compare the structures below with those of the standard bases shown in Figure 13.4 and notice why these drugs are called "acyclic."

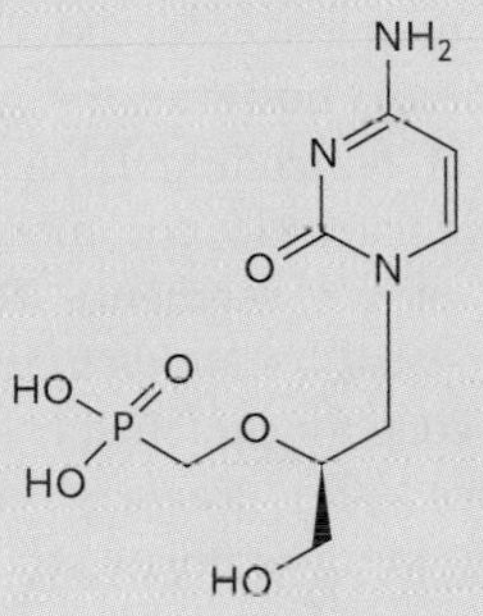

Cidofovir

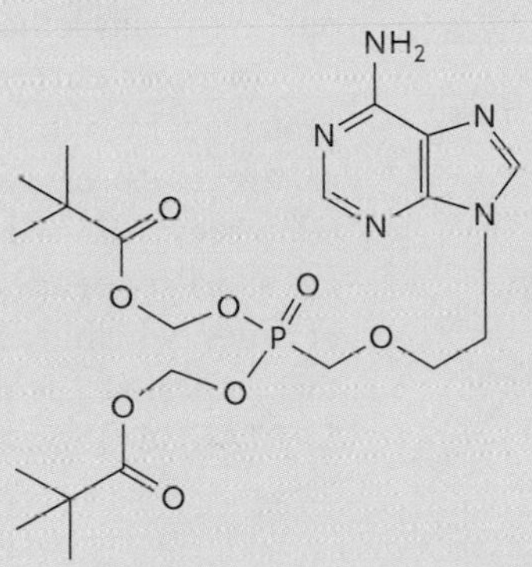

Adefovir dipivoxil

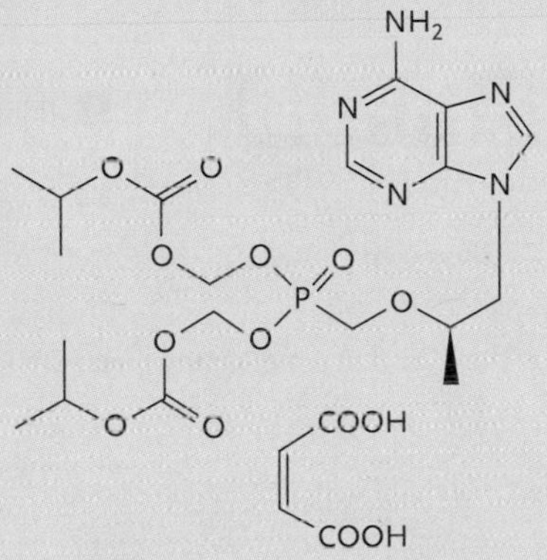

Tenofovir disoproxil fumarate

joining the two fragments into one larger fragment (step 5). The replication process continues in the same way until the entire DNA molecule is copied (step 6). **Table 13.1** summarizes the activities of the major enzymes replicating DNA.

The entire replication mechanism, including the activities of the helicase, primase, DNA polymerases, DNA ligase, and other proteins involved in the process, advances at a rate of about 500 to 1000 nucleotides per second in prokaryotes and at a rate of about 50 to 100 per second in eukaryotes. The entire process is so rapid that the RNA primers and gaps left by discontinuous synthesis persist for only seconds or fractions of a second. Consequently, the replication enzymes operate only at the replication fork. A short distance behind the fork, the new DNA chains are fully continuous and wound with their template strands into complete DNA double helices. Each helix consists of one "old" and one "new" polynucleotide chain.

Table 13.1 Major Enzymes of DNA Replication

Enzyme	Activity
Helicase	Unwinds DNA helix
Single-stranded binding proteins	Stabilize DNA in single-chain form
Primase	Assembles RNA primers
DNA polymerases	Assemble DNA chains on primers; replace primers while simultaneously replacing primer nucleotides with DNA nucleotides
DNA ligase	Seals nicks left after RNA primers replaced with DNA
Topoisomerases	Relieve overtwisting and strain of DNA ahead of replication fork (in circular DNA)

Researchers identified the enzymes that replicate DNA through experiments with a variety of prokaryotes and eukaryotes and with viruses that infect both types of cells. Experiments with the bacterium *E. coli* have provided the most complete information about DNA replication, particularly in the laboratory of Arthur Kornberg at Stanford University. Kornberg received a Nobel Prize in 1959 for his discovery of the mechanism for DNA synthesis.

13.3g Telomerases Solve a Specialized Replication Problem at the Ends of Linear DNA Molecules

The priming mechanism outlined in Figure 13.12 leaves one major problem unsolved for linear chromosomes, such as those in eukaryotes. Think about replication

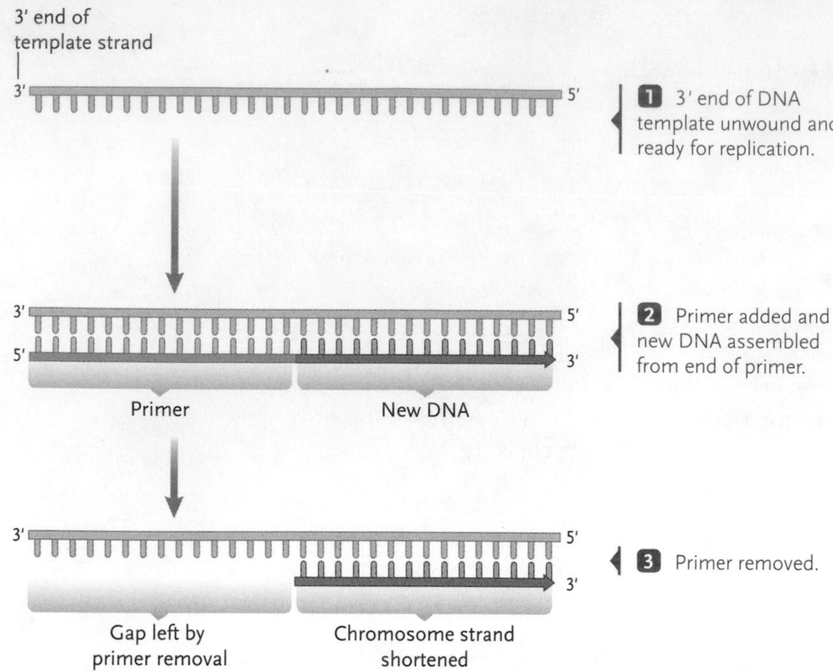

Figure 13.13
How a gap is left by primer removal at the 5′ end of a replicating linear DNA molecule.

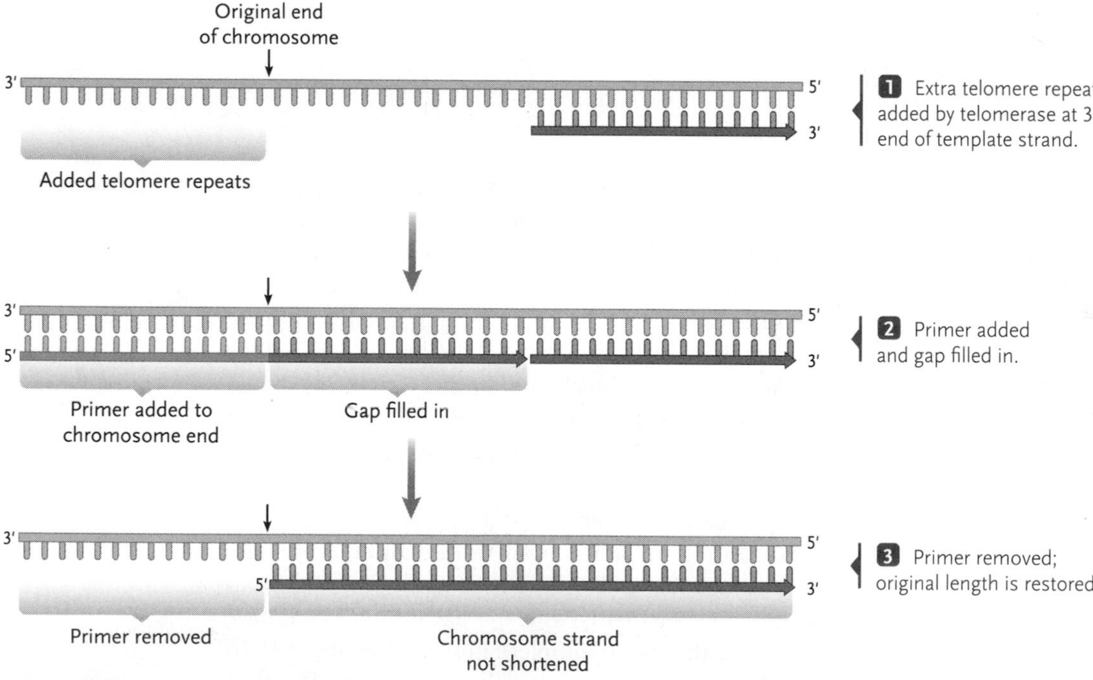

Figure 13.14
How telomere repeats added to eukaryotic chromosomes prevent chromosome shortening.

that occurs at one end of a chromosome (**Figure 13.13**, step 1). To begin the new strand, an RNA primer is laid down opposite the end of the template strand and then a DNA polymerase adds new DNA nucleotides from the end of this primer (step 2). Once replication is under way, this first primer is removed, leaving a gap at the beginning (5′) end of the new strand (as in step 3). It is important to understand why this gap is formed.

If you look at step 4 in Figure 13.12, you will see that the blue RNA is removed and replaced with red DNA just by elongating the 3′ end of an Okazaki fragment. However, at the very end of a chromosome, no such fragment is available to be extended. Although it looks theoretically easy to repair the gap by extending the 5′ end of the DNA, there are no polymerases known to have this ability. In a similar way, a gap is produced at the 5′ end of the new strand made starting at the other end of the chromosome. Therefore, when these new, now shortened DNA strands are used as a template for the next round of DNA replication, the new chromosome will be shorter. Indeed, when most somatic cells go through the cell cycle, the chromosomes shorten with each division. Deletion of genes by such shortening would have serious, eventually lethal, consequences for the cell.

In most chromosomes, however, the genes are protected by a buffer of noncoding DNA. That is, at the ends of each eukaryotic chromosome are telomeres (*telo* = end; *mere* = segment). **Telomeres** are short sequences repeated hundreds to thousands of times, which do not code for proteins. In humans, the repeated sequence, the *telomere repeat*, is 5′-TTAGGG-3′ on the leading template strand. With each replication, a fraction of the telomere repeats is lost, but the genes are unaffected. The buffering fails only when the entire telomere is lost.

The enzyme **telomerase** can maintain the buffer by adding telomere repeats to the chromosome ends. Discovered in 1985 by Elizabeth H. Blackburn and her graduate student Carol W. Greider at the University of California, Berkeley, telomerase adds additional telomere repeats to the end of the *template strand* before DNA replication begins (see **Figure 13.14**, step 1; compare with Figure 13.13, step 1). After the addition, the primer of the leading strand is laid down, using the newly added telomere repeats as the template. A DNA polymerase then extends the new DNA strand as usual (see Figure 13.14, step 2). The primer is removed, which still leaves an unfilled gap at the beginning of the leading chain (step 3). However, this gap is now out on the end of the chromosome, far from coding regions. The telomerase enzyme, which appears to be present in all eukaryotes, is an unusual enzyme that consists of protein subunits complexed with RNA; the

RNA part is the template for making the extra telomere repeats.

Telomerase is active in some cells but not in others. In particular, telomerase is active in sperm and eggs, which is necessary to maintain chromosome length from generation to generation. It is also active in the rapidly dividing cells of the early embryo. However, telomerase becomes inactive after a number of divisions, meaning that subsequent telomeres shorten as the cells continue to divide. As a result, a cell is capable of only a certain number of mitotic divisions before it stops dividing and dies. Could telomere shortening, then, contribute to the aging process in multicellular animals? Telomere shortening has indeed been linked to the aging process, but it is unknown whether it contributes to or is a result of aging. Some observations have made it difficult to draw firm conclusions on this issue. For example, humans, a long-lived species, have telomeres that are much shorter than mice, which live just a few years. Clearly, telomeres alone do not determine the life span of an organism.

An unexpected link between telomerases and cancer was found when investigators discovered that more than 90% of cancer cells have fully active telomerase enzymes, regardless of the type of body cell from which they are derived. Evidently, as body cells develop into cancer cells, their telomerases are reactivated, preserving chromosome length during the rapid divisions characteristic of cancer. A positive side of this discovery is that it may lead to an effective cancer treatment if a means can be found to switch off the telomerases in tumour cells. The chromosomes in the rapidly dividing cancer cells would then eventually shorten to the length at which they break down, leading to cell death and elimination of the tumour.

13.3h DNA Replication Begins at Replication Origins

Replication begins at sites called **replication origins.** Hundreds of replication origins may be present in the long chromosomes of eukaryotes. The origins are recognized by proteins that bind to the DNA and stimulate helicases to start the unwinding, followed by primer synthesis and DNA replication. In most cases, replication proceeds from both sides of a replication origin, producing two replication forks that move in opposite directions **(Figure 13.15).** (This means that the leading strands and lagging strands are reversed on the two sides.) The forks eventually meet along the chromosomes to produce fully replicated DNA molecules.

Normally, a replication origin is activated only once during the S phase of a eukaryotic cell cycle, so no portion of the DNA is replicated more than once.

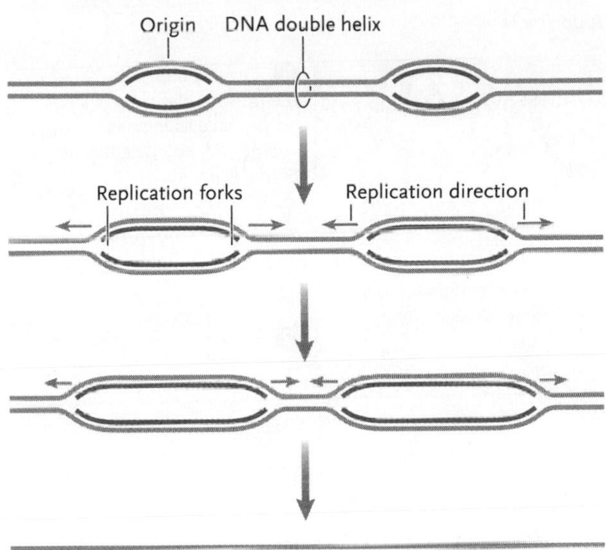

Figure 13.15
Replication from multiple origins in the chromosomes of eukaryotes.

Study Break

1. What is the importance of complementary base pairing to DNA replication?
2. Why is a primer needed for DNA replication on both strands?
3. Two DNA polymerases are used in DNA replication. What are their roles?
4. Why are telomeres important?

13.4 Mechanisms That Correct Replication Errors

DNA polymerases make very few errors as they assemble new nucleotide chains. Most of the mistakes that do occur, called **base-pair mismatches,** are corrected, either by a proofreading mechanism carried out during replication by the DNA polymerases themselves or by a DNA repair mechanism that corrects mismatched base pairs after replication is complete.

13.4a Proofreading Depends on the Ability of DNA Polymerases to Reverse and Remove Mismatched Bases

The **proofreading mechanism,** first proposed in 1972 by Arthur Kornberg and Douglas L. Brutlag of Stanford University, depends on the ability of DNA polymerases to back up and remove mispaired nucleotides from a DNA strand. Only when the most recently added base is correctly paired with its complementary base on the

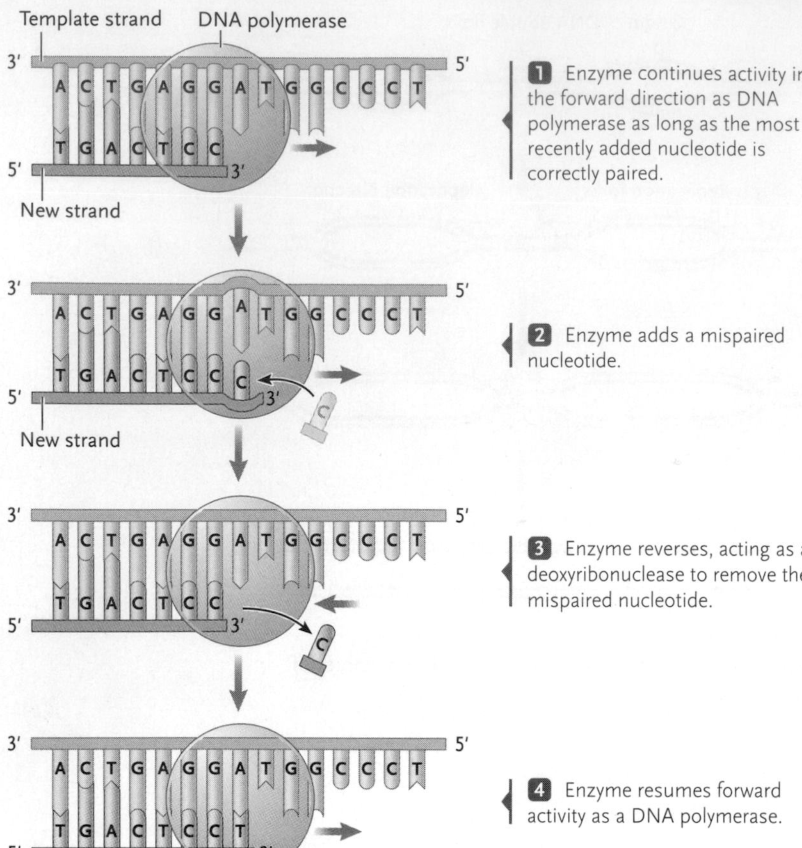
Template strand
DNA polymerase
3'
5'
A C T G A G G A T G G C C C T
T G A C T C C
3'
5'
New strand
1 Enzyme continues activity in the forward direction as DNA polymerase as long as the most recently added nucleotide is correctly paired.
2 Enzyme adds a mispaired nucleotide.
3 Enzyme reverses, acting as a deoxyribonuclease to remove the mispaired nucleotide.
4 Enzyme resumes forward activity as a DNA polymerase.

Figure 13.16
Proofreading by a DNA polymerase.

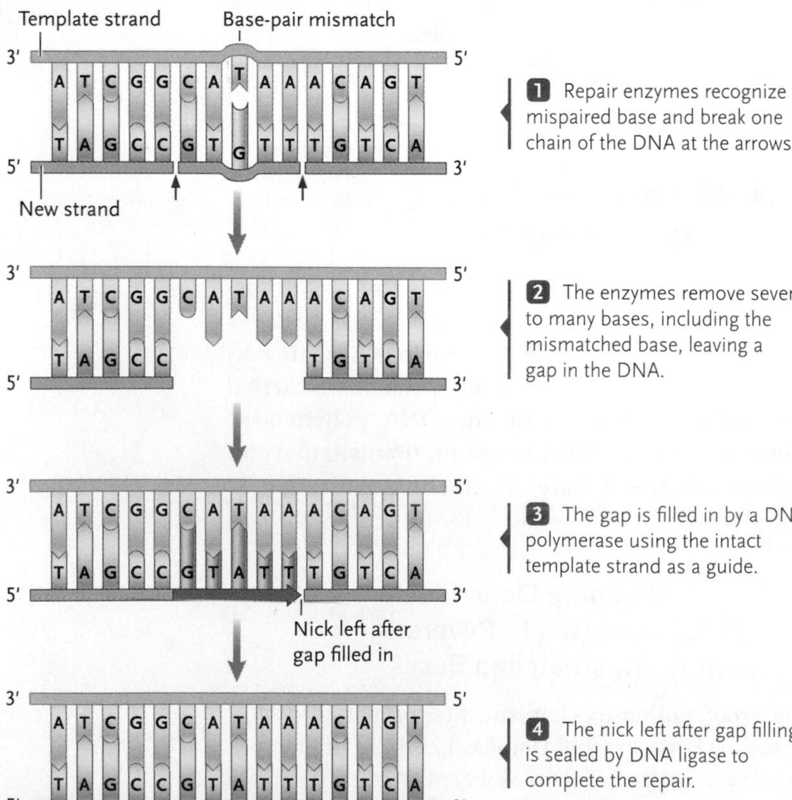
Template strand
Base-pair mismatch
3'
5'
A T C G G C A T A A A C A G T
T A G C C G T G T T T G T C A
New strand
1 Repair enzymes recognize a mispaired base and break one chain of the DNA at the arrows.
2 The enzymes remove several to many bases, including the mismatched base, leaving a gap in the DNA.
3 The gap is filled in by a DNA polymerase using the intact template strand as a guide.
Nick left after gap filled in
4 The nick left after gap filling is sealed by DNA ligase to complete the repair.

Figure 13.17
Repair of mismatched bases in replicated DNA.

template strand can the DNA polymerases continue to add nucleotides to a growing chain. The correct pairs allow the fully stabilizing hydrogen bonds to form (**Figure 13.16,** step 1). If a newly added nucleotide is mismatched (step 2), the DNA polymerase reverses, using a built-in deoxyribonuclease to remove the newly added incorrect nucleotide (step 3). The enzyme resumes working forward, now inserting the correct nucleotide (step 4).

Several experiments have confirmed that the major DNA polymerases of replication can actually proofread their work. For example, when the primary DNA polymerase that replicates DNA in bacteria is intact, with its reverse activity working, its overall error rate is astonishingly low—only about 1 mispair survives in the DNA for every 1 million nucleotides assembled in the test tube. If the proofreading activity of the enzyme is experimentally inhibited, the error rate increases to about 1 mistake for every 1000 to 10 000 nucleotides assembled. Experiments with eukaryotes have yielded similar results.

13.4b DNA Repair Corrects Errors That Escape Proofreading

Any base-pair mismatches that remain after proofreading face still another round of correction by **DNA repair mechanisms.** These **mismatch repair** mechanisms increase the accuracy of DNA replication well beyond the one-in-a million errors that persist after proofreading. As noted earlier, the "correct" A-T and G-C base pairs fit together like pieces of a jigsaw puzzle, and their dimensions separate the sugar–phosphate backbone chains by a constant distance. Mispaired bases are too large or small to maintain the correct separation, and they cannot form the hydrogen bonds characteristic of the normal base pairs. As a result, base mismatches distort the structure of the DNA helix. These distortions provide recognition sites for the enzymes catalyzing mismatch repair.

The repair enzymes move along newly replicated DNA molecules, "scanning" the DNA for distortions in the newly synthesized nucleotide chain. If the enzymes encounter a distortion, they remove a portion of the new chain, including the mismatched nucleotides (**Figure 13.17,** step 1). The gap left by the removal (step 2) is then filled by a DNA polymerase, using the template strand as a guide (step 3). The repair is completed by a DNA ligase, which seals the nucleotide chain into a continuous DNA molecule (step 4).

The same repair mechanisms also detect and correct alterations in DNA caused by the damaging effects of chemicals and radiation, including the ultraviolet light in sunlight. Some idea of the importance of the repair mechanisms comes from the unfortunate plight of individuals with *xeroderma pigmentosum,* a hereditary disorder in which the repair mechanism is faulty. Because of the effects of unrepaired alterations in their DNA, skin cancer can develop quickly in these individuals if they are exposed to sunlight.

People Behind Biology

Dr. Robert (Bob) Haynes, Distinguished Research Professor of Biology, York University, Toronto

In 1944, the Austrian physicist Erwin Schrödinger published *What Is Life?* This small book speculated about the theoretical nature of the genetic material and prompted several physicists to turn their creativity to solving fundamental problems in the field of biology.

Cross-fertilization of these scientific disciplines energized research into the molecular biology of the gene and, specifically through the career of Dr. Bob Haynes, provided pioneering insights into the ways in which cells suffer and respond to DNA damage. Subsequent research has revealed that a breakdown in repair of DNA damage has important implications for cancer, aging, certain genetic diseases, and exposure to physical and chemical mutagens.

Born in 1931, Dr. Haynes earned undergraduate and Ph.D. degrees in biophysics from the University of Western Ontario before working as a postdoctoral fellow in physics at St. Bartholomew's Hospital Medical College, University of London. He joined the Biophysics Departments of the University of Chicago and the University of California at Berkeley before returning to Canada in 1968 as chair of the Biology Department at York University in Toronto. Upon his death in 1998, Dr. Haynes was a fellow of the Royal Society of Canada and an officer of the Order of Canada in recognition of his broad contributions to research in environmental mutagenesis, international leadership, and science education.

Very few replication errors remain in DNA after proofreading and DNA repair. The errors that persist, although extremely rare, are a primary source of **mutations**, differences in DNA sequence that appear and remain in the replicated copies. When a mutation occurs in a gene, it can alter the property of the protein encoded by the gene, which, in turn, may alter how the organism functions. Hence, mutations are highly important to the evolutionary process because they are the ultimate source of the variability in offspring acted on by natural selection.

We now turn from DNA replication and error correction to the arrangements of DNA in eukaryotic and prokaryotic cells. These arrangements organize superstructures that fit the long DNA molecules into the microscopic dimensions of cells and also contribute to the regulation of DNA activity.

Study Break

Why is a proofreading mechanism important for DNA replication?

13.5 DNA Organization in Eukaryotes and Prokaryotes

Enzymatic proteins are the essential catalysts of every step in DNA replication. In addition, numerous proteins of other types organize the DNA in both eukaryotes and prokaryotes and control its function.

In eukaryotes, two major types of proteins, the histone and nonhistone proteins, are associated with DNA structure and regulation in the nucleus. These proteins are known collectively as the **chromosomal proteins** of eukaryotes. The complex of DNA and its associated proteins, termed **chromatin**, is the structural building block of a chromosome.

By comparison, the single DNA molecule of a prokaryotic cell is more simply organized and has fewer associated proteins. However, prokaryotic DNA is still associated with two classes of proteins with functions similar to those of the eukaryotic histones and nonhistones: one class that organizes the DNA structurally and one that regulates gene activity. We begin this section with the major DNA-associated proteins of eukaryotes.

13.5a Histones Pack Eukaryotic DNA at Successive Levels of Organization

The **histones** are a class of small, positively charged (basic) proteins that are complexed with DNA in the chromosomes of eukaryotes. (Most other cellular proteins are larger and are neutral or negatively charged.) The histones link to DNA by an attraction between their positive charges and the negatively charged phosphate groups of the DNA.

Five types of histones exist in most eukaryotic cells: H1, H2A, H2B, H3, and H4. The amino acid sequences of these proteins are highly similar among eukaryotes, suggesting that they perform the same functions in all eukaryotic organisms.

One function of histones is to pack DNA molecules into the narrow confines of the cell nucleus. For example, each human cell nucleus contains 2 metres of DNA. Combination with the histones compacts this length so much that it fits into nuclei that are only about 10 μm in diameter. Another function is the regulation of DNA activity.

Histones and DNA Packing. The histones pack DNA at several levels of chromatin structure. In the most fundamental structure, called a **nucleosome**, two molecules each of H2A, H2B, H3, and H4 combine to form a bead-like, eight-protein **nucleosome core particle** around which DNA winds for almost two turns **(Figure 13.18)**. A short segment of DNA, the **linker**, extends between one nucleosome and the next. Under the electron microscope, this structure looks like beads on a string. The diameter of the beads (the nucleosomes) gives this structure its name—the **10 nm chromatin fibre** (see Figure 13.18).

Each nucleosome and linker includes about 200 base pairs of DNA. Nucleosomes compact DNA by a factor of about 7; that is, a length of DNA becomes about 7 times shorter when it is wrapped into nucleosomes.

Histones and Chromatin Fibres. The fifth histone, H1, brings about the next level of chromatin packing. One H1 molecule binds both to the nucleosome at the point where the DNA enters and leaves the core particle and to the linker DNA. This binding causes the nucleosomes to package into a coiled structure 30 nm in diameter, called the **30 nm chromatin fibre** or **solenoid**, with about six nucleosomes per turn (see Figure 13.18).

The arrangement of DNA in nucleosomes and solenoids compacts the DNA and probably also protects it from chemical and mechanical damage. In the test tube, DNA wound into nucleosomes and chromatin fibres is much more resistant to attack by deoxyribonuclease (a DNA-digesting enzyme) than when it is not bound to histone proteins. Therefore, DNA must unwind almost entirely from solenoids and nucleosomes when it becomes active. When genes become active, however, their DNA becomes almost as susceptible to attack as naked DNA in the test tube.

Packing at Still Higher Levels: Euchromatin and Heterochromatin. In interphase nuclei, chromatin fibres are loosely packed in some regions and densely packed in others. The loosely packed regions are known as **euchromatin** (*eu* = true, regular, or typical), and the densely packed regions are called **heterochromatin** (*hetero* = different). Chromatin fibres also fold and pack into the thick, rodlike chromosomes visible during mitosis and meiosis. Some experiments indicate that links formed between H1 histone molecules contribute to the packing of chromatin fibres, both into heterochromatin and into the chromosomes visible during nuclear division (see discussion in Section 9.2, as well as the more detailed discussion in Section 14.2). However, the exact mechanism for the more complex folding and packing is not known.

Several experiments indicate that heterochromatin represents large blocks of genes that have been turned off and placed in a compact storage form. For example, recall the process of X-chromosome inactivation in mammalian females (see Section 12.2). As one of the two X chromosomes becomes inactive in cells early in development, it packs down into a block of heterochromatin called the *Barr body*, which is large enough to see under the light microscope. These findings support the idea that, in addition to organizing nuclear DNA, histones play a role in regulating gene activity.

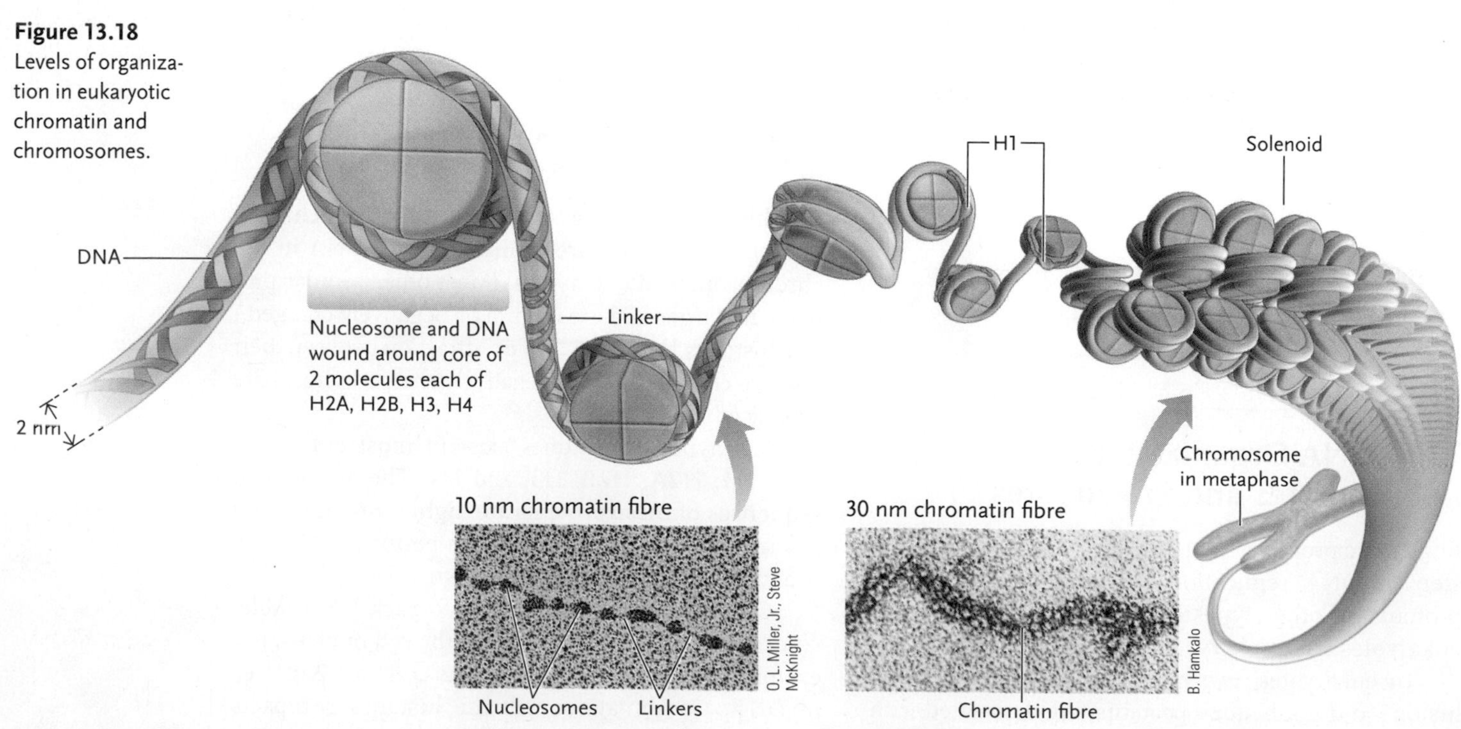

Figure 13.18
Levels of organization in eukaryotic chromatin and chromosomes.

13.5b Many Nonhistone Proteins Have Key Roles in the Regulation of Gene Expression

Nonhistone proteins are loosely defined as all the proteins associated with DNA that are not histones. Nonhistones vary widely in structure; most are negatively charged or neutral, but some are positively charged. They range in size from polypeptides smaller than histones to some of the largest cellular proteins.

Many nonhistone proteins help control the expression of individual genes. (The regulation of gene expression is the subject of Chapter 15.) For example, expression of a gene requires that the enzymes and proteins for that process be able to access the gene in the chromatin. If a gene is packed into heterochromatin, it is unavailable for activation. If the gene is in the more extended euchromatin, it is more accessible. Many nonhistone proteins affect gene accessibility by modifying histones to change how the histones associate with DNA in chromatin, either loosening or tightening the association. Other nonhistone proteins are regulatory proteins that activate or repress the expression of a gene. Yet others are components of the enzyme–protein complexes that are needed for the expression of any gene.

13.5c DNA Is Organized More Simply in Prokaryotes than in Eukaryotes

Several features of DNA organization in prokaryotes differ fundamentally from eukaryotic DNA. In contrast to the linear DNA in eukaryotes, the primary DNA molecule of most prokaryotic cells is circular, with only one copy per cell. In parallel with eukaryotic terminology, the DNA molecule is called a **bacterial chromosome.** The chromosome of the best-known bacterium, *E. coli*, includes about 1360 μm of DNA, which is equivalent to 4.6 million base pairs. There are exceptions: some bacteria have two or more different chromosomes in the cell, and some bacterial chromosomes are linear.

Replication begins from a single origin in the DNA circle, forming two forks that travel around the circle in opposite directions. Eventually, the forks meet at the opposite side from the origin to complete replication **(Figure 13.19)**.

Inside prokaryotic cells, the DNA circle is packed and folded into an irregularly shaped mass called the **nucleoid** (shown in Figure 2.4). The DNA of the nucleoid is suspended directly in the cytoplasm with no surrounding membrane.

Many prokaryotic cells also contain other DNA molecules, called **plasmids,** in addition to the main chromosome of the nucleoid. Most plasmids are circular, although some are linear. Plasmids have replication origins and are duplicated and distributed to daughter cells together with the bacterial chromosome during cell division. Chapter 10 describes the process of conjugation, in which plasmids are replicated while being transferred from a donor cell to a recipient cell. The DNA is replicated by a mechanism called "rolling circle" replication, in which one strand of the plasmid is cut and travels into a recipient cell as a linear molecule; the other strand remains circular in the donor cell **(Figure 13.20, p. 292)**. DNA replication restores both strands to double-strandedness, and the linear molecule recircularizes. Although rolling circle replication follows the usual rules of DNA replication, notice that the leading and lagging strand synthesis occur in separate cells rather than at one replication fork.

Although bacterial DNA is not organized into nucleosomes, there are positively charged proteins that combine with bacterial DNA. Some of these proteins help organize the DNA into loops, thereby providing some compaction of the molecule. Bacterial DNA also combines with many types of genetic regulatory proteins that have functions similar to those of the nonhistone proteins of eukaryotes (see Chapter 15).

With this description of prokaryotic DNA organization, our survey of DNA structure and its replication and organization is complete. The next chapter revisits the same structures and discusses how they function in the expression of information encoded in DNA.

Study Break

1. What is the structure of the nucleosome?
2. What is the role of histone H1 in eukaryotic chromosome structure?

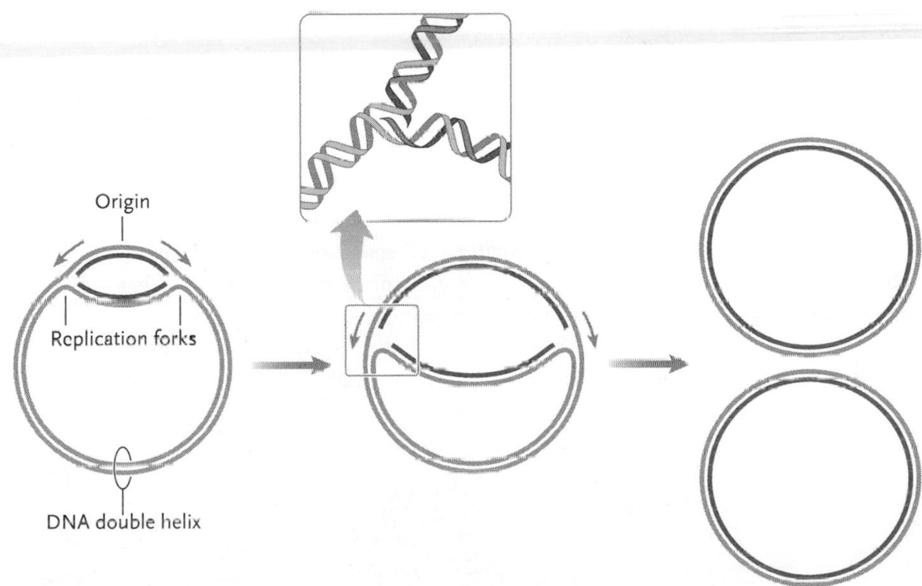

Figure 13.19
Replication from a single origin in the DNA circle of prokaryotes.

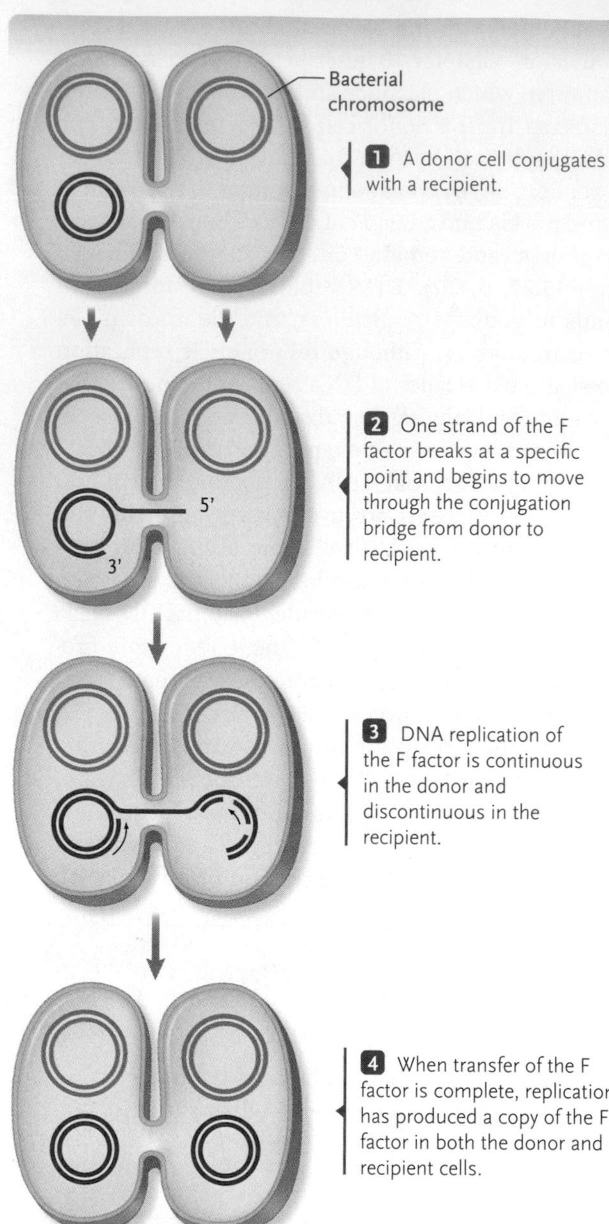

Bacterial chromosome
1 A donor cell conjugates with a recipient.
2 One strand of the F factor breaks at a specific point and begins to move through the conjugation bridge from donor to recipient.
5'
3'
3 DNA replication of the F factor is continuous in the donor and discontinuous in the recipient.
4 When transfer of the F factor is complete, replication has produced a copy of the F factor in both the donor and recipient cells.

Figure 13.20

Transfer of F factor by Rolling Circle Replication during conjugation. One of the two strands of the plasmid is nicked and the 5' end moves from the donor into a recipient cell. The remaining circular strand "rolls" like a tape dispenser. DNA synthesis is continuous in the donor cell and discontinuous in the recipient resulting in two complete plasmids

Unanswered Questions

In this chapter, we learned about the structure and replication of DNA, the key role of telomeres in maintaining the ends of chromosomes, and the packaging of DNA into chromosomes in eukaryotes.

Although research is ongoing in these areas, several big questions remain. For instance, the evolutionary relationship between DNA and RNA is intriguing. Why do all organisms have DNA as their genetic material? What does it mean that several types of viruses have RNA instead?

Chapter 9 described Hayflick factors that limit the life span of cells. Both DNA polymerase and telomerase influence cellular aging and senescence in ways that we are only beginning to understand.

Review

Go to CENGAGENOW™ at http://hed.nelson.com/ to access quizzing, animations, exercises, articles, and personalized homework help.

13.1 Establishing DNA as the Hereditary Molecule

- Griffith found that a substance derived from killed infective pneumonia bacteria could transform noninfective living pneumonia bacteria to the infective type (see Figure 13.2).
- Avery and his coworkers showed that DNA, not protein or RNA, was the molecule responsible for transforming pneumonia bacteria into the infective form.
- Hershey and Chase showed that the DNA of a phage, not the protein, enters bacterial cells to direct the life cycle of the virus. Taken together, the experiments of Griffith, Avery and his coworkers, and Hershey and Chase established that DNA is the hereditary molecule (see Figure 13.3).

13.2 DNA Structure

- Watson and Crick discovered that a DNA molecule consists of two polynucleotide chains twisted around each other into a right-handed double helix. Each nucleotide of the chains consists of deoxyribose, a phosphate group, and either adenine, thymine, guanine, or cytosine. The deoxyribose sugars are linked by phosphate groups to form an alternating sugar–phosphate backbone. The two strands are held together by adenine–thymine and guanine–cytosine base pairs. Each full turn of the double helix involves 10 base pairs (see Figures 13.4 and 13.6).
- The two strands of the DNA double helix are antiparallel.

13.3 DNA Replication

- DNA is duplicated by semiconservative replication, in which the two strands of a parental DNA molecule unwind and each serves as a template for the synthesis of a complementary copy (see Figures 13.7–13.9).
- DNA replication is catalyzed by several enzymes. Helicase unwinds the DNA; primase synthesizes an RNA primer used as a starting point for nucleotide assembly by DNA polymerases. DNA polymerases assemble nucleotides into a chain one at a time, in a sequence complementary to the sequence of bases in the template strand. After a DNA polymerase removes the primers and fills in the resulting gaps, DNA ligase closes the remaining single-chain nicks (see Figures 13.10 and 13.12).
- As the DNA helix unwinds, only one template strand runs in a direction allowing the new DNA strand to be made continuously in the direction of unwinding. The other template strand is copied in short lengths that run in the direction opposite to unwinding. The short lengths produced by this discontinuous replication are then linked into a continuous strand (see Figures 13.11 and 13.12).
- The ends of eukaryotic chromosomes consist of telomeres, short sequences repeated hundreds to thousands of times. These repeats provide a buffer against chromosome shortening during replication. Although most somatic cells show this chromosome shortening, some cell types do not because they have a telomerase enzyme that adds telomere repeats to the chromosome ends (see Figures 13.13 and 13.14).
- DNA synthesis begins at sites that act as replication origins and proceeds from the origins as two replication forks moving in opposite directions (see Figure 13.14).

13.4 Mechanisms That Correct Replication Errors

- In proofreading, the DNA polymerase reverses and removes the most recently added base if it is mispaired as a result of a replication error. The enzyme then resumes DNA synthesis in the forward direction (see Figure 13.16).
- In DNA mismatch repair, enzymes recognize distorted regions caused by mispaired base pairs and remove a section of DNA that includes the mispaired base from the newly synthesized nucleotide chain. A DNA polymerase then resynthesizes the section correctly, using the original template chain as a guide (see Figure 13.17).

13.5 DNA Organization in Eukaryotes and Prokaryotes

- Eukaryotic chromosomes consist of DNA complexed with histone and nonhistone proteins.
- In eukaryotic chromosomes, DNA is wrapped around a nucleosome consisting of two molecules each of histones H2A, H2B, H3, and H4. Linker DNA connects adjacent nucleosomes. The binding of histone H1 causes the nucleosomes to package into a coiled structure called a solenoid (see Figure 13.18).
- Chromatin is distributed between euchromatin, a loosely packed region in which genes are active in RNA transcription, and heterochromatin, densely packed masses in which the genes are inactive. Chromatin also folds and packs to form thick, rodlike chromosomes during nuclear division.
- Nonhistone proteins help control the expression of individual genes.
- The bacterial chromosome is a closed, circular molecule of DNA that is packed into the nucleoid region of the cell. Replication begins from a single origin and proceeds in both directions. Many bacteria also contain plasmids, which replicate independently of the host chromosome (see Figure 13.19).
- Bacterial DNA is organized into loops through interaction with proteins. Other proteins similar to eukaryotic nonhistones regulate gene activity in prokaryotes.

Questions

Self-Test Questions

1. Working on the Amazon River, a biologist isolated DNA from two unknown organisms, P and Q. He discovered that the adenine content of P was 15% and the cytosine content of Q was 42%. This means that
   a. the amount of guanine in P is 15%.
   b. the amount of guanine and cytosine combined in P is 70%.
   c. the amount of adenine in Q is 42%.
   d. the amount of thymine in Q is 21%.
   e. it takes more energy to unwind the DNA of P than the DNA of Q.

2. The Hershey and Chase experiment showed that viral
   a. ^{35}S entered bacterial cells.
   b. ^{32}P remained outside of bacterial cells.
   c. protein entered bacterial cells.
   d. DNA entered bacterial cells.
   e. DNA mutated in bacterial cells.
3. Pyrimidines include
   a. cytosine and thymine.
   b. adenine, cytosine, and guanine.
   c. adenine and thymine.
   d. cytosine and guanine.
   e. adenine and guanine.
4. Which of the following statements about DNA replication is *false*?
   a. Synthesis of the new DNA strand is from 3′ to 5′.
   b. Synthesis of the new DNA strand is from 5′ to 3′.
   c. DNA unwinds, primase adds RNA primer, and DNA polymerases synthesize the new strand and remove the RNA primer.
   d. Many initiation points exist in each eukaryotic chromosome.
   e. Okazaki fragments are synthesized in the opposite direction from the direction in which the replication fork moves.
5. Which of the following statements about DNA is *false*?
   a. Phosphate is linked to the 5′ and 3′ carbons of adjacent deoxyribose molecules.
   b. DNA is bidirectional in its synthesis.
   c. Each side of the helix is antiparallel to the other.
   d. The binding of adenine to thymine is through three hydrogen bonds.
   e. Avery identified DNA as the transforming factor in crosses between smooth and rough bacteria.
6. In the Meselson and Stahl experiment, the DNA in the parental generation was all $^{15}N^{15}N$, and after one round of replication, the DNA was all $^{15}N^{13}N$. What DNAs were seen after three rounds of replication, and in what ratio were they found?
   a. one $^{15}N^{13}N$: one ^{13}N:^{13}N
   b. one $^{15}N^{13}N$: two ^{13}N:^{13}N
   c. one $^{15}N^{13}N$: three ^{13}N:^{13}N
   d. one $^{15}N^{13}N$: four ^{13}N:^{13}N
   e. one $^{15}N^{13}N$: seven ^{13}N:^{13}N
7. During replication, DNA is synthesized in a $5' \rightarrow 3'$ direction. This implies that
   a. the template is read in a $5' \rightarrow 3'$ direction.
   b. successive nucleotides are added to the 3′–OH end of the newly forming chain.
   c. because both strands are replicated nearly simultaneously, replication must be continuous on both.
   d. ligase unwinds DNA in a $5' \rightarrow 3'$ direction.
   e. primase acts on the 3′ end of the replicating strand.
8. Telomerase
   a. is active in cancer cells.
   b. is more active in adult than in embryonic cells.
   c. complexes with the ribosome to form telomeres.
   d. acts on unique genes called telomeres.
   e. shortens the ends of chromosomes.
9. Mismatch repair is the ability
   a. to seal Okazaki fragments with ligase into a continual DNA strand.
   b. of primase to remove the RNA primer and replace it with the correct DNA.
   c. of some enzymes to sense the insertion of an incorrect nucleotide, remove it, and use a DNA polymerase to insert the correct one.
   d. to correct mispaired chromosomes in prophase I of meiosis.
   e. to remove worn-out DNA by telomerase and replace it with newly synthesized nucleotides.
10. Prokaryotic DNA
   a. is surrounded by densely packed histones.
   b. has many sites for the initiation of DNA replication.
   c. has both strands synthesized in the same direction.
   d. is packaged as euchromatin and heterochromatin.
   e. is packaged as a large circular chromosome.

Questions for Discussion

1. Chargaffs data suggested that adenine pairs with thymine and guanine pairs with cytosine. What other data available to Watson and Crick suggested that adenine–guanine and cytosine–thymine pairs normally do not form?
2. Eukaryotic chromosomes can be labelled by exposing cells to radioactive thymidine during the S phase of interphase. If cells are exposed to radioactive thymidine during the S phase, would you expect both or only one of the sister chromatids of a duplicated chromosome to be labelled at metaphase of the following mitosis (see Section 9.2)?
3. If the cells in question 2 finish division and then enter another round of DNA replication in a medium that has been washed free of radioactive label, would you expect both or only one of the sister chromatids of a duplicated chromosome to be labelled at metaphase of the following mitosis?
4. During replication, an error uncorrected by proofreading or mismatch repair produces a DNA molecule with a base mismatch at the indicated position:

   AATTCCGACTCCTATGG
   TTAAGGTTGAGGATACC
   ↑

   The mismatch results in a mutation. This DNA molecule is received by one of the two daughter cells produced by mitosis. In the next round of replication and division, the mutation appears in only one of the two daughter cells. Develop a hypothesis to explain this observation.
5. Strains of bacteria that are resistant to an antibiotic sometimes appear spontaneously among other bacteria of the same type that are killed by the antibiotic. In view of the information in this chapter about DNA replication, what might account for the appearance of this resistance?

Transcription of a eukaryotic gene to produce messenger RNA (mRNA), a type of RNA that acts as a template for protein synthesis. The DNA of the gene unwinds from the nucleosome (left side) and is copied by an RNA polymerase (center) into mRNA (exiting the top).

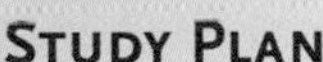

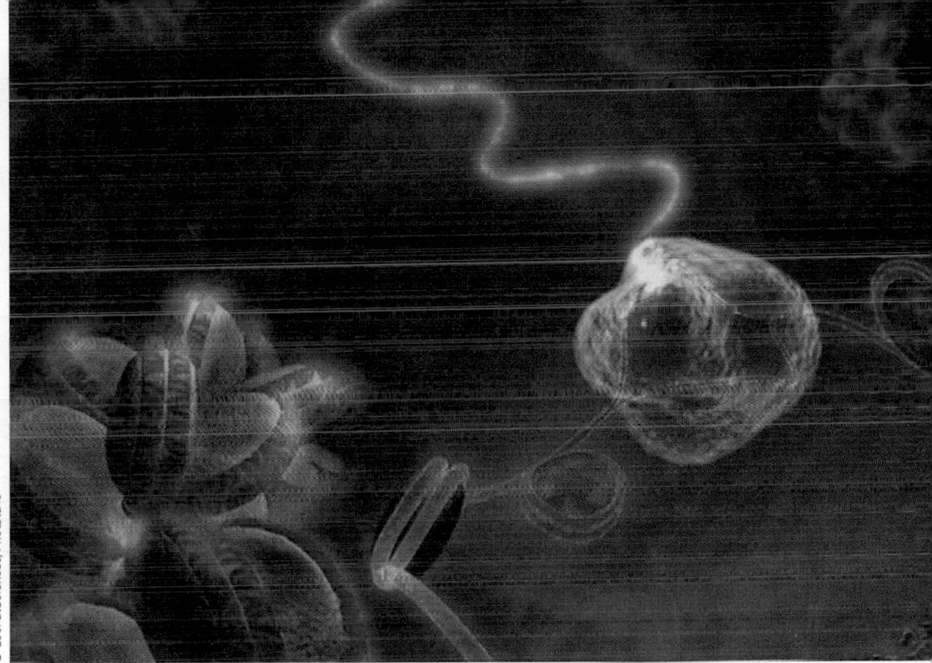

Study Plan

14 Gene Structure and Expression

Why It Matters

The marine mussel *Mytilus* **(Figure 14.1, p. 296)** lives in one of the most demanding environments on the Earth—it clings permanently to rocks pounded by surf day in and day out, constantly in danger of being dashed to pieces or torn loose by foraging predators. The mussel is remarkably resistant to disturbance. If you try to pry one loose, you will find how difficult it is to tear the tough, elastic fibres that hold it fast. They are even hard to cut with a knife.

The fibres holding mussels to rocks are proteins secreted by the muscular foot of the animal. The proteins include keratin (an intermediate filament protein) and another resinous protein. Along with other proteins, they form a tough, adhesive material called byssus.

Byssus is one of the world's premier underwater adhesives. It fascinates biochemists, adhesive manufacturers, dentists, and surgeons looking for better ways to hold repaired body parts together. Genetic engineers are inserting segments of mussel deoxyribonucleic acid (DNA) into yeast cells, which reproduce in large numbers and serve as "factories" translating the mussel genes into proteins. Among the proteins produced may be those of byssus, allowing investigators to figure out how to use or imitate the mussel glue for human needs. This exciting

Figure 14.1
The marine mussel *Mytilus* and its natural habitat.

work, like the mussel's own byssus building, starts with one of life's universal truths: *Every protein is assembled on ribosomes according to instructions copied from genes coded in DNA.*

In this chapter, we trace the basic process that produces proteins in all organisms, beginning with the instructions encoded in DNA and leading through ribonucleic acid (RNA) to the sequence of amino acids in a protein. Many enzymes and other proteins are players as well as products in this story, as are several kinds of RNA and the cell's protein-making machines, the ribosomes. As your understanding of the fundamental elements of all protein production grows, be sure to notice the differences in the kinds of information coded in DNA, differences in the mechanisms in prokaryotes and eukaryotes, and differences in the structure of genes that code for protein versus those that code for RNA.

14.1 The Connection between DNA, RNA, and Protein

We know that genes encode proteins. In this section, you will learn how that connection was discovered. We also present an overview of the molecular steps needed to go from gene to protein: transcription and translation.

14.1a Genes Specify Either Protein or RNA Products

How do we know that genes encode—specify the amino acid sequence of—proteins? Two key pieces of research involving defects in metabolism illustrated this connection unequivocally. The first began in 1896 with Archibald Garrod, an English physician. He studied *alkaptonuria*, a human disease that does little harm but is detected easily by the fact that a patient's urine turns black in air. Garrod and William Bateson, a geneticist, studied families of patients with the disease and concluded that it is an inherited trait. Garrod also found that people with alkaptonuria excrete a particular chemical in their urine. It is this chemical that turns black in air. Garrod concluded that normal people are able to metabolize the chemical, whereas people with alkaptonuria cannot. By 1908, Garrod had concluded that the disease was an inborn error of metabolism. He did not know it then, but the defect causing alkaptonuria is the result of an alteration of a gene that encodes an enzyme that metabolizes a key chemical. The altered gene causes a defect in the function of the enzyme, which leads to the phenotype of the disease. Garrod's work was the first to show a specific relationship between genes and metabolism.

In the second piece of research, George Beadle and Edward Tatum, working in the 1940s with the orange bread mould *Neurospora crassa*, collected data showing a direct relationship between genes and enzymes. Beadle and Tatum chose *Neurospora* for their work because it is a haploid fungus with simple nutritional needs. That is, wild-type *Neurospora*—the form of the mould found in nature—grows readily on a minimal medium (MM) consisting of a number of inorganic salts, sucrose, and a vitamin. The researchers reasoned that the fungus uses the simple chemicals in the medium to synthesize all of the more complex molecules needed for growth and reproduction, including amino acids for proteins and nucleotides for DNA and RNA.

Beadle and Tatum exposed spores of wild-type *Neurospora* to X-rays. X-rays are a mutagen, an agent that causes mutations. They found that some of the treated spores would not germinate and grow unless MM was supplemented with additional nutrients, such as amino acids or vitamins. Mutant strains that are unable to grow on MM are called auxotrophs (*auxo* = increased; *troph* = eater), or nutritional mutants. Beadle and Tatum hypothesized that each auxotrophic strain had a defect in a gene coding for an enzyme needed to synthesize a nutrient that now had to be added to the MM. The wild-type strain could make the nutrient for itself from raw materials in the MM, but the mutant strain could grow only if the researchers supplied the nutrient. By testing to see if each mutant strain would grow on MM supplemented with a given nutrient, Beadle and Tatum discovered which specific nutrient each mutant needed to grow and, therefore, which gene defect it had. For example, a mutant that required the addition of the amino acid arginine to grow had a defect in a gene for an enzyme involved in the synthesis of arginine. Such arginine auxotrophs are known as *arg* mutants. The assembly of arginine from raw materials is a multistep "assembly-line" process with a different enzyme catalyzing each step. Therefore, different *arg* mutants might differ in the particular enzyme that is defective and therefore in which step of the assembly pathway is blocked. (This is conceptually similar to Lederberg's work with auxotrophic bacteria described in Chapter 10.)

Beadle and Tatum determined where in the arginine synthesis pathway each of four mutants (*argE*, *argF*, *argG*, and *argH*) was blocked. They tested whether each mutant could grow on MM or on MM supplemented with either ornithine, citrulline, argininosuccinate—three compounds known to be involved in the synthesis of arginine—or arginine itself **(Figure 14.2, p. 298)**. None of the four mutants grew on MM, but, of course, they all grew on MM + arginine. Each of the *arg* mutants showed a different pattern of growth on the supplemented MM (see Figure 14.2). Beadle and Tatum deduced that the biosynthesis of arginine occurred in a number of steps, with each step controlled by a gene that encoded the enzyme for the step (see Figure 14.2, bottom). For example, the *argH* mutant grows on MM + arginine but not on MM + any of the other three compounds; this means that the mutant is blocked at the last step in the pathway, which produces arginine. Similarly, the *argG* mutant grows on MM + arginine or argininosuccinate but not on MM + any of the other supplements; this means that *argG* is blocked in the pathway before argininosuccinate is made (see Figure 14.2, bottom). With similar analysis, the researchers deduced the whole pathway from precursor to arginine and showed which gene encoded the enzyme that carried out each step. In sum, Beadle and Tatum had shown the direct relationship between genes and enzymes, which they put forward as the **one gene–one enzyme hypothesis**. Their experiment was a keystone in the development of molecular biology. As a result of their work, they were awarded a Nobel Prize in 1958.

It is important to understand that many proteins are not enzymes and many consist of more than one subunit, called a polypeptide. For instance, the protein hemoglobin is made up of four polypeptides, two each of an α subunit and a β subunit; this composition gives the protein its functional property of transporting oxygen rather than catalyzing a chemical reaction. Two different genes are needed to encode the hemoglobin protein: one for the α polypeptide and one for the β polypeptide. Beadle and Tatum's hypothesis was later restated as the **one gene–one polypeptide hypothesis**. It is important to keep the distinction between protein, the functional molecule, and polypeptide, the molecule encoded by a gene, clear as we discuss transcription and translation in the rest of this chapter.

14.1b The Pathway from Gene to Polypeptide Involves Transcription and Translation

The pathway from gene to polypeptide has two major steps, transcription and translation. **Transcription** is the mechanism by which the information encoded in DNA is made into a complementary RNA copy. It is called transcription because the information in one nucleic acid type is transferred to another nucleic acid type. **Translation** is the use of the information encoded in the RNA to assemble amino acids into a polypeptide. It is called translation because the information in a nucleic acid, in the form of nucleotides, is converted into a different kind of molecule—amino acids. In 1956, Francis Crick gave the name central dogma to the flow of information from DNA to RNA to protein.

In transcription, the enzyme RNA polymerase creates an RNA sequence that is complementary to the DNA sequence of a given gene. The process follows the same basic rules of complementary base pairing and nucleic acid chemistry that we first encountered in DNA replication (see Chapter 13). For each of the several thousand genes that will be appropriate to express in a given cell, one DNA strand or the other is the **template strand** and is read by the RNA polymerase. The RNA transcribed from a gene encoding a polypeptide is called **messenger RNA (mRNA)**.

In translation, an mRNA associates with a **ribosome**, a particle on which amino acids are linked into polypeptide chains. As the ribosome moves along the mRNA, the amino acids specified by the mRNA are joined one by one to form the polypeptide encoded by the gene.

The processes of transcription and translation are similar in prokaryotes and eukaryotes **(Figure 14.3, p. 299)**. One key difference is that whereas prokaryotes can transcribe and translate a given gene simultaneously, eukaryotes transcribe and process mRNA in the nucleus before exporting it to the cytoplasm for translation.

14.1c The Genetic Code Is Written in Three-Letter Words Using a Four-Letter Alphabet

Conceptually, the transcription of DNA into RNA is straightforward. The DNA "alphabet" consists of the four letters A, T, G, and C, representing the four

Figure 14.2 Beadle and Tatum's experiment showing the direct relationship between genes and proteins.

QUESTION: Do genes specify enzymes?

EXPERIMENT: Test *arg* mutants of the orange bread mold *Neurospora crassa* for growth on MM (minimal medium), MM + ornithine, MM + citrulline, MM + argininosuccinate, and MM + arginine. *Arg* mutants are unable to synthesize the amino acid arginine, which is essential for growth.

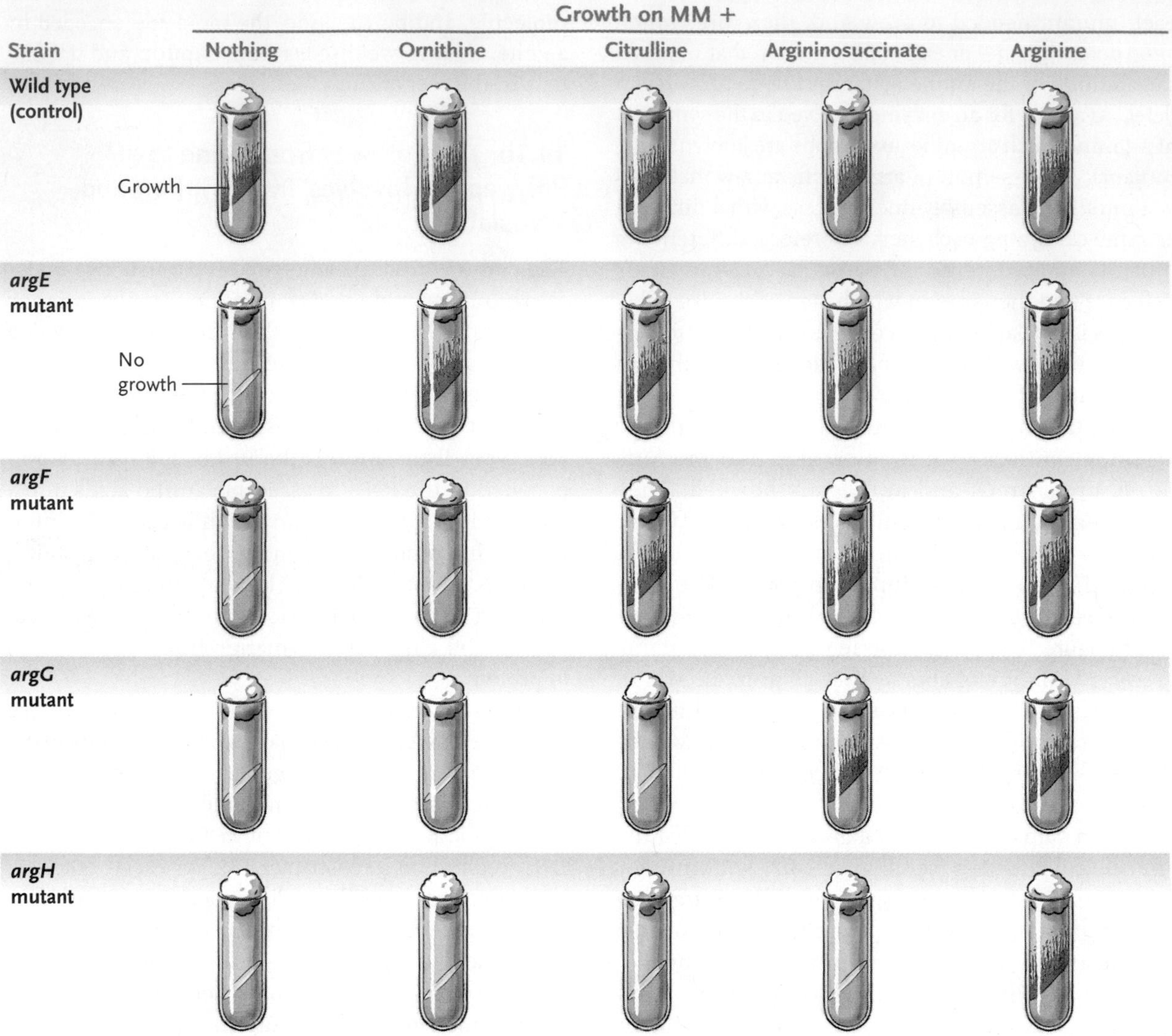

Growth on MM +

Strain | Nothing | Ornithine | Citrulline | Argininosuccinate | Arginine

Wild type (control)

Growth

***argE* mutant**

No growth

***argF* mutant**

***argG* mutant**

***argH* mutant**

CONCLUSION: Arginine is synthesized in a biochemical pathway. Each step of the pathway is catalyzed by an enzyme, and each enzyme is encoded by a gene:

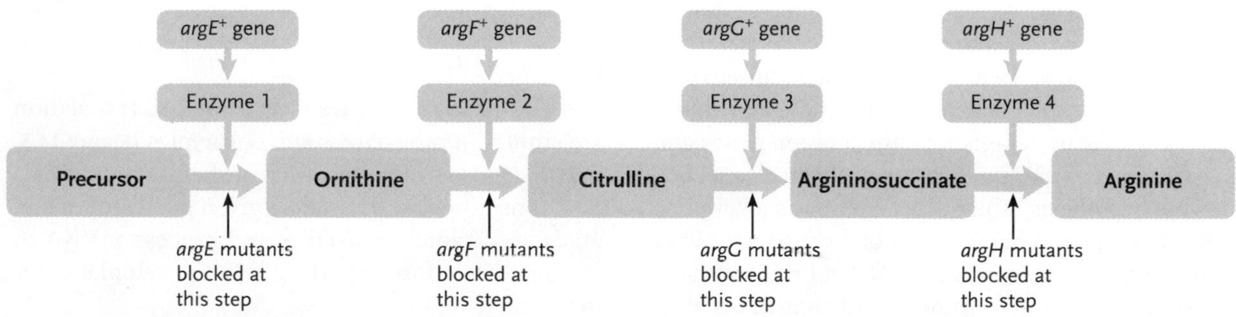

DNA nucleotide bases, adenine, thymine, guanine, and cytosine, and the RNA "alphabet" consists of the four letters A, U, G, and C, representing the four RNA bases, adenine, uracil, guanine, and cytosine. In other words, both nucleic acids share three of the four bases but differ in the other one: T in DNA is equivalent to U in RNA. But whereas there are 4 RNA bases, there are 20 amino acids. How is nucleotide information in an mRNA translated into the amino acid sequence of a polypeptide?

Breaking the Genetic Code. The nucleotide information that specifies the amino acid sequence of a polypeptide is called the **genetic code.** Scientists realized that the 4 bases in an mRNA (A, U, G, C) would have to be used in combinations of at least 3 to provide the capacity to code for 20 amino acids. One- and 2-letter words were eliminated because if the code used 1-letter words, only 4 different amino acids could be specified (that is, 4^1); if 2-letter words were used, only 16 different amino acids could be specified (that is, 4^2). But if the code used three-letter words, 64 different amino acids could be specified (that is, 4^3), more than enough to specify 20 amino acids. We know now that the genetic code is indeed a three-letter code; each three-letter word (triplet) is called a **codon.** **Figure 14.4,** illustrates the relationship between a gene, codons in an mRNA, and the amino acid sequence of a polypeptide. The three-letter codons in DNA are first transcribed into complementary three-letter RNA codons (the RNA complement to adenine [A] in the template strand is uracil [U] instead of thymine [T]). The template strand for a given gene is always read 3′ to 5′. For Gene *a* in Figure 14.4, the bottom strand is the template, and is therefore read left to right. However, the template for Gene b might be the top strand; RNA polymerase would then have to read right to left.

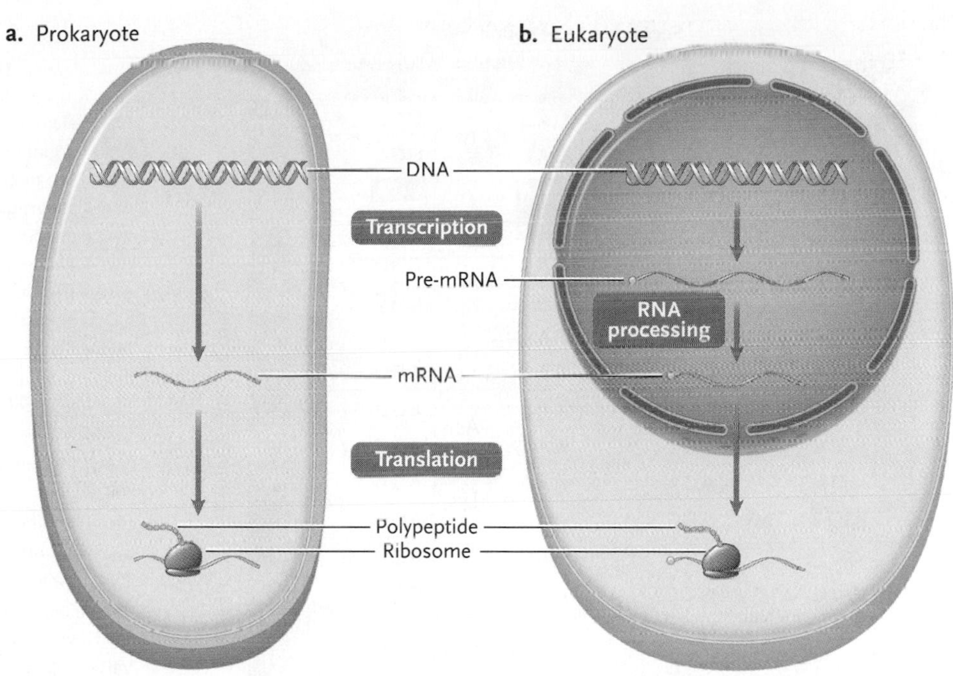

Figure 14.3
Transcription and translation in **(a)** prokaryotes and **(b)** eukaryotes. In prokaryotes, RNA polymerase synthesizes an mRNA molecule that is ready for translation on ribosomes. In eukaryotes, RNA polymerase synthesizes a precursor–mRNA (pre-mRNA molecule) containing extra segments that are removed by RNA processing to produce a translatable mRNA. That mRNA exits the nucleus through a nuclear pore and is translated on ribosomes in the cytoplasm.

How do the codons correspond to the amino acids? Marshall Nirenberg and Philip Leder of the National Institutes of Health (NIH) established the identity of most of the codons in 1964. These researchers found that short, artificial mRNAs of codon length—three nucleotides—could bind to ribosomes in a test tube and cause a single transfer RNA (tRNA), with its linked amino acid, to bind to the ribosome. (As we will discuss in Section 14.4, tRNAs are a special class of RNA molecules that bring amino acids to the ribosome for assembly into the polypeptide chain.) Nirenberg and Leder then made 64 of the short mRNAs, each consisting of a different, single codon. They added the mRNAs, one at a time, to a mixture in a test tube containing ribosomes and all the different tRNAs, each linked to its own amino acid. The idea was that, from the mixture of tRNAs, each single-codon mRNA would link to the tRNA carrying the amino acid corresponding to the codon. The experiment worked for 50 of the 64 codons, allowing those codons to be assigned to amino acids definitively.

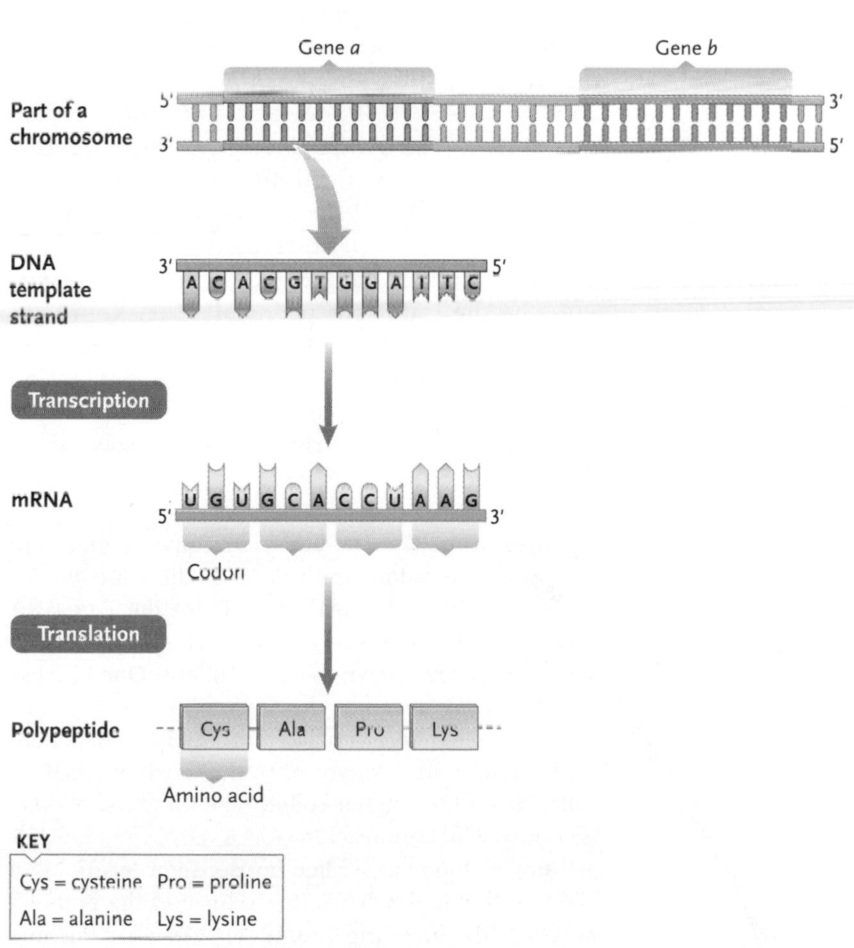

Figure 14.4
Relationship between a gene, codons in an mRNA, and the amino acid sequence of a polypeptide.

Second base of codon

First base of codon	U		C		A		G		Third base of codon
U	UUU	Phe	UCU	Ser	UAU	Tyr	UGU	Cys	U
U	UUC	Phe	UCC	Ser	UAC	Tyr	UGC	Cys	C
U	UUA	Leu	UCA	Ser	UAA		UGA		A
U	UUG	Leu	UCG	Ser	UAG		UGG	Trp	G
C	CUU	Leu	CCU	Pro	CAU	His	CGU	Arg	U
C	CUC	Leu	CCC	Pro	CAC	His	CGC	Arg	C
C	CUA	Leu	CCA	Pro	CAA	Gln	CGA	Arg	A
C	CUG	Leu	CCG	Pro	CAG	Gln	CGG	Arg	G
A	AUU	Ile	ACU	Thr	AAU	Asn	AGU	Ser	U
A	AUC	Ile	ACC	Thr	AAC	Asn	AGC	Ser	C
A	AUA	Ile	ACA	Thr	AAA	Lys	AGA	Arg	A
A	AUG	Met	ACG	Thr	AAG	Lys	AGG	Arg	G
G	GUU	Val	GCU	Ala	GAU	Asp	GGU	Gly	U
G	GUC	Val	GCC	Ala	GAC	Asp	GGC	Gly	C
G	GUA	Val	GCA	Ala	GAA	Glu	GGA	Gly	A
G	GUG	Val	GCG	Ala	GAG	Glu	GGG	Gly	G

KEY

Ala = alanine
Arg = arginine
Asn = asparagine
Asp = aspartic acid
Cys = cysteine
Gln = glutamine
Glu = glutamic acid
Gly = glycine
His = histidine
Ile = isoleucine
Leu = leucine
Lys = lysine
Met = methionine
Phe = phenylalanine
Pro = proline
Ser = serine
Thr = threonine
Trp = tryptophan
Tyr = tyrosine
Val = valine

Figure 14.5
The genetic code, written in the form in which the codons appear in mRNA. The AUG initiator codon, which codes for methionine, is shown in green; the three terminator codons are boxed in red.

Another approach, carried out in 1966 by H. Ghobind Khorana and his coworkers, used long, artificial mRNA molecules containing only one nucleotide repeated continuously or different nucleotides in repeating patterns. Each artificial mRNA was added to ribosomes in a test tube, and the sequence of amino acids in the polypeptide chain made by the ribosomes was analyzed. For example, an artificial mRNA containing only uracil nucleotides in the sequence UUUUUU . . . resulted in a polypeptide containing only the amino acid phenylalanine; they deduced that UUU must be the codon for phenylalanine. Khorana's approach, combined with the results of Nirenberg and Leder's experiments, identified the coding assignments of all the codons. Nirenberg and Khorana received a Nobel Prize in 1968 for solving the nucleic acid code.

Features of the Genetic Code. By convention, scientists write the codons in the $5' \rightarrow 3'$ direction as they appear in mRNAs, substituting U for the T of DNA **(Figure 14.5)**. Of the 64 codons, 61 specify amino acids. These are known as sense codons. One of these codons, AUG, specifies the amino acid methionine. It is the first codon translated in any mRNA in both prokaryotes and eukaryotes. In that position, AUG is called a **start** or **initiator codon.** The three codons that do not specify amino acids—UAA, UAG, and UGA—are **stop codons** (also called **nonsense** or **termination codons**) that act as "periods" indicating the end of a polypeptide-encoding sentence. When a ribosome reaches one of the stop codons, polypeptide synthesis stops and the new polypeptide chain is released from the ribosome.

Only two amino acids, methionine and tryptophan, are specified by a single codon. All the rest are represented by at least two, some by as many as six. In other words, there are many synonyms in the nucleic acid code, a feature known as **degeneracy** (or redundancy). For example, UGU and UGC both specify cysteine, whereas CCU, CCC, CCA, and CCG all specify proline.

Another feature of the genetic code is that it is **commaless**; that is, the words of the nucleic acid code are sequential, with no indicators such as commas or spaces to mark the end of one codon and the beginning of the next. Therefore, the code can be read correctly only by starting at the right place—at the first base of the first three-letter codon at the beginning of a coded message (the start codon)—and reading three nucleotides at a time. In other words, there is only one correct **reading frame** for each mRNA. For example, if you read the message SADMOMHASMOPCUTOFFBOYTOT three letters at a time, starting with the first letter of the first "codon," you would find that a mother reluctantly had her small child's hair cut. However, if you start incorrectly at the second letter of the first codon, you read the gibberish message ADM OMH ASM OPC UTO FFB OYT OT.

The code is also **universal.** With a few exceptions, the same codons specify the same amino acids in all living organisms, and also in viruses. The universality of the nucleic acid code indicates that it was established in its present form very early in the evolution of life and has remained virtually unchanged through billions of years of evolutionary history. Minor exceptions to the universality of the genetic code have been found in a few organisms, including yeast, some protozoans, a prokaryote, and in the genetic systems of mitochondria and chloroplasts.

STUDY BREAK

1. On the basis of their work with auxotrophic mutants of the fungus *Neurospora crassa,* Beadle and Tatum proposed the one gene–one enzyme hypothesis. Why was this hypothesis updated subsequently to the one gene–one polypeptide hypothesis?
2. Why is the sequence of bases different in the mRNA relative to the DNA of a given gene?

14.2 Transcription: DNA-Directed RNA Synthesis

Transcription is the process by which information coded in sequential DNA bases is transferred to a complementary RNA strand. Although certain aspects of this mechanism **(Figure 14.6, p. 302)** are similar to those of DNA replication (see Figure 13.11), it is important for you to understand how these processes are different. In transcription,

- in a given gene, only one of the two DNA nucleotide strands acts as a template for synthesis of a complementary copy, instead of both, as in replication.
- only a relatively small part of a DNA molecule—the sequence encoding a single gene—serves as a template, rather than all of both strands, as in DNA replication.
- **RNA polymerases** catalyze the assembly of nucleotides into an RNA strand, rather than the DNA polymerases that catalyze replication.
- the RNA molecules resulting from transcription are single polynucleotide chains, not double ones, as in DNA replication.

Although the mechanism of transcription is similar in prokaryotes and eukaryotes, watch for the important differences pointed out in this section.

14.2a RNA Polymerases Work Like DNA Polymerases but Require No Primer

Transcription begins as RNA polymerase binds to the DNA and unwinds it near the beginning of a gene (see Figure 14.6, steps 1 to 2). Unlike DNA polymerases, RNA polymerases can start the complementary copy with no need for a primer already in place (DNA primers are discussed in Section 14.3). Like DNA, RNA is made in the 5′→3′ direction using the 3′→5′ DNA strand as a template (step 3). Thus, we refer to the beginning of the RNA strand as the 5′ end and the other end as the 3′ end. The RNA polymerase continues adding nucleotides one at a time until the gene is transcribed completely. At this point, the newly synthesized RNA molecule and the enzyme are released from the DNA template (step 4).

14.2b Specific Sequences of Nucleotides in the DNA Indicate Where Transcription of a Gene Begins and Ends

An organism's genome contains a large number of genes. For example, scientists analyzing data from the human genome sequence suggest that between 20 000 and 25 000 protein-coding genes are needed to make a human. Transcription is the first step in a process whereby particular genes are expressed in any given cell at a given time. Some of those genes are protein-coding genes that encode mRNAs to be translated; others are non–protein-coding genes that encode RNAs that are never translated, such as ribosomal RNAs (rRNAs), transfer RNAs (tRNAs), and small nuclear RNAs (snRNAs). The following sections describe the basic steps of transcription for protein-coding genes.

Organization of a Gene and the Steps of Transcription. Let us first outline the structure of a gene and how it is transcribed into an RNA **(Figure 14.7, p. 303).** At one end of a gene is a control sequence called a **promoter** (Figure 14.7, step 1). The part of the gene that is to be transcribed into RNA is called the **transcription unit.** To *initiate* transcription, RNA polymerase binds to the promoter, unwinds the DNA in that region, and starts synthesizing an RNA molecule at the transcription start point (step 2). As RNA polymerase moves along the DNA, unwinding it at the forward end of the enzyme, the new RNA molecule *elongates* as nucleotides are added one by one (step 3). The new RNA molecule winds temporarily with the template strand of the DNA into a hybrid RNA–DNA double helix. Beyond this short region of pairing, the growing RNA strand unwinds from the DNA and extends from the RNA polymerase as a single nucleotide chain. As the RNA polymerase passes, the DNA double helix reforms. Elongation of the RNA chain continues until the end of the transcription unit, at which point, RNA synthesis *terminates*, and the completed RNA transcript and RNA polymerase are released from the DNA (step 4).

Once an RNA polymerase molecule has started transcription and progressed past the beginning of a gene, another molecule of RNA polymerase may start creating another RNA as soon as there is room at the promoter. For most genes, there are many RNA polymerase molecules spaced closely along a gene, each making an RNA transcript.

The Promoter of Protein-Coding Genes and Transcription Initiation. The promoter specifies where on the DNA transcription begins. In prokaryotes, the promoters are immediately upstream of where transcription initiates. With the help of another protein, RNA polymerase recognizes key DNA sequences in the promoter, binds, and begins transcription of the mRNA. Since all the other types of genes in prokaryotes (for example, tRNA and rRNA genes) have similar promoters, the same RNA polymerase complex can transcribe them all.

In eukaryotes, there are different polymerases for transcribing different types of genes. RNA polymerase II transcribes protein-coding genes. RNA polymerases I and III transcribe genes for non-protein-coding RNAs. The promoters of protein-coding genes are immediately upstream of the transcription start point and are typically more complex than in prokaryotes. Other sequences further upstream of the gene regulate the rate of transcription (discussed in Chapter 15).

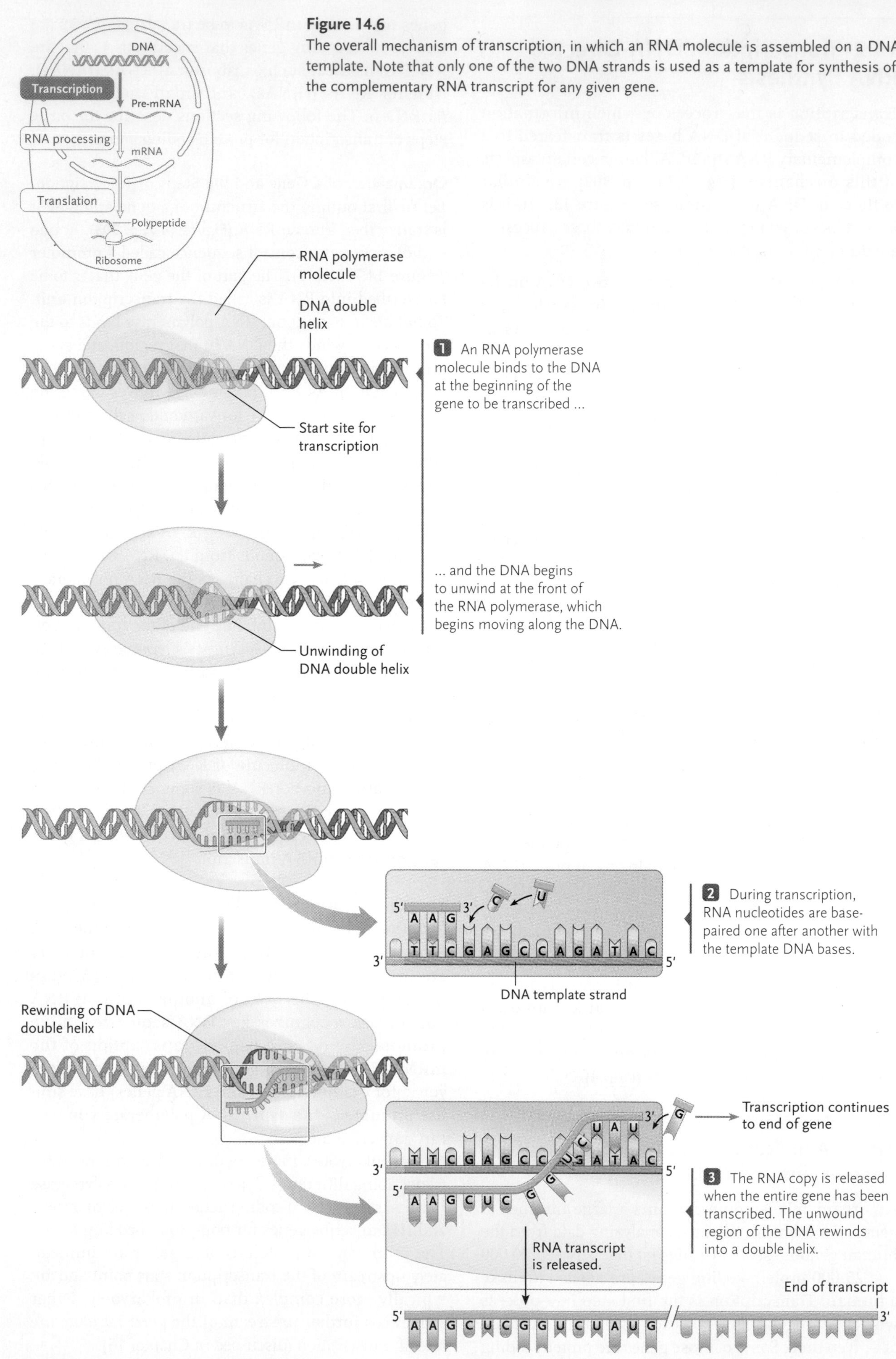

Figure 14.6
The overall mechanism of transcription, in which an RNA molecule is assembled on a DNA template. Note that only one of the two DNA strands is used as a template for synthesis of the complementary RNA transcript for any given gene.

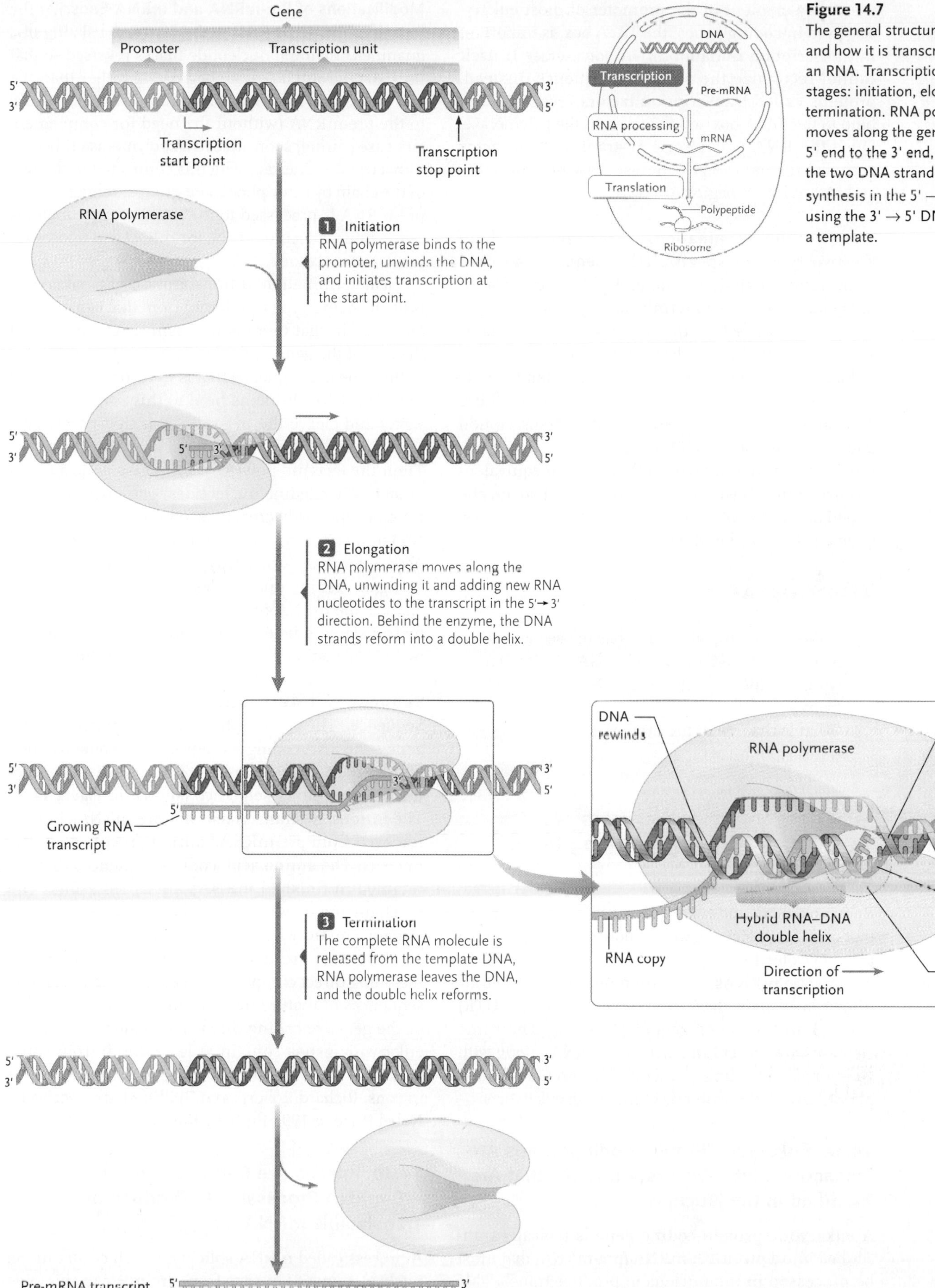

Gene
Promoter
Transcription unit
5'
3'
3'
5'
Transcription start point
Transcription stop point
RNA polymerase
1 Initiation
RNA polymerase binds to the promoter, unwinds the DNA, and initiates transcription at the start point.
2 Elongation
RNA polymerase moves along the DNA, unwinding it and adding new RNA nucleotides to the transcript in the 5'→3' direction. Behind the enzyme, the DNA strands reform into a double helix.
Growing RNA transcript
3 Termination
The complete RNA molecule is released from the template DNA, RNA polymerase leaves the DNA, and the double helix reforms.
Pre-mRNA transcript
DNA
Transcription
Pre-mRNA
RNA processing
mRNA
Translation
Polypeptide
Ribosome
DNA rewinds
DNA unwinds
RNA polymerase
DNA template chain
Hybrid RNA–DNA double helix
RNA copy
Direction of transcription
Site of RNA assembly

Figure 14.7
The general structure of a gene and how it is transcribed into an RNA. Transcription has three stages: initiation, elongation, and termination. RNA polymerase moves along the gene from the 5' end to the 3' end, separating the two DNA strands to allow RNA synthesis in the 5' → 3' direction using the 3' → 5' DNA strand as a template.

A key element of the promoter of most eukaryotic protein-coding genes, the **TATA box**, is important in transcription initiation. RNA polymerase II itself cannot recognize the promoter sequence. Instead, proteins called **transcription factors** recognize and bind to the TATA box and then recruit the polymerase. Once the RNA polymerase II–transcription factor complex forms, the polymerase unwinds the DNA and transcription begins.

Transcription Termination. In prokaryotes, there are two types of specific DNA sequences called **terminators** that signal the end of transcription of the gene. Both types of terminator sequences act *after they are transcribed*. In the first case, the terminator sequence on the mRNA base-pairs with itself to form a "hairpin." In the second case, a protein binds to the terminator sequence on the mRNA. Both of these mechanisms trigger the termination of transcription and the release of the RNA and RNA polymerase from the template. In eukaryotes, there are no equivalent "transcription terminator" sequences. Instead, the 3′ end of the mRNA is specified by a different process, which is discussed in the next section.

Study Break

1. If the DNA template strand has the sequence 3′-CAAATTGGCTTATTACCGGATG-5′, what would be the sequence of an RNA transcribed from it?
2. What is the role of the promoter in transcription?

14.3 Processing of mRNAs in Eukaryotes

Both prokaryotic and eukaryotic mRNAs contain regions that code for protein as well as noncoding regions that play key roles in the process of protein synthesis. In prokaryotic mRNAs, the coding region is flanked by untranslated ends, the 5′ untranslated region (5′ UTR) and a 3′ untranslated region (3′ UTR). The same elements are present in eukaryotic mRNAs along with additional noncoding elements. This section focuses particularly on the synthesis of mRNA in eukaryotes.

14.3a Eukaryotic Protein-Coding Genes Are Transcribed into Precursor-mRNAs that Are Modified in the Nucleus

A eukaryotic protein-coding gene is typically transcribed into a **precursor-mRNA (pre-mRNA)** that must be processed in the nucleus to produce translatable mRNA (see Figures 14.3 and 14.9). The mature mRNA exits the nucleus and is translated in the cytoplasm.

Modifications of Pre-mRNA and mRNA Ends. At the 5′ end of the pre-mRNA is the **5′ cap**, consisting of a guanine-containing nucleotide that is reversed so that its 3′-OH group faces the beginning rather than the end of the molecule. A capping enzyme adds the 5′ cap to the pre-mRNA (without the need for complementary base pairing) soon after RNA polymerase II begins transcription. The cap, which is connected to the rest of the chain by three phosphate groups, remains when pre-mRNA is processed to mRNA. The cap functions as the initial attachment site for mRNAs to ribosomes to allow translation.

The termination of transcription of a eukaryotic protein-coding gene is different from that of a prokaryotic gene in that there is no terminator sequence at the end of the gene in the DNA. Instead, at the 3′ end of the gene is a sequence that is to be transcribed into the pre-mRNA. Proteins bind to this *polyadenylation signal* and cleave the pre-mRNA at that point. This signals the RNA polymerase to stop transcription. Then the enzyme poly(A) polymerase adds a chain of 50 to 250 adenine nucleotides, one nucleotide at a time, to the newly created 3′ end of the pre-mRNA. No complementary base pairing with a template is needed for this particular type of RNA synthesis. The string of adenine nucleotides, called the **poly(A) tail**, enables the mRNA produced from the pre-mRNA to be translated efficiently and protects it from attack by RNA-digesting enzymes in the cytoplasm.

Sequences Interrupting the Protein-Coding Sequence. The transcription unit of a protein-coding gene—the RNA-coding sequence—also contains non–protein-coding sequences called **introns** that interrupt the protein-coding sequence (shown in **Figure 14.8**). The introns are transcribed into pre-mRNAs but are removed from pre-mRNAs during processing in the nucleus. The amino acid–coding sequences that are retained in finished mRNAs are called **exons.** The mechanisms by which introns originated in genes remain a mystery.

Introns were discovered by several methods, including direct comparisons between the nucleotide sequences of mature mRNAs and either pre-mRNAs or the genes encoding them. The majority of known eukaryotic genes contain at least one intron; some contain more than 60. The original discoverers of introns, Richard Roberts and Phillip Sharp, received a Nobel Prize in 1993 for their findings.

14.3b Introns Are Removed during Pre-mRNA Processing to Produce the Translatable mRNA

A process called **mRNA splicing**, which occurs in the nucleus, removes introns from pre-mRNAs and joins exons together. How does this occur? mRNA splicing occurs in a **spliceosome**, a complex formed between

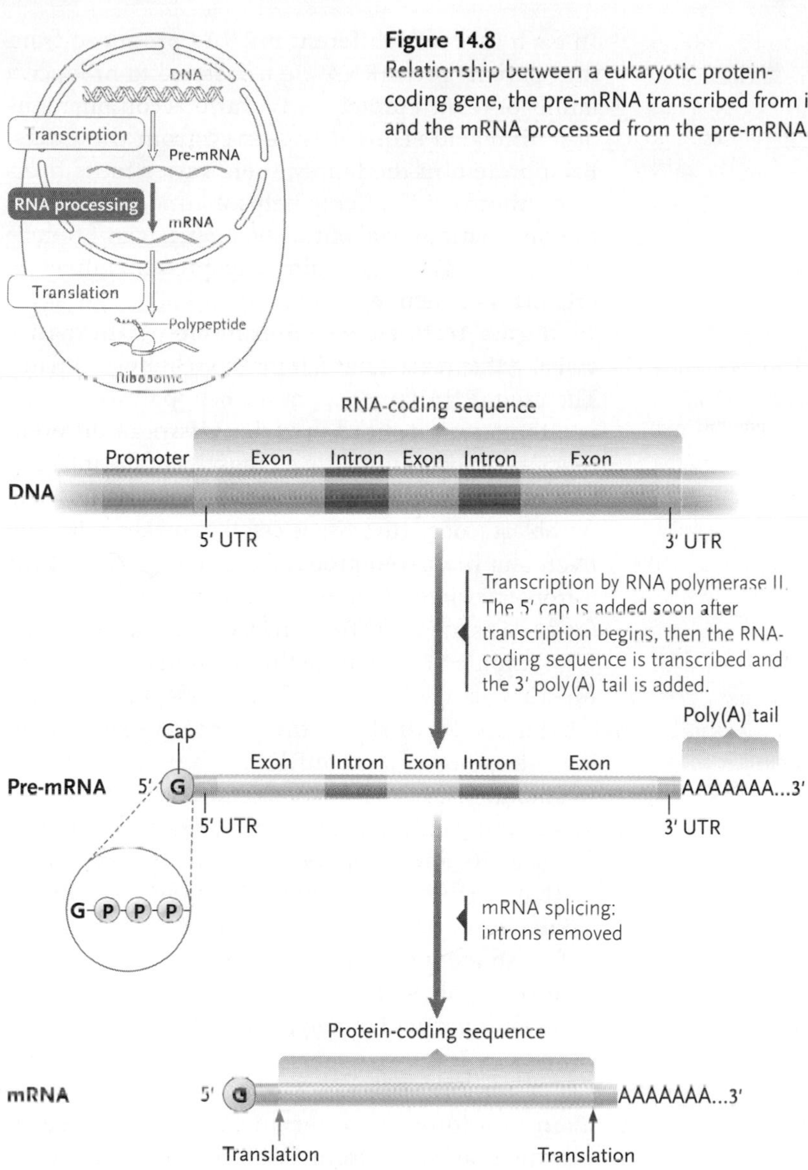

Figure 14.8
Relationship between a eukaryotic protein-coding gene, the pre-mRNA transcribed from it, and the mRNA processed from the pre-mRNA.

the pre-mRNA and a handful of **small ribonucleoprotein particles** (snRNPs; pronounced "snurps") **(Figure 14.9, p. 306).** (Generally, a complex of RNA and proteins is called a ribonucleoprotein.) Located in the nucleus, each type of snRNP contains a relatively short RNA called a small nuclear RNA (snRNA) bound to a number of proteins.

The snRNPs bind in a particular order to an intron in the pre-mRNA. The first snRNPs are those with snRNAs that recognize and form complementary base pairs with mRNA sequences at the junctions of the intron and adjacent exons. Other snRNPs are then recruited, leading to looping out of the intron and bringing the two exon ends close together. At this point, the active spliceosome has been formed. The spliceosome cleaves the pre-mRNA at the junction between the 5′ end of the intron and the adjacent exon (exon 1 in Figure 14.9), and the intron loops back to bond with itself near the intron's 3′ end. The spliceosome then cleaves the pre-mRNA at the junction between the 3′ end of the intron and exon 2, releasing the intron and joining together the two exons (exon 1 and exon 2 in Figure 14.9). Because of the shape of the released intron, it is called a lariat structure. Enzymes degrade the intron, and the snRNPs are used in other mRNA splicing reactions. Researchers were surprised to discover that the catalytic activity in splicing resides not in the proteins but in the RNA component of spliceosomes. Some introns can even splice themselves! An RNA molecule that catalyzes a reaction like a protein enzyme is called a catalytic RNA or a **ribozyme** (ribonucleic acid enzyme).

The cutting and splicing are so exact that not a single base of an intron is retained in the finished mRNA, nor is a single base removed from the exons. Without this precision, removing introns would change the reading frame of the coding portion of the mRNA, producing gibberish from the point of a mistake onward.

14.3c Introns Contribute to Protein Variability

Introns seem wasteful in terms of the energy and raw materials required to replicate and transcribe them and the elaborate cellular machinery required to remove them during pre-mRNA processing. Why are they present in mRNA-encoding genes? Among a number of possibilities, introns may provide a selective advantage to organisms by increasing the coding capacity of existing genes through a process called alternative splicing and in a process generating new proteins by exon shuffling.

Alternative Splicing. The removal of introns from a given gene is not absolute. That is, in certain tissues, or under certain environmental conditions, exons may be joined in different combinations to produce different mRNAs from a single DNA gene sequence. The mechanism, called **alternative splicing,** greatly increases the number and variety of proteins encoded in the cell nucleus without increasing the size of the genome. For example, current data suggest that three-quarters of all human pre-mRNAs are subjected to alternative splicing.

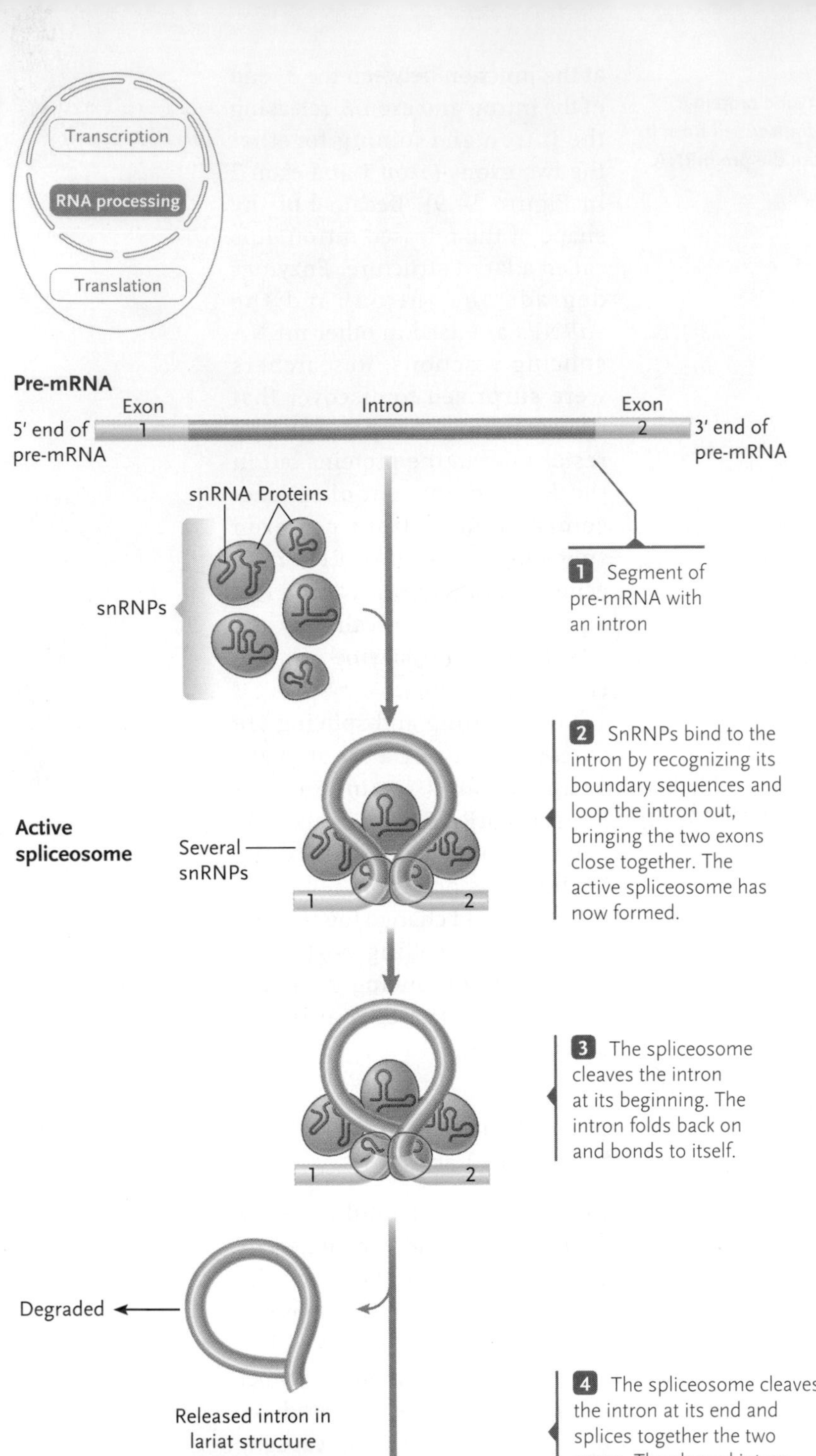
Transcription
RNA processing
Translation
Pre-mRNA
Exon
1
Intron
Exon
2
5′ end of pre-mRNA
3′ end of pre-mRNA
snRNA Proteins
snRNPs
1 Segment of pre-mRNA with an intron
2 SnRNPs bind to the intron by recognizing its boundary sequences and loop the intron out, bringing the two exons close together. The active spliceosome has now formed.
Active spliceosome
Several snRNPs
3 The spliceosome cleaves the intron at its beginning. The intron folds back on and bonds to itself.
Degraded
Released intron in lariat structure
4 The spliceosome cleaves the intron at its end and splices together the two exons. The cleaved intron and snRNPs are released.
Reused
Released snRNPs

Figure 14.9
mRNA splicing—the removal of introns from pre-mRNA and joining of exons in the spliceosome.

In each case, the different mRNAs produced from the "parent" pre-mRNA are translated to produce a family of related proteins with various combinations of amino acid sequences derived from the exons. Each protein in the family, then, varies in its function. Alternative splicing helps us understand why humans with only about 25 000 genes can produce many more proteins. Ultimately, proteins direct an organism's functions.

Figure 14.10 shows an example of alternative splicing that occurs in mammals, including humans. The pre-mRNA transcript of the α-tropomyosin gene is alternatively spliced in various ways in different tissues—smooth muscle (e.g., muscles of the intestine and bladder), skeletal muscle (e.g., biceps, gluteus), fibroblast (connective tissue cell that makes collagen), liver, and brain—to produce different forms of the α-tropomyosin protein that are functionally optimized for each tissue type. Tropomyosins play a role in the regulation of cell contraction in muscle and non-muscle cells.

Figure 14.10 shows the alternative splicing of the α-tropomyosin pre-mRNA to the mRNAs found in smooth muscle and striated muscle. Exons 2 and 12 are found only in smooth muscle mRNA, whereas exons 3, 10, and 11 are exclusive to striated muscle mRNA. Different proteins are made in different tissues from the same DNA gene. Notice that alternative splicing causes us to further refine the "one gene–one polypeptide" idea to something like "one gene–one particular polypeptide under particular conditions."

Exon Shuffling. Another advantage provided by introns may come from the fact that intron–exon junctions often fall at points dividing major functional regions in encoded proteins, for example, genes for antibody proteins, hemoglobin blood proteins, and the peptide hormone insulin. The functional divisions may have allowed new proteins to evolve by exon shuffling, a process by which existing protein regions or domains, already selected for due to their functions, are mixed into novel combinations to create new proteins. Evolution of new proteins by this mechanism would produce changes much more quickly than by changes in individual amino acids at random points.

Study Break

1. What are the similarities and differences between pre-mRNAs and mRNAs?
2. What is the role of base pairing in mRNA splicing?
3. How is it possible for an organism to produce more proteins than it has genes for?

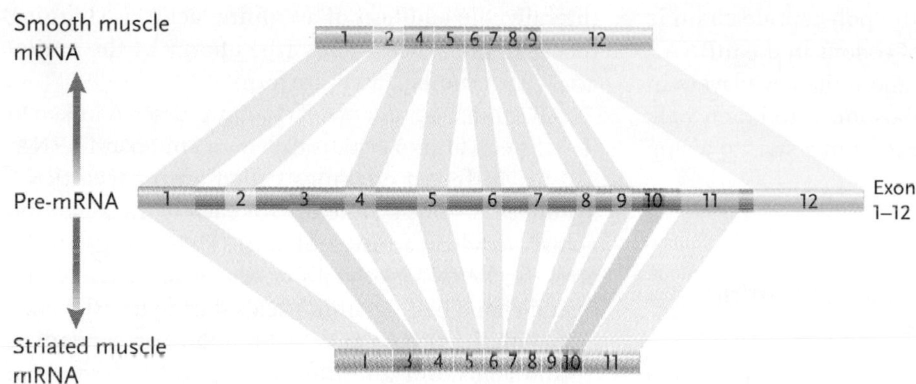

Figure 14.10
Alternative splicing of the α-tropomyosin pre-mRNA to distinct mRNA forms found in smooth muscle and striated muscle. All of the introns are removed in both mRNA splicing pathways. However, to produce smooth muscle mRNA, "exons" 3, 10, and 11 are also removed; to produce the striated muscle mRNA, "exons" 2 and 12 are also removed.

14.4 Translation: mRNA-Directed Polypeptide Synthesis

Translation is the assembly of amino acids into polypeptides. In prokaryotes, translation takes place throughout the cell, whereas in eukaryotes, it occurs mostly in the cytoplasm, although, as we will see, a few specialized genes are transcribed and translated in mitochondria and chloroplasts.

Figure 14.11 (p. 309) summarizes the translation process. In prokaryotes, the mRNA produced by transcription is not confined within a nucleus and is therefore available immediately for translation. For eukaryotes, the mRNA produced by splicing of the pre-mRNA first exits the nucleus and then is translated in the cytoplasm. In translation, the mRNA associates with a ribosome and another type of RNA, transfer RNAs (tRNAs), brings amino acids to the complex to be joined one by one into the polypeptide chain. The

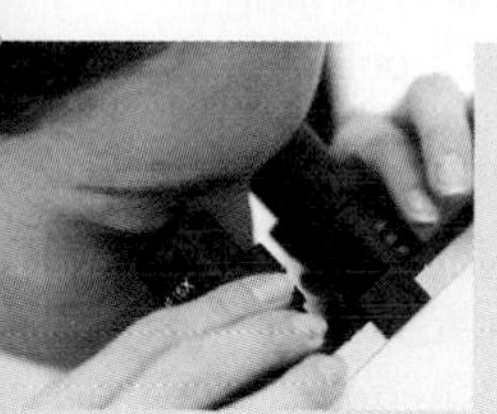

People Behind Biology

Dr. Steve Zimmerly, University of Calgary, Alberta

Dr. Steve Zimmerly and his colleagues think they know where introns came from.

Biology students (and researchers) often wonder about the origins of introns, and to investigate this question, Dr. Zimmerly collected and analyzed a large number of examples of a type of intron called "Group II" from plant organelles and bacteria. Group II introns have two fascinating abilities. First, they can splice themselves out of RNA without the need for proteins. Second, they are mobile; these elements can copy themselves and insert at a new location **(Figure 1)**.

The Zimmerly lab proposed a model for intron evolution that suggests the introns in nuclear genes of higher eukaryotes evolved from mobile Group II introns originating in prokaryotes. These Group II introns may have spread to eukaryotes at the time when their bacterial hosts were engulfed by eukaryotic cells to become endosymbiotic mitochondria and chloroplasts. Over evolutionary time, the nuclear introns lost their mobility and became dependent on spliceosomes for accurate splicing.

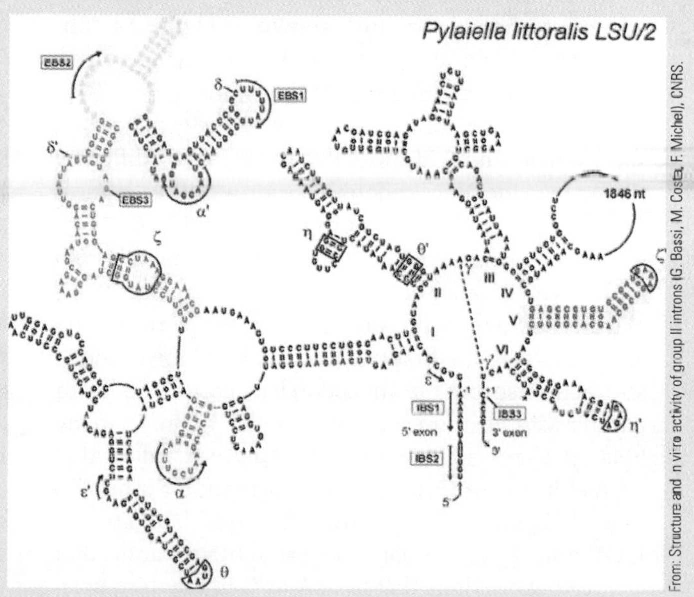

Figure 1
Sequence of a Group II intron showing extensive pairing with itself.

sequence of amino acids in the polypeptide chain is determined by the sequence of codons in the mRNA.

We will start by learning about the key players in the process, the tRNAs and ribosomes, and then walk through the translation process from a start to a stop codon.

14.4a tRNAs Are Small RNAs of a Highly Distinctive Structure that Bring Amino Acids to the Ribosome

Transfer RNAs (tRNAs) bring amino acids to the ribosome for addition to the polypeptide chain.

tRNA Structure. tRNAs are small RNAs, about 75 to 90 nucleotides long (mRNAs are typically hundreds of nucleotides long), with a highly distinctive structure that accomplishes their role in translation **(Figure 14.12).** All tRNAs can base-pair with themselves to wind into four double-helical segments, forming a cloverleaf pattern in two dimensions. At the tip of one of the double-helical segments is the **anticodon,** the three-nucleotide segment that pairs with a codon in mRNAs. At the other end of the cloverleaf is a double-helical segment that links to the amino acid corresponding to the anticodon. For example, a tRNA that is linked to serine (Ser) pairs with the codon 5′-AGU-3′ in mRNA (see Figure 14.12). The anticodon of the tRNA that pairs with this codon is 3′-UCA-5′. (The anticodon and codon pair in an antiparallel manner, as do the strands in DNA. We will write anticodons in the 3′ → 5′ direction to make it easy to see how they pair with codons normally written 5′ → 3′.)

The tRNA cloverleaf folds in three dimensions into the L-shaped structure shown in Figure 14.12b. The anticodon and the segment binding the amino acid are located at the opposite tips of the L.

Recall that 61 of the 64 codons of the genetic code specify an amino acid. Does this mean that 61 different tRNAs read the sense codons? The answer is no. Francis Crick's **wobble hypothesis** proposed that the complete set of 61 sense codons can be read by fewer than 61 distinct tRNAs because of the particular pairing properties of the bases in the anticodons. That is, the pairing of the anticodon with the first two nucleotides of the codon is always precise, but the anticodon has more flexibility in pairing with the third nucleotide of the codon. In many cases, the same tRNA's anticodon can read codons that have either U or C in the third position; for example, a tRNA carrying phenylalanine can read both codons UUU and UUC. Similarly, the same tRNA's anticodon can read two codons that have A or G in the third position; for example, a tRNA carrying glutamine can pair with both CAA and CAG codons.

Addition of Amino Acids to Their Corresponding tRNAs. The correct amino acid must be present on a tRNA if translation is to be accurate. The process of adding an amino acid to a tRNA is called **aminoacylation** (literally, the addition of an amino acid) or **charging** (because the process adds free energy as the amino acid–tRNA combinations are formed).

The finished product of charging, a tRNA linked to its "correct" amino acid, is called an **aminoacyl–tRNA.** Twenty different enzymes called **aminoacyl–tRNA synthetases**—one synthetase for each of the 20 amino acids—catalyze aminoacylation. This energy in the aminoacyl–tRNA eventually drives the formation of the peptide bond linking amino acids during translation.

With the tRNAs attached to their corresponding amino acids, our attention moves to the ribosome, where the amino acids are removed from tRNAs and linked together into polypeptide chains.

14.4b Ribosomes Are rRNA–Protein Complexes that Work as Automated Protein Assembly Machines

Ribosomes are ribonucleoprotein particles that carry out protein synthesis by translating mRNA into chains of amino acids. Like some automated machines, such as those forming complicated metal parts by a series of machining steps, ribosomes use an information tape—an mRNA molecule—as the directions required to accomplish a task. For ribosomes, the task is joining amino acids in ordered sequences to make a polypeptide chain.

In prokaryotes, ribosomes carry out their assembly functions throughout the cell. In eukaryotes, ribosomes function in the cytoplasm, either suspended freely in the cytoplasmic solution or attached to the membranes of the endoplasmic reticulum (ER), the system of tubular or flattened sacs in the cytoplasm. Chloroplasts and mitochondria each have their own ribosomes in addition to those in the cytoplasm.

A finished ribosome is made up of two parts of dissimilar size, called the *large* and *small ribosomal subunits* **(Figure 14.13, p. 310).** Each subunit is made up of a combination of ribosomal RNA (rRNA) and ribosomal proteins.

Prokaryotic and eukaryotic ribosomes are similar in structure and function. However, the differences in their molecular structure, particularly in the ribosomal proteins, give them distinct properties. For example, the antibiotics streptomycin and erythromycin are effective antibacterial agents because they inhibit bacterial, but not eukaryotic, ribosomes.

To fulfill its role in translation, the ribosome has special binding sites active in bringing together mRNA with aminoacyl–tRNAs (see Figure 14.13 and refer also to Figure 14.11). One such site is where the mRNA threads through the ribosome. The **A site** (aminoacyl site) is where the incoming aminoacyl–tRNA (carrying the next amino acid to be added to the polypeptide chain) binds to the mRNA. The **P site** (peptidyl site) is where the tRNA carrying the growing polypeptide chain is bound. The **E site** (exit site) is where an exiting tRNA binds as it leaves the ribosome.

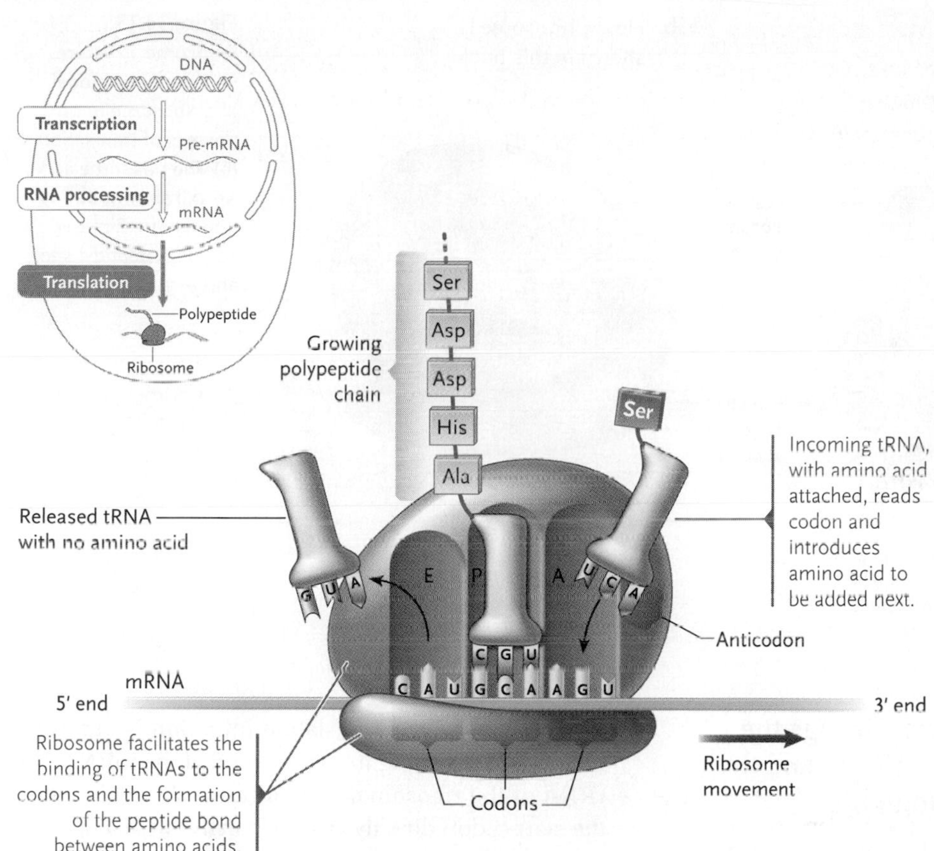

Figure 14.11
An overview of translation, in which ribosomes assemble amino acids into a polypeptide chain. The figure shows a ribosome in the process of translation. A tRNA molecule with an amino acid bound to it is entering the ribosome on the right. The anticodon on the tRNA will pair with the codon in the mRNA. Its amino acid will then be added to the growing polypeptide, which is currently attached to the tRNA in the middle of the ribosome.

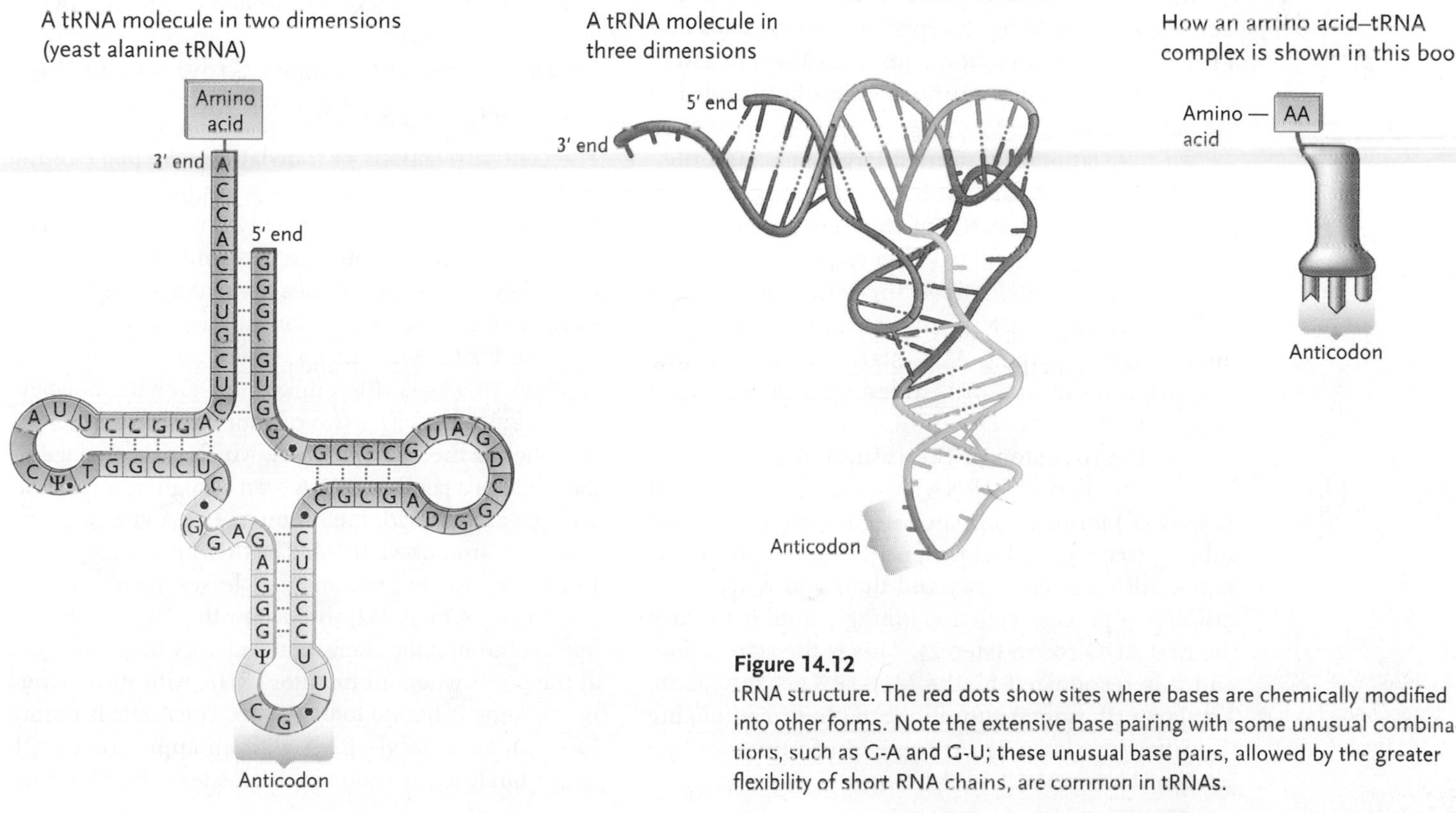

Figure 14.12
tRNA structure. The red dots show sites where bases are chemically modified into other forms. Note the extensive base pairing with some unusual combinations, such as G-A and G-U; these unusual base pairs, allowed by the greater flexibility of short RNA chains, are common in tRNAs.

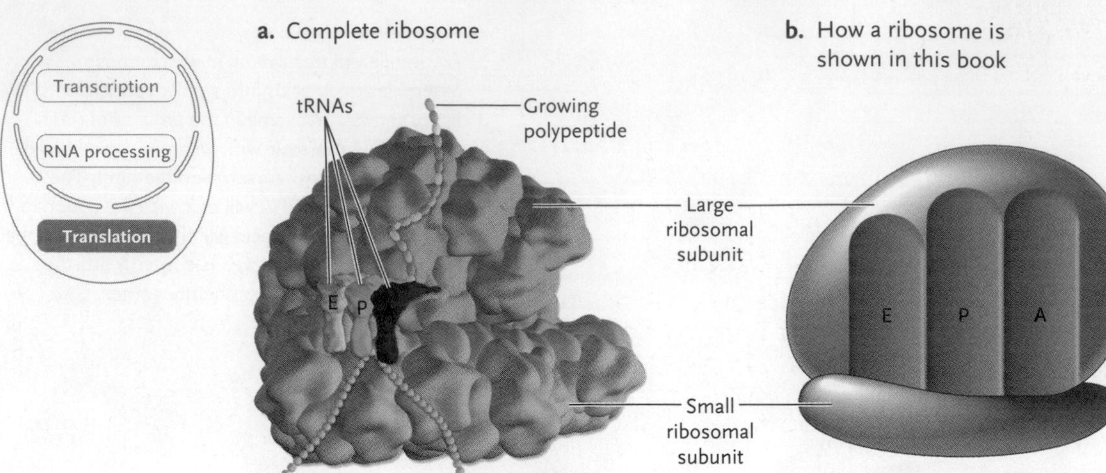

Figure 14.13 Ribosome structure. **(a)** Computer model of a ribosome in the process of translation. **(b)** The ribosome as we will show it during translation. E = exit site, P = peptidyl site, and A = aminoacyl site.

14.4c Translation Initiation Brings the Ribosomal Subunits, an mRNA, and the First Aminoacyl–tRNA Together

Translation is similar in prokaryotes and eukaryotes. In this section we present translation in a eukaryote but will point out along the way how it differs in prokaryotes.

There are three major stages of translation: initiation, elongation, and termination. Initiation involves the assembly of all the translation components on the start codon of the mRNA. Elongation involves reading the string of codons in the mRNA one at a time while assembling the specified amino acids into a polypeptide. Termination completes the translation process when the last amino acid has been added to the polypeptide.

In translation initiation, a large and small ribosomal subunit associates with an mRNA molecule and the first aminoacyl–tRNA of the new protein chain becomes bound to the AUG start codon **(Figure 14.14)**. That aminoacyl–tRNA used for initiation is a specialized **initiator tRNA** with an anticodon to the methionine-specifying AUG start codon. Each step in translation initiation is aided by proteins called initiation factors.

In the first step of the initiation process, the initiator methionine–tRNA (Met–tRNA—anticodon 3′-UAC-5′) forms a complex with the small ribosomal subunit (see Figure 14.14, step 1). The complex binds to the mRNA at the 5′ cap and then moves along the mRNA—a process called *scanning*—until it reaches the first AUG codon (step 2). This is the start codon, and it is recognized by the Met–tRNA's anticodon. The large ribosomal subunit then binds, completing the ribosome (step 3). At the end of initiation, the initiator Met–tRNA is in the P site.

In prokaryotes, translation initiation is different: rather than scanning from the 5′ end of the mRNA, the rRNA of the ribosomal subunit finds the region with the start codon directly by base pairing with a specific ribosome binding site on the mRNA just upstream of the start codon. The large ribosomal subunit then binds to the small one to complete the ribosome.

After the initiator tRNA pairs with the AUG initiator codon, the subsequent stages of translation simply read the nucleotide bases three at a time on the mRNA. The initiator tRNA–AUG pairing thus establishes the correct reading frame—the series of codons for the polypeptide encoded by the mRNA.

14.4d Polypeptide Chains Grow during the Elongation Stage of Translation

The central reactions of translation take place in the elongation stage, which adds single amino acids sequentially to a growing polypeptide chain. The individual steps of elongation depend on the binding properties of P, A, and E sites of the ribosome. Protein elongation factors aid the elongation events.

The P site, with one exception, can only bind to a **peptidyl–tRNA**—a tRNA linked to a growing polypeptide chain containing two or more amino acids. The exception is the initiator tRNA, which is recognized by the P site as a peptidyl–tRNA even though it carries only a single amino acid, methionine. The A site can bind only to an aminoacyl–tRNA. The tRNA previously in the P site binds to the E site and then leaves the ribosome.

Figure 14.15 (p. 312) shows how the P, A, and E sites operate through the elongation cycle. We begin the cycle at the point when an initiator tRNA with its attached methionine is bound to the P site. The A site is empty. First, an aminoacyl–tRNA with an appropriate anticodon binds to the codon in the A site of the ribosome;

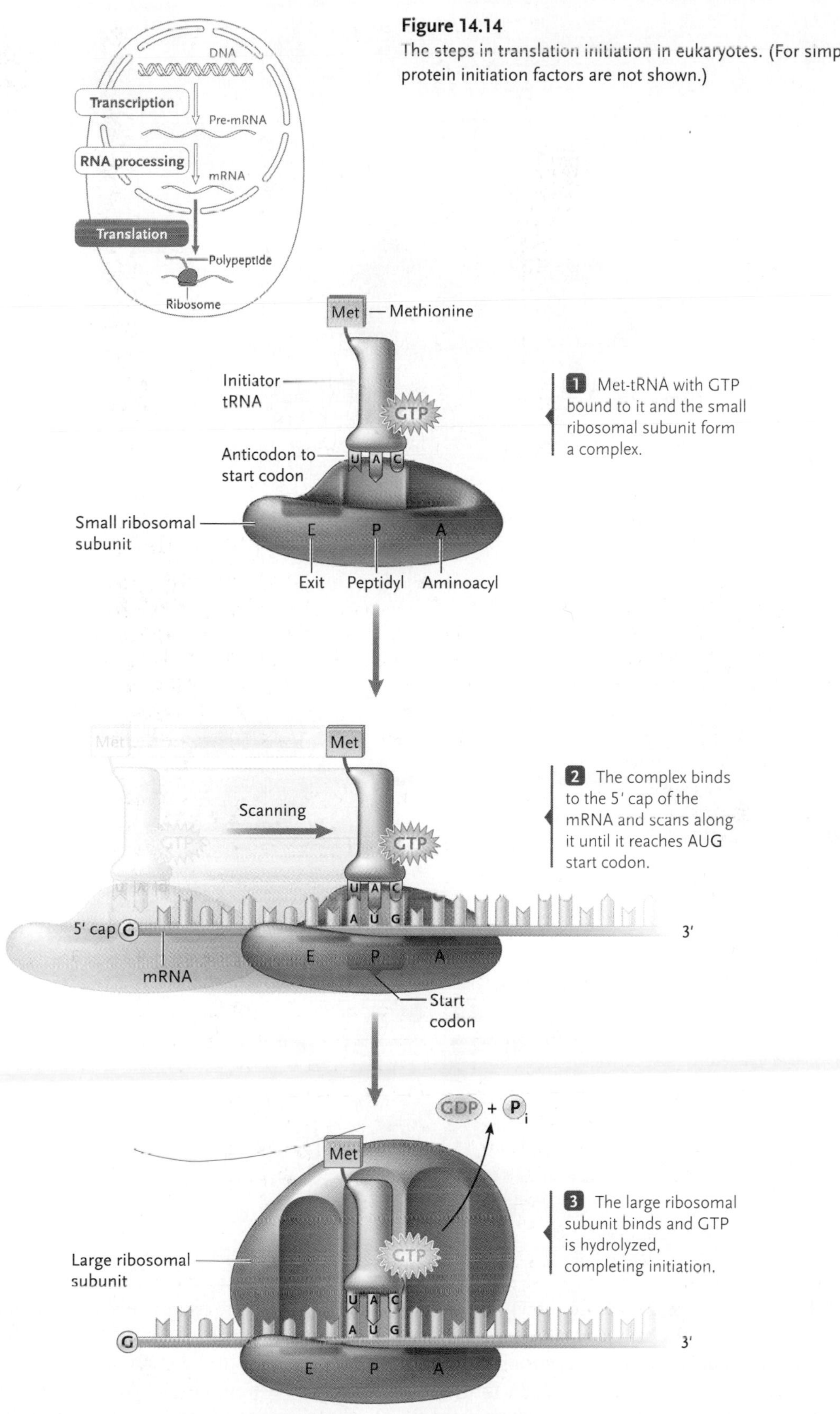

Figure 14.14
The steps in translation initiation in eukaryotes. (For simplicity, protein initiation factors are not shown.)

guanosine triphosphate (GTP) is hydrolyzed to provide energy for this step (see **Figure 14.16, p. 314,** step 1).

Next, the amino acid (here, the initiator methionine) is cleaved from the tRNA in the P site and forms a peptide bond with the amino acid on the tRNA in the A site (step 2). **Peptidyl transferase** catalyzes this reaction. As we saw previously in the case of spliceosomes, catalytic activity of ribosomes resides in the rRNA component rather than the protein component, as was originally thought.

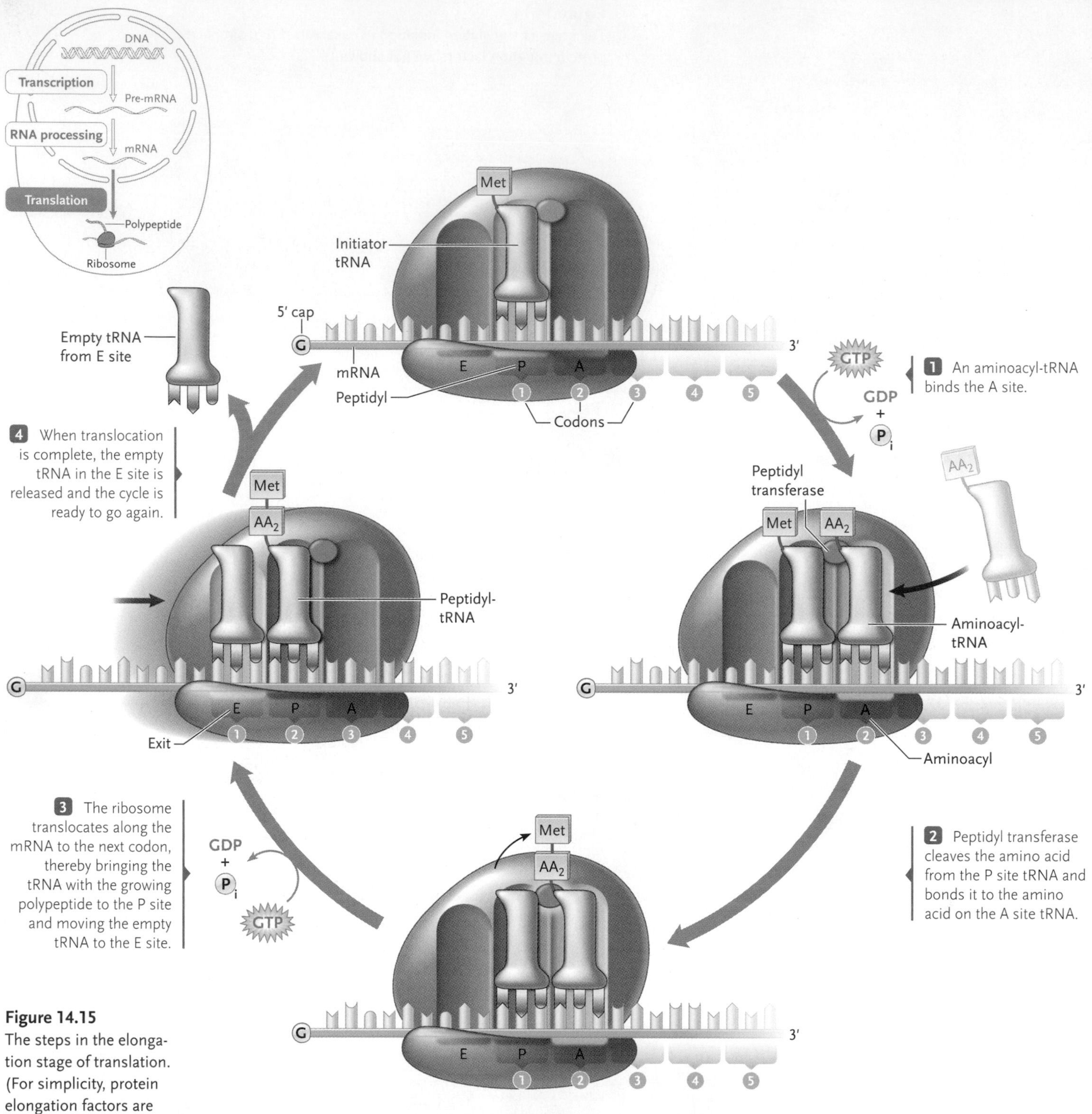
DNA
Transcription
Pre-mRNA
RNA processing
mRNA
Translation
Polypeptide
Ribosome
Met
Initiator tRNA
5′ cap
G
3′
mRNA
Peptidyl
E
P
A
Codons
GTP
GDP
+
P
1 An aminoacyl-tRNA binds the A site.
Empty tRNA from E site
4 When translocation is complete, the empty tRNA in the E site is released and the cycle is ready to go again.
AA2
Peptidyl-tRNA
Peptidyl transferase
Aminoacyl-tRNA
Exit
Aminoacyl
3 The ribosome translocates along the mRNA to the next codon, thereby bringing the tRNA with the growing polypeptide to the P site and moving the empty tRNA to the E site.
2 Peptidyl transferase cleaves the amino acid from the P site tRNA and bonds it to the amino acid on the A site tRNA.

Figure 14.15
The steps in the elongation stage of translation. (For simplicity, protein elongation factors are not shown.)

At the end of the reaction, the (now) polypeptide chain is attached to the tRNA in the A site and an "empty" tRNA remains at the P site. Next, the ribosome moves—translocates—along the mRNA to the next codon, using energy from GTP hydrolysis (step 3). The two tRNAs remain bound to their respective codons, so this step positions the just-formed peptidyl–tRNA in the P site and generates a vacant A site. The empty tRNA that was in the P site moves to the E site, from where it is released from the ribosome (step 4). With the A site empty and a peptidyl–tRNA in the P site, the ribosome repeats the elongation cycle. In subsequent turns of the cycle, the growing polypeptide on the tRNA in the P site is transferred to the amino acid on the A site tRNA. The growing polypeptide chain extends from the ribosome through the exit tunnel (see Figure 14.13) as elongation continues.

Elongation is similar in prokaryotes and eukaryotes, with no substantive differences beyond being faster in prokaryotes. Each elongation cycle turns about 1 to 3 times per second in eukaryotes and 15 to 20 times per second in prokaryotes.

Molecule Behind Biology

Amanitin

Alpha-amanitin is one of several potent toxins found in various species of the mushroom *Amanita* **(Figure 1).** Although composed of many amino acid backbones linked in a ring, this interesting molecule is not a protein and is not produced by translation. In the laboratory, amanitin is a useful inhibitor of eukaryotic RNA polymerase. However, on the dinner table, amanitin is a powerful poison. People suffering from amanitin poisoning show extensive, and usually fatal, liver and kidney damage.

a.

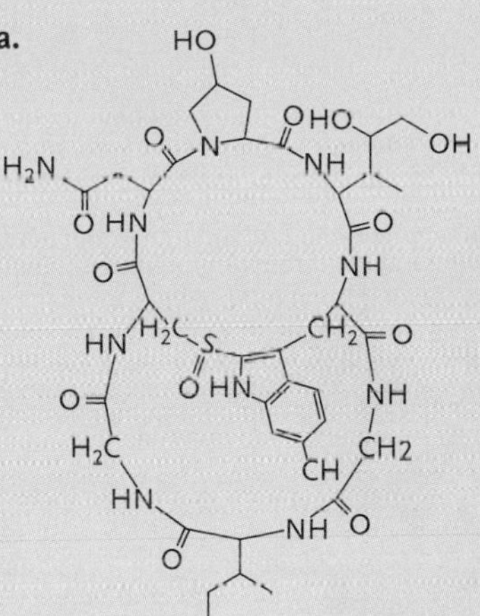

b.

Figure 1
(a) The very striking double circular structure of amanitin. **(b)** *Amanita phalloides.*

14.4e Termination Releases a Completed Polypeptide from the Ribosome

Translation switches from the elongation to the termination stage when the A site of a ribosome arrives at one of the stop codons (UAA, UAG, or UGA) on the mRNA (Figure 14.16, step 1). When a stop codon appears at the A site, a protein **release factor** (RF; also called a **termination factor**) binds at this site instead of an aminoacyl–tRNA (step 2). In response, the polypeptide chain is released from the tRNA at the P site as usual (step 3). However, because no amino acid is present at the A site, the freed polypeptide chain is released from the ribosome (step 4). At the same time, the ribosomal subunits separate and detach from the mRNA. The empty tRNA and the release factor are also released. Termination is the same in prokaryotes and eukaryotes.

14.4f Multiple Ribosomes Simultaneously Translate a Single mRNA

In the previous section describing transcription, we noted that several RNA polymerases can transcribe a gene at the same time; the same idea applies in translation. Once the first ribosome has begun translating, another one can assemble with an initiator tRNA as soon as there is room on the mRNA. Ribosomes continue to attach as translation continues and become spaced along the mRNA like beads on a string. The entire structure of an mRNA molecule and the multiple ribosomes attached to it is known as a **polysome** (a contraction of polyribosome; **Figure 14.17, p. 314**. Multiple ribosomes greatly increase the overall rate of polypeptide synthesis from a single mRNA.

In prokaryotes, the absence of a nuclear envelope allows transcription and translation to be tightly coupled. That is, as soon as the 5′ end of a new mRNA emerges from the RNA polymerase, ribosomal subunits may attach and initiate translation **(Figure 14.18, p. 314).** In essence, the polysome forms while the mRNA is still being created. By the time the mRNA is completely transcribed, it is covered with ribosomes from end to end, each assembling a copy of the encoded polypeptide. Meanwhile, several other RNA polymerases have likely begun transcribing the same gene, each one trailing a collection of translating ribosomes. You can see that such a system allows prokaryotes to regulate the production of proteins very quickly in response to changing environmental conditions.

14.4g Newly Synthesized Polypeptides Are Processed and Folded into Finished Form

Most eukaryotic proteins are in an inactive, unfinished form when ribosomes release them. Processing reactions that convert the new proteins into finished form include the removal of amino acids from the ends or interior of the polypeptide chain and the addition of larger organic groups, including carbohydrate or lipid structures.

Proteins fold into their final three-dimensional shapes as the processing reactions take place. For many proteins, helper proteins called chaperones or chaperonins assist the folding process by combining with the folding protein, promoting "correct" three-dimensional structures, and inhibiting incorrect ones.

In some cases, the same initial polypeptide may be processed by alternative pathways that produce different mature polypeptides, usually by removing different, long stretches of amino acids from the interior of the polypeptide chain. Alternative processing is another mechanism, distinct from alternative splicing of mRNA, that increases the number of proteins encoded by a single gene.

Other proteins are processed into an initial, inactive form that is later activated at a particular time or location by removal of a covering segment of the

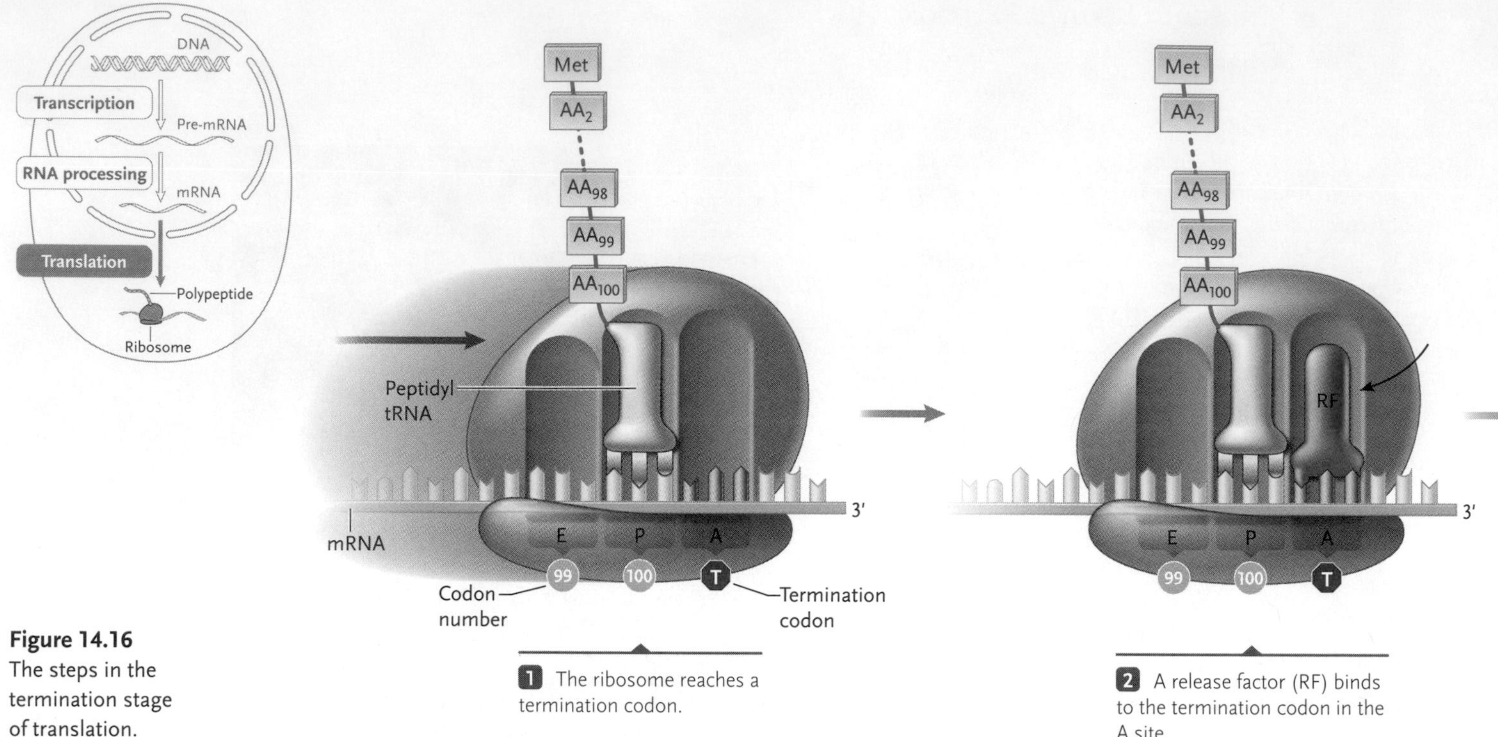

Figure 14.16
The steps in the termination stage of translation.

amino acid chain. The digestive enzyme pepsin, for example, is made by cells lining the stomach in an inactive form called pepsinogen. When the cells secrete pepsinogen into the stomach, the high acidity of that organ triggers removal of a segment of amino acids, thus converting the enzyme into the active form in which it rapidly degrades proteins in food particles. The initial production of the protein as inactive pepsinogen protects the cells that make it from having their proteins degraded by the enzyme.

14.4h Finished Proteins Contain Sorting Signals that Direct Them to Cellular Locations

Proteins are found in all parts of the eukaryotic cell, including the soluble cytoplasm, the nucleus, and the plasma membrane, as well as in the membranes or interior of various organelles; they are also transported to the cell exterior. How are newly synthesized proteins directed to these locations? Proteins that remain in the cytoplasmic solution, such as microtubule proteins or the enzymes used in glycolysis, have no signals; these proteins are made on ribosomes called free ribosomes that

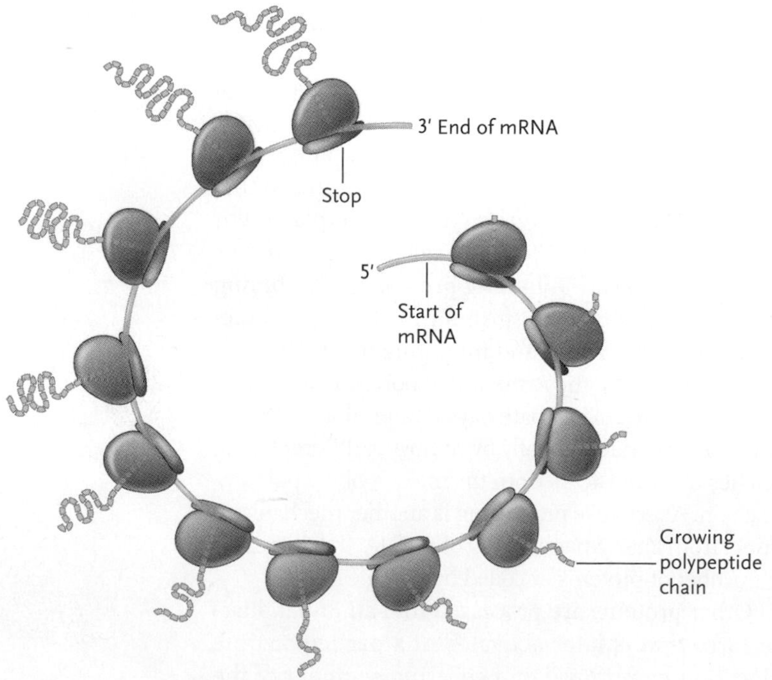

Figure 14.17
Polysomes, consisting of a series of ribosomes "reading" the same mRNA.

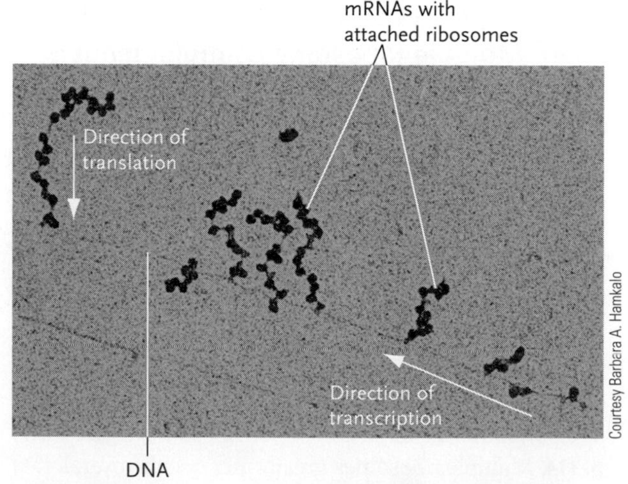

Figure 14.18
Simultaneous transcription and translation in progress in an electron microscope preparation extracted from *E. coli*, × 5 700 000. Courtesy of O.L. Miller Jr, Barbara A. Hamkalo, and C.A. Thomas Jr.

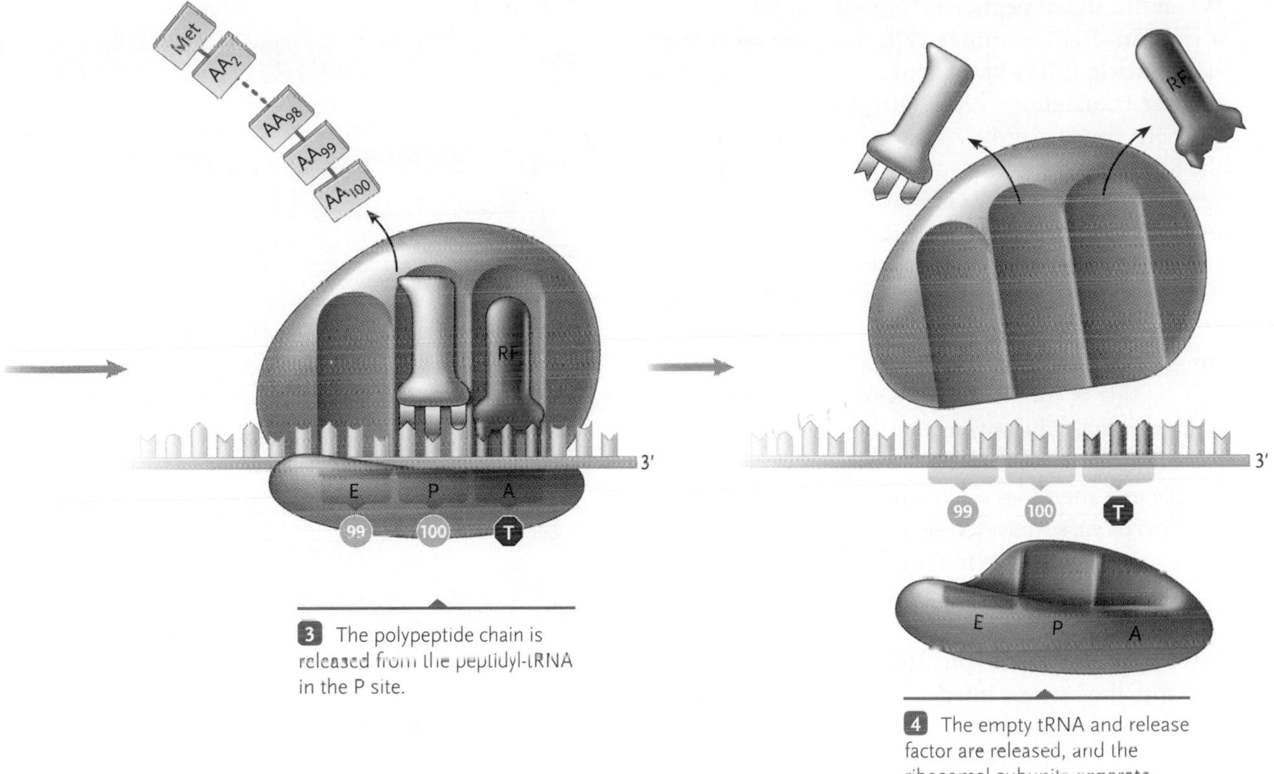

3 The polypeptide chain is released from the peptidyl-tRNA in the P site.

4 The empty tRNA and release factor are released, and the ribosomal subunits separate.

remain suspended in the cytosol. These proteins simply remain in the cytoplasmic solution as they are made.

For all other proteins, an amazing system of "address codes," written in the form of amino acid sequences, serves as sorting signals, directing the proteins to their cellular locations, or out of the cell. The signals are coded in the DNA, transcribed into mRNAs, and "printed" in proteins as they are made. The signals, first discovered by Günter Blobel and his coworkers, are recognized and bound by receptors in the locations to which the proteins are addressed. Blobel received a Nobel Prize in 1999 for his work with the mechanism sorting proteins in cells.

One major signal pathway sends proteins to the ER **(Figure 14.19)**. In these proteins, a short segment of amino acids called the **signal peptide** (or **signal sequence**) is in the first part of the polypeptide chain.

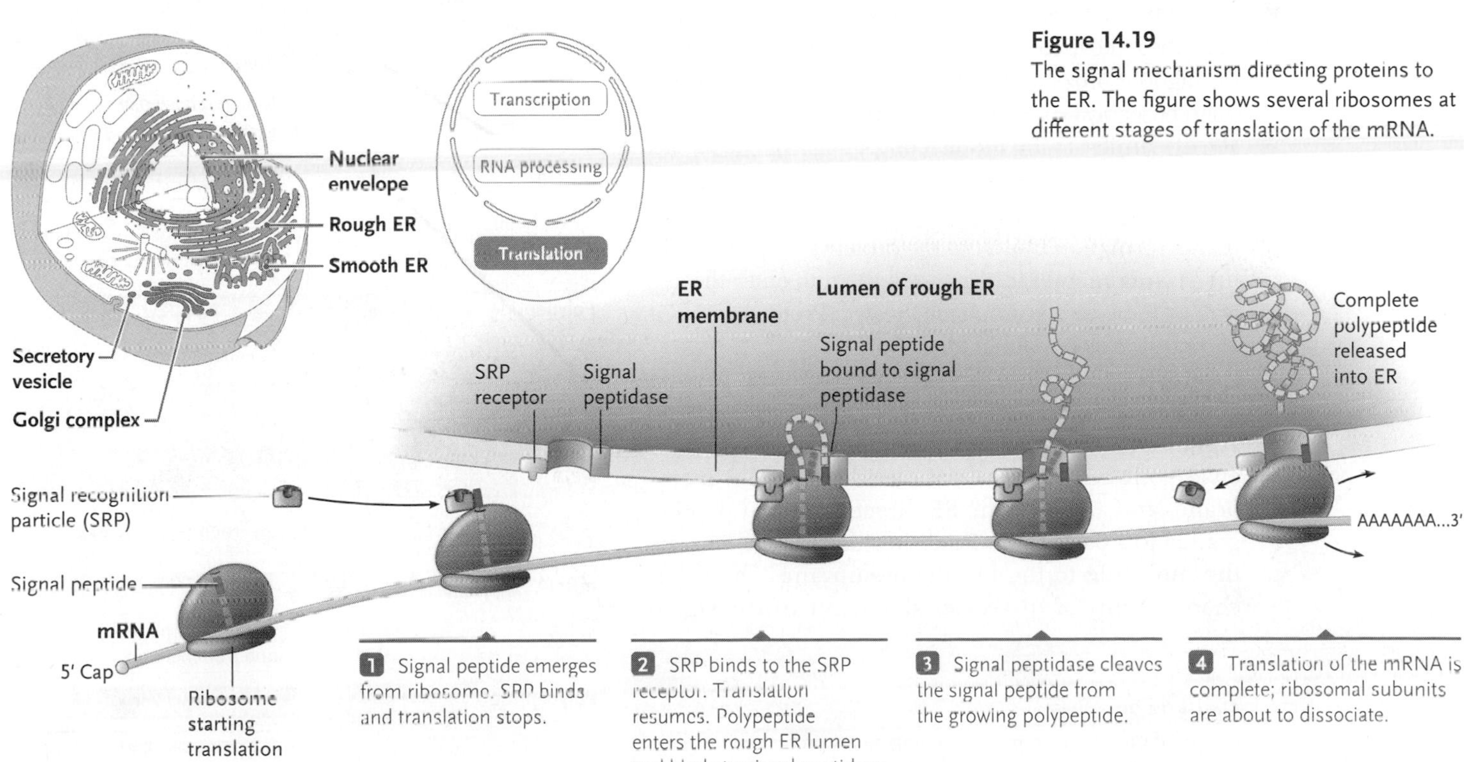

Figure 14.19
The signal mechanism directing proteins to the ER. The figure shows several ribosomes at different stages of translation of the mRNA.

When the signal peptide emerges from the ribosome, a protein–RNA complex called the **signal recognition particle (SRP)** binds to it and temporarily blocks further translation (see Figure 14.19, step 1). Next, the SRP binds a protein in the ER membrane called the **SRP receptor**; this step "docks" the ribosome on the ER membrane (step 2). (The docked ribosomes give the the "roughness" to the rough ER.) The ribosome can now continue protein synthesis, and the growing polypeptide is pushed through the ER membrane into the ER lumen (see step 2). Here an enzyme, signal peptidase, removes the signal sequence (step 3), and synthesis of the polypeptide is completed (step 4). Depending on other built-in signals, the polypeptide may move to any part of the ER-based system (the ER itself, the Golgi complex, the plasma membrane, the nuclear envelope, secretory vesicles) or via secretory vesicles to the cell exterior (these destinations are shown in the inset to Figure 14.19).

Nuclear proteins include a signal bound by receptors in the pore complexes of the nuclear envelope. Once bound, they are pushed through the pore complex into the nuclear interior, in a process that requires adenosine triphosphate (ATP) energy. These proteins retain their signal because they need to reenter the nucleus each time the nuclear envelope is broken down and reforms during the cell division cycle.

Many proteins that are to become part of organelles, such as mitochondria, chloroplasts, or microbodies, are also made on free ribosomes. However, these proteins have signals that are bound by receptors in the organelle membranes, targeting them for entry into the organelles. Further signals on the proteins direct them to the different membranes or compartments inside the organelles.

The same basic system of sorting protein signals described above for eukaryotes also distributes proteins throughout prokaryotic cells, indicating that this mechanism probably evolved with the first cells. In prokaryotes, signals similar to the ER-directing signals of eukaryotes direct newly synthesized bacterial proteins to the plasma membrane (bacteria do not have ER membranes); further information built into the proteins keeps them in the plasma membrane or allows them to enter the cell wall or to be secreted outside the cell. Proteins without sorting signals remain in the cytoplasm.

Interestingly, prokaryotic and eukaryotic routing signals are interchangeable. That is, a prokaryotic signal peptide added to a polypeptide made in a eukaryotic cell routes the molecule to the ER membrane, and a eukaryotic ER-directing signal peptide grafted to a polypeptide made in a bacterial cell directs the molecule to the plasma membrane. The interchangeability of the bacterial and eukaryotic signal

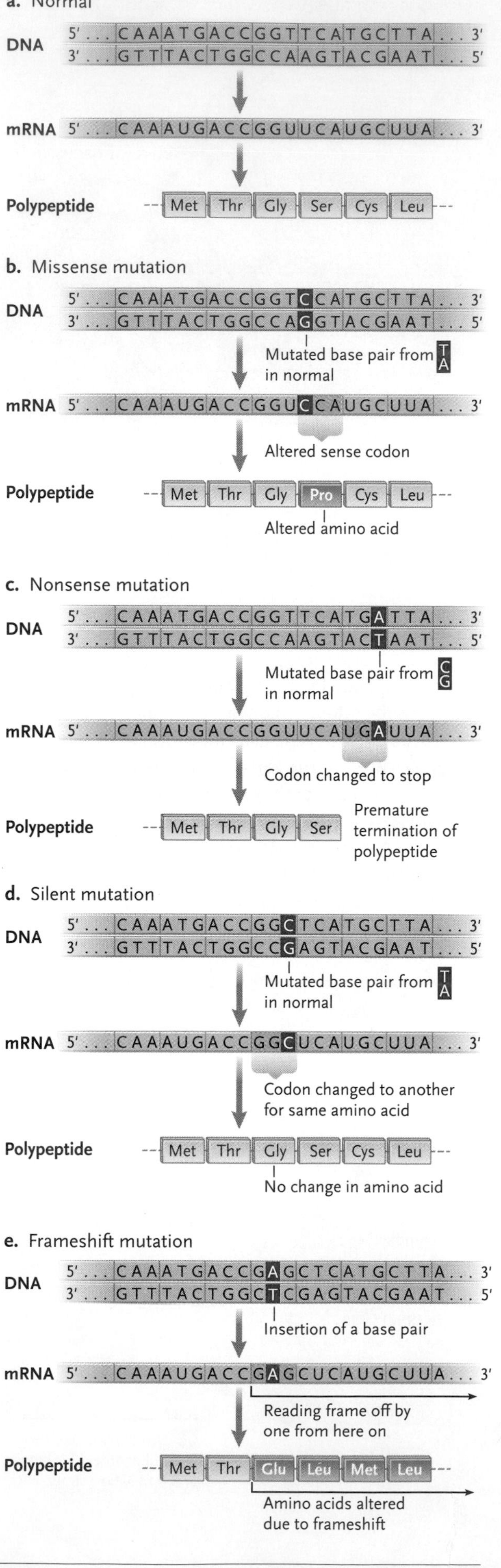

Figure 14.20
Effects of mutations in protein-coding genes on the amino acid sequence of the encoded polypeptide.

peptides provides further evidence that the sorting mechanism evolved early in the cells.

14.4i Base-Pair Mutations Can Affect Protein Structure and Function

Mutations are changes in the sequence of bases in the genetic material. How will mutations affect protein structure and function? It is hoped that your understanding of this chapter will lead you to respond, "It depends." For instance, let's consider several different mutations in the protein-coding region of a gene as shown in **Figure 14.20. Base-pair substitution mutations** involve a change of one particular base to another in the genetic material. This will change a base in a codon.

The normal (unmutated) DNA and amino acid sequences are shown in Figure 14.20a. If a mutation alters the codon to specify a different amino acid, then the resulting protein will have a different amino acid sequence. We call this a **missense mutation** because although an amino acid is placed in the polypeptide, it is the wrong one (see Figure 14.20b). Whether the polypeptide's function is altered significantly or not depends on which amino acid is changed and what it is changed to. A missense mutation in the gene for one of the two hemoglobin polypeptides **(Figure 14.21)** results in the genetic disease sickle cell anemia, described in Chapter 11.

A second type of base-pair substitution mutation is a **nonsense mutation** (see Figure 14.20c). In this case, the mutation changes a sense (amino acid–coding) codon to a nonsense (termination) codon in the mRNA. Translation of an mRNA containing a nonsense mutation results in a premature "stop" and a shorter-than-normal polypeptide. This polypeptide will likely be partially functional at best.

Because of the degeneracy of the genetic code, some base-pair substitution mutations do not alter the amino acid specified by the gene because the changed codon specifies the same amino acid as in the normal polypeptide. Such mutations are known as **silent mutations** (see Figure 14.20d).

If a single base pair is deleted or inserted in the coding region of a gene, the reading frame of the resulting mRNA is altered. That is, after that point, the ribosome reads codons that are not the same as for the normal mRNA, typically producing a completely different amino acid sequence in the polypeptide from then on. This type of mutation is called a **frameshift mutation** (see Figure 14.20e; insertion mutation shown); the resulting polypeptide is usually nonfunctional because of the significantly altered amino acid sequence.

Both transcription and translation are steps in the process of gene expression, the realization of the gene's coded information in the makeup and activities of a cell. However, we will see in the next chapter that the flow of information is not one way; organisms and cells also exert control over how their genes are expressed.

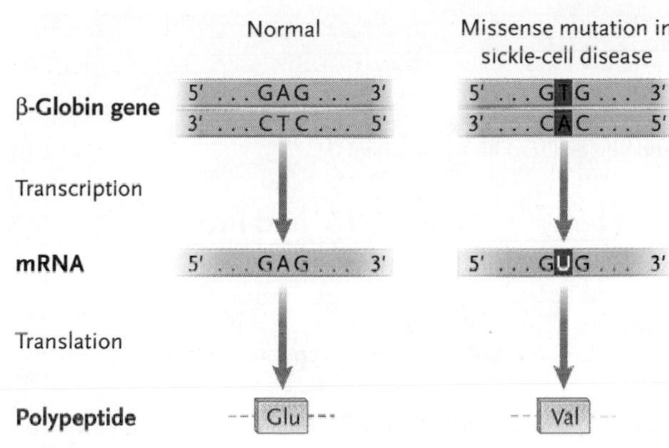

Figure 14.21
Missense mutation in a gene for one of the two polypeptides of hemoglobin that is the cause of sickle cell anemia.

Study Break

1. How does translation initiation occur in eukaryotes versus prokaryotes?
2. Distinguish between the E, P, and A sites of the ribosome.
3. How are proteins directed to different parts of a eukaryotic cell?

Unanswered Questions

The universality of the genetic code and the machinery that expresses it is a strikingly common feature of modern life. The same basic mechanism of transcription and translation is used by literally every cell on the planet to express its protein-coding genes. In spite of great progress in working out the specific functions of the multitude of components of the machinery, science is left with some big questions: Why is there only one system? How did it get started? What is the evolutionary origin and history of introns?

Review

Go to CENGAGENOW™ at http://hed.nelson.com/ to access quizzing, animations, exercises, articles, and personalized homework help.

14.1 The Connection between DNA, RNA, and Protein

- In their genetic experiments with *Neurospora crassa,* Beadle and Tatum found a direct correspondence between gene mutations and alterations of enzymes. Their one gene–one enzyme hypothesis is now restated as the one gene–one polypeptide hypothesis (Figure 14.2).
- The pathway from genes to proteins involves transcription then translation. In transcription, a sequence of nucleotides in DNA is copied into a complementary sequence in an RNA molecule. In translation, the sequence of nucleotides in an mRNA molecule specifies an amino acid sequence in a polypeptide (Figure 14.3).
- The genetic code is a triplet code. AUG at the beginning of a coded message establishes a reading frame for reading the codons three nucleotides at a time. The code is redundant: most of the amino acids are specified by more than one codon (Figures 14.4 and 14.5).
- The genetic code is essentially universal.
- Aside from genes that code for protein through translation of mRNA, other genes code directly for RNA products, such as tRNA, rRNA and snRNA, that are not translated.

14.2 Transcription: DNA-Directed RNA Synthesis

- Transcription is the process by which information coded in DNA is transferred to a complementary RNA copy (Figure 14.6).
- Transcription begins when an RNA polymerase binds to a promoter sequence in the DNA and starts synthesizing an RNA molecule. The enzyme then adds RNA nucleotides in sequence according to the DNA template. At the end of the transcribed sequence, the enzyme and the completed RNA transcript release from the DNA template. The mechanism of termination is different in eukaryotes and prokaryotes (Figure 14.7).
- In addition to sequences coding for amino acids, the DNA of protein-coding genes also contains several types of sequences that regulate transcription and translation.

14.3 Processing of mRNAs in Eukaryotes

- A gene encoding an mRNA molecule includes the promoter, which is recognized by the regulatory proteins and transcription factors that promote DNA unwinding and the initiation of transcription by an RNA polymerase. Transcription in eukaryotes produces a pre-mRNA molecule that consists of a 5′ cap, the 5′ untranslated region, interspersed exons (amino acid-coding segments) and introns, the 3′ untranslated region, and the 3′ poly(A) tail. All are copied from DNA except the 5′ cap and poly(A) tail, which are added during transcription (Figure 14.8).
- Introns in pre-mRNAs are removed to produce functional mRNAs by splicing. snRNPs bind to the introns, loop them out of the pre-mRNA, clip the intron at each exon boundary, and join the adjacent exons together (Figure 14.9).
- Many pre-mRNAs are subjected to alternative splicing, a process that joins exons in different combinations to produce different mRNAs encoded by the same gene. Translation of each mRNA produced in this way generates a protein with different function (Figure 14.10).

14.4 Translation: mRNA-Directed Polypeptide Synthesis

- Translation is the assembly of amino acids into polypeptides. Translation occurs on ribosomes. The P, A, and E sites of the ribosome are used for the stepwise addition of amino acids to the polypeptide as directed by the mRNA (Figures 14.11 and 14.14).
- Amino acids are brought to the ribosome attached to specific tRNAs. Amino acids are linked to their corresponding tRNAs by aminoacyl-tRNA synthetases. By matching amino acids with tRNAs, the reactions also provide the ultimate basis for the accuracy of translation (Figures 14.12 and 14.13).
- Translation proceeds through the stages of initiation, elongation, and termination. In initiation, a ribosome assembles with an mRNA molecule and an initiator methionine-tRNA. In elongation, amino acids linked to tRNAs add one at a time to the growing polypeptide chain. In termination, the new polypeptide is released from the ribosome and the ribosomal subunits separate from the mRNA (Figures 14.15–14.17).
- After they are synthesized on ribosomes, polypeptides are converted into finished form by processing reactions, which include removal of one or more amino acids from the protein chains, addition of organic groups, and folding guided by chaperones.
- Proteins are distributed in cells by means of signals spelled out by amino acid sequences (Figure 14.20).
- Base-pair substitution mutations alter the mRNA and can lead to changes in the amino acid sequence of the encoded polypeptide. A missense mutation changes one sense codon to one that specifies a different amino acid, a nonsense mutation changes a sense codon to a stop codon, and a silent mutation changes one sense codon to another sense codon that specifies the same amino acid. A base-pair insertion or deletion is a frameshift mutation that alters the reading frame beyond the point of the mutation, leading to a different amino acid sequence from then on in the polypeptide (Figures 14.21 and 14.22).

Questions

Self-Test Questions

1. Which statement about the following pathway is false?

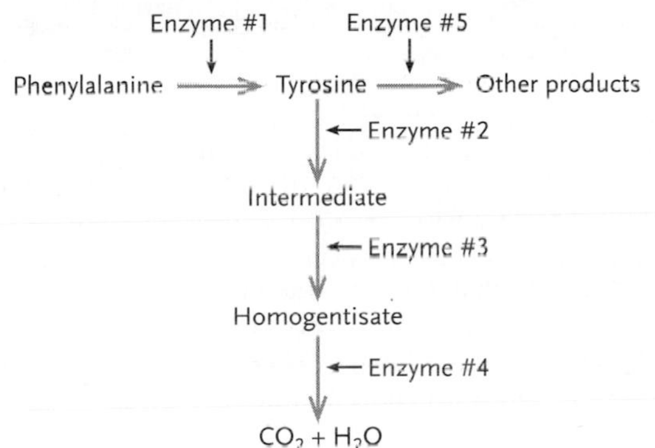

   a. A mutation for enzyme #1 causes phenylalanine to build up.
   b. A mutation for enzyme #2 prevents tyrosine from being synthesized.
   c. A mutation at enzyme #3 prevents homogentistate from being synthesized.
   d. A mutation for enzyme #2 could hide a mutation in enzyme #4.
   e. Each step in a pathway such as this is catalyzed by an enzyme, which is coded by a gene.

2. Eukaryotic mRNA:
   a. uses snRNPs to cut out introns and seal together translatable exons.
   b. uses a spliceosome mechanism made of DNA to recognize consensus regions to cut and splice.
   c. has a guanine cap on its 3′ end and a poly(A) tail on its 5′ end.
   d. is composed of adenine, thymine, guanine, and cytosine.
   e. codes the guanine cap and poly(A) tail from the DNA template.

3. A segment strand of DNA has a base sequence of 5′-GCATTAGAC-3′. What would be the sequence of an RNA molecule complementary to that sequence?
   a. 5′-GUCTAATGC-3′
   b. 5′-GCAUUAGAC-3′
   c. 5′-CGTAATCTG-3′
   d. 5′-GUCUAAUGC-3′
   e. 5′-CGUAAUCUG-3′

4. Which of the following statements about the initiation phase of translation is false?
   a. An initiation factor allows 5′ mRNA to attach to the small ribosomal subunit.
   b. Initiation factors complex with GTP to help Met-tRNA and AUG pair.
   c. mRNA attaches first to the small ribosomal subunit.
   d. GTP is synthesized.
   e. 3′-UAC-5′ on the tRNA binds 5′-AUG-3′ on mRNA.

5. Which of the following types of bonding DOES NOT involve complementary base pairing?
   a. codon to anticodon
   b. signal peptide to signal recognition particle
   c. RNA to RNA in hairpin transcription terminator
   d. DNA to RNA in transcription of snRNA gene
   e. rRNA to mRNA in prokaryotic translation initiation

6. Translation is in progress, with methionine bound to a tRNA in the P site, and a phenylalanine bound to a tRNA in the A site. The order of the next steps in the elongation cycle is:
   a. the ribosome translocates → a new aminoacyl-tRNA enters the A site → peptidyl transferase catalyzes a peptide bond between the two amino acids → empty tRNA is released from the ribosome.
   b. peptidyl transferase catalyzes a peptide bond between the two amino acids → a new aminoacyl tRNA enters the A site → empty tRNA is released from the ribosome → the ribosome translocates.
   c. peptidyl transferase catalyzes a peptide bond between the two amino acids → empty tRNA is released from the ribosome → a new aminoacyl-tRNA enters the A site → the ribosome translocates.
   d. peptidyl transferase catalyzes a peptide bond between the two amino acids → the ribosome translocates → empty tRNA is released from the ribosome → a new aminoacyl-tRNA enters the A site.
   e. the ribosome translocates → peptidyl transferase catalyzes a peptide bond between the two amino acids → empty tRNA is released from the ribosome → a new aminoacyl-tRNA enters the A site.

7. Which of the following statements is false?
   a. GTP is an energy source during various stages of translation.
   b. In the ribosome, peptidyl transferase catalyses peptide bond formation between amino acids.
   c. When the mRNA code UAA reaches the ribosome, there is no tRNA to bind to it.
   d. A long polypeptide is cut off the tRNA in the A site so its Met amino acid links to the amino acid in the P site.
   e. Forty-two amino acids of a protein are encoded by 126 nucleotides of the mRNA.

8. Which item binds to SRP receptor and to the signal sequence to guide a newly synthesized protein to be secreted to its proper "channel"?
   a. ribosome
   b. signal recognition particle
   c. endoplasmic reticulum
   d. signal peptidase
   e. receptor protein

9. A part of an mRNA molecule with the sequence 5′-UGC GCA-3′ is being translated by a ribosome. The following activated tRNA molecules are available. Two of them can correctly bind the mRNA so that a dipeptide can form.

tRNA Anticodon	Amino Acid
3′-GGC-5′	Proline
3′-CGU-5′	Alanine
3′-UGC-5′	Threonine
3′-CCG-5′	Glycine
3′-ACG-5′	Cysteine
3′-CGG-5′	Alanine

   a. cysteine-alanine
   b. proline-cysteine
   c. glycine-cysteine
   d. alanine-alanine
   e. threonine-glycine

10. A missense mutation cannot be:
    a. the code for the sickle-cell gene.
    b. caused by a frameshift.
    c. the deletion of a base in a coding sequence.
    d. the addition of two bases in a coding sequence.
    e. the same as a silent mutation.

Questions for Discussion

1. Would you expect rRNA genes to have "start" codons? Why, or why not?
2. A mutation appears that alters an anticodon in a tRNA from AAU to AUU. What effect will this change have on protein synthesis in cells carrying this mutation?
3. The normal form of a gene contains the nucleotide sequence:

   5′- ATGCCCGCCTTTGCTACTTGGTAG - 3′
   3′- TACGGGCGGAAACGATGAACCATC - 5′

   When this gene is transcribed, the result is the following mRNA molecule:

   5′- AUGCCCGCCUUUGCUACUUGGUAG - 3′

   In a mutated form of the gene, two extra base pairs (underlined) are inserted:

   5′- ATGCCCGCCTAATTGCTACTTGGTAG - 3′
   3′- TACGGGCGGATTAACGATGAACCATC - 5′

   What effect will this particular mutation have on the structure of the protein encoded in the gene?
4. A geneticist is attempting to isolate mutations in the genes for four enzymes acting in a metabolic pathway in the bacterium *Escherichia coli*. The end product *E* of the pathway is absolutely essential for life:

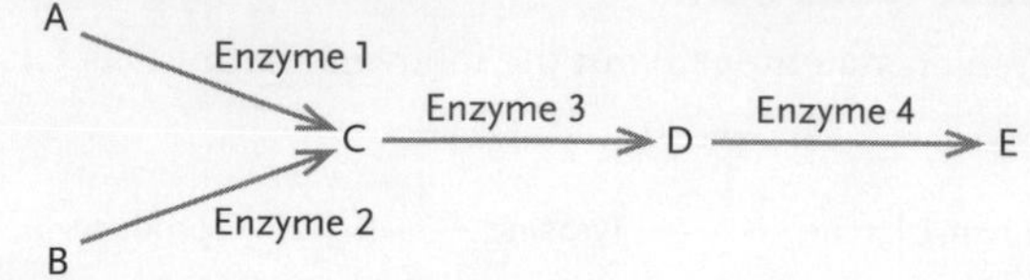

   The geneticist has been able to isolate mutations in the genes for enzymes 1 and 2, but not for enzymes 3 and 4. Develop a hypothesis to explain why.
5. How could you show experimentally that the genetic code is universal; namely, that it is the same in bacteria as it is in eukaryotes such as fungi, plants, and animals?

   How might the process of alternative splicing and exon shuffling affect the rate at which new proteins evolve?

Chromatin remodelling proteins (gold) binding to chromatin (blue). Chromatin remodelling, a change in chromosome structure in the region of a gene, is a key step in the activation of genes in eukaryotes.

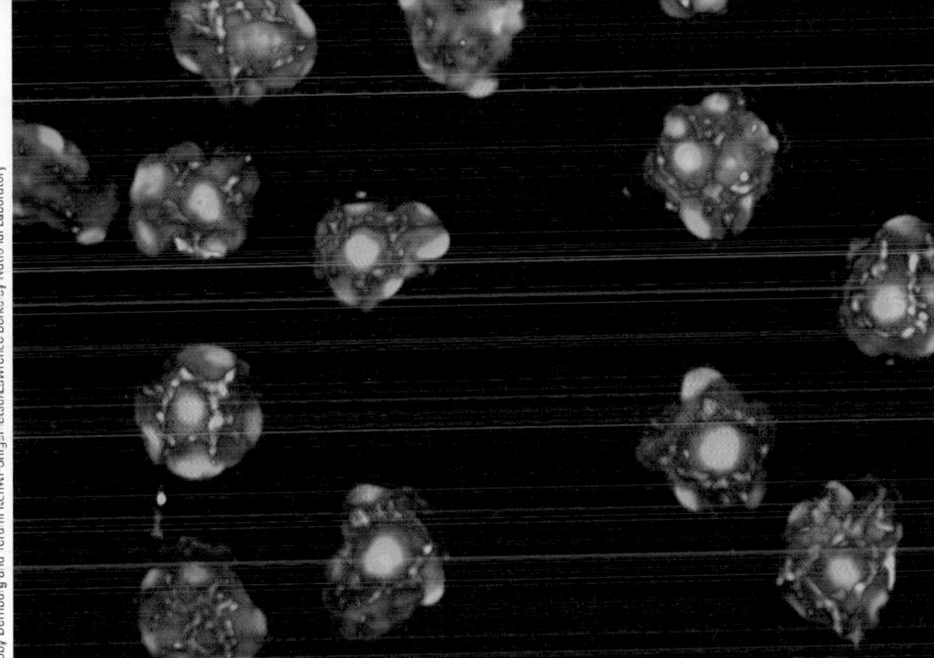

Abby Dernburg and Terumi Kohwi-Shigematsu/Lawrence Berkeley National Laboratory

Study Plan

15 Control of Gene Expression

Why It Matters

A human egg cell is almost completely inactive metabolically when it is released from the ovary. It remains quiescent as it begins its travel down a fallopian tube leading from the ovary to the uterus, carried along by movements of cilia lining the walls of the tube **(Figure 15.1, p. 322)**. It is here, in the fallopian tube, that egg and sperm cells meet and embryonic development begins. Within seconds after the cells unite, the fertilized egg breaks its quiescent state and begins a series of divisions that continues as the egg moves through the fallopian tube and enters the uterus. Subsequent divisions produce specialized cells that *differentiate* into the distinct types tailored for specific functions in the body, such as muscle cells and cells of the nervous system.

At first glance, you might think it most efficient for each differentiated cell type to retain only those genes needed to carry out its specific function; that is, liver cells might be expected to have a different collection of genes than bone cells. However, biochemical and cytogenetic analyses do not support this model and have, in fact, demonstrated that all nucleated cells of a developing embryo retain essentially the same set of genes that was created in the original single-celled zygote resulting from fertilization. Structural and functional differences in cell types

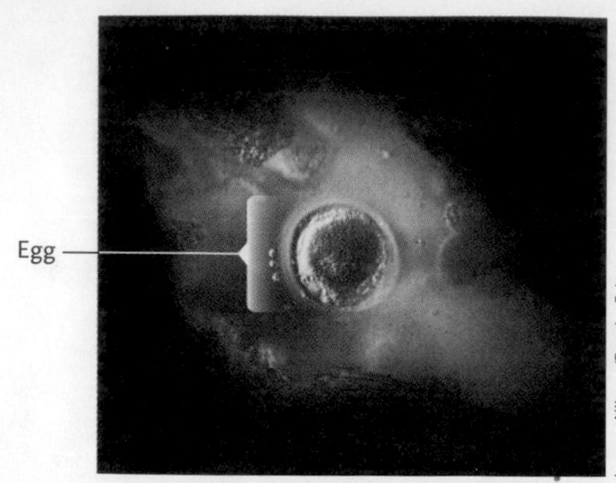

Figure 15.1 **A human egg released from the ovary.** The outer layer appearing light blue is a coat of polysaccharides and glycoproteins that surrounds the egg. Within the egg, genes and regulatory proteins are poised to enter the pathways initiating embryonic development.

result from the presence or absence of *the products resulting from expression of genes* rather than the actual genes themselves. The products of some genes, known as housekeeping genes, are expressed in nearly all cells, whereas the products of other genes may be found only in certain cell types under particular environmental conditions. For example, all cells contain genes coding for the enzymes needed for basic cellular metabolism (that is, the Krebs cycle), as well as genes coding for various hemoglobin polypeptides. While Krebs cycle gene products are found in all cells, particular hemoglobins are found only in those cells that give rise to red blood cells in the fetus, newborn, or adult.

What determines whether a gene product will be produced or not? The overall expression of a gene is subject to a number of fundamental mechanisms that provide fine-detail control over when, where, and how much a gene product is produced. The material in the previous chapter on transcription and translation hinted at these mechanisms. Usually, when we say that a gene is "turned on," we mean that it is being transcribed actively. Beyond transcription, the expression of gene products is subject to further controls affecting the processing of ribonucleic acid (RNA), possible translation into protein, and the activity and "life span" of the product itself. You saw in the previous chapter that transcription and translation are coincident in prokaryotes. This enables a rapid response to environmental conditions through regulation of transcription initiation. Eukaryotes, particularly multicellular organisms, exhibit both short-term response and long-term differentiation through a variety of mechanisms not used by prokaryotes.

In this chapter, we examine the mechanisms of transcriptional regulation and its fine-tuning by additional controls at the posttranscriptional, translational, and posttranslational levels. Our discussion begins with bacterial systems, where researchers first discovered a mechanism for transcriptional regulation, and then moves to eukaryotic systems, where the regulation of gene activity is more complicated. How genes regulate development is discussed in Chapters 30 and 39.

15.1 Regulation of Gene Expression in Prokaryotes

Transcription and translation are closely regulated in prokaryotes in ways that reflect prokaryotic life histories. Prokaryotes are relatively simple, single-celled organisms with generation times measured in minutes. Rather than the complex patterns of long-term cell differentiation and development typical of multicellular eukaryotes, prokaryotic cells typically undergo rapid and reversible alterations in biochemical pathways that allow them to adapt quickly to changes in their environment.

The bacterium *Escherichia coli,* for example, can find itself in the intestinal tract of a cow one minute and then in a treated municipal water supply soon after. Sugars such as lactose might be more available in the water environment, and genes coding for enzymes needed to metabolize this energy source need to be "turned on." Other nutrients, such as the amino acid tryptophan, may also be available in the water. Therefore, genes coding for enzymes needed to manufacture the amino acid "from scratch" need to be "turned off." The versatile and responsive control system allows the bacterium to make the most efficient use of the particular array of nutrients available at any given time.

15.1a The Operon Is a Unit of Transcription

When the environment in which a bacterium lives changes, some metabolic processes are stopped and others are started. Typically, this involves turning off the genes for the metabolic processes not needed and turning on the genes for the new metabolic processes. For each metabolic process, a few to many genes are involved, and the regulation of those genes must be coordinated. For example, three genes encode proteins for the metabolism of lactose by *E. coli.* In the absence of lactose, the three genes are not expressed, whereas in the presence of lactose, the genes are expressed. That is, the control of these genes is at the transcription level.

In 1961, François Jacob and Jacques Monod of the Pasteur Institute in Paris proposed the *operon model* for the control of the expression of genes for lactose metabolism in *E. coli*. Subsequently, data have shown the *operon model* to be widely applicable to the regulation of gene expression in bacteria and their viruses. Jacob and Monod received the Nobel Prize in 1965 for their explanation of bacterial operons and their regulation by repressors.

An **operon** is a cluster of prokaryotic genes and the DNA sequences involved in their regulation. The promoter, as we saw in the previous chapter, is a region where the RNA polymerase begins transcription. Each operon, which can contain several to many genes, is transcribed as a unit from the promoter into a single messenger RNA (mRNA), and as a result, the mRNA contains codes for several proteins. The cluster of genes transcribed into a single mRNA is called a **transcription unit.** A ribosome translates the mRNA from one end to the other, sequentially making each protein encoded in the mRNA. Typically, the proteins encoded by an operon catalyze steps in the same function, such as enzymes acting in sequence in a biochemical pathway.

The other regulatory DNA sequence in the operon is the **operator,** a short segment to which a regulatory protein binds. The regulatory protein is encoded by a gene separate from the operon that the protein controls. Some operons are controlled by a regulatory protein termed a **repressor,** which, when active, prevents the genes of the operon from being expressed. Other operons are controlled by a regulatory protein termed an *activator,* which, when active, stimulates the expression of genes.

Many operons are controlled by more than one regulatory mechanism, and a number of the repressors or activators control more than one operon. The result is a complex network of superimposed controls that provides regulation of transcription, allowing almost instantaneous responses to changing environmental conditions.

15.1b The *lac* Operon for Lactose Metabolism Is Transcribed When an Inducer Inactivates a Repressor

Jacob and Monod researched the genetic control of lactose metabolism in *E. coli.* Lactose is a sugar that, when metabolized, provides energy for the cell. Jacob and Monod used genetic and biochemical approaches to study the genetic control of lactose metabolism in *E. coli.* Their genetic studies showed that for lactose metabolism, three genes are involved: *lacZ, lacY,* and *lacA* **(Figure 15.2).** These three genes are adjacent to one another on the chromosome in the order *Z-Y-A.* The genes are transcribed as a unit into a single mRNA starting with the *lacZ* gene; the promoter for the transcription unit is upstream of *lacZ.* The *lacZ* gene encodes the enzyme β-galactosidase, which catalyzes the conversion of the disaccharide sugar, lactose, into the monosaccharide sugars, glucose and galactose. These sugars are then metabolized by other enzymes, producing energy for the cell. The *lacY* gene encodes a permease enzyme that transports lactose actively into the cell, and the *lacA* gene encodes a transacetylase enzyme, the function of which is unknown.

Jacob and Monod called the cluster of genes and adjacent sequences that control their expression the *lac operon* (see Figure 15.2). They coined the name *operon* from a key DNA sequence they discovered for regulating transcription of the operon—the **operator.** The operator was named because it controls the operation of the genes adjacent to it. For the *lac* operon, the operator is a short DNA sequence between the promoter and the *lacZ* gene.

These two investigators showed that the *lac* operon was controlled by a regulatory protein that they termed the *Lac repressor.* The Lac repressor is encoded by the regulatory gene *lacI,* which is nearby but separate from the *lac* operon (see Figure 15.2), and is synthesized in active form. When lactose is absent from the medium, active Lac repressor binds to the operator, thereby blocking the RNA polymerase from binding to the promoter; as a result, transcription cannot occur **(Figure 15.3a, p. 324).** Actually, the repressor occasionally falls off, allowing transcription to occur—but at a very slow rate, leading to just a few molecules of each encoded enzyme in the cell.

When lactose is added to the medium, the *lac* operon is turned on and all three enzymes are synthesized rapidly **(Figure 15.3b, p. 324).** How does this occur? Lactose enters the cell and the β-galactosidase molecules already present convert some of it to *allolactose,* an isomer of lactose. Allolactose is an **inducer** for the *lac* operon—the isomer turns on the three genes in the operon. Allolactose does this by binding to the Lac repressor, inactivating it by altering its shape so that it can no longer bind to the operator. With the repressor out of the way, RNA polymerase is then able to bind to the promoter, and it transcribes the three genes. The *lac* operon is called an **inducible operon** because an inducer molecule increases its expression.

When the lactose is used up, the regulatory system again switches the *lac* operon off. That is, the absence of lactose means that there are no allolactose inducer molecules to inactivate the repressor; the again-active repressor binds to the operator, blocking transcription of the

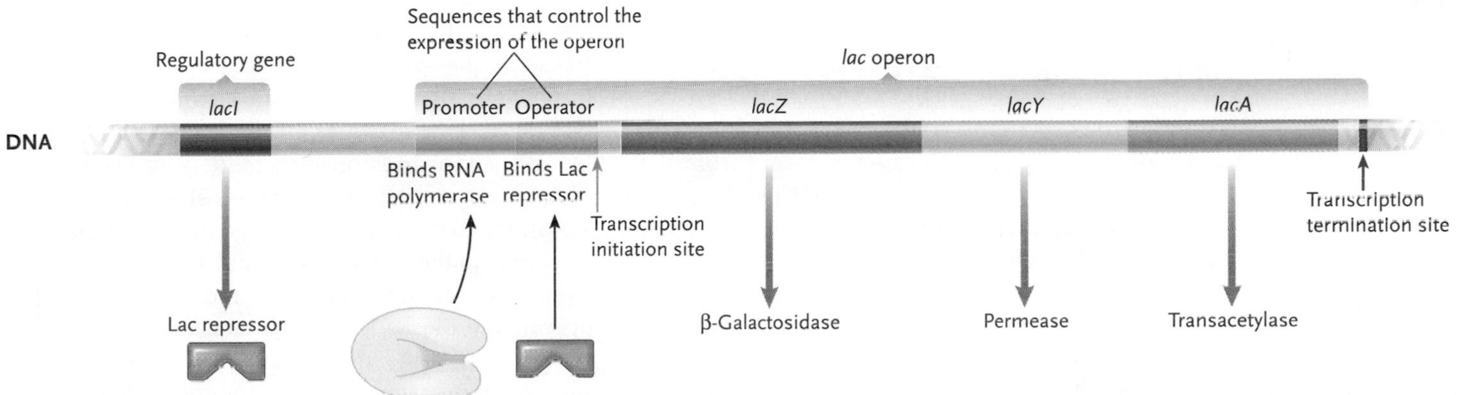

Figure 15.2
The *E. coli lac* operon. The *lacZ, lacY,* and *lacA* genes encode the enzymes taking part in lactose metabolism. The separate regulatory gene, *lacI,* encodes the Lac repressor, which plays a pivotal role in the control of the operon. The promoter binds RNA polymerase, and the operator binds activated Lac repressor. The transcription unit, which extends from the transcription initiation site to the transcription termination site, contains the genes.

a. Lactose absent from medium

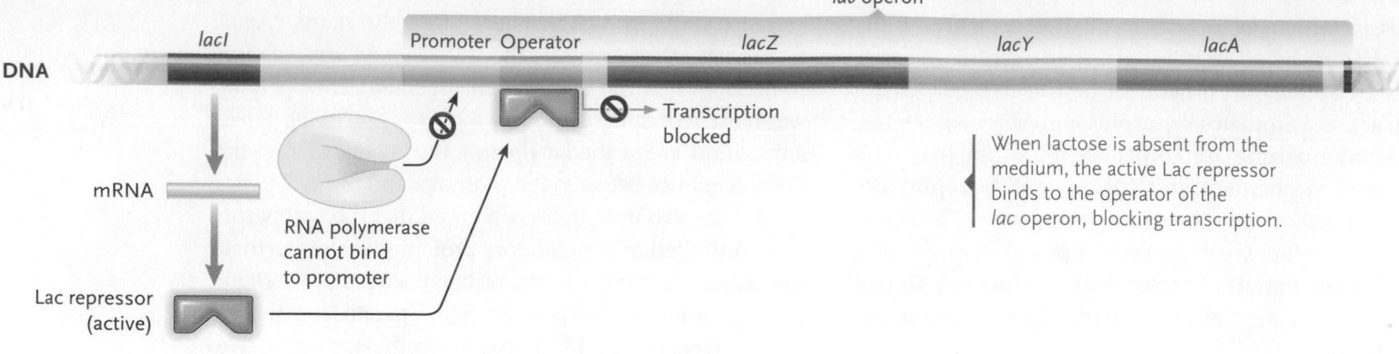

lac operon
lacI
Promoter
Operator
lacZ
lacY
lacA
DNA
mRNA
Transcription blocked
RNA polymerase cannot bind to promoter
Lac repressor (active)
When lactose is absent from the medium, the active Lac repressor binds to the operator of the lac operon, blocking transcription.

b. Lactose present in medium

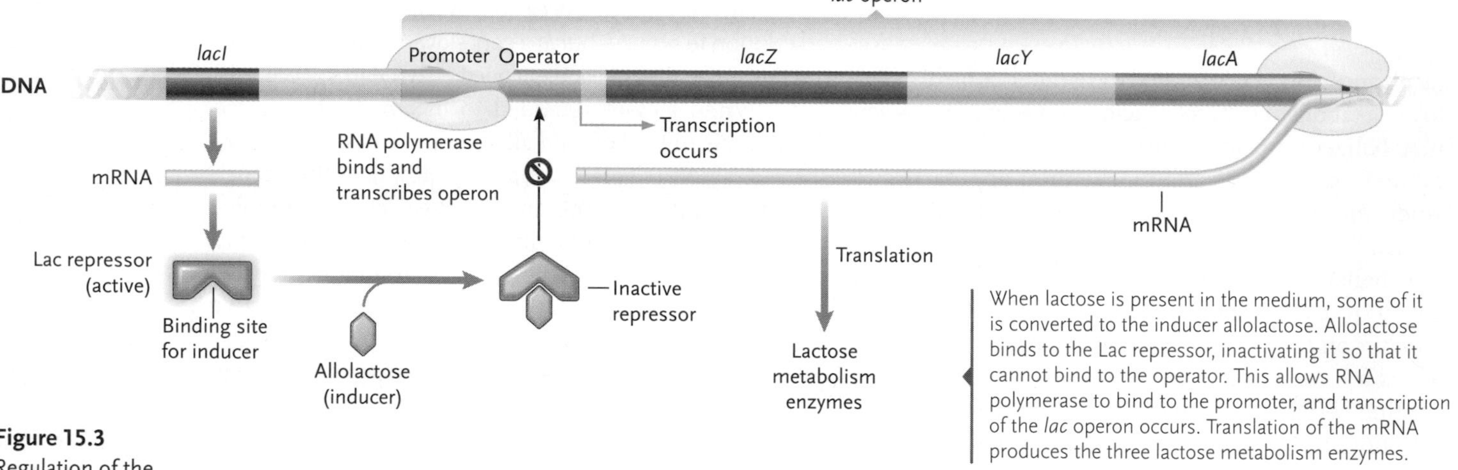

lac operon
lacI
Promoter
Operator
lacZ
lacY
lacA
DNA
mRNA
RNA polymerase binds and transcribes operon
Transcription occurs
mRNA
Translation
Lac repressor (active)
Binding site for inducer
Allolactose (inducer)
Inactive repressor
Lactose metabolism enzymes
When lactose is present in the medium, some of it is converted to the inducer allolactose. Allolactose binds to the Lac repressor, inactivating it so that it cannot bind to the operator. This allows RNA polymerase to bind to the promoter, and transcription of the lac operon occurs. Translation of the mRNA produces the three lactose metabolism enzymes.

Figure 15.3
Regulation of the inducible *lac* operon by the Lac repressor in the absence **(a)** and presence **(b)** of lactose.

operon. The controls are aided by the fact that bacterial mRNAs are very short-lived, about three minutes on average. This quick turnover permits the cytoplasm to be cleared quickly of the mRNAs transcribed from an operon. The enzymes themselves also have short lifetimes and are quickly degraded.

15.1c Transcription of the *trp* Operon Genes for Tryptophan Biosynthesis Is Repressed When Tryptophan Activates a Repressor

Tryptophan is an amino acid that is used in the synthesis of proteins. If tryptophan is absent from the medium, *E. coli* must make it so that proteins can be synthesized. If tryptophan is present in the medium, then the cell will use that source rather than make its own.

Tryptophan biosynthesis also involves an operon, the *trp* operon **(Figure 15.4)**. The five genes in this operon, *trpA–trpE*, encode the enzymes for the steps in the tryptophan biosynthesis pathway. Upstream of the *trpE* gene are the operon's promoter and operator sequences. Expression of the *trp* operon is controlled by the Trp repressor, a regulatory protein encoded by the *trpR* gene, which is located elsewhere in the genome (not nearby, as was the case for the repressor gene for the *lac* operon). In contrast to the Lac repressor, the Trp repressor is synthesized in an inactive form in which it cannot bind to the operator.

When tryptophan is absent from the medium and must be made by the cell, the *trp* operon genes are expressed (see **Figure 15.4a**). This is the default state: since the Trp repressor is inactive and cannot bind to the operator, RNA polymerase can bind to the promoter and transcribe the operon. The resulting mRNA is translated to produce the five tryptophan biosynthetic enzymes that catalyze the reactions for tryptophan synthesis.

If tryptophan is present, there is no need for the cell to make it, so the *trp* operon is shut off (see **Figure 15.4b**). This occurs because the tryptophan entering the cell binds to the Trp repressor and activates it. The active Trp repressor then binds to the operator of the *trp* operon and blocks RNA polymerase from binding to the promoter—the operon cannot be transcribed.

For the *trp* operon, then, the presence of tryptophan represses the expression of the tryptophan biosynthesis genes; hence, this operon is an example of a **repressible operon.** Here, tryptophan acts as a **corepressor**, a regulatory molecule that combines with a repressor to activate it and thus shut off the operon.

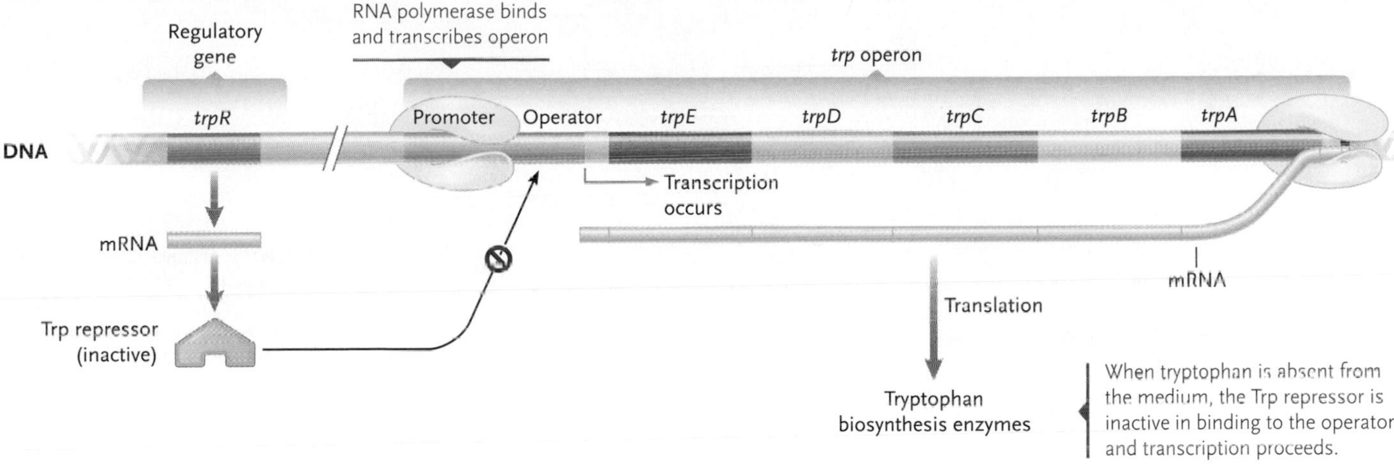
a. Tryptophan absent from medium
Regulatory gene
RNA polymerase binds and transcribes operon
trp operon
trpR
Promoter
Operator
trpE
trpD
trpC
trpB
trpA
DNA
Transcription occurs
mRNA
Trp repressor (inactive)
mRNA
Translation
Tryptophan biosynthesis enzymes
When tryptophan is absent from the medium, the Trp repressor is inactive in binding to the operator and transcription proceeds.

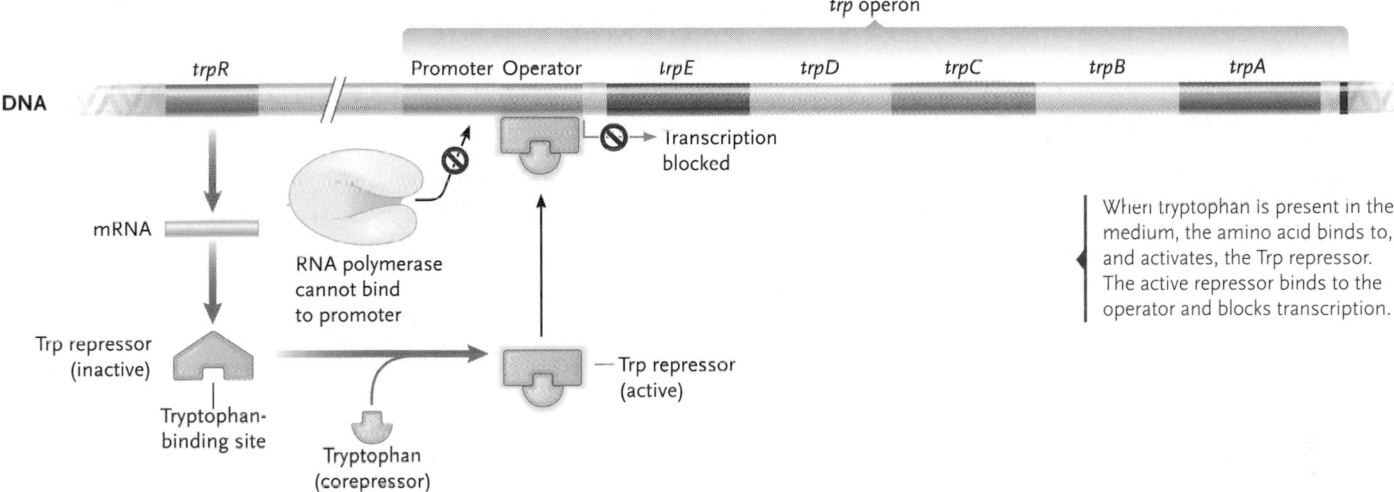
b. Tryptophan present in medium
trp operon
trpR
Promoter Operator
trpE
trpD
trpC
trpB
trpA
DNA
Transcription blocked
mRNA
RNA polymerase cannot bind to promoter
When tryptophan is present in the medium, the amino acid binds to, and activates, the Trp repressor. The active repressor binds to the operator and blocks transcription.
Trp repressor (inactive)
Trp repressor (active)
Tryptophan-binding site
Tryptophan (corepressor)

Figure 15.4 Regulation of the repressible *trp* operon by the Trp repressor in the absence **(a)** and presence **(b)** of tryptophan.

To compare and contrast the two operons we have discussed: (1) In the *lac* operon, the repressor is synthesized in an active form. When the inducer (allolactose) is present, it binds to the repressor and inactivates it. The operon is then transcribed. (2) In the *trp* operon, the repressor is synthesized in an inactive form. When the corepressor (tryptophan) is present, it binds to the repressor and activates it. The active repressor blocks transcription of the operon.

Inducible and repressible operons illustrate two types of *negative gene regulation* because both are regulated by a repressor that turns off gene expression when it is in active form. Genes are expressed only when the repressor is in inactive form.

15.1d Transcription of the *lac* Operon Is Also Controlled by a Positive Regulatory System

Several years after Jacob and Monod proposed their operon model for the lactose metabolism genes, researchers found a *positive gene regulation* system that also regulates the *lac* operon. This system ensures that the *lac* operon is transcribed if lactose is provided as an energy source, but not if glucose is present in addition to lactose. This is because glucose is a more efficient source of energy than is lactose. Glucose can be used directly in the glycolysis pathway to produce energy for the cell (see Chapter 6). Lactose, on the other hand, must first be converted into glucose and galactose, and the galactose then converted into glucose. These conversions require energy. Thus, the cell gains more by metabolizing glucose than lactose, or for that matter any other sugar.

Figure 15.5a (p. 326) shows the positive gene regulation system working when lactose is present and glucose is absent in the growth medium. In essence, this adds to the model shown earlier in Figure 15.3b. Lactose is metabolized to the inducer, allolactose, which binds to and inactivates the Lac repressor. RNA polymerase is then recruited to the promoter by active *CAP (catabolite activator protein)* at the *CAP site*, a DNA sequence immediately upstream of the promoter. CAP is an **activator**, a regulatory protein that stimulates gene

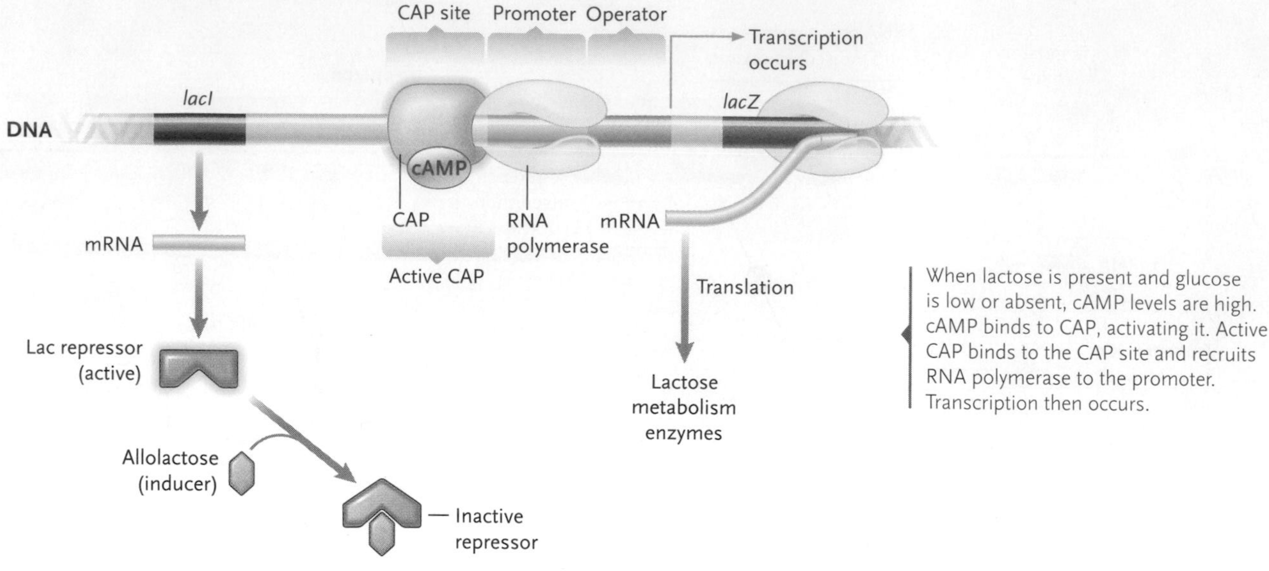
a. Lactose present; glucose low or absent
CAP site
Promoter
Operator
Transcription occurs
lacI
lacZ
DNA
cAMP
CAP
RNA polymerase
mRNA
mRNA
Active CAP
Translation
Lac repressor (active)
Lactose metabolism enzymes
Allolactose (inducer)
Inactive repressor
When lactose is present and glucose is low or absent, cAMP levels are high. cAMP binds to CAP, activating it. Active CAP binds to the CAP site and recruits RNA polymerase to the promoter. Transcription then occurs.

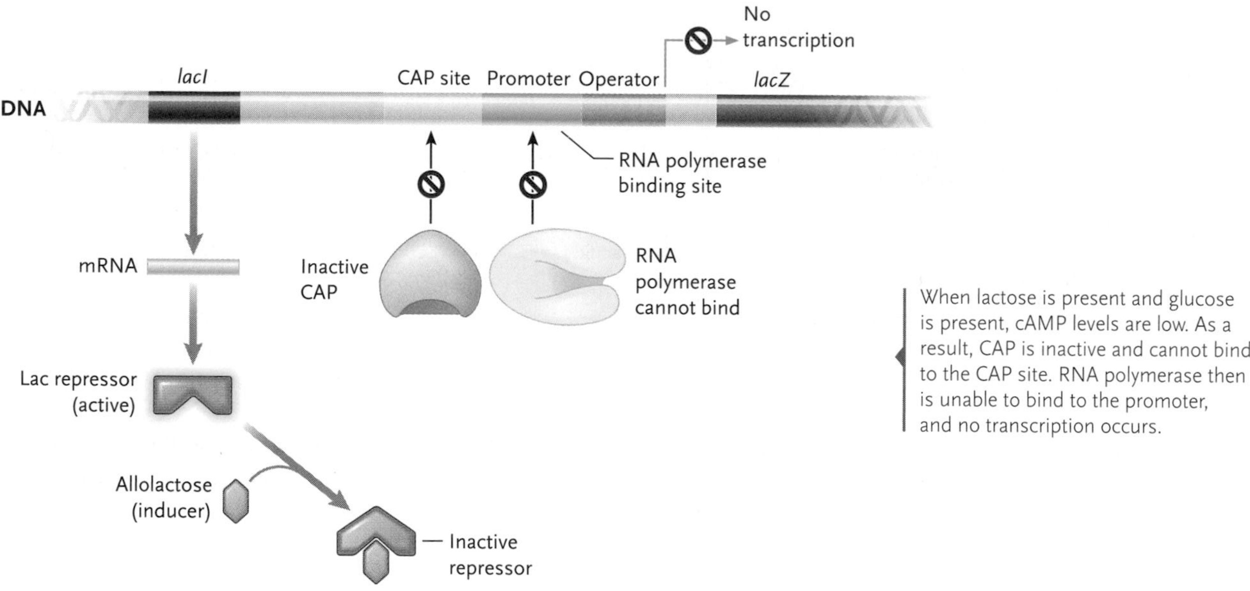
b. Lactose present; glucose present
No transcription
lacI
CAP site
Promoter
Operator
lacZ
DNA
RNA polymerase binding site
mRNA
Inactive CAP
RNA polymerase cannot bind
Lac repressor (active)
Allolactose (inducer)
Inactive repressor
When lactose is present and glucose is present, cAMP levels are low. As a result, CAP is inactive and cannot bind to the CAP site. RNA polymerase then is unable to bind to the promoter, and no transcription occurs.

Figure 15.5 Positive regulation of the *lac* operon by the CAP activator. Other operons involved in the metabolism of various sugars are regulated in the same way.

expression. It is synthesized in *inactive* form and is activated when cyclic adenine monophosphate (cAMP) binds to it (cAMP is a nucleotide that plays a role in regulating cellular processes in both prokaryotes and eukaryotes; see Section 8.4). When glucose is absent from the medium, cAMP is abundant in the cell, so CAP is active under these conditions and can bind to the CAP site.

If both lactose and glucose are present in the medium, the *lac* operon is not transcribed **(Figure 15.5b)**. Metabolism of the incoming glucose triggers a series of events leading to inactivation of adenylyl cyclase, the enzyme that catalyzes the synthesis of cAMP from ATP. The level of cAMP drops drastically, reaching a point where it is too low to activate CAP. Without active CAP bound to the CAP site, RNA polymerase is unable to bind to the promoter, and the operon cannot be transcribed. In short, gene expression cannot be activated under these conditions. When glucose is depleted, the bacteria then shift to metabolizing lactose. Inactivation of adenylyl cyclase is reversed, cAMP levels rise again, and CAP is activated. The events of Figure 15.5a then occur.

The same positive gene regulation system using CAP and cAMP regulates a large number of other operons that control the metabolism of many sugars. In each case, the system functions so that glucose, if it is present in the growth medium, is metabolized first. This type of regulatory system, in which several operons are under the control of a common regulator, is called a regulon.

In sum, regulation of gene expression in prokaryotes occurs primarily at the transcription level. There are

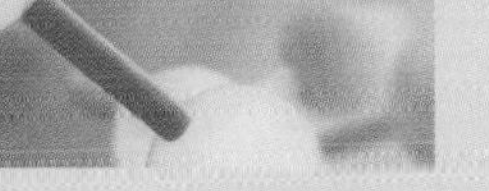

Molecule Behind Biology

AI-2

Bacterial cells can communicate with one another through the production and detection of molecules called autoinducers. When an autoinducer accumulates to high concentration in the local environment, it binds to membrane receptors that initiate a signal cascade, resulting in transcriptional activation of genes. This process, called quorum sensing, provides a mechanism for populations of cells to determine their density and thus coordinate gene expression as a community. For instance, although it is rather futile for an isolated single cell of *Vibrio harveyi* to express genes from its *lux* operon in order to bioluminesce, hundreds of millions of cells, all expressing *lux* genes, collectively produce biologically significant amounts of light. In a way, these populations of cells are behaving like multicellular organisms. Although various autoinducers are known to mediate communication among members of the same species, a novel compound, called AI-2 **(Figure 1)**, has been found to facilitate communication between members of *different* species. AI-2 is unlike any other known autoinducer and is particularly interesting in that it contains an atom of boron, an element whose function in biological systems has been quite mysterious.

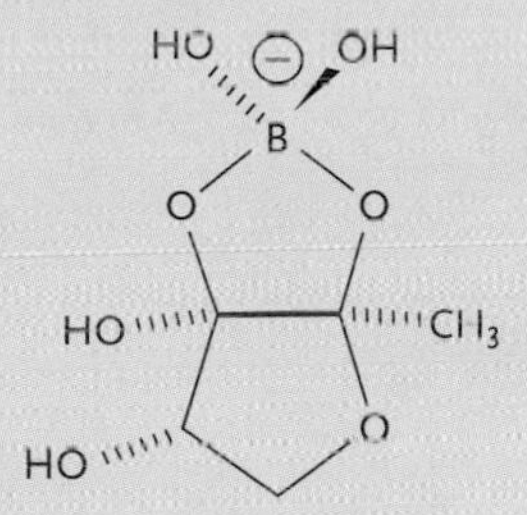

AI-2

Figure 1
AI-2, a universal autoinducer containing boron.

also some examples of regulation at the translation level. For example, some proteins can bind to the mRNAs that produce them and modulate their translation. This serves as a feedback mechanism to fine-tune the amounts of the proteins in the cell. In the remainder of the chapter, we discuss the regulation of gene expression in eukaryotes. You will see that regulation occurs at several points between the gene and the protein and that regulatory mechanisms are more complex than those in prokaryotes.

Study Break

1. Suppose the *lacI* gene is mutated so that the Lac repressor is not made. How does this mutation affect the regulation of the *lac* operon?
2. Answer the equivalent question for the *trp* operon: How would a mutation that prevents the Trp repressor from being made affect the regulation of the *trp* operon?

15.2 Regulation of Transcription in Eukaryotes

As you just learned, gene expression in prokaryotes is commonly regulated at the transcription level with genes organized in functional units called operons. The molecular mechanisms in operon function are a simple means of coordinating synthesis of proteins with related functions. In eukaryotes, the coordinated synthesis of proteins with related functions also occurs, but the genes involved are usually scattered around the genomes; that is, they are not organized into operons. Nonetheless, like operons, individual eukaryotic genes also consist of protein-coding sequences and adjacent regulatory sequences.

There are two general categories of eukaryotic gene regulation. Short-term regulation involves regulatory events in which gene sets are quickly turned on or off in response to changes in environmental or physiological conditions in the cell's or organism's environment. This type of regulation is most similar to prokaryotic gene regulation. Long-term gene regulation involves regulatory events required for an organism to develop and differentiate. Long-term gene regulation occurs in multicellular eukaryotes and not in simpler, unicellular eukaryotes. The mechanisms we discuss in this and the next section are applicable to both short-term and long-term regulation. The specific molecules and genes involved are different and, of course, so is the outcome to the cell or organism.

15.2a In Eukaryotes, Regulation of Gene Expression Occurs at Several Levels

The regulation of gene expression is more complicated in eukaryotes than in prokaryotes because eukaryotic cells are more complex, because the nuclear DNA is organized with histones into chromatin, and because multicellular eukaryotes produce large numbers and different types of cells. Further, the eukaryotic nuclear envelope separates the processes of transcription and translation, whereas in prokaryotes, translation can start on an mRNA that is still being made. Consequently, gene expression in eukaryotes is regulated at more levels. That is, there is transcriptional regulation, posttranscriptional regulation, translational regulation, and posttranslational regulation **(Figure 15.6, p. 328)**. The most important of these is transcriptional regulation.

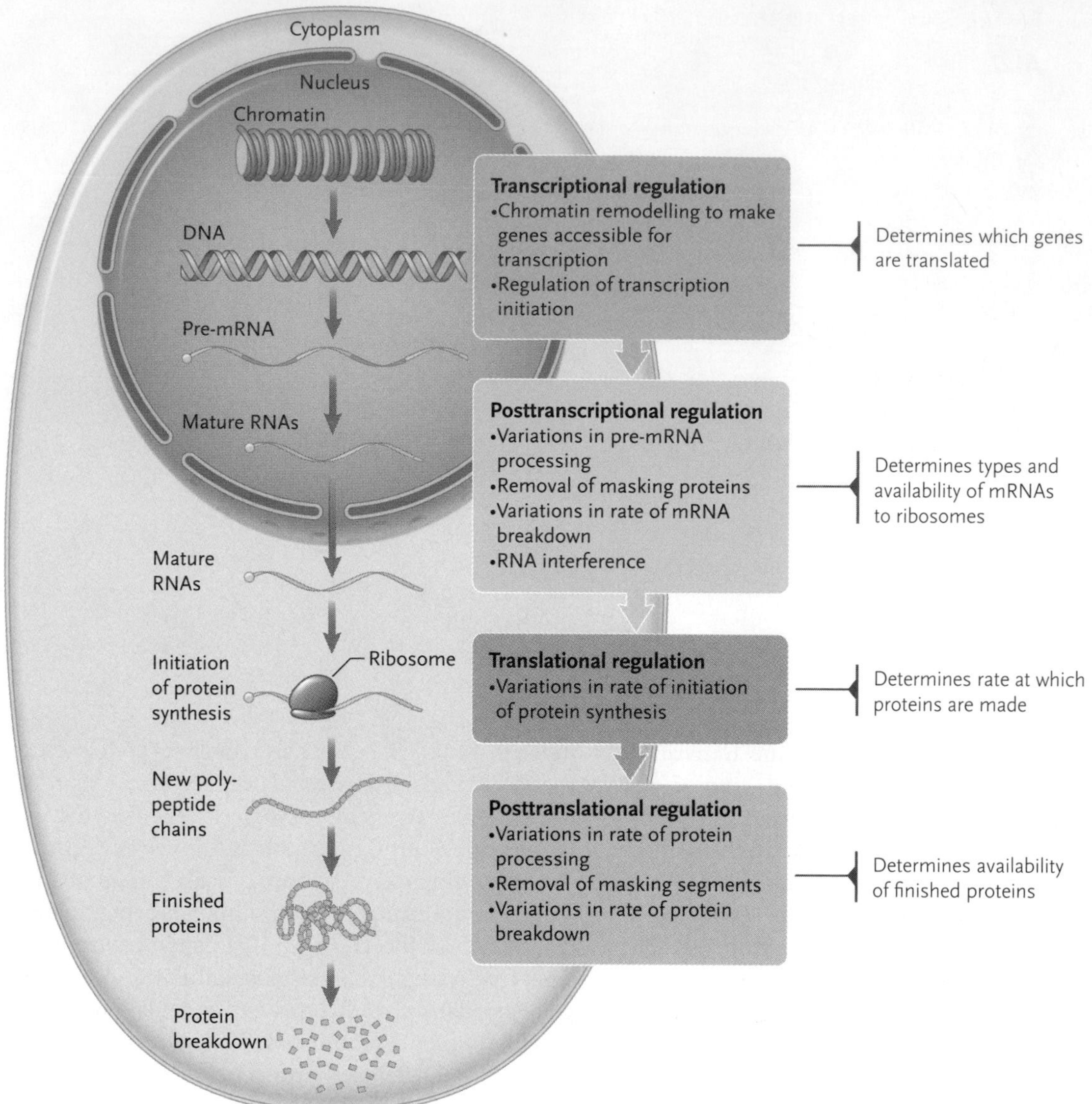

Figure 15.6
Steps in transcriptional, posttranscriptional, translational, and posttranslational regulation of gene expression in eukaryotes.

15.2b Chromatin Structure Plays an Important Role in Whether a Gene Is Active or Inactive

Eukaryotic DNA is organized into chromatin by combination with histone proteins (discussed in Section 13.5). Recall that DNA is wrapped around a core of two molecules each made of histones H2A, H2B, H3, and H4, forming the nucleosome (see Figure 13.18). Higher levels of chromatin organization occur when histone H1 is linked to adjacent nucleosomes.

Genes in regions of the DNA that are tightly wound around histones in chromatin are inactive because their promoters are not accessible to the proteins that initiate transcription. Activating a gene involves changing the state of the chromatin so that the proteins that initiate transcription can bind to their promoters, a process called **chromatin remodelling.** In one type of chromatin remodelling, an activator binds to a regulatory sequence upstream of the gene's promoter and recruits a *remodelling complex,* a protein complex that displaces a nucleosome from the chromatin, exposing the promoter **(Figure 15.7).** In a second type of chromatin remodelling, an activator binds to a regulatory sequence upstream of the gene's promoter and recruits an enzyme that acetylates (adds acetyl groups: CH_3CO—) to histones in the nucleosome where the promoter is located. Acetylation causes the histones to loosen their association with DNA, and the promoter becomes accessible. This type of remodelling is reversed by deacetylation enzymes that remove the acetyl groups from the histones. Many activators use both of these chromatin remodelling mechanisms to regulate gene activity.

15.2c Regulation of Transcription Initiation Involves the Effects of Proteins Binding to a Gene's Promoter and Regulatory Sites

Chromatin remodelling is a crucial initial event in facilitating gene expression. Remodelling opens the way for transcription initiation to occur. Transcription initiation is the most important level at which the regulation of gene expression takes place.

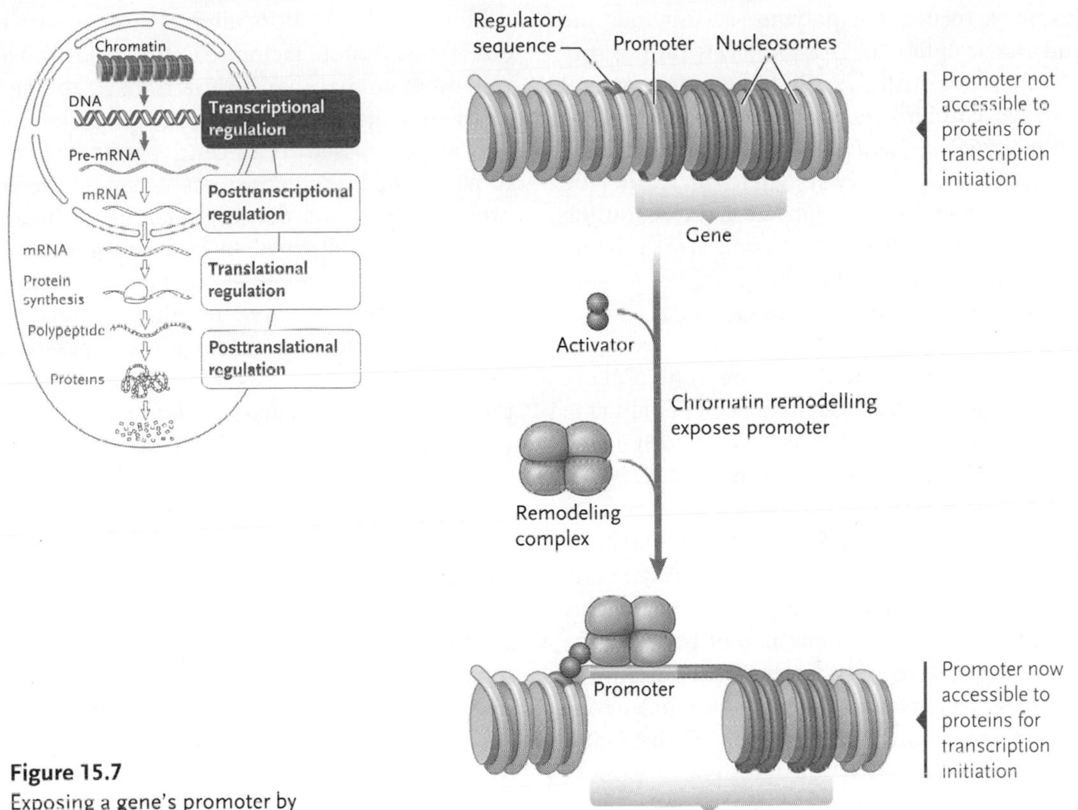

Figure 15.7
Exposing a gene's promoter by chromatin remodelling.

Organization of a Eukaryotic Protein-Coding Gene. **Figure 15.8** shows a eukaryotic gene, emphasizing the regulatory sites involved in its expression. Immediately upstream of the transcription unit is the promoter, a short region often containing the TATA box. The TATA box plays an important role in transcription initiation. RNA polymerase II itself cannot recognize the promoter sequence. Instead, proteins called transcription factors recognize and bind to the TATA box and then recruit the polymerase. Once the RNA polymerase II–transcription

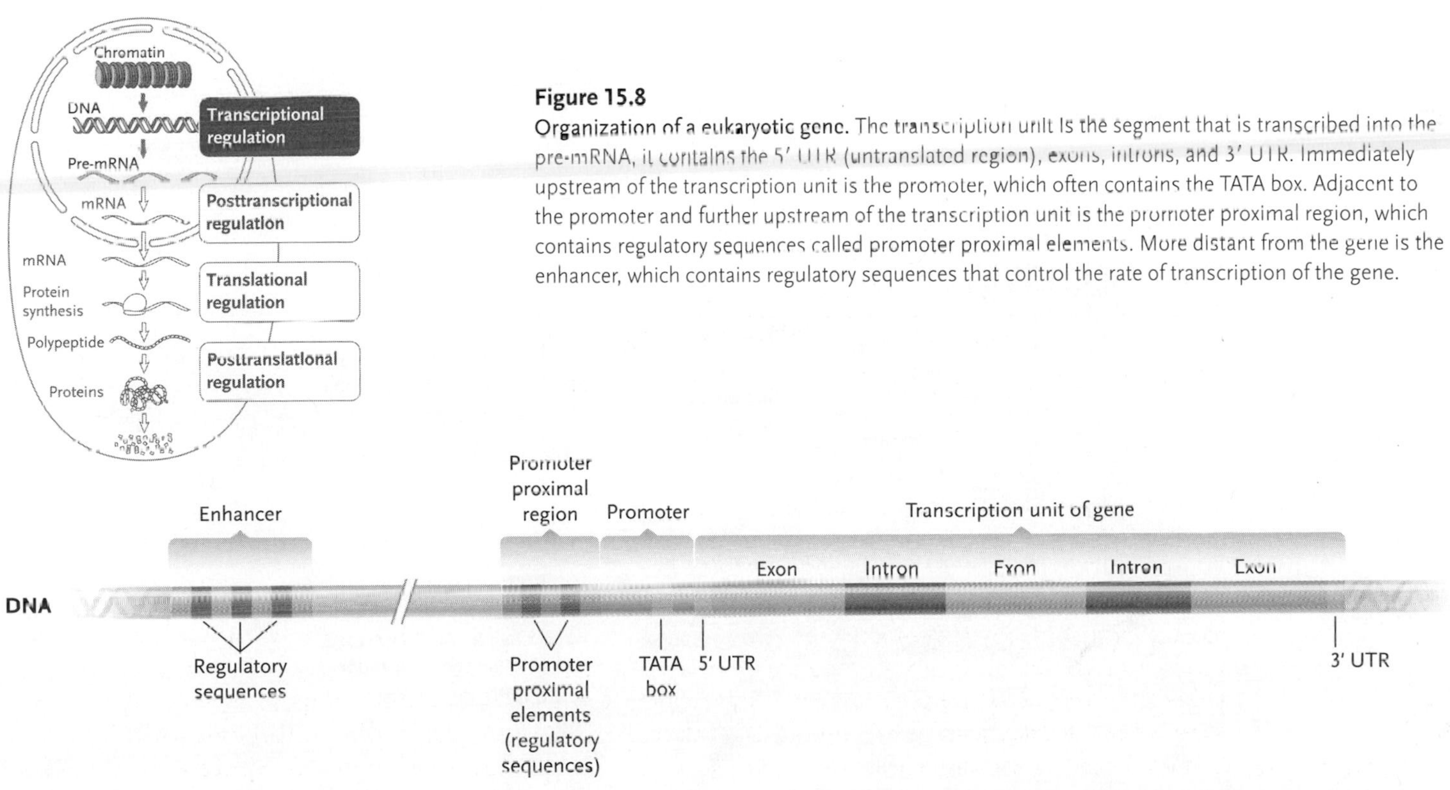

Figure 15.8
Organization of a eukaryotic gene. The transcription unit is the segment that is transcribed into the pre-mRNA; it contains the 5′ UTR (untranslated region), exons, introns, and 3′ UTR. Immediately upstream of the transcription unit is the promoter, which often contains the TATA box. Adjacent to the promoter and further upstream of the transcription unit is the promoter proximal region, which contains regulatory sequences called promoter proximal elements. More distant from the gene is the enhancer, which contains regulatory sequences that control the rate of transcription of the gene.

factor complex forms, the polymerase unwinds the DNA and transcription begins. Adjacent to the promoter, further upstream, is the **promoter proximal region**, which contains regulatory sequences called *promoter proximal elements*. Promoter proximal elements are part of a regulatory system for increasing the rate of transcription. More distant from the beginning of the gene is the **enhancer**, which contains regulatory sequences that determine whether the gene is transcribed at its maximum possible rate.

Activation of Transcription. To initiate transcription, proteins called **general transcription factors** bind to the promoter in the area of the TATA box **(Figure 15.9).** These factors recruit the enzyme RNA polymerase II, which alone cannot bind to the promoter, and orient the enzyme to start transcription at the correct place. The combination of general transcription factors with RNA polymerase II is the **transcription initiation complex.** On its own, this complex brings about only a low rate of transcription initiation, which leads to just a few mRNA transcripts.

Activators—regulatory proteins that control the expression of one or more genes—bind to the promoter proximal elements to increase the rate of transcription. When bound, activators interact directly with the general transcription factors to stimulate transcription initiation, so that many more transcripts are synthesized in a given time. Housekeeping genes—genes that are expressed in all cell types for basic cellular functions such as glucose metabolism—have promoter proximal elements that are recognized by activators present in all cell types. By contrast, genes expressed only in particular cell types or at particular times have promoter proximal elements that are recognized by activators found only in those cell types or at those times. Said another way, the particular set of activators present within a cell at a given time is responsible for determining which genes in that cell are expressed.

Events at the enhancer determine whether a gene is transcribed at its maximal rate **(Figure 15.10).** Particular activators bind to the regulatory sequences within the enhancer. A **coactivator**, a large multiprotein complex, forms a bridge between the activators at the enhancer and the proteins at the promoter and promoter proximal region and causes the DNA to loop around on itself. The interactions between the coactivator, the proteins at the promoter, and the RNA polymerase stimulate transcription to its maximal rate.

Figure 15.9
Formation of the transcription complex on the promoter of a protein-coding gene by the combination of general transcription factors with RNA polymerase. The general transcription factors are needed for RNA polymerase to bind and initiate transcription at the correct place.

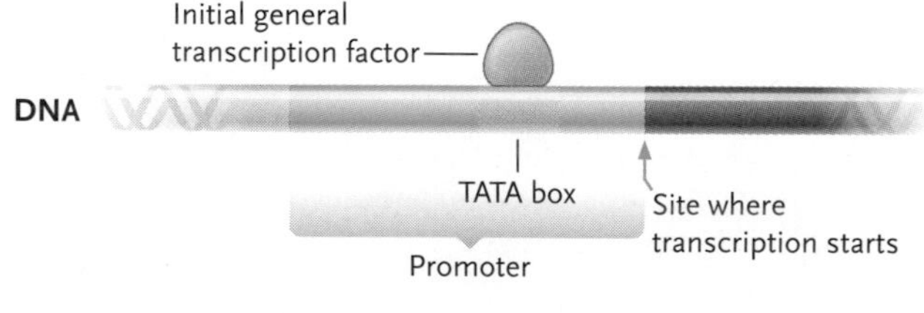

1 The first general transcription factor recognizes and binds to the TATA box of a protein-coding gene's promoter.

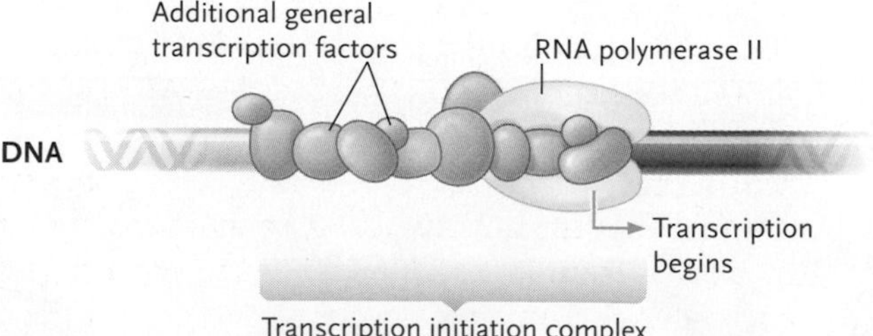

2 Additional general transcription factors and then RNA polymerase add to the complex, and then transcription begins.

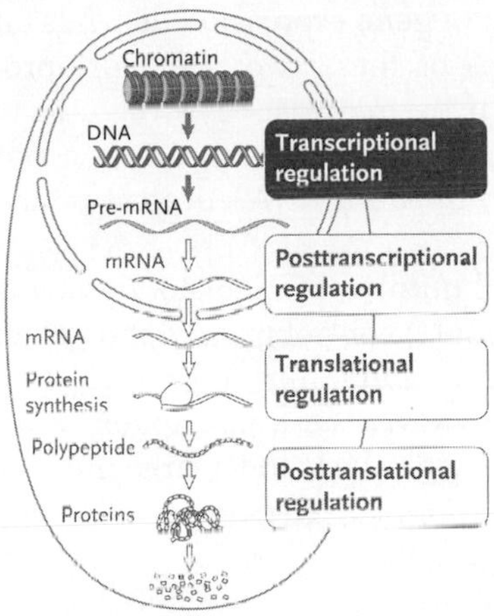

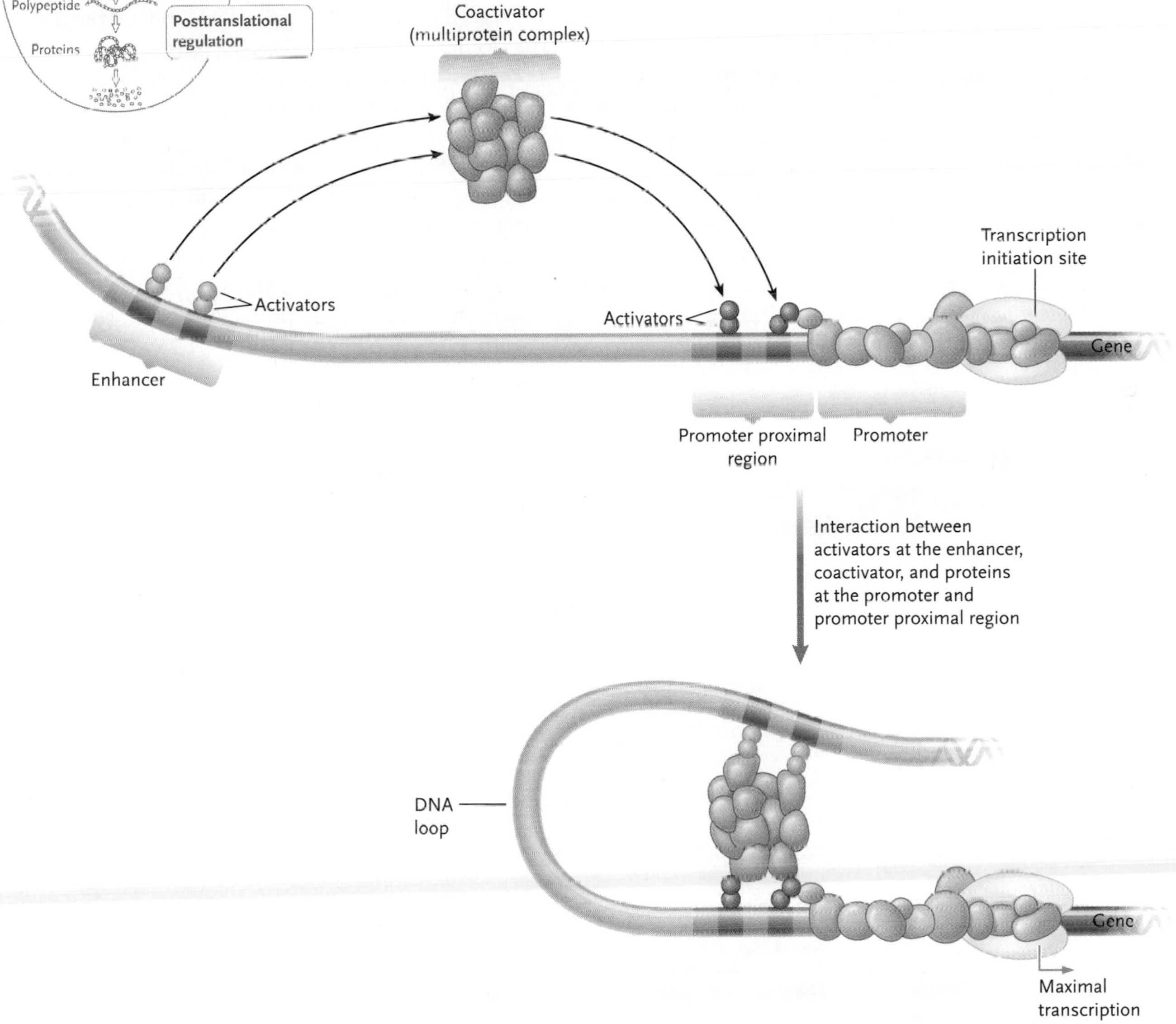

Figure 15.10
Interactions between activators at the enhancer, a coactivator, and general transcription factors at the promoter lead to maximal transcription of the gene.

Repression of Transcription. In some genes, repressors oppose the effect of activators, thereby blocking or reducing the rate of transcription. The final rate of transcription then depends on the "battle" between the activation signal and the repression signal.

Repressors in eukaryotes work in various ways. Some repressors bind to the same regulatory sequence to which activators bind (often in the enhancer), thereby preventing activators from binding to that site. Other repressors bind to their own specific site in the DNA near where the activator binds and interact with the activator so that it cannot interact with the coactivator. Yet other repressors recruit histone deacetylation enzymes that modify histones, leading to chromatin compaction and making a gene's promoter inaccessible to the transcription machinery.

Combinatorial Gene Regulation. Let's review the key elements of regulation of transcription of a protein-coding gene. General transcription factors bind to certain promoter sequences such as the TATA box and recruit RNA polymerase II; this results in a basal level of transcription. Specific activators bind to promoter proximal elements and stimulate the rate of transcription initiation. Activators also bind to the enhancer to give maximal transcription of the gene.

How are these events coordinated in regulating gene expression? Characteristic of any given gene is the number and types of promoter proximal elements. In some genes, there may be only one regulatory element, but genes under complex regulatory control have many regulatory elements. Similarly, the number and types of regulatory sequences in the enhancer are specific to each gene.

Both promoter proximal regions and enhancers are important in regulating the transcription of a gene. Each different regulatory sequence in those two regions binds a specific regulatory protein. Since some regulatory proteins are activators and others are repressors, the overall effect of regulatory sequences on transcription depends on the particular proteins that bind to them. If activators bind to both the regulatory sequences in the promoter proximal region and to the enhancer, transcription is activated maximally, meaning a high rate of transcription and therefore the production of a high level of the mRNA encoded by the gene. But if a repressor binds to the enhancer and an activator binds to the promoter proximal element, the amount of gene expression depends on the relative strengths of these two regulatory proteins. For example, if the repressor is strong, gene expression, in terms of the rate of transcription and the consequent level of the mRNA encoded by the gene, will be low.

A relatively small number of regulatory proteins (activators and repressors) control transcription of all protein-coding genes. By combining a few regulatory proteins in particular ways, the transcription of an array of genes can be controlled, and a large number of cell types can be specified. The process is called **combinatorial gene regulation.** Let us consider a theoretical example of two genes, each with activators already bound to the respective promoter proximal elements **(Figure 15.11).** Maximal transcription of gene *A* requires activators 2, 5, 7, and 8 binding to their regulatory sequences in the enhancer, whereas maximal transcription of gene *B* requires activators 1, 5, 8, and 11 binding to its enhancer. That is, both genes require activators 5 and 8 for full activation in combination with different other activators.

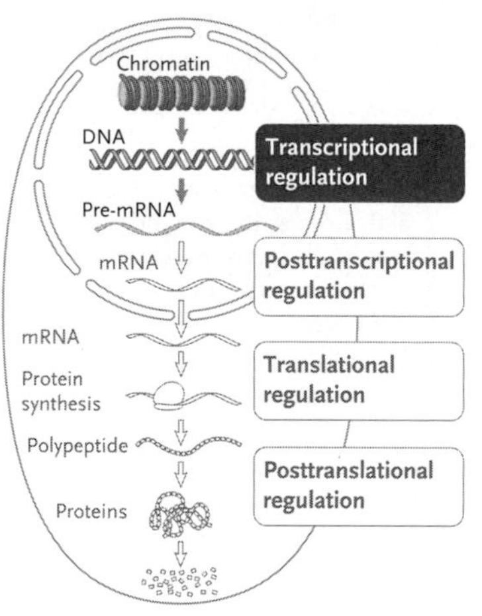

Figure 15.11
Combinatorial gene regulation. A relatively small number of regulatory proteins control transcription of all protein-coding genes. Different combinations of activators bind to enhancer regulatory sequences to control the rate of transcription of each gene.

a. A unique combination of activators controls gene *A*.

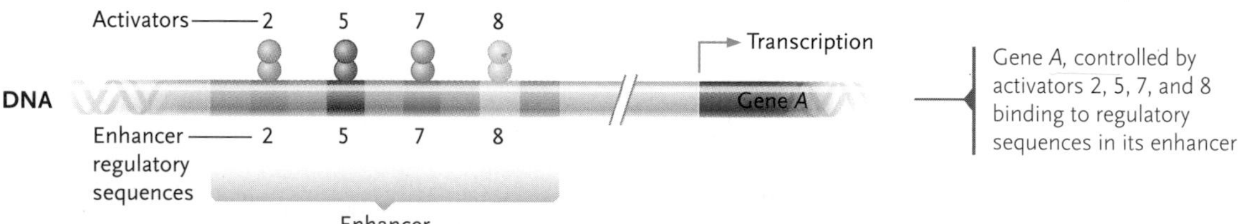

b. A different combination of activators controls gene *B*.

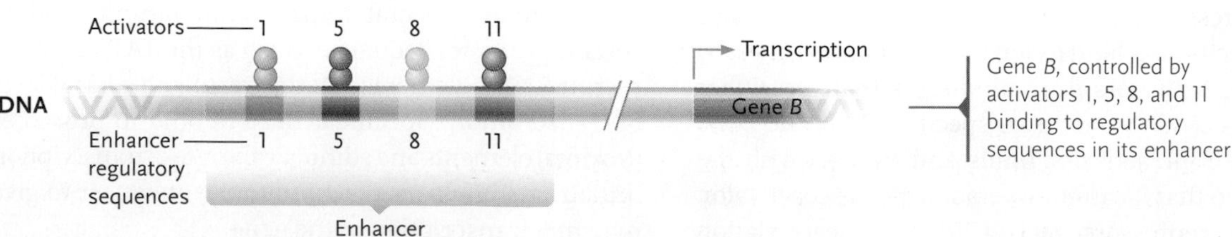

This operating principle solves a basic dilemma in gene regulation—if each gene were regulated by a single, distinct protein, the number of genes encoding regulatory proteins would have to equal the number of genes to be regulated. Regulating the regulators would require another set of genes of equal number and so on until the coding capacity of any chromosome set, no matter how large, would be exhausted. But because different genes require different combinations of regulatory proteins, the number of genes encoding regulatory proteins can be much lower than the number of genes they control.

Coordinated Regulation of Transcription of Genes with Related Functions. In the discussion of prokaryotic operons, you learned that genes with related function are often clustered *and* they are transcribed from one promoter onto a single mRNA. That mRNA is translated from one end to the other to produce the several proteins encoded by the genes. There are no operons in eukaryotes, yet the transcription of genes with related functions is coordinated. How is this accomplished?

The answer is that all genes that are coordinately regulated have the same regulatory sequences associated with them. Therefore, with one signal, the transcription of all the genes can be controlled simultaneously. Let us consider an example of this: the control of gene expression by steroid hormones in mammals. A **hormone** is a molecule produced by one tissue and transported via the bloodstream to another specific tissue to alter its physiological activity. A **steroid** is a type of lipid derived from cholesterol. Examples of steroid hormones are testosterone and glucocorticoid. Testosterone regulates the expression of a large number of genes associated with the maintenance of primary and secondary male characteristics. Glucocorticoid, among other actions, regulates the expression of genes involved in the maintenance of the concentration of glucose and other fuel molecules in the blood.

A steroid hormone acts on specific target tissues in the body because only cells in those tissues have *steroid hormone receptors* in their cytoplasm that recognize and bind the hormone (see Chapter 8). The steroid hormone moves through the plasma membrane into the cytoplasm and the receptor binds to it **(Figure 15.12)**. The hormone–receptor complex then enters the nucleus and binds to specific regulatory sequences adjacent to the genes whose expression is controlled by the hormone. This binding activates transcription, and proteins encoded by the genes are made rapidly.

All genes regulated by a specific steroid hormone have the same DNA sequence to which the hormone–receptor complex binds. This sequence is called a **steroid hormone response element.** For example, all genes controlled by glucocorticoid have a glucocorticoid response element associated with them. Therefore, the release of glucocorticoid into the bloodstream coordinately activates the transcription of genes through that response element.

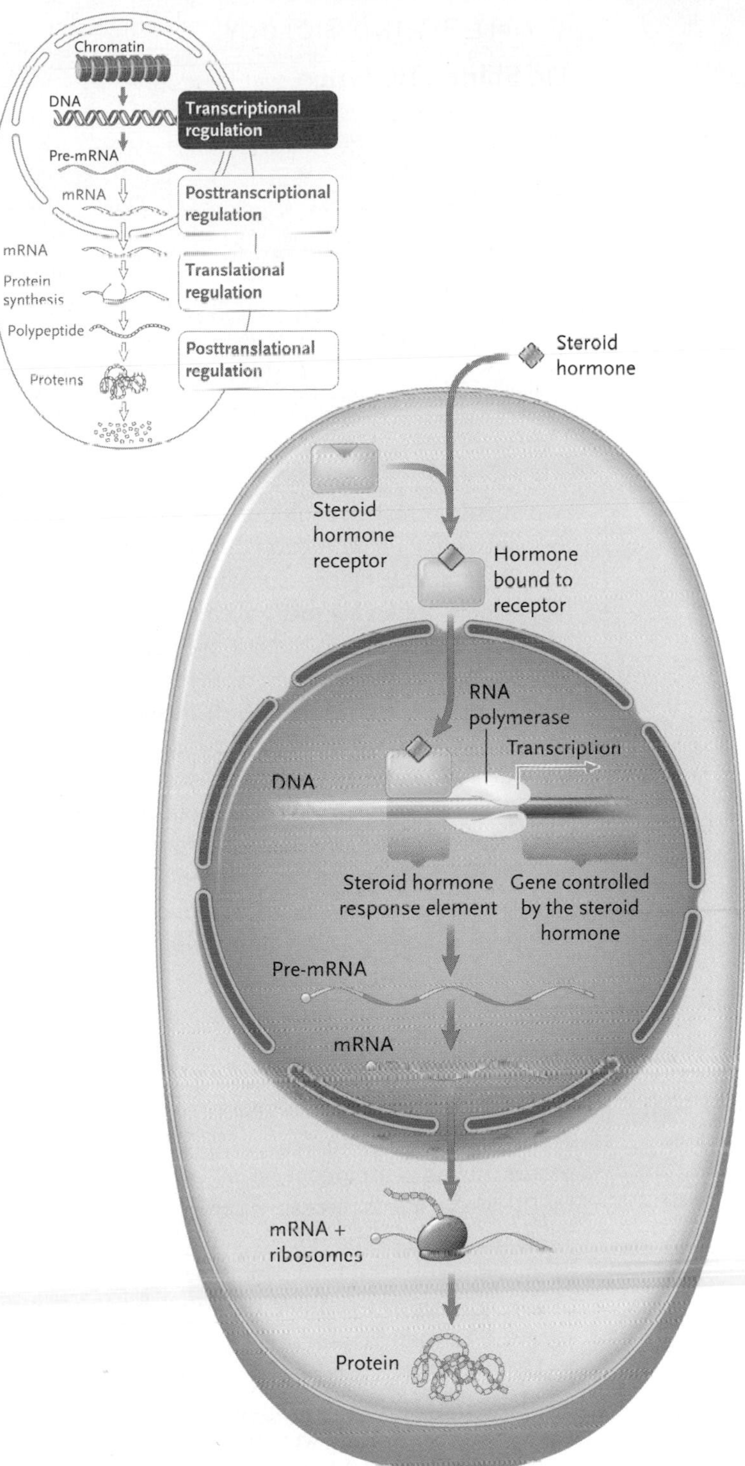

Figure 15.12
Steroid hormone regulation of gene expression. A steroid hormone enters the cell and forms a complex in the cytoplasm with a steroid hormone receptor that is specific to the hormone. Steroid hormone–receptor complexes migrate to the nucleus, bind to the steroid hormone response element next to each gene they control (one such gene is shown in the figure), and affect transcription of those genes.

15.2d Methylation of DNA Can Control Gene Transcription

DNA methylation, in which a methyl group (—CH_3) is added enzymatically to cytosine bases in the DNA, can also regulate transcription. Specifically, methylation of

People Behind Biology
Dr. Shirley Tilghman

Dr. Tilghman was elected the nineteenth president of Princeton University in 2001. She is a distinguished teacher, a strong supporter of women in science, a world-renowned molecular biologist, and a director of Google Inc. Dr. Tilghman, who did her undergraduate study at Queen's University in Kingston and Ph.D. at Temple University in Philadelphia, was involved in the cloning of the first mammalian gene and the subsequent discovery of introns. She is now an international authority on the molecular understanding of gene regulation by genomic imprinting and its implications for cloning in mammals, including humans.

cytosines in promoters inhibits transcription and turns the genes off, a phenomenon called **silencing.**

For example, genes encoding the blood protein hemoglobin are highly methylated and inactive in most vertebrate body cells. In the cell lines giving rise to red blood cells, however, enzymes remove the methyl groups from the hemoglobin genes, which are then transcribed.

DNA methylation in some cases silences large blocks of genes, or even chromosomes. For example, in body cells of female placental mammals, including humans, one of the two X chromosomes packs tightly into a mass known as a Barr body, in which essentially all the genes of the X chromosome are turned off. As part of this general inactivation, which also includes chromatin modifications, cytosines in the DNA become methylated.

DNA methylation underlies **genomic imprinting**, in which methylation permanently silences transcription of either the inherited maternal or paternal allele of a particular gene (see Section 12.5). The methylation occurs during gametogenesis in a parent. An inherited methylated allele is not expressed—it is silenced. That allele is known as the *imprinted allele*. The expression of the gene involved therefore depends on expression of the nonimprinted allele inherited from the other parent. The methylation of the parental allele is maintained as the DNA is replicated, so that the silenced allele remains inactive in progeny cells. Some examples of genomic imprinting were presented in Section 12.5. In one of those examples, the mammalian *Igf2* (insulin growth factor 2) gene is inherited with the paternally derived allele nonmethylated and, therefore, active and with the maternally derived allele methylated and, therefore, silenced.

Once mRNAs are transcribed, further regulation occurs at each major step in the pathway from genes to proteins: during pre-mRNA processing and the movement of finished mRNAs to the cytoplasm (posttranslational regulation), during protein synthesis (translational regulation), and after translation is complete (posttranslational regulation). The next section describes the regulatory mechanisms operating at each of these steps.

Study Break

1. What is the role of histones in gene expression? How does acetylation of the histones affect gene expression?
2. What are the roles of general transcription factors, activators, and coactivators in transcription of a protein-coding gene?

15.3 Posttranscriptional, Translational, and Posttranslational Regulation

Transcriptional regulation determines which genes are copied into mRNAs. This basic level of regulation is fine-tuned by posttranscriptional, translational, and posttranslational controls, the subjects of this section (refer again to Figure 15.6).

15.3a Posttranscriptional Regulation Controls mRNA Availability

Posttranscriptional regulation directs translation by controlling the availability of mRNAs to ribosomes. The controls work by several mechanisms, including changes in pre-mRNA processing and the rate at which mRNAs are degraded.

Variations in Pre-mRNA Processing. In Chapter 14, we noted that mRNAs are transcribed initially as pre-mRNA molecules. These pre-mRNAs are processed to produce the finished mRNAs, which then enter protein synthesis. Variations in pre-mRNA processing can regulate *which* proteins are made in cells. As described in Section 14.3, pre-mRNAs can be processed by *alternative splicing*. Alternative splicing produces different mRNAs from the same pre-mRNA by removing different combinations of exons (the amino acid–coding segments) along with the introns (the noncoding spacers). The resulting mRNAs are translated to produce a family of related proteins with various combinations of amino acid sequences derived from the exons. Alternative splicing itself is under regulatory control. Regulatory proteins specific to the type of cell control which exons are removed from pre-mRNA molecules by binding to regulatory sequences within those molecules. The outcome of alternative splicing is that appropriate proteins within a family are synthesized in cell types or tissues in which they function optimally. Perhaps three-quarters of human genes are alternatively spliced at the pre-mRNA level.

Posttranscriptional Control by Masking Proteins. Some posttranscriptional controls operate by means of "masking" proteins that bind to mRNAs and make them unavailable for protein synthesis. These controls are important in many animal eggs, keeping mRNAs in an inactive form until the egg has been fertilized and embryonic development is under way. When an mRNA is to become active, other factors—other proteins, made as part of the developmental pathway—remove the masking proteins and allow the mRNA to enter protein synthesis.

Variations in the Rate of mRNA Breakdown. The rate at which eukaryotic mRNAs break down can also be controlled posttranscriptionally. The mechanism involves a regulatory molecule, such as a steroid hormone, directly or indirectly affecting the mRNA breakdown steps, either slowing or increasing the rate of those steps. For example, in the mammary gland of the rat, the mRNA for casein (a milk protein) has a half-life of about 5 hours (meaning that it takes 5 hours for half of the mRNA present at a given time to break down). The half-life of casein mRNA changes to about 92 hours if the peptide hormone prolactin is present. Prolactin is synthesized in the brain and in other tissues, including the breast. The most important effect of prolactin is to stimulate the mammary glands to produce milk (that is, it stimulates lactation). During milk production, a large amount of casein must be synthesized, and this is accomplished in part by radically decreasing the rate of breakdown of the casein mRNA.

Nucleotide sequences in the 5′ UTR (untranslated region; see Section 14.3) appear also to be important in determining mRNA half-life. If the 5′ UTR is transferred experimentally from one mRNA to another, the half-life of the receiving mRNA becomes the same as that of the donor mRNA. The controlling sequences in the 5′ UTR of an mRNA might be recognized by proteins that regulate its stability.

Regulation of Gene Expression by Small RNAs. The relatively recent discovery of *micro-RNAs* (miRNAs) has revolutionized our understanding of gene control. miRNAs are small, single-stranded RNAs found in organisms as diverse as worms, flies, plants, and mammals, where they regulate important processes such as development, growth, and behaviour. What are miRNAs and how do they work?

Each miRNA is encoded by a non–protein-coding gene. Transcription of the gene produces an RNA that is the precursor to the miRNA (**Figure 15.13, p. 336**). The precursor RNA folds and base-pairs with itself, forming a stem-loop structure. An enzyme named Dicer cuts the stem-loop to produce a double-stranded RNA, about 21 to 22 base pairs long. A protein complex then binds to the double-stranded RNA and degrades one of the two RNA strands, leaving a small, single-stranded RNA—the miRNA. Still bound to the protein complex, the miRNA binds to any mRNA that has a complementary sequence. Gene expression is then silenced in one of two ways: either the proteins in the complex cleave the mRNA where the miRNA is bound to it, or the double-stranded segment formed between the miRNA and the mRNA blocks ribosomes from translating the mRNA.

Researchers think that there are 120 genes for miRNAs in worms and 250 genes in humans. Many of these miRNAs are expressed in developmentally regulated patterns. The targets of the miRNA's action are often mRNAs for regulatory proteins that control the development of the organism.

The phenomenon of silencing a gene posttranscriptionally by a small, single-stranded RNA that is complementary to part of an mRNA is termed **RNA interference (RNAi)**. miRNAs are one class of single-stranded RNAs that cause RNAi; another class is known as **small interfering RNA (siRNA)**. Whereas miRNA is produced from RNA that is encoded in the cell's genome, siRNA is produced from double-stranded RNA that is *not* encoded by nuclear genes. For example, the life cycle and replication of many viruses involves a double-stranded RNA stage. Viral double-stranded RNA enters the RNAi process as described for miRNAs: double-stranded RNA is cut by Dicer into short double-stranded RNA molecules, and then a protein complex binds to the molecules and degrades one of the RNA strands to produce siRNA. The protein complex is the same one that acts on the double-stranded RNA precursors of miRNAs. In the RNAi process, siRNA acts exactly like microRNA—mRNAs complementary to the siRNA are targeted and either they are degraded or their translation is blocked. In our viral example, the targeted mRNAs would be mRNAs for proteins needed for viral genome replication and the production of new virus particles.

Any gene can be silenced experimentally by RNAi. To silence a gene, researchers introduce a double-stranded RNA into a cell that can be processed by Dicer and the protein complex into an siRNA complementary to the mRNA transcribed from that gene. Indeed, RNAi has become a powerful new technique for silencing specific genes experimentally in a variety of organisms. Andrew Fire of the Massachusetts Institute of Technology and Craig Mello of Harvard University received a Nobel Prize in 2006 for their discovery of RNA interference.

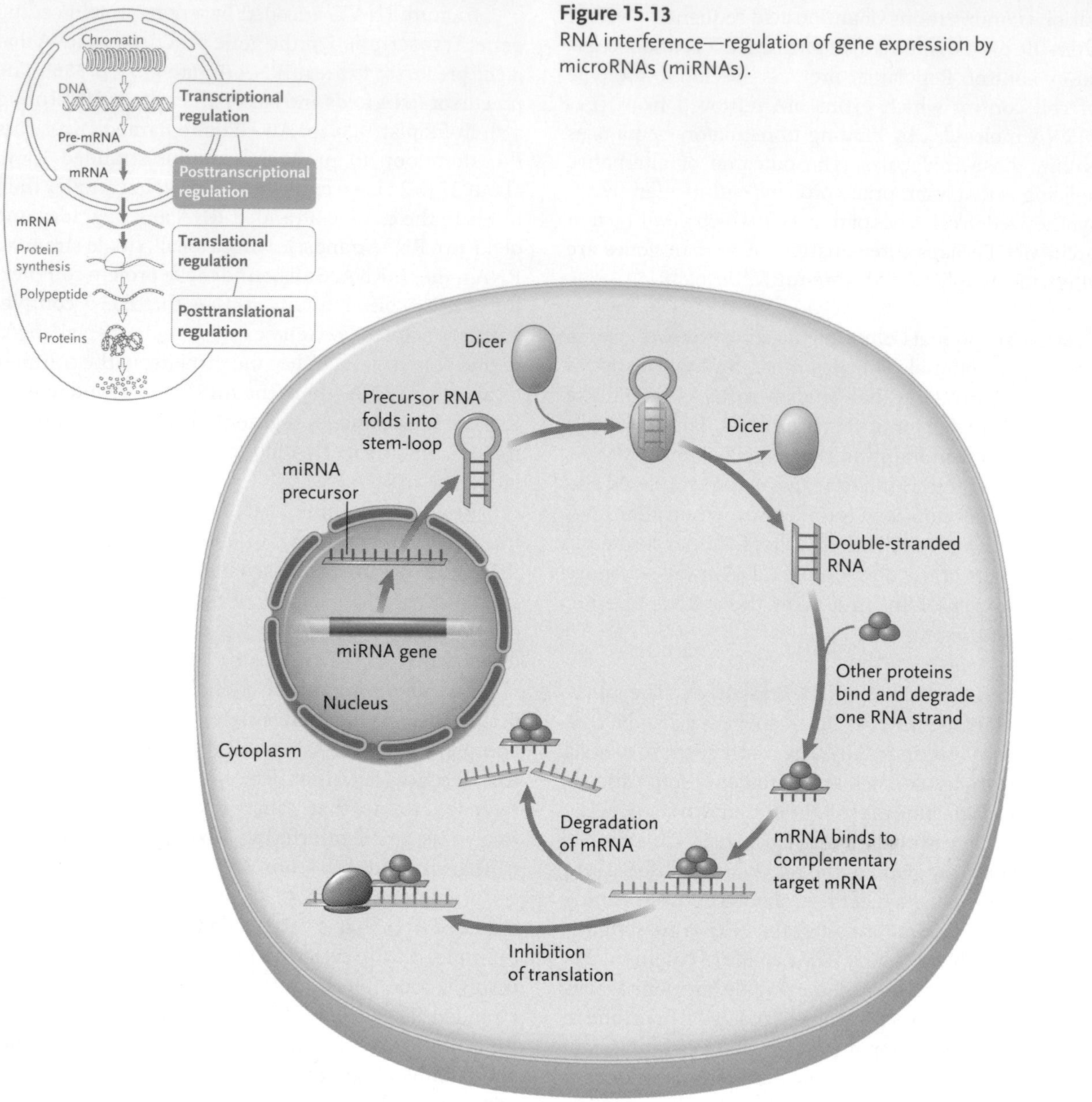

Figure 15.13
RNA interference—regulation of gene expression by microRNAs (miRNAs).

15.3b Translational Regulation Controls the Rate of Protein Synthesis

At the next regulatory level, translational regulation controls the rate at which mRNAs are used in protein synthesis. Translational regulation occurs in essentially all cell types and species. For example, translational regulation is involved in cell cycle control in all eukaryotes and in many processes during development in multicellular eukaryotes, such as red blood cell differentiation in animals. Significantly, many viruses exploit translational regulation to control their infection of cells and to shut off the host cell's own genes.

Let us consider the general role of translational regulation in animal development. During early development of most animals, little transcription occurs. The changes in protein synthesis patterns seen in developing cell types and tissues instead derive from the activation, repression, or degradation of maternal mRNAs, the mRNAs that were present in the mother's egg before fertilization. One important mechanism for translational regulation involves adjusting the length of the poly(A) tail of the mRNA. (Recall from Section 14.3 that the poly(A) tail—a string of adenine-containing nucleotides—is added to the 3′ end of pre-mRNA and is retained on the mRNA produced from the pre-mRNA after introns are removed.) That is, enzymes can change the length of the poly(A) tail on an mRNA in the cytoplasm in either direction: by shortening it or lengthening it. Increases in poly(A) tail length result in increased translation; decreases in length result in decreased translation. For example, during embryogenesis (the formation of the embryo) of the fruit fly, *Drosophila*, key proteins are synthesized when the poly(A) tails on the mRNAs for those proteins are lengthened in a regulated way. Evidence for this came from experiments in which poly(A) tail lengthening was blocked; the result was that embryogenesis was inhibited. But although researchers know that the length of poly(A) tails is regulated in the cytoplasm, how this process occurs is not completely understood.

15.3c Posttranslational Regulation Controls the Availability of Functional Proteins

Posttranslational regulation controls the availability of functional proteins primarily in three ways: chemical modification, processing, and degradation. Chemical modification involves the addition or removal of chemical groups, which reversibly alters the activity of the protein. For example, you saw in Section 8.2 how the addition of phosphate groups to proteins involved in signal transduction pathways either stimulates or inhibits the activity of those proteins. Further, in Section 9.4, you learned how the addition of phosphate groups to target proteins plays a crucial role in regulating how a cell progresses through the cell division cycle. And in Section 15.2, you saw how acetylation of histones altered the properties of the nucleosome, loosening its association with DNA in chromatin.

In processing, proteins are synthesized as inactive precursors, which are converted to an active form under regulatory control. For example, you saw in Section 14.4 that the digestive enzyme pepsin is synthesized as pepsinogen, an inactive precursor that activates by removal of a segment of amino acids. Similarly, the glucose-regulating hormone insulin is synthesized as a precursor called proinsulin; processing of the precursor removes a central segment but leaves the insulin molecule, which consists of two polypeptide chains linked by disulphide bridges.

The rate of degradation of proteins is also under regulatory control. Some proteins in eukaryotic cells last for the lifetime of the individual, whereas others persist only for minutes. Proteins with relatively short cellular lives include many of the proteins regulating transcription. Typically, these short-lived proteins are marked for breakdown by enzymes that attach a "doom tag" consisting of a small protein called *ubiquitin* (**Figure 15.14**, step 1). The protein is given this name because it is indeed ubiquitous—present in almost the same form in essentially all eukaryotes. The ubiquitin tag labels the doomed proteins so that they are recognized and attacked by a *proteasome*, a large cytoplasmic complex of a number of different proteins (step 2). The proteasome unfolds the protein, and protein-digesting enzymes within the core digest the protein into small peptides. The peptides are released from the proteasome, and cytosolic enzymes further digest the peptides into individual amino acids, which are recycled for use in protein synthesis or oxidized as an energy source (step 3). The ubiquitin protein and proteasome are also recycled. Aaron Ciechanover and Avram Hershko, both of the Israel Institute of Technology, Haifa, Israel, and Irwin Rose of the University of California, Irvine, received a Nobel Prize in 2004 for the discovery of ubiquitin-mediated protein degradation.

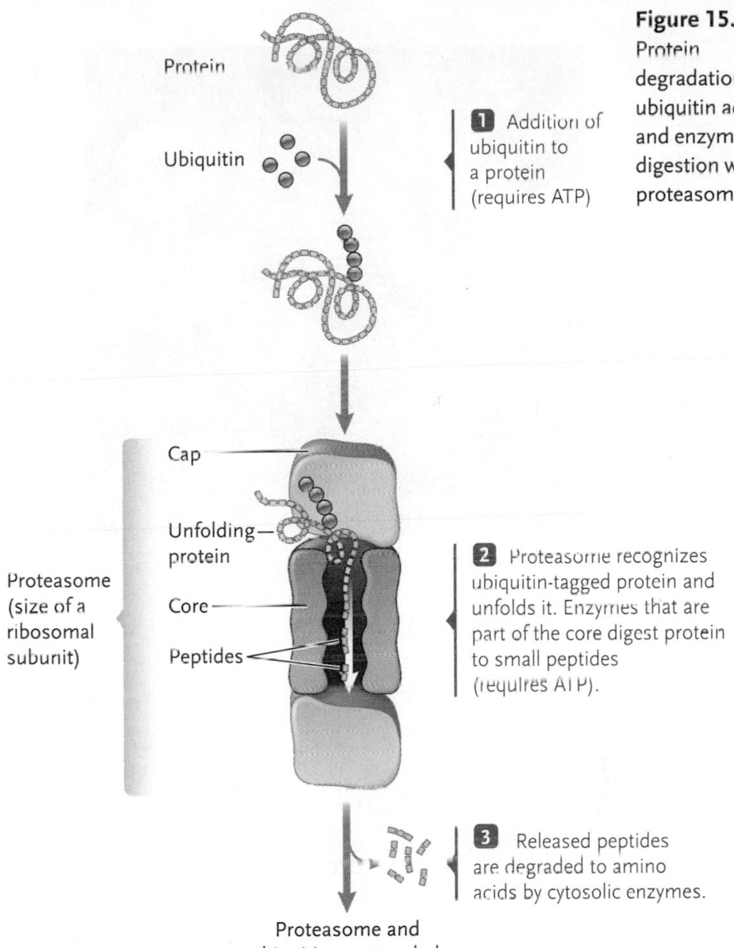
Protein
Ubiquitin
1 Addition of ubiquitin to a protein (requires ATP)
Cap
Unfolding protein
Proteasome (size of a ribosomal subunit)
Core
Peptides
2 Proteasome recognizes ubiquitin-tagged protein and unfolds it. Enzymes that are part of the core digest protein to small peptides (requires ATP).
3 Released peptides are degraded to amino acids by cytosolic enzymes.
Proteasome and ubiquitin are recycled.

Figure 15.14 Protein degradation by ubiquitin addition and enzymatic digestion within a proteasome.

Control of protein breakdown is the last opportunity for control of gene expression. We now describe cancer, a disease in which the control of gene expression goes awry.

Study Break

1. How does a microRNA silence gene expression?
2. If the poly(A) tail on a mRNA was removed, what would likely be the effect on the translation of that mRNA?

15.4 The Loss of Regulatory Controls in Cancer

The cell division cycle of all eukaryotic cells from single-celled microorganisms to cells that are components of multicellular organisms is controlled by genes. The types of genes exerting this control are basically the same in terms of functions in all eukaryotes. Mutations in these genes can disrupt normal cell

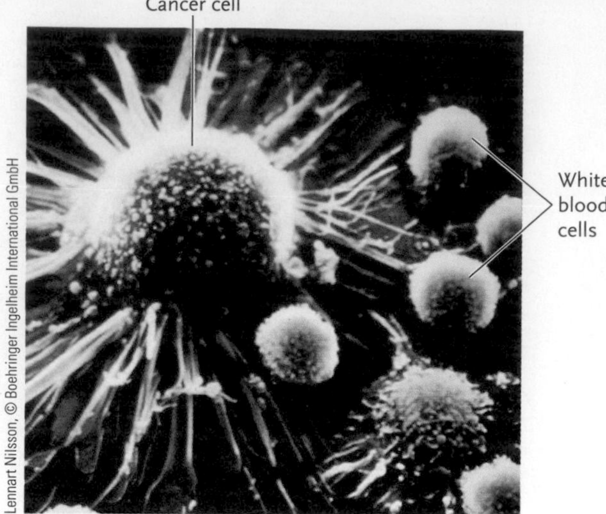

Figure 15.15
A scanning electron micrograph of a cancer cell surrounded by several white blood cells.

growth and division. The effects of such mutations are more significant and profound in complex multicellular organisms. For example, occasionally, dividing and differentiating cells deviate from their normal genetic program and give rise to tissue masses called *tumours*. In other words, the cells lose their normal regulatory controls and revert partially or completely to an embryonic developmental state, in a process called *dedifferentiation*. If the deviant cells stay together in a single mass, the tumour is said to be *benign*. Benign tumours are usually not life threatening, and their surgical removal generally results in a complete cure. If the cells of a tumour invade and disrupt surrounding tissues, the tumour is said to be *malignant* and is called a cancer (**Figure 15.15** shows a cancer cell). Sometimes, cells from malignant tumours break off and move through the blood system or lymphatic system, forming new tumours at other locations in the body. The spreading of a malignant tumour is called *metastasis* (meaning "change of state"). Malignant tumours can result in debilitation and death in various ways, including damage to critical organs, metabolic problems, hemorrhage, and secondary malignancies. In some cases, malignant tumours can be eliminated from the body by surgery or destroyed by chemicals (*chemotherapy*) or radiation.

15.4a Most Cancers Are Caused by Genes That Have Lost Their Normal Controls

All the characteristics of cancer cells—dedifferentiation, uncontrolled division, and metastasis—reflect changes in gene activity. Many of the genes that become altered encode proteins that control the cell division cycle of normal cells. That is, healthy cells grow and divide only when the balance of stimulatory and inhibitory signals received from outside the cell favours cell division. A cancer cell, by contrast, does not respond properly to the usual signals and divides without the usual constraints.

Two main types of genes commonly show altered activities as cells become cancerous. One class is the **proto-oncogenes** (*oncos* = bulk or mass), genes in normal cells that encode various kinds of proteins that stimulate cell division. In cancer cells, the proto-oncogenes are altered to become **oncogenes**, genes that stimulate the cell to progress to the cancerous state. Among the mechanisms that can convert proto-oncogenes to oncogenes:

- Mutations in a gene's promoter or other control sequences may disrupt normal regulatory controls, making the gene abnormally active. The mutations can occur spontaneously or be induced by radiation or by particular chemicals.
- Mutations in the coding segment of the gene may produce an altered form of the encoded protein that is abnormally active.
- Translocation, in which a segment of a chromosome breaks off and attaches to a different chromosome (discussed in Section 12.3), may move a gene that controls cell division to a new location near the promoter or enhancer sequence of a highly active gene, making the cell division gene overactive.
- Infecting viruses may introduce genes to regions in the chromosomes where the expression of the genes disrupts cell cycle control or alters regulatory proteins to turn genes on.

For example, translocation may affect *MYC*, a proto-oncogene controlling cell division. The activity of *MYC* is normally tightly regulated. However, *MYC* lies in a chromosome region that often breaks, causing a translocation that places *MYC* near the enhancer and promoter of a highly active antibody gene. The placement makes *MYC* continuously active, converting it into an oncogene that triggers rapid and uncontrolled cell division.

Several proto-oncogenes encode cell surface receptors that bind extracellular signal molecules such as peptide hormones or growth factors. In general, the oncogene forms of these receptors are continually activated, whether they are bound to the external signal molecule or not. As a result, the internal pathways they trigger, including those that cause cells to divide, are also continually active.

Another key group of proto-oncogenes encodes enzymes forming parts of the internal reaction pathways triggered by surface receptors (see Chapter 8). Most important are genes encoding the protein kinases, which regulate the activity of other proteins by adding phosphate groups to them. Some of the proteins phosphorylated by the protein kinases directly take part in gene regulation or initiation of

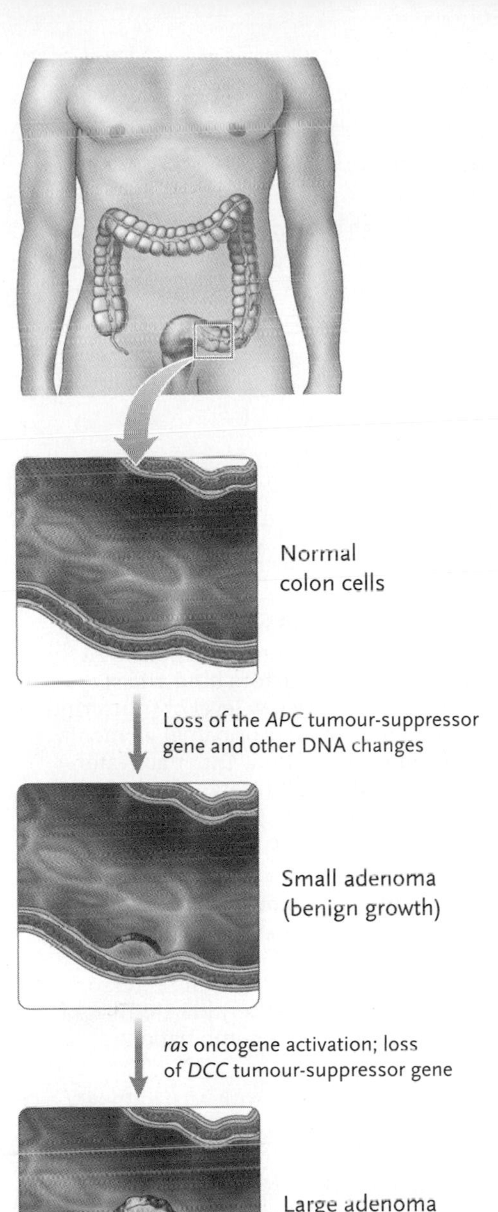

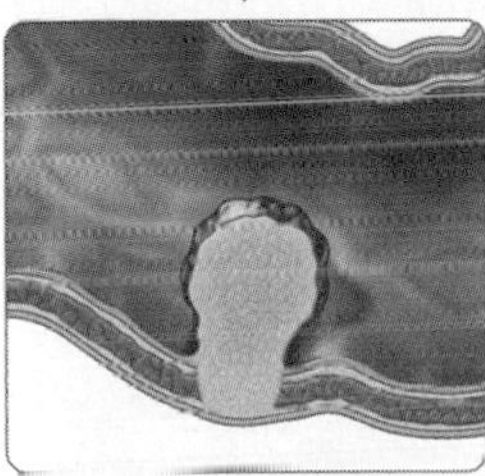

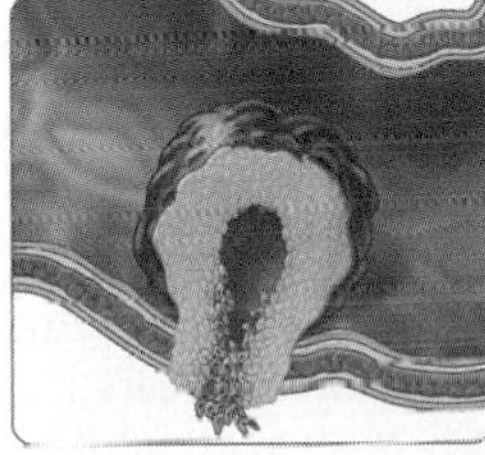

Figure 15.16
A multistep model for the development of a type of colorectal cancer.

cell division; others form parts of the cellular response pathways linked to surface receptors. The protein kinases encoded by the oncogene forms of the genes are continually active, constantly phosphorylating the control protein so that cell division continues at high and uncontrolled rates.

The other main class of genes that shows altered activity in cancer cells is the **tumour-suppressor genes,** which, in normal cells, encode proteins that inhibit cell division. Both alleles of a tumour-suppressor gene must be inactivated for inhibitory activity to be lost in cancer cells. The best known of these genes is *TP53*, so called because its encoded protein, p53, has a molecular weight of 53 000 daltons. Among other activities, normal p53 stops cell division by combining with and inhibiting cyclin-dependent protein kinases that trigger entry into critical stages of DNA replication and mitosis (discussed in Section 9.4). Without the normal form of the p53 protein, the cyclin-dependent protein kinases are continually active in triggering cell division. Inactive *TP53* genes are found in many types of cancers.

15.4b Cancer Develops Gradually by Multiple Steps

Cancer rarely develops by alteration of a single proto-oncogene to an oncogene, or inactivation of a single tumour-suppressor gene. Instead, in almost all cancers, successive alterations in several to many genes gradually accumulate to change normal cells into cancer cells. This is the *multistep progression of cancer* **(Figure 15.16).** The gradual nature of the process explains why smokers, for example, may not develop cancer until years after the first mutations caused by chemicals in tobacco smoke occur, soon after smoking begins. It also offers some hope to those who quit smoking, for stopping the exposure to the carcinogenic smoke may halt multistep progression before it reaches its deadly conclusion in cancer.

The ravages of cancer, probably more than any other example, bring home the critical extent to which humans and all other multicellular organisms depend on the mechanisms controlling gene expression to develop and live normally. In a sense, the most amazing thing about these control mechanisms is that, in spite of their complexity, they operate without failures throughout most of the lives of all eukaryotes.

Study Break

1. What is the normal function of a tumour-suppressor gene? How do mutations in tumour-suppressor genes contribute to the onset of cancer?
2. What is the normal function of a proto-oncogene? How can mutations in proto-oncogenes contribute to the onset of cancer?

UNANSWERED QUESTIONS

How are specific patterns of gene expression generated and maintained in a developing eukaryotic organism?

You learned in this chapter that chromatin remodelling is necessary to "open the door" for the transcription machinery to assemble at a promoter. However, researchers do not understand completely how the chromatin remodelling complexes are targeted to particular genes and regulated to give specific patterns of gene expression in a eukaryotic cell, or throughout the development of multicellular eukaryotic organism to maturity, and then through subsequent life. Since mutations in genes encoding chromatin remodelling components are directly linked to human cancers, understanding such basic functions of the complexes is a highly important goal.

Review

Go to CENGAGENOW™ at http://hed.nelson.com/ to access quizzing, animations, exercises, articles, and personalized homework help.

15.1 Regulation of Gene Expression in Prokaryotes

- Transcriptional control in prokaryotes involves short-term changes that turn specific genes on or off in response to changes in environmental conditions. The changes in gene activity are controlled by regulatory proteins that recognize operators of operons (see Figure 15.2).
- Regulatory proteins may be repressors, which slow the rate of transcription of operons, or activators, which increase the rate of transcription.
- Some repressors are made in an active form, in which they bind to the operator of an operon and inhibit its transcription. Combination with an inducer blocks the activity of the repressor and allows the operon to be transcribed (see Figure 15.3). Loss of repressor activity results in constant transcription.
- Other repressors are made in an inactive form, in which they are unable to inhibit transcription of an operon unless they combine with a corepressor (see Figure 15.4).
- Activators typically are made in inactive form, in which they cannot bind to their binding site next to an operon. Combining with another molecule, often a nucleotide, converts the activator into the form in which it binds with its binding site and recruits RNA polymerase, thereby stimulating transcription of the operon (see Figure 15.5).

15.2 Regulation of Transcription in Eukaryotes

- Operons are not found in eukaryotes. Instead, genes that encode proteins with related functions typically are scattered through the genome, while being regulated in a coordinated manner.
- Two general types of gene regulation occur in eukaryotes. Short-term regulation involves relatively rapid changes in gene expression in response to changes in environmental or physiological conditions. Long-term regulation involves changes in gene expression associated with the development and differentiation of an organism.
- Gene expression in eukaryotes is regulated at the transcriptional level (where most regulation occurs) and at posttranscriptional, translational, and posttranslational levels (see Figure 15.6).
- Transcriptionally active genes have a looser chromatin structure than transcriptionally inactive genes. The change in chromatin structure that accompanies the activation of transcription of a gene involves chromatin remodelling—specific histone modifications—particularly in the region of a gene's promoter (see Figure 15.7).
- Regulation of transcription initiation involves proteins binding to a gene's promoter and regulatory sites. At the promoter, general transcription factors bind and recruit RNA polymerase II, giving a very low level of transcription. Activator proteins bind to promoter proximal elements and increase the rate of transcription. Other activators bind to the enhancer and, through interaction with a coactivator, which binds also to the proteins at the promoter, greatly stimulate the rate of transcription (see Figures 15.8–15.10).
- The overall control of transcription of a gene depends on the particular regulatory proteins that bind to promoter proximal elements and enhancers. The regulatory proteins are cell type specific and may be activators or repressors. This gene regulation is achieved by a relatively low number of regulatory proteins, acting in various combinations (see Figure 15.11).
- The coordinated expression of genes with related functions is achieved by each of the related genes having the same regulatory sequences associated with them.
- Sections of chromosomes or whole chromosomes can be inactivated by DNA methylation, a phenomenon called silencing. DNA methylation is also involved in genomic imprinting, in which transcription of either the inherited maternal or paternal allele of a gene is inhibited permanently.

15.3 Posttranscriptional, Translational, and Posttranslational Regulation

- Posttranscriptional, translational, and posttranslational controls operate primarily to regulate the quantities of proteins synthesized in cells (see Figure 15.6).
- Posttranscriptional controls regulate pre-mRNA processing, mRNA availability for translation, and the rate at which mRNAs are degraded. In alternative splicing, different mRNAs are derived from the same pre-mRNA. In another process, small single-stranded RNAs complexed with proteins bind to mRNAs that have complementary sequences, and either the mRNA is cleaved or translation is blocked (see Figure 15.13).
- Translational regulation controls the rate at which mRNAs are used by ribosomes in protein synthesis.
- Posttranslational controls regulate the availability of functional proteins. Mechanisms of regulation include the alteration of protein activity by chemical modification, protein activation by processing of inactive precursors, and affecting the rate of degradation of a protein.

15.4 The Loss of Regulatory Controls in Cancer

- In cancer, cells partially or completely dedifferentiate, divide rapidly and uncontrollably, and break loose to form additional tumours in other parts of the body.
- Proto-oncogenes and tumour-suppressor genes typically are altered in cancer cells. Proto-oncogenes encode proteins that stimulate cell division. Their altered forms, oncogenes, are abnormally active. Tumour-suppressor genes in their normal form encode proteins that inhibit cell division. Mutated forms of these genes lose this inhibitory activity.
- Most cancers develop by multistep progression involving the successive alteration of several to many genes (see Figure 15.16).

Questions

Self-Test Questions

1. The control of the delivery of mRNA to the cytoplasm is an example of
   a. translational regulation.
   b. posttranslational regulation.
   c. transcriptional regulation.
   d. posttranscriptional regulation.
   e. deoxyribonucleic regulation.
2. For the *E. coli lac* operon, when glucose is absent and lactose is added,
   a. allolactose binds to the operator.
   b. the *lac* gene cannot make Lac repressor protein.
   c. allolactose binds the Lac repressor protein to remove it from the operator.
   d. the genes *lacZ*, *lacY*, and *lacA* are turned off.
   e. β-galactosidase decreases in the cell.
3. For the *E. coli lac* operon, when lactose is present
   a. and glucose is absent, cAMP binds and activates catabolic activator protein (CAP).
   b. and glucose is absent, the level of cAMP decreases.
   c. activated CAP binds the repressor protein to remove it from the operator gene.
   d. the cell prefers lactose over glucose.
   e. RNA polymerase cannot bind to the promoter.
4. For the *trp* operon,
   a. tryptophan is an inducer.
   b. when end-product tryptophan binds to the Trp repressor, it stops transcription of the tryptophan biosynthesis genes.
   c. Trp repressor is synthesized in active form.
   d. low levels of tryptophan bind to the *trp* operator and block transcription of the tryptophan biosynthesis genes.
   e. high levels of tryptophan activate RNA polymerase and induce transcription.
5. Chromatin remodelling activates gene expression when it:
   a. allows proteins initiating transcription to disengage from the promoter.
   b. winds genes tightly around histones.
   c. deacetylates histones.
   d. inserts nucleosomes into chromatin.
   e. recruits a protein complex that displaces nucleosome from the promoter.
6. Which statement about activation of transcription is *not correct*?
   a. A transcription factor binds the TATA box.
   b. A coactivator called a mediator forms a bridge between the promoter and the gene to be transcribed.
   c. Transcription factors bind the promoter and RNA polymerase.
   d. Activators bind to the enhancer region on DNA.
   e. RNA is transcribed downstream from the promoter region.
7. Which of the following statements does not support the idea of combinatorial gene regulation?
   a. Promoter proximal regions and enhancers regulate transcription of genes.
   b. A few regulatory genes can control a large number of transcribable genes.
   c. If repressor binding to enhancer is strong, gene expression is reduced.
   d. Genes requiring complex regulation have a single regulatory element.
   e. The number and types of regulatory sequences in the enhancer vary with each gene.
8. Normal ears in a certain mammal are perky; mutants have droopy ears. In males of these mammals, the gene encoding perky ears is transcribed only from the female parent. This is because the gene from the male parent is silenced by methylation. If the maternal gene is mutated,
   a. male offspring have droopy ears.
   b. male offspring have perky ears.
   c. male offspring have one droopy ear and one perky ear.
   d. the genetic mechanism is called alternative splicing.
   e. this is an example of posttranscriptional regulation.
9. Which of the following statements does not describe microRNA?
   a. MicroRNA is encoded by non–protein-coding genes.
   b. MicroRNA has a precursor that is folded and then cut by a Dicer enzyme.
   c. MicroRNA is an example of a molecule that induces RNA interference or gene silencing.
   d. MicroRNA is synthesized *in vitro* but not *in vivo*.
   e. MicroRNA has a function similar to that of small interfering RNAs.
10. Which of the following is not a characteristic of cancer cells?
    a. proto-oncogenes converting to active oncogenes
    b. the position of the *MYC* gene near a repressor gene
    c. the mutation of the *TP53* gene
    d. their stepwise developmental stages
    e. amplification of growth factors and growth factor receptors

Questions for Discussion

1. In a mutant strain of *E. coli*, the CAP protein is unable to combine with its target region of the *lac* operon. How would you expect the mutation to affect transcription when cells of this strain are subjected to the following conditions?
   a. Lactose and glucose are both available.
   b. Lactose is available, but glucose is not.
   c. Both lactose and glucose are unavailable.
2. Duchenne muscular dystrophy, an inherited genetic disorder, affects boys almost exclusively. Early in childhood, muscle tissue begins to break down in affected individuals, who typically die in their teens or early twenties as a result of respiratory failure. Muscle samples from women who carry the mutation reveal some regions of degenerating muscle tissue adjacent to other regions that are normal. Develop a hypothesis explaining these observations.
3. Eukaryotic transcription is generally controlled by binding of regulatory proteins to DNA sequences rather than by modification of RNA polymerases. Develop a hypothesis explaining why this is so.

Protein microarray, a key tool of proteomics, the study of the complete set of proteins that can be expressed by an organism's genome. Each coloured dot is a protein, with a specific colour for each protein being studied.

Pastaka/SPL/Photo Researchers, Inc.

Study Plan

16 DNA Technologies and Genomics

Why It Matters

Imagine yourself as a member of the crew of *Sorcerer II*, a private yacht renovated by maverick biologist J. Craig Venter to serve as an oceanic survey laboratory. Several months out of Halifax, down the Atlantic coast of the United States, and through the Panama Canal into the Pacific, you are now threading among the famed Galapagos Islands. Of course, your mind wanders to the historic voyage of the H.M.S. *Beagle* that brought Charles Darwin to these same waters some 170 years ago. Darwin returned home with specimens of novel species and notebooks filled with the scientific observations, illustrations, and ideas that would revolutionize our understanding of biology; you will return home with frozen seawater samples containing billions of base pairs of DNA sequence that may well, once again, cause us to reconsider cherished beliefs.

Back on land, the DNA is isolated, broken into random fragments, and then sequenced by industrial sequencing robots. Computer programs compare the individual sequences, looking for novel genes and areas of overlap that will help reconstruct the entire genomes of previously unknown organisms and viruses. Analysis of the massive data set reveals a staggering degree of genetic diversity among the unicellular microorganisms in the marine environment; 400 new species are discovered. Scanning for potential protein-coding genes predicts hundreds of thousands of likely proteins, a surprising fraction of them unknown to science.

Venter's survey of genetic diversity in the ocean is an example of the emerging field of metagenomics, in which DNA from an entire community of organisms in a particular niche is harvested collectively, sequenced, and analyzed using some of the DNA technologies described in this chapter. This approach is significant because, until very recently, our understanding of the genetics of the microbial world was based almost exclusively on the very small proportion of species that can be cultivated in the laboratory. With the tools of modern metagenomics, we gain access to the genomes of a whole new world of previously inaccessible organisms.

Metagenomic studies targeted to microbial communities in such diverse environments as the termite gut, deep sea hydrothermal vents, glaciers, geysers, the bovine rumen, and desert soil will certainly identify tens of thousands of novel genes that code for enzymes that may have applications in industrial biofuel production, food processing, pollution control, and drug development. The use of such genes for practical purposes is called genetic engineering.

Genetic engineering is the latest addition to the broad area known as *biotechnology,* which is any technique applied to biological systems or living organisms to make or modify products or processes for a specific purpose. Thus, biotechnology includes manipulations that do not involve DNA technologies, such as the use of yeast to brew beer and bake bread, and the use of bacteria to make yogurt and cheese.

In this chapter, we focus on how biologists isolate genes and manipulate them for basic and applied research. You will learn about the basic DNA technologies and their applications to research in biology, to genetic engineering, and to the analysis of genomes. You will also learn about some of the risks and controversies surrounding genetic engineering and about some of the scientific, social, and ethical questions related to its application.

We begin our discussion with a description of methods used to obtain genes in large quantities, an essential step for their analysis or manipulation.

16.1 DNA Cloning

Remember from Chapter 10 that a *clone* is a line of genetically identical cells or individuals derived from a single ancestor. DNA cloning is a method for producing many copies of a piece of DNA; the piece of DNA is referred to as a "gene of interest", which is a gene that a researcher wants to study or manipulate. Scientists clone DNA for many reasons. For example, a researcher might be interested in how a particular human gene functions. Each human cell contains only two copies of most genes, amounting to a very small fraction of the total amount of DNA in a diploid cell. In its natural state in the genome, then, the gene is extremely difficult to study. However, through DNA cloning, a researcher can produce a sample large enough for scientific experimentation.

Cloned genes are used in basic research to find out about their biological functions. For example, researchers can determine the DNA sequence of a cloned gene, giving them the ultimate information about its structure. Also, by manipulating the gene and inducing mutations in it, they can gain information about its function and about how its expression is regulated. Cloned genes can be expressed in bacteria, and the proteins encoded by the cloned genes can be produced in quantity and purified. Those proteins can be used in basic research, or, in the case of genes that encode proteins of pharmaceutical or clinical importance, they can be used in applied research.

An overview of one common method for cloning a gene of interest from a genome is shown in **Figure 16.1;** the method uses bacteria (commonly, *Escherichia coli*) and plasmids, the small circular DNA molecules that replicate separately from the bacterial chromosome (see Section 10.2). The researcher extracts DNA that contains a gene of interest from cells and cuts it into fragments. The fragments are inserted into plasmids producing *recombinant DNA molecules*—**recombinant DNA** is DNA from two or more different sources that are joined together. The recombinant plasmids are introduced into bacteria; each bacterium receives a different plasmid. The bacterium continues growing and dividing, and as it does, the plasmid continues to replicate. Through replication of the plasmid, amplification of the piece of DNA inserted into the plasmid occurs. The final step, then, is to identify the bacterium containing the plasmid with the gene of interest and isolate it for further study.

16.1a Bacterial Enzymes Called Restriction Endonucleases Form the Basis of DNA Cloning

The key to DNA cloning is the specific joining of two DNA molecules from different sources, such as a genomic DNA fragment and a bacterial plasmid (see Figure 16.1). This specific joining of DNA is made possible, in part, by bacterial enzymes called **restriction endonucleases** (also called **restriction enzymes**), discovered in the late 1960s. Restriction enzymes recognize short, specific DNA sequences called *restriction sites,* typically four to eight base pairs long, and cut the DNA at specific locations within those sequences. The DNA fragments produced by cutting a long DNA molecule with a restriction enzyme are known as **restriction fragments.**

The "restriction" in the name of the enzymes refers to their normal role inside bacteria, in which the enzymes defend against viral attack by breaking down (restricting) the DNA molecules of infecting viruses. The bacterium protects the restriction sites in its own DNA from cutting by modifying bases in those sites enzymatically, thereby blocking the action of its restriction enzyme.

Hundreds of different restriction enzymes have been identified, each one cutting DNA at a specific restriction site. As illustrated by the restriction site of *Eco*RI **(Figure 16.2, p. 346),** most restriction sites are symmetrical in that the sequence of nucleotides read in the 5′→3′ direction on one strand is the same as the sequence read in the 5′→3′ direction on the complementary strand. The restriction enzymes most used in cloning—such as *Eco*RI—cleave the sugar–phosphate backbones of DNA to produce DNA fragments with single-stranded ends (step 1). The ends are called **sticky ends** because the short, single-stranded regions can form hydrogen bonds with complementary sticky ends on any other DNA molecules cut with the same enzyme. For example, step 2 shows the insertion of a DNA molecule with sticky ends produced by *Eco*RI between two other DNA molecules with the same sticky ends. The pairings leave nicks in the sugar–phosphate backbones of the DNA strands that are sealed by *DNA ligase,* an enzyme that has the same function in DNA replication (step 3; see Section 13.3). The result is DNA from two different sources joined together—a recombinant DNA molecule.

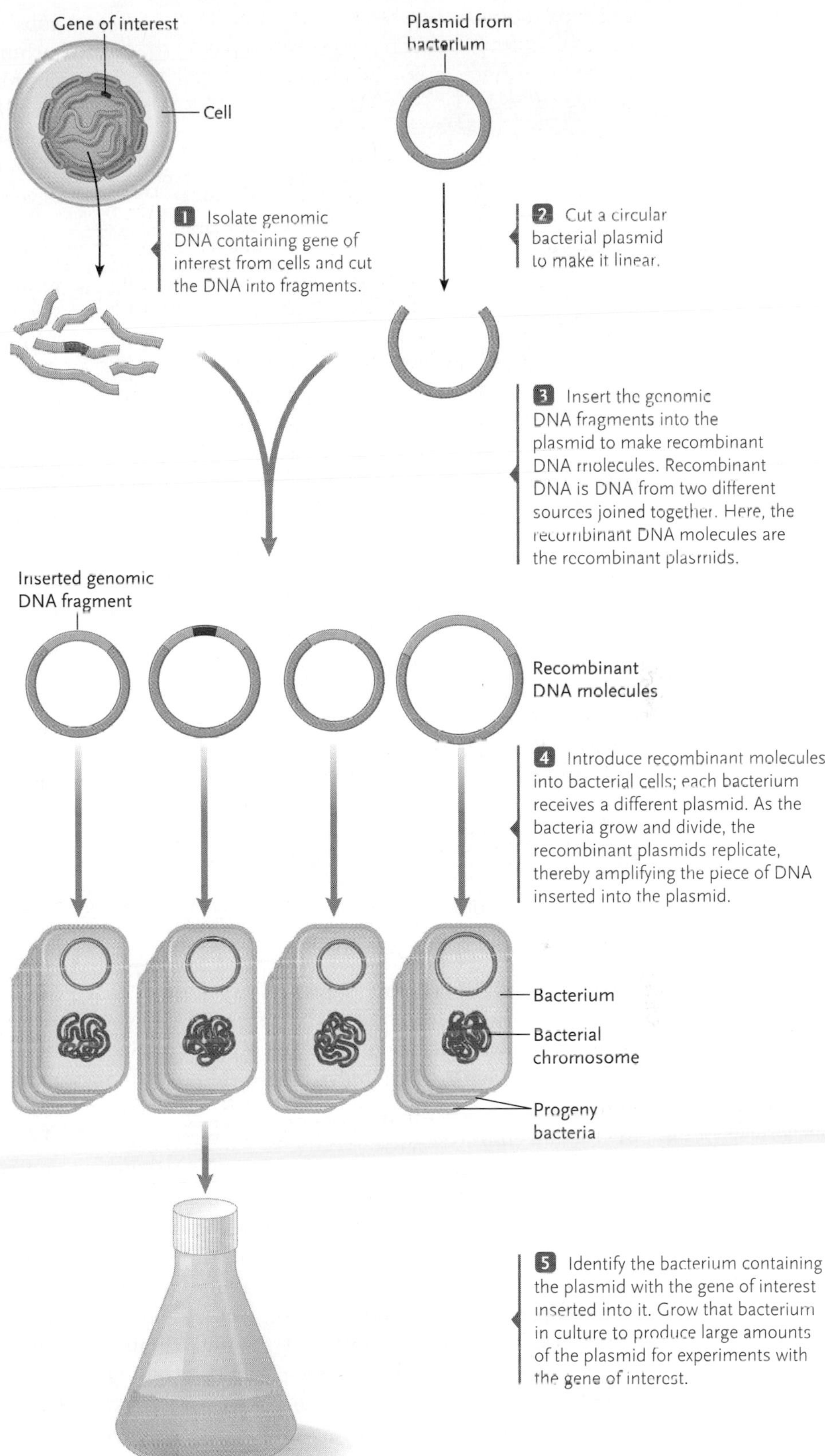

Gene of interest
Plasmid from bacterium
Cell
1 Isolate genomic DNA containing gene of interest from cells and cut the DNA into fragments.
2 Cut a circular bacterial plasmid to make it linear.
3 Insert the genomic DNA fragments into the plasmid to make recombinant DNA molecules. Recombinant DNA is DNA from two different sources joined together. Here, the recombinant DNA molecules are the recombinant plasmids.
Inserted genomic DNA fragment
Recombinant DNA molecules
4 Introduce recombinant molecules into bacterial cells; each bacterium receives a different plasmid. As the bacteria grow and divide, the recombinant plasmids replicate, thereby amplifying the piece of DNA inserted into the plasmid.
Bacterium
Bacterial chromosome
Progeny bacteria
5 Identify the bacterium containing the plasmid with the gene of interest inserted into it. Grow that bacterium in culture to produce large amounts of the plasmid for experiments with the gene of interest.

Figure 16.1
Overview of cloning DNA fragments in a bacterial plasmid.

16.1b Bacterial Plasmids Illustrate the Use of Restriction Enzymes in Cloning

The bacterial plasmids used for cloning are examples of cloning vectors—DNA molecules into which a DNA fragment can be inserted to form a recombinant DNA molecule for cloning. Bacterial plasmid cloning vectors do not naturally occur in bacteria; they are plasmids modified to have special features. Commonly, plasmid cloning vectors are engineered to contain two genes that are useful in the final steps of a cloning experiment for identifying bacteria that have recombinant plasmids from those that do not. The amp^R gene encodes an enzyme that breaks down the antibiotic ampicillin; when the plasmid is introduced into *E. coli* and the amp^R gene is expressed, the bacteria become resistant to ampicillin. The $lacZ^+$ gene encodes β-galactosidase (recall the *lac* operon from Section 15.1), which hydrolyzes the sugar lactose, as well as a number of synthetic substrates. Restriction sites are located within the $lacZ^+$ gene but do not alter the gene's function. For a given cloning experiment, one of these restriction sites is chosen.

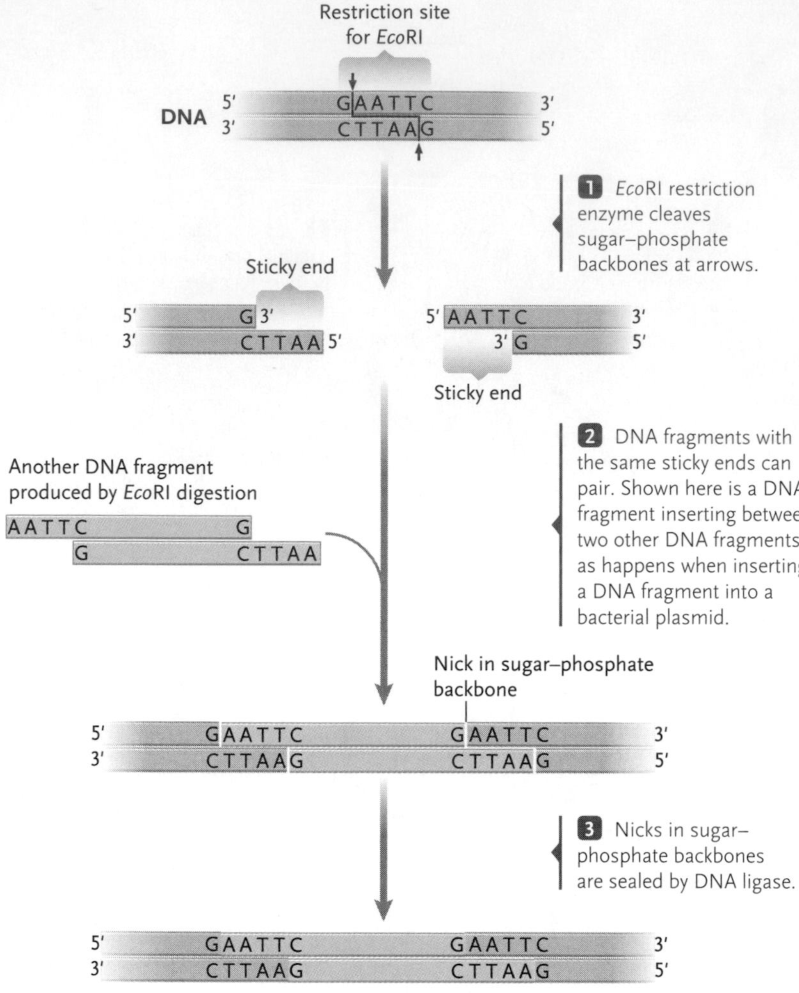
Restriction site
for EcoRI
DNA
5'
3'
GAATTC
CTTAAG
3'
5'
1 EcoRI restriction enzyme cleaves sugar–phosphate backbones at arrows.
Sticky end
5' G 3'
3' CTTAA 5'
5' AATTC 3'
3' G 5'
Sticky end
2 DNA fragments with the same sticky ends can pair. Shown here is a DNA fragment inserting between two other DNA fragments, as happens when inserting a DNA fragment into a bacterial plasmid.
Another DNA fragment
produced by EcoRI digestion
AATTC G
G CTTAA
Nick in sugar–phosphate
backbone
5' GAATTC GAATTC 3'
3' CTTAAG CTTAAG 5'
3 Nicks in sugar–phosphate backbones are sealed by DNA ligase.
5' GAATTC GAATTC 3'
3' CTTAAG CTTAAG 5'
Recombinant DNA molecule

Figure 16.2
The restriction site for the restriction enzyme *Eco*RI, and the generation of a recombinant DNA molecule by complementary base pairing of DNA fragments produced by digestion with the same restriction enzyme.

Cloning a Gene of Interest. **Figure 16.3** expands on the overview of Figure 16.1 to show the steps used to clone a gene of interest using a plasmid cloning vector and restriction enzymes. Genomic DNA isolated from the organism in which the gene is found is cut with a restriction enzyme, and a plasmid cloning vector is cut within the *lacZ*$^+$ gene with the same restriction enzyme (steps 1 and 2). Mixing the DNA fragments and cut plasmid together with DNA ligase produces various joined molecules as the sticky ends pair and the enzyme seals them together. Some of these molecules are recombinant plasmids consisting of, in each case, a DNA fragment inserted into the plasmid cloning vector; others are nonrecombinant plasmids resulting from the cut plasmid resealed into a circle without an inserted fragment (step 3). In addition, ligase joins together pieces of genomic DNA with no plasmid involved. Only the recombinant plasmids are important in the cloning of the gene of interest; we sort out the other two undesired molecules in later steps.

Next, the DNA molecules are transformed—introduced—into ampicillin-sensitive, *lacZ*$^-$ *E. coli* (which cannot make β-galactosidase), and the transformed bacteria are spread on a plate of agar growth medium containing ampicillin and the β-galactosidase substrate X-gal (steps 4 and 5). (Section 10.2 describes techniques for transformation of DNA into bacteria.) Only bacteria with a plasmid can grow and form colonies because expression of the plasmid's *amp*^{R} gene makes the bacteria resistant to ampicillin (see Figure 16.3 results). Within each cell of a colony, the plasmids have replicated until a hundred or so are present.

The X-gal in the medium distinguishes between bacteria that have been transformed with recombinant plasmids and nonrecombinant plasmids by *blue-white screening* (see Figure 16.3, Interpreting the Results). If a colony produces β-galactosidase, it converts X-gal to a blue product and the colony turns blue, but if a colony does not produce the enzyme, X-gal is unchanged and the colony remains white. Colonies containing nonrecombinant plasmids have an intact *lacZ*$^+$ gene, produce the enzyme, and turn blue. Colonies containing recombinant plasmids are white because those plasmids each contain a DNA fragment inserted into the *lacZ*$^+$ gene, so they do not produce the enzyme. The white colonies are examined to find the one containing a recombinant plasmid with the gene of interest.

Two researchers, Paul Berg and Stanley Cohen, were prime movers in the development of DNA cloning techniques using restriction enzymes and bacterial plasmids. Berg and Cohen received a Nobel Prize in 1980 for their research, which pushed DNA technology to the forefront of biological investigations.

Identifying the Clone Containing the Gene of Interest. How is a clone containing the gene of interest identified among the population of clones? The gene of interest has a unique DNA sequence, which is the basis for one commonly used identification technique. In this technique, called **DNA hybridization**, the gene of interest is identified in the set of clones when it base-pairs with a short, single-stranded complementary DNA or RNA molecule called a *nucleic acid probe* **(Figure 16.4, p. 348).** The probe is typically labelled with a radioactive or a nonradioactive tag so investigators can detect it. In our example, if we know the sequence of part of the gene of interest, we can use that information to design and synthesize a nucleic acid probe. Or we can take advantage of DNA sequence similarities of evolutionarily related organisms. For instance, we could make a probe for a human gene based on the sequence of an equivalent mouse gene. Once a colony containing plasmids with the gene of interest has been identified, that colony can be used to produce large quantities of the cloned gene.

16.1c DNA Libraries Contain Collections of Cloned DNA Fragments

As you have seen, the starting point for cloning a gene of interest is a large set of plasmid clones carrying fragments representing all of the DNA of an organism's genome. A collection of clones that contains a copy of every DNA sequence in a genome is called a **genomic library.**

Figure 16.3
Cloning a gene of interest in a plasmid cloning vector.

PURPOSE: Cloning a gene produces many copies of a gene of interest that can be used, for example, to determine the DNA sequence of the gene, to manipulate the gene in basic research experiments, to understand its function, and to produce the protein encoded by the gene.

PROTOCOL:

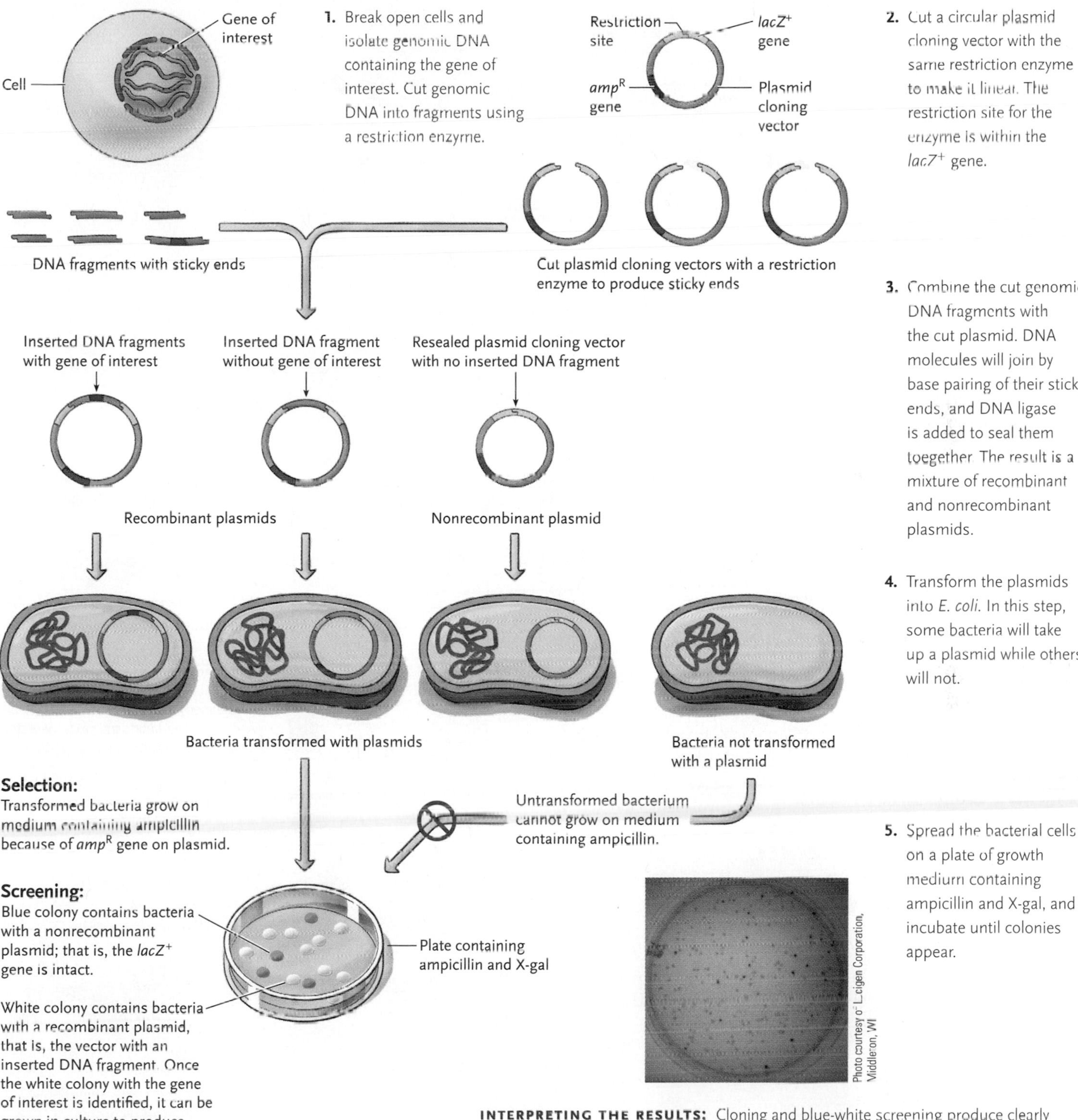

Gene of interest
Cell
1. Break open cells and isolate genomic DNA containing the gene of interest. Cut genomic DNA into fragments using a restriction enzyme.
Restriction site
lacZ+ gene
ampR gene
Plasmid cloning vector
2. Cut a circular plasmid cloning vector with the same restriction enzyme to make it linear. The restriction site for the enzyme is within the lacZ+ gene.
DNA fragments with sticky ends
Cut plasmid cloning vectors with a restriction enzyme to produce sticky ends
3. Combine the cut genomic DNA fragments with the cut plasmid. DNA molecules will join by base pairing of their sticky ends, and DNA ligase is added to seal them together. The result is a mixture of recombinant and nonrecombinant plasmids.
Inserted DNA fragments with gene of interest
Inserted DNA fragment without gene of interest
Resealed plasmid cloning vector with no inserted DNA fragment
Recombinant plasmids
Nonrecombinant plasmid
4. Transform the plasmids into E. coli. In this step, some bacteria will take up a plasmid while others will not.
Bacteria transformed with plasmids
Bacteria not transformed with a plasmid
Selection:
Transformed bacteria grow on medium containing ampicillin because of ampR gene on plasmid.
Untransformed bacterium cannot grow on medium containing ampicillin.
5. Spread the bacterial cells on a plate of growth medium containing ampicillin and X-gal, and incubate until colonies appear.
Screening:
Blue colony contains bacteria with a nonrecombinant plasmid; that is, the lacZ+ gene is intact.
White colony contains bacteria with a recombinant plasmid, that is, the vector with an inserted DNA fragment. Once the white colony with the gene of interest is identified, it can be grown in culture to produce large quantities of the plasmid.
Plate containing ampicillin and X-gal
Photo courtesy of Lucigen Corporation, Middleton, WI

INTERPRETING THE RESULTS: Cloning and blue-white screening produce clearly identifiable white colonies containing recombinant plasmids. Most of the white colonies will contain plasmids that do not contain the gene of interest. Further screening will be done to identify the particular white colony that contains a plasmid with the gene of interest (Figure 16.4). Once identified, the colony can be cultured to produce large quantities of the plasmid for analysis or manipulation of the gene.

Figure 16.4
DNA hybridization to identify a DNA sequence of interest.

PURPOSE: Hybridization with a specific DNA probe allows researchers to detect a specific DNA sequence, such as a gene, within a population of DNA molecules. Here, DNA hybridization is used to screen a collection of bacterial colonies to identify those containing a recombinant plasmid with a gene of interest.

PROTOCOL:

1. Prepare master plates of white colonies detected in the blue-white screening step of Figure 16.3. These colonies contain bacteria with recombinant plasmids. Hundreds or thousands of colonies can be screened for the gene of interest by using many master plates.

2. Lay a special filter paper on the plate to pick up some cells from each colony. This produces a replica of the colony pattern on the filter.

3. Treat the filter to break open the cells and to denature the released DNA to single strands. The single-stranded DNA sticks to the filter in the same position as the colony from which it was derived.

4. Add a labelled single-stranded probe (DNA or RNA) for the gene of interest and incubate. The label can be radioactive or nonradioactive. If a recombinant plasmid's inserted DNA fragment is complementary to the probe, the two will hybridize, that is, form base pairs. Wash off excess labelled probe.

5. Detect the hybridization event by looking for the labelled tag on the probe. If the probe was radioactively labelled, place the filter against photographic film. The decaying radioactive compound exposes the film, giving a dark spot when the film is developed. Correlate the position of any dark spot on the film to the original colony pattern on the master plate. Isolate the colony and use it to produce large quantities of the gene of interest.

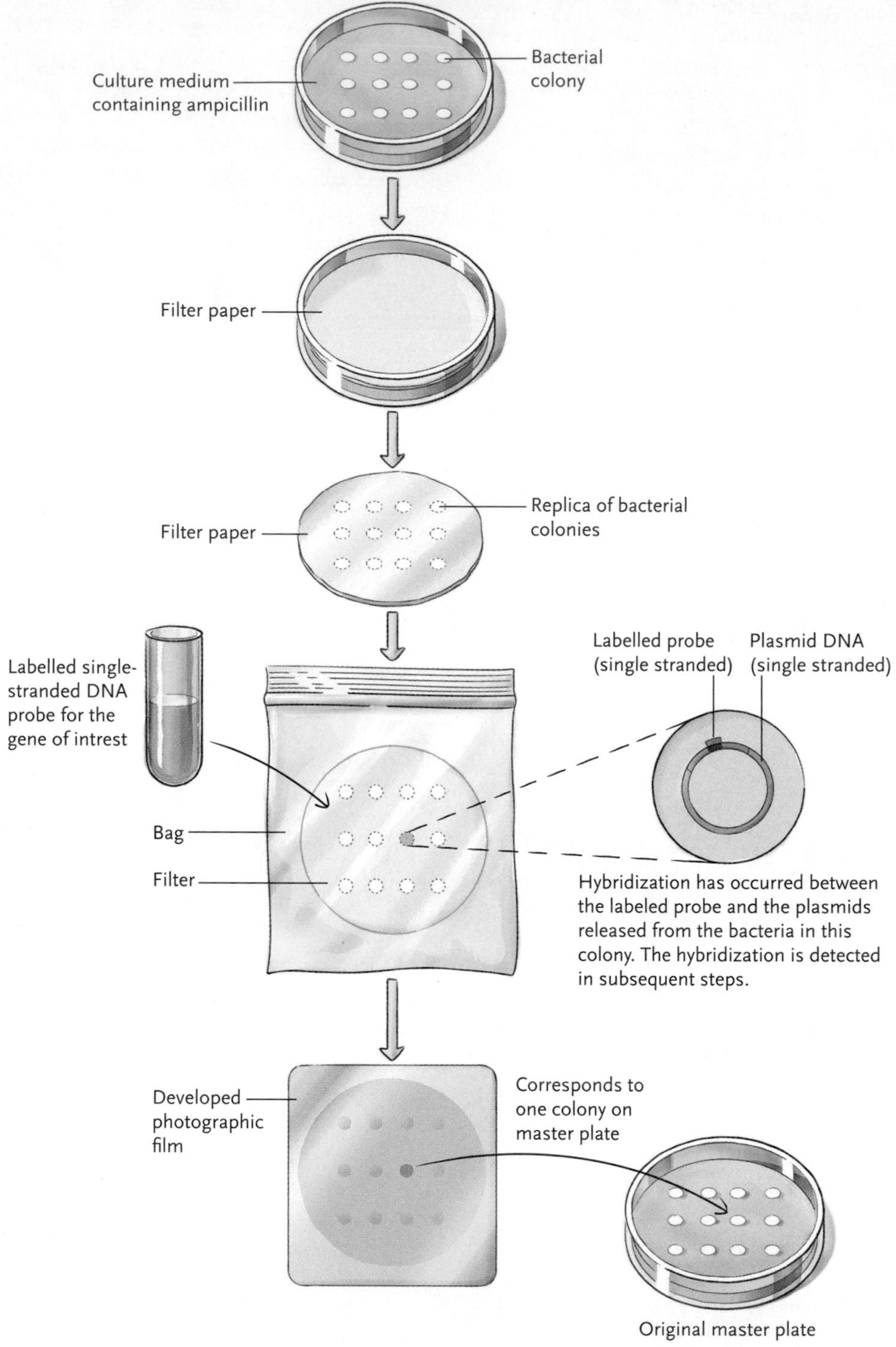

INTERPRETING THE RESULTS: DNA hybridization with a labelled probe enables a researcher to home in on a sequence of interest. If the probe is for a particular gene, it allows the specific identification of a colony containing bacteria with recombinant plasmids carrying that gene. The specificity of the method depends directly on the probe used. The same collection of bacterial clones can be used again and again to search for recombinant plasmids carrying different genes or different plasmids of interest simply by changing the probe used in the experiment.

A genomic library can be made using plasmid cloning vectors or any other kind of cloning vector. The number of clones in a genomic library increases with the size of the genome. For example, a yeast genomic library of plasmid clones consists of hundreds of plasmids, whereas a human genomic library of plasmid clones consists of thousands of plasmids.

A genomic library is a resource containing all of the DNA of an organism cut into pieces. Just as for a book library, where you can search through the same set of books on various occasions to find different passages of interest, you can search through the same genomic library on various occasions to find and isolate different genes or other DNA sequences.

Researchers also commonly use another kind of DNA library that is made starting with mRNA molecules isolated from a cell. To convert single-stranded mRNA to double-stranded DNA for cloning (RNA cannot be cloned), first they use the enzyme *reverse transcriptase* (made by retroviruses) to make a single-stranded DNA that is complementary to the mRNA. Then they degrade the mRNA strand with an enzyme and use DNA polymerase to make a second DNA strand that is complementary to the first. The result is **complementary DNA (cDNA).** After adding restriction sites to each end, they insert the cDNA into a cloning vector as described for the genomic library. The entire collection of cloned cDNAs made from the mRNAs isolated from a cell is a **cDNA library.**

Not all genes are active in every cell. Therefore, a cDNA library is limited in that it includes copies of only the genes that were active in the cells used as the starting point for creation of the library. This limitation can be an advantage, however, in identifying genes active in one cell type and not another. cDNA libraries are useful, therefore, for providing clues to the changes in gene activity that are responsible for cell differentiation and specialization. An ingenious method for comparing the cDNA libraries produced by different cell types—the DNA chip—is described later in this chapter.

cDNA libraries provide a critical advantage to genetic engineers who wish to insert eukaryotic genes into bacteria, particularly when the bacteria are to be used as "factories" for making the protein encoded in the gene. The genes in eukaryotic nuclear DNA typically contain many *introns,* spacer sequences that interrupt the amino acid–coding sequence of a gene (see Section 14.3). Because bacterial DNA does not contain introns, bacteria are not equipped to process eukaryotic genes correctly. However, the cDNA copy of a eukaryotic mRNA already has the introns removed, so bacteria can transcribe and translate it accurately to make eukaryotic proteins.

Genomic and cDNA libraries both depend on cloning in a living cell to produce multiple copies of the DNA of interest. Next we look at a highly automated method of making copies of a targeted piece of DNA in a genome.

16.1d The Polymerase Chain Reaction (PCR) Amplifies DNA *In Vitro*

Producing multiple DNA copies by cloning requires a series of techniques and considerable time. A much more rapid process, **polymerase chain reaction (PCR),** produces an extremely large number of copies of a specific DNA sequence from a DNA mixture without having to clone the sequence in a host organism. The process is called *amplification* because it increases the amount of DNA to the point where it can be analyzed or manipulated easily. Developed in 1983 by Kary B. Mullis and F. Faloona at Cetus Corporation (Emeryville, CA), PCR has become one of the most important tools in modern molecular biology, finding wide application in all areas of biology. Mullis received a Nobel Prize in 1993 for his role in the development of PCR.

How PCR is performed is shown in **Figure 16.5 (p. 350).** PCR essentially is DNA replication, but a special case in which a DNA polymerase replicates just a portion of a DNA molecule rather than the whole molecule. PCR takes advantage of a characteristic common to all DNA polymerases: these enzymes add nucleotides only to the end of an existing chain called the *primer* (see Section 13.3). For replication to take place, a primer therefore must be in place, base-paired to the template chain at which replication is to begin. By cycling 20 to 30 times through a series of steps, PCR amplifies the target sequence, producing millions of copies.

Since the primers used in PCR are designed to bracket only the sequence of interest, the cycles replicate only this sequence from a mixture of essentially any DNA molecules. Thus, PCR not only finds the "needle in the haystack" among all the sequences in a mixture but also makes millions of copies of the "needle"—the DNA sequence of interest. Usually, no further purification of the amplified sequence is necessary.

The characteristics of PCR allow extremely small DNA samples to be amplified to concentrations high enough for analysis. PCR is used, for example, to produce enough DNA for analysis from the root of a single human hair, or from a small amount of blood, semen, or saliva, such as the traces left at the scene of a crime. It is also used to extract and multiply DNA sequences from skeletal remains; ancient sources such as mammoths, Neanderthals, and Egyptian mummies; and, in rare cases, amber-entombed fossils, fossil bones, and fossil plant remains.

A successful outcome of PCR is shown by analyzing a sample of the amplified DNA using **agarose gel electrophoresis** to see if the copies are the same length as the target **(Figure 16.6, p. 351).** Gel electrophoresis is a technique by which DNA, RNA, or protein molecules are separated in a gel subjected to an electric field. The type of gel and the conditions used vary with the experiment, but in each case, the gel functions as a molecular sieve to separate the macromolecules based on size, electrical

Figure 16.5
The polymerase chain reaction (PCR).

PURPOSE: To amplify—produce large numbers of copies of—a target DNA sequence in the test tube without cloning.

PROTOCOL: A polymerase chain reaction mixture has four key elements: **(1)** the DNA with the target sequence to be amplified; **(2)** a pair of DNA primers, one complementary to one end of the target sequence and the other complementary to the other end of the target sequence; **(3)** the four nucleoside triphosphate precursors for DNA synthesis (dATP, dTTP, dGTP, and dCTP); and **(4)** DNA polymerase. Since PCR uses high temperatures for some of the steps, a heat-stable DNA polymerase is used, typically one isolated from a microorganism that grows in a high-temperature area such as a thermal pool or near a deep-sea vent.

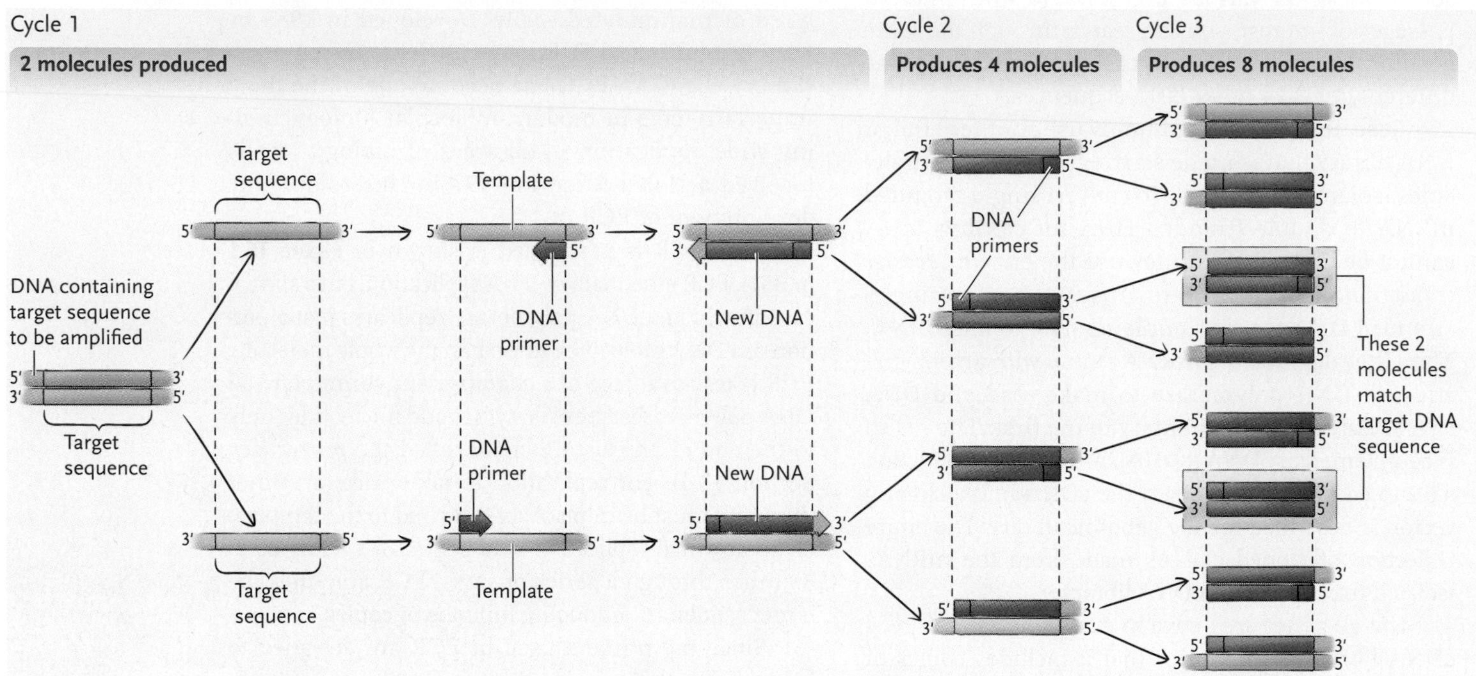

1. Denaturation: Heat DNA containing target sequence to denature it to single strands.
2. Annealing: Cool the mixture to allow the two primers to anneal to their complementary sequences at the two ends of the target sequence.
3. Heat to the optimal temperature for DNA polymerase to extend the primers, using the four nucleoside triphosphate precursors to make complementary copies of the two template strands. This completes cycle 1 of PCR; the end result is two molecules.
4. Repeat the same steps of denaturation, annealing of primers, and extension in cycle 2, producing a total of four molecules.
5. Repeat the same steps in cycle 3, producing a total of eight molecules. Two of the eight match the exact length of the target DNA sequence (highlighted in yellow).

INTERPRETING THE RESULTS: After three cycles, PCR produces a pair of molecules matching the target sequence. Subsequent cycles amplify these molecules to the point where they outnumber all other molecules in the reaction by many orders of magnitude.

charge, or other properties. For separating large DNA molecules, such as those typically produced by PCR, a gel made of agarose, a natural molecule isolated from seaweed, is used because of its large pore size.

For PCR experiments, the size of the amplified DNA is determined by comparing the position of the DNA band with the positions of DNA fragments of known size separated on the gel at the same time. If that size matches the predicted size for the target DNA, PCR is deemed successful. In some cases, such as DNA from ancient sources, a size prediction may not be possible; in this case, agarose gel electrophoresis

Figure 16.6
Separation of DNA fragments by agarose gel electrophoresis.

PURPOSE: Gel electrophoresis separates DNA molecules, RNA molecules, or proteins according to their sizes, electrical charges, or other properties through a gel in an electric field. Different gel types and conditions are used for different molecules and types of applications. A common gel for separating large DNA fragments is made of agarose.

PROTOCOL:

1. Prepare a gel consisting of a thin slab of agarose and place it in a gel box in between two electrodes. The gel has wells for placing the DNA samples to be analyzed. Add buffer to cover the gel.
2. Load DNA sample solutions, such as PCR products, into wells of the gel, alongside a well loaded with marker DNA fragments of known sizes.

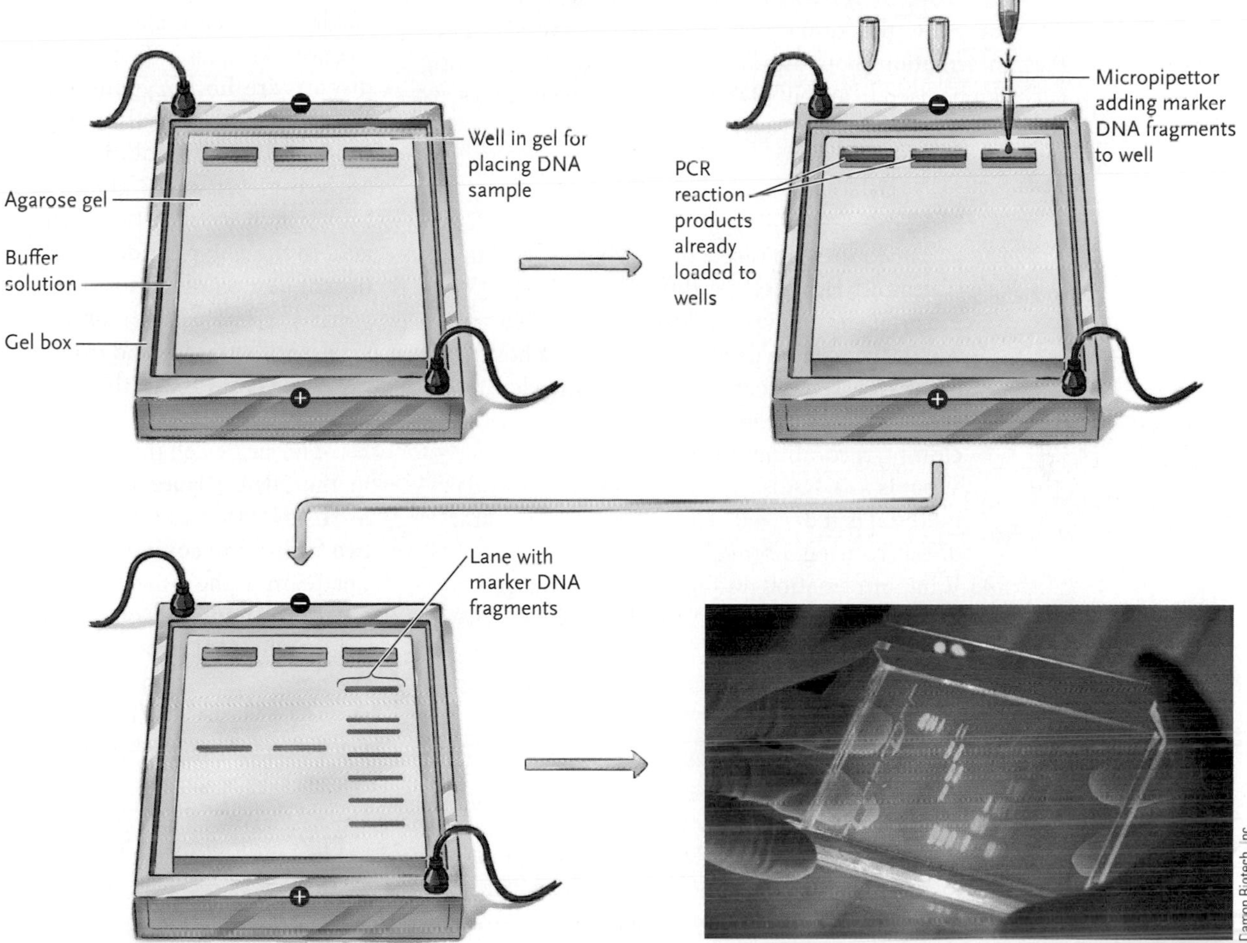

3. Apply an electric current to the gel; DNA fragments are negatively charged, so they migrate to the positive pole. Shorter DNA fragments migrate faster than longer DNA fragments. At the completion of the separation, DNA fragments of the same length have formed bands in the gel. At this point, the bands are invisible.
4. Stain the gel with a dye that binds to DNA. The dye fluoresces under UV light, enabling the DNA bands to be seen and photographed. An actual gel showing separated DNA bands stained and visualized this way is shown.

INTERPRETING THE RESULTS: Agarose gel electrophoresis separates DNA fragments according to their length. The lengths of the DNA fragments being analyzed are determined by measuring their migration distances and comparing those distances to a calibration curve of the migration distances of the marker bands, which have known length. For PCR, agarose gel electrophoresis shows whether DNA of the correct length was amplified. For restriction enzyme digests, this technique shows whether fragments are produced as expected.

analysis simply indicates whether there was DNA in the sample that could be amplified.

The advantages of PCR have made it the technique of choice for researchers, law enforcement agencies, and forensic specialists whose primary interest is in the amplification of specific DNA fragments up to a practical maximum of a few thousand base pairs. Cloning remains the technique of choice for amplification of longer fragments. The major limitation of PCR relates to the primers. To design a primer for PCR, the researcher must first have sequence information about the target DNA. By contrast, cloning can be used to amplify DNA of unknown sequence.

Study Break

1. What features do restriction enzymes have in common? How do they differ?
2. Plasmid cloning vectors are one type of cloning vector that can be used with *E. coli* as a host organism. What features of a plasmid cloning vector make it useful for constructing and cloning recombinant DNA molecules?
3. What is a cDNA library, and from what cellular material is it derived? How does a cDNA library differ from a genomic library?
4. What information and materials are needed to amplify a region of DNA using PCR?

16.2 Applications of DNA Technologies

The ability to clone pieces of DNA—genes, especially—and to amplify specific segments of DNA by PCR revolutionized biology. These and other DNA technologies are now used for research in all areas of biology, including cloning genes to determine their structure, function, and regulation of expression; manipulating genes to determine how their products function in cellular or developmental processes; and identifying differences in DNA sequences among individuals in ecological studies. The same DNA technologies also have practical applications, including medical and forensic detection, modification of animals and plants, and the manufacture of commercial products. In this section, case studies provide examples of how the techniques are used to answer questions and solve problems.

16.2a DNA Technologies Are Used in Molecular Testing for Many Human Genetic Diseases

Many human genetic diseases are caused by defects in enzymes or other proteins that result from mutations at the DNA level. Once scientists have identified the specific mutations responsible for human genetic diseases, they can often use DNA technologies to develop molecular tests for those diseases. One example is sickle cell disease (see *Why It Matters* in Chapter 11, Section 11.2, and Section 12.4). People with this disease are homozygous for a DNA mutation that affects hemoglobin, the oxygen-carrying molecule of the blood. Hemoglobin consists of two copies each of the α-globin and β-globin polypeptides. The mutation, which is in the β-globin gene, alters one amino acid in the polypeptide. As a consequence, the function of hemoglobin is significantly impaired in individuals homozygous for the mutation (who have sickle cell anemia) and mildly impaired in individuals heterozygous for the mutation (who have sickle cell trait).

The sickle cell mutation changes a restriction site in the DNA **(Figure 16.7)**. Three restriction sites for *Mst*II are associated with the normal β-globin gene, two within the coding sequence of the gene and one upstream of the gene. The sickle cell mutation eliminates the middle site of the three. Cutting the β-globin gene with *Mst*II produces two DNA fragments from the normal gene and one fragment from the mutated gene (see Figure 16.7). Restriction enzyme–generated DNA fragments of different lengths from the same region of the genome such as in this example are known as **restriction fragment length polymorphisms** (RFLPs, pronounced "riff-lips").

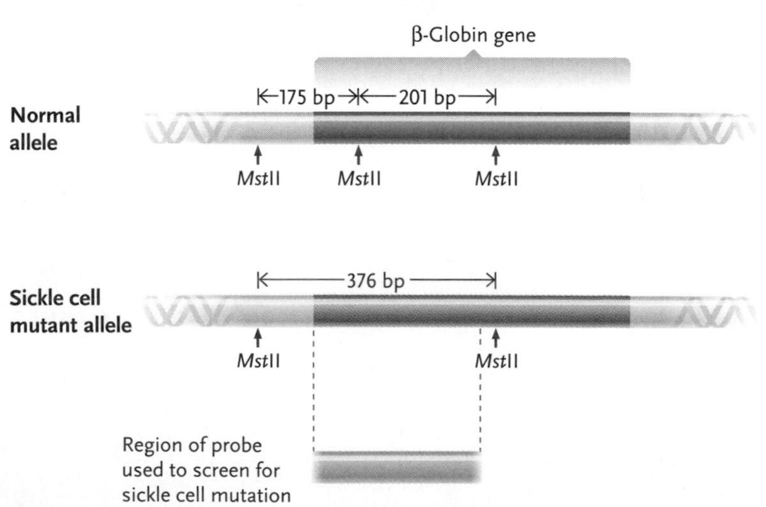

Figure 16.7
Restriction site differences between the normal and sickle cell mutant alleles of the β-globin gene. The figure shows a DNA segment that can be used as a probe to identify these alleles in subsequent analysis (see Figure 16.8).

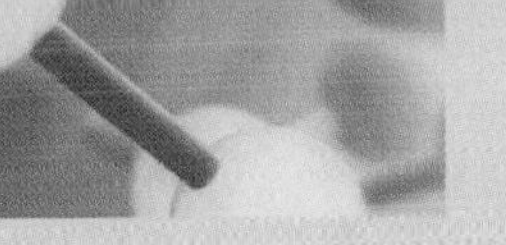

MOLECULE BEHIND BIOLOGY
Ethidium Bromide

Figure 16.6 shows an agarose gel containing DNA fragments separated by electrophoresis. The fragments appear orange because a stain has bound to the DNA and is fluorescing under ultraviolet light. The stain is ethidium bromide **(Figure 1).** This relatively flat molecule slides neatly between the bases of DNA by a process called intercalation—hence, its usefulness as a stain. However, intercalation into DNA around replication forks can increase the frequency of addition/deletion mutations in cultured cells.

Figure 1
Ethidium bromide.

RFLPs typically are analyzed using **Southern blot analysis** (named after its inventor, researcher Edward Southern) **(Figure 16.8, p. 354).** In this technique, genomic DNA is digested with a restriction enzyme, and the DNA fragments are separated using agarose gel electrophoresis. The fragments are then transferred—blotted—to a filter paper, and a labelled probe is used to identify a DNA sequence of interest from among the many thousands of fragments on the filter paper.

Analyzing DNA for the sickle cell mutation by *Mst*II digestion and Southern blot analysis is straightforward (see Figure 16.8). An individual with sickle cell disease will have one DNA band of 376 bp detected by the probe (lane A), a healthy individual will have two DNA bands of 175 and 201 bp (lane B), and an individual with sickle cell trait (heterozygous for normal and mutant alleles) will have three DNA bands of 376 bp (mutant allele) and 201 and 175 bp (normal allele) (lane C). The same probe detects all three RFLP fragments by binding to all or part of the sequence.

Restriction enzyme digestion and Southern blot analysis may be used to test for a number of other human genetic diseases, including phenylketonuria and Duchenne muscular dystrophy. In some cases, restriction enzyme digestion is combined with PCR for a quicker, easier analysis. The gene or region of the gene with the restriction enzyme variation is first amplified using PCR, and the amplified DNA is then cut with the diagnostic restriction enzyme. Amplification produces enough DNA so that separation by size on an agarose gel produces clearly visible bands, positioned according to fragment length. Researchers can then determine whether the fragment lengths match a normal or abnormal RFLP pattern. This method eliminates the need for a probe or for Southern blotting.

16.2b DNA Fingerprinting Is Used to Identify Human Individuals and Individuals of Other Species

Just as each human has a unique set of fingerprints, each also has unique combinations and variations of DNA sequences (with the exception of identical twins) known as *DNA fingerprints*. **DNA fingerprinting** is a technique used to distinguish between individuals of the same species using DNA samples. Invented by Sir Alec Jeffreys in 1985, DNA fingerprinting has become a mainstream technique for distinguishing human individuals, notably in forensics and paternity testing. Although the technique can be applied to all kinds of animals and plants, in this chapter we focus on humans.

DNA Fingerprinting Principles. In DNA fingerprinting, scientists use molecular techniques, most typically PCR, to analyze DNA variations at various loci in the genome. Several loci in noncoding regions of the genome are used for analysis. Each locus is an example of a *short tandem repeat* (STR) sequence, meaning that it has a short sequence of DNA repeated in series, with each repeat about 3 to 5 bp. Each locus has a different repeated sequence, and the number of repeats varies among individuals in a population. For example, one STR locus has the sequence AGAT repeated between 8 and 20 times. As a further source of variation, a given individual is either homozygous or heterozygous for an STR allele; perhaps you are homozygous for the 11-repeat allele or heterozygous for a 9-repeat allele and a 15-repeat allele. Likely your DNA fingerprint for this locus is different from most of the others in your class. Because each individual has an essentially unique combination of alleles (identical twins are the exception), analysis of multiple STR loci can discriminate between DNA of different individuals.

Figure 16.8
Southern blot analysis.

PURPOSE: The Southern blot technique allows researchers to identify DNA fragments of interest after separating DNA fragments on a gel. One application is to compare different samples of genomic DNA cut with a restriction enzyme to detect specific restriction fragment length polymorphisms. Here the technique is used to distinguish between individuals with sickle cell disease, individuals with sickle cell trait, and normal individuals.

PROTOCOL:

1. Isolate genomic DNA and digest with a restriction enzyme. Here, genomic DNA is isolated from three individuals: A, sickle cell disease (homozygous for the sickle cell mutant allele); B, normal (homozygous for the normal allele); and C, sickle cell trait (heterozygote for sickle cell mutant allele). Digest the DNA with *Mst*II.

2. Separate the DNA fragments by agarose gel electrophoresis. The thousands of differently sized DNA fragments generated results in a smear of DNA down the length of each lane in the gel, which can be seen after staining the DNA. (Gel electrophoresis and gel staining are shown in Figure 16.6).

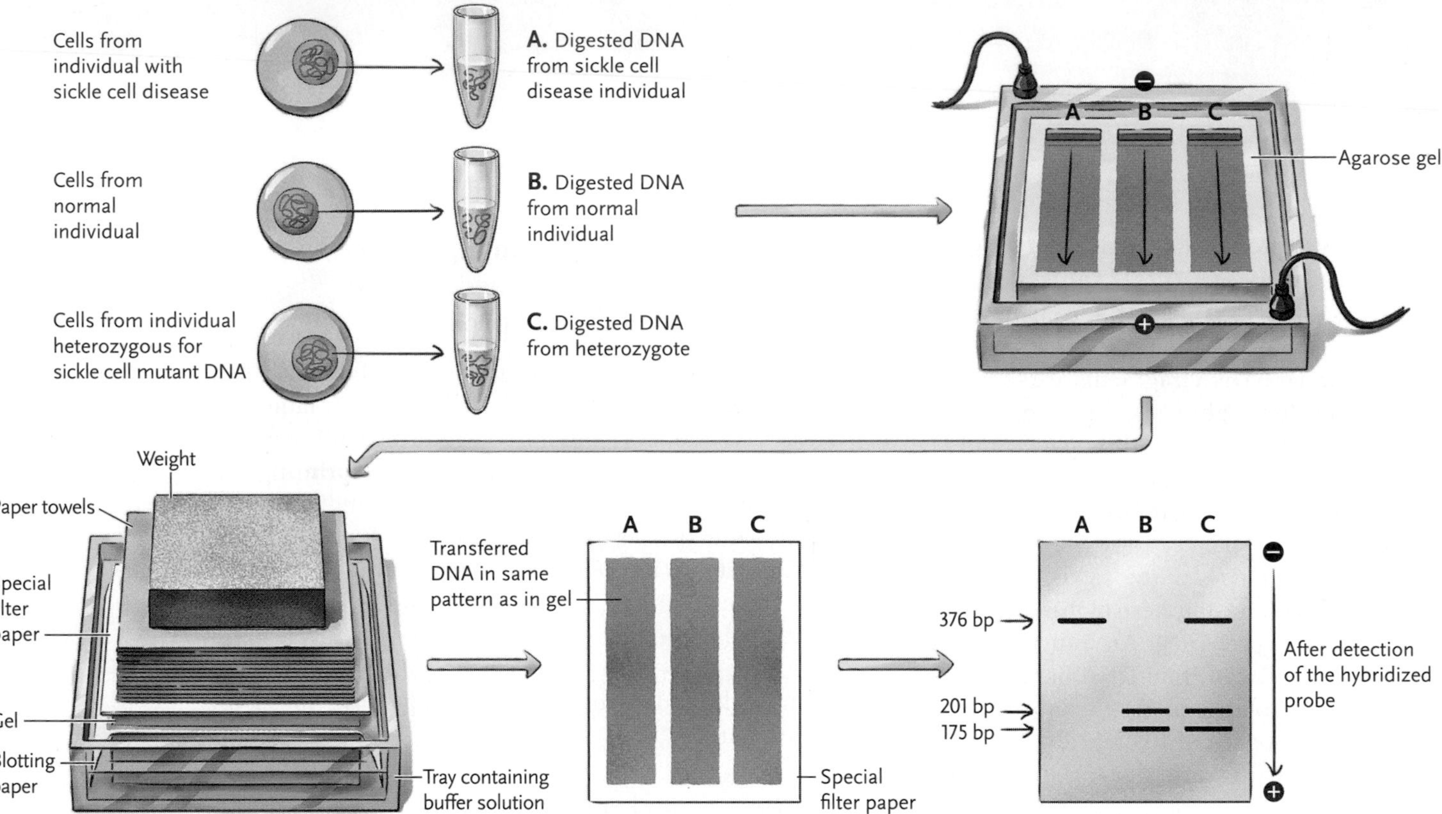

3. Hybridization with a labelled DNA probe to identify DNA fragments of interest cannot be done directly with an agarose gel. Edward Southern devised a method to transfer the DNA fragments from a gel to a special filter paper. First, treat the gel with a solution to denature the DNA to single strands. Next, place the gel on a piece of blotting paper with ends of the paper in the buffer solution and place the special filter paper on top of the gel. Capillary action wicks the buffer solution in the tray up the blotting paper, through the gel and special filter paper, and into the weighted stack of paper towels on top of the gel. The movement of the solution transfers—blots—the single-stranded DNA fragments to the filter paper, where they stick. The pattern of DNA fragments is the same as it was in the gel.

4. To home in on a particular region of the genome, use DNA hybridization with a labelled probe. That is, incubate a labelled, single-stranded probe with the filter and, after washing off excess probe, detect hybridization of the probe with DNA fragments on the filter. For a radioactive probe, the filter is placed against photographic film, which, after development will show a band or bands where the probe hybridized. In this experiment, the probe is a cloned piece of DNA from the area shown in Figure 16.7 that can bind to all three of the *Mst*II fragments of interest.

INTERPRETING THE RESULTS: The hybridization result indicates that the probe has identified a very specific DNA fragment or fragments in the digested genomic DNA. The RFLPs for the β-globin gene can be seen in Figure 16.7. DNA from the sickle cell disease individual cut with *Mst*II results in a single band of 376 bp detected by the probe, while DNA from the normal individual results in two bands of 201, and 175 bp. DNA from a sickle cell trait heterozygote results in three bands of 376 bp (from the sickle cell mutant allele), and 201 and 175 bp (the latter two from the normal allele). This type of analysis in general is useful for distinguishing normal and mutant alleles of genes where the mutation involved alters a restriction site.

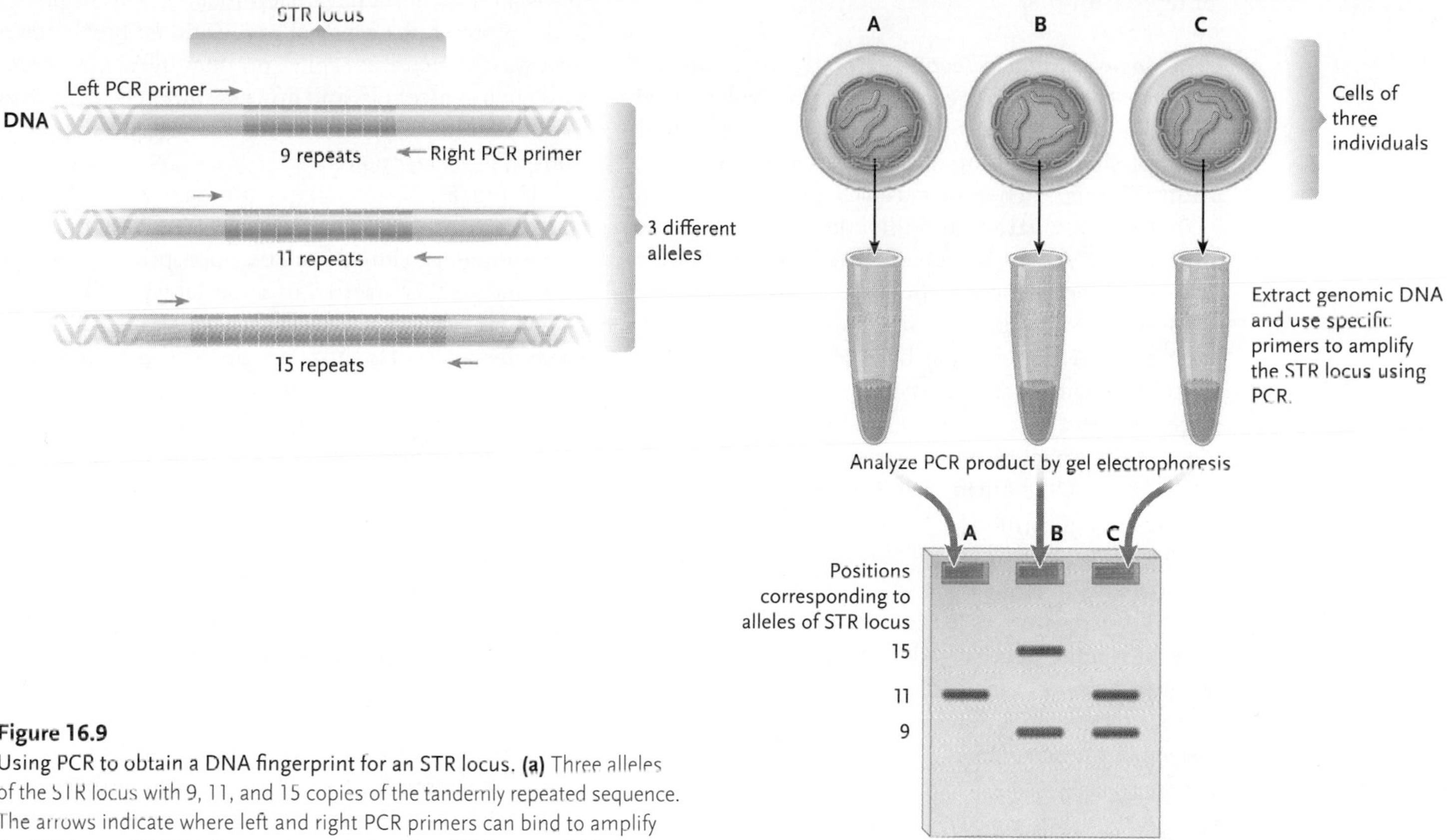

Figure 16.9
Using PCR to obtain a DNA fingerprint for an STR locus. **(a)** Three alleles of the STR locus with 9, 11, and 15 copies of the tandemly repeated sequence. The arrows indicate where left and right PCR primers can bind to amplify the STR locus. **(b)** DNA fingerprint analysis of the STR locus by PCR.

Figure 16.9 illustrates how PCR is used to obtain a DNA fingerprint for a theoretical STR locus with three alleles of 9, 11, and 15 tandem repeats (see Figure 16.9a). Using primers that flank the STR locus, the locus is amplified from genomic DNA using PCR, and the PCR products are analyzed by gel electrophoresis (see Figure 16.9b). The number of bands on the gel and the sizes of the DNA in the bands show the STR alleles that were amplified. One band indicates that the individual was homozygous for an STR allele with a particular number of repeats, whereas two bands indicate that the individual is heterozygous for two STR alleles with different numbers of repeats. In the result shown in Figure 16.9b, the A individual is homozygous for an 11-repeat allele (designated 11,11), B is heterozygous for a 15-repeat allele and a 9-repeat allele (15,9), and C is heterozygous for the 11-repeat allele and the 9 repeat allele (11,9).

DNA Fingerprinting in Forensics. DNA fingerprints are routinely used to identify criminals or eliminate innocent persons as suspects in legal proceedings. For example, a DNA fingerprint prepared from a hair found at the scene of a crime or from a semen sample might be compared with the DNA fingerprint of a suspect to link the suspect with the crime. Or a DNA fingerprint of blood found on a suspect's clothing or possessions might be compared with the DNA fingerprint of a victim. Typically, the evidence is presented in terms of the probability that the particular DNA sample could have come from a random individual. Hence, the media report probability values, such as one in several million, or in several billion, that a person other than the accused could have left his or her DNA at the crime scene.

Although courts initially met with legal challenges to the admissibility of DNA fingerprints, experience has shown that they are highly dependable as a line of evidence if DNA samples are collected and prepared with care and if a sufficient number of polymorphic loci are examined. There is always concern, however, about the possibility of contamination of the sample with DNA from another source during the path from crime scene to forensic lab analysis. Moreover, in some cases, criminals themselves have planted fake DNA samples at crime scenes to confuse the investigation.

There are many examples of the use of DNA fingerprinting to identify a criminal. For example, in a case in England, the DNA fingerprints of more than 4000 men were made during an investigation of the rape and murder of two teenage girls. The results led to the release of a man wrongly imprisoned for the crimes and to the confession and conviction of the actual killer. And the application of DNA fingerprinting techniques to stored forensic samples has led to the release of a number of persons wrongly convicted for rape or murder.

DNA Fingerprinting in Testing Paternity and Establishing Ancestry. DNA fingerprints are also widely used as evidence of paternity because parents and their children share common alleles in their DNA fingerprints. That is, each child receives one allele of each locus from one parent and the other allele from the other parent. A comparison of DNA fingerprints for a number of loci can prove almost infallibly whether a child has been fathered or mothered by a given person. DNA fingerprints have also been used for other investigations, such as confirming that remains discovered in a remote region of Russia were actually those of Czar Nicholas II and members of his family, murdered in 1918 during the Russian revolution.

DNA fingerprinting is also widely used in studies of other organisms, including other animals, plants, and bacteria. Examples include testing for pathogenic *E. coli* in food sources such as hamburger meat, investigating cases of wildlife poaching, detecting genetically modified organisms among living organisms or in food, and comparing the DNA of ancient organisms with that of present-day descendants.

16.2c Genetic Engineering Uses DNA Technologies to Alter the Genes of a Cell or Organism

We have seen the many ways scientists use DNA technologies to ask and answer questions that were once completely inaccessible. Genetic engineering goes beyond gathering information; it is the use of DNA technologies to modify genes of a cell or organism. The goals of genetic engineering include using prokaryotes, fungi, animals, and plants as factories for the production of proteins needed in medicine and scientific research; correcting hereditary disorders; and improving animals and crop plants of agricultural importance. In many of these areas, genetic engineering has already been spectacularly successful. The successes and potential benefits of genetic engineering, however, are tempered by ethical and social concerns about its use, along with the fear that the methods may produce toxic or damaging foods or release dangerous and uncontrollable organisms to the environment.

Genetic engineering uses DNA technologies of the kind discussed already in this chapter. DNA—perhaps a modified gene—is introduced into target cells of an organism. Organisms that have undergone a gene transfer are called **transgenic,** meaning that they have been modified to contain genetic information—the *transgene*—from an external source.

The following sections discuss examples of applications of genetic engineering to bacteria, animals, and plants and assess major controversies arising from these projects.

Genetic Engineering of Bacteria to Produce Proteins. Transgenic bacteria have been made, for example, to make proteins for medical applications, break down toxic wastes such as oil spills, produce industrial chemicals such as alcohols, and process minerals. *E. coli* has been the organism of choice for many of these applications of DNA technologies.

Using *E. coli* to make a protein from a foreign source is conceptually straightforward. First, the gene for the protein is cloned from the appropriate organism. Then the gene is inserted in a special type of bacterial plasmid called an *expression vector,* which has a bacterial promoter adjacent to the restriction site used for inserting the gene. The resulting recombinant plasmid is transformed into *E. coli,* which transcribes the gene and translates the resulting mRNA to make the desired protein. The protein is either extracted from the bacterial cells and purified, or if the protein is secreted, it is purified from the culture medium.

For example, *E. coli* bacteria have been genetically engineered to make the human hormone insulin; the commercial product is called HUMULIN®. Insulin is required by persons with some forms of diabetes. Humulin is a perfect copy of the human insulin hormone. Many other proteins, including human growth hormone to treat human growth disorders, tissue plasminogen activator to dissolve blood clots that cause heart attacks, and a vaccine against hoof-and-mouth disease of cattle (a highly contagious and sometimes fatal viral disease), have been developed for commercial production in bacteria by similar methods.

Although they offer many benefits, genetically engineered bacteria pose the risk that they may be released accidentally into the environment, where any adverse effects are currently unknown. Scientists minimize the danger of accidental release by growing the bacteria in laboratories that follow appropriate biosafety protocols. In addition, the bacterial strains typically used are genetically modified so that they will not survive outside of the growth media used in the laboratory.

Genetic Engineering of Animals. Many animals, including fruit flies, fish, mice, pigs, sheep, goats, and cows, have been altered successfully by genetic engineering. There are many purposes for these alterations, including basic research, correcting genetic disorders in humans and other mammals, and producing pharmaceutically important proteins.

Genetic Engineering Methods for Animals. Several methods are used to introduce a gene of interest into animal cells. The gene may be introduced into *germ-line cells,* which develop into sperm or eggs and thus enable the introduced gene to be passed from generation to generation. Or, the gene may be introduced into *somatic* (body) *cells,* differentiated cells that are not part of lines producing sperm or eggs, in which case, the gene is not transmitted from generation to generation.

Germ-line cells of embryos are often used as targets for introducing genes, particularly in mammals **(Figure 16.10)**. The treated cells are then cultured in quantity and reintroduced into early embryos. If the technique is successful, some of the introduced cells become founders of cell lines that develop into eggs or sperm with the desired genetic information integrated into their DNA. Individuals produced by crosses using the engineered eggs and sperm then contain the introduced sequences in all of their cells. Several genes have been introduced into the germ lines of mice by this approach, resulting in permanent, heritable changes in the engineered individuals.

A related technique involves introducing desired genes into *stem cells,* which are capable of differentiating into almost any adult cell type and tissue. Stem cells that have taken up the gene are then injected into an early embryo, where they differentiate into a variety of tissues along with cells of the embryo itself, including sperm and egg cells. Males and females are then bred, leading to offspring that are either homozygotes, containing two copies of the introduced gene, or heterozygotes, containing one introduced gene and one gene that was native to the embryo receiving the engineered stem cells.

Introduction of genes into stem cells has been performed mostly in mice. One of the highly useful results is the production of a "knockout mouse," a homozygous recessive that receives two copies of a gene altered to a nonfunctional state and thus has no functional copies. The effect of the missing gene on the knockout mouse is a clue to the normal function of the gene. In some cases, knockout mice are used to model human genetic diseases.

For introducing genes into somatic cells, typically somatic cells are removed from the body, cultured, and then transformed with DNA containing the transgene. The modified cells are then reintroduced into the body where the transgene functions. Because germ cells and their products are not involved, the transgene remains in the individual and is not passed to offspring.

Gene Therapy: Correcting Genetic Disorders. The path to **gene therapy**—correcting genetic disorders—in humans began with experiments using mice. In 1982, Richard Palmiter at the University of Washington, Ralph Brinster of the University of Pennsylvania, and their colleagues injected a growth hormone gene from rats into fertilized mouse eggs and implanted the eggs into a surrogate mother. She gave birth to some normal-sized mouse pups that grew faster than normal and became about twice the size of their normal litter mates. These *giant mice* **(Figure 16.11, p. 358)** attracted extensive media attention from around the world.

Figure 16.10
Introduction of genes into mouse embryos using embryonic germ-line cells.

PURPOSE: To make a transgenic animal that can transmit the transgene to offspring. The embryonic germ-line cells that receive the transgene develop into the reproductive cells of the animal.

PROTOCOL:

Germ-line cells derived from mouse embryo

1. Introduce desired gene into germ-line cells from an embryo by injection or electroporation.

Transgene

Cell with transgene

2. Clone cell that has the incorporated transgene to produce a pure culture of transgenic cells.

Pure population of transgenic cells

3. Inject transgenic cells into early-stage embryos (called a blastocyst).

4. Implant embryos into surrogate (foster) mothers.

5. Allow embryos to grow to maturity and be born.

6. Interbreed the progeny mice.

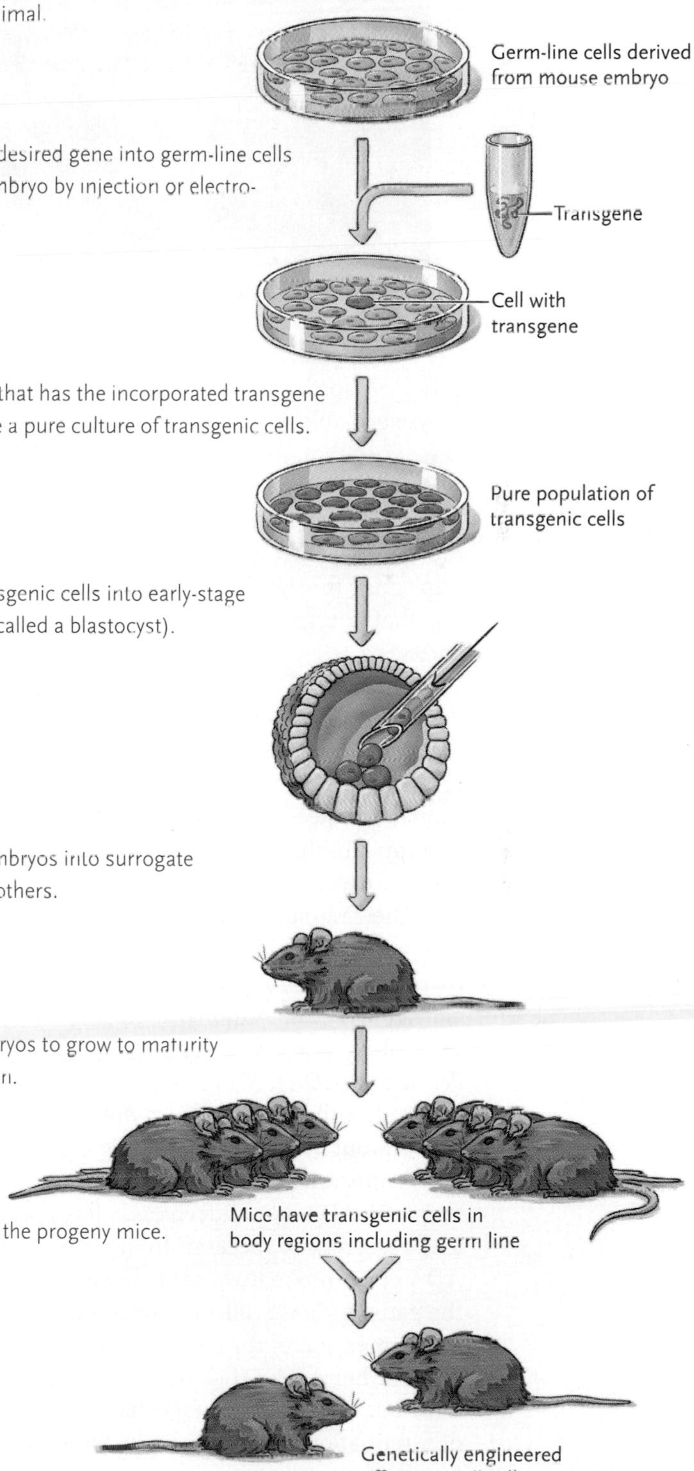

Mice have transgenic cells in body regions including germ line

Genetically engineered offspring—all cells transgenic

INTERPRETING THE RESULTS: The result of the breeding is some offspring in which all cells are transgenic—a genetically engineered animal has been produced.

Figure 16.11
A genetically engineered giant mouse (right) produced by the introduction of a rat growth hormone gene into the animal. A mouse of normal size is on the left.

Palmiter and Brinster next attempted to cure a genetic disorder by gene therapy. In this experiment, they were able to correct a genetic growth hormone deficiency that produces dwarf mice. They introduced a normal copy of the growth hormone gene into fertilized eggs taken from mutant dwarf mice and implanted them into a surrogate mother. The transgenic mouse pups grew to slightly larger than normal, demonstrating that the genetic defect in those mice had been corrected.

This sort of experiment, in which a gene is introduced into germ-line cells of an animal to correct a genetic disorder, is **germ-line gene therapy.** For ethical reasons, germ-line gene therapy is not permitted with humans. Instead, humans are treated with **somatic gene therapy**, in which genes are introduced into somatic cells (as described in the previous section).

The first successful use of somatic gene therapy with a human subject who had a genetic disorder was carried out in the 1990s by W. French Anderson and his colleagues at the National Institutes of Health (NIH). The subject was a young girl with *adenosine deaminase deficiency (ADA)*. Without the adenosine deaminase enzyme, white blood cells cannot mature (see Chapter 44); without normally functioning white blood cells, the body's immune response is so deficient that most children with ADA die of infections before reaching puberty. The researchers successfully introduced a functional ADA gene into mature white blood cells isolated from the patient. Those cells were reintroduced into the girl, and expression of the ADA gene provided a temporary cure for her ADA deficiency. The cure was not permanent because mature white blood cells, produced by differentiation of stem cells in the bone marrow, are nondividing cells with a finite lifetime. Therefore, the somatic gene therapy procedure has to be repeated every few months. Indeed, the subject of this example still receives periodic gene therapy to maintain the necessary levels of the ADA enzyme in her blood. In addition, she receives direct doses of the normal enzyme.

Successful somatic gene therapy has also been achieved for sickle cell disease. In December 1998, a 13-year-old boy's bone marrow cells were replaced with stem cells from the umbilical cord of an unrelated infant. The hope was that the stem cells would produce healthy bone marrow cells, the source of blood cells. The procedure worked, and the patient has been declared cured of the disease.

However, despite enormous efforts, human somatic gene therapy has not been the panacea people expected. Relatively little progress has been made since the first gene therapy clinical trial for ADA deficiency was described, and, in fact, there have been major setbacks. In 1999, for example, a teenage patient in a somatic gene therapy trial died as a result of a severe immune response to the viral vector being used to introduce a normal gene to correct his genetic deficiency. Furthermore, some children in gene therapy trials involving the use of retrovirus vectors to introduce genes into blood stem cells have developed a leukemia-like condition. In short, somatic gene therapy is not yet an effective treatment for human genetic disease, even though the approach has been successful in a number of cases to correct models of human genetic disorders in experimental mammals. Although no commercial human gene therapy product has been approved for use, research and clinical trials continue as scientists try to circumvent the difficulties.

Turning Domestic Animals into Protein Factories. Another successful application of genetic engineering turns animals into pharmaceutical factories for the production of proteins required to treat human diseases or other medical conditions. Most of these *pharming* projects, as they are called, engineer the animals to produce the desired proteins in milk, making the production, extraction, and purification of the proteins harmless to the animals.

One of the first successful applications of this approach was carried out with sheep engineered to produce a protein required for normal blood clotting in humans. The protein, called a *clotting factor,* is deficient in persons with one form of hemophilia, who require frequent injections of the factor to avoid bleeding to death from even minor injuries. Using DNA cloning techniques, researchers joined the gene encoding the normal form of the clotting factor to the promoter sequences of the β-lactoglobin gene, which encodes a protein secreted in milk, and introduced it into fertilized eggs. Those cells were implanted into a surrogate mother, and the transgenic sheep born were allowed to mature. The β-lactoglobin promoter controlling the clotting factor gene became activated in mammary gland cells of females, resulting in the production of clotting factor. The clotting factor was then secreted into the milk. Production in the milk is harmless to the sheep and yields the protein in a form that can easily be obtained and purified.

Other similar projects are under development to produce particular proteins in transgenic mammals. These include a protein to treat cystic fibrosis, collagen to correct scars and wrinkles, human milk proteins to be added to infant formulas, and normal hemoglobin for use as an additive to blood transfusions.

Producing Animal Clones. Making transgenic mammals is expensive and inefficient. And because only one copy of the transgene typically becomes incorporated into the treated cell, not all progeny of a transgenic animal inherit that gene. Scientists reasoned that an alternative to breeding a valuable transgenic mammal to produce progeny with the transgene would be to clone the mammal. Each clone would be identical to the original, including the expression of the transgene. That this is possible was shown in 1997 when two Scottish scientists, Ian Wilmut and Keith H. S. Campbell of the Roslin Institute, Edinburgh, announced that they had successfully cloned a sheep from a single somatic cell derived from an adult sheep **(Figure 16.12)**—the first mammalian clone made. For their experiment, the researchers fused a diploid cell derived from the mammary gland of a 6-year-old adult sheep with an unfertilized egg cell from which the nucleus had been removed. Signals from the egg cytoplasm triggered DNA replication and cell division, producing a cluster of cells derived from the mammary gland cell. The cluster was implanted into the uterus of an adult female sheep, where it developed into an embryo that grew to full term and was delivered as an apparently normal lamb, named Dolly. Their cloning success rate, however, was very low—Dolly represents less than 0.4% of the transgenic cells they made. Dolly developed to sexual maturity and produced four normal offspring. She was euthanized at age 6 after contracting a fatal, virus-induced lung disease that her cloners believe was unrelated to the cloning.

After the successful cloning experiment producing Dolly, many additional mammals have been cloned, including mice, goats, pigs, monkeys, rabbits, dogs, a male calf appropriately named Gene, and a domestic cat called *CC* (for *Copy Cat*).

Cloning farm animals has been so successful that several commercial enterprises now provide cloned copies of champion animals. One example is a clone of an American Holstein cow, Zita, who was the U.S. national champion milk producer for many years. Animal breeders estimate that there are now more than 100 cloned animals on American farms, and breeders plan to produce entire herds if government approval is granted.

The cloning of domestic animals has its drawbacks. Many cloning attempts fail, leading to the death of the transplanted embryos. Cloned animals often suffer from health defects from conditions such as birth defects and poor lung development. Genes may be lost during the cloning process or may be expressed abnormally in the cloned animal. For example, molecular studies have shown that the expression of perhaps hundreds of genes in the genomes of clones is regulated abnormally.

PA News Photo Library/AP Wide World Photos

Figure 16.12
Dolly, the cloned sheep.

Genetic Engineering of Plants. Genetic engineering of plants has led to increased resistance to pests and disease; greater tolerance to heat, drought, and salinity; greater crop yields; faster growth; and resistance to herbicides. Another aim is to produce seeds with higher levels of amino acids. The essential amino acid lysine, for example, is present only in limited quantities in cereal grains such as wheat, rice, oats, barley, and corn; the seeds of legumes such as beans, peas, lentils, soybeans, and peanuts are deficient in the essential amino acids methionine or cysteine. Increasing the amounts of the deficient amino acids in plant seeds by genetic engineering would greatly improve the diet of domestic animals and human populations that rely on seeds as a primary food source. Efforts are also under way to increase the content of vitamins and minerals in crop plants.

Other possibilities for plant genetic engineering include plant pharming to produce pharmaceutical products. Plants are ideal for this purpose because they are primary producers at the bottom rung of the food chain and can be grown in huge numbers with maximum conservation of the sun's energy captured in photosynthesis.

Some plants, such as *Arabidopsis*, tobacco, potato, cabbage, and carrot, have special advantages for genetic engineering because individual cells can be removed from an adult, altered by the introduction of a desired gene, and then grown in cultures into a multicellular mass of cloned cells called a *callus*. Subsequently, roots, stems, and leaves develop in the callus, forming a young plant that can then be grown in containers or fields by the usual methods. In the plant, each cell contains the introduced gene. The gametes produced by the transgenic plants can then be used in crosses to produce

Figure 16.13 A crown gall tumour on the trunk of a California pepper tree. The tumour, stimulated by genes introduced from the bacterium *Rhizobium radiobacter*, is the bulbous, irregular growth extending from the trunk.

offspring, some of which will have the transgene, as in the similar experiments with animals.

Methods Used to Insert Genes into Plants. Genes are inserted into plant cells by several techniques. One commonly used method takes advantage of a natural process that causes crown gall disease, which is characterized by bulbous, irregular growths—tumours, essentially—that can develop at wound sites on the trunks and limbs of deciduous trees **(Figure 16.13).** Crown gall disease is caused by the bacterium *Rhizobium radiobacter* (formerly *Agrobacterium tumefaciens,* recently reclassified on the basis of genome analysis). This bacterium contains a large, circular plasmid called the **Ti (tumour inducing) plasmid.** The interaction between the bacterium and the plant cell it infects stimulates the excision of a segment of the Ti plasmid called *T DNA* (for transforming DNA), which then integrates into the plant cell's genome. Genes on the T DNA are then expressed; the products stimulate the transformed cell to grow and divide and therefore to produce a tumour. The tumours provide essential nutrients for the bacterium. The Ti plasmid is used as a vector for making transgenic plants in much the same way as bacterial plasmids are used as vectors to introduce genes into bacteria **(Figure 16.14).**

Successful Plant Genetic Engineering Projects. An early visual demonstration of the successful use of genetic engineering techniques to produce a transgenic plant is the glowing tobacco plant **(Figure 16.15, p. 362).** The transgenic plant contained luciferase, the gene for the firefly enzyme. When the plant was soaked in the substrate for the enzyme, it became luminescent.

The most widespread application of genetic engineering of plants involves the production of transgenic crops. Thousands of such crops have been developed and field tested, and many have been approved for commercial use. If you analyze the processed plant-based foods at a national supermarket chain, you will likely find that at least two-thirds contain transgenic plants.

In many cases, plants are modified to make them resistant to insect pests, viruses, or herbicides. Crops modified for insect resistance include corn, cotton, and potatoes. The most common approach to making plants resistant to insects is to introduce the gene from the bacterium *Bacillus thuringiensis* that encodes the *Bt* toxin, an organic pesticide. This toxin has been used in powder form to kill insects in agriculture for many years, and now transgenic plants making their own *Bt* toxin are resistant to specific groups of insects that feed on them. Millions of acres of crop plants planted in the United States and Canada are *Bt*-engineered varieties.

Virus infections cause enormous crop losses worldwide. Transgenic crops that are virus-resistant would be highly valuable to the agricultural community. There is some promise in this area. By some unknown process, transgenic plants expressing certain viral proteins become resistant to infections by whole viruses that contain those same proteins. Two virus-resistant genetically modified crops made so far are papaya and squash.

Several crops have also been engineered to become resistant to herbicides. For example, *glyphosate* (commonly known by its brand name, Roundup) is a highly potent herbicide that is widely used in weed control. The herbicide works by inhibiting a particular enzyme in the chloroplast. Unfortunately, it also kills crops. But transgenic crops have been made in which a bacterial form of the chloroplast enzyme has been added to the plants. The bacteria-derived enzyme is not affected by Roundup, and farmers who use these herbicide-resistant crops can spray fields of crops to kill weeds without killing the crops. Now most of the corn, soybean, canola, and cotton plants grown in North America are the genetically engineered, glyphosate-resistant ("Roundup-ready") varieties.

Crop plants are also being engineered to alter their nutritional qualities. For example, a strain of rice plants has been produced with seeds rich in β-carotene, a precursor of vitamin A, as well as iron **(Figure 16.16, p. 362).** The new rice, which is given a yellow or golden colour by the carotene, may provide improved nutrition for the billions of people who depend on rice as a diet staple. In particular, the rice may help improve the nutrition of children younger than age 5 in southeast Asia, 70% of whom suffer from impaired vision because of vitamin A deficiency.

Plant pharming is also an active area both in university research labs and at biotechnology companies. Plant pharming involves the engineering of transgenic plants to produce medically valuable products. The approach is one described earlier: the gene for the product is cloned into a cloning vector adjacent to a promoter, in this case one active in plants, and the recombinant DNA molecule is introduced into plants. Products under development include vaccines for various bacterial and viral diseases, protease inhibitors to treat or prevent virus infections, collagen to treat scars and wrinkles, and aprotinin to reduce bleeding and clotting during heart surgery.

In contrast to animal genetic engineering, genetically altered plants have been widely developed and appear to be here to stay as mainstays of agriculture. But, as the next section discusses, both animal and plant genetic engineering have not proceeded without concerns.

16.2d DNA Technologies and Genetic Engineering Are a Subject of Public Concern

When recombinant DNA technology was developed in the early 1970s, researchers quickly recognized that in addition to the many anticipated benefits, there might be deleterious outcomes. One key concern at the time was that a bacterium carrying a recombinant DNA molecule might escape into the environment. Perhaps it could transfer that molecule to other bacteria and produce new, potentially harmful, strains. To address these concerns, the U.S. scientists who developed the technology drew up safety guidelines for recombinant DNA research in the United States. Adopted by the NIH, the guidelines listed the precautions to be used in the laboratory when constructing recombinant DNA molecules and included the design and use of host organisms that could survive only in growth media in the laboratory. Since that time, countless thousands of experiments involving recombinant DNA molecules have been done in laboratories around the world. Those experiments have shown that recombinant DNA manipulations can be done safely. Over time, therefore, the recombinant DNA guidelines have become more relaxed. Nonetheless, stringent regulations still exist for certain areas of recombinant DNA research that pose significant risk, such as cloning genes from highly pathogenic bacteria or viruses, or gene therapy experiments. In essence, as the risk increases, the research facility must increase its security and must obtain more levels of approval by peer scientist groups.

Guidelines for genetic engineering also extend to research in several areas that have been the subject of public concern and debate. Although the public does not seem to be very concerned about genetically engineered microorganisms, for example, those cleaning up oil spills and hazardous chemicals, it is concerned about possible problems with **genetically modified organisms (GMOs)** used as food. A GMO is a transgenic organism; the majority of GMOs are crop plants. Issues are the safety of GMO-containing food and the possible adverse effects of the GMOs to the environment, such as by interbreeding with natural species or by harming beneficial insect species. For example, could introduced genes providing herbicide or insect resistance move from crop plants into related weed species through cross-pollination, producing "super weeds" that might be difficult or impossible to control? *Bt*-expressing corn was originally thought to have adverse effects on monarch butterflies who fed on the

Figure 16.14
Using the Ti plasmid of Rhizobium radiobacter to produce transgenic plants.

PURPOSE: To make transgenic plants. This technique is one way to introduce a transgene into a plant for genetic engineering purposes.

PROTOCOL:

1. Isolate the Ti plasmid from *Rhizobium radiobacter.* The plasmid contains a segment called T DNA (T = transforming), which induces tumours in plants.
2. Digest the Ti plasmid with a restriction enzyme that cuts within the T DNA segment. Mix with a gene of interest on a DNA fragment that was produced by digesting with the same enzyme. Use DNA ligase to join the two DNA molecules together to produce a recombinant plasmid.
3. Transform the recombinant Ti plasmid into a disarmed *Rhizobium radiobacter* that cannot induce tumours, and use the transformed bacterium to infect cells in plant fragments in a test tube. In infected cells, the T DNA with the inserted gene of interest excises from the Ti plasmid and integrates into the plant cell genome. 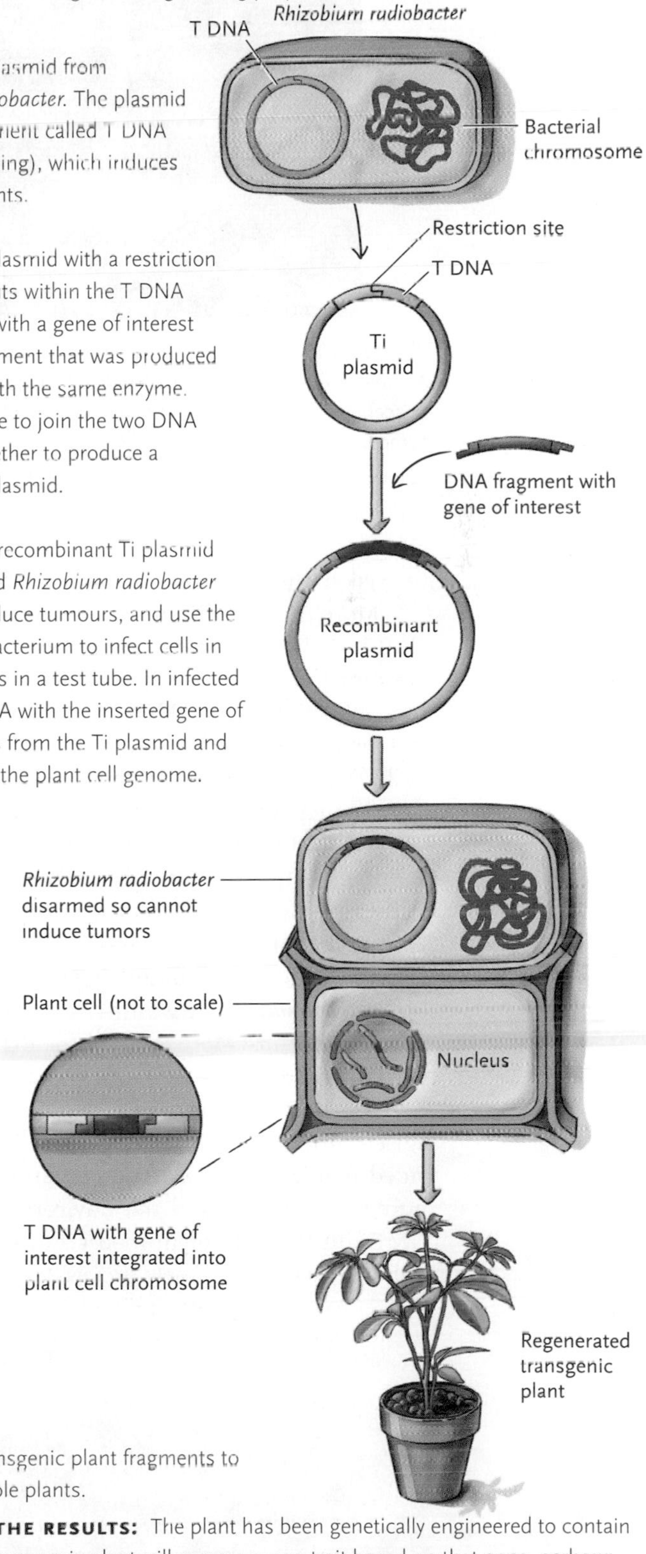
4. Culture the transgenic plant fragments to regenerate whole plants.

INTERPRETING THE RESULTS: The plant has been genetically engineered to contain a new gene. The transgenic plant will express a new trait based on that gene, perhaps resistance to an herbicide or the production of an insect toxin according to the goal of the experiment.

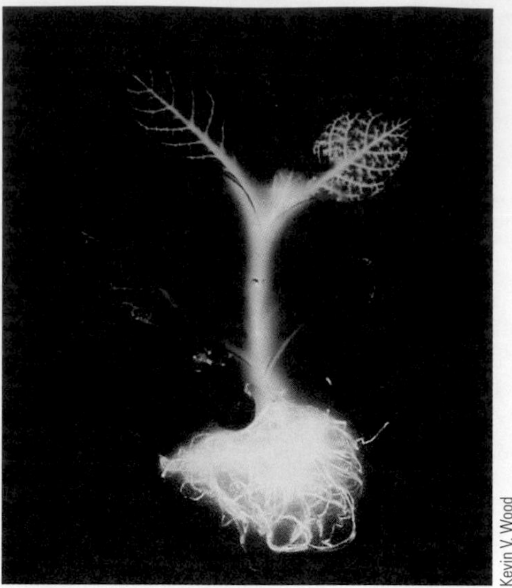
Kevin V. Wood

Figure 16.15
A genetically engineered tobacco plant, made capable of luminescence by the introduction of a firefly gene coding for the enzyme luciferase.

pollen. The most recent of a series of independent studies investigating this possibility has indicated that the risk to the butterflies is extremely low.

More broadly, different countries have reacted to GMOs in different ways. In Canada, transgenic crops are quite widely planted and harvested. Before commercialization, such GMOs are evaluated for potential risk by appropriate government regulatory agencies, including Health Canada, the Canadian Food Inspection Agency, and Environment Canada.

Political opposition to GMOs has been greater in Europe, dampening the use of transgenic crop plants in the fields and GMOs in food. In 1999, the European Union (EU) imposed a six-year moratorium on all GMOs, leading to a bitter dispute with the United States, Canada, and Argentina, the leading growers of transgenic crops. More recently, the EU has revised the GMO regulations in all member states. Basically, the EU has decided that using genetic engineering in agriculture and food production is permissible provided that the GMO or food containing it is safe for humans, animals, and the environment. All use of GMOs in the field or in food requires authorization following a careful review process.

Dr. Jorge Mayer, Golden Rice Project

Figure 16.16
Rice genetically engineered to contain β-carotene.

On a global level, an international agreement, the **Cartagena Protocol on Biosafety**, "promotes biosafety by establishing practical rules and procedures for the safe transfer [between countries], handling and use of GMOs." Separate procedures have been set up for GMOs that are to be introduced into the environment and those that are to be used as food or feed or for processing. To date, several countries, mainly GMO exporters, have failed to ratify the protocol.

In sum, the use of DNA technologies in biotechnology has the potential for tremendous benefits to humankind. Such experimentation is not without risk, so for each experiment, researchers must assess that risk and make a judgment about whether to proceed and, if so, how to do so safely. Furthermore, agreed-upon guidelines and protocols should ensure a level of biosafety for researchers, consumers, politicians, and governments.

We now turn to the analysis of whole genomes.

Study Break

1. What are the principles of DNA fingerprinting?
2. What is a transgenic organism?
3. What is the difference between using germ-line cells and somatic cells for gene therapy?

16.3 Genome Analysis

The development of DNA technologies for analyzing genes and gene expression revolutionized experimental biology. DNA sequencing techniques (described in this section) have made it possible to analyze the sequences of cloned genes and genes amplified by PCR. Having the complete sequence of a gene aids researchers tremendously in unravelling how that gene functions. But a gene is only part of a genome. Researchers want to know about the organization of genes in a complete genome and how genes work together in networks to control life. Of particular interest, of course, is the human genome. The complete sequencing of the approximately 3 billion base-pair human genome—the Human Genome Project (HGP)—began in 1990. The task was completed in 2003 by an international consortium of researchers and by a private company, Celera Genomics. As part of the official HGP, for purposes of comparison, the genomes of several important model organisms commonly used in genetic studies were sequenced: *E. coli* (representing prokaryotes), the yeast *Saccharomyces cerevisiae* (representing single-celled eukaryotes), *Drosophila melanogaster* and *Caenorhabditis elegans* (the fruit fly and nematode worm, respectively, representing multicellular animals of moderate genome complexity), and *Mus musculus* (the house mouse, representing a mammal of genome complexity comparable to that of humans). In addition, the sequences of the genomes of many organisms beyond this list, including plants, have been completed or are in progress at this time. What researchers are learning from analyzing complete genomes is of enormous importance to our understanding of biology and the evolution of organisms.

16.3a DNA Sequencing Techniques Are Based on DNA Replication

DNA sequencing is the key technology for genome sequencing projects. DNA sequencing is also used on a smaller scale, for example, in determining the sequence of individual genes that have been cloned or amplified by PCR.

DNA sequencing was first developed in the late 1970s by Allan M. Maxam, a graduate student, and his mentor, Walter Gilbert of Harvard University; within a few years, another investigator, Frederick Sanger of Cambridge University, designed the method that is most used today. Gilbert and Sanger were awarded a Nobel Prize in 1980.

The Sanger method is based on the properties of nucleotides known as *dideoxyribonucleotides*—the method, therefore, is also called *dideoxy sequencing* **(Figure 16.17, p. 364)**. Dideoxyribonucleotides have a single —H bound to the 3′ carbon of the deoxyribose sugar instead of the —OH normally appearing at this position in deoxyribonucleotides. DNA polymerases, the replication enzymes, recognize the dideoxyribonucleotides and place them in the DNA just as they do the normal deoxyribonucleotides. However, because a dideoxyribonucleotide has no 3′-OH group available for addition of the next base, replication of a nucleotide chain stops when one of these nucleotides is added to a growing nucleotide chain. (Remember from Section 13.3 that a 3′-OH group must be present at the growing end of a nucleotide chain for the next nucleotide to be added during DNA replication.) In a dideoxy sequencing reaction, researchers use a mixture of dideoxyribonucleotides and normal nucleotides, so that chain termination will occur randomly at each position where a particular nucleotide appears in the population of DNA molecules being replicated. Each chain-termination event generates a newly synthesized DNA strand that ends with the dideoxyribonucleotide; hence, for this particular strand, the base at the 3′ end is known, and because of base-pairing rules, the base on the template strand being sequenced is deduced. Once they know the base at the end of each terminated DNA strand, researchers can work out the complete sequence of the template DNA strand.

The dideoxy sequencing method can be used with any pure piece of DNA, such as a cloned DNA fragment or a fragment amplified by PCR. An unambiguous sequence of about 500 to 750 nucleotides can be obtained from each sequencing experiment.

16.3b Structural Genomics Determines the Complete DNA Sequence of Genomes

Genome analysis consists of two main areas: *structural genomics* and *functional genomics*. **Structural genomics** is the actual sequencing of genomes and the analysis of the nucleotide sequences to locate genes and other functionally important sequences within the genome. **Functional genomics** is the study of the functions of genes and of other parts of the genome. In the case of genes, this includes developing an understanding of the regulation of their expression, the proteins they encode, and the role played by the proteins in the organism's metabolic processes.

The most widely used method for sequencing a genome is the *whole-genome shotgun method* **(Figure 16.18, p. 365)**. In this method, the entire genome is broken into thousands to millions of random, overlapping fragments, and each fragment is cloned and sequenced. The genome sequence then is assembled by computer on the basis of the sequence overlaps between fragments.

The first genome sequence reported, that of the bacterium *Haemophilus influenzae,* was determined using the whole-genome shotgun method by J. Craig Venter and his associates at Celera Genomics (the developers of the method). Originally, it was thought that the much larger genomes of eukaryotes would be too difficult to sequence using this method. But improvements in sequencing technologies and in the computer algorithms used to identify overlapping sequences have made it easier to assemble the segment sequences into the sequence of a whole genome. Whole-genome shotgun sequencing is now the method of choice for sequencing essentially any genome.

16.3c Functional Genomics Focuses on the Functions of Genes and Other Parts of the Genome

The genomes of a large number of viruses and more than 180 organisms have been sequenced, and those of more species are continually being added to the total. Among those already sequenced are the cytomegalovirus, bacteria including *E. coli,* various archaean species, and eukaryotes including the brewer's yeast *Saccharomyces cerevisiae,* the protozoan *Plasmodium falciparium* (the malarial parasite), the roundworm *Caenorhabditis elegans,* the plants *Arabidopsis thaliana* and rice, the fruit fly *Drosophila melanogaster,* the chicken, the mouse, the rat, the dog, the chimpanzee, and human. In fact, the entire diploid DNA sequence of two humans, J. Craig Venter and James Watson, has been determined.

Analysis of Genome Sequences. The complete genome sequence for an organism is basically a very long string of letters, which means little without further analysis.

Figure 16.17
Dideoxy (Sanger) method for sequencing DNA.

PURPOSE: Obtain the sequence of a piece of DNA, such as in gene sequencing or genome sequencing. The method is shown here with an automated sequencing system.

PROTOCOL:

1. A dideoxy sequencing reaction has the following components: the fragment of DNA to be sequenced (denatured to single strands); a DNA primer that will bind to the 3′ end of the sequence to be determined; a mixture of the four deoxyribonucleotide precursors for DNA synthesis; and a mixture of the four dideoxyribonucleotides (dd) precursors, each labelled with a different fluorescent molecule, and DNA polymerase to catalyze the DNA synthesis reaction.

2. Synthesis of the new DNA strand is in the 5′→3′ direction starting at the 3′ end of the primer. New synthesis continues until a dideoxyribonucleotide is incorporated into the DNA instead of a normal deoxyribonucleotide. For a large population of template DNA strands, the dideoxy sequencing reaction produces a series of new strands, with lengths from one on up. At the 3′ end of each new strand is the labelled dideoxyribonucleotide that terminated the synthesis.

3. The labelled strands produced by the reaction are separated by gel electrophoresis. The principle of separation is the same as for agarose gel electrophoresis described in Figure 16.8. But here it is necessary to discriminate between DNA strands that differ in length by one nucleotide, which agarose gels cannot do. In this case, therefore, a gel made of polyacrylamide is prepared in a capillary tube for separating the DNA fragments. As the bands of DNA fragments move near the bottom of the tube, a laser beam shining through the gel excites the fluorescent labels on each DNA fragment. The fluorescence is registered by a detector with the wavelength of the fluorescence indicating which of the four dideoxyribonucleotides is at the end of the fragment in each case.

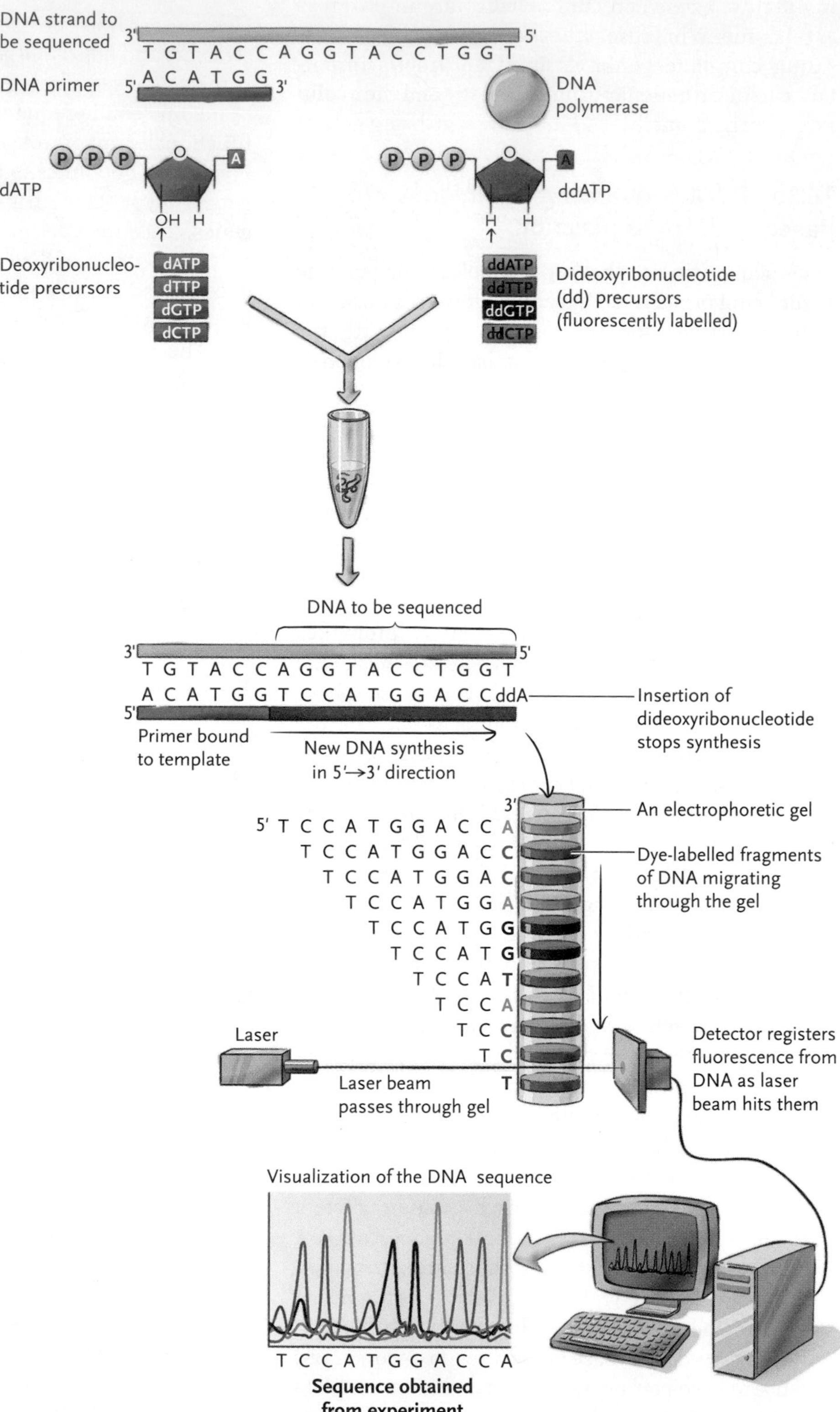

INTERPRETING THE RESULTS: The data from the laser system are sent to a computer that interprets which of the four possible fluorescent labels is at the end of each DNA strand. The results show the colours of the labels as the DNA bands passed the detector. They may be seen on the computer screen or in printouts. The sequence of the newly synthesized DNA, which is complementary to the template strand, is read from left (5′) to right (3′). (The sequence shown here begins after the primer.)

Discovering the functions of genes and other parts of the genome is one important goal of this analysis. Most research is focused on the genes because they control the functions of cells and, therefore, of organisms. Functional genomics relies on laboratory experiments by molecular biologists and sophisticated computer analyses by researchers in the rapidly growing field of **bioinformatics,** which fuses biology with mathematics and computer science. Bioinformatics is used, for example, to find genes within a genomic sequence, align sequences in databases to determine the degree of matching, predict the structure and function of gene products, and postulate evolutionary relationships for sequences.

Protein-coding genes are of particular interest in genome analysis. Once a genome sequence is determined, researchers use computer algorithms to search both strands of the sequence for these genes. They identify possible protein-coding genes by searching for open reading frames, that is, a start codon (ATG, at the DNA level) in frame (separated by a multiple of three nucleotides) with one of the stop codons (TAG, TAA, or TGA at the DNA level). This process is easy for prokaryotic genomes, because the genes have no introns. In eukaryotic protein-coding genes, which typically have introns, more sophisticated algorithms are used to try to identify the junctions between exons and introns in scanning for open reading frames.

Each open reading frame found by computer analysis of a genome can be "translated" by computer to give the amino acid sequence of the protein it could encode. Researchers may then be able to assign a function to the open reading frame by performing a *sequence similarity search,* a computer-based comparison of a DNA or amino acid sequence with databases of sequences of known genes or proteins. That is, if an open reading frame or its protein product resembles those of a previously sequenced gene, the two genes are related in an evolutionary sense and are likely to have similar functions.

Many new features of genetic organization have been discovered, or previous conclusions reinforced, through the findings of genome sequencing. One of the more surprising discoveries is that the eukaryotic genomes sequenced to date contain large numbers of previously unknown genes, many more than scientists expected to find. In *Caenorhabditis,* for example, 12 000 of the 19 000 genes are of unknown function. Identifying these genes and their functions is one of the major challenges of contemporary molecular genetics.

Another revelation is the degree to which different organisms, some of them widely separated in evolutionary origins, contain similar genes. For example, even though the yeast *Saccharomyces* is a fungus separated from our species by millions of years of evolutionary history, about 2300 of its approximately 6000 genes are

Figure 16.18
Whole-genome shotgun sequencing.

PURPOSE: Obtain the complete sequence of the genome of an organism.

PROTOCOL:

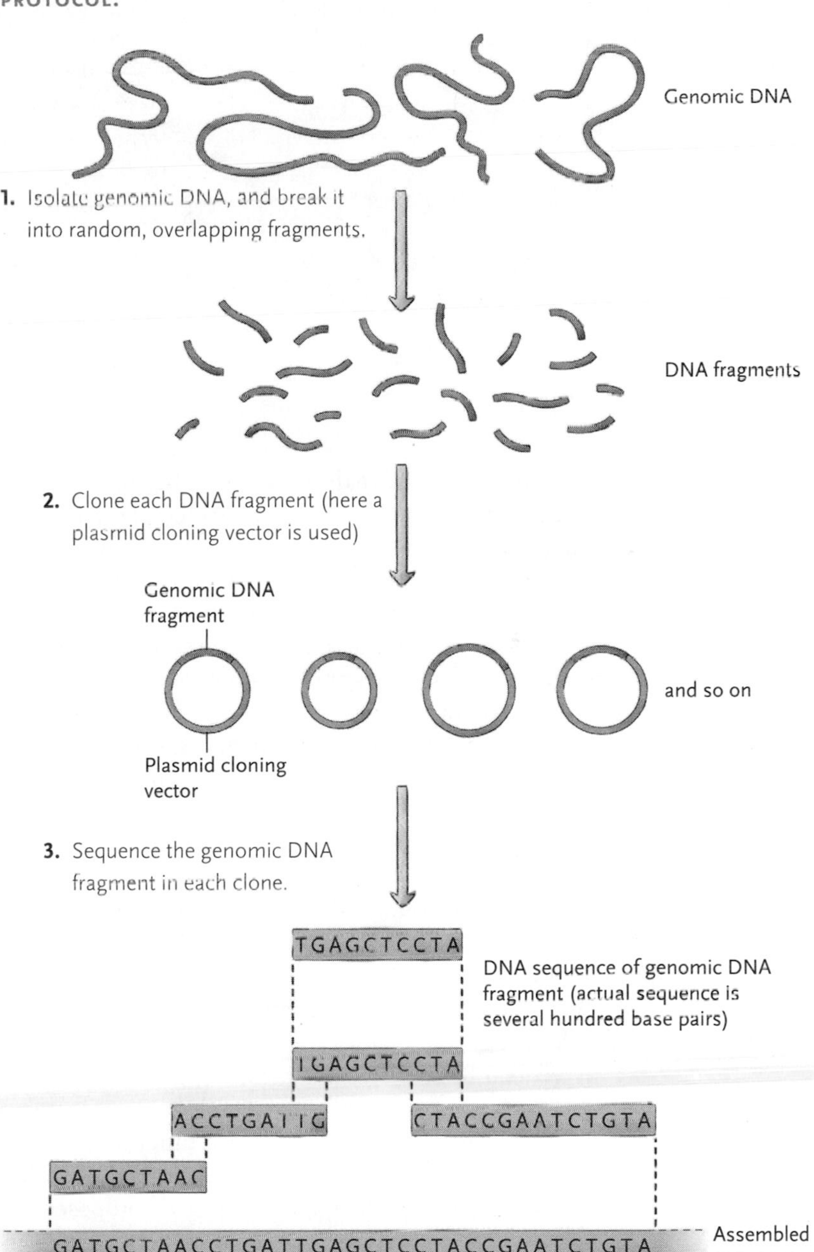

Genomic DNA
1. Isolate genomic DNA, and break it into random, overlapping fragments.
DNA fragments
2. Clone each DNA fragment (here a plasmid cloning vector is used)
Genomic DNA fragment
and so on
Plasmid cloning vector
3. Sequence the genomic DNA fragment in each clone.
TGAGCTCCTA
DNA sequence of genomic DNA fragment (actual sequence is several hundred base pairs)
TGAGCTCCTA
ACCTGATTG
CTACCGAATCTGTA
GATGCTAAC
GATGCTAACCTGATTGAGCTCCTACCGAATCTGTA
Assembled sequence

4. Enter the DNA sequences of the fragments into a computer program, to assemble overlapping sequences into the continuous sequences of each chromosome of the organism. This technique is analogous to taking 10 copies of a book that have been torn randomly into smaller sets of a few pages each and, by matching overlapping pages of the leaflets, assembling a complete copy of the book with the pages in the correct order.

INTERPRETING THE RESULTS: The method generates the complete sequence of the genome of an organism.

People Behind Biology

The Late Dr. Michael Smith, Nobel Laureate, Distinguished Professor of Biotechnology, University of British Columbia

The discipline of genetics was originally built on the study of rare, naturally occurring mutations. Researchers routinely screened thousands (or sometimes millions) of individuals to collect a handful of useful mutations. Agents that increased the frequency of mutations were often used, but they tended to be nonspecific, and the isolation of particular mutations in specific genes remained a lottery with unfavourable odds.

Michael Smith changed all of that in the late 1970s by demonstrating that *in vitro* DNA synthesis techniques could be used to create mutated sequences. This method of site-directed mutagenesis allowed specific mutations to be introduced into any given DNA sequence. For the first time, geneticists could create the exact changes they were interested in. Smith's work was recognized with the 1993 Nobel Prize in Chemistry.

In addition to his legacy as a scientist, Michael Smith was a generous philanthropist and a strong supporter of public education in science.

related to those of mammals, including many genes that control progress through the cell cycle. The similarities are so close that the yeast and human versions of many genes can be interchanged with little or no effect on cell functions in either organism.

The sequences also confirm that eukaryotic genomes contain large numbers of noncoding sequences, most of them in the form of repeated sequences of various lengths and numbers. Most of these sequences, which make up from about 25% to 50% of the total genomic DNA in different eukaryotic species, have no determined function at this point in time.

Features of the Human Genome Sequence. The human genome sequence consists of 3.2 *billion* base pairs. Until the genome was sequenced, researchers expected that human cells might contain as many as 100 000 different protein-coding genes. The best current estimate is 20 000 to 25 000 protein-coding genes. However, although the number of protein-coding genes is unexpectedly small, the total number of different proteins produced in humans is much greater and probably approaches the 100 000 figure originally proposed for genes. The additional proteins arise through such processes as alternative splicing during mRNA processing (see Section 14.3) and differences in protein processing (discussed further in the following sections).

All the protein-coding sequences occupy less than 2% of the human genome. Introns—the noncoding spacers in genes—occupy another 24% of the genome. The rest of the DNA, almost three-quarters of the genome, occupies the spaces between genes. Some of this intergenic DNA is functional and includes regulatory sequences such as promoters and enhancers, but much of it, more than 50% of the total genome, consists of repeated sequences that have no known function.

Completing the human genome sequence is only the beginning of human genomics. The next steps are to determine the functions of the unknown genes and of the sequence elements in intergenic regions. This *data mining*, as it is called, may answer fundamental questions about genome organization and the mechanisms controlling genes in development and cell differentiation. Genes related to human health and disease, including cancer, are of particular interest. The analysis of these disease-related genes may suggest methods to predict individual susceptibility to diseases and may possibly lead to means for their diagnosis and treatment.

On an even larger scale, the human genome is being compared with the genomes of other species to determine the molecular basis of differences in anatomy, physiology, and developmental patterns between species. Ultimately, species comparisons may reveal the mutational changes underlying the evolution of our species and many others. This area of genomics is known as *comparative genomics*.

There are bioethics issues concerning the human genome. To address those issues, the U.S. Department of Energy and the NIH have funded studies of the ethical, legal, and social issues surrounding the availability of genetic information from human genome research. The following are among the questions being looked at: Who should have access to personal genetic information, and how should it be used? To what extent should genetic information be private and confidential? How will genetic tests be evaluated and regulated? How can people be informed sufficiently about the genetic information from genomic analysis so that they can make informed personal medical choices? Does a set of genes predispose a person's behaviour, and can the person control that behaviour?

Studying Differential Gene Activity in Entire Genomes with DNA Microarrays. As part of genome research, investigators are interested in comparing which genes are active in different cell types of humans and other organisms, and tracking the changes in total gene activity in the same cell types as development progresses. In some cases, the researcher wants to know whether or not particular genes are being expressed, and in other cases how the level of expression varies in different circumstances. This research has been revolutionized by a technique using **DNA microarrays.** The microarrays are also called **DNA chips** for short because the techniques used to "print" the arrays resemble those used to lay out electronic circuits on a computer chip. The surface of a DNA chip is divided into a microscopic grid of about 60 000 spaces. On each space of the grid, a computerized system deposits a microscopic spot containing about 10 000 000 copies of a DNA probe about 20 nucleotides long.

Studies of gene activity using DNA microarrays involve comparing gene expression under a defined experimental condition with expression under a reference (control) condition. For instance, DNA microarrays can be used to answer basic biological questions, such as: How does gene expression change when a cell goes from a resting state (reference condition) to a dividing state (experimental condition). In other words: how is gene expression different in different stages of development? DNA microarrays can also be used to address many questions of medical significance, such as How are genes differentially expressed in normal cells and cells of various cancers? In these experiments, investigators might focus on which genes are active and inactive under the two conditions or on how the levels of expression of genes change under the two conditions.

Figure 16.19 (p. 368) shows how a DNA microarray is used to compare gene expression in normal cells and in cancer cells in humans. mRNAs are isolated from each cell type, and cDNAs are made from them, incorporating different fluorescent labels: green for one, red for the other. The two cDNAs are mixed and added to the DNA chip, where they hybridize with any complementary probes. A laser locates and quantifies the green and red fluorescence, enabling a researcher to see which genes are expressed in the cells and, for those that are expressed, to quantify differences in gene expression between the two cell types (see Interpreting the Results in Figure 16.19). The results can help researchers understand how the cancer develops and progresses.

DNA microarrays are also used to screen individuals for particular mutations. To detect mutations, the probes spotted onto the chip include probes for the normal sequence of the genes of interest along with probes for sequences of all known mutations. A fluorescent spot at a site on the chip printed with a probe for a given mutation immediately shows the presence of the mutation in the individual. Such a test is currently used to screen patients for whether they carry any one of a number of mutations of the *breast cancer 1* (*BRCA1*) gene known to be associated with the possible development of breast cancer.

16.3d Studying the Array of Expressed Proteins Is the Next Level of Genomic Analysis

Given that proteins are largely responsible for cell function, and therefore for all of an organism's functions, genome research also includes the analysis of the proteins that are encoded by a genome. The term **proteome** has been coined to refer to the complete set of proteins that can be expressed by an organism's genome. A *cellular proteome* is a subset of those proteins, the collection of proteins found in a particular cell type under a particular set of environmental conditions.

The study of the proteome is the field of **proteomics**. The number of possible proteins encoded by the genome is larger than the number of protein-coding genes in the genome, at least in eukaryotes. In eukaryotes, alternative splicing of gene transcripts and variation in protein processing means that expression of a gene may yield more than one protein product. Therefore, proteomics is a more challenging area of research than is genomics.

The two major immediate goals of proteomics are to determine (1) the number and structure of proteins in the proteome, and (2) the functional interactions between the proteins. The interactions are particularly important because they help us understand how proteins work together to determine the phenotype of the cell. For instance, if a particular set of interacting proteins characterized a lung tumour cell, then drugs could be developed that specifically target the interactions.

What are the tools of proteomics? For many years, it has been possible to separate and identify proteins by gel electrophoresis (using polyacrylamide to make the gels, the same material used for separating DNA fragments in DNA sequencing) or mass spectrometry. However, to study an entire cellular proteome, many more proteins must be analyzed simultaneously than is possible with either of those techniques. A big step in that direction is the development of **protein microarrays (protein chips)**, which are similar in concept to DNA microarrays. For example, one type of protein microarray involves binding antibodies prepared against different proteins to different locations on the protein chip. An antibody for a foreign substance, such as a protein, is generated by the immune system of an animal that has been injected with that substance. The antibody is isolated from the blood of that animal and can be used to bind specifically to the protein in experiments. Proteins are isolated from cells, labelled, and then pumped over the surface of the protein microarray. Each labelled protein binds to the antibody for that protein. After washing off excess proteins, the protein microarray is analyzed much as for DNA microarrays to determine where the proteins bound and to quantify that binding. With this technique, a researcher can quantify proteins in different cell types and different tissues. Researchers can also compare proteins under different conditions, such as during differentiation, or

Figure 16.19
DNA microarray analysis of gene expression levels.

PURPOSE: DNA microarrays can be used in various experiments, including comparing the levels of gene expression in two different tissues, as illustrated here. The power of the technique is that the entire set of genes in a genome can be analyzed simultaneously.

PROTOCOL:

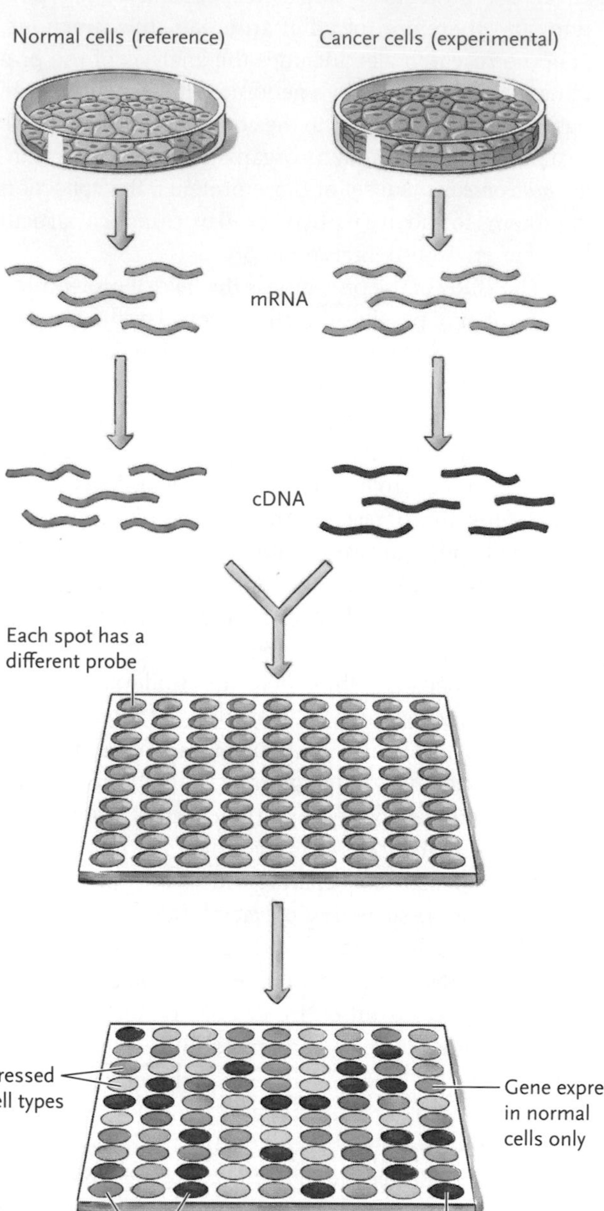

1. Isolate mRNAs from a control cell type (here, normal cells) and an experimental cell type (here, cancer cells).

2. Prepare cDNA libraries from each mRNA sample. For the normal cell (control) library use nucleotides with a green fluorescent label, and for the cancer cell (experimental) library use nucleotides with a red fluorescent label.

3. Denature the cDNAs to single strands, mix them, and pump them across the surface of a DNA microarray containing a set of single-stranded probes representing every protein-coding gene in the human genome. The probes are spotted on the surface, with each spot containing a probe for a different gene. Allow the labelled cDNAs to hybridize with the gene probes on the surface of the chip, and then wash excess cDNAs off.

4. Locate and quantify the fluorescence of the labels on the hybridized cDNAs with a laser detection system.

Actual DNA microarray result

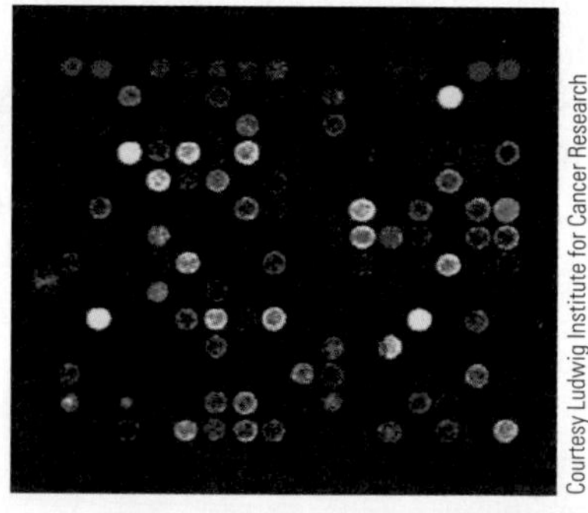

Courtesy Ludwig Institute for Cancer Research

INTERPRETING THE RESULTS: The coloured spots on the microarray indicate where the labelled cDNAs have bound to the gene probes attached to the chip and, therefore, which genes were active in normal and/or cancer cells. Moreover, we can quantify the gene expression in the two cell types by the colour detected. A purely green spot indicates the gene was active in the normal cell, but not in the cancer cell. A purely red spot indicates the gene was active in the cancer cell, but not in the normal cell. A yellow spot indicates the gene was equally active in the two cell types, and other colours tell us the relative levels of gene expression in the two cell types. For this particular experiment, we would be able to see how many genes have altered expression in the cancer cells, and exactly how their expression was changed.

with and without a particular disease condition, or with and without a particular drug treatment. In the future, we can expect protein arrays to become routine for studying cellular proteomes.

Overall, taking an "omics" approach to biology—considering all of the genes, or all of the proteins, or all of the mRNA, or all of the interactions between these components in a system—reveals a picture of complexity that was only glimpsed through past studies of each isolated component. This more holistic understanding extends beyond individual cells or organisms to consider relationships to the populations, communities, and ecosystems in which they reside.

Study Break

1. How are possible protein-coding genes identified in a genome sequence of a bacterium? Of a mammal?
2. What are the steps in whole-genome shotgun cloning?

Unanswered Questions

This chapter leaves us with two big questions.

First, how much diversity is out there?
Metagenomic studies increase the number of known genes by leaps and bounds each year. Will we ever know them all? Leaving aside genes, will we ever even find all of the different organisms and viruses on the planet?

Second, how can this diversity be used to our benefit?
In just over 50 years since the structure of DNA was published by Watson and Crick, scientists have learned to cut it, paste it, amplify it, sequence it, and synthesize it "from scratch." These technologies enable the creation of "custom-designed" organisms with novel qualities or abilities. The challenge will be in determining how to effectively apply these tools toward some of the significant problems facing the world in the coming years.

Review

Go to CENGAGENOW™ at http://hed.nelson.com/ to access quizzing, animations, exercises, articles, and personalized homework help.

16.1 DNA Cloning

- Producing multiple copies of genes by cloning is a common first step for studying the structure and function of genes or for manipulating genes. Cloning involves cutting genomic DNA and a cloning vector with the same restriction enzyme, joining the fragments to produce recombinant plasmids, and introducing those plasmids into a living cell such as a bacterium, where replication of the plasmid takes place (see Figures 16.1–16.3).
- A clone containing a gene of interest may be identified among a population of clones by using DNA hybridization with a labelled nucleic acid probe (see Figure 16.4).
- A genomic library is a collection of clones that contains a copy of every DNA sequence in the genome. A cDNA (complementary DNA) library is the entire collection of cloned cDNAs made from the mRNAs isolated from a cell. A cDNA library contains only sequences from the genes that are active in the cell when the mRNAs are isolated.
- PCR amplifies a specific target sequence in DNA, such as a gene, defined by a pair of primers. PCR increases DNA quantities by successive cycles of denaturing the template DNA, annealing the primers, and extending the primers in a DNA synthesis reaction catalyzed by DNA polymerase; with each cycle, the amount of DNA doubles (see Figure 18.5).

16.2 Applications of DNA Technologies

- Recombinant DNA and PCR techniques are used in DNA molecular testing for human genetic disease mutations. One approach exploits restriction site differences between normal and mutant alleles of a gene that create restriction fragment length polymorphisms (RFLPs) detectable by DNA hybridization with a labelled nucleic acid probe (see Figures 16.7 and 16.8).
- Human DNA fingerprints are produced from a number of loci in the genome characterized by tandemly repeated sequences that vary in number in all individuals (except identical twins). To produce a fingerprint, the PCR is used to amplify the region of genomic DNA for each locus, and the lengths of the PCR products indicate the alleles an individual has for the repeated sequences at each locus. DNA fingerprints are widely used to establish paternity, ancestry, or criminal guilt (see Figure 16.9).
- Genetic engineering is the introduction of new genes or genetic information to alter the genetic makeup of humans, other animals, plants, and microorganisms such as bacteria and yeast. Genetic engineering primarily aims to correct hereditary defects, improve domestic animals and crop plants, and provide proteins for medicine, research, and other applications (see Figures 16.10, 16.11, and 16.14).
- Genetic engineering has enormous potential for research and applications in medicine, agriculture, and industry. Potential risks include unintended damage to living organisms or the environment.

16.3 Genome Analysis

- Genome analysis consists of two main areas: structural genomics, the sequencing of genomes and the identification of the genes the sequences contain, and functional genomics, the study of the function of genes and other parts of the genome.
- Sequencing a genome involves a replication reaction with a DNA template, a DNA primer, the four normal deoxyribonucleotides, and a mixture of four dideoxyribonucleotides, each labelled with a different fluorescent tag, and DNA polymerase. Replication stops at any place in the sequence in which a dideoxyribonucleotide

is substituted for the normal deoxyribonucleotide. The lengths of the terminated DNA chains and the label on them indicate the overall sequence of the DNA chain being sequenced (see Figure 16.17).

- The whole-genome shotgun method of sequencing a genome involves breaking up the entire genome into random, overlapping fragments, cloning each fragment, determining the sequence of the fragment in each clone, and using computer algorithms to assemble overlapping sequences into the sequence of the complete genome (see Figure 16.18).
- Once a gene is sequenced, the sequence of the protein encoded in a prokaryotic gene can be deduced by reading the coding portion of the gene three nucleotides at a time, starting at the AUG codon that indicates the beginning of a coding sequence.
- Complete genome sequences have been obtained for many viruses, a large number of prokaryotes, and many eukaryotes, including the human. The sequences have revealed that all eukaryotes share related gene sequences, and they have also revealed a significant proportion of genes whose functions are not presently known.
- Having the complete genome of an organism makes it possible to study the expression of all of the genes in the genome simultaneously, including comparing gene expression in two different cell types. The DNA microarray (or DNA chip) is typically used for the comparison; this technique can provide information about which genes are active in the two cell types, as well as relative levels of expression of those genes (see Figure 16.19).
- Proteomics is the study of the complete set of proteins in an organism or in a particular cell type. Protein numbers, protein structure, and protein interactions are all topics of proteomics.
- Systems biology combines data derived from genomics, proteomics, and other sources of information. Using sophisticated quantitative analysis, it seeks to model the total array of interactions responsible for an organism's form and function.

Questions

Self-Test Questions

1. Using cDNA is associated with which of the following?
   a. Introns can be identified and sequenced by this method.
   b. It measures both active and inactive DNA.
   c. Promoter regions can be identified by this method.
   d. One can identify start and stop regions by this method.
   e. One can identify active mRNA and make a complementary DNA sequence to the mRNA.
2. Restriction endonucleases, ligases, plasmids, viral or yeast vectors, electrophoretic gels, and a bacterial gene resistant to an antibiotic are all required for:
   a. dideoxyribonucleotide analysis.
   b. PCR.
   c. DNA cloning.
   d. DNA fingerprinting.
   e. DNA sequencing.
3. The PCR technique is distinguished from other processes discussed in this chapter by the use of:
   a. primers.
   b. DNA.
   c. RNA.
   d. Taq polymerase.
   e. the four nucleoside triphosphates.
4. Restriction fragment length polymorphisms:
   a. are produced by reaction with restriction endonucleases and are detected by Southern blot analysis.
   b. are of the same length for mutant and normal β-globin alleles.
   c. determine the sequence of bases in a DNA fragment.
   d. have in their middle short fragments of DNA that are palindromic.
   e. are used as vectors.
5. DNA fingerprinting:
   a. compares one stretch of the same DNA between two or more people.
   b. measures different lengths of DNA from many repeating noncoding regions for comparison between two or more people.
   c. requires the largest DNA lengths to run the greatest distance on a gel.
   d. requires amplification after the gels are run.
   e. can easily differentiate DNA between identical twins.
6. Dolly, a sheep, was an example of reproductive (germ line) cloning. Required to perform this process was:
   a. implantation of uterine cells from one strain into the mammary gland of another.
   b. the fusion of the mammary cell from one strain with an enucleated egg of another strain.
   c. the fusion of an egg from one strain with the egg of a different strain.
   d. the fusion of an embryonic diploid cell with an adult haploid cell.
   e. the fusion of two nucleated mammary cells from two different strains.
7. Which of the following statements is NOT true for somatic cell gene therapy?
   a. White blood cells can be used.
   b. Somatic cells are cultured, and the desired DNA is introduced into them.
   c. Cells with the introduced DNA are returned to the body.
   d. The technique is still very experimental.
   e. The inserted genes are passed on to the offspring.
8. The sequence of the human genome
   a. was obtained by sequencing overlapping DNA fragments.
   b. revealed far more genes than expected.
   c. revealed 3 trillion base pairs.
   d. used techniques not applicable to mapping other species.
   e. revealed 250 000 protein-coding genes.
9. Sanger's DNA sequencing technique:
   a. uses dideoxyribonucleotides to make new full-length strands of DNA.
   b. is based on cellular transcription.
   c. requires an RNA template, an RNA primer, RNA polymerase, reverse transcriptase, and the dideoxyribonucleotides, ddATP, ddUTP, ddCTP, and ddGTP.
   d. places the RNA template to be sequenced on a gel and then adds the other ingredients from (c).
   e. is based on DNA replication.
10. A microarray could be used to
    a. sequence DNA from several chromosomes in one individual.
    b. synthesize multiple copies of DNA from several sources.
    c. propagate human germ-line cells for cloning.
    d. compare coding DNA from a patient's normal lung cells with coding DNA from his cancerous lung cells.
    e. determine proteins that are expressed under certain environmental conditions.

Questions for Discussion

1. Do you think that genetic engineering is worth the risk? Who do you think should decide whether genetic engineering experiments and projects should be carried out: scientists, judges, politicians?
2. Do you think that human germ-line cells should be modified by genetic engineering to cure birth defects? To increase intelligence or beauty?
3. Write a paragraph supporting genetic engineering and one arguing against it. Which argument carries more weight, in your opinion?
4. What should juries know to interpret DNA evidence? Why might juries sometimes ignore DNA evidence?
5. A forensic scientist obtained a small DNA sample from a crime scene. To examine the sample, he increased its quantity by PCR. He estimated that there were 50 000 copies of the DNA in his original sample. Derive a simple formula and calculate the number of copies he will have after 15 cycles of PCR.
6. A market puts out a bin of tomatoes that have outstanding colour, flavour, and texture. A sign posted above them identifies them as genetically engineered produce. Most shoppers pick unmodified tomatoes in an adjacent bin, even though they are pale, mealy, and nearly tasteless. Which tomatoes would you pick? Why?
7. Suppose a biotechnology company has developed a GMO, a transgenic plant that expresses *Bt* toxin. The company sells its seeds to a farmer under the condition that the farmer may plant the seed, but not collect seed from the plants that grow and use it to produce crops in the subsequent season. The seeds are expensive, and the farmer buys seeds from the company only once. How could the company show experimentally that the farmer has violated the agreement and is using seeds collected from the first crop to grow the next crop?

Phenotypic variation. The frog *Dendrobates pumilio* exhibits dramatic colour variation in populations that inhabit the Bocas del Toro Islands, Panama.

© Mark Moffett/Foto Natura/Minden Pictures

Study Plan

17 Microevolution: Genetic Changes within Populations

Why It Matters

On November 28, 1942, at the height of American involvement in World War II, a disastrous fire killed more than 400 people in Boston's Cocoanut Grove nightclub. Many more would have died later but for a new experimental drug, penicillin. A product of *Penicillium* mould, penicillin fought the usually fatal infections of *Staphylococcus aureus,* a bacterium that enters the body through damaged skin. Penicillin was the first antibiotic drug based on a naturally occurring substance that kills bacteria.

Until the disaster at the Cocoanut Grove, the production and use of penicillin had been a closely guarded military secret. But after its public debut, the pharmaceutical industry hailed penicillin as a wonder drug, promoting its use for the treatment of the many diseases caused by infectious microorganisms. Penicillin became widely available as an over-the-counter remedy, and Americans dosed themselves with it, hoping to cure all sorts of ills **(Figure 17.1, p. 374).** But in 1945, Alexander Fleming, the scientist who discovered penicillin, predicted that some bacteria could survive low doses and that the offspring of those germs would be more resistant to its effects. In 1946—just 4 years after penicillin's use in Boston—14% of the *Staphylococcus* strains isolated

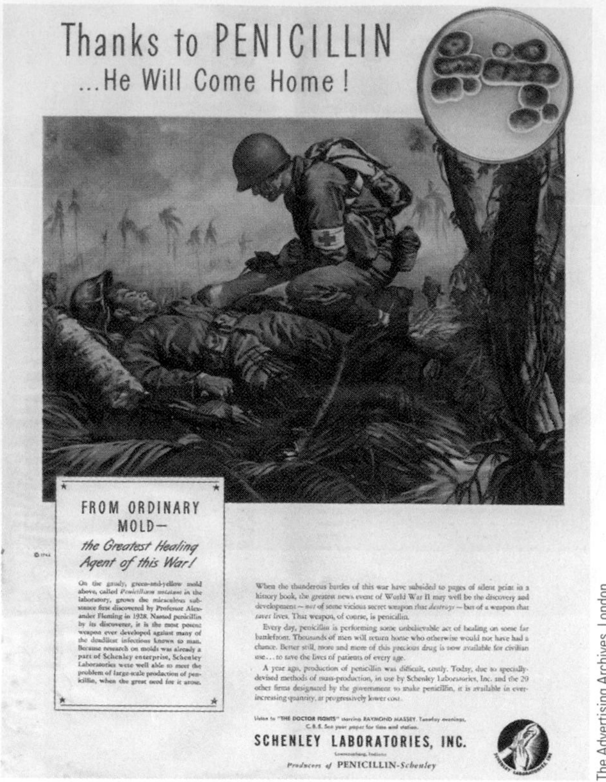

The Advertising Archives, London

Figure 17.1
Selling penicillin. This ad, from a 1944 issue of *Life* magazine, credits penicillin with saving the lives of wounded soldiers.

from patients in a London hospital were resistant. By 1950, more than half the strains were resistant.

Scientists and physicians have discovered numerous antibiotics since the 1940s, and many strains of bacteria have developed resistance to these drugs. *Streptococcus pneumoniae* is the leading cause of infectious death worldwide. In Canada, over 12 000 people require hospitalization for *Streptococcus* infections annually, and the rate of drug resistance nearly doubled between 1999 and 2000. In the face of such increases, it is alarming that a recent study revealed that misunderstandings about the biology of antibiotic resistance are widespread among Canadians.

How do bacteria become resistant to antibiotics? The genomes of bacteria—like those of all other organisms—vary among individuals, and some bacteria have genetic traits that allow them to withstand attack by antibiotics. When we administer antibiotics to an infected patient, we create an environment favouring bacteria that are even slightly resistant to the drug. The surviving bacteria reproduce, and resistant microorganisms—along with the genes that confer antibiotic resistance—become more common in later generations. In other words, bacterial populations change in response to antibiotics through the evolutionary process of selection. Our use of antibiotics is comparable to artificial selection by plant and animal breeders (see Chapter 49), but when we use antibiotics, we inadvertently select for the success of organisms that we are trying to eradicate.

The evolution of antibiotic resistance in bacteria is an example of **microevolution**, which is a heritable change in the genetics of a population. A **population** of organisms includes all the individuals of a single species that live together in the same place and time. Today, when scientists study microevolution, they analyze variation—the differences between individuals—in natural populations and determine how and why these variations are inherited. Darwin recognized the importance of heritable variation within populations; he also realized that natural selection can change the pattern of variation in a population from one generation to the next. Scientists have since learned that microevolutionary change results from several processes, not just natural selection, and that sometimes these processes counteract each other.

In this chapter, we first examine the extensive variation that exists within natural populations. We then take a detailed look at the most important processes that alter genetic variation within populations, causing microevolutionary change. Finally, we consider how microevolution can fine-tune the functioning of populations within their environments.

17.1 Variation in Natural Populations

In some species, individuals vary dramatically in appearance, but in most species, the members of a population look pretty much alike **(Figure 17.2)**. Even those that look alike, such as the *Cerion* snails in Figure 17.2b, are not identical, however. With a scale and a ruler, you could detect differences in their mass as well as in the length

a. European garden snails

George Bernard/Foto Natura/Photo Researchers, Inc.

b. Bahaman land snails

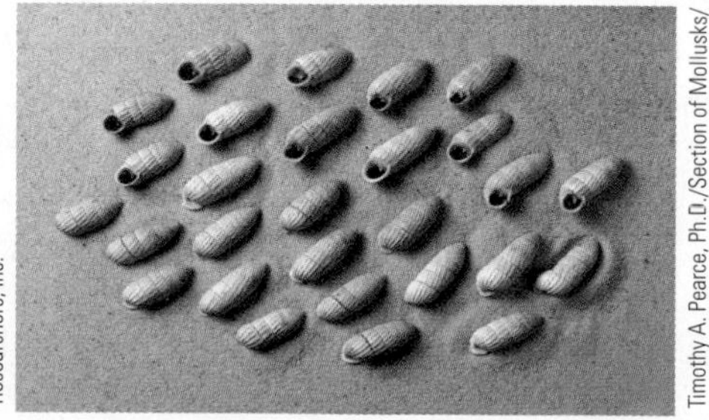

Timothy A. Pearce, Ph.D./Section of Mollusks/ Carnegie Museum of Natural History. Photograph by Mindy McNaugher

Figure 17.2
Phenotypic variation. **(a)** Shells of the European garden snail (*Cepaea nemoralis*) from a population in Scotland vary considerably in appearance. **(b)** By contrast, shells of *Cerion christophei* from a population in the Bahamas look very similar.

and diameter of their shells. With suitable techniques, you could also document variations in their individual biochemistry, physiology, internal anatomy, and behaviour. All of these are examples of **phenotypic variation,** differences in appearance or function that are passed from generation to generation.

17.1a Evolutionary Biologists Describe and Quantify Phenotypic Variation

Darwin's theory recognized the importance of heritable phenotypic variation, and today, microevolutionary studies often begin by assessing phenotypic variation within populations. Most characters exhibit **quantitative variation:** individuals differ in small, incremental ways. If you weighed everyone in your biology class, for example, you would see that mass varies almost continuously from your lightest to your heaviest classmate. Humans also exhibit quantitative variation in the length of their toes, the number of hairs on their heads, and their height, as discussed in Chapter 11.

We usually display data on quantitative variation in a bar graph or, if the sample is large enough, as a curve **(Figure 17.3).** The width of the curve is proportional to the variability—the amount of variation—among individuals, and the *mean* describes the average value of the character. As you will see shortly, natural selection often changes the mean value of a character or its variability within populations.

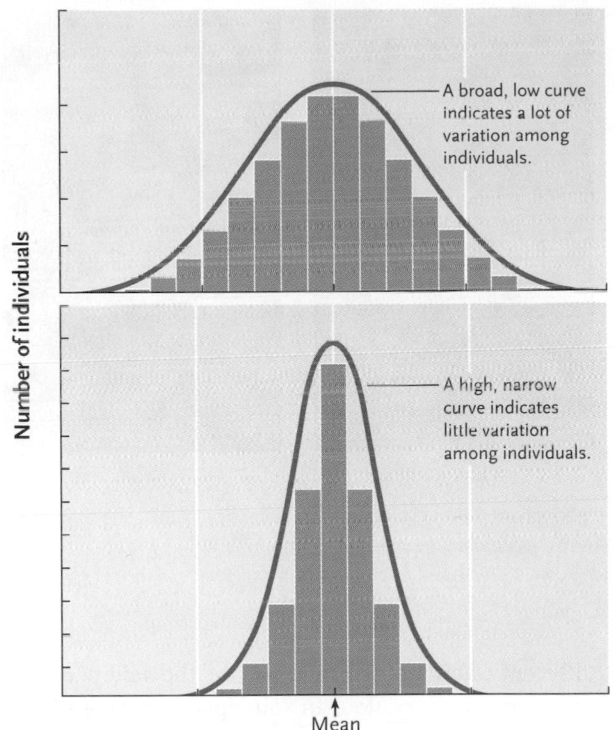

Figure 17.3
Quantitative variation. Many traits vary continuously among members of a population, and a bar graph of the data often approximates a bell-shaped curve. The mean defines the average value of the trait in the population, and the width of the curve is proportional to the variability among individuals.

Other characters, like those Mendel studied (see Section 11.1), exhibit **qualitative variation:** they exist in two or more discrete states, and intermediate forms are often absent. Snow geese, for example, have *either* blue *or* white feathers **(Figure 17.4).** The existence of discrete variants of a character is called a **polymorphism** (*poly* = many; *morphos* = form); we describe such traits as *polymorphic.* The *Cepaea nemoralis* snail shells in Figure 17.2a are polymorphic in background colour, number of stripes, and colour of stripes. Biochemical polymorphisms, like the human A, B, AB, and O blood groups (described in Section 11.2), are also common.

We describe phenotypic polymorphisms quantitatively by calculating the percentage or *frequency* of each trait. For example, if you counted 123 blue snow geese and 369 white ones in a population of 492 geese, the frequency of the blue phenotype would be 123/492 or 0.25, and the frequency of the white phenotype would be 369/492 or 0.75.

17.1b Phenotypic Variation Can Have Genetic and Environmental Causes

Phenotypic variation within populations may be caused by genetic differences between individuals, by differences in the environmental factors that individuals experience, or by an interaction between genetics and the environment. As a result, genetic and phenotypic variations may not be perfectly correlated. Under some circumstances, organisms with different genotypes exhibit the same phenotype. For example, the black colouration of some rock pocket mice from Arizona is caused by certain mutations in the *Mc1r* gene, but black mice from New Mexico do not share those mutations—that is, they have different genotypes—even though they exhibit the same phenotype. On the other hand, organisms with the same genotype sometimes exhibit

Figure 17.4
Qualitative variation. Individual snow geese (*Chen caerulescens*) are either blue or white. Although both colours are present in many populations, geese tend to associate with others of the same colour.

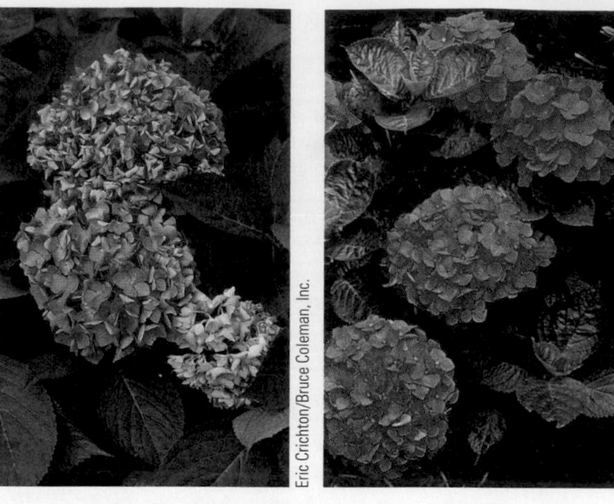

Figure 17.5
Environmental effects on phenotype. Soil acidity affects the expression of the gene controlling flower colour in the common garden plant *Hydrangea macrophylla*. When grown in acid soil, it produces deep blue flowers. In neutral or alkaline soil, its flowers are bright pink.

different phenotypes. For example, the acidity of soil influences flower colour in some plants **(Figure 17.5)**.

Knowing whether phenotypic variation is caused by genetic differences, environmental factors, or an interaction of the two is important because *only genetically based variation is subject to evolutionary change*. Moreover, knowing the causes of phenotypic variation has important practical applications. Suppose, for example, that one field of wheat produced more grain than another. If a difference in the availability of nutrients or water caused the difference in yield, a farmer might choose to fertilize or irrigate the less productive field. But if the difference in productivity resulted from genetic differences between plants in the two fields, a farmer might plant only the more productive genotype. Because environmental factors can influence the expression of genes, an organism's phenotype is frequently the product of an interaction between its genotype and its environment. In our hypothetical example, the farmer may maximize yield by fertilizing and irrigating the better genotype of wheat.

How can we determine whether phenotypic variation is caused by environmental factors or by genetic differences? We can test for an environmental cause experimentally by changing one environmental variable and measuring the effects on genetically similar subjects. You can try this yourself by growing some cuttings from an ivy plant in shade and other cuttings from the same plant in full sun. Although they all have the same genotype, the cuttings grown in sun will produce smaller leaves and shorter stems.

Breeding experiments can demonstrate the genetic basis of phenotypic variation. For example, Mendel inferred the genetic basis of qualitative traits, such as flower colour in peas, by crossing plants with different phenotypes. Moreover, traits that vary quantitatively will respond to artificial selection only if the variation has some genetic basis. For example, researchers observed that individual house mice (*Mus musculus*) differ in activity levels, as measured by how much they use an exercise wheel and how fast they run. John G. Swallow, Patrick A. Carter, and Theodore Garland Jr., then at the University of Wisconsin at Madison, used artificial selection to produce lines of mice that exhibit increased wheel-running behaviour, demonstrating that the observed differences in these two aspects of activity level have a genetic basis **(Figure 17.6)**.

Breeding experiments are not always practical, however, particularly for organisms with long generation times. Ethical concerns also render these techniques unthinkable for humans. Instead, researchers sometimes study the inheritance of particular traits by analyzing genealogical pedigrees, as discussed in Section 12.2, but this approach often provides poor results for analyses of complex traits.

17.1c Several Processes Generate Genetic Variation

Genetic variation, the raw material moulded by microevolutionary processes, has two potential sources: the production of new alleles and the rearrangement of existing alleles. Most new alleles probably arise from small-scale mutations in DNA (described later in this chapter). The rearrangement of existing alleles into new combinations can result from larger scale changes in chromosome structure or number and from several forms of genetic recombination, including crossing over between homologous chromosomes during meiosis, the independent assortment of nonhomologous chromosomes during meiosis, and random fertilizations between genetically different sperm and eggs. (These processes are described in Chapter 10.)

The shuffling of *existing* alleles into new combinations can produce an extraordinary number of novel genotypes and phenotypes in the next generation. By one estimate, more than 10^{600} combinations of alleles are possible in human gametes, yet fewer than 10^{10} humans are alive today. So unless you have an identical twin, it is extremely unlikely that another person with your genotype has ever lived or ever will.

17.1d Populations Often Contain Substantial Genetic Variation

How much genetic variation actually exists within populations? In the 1960s, evolutionary biologists began to use gel electrophoresis (see Figure 16.7) to identify biochemical polymorphisms in diverse organisms. This technique separates two or more forms of a given protein if they differ significantly in shape, mass, or net electrical charge. The identification of a protein polymorphism allows researchers to infer genetic variation at the locus coding for that protein.

Figure 17.6
Using artificial selection to demonstrate that activity level in mice has a genetic basis.

QUESTION: Do observed differences in activity level among house mice have a genetic basis?

EXPERIMENT: Swallow, Carter, and Garland knew that a phenotypic character responds to artificial selection only if it has a genetic, rather than an environmental, basis. In an experiment with house mice (*Mus domesticus*), they selected for the phenotypic character of increased wheel-running activity. In four experimental lines, they bred those mice that ran the most. Four other lines, in which breeders were selected at random with respect to activity level, served as controls.

RESULTS: After 10 generations of artificial selection, mice in the experimental lines ran longer distances and ran faster than mice in the control lines. Thus, artificial selection on wheel-running activity in house mice increased **(a)** the distance that mice run per day and **(b)** their average speed. The data illustrate responses of females in four experimental lines and four control lines. Males showed similar responses.

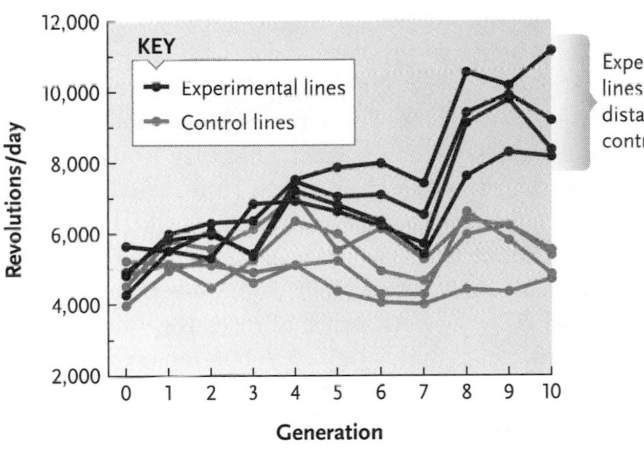

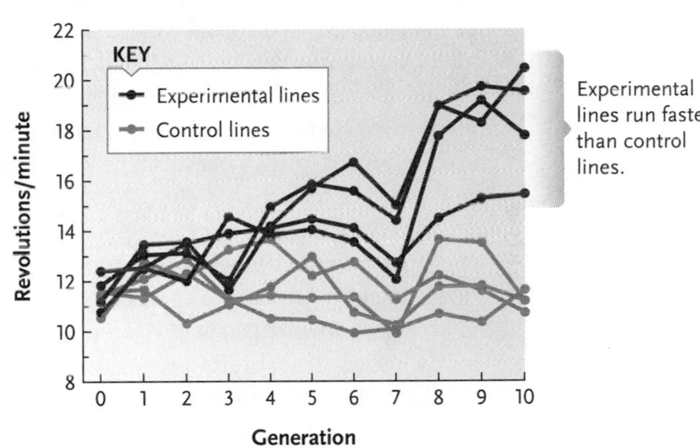

CONCLUSION: Because two measures of activity level responded to artificial selection, researchers concluded that variation in this behavioural character has a genetic basis.

Researchers discovered much more genetic variation than anyone had imagined. For example, nearly half the loci surveyed in many populations of plants and invertebrates are polymorphic. Moreover, gel electrophoresis actually underestimates genetic variation because it doesn't detect different amino acid substitutions if the proteins for which they code migrate at the same rate.

Advances in molecular biology now allow scientists to survey genetic variation directly, and researchers have accumulated an astounding knowledge of the structure of DNA and its nucleotide sequences. In general, studies of chromosomal and mitochondrial DNA suggest that every locus exhibits some variability in its nucleotide sequence. The variability is apparent in comparisons of individuals from a single population, populations of one species, and related species. However, some variations detected in the protein-coding regions of DNA may not affect phenotypes because, as explained in the following they do not change the amino acid sequences of the proteins for which the genes code.

Study Break

1. What is a genetic polymorphism?
2. If a population of skunks includes some individuals with stripes and others with spots, would you describe the variation as quantitative or qualitative?
3. What factors contribute to phenotypic variation in a population?

17.2 Population Genetics

To predict how certain factors may influence genetic variation, population geneticists first describe the genetic structure of a population. They then create hypotheses, which they formalize in mathematical models, to describe how evolutionary processes may change the genetic structure under specified conditions. Finally, researchers test the predictions of these models to evaluate the ideas about evolution that are embodied within them.

17.2a All Populations Have a Genetic Structure

Populations are made up of individuals, each with its own genotype. In diploid organisms, which have pairs of homologous chromosomes, an individual's genotype includes two alleles at every gene locus. The sum of all alleles at all gene loci in all individuals is called the population's **gene pool.**

To describe the structure of a gene pool, scientists first identify the genotypes in a representative sample and calculate **genotype frequencies,** the percentages of individuals possessing each genotype. Knowing that each diploid organism has two alleles (either two copies of the same allele or two different alleles) at each gene locus, a scientist can then calculate **allele frequencies,** the relative abundances of the different alleles. For a locus with two alleles, scientists use the symbol p to identify the frequency of one allele, and q to identify the frequency of the other allele.

The calculation of genotype and allele frequencies for the two alleles at the gene locus governing flower colour in snapdragons (genus *Antirrhinum*) is straightforward **(Table 17.1).** This locus is easy to study because it exhibits incomplete dominance (see Section 11.2). Individuals that are homozygous for the C^R allele (C^RC^R) have red flowers; those homozygous for the C^W allele (C^WC^W) have white flowers; and heterozygotes (C^RC^W) have pink flowers. Genotype frequencies represent how the C^R and C^W alleles are distributed among individuals. In this example, examination of the plants reveals that 45% of individuals have the C^RC^R genotype, 50% have the heterozygous C^RC^W genotype, and the remaining 5% have the C^WC^W genotype. Allele frequencies represent the commonness or rarity of each allele in the gene pool. As calculated in the table, 70% of the alleles in the population are C^R and 30% are C^W. Remember that for a gene locus with two alleles, there are three genotype frequencies, but only two allele frequencies (p and q). The sum of the three genotype frequencies must equal 1; so must the sum of the two allele frequencies.

17.2b The Hardy–Weinberg Principle Is a Null Model That Defines How Evolution Does Not Occur

When designing experiments, scientists often use control treatments to evaluate the effect of a particular factor. The control tells us what we would see if the experimental treatment had no effect. However, in studies that use observational rather than experimental data, there is often no suitable control. In such cases, investigators develop conceptual models, called **null models,** which predict what they would see if a particular factor had no effect. Null models serve as theoretical reference points against which observations can be evaluated.

Early in the twentieth century, geneticists were puzzled by the persistence of recessive traits because they assumed that natural selection replaced recessive or rare alleles with dominant or common ones. An English mathematician, G. H. Hardy, and a German physician, Wilhelm Weinberg, tackled this problem independently in 1908. Their analysis, now known as the **Hardy–Weinberg principle,** specifies the conditions under which a population of diploid organisms achieves **genetic equilibrium,** the point at which neither allele frequencies nor genotype frequencies change in succeeding generations. Their work also showed that

Table 17.1 Calculation of Genotype Frequencies and Allele Frequencies for the Snapdragon Flower Colour Locus

Because each diploid individual has two alleles at each gene locus, the entire sample of 1000 individuals has a total of 2000 alleles at the *C* locus.

Flower Colour Phenotype	Genotype	Number of Individuals	Genotype Frequency[1]	Total Number of C^R Alleles[2]	Total Number of C^W Alleles[2]
Red	C^RC^R	450	$450/1000 = 0.45$	$2 \times 450 = 900$	$0 \times 450 = 0$
Pink	C^RC^W	500	$500/1000 = 0.50$	$1 \times 500 = 500$	$1 \times 500 = 500$
White	C^WC^W	50	$50/1000 = 0.05$	$0 \times 50 = 0$	$2 \times 50 = 100$
	Total	1000	$0.45 + 0.50 + 0.05 = 1.0$	1400	600

Calculate allele frequencies using the total of 1400 + 600 = 2000 alleles in the sample:

$$p = \text{frequency of } C^R \text{ allele} = 1400/2000 = 0.7$$
$$q = \text{frequency of } C^W \text{ allele} + 600/2000 = 0.3$$
$$p + q = 0.7 + 0.3 = 1.0$$

[1]Genotype frequency = the number of individuals possessing a particular genotype divided by the total number of individuals in the sample.
[2]Total number of C^R or C^W alleles = the number of C^R or C^W alleles present in one individual with a particular genotype multiplied by the number of individuals with that genotype.

dominant alleles need not replace recessive ones, and that the shuffling of genes in sexual reproduction does not in itself cause the gene pool to change.

The Hardy–Weinberg principle is a mathematical model that describes how genotype frequencies are established in sexually reproducing organisms. According to this model, genetic equilibrium is possible only if *all* of the following conditions are met:

1. No mutations are occurring.
2. The population is closed to migration from other populations.
3. The population is infinite in size.
4. All genotypes in the population survive and reproduce equally well.
5. Individuals in the population mate randomly with respect to genotypes.

If the conditions of the model are met, the allele frequencies of the population will never change, and the genotype frequencies will stop changing after one generation. In short, under these restrictive conditions, microevolution will *not* occur. The Hardy–Weinberg principle is thus a null model that serves as a reference point for evaluating the circumstances under which evolution *may* occur.

If a population's genotype frequencies do not match the predictions of this model or if its allele frequencies change over time, microevolution may be occurring. Determining which of the model's conditions are not met is a first step in understanding how and why the gene pool is changing.

Study Break

1. What comprises the gene pool of a population?
2. Why is the Hardy–Weinberg principle considered a null model of evolution?

Table 17.2 Agents of Microevolutionary Change

Agent	Definition	Effect on Genetic Variation
Mutation	A heritable change in DNA	Introduces new genetic variation into population
Gene flow	Change in allele frequencies as individuals join a population and reproduce	May introduce genetic variation from another population
Genetic drift	Random changes in allele frequencies caused by chance events	Reduces genetic variation, especially in small populations; can eliminate alleles
Natural selection	Differential survivorship or reproduction of individuals with different genotypes	One allele can replace another or allelic variation can be preserved
Nonrandom mating	Choice of mates based on their phenotypes and genotypes	Does not directly affect allele frequencies, but usually prevents genetic equilibrium

17.3 The Agents of Microevolution

A population's allele frequencies will change over time if the conditions of the Hardy–Weinberg model are violated. The processes that foster microevolutionary change—which include mutation, gene flow, genetic drift, natural selection, and nonrandom mating—are summarized in **Table 17.2.**

17.3a Mutations Create New Genetic Variations

A **mutation** is a heritable change in DNA. In nature, mutations are usually rare events; during any particular breeding season, between 1 gamete in 100 000 and 1 in 1 million will include a new mutation at a particular gene locus. New mutations are so infrequent, in fact, that they exert little or no immediate effect on allele frequencies in most populations. But over evolutionary time scales, their numbers are significant—mutations have been accumulating in biological lineages for billions of years. And because it is a mechanism through which entirely new genetic variations arise, *mutation is a major source of heritable variation.*

For most animals, only mutations in the germ line (the cell lineage that produces gametes) are heritable; mutations in other cell lineages have no direct effect on the next generation. In plants, however, mutations may occur in meristem cells, which eventually produce flowers as well as nonreproductive structures (see Chapter 28); in such cases, a mutation may be passed to the next generation and ultimately influence the gene pool.

Deleterious mutations alter an individual's structure, function, or behaviour in harmful ways. In mammals, for example, a protein called collagen is an essential component of most extracellular structures. Several simple mutations in humans cause forms of Ehlers–Danlos syndrome, a disruption of collagen synthesis that may result in loose skin, weak joints, or sudden death from the rupture of major blood vessels, the colon, or the uterus.

By definition, *lethal mutations* cause the death of organisms carrying them. If a lethal allele is dominant, both homozygous and heterozygous carriers suffer from its effects; if recessive, it affects only homozygous recessive individuals. A lethal mutation that causes death before the individual reproduces is eliminated from the population.

Neutral mutations are neither harmful nor helpful. Recall from Section 14.1 that in the construction of a polypeptide chain, a particular amino acid can be specified by several different codons. As a result, some DNA sequence changes—especially certain changes

Research Example: Using the Hardy–Weinberg Principle

To see how the Hardy–Weinberg principle can be applied, we will analyze the snapdragon flower colour locus using the hypothetical population of 1000 plants described in Table 17.1. This locus includes two alleles—C^R (with its frequency designated as p) and C^W (with its frequency designated as q)—and three genotypes—homozygous C^RC^R, heterozygous C^RC^W, and homozygous C^WC^W. Table 17.1 lists the number of plants with each genotype: 450 have red flowers (C^RC^R), 500 have pink flowers (C^RC^W), and 50 have white flowers (C^WC^W). It also shows the calculation of both the genotype frequencies ($C^RC^R = 0.45$, $C^RC^W = 0.50$, and $C^WC^W = 0.05$) and the allele frequencies ($p = 0.7$ and $q = 0.3$) for the population.

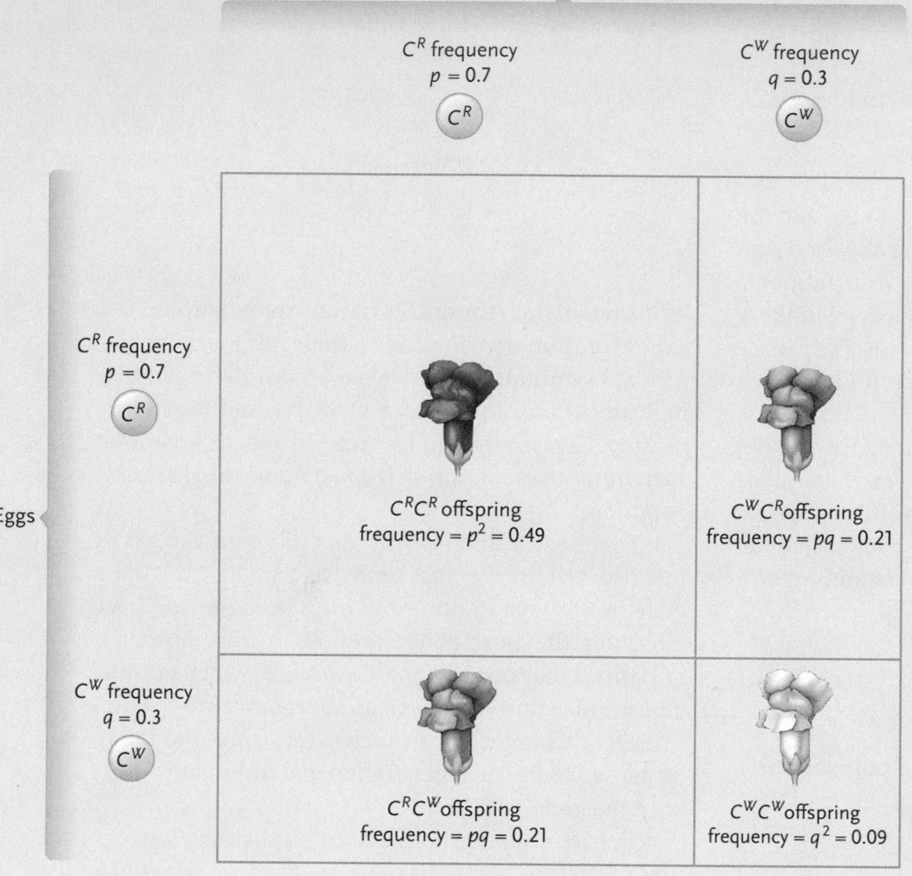

Let's assume for simplicity that each individual produces only two gametes and that both gametes contribute to the production of offspring. This assumption is unrealistic, of course, but it meets the Hardy–Weinberg requirement that all individuals in the population contribute equally to the next generation. In each parent, the two alleles segregate and end up in different gametes:

450 C^RC^R individuals produce	→	900 C^R gametes		
500 C^RC^W individuals produce	→	500 C^R gametes	+	500 C^W gametes
50 C^WC^W individuals produce	→			100 C^W gametes

You can readily see that 1400 of the 2000 total gametes carry the C^R allele and 600 carry the C^W allele. The frequency of C^R gametes is 1400/2000 or 0.7, which is equal to p; the frequency of C^W gametes is 600/2000 or 0.3, which is equal to q. Thus, the allele frequencies in the gametes are exactly the same as the allele frequencies in the parent generation—it could not be

at the third nucleotide of the codon—do not alter the amino acid sequence. Not surprisingly, mutations at the third position appear to persist longer in populations than those at the first two positions. Other mutations may change an organism's phenotype without influencing its survival and reproduction. A neutral mutation might even be beneficial later if the environment changes.

Sometimes a change in DNA produces an *advantageous mutation,* which confers some benefit on an individual that carries it. However slight the advantage, natural selection may preserve the new allele and even increase its frequency over time. Once the mutation has been passed to a new generation, other agents of microevolution determine its long-term fate.

17.3b Gene Flow Introduces Novel Genetic Variants into Populations

Organisms or their gametes (for example, pollen) sometimes move from one population to another. If the immigrants reproduce, they may introduce novel alleles into the population they have joined. This phenomenon, called **gene flow**, violates the Hardy–Weinberg requirement that populations must be closed to migration.

Gene flow is common in some animal species. For example, young male baboons typically move from one local population to another after experiencing aggressive behaviour by older males. And many marine invertebrates disperse long distances as larvae carried by ocean currents.

Research Example: Using the Hardy–Weinberg Principle (*continued*)

otherwise because each gamete carries one allele at each locus.

Now assume that these gametes, both sperm and eggs, encounter each other at random. In other words, individuals reproduce without regard to the genotype of a potential mate. We can visualize the process of random mating in the mating table on the left.

We can also describe the consequences of random mating—$(p + q)$ sperm fertilizing $(p + q)$ eggs—with an equation that predicts the genotype frequencies in the offspring generation:

$$(p + q) \times (p + q) = p^2 + 2pq + q^2$$

If the population is at genetic equilibrium for this locus, p^2 is the predicted frequency of the C^RC^R genotype, $2pq$ the predicted frequency of the C^RC^W genotype, and q^2 the predicted frequency of the C^WC^W genotype. Using the gamete frequencies determined above, we can calculate the predicted genotype frequencies in the next generation:

frequency of C^RC^R =
$$p^2 = (0.7 \times 0.7) = 0.49$$

frequency of C^RC^W =
$$2pq = 2(0.7 \times 0.3) = 0.42$$

frequency of C^WC^W =
$$q^2 = (0.3 \times 0.3) = 0.09$$

Notice that the predicted genotype frequencies in the offspring generation have changed from those in the parent generation: the frequency of heterozygous individuals has decreased, and the frequencies of both types of homozygous individuals have increased. This result occurred because the starting population was *not already* in equilibrium at this gene locus. In other words, the distribution of parent genotypes did not conform to the predicted $p^2 + 2pq + q^2$ distribution.

The 2000 gametes in our hypothetical population produced 1000 offspring. Using the genotype frequencies we just calculated, we can predict how many offspring will carry each genotype:

490 red (C^RC^R)
420 pink (C^RC^W)
90 white (C^WC^W)

In a real study, we would examine the offspring to see how well their numbers match these predictions.

What about the allele frequencies in the offspring? The Hardy–Weinberg principle predicts that they did not change. Let's calculate them and see. Using the method shown in Table 17.1 and the prime symbol (′) to indicate offspring allele frequencies,

$$p' = ([2 \times 490] + 420)/2000 = 1400/2000 = 0.7$$

$$q' = ([2 \times 90] + 420)/2000 = 600/2000 = 0.3$$

You can see from this calculation that the allele frequencies did not change from one generation to the next, even though the alleles were rearranged to produce different proportions of the three genotypes. Thus, the population is now at genetic equilibrium for the flower colour locus; neither the genotype frequencies nor the allele frequencies will change in succeeding generations as long as the population meets the conditions specified in the Hardy–Weinberg model.

To verify this, you can calculate the allele frequencies of the gametes for this offspring generation and predict the genotype frequencies and allele frequencies for a third generation. You could continue calculating until you ran out of either paper or patience, but these frequencies will not change.

Researchers use calculations like these to determine whether an actual population is near its predicted genetic equilibrium for one or more gene loci. When they discover that a population is not at equilibrium, they infer that microevolution is occurring and can investigate the factors that might be responsible.

Dispersal agents, such as pollen-carrying wind or seed-carrying animals, are responsible for gene flow in most plant populations. For example, blue jays foster gene flow among populations of oaks by carrying acorns from nut-bearing trees to their winter caches, which may be as much as a 1.5 kilometres away **(Figure 17.7).** Transported acorns that go uneaten may germinate and contribute to the gene pool of a neighbouring oak population.

Documenting gene flow among populations is not always easy, particularly if it occurs infrequently. Researchers can use phenotypic or genetic markers to identify immigrants in a population, but they must also demonstrate that immigrants reproduced, thereby contributing to the gene pool of their adopted population. In the San Francisco Bay area, for example, Bay checkerspot butterflies (*Euphydryas editha bayensis*)

David Nea Parks

W Carter Johnson

Figure 17.7
Gene flow. Blue jays (*Cyanocitta cristata*) serve as agents of gene flow for oaks (genus *Quercus*) when they carry acorns from one oak population to another. An uneaten acorn may germinate and contribute to the gene pool of the population into which it was carried.

rarely move from one population to another because they are poor fliers. When adult females do change populations, it is often late in the breeding season, and their offspring have virtually no chance of finding enough food to mature. Thus, many immigrant females do not foster gene flow because they do not contribute to the gene pool of the population they join.

The evolutionary importance of gene flow depends on the degree of genetic differentiation between populations and the rate of gene flow between them. If two gene pools are very different, a little gene flow may increase genetic variability within the population that receives immigrants, and it will make the two populations more similar. But if populations are already genetically similar, even a lot of gene flow will have little effect.

Frans Lanting/Minden Pictures

Figure 17.8
Population bottleneck. Northern elephant seals (*Mirounga angustirostris*) at the Año Nuevo State Reserve in California are descended from a population that was decimated by hunting late in the nineteenth century. In this photo, two large bulls fight to control a harem of females.

17.3c Genetic Drift Reduces Genetic Variability within Populations

Chance events sometimes cause allele frequencies in a population to change unpredictably. This phenomenon, known as **genetic drift,** has especially dramatic effects on small populations, which clearly violate the Hardy–Weinberg assumption of infinite population size.

A simple analogy clarifies why genetic drift is more pronounced in small populations than in large ones. When individuals reproduce, male and female gametes often pair up randomly, as though the allele in any particular sperm or ovum was determined by a coin toss. Imagine that "heads" specifies the R allele and "tails" specifies the r allele. If the two alleles are equally common (that is, their frequencies, p and q, are both equal to 0.5), heads should be as likely an outcome as tails. But if you toss the coin 20 or 30 times to simulate random mating in a small population, you won't often see a 50:50 ratio of heads and tails. Sometimes heads will predominate and sometimes tails will—just by chance. Tossing the coin 500 times to simulate random mating in a somewhat larger population is more likely to produce a 50:50 ratio of heads and tails. And if you tossed the coin 5000 times, you would get even closer to a 50:50 ratio.

Chance deviations from expected results—which cause genetic drift—occur whenever organisms engage in sexual reproduction, simply because their population sizes are not infinitely large. But genetic drift is particularly common in small populations because only a few individuals contribute to the gene pool and because any given allele is present in very few individuals.

Genetic drift generally leads to the loss of alleles and reduced genetic variability. Two general circumstances, population bottlenecks and founder effects, often foster genetic drift.

Population Bottlenecks. On occasion, a stressful factor such as disease, starvation, or drought kills a great many individuals and eliminates some alleles from a population, producing a **population bottleneck.** This cause of genetic drift greatly reduces genetic variation even if the population numbers later rebound.

In the late nineteenth century, for example, hunters nearly wiped out northern elephant seals (*Mirounga angustirostris*) along the Pacific coast of North America **(Figure 17.8).** Since the 1880s, when the species received protected status, the population has increased to more than 30 000, all descended from a group of about 20 survivors. Today, the population exhibits no variation in 24 proteins studied by gel electrophoresis. This low level of genetic variation, which is unique among seal species, is consistent with the hypothesis that genetic drift eliminated many alleles when the population experienced the bottleneck.

Founder Effect. When a few individuals colonize a distant locality and start a new population, they carry only a small sample of the parent population's genetic variation. By chance, some alleles may be totally missing from the new population, whereas other alleles that were rare "back home" might occur at relatively high frequencies. This change in the gene pool is called the **founder effect.**

The human medical literature provides some of the best-documented examples of the founder effect. For example, populations in the Charlevoix and Saguenay-Lac-Saint-John regions of northeastern Quebec show an unusually high incidence of myotonic dystrophy. This dominant disorder is characterized by progressive muscle weakness and wasting, often arising in early adulthood. Whereas the frequency of people carrying an allele for this trait ranges from 1 in 5000 to 1 in 50 000 in other parts of the world, this region of Quebec shows a frequency as high as 1 in 550. Analysis of the age of the founder effect suggests that the allele was brought into the

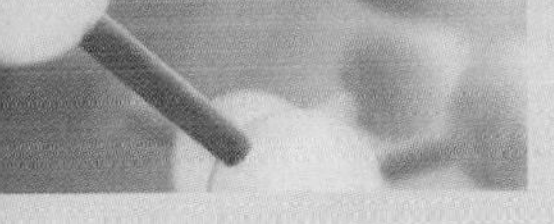

Molecule Behind Biology

Warfarin

Coumarins are anticoagulant compounds that interfere with the metabolism of vitamin K by inhibiting an enzyme called vitamin K epoxide reductase. This vitamin is required for the synthesis of prothrombin and other essential blood-clotting factors. Warfarin is a tasteless and colourless synthetic derivative of coumarin that was first developed as a rat poison in the mid-1900s **(Figure 1)**.

Warfarin was very effective when first introduced because the frequency of susceptible alleles was high in wild rodent populations. The vast majority of individuals had susceptible genotypes and therefore died from reduced clotting ability. However, those few rats carrying dominant resistance alleles tended to survive and reproduce. (Perhaps their vitamin K epoxide reductase gene had suffered a spontaneous mutation that resulted in an altered enzyme that warfarin could no longer bind to.) With continued exposure to warfarin, populations tend to accumulate resistant alleles and expand in spite of exposure to the pesticide.

Figure 1
Warfarin, an anticoagulant rat poison.

region about nine generations ago, about the time of settlement of the area by Europeans at the turn of the seventeenth century.

Conservation Implications. Genetic drift has important implications for conservation biology. By definition, endangered species experience severe population bottlenecks, which result in the loss of genetic variability. Moreover, the small number of individuals available for captive breeding programs may not fully represent a species' genetic diversity. Without such variation, no matter how large a population may become in the future, it will be less resistant to diseases or less able to cope with environmental change.

For example, scientists believe that an environmental catastrophe produced a population bottleneck in the African cheetah (*Acinonyx jubatus*) 10 000 years ago. Cheetahs today are remarkably uniform in genetic make-up. Their populations are highly susceptible to diseases; they also have a high proportion of sperm cell abnormalities and a reduced reproductive capacity. Thus, limited genetic variation, as well as small numbers, threatens populations of endangered species.

17.3d Natural Selection Shapes Genetic Variability by Favouring Some Traits over Others

Recall that the Hardy–Weinberg relationship is just a theoretical model that predicts how given allele frequencies would give rise to respective genotypic frequencies in a population over time. However, the conditions necessary for Hardy–Weinberg equilibrium, such as the requirement for all genotypes to survive and reproduce equally well, are seldom met in nature. You know from Section 20 that heritable traits enable some individuals to survive better and reproduce more than others. **Natural selection** is the process by which such traits become more common in subsequent generations. Thus, natural selection violates a requirement of the Hardy–Weinberg equilibrium.

Although natural selection can change allele frequencies, *it is the phenotype of an individual organism, rather than any particular allele, that is successful or not.* When individuals survive and reproduce, their alleles—both favourable and unfavourable—are passed to the next generation. Of course, an organism with harmful or lethal dominant alleles will probably die before reproducing, and all the alleles it carries will share that unhappy fate, even those that are advantageous.

To evaluate reproductive success, evolutionary biologists consider **relative fitness**, the number of surviving offspring that an individual produces compared with the number left by others in the population. Thus, a particular allele will increase in frequency in the next generation if individuals carrying that allele leave *more* offspring than individuals carrying other alleles. Differences in the *relative* success of individuals are the essence of natural selection.

Natural selection tests fitness differences at nearly every stage of the life cycle. One plant may be fitter than others in the population because its seeds survive colder conditions, because the arrangement of its leaves captures sunlight more efficiently, or because its flowers are more attractive to pollinators. However, natural selection exerts little or no effect on traits that appear during an individual's postreproductive life. For example, Huntington disease, a dominant-allele disorder that first strikes humans after the age of 40, is not subject to strong selection. Carriers of the disease-causing allele reproduce before the onset of the condition, passing it to the next generation.

Biologists measure the effects of natural selection on phenotypic variation by recording changes in the mean and variability of characters over time (see Figure 17.3). Three modes of natural selection have been identified: directional selection, stabilizing selection, and disruptive selection **(Figure 17.9)**.

Directional Selection. Traits undergo **directional selection** when individuals near one end of the phenotypic spectrum have the highest relative fitness. Directional selection shifts a trait away from the existing mean and toward the favoured extreme (see Figure 17.9a). After selection, the trait's mean value is higher or lower than before.

Directional selection is extremely common. For example, predatory fish promote directional selection for larger body size in guppies when they selectively feed on the smallest individuals in a guppy population. And most cases of artificial selection, including the experiment on the activity levels of house mice, are directional, aimed at increasing or decreasing specific phenotypic traits. Humans routinely use directional selection to produce domestic animals and crops with desired characteristics, such

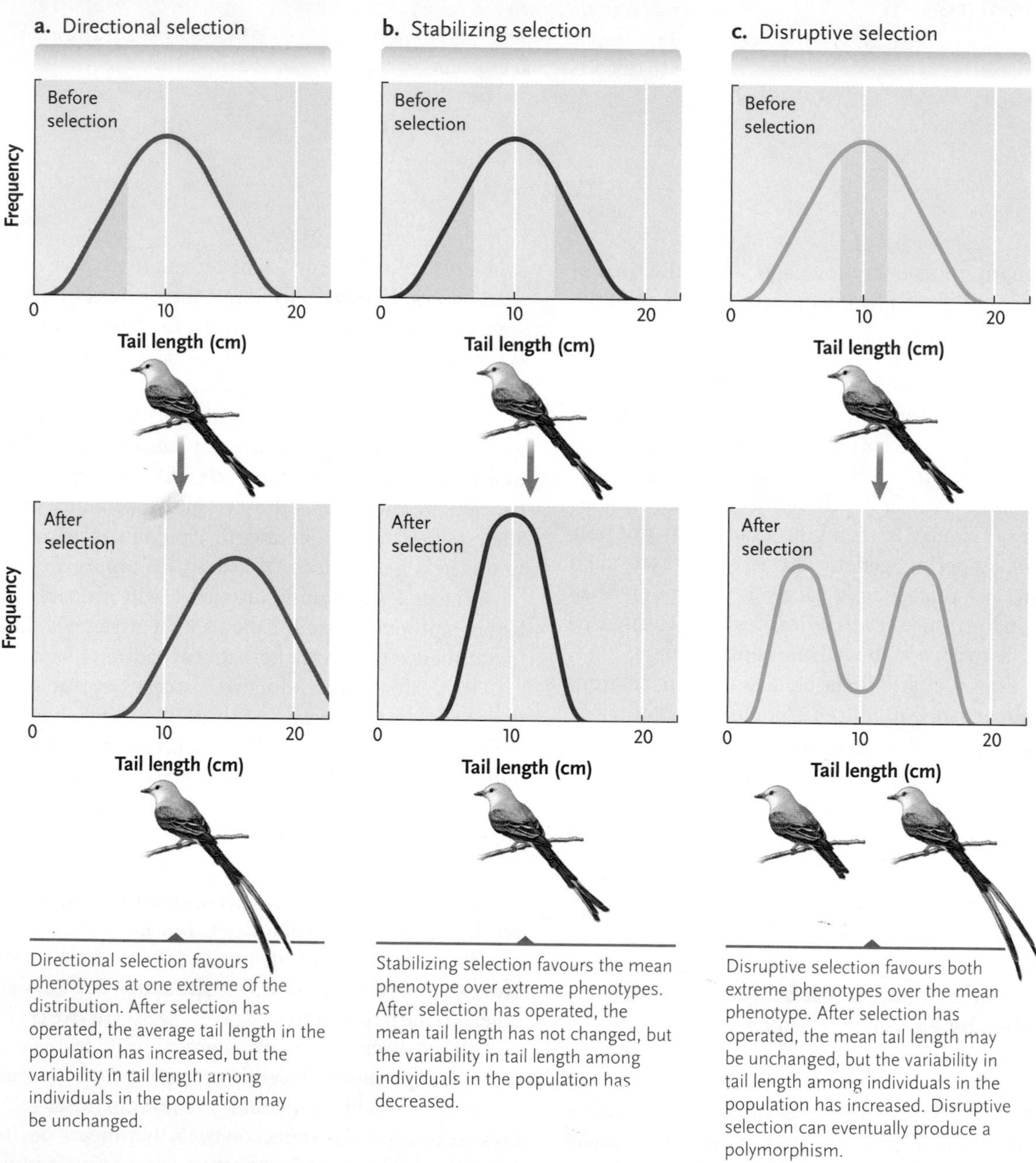

a. Directional selection
b. Stabilizing selection
c. Disruptive selection
Before selection
After selection
Frequency
Tail length (cm)
0
10
20
Directional selection favours phenotypes at one extreme of the distribution. After selection has operated, the average tail length in the population has increased, but the variability in tail length among individuals in the population may be unchanged.
Stabilizing selection favours the mean phenotype over extreme phenotypes. After selection has operated, the mean tail length has not changed, but the variability in tail length among individuals in the population has decreased.
Disruptive selection favours both extreme phenotypes over the mean phenotype. After selection has operated, the mean tail length may be unchanged, but the variability in tail length among individuals in the population has increased. Disruptive selection can eventually produce a polymorphism.

Figure 17.9
Three modes of natural selection. This hypothetical example uses tail length of birds as the quantitative trait subject to selection. The yellow shading in the top graphs indicates phenotypes that natural selection does *not* favour. Notice that the area under each curve is constant because each curve presents the frequencies of all phenotypes in the population. When stabilizing selection **(b)** reduces variability in the trait, the curve becomes higher and narrower.

as the small size of chihuahuas and the intense "bite" of chili peppers.

Stabilizing Selection. Traits undergo **stabilizing selection** when individuals expressing intermediate phenotypes have the highest relative fitness (see Figure 17.9b). By eliminating phenotypic extremes, stabilizing selection reduces genetic and phenotypic variation and increases the frequency of intermediate phenotypes. Stabilizing selection is probably the most common mode of natural selection, affecting many familiar traits. For example, very small and very large human newborns are less likely to survive than those born at an intermediate mass **(Figure 17.10).**

Warren G. Abrahamson and Arthur E. Weis of Bucknell University have shown that opposing forces of directional selection can sometimes produce an overall pattern of stabilizing selection **(Figure 17.11, p. 386).** The gallmaking fly (*Eurosta solidaginis*) is a small insect that feeds on the tall goldenrod plant (*Solidago altissima*). When a fly larva hatches from its egg, it bores into a goldenrod stem, and the plant responds by producing a spherical growth deformity called a gall. The larva feeds on plant tissues inside the gall. Galls vary dramatically in size; genetic experiments indicate that gall size is a heritable trait of the fly, although plant genotype also has an effect.

Fly larvae inside galls are subjected to two opposing patterns of directional selection. On the one hand, a tiny wasp (*Eurytoma gigantea*) parasitizes gallmaking flies by laying eggs in fly larvae inside their galls. After hatching, the young wasps feed on the fly larvae, killing them in the process. However, adult wasps are so small that they cannot easily penetrate the thick walls of a large gall; they generally lay eggs in fly larvae occupying small galls. Thus, wasps establish directional selection favouring flies that produce large galls, which are less likely to be parasitized. On the other hand, several bird species open galls to feed on mature fly larvae; these predators preferentially open large galls, fostering directional selection in favour of small galls.

In about one-third of the populations surveyed in central Pennsylvania, wasps and birds attacked galls with equal frequency, and flies producing galls of intermediate size had the highest survival rate. The smallest and largest galls—as well as the genetic predisposition to make very small or very large galls—were eliminated from the population.

Disruptive Selection. Traits undergo **disruptive selection** when extreme phenotypes have higher relative fitness than intermediate phenotypes (see Figure 17.9c). Thus, alleles producing extreme phenotypes become more common, promoting polymorphism. Under natural conditions, disruptive selection is much less common than directional selection and stabilizing selection.

Figure 17.10
Evidence for stabilizing selection in humans.

HYPOTHESIS: Human birth mass has been adjusted by natural selection.

NULL HYPOTHESIS: Natural selection has not affected human birth mass.

METHOD: Two noted human geneticists, Luigi Cavalli-Sforza and Sir Walter Bodmer of Stanford University, collected data on the variability in human birth mass, a character exhibiting quantitative variation, and on the mortality rates of babies born at different weights. The researchers then searched for a relationship between birth mass and mortality rate by plotting both data sets on the same graph. A lack of correlation between birth mass and mortality rate would support the null hypothesis.

RESULTS: When plotted together on the same graph, the bar graph (birth mass) and the curve (mortality rate) illustrate that the mean birth mass is very close to the optimum birth mass (the mass at which mortality is lowest). The two data sets also show that few babies are born at the very low and very high mass associated with high mortality.

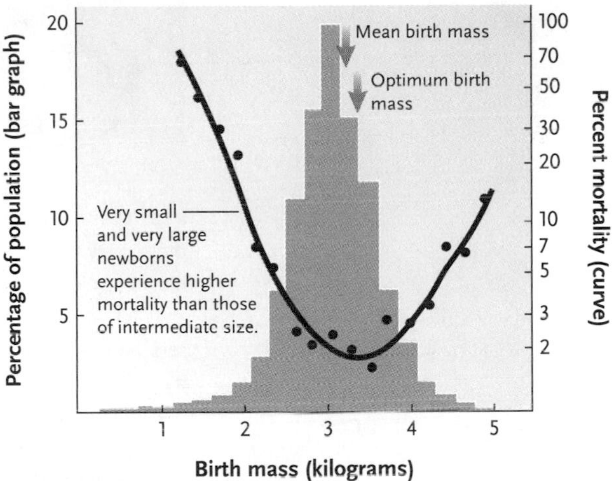

CONCLUSION: The shapes and positions of the birth mass bar graph and the mortality rate curve suggest that stabilizing selection has adjusted human birth weight to an average of 3.8 kilograms.

Peter Grant of Princeton University, one of the world's expert on the ecology and evolution of the Galápagos finches, has analyzed a likely case of disruptive selection on the size and shape of the bill in a population of cactus finches (*Geospiza conirostris*) on the island of Genovesa. During normal weather cycles, the finches feed on ripe cactus fruits, seeds, and exposed insects. During drought years, when food is scarce, they also search for insects by stripping bark from the branches of bushes and trees.

During the long drought of 1977, about 70% of the cactus finches on Genovesa died; the survivors exhibited unusually high variability in their bills **(Figure 17.12, p. 386).** Grant suggested that this morphological variability allowed birds to specialize on particular foods.

Figure 17.11
How opposing forces of directional selection produce stabilizing selection.

HYPOTHESIS: The size of galls made by larvae of the gallmaking fly (*Eurosta solidaginis*) is governed by conflicting selection pressures established by parasitic wasps and predatory birds.

PREDICTION: Gallmaking flies that produce galls of intermediate size will be more likely to survive than those that make either small galls or large galls.

METHOD: Abrahamson and his colleagues surveyed galls made by the larvae of the gallmaking fly in Pennsylvania. They measured the diameters of the galls they encountered, and for those galls in which the larvae had died, they determined whether they had been killed by **(a)** a parasitic wasp (*Eurytoma gigantea*) or **(b)** a predatory bird, such as the downy woodpecker (*Dendrocopus pubescens*).

a. *Eurytoma gigantea*, a parasitic wasp

Forrest W. Buchanan/Visuals Unlimited

b. *Dendrocopus pubescens*, a predatory bird

Gregory K. Scott/Photo Researchers, Inc.

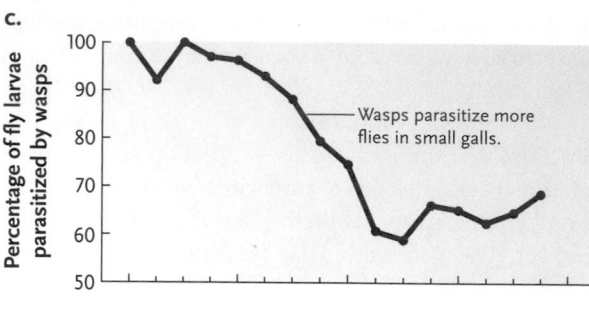

c.

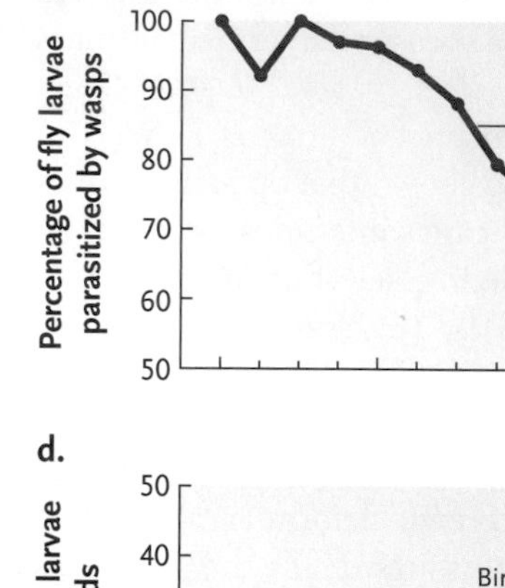

d.

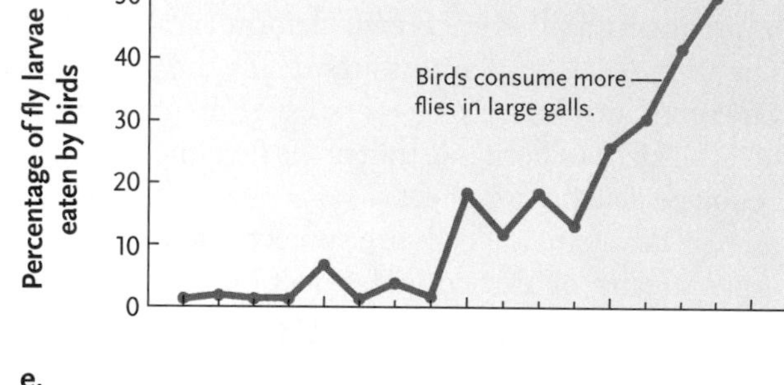

e.

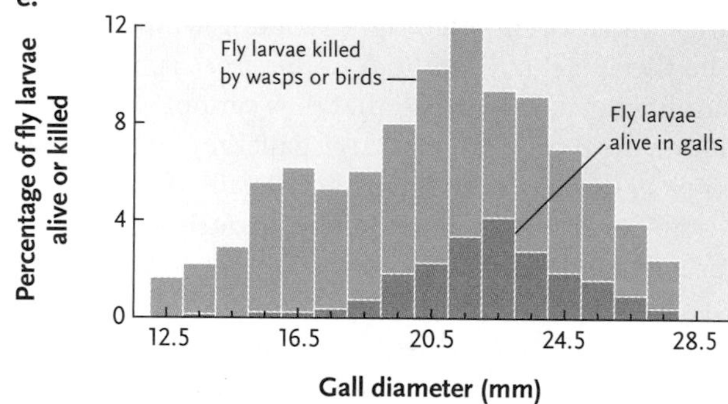

RESULTS: Tiny wasps are more likely to parasitize gallmaking fly larvae inside small galls **(c),** fostering directional selection in favour of large galls. By contrast, birds usually feed on fly larvae inside large galls **(d),** fostering directional selection in favour of small galls. These opposing patterns of directional selection create stabilizing selection for the size of galls that the fly larvae make **(e).**

CONCLUSION: Because wasps preferentially parasitize fly larvae in small galls, and birds preferentially eat fly larvae in large galls, the opposing forces of directional selection establish an overall pattern of stabilizing selection in favour of medium-sized galls.

Figure 17.12
Disruptive selection. Cactus finches (*Geospiza conirostris*) on Genovesa exhibit extreme variability in the size and shape of their bills.

Geospiza conirostris

Heather Angel/Natural Visions

Birds with long bills open cactus fruits to feed on the fleshy pulp.

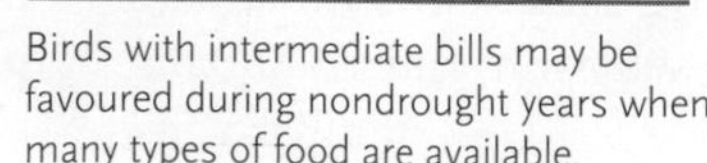

Birds with intermediate bills may be favoured during nondrought years when many types of food are available.

Birds with deep bills strip bark from trees to locate insects.

Figure 17.13
Sexual selection in action.

QUESTION: Is the long tail of the male long-tailed widowbird (*Euplectes progne*) the product of intrasexual selection, intersexual selection, or both?

EXPERIMENT: Andersson counted the number of females that associated with individual male widowbirds in the grasslands of Kenya. He then shortened the tails of some individuals by cutting the feathers, lengthened the tails of others by gluing feather extensions to their tails, and left a third group essentially unaltered as a control. One month later, he again counted the number of females associating with each male and compared the results from the three groups.

RESULTS: Males with experimentally lengthened tails attracted more than twice as many mates as males in the control group, and males with experimentally shortened tails attracted fewer. Andersson observed no differences in the ability of altered males and control group males to maintain their display areas.

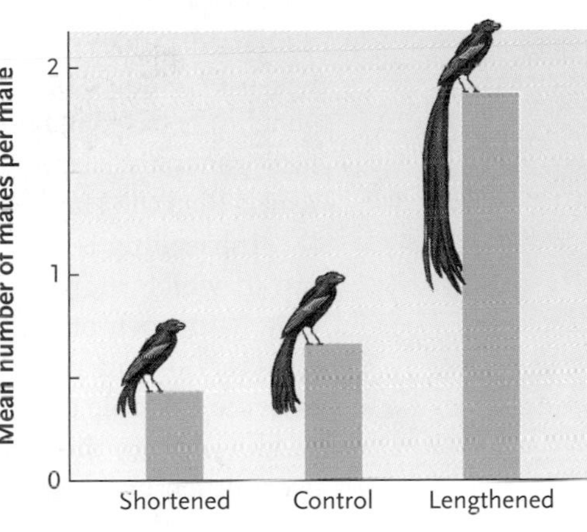

CONCLUSION: Female widowbirds clearly prefer males with experimentally lengthened tails to those with normal tails or experimentally shortened tails. Tail length had no obvious effect on the interactions between males. Thus, the long tail of male widowbirds is the product of intersexual selection.

Birds that stripped bark from branches to look for insects had particularly deep bills, and birds that opened cactus fruits to feed on the fleshy interior had especially long bills. Thus, birds with extreme bill phenotypes appeared to feed efficiently on specific resources, establishing disruptive selection on the size and shape of their bills. The selection may be particularly strong when drought limits the variety and overall availability of food. However, intermediate bill morphologies may be favoured during nondrought years when insects and small seeds are abundant.

17.3e Sexual Selection Often Exaggerates Showy Structures in Males

Darwin hypothesized that a special process, which he called **sexual selection**, has fostered the evolution of showy structures—such as brightly coloured feathers, long tails, or impressive antlers—as well as elaborate courtship behaviour in the males of many animal species. Sexual selection encompasses two related processes. As the result of *intersexual selection* (that is, selection based on the interactions between males and females), males produce these otherwise useless structures simply as a result of females finding them irresistibly attractive in the past. Under *intrasexual selection* (that is, selection based on the interactions between members of the same sex), males use their large body size, antlers, or tusks to intimidate, injure, or kill rival males. In many species, sexual selection is the most probable cause of **sexual dimorphism**, differences in the size or appearance of males and females.

Behavioural aspects of sexual selection are described further in Chapter 40.

Like directional selection, sexual selection pushes phenotypes toward one extreme. But the products of sexual selection are sometimes bizarre—such as the ridiculously long tail feathers of male African widowbirds. How could evolutionary processes favour the production of such costly structures? Malte Andersson of the University of Gothenburg, Sweden, conducted a field experiment to determine whether the long tail feathers were the product of either intersexual selection or intrasexual selection **(Figure 17.13).**

17.3f Nonrandom Mating Can Influence Genotype Frequencies

To fulfill the assumptions of the Hardy–Weinberg model requires individuals to select mates randomly with respect to their genotypes. This requirement is, in fact, often met; humans, for example, generally marry one another in total ignorance of their genotypes for digestive enzymes or blood types.

Nevertheless, many organisms mate nonrandomly, selecting a mate with a particular phenotype and underlying genotype. Snow geese, for example, usually select mates of their own colour, and a tall woman is more likely to marry a tall man than a short man. If no one phenotype is preferred by all potential mates, nonrandom mating does not establish selection for one phenotype over another. But because individuals with similar genetically based phenotypes mate with each other, the next generation will contain fewer heterozygous offspring than the Hardy–Weinberg model predicts.

Inbreeding is a special form of nonrandom mating in which individuals that are genetically related mate with each other. Self-fertilization in plants (see Chapter 30) and a few animals (see Chapter 38) is an extreme example of inbreeding because offspring are produced from the gametes of a single parent. However, other organisms that live in small, relatively closed populations often mate with related individuals. Because relatives often carry the same alleles, inbreeding generally increases the frequency of homozygous genotypes and decreases the frequency of heterozygotes. Thus, recessive phenotypes are often expressed. For example, the high incidence of Ellis–van Creveld syndrome among the Old Order Amish population is caused by inbreeding. Although the founder effect originally established the disease-causing allele in this population, inbreeding increases the likelihood that it will be expressed. Most human societies discourage matings between genetically close relatives, thereby reducing inbreeding and the production of recessive homozygotes.

Table 17.3 Masking of Recessive Alleles in Diploid Organisms

When a recessive allele is common in a population (top rows), most copies of the allele are present in homozygotes. But when the allele is rare (bottom rows), most copies of it exist in heterozygotes. Thus, rare alleles that are completely recessive are protected from the action of natural selection because they are masked by dominant alleles in heterozygous individuals.

Frequency of Allele *a*	Genotype Frequencies*			% of Allele *a* Copies in	
	AA	*Aa*	*aa*	*Aa*	*aa*
0.99	0.0001	0.0198	0.9801	1	99
0.90	0.0100	0.1800	0.8100	10	90
0.75	0.0625	0.3750	0.5625	25	75
0.50	0.2500	0.5000	0.2500	50	50
0.25	0.5625	0.3750	0.0625	75	25
0.10	0.8100	0.1800	0.0100	90	10
0.01	0.9801	0.0198	0.0001	99	1

*Population is assumed to be in genetic equilibrium.

STUDY BREAK

1. Which agents of microevolution tend to increase genetic variation within populations, and which ones tend to decrease it?
2. In what way does nonrandom mating affect the predictions of the Hardy–Weinberg equation?

17.4 Maintaining Genetic and Phenotypic Variation

Evolutionary biologists continue to discover extraordinary amounts of genetic and phenotypic variation in most natural populations. How can so much variation persist in the face of stabilizing selection and genetic drift?

17.4a Diploidy Can Hide Recessive Alleles from the Action of Natural Selection

The diploid condition reduces the effectiveness of natural selection in eliminating harmful recessive alleles from a population. Although such alleles are disadvantageous in the homozygous state, they may have little or no effect on heterozygotes. Thus, recessive alleles can be protected from natural selection by the phenotypic expression of the dominant allele.

In most cases, the masking of recessive alleles in heterozygotes makes it almost impossible to eliminate them completely through selective breeding. Experimentally, we can prevent homozygous recessive organisms from mating. But, as the frequency of a recessive allele decreases, an increasing proportion of its remaining copies is "hidden" in heterozygotes **(Table 17.3).** Thus, the diploid state preserves recessive alleles at low frequencies, at least in large populations. In small populations, a combination of natural selection and genetic drift can eliminate harmful recessive alleles.

17.4b Natural Selection Can Maintain Balanced Polymorphisms

A **balanced polymorphism** is one in which two or more phenotypes are maintained in fairly stable proportions over many generations. Natural selection preserves balanced polymorphisms when heterozygotes have higher relative fitness, when different alleles are favoured in different environments, and when the rarity of a phenotype provides an advantage.

Heterozygote Advantage. A balanced polymorphism can be maintained by **heterozygote advantage**, when heterozygotes for a particular locus have higher relative fitness than either homozygote. The best-documented example of heterozygote advantage is the maintenance of the *HbS* (sickle) allele, which codes for a defective form of hemoglobin in humans. As you learned in Chapter 11, hemoglobin is an oxygen-transporting molecule in red blood cells. The hemoglobin produced by the *HbS* allele differs from normal hemoglobin (coded by the *HbA* allele) by just one amino acid. In *HbS*/*HbS* homozygotes, the faulty hemoglobin forms long fibrous chains under low oxygen conditions, causing red blood cells to assume a sickle shape (as shown in Figure 11.1). Homozygous *HbS*/*HbS* individuals often die of sickle cell disease before reproducing, yet in tropical and subtropical Africa, *HbS*/*HbA* heterozygotes make up nearly 25% of many populations.

Why is the harmful allele maintained at such high frequency? It turns out that sickle cell disease is most common in regions where malarial parasites infect red blood cells in humans **(Figure 17.14).** When heterozygous *HbA*/*HbS* individuals contract malaria, their infected red blood cells assume the same sickle shape as those of homozygous *HbS*/*HbS* individuals. The sickled cells lose potassium, killing the parasites, which limits their spread within the infected individual. Heterozygous individuals often survive malaria because the parasites do not multiply quickly inside them; their immune systems can effectively fight the infection; and they retain a large population of uninfected red blood cells. Homozygous *HbA*/*HbA* individuals are also subject to malarial infection, but because their infected cells do not sickle, the parasites multiply rapidly, causing a severe infection with a high mortality rate.

Therefore, *HbA*/*HbS* heterozygotes have greater resistance to malaria and are more likely to survive severe infections in areas where malaria is prevalent. Natural selection preserves the *HbS* allele in these populations because heterozygotes in malaria-prone areas have higher relative fitness than homozygotes for the normal *HbA* allele.

Selection in Varying Environments. Genetic variability can also be maintained within a population when different alleles are favoured in different places or at different times. For example, the shells of European garden snails range in colour from nearly white to pink, yellow, or brown and may be patterned by one to five stripes of varying colour (see Figure 17.2a). This polymorphism, which is relatively stable through time, is controlled by several gene loci. The variability in colour and in striping pattern can be partially explained by selection for camouflage in different habitats.

Predation by song thrushes (*Turdus ericetorum*) is a major agent of selection on the colour and pattern of these snails in England. When a thrush finds a snail, it smacks it against a rock to break the shell. The bird eats the snail but leaves the shell near its "anvil."

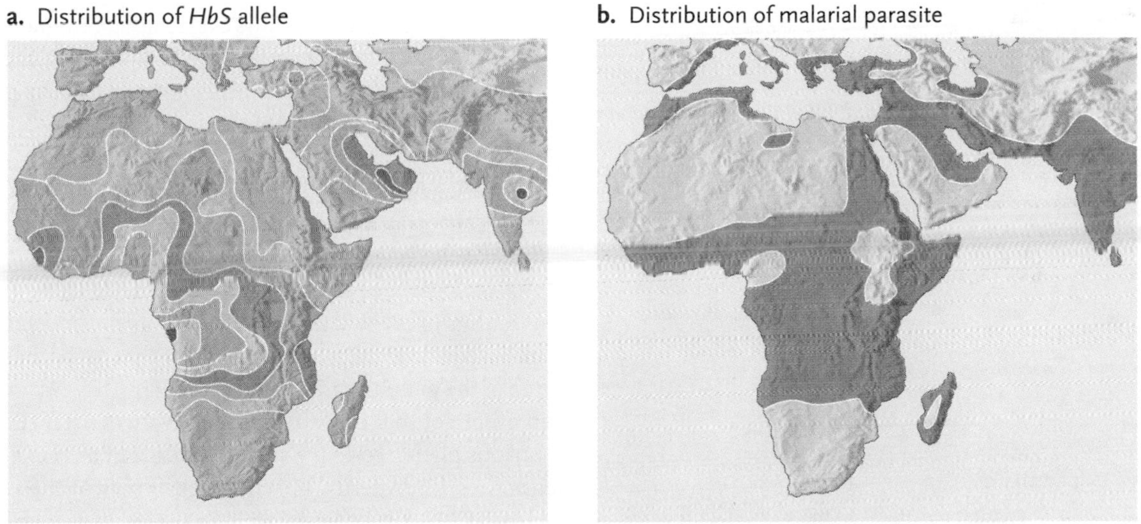

a. Distribution of *HbS* allele

b. Distribution of malarial parasite

KEY

Allele frequencies of *HbS* allele

>0.14	0.11–0.12	0.06–0.08	0.02–0.04
0.12–0.14	0.08–0.10	0.04–0.06	0.00–0.02

Regions with malaria

Figure 17.14
Heterozygote advantage. The distribution of the *HbS* allele **(a),** which causes sickle cell disease in homozygotes, roughly matches the distribution of the malarial parasite *Plasmodium falciparum* **(b)** in southern Europe, Africa, the Middle East, and India. Gene flow among human populations has carried the *HbS* allele to some malaria-free regions.

Figure 17.15
Habitat variation in colour and striping patterns of European garden snails.

HYPOTHESIS: Genetically based variation in the shell colour and striping patterns of the European garden snail (*Cepaea nemoralis*) differ substantially from one type of vegetation to another because birds and other visual predators establish strong selection for camouflage in local populations.

PREDICTION: Snails with plain, dark-coloured shells will be most abundant in woodland habitats, but snails with striped, light-coloured shells will be most abundant in hedges and fields.

METHOD: Two British researchers, A. J. Cain and P. M. Shepard, surveyed the distribution of colour and striping patterns of snails in many local populations. They plotted the data on a graph showing the percentage of snails with yellow shells versus the percentage of snails with striped shells, noting the vegetation type where each local population lived.

RESULTS: The shell colour and striping patterns of snails living in a particular vegetation type tend to be clustered on the graph, reflecting phenotypic differences that enable the snails to be camouflaged in different habitats. Thus, the alleles that control these characters vary from one local population to another.

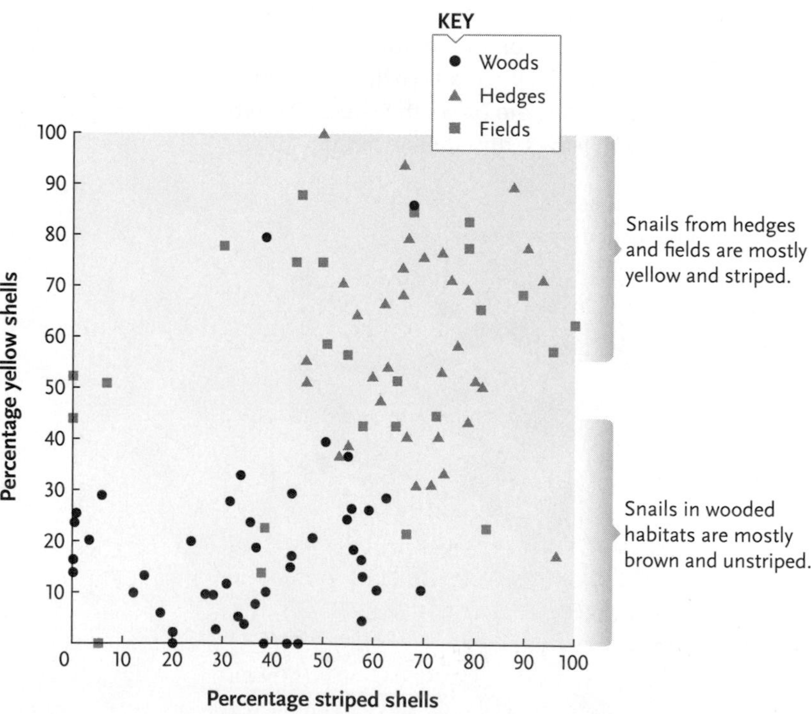

CONCLUSION: Variations in the colour and striping patterns of the shells of European garden snails allow most snails to be camouflaged in whatever habitat they occupy. Because these traits are genetically based, the frequencies of the alleles that control them also differ among snails living in different vegetation types. Natural selection therefore favours different alleles in different local populations, maintaining genetic variability in populations that span several vegetation types.

Researchers used the broken shells near an anvil to compare the phenotypes of captured snails with a random sample of the entire snail population. Their analyses indicated that thrushes are visual predators, usually capturing snails that are easy to find. Thus, well-camouflaged snails survive, and the alleles that specify their phenotypes increase in frequency.

The success of camouflage varies with habitat, however; local subpopulations of the snail, which occupy different habitats, often differ markedly in shell colour and pattern. The predators eliminate the most conspicuous individuals in each habitat; thus, natural selection differs from place to place (**Figure 17.15**). In woods where the ground is covered with dead leaves, snails with unstriped pink or brown shells predominate. In hedges and fields, where the vegetation includes thin stems and grass, snails with striped yellow shells are the most common. In populations that span several habitats, selection preserves different alleles in different places, thus maintaining variability in the population as a whole.

Frequency-Dependent Selection. Sometimes genetic variability is maintained in a population simply because rare phenotypes—whatever they happen to be—have higher relative fitness than more common phenotypes. The rare phenotype will increase in frequency until it becomes so common that it loses its advantage. Such phenomena are examples of **frequency-dependent selection** because the selective advantage enjoyed by a particular phenotype depends on its frequency in the population.

Predator–prey interactions can establish frequency-dependent selection because predators often focus their attention on the most common types of prey (see Chapter 46 and **Figure 17.16**).

17.4c Some Genetic Variations May Be Selectively Neutral

Many biologists believe that some genetic variations are neither preserved nor eliminated by natural selection. According to the **neutral variation hypothesis**, some of the genetic variation at loci coding for enzymes and other soluble proteins is **selectively neutral**. Even if various alleles code for slightly different amino acid sequences in proteins, the different forms of the proteins may function equally well. In those cases, natural selection would not favour some alleles over others.

Biologists who support the neutral variation hypothesis do not question the role of natural selection in producing complex anatomical structures or useful biochemical traits. They also recognize that selection reduces the frequency of harmful alleles. But they argue that we should not simply assume that every genetic variant that persists in a population has been preserved by natural selection. In practice, it is often very difficult to test the natural variation hypothesis because the fitness effects of different alleles are often subtle and vary with small changes in the environment.

The neutral variation hypothesis helps explain why we see different levels of genetic variation in different populations. It proposes that genetic variation is directly proportional to a population's size and the length of time over which variations have accumulated. Small populations experience fewer mutations than large populations simply because they include fewer replicating genomes. Small populations also lose rare alleles more readily through genetic drift. Thus, small populations should exhibit less genetic variation than large ones, and a population, like the northern elephant seals, that has experienced a recent population bottleneck should exhibit an exceptionally low level of genetic variation. These predictions of the neutral variation hypothesis are generally supported by empirical data.

Study Break

1. How does the diploid condition protect harmful recessive alleles from natural selection?
2. What is a balanced polymorphism?
3. Why is the allele that causes sickle cell disease very rare in human populations that are native to northern Europe?

Figure 17.16
Demonstration of frequency-dependent selection.

QUESTION: How does the frequency of a prey type influence the likelihood that it will be captured by predators?

EXPERIMENT: Water boatmen (*Sigara distincta*) occur in three colour forms, which vary in the effectiveness of their camouflage. Researchers offered different proportions of the three colour forms to predatory fishes in the laboratory and recorded how many of each form were eaten.

RESULTS: When all three phenotypes were available, predatory fishes consumed a disproportionately large number of the most common form, thereby reducing its frequency in the population.

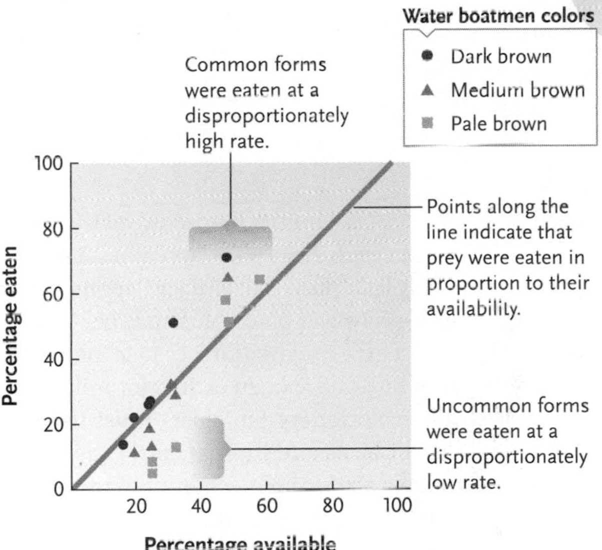

CONCLUSION: Predators tend to feed disproportionately on whatever form of their prey is most abundant, thereby reducing its frequency in the prey population.

17.5 Adaptation and Evolutionary Constraints

Although natural selection preserves alleles that confer high relative fitness on the individuals that carry them, researchers are cautious about interpreting the benefits that particular traits may provide.

17.5a Scientists Construct Hypotheses about the Evolution of Adaptive Traits

An **adaptive trait** is any product of natural selection that increases the relative fitness of an organism in its environment. **Adaptation** is the accumulation of adaptive traits over time, and this book describes many examples. The change in the oxygen-binding capacity of hemoglobin in response to carbon dioxide concentration, the water-retaining structures and special photosynthetic pathways of desert plants, and the warning colouration of poisonous animals can all be interpreted as adaptive traits.

In fact, we can concoct an adaptive explanation for almost any characteristic we observe in nature. But such explanations are just fanciful stories unless they are framed as testable hypotheses about the relative fitness of different phenotypes and genotypes. Unfortunately, evolutionary biologists cannot always conduct straightforward experiments because they sometimes study traits that do not vary much within a population or species. In such cases, they may compare variations of a trait in closely related species living in different environments. For example, one can test how the traits of desert plants are adaptive by comparing them with traits in related species from moister habitats.

When biologists try to unravel how and why a particular characteristic evolved, they must also remember that a trait they observe today may have had a different function in the past. For example, the structure of the shoulder joint in birds allows them to move their wings first upward and backward and then downward and forward during flapping flight. But analyses of the fossil record reveal that this adaptation, which is essential for flight, did not originate in birds: some predatory nonflying dinosaurs, including the ancestors of birds, had a similarly constructed shoulder joint. Researchers hypothesize that these fast-running predators may have struck at prey with a flapping motion similar to that

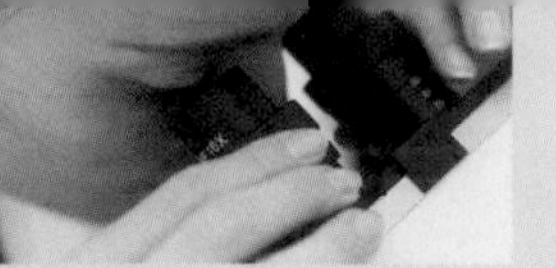

People Behind Biology

Dr. Dolph Schluter, Centre for Biodiversity Research, University of British Columbia

This chapter closes with the idea that "genetic divergence is sometimes sufficient to cause the populations to evolve into different species." The work of Dr. Dolph Schluter, first with Darwin's finches and then with three-spine stickleback fish (*Gasterosteus aculeatus*), has helped answer important questions about "ecological speciation." Which genetic differences are ecologically determined? Under what conditions are these differences selected?

Marine sticklebacks are widespread in the oceans of the northern hemisphere, returning annually to freshwater streams to spawn (this lifestyle is called anadromous). Freshwater populations, believed to be derived from the anadromous population, inhabit streams and lakes. No matter where they are found in the world, the stream-dwelling fish are consistently small and lightly armoured relative to their anadromous relatives. Therefore, body size seems to be an adaptation to a particular environment.

Schluter and colleagues collected fish from geographically isolated stickleback populations and noted their choice of partners in mating trials. Females were almost twice as likely to choose mates from their own population. The data suggested that this assortive mating was on the basis of differences in body size. Experimental manipulation of body size confirmed that females preferred males that were close to them in body size, regardless of their population of origin. This work provides important evidence in support of reproductive isolation of populations (and potential speciation) on the basis of a single, ecologically related trait (body size).

used by modern birds. Thus, the structure of the shoulder may have first evolved as an adaptation for capturing prey, and only later proved useful for flapping flight. This hypothesis—however plausible it may be—cannot be tested by direct experimentation because the nonflying ancestors of birds have been extinct for millions of years. Instead, evolutionary biologists must use anatomical studies of birds and their ancestors as well as theoretical models about the mechanics of movement to challenge and refine the hypothesis.

Finally, although evolution has produced all the characteristics of organisms, not all are necessarily adaptive. Some traits may be the products of chance events and genetic drift. Others are produced by alleles that were selected for unrelated reasons (see Section 11.2). Still other characteristics result from the action of basic physical laws. For example, the seeds of many plants fall to the ground when they mature, reflecting the inevitable effect of gravity.

17.5b Several Factors Constrain Adaptive Evolution

When we analyze the structure and function of an organism, we often marvel at how well adapted it is to its environment and mode of life. However, the adaptive traits of most organisms are compromises produced by competing selection pressures. Sea turtles, for example, must lay their eggs on beaches because their embryos cannot acquire oxygen under water. Although flippers allow females to crawl to nesting sites on beaches, they are not ideally suited for terrestrial locomotion. Their structure reflects their primary function in underwater locomotion.

Moreover, no organism can be perfectly adapted to its environment because environments change over time. When selection occurs in a population, it preserves alleles that are successful under the prevailing environmental conditions. Thus, each generation is adapted to the environmental conditions under which its parents lived. If the environment changes from one generation to the next, adaptation will always lag behind.

Another constraint on the evolution of adaptive traits is historical. Natural selection is not an engineer that designs new organisms from scratch. Instead, it acts on new mutations and existing genetic variation. Because new mutations are fairly rare, natural selection works primarily with alleles that have been present for many generations. Thus, adaptive changes in the morphology of an organism are almost inevitably based on small modifications of existing structures. The bipedal (two-footed) posture of humans, for example, evolved from the quadrupedal (four-footed) posture of our ancestors. Natural selection did not produce an entirely new skeletal design to accompany this radical behavioural shift. Instead, existing characteristics of the spinal column and the musculature of the legs and back were modified, albeit imperfectly, for an upright stance.

The agents of evolution cause microevolutionary changes in the gene pools of populations. In the next chapter, we examine how microevolution in different populations can cause their gene pools to diverge. The extent of genetic divergence is sometimes sufficient to cause the populations to evolve into different species.

Study Break

1. What is an adaptive trait?
2. Why can organisms never be perfectly adapted to their environment?

Unanswered Questions

What are the evolutionary forces affecting molecular variation within populations?

This question may sound like a simple restatement of the entire chapter you have just read, but it is one of the *fundamental* questions in population genetics today—and we have only begun to scratch its surface. The Hardy–Weinberg principle provides a useful null hypothesis, but since we know that evolution happens routinely, that null hypothesis is very frequently rejected. Recent studies have attempted to address this question using theoretical models, extensive DNA sequence data, and detailed measures of recombination rate.

Review

Go to CENGAGENOW™ at http://hed.nelson.com/ to access quizzing, animations, exercises, articles, and personalized homework help.

17.1 Variation in Natural Populations

- Phenotypic traits exhibit either quantitative or qualitative variation within populations of all organisms (see Figures 17.2 and 17.3). These discrete differences are called polymorphisms.
- Genetic variation, environmental factors, or an interaction between the two cause phenotypic variation within populations. Only genetically based phenotypic variation is heritable and subject to evolutionary change.
- Genetic variation arises within populations largely through mutation and genetic recombination. Artificial selection experiments and analyses of protein and DNA sequences reveal that most populations include significant genetic variation (see Figure 17.6).

17.2 Population Genetics

- All the alleles in a population comprise its gene pool, which can be described in terms of allele frequencies and genotype frequencies.
- The Hardy–Weinberg principle of genetic equilibrium is a null model that describes the conditions under which microevolution will not occur: mutations do not occur; populations are closed to migration; populations are infinitely large; natural selection does not operate; and individuals select mates at random. Microevolution, a change in allele frequencies through time, occurs frequently in natural populations since the restrictive requirements of the model are seldom met.

17.3 The Agents of Microevolution

- Several processes cause microevolution in populations. Mutation introduces completely new genetic variation. Gene flow carries novel genetic variation into a population through the arrival and reproduction of immigrants. Genetic drift causes random changes in allele frequencies, especially in small populations. Natural selection occurs when the genotypes of some individuals enable them to survive and reproduce more than others. Nonrandom mating within a population can cause its genotype frequencies to depart from the predictions of the Hardy–Weinberg equilibrium.
- Natural selection alters phenotypic variation in one of three ways (see Figure 17.9). Directional selection increases or decreases the mean value of a trait, shifting it toward a phenotypic extreme. Stabilizing selection increases the frequency of the mean phenotype and reduces variability in the trait (see Figure 17.10). Disruptive selection increases the frequencies of extreme phenotypes and decreases the frequency of intermediate phenotypes (see Figure 17.12).
- Sexual selection promotes the evolution of exaggerated structures and behaviours (see Figure 17.13).
- Although nonrandom mating does not change allele frequencies, it can affect genotype frequencies, producing more homozygotes and fewer heterozygotes than the Hardy–Weinberg model predicts.

17.4 Maintaining Genetic and Phenotypic Variation

- Diploidy can maintain genetic variation in a population if alleles coding for recessive traits are not expressed in heterozygotes and are thus hidden from natural selection.
- Polymorphisms are maintained in populations when heterozygotes have higher relative fitness than both homozygotes (see Figure 17.14), when natural selection occurs in variable environments (see Figure 17.15), or when the relative fitness of a phenotype varies with its frequency in the population (see Figure 17.16).
- Some biologists believe that many genetic variations are selectively neutral, conferring neither advantages nor disadvantages on the individuals that carry them. The neutral variation hypothesis explains why large populations and those that have not experienced a recent population bottleneck exhibit the highest levels of genetic variation.

17.5 Adaptation and Evolutionary Constraints

- Adaptive traits increase the relative fitness of individuals carrying them. Adaptive explanations of traits must be framed as testable hypotheses.
- Natural selection cannot result in perfectly adapted organisms because most adaptive traits represent compromises among conflicting needs; because most environments are constantly changing; and because natural selection can affect only existing genetic variation.

Questions

Self-Test Questions

1. Which of the following represents an example of qualitative phenotypic variation?
   a. the lengths of people's toes.
   b. the body sizes of pigeons.
   c. human ABO blood groups.
   d. the birth mass of humans.
   e. the number of leaves on oak trees.
2. A population of mice is at Hardy–Weinberg equilibrium at a gene locus that controls fur colour. The locus has two alleles, *M* and *m*. A genetic analysis of one population reveals that 60% of its gametes carry the *M* allele. What percentage of mice contains both the *M* and *m* alleles?
   a. 60%
   b. 48%
   c. 40%
   d. 36%
   e. 16%
3. If the genotype frequencies in a population are 0.60 *AA*, 0.20 *Aa*, and 0.20 *aa*, and if the requirements of the Hardy–Weinberg principle apply, the genotype frequencies in the offspring generation will be
   a. 0.60 *AA*, 0.20 *Aa*, 0.20 *aa*.
   b. 0.36 *AA*, 0.60 *Aa*, 0.04 *aa*.
   c. 0.49 *AA*, 0.42 *Aa*, 0.09 *aa*.
   d. 0.70 *AA*, 0.00 *Aa*, 0.30 *aa*.
   e. 0.64 *AA*, 0.32 *Aa*, 0.04 *aa*.
4. The reason spontaneous mutations do not have an immediate effect on allele frequencies in a large population is that
   a. mutations are random events, and mutations may be either beneficial or harmful.
   b. mutations usually occur in males and have little effect on eggs.
   c. many mutations exert their effects after an organism has stopped reproducing.
   d. mutations are so rare that mutated alleles are greatly outnumbered by nonmutated alleles.
   e. most mutations do not change the amino acid sequence of a protein.
5. The phenomenon in which chance events cause unpredictable changes in allele frequencies is called
   a. gene flow.
   b. genetic drift.
   c. inbreeding.
   d. balanced polymorphism.
   e. stabilizing selection.
6. An Eastern European immigrant carrying the allele for Tay–Sachs disease settled in a small village on the St. Lawrence River. Many generations later, the frequency of the allele in that village is statistically higher than it is in the immigrant's homeland. The high frequency of the allele in the village probably provides an example of
   a. natural selection.
   b. the concept of relative fitness.
   c. the Hardy–Weinberg genetic equilibrium.
   d. phenotypic variation.
   e. the founder effect.
7. If a storm kills many small sparrows in a population, but only a few medium-sized and large ones, which type of selection is probably operating?
   a. directional selection.
   b. stabilizing selection.
   c. disruptive selection.
   d. intersexual selection.
   e. intrasexual selection.
8. Which of the following phenomena explains why the allele for sickle cell hemoglobin is common in some tropical and subtropical areas where the malaria parasite is prevalent?
   a. balanced polymorphism.
   b. heterozygote advantage.
   c. sexual dimorphism.
   d. neutral selection.
   e. stabilizing selection.
9. The neutral variation hypothesis proposes that
   a. complex structures in most organisms have not been fostered by natural selection.
   b. most mutations have a strongly harmful effect.
   c. some mutations are not affected by natural selection.
   d. natural selection cannot counteract the action of gene flow.
   e. large populations are subject to stronger natural selection than small populations.
10. Phenotypic characteristics that increase the fitness of individuals are called
    a. mutations.
    b. founder effects.
    c. heterozygote advantages.
    d. adaptive traits.
    e. polymorphisms.

Questions for Discussion

1. Most large commercial farms routinely administer antibiotics to farm animals to prevent the rapid spread of diseases through a flock or herd. Explain why you think that this practice is either wise or unwise.
2. Many human diseases are caused by recessive alleles that are not expressed in heterozygotes. Explain why it is almost impossible to eliminate such genetic traits from human populations.
3. Using two types of beans to represent two alleles at the same gene locus, design an exercise to illustrate how population size affects genetic drift.
4. In what ways are the effects of sexual selection, disruptive selection, and nonrandom mating different? How are they similar?
5. Design an experiment to test the hypothesis that the differences in size among adult guppies are determined by the amount of food they eat rather than by genetic factors.

The bacterium *Clostridium difficile*, which often is responsible for outbreaks of disease in hospitals and chronic care facilities.

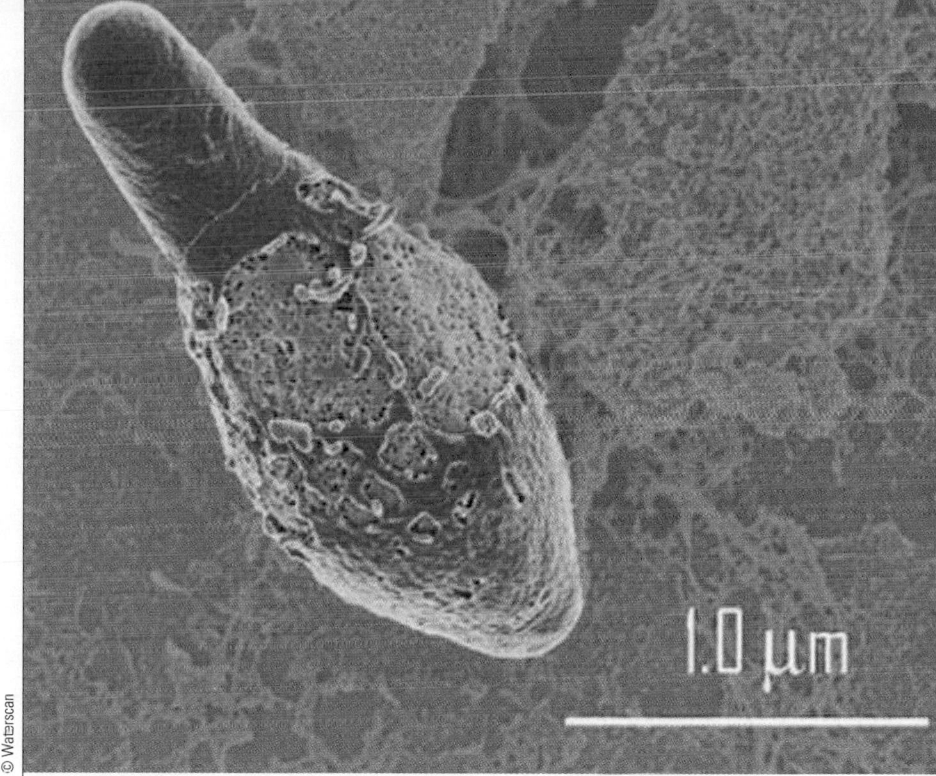

STUDY PLAN

18 Species

WHY IT MATTERS

Names can contribute to the precision of communication. Whether you are looking for a product in a grocery store, a book in a library, or a restaurant, knowing the name is an important first step. As noted in Chapter 1, biologists use formal scientific names to report information about organisms.

In a hospital or chronic care facility, knowing that an epidemic can be attributed to *Clostridium difficile* (*C. difficile*) helps authorities take steps to contain the outbreak and ensure that patients receive appropriate treatment. If the illness has been caused by West Nile virus, then the situation will require a different approach from prevention to treatment. Here, knowing the identity of the disease-causing agent means using the appropriate characteristics to recognize it (or the symptoms it causes).

Meanwhile, a bird watcher trying to convince colleagues about an unusual sighting in the neighbourhood understands that knowing how to recognize the bird means knowing its name. Dedicated birders will respond to the opportunity to see an Ivory-billed Woodpecker (*Campephilus principalis*) much more quickly than if you just say that you saw a crow-sized bird sitting on a tree. This woodpecker had long been thought to be extinct, so in 2007, people flocked to try to see one when it was reported that they were still alive. Although we have common names for birds, this is not true for most other organisms.

18.1 What's in a Name?

The purpose of this chapter is to explore the species concept, identify mechanisms involved in speciation, and develop an appreciation of the importance of names of organisms in biology. We will see how names/labels can convey a great deal of information.

Anyone who has watched an experienced shepherd work with a border collie knows that different signals (whistles) carry specific meanings that are well known to dog and handler. Use of specific signals (labels) to communicate information to other organisms is not unique to *Homo sapiens*. When a vervet monkey (*Chlorocebus pygerythrus*; **Figure 18.1**) gives the "eagle" alarm call, its fellows look skyward and move closer to the trunks of trees. When the same monkey gives a "leopard" alarm call, others within earshot look down, and those on the ground climb trees.

Communication can affect both inter- and intraspecific behaviour. Vervet monkeys use different signals (or names) for the different threats. Similarly, humans use names (signals) to distinguish between different categories of objects. "Fish" means something different from "bird," and almost everyone knows some fundamental differences between these two kinds of animals. But what about "sharks"? They are not birds, but are they really fish? When we say "eel," do we mean a fishlike creature with an elongated body? But there are "eels," bony fish with jaws, and there are "lamprey eels," jawless fish with cartilaginous skeletons (see Chapter 27).

As we have seen (see Chapter 1), biologists use scientific names, Latinized descriptions of the organism bearing the name, for precise communication. Each described species has a scientific name.

Figure 18.1
Vervet monkeys (*Chlorocebus pygerythrus*) are widespread in Africa and have predator-specific alarm calls.

18.2 Definition of "Species"

What is a species? According to the *Stanford Encyclopedia of Philosophy* (http://plato.stanford.edu/entries/species/), "...the nature of species is controversial in biology and philosophy. Biologists disagree on the definition of the term species." A proper understanding of species is important for a number of reasons. Species are the fundamental taxonomic units of biological classification. Environmental laws are framed in terms of species (see Chapter 48). Even our concept of human nature is affected by our understanding of species.

This source goes on to say that "...The **Biological Species Concept** defines a species as a group of organisms that can successfully interbreed and produce fertile offspring. The **Phylogenetic Species Concept** (which itself has multiple versions) defines a species as a group of organisms bound by a unique ancestry. The **Ecological Species Concept** defines a species as a group of organisms that share a distinct ecological niche. These species concepts are just three of a dozen prominent species concepts in the biological literature."

How can so many definitions of "species" be used in a biological context?

There are several problems with the "Biological Species Concept" defined above. One important problem is that although the definition can work for species that reproduce sexually, it does not deal as well with the many species that reproduce asexually. By their approach to reproduction, whole groups of organisms in the biological kingdom sit outside the "conventional" definition of species. Thus, patterns of reproduction can blur the definition of species.

But try looking up the scientific name of West Nile virus. Are scientific names used for viruses? Prokaryotes reproduce by binary fission, yet they have scientific names. You would not want to confuse *Bacillus subtilis*, which causes food poisoning, with *Bacillus anthracis*, which causes anthrax. Similarly, the bacterium *Vibrio fisheri* is a symbiont that makes some squid bioluminescent, whereas *Vibrio cholera* has an entirely different effect, one that frequently kills people. Whatever the mode of reproduction and the comfort of fit with the Biological Species Concept, there are compelling reasons to know the species or kind of organism you are facing.

Androdioecy (*andro* = male; *dioeciocy* = male and female) and gynogenetic (*gyno* = female) species are two interesting variations in patterns of reproduction. As the name implies, androdioecous organisms exist as natural populations of functional males and hermaphrodites but include no true females. *Krytolebias mormoratus*, the mangrove killifish **(Figure 18.2)**, and clam shrimps (*Eulimnadia texana*) are androdioecous species. Gynogenetic species, as the name implies, have only females. One example is *Poecilia formosa* (Amazon molly; **Figure 18.3**). Like many other species in the genus *Poecilia*, *P. formosa* uses internal fertilization. Within these females, the eggs require mechanical stimulation by sperm to initiate development. This means that female *P. formosa* must seduce and mate with males of other species to obtain the sperm needed to achieve reproduction. Using the Biological Species Concept, neither androdioecous nor gynogenetic species are covered by the traditional definition of species. Does this mean that they are not species?

The definition also does not apply where there is **hybridization**, when two species interbreed and produce fertile offspring. Many "species" hybridize naturally in the wild. As many as 10% of the ~8000 species of birds hybridize naturally and produce fertile offspring. Hybridization between species that produces sterile offspring does not put them outside the definition of the Biological Species Concept. Sterile hybrids result when horses (*Equus calabus*) are crossed with zebras (*Equus burchellii*) and lions (*Panthera leo*) with tigers (*Panthera tigris*). Mules are the sterile hybrids resulting when a male donkey (jack) breeds with a female horse (mare), whereas hinnies are sterile hybrids resulting when a male horse (stallion) breeds with a female donkey (jennet).

Hybrid vigour is usually discussed in the context of crossbreeding between strains of domesticated organisms (see Chapter 49). Breeders of animals and plants have long used the situation to advantage, even well before the work of Gregor Mendel and the birth of the study of genetics. From the work of Peter and Rosemary Grant, we know that some species of Darwin's finches interbreed, and the hybrids are both fertile and strong competitors (see *Hybridization of Bird Species*).

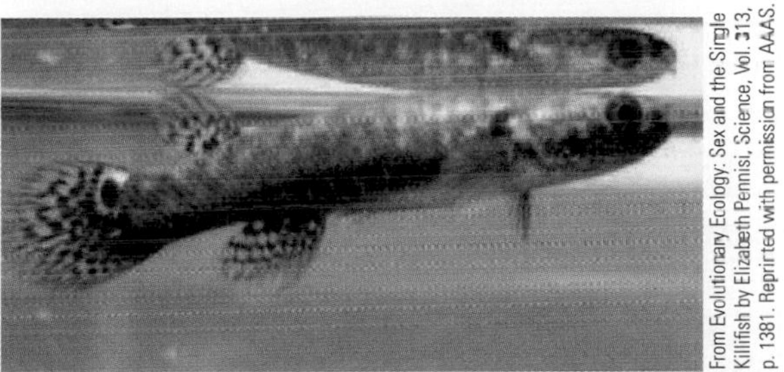

From Evolutionary Ecology: Sex and the Single Killifish by Elizabeth Pennisi, Science, Vol. 313, p. 1381. Reprinted with permission from AAAS.

Figure 18.2
Mangrove killifish (*Krytolebias mormoratus*) is an androdioecous species.

Ingo Schlupp photo

Figure 18.3
Amazon molly (*Poecilia formosa*) is a gynogenetic species.

Recombination is a principal advantage of sexual reproduction (see Chapter 10), one that explains its prevalence among living organisms. Working with *Daphnia pulex*, a water flea in which some populations reproduce sexually and others reproduce asexually, researchers demonstrated the advantages of recombination. Asexually reproducing populations had a higher frequency of mutations in mitochondrial protein-coding genes than sexually reproducing populations.

Study Break

1. What is a species, according to the Biological Species Concept? Name two problems with this definition.
2. What is a species as defined by the Phylogenetic Species Concept? As defined by the Ecological Species Concept?
3. What is a hermaphrodite? What is the difference between an androdioecous species and a gynogenetic species? Name an example of each.

18.3 One Size Does Not Fit All

Anyone who has exchanged clothing or accessories with someone else will know that "one size fits all" can be a plausible strategy for people selling socks but not for those selling jeans or contact lenses. Therefore, we should not be surprised that any one definition of "species" in biology is not uniformly used or subscribed to by all biologists. Organisms are the product of evolution, a dynamic process that does not easily accommodate rigid definitions. Our concepts of species appears to be most readily applicable to static situations but not to all species in all situations.

Hybridization in Bird Species

Darwin's original descriptions of finches on the Galapágos Islands reflected the impact of his visit there on his thinking. Therefore, it is fitting that Rosemary and Peter Grant, who study Darwin's finches **(Figure 1)**, should document hybridization between different species, interbreeding that produces fertile and fit hybrids. Hybridization can be an effective way of achieving major and rapid evolution. Grant and Grant note that the discovery of superior fitness of hybrids over parent stock **(Table 1)** brings into question the designation of the parent stocks as "species." Indeed, in birds, hybridization may be a common and persistent route to rapid evolution **(Table 2).**

Biologists are obliged to be more open-mined about hybridization when given the data from birds and those from plants where polyploidy is common. Hybridization could result in major and rapid evolution. Indeed, characterization of hybridization as a gross blunder in sexual preference may be a mistake. Polyploidy is common in plants (2–7% of vascular plant species) and has been thought to be less common in animals. However, the adaptive radiation of African cichlid fish and Darwin's finches may be examples of jumps in evolution aided and abetted by hybridization.

Figure 1
Geospiza fortis, a large, ground-dwelling Darwin's finch that often interbreeds with *G. fuliginosa* and *G. scandens*.

Table 1 A Comparison of the Breeding Success of Hybridizing and Nonhybridizing Darwin's Finches (Genus *Geospiza*) from 1983 to 1991

Pairs	Clutches (C)	Eggs (E)	Nestlings (N)	Fledglings (F)	N/E	F/C
Fortis × fuliginosa	31	122	107	92	0.88	2.97
Fortis × scandens	12	44	31	27	0.70	2.25
Fortis × fortis	1141	4462	3446	2953	0.77	2.59
Fuliginosa × fuliginosa	7	28	24	24	0.86	3.43
Scandens × scandens	559	2071	1550	1264	0.75	2.26

Table 2 Incidence of Hybridization Among Bird Species Belonging to 23 Orders

Order	Species (*n*)	Species hybridizing		Pairs hybridizing (*n*)	Intergeneric pairs of hybridizing species	
		n	%		*n*	%
Struthioniformes	10	0	0.0	0	0	0.0
Tinamiformes	47	0	0.0	0	0	0.0
Craciformes	69	2	2.9	1	0	0.0
Galiformes	214	46	21.5	46	6	13.0
Anseriformes	161	67	41.6	114	35	30.7
Tumiciformes	17	0	0.0	0	0	0.0
Piciformes	355	49	13.5	32	0	0.0
Galbulformes	51	2	3.9	1	0	0.0
Bucenotiformes	56	0	0.0	0	0	0.0
Upupiformes	10	0	0.0	0	0	0.0
Trogoniformes	39	0	0.0	0	0	0.0
Coraciformes	152	8	5.3	4	0	0.0
Coliiformes	6	2	16.7	1	0	0.0
Cuculiformes	143	4	2.8	2	0	0.0
Psittaciformes	358	27	7.5	17	5	29.4
Apodiformes	103	0	0.0	0	0	0.0
Trochiliformes	319	61	19.1	52	36	69.2
Musophagiformes	23	0	0.0	0	0	0.0
Strigiformes	291	2	0.7	1	0	0.0
Columbiformes	313	10	3.2	5	0	0.0
Gruiformes	196	17	8.7	10	3	30.0
Ciconiiformes	1027	139	13.5	92	3	3.3
Passeriformes	5712	460	8.0	320	58	18.2
Total	9672	895	9.2	698	136	19.5

The diversity of species and of their lifestyles partly reflects the mechanisms underlying the processes of speciation. The Biological Species Concept defines species in terms of population genetics and evolutionary theory in a static world. The definition alludes to the genetic *cohesiveness* of species. Populations of the same species are said to experience gene flow that mixes their genetic material and could be the "glue" holding a species together. The second part of this concept emphasizes the genetic *distinctness* of each species. Because populations of different species are reproductively isolated, they cannot exchange genetic information. In fact, the process of speciation is frequently defined as the evolution of reproductive isolation between populations.

The Biological Species Concept could explain why individuals of a species generally look alike. If phenotype reflects genotype, members of the same gene pool should share genetic traits (genotype) that determine phenotype. Individuals of different species generally do not resemble one another as closely because they share fewer genetic characteristics. In practice, biologists often use similarities or differences in morphological traits as convenient markers of genetic similarity or reproductive isolation. But remember that Linnaeus's binomial system predated the work of Charles Darwin and Gregor Mendel (see Chapters 11 and 20).

Biologists often describe new species and use visible morphological traits to allow other biologists to distinguish the new species from those previously known. This process dates back to Linnaeus's classification of organisms in the eighteenth century (see Chapter 20). This approach is based on the **Morphological Species Concept**, the idea that all individuals of a species share measurable traits that distinguish them from individuals of other species. The Morphological Species Concept has many practical applications. Paleontologists use morphology to identify fossils to species but also depend on information about the fossils' ages (see Chapter 19). External traits of organisms are presented in field guides, which help the users recognize species, for example, to tell yellow-throated warblers from yellow-rumped warblers **(Figure 18.4).** Visit the natural history section in a bookstore to get an idea of the range of field guides available for identifying everything from butterflies to mushrooms.

Study Break

1. What contributes to the genetic cohesiveness and genetic distinctiveness of species?
2. What is the Morphological Species Concept? What are some practical applications of this concept?

Figure 18.4
Diagnostic characters. Yellow-throated Warblers (*Dendroica dominica*) and yellow-rumped Warblers (*Dendroica coronata*) can be distinguished by the colours of feathers on the throat and rump. Yellow-rumped Warblers used to be known as Myrtle Warblers. Arrows identify diagnostic differences.

18.4 Gene Flow: Four Examples

It is traditional for biologists to presume that gene flow occurs within populations of single species. For many species that reproduce sexually and whose geographic distributions are relatively continuous, this may be true. But do *Rattus norvegicus* (Norway rats; **Figure 18.5**) in London, England, look like those in London, Ontario, or Sydney, Australia, or Cape Town, South Africa, because gene flow occurs among these populations? Or do they look the same because they fill the same basic niche (role in nature) in similar, human-created habitats? You will recognize this as a variant on the nature–nurture debate. Are we what we are because of our genes or because of the environment in which we were raised?

The four examples below illustrate how ecology, habitat availability, and behaviour can affect distribution patterns and genetic differences.

Figure 18.5
Rattus norvegicus, Norway rats, a cosmopolitan species that is often commensal with humans.

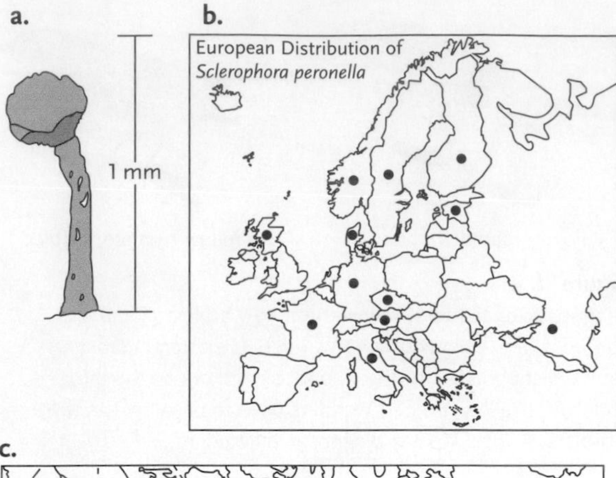

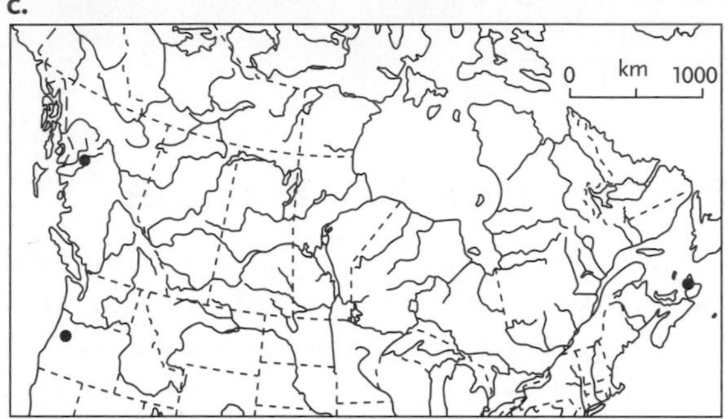

Figure 18.6
The lichen *Sclerophora peronella* (frosted glass whiskers) **(a)** and its European **(b)** and North American **(c)** distribution.

First, at one extreme are organisms such as Norway rats that occur everywhere you find humans, whereas other species, such as mosses and lichens, have very restricted distributions. The frosted glass whiskers, a lichen, is known from very few locations in the world **(Figure 18.6)**. The same is true of the cryptic paw lichen **(Figure 18.7)**. Many other organisms are widely but sparsely distributed, raising questions about gene flow as a cohesive force.

Second, the tools of modern genetics (see Chapter 16) have given biologists more opportunities to measure gene flow and document the relatedness between populations. From a genetic database, it was possible to look at the dispersal of *Balea perversa* **(Figure 18.8)**, an oviparous (egg-laying), hermaphroditic snail. Biologists showed that the distribution of snails from Tristan da Cunha to Iceland reflected the migratory pathways of birds because *B. perversa* hitchhiked with the birds (see Figure 18.8). Without knowing about the hitchhiking behaviour, the distribution of the snails and the genetic relatedness between populations would have made little sense.

Third is evidence from behaviour. In the 1960s, gel electrophoretic studies of proteins were used to examine population genetics of *Mus musculus* (house mice; see Chapter 16). At that time, examining variation in proteins was deemed to be a proxy for genetic variation, and the results demonstrated how social structures in mouse populations limited genetic exchange. The data revealed that within a single barn lived groups of mice that did not interbreed. Although these mice could interbreed, social behaviour appeared to prevent gene flow. Then, in the 1970s, Ann Eileen Miller Baker introduced some female house mice that had genetic markers into both captive and wild populations. These females bred with males, and through the progeny of these matings, the genetic markers moved rapidly through wild and captive populations. A key factor was using females to introduce the markers because males were less often assimilated into mouse populations. Genetic markers provided a more representative view of mouse population genetics than variation in allozymes.

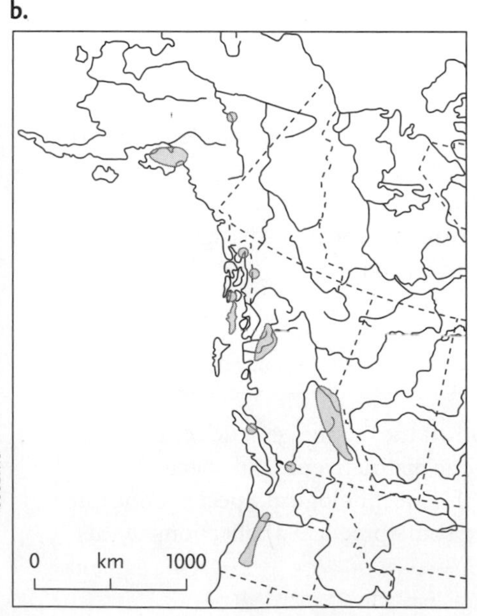

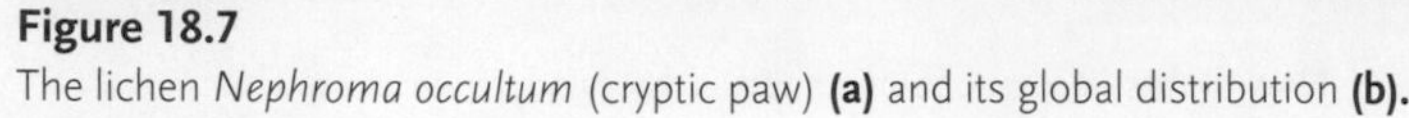
Figure 18.7
The lichen *Nephroma occultum* (cryptic paw) **(a)** and its global distribution **(b)**.

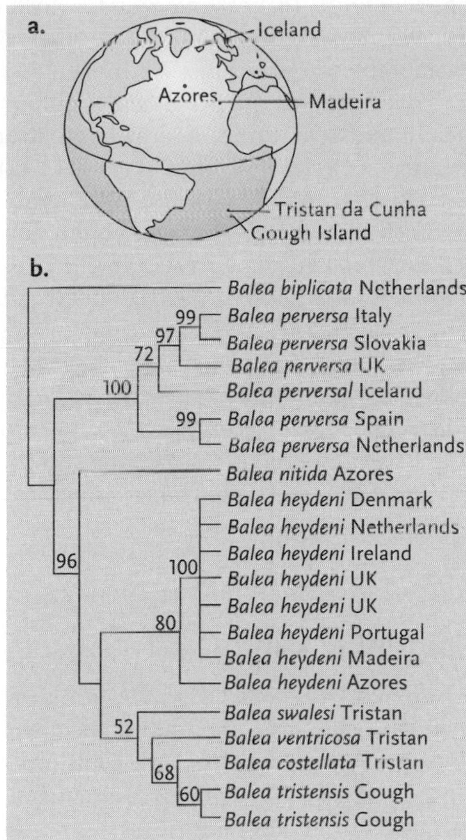

Figure 18.8
The snail, *Balea perversa* **(c),** hitchhikes on migrating birds and achieves an extensive distribution on islands in and continents adjoining the North and South Atlantic **(a, b).** Numbers on the neighbour-joining tree are bootstrap support values derived from analysis of DNA sequences of cytochrome oxidase subunit 1.

Fourth, DNA technology tools (see Chapter 16) allowed biologists to track the responses of *Sciurus vulgaris* (Eurasian red squirrel) to changes in forest availability along the border between England and Scotland **(Figure 18.9).** There, extensive pine plantations have allowed Cumbrian (northern England) populations of the squirrels to spread into isolated woodlands in Scotland. This is reflected by genetic changes **(Figure 18.10, p. 402).** This situation has changed the genetic face of *S. vulgaris* populations and demonstrates responses associated with habitat change. It also demonstrates how changes in landscape and habitat can alter genetic patterns, sometimes creating problems for those concerned about conserving biodiversity (see Chapter 48).

Study Break

Identify three different factors that can influence gene flow within populations.

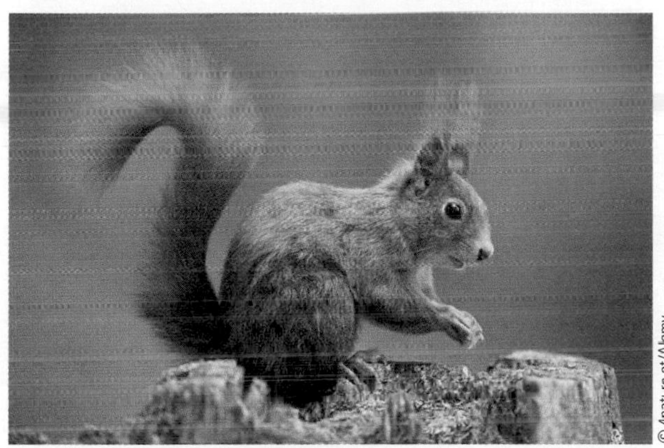

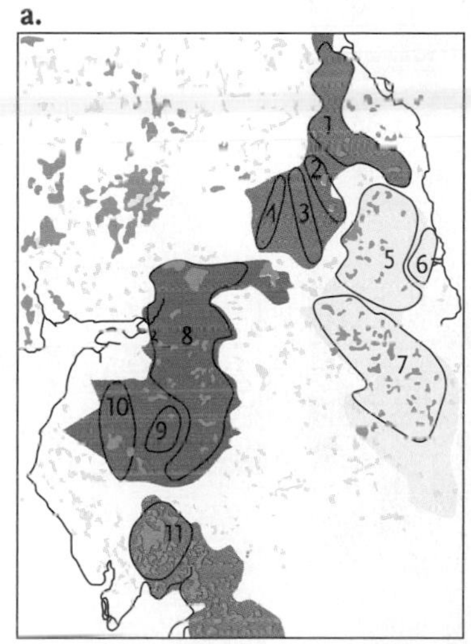

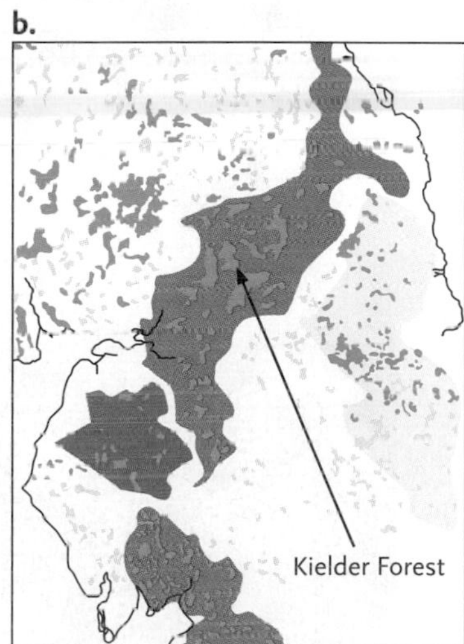

Figure 18.9
Eurasian red squirrels (*Sciurus vulgaris*) (left) occur in woodlands and pine plantations in northern England (Cumbria) and adjacent Scotland. The extent of woodland coverage from low **(a)** to high **(b)** in the Kielder Forest. Three basic squirrel genetic groups are shown. Orange is the northern group, yellow is the eastern group, and blue is the western group. Coloured areas depict all woods within 1.5 km; black outlines the area over which specimens were collected. When the Kielder Forest is included, Cumbria is part of the northern genetic group.

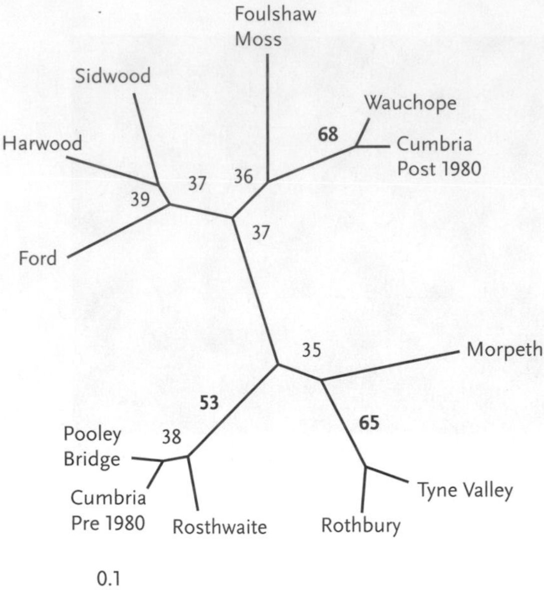

Figure 18.10
Genetic distances between populations of *S. vulgaris* in the woodlands shown in Figure 18.9.

18.5 A Dynamic Situation

The case of *Acanthinucella spirata*, a marine snail **(Figure 18.11)**, illustrates how a species can vary in space and in time. The story involves data about distribution in space (today) and in time (from 125 000 years B.P. to 2006), the morphology of their shells, and their genetics. Along 1050 km of California coast (see Figure 18.11, from Baja California to Tomales Bay), the 14 living populations of snails showed considerable variation in shell morphology and mitochondrial DNA sequences. Northern populations did not show as much within-population genetic variation as southern ones **(Figure 18.12)**, suggesting that the snails have expanded their range to the north. Recently colonized populations showed shell morphologies not present in either the southern populations or the 125 000-year-old fossils (Pleistocene; **Figure 18.13**).

A. spirata demonstrates how a snail can change its distribution in space and in time. Furthermore, recent expansion of snail populations coincide with novel (for the species) morphological changes. Changes in the snails appear to be in response to changes in climate (see Chapter 46).

18.6 Geographic Variation

When geographically separated populations of a species exhibit dramatic, easily recognized phenotypic variation, biologists may identify them as different **subspecies (Figure 18.14)**, which are local variants of a species. Individuals from different subspecies usually interbreed where their geographic distributions meet, and their offspring often exhibit intermediate phenotypes. Zoologists sometimes use the word "race" as shorthand for the term "subspecies." Botanists more often refer to "variants" or, for domesticated stock, "cultivars."

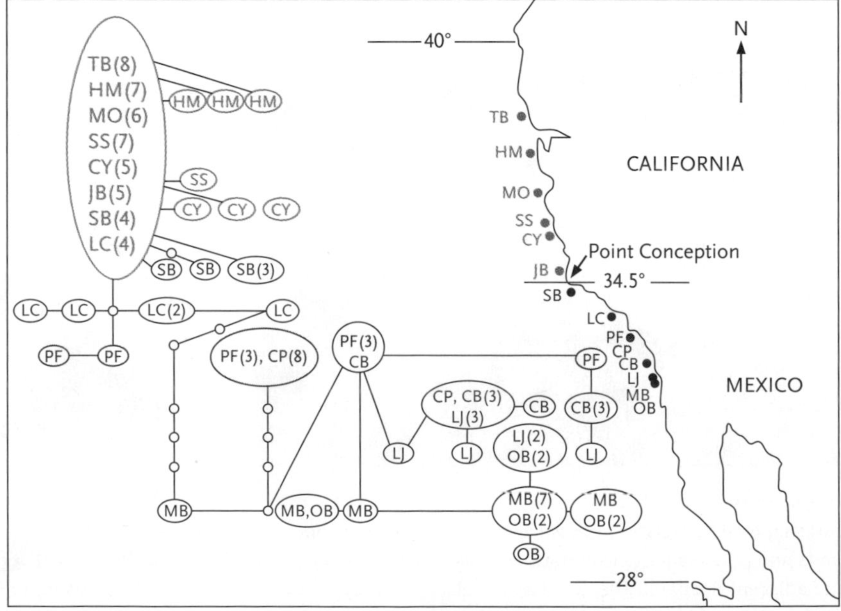

Figure 18.11
The genetic diversity of *Acanthinucella spirata* (left) from 14 populations along the coast of California (right). Locations are shown on the map, as well as a parsimony network for 33 unique cytochrome oxidase subunit 1 genes. SB and LC (blue) are located south of Point Conception. TB stands for Tomales Bay, HM for Half Moon Bay, MO for Monterey Bay, SS for San Simeon, CY for Cayucos, JB for Jalama Bay, SB for Santa Barbara, LC for Leo Carillo State Beach, PF for Point Fermin, CP for Cabrillo Beach, CB for Carlsbad, LJ for La Jolla, MB for Mission Bay, and OB for Ocean Beach.

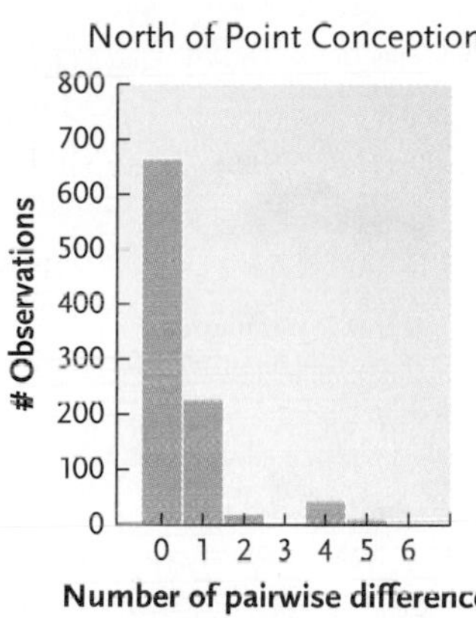

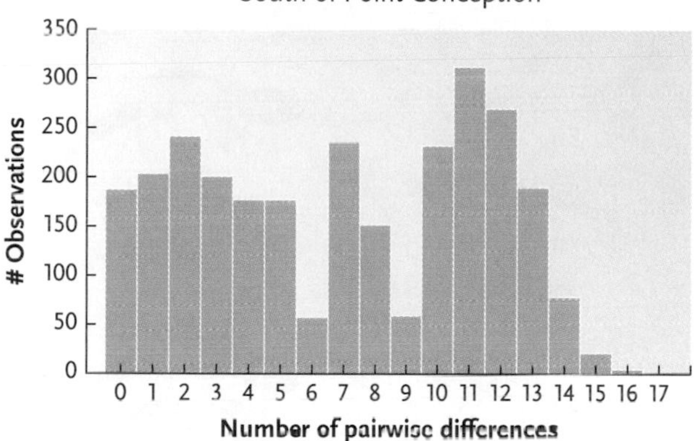

Figure 18.12
Northern and southern populations of *A. spirata* compared using pairwise base-pair differences in COI sequences.

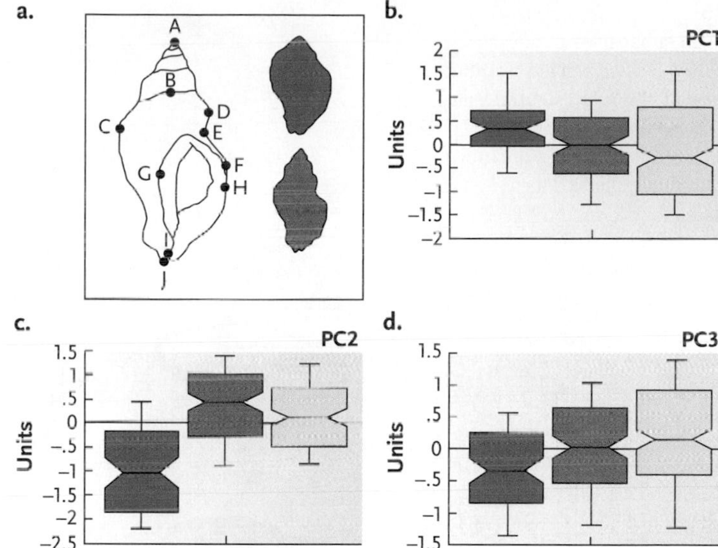

Figure 18.13
Trends in shell shape and size based on shell landmarks (A), for northern (blue), southern (red), and fossil (grey = Pleistocene) materials. The plots show scores on the first three principal components (PC in B, C, and D). PCs are statistical representations of groups of measurements.

Various patterns of geographic variation have provided insight into the speciation process. Two of the best-studied patterns are ring species and clinal variation.

18.6a Ring Species: Genes Flowing between Some Populations

Some plant and animal species have a ring-shaped geographic distribution that surrounds uninhabitable terrain. Adjacent populations of these so-called **ring species** can exchange genetic material directly, but gene flow between distant populations occurs only through intermediary populations.

The lungless salamander *Ensatina eschscholtzi*, an example of a ring species, is widely distributed in the coastal mountains and the Sierra Nevada of California, but it cannot survive in the hot, dry Central Valley **(Figure 18.15, p. 404).** Seven subspecies differ in biochemical traits, colour, size, and ecology. Individuals from adjacent subspecies often interbreed where their geographic distributions overlap, and intermediate phenotypes are fairly common. In the south, where the ring is not completely closed, the two subspecies rarely interbreed as they appear to have differentiated to an extent that they can no longer exchange genetic material.

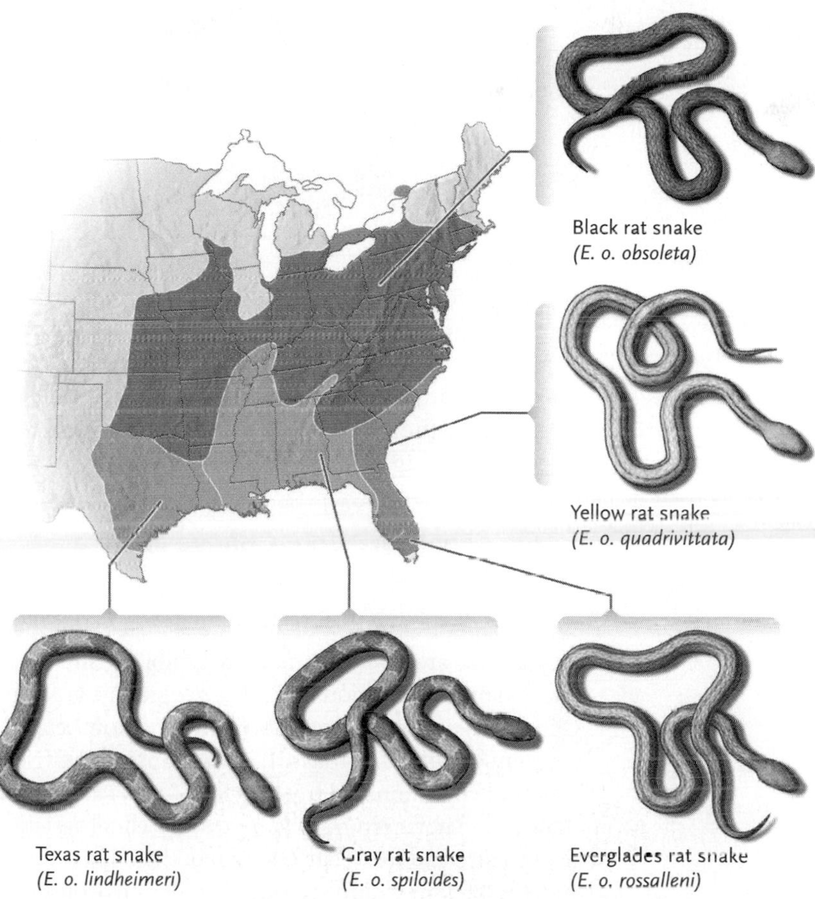

Figure 18.14
Five subspecies of rat snake (*Elaphe obsoleta*) in eastern North America differ in colour and in the presence or absence of stripes.

Are the southernmost populations of this salamander subspecies or different species? A biologist who saw *only* the southern populations, which coexist without interbreeding, might call them separate

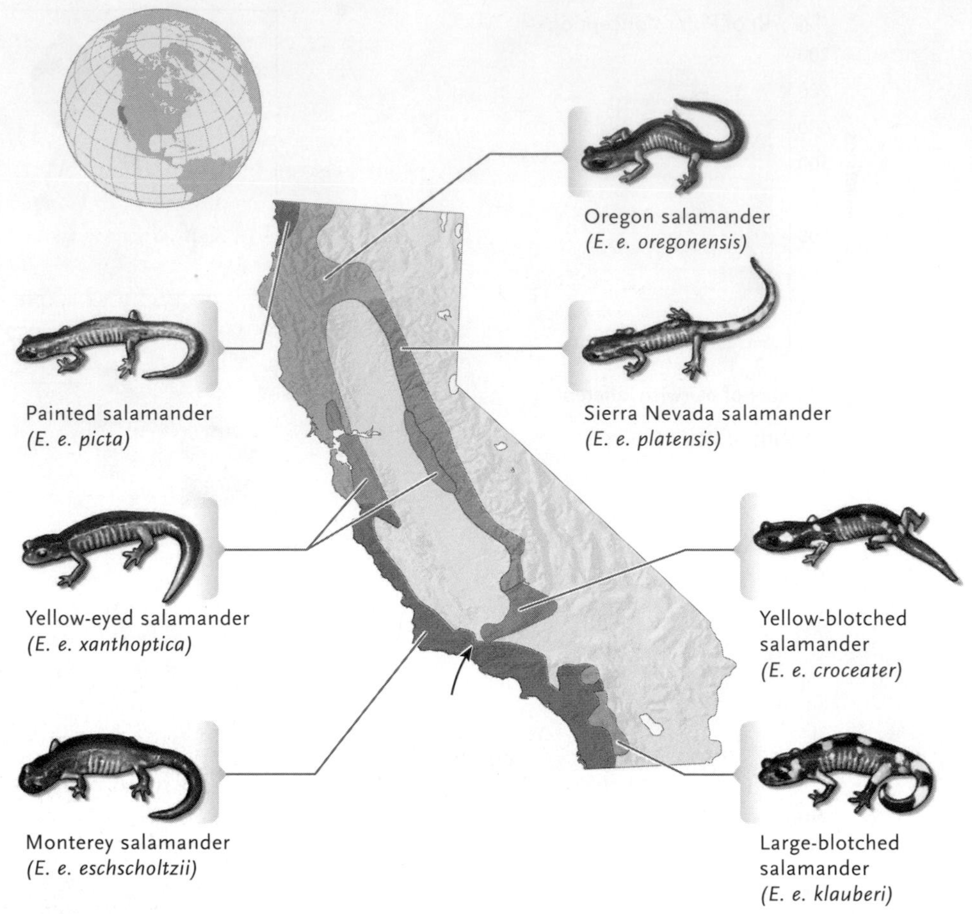

Figure 18.15
Six of the seven subspecies of the salamander *Ensatina eschscholtzi* are distributed in a ring around California's Central Valley. However, the two subspecies that nearly close the ring in the south (marked by an arrow), the Monterey salamander and the yellow-blotched salamander, rarely interbreed.

species. However, they still have the potential to exchange genetic material through the intervening populations that form the ring. Hence, we recognize these populations as belonging to the same species. Most likely, the southern subspecies represent an intermediate stage of new species formation.

18.6b Clinal Variation: Change along a Gradient

When a species is distributed over a large, environmentally diverse area, some traits may exhibit a **cline**, a pattern of smooth variation along the geographic gradient. Clinal variation usually results from gene flow between adjacent populations that are each adapting to slightly different conditions. Many species of birds and mammals in the northern hemisphere show clinal variation in body size and the relative length of their appendages. In general, populations living in colder environments have larger bodies and shorter appendages, a pattern usually interpreted as a mechanism to conserve heat (see Chapter 43). When a cline extends over a large geographic gradient, populations at the opposite ends of the cline may be very different.

Most species are morphologically or behaviourally distinct from other species, but local and geographic variation can mask interspecific (between species) differences. In the next section, we consider mechanisms that establish and maintain reproductive isolation between species that are descended from a common ancestor.

Study Break

1. What is a subspecies? Do subspecies interbreed?
2. What kind of geographic distribution is characteristic of a ring species? Name an example of a ring species.

18.7 Reproductive Isolation

Reproductive isolation is fundamental to the Biological Species Concept. A **reproductive isolating mechanism** is a biological characteristic that prevents the gene pools of two species from mixing even when they are **sympatric** (occupying the same spaces at the same time). Reproductive isolation can be achieved in two basic ways **(Table 18.1).** Prezygotic isolating mechanisms exert their effects before the production of a zygote, or fertilized egg, and **postzygotic isolating**

Table 18.1 Reproductive Isolating Mechanisms

Timing Relative to Fertilization	Mechanism	Mode of Action
Prezygotic ("premating") mechanisms	Ecological isolation	Species live in different habitats
	Temporal isolation	Species breed at different times
	Behavioural isolation	Species cannot communicate
	Mechanical isolation	Species cannot physically mate
	Gametic isolation	Species have nonmatching receptors on gametes
Postzygotic ("postmating") mechanisms	Hybrid inviability	Hybrid offspring do not complete development
	Hybrid sterility	Hybrid offspring cannot produce gametes
	Hybrid breakdown	Hybrid offspring have reduced survival or fertility

mechanisms operate after zygote formation. These isolating mechanisms are not mutually exclusive, and two or more may operate simultaneously.

18.7a Prezygotic Isolating Mechanisms: Isolation before Fertilization

At least five mechanisms can prevent interspecific matings or fertilizations and the production of hybrid (mixed species) offspring. Included here are ecological, temporal, behavioural, mechanical, and gametic isolation.

Species living in the same geographic region may experience **ecological isolation** if they live in different habitats. Lions and tigers were both common in India until the mid-nineteenth century, when hunters virtually exterminated the Asian lions. However, because lions lived in open grasslands and tigers in dense forests, the two species did not encounter one another and did not interbreed. Lion–tiger hybrids are sometimes born in captivity but do not occur under natural conditions.

Species living in the same habitat can experience **temporal isolation** if they mate at different times of the day or different times of the year. The fruit flies *Drosophila persimilis* and *D. pseudoobscura* overlap extensively in their geographic distributions, but they do not interbreed, in part because *D. persimilis* mates in the morning and *D. pseudoobscura* in the afternoon. Two species of pine in California are reproductively isolated where their geographic distributions overlap: even though both rely on the wind to carry male gametes (pollen grains) to female gametes (ova) in other cones, *Pinus radiata* releases pollen in February and *P. muricata* releases it in April.

Many animals rely on specific signals, which often differ dramatically between species, to identify the species of a potential mate. **Behavioural isolation** results when the signals used by one species are not recognized by another. Female songbirds often rely on the song, colour, and displays of males to identify members of their own species. Female fireflies identify males by their flashing patterns **(Figure 18.16)**. These behaviours (collectively called *courtship displays*) may be so complicated that signals sent by one species are not recognized by another. Mate choice by females and sexual selection (see Chapters 38 and 40) generally drive the evolution of mate recognition signals. The energetic cost of producing eggs or rearing young is substantial, and mating with a male of a different

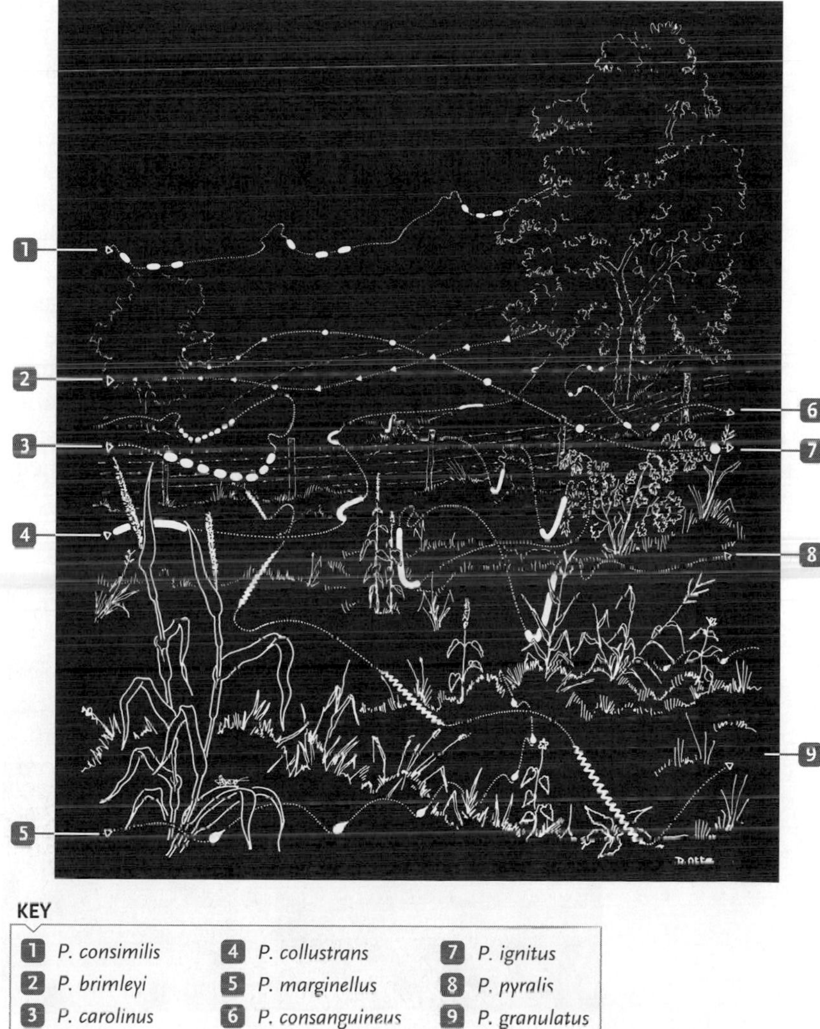

Figure 18.16
Behavioural reproductive isolation. Male beetles (*Photinus* species) use bioluminescent signals to attract potential mates. The different flight paths and flashing patterns of males in nine North American species are represented here. Courtesy of James E. Lloyd. Miscellaneous Publications of the Museum of Zoology of the University of Michigan, 130:1-195, 1966.

species reduces a female's production of fertile offspring. By contrast, females that choose appropriate mates are likely to produce more surviving young. Over time, the number of males with recognizable traits, as well as the number of females able to recognize the traits, increases in the population.

Mechanical isolation results when differences in the structure of copulatory organs prevent successful mating between individuals of different species. This also could be true of other body parts. In particular, many plants have anatomical features that allow only certain pollinators, usually particular bird or insect species, to collect and distribute pollen (see Chapter 30). The flowers and nectar of two native California plants, the monkey-flowers *Mimulus lewisii* and *M. cardinalis,* attract different animal pollinators **(Figure 18.17).** *Mimulus lewisii,* pollinated by bumblebees, has shallow pink flowers with broad petals that provide a landing platform for the bees. Bright yellow streaks on the petals serve as "nectar guides," directing bumblebees to the short nectar tube and reproductive parts located among the petals. Bees enter the flowers to drink nectar and pick up and deliver pollen as they brush against the reproductive parts of the flowers. *Mimulus cardinalis,* pollinated by hummingbirds, has long red flowers with no yellow streaks, and the reproductive parts extend above the petals. The red colour attracts hummingbirds but lies outside the colour range detected by bumblebees. The nectar of *M. cardinalis* is more dilute than that of *M. lewisii,* but it is produced in much greater quantity, making it easier for hummingbirds to ingest. When a hummingbird visits *M. cardinalis* flowers, it pushes its long bill down the nectar tube, and its forehead touches the reproductive parts, picking up and delivering pollen. Where the two monkey flower species grow side by side, animal pollinators restrict their visits to either one species or the other 98% of the time, providing nearly complete reproductive isolation.

Mimulus lewisii

Reny Parker

Mimulus cardinalis

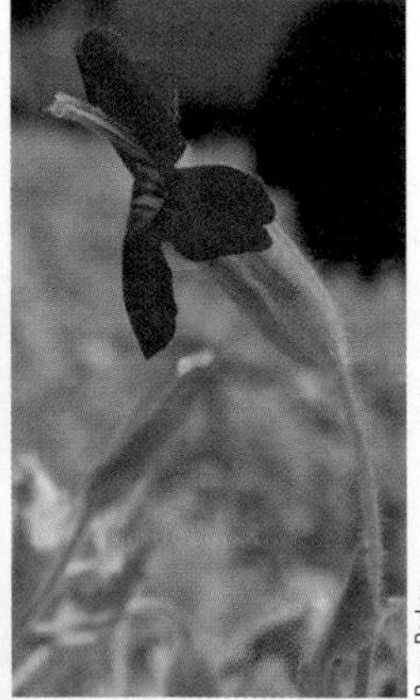

Reny Parker

Figure 18.17
Mechanical reproductive isolation. Because of differences in floral structure, two species of monkey-flower attract different animal pollinators. *Mimulus lewisii* attracts bumblebees, and *Mimulus cardinalis* attracts hummingbirds.

Even when individuals of different species do mate, **gametic isolation**, or incompatibility between the sperm of one species and the eggs of another, may prevent fertilization. Many marine invertebrates release gametes into the environment for external fertilization. The sperm and eggs of each species recognize one another's complementary surface proteins (see Chapter 40), but the surface proteins on the gametes of different species do not match. In animals with internal fertilization, the sperm of one species may not survive or function within the reproductive tract of another. Interspecific matings between some *Drosophila* species induce a reaction in the female's reproductive tract that blocks "foreign" sperm from reaching the eggs. Parallel physiological incompatibilities between a pollen tube and a stigma can prevent interspecific fertilization in some plants.

18.7b Postzygotic Isolating Mechanisms: Barriers after Fertilization

Despite the existence of prezygotic isolating mechanisms, sperm from one species sometimes fertilizes an egg of another species. In such cases, the two species are reproductively isolated if their offspring, called interspecific (between species) hybrids, have lower fitness than those produced by intraspecific (within species) matings. Three postzygotic isolating mechanisms (hybrid inviability, hybrid sterility, and hybrid breakdown) can reduce the fitness of hybrid individuals.

Hybrid inviability can occur because many genes govern the complex processes that transform a zygote into a mature organism (see Chapter 39). Hybrid individuals have two sets of developmental instructions, one from each parent, which may not interact properly for the successful completion of embryonic development. As a result, hybrid organisms frequently die as embryos or at an early age, a phenomenon called hybrid inviability. Domestic sheep and goats can mate and fertilize one another's ova, but the hybrid embryos die before reaching term, presumably because the developmental programs of the two parent species are incompatible.

Although some hybrids between closely related species develop into healthy and vigorous adults, they may not produce functional gametes. This **hybrid sterility** often results when the parent species differ in the number or structure of their chromosomes, which cannot pair properly during meiosis. Such hybrids have zero fitness because they leave no descendants. The most familiar example is a mule, the product of mating between a female horse ($2n = 64$) and a male donkey ($2n = 62$). Zebroids, the offspring of matings between horses and zebras, are also sterile.

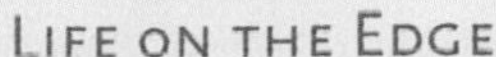

Life on the Edge

Rate of Evolutionary Change

How quickly can evolution occur? The role of the fossil record in our knowledge and understanding of evolution can leave the impression that evolution occurs over millions of years, or at least millions of generations. But this is not always true.

In 1971, five adult pairs of Italian wall lizards (*Podarcis sicula*) were introduced to Pod Kopište a 0.09 km^2 islet in the South Adriatic, and five other pairs to the nearby Pod Mrčaru (0.03 km^2). In 1971, another lacertid lizard, *Podarcis melisellensis*, occurred on Pod Mrčaru, but they had vanished by 2007. In 2007, densities of *P. sicula* on Pod Mrčaru were significantly greater than those on Pod Kopište. Female Italian wall lizards may lay several clutches of eggs in one season, translating into a short generation time and high values of R, the intrinsic rate of population increase (see Chapter 45).

In 36 years, *P. sicula* established viable populations on both islets. In 2007, the *P. sicula* on both islets were genetically indistinguishable from the mainland source population. However, their populations had changed in morphology. Specifically, introduced lizards differed both from source populations and from one another in head morphology, bite strength, and digestive tracts. On Pod Mrčaru, *P. sicula* have longer, wider, and taller heads than those on Pod Kopište, corresponding with a difference in diet. *P. sicula* on Pod Mrčaru ate more plant material than those on Pod Kopište.

The changes in morphology and performance of *P. sicula* after introduction to the islets are similar to those documented among other species and families of lizards. Italian wall lizards on small islands demonstrate adaptability, a foundation for evolution. Italian wall lizards have also been introduced to Long Island, New York, where they have thrived. The situation reminds us how introduced species may adapt to and thrive in new settings. However, we will see how such introductions can pose significant problems for conservation (see Chapter 48). Adapting to life on the edge can be a recipe for success.

But some F_1 hybrids are healthy, vigorous, and fully fertile and can breed with other hybrids and with both parental species. Sometimes the F_2 generation, produced by matings between F_1 hybrids, or between F_1 hybrids and either parental species, may exhibit reduced survival or fertility, a phenomenon known as **hybrid breakdown.** Experimental crosses between fruit fly (*Drosophila*) species may produce functional interspecific hybrids, but their offspring experience a high rate of chromosomal abnormalities and harmful types of genetic recombination. Thus, reproductive isolation is maintained between the species because there is little long-term mixing of their gene pools.

Study Break

1. What is a reproductive isolating mechanism? Distinguish between two major types of reproductive isolating mechanisms.
2. Define five types of prezygotic isolating mechanisms that can prevent interspecific mating.
3. Prezygotic isolating mechanisms prevent gene pools of two species from mixing, so why do postzygotic isolating mechanisms exist? Distinguish between three types of postzygotic isolating mechanisms.

18.8 Geography of Speciation

Geography has a huge impact on whether gene pools have the opportunity to mix. Biologists define three modes of speciation based on the geographic relationship of populations as they become reproductively isolated: allopatric speciation (*allo* = different; *patria* = homeland), parapatric speciation (*para* = beside), and sympatric speciation (*sym* = together).

18.8a Allopatric Speciation: New Species Develop from Isolated Populations

Allopatric speciation can occur when a physical barrier subdivides a large population or when a small population becomes separated from a species' main geographic distribution. Allopatric speciation, probably the most common mode of speciation in large animals, occurs in two stages. First, two populations become *geographically* separated, preventing gene flow between them. Then, as the populations experience distinct mutations as well as different patterns of natural selection and genetic drift, they may accumulate genetic differences that isolate them *reproductively*.

Geographic separation sometimes occurs when a barrier divides a large population into two or more

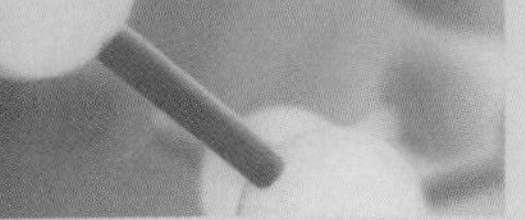

Molecule Behind Biology

Champignon Scents

People associate the aroma of mushrooms (champignon scent) with edible fungi. The aroma is mainly associated with four constituents that comprise >70% of the volaties: oct-1-en-3-ol, oct-1-en-3-one, octan-3-ol, and octan-3-one **(Figure 1).**

The floral fragrance of the orchid *Dracula chestertonii* emits the champignon scent that attracts fungus gnats to pollinate the flowers that are astonishingly mushroom-like in appearance.

Flowers in the genera *Asarum* and *Arisaema* (family Araceae) and *Aristolochia arborea* (family Aristolochiaceae) also use champignon-like scents to attract fungus gnats. Whereas *Asarum* and *Arisaema* attract pollinators, *Aristolochia arborea* **(Figure 2)** is an insectivorous plant (see Chapter 3 and Box 47.6), and the fungus gnats are food.

Precision in communication often crosses species boundaries.

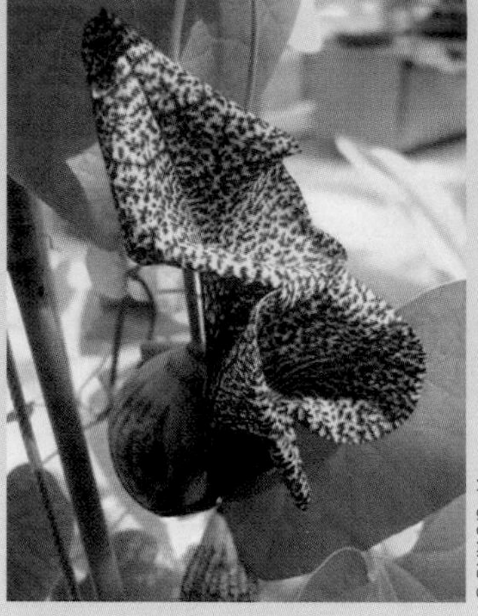

Figure 2
Aristochia arborea, a carnivorous plant that uses champignon scents to attract the fungus gnats it catches and eats.

Figure 1
The four main volatile constituents of champignon scent used by *Dracula chesteronii* to attract fungus gnats that serve as its pollinators.

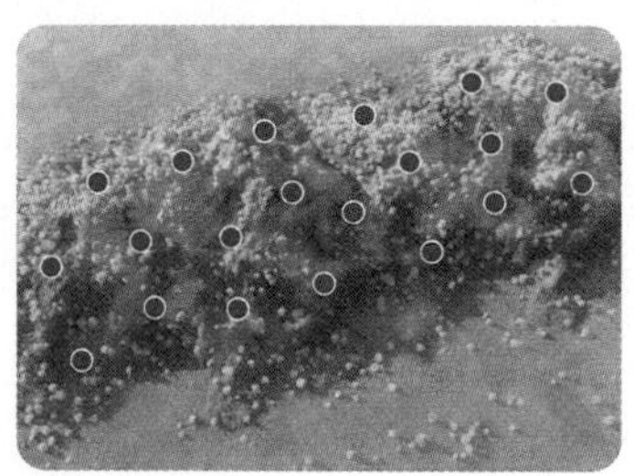

1 At first, a population is distributed over a large geographical area.

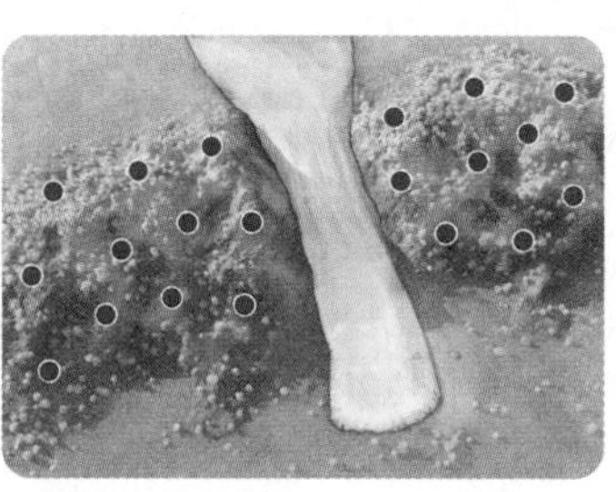

2 A geographical change, such as the advance of a narrow glacier, separates the original population, creating a barrier to gene flow.

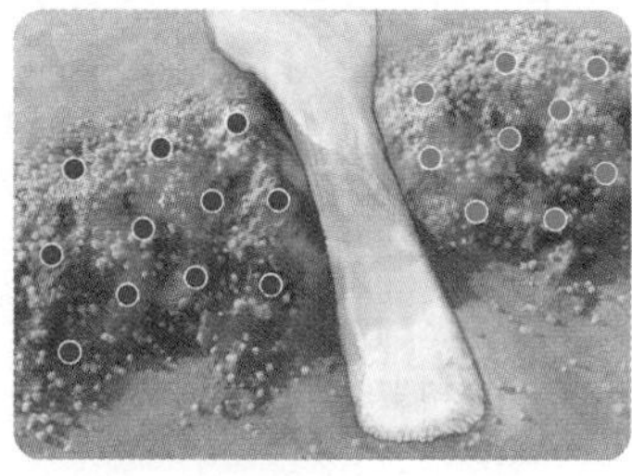

3 In the absence of gene flow, the separated populations evolve independently and diverge into different species.

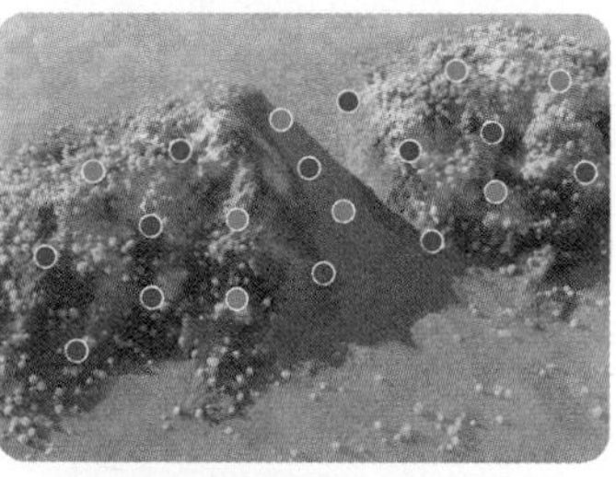

4 When the glacier later melts, allowing individuals of the two species to come into secondary contact, they do not interbreed.

Figure 18.18
The model of allopatric speciation and secondary contact.

units **(Figure 18.18).** Hurricanes may create new channels that divide low coastal islands and the populations inhabiting them. Uplifting mountains or landmasses, as well as advancing glaciers, can also produce barriers that subdivide populations. Movements of Earth's crust about 5 million years ago caused the uplift of the Isthmus of Panama, separating the once continuous shallow sea into the eastern tropical Pacific Ocean and the western tropical Atlantic Ocean. Populations of marine organisms such as wrasses (fish in the genus *Thalassoma*) were subdivided by this event, and pairs of closely related species now live on either side of this divide **(Figure 18.19).**

In other cases, small populations become isolated at the edge of a species' geographic distribution. Such peripheral populations often differ genetically from the central population because they are adapted to somewhat different environments. Once a small population is isolated, genetic drift and natural selection, as well as limited gene flow from the parent population, foster further genetic differentiation. In time, the accumulated genetic differences may lead to reproductive isolation.

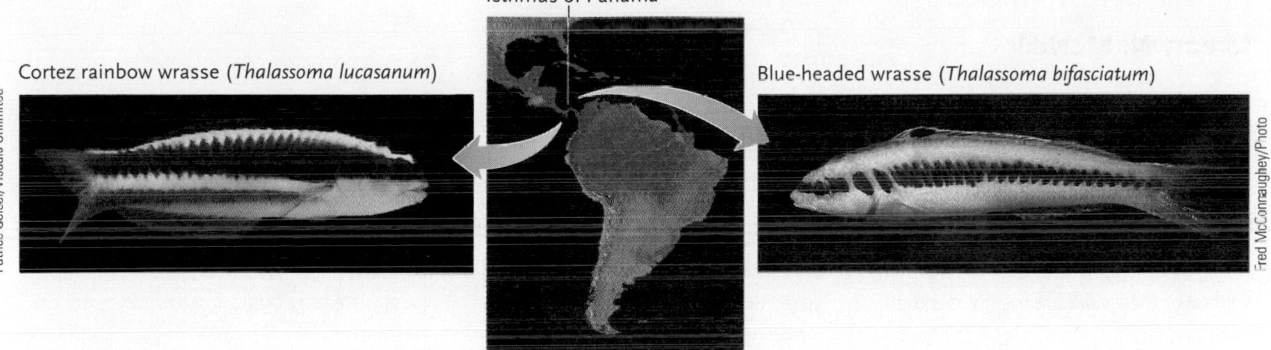

Figure 18.19
Geographic separation. The uplift of the Isthmus of Panama divided an ancestral wrasse population. The Cortez rainbow wrasse (*Thalassoma lucasanum*) now occupies the eastern Pacific Ocean, and the blue-headed wrassed (*T. bifasciatum*) now occupies the western Atlantic Ocean.

Populations on oceanic islands show extreme examples of this phenomenon. Founder effects, an example of genetic drift (see Chapter 17), make the populations genetically distinct. On oceanic archipelagos, such as the Galápagos and Hawaiian Islands, individuals from one island may colonize nearby islands, founding populations that differentiate into distinct species. Each island may experience multiple invasions, and the process may be repeated many times within the archipelago, leading to the evolution of a **species cluster (Figure 18.20).** The nearly 800 species of fruit flies on the Hawaiian Islands form several species clusters.

Allopatric populations may reestablish contact when a geographic barrier is eliminated or breached (see Figure 18.18, step 4). This *secondary contact* provides a test of whether or not the populations have diverged into separate species. If their gene pools did not differentiate much during geographic separation, the populations will interbreed and merge. But if the populations have differentiated enough to be reproductively isolated, they have become separate species. Morphological and gametic isolation could involve chemical or genetic factors as well as the timing of reproduction.

During the early stages of secondary contact, prezygotic reproductive isolation may be incomplete. Some members of each population may mate with individuals from the other, producing viable, fertile offspring in areas called **hybrid zones.** Although some hybrid zones have persisted for hundreds or thousands of years, they are generally narrow, and ecological or geographic factors maintain the separation of the gene pools for the majority of individuals in both species.

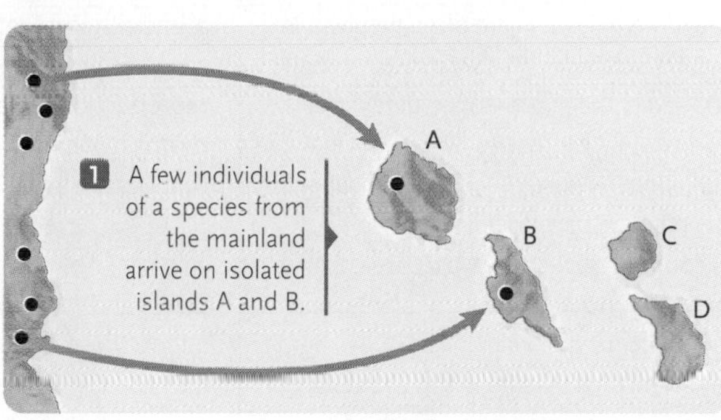

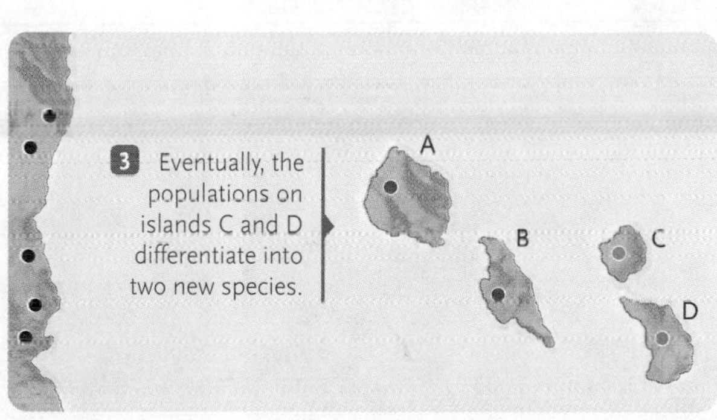

3 Eventually, the populations on islands C and D differentiate into two new species.
A
B
C
D

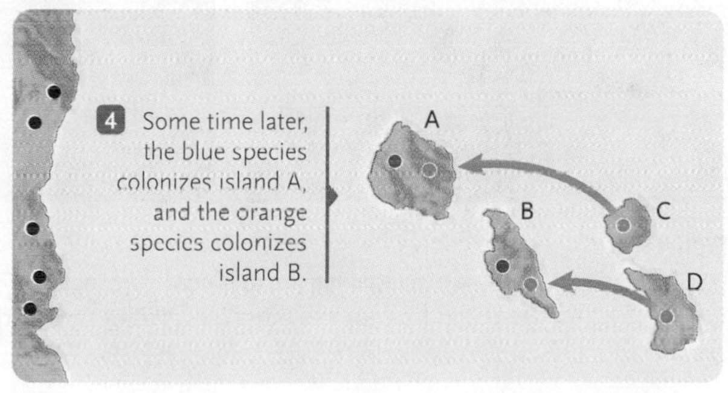

4 Some time later, the blue species colonizes island A, and the orange species colonizes island B.
A
B
C
D

Figure 18.20
Evolution of a species cluster on an archipelago. Letters identify four islands in a hypothetical archipelago, and coloured dots represent different species. The ancestor of all species is represented by black dots on the mainland. At the end of the process, islands A and B are each occupied by two species, and islands C and D are each occupied by one species, all of which evolved on the islands.

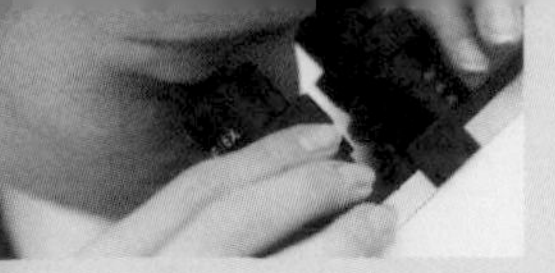

PEOPLE BEHIND BIOLOGY

Jeremy N. McNeil

Jeremy McNeil is a visiting professor in the Department of Biology at the University of Western Ontario, in London, Ontario. He and his students study reproductive behaviour, focusing on insects, particularly species that migrate. Central to their work are the signals that males use to find females and the various processes involved in mate choice. Pheromones or chemical signals (see Chapter 34) may be produced by males and/or females and are often involved in mating behaviour. In some insects, males can detect the pheromones of females from several kilometres away. Information about intraspecific communication can often be used to advantage in efforts to control insect species that are commercially important pests of plants, such as spruce trees or corn.

Pheromonostasis is the process of inhibiting pheromone production. In insects such as spruce budworms (*Choristoneura fumiferana*), males produce two kinds of sperm, one that is nucleate (eupyrene) and the other anucleate (apyrene). McNeil and two colleagues determined that in *C. fumiferana*, apyrene sperm arrive in the spermatheca (females' storage organ for sperm) three to five hours after mating. Therefore, it is possible that apyrene sperm are responsible, at least in part, for pheromonostasis. In the oblique-banded leafroller *C. rosaceana*, the timing of arrival of apyrene sperm in the spermathecae makes it unlikely that the sperm are involved in pheromonostasis. The results demonstrate variations that occur within a genus. The potential to artificially stimulate pheromonostasis could be another way to interrupt reproduction in spruce budworm moths, which are economically important pests of spruce trees.

As we have seen, chemical signals also can mediate interactions between plants and their pollinators. In many situations, these are economically important interactions. One example that McNeil and his students have explored is fruit production in cranberries (*Vaccinium macrocarpon*). In these cranberries, most reproductive stems produce one to three fruits even though there usually are five to seven flowers (**Figure 1**). Flowers higher on the reproductive stems tend to have fewer ovules than lower flowers and often abort without producing fruit. By hand-pollinating flowers along the stems, McNeil and his colleagues demonstrated that the failure of each flower to produce fruit was not a function of insufficient pollination. The upper flowers appeared to be a backup for loss of the earlier blooming lower flowers on the stem.

Chemical communication is often vital in interactions between individuals, whether interspecific or intraspecific. Another intriguing example involves insects that are nest parasites of ants. In Europe, ants (*Myrmica rubra*) adopt the larvae of Alcon blue butterflies (*Maculinea alcon*), take them into their nests, and feed them even before they feed their own young. Female butterflies lay their eggs on marsh gentian plants (*Gentiana pneumonanthe*). The eggs hatch, and young caterpillars (early instars) feed on the plants. Chemical signals from the caterpillars fool the ants. Alcon blue butterflies are social parasites (see Chapter 46) of the ants, and the interaction is an example of one mediated by semiochemicals (see Chapter 34), demonstrating yet another example of precision in interspecific communication.

a.

Photo by Jeremy McNeil

b.

Photo by Jeremy McNeil

Figure 1

(a) Cranberries (*Vaccinium macrocarpon*) are produced from individual flowers that grow on stalks. Each plant typically produces more flowers (five to seven) than fruit (one to three). Increasing production from individual plants could increase overall production **(b)**. The extra flowers (over fruit) appear to be backup for fruit loss.

If hybrid offspring have lower fitness than those produced within each population, natural selection will favour individuals that mate only with members of their own population. Recent studies of *Drosophila* suggest that this phenomenon, called **reinforcement**, enhances reproductive isolation that had begun to develop while the populations were geographically separated. Thus, natural selection may promote the evolution of prezygotic isolating mechanisms.

18.8b Parapatric Speciation: New Species Develop When Populations Span a Barrier

Isolation may occur in a situation where a single species is distributed across a discontinuity in environmental conditions, such as a major change in soil type. Although organisms from both sides of the discontinuity can interbreed freely, natural selection may favour different alleles on either side, limiting gene flow. In such cases, parapatric speciation, speciation arising between adjacent populations, may occur if hybrid offspring have low relative fitness.

Some strains of bent grass (*Agrostis tenuis*), a common pasture plant in Great Britain, have the physiological ability to grow on mine tailings where soil is heavily polluted by copper or other metals. Plants of the copper-tolerant strains grow well on polluted soils, but plants of the pasture strain do not. Conversely, copper-tolerant plants don't survive as well as pasture plants on unpolluted soils. These strains often grow within a few metres of each other where polluted and unpolluted soils form an intricate mosaic. Because bent grass is wind pollinated, pollen is readily transferred from one strain to another.

Thomas McNeilly and Janis Antonovics crossed these strains in the laboratory and determined that they are fully interfertile (pre- and post-zygotically). However, the copper-tolerant plants flower about one week earlier than nearby pasture plants, which promotes pre-zygotic (temporal) isolation of the two strains **(Figure 18.21)**. If the flowering times become further separated, the two strains may attain complete reproductive isolation and become separate species.

Some biologists argue that the places where parapatric populations of bent grass interbreed are hybrid zones where allopatric populations have established secondary contact. Unfortunately, there is no way to determine whether the hybridizing populations were parapatric or allopatric in the past. Thus, a thorough evaluation of the parapatric speciation hypothesis must await the development of techniques that enable biologists to distinguish clearly between the products of allopatric and parapatric speciation.

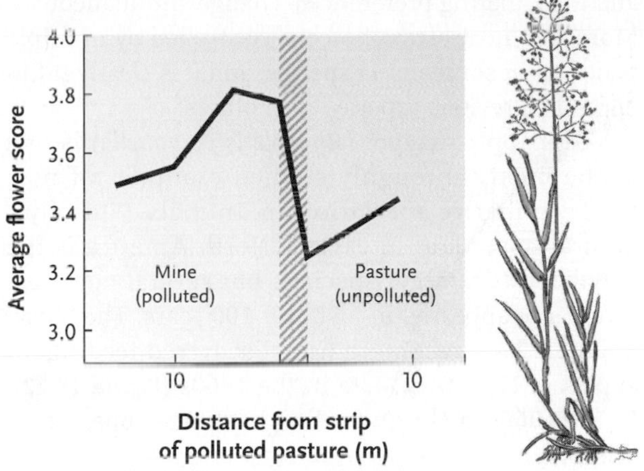

Figure 18.21
Evidence for reproductive isolation in bent grass (*Agrostis tenuis*). Comparison of flowers on bent grass growing on polluted and unpolluted soils revealed differences in flower maturity. Individual bent grass plants growing on polluted soil flowered earlier than individuals growing on unpolluted soil. The differences translated into reproductive isolation of the two populations.

18.8c Sympatric Speciation: New Species Develop in Contiguous Populations

In **sympatric speciation**, reproductive isolation evolves between distinct subgroups that arise within one population. Models of sympatric speciation do not require that the populations be either geographically or environmentally separated as their gene pools diverge. Changes in diet, behaviour, or chromosomes could effect reproductive isolation.

Insects that feed on just one or two plant species are among the animals most likely to evolve by sympatric speciation. These insects generally carry out most important life cycle activities on or near their "host" plants. Adults mate on the host plant, females lay their eggs on it, and larvae feed on the host plant's tissues, eventually developing into adults, which initiate another round of the life cycle. In many insect species, host plant choice is genetically determined. In others, individuals associate with the host plant species they ate as larvae.

Theoretically, a genetic mutation could suddenly change some insects' choice of host plant. Mutant individuals would shift their life cycle activities to the new host species and then interact primarily with others preferring the same new host, an example of ecological isolation. These individuals would collectively form a separate subpopulation, called a **host race**. Reproductive isolation could evolve between different host races if the individuals of each host race are more likely to mate with members of their own host race than with members of another. Some biologists criticize this model because it assumes that the genes controlling two traits, the insects' host plant choice and their mating preferences, change simultaneously. Moreover, host plant choice is controlled by multiple gene loci in some insect species, and it is clearly influenced by previous experience in others.

The apple maggot (*Rhagoletis pomonella*) is one of the most thoroughly studied examples of possible sympatric speciation in animals. This fly's natural host plant in eastern North America is the hawthorn (*Crataegus* species), but several new host races have appeared in just over 100 years. The larvae of a new host race were first discovered feeding on apples in New York state in the 1860s **(Figure 18.22).** In the 1960s, a cherry-feeding host race appeared in Wisconsin.

Recent research has shown that variations at a few gene loci underlie differences in the feeding preferences of *Rhagoletis* host races. Other genetic differences cause them to develop at different rates. Moreover, adults of the three races mate during different summer months. Nevertheless, individuals show no particular preference for mates of their own host race, at least under laboratory conditions. Thus, although behavioural isolation has not developed between races, ecological and temporal isolation may separate adults in nature. Researchers are still not certain that the different host races are reproductively isolated under natural conditions.

Study Break

1. What are the three modes of speciation? What do each of their prefixes mean? How do they occur?
2. What is allopatric speciation? What are the two stages in which it occurs?
3. What is a species cluster? When does it occur?

Dr. Jim Smith, Michigan State University

Figure 18.22
Sympatric speciation in animals. Male and female apple maggots (*Rhagoletis pomonella*) court on a hawthorn leaf. The female will later lay her eggs on the fruit, and the offspring will feed, mate, and lay their eggs on hawthorns as well.

18.9 Genetic Mechanisms of Speciation

What genetic changes lead to reproductive isolation between populations, and how do these changes arise? We examine three genetic mechanisms that can lead to reproductive isolation: *genetic divergence* between allopatric populations, *polyploidy* in sympatric populations, and *chromosome alterations*, which occur independently of the geographic distributions of populations.

18.9a Genetic Divergence: When Isolated Pockets Develop in Continuous Populations

In the absence of gene flow, geographically separated populations inevitably accumulate genetic differences. Most postzygotic isolating mechanisms probably develop as accidental by-products of mutation, genetic drift, and natural selection. Natural selection cannot directly promote the evolution of reproductive isolating mechanisms between *allopatric* populations. Individuals in allopatric populations do not encounter one another and therefore have no opportunity to produce hybrids. In the absence of hybrids, natural selection cannot select against the matings that would have produced them. Natural selection may foster adaptive changes that create postzygotic reproductive isolation between populations after they reestablish contact. If postzygotic isolating mechanisms reduce the fitness of hybrids, natural selection can reinforce the evolution of prezygotic isolating mechanisms.

How much genetic divergence is necessary for speciation to occur? To understand the genetic basis of speciation in closely related species, researchers must first identify the specific causes of reproductive isolation. They then use standard techniques of genetic analysis, along with new molecular approaches such as gene mapping and sequencing, to analyze the genetic mechanisms that establish reproductive isolation. These techniques now allow researchers to determine the minimum number of genes responsible for reproductive isolation in particular pairs of species.

In cases of postzygotic reproductive isolation, mutations in a few gene loci may establish reproductive isolation. If two common species of aquarium fishes, swordtails (*Xiphophorus helleri*) and platys (*X. maculatus*), mate, two genes induce the development of lethal tumours in hybrid offspring. When hybrid sterility is the primary cause of reproductive isolation between *Drosophila* species, at least 5 to 10 gene loci are responsible. Approximately 55 gene loci contribute to postzygotic reproductive isolation between the toads *Bombina bombina* and *B. variegata*.

In cases of prezygotic reproductive isolation, some mechanisms have a surprisingly simple genetic

Mallard Ducks

Andrew Perkinson/Frank Lane Photo Agency

Pintail Ducks

Eric Soder/Foto Natura/Photo Researchers, Inc

Figure 18.23
Sexual selection and prezygotic isolation. In closely related species, such as Mallard Ducks (*Anas platyrhynchos*) and Pintails (*Anas acuta*), males have much more distinctive coloration than females, a sure sign of sexual selection.

basis. A single mutation reverses the direction of coiling (clockwise or counterclockwise) in the shells of some species of snails. Snails with shells that coil in opposite directions cannot approach each other closely enough to mate, making reproduction between them mechanically impossible.

Many traits that now function as prezygotic isolating mechanisms may originally have evolved in response to sexual selection (see Chapters 38 and 40). This evolutionary process exaggerates showy structures and courtship behaviours in males, traits that females use to identify appropriate mates. When two species encounter one another on secondary contact, these traits may also prevent interspecific mating. Many closely related species of ducks exhibit dramatic variation in the appearance of males but not females **(Figure 18.23)**, an almost certain sign of sexual selection. Yet these species hybridize readily in captivity, producing offspring that are both viable and fertile. Speciation in these ducks probably resulted from geographic isolation and sexual selection without significant genetic divergence; only a few morphological and behavioural characters are responsible for their reproductive isolation. Sometimes the evolution of reproductive isolation may not require much genetic change at all.

18.9b Polyploidy: Multiples of Haploid (N) Chromosomes

Polyploidy, individuals with >2*n* sets of chromosomes, is common among plants, where it plays an important role in diversification and speciation. Polyploidy may also have been an important factor in the evolution of some species of fishes, amphibians, and reptiles. Polyploid individuals can arise from chromosome duplications within a single species (autopolyploidy) or through hybridization of different species (allopolyploidy). In plants, polyploids can maintain themselves for long periods of time without sexual reproduction because they reproduce vegetatively. This is not known in polyploid animals.

In **autopolyploidy (Figure 18.24)**, a diploid (2*n*) individual may produce tetraploid (4*n*) offspring, each with four complete chromosome sets. Autopolyploidy occurs through an error in either mitosis or meiosis, so that gametes spontaneously receive the same number of chromosomes as a somatic cell. Again, **unreduced gametes** do not have reduced chromosome numbers compared with somatic cells.

Tetraploids also arise when diploid pollen fertilizes diploid ovules of a self-fertilizing individual or when it fertilizes diploid eggs on another plant with unreduced gametes. Tetraploid offspring can reproduce either by self-pollination or by breeding with other tetraploid individuals. However, tetraploid plants cannot produce fertile offspring by hybridizing with its diploid parents. Fusion of a diploid gamete with a normal haploid gamete produces a triploid (3*n*) offspring, which is usually sterile because the odd number of chromosomes cannot segregate properly during meiosis. Thus, the tetraploid is reproductively isolated from the original diploid population. Many species of grasses, shrubs, and ornamental plants, including violets (*Viola* species), chrysanthemums (*Chrysanthemum* spp.), and nasturtiums (*Tropaelolum majus*), are autopolyploids, having anywhere from 4 to 20 complete chromosome sets.

In **allopolyploidy (Figure 18.25, p. 414)**, two closely related species hybridize and subsequently form polyploid offspring. When two parent species

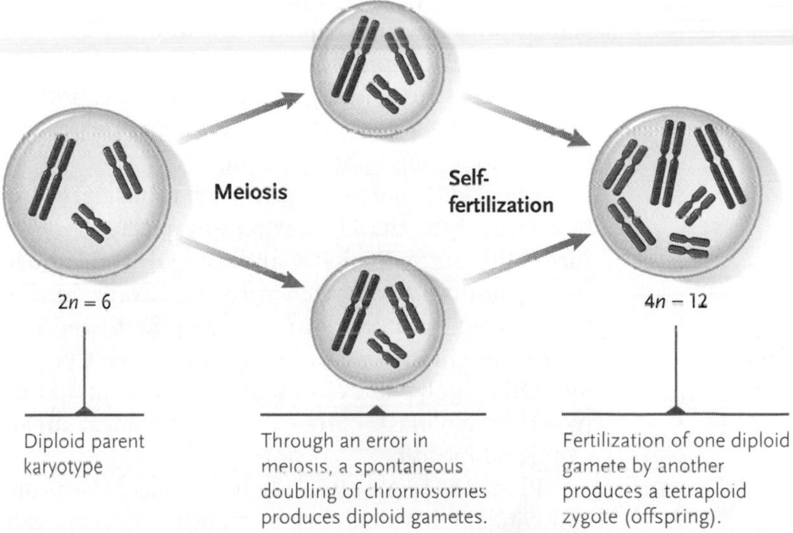

Meiosis
Self-fertilization
2n = 6
4n = 12
Diploid parent karyotype
Through an error in meiosis, a spontaneous doubling of chromosomes produces diploid gametes.
Fertilization of one diploid gamete by another produces a tetraploid zygote (offspring).

Figure 18.24
Speciation by autopolyploidy in plants. A spontaneous doubling of chromosomes during meiosis produces diploid gametes. If the plant fertilizes itself, a tetraploid zygote will be produced.

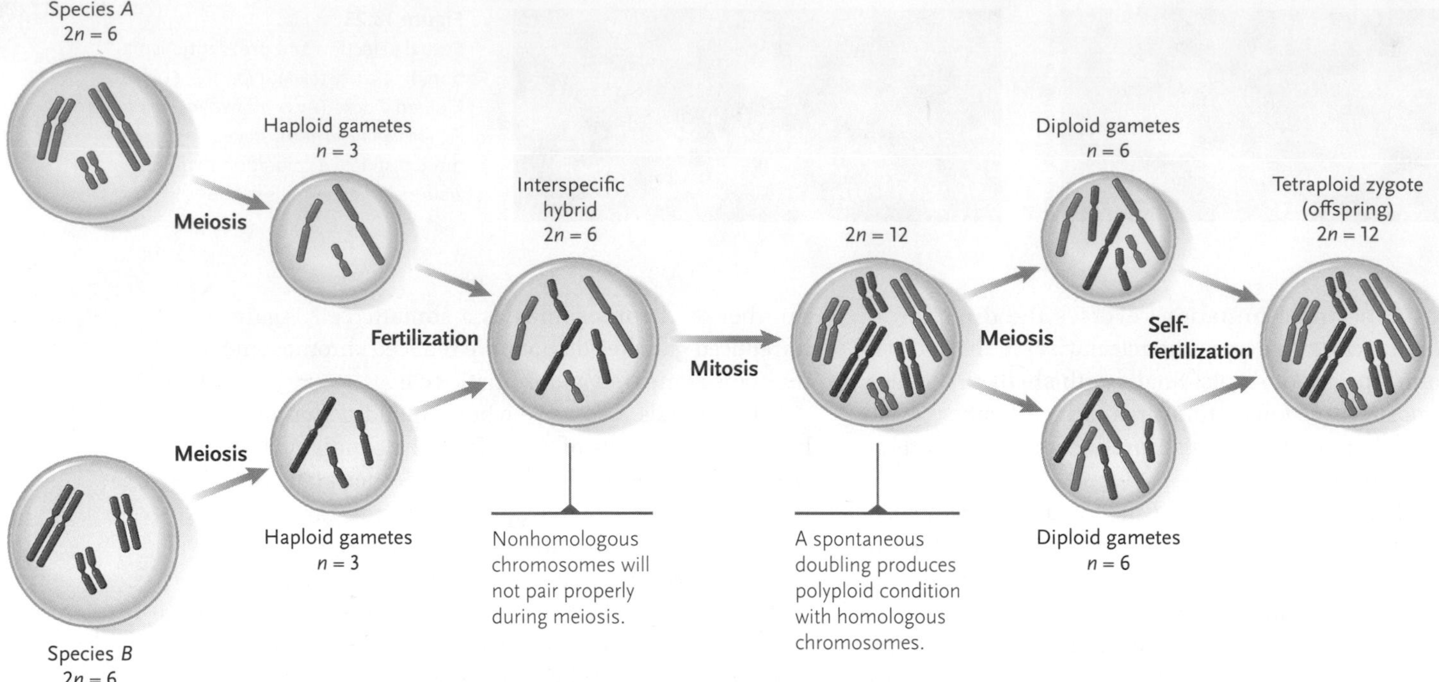

Figure 18.25
Speciation by allopolyploidy in plants. A hybrid mating between two species followed by a doubling of chromosomes during mitosis in gametes of the hybrid can instantly create sets of homologous chromosomes. Self-fertilization can then generate polyploid individuals that are reproductively isolated from both parent species.

have diverged sufficiently, their hybrid offspring are sterile because chromosomes from the two parents do not pair properly during meiosis. However, if chromosome numbers double in the interspecific hybrid, the chromosome complement of the gametes is also doubled, producing homologous chromosomes that *can* pair during meiosis. The hybrid can establish a population of a new polyploid species provided that it can produce polyploid gametes. The route to a new polyploid species can be through self-fertilization or fertilization with other doubled hybrids. When compared with speciation by genetic divergence, speciation by allopolyploidy is extremely rapid, causing a new species to arise in one generation without geographic isolation.

Even sterile polyploids are often robust, growing to a larger size than either parent species. Therefore, both autopolyploids and allopolyploids have been important to agriculture. For example, the wheat used to make flour (*Triticum aestivum*) has six sets of chromosomes (**Figure 18.26**; see Chapter 49). Other polyploid crop plants include plantains (cooking bananas), coffee, cotton, potatoes, sugarcane, and tobacco.

Plant breeders often try to increase the probability of allopolyploid formation by using chemicals that foster nondisjunction of chromosomes during mitosis (see Chapter 10). In the first such experiment, undertaken in the 1920s, scientists crossed a radish (*Raphanus sativus*) and a cabbage (*Brassica oleracea*), hoping to develop a plant with both edible roots and leaves. Instead, the new species, *Raphanobrassica*, combined the least desirable characteristics of each parent, growing a cabbage-like root and radish-like leaves. Recent experiments have been more successful. Plant scientists have produced an allopolyploid grain, triticale, that has the disease resistance of rye and the high productivity of wheat (see Chapter 49).

18.9c Chromosome Alterations Can Lead to Genetic Isolation and Speciation

Other changes in chromosome structure or number may also foster speciation. Surveys of closely related species often uncover a substantial number of chromosome differences between them, including inversions, translocations, deletions, and duplications (see Chapter 12). These differences may foster postzygotic isolation.

Biologists use different chemical or enzymatic treatments and staining to highlight alternating light and dark bands in metaphase chromosomes. The resulting banding patterns are constant and chromosome specific, making them useful in cytogenetic mapping and karyotype analysis. In all species, banding patterns vary from one chromosome segment to another. Identical banding patterns in chromosome segments from two or more related species identify comparable portions of genomes. Banding patterns allow scientists to identify specific

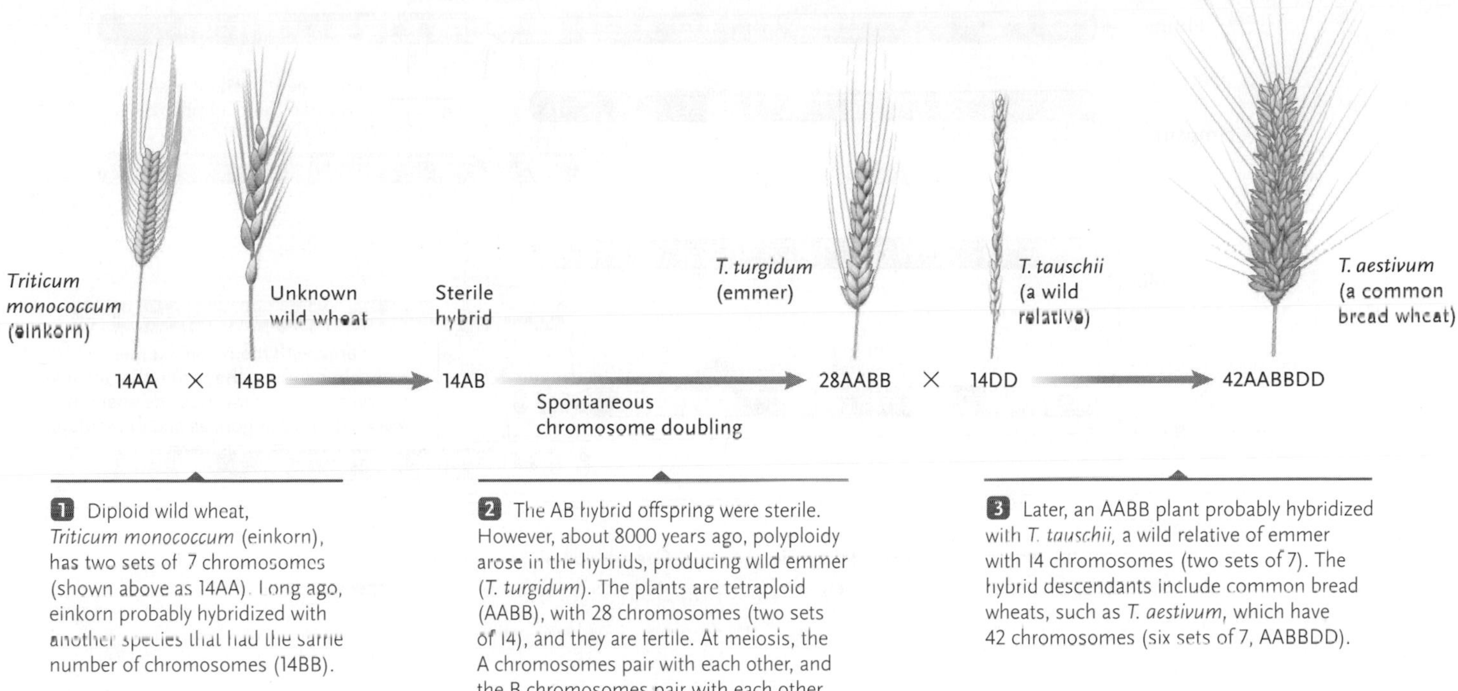

Triticum monococcum (einkorn)
Unknown wild wheat
Sterile hybrid
T. turgidum (emmer)
T. tauschii (a wild relative)
T. aestivum (a common bread wheat)
14AA × 14BB
14AB
Spontaneous chromosome doubling
28AABB × 14DD
42AABBDD
1 Diploid wild wheat, Triticum monococcum (einkorn), has two sets of 7 chromosomes (shown above as 14AA). Long ago, einkorn probably hybridized with another species that had the same number of chromosomes (14BB).
2 The AB hybrid offspring were sterile. However, about 8000 years ago, polyploidy arose in the hybrids, producing wild emmer (T. turgidum). The plants are tetraploid (AABB), with 28 chromosomes (two sets of 14), and they are fertile. At meiosis, the A chromosomes pair with each other, and the B chromosomes pair with each other.
3 Later, an AABB plant probably hybridized with T. tauschii, a wild relative of emmer with 14 chromosomes (two sets of 7). The hybrid descendants include common bread wheats, such as T. aestivum, which have 42 chromosomes (six sets of 7, AABBDD).

Figure 18.26

The evolution of wheat (*Triticum*). Cultivated wheat grains more than 11 000 years old have been found in the eastern Mediterranean region. Researchers believe that speciation in wheat occurred through hydridization and polyploidy (see also Chapter 49).

chromosome segments and compare their positions in the chromosomes of different species.

In 1982, Jorge J. Younis and Om Prakash compared the chromosome structures of humans and their closest relatives among the apes, chimpanzees (*Pan troglodytes*), gorillas (*Gorilla gorilla*), and orangutans (*Pongo pygmaeus*). Nearly all of the 1000 bands that Younis and Prakash identified were present in all taxa, but whole sections of chromosomes have been rearranged over evolutionary time **(Figure 18.27, p. 416)**. Humans have a diploid chromosome complement of 46 chromosomes, whereas chimpanzees, gorillas, and orangutans have 48. The difference can be traced to the fusion (joining together) of two ancestral chromosomes into chromosome 2 of humans. The ancestral chromosomes are separate in the other three species.

Moreover, banding patterns suggest that the position of the centromere in human chromosome 2 closely matches that of a centromere in one chimpanzee chromosome **(Figure 18.28, p. 416)**, reflecting a close evolutionary relationship. But this centromere falls within an inverted region of the chromosome in gorillas and orangutans, reflecting their evolutionary divergence from chimpanzees and humans. Humans and chimps have different centromeric inversions in six other chromosomes.

How might such chromosome rearrangements promote speciation? In 2003, Arcadi Navarro and Nick H. Barton compared the rates of evolution in protein-coding genes within rearranged chromosome segments of humans and chimpanzees with those in genes outside rearranged segments. Proteins evolved more than twice as quickly in rearranged chromosome segments. Chromosome rearrangements inhibit chromosome pairing and recombination during meiosis. Therefore, new genetic variations favoured by natural selection would be conserved within the rearranged segments. These variations accumulate over time, contributing to genetic divergence between populations with the rearrangement and those without it. Chromosome rearrangements can be a trigger for speciation. Once a chromosome rearrangement becomes established within a population, that population will diverge more rapidly from populations lacking the rearrangement than if the rearrangement did not exist. The genetic divergence eventually causes reproductive isolation.

As important, however, are the more general genetic similarities between humans and closely related species. In 1975, genetic evidence suggested that the genomes of humans and chimps were 99% similar. Yet few people would mistake humans for chimps. Humans walk upright and have bigger brains, whereas chimps are resistant to AIDS—the list goes on and on. Genetic similarity between the two species reflects base substitutions (see Chapter 27). There are obvious differences between the brains of the two species, and in the cortex, 17.4% of the connections are specific to humans. Differences in the genomes between species can inform us about genetic isolation, but they do not provide a quantitative

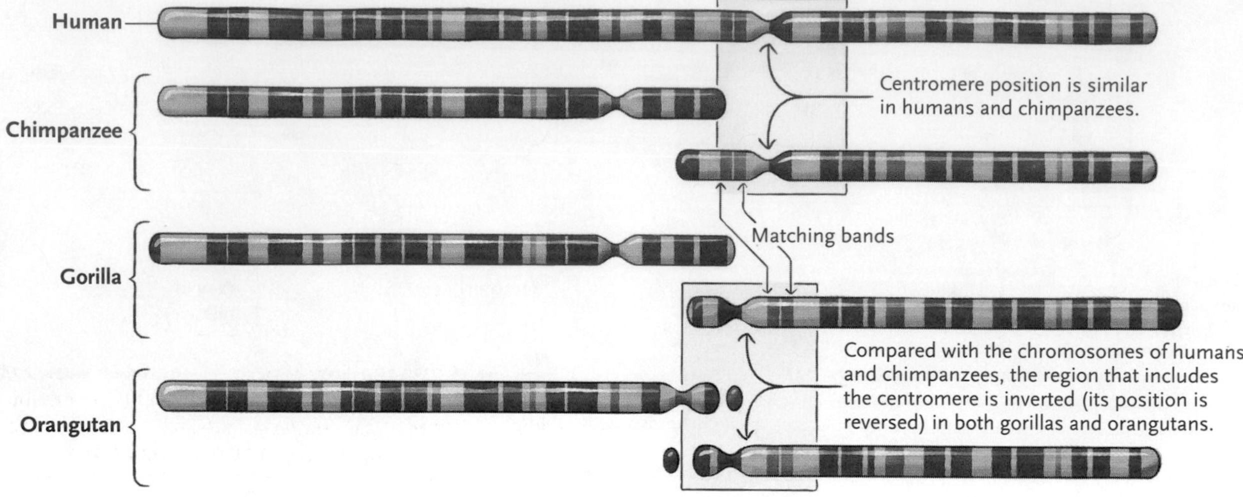

Figure 18.27
Banding patterns in chromosomes revealed by Giemsa stain. Comparison of the banding patterns of humans, chimpanzees, orangutans, and gorillas provides evidence of genetic changes associated with the evolution of these species.

measure of differences between species (see Figure 18.28). For more discussion of humans and chimps, see Chapter 27.

Study Break

1. How does genetic divergence occur between geographically separated populations? Why does natural selection not promote the evolution of reproductive isolating mechanisms between allopatric populations?
2. In what organisms is polyploidy most common? What is the difference between autopolyploidy and allopolyploidy?

18.10 Back to the Species Concept in Biology

At this point, the dynamics of speciation should be obvious to you. Perhaps you are now better able to appreciate how species reflect the richness of biology. Species are the products of evolution, the very essence of biodiversity. But you also will know that it is naive to believe that one definition of species will apply across biology. Be cautious of evidence that does not make sense, of claims that do not seem entirely credible. Differences and similarities between humans and chimps (for example) are no better expressed by a few linear measurements of bones or organs than they are by genomes.

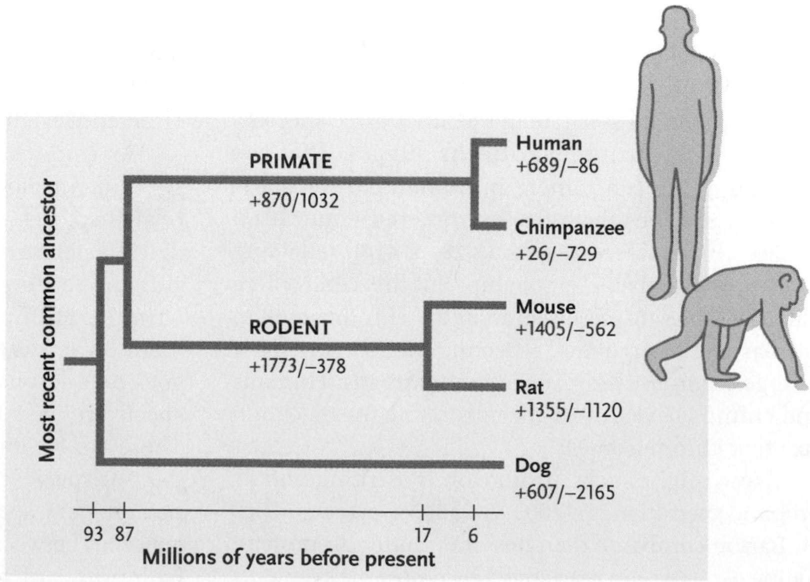

Figure 18.28
Through evolution, the gain (+) in the number of copies of some genes and the loss (−) of others have contributed to human–chimp differences. Shown here are gain and loss data for rodents (mouse and rat) and primates (human and chimpanzee). These changes contributed to differences between these animals.

Unanswered Questions

Should gardeners be permitted to use introduced plants in their gardens? How would you define "introduced"?

How do data on the distribution and genetics of starlings (*Sturnis vulgaris*) and Italian wall lizards influence your concept of species?

Review

Go to CENGAGENOW™ at http://hed.nelson.com/ to access quizzing, animations, exercises, articles, and personalized homework help.

18.1 What's in a "Name?"

- Biologists use names to precisely identify species, subspecies, or varieties. Other animals also use "names" or signals to refer to different organisms.
- Biologists use almost any available feature to identify species. Traditionally, morphological features were most important, but now behavioural and genetic features also are commonly used.

18.2 Definition of "Species"

- According to the Biological Species Concept, a species is a group of organisms that can interbreed and produce fertile offspring; however, this definition does not deal with organisms that reproduce asexually, nor does it apply well to species that hybridize and produce fertile offspring. Other species concepts are phylogenetic (a species is a group of organisms bound by a unique evolutionary ancestry) and ecological (a species is a group of organisms sharing a distinct ecological niche).
- Androdioecous species are composed of males and hermaphrodites (which produce both sperm and eggs), whereas gynogenetic species consist only of females. The egg of gynogenetic species requires mechanical stimulation by sperm donated from males of other species to begin development and achieve reproduction.
- Sexual reproduction involves genetic recombination. In *Daphnia pulex,* mutations in mitochondrial protein-coding genes are more frequent in individuals reproducing asexually compared with those reproducing sexually, demonstrating an advantage of recombination, the reduction in the number of mutations.

18.3 One Size Does Not Fit All

- Gene flow among individuals in a population of conspecifics mixes their genetic material and is said to act like "glue" holding that species together. Individuals of different species are genetically isolated, but species that produce fertile hybrids may not be naturally isolated (are they, in fact, species?).
- According to the Morphological Species Concept, individuals of the same species share measurable traits that distinguish them from individuals of other species. Paleontologists use morphology to identify fossils to species, as do naturalists identifying animals and plants in the field.

18.4 Gene Flow: Four Examples

- Distribution influences gene flow, and sparsely distributed species may experience less gene flow than those with a continuous distribution. Species may depend on other species for dispersal (hitchhike). Social behaviour also can limit gene flow within continuous populations. Changes in habitat continuity affect gene flow, and a discontinuous habitat may inhibit gene flow between populations.

18.6 Geographic Variation

- Subspecies are local variants of a species that consist of usually geographically separated populations exhibiting recognizable phenotypic and/or genotypic variations. Subspecies may interbreed where their distributions overlap. Terms such as variants, cultivars, or breeds are used to identify distinct populations.
- In ring species, adjacent populations exchange genetic material directly, and gene flow between distant populations occurs only through the intermediate populations. Clinal changes are smooth patterns of variation along a geographic gradient. Clines occur when there is gene flow between adjacent populations that are adapting to slightly different conditions.

18.7 Reproductive Isolation

- Reproductive isolating mechanisms are biological characteristics preventing gene pools of two sympatric species from mixing. Prezygotic isolating mechanisms prevent fertilization. Postzygotic isolating mechanisms operate after fertilization.
- Ecological isolation occurs between species that live in different habitats in the same area. Temporal isolation occurs between species living in the same habitat but mating at different times (of the day or year). Behavioural isolation results when the signals used by one species to identify a potential mate are not recognized by the other species. Mechanical isolation occurs when differences in the structure of reproductive organs or other body parts prevent interbreeding of species. Gametic isolation occurs when the sperm of one species are incompatible with the eggs of another.
- When sperm from one species does fertilize an egg of another species, postzygotic isolating mechanisms may reduce the fitness of hybrids. Hybrid inviability results when developmental programs of the two parent species are incompatible. Some hybrids develop into healthy adults but cannot produce functional gametes. Hybrid breakdown happens when hybrids are healthy and fully fertile, but their offspring exhibit reduced fitness.

18.8 Geography of Speciation

- Allopatric, parapatric, and sympatric speciation reflect the meanings of *allo* = different, *para* = beside, and *sym* = together.
- Allopatric speciation occurs when a physical barrier subdivides a large population or when a small population becomes separated from the species' main geographic distribution. A species cluster results after founding populations colonize an island or isolated land mass. Secondary contact occurs when allopatric populations reestablish contact after a barrier between them is eliminated.
- Parapatric speciation occurs when a species is distributed across a discontinuity in environmental conditions so that natural selection favours different alleles and phenotypes on either side of the discontinuity.

- Sympatric speciation occurs among subgroups of a population. Neither geographic nor reproductive isolation is necessary for sympatric speciation to occur. Changes in diet, behaviour, or chromosomes can cause sympatric speciation.

18.9 Genetic Mechanisms of Speciation

- Geographically separated populations experience no gene flow, allowing accumulation of genetic differences. Natural selection cannot directly promote speciation between allopatric populations.
- Polyploidy, multiples of N (haploid) chromosomes, is more common in plants than in animals. Autopolyploidy arises from chromosome duplications within a single species. It results when an error in mitosis or meiosis causes individuals to spontaneously receive the same number of chromosomes as a somatic cell. Polyploid individuals are produced when unreduced gametes join in fertilization. Allopolyploidy results from the hybridization of different species. Polyploidy is often important in the development of domesticated species.

Questions

Self-Test Questions

1. The Biological Species Concept defines species on the basis of
   a. reproductive characteristics.
   b. genetic characteristics.
   c. morphological characteristics.
   d. behavioural characteristics.
   e. all of the above.
2. Biologists can apply the Biological Species Concept most confidently to species that
   a. reproduce asexually.
   b. lived in the past.
   c. are allopatric.
   d. hybridize in captivity.
   e. reproduce sexually.
3. A ________ occurs when there are smooth changes in populations distributed along a geographic gradient.
   a. ring species
   b. subspecies
   c. cline
   d. hybridization zone
   e. subspecies
4. Gene flow in marine snails (*Balea perversa*) is directly assisted by
   a. ocean currents.
   b. migrating birds.
   c. migrating whales.
   d. shipping.
   e. none of the above.
5. Prezygotic isolating mechanisms
   a. reduce the fitness of hybrid offspring.
   b. generally prevent individuals of different species from mating.
   c. are found only in animals.
   d. are found only in plants.
   e. are observed only in organisms that reproduce asexually.
6. In allopatric speciation, geographic separation of two populations
   a. is sufficient for speciation to occur.
   b. occurs only after speciation is complete.
   c. allows gene flow between them.
   d. reduces the relative fitness of hybrid offspring.
   e. inhibits gene flow between them.
7. Adjacent populations producing hybrid offspring with low relative fitness may be undergoing
   a. clinal isolation.
   b. parapatric speciation.
   c. allopatric speciation.
   d. sympatric speciation.
   e. geographic isolation.
8. Lack of gene flow is a major contributor to speciation in
   a. rodents.
   b. birds.
   c. lichens.
   d. polyploids.
   e. hermaphrodites.
9. Which of the following could be an example of allopolyploidy?
   a. One parent has 32 chromosomes, the other has 10, and their offspring have 42.
   b. Gametes and somatic cells have the same number of chromosomes.
   c. Chromosome number increases by one in a gamete and in the offspring it produces.
   d. Chromosome number decreases by one in a gamete and in the offspring it produces.
   e. Chromosome number in the offspring is exactly half of what it is in the parents.
10. Which of the following genetic characteristics is shared by humans and chimpanzees?
    a. They have the same number of chromosomes.
    b. The position of the centromere on human chromosome 2 matches the position of a centromere on a chimpanzee chromosome.
    c. A fusion of ancestral chromosomes formed chromosome 2 in humans.
    d. Centromeres on all of their chromosomes fall within inverted chromosome segments.
    e. All of the above.

Questions for Discussion

1. Domestic dogs (*Canis familiaris*) and cats (*Felis cattus*) each represent a single species. How do you explain differences in the range of size and appearance in these two species? Do they interbreed with other species? How does this reconcile with the definition of species? (See also Chapter 49.)
2. How do genetic differences between humans and other species of great apes translate into evolution in this group? (See also Chapter 27.)
3. If intermediate populations in a ring species go extinct, eliminating the possibility of gene flow between populations at the two ends of the ring, would you now identify those remaining populations as full species? Explain your answer.
4. What will happen when the genetic integrity of a species is extensively compromised? Consider the case of peregrine falcons (*Falco peregrinus*). This species was listed as endangered, but widespread reintroductions, reproductive success, and reduced levels of DDT have brought it back from the brink of extinction. Some of the reintroductions were from stock not native to the areas of reintroduction. Or consider the case of wild grapes (*Vitus vinifera*) contaminated by genes from domesticated grapes, or grey wolves (*Canis lupis*) and red wolves (*Canis rufus*) contaminated by genes from coyotes (*Canis latrans*).

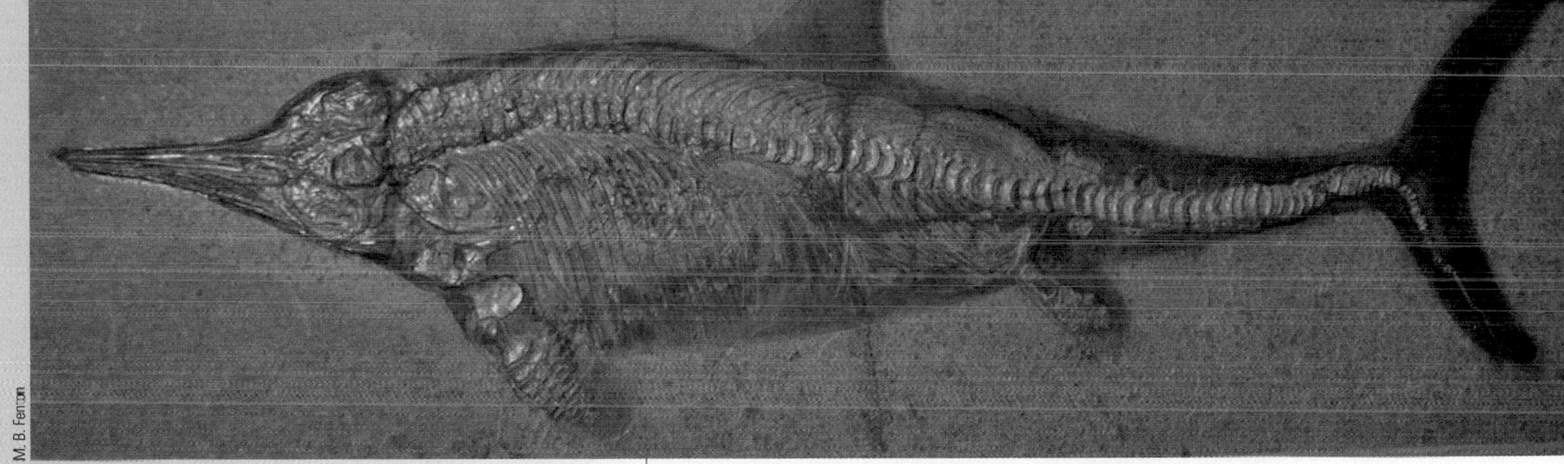

M. B. Fenton

An ichthyosaur (*Stenopterygius* spp.) from Germany on display in the Royal Tyrrell Museum in Drumheller, Alberta. Although this specimen is about 2 m long, the largest ichthyosaurs were up to 15 m in length. As adults, the smallest were about 70 cm long.

19 Evolution and Classification

Study Plan

Why It Matters

Understanding and documenting the diversity of life is a major challenge to biologists. This exercise means determining evolutionary relationships between organisms and deciding if similar structures or similar-looking structures are grounds for grouping species together. In other words, if they look the same, are they closely related in an evolutionary sense? Before you dismiss this as an easy exercise, remember that when first discovered, fossil ichthyosaurs were thought to be the remains of fish. Only later were they recognized as reptiles. Small wonder: ichthyosaurs have fishlike bodies, but so do dolphins and other whales (Cetacea), and they are mammals. Many aquatic vertebrates have fishlike bodies—think of sharks (cartilaginous fishes) and tunas (bony fishes). But these are two very different kinds of "fish." Other fish have very different bodies—think of eels, flatfish, anglerfish, or sea horses.

There is a tendency among organisms living under the same conditions to develop similar body forms. This can be called parallel or convergent evolution, depending on the evolutionary relatedness of the organisms involved. Convergent evolution refers to more distantly related organisms, parallel to more closely related ones. How do you tell?

Cacti and euphorbs are two groups of desert plants that can be strikingly similar in appearance **(Figure 19.1)**. But cacti and euphorbs are not closely related in an evolutionary sense. Similarity in appearance does not always mean relatedness. The same applies to earthworms (phylum Annelida) and caecilians (phylum Chordata), two terrestrial "worm-like" animals **(Figure 19.2)**. Resemblance does not necessarily mean relatedness.

Knowing what an organism is can be crucial. This sometimes means making an accurate identification by looking beyond superficial resemblances. Many people collect and eat mushrooms. Now, the fruiting bodies of many species of mushrooms are superficially similar, but you need to be sure what you are eating. There are some obvious "right" and "wrong" choices for the table **(Figure 19.3)**. Whereas true morels (*Morchella* species) are delicacies, false morels (*Gyromitra esculenta*) can be deadly because they contain gyromitrin, a hemolytic toxin (see *Molecule Behind Biology*). In the same spirit, choosing *Cantherellus ciabarius* (chanterelle) for dinner is epicurian, whereas *Omphalotus illudens* (jack-o'-lantern) is not. Jack-o'-lanterns are very poisonous. *Hygrophoropsis aurantiacus* (false chanterelle) looks like *C. ciabarius* and *O. illudens* but may not be poisonous. Why do they resemble one another?

If you are going mushroom hunting, know your quarry or at least work with someone who really does.

a. Cactus

b. Spurge

Figure 19.1
Convergent evolution in plants. **(a)** *Echinocereus* and other North American cacti (family Cactaceae) are strikingly similar to **(b)** *Euphorbia* and other African spurges (Euphorbeaceae). Convergent evolution adapted both groups to desert environments. Each has thick, water-storing stems, spiny structures that discourage animals from feeding on them, CAM photosynthesis (see Chapter 7), and stomata that open only at night.

a.

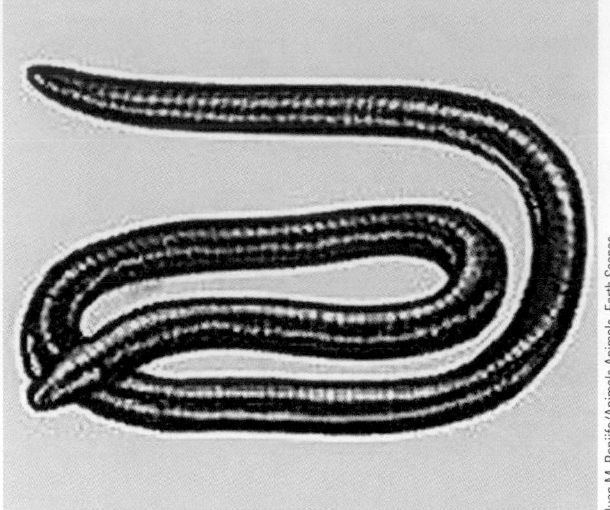

b.

Figure 19.2
Two wormlike animals from different phyla. **(a)** The caecilian (Phylum Chordata) and **(b)** the earthworm (Phylum Annelida) are superficially similar, but the former has a backbone, a skull, and jaws, whereas the latter does not.

Molecule Behind Biology

Gyromitrin

First isolated in 1885, gyromitrin **(Figure 1)** was originally known as "helvellic acid." This toxin can kill people, demonstrated by 74 of 513 fatal cases described in the medical literature between 1782 and 1965. In 1975, a case report described the death of a 53-year-old woman who had eaten some raw mushrooms she picked in the fields. The day after eating them, she was vomiting and had diarrhea. After receiving treatment in a "minor" hospital, she was transferred to a university hospital, where she was placed in the intensive care unit. She died there a few hours after being admitted. Her symptoms included a severely swollen liver, edema, necrosis, fatty degeneration in the liver, nephrosis—the list goes on.

The moral: know your mushrooms. By the way, although there is a folk tradition that toxins such as gyromitrin are neutralized by cooking, it is not wise to count on this view because human fatalities have been reported after people ate mushrooms that had been cooked and whose juices had been removed. Her case demonstrates the folly of eating raw wild mushrooms and the importance of knowing how to identify the mushrooms you pick for consumption.

Gyromitrin is the toxin produced by false morels (*Gyromitra esculenta;* see Figure 19.3b). It is important to be able to distinguish false morels from real morels (*Morchellus esculenta;* see Figure 19.3a) because eating false morels can kill you. Poisoning by gyromitrin appears to be most common in Eastern Europe and Germany.

As we have seen (see Chapter 18), other fungi use odours to attract animals to disperse spores, and rusts may use false flowers to effect fertilization (see Figure 19.4). Why do mushrooms have toxins? The topic of mushroom toxins was addressed by Discorides, a Greek surgeon, who was in Nero's army during the first century A.D. He is reported as saying that "of fungi there is a double difference, for either they are edible, or they are poisonous." How do toxic mushrooms signal their condition? Many species of organisms use visual, olfactory, or acoustic signals to warn would-be predators of the risks they pose (see Chapter 46). It is possible that poisonous mushrooms use olfactory cues to signal their condition. If so, humans are not the main predators of false morels.

H_3C, N, N, O, H, H, CH_3

Figure 1
Gyromitrin is produced by the false morel, *Gyromitra esculenta.*

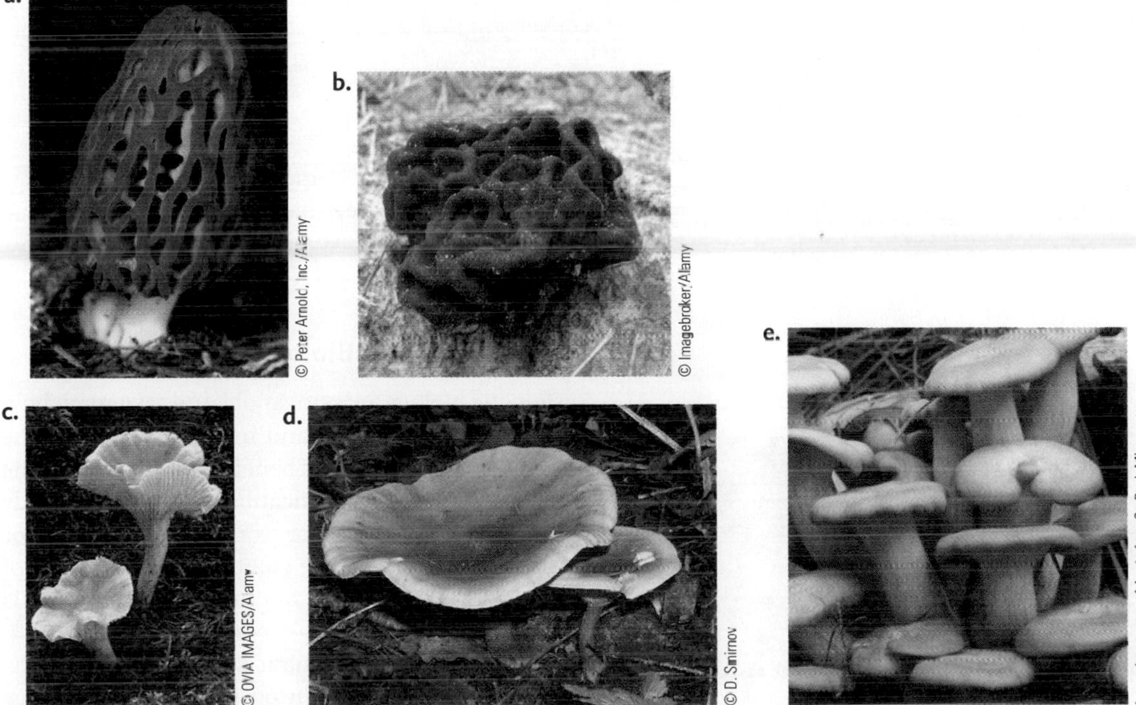

Figure 19.3
People who know their mushrooms collect, cook, and eat **(a)** *Morchellus esculenta* and **(c)** *Cantherellus ciabrius,* a morel and a chanterelle, respectively. They never eat **(b)** *Gromitra esculenta,* the false morel, or **(e)** *Omphalotus illudens* (jack-o'-lantern) because they are deadly. They might watch someone else try **(d)** *Hygrophoropsis aurantiacus,* the false chanterelle that may (or may not) be toxic.

19.1 The Significance of Similarities and Differences

One of the excitements and satisfactions in biology is learning to look at something, recognize it, and understand just what you are seeing. Below are three cases, examples of where even an experienced biologist might be fooled. At first, this may seem strange or even preposterous when you know what a flower looks like; surely, you will always recognize one. Read on to see that things are not always as they appear.

19.1a Case 1: Fake Flowers

You may be astonished to realize that what you thought was a flower **(Figure 19.4a, b)** is actually a leaf modified by a fungus. The fungus, the rust *Puccinia monoica,* affects the growth of the leaves, changing their appearance and odour. The fungus-induced "flowers" have nectaries (glands that produce nectar; **Figure 19.4c**). Just as many biologists are fooled by the flower-like leaves, so are insects that come to pollinate the flowers. In this way, the rust effects fertilization. The rust also inhibits the formation of the plant's own flowers, minimizing confusion among pollinators. So when is a flower not a flower?

19.1b Case 2: Carnivorous Plants

In some places, there may be an abundance of water and sunlight, but nitrogen is in short supply for plants. Here we find a diversity of ways that plants trap insects to directly (or indirectly) obtain nitrogen (**Figure 19.5;** see Figure 3.21, Box 47.5). Like people trying to catch insects (but perhaps not for their nitrogen), plants use different methods, including sticky traps (flypaper), snap traps, and pitfall traps (pitchers). Flypaper traps have appeared in at least five evolutionary lines of plants and pitchers at least three times. Not all carnivorous plants share a close common ancestor.

a.

b.

c.

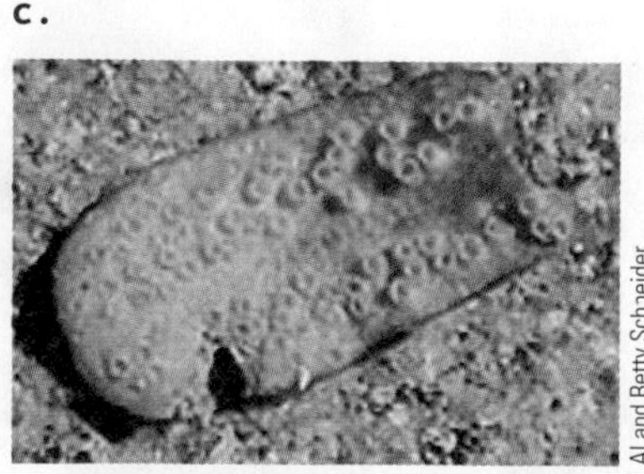

Figure 19.4
(a) There is an obvious difference between an uninfected *Boerchera* species (left) and an infected one (right). **(b)** When infected by the fungus *Puccinia monoica,* a rust, the leaves of *Boerchera* become flower-like and **(c)** appear to produce nectar. The rust inhibits flowering so that insects visiting the "flowers" to collect nectar fertilize the rust. The insects do not visit the host plant's flowers.

19.1c Case 3: Mammals with Flat Tails Are Not Always Beavers

In 2006, the news media reported a science story about a "Mesozoic beaver" **(Figure 19.6).** This was an exciting fossil find from China, and as long as you focused on the broad, flattened tail, the "beaver" part of the name made sense. This mammal, *Castorocauda lutrasimilis* (see **Figure 19.6a**), had modified tail vertebrae flattened like those of living beavers (rodents in the genus *Castor*) (see **Figure 19.6b**). But beavers are not the only aquatic mammals with flattened tails. Another good example is *Ornithorhynchus anatinus,* the duck-billed platypus of Australia (see **Figure 19.6c**). If you look at the skulls of the Mesozoic beaver, a modern beaver, and a platypus, the differences are striking **(Figure 19.7).** It appears that the giant beaver (*Casteroides ohioensis*) of the North American Pleistocene may not have had a flattened tail, so there is more to being a beaver than having a flat tail!

These examples demonstrate why biologists must look closely at the details. Flowerlike structures are not always flowers. Carnivorous plants are not necessarily closely related. Looking at a mammal's tail may give you a different picture of its relationships than its skull.

The purpose of this chapter is to introduce you to classification, systematic biology, and taxonomy and give you an idea of how biologists proceed to document and understand diversity and evolution. This means giving you information about how biologists assess the importance of characters when studying evolution. Put another way, we will try to understand how biologists distinguish between parallel and convergent evolution.

Study Break

1. What is a flower? Name an example of a flowerlike structure that is not a flower.
2. How do carnivorous plants catch insects? Why?

19.2 Systematic Biology: An Overview

Systematic biology, classification, and taxonomy help us organize and understand information about the biological world. Biologists benefit from the work done on systematics and classification whether they study molecules or ecosystems or work in biotechnology or conservation. Knowing the identity of the organism of interest is the first step to finding out what already is known about it.

The science of **systematics** has two major goals. One is to reconstruct the **phylogeny** or evolutionary history of a group of organisms. Phylogenies are presented as **phylogenetic trees,** which are formal hypotheses identifying likely relationships among species. Like all hypotheses, they can be tested with data and often are revised as scientists gather new data.

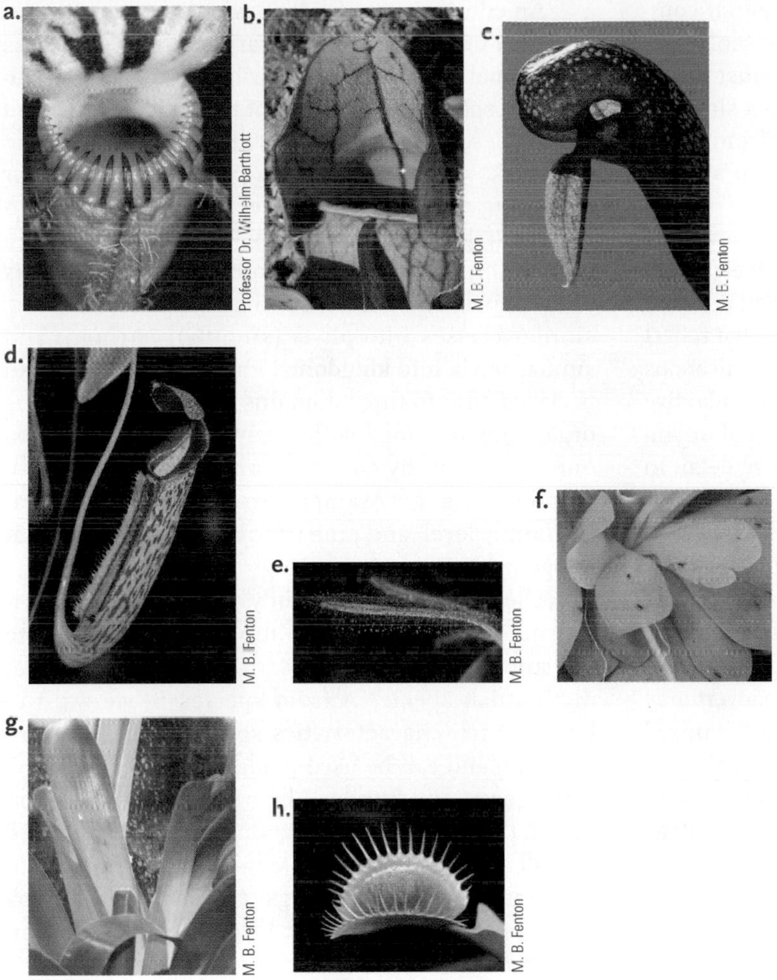

Figure 19.5
Plants that catch insects in pitchers **(a)** *Cephalotus follicularis;* **(b)** *Sarracenia purpurea;* **(c)** *Darlingtonia california;* **(d)** *Nepenthes* species on flypaper; **(e)** *Drosera capensis;* **(f)** *Pinguicula* spp.; **(g)** *Brocchinia reducta,* or in a snap trap **(h)** *Dioneae muscipula.*

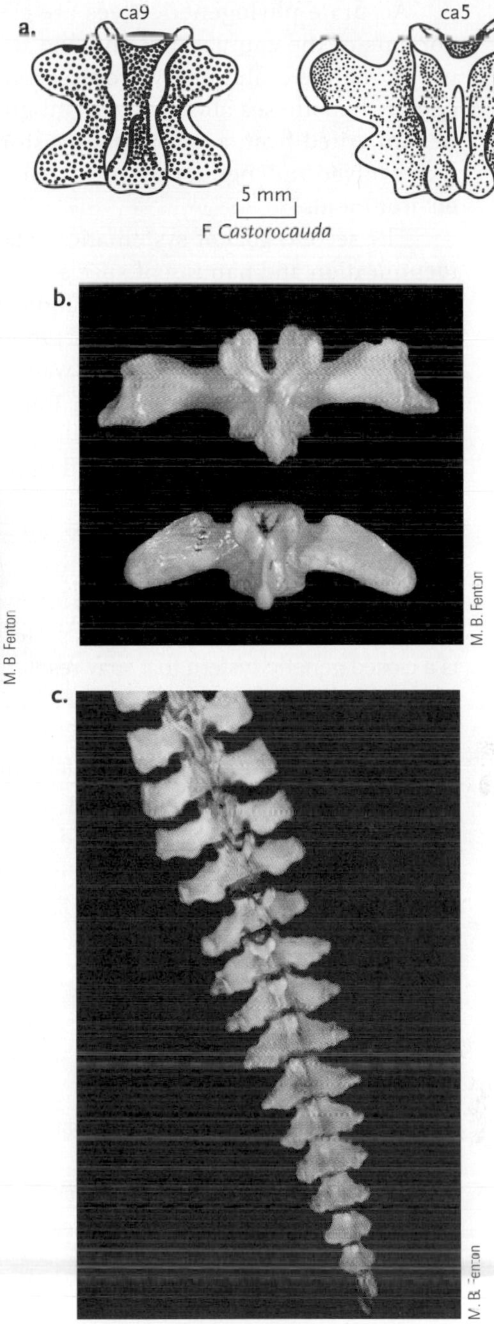

Figure 19.6
Aquatic mammals with flattened tails have similar flattened caudal (tail) vertebrae. Dorsal and ventral views of caudal vertebrae of **(a)** a Mesozoic "beaver" (*Castorocauda lutrasimilis*), **(b)** a modern beaver (*Castor canadensis*), and **(c)** a duck-billed platypus (*Ornithorhynchos anatinus*). Note the similarities in structure.

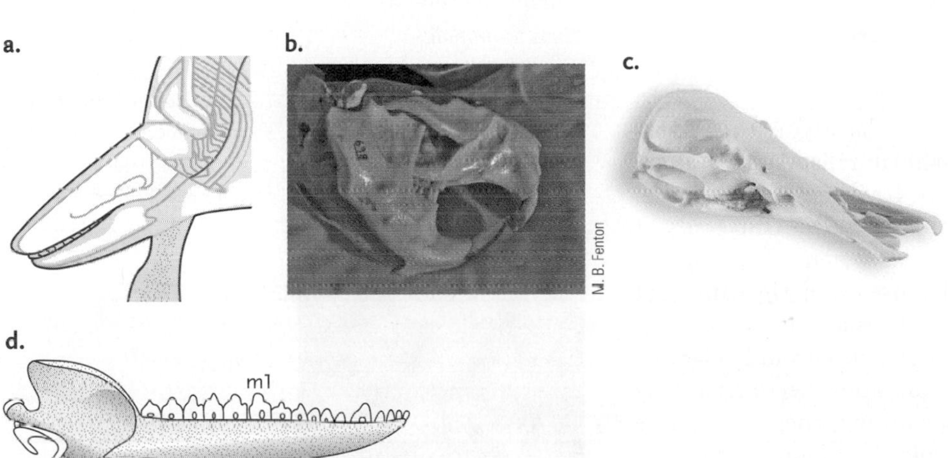

Figure 19.7
A comparison of the skulls of *Castorocauda* (a), *Castor* (b), and *Ornithorhynchus* (c). Although the tails in each species are broad and flat with similarities in caudal vertebrate, the skulls and teeth are different. *Ornithorhynchus* lacks teeth.

Accurate phylogenetic trees are essential components of the comparative method that biologists use to analyze evolutionary processes. Robust phylogenetic hypotheses allow us to distinguish similarities inherited from a common ancestor from those that evolved independently in response to similar environments.

The second goal of systematics is **taxonomy**, the identification and naming of species and their placement in a classification. A **classification** is an arrangement of organisms into hierarchical groups that reflect their relatedness. Most systematists want classifications to mirror phylogenetic history and, thus, the adaptive radiation (evolutionary history) of the group of organisms in question. This is discussed in more detail in Sections 19.4 and 19.5.

Data collected and organized by systematists allow biologists to select appropriate organisms for their work. Many biological experiments are first conducted with individuals of a single species, preferably one that is a closed genetic system that may respond uniquely to experimental conditions. If a researcher inadvertently used two species that responded differently, the mixed results probably would not make much sense. Selecting a species that is androdieocous or gynogenetic (see Chapter 18) could be a mistake—or a canny strategy depending on the research question driving the work.

Study Break

1. What evolutionary process explains why organisms living in the same conditions develop similar body forms?
2. What are two major goals of systematics, and how are they presented?
3. Why are phylogenetic trees essential for comparison and analysis of evolutionary processes?

19.3 The Linnaean System of Classification

The practice of naming and classifying organisms originated with the Swedish naturalist Carl von Linné (1707–1778), better known by his Latinized name, Carolus Linnaeus. A professor at the University of Uppsala, he developed the basic system of naming and classifying organisms still in use today. The naming of newly discovered species follows a formal process of publishing a description of the species in a scientific journal. International commissions meet periodically to settle disputes about scientific names. As we have seen (see Chapter 1), the rules for naming organisms differ between botanists and zoologists.

An effective classification, whether of organisms on Earth or of books in a library, gives users access to information. Linnaeus described and named thousands of species on the basis of their similarities and differences. Keeping track of so many species was no easy task, so he devised a **taxonomic hierarchy** for arranging organisms into ever more inclusive categories (**Figure 19.8**). A **family** is a group of genera that closely resemble one another. Similar families are grouped into **orders**, similar orders into **classes**, similar classes into **phyla** (singular, *phylum*), and similar phyla into **kingdoms.** Finally, all life on Earth is classified into three **domains** (see Chapter 3). The organisms included within any category of the taxonomic hierarchy comprise a **taxon** (plural, *taxa*). Woodpeckers, for example, are a taxon (Picidae) at the family level, and pine trees are a taxon (*Pinus*) at the genus level.

The next step in the study of evolution is determining which species are most closely related to one another. Rather than learning the features that distinguish species A from species B, we want to know which characteristics some species have in common and can be used to place the species in the same genus and family. When Linnaeus focused on external anatomy and considered birds, he noted that all birds are oviparous (egg-laying) animals with feathered bodies, two wings, two feet, and a bony beak. Is this evidence that birds share a common ancestor?

Study Break

1. What is a taxonomic hierarchy?
2. What categories are used in the Linnaean system of classification?

Domain *Eukarya*
Kingdom *Animalia*
Phylum *Chordata*
Class *Mammalia*
Order *Rodentia*
Family *Castoridae*
Genus *Castor*
Species *Castor canadensis*

Figure 19.8
The Linnaean hierarchy of classification. The classification of the Canadian beaver (*Castor canadensis*) reflects its similarity to other species in the genus *Castor* and its placement by family, order, class, phylum, kingdom, and domain.

19.4 From Classification to Phylogeny

For at least 200 years, systematists relied on organismal traits (mainly morphology) when analyzing evolutionary relationships and classifying organisms. In the wake of Linnaeus, they developed phylogenies based on characteristics such as chromosomal anatomy; details of physiological functioning; morphology of subcellular structures, cells, organ systems, and whole organisms; and patterns of behaviour. Today, systematists also use molecular sequences of nucleic acids and proteins as additional characters when deriving phylogenies.

19.5 Evaluating Systematic Characters

Systematists use guidelines to select characters for study. As we saw previously, there is more to being a beaver than being a mammal with a flattened tail. Systematists seek characters that are independent markers of underlying genetic similarity and differentiation. Ideally, systematists create phylogenetic hypotheses and classifications by analyzing the genetic changes that caused speciation and differentiation. But the fossil record is not complete, so often systematists must rely on phenotypic traits as indicators of genetic similarity or divergence. Systematists study traits in which phenotypic variation reflects genetic differences. They try to exclude differences caused by environmental conditions.

Useful systematic characters must be genetically *independent*, reflecting different parts of organisms' genomes. This precaution is necessary because different organismal characters can have the same genetic basis. We want to use each genetic variation only once in an analysis. For example, tropical lizards in the genus *Anolis* can climb trees because they get a grip (purchase) on the bark from small adhesive pads on the underside of their toes. The number of pads varies from species to species and toe to toe. Researchers have used the number of pads on the fourth toe of the left hind foot as a systematic character. They do not use the number of pads on the fourth toe of the right hind foot as a *separate* character because the same genes almost certainly control the number of pads on the toes of both feet. The point here is not the fine-grained detail about toes, but rather the kinds of characters that can be used when assembling a picture of adaptive radiation.

The limbs of tetrapod vertebrates are homologous characters, and they are useful in preparing phylogenies. Such phenotypic similarities between organisms reflect underlying genetic similarities. Systematic analyses rely on the comparison of homologous characters as indicators of common ancestry and genetic relatedness.

Analogous characters are homoplasious (homoplasies), phenotypic similarities that evolved independently in different lineages. For example, the flattened tails of aquatic mammals noted above appear to be homoplasious. By definition, analogous characters serve a similar function in different species. Systematists exclude homoplasies from their analyses because homoplasies provide no information about shared (genetic) ancestry.

But where their function has changed, homologous structures (inherited from a common ancestor) can differ considerably among species. The stapes, a bone in the middle ear of tetrapod vertebrates, evolved from (is homologous to) the hyomandibula, a bone that supports the jaw joint of most fishes. The structure, position, and function of the hyomandibular are different in tetrapods than they are in fishes **(Figure 19.9)**.

The situation can be complex. For example, flight in animals has evolved at least four times (bats, birds, insects, pterosaurs). Bones in the wings of flying vertebrates (bats, birds, and pterosaurs) are homologous **(Figure 19.10, p. 426)**. They have the same basic structural elements (arm, wrist, and hand) with similar spatial relationships to each other and to the bones that attach the wing to the rest of the skeleton (shoulder girdle). Wing bones of bats, birds, and pterosaurs are homologous to the forelimbs of other tetrapods.

But the large flat surfaces of bird wings are homoplasious with those of bats and pterosaurs. The flight surfaces of birds are made of feathers, whereas those of

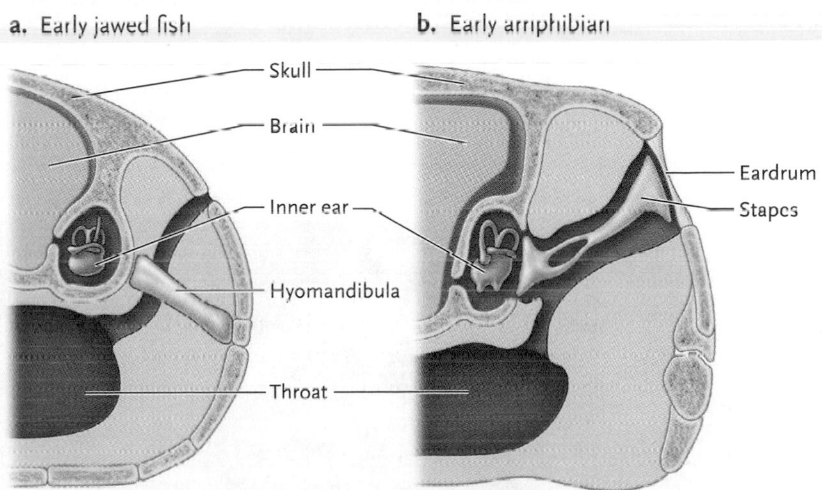

Figure 19.9
Homologous bones, different structures and functions. (a) The hyomandibula, which braced the jaw joint against the skull in early jawed fishes, is homologous to **(b)** the stapes, which transmits sound to the inner ear in four-legged vertebrates, exemplified here by an early amphibian. Both diagrams show a cross section through the head just behind the jaw joint.

Figure 19.10
Arm, hand, and finger bones supporting the wings of a bat **(a)**, a bird **(b)**, and a pterosaur **(c)**. Note the position of the wrists (arrow). In this feature, bats and birds are more similar to one another than either is to the pterosaur.

bats and pterosaurs are made of skin. Therefore, one could assert that in their flight membranes, birds are convergent with bats and pterosaurs.When we add insects to the comparison **(Figure 19.11)**, their wings are surely convergent with those of bats, birds, and pterosaurs. In this situation, the wings of vertebrates could be considered examples of parallel evolution. If you go to the fine details, the basic elements supporting the wings of bats, birds, and pterosaurs are homologous. However, the details of the forearm, hand, and finger bones differ substantially among these three groups of animals. The example of wings illustrates that the distinction between parallel and convergent evolution is based on closeness of relationships.

Homologous characters emerge from comparable embryonic structures and grow in similar ways during development. Systematists have put great stock in embryological indications of homology on the assumption that evolution has conserved the pattern of embryonic development in related organisms. Indeed, recent discoveries in evolutionary developmental biology have revealed that some genetic controls of developmental pathways can be very similar across a wide variety of organisms (e.g., *Pax6* genes control the development of eyes; see Chapters 1 and 39).

Mosaic evolution refers to the reality that in all evolutionary lineages, some characteristics evolve slowly, whereas others evolve rapidly. Mosaic evolution is pervasive. Every species displays a mixture of **ancestral characters** (old forms of traits) and **derived characters** (new forms of traits). Derived characters provide the most useful information about evolutionary relationships because once a derived character becomes established, it is usually present in all of that species' descendants. Thus, unless they are lost or replaced by newer characters over evolutionary time, derived characters can serve as markers for entire evolutionary lineages.

Systematists score characters as either ancestral or derived only when comparing them among organisms. Thus, any particular character is derived *only in relation to* what occurs in other organisms, which could be either an older version of the same character or, in the case of an entirely new trait, the absence of it altogether.

Most species of animals lack a vertebral column, which is a defining feature for vertebrates, the animal lineage that includes fishes, amphibians, reptiles, birds, and mammals. Thus, when systematists compare vertebrates with all animals lacking a vertebral column, they score the absence of a vertebral column as the ancestral condition and the presence of a vertebral column as derived.

Systematists distinguish between ancestral and derived characters to ascertain in which direction a character has evolved. In some cases, the fossil record is detailed enough to provide unambiguous information about the direction of evolution. For example, biologists are confident that the presence of a vertebral

a. Caddis fly

Nature's Images/Photo Researchers, Inc.

b. Orange palm dart butterfly

Neil Bowman/Frank Lane Picture Agency

c. Monarch butterfly

Millard Sharp/Photo Researchers, Inc.

Figure 19.11
Outgroup comparison. Most adult insects, like **(a)** the caddis fly (family Limnephilidae) and **(b)** the orange palm dart butterfly (*Cephrenes auglades*, family Hesperiidae), have six walking legs. This comparison of butterflies with other insects suggests that the four walking legs of the **(c)** monarch butterfly (*Danaeus plexippus*, family Nymphalidae) represent the derived character state.

column is a derived character because fossils of the earliest animals lack backbones.

Systematists frequently use **outgroup comparison** to identify ancestral and derived characters. This involves comparing the group under study with more distantly related species not otherwise included in the analysis. Most modern butterflies have six walking legs. But some species in two families (Nymphalidae and Papillionidae) have four walking legs and two small, nonwalking legs (see Figure 19.11). Which is the ancestral character state, and which is derived? Outgroup comparison with other insects, most of which have six walking legs as adults, suggests that six walking legs is an ancestral character and four is a derived character. The same would apply when trying to understand the almost legless condition of female bagworms (Psychidae), another group of butterflies.

Study Break

1. What are outgroup comparisons?
2. How are ancestral characters different from derived ones?
3. What do *Pax* 6 genes do? Where are they found?

19.6 Phylogenetic Inference and Classification

Phylogenetic trees portray the evolutionary diversification of lineages as a hierarchy that reflects the branching pattern of evolution. Each branch represents the descendants of a single ancestral species. When converting the phylogenetic tree into a classification, systematists use the **principle of monophyly.** They try to define **monophyletic taxa**, those derived from a single ancestral species (**Figure 19.12**). By contrast, **polyphyletic taxa** include species from separate evolutionary lineages. If, based on the presence of wings, bats, birds, pterosaurs, and insects were placed in one taxonomic group (flying animals), it would be polyphyletic. A **paraphyletic taxon** includes an ancestor and some, but not all, of its descendants. The traditional taxon class Reptilia is paraphyletic (see Chapter 27).

Many systematists also strive to create parsimonious phylogenetic hypotheses. Here they include the fewest possible evolutionary changes to account for the diversity within a lineage. The justification of this approach is the **assumption of parsimony**, or that the simplest explanation should be the most accurate. This means that any particular evolutionary change is an unlikely event and presumably happened only once in any evolutionary lineage. Following this assumption, it is unlikely that the same change evolved twice in one lineage. Phylogenetic trees are representations of hypotheses that place all organisms on a single branch. For example, the portrayal of birds on a single evolutionary branch implies that feathered wings evolved once in their common ancestor. This hypothesis is more parsimonious than one proposing that feathered wings evolved independently in two or more vertebrate lineages. The monophyly of birds is not contradicted by the repeated evolution of flightlessness in this group.

19.6a Traditional Evolutionary Systematics: Using Phenotypic Similarities and Differences to Classify Organisms According to Their Evolutionary History

For a century after the publication of Charles Darwin's book *On the Origin of Species by Means of Natural Selection* (see Chapter 20), most systematists followed Linnaeus's practice of using phenotypic similarities and differences to infer evolutionary relationships. This approach, called **traditional evolutionary systematics,** groups together species that share ancestral and derived

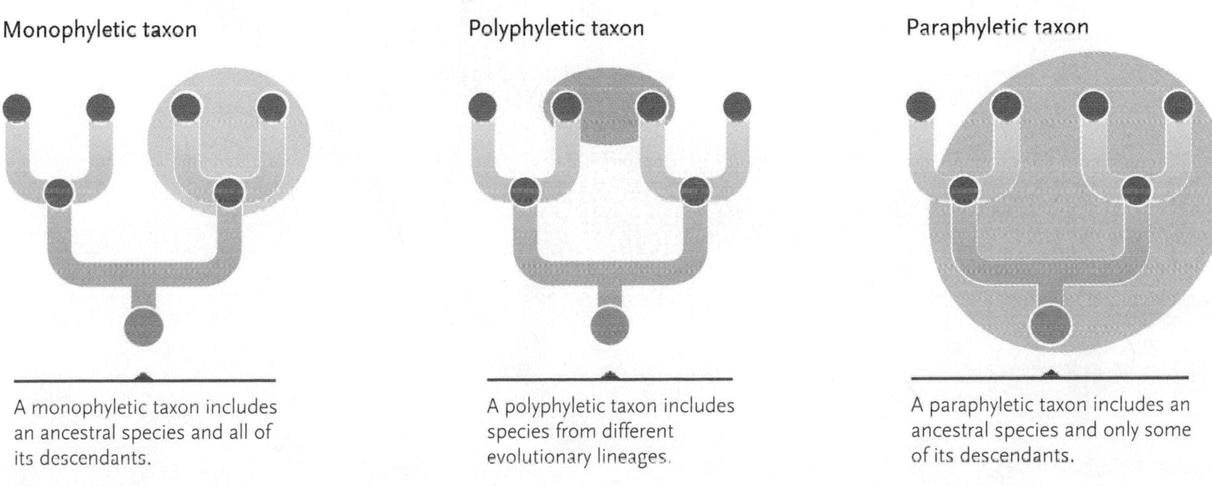

Monophyletic taxon
Polyphyletic taxon
Paraphyletic taxon
A monophyletic taxon includes an ancestral species and all of its descendants.
A polyphyletic taxon includes species from different evolutionary lineages.
A paraphyletic taxon includes an ancestral species and only some of its descendants.

Figure 19.12
Defining taxa in a classification. Systematists can create different classifications from the same phylogenetic tree by identifying different groups of species as a single taxon (shaded).

characters. Mammals are defined by their internal skeleton, vertebral column, and four limbs—ancestral characters among tetrapod vertebrates. But mammals also have hair, mammary glands, and a four-chambered heart (see Chapter 27). These are derived characters.

Classifications produced by traditional systematics reflect evolutionary branching and morphological divergence **(Figure 19.13a)**. Among tetrapod vertebrates, the amphibian and mammalian lineages diverged early, followed shortly by the divergence of the turtle lineage and then that of other reptiles. After this, subsequent divergences produced two groups: lepidosaurs that gave rise to lizards and snakes and archosaurs that gave rise to crocodilians, dinosaurs, and birds. Although crocodilians outwardly resemble lizards, they share a more recent common ancestor with birds. Yet birds differ from crocodilians in many morphological characters.

Even though the phylogenetic tree of tetrapod vertebrates shows six living groups, the traditional classification recognizes four classes: Amphibia, Mammalia, Reptilia, and Aves (birds). These groups (classes in classification) are given equal ranking because each represents a distinctive body plan and way of life. The class Reptilia, however, is a paraphyletic taxon because it includes *some* descendants of the common ancestor (located at A in Figure 19.13a), namely turtles, lizards, snakes, and crocodilians, but omits birds and therefore does not include all of the descendants.

Traditional evolutionary systematists justify this definition of Reptilia because it includes morphologically similar animals with close evolutionary relationships. Crocodilians are classified with lizards, snakes, and turtles because they share a common ancestry and are covered with dry, scaly skin. Traditional systematists also argue that the key innovations thought to have initiated the adaptive radiation of birds—wings, feathers, high metabolic rates, and flight—are extreme divergences from the ancestral morphology. Therefore, birds merit recognition as a separate class.

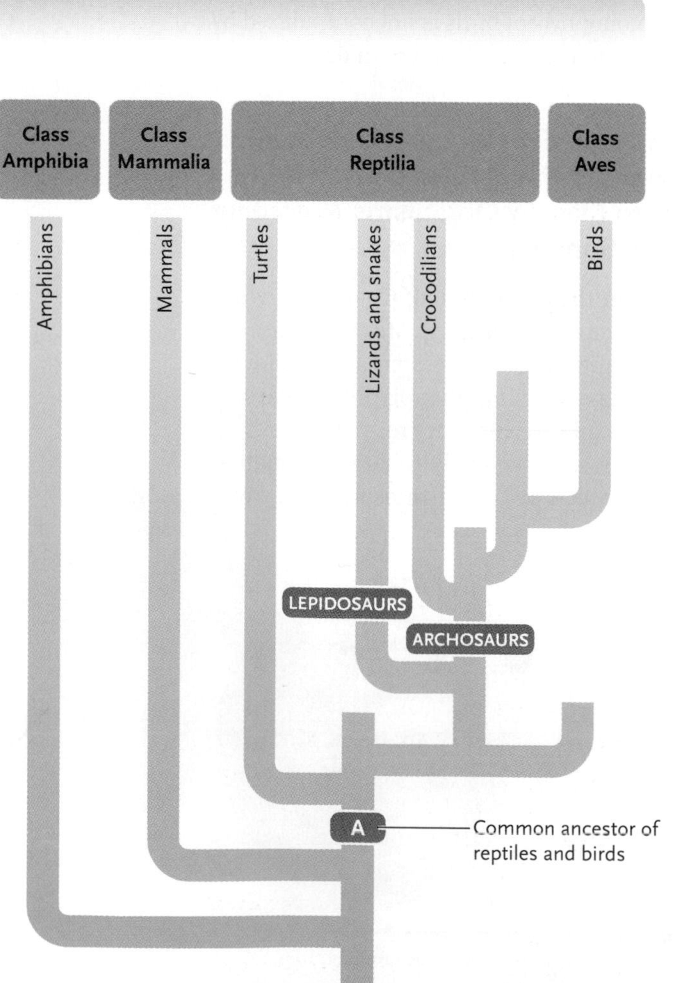

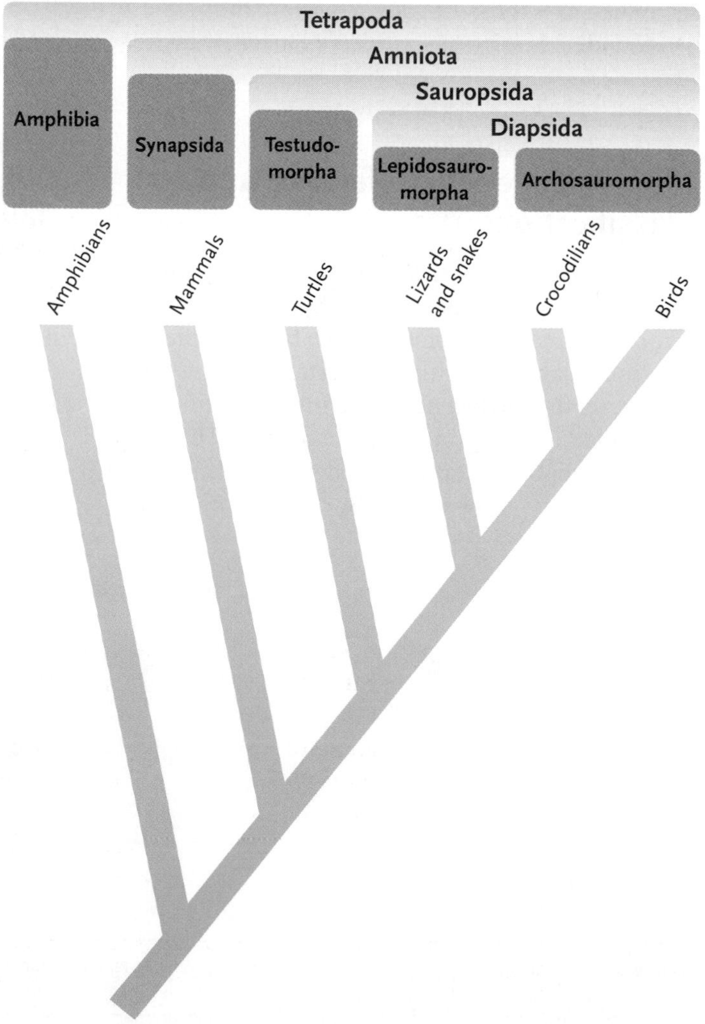

Figure 19.13
Phylogenetic trees and classifications for tetrapod vertebrates. Traditional **(a)** and cladistic **(b)** phylogenies produce different phylogenetic trees and classifications. Classifications are presented above the trees.

19.6b Cladistics: Classifications Based on Shared Derived Characters

Cladistics emerged in the 1950s and 1960s when some researchers criticized the inherent lack of clarity in classifications based on two distinct phenomena, branching evolution and morphological divergence. After all, how can we tell *why* two groups are classified in the same higher taxon? Sometimes they have shared a recent common ancestor (e.g., lizards and snakes), but other times they have not (e.g., lizards and crocodilians).

To minimize such confusion, many systematists followed the philosophical and analytical lead of Willi Hennig, a German entomologist who wrote *Phylogenetic Systematics,* published in 1966. Hennig and his followers argued that classifications should be based solely on evolutionary relationships. **Cladistics** produces phylogenetic hypotheses and classifications that reflect only the branching pattern of evolution. Cladistics ignores morphological divergence.

Cladists group together species that *share derived characters.* Cladists argue that mammals form a monophyletic lineage, a **clade,** because they have a unique set of derived characters, including hair, mammary glands, reduction of bones in the lower jaw, and a four-chambered heart. The ancestral characters found in mammals, such as an internal skeleton, a vertebral column, and four legs, do not distinguish them from other tetrapod vertebrates, so these traits are excluded from analysis.

Phylogenetic trees produced by cladists **(cladograms)** illustrate the hypothesized sequence of evolutionary branchings, with a hypothetical ancestor at each branching point **(Figure 19.13b).** Cladograms portray strictly monophyletic groups and are usually constructed using the principle of parsimony. Once a researcher identifies derived, homologous characters, constructing a cladogram is straightforward (see *Constructing a Cladogram*).

Classifications produced by cladistic analysis often differ radically from those of traditional evolutionary systematics (compare Figure 1a and b in *Constructing a Cladogram*). Pairs of higher taxa are defined directly from the two-way branching pattern of the cladogram. Thus, the clade Tetrapoda (the traditional amphibians, reptiles, birds, and mammals) is divided into two taxa, Amphibia (tetrapods lacking an amnion; see Chapters 27 and Chapter 39) and Amniota (tetrapods with an amnion). Amniota is subdivided into two taxa on the basis of skull morphology and other characteristics, namely Synapsida (mammals) and Sauropsida (turtles, lizards, snakes, crocodilians, and birds). Based on cranial structure, Sauropsida is further divided into Testudomorpha (turtles) and Diapsida (lizards and snakes, crocodilians, and birds). Finally, based on anatomical details, Diapsida is subdivided into two more recently evolved taxa, Lepidosauromorpha (lizards and snakes) and Archosauromorpha (crocodilians and birds). The strictly cladistic classification parallels the pattern of branching evolution that produced the organisms included in the classification. These parallels are the essence and strength of the cladistic method.

Today most biologists use the cladistic approach because of its evolutionary focus, clear goals, and precise methods. Some systematists advocate abandoning the Linnaean hierarchy for classifying and naming organisms. They propose using a strictly cladistic system, called **PhyloCode,** that identifies and names clades instead of placing organisms into the familiar taxonomic groups. However, traditional evolutionary systematics has guided most people's understanding of biological diversity.

Study Break

1. What kinds of traits are studied by systematists?
2. What is the difference between homologous and analogous characters? Which are used in systematics? Why?
3. What is mosaic evolution? Distinguish between ancestral and derived characters.

19.7 Add Molecular Data

Most systematists working on living organisms use molecular characters as part of the data set when conducting phylogenetic analyses. Molecular data include nucleotide base sequences of DNA and RNA or the amino acid sequences of the proteins for which they code. Because DNA is inherited, shared changes in molecular sequences (insertions, deletions, or substitutions) provide clues to the evolutionary relationships of organisms. Technological advances have automated many of the necessary laboratory techniques, and analytical software makes it easy to compare new data with information filed in data banks accessible over the Internet, for example, the Barcode of Life project (see Chapter 3).

Molecular sequences have some practical advantages over organismal characters. First, they provide abundant data because every amino acid in a protein and every base in a nucleic acid can serve as a separate, independent character for analysis. Moreover, because many genes have been conserved by evolution, molecular sequences can be compared between distantly related organisms that share no organismal characteristics. Molecular characters can also be used to study closely related species that have only minor morphological differences. Finally, many proteins and nucleic acids are not directly affected by the developmental or environmental factors that cause nongenetic morphological variations (see Chapter 17).

But there are drawbacks to molecular characters. There are only 4 alternative character states (the

Constructing a Cladogram

Cladograms allow systematists (and others) to visualize hypothesized evolutionary relationships by grouping together organisms that share derived characters. The cladogram also indicates where derived characters evolved.

Here we develop a cladogram for the nine extant groups of chordates, vertebrates, lampreys (Agnatha), sharks (Chondrichthyes), bony fishes (Osteichthyes), amphibians (Amphibia), reptiles (turtles, lizards and snakes, crocodilians), birds, and mammals (see also Chapter 27). We also include lancelets (marine organisms in the subphylum Cephalochordata). Lancelets serve as the outgroup in our comparison.

We have chosen characters on which to base the cladogram **(Table 1)**, noting the presence or absence of (1) a vertebral column (backbone), (2) jaws, (3) a swim bladder or lungs, (4) paired limbs, (5) extraembryonic membranes (the amnion), (6) mammary glands, (7) dry, scaly skin, (8) two openings at the back of the skull (temporal fenestrae), (9) one opening on each side of the skull in front of the eye, and (10) feathers.

The characters are ancestral or derived in each group, but the outgroup (the lancelets) lacks all of these features. We tabulate the presence (+) and absence (−) of characters starting with lancelets and followed, in alphabetical order, by the other organisms (see Table 1).

We construct the cladogram from the information in the table, grouping organisms that share derived characters (right branch, **Figure 1a**), whereas the lancelets form the left branch because they lack the derived characters.

The remaining organisms except lancelets and lampreys have jaws. Now the right branch **(Figure 1b)** includes all living vertebrates sharing derived characters, separating them from lancelets and lampreys. The selection of different characteristics might give different outcomes. For further discussion of the evolution of chordates, see Chapter 27.

Table 1 **The Presence of Derived Characters in Lancelets and Living Chordates**

	Vertebrae	Jaws	Swim Bladder or Lungs	Paired Limbs	Extra-embryonic Membranes	Mammary Glands	Dry, Scaly Skin	Two Openings at Back of Skull	One Opening in Front of Each Eye	Feathers
Lancelets	−	−	−	−	−	−	−	−	−	−
Amphibians	+	+	+	+	−	−	−	−	−	−
Birds	+	+	+	+	+	−	+	+	+	+
Bony fishes	+	+	+	−	−	−	−	−	−	−
Crocodilians	+	+	+	+	+	−	+	+	+	−
Lampreys	+	−	+	+	−	−	−	−	−	−
Lizards	+	+	+	+	+	−	+	+	−	−
Mammals	+	+	+	+	+	+	−	−	−	−
Sharks	+	+	−	−	−	−	−	−	−	−
Turtles	+	+	+	+	+	−	+	−	−	−

Figure 1
The first cladogram **(a)** shows the separation of lancelets from living chordates. The second cladogram **(b)** shows the separation of lancelets and lampreys from most living chordates. Lampreys are chordates, but the cladogram suggests that they are the earliest chordates. These cladograms were prepared from the data in Table 1.

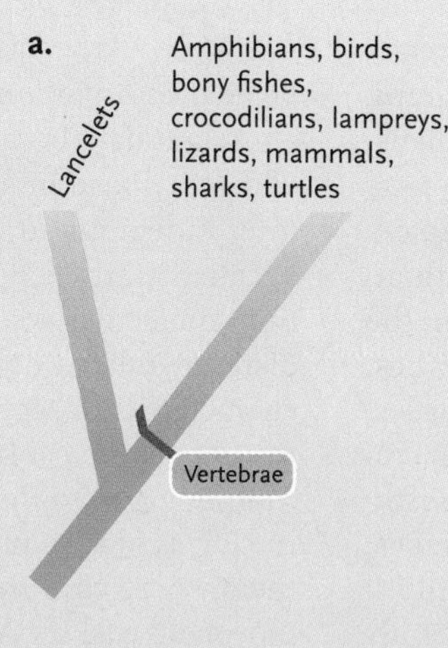

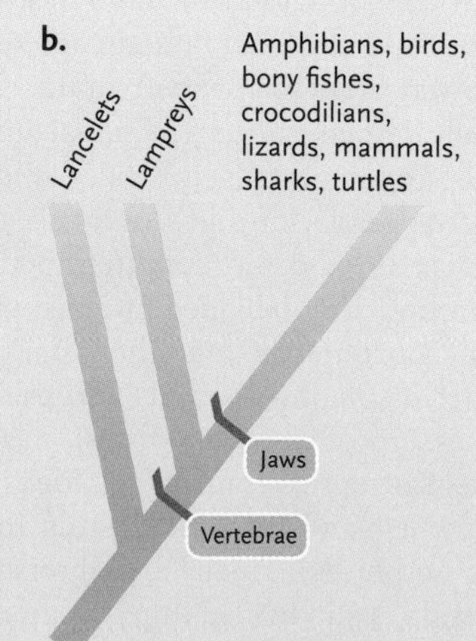

4 nucleotide bases) at each position in a DNA or RNA sequence and only 20 alternative character states (the 20 amino acids) at each position in a protein (see Chapter 12). If two species have the same nucleotide base substitution at a given position in a DNA segment, their similarity may have evolved independently. As a result, systematists often find it difficult to verify that molecular similarities were inherited from a common ancestor.

For organismal characters, biologists can establish that similarities are homologous by analyzing the characters' embryonic development or details of their function. But molecular characters have no embryonic development, and biologists still do not understand the functional significance of most molecular differences. Despite these disadvantages, molecular characters represent the genome directly, and researchers use them with great success in phylogenetic analyses.

19.7a Molecular Clocks: Using Shared Mutations to Estimate Times of Divergences

Molecular phylogenetics is based on the observation that many molecules have been conserved by evolution. But different adaptive changes and neutral mutations accumulate in separate lineages from the moment they first diverge. Mutations in some types of DNA appear to arise at a relatively constant rate. Therefore, differences in the DNA sequences of two species can serve as a **molecular clock**, indexing their time of divergence. Large differences imply divergence in the distant past. Small differences suggest a more recent common ancestor.

Mosaic evolution occurs at the molecular level, so different molecules exhibit individual rates of change, and each molecule is an independent clock ticking at its own rate. Researchers study different molecules to track evolutionary divergences over different time scales.

Mitochondrial DNA (mtDNA) evolves relatively quickly; it is useful for dating evolutionary divergences that occurred within the last few million years. Studies of mtDNA have illuminated aspects of the evolutionary history of humans, as described in Chapter 27. By contrast, chloroplast DNA (cpDNA) and genes that encode ribosomal RNA evolve much more slowly, providing information about divergences that are hundreds of millions of years old.

To synchronize molecular clocks, some researchers study DNA sequences that are not parts of protein-encoding genes. Because they don't affect protein structure, mutations in these sequences are probably not often eliminated by natural selection. Thus, sequence differences between species in noncoding areas probably result from mutation alone and therefore reflect the ticking of the molecular clock more directly. Some researchers also calibrate molecular clocks to the fossil record, so that actual times of divergence can be estimated from molecular data with a fair degree of certainty.

19.7b Extracting Molecular Data: Using Segments of Nucleic Acid for Analysis

Molecular phylogenetics relies on the same basic logic that underlies analyses based on organismal characters. Species that diverged recently from a common ancestor should share many similarities in their molecular sequences, whereas more distantly related species should exhibit fewer similarities. Nevertheless, the practice of molecular phylogenetics is based on a set of distinctive methods.

After selecting a protein molecule or appropriate segment of a nucleic acid for analysis, systematists determine the exact sequence of amino acids (in the case of proteins) or nucleotide bases (in the case of DNA or RNA) that comprise the molecule.

Amino acid sequencing allows systematists to compare the primary structure of protein molecules directly. In Chapters 12 and 13, we learned that the amino acid sequence of a protein is determined by the sequence of nucleotide bases in the gene encoding that protein. When two species exhibit similar amino acid sequences for the same protein, systematists infer their genetic similarity and evolutionary relationship. Researchers have used sequence data from the protein cytochrome *c* to construct a phylogenetic tree for organisms as different as slime moulds, vascular plants, and humans (see *Using Amino Acid Sequences to Construct a Phylogenetic Tree*).

Most systematic studies are now based, at least in part, on DNA sequencing data, which provide a detailed view of the genetic material that is changed by evolutionary processes. The polymerase chain reaction (PCR) makes it easy for researchers to produce numerous copies of specific segments of DNA (see Chapter 16) for comparison. This technique allows scientists to sequence minute quantities of DNA taken from dried or preserved specimens in museums and even from some fossils.

19.7c Aligning Molecular Sequences: Correcting for the Effects of Insertions and Deletions

Before comparing molecular sequences from different organisms, a systematist must ensure that the homologous sequences being compared are properly "aligned." We compare nucleotide bases or amino acids at exactly the same positions in the nucleic acid or protein molecule because mutations often change along the length of a DNA sequence. This can change the relative locations of specific positions through the insertion or deletion of base pairs, making sequence comparisons more difficult. By determining where insertions or deletions have occurred, systematists can match up (align) the positions of nucleotides for comparison. Although alignments can be done "by eye," they often are done using computer programs **(Figure 19.14, p. 433)**.

Using Amino Acid Sequences to Construct a Phylogenetic Tree

Amino acid sequences of proteins change over evolutionary time, so differences in sequences between organisms should reflect evolutionary patterns. We expect closely related species to have similar amino acid sequences compared with distantly related species. Using amino acid sequences of cytochrome *c* from eukaryotic organisms classified in four different kingdoms, biologists developed a phylogenetic tree. Cytochrome *c* is a protein in the electron transport system that has been conserved in evolution (see Chapter 6).

The amino acid sequences of cytochrome *c* are surprisingly similar across organisms from evolutionary lines that have been distinct for millions of years. In **Figure 1,** gold shading marks amino acids that are identical in sequences for yeast (top row), wheat (middle row), and humans (bottom row).

Using similarities and differences in cytochrome c sequences, biologists constructed a phylogenetic tree **(Figure 2).** The vertical axis gives approximate time for each evolutionary branching estimated from amino acid sequence data. The exercise demonstrates how differences in amino acid sequences can be used to construct phylogenetic trees for organisms that share virtually no organismal characters.

Yeast

$^{+}NH_3$-GDVEKGKKIFIMKCSQCHTVEKGGKHKTGPNLHGLFGRKTGQAPGYSYTAANKNKGIIWGEDTLMEYLENPKKYIPGTKMIFVGIKKKEERADLIAYLKKATNE-COO^-

Wheat

$^{+}NH_3$-ASFSEAPPGNPDAGAKIFKTKCAQCHTVDAGAGHKQGPNLHGLFGRQSGTTAGYSYSAANKNKAVEWEENTLYDYLLNPKKYIPGTKMVFPGLKKPQDRADLIAYLKKATSS-COO^-

Human

$^{+}NH_3$-TEFKAGSAKKGATLFKTRCLQCHTVEKGGPHKVGPNLHGIFGRHSGQAEGYSYTDANIKKNVLWDENNMSEYLTNPKKYIPGTKMAFGGLKKEKDRNDLITYLKKACE-COO^-

Figure 1
Amino acid sequences of cytochrome *c* for yeast, wheat, and humans. Gold shading marks areas where the organisms are similar.

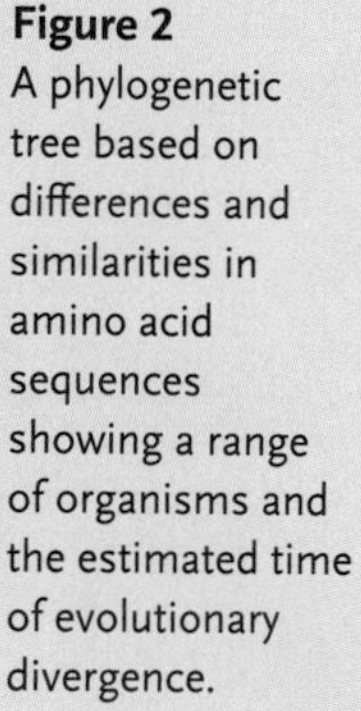

Figure 2
A phylogenetic tree based on differences and similarities in amino acid sequences showing a range of organisms and the estimated time of evolutionary divergence.

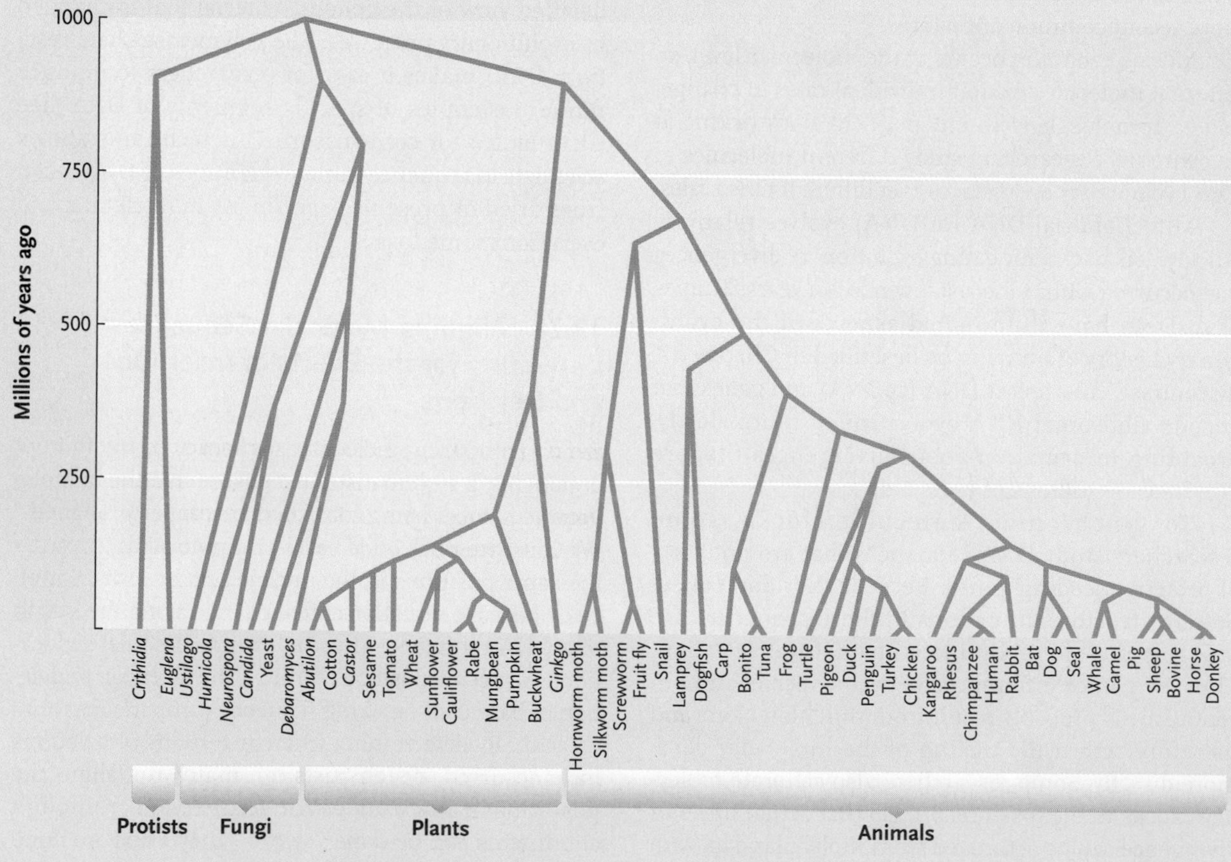

People Behind Biology
Alfred Sherwood Romer

Our knowledge of the evolution of vertebrate animals was strongly influenced by the work of Alfred Sherwood Romer (1894–1973). Romer's interest in fossils was sparked in his childhood by visits to the American Museum of Natural History, particularly the dinosaur exhibits there. His Ph.D. thesis, submitted to Columbia University, was a classic contribution to the study of muscles in vertebrates and led to his many contributions in the fields of functional anatomy and evolution.

His textbook *Vertebrate Paleontology* first appeared in 1933 and went through three editions, influencing the studies and academic development of many students of vertebrate evolution. He moved to Harvard University in 1945 to become director of the Biological Laboratories and the Museum of Comparative Zoology.

One of his main research foci was the evolution of pelycosaurian reptiles (see Chapter 27), and he continued to be active as a researcher after his retirement from Harvard in 1965. Romer is an example of an academic whose contributions spanned the spectrum from his own research endeavours to presenting information to students (through texts such as *Vertebrate Paleontology* and *The Vertebrate Body*) and as an academic leader in the various positions he filled. He was an enthusiastic and articulate speaker with a great talent for presenting his material in a format that was readily accessible to students.

Once the molecules are aligned, a systematist can compare the nucleotide base or amino acid sequences and determine whether mutations or other processes have produced evolutionary changes in the sequences. Similarities and differences can then be used to reconstruct a phylogenetic tree. Each phylogenetic tree is a hypothesis about evolutionary relationships, and different assumptions can yield alternative trees for any data set. Indeed, systematists have developed several approaches for comparing molecular sequences and constructing trees.

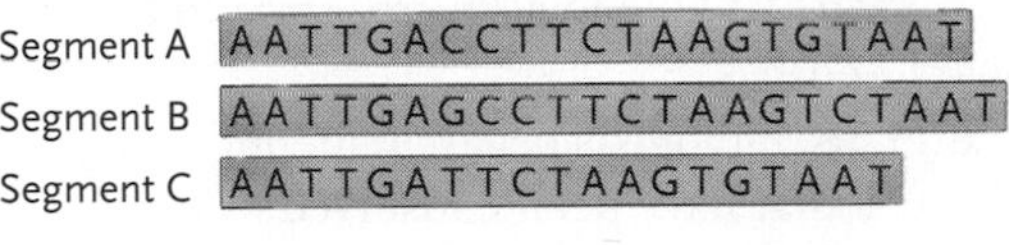

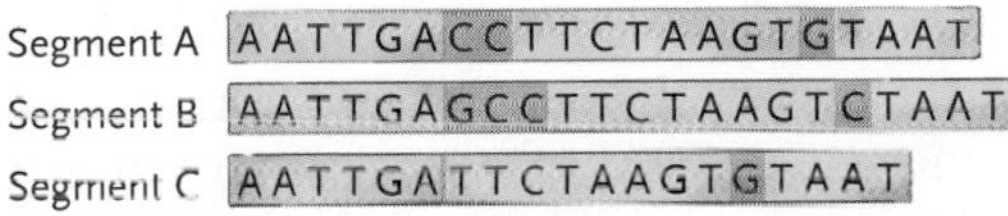

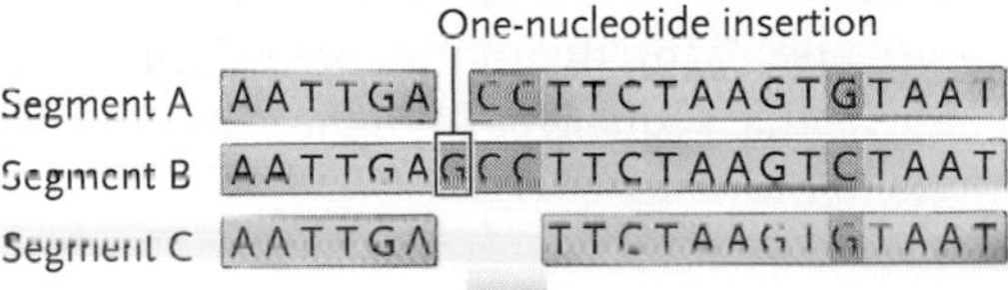

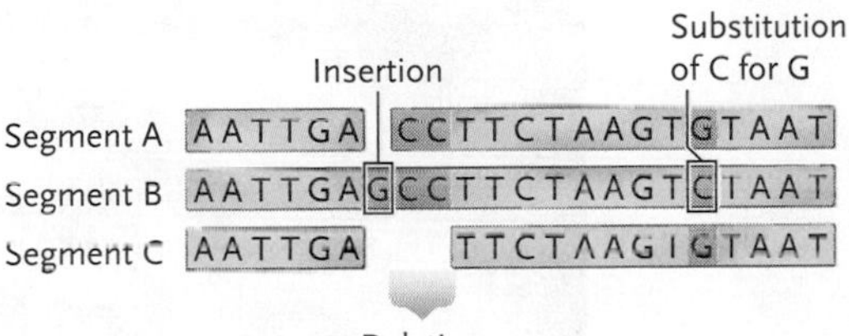

Figure 19.14
Insertion or deletion of base pairs can change the length of a DNA sequence and the relative locations of the specific positions along its length. Therefore, systematists "align" the sequences they are comparing to ensure that the nucleotide bases being compared are at exactly the same positions in the nucleic acid molecules. By determining where insertions or deletions have occurred, systematists match up the positions of the nucleotides. In this hypothetical example, DNA sequences were obtained from three species and aligned.

For DNA sequences, the simplest approach is to count the number of similarities and differences between each pair of organisms being compared. Systematists use data from these comparisons to estimate *genetic distances* between species and construct a phylogenetic tree by grouping together organisms exhibiting the smallest genetic distances. This approach, however, can produce phylogenies based on both ancestral and derived characters. Recall that this is the same problem involved in traditional evolutionary systematics.

Using cladistics and the principle of parsimony, molecular sequence data can be converted into a phylogenetic tree. To achieve this requires identification of ancestral and derived character states. For each position in the sequence, systematists must determine which nucleotide bases are ancestral and which are derived. As for organismal characters, analysis of homologous sequences in a designated outgroup can provide information that allows researchers to distinguish between ancestral and derived conditions. In the parsimony approach, a computer program is used to test all possible phylogenetic trees and identify the one that accounts for the diversity of organisms in the group using the fewest evolutionary changes in molecular sequences.

In recent years, researchers have faulted the parsimony approach because identical changes in nucleotides can arise independently. To avoid this problem, systematists have begun to use a series of statistical techniques collectively known as *maximum likelihood methods*. This approach reconstructs phylogenetic history from molecular sequence data by making assumptions about variations in the rate at which different segments of DNA evolve. These statistical models can take into account variations in the rates of evolution between genes or between species as well as changes in evolutionary rates over time. Maximum likelihood programs construct numerous alternative phylogenetic trees and estimate how likely it is that each tree represents the true evolutionary history. Systematists then accept the phylogenetic tree that is most likely to be true until more data are available.

Study Break

1. What are some advantages and disadvantages to using molecular data as clues to the evolutionary relationships among organisms?
2. How can the concept of a molecular clock indicate the time of divergence for traits? What are two types of DNA used for dating evolutionary divergence, and when are they used?
3. Why must molecular sequences be aligned before they are compared?

19.8 Clarifications from Molecular Phylogenetics

Analyses of morphological data sometimes produced conflicting hypotheses about the origin and relationships of flowering plants. Molecular phylogenetics have been used to resolve these conflicts. In 1999, four teams of researchers, analyzing different parts of flowering plant genomes, independently identified *Amborella trichopoda*, a bush native to the South Pacific island of New Caledonia, as a living representative of the most ancient group of flowering plants yet discovered **(Figure 19.15)**. The first team to publish their results, Sarah Mathews and Michael Donoghue, studied phytochrome genes (*PHYA* and *PHYC*) that had duplicated early in the evolutionary history of this group. Other researchers, who studied chloroplast, mitochondrial, and ribosomal sequences, obtained similar results, providing strong support for this phylogenetic hypothesis.

On a grander scale, molecular phylogenetics has revolutionized our view of the entire tree of life (look back at Figure 3.7). The first efforts to create a phylogenetic tree for all forms of life were based on morphological analyses that did not resolve branches of the tree containing prokaryotes. Prokaryotes lack significant structural variability to allow earlier efforts to resolve their relationships to eukaryotes.

In the 1960s and early 1970s, biologists organized living systems into five kingdoms. Prokaryotes were grouped in the kingdom Monera. Eukaryotes were grouped into four kingdoms, Fungi, Plantae, Animalia, and Protista. Protista was always recognized as a polyphyletic "grab bag" of unicellular or acellular eukaryotic organisms. Phylogenetic analyses based on morphology were unable to sort Protista into distinct evolutionary lineages.

In the 1970s, biologists began to identify and analyze molecules that have been conserved by evolution over billions of years. Carl R. Woese identified the small subunit of ribosomal RNA (rRNA) as a suitable molecule for analysis. Ribosomes, the structures that translate messenger RNA molecules into proteins (see Chapter 13), are remarkably similar in all forms of life. Ribosomes are so essential to cellular processes that the genes specifying their structure exhibit similarities in nucleotide sequences in organisms ranging from bacteria to humans.

Figure 19.15
The ancestral flowering plant. DNA sequencing studies identified *Amborella trichopoda* **(a)** as a living representative of the earliest group of flowering plants. Its flower is shown in **(b)**.

a. *Amborella trichopoda* branch

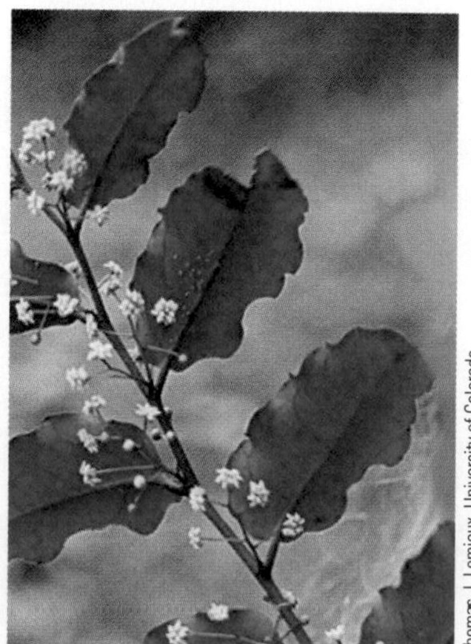

Thomas J. Lemieux, University of Colorado

b. *Amborella trichopoda* flower

Sandra Floyd, University of Colorado

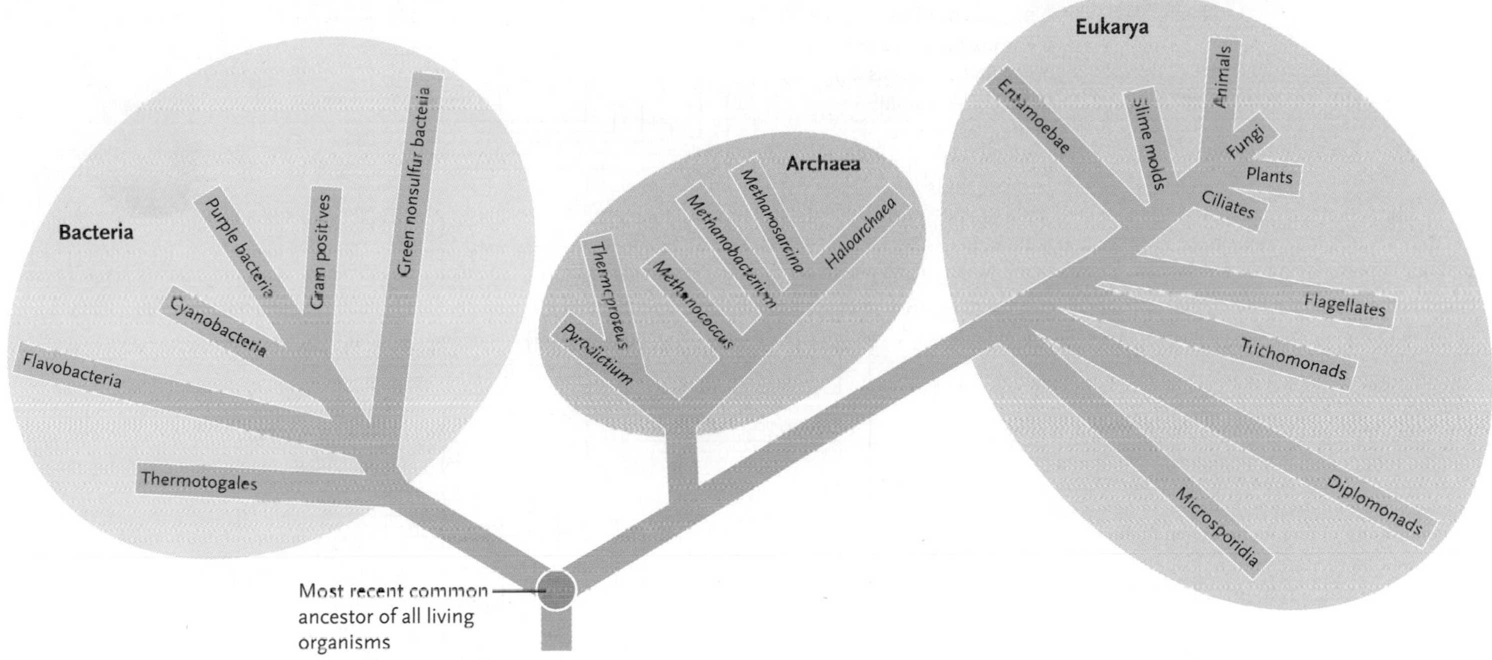

Figure 19.16
Three domains: the tree of life. Carl R. Woese's 1996 analysis of rRNA sequences suggests that all living organisms can be classified into one of three domains, identified here on branches shaded in different colours.

The phylogenetic tree based on rRNA sequences divides living organisms into three primary lineages called domains: Bacteria, Archaea, and Eukarya **(Figure 19.16)**. According to this hypothesis, two domains, Bacteria and Archaea, include prokaryotic organisms, and one, Eukarya, includes eukaryotes. Bacteria includes well-known microorganisms, and Archaea comprises microorganisms that live in physiologically harsh environments, such as hot springs or very salty habitats. Eukarya includes the familiar animals, plants, and fungi, as well as the many lineages formerly included among the Protista.

Study Break

1. What characters (features) do systematists use when constructing phylogenetic trees?
2. What constitutes a "kingdom" in biology? Name four kingdoms.

19.9 Putting It Together

Returning to the evolution of carnivory in plants, we can see how phylogeny derived from nucleotide sequence data helped clarify the situation **(Figure 19.17, p. 436)**. The plastid gene *rbcL* encodes a large subunit of ribulolse-1,5-biphosphate carboxylase/oxygenase (rubisco). This is a primary enzyme in the Calvin cycle (see Chapter 7). Rates of substitution in *rbcL* make it well suited to parsimony analyses in seed plants. This work made it easier to understand the evolution of carnivory in plants and their adaptive radiation.

When traditional data are combined with molecular data, we can see advances in our understanding of evolution and adaptive radiation. Bats provide an interesting example. Today there are ~1100 species arrayed in 17 families and distributed worldwide aside from remote oceanic islands and the polar regions. The first known fossil bats are found in Eocene rocks, dating to about 50 million years ago. At that time, the fossil record contains the remains of species from at least 10 families of bats. From 1990 to 2005, more fossil bats have been discovered, and detailed phylogenetic analyses of molecular (living bats) and morphological data (living and fossil bats) have changed our understanding of the relationships among families **(Figure 19.18, p. 436)**. The combination of molecular evidence with detailed morphological analyses of living and fossil species is responsible for our new view of their evolution. However, the ancestors of bats remain undiscovered.

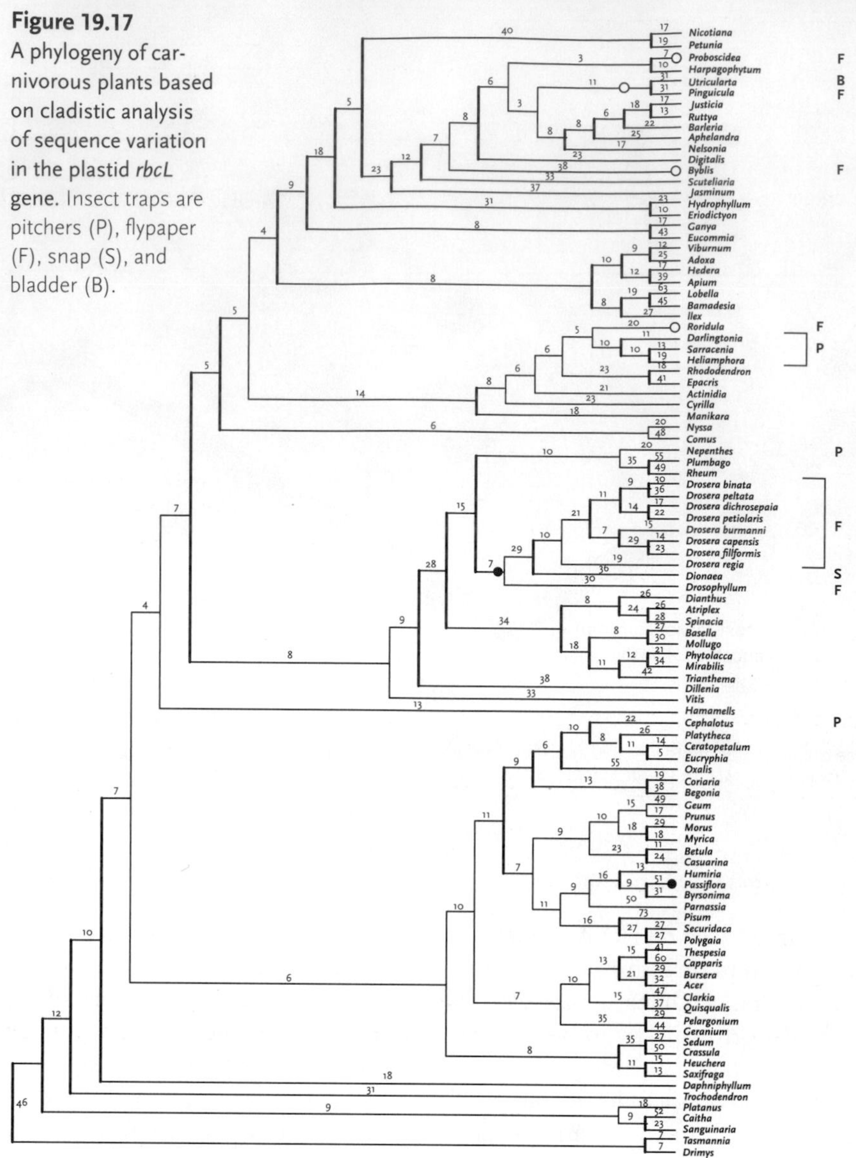

Figure 19.17
A phylogeny of carnivorous plants based on cladistic analysis of sequence variation in the plastid *rbcL* gene. Insect traps are pitchers (P), flypaper (F), snap (S), and bladder (B).

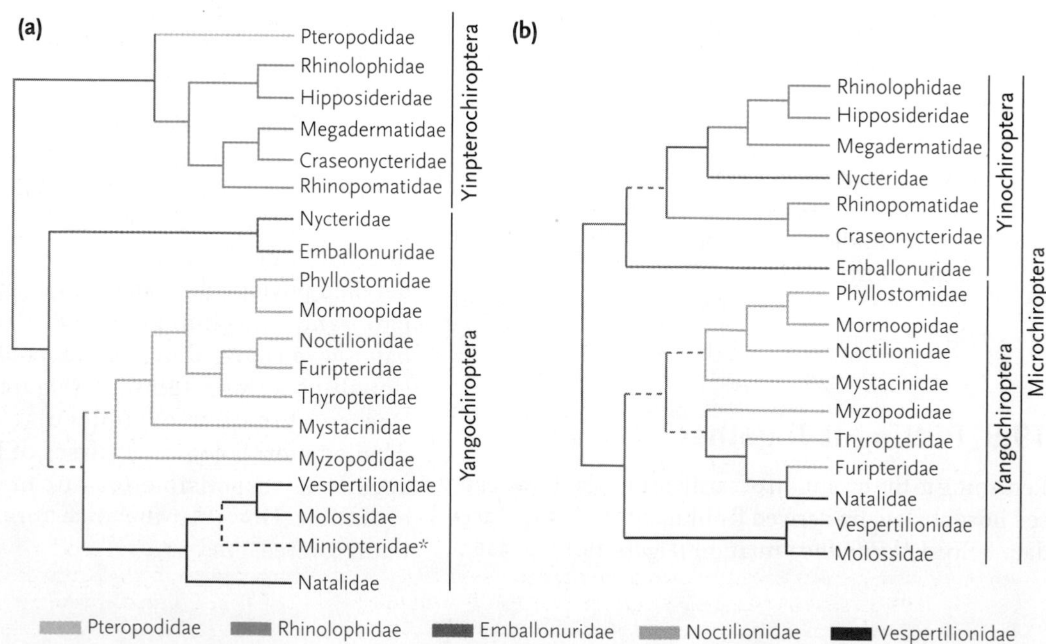

Figure 19.18
A comparison of two phylogenies of bats identifies the changes in our view of the relationships between families with the publication of additional molecular and morphological data. The newer view **(a)** is substantially different in many details from the more traditional one **(b)**.

Unanswered Questions

To what extent should systematists be able to use data about the structure of chemicals used by organisms? Included could be odourants used to attract pollinators or venom used to immobilize prey.

Think back to the origin of life (see Chapter 2) and the tree of life (see Figure 3.7). Do you think that all living organisms are monophyletic? Diphyletic? Polyphyletic? What data would you use to support your point of view?

Review

Go to CENGAGENOW™ at http://hed.nelson.com/ to access quizzing, animations, exercises, articles, and personalized homework help.

19.2 Systematic Biology and Classification

- Convergent evolution refers more to distantly related organisms and parallel evolution to more closely related ones. The evolution of flight is convergent between insects (phylum Arthropoda) and vertebrates (phylum Chordata, birds, pterosaurs, and bats) and parallel within the vertebrates.
- Systematics is used to reconstruct the phylogeny (evolutionary history) of a group of organisms and is portrayed as a phylogenetic tree. Systematics also assists in the identification and naming of species and their placement in a classification. A classification arranges organisms into hierarchical groups reflecting their relatedness.
- Phylogenetic trees can be used to distinguish similarities inherited from a common ancestor from those that evolved independently (e.g., wings).
- A taxonomic hierarchy arranges organisms into ever more exclusive categories. In the Linnaean system, a family is a group of genera that closely resemble one another. Families are grouped into orders, orders into classes, etc.
- Organisms are classified based on features such as morphological traits; chromosomal anatomy; gene sequences; details of physiological functioning; morphology of subcellular structures, cells, and organ systems; and patterns of behaviour.

19.5 Evaluating Systematic Characters

- In preparing a phylogeny, systematists seek traits in which phenotypic variation reflects genetic differences rather than environmental variation. Systematists also use genetically independent traits, which reflect different parts of an organism's genome.
- Homologous characters have been inherited from a common ancestor, so phenotypic similarities between organisms reflect underlying genetic similarities. Homologous characters can differ considerably among species. Analogous (homoplasious) characters are phenotypically similar and have similar functions but evolved independently in different lineages.
- Systematists compare homologous characters to determine common ancestry and genetic relatedness. They exclude analogous structures because they provide no information about shared ancestry or genetic relatedness.
- Mosaic evolution refers to the reality that some characteristics evolve more slowly or more quickly than others. Ancestral characters are old forms of traits, and derived characters are new forms. Once a derived characteristic becomes established, it occurs in all the species' descendants and is a marker for evolutionary lineages.
- An outgroup comparison can be used to identify ancestral and derived traits because it compares the group under study with more distantly related species not otherwise included in the analysis.

19.6 Phylogenetic Inference and Classification

- A monophyletic taxon is a group of species derived from a single ancestral species. A polyphyletic taxon includes species from separate evolutionary lineages. A paraphyletic taxon includes an ancestor and some, but not all, of its descendants.
- According to the principle of parsimony, any particular evolutionary change is a rare event, unlikely to have occurred twice in one lineage. Therefore, the fewest possible evolutionary changes should be used to account for within-lineage diversity.
- Traditional evolutionary systematics groups together species that share what are considered to be ancestral and derived characters. Classifications reflect evolutionary branching and morphological divergence. Cladistics investigates branching patterns of evolution, ignoring morphological divergence. Cladistics groups together species sharing derived characters and uses cladograms based on the principle of parsimony to illustrate sequences of evolutionary branching and the ancestors at each branching point.

19.7 Add Molecular Data

- Every amino acid in a protein and every base in a nucleic acid can serve as independent characters for analysis. DNA can be compared between distantly related species sharing no organismal characteristics and between closely related species exhibiting minor morphological differences. Molecular data are not affected by developmental and environmental factors.
- It can be difficult to verify that similarities at the molecular level were inherited from a common ancestor because there are only 4 DNA bases and only 20 amino acids. The same base substitution in a given DNA segment may have evolved independently in two different species.
- Mutations in certain types of DNA appear at a constant rate, so the DNA sequences of two species can index their time of divergence, with large differences implying divergence in the distant past and small differences suggesting a more recent common ancestor.
- When molecular clocks can be calibrated to the fossil record, biologists can predict the times of evolutionary divergence. Mitochondrial DNA evolves relatively quickly, making it useful for dating evolutionary divergences that occurred within the last few million years. Choloroplast DNA evolves much more slowly, providing information about divergences that are hundreds of millions of years old.
- DNA molecules must be aligned to allow for comparison of changes in bases or amino acids. The comparisons must be made at exactly the same positions because mutations often change along the length of a DNA sequence. After alignment, sequences can be compared to determine if mutations or other processes have produced evolutionary changes in the sequences. Similarities and differences can then be used to construct phylogenetic trees.
- Maximum likelihood methods are statistical techniques used to reconstruct phylogenetic history from molecular sequence data. These methods make assumptions about variations because identical changes in nucleotides can arise independently and

there are variations in the rates at which different segments of DNA evolve. Maximum likelihood methods account for variations in the rates of evolution between genes or species, as well as over time. The process involves constructing numerous phylogenetic trees and selecting the one that best represents the true evolutionary history.

Questions

Self-Test Questions

1. A phylogenetic tree portrays the ____________ of a group of organisms.
   a. classification
   b. evolutionary history
   c. domain
   d. distribution
   e. all of the above
2. Species in the same genus should
   a. belong to the same family.
   b. share a recent common evolutionary history.
   c. be animals.
   d. be plants.
   e. reproduce sexually.
3. When systematists use morphological or behavioural traits to reconstruct the evolutionary history of a group of animals, they assume that
   a. phenotypic characters reflect underlying genetic similarities and differences.
   b. the animals use exactly the same traits to identify appropriate mates.
   c. these traits were responsible for speciation events in the past.
   d. the adaptive value of these traits can be explained.
   e. variations are produced by environmental effects during development.
4. Which statement best describes the concept of mosaic evolution?
   a. Some phenotypic variation is caused by environmental factors.
   b. Homologous characters are inherited from a common ancestor.
   c. Different organismal traits may reflect the same part of an organism's genome.
   d. Some characters evolve more quickly than others.
   e. The fossil record provides clues about the ancestral versions of characters.
5. Which of the following pairs of structures are homoplasious?
   a. the wing skeleton of a bird and the wing skeleton of a bat
   b. the wing of a bird and the wing of a fly
   c. the eye of a fish and the eye of a human
   d. the bones in the foot of a duck and the bones in the foot of a chicken
   e. the wing structures of a pterosaur and those of a bird
6. Which of the following does *not* help systematists determine which version of a morphological character is ancestral and which is derived?
   a. outgroup comparison
   b. patterns of embryonic development
   c. studies of the fossil record
   d. studies of the character in more related species
   e. dating of the character by molecular clocks
7. In a cladistic analysis, a systematist groups together organisms that share
   a. derived homologous traits.
   b. derived homoplasious traits.
   c. ancestral homologous traits.
   d. ancestral homoplasious traits.
   e. all of the above.
8. A monophyletic taxon includes
   a. an ancestor and all of its descendants.
   b. an ancestor and some of its descendants.
   c. organisms from different evolutionary lineages.
   d. an ancestor and those descendants that still resemble it.
   e. organisms that resemble each other because they live in similar environments.
9. Which of the following is *not* an advantage of using molecular characters in a systematic analysis?
   a. Molecular characters provide abundant data.
   b. Systematists can compare molecules among morphologically similar species.
   c. Systematists can compare molecules among species that share few morphological characters.
   d. Amino acid sequences in proteins are generally not influenced by environmental factors.
   e. Systematists can easily determine if nucleotide base substitutions in DNA are homologous.
10. To construct a cladogram by applying the principles of parsimony to molecular sequence data, one would
    a. start by making assumptions about variations in the rates at which different DNA segments evolve.
    b. group together organisms sharing the largest number of ancestral sequences.
    c. group together organisms that share derived sequences, matching the groups to those defined by morphological characters.
    d. group together organisms sharing derived sequences, minimizing the number of hypothesized evolutionary changes.
    e. identify derived sequences by studying the embryology of the organisms.

Questions for Discussion

1. Systematists use both amino acid sequences and DNA sequences to determine evolutionary relationships. Think about the genetic code (DNA structure; see Chapter 13) and explain why phylogenetic hypotheses based on DNA sequences may be more accurate than those based on amino acid sequences.
2. Traditional evolutionary systematists identify the Reptilia as one class of vertebrates, even though this taxon is paraphyletic. What are the advantages and disadvantages of defining paraphyletic taxa in a classification?
3. The table below includes information about the distribution of ancestral and derived states for six systematic characters (1 through 6) in five species (A through E). A "d" denotes the presence of the derived form of the character and an "a" the ancestral form. Construct a cladogram for the five species using the principle of parsimony. Assume that each derived character evolved only once in this group of organisms. Mark the branches of the cladogram to show where each character changed from the ancestral to the derived state.

	Character					
Species	**1**	**2**	**3**	**4**	**5**	**6**
A	a	a	a	a	a	a
B	d	a	a	a	a	d
C	d	d	d	a	a	a
D	d	d	d	a	d	a
E	d	d	a	d	a	a

A fossil ammonite

M. B. Fenton

Study Plan

20 Darwin, Fossils, and Developmental Biology

Why It Matters

Many cities and towns are built on the remains of earlier life. Medicine Hat, Alberta, is a good example **(Figure 20.1, p. 440)**. There the South Saskatchewan River has cut a deep valley through sediments. Every year, more and more fossils are eroded from the river's banks, providing paleontologists with a picture of life in the area over the last ~100 000 years (dating back to the Pleistocene). Many of the animals we find there as fossils do not occur in the area today. Equids, camels, several species of ground sloths, sabre-toothed cats, mammoths, and other species disappeared by 11 000 years ago. The horses (equids; see Chapter 27) there today are descendants of those reintroduced by European explorers and settlers beginning with the Spanish. Humans probably lived along the South Saskatchewan River before many of these now extinct species disappeared.

Imagine looking out and seeing a giant ground sloth (*Megalotherium*) or a sabre-toothed cat (*Smilodon*) in your garden. This would have been possible 15 000 years ago. Look at the roster of mammals (see Figure 20.1). But sharks' teeth have also been found in the deposits. Does that mean that swimmers in the South

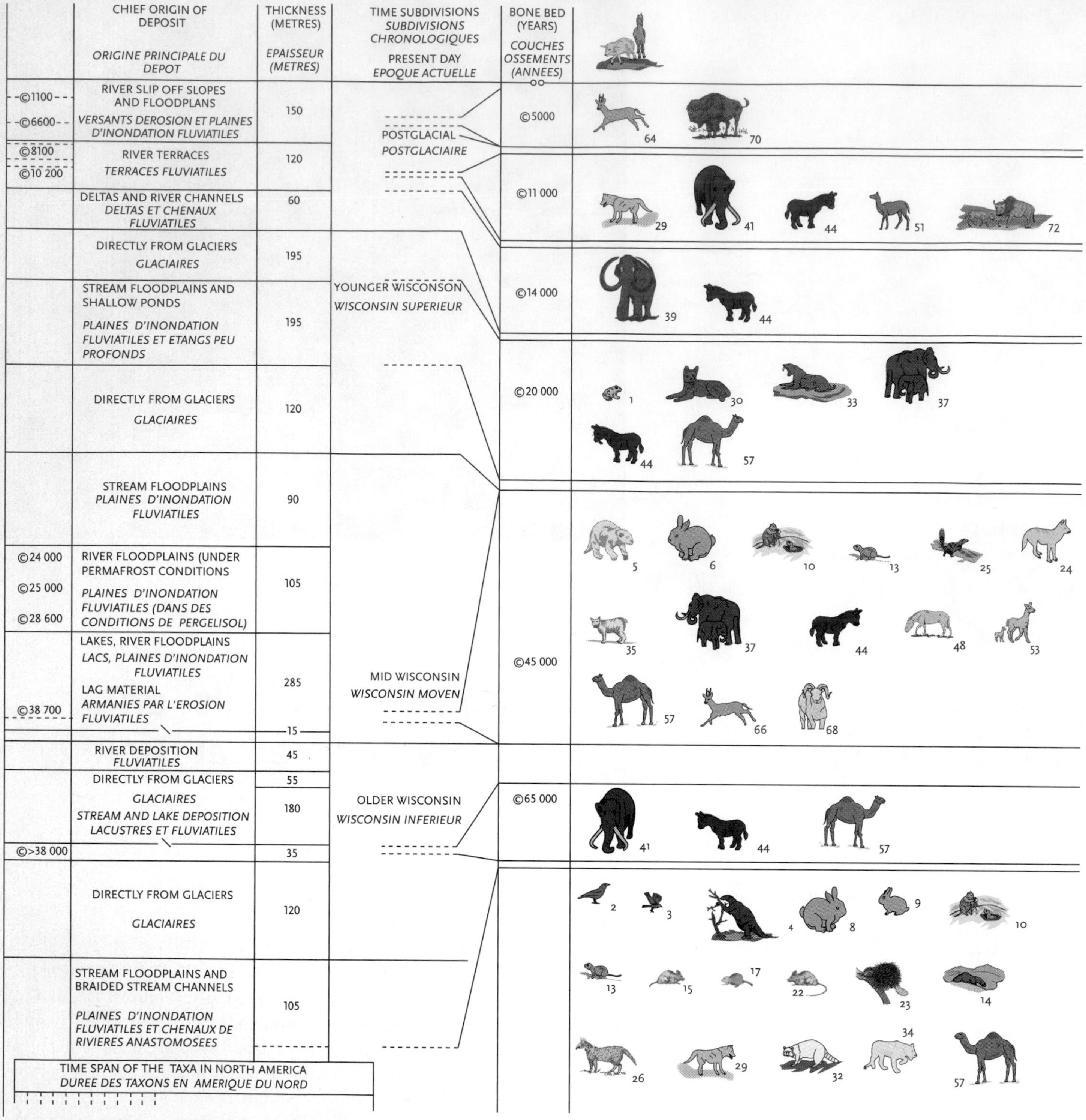

	CHIEF ORIGIN OF DEPOSIT *ORIGINE PRINCIPALE DU DEPOT*	THICKNESS (METRES) *EPAISSEUR (METRES)*	TIME SUBDIVISIONS *SUBDIVISIONS CHRONOLOGIQUES* PRESENT DAY *EPOQUE ACTUELLE*	BONE BED (YEARS) *COUCHES OSSEMENTS (ANNEES)*	
©1100 ©6600	RIVER SLIP OFF SLOPES AND FLOODPLANS *VERSANTS DEROSION ET PLAINES D'INONDATION FLUVIATILES*	150	POSTGLACIAL *POSTGLACIAIRE*	©5000	64, 70
©8100 ©10 200	RIVER TERRACES *TERRACES FLUVIATILES*	120		©11 000	29, 41, 44, 51, 72
	DELTAS AND RIVER CHANNELS *DELTAS ET CHENAUX FLUVIATILES*	60			
	DIRECTLY FROM GLACIERS *GLACIAIRES*	195		©14 000	39, 44
	STREAM FLOODPLAINS AND SHALLOW PONDS *PLAINES D'INONDATION FLUVIATILES ET ETANGS PEU PROFONDS*	195	YOUNGER WISCONSON *WISCONSIN SUPERIEUR*		
	DIRECTLY FROM GLACIERS *GLACIAIRES*	120		©20 000	1, 30, 33, 37, 44, 57
	STREAM FLOODPLAINS *PLAINES D'INONDATION FLUVIATILES*	90			
©24 000 ©25 000 ©28 600	RIVER FLOODPLAINS (UNDER PERMAFROST CONDITIONS) *PLAINES D'INONDATION FLUVIATILES (DANS DES CONDITIONS DE PERGELISOL)*	105		©45 000	5, 6, 10, 13, 25, 24, 35, 37, 44, 48, 53, 57, 66, 68
©38 700	LAKES, RIVER FLOODPLAINS *LACS, PLAINES D'INONDATION FLUVIATILES* LAG MATERIAL *ARMANIES PAR L'EROSION FLUVIATILES*	285	MID WISCONSIN *WISCONSIN MOVEN*		
		15			
	RIVER DEPOSITION *FLUVIATILES*	45			
	DIRECTLY FROM GLACIERS	55			
	GLACIAIRES *STREAM AND LAKE DEPOSITION* *LACUSTRES ET FLUVIATILES*	180	OLDER WISCONSIN *WISCONSIN INFERIEUR*	©65 000	41, 44, 57
©>38 000		35			
	DIRECTLY FROM GLACIERS *GLACIAIRES*	120			2, 3, 4, 8, 9, 10, 13, 15, 17, 22, 23, 14, 26, 29, 32, 34, 57
	STREAM FLOODPLAINS AND BRAIDED STREAM CHANNELS *PLAINES D'INONDATION FLUVIATILES ET CHENAUX DE RIVIERES ANASTOMOSEES*	105			

TIME SPAN OF THE TAXA IN NORTH AMERICA
DUREE DES TAXONS EN AMERIQUE DU NORD

Figure 20.1

Pleistocene sequence from Medicine Hat, Alberta. Erosion of the banks of the South Saskatachewan River provides access to (right) fossil deposits. This sequence goes from the present to about 80 000 years ago and portrays the changes in the vertebrate fauna over this period. Included are (1) prairie toad; (2) grouse; (3) hawk; (4) ground sloth; (5) shasta ground sloth; (6) Hartan's ground sloth; (7) Gazin's marsh rabbit; (8) Townsend's hare; (9) eastern cottontail rabbit; (10) white-tailed prairie dog; (11) meade prairie dog; (12) meade ground squirrel; (13) ground squirrel; (14) undescribed species of pocket gopher; (15) northern pocket gopher; (16) Canadian beaver; (17) field vole; (18) extinct vole; (19) undescribed species of extinct vole; (20) Osborn's extinct tree vole; (21) Kansas southern bog lemming; (22) muskrat; (23) porcupine; (24) black-footed ferret; (25) eastern striped skunk; (26) red fox; (27) Cope's bone-eating dog; (28) coyote; (29) grey wolf; (30) dire wolf; (31) dog or wolf; (32) raccoon; (33) sabre-toothed cat; (34) Pleistocene lion; (35) Canada lynx; (36) bobcat; (37) mammoth; (38) Cook's mammoth; (39) Imperial mammoth; (40) Siberian or northern mammoth; (41) eastern horse; (42) stilt-legged ass; (43) Pacific horse; (44) Mexican ass; (45) Pacific horse; (46) Niobrara horse; (47) Scott's horse; (48) giant horse; (49) neogene horse; (50) Cope's peccary; (51) unidentified camel; (52) plains llama; (53) Steven's plains llama; (54) Holloman's plains llama; (55) camel; (56) Irvingtonian camel; (57) Western camel; (58) Nearctic deer; (59) white-tailed deer; (60) waipiti or elk; (61) caribou; (62) small caribou; (63) moose deer; (64) mountain sheep; (65) unidentified pronghorned antelope; (66) pronghorn; (67) mountain sheep; (68) woodland muskox; (69) woodland scrub ox; (70) bison; (71) giant long-horned bison; and (72) large extinct bison.

Saskatchewan River had to cope with sharks 11 000 years ago? The answer is "no." The sharks' teeth are much older than the Pleistocene sediments. They are fossils from the Cretaceous that had weathered out of their bedrocks and were redeposited during the Pleistocene (see Table 1.1).

The ground on which Medicine Hat is built contains a treasure trove of earlier life. This pattern repeats itself in many cities around the world. It can give people a sense of history that extends well beyond their current situation. The fossils bring mysteries: Why did so many animals disappear at the end of the Pleistocene? Did early humans arriving in the New World encounter these animals? We know that in the American southwest, early North Americans hunted mammoths (*Mammuthus* spp.), mastodons (*Mastodon* spp.), and ground sloths (*Megalotherium* spp.). Did this hunting pressure contribute to the extinction of large mammals in the Pleistocene?

In biology, unanswered questions outnumber answered ones.

20.1 Recognition of Evolutionary Change

It is timely to reflect on the historical development of evolutionary theory. We know that the Greek philosopher Aristotle (384–322 B.C.E.) was a keen observer of nature and natural history, the branch of biology that examines the form and variety of organisms in their natural environments. Aristotle believed that both inanimate objects and living species had fixed characteristics. Careful study of their differences and similarities enabled him to create a ladder-like classification of nature from simplest to most complex: minerals ranked below plants, plants below animals, animals below humans, and humans below the gods of the spiritual realm.

By the fourteenth century, Europeans had merged Aristotle's classification with the biblical account of creation. At that time, a prevailing view in Europe was that all of the different kinds of organisms had been specially created by a god, that species could never change or become extinct, and that new species could never arise. Biological research was dominated by **natural theology**, which sought to name and catalogue all of God's creation. Careful study of each species would identify its position and purpose in the *Scala Naturae*, or Great Chain of Being, as Aristotle's ladder of life was called. This approach to nature and history was clear in the work of Carolus Linnaeus (1707–1778), whose efforts were *ad majorem Dei gloriam* (for the greater glory of God).

In the Western world, modern science began to come of age in the fifteenth through eighteenth centuries. The English philosopher and statesman Sir Francis Bacon (1561–1626) established the importance of observation, experimentation, and inductive reasoning. Other scientists proposed mechanistic theories to explain physical events, notably Nicolaus Copernicus (1473–1543), Galileo Galilei (1564–1642), René Descartes (1596–1650), and Sir Isaac Newton (1643–1727). Three new disciplines—biogeography, comparative morphology, and geology—promoted a growing awareness of change.

A French scientist, George-Louis Leclerc (1707–1788), le Comte (Count) de Buffon, was puzzled by the existence of body parts with no apparent function. He noted, for example, that the feet of pigs and some other mammals have two toes that never touch the ground. If each species is anatomically perfect for its particular way of life, why do useless structures exist?

Buffon proposed that some animals must have *changed* since their creation. He suggested that **vestigial structures**, the useless body parts we observe today, must have functioned in ancestral organisms. Buffon offered no explanation of how functional structures became vestigial, but he clearly recognized that some species were "conceived by Nature and produced by Time."

Georges Cuvier (1769–1832), a French zoologist, realized that the layers of fossils represented organisms that had lived at successive times in the past. He suggested that abrupt changes between geologic strata marked dramatic shifts in ancient environments. Cuvier and his followers developed the theory of **catastrophism**, reasoning that each layer of fossils represented the remains of organisms that had died in a local catastrophe such as a flood. Somewhat different species then recolonized the area, and when another catastrophe struck, they formed a different set of fossils in the next higher layer.

A contemporary of Cuvier and a student of Buffon, Jean Baptiste de Lamarck (1744–1829) proposed the first comprehensive theory of biological evolution based on specific mechanisms. He proposed that a metaphysical "perfecting principle" caused organisms to become better suited to their environments. Simple organisms evolved into more complex ones, moving up the ladder of life. Microscopic organisms were replaced at the bottom by spontaneous generation.

Lamarck theorized that two mechanisms fostered evolutionary change. According to his *principle of use and disuse*, body parts grow in proportion to how much they are used, as anyone who "pumps iron" well knows. Conversely, unused structures get weaker and shrink, like the muscles of an arm immobilized in a cast. According to his second principle, the *inheritance of acquired characteristics*, changes that an animal acquires during its lifetime

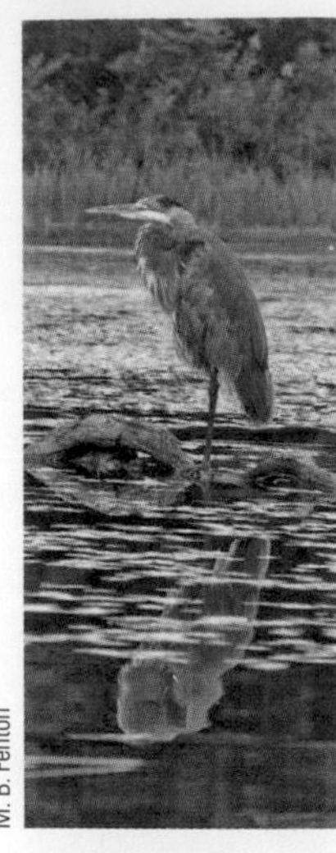
M. B. Fenton

Figure 20.2
Great blue heron, *Ardea herodias.*

are inherited by its offspring. Thus, Lamarck argued that long-legged wading birds, such as herons **(Figure 20.2)**, are descended from short-legged ancestors that stretched their legs to stay dry while feeding in shallow water. Their offspring inherited slightly longer legs, and after many generations, their legs became extremely long.

Today we know that Lamarck's proposed mechanisms do not cause evolutionary change. Although muscles do grow larger through continued use, most structures do not respond in the way Lamarck predicted. Structural changes acquired during an organism's lifetime are not inherited by the next generation.

Despite the shortcomings of his theory, Lamarck made four important contributions to the development of an evolutionary world-view:

- He proposed that all species change through time.
- He recognized that changes are passed from one generation to the next.
- He suggested that organisms change in response to their environments.
- He hypothesized the existence of specific mechanisms that caused evolutionary change.

The first three of these ideas became cornerstones of Darwin's evolutionary theory. Perhaps Lamarck's most important contribution was to foster discussion. By the mid-nineteenth century, most educated Europeans were talking about evolutionary change, whether they believed in it or not.

Study Break

1. Why can one find fossil shark teeth in the bluffs at Medicine Hat?
2. What four main points did Darwin make with his theory about evolution?

20.2 Changes in Earth

In 1795, the Scottish geologist James Hutton (1726–1797) argued that slow and continuous physical processes, *acting over long periods of time*, produced Earth's major geologic features. The movement of water in a river slowly erodes the land and deposits sediments near the river's mouth. Given enough time, erosion creates deep canyons, and sedimentation creates thick topsoil on flood plains. Hutton's **gradualism**, the view that Earth changed *slowly* over its history, contrasted sharply with Cuvier's catastrophism.

The English geologist Charles Lyell (1797–1875) championed and extended Hutton's ideas in an influential series of books, *Principles of Geology*. Lyell argued that the geologic processes that sculpted Earth's surface over long periods of time, such as volcanic eruptions, earthquakes, erosion, and the formation and movement of glaciers, are exactly the same as the processes we observe today. This concept, **uniformitarianism**, undermined any remaining notions of an unchanging Earth. Because geologic processes proceed very slowly, it must have taken millions of years, not just a few thousand, to mould the landscape into its current configuration.

Study Break

What is the theory of catastrophism?

20.3 Charles Darwin

Charles Darwin (1809–1882) changed biologists' view of evolution. But around 1830, Charles Darwin wondered what to do with his life. Raised in a wealthy English household, Darwin had always collected shells and studied the habits of insects and birds. He preferred hunting and fishing to classical studies. Despite his lacklustre performance as a student, Darwin was expected to continue the family tradition of practising medicine. He abandoned medical studies after two years and followed his interest in natural history.

20.3a HMS *Beagle*: Darwin's Voyage

In 1831, Darwin set sail as a dining companion for the captain of HMS *Beagle*, first going westward to map the coastline of South America and then on to circumnavigate the globe **(Figure 20.3)**. When the ship's naturalist quit his post mid-journey, Darwin replaced him in an unofficial capacity. For nearly five years, Darwin toured the world, and because he suffered from seasickness, he seized every chance to go ashore. He collected plants and animals in Brazilian rain forests and fossils in Patagonia. He hiked the grasslands of the pampas and climbed the Andes in Chile. Armed with the first volume of Lyell's *Principles of Geology*, Darwin was primed to apply gradualism and uniformitarianism to the living world.

Darwin observed fascinating patterns in the distributions of species on the Galápagos Islands **(Figure 20.4)**. There he found strange and wonderful creatures, including giant tortoises and lizards that dived into the sea to eat algae. Darwin noted that the animals on different islands varied slightly in form. Indeed, experienced sailors could easily identify

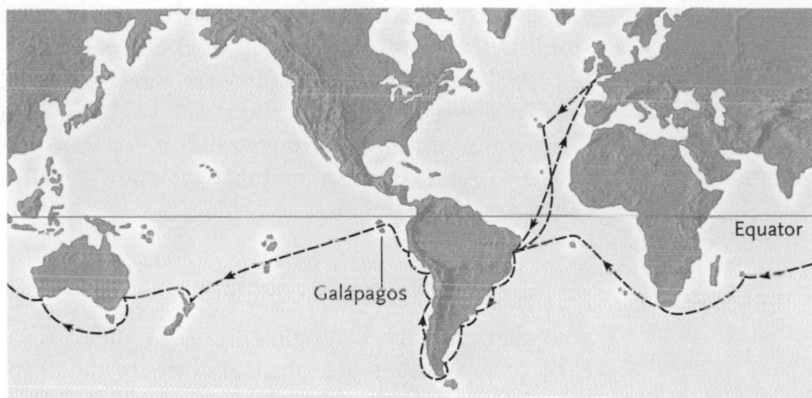

Figure 20.3
Darwin's voyage—map of the path followed by HMS *Beagle*.

a tortoise's island of origin by the shape of its shell. Moreover, many species resembled those on the distant South American mainland. Why did so many different organisms occupy one small island cluster? Why did these species resemble others from the nearest continent? Darwin later hypothesized that the plants and animals of the Galápagos were descended from South American ancestors and that each species had changed after being isolated on a particular island.

20.3b Selective Breeding and Heredity: Like Begets Like

Having grown up in the country, Darwin was well aware that "like begets like": offspring resemble their parents. Plant and animal breeders had applied this basic truth of inheritance for thousands of years. By selectively breeding individuals with favourable characteristics, breeders enhanced those traits in future generations. Darwin was well aware of this process, which he called **artificial selection** (see Chapter 49), but he puzzled over how it could operate in nature.

a. The Galápagos

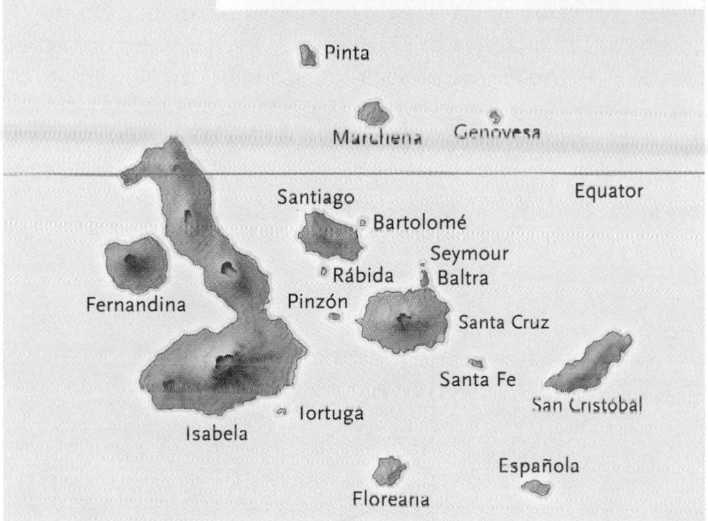

Darwin
Wolf
Pinta
Marchena
Genovesa
Equator
Santiago
Bartolomé
Seymour
Rábida
Baltra
Fernandina
Pinzón
Santa Cruz
Santa Fe
San Cristóbal
Tortuga
Isabela
Española
Floreana

b. Galápagos tortoise

D. Kaleth/Image Bank/Getty Images

c. Marine iguana

William Paton/Foto Natura/Photo Researchers, Inc.

d. Blue-footed booby

Heather Angel/Natural Visions

Figure 20.4
The Galápagos Islands. Between 3 and 5 million years ago, volcanic eruptions created the Galápagos Islands **(a)** about 1000 km west of Ecuador. The islands were named for the giant tortoises **(b)** found there (in Spanish, *galápa* means tortoise). This tortoise (*Geochelone elephantopus*) is native to Isla Santa Cruz. Marine iguanas **(c,** *Amblyrhynchus cristatus***)** dive into the Pacific Ocean to feed on algae. A male blue-footed booby **(d,** *Sula nebouxii***)** engages in courtship display.

20.3c Struggle For Existence: Survival of the Fittest

Darwin had a revelation about how selective breeding could occur naturally when he read Thomas Malthus's famous *Essay on the Principles of Population*. Malthus, an English clergyman and economist, observed that England's population was growing much faster than its agricultural capacity. This situation meant that individuals competed for food, and some of them would inevitably starve.

Darwin applied Malthus's argument to organisms in nature. Species typically produce many more offspring than are needed to replace the parent generation, yet the world is not overrun with sunflowers, tortoises, or bears. Darwin even calculated that if its reproduction went unchecked, a single pair of elephants (the slowest breeding animal known) would leave roughly 19 million descendants after only 750 years. Happily for us (and all other species that might be underfoot), the world is not so crowded with elephants. Instead, some members of every population survive and reproduce, whereas others die without reproducing.

20.3d Darwin's Inferences: The Theory of Evolution by Natural Selection

Darwin's discovery of a mechanism for evolutionary change required him to infer the nature of a process that no one previously had envisioned or documented **(Table 20.1)**. First, individuals within populations vary in size, form, colour, behaviour, and other characteristics. Second, many of these variations are hereditary. What if variations in hereditary traits enabled some individuals to survive and reproduce more readily than others? Organisms with favourable traits would leave many young, whereas those that lacked favourable traits would die, leaving few, if any, descendants. Thus, favourable hereditary traits would become more common in the next generation. And if the next generation were subjected to the same process of selection, the traits would be even more common in the third generation. Because this process is analogous to artificial selection, Darwin called it **natural selection.**

20.3e Darwin's Innovations

Four characteristics distinguish Darwin's theory from earlier explanations of biological diversity and adaptive traits:

1. Darwin provided purely physical rather than spiritual explanations about the origins of biological diversity.
2. Darwin recognized that evolutionary change occurs in groups of organisms rather than in individuals. Some members of a group survive and reproduce more successfully than others do.
3. Darwin described evolution as a multistage process. Variations arise within groups, natural selection eliminates unsuccessful variations, and the next generation inherits successful variations.
4. Like Lamarck, Darwin understood that evolution occurs because some organisms function better than others *in a particular environment.*

One of the most interesting parts of the story of Darwin's development and publication of his theory is its parallel with work by Alfred Russell Wallace. On June 18, 1858, Darwin received a letter from Wallace outlining his ideas about how species change over time. To his credit, Darwin forwarded Wallace's manuscript to Charles Lyell, who had been encouraging Darwin to publish his theory. On July 1, 1858, papers by Darwin and Wallace were presented to the Linnaean Society of London. On November 24,

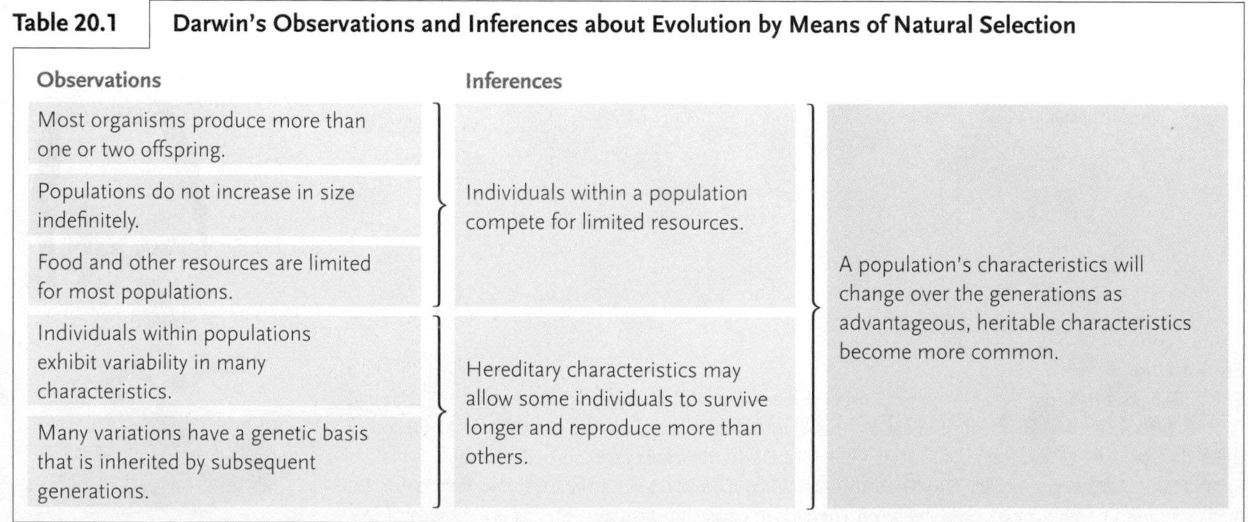

Table 20.1 Darwin's Observations and Inferences about Evolution by Means of Natural Selection

Observations	Inferences	
Most organisms produce more than one or two offspring.	Individuals within a population compete for limited resources.	A population's characteristics will change over the generations as advantageous, heritable characteristics become more common.
Populations do not increase in size indefinitely.		
Food and other resources are limited for most populations.		
Individuals within populations exhibit variability in many characteristics.	Hereditary characteristics may allow some individuals to survive longer and reproduce more than others.	
Many variations have a genetic basis that is inherited by subsequent generations.		

1859, Darwin's book *On the Origin of Species by Means of Natural Selection* was published.

Just as species on different continents converge in their appearance, so do similar theories and ideas in biology arise from different biologists.

20.3f Darwin's Impact on Biological Thought and Society

It would be hard to overestimate the impact of Darwin's theory on Western thought. In *On the Origin of Species*, he proposed a logical mechanism for evolutionary change and provided enough supporting evidence to convince the educated public. Darwin argued that all the organisms that have ever lived arose through **descent with modification**, the evolutionary alteration and diversification of ancestral species. Darwin proposed natural selection as the mechanism that drives evolutionary change. In fact, most of *On the Origin of Species* was an explanation of how natural selection acted on the variability within groups of organisms, preserving favourable traits and eliminating unfavourable ones. Remember that as he wrote, Darwin knew nothing about Mendelian genetics (see Chapter 11). He had no clear idea of how variation arose or how it was passed from one generation to the next.

Evolution was a popular topic in Victorian England, and Darwin's theory received both praise and ridicule. Although he had not speculated about the evolution of humans in *On the Origin of Species*, many readers were quick to extrapolate Darwin's ideas to our own species. Needless to say, certain influential Victorians were not amused by the suggestion that humans and apes shared a common ancestry. The problem of this perception lingers still.

Study Break

1. How did historical thinkers pave the way for the acceptance of the theory of evolution by the scientific community?
2. How did Lyell's ideas influence Darwin's development of the theory of evolution by natural selection?
3. What makes Darwin's theory a scientific theory?

20.4 The Fossil Record

Paleontology is our primary source of data about the evolutionary history of many organisms. Paleontologists discover, describe, and name species of fossils (e.g., the ichthyosaur shown in Figure 19.1). They also analyze the morphology and ecology (deduced from the sediments and the other species in them) of extinct organisms. Most fossils are found in sedimentary rocks, which formed when rain and runoff eroded the land, carrying fine particles of rock and soil downstream to a swamp, a lake, or the sea. Particles settled to the bottom as sediments, forming successive layers over millions of years. The weight of newer sediments compressed the older layers beneath them into a solid matrix: sand into sandstone and silt or mud into shale. When organisms were buried in the sediments, their fossils formed within that layer.

The process of fossilization is a race against time because usually the soft remains of organisms are quickly consumed by scavengers or decomposed by microorganisms. Thus, fossils usually preserve the details of hard structures—bones, teeth, and shells of animals or wood, leaves, and pollen of plants. During fossilization, dissolved minerals replace some of an organism's parts, molecule by molecule **(Figure 20.5a, p. 446)**. Other fossils are moulds, casts, or impressions **(Figure 20.5b)**. In environments where oxygen is scarce, decomposition does not occur and even soft-bodied organisms may be preserved. The Burgess Shale, a deposit in the Canadian Rockies, is rich in extremely well-preserved soft-bodied animals (see Chapter 26). Amber, the fossilized resin of coniferous trees, can include the remains of insects, plants, tiny lizards, and frogs **(Figure 20.5c)**. Other organisms are preserved in glacial ice, coal, tar pits, or the highly acidic water of peat bogs **(Figure 20.5d)**. Sometimes organisms are well enough preserved that their internal anatomy and cell structure, even food in their digestive tracts, can be examined. Biologists have obtained and analyzed DNA from a 40-million-year-old magnolia leaf.

Still, the odds are against almost anything being fossilized, let alone against the discovery of fossils by paleontologists. The ~300 000 described fossil species represent less than 1% of the estimated number of species that have ever lived. Inevitably, absence of skeletons and hard parts means that fossil jellyfish (Cnidaria) are much less common than fossil trilobites (Arthropoda; see Chapter 26), even if both kinds of organisms were equally abundant in the same Ordovician sea. Fossils rarely form in habitats where sediments do not accumulate (e.g., mountain forests) or where soils are acidic (e.g., many forests). Furthermore, although most fossils are composed of stone, they do not last forever. Many are deformed by pressure from overlying rocks **(Figure 20.6, p. 447)** or destroyed by geologic processes (erosion) or disturbances, such as volcanic eruptions. The effects of erosion mean that fossils from older rocks are less common than those in younger rocks because the latter have been around for less time and therefore exposed to less erosion.

a. Petrified wood

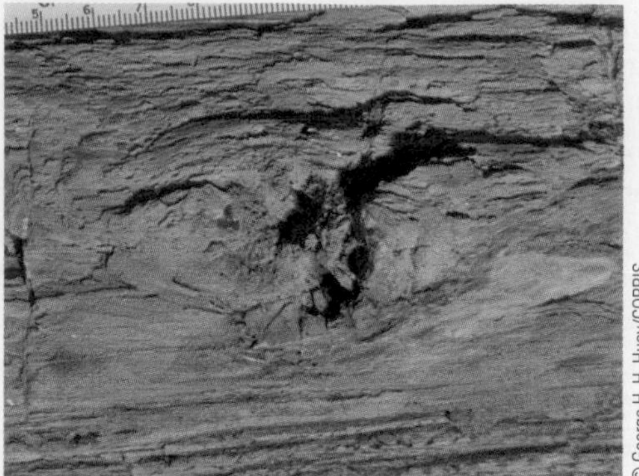

© George H. H. Huey/CORBIS

b. An invertebrate

Neville Pledge/South Australian Museum

c. Insects in amber

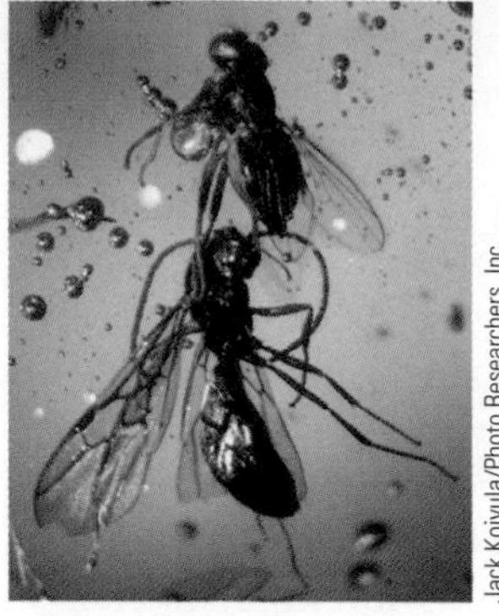

Jack Koivula/Photo Researchers, Inc.

d. Mammoth in permafrost

Novosti/Photo Researchers, Inc.

Figure 20.5
In petrified wood **(a)** from Dinosaur Provincial Park in Alberta, minerals have replaced the wood of dead trees molecule by molecule. **(b)** The soft tissues of an invertebrate (genus *Dickinsonia*) from the Proterozoic preserved as an impression in very fine sediments; **(c)** a 20-million-year-old fly (left) and a wasp were trapped in the oozing resin of a coniferous tree and are now encased in amber; **(d)** a frozen baby mammoth, genus *Mammuthus*, that lived about 40 000 years ago was discovered embedded in ice in Siberia in 1977.

20.4a Dating: How Old Is That Fossil in Relative or in Absolute Time?

Scientists can assign relative and absolute dates to geologic strata and the fossils they contain. Sediments found in any one place form distinctive strata (layers) that usually differ in colour, mineral composition, particle size, and thickness **(Figure 20.7)**. If they have not been disturbed, the strata are arranged in the order in which they formed, with the youngest layers on top. But strata sometimes have been uplifted, warped, or even inverted by geologic processes.

Geologists of the early nineteenth century deduced that the fossils discovered in a particular sedimentary stratum, no matter where it is found, represent organisms that lived and died at roughly the same time in the past. Because each stratum formed at a specific time, the sequence of fossils in the lowest (oldest) to the highest (newest) strata reveals their *relative ages*. Geologists used the sequence of strata and their distinctive fossil assemblages to establish the geologic time scale (see Table 1.1).

The geologic time scale provides a relative dating system for sedimentary strata rather than actual ages of rocks and fossils. Radiometric dating involves the use of isotopes and sometimes allows actual ages (with error bars) to be associated with different rock strata. Radiometric dating exploits the fact that isotopes begin to decay (break down into more stable elements) from the moment they form. Isotopes decay at steady rates; thus, rocks containing isotopes can be dated (see Chapter 3) when the amounts of isotopes can be measured and the rates of decay are known.

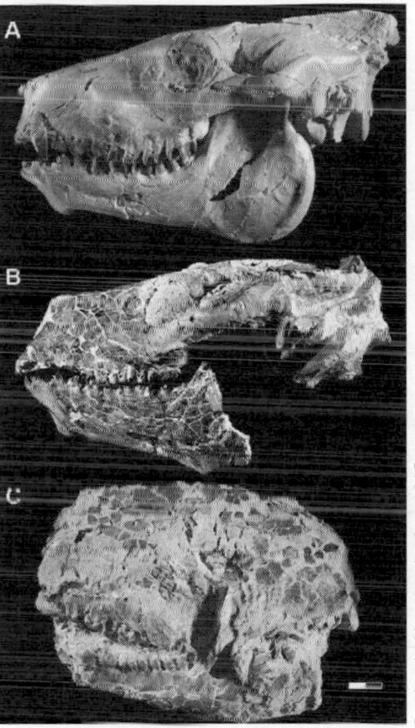

Reprinted with permission from AAAS.

Figure 20.6
Fossils can be distorted. These fossil mammals (creodonts) are from the Day Formation in Oregon. The three fossils are of the same species.

David Noble/FPG/Getty Images

Figure 20.7
Geologic strata in the Grand Canyon. Millions of years of sedimentation in an old ocean basin produced layers of rock that differ in colour and particle size. Tectonic forces later lifted the land above sea level, and the flow of the Colorado River carved this natural wonder.

This approach to dating is limited by the half-life of the isotope, which is the amount of time it takes half of the initial amount of isotope to decay into more stable elements.

Radiometric dating works best with volcanic rocks, which form when lava cools and solidifies. But most fossils are found in sedimentary rocks. To date sedimentary fossils, scientists determine the age of volcanic rocks from the same strata. Using this method, investigators have linked fossils to deposits that are hundreds of millions of years old.

Fossils that still contain organic matter, such as the remains of bones or wood, can be dated directly by measuring the amount of the isotope ^{14}C. Living organisms absorb traces of ^{14}C and large quantities of the stable ^{12}C from the environment and incorporate them into biological molecules. As long as an organism is still alive, its ^{14}C content remains constant because any ^{14}C that decays is replaced by the uptake of other ^{14}C atoms. But as soon as the organism dies, no further replacement occurs, and ^{14}C begins its steady radioactive decay. Scientists use the ratio of ^{14}C to ^{12}C present in a fossil to determine its age.

Study Break

1. What is the difference between absolute and relative dates?
2. How are isotopes used in dating rocks?

20.5 Earth History, Biogeography, and Convergent Evolution

Living organisms are affected profoundly by prevailing climates and environmental conditions. Organisms also affect their surroundings, a striking example being the development of oxygenic photosynthesis (see Section 2.4). A more modest example is the impact of a beaver dam on a stream. Environments on Earth are affected by shifts in geography and climate, whether brief or prolonged, and by catastrophic events. Major geologic shifts occur because the planet's crust is in motion.

20.5a Continental Drift: Movements in Space and Time

According to the theory of **plate tectonics**, Earth's crust is broken into irregularly shaped plates of rock that float on its semisolid mantle **(Figure 20.8, p. 448)**. Currents in the mantle cause the plates, and the continents embedded in them, to move, a phenomenon called **continental drift**. About 250 million years ago, Earth's landmasses coalesced into a single supercontinent named Pangea. Later continental drift separated Pangea into a northern continent, Laurasia, and a southern continent, Gondwana. Laurasia and Gondwana subsequently broke into the continents we know today **(Figure 20.9, p. 449)**.

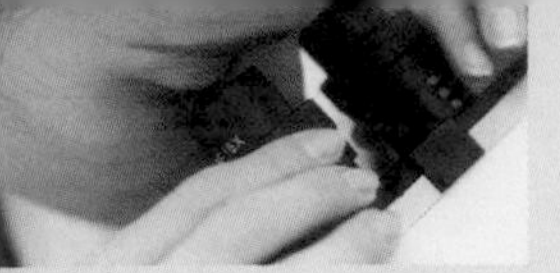

People Behind Biology

J. Tuzo Wilson

In 1963, Canadian geophysicist J. Tuzo Wilson (1908–1993) published a paper suggesting that the Hawaiian Islands and other volcanic island chains formed because of "hot spots" in Earth's mantle. With this concept, Tuzo Wilson explained the presence of active volcanoes thousands of kilometres from the boundaries between tectonic plates. His manuscript was rejected by many major international journals because it was too radical. The hot spot theory, published in the relatively obscure journal *Canadian Journal of Physics*, is one of the milestone papers in the development of our understanding of the theory of plate tectonics.

In 1965, Tuzo published two more papers that further advanced this theory. He asserted that a third type of plate boundary connects oceanic ridges and trenches. This third type of boundary can end abruptly and transform into major faults. The San Andreas Fault zone in California is now recognized as an example of the third type of plate boundary.

Tuzo Wilson was an accomplished teacher, but he also contributed to science in other ways. He was the first principal of Erindale College, which became the University of Toronto, Mississauga, and later was the director of the Ontario Science Centre.

Tuzo Wilson was a geophysicist whose work had a strong impact on our understanding of evolution and biogeography.

Drifting continents induced global changes in Earth's climate. The movement of continents toward the poles encouraged the formation of glaciers, which caused temperature and rainfall to decrease worldwide. Earth's average temperature has fluctuated widely because of complex continental movements.

Unpredictable events have also changed physical environments on Earth. Massive volcanic eruptions and asteroid impacts have occasionally altered the planet's atmosphere and climate drastically. These cataclysmic events have sometimes caused the extinction of many forms of life in relatively short periods of geologic time.

More than a century after Darwin published his observations, the theory of plate tectonics refocused attention on biogeography. Historical biogeographers try to explain how organisms acquired their geographic distributions over evolutionary time.

a. Earth's crustal plates

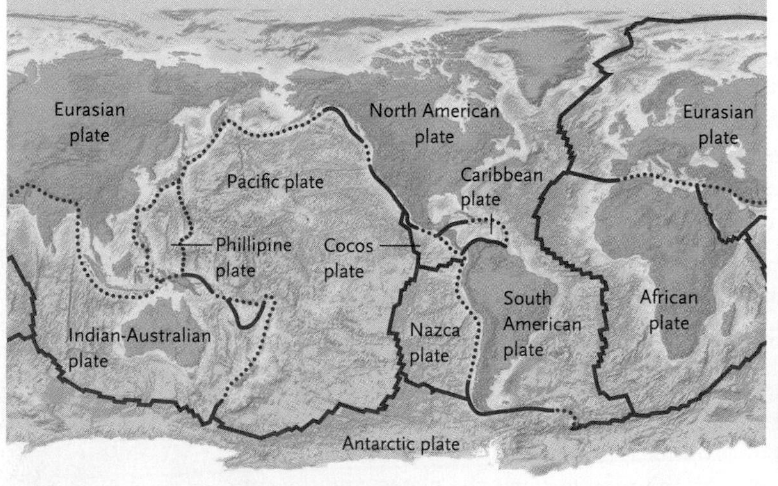

b. Model of plate tectonics

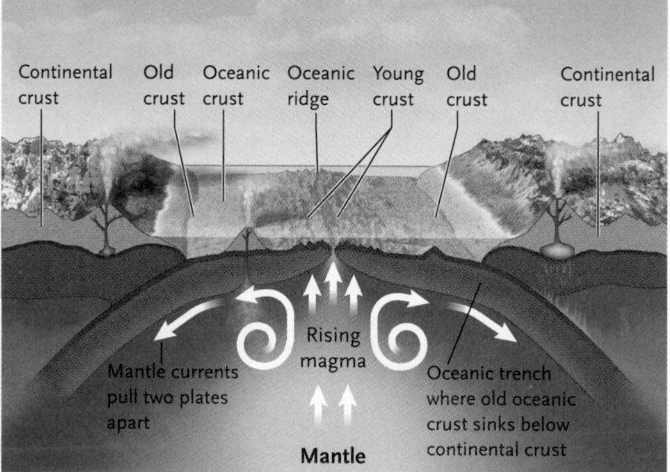

Figure 20.8
Plate tectonics. Earth's crust **(a)** is broken into large rigid plates. New crust is added at oceanic ridges (red), and old crust is recycled into the mantle at oceanic trenches (blue). Oceanic ridges **(b)** form where pressure in the mantle forces magma (molten rock) through fissures in the sea floor. Mantle currents pull the plates apart on either side of the ridge, forcing the sea floor to move laterally away from the ridge. This phenomenon, sea-floor spreading, is widening the Atlantic Ocean about 3 cm per year. Oceanic trenches form where plates collide. The heavier oceanic crust sinks below the lighter continental crust and is recycled into the mantle, a process called subduction. The highest mountain ridges (including the Rockies, Himalayas, Alps, and Andes) formed where subduction uplifted continental crust. Earthquakes and volcanoes are also common near trenches.

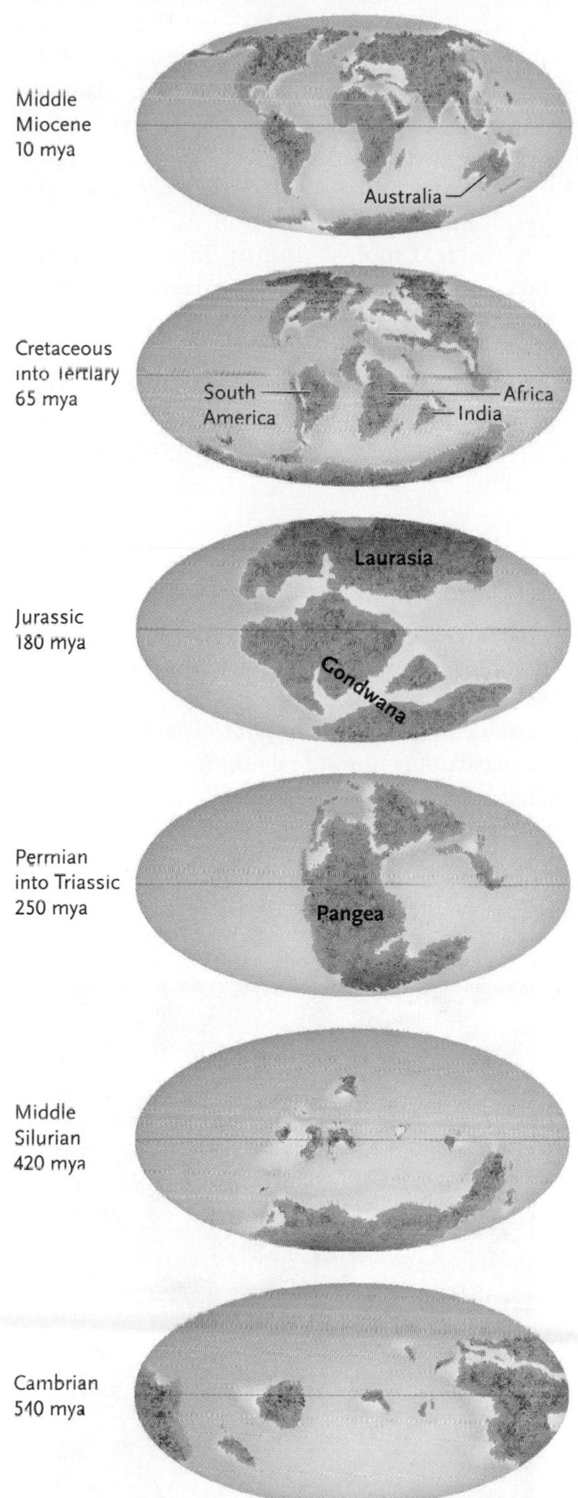

Figure 20.9
History of long-term changes in the positions of continents. Earth's many landmasses coalesced during the Permian, forming the super continent Pangea. About 180 million years ago, Pangea separated into Gondwana and Laurasia. Then Gondwana began to break apart. Africa and India pulled way first, opening the South Atlantic and Indian Oceans. Australia separated from Antarctica about 55 million years ago and slowly drifted northward. South America separated from Antartica shortly thereafter. Laurasia remained nearly intact until 43 million years ago when North America and Greenland together separated from Europe and Asia. Movement of the continents also changed the shapes and sizes of the oceans.

Continuous and Disjunct Distributions Many species have a **continuous distribution**, living in suitable habitats throughout large areas. For example, herring gulls (*Larus argentatus*) live along the coastlines of all northern continents. Continuous distributions usually require no special historical explanations. Other groups exhibit **disjunct distributions.** Here, closely related species live in widely separated locations. Magnolia trees (*Magnolia* spp.) occur in parts of North, Central, and South America, as well as in China and Southeast Asia, but nowhere in between.

Dispersal and vicariance create disjunct distributions. **Dispersal** is the movement of organisms away from their place of origin; it can produce a disjunct distribution if a new population becomes established on the far side of a geographic barrier. **Vicariance** is the fragmentation of a continuous geographic distribution by external factors. Over the course of evolutionary history, dispersal and vicariance have together influenced the geographic distributions of organisms on a very grand scale.

20.5b Biogeographic Regions: Regional Influences on Flora and Fauna

Pangea's breakup was a powerful vicariant experience for species that were widespread in the Mesozoic. The subsequent geographic isolation of continents fostered the evolution of distinctive regional **biotas** (all organisms living in a region). Alfred Russel Wallace used biotas to define six **biogeographic regions** that we still recognize today **(Figure 20.10).**

The Australian and Neotropical realms have been geographically isolated since the Mesozoic. Each contains many **endemic species** (those that occur nowhere else on Earth). The Australian region, in particular, has had no complete land connection to any other continent for approximately 55 million years. The biota of the Australian region reflects this isolation, especially the mammals. Of the 247 species of living terrestrial mammals native to Australia, 64% of them are marsupials, unlike the situation

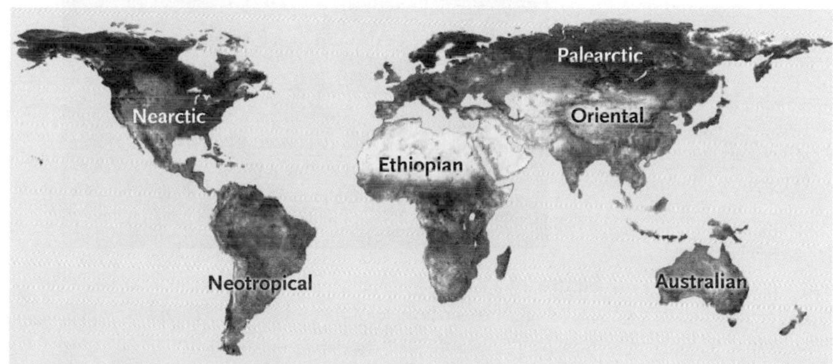

Figure 20.10
Wallace's biogeographic realms. Each realm contains a distinctive biota.

on any other continent. There are also two species of monotremes (egg-laying mammals). The rest of the native mammal species are placentals: mostly bats (77 species), but some rodents (10 species) and one carnivore, the dingo (*Canis familiaris*). The dingo arrived with humans, whereas the rodents apparently arrived on their own. For more about mammals, see Chapter 27.

In comparison, the biotas of the Nearctic and Palearctic realms (including mammals) are fairly similar. North America and Eurasia were frequently connected by land bridges; eastern North America was attached to Western Europe until the breakup of Laurasia 43 million years ago, and northwestern North America has had periodic contact with northeastern Asia over the Bering land bridge during much of the last 60 million years.

20.5c Convergences in Life Forms: Parallel and Convergent Evolution

Distantly related species living in different biogeographic realms can be similar in appearance. We have seen that cacti can be almost identical to spurges (see Figure 19.2). But these lineages arose independently long after the continents had separated. Cacti and spurges did not inherit their similarities from a shared ancestor; rather, their overall resemblance is the product of **convergent evolution**, the evolution of similar adaptations in distantly related organisms that occupy similar environments.

A comparison of some mammals provides impressive examples of convergence between marsupials and placental mammals. *Canis lupis*, the grey wolf of the Palearctic, is strikingly similar to the extinct *Thylacinus cynocephalus* (marsupial wolf or thalacine, **Figure 20.11**). Similarly, in the Pleistocene, *Thylacoleo carnifex* was a lion-like Australian marsupial. Sabre-toothed "lions" lived among South American marsupials (*Thylacosmilus* of the Pliocene), whereas *Smilodon*, a Pleistocene placental sabre-toothed lion, lived in the Northern Hemisphere (and spread into South America) **(Figure 20.12)**. Other exceptional examples are *Notorytes typhlops*, a marsupial mole from Australia, compared with "real moles" (family Talpidae), which are placentals from the Northern Hemisphere, or "golden moles" (family Chrysochloridae), which are placentals from Africa.

Carnivorous plants such as living flypaper and pitcher plants are other variations on the themes of convergent and parallel evolution (see Figure 19.6).

Study Break

1. What conditions lead to fossilization? How would these affect the sample of fossils available?
2. What techniques for dating fossils provide relative dating? Absolute dating?
3. What historical conditions lead to continuous distributions? Disjunct distributions?

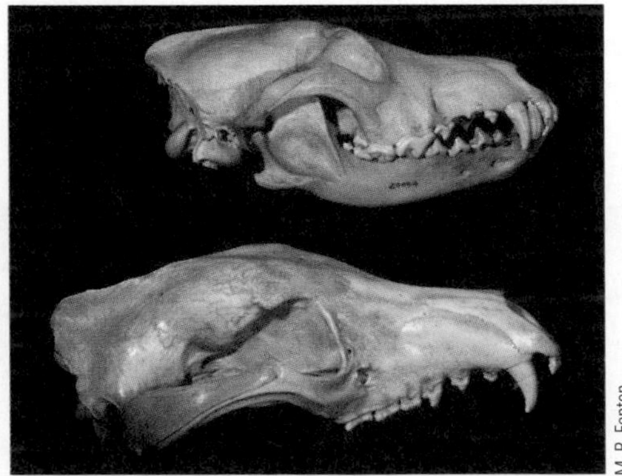

M. B. Fenton

Figure 20.11
Convergent evolution. Wolf-like mammals such as *Canis lupis* (top) and *Thylacinus cynocephalus* (bottom). The grey wolf occurs widely in the Northern Hemisphere, whereas the now extinct thalacine (marsupial wolf) formerly occurred in Tasmania.

a.

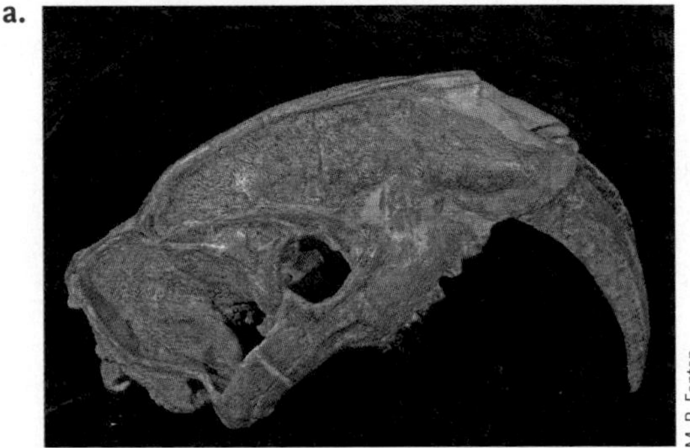

M. B. Fenton

b.

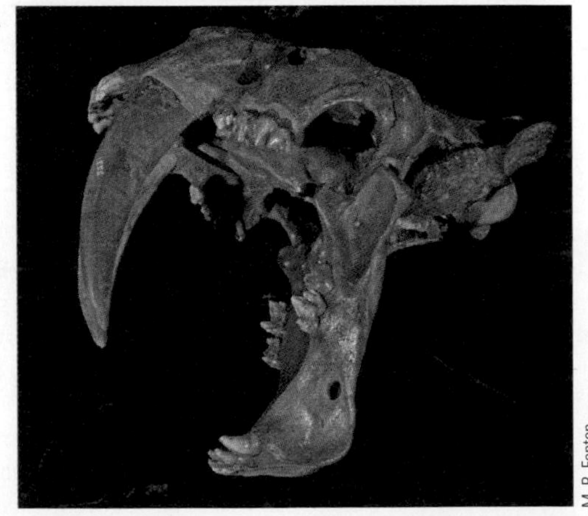

M. B. Fenton

Figure 20.12
Convergent evolution. (a) Sabre-toothed marsupial lion (*Thylacosmilus atrox*) of South America, compared with the **(b)** placental sabre-toothed cat (*Smilodon* spp.) from North America.

20.6 Interpreting Evolutionary Lineages

As newly discovered fossils demanded the reinterpretation of old hypotheses, biologists have refined their ideas about the history of life. The evolution of horses is a case in point.

20.6a Evolution of Horses: An Adaptive Radiation

The earliest known ancestors of modern horses were first identified by Othniel C. Marsh a year after Darwin published *On the Origin of Species*. These early horses, *Hyracotherium*, stood 25 to 50 cm high at the shoulder. Each of their toes (four on the front feet and three on the hind) was capped with a tiny hoof, but the animals walked on soft pads, as dogs do today. Their faces were short, their teeth were small, and they browsed on soft leaves in woodland habitats.

In 1879, Marsh published his analysis of 60 million years of horse family history. He described their evolution in a series of stages from the tiny *Hyracotherium* through intermediates (*Mesohippus* spp., *Merychippus* spp., and *Pliohippus* spp.) to the modern *Equus* **(Figure 20.13a, p. 452)**. Marsh inferred a pattern of descent characterized by gradual, directional evolution in several skeletal features. Changes in the legs and feet allowed horses to run faster, and changes in the face and teeth accompanied a switch in diet from soft leaves to tough grasses. The pattern of evolution appeared to progress from living in wooded habitats to open grasslands.

The fossil record for horses is superb, and we now have fossils of more than 100 extinct species from five continents. These fossils reveal a macroevolutionary history that differs from Marsh's interpretation. *Hyracotherium* was not gradually transformed into *Equus* along a linear track. Rather, the evolutionary tree for horses was highly branched **(Figure 20.13b)**, and *Hyracotherium*'s descendants differed in size, numbers of toes, tooth structure, and other traits. Although there were many branches of the horse lineage in the Miocene and Pliocene epochs, today only one genus (*Equus*) remains, and it includes several species. Today's horses and their close relatives (donkeys and zebras) are the surviving tips of one evolutionary line.

When we study extinct organisms, we tend to focus on traits that characterize modern species. Marsh had assumed that the differences between *Hyracotherium* and *Equus* were typical of the changes that characterized the group's evolutionary history. But not all fossil horses were larger **(Figure 20.13c)**, had fewer toes, or were better adapted to feed on grass than their ancestors. Furthermore, if a branch other than *Equus* survived today, Marsh's description of trends in horse evolution could have been very different. All evolutionary lineages have extinct branches. Any attempt to trace a linear evolutionary path, as Marsh did for horses and many people do for humans, imposes artificial order on an inherently disorderly history. This is a variation on the problem of defining a species where we impose a set of conditions on a natural continuum.

20.6b Time for Evolution to Occur: Rapid or Slow Change?

Which evolutionary processes produce the numerous branches of a lineage such as the horse lineage? Over what time scale does a lineage evolve? To put this in perspective, remember the example of *Acanthinucella spirata*, a marine gastropod from the California coast (see Figure 18.12), or the Italian wall lizard (see Section 18.11).

Evolution can occur by gradual changes, by anagenesis or by cladogenesis. **Anagenesis** is the accumulation of changes in a lineage as it adapts to changing environments. If morphological changes are large, we may give the organisms different names at different times in their history. One might say that Species A from the late Mesozoic evolved into Species B from the middle Cenozoic **(Figure 20.14a, p. 453)**. Anagenesis does not increase the number of species; it is the evolutionary transformation of an existing species rather than the production of new ones.

Evolution also occurs by **cladogenesis**, the evolution of two or more descendant species from a common ancestor. If the fossilized remains of the descendants are distinct, paleontologists will recognize them as different species **(Figure 20.14b)**. Cladogenesis increases the number of species on Earth.

The **gradualist hypothesis** suggests that large changes result from slow, continuous accumulations of small changes over time. If this hypothesis is correct, in any lineage we expect to find a series of transitional fossils documenting gradual evolution. However, we rarely find evidence of gradual changes in any lineage. Most species appear suddenly in a particular stratum, persist for some time with little change, and then disappear from the fossil record. Then another species, a variant on the first with different traits, suddenly appears in the next higher stratum.

Alternatively, evolution also can occur rapidly, as predicted by the **punctuated equilibrium hypothesis** proposed in the early 1970s by Niles Eldredge and Stephen Jay Gould. The punctuated equilibrium hypothesis suggested that speciation occurs in isolated populations at the edge of a species' geographic distribution. Marginal populations experience substantial genetic drift and distinctive patterns of natural selection. According to this hypothesis,

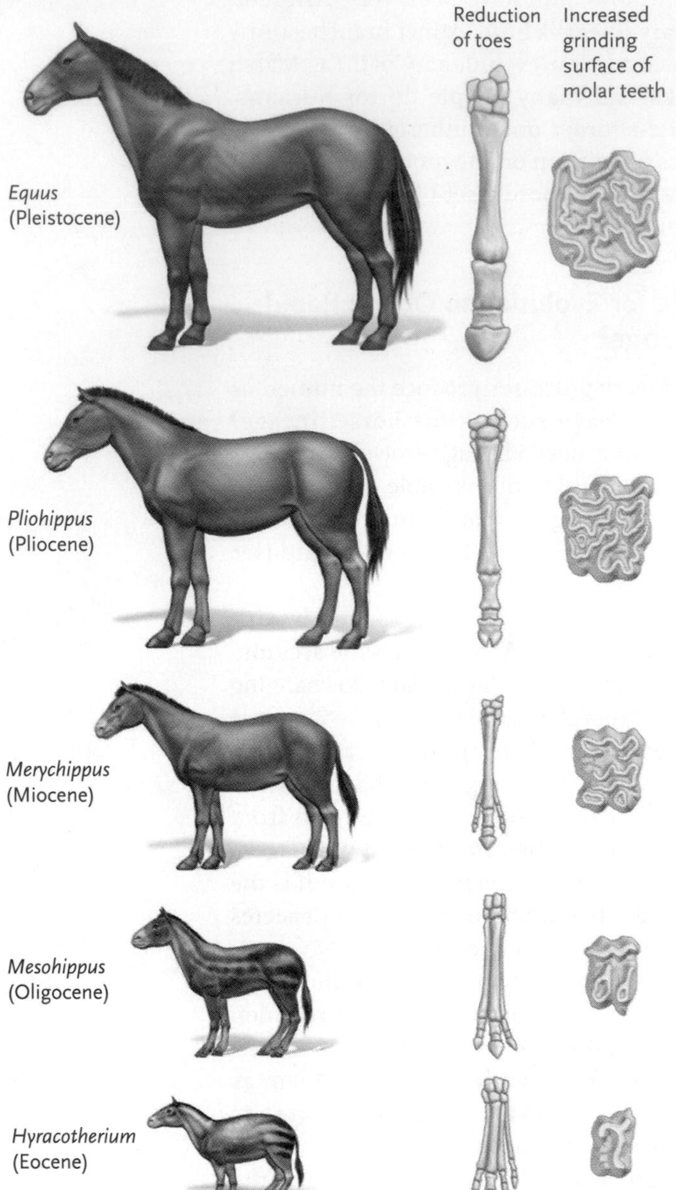

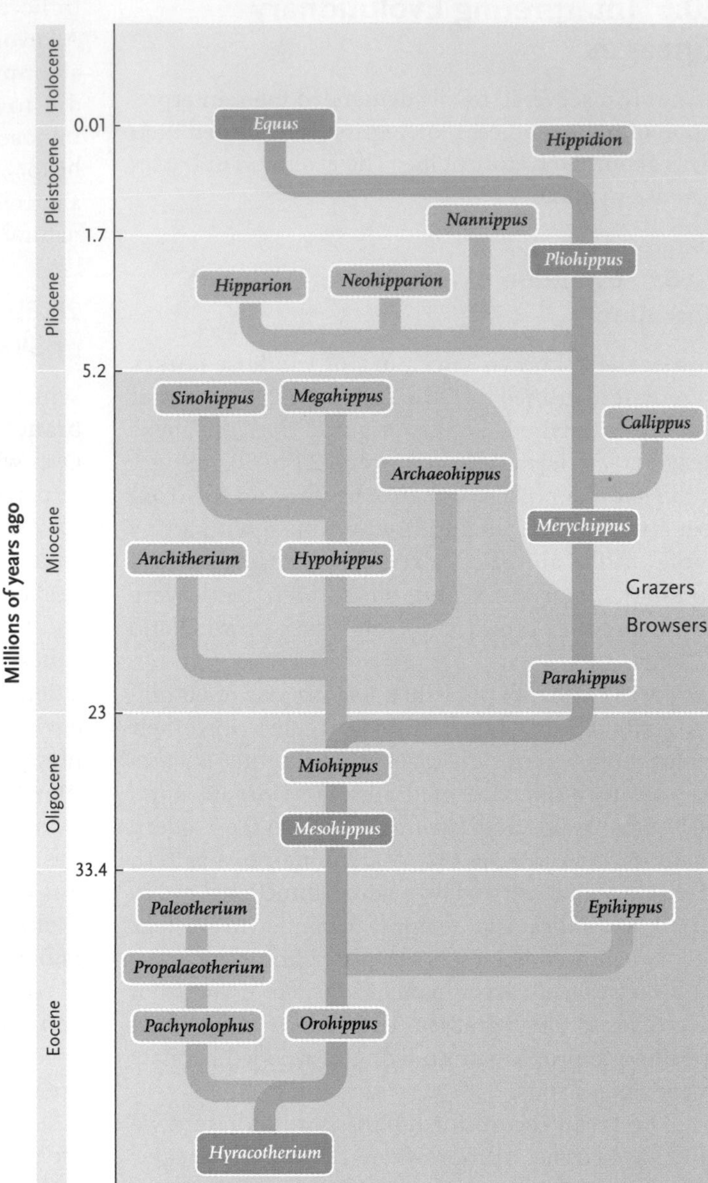

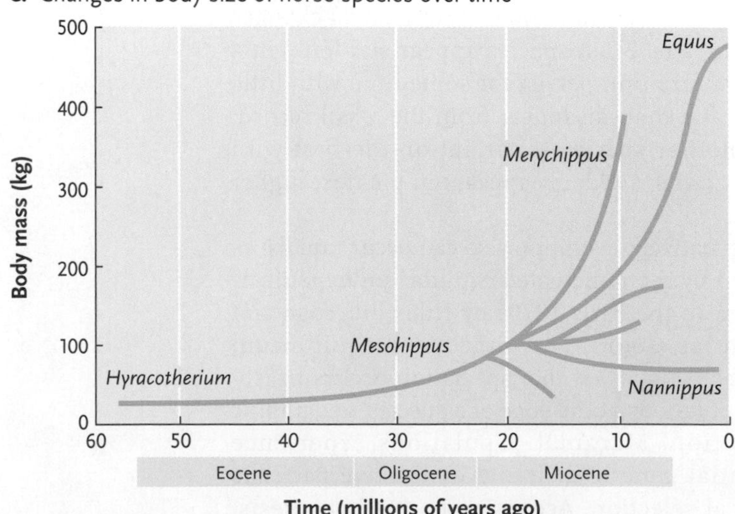

Figure 20.13
Evolution of horses. Marsh depicted the evolution of horses **(a)** as a linear pattern of descent characterized by an increase in body size, a reduction in the number of toes, increased fusion of bones in the lower leg, elongation of the face, and an increase in the sizes of grinding (molar) teeth. Recent studies **(b)** indicated that the horse family included numerous evolutionary branches with variable morphology. Although many branches of the lineage developed larger bodies, some remained as small as the earliest horses **(c)**.

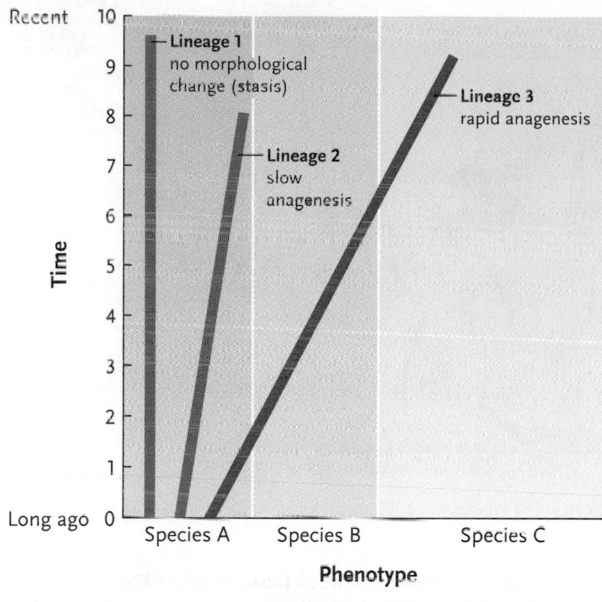

Three lineages begin with the same phenotype, identified as fossil Species A, at time 0. The rate of evolutionary change is shown by the angle of the line for each lineage: lineage 1 undergoes no change over time, lineage 2 changes slowly, and lineage 3 changes so rapidly that its phenotype shifts far to the right in the graph. Paleobiologists might assign different names to the fossils of lineage 3 at different times in its history—Species A at time 1, Species B at times 2 through 6, and Species C at times 7 through 9—even though no additional species evolved. By contrast, fossils of lineages 1 and 2 change so little over time that they would be identified as Species A throughout their evolutionary history.

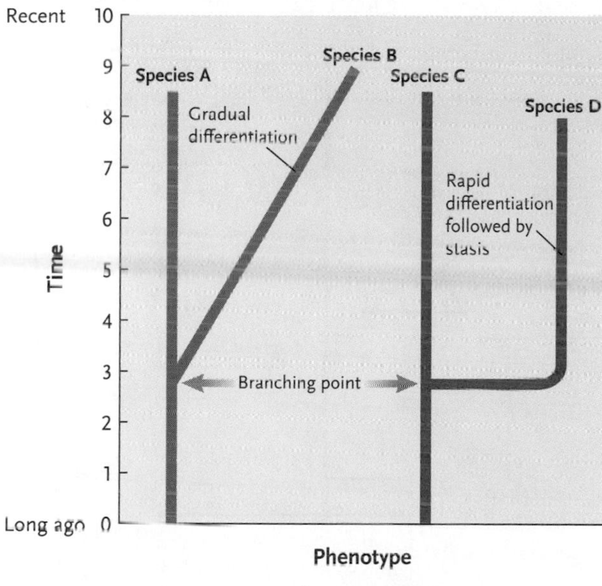

Each branching point represents a new line of descent. The branching may show either gradual (left) or rapid (right) morphological differentiation from the parent species.

Figure 20.14
Patterns of evolution. In these hypothetical examples, the vertical axis represents geologic time and the horizontal axis represents variation in a phenotypic trait.

morphological variations arise rapidly during cladogenesis. Thus, most species exhibit long periods of morphological equilibrium (stasis), punctuated by brief periods of cladogenesis and rapid morphological evolution. If this hypothesis is correct, transitional forms are uncommon in the fossil record because they live only for short periods of time in small, localized populations. Darwin had used a similar line of reasoning to explain puzzling gaps in the fossil record.

The fossil record supports both hypotheses. Data from work on Ordovician trilobites (Arthropoda) support the gradualist hypothesis. The number of "ribs" in the tail regions of trilobites changed continuously over 3 million years. The change was so gradual that a sample from any given stratum is almost always intermediate between samples from the strata just above and below it. The changes in rib number probably evolved without cladogenesis **(Figure 20.15, p. 454).**

A punctuated pattern is evident in the evolutionary history of *Metrarabdotus*, a genus of ectoprocts from the Caribbean Sea. Ectoprocts are small colonial animals that build hard skeletons **(Figure 20.16, p. 454),** the details of which are well preserved in fossils. Alan Cheetham measured 46 morphological traits in fossils of 18 *Metrarabdotus* species. He used a single statistic to summarize the morphological differences between populations of a single species over time and between ancestral species and their descendants. He found that most species did not change much over millions of years, but new species, which were morphologically different from their ancestors, often appeared quite suddenly (see Figure 20.16).

The punctuationalist and gradualist hypotheses are extremes along a continuum of possible macroevolutionary patterns. The mode and tempo of evolution vary among lineages, and both viewpoints are validated by data on some organisms but not on others. Some of the most interesting results have come from work focused on morphological changes within lineages and on long-term changes in the number of living species (e.g., *Acanthinucella spirata*; see Figure 18.12).

Study Break

1. Why would it be a mistake to classify a fossil as an ancestor to an extant species based on the possession of intermediate traits?
2. Which sort of evolution does not increase the number of species? How does it work?
3. Compare the gradualist hypothesis with the punctuated equilibrium hypothesis. Why should a biologist consider both hypotheses when looking at the evolution of a species?

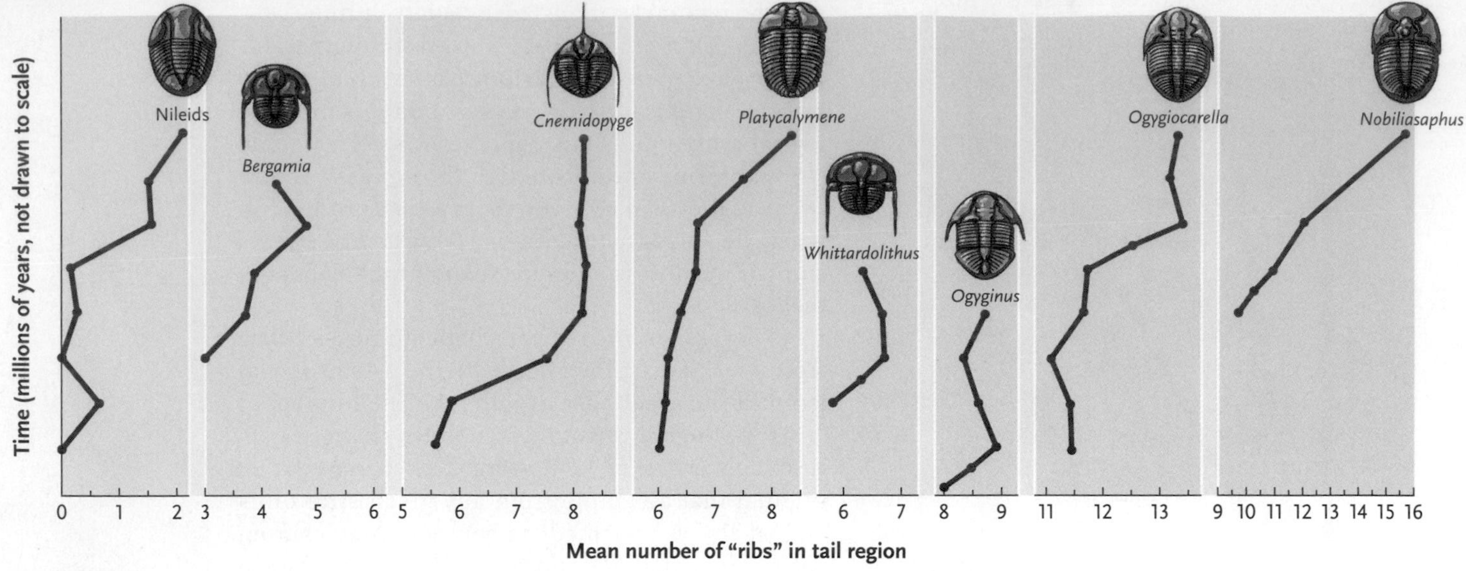

Figure 20.15
The gradualist hypothesis predicts that in morphology, the fossils from any layer of rock (stratum) will be intermediate between those in strata above and below (younger and older, respectively). Analysis of the number of riblike structures in the tail regions of 15 000 trilobites from northern Wales revealed gradual changes as illustrated in this figure. The fossils had been deposited over 3 million years in the Ordovician.

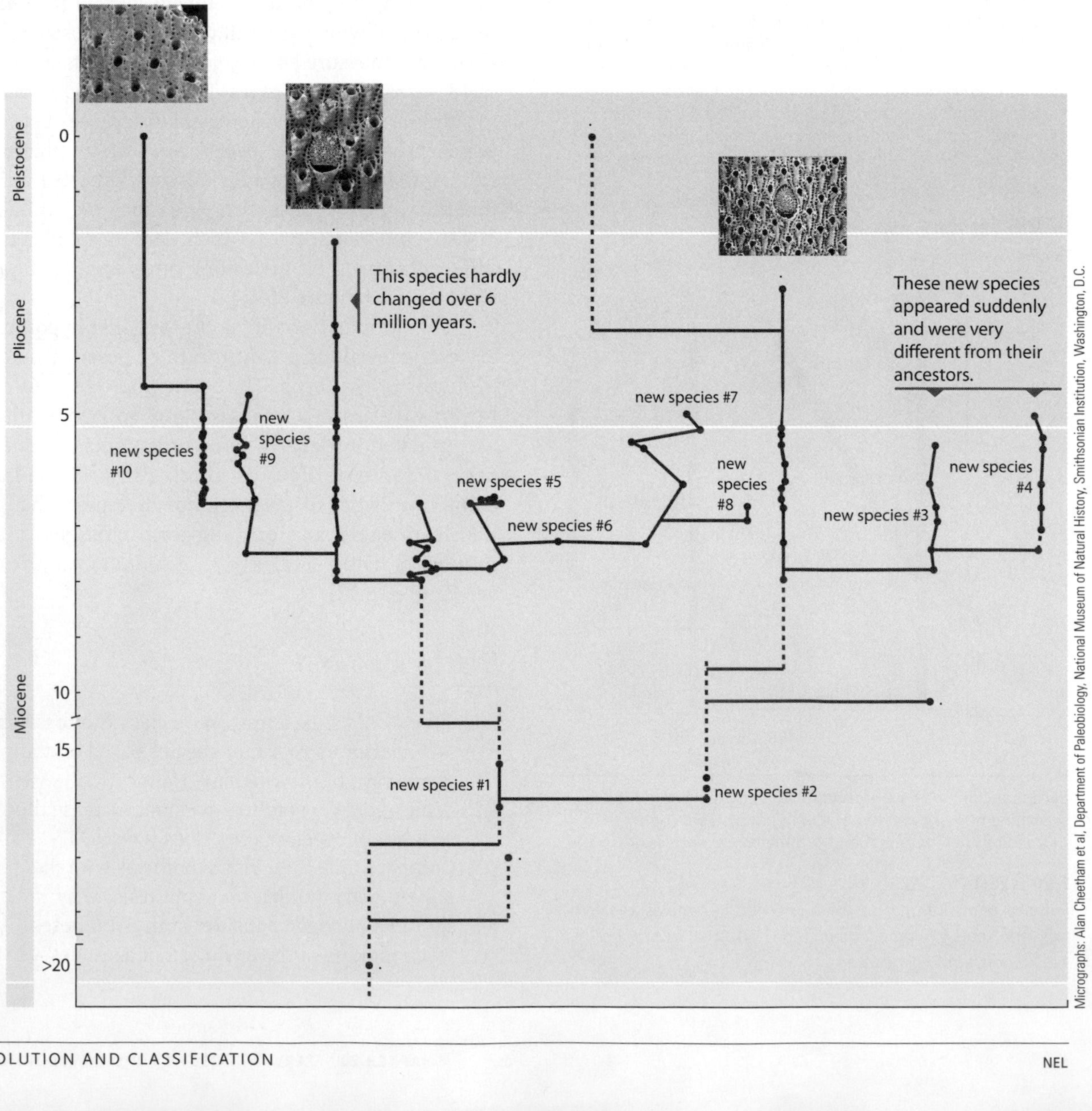

Pleistocene
Pliocene
Miocene
0
5
10
15
>20
This species hardly changed over 6 million years.
These new species appeared suddenly and were very different from their ancestors.
new species #10
new species #9
new species #5
new species #6
new species #7
new species #8
new species #3
new species #4
new species #1
new species #2

Micrographs: Alan Cheetham et al, Department of Paleobiology, National Museum of Natural History, Smithsonian Institution, Washington, D.C.

Figure 20.16
Changes in the morphology of 18 fossil species of ectoprocts (genus *Metrarabdotus*) from the Dominican Republic support the punctuated equilibrium hypothesis. Although the morphology of most fossil species of *Metrarabdotus* changed relatively little, new species often appeared "suddenly" in the fossil record. The dashed lines represent gaps in the fossil record. The time scale is shown on the vertical axis.

20.7 Macroevolutionary Trends in Morphology

Some evolutionary lineages exhibit trends toward larger size and greater morphological complexity. Others are marked by the development of novel structures.

Body size affects most aspects of an organism's physiology and ecology. When we look at the entire history of life, some organisms have become larger over time, but others have not. Within some evolutionary lineages, increases in body size are common, but not universal. The nineteenth-century paleobiologist Edward Drinker Cope noted this trend in vertebrates, now known as *Cope's Rule*. Although Cope's Rule also applies to some lineages of invertebrates and plants, no truly broad survey has been done to test the generality of the hypothesis underlying it. Insects appear to be a major exception to Cope's Rule. Most insects have remained small since their appearance in the Devonian, perhaps reflecting the prevalence of a life history strategy that permits production of large numbers of offspring and thus the ability to withstand high levels of mortality (see Chapter 45).

20.7a Novel Features: Innovation in Evolution

Novel morphological structures, such as the wings of birds, often appear suddenly in the fossil record. How do novel features evolve? Scientists have identified several mechanisms, including preadaptation, allometric growth, and heterochrony.

Preadaptations are said to occur when a trait that is adaptive in one context is also advantageous in another. In this situation, the trait may be enhanced by natural selection, modifying and enhancing the feature to enhance its new function. Such preadaptations are lucky accidents; they never evolve *in anticipation* of future evolutionary needs.

John Ostrom described how some evolutionary lines of carnivorous dinosaurs, the immediate ancestors of *Archaeopteryx* and modern birds, were preadapted for flight **(Figure 20.17)**. Some of these small, agile, nonflying creatures were bipedal, with light hollow bones and long forelimbs that they used to capture prey. Feathers appeared in some of these lineages, where they probably served in thermoregulation (either as heat shields or insulation). The collection of traits developed because they conferred high levels of activity and mobility, combined with access to elusive prey, such as flying insects. Other branches of carnivorous dinosaurs related to birds were active and predatory but did not fly. At least one was a large bipedal predator, the size of *Tyrannosaurus* (see Figure 20.17). We have no fossils of animals that were intermediate between *Archaeopteryx* and its ancestors, just as we lack fossils of animals whose descendants were on their way to becoming pterosaurs or bats. The absence of intermediate forms does not mean that they did not exist. In 1990, most biologists would have considered feathers to be a diagnostic feature of birds. Within

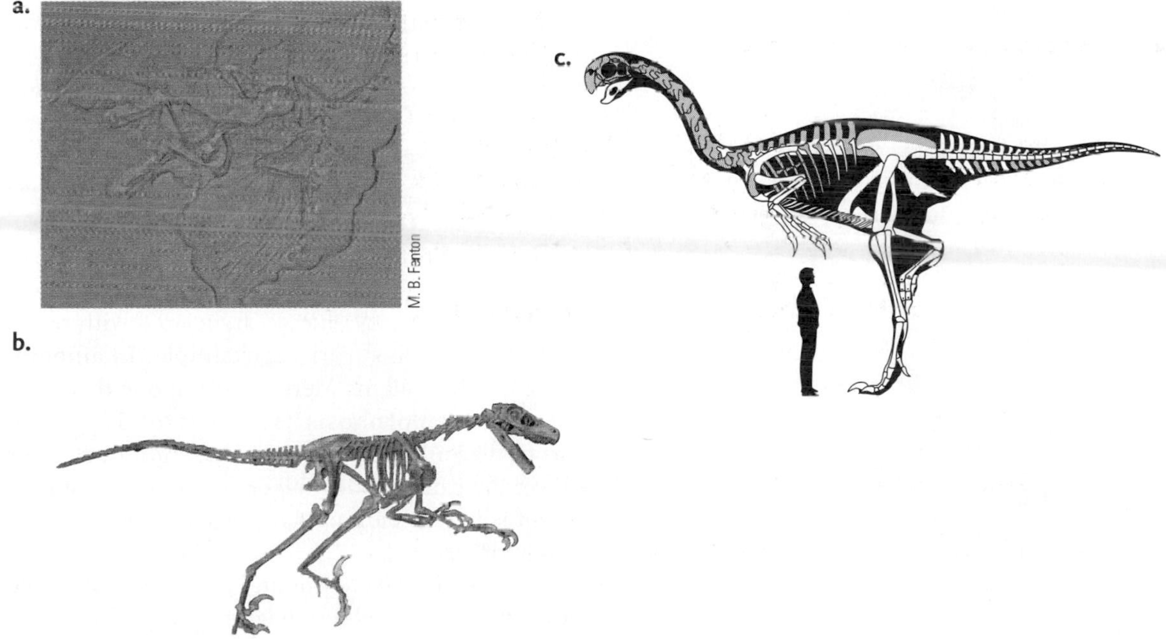

Figure 20.17
Bird-like fossils. (a) Skeleton of *Archaeopteryx lithographica* from the German Jurassic. Bird-like features include a furculum (wishbone) and feathers. **(b)** This bird-like dinosaur, *Saurornitholestes langstoni*, from the Cretaceous of western Canada, probably had feathers and was closely related to birds but did not fly. **(c)** This bird-like dinosaur, *Gigantoraptor erlianensis*, from the Late Cretaceous of China, probably had feathers and was closely related to birds but did not fly. The human silhouette puts *Gigantoraptor* in perspective.

10 years, it was obvious that other species of carnivorous dinosaurs had feathers but were not birds (see Chapter 27).

20.7b Allometric Growth: Changes in Shape through Differential Growth

Allometric growth occurs when different parts of the body grow at different rates. Allometry can result in changes in the morphology of individuals over time (*allo* = different; *metro* = measure). Allometric growth occurs in humans. The relative sizes of different body parts change because human heads, torsos, and limbs grow at different rates **(Figure 20.18a)**. Allometric growth also occurred in dinosaurs. It can create morphological differences in closely related species. The skulls of chimpanzees and humans are similar in newborns but markedly different in adults **(Figure 20.18b)**. Some regions of the chimp skull grow much more quickly than others, whereas the proportions of the human skull change much less. Differences in the adult skulls may simply reflect changes in one or a few genes that regulate the pattern of growth.

Figure 20.18
Examples of allometric growth.

a. Allometric growth in humans

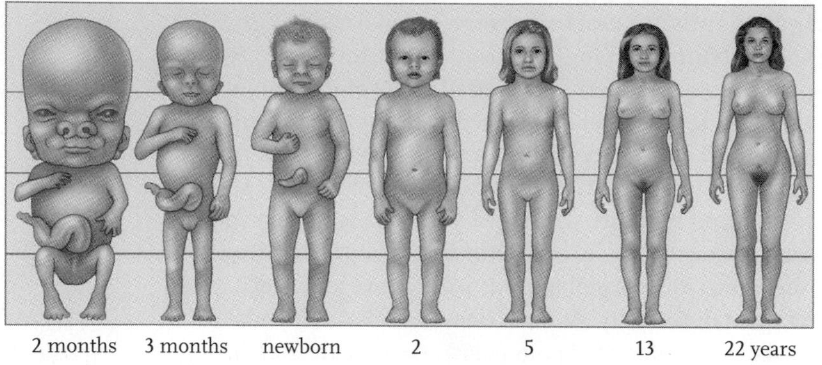

Humans exhibit allometric growth from prenatal development until adulthood. Our heads grow more slowly than other body parts; our legs grow faster.

b. Differential growth in the skulls of chimpanzees and humans

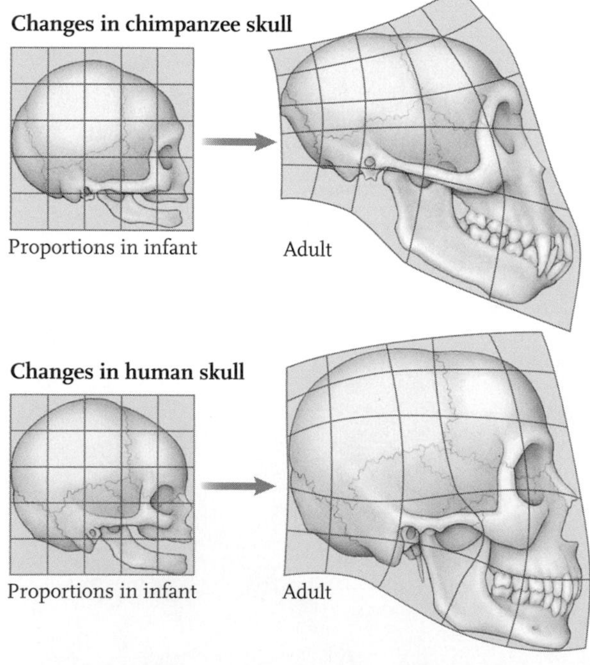

Although the skulls of newborn humans and chimpanzees are remarkably similar, differential patterns of growth make them diverge during development. Imagine that the skulls are painted on a blue rubber sheet marked with a grid. Stretching the sheet deforms the grid in particular ways, mimicking the differential growth of various parts of the skull.

20.7c Heterochrony: Timing of Developmental Events and Larval Stages

Heterochrony, changes in the timing of developmental events (*hetero* = different; *chronos* = time), can cause the morphology of closely related species to differ. At least two phenomena can be involved, neoteny and pedomorphosis (*paedo* = child; *morpho* = form). We use the ability to reproduce to distinguish juveniles (no reproduction) from adults (reproduction). Neoteny occurs when larvae acquire the ability to reproduce. Pedomorphosis occurs when adults retain juvenile characters. In many protostomes, larvae contain totipotent cells that develop into adults (see Chapter 26).

Metamorphosis, the change from a juvenile form to an adult form, can involve significant reorganization of internal organs. The distinctiveness of larval versus adult forms is obvious in some insects and in many other protostomes (see Chapter 26). Metamorphosis also occurs in many species of salamanders and frogs, coincident with the change from aquatic (juvenile) to terrestrial (adult) forms. Populations of several salamander species are pedomorphic because the organisms grow to adult size and become reproductively mature without changing to the adult form **(Figure 20.19)**.

The evolutionary change associated with pedomorphosis can be surprisingly simple. In amphibians, including salamanders, the hormone thyroxine induces metamorphosis (see Chapter 35). Pedomorphosis could result from a mutation that either reduces thyroxine production or limits the responsiveness of some developmental processes to thyroxine concentration.

Changes in developmental rates also influence the morphology of plants **(Figure 20.20)**. The flower of a larkspur species, *Delphinium decorum*, includes a ring of petals that guide bees to its nectar tube and other structures on which bees can perch. By contrast, *D. nudicaule*, a more recently evolved species, has tight flowers that attract hummingbird pollinators, which

David Scott/SREL

Figure 20.19
Pedomorphosis in salamanders. Some populations of the small-mouthed salamander *Amblystoma talpoideum* undergo metamorphosis, losing their gills and developing lungs (left). Other populations are pedomorphic (right); they retain juvenile morphological characters such as gills after attaining sexual maturity.

a. *D. decorum*

Gary Head

b. *D. nudicaule*

Gary Head

c.

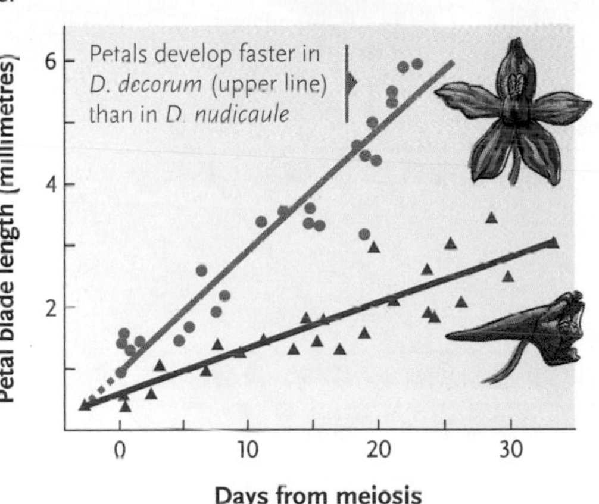

Figure 20.20
Delphinium decorum flowers are pollinated by bees **(a)** and *D. nudicaule* flowers by hummingbirds **(b).** Using days since completion of meiosis in pollen grains, it is clear in the graph that the rate of petal growth differs between the two species **(c).** Petals of *D. decorum* develop faster and are pollinated by bees.

can hover in front of the flowers. Slower development in *D. nudicaule* flowers causes the structural difference. A mature flower in the descendant species resembles an unopened (juvenile) flower of the ancestral species.

Study Break

1. What is a preadaptation?
2. How can allometric growth lead to novel structures?
3. What is pedomorphosis?

20.8 Evolutionary Developmental Biology

Historically, evolutionary biologists studied evolutionary history by comparing the embryos of different species, often independently from scientists studying embryonic development. Therefore, we did not see the development of a coherent picture of specific developmental mechanisms contributing to morphological innovations. Since the late 1980s, advances in molecular genetics have allowed scientists to explore the genomes of organisms in great detail, fostering a new approach to these studies. **Evolutionary developmental biology**, "evo-devo" for short, asks how evolutionary changes in genes regulating embryonic development can lead to changes in body shape and form.

The study of development helps advance the understanding of macroevolutionary trends because changes in genes that regulate development often promote evolution of morphological innovations. Moreover, the resulting changes in body plan have sometimes fostered adaptive radiations, increasing biodiversity over geologic time. In the life cycle of a multicellular organism, the many different body parts of the adult develop in a highly controlled sequence of steps specified by genetic instructions in the single cell of a fertilized egg. Developmental biologists study how regulatory genes control the development of phenotypes and their variations. (Gene regulation was described in Chapter 14). Homeotic genes are regulatory genes that code for transcription factors that bind regulatory sites on DNA, either activating or repressing the expression of other genes that contribute to an organism's form (see Chapter 13).

20.8a Genetic Tool-Kits: Controlling Growth and Development

Comparisons of genome sequence data reveal that most animals, regardless of their complexity or position in the tree of life (see Figure 3.7), share a set of several hundred homeotic genes that control their development. This "genetic tool-kit" governs the basic design of the body plan by controlling the activity of thousands of other genes. Some of the homeotic genes must be at least 500 million years old because all living animals inherited them from a common ancestor alive then. Some of the same tool kit genes are present in plants, fungi, and prokaryotes, suggesting that those genes could date back to the earliest forms of life.

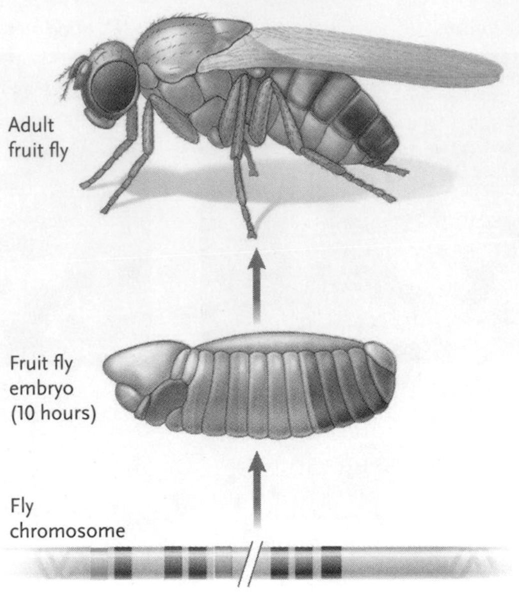

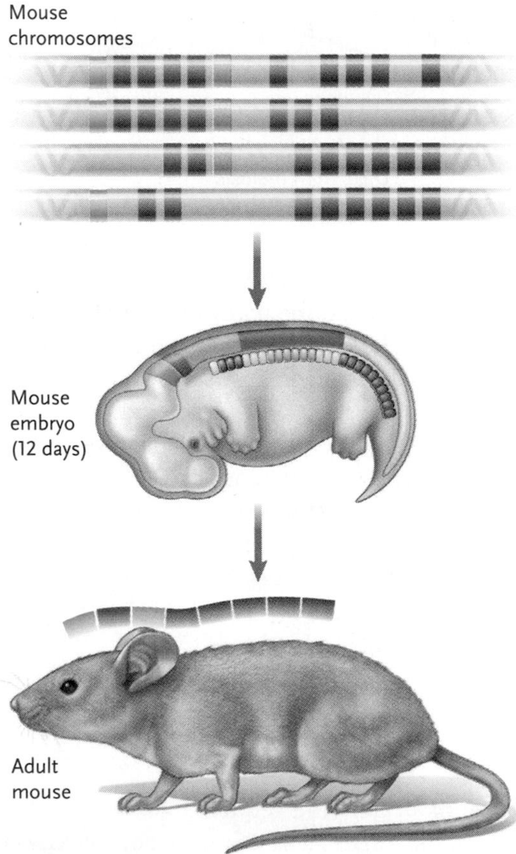

Figure 20.21
Hox **genes.** The linear sequence of *Hox* genes on chromosomes and their expression in different body regions have been conserved by evolution. Each colour-coded band on the chromosomes in the illustration represents a different gene in the *Hox* family. Fruit flies have one set of *Hox* genes, which are arranged on a single chromosome in the same order that they are expressed in the fruit fly embryo. Like all mammals, mice have four sets of *Hox* genes, arranged on four chromosomes that are expressed in mouse embryos in the same order as the *Hox* genes in fruit flies. The illustrations of the adult fruit fly and mouse show the adult body regions influenced by the expression of *Hox* genes in their embryos.

Structurally, tool-kit genes do not differ much among the animals that have them and generally play the same role in development in all species. Genes in the *Hox* family control the overall body plan of animals. *Hox* genes always include a 180-nucleotide sequence (a **homeobox**) that codes for a **homeodomain**, part of a protein that functions as a transcription factor. When bound to a regulatory site on a strand of DNA, the homeodomain either activates or represses a downstream gene involved in development.

Among other functions, *Hox* genes specify where appendages such as wings in flies and legs in mice will develop on the animal's body. They do so by producing transcription factors that activate the genes that produce wings or legs in the body regions where these appendages typically grow. Different *Hox* genes are expressed at different positions along the head-to-tail axis of a developing embryo. These genes are arranged on a chromosome in the same sequence in which they are expressed in the body. Remarkably, the *Hox* genes and their relative positions on chromosomes have been conserved by evolution. Nearly identical genes are found in animals as different as fruit flies (phylum Arthropoda) and mice (phylum Chordata) **(Figure 20.21).** Genes with comparable functions control aspects of development in plants (see Chapter 31).

Pax-6 is another highly conserved and widely distributed tool-kit gene. The *Pax-6* gene triggers the formation of light-sensing organs as diverse as the eye spots in flatworms, the compound eyes of insects and other arthropods, and the camera eyes of vertebrates (see Chapter 34). Like *Hox* genes, *Pax-6* contains a homeobox, indicating that the protein for which it codes either activates or represses gene transcription. Proteins coded by *Pax-6* in different animals are so similar that when researchers genetically engineered fruit fly larvae to express the *Pax-6* gene taken from either a squid or a mouse, the flies responded by developing eyes. The induced eyes were, however, fruit fly eyes, not squid eyes or mouse eyes. Thus, *Pax-6* triggers activity in genes that carry the specific instructions for making an eye typical of the species. Apparently, the ancient genetic sequence for *Pax-6*, the master regulatory gene for eye development, has been conserved over the hundreds of millions of years since squids, fruit flies, and mice shared a common ancestor.

20.8b Evolutionary Changes in Development Switches: Changes in Gene Expression

If most animals share the same tool-kit genes, how has evolution produced different body plans among species? What makes a squid, a fruit fly, and a mouse different? Researchers in evo-devo have proposed that morphological differences among species arise when mutations alter the effects of developmental regulatory genes. As you will discover in Chapter 39, developmental programs of animals involve complex networks of many interacting genes. Continuously changing combinations of tool-kit genes may be expressed at different times and in different body regions. According to this hypothesis, the several hundred tool-kit genes encode proteins that work either as activators or repressors in a multitude of possible combinations. Thus, they can generate an unimaginably large number of different gene expression patterns, each with the potential to alter morphology.

Sean Carroll described the regulatory sites that transcription factors can bind as *switches*, like those that we use to turn lights on or off. When a combination of transcription factors turns a regulatory switch on, they activate a gene further downstream. When they turn it off, their activity represses the gene.

Although all the cells in an animal contain exactly the same set of genes, the differential expression of genes in different body regions and at different times during embryonic development causes different structures to be made. Allometric growth can result from evolutionary changes in developmental switches that cause certain body parts to grow larger or more quickly than others. Similarly, heterochrony can be explained as an evolutionary change in the switches that either delays the development of adult characteristics or speeds up the development of reproductive maturity.

If Carroll's hypothesis is correct, morphological novelties arise when evolutionary changes in developmental switches alter the expression patterns of *existing* genes. This view contrasts markedly with the explanation that most morphological novelties arise as mutations that slowly accumulate in genes that carry the blueprints for building particular structures. In this scenario, accumulated mutations eventually create *new* genes that specify the creation of new structures.

Although Carroll's hypothesis argues that changes in the genes that regulate development cause most morphological change, proponents of evo-devo recognize that mutations in developmental regulatory genes and their effects on morphology are subject to the action of the same microevolutionary processes—natural selection, genetic drift, and gene flow—that influence the frequencies of genotypes and phenotypes in populations. Thus, every morphological change induced by a mutation in a homeotic gene or in a developmental switch is tested by the success or failure of the individual that carries it.

Numerous studies have shown that changes in the expression of homeotic genes can have dramatic effects on morphology. Fancy footwork from fins to fingers explains how a change in the number and expression of *Hox* genes produced a striking alteration in the structure of vertebrate limbs (see *From Fins to Fingers*).

In another example, researchers have determined how an adaptive morphological change in a small fish, the three-spined stickleback (*Gasterosteus aculeatus*), results from the deactivation of a homeotic gene. The freshwater stickleback populations in North American lakes are the descendants of marine ancestors that colonized the lakes after the retreat of glaciers between 10 000 and 20 000 years ago. Marine sticklebacks have bony armour along their sides and prominent spines; lake-dwelling sticklebacks have greatly reduced armour and, in many populations, lack spines on their pelvic fins **(Figure 20.22)**.

Natural selection has apparently fostered these morphological differences in response to the dominant predators in each habitat. In marine environments, long spines prevent some predatory fishes from swallowing sticklebacks. But long spines are a liability in lakes, where voracious dragonfly larvae grab sticklebacks by their spines and then devour them. Freshwater sticklebacks that lack spines are more likely to escape from their clutches.

The presence or absence of spines on the pelvic fins of sticklebacks is governed by the expression of the gene *Pitx1*. Pelvic spines are part of the pelvic fin skeleton, the fishes' equivalent of a hind limb. In fact, *Pitx1* also contributes to the development of hind limbs in four-legged vertebrates as well as certain glands and sensory organs in the head. In long-spined marine sticklebacks, *Pitx1* is expressed in the embryonic buds from which pelvic fins develop, promoting the development of spines. But *Pitx1* is not expressed in the fin buds of the freshwater sticklebacks, and pelvic spines do not develop in them. However, freshwater sticklebacks have not *lost* the *Pitx1* gene, which is still expressed elsewhere in the fishes' bodies. Apparently, a mutation somehow blocks its expression in the developing pelvic fin, thereby blocking the production of pelvic spines.

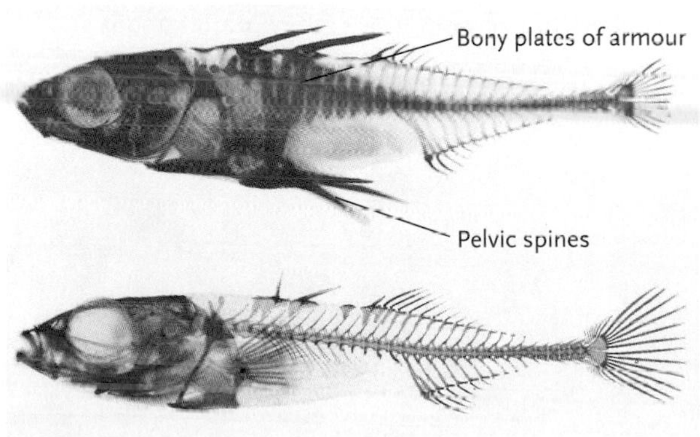

Figure 20.22
Stickleback marine populations (top) of three-spined sticklebacks (*Gasterosteus aculeatus*) have bony plates along their sides and large spines on their dorsal and pelvic fins. Many freshwater populations of the same species (bottom) lack the bony plates and spines. Pelvic spines do not develop in the freshwater fishes because they do not express the *Pitx1* gene in their fin buds during embryonic development. The skeletons of these specimens, each about 8 cm long, were dyed bright red.

From Fins to Fingers

The early embryonic development of the limbs of fishes and tetrapods is similar. The limbs start as buds of mesoderm, which thicken by increased cell division. As the buds elongate, cartilage is deposited at localized centres, the precursors of later limb bones. In fishes, bones develop along a central axis from base to tip **(Figure 1a).** In tetrapods, centres of cartilage formation generate the long bones of the limb and the five digits of the foot (or hand; **Figure 1b**).

To assess the patterns of development and determine if the digits of tetrapods were modifications of the bones radiating from the central axis in fish, biologists used molecular techniques. In tetrapods with paired forelimbs and hind limbs, groups of homeobox genes control their development. A comparison of *HoxD* genes in zebrafish (*Danio rerio*) and previously available data from birds and mammals revealed the details of development. Using the DNA from a rodent *HoxD* gene as a probe, researchers searched for similar genes in fragmented zebrafish DNA. After cloning and sequencing, it was clear that the *HoxD-11*, *HoxD-12*, and *HoxD-13* genes in zebrafish are arranged in the same order as they are in rodents.

Paolo Sordino, Franks van der Hoeven, and Denis Duboule then tested the activity of *HoxD* genes in developing zebrafish using a nucleic acid probe that could pair with mRNA products of the genes. The probe was linked to a blue dye molecule so that the cells in which a particular *HoxD* gene was active would appear blue in the light microscope. In zebrafish, the *HoxD* genes became active in cells along the posterior side of the central axis **(Figure 1c).** As limb development neared completion, the activity of *HoxD* genes dropped off.

Using the same approach in tetrapods, the researchers found that the *HoxD* genes were activated in two distinct phases **(Figure 1d).** In phase 1, gene activity was restricted to the posterior half of the limb, as it had been in zebrafish. This period of activity corresponded to the development of long limb bones. In phase 2, the *HoxD* genes became active in a band of cells perpendicular to the central axis. Here, cartilage centres formed the bones of the digits that developed in an anterior–posterior band. These patterns differed from those in zebrafish, suggesting morphological novelty in tetrapods. These changes in *HoxD* activity must have preceded the development of tetrapod limbs.

A comparison of levels of activity of bone morphogenetic protein 2 (*Bmp2*) house mice (*Mus musculus*) and short-tailed fruit bats (*Carollia perspicillata*) may help explain the development of elongated fingers that support the wings of bats. Elongation of bat fingers reflects growth of cartilage, which depends on relative proliferation and differentiation of cartilage cells (chondrocytes). The developing forelimbs of bats have higher levels of *Bmp2* compared with the hind limbs of the bats or the forelimbs and hind limbs of mice.

Differences in developmental patterns reflect genetic differences.

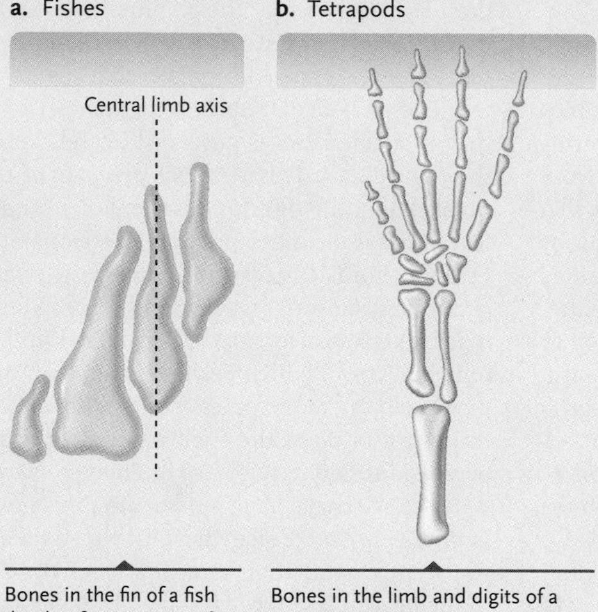

Bones in the fin of a fish develop from centers of cartilage formation along a central axis (dashed line).

Bones in the limb and digits of a tetrapod also develop from centers of cartilage formation in the central axis.

c. Fishes

d. Tetrapods

Phase 2 activity

Phase 1 activity

Anterior

Posterior

During development of the fin in fishes, *HoxD* genes become active in cells posterior to the central axis of the fin (shown in blue).

During development of the limb and digits in tetrapods, *HoxD* genes first become active in cells posterior to the central axis of the limb (blue). Later, these genes are active in a band of cells perpendicular to the central axis of the limb (green).

Figure 1
Fins versus fingers: *HoxD* genes in action.

Spidroin

Spider and their webs have always fascinated people. Ancient Greeks are said to have used spider webs to staunch bleeding wounds. Some Australian aborigines used webs for fishing. In the American Civil War, a surgeon, Burt G. Wilder, built a device to hold spider webs and collected 137 metres from one cooperative spider.

Spider silk (also known as spidroin) is very strong, but its thinness makes it workable. It can stretch to 40% of its normal length and return to its original length. Spider webs may include both a supporting architecture and an overlay of sticky capture spiral.

Spiders produce more than one kind of silk. Spidroins **(Figure 1)** are the proteins comprising spider silk. Spidroins have been reported in two lineages of orb-weaving spiders (araneoids and deinopoids) and from six non–orb weavers.

Orthologues are genes that evolved from a common ancestor through speciation. In spiders, the silk proteins MaSp1 and MaSp2 are orthologues.

The dragline web silk of orb-web spiders is a composite of MaSp1 and MaSp2, and both proteins are encoded at multiple loci.

Silk gland cDNAs were characterized from both groups of orb weavers (the araneoid ***Uloborus diversus*** and the deinopid ***Deinopis spinosa***) and other spiders **(Figure 2).** Both the araneoid and the dinopid use MaSp2, and both have flagelliform-like spigots that are used to make silk capture spirals. In the silk glands, spidroins are soluble but turn into an insoluble solid after leaving the body. The cDNA data suggest that the ancestor of orb weavers had the genetic tools for effecting orb web construction.

The fossil record of spiders reveals some information on the first appearance of webs. The first fossil webs found are from the Early Cretaceous (~110 million years old) and have been reported from Lebanon and Spain. The Spanish fossils (see Figure 2) suggest an orb web with supporting architecture and capture spiral.

The radiation of insects, probably just after that of angiosperms, is thought to predate the diversification of spiders. Using webs, spiders were able to catch flying insects not otherwise available to predators that did not fly. Of special importance was the radiation of small flying insects (flies: Diptera; bees and wasps: Hymenoptera; and beetles: Coleoptera), the main prey of today's araneid spiders. Wood spiders **(Figure 3)** are commonly used by biologists and chemists studying webs.

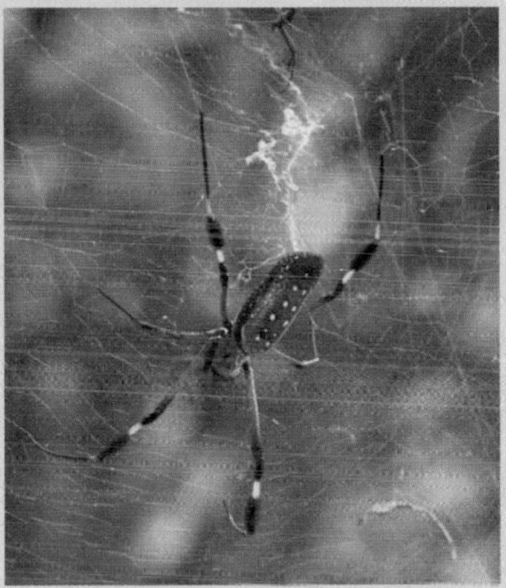

Figure 3
A 2 cm-long *Nephila* (wood spider) female on its web in Costa Rica.

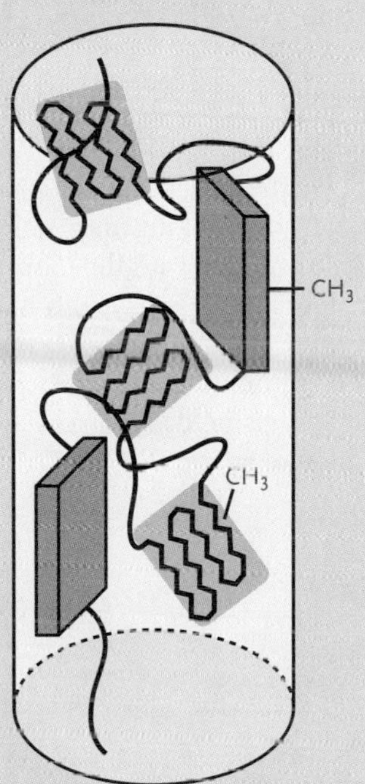

Figure 1
Spidroin.

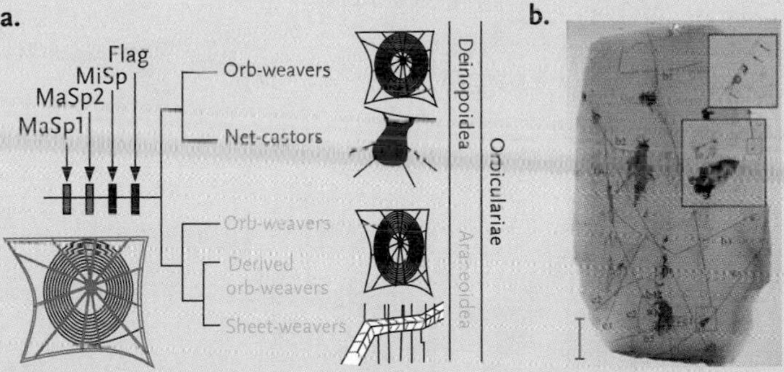

Figure 2
Relationships **(a)** of orb-weaving spiders and spidroins showing inferred ancestral web and spidroins. Orb-web frame and radii composed of MaSp1 (blue) and MaSp2 (brown) are shown with MiSp (black) capture spiral with flag. Spider web in amber **(b)** with arthropods sticking to it. Amber is from Early Cretaceous of Spain. Scale bar is 1 mm. Strands of web are identified by lettered lines.

Study Break

1. Name three examples of regulatory genes.
2. Why are sticklebacks a good example of developmental biology?
3. What is allometric growth? Give an example of it.

20.9 Evolutionary Biology since Darwin

Our ideas about evolution have changed over time (evolved!) and expanded as more people enter the field, we obtain more data, and from different organisms. Having access to more data and more points of view stimulates further thought and reflection, as well as the design of new experiments. The discovery of previously unknown fossils also changes our view of evolutionary history.

Biologists and paleontologists had known for some time that dinosaurs originated 200 to 230 million years ago (Late Triassic). Before 2007, the only evidence of precursors to dinosaurs was fossils from the Middle Triassic of Argentina. The fossil record appeared to indicate that dinosaurs appeared abruptly in the Late Triassic. Writing in *Science* on July 20, 2007, Randall B. Irmis and colleagues reported Upper Triassic fossils from New Mexico **(Figure 20.23)** and suggested that the transition to a fauna dominated by dinosaurs took 15 to 20 million years.

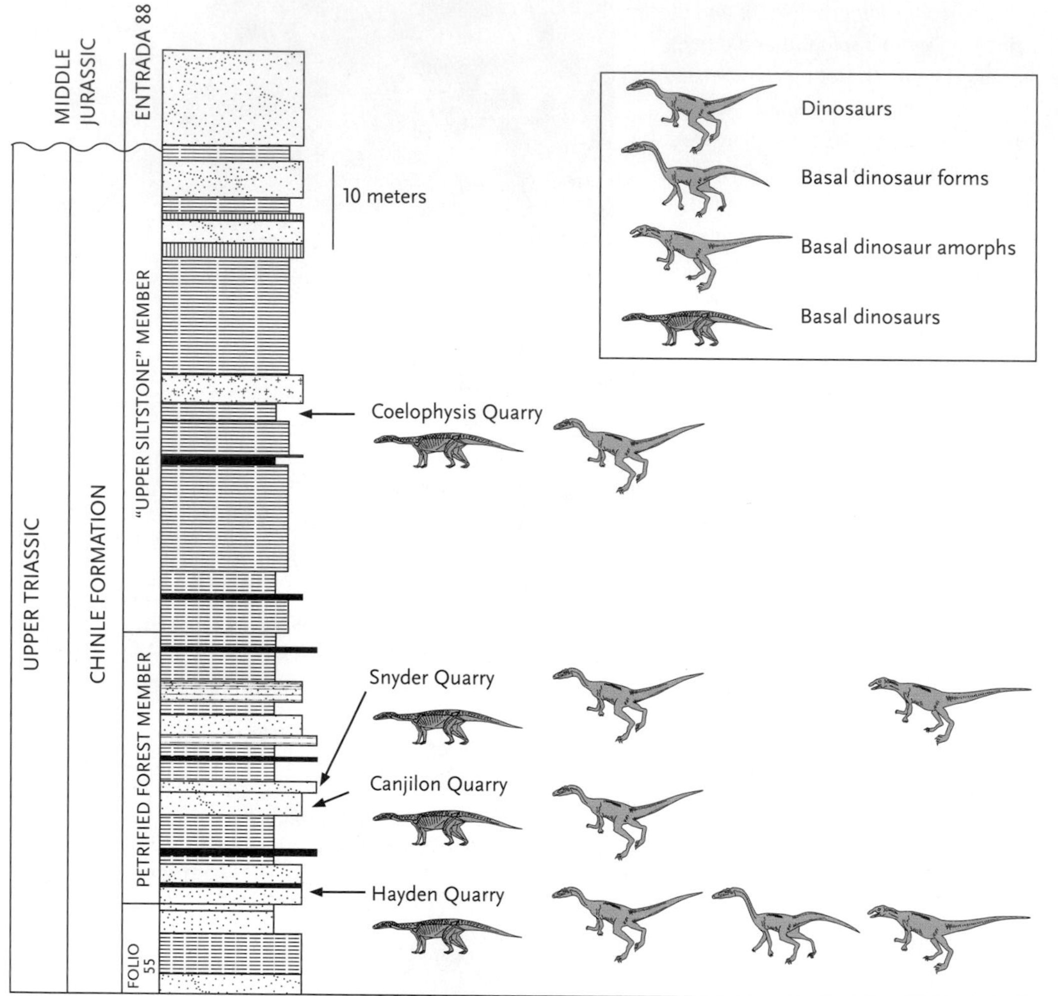

Figure 20.23
The rise of dinosaurs. Stratigraphic position of Middle Triassic fossil beds containing early dinosaurs and other reptiles.

Study Break

1. What are the general functions of tool-kit genes?
2. How can species with the same tool-kit genes have different morphologies?
3. Why is it important that flying insects predated diversification of spiders?

Unanswered Questions

Imagine a population of mice that includes brown and black individuals. They live in a habitat with brown soil, where predatory hawks can see black mice more easily than they can see brown ones. Design a study that would allow you to determine whether brown or black mice are better adapted to this environment. What would happen if you used different predators, for example, owls or rattlesnakes?

Find examples from popular publications or advertisements for consumer products that misrepresent the theory of biological evolution. Explain how the theory is misrepresented.

Review

Go to CENGAGENOW™ at http://hed.nelson.com/ to access quizzing, animations, exercises, articles, and personalized homework help.

20.1 Recognition of Evolutionary Change

- Well before Darwin published his theory of evolution by natural selection, changes in scientific thought and methods paved the way for its appearance. Natural theology promoted investigation of living organisms, giving rise to ideas that species had changed since their creation. Fields such as geology contributed through documentation of the fossil record and the discovery that Earth was very, very old.
- Remember the contributions of people such as Aristotle, Bacon, Buffon, Copernicus, Cuvier, Hutton, Lamarck, Linnaeus, Lyell, Malthus, Newton, and Wallace.

20.2 Changes in Earth

- Plate tectonics can be responsible for phenomena such as continental drift and have strong influences on the distribution and evolution of organisms.
- Changes in Earth's crust can also cause calamitous events, such as earthquakes, which also have implications for living organisms.

20.3 Charles Darwin

- A five-year voyage on HMS *Beagle* introduced Charles Darwin to many variations in the natural world. Darwin's theory of evolution recognized the importance of variation and provided a mechanism (natural selection) that can be tested using data from nature.

20.4 The Fossil Record

- Conditions of low oxygen or high acidity are ideal for fossilization. Hard structures such as skeletons and teeth do not readily decompose and are more often fossilized than softer structures. Some fossils are casts or moulds; in others, the original materials are replaced by dissolved minerals. The availability of fossils is highly skewed toward certain areas, certain organisms, or parts of organisms.
- Relative dating involves comparisons of deeper (older) strata to shallower (younger) strata. Radiometric dating is based on the decay rates of unstable isotopes and permits absolute dating.

20.5 Earth History, Biogeography, and Convergent Evolution

- Continuous distributions require no special explanation, but disjunct distributions result from dispersal and/or vicariance. In vicariance, external conditions fragment a continuous distribution and create new geographic barriers. Dispersing organisms may cross geographic barriers.
- Under similar environmental pressures and lifestyles, similar structures are favoured by natural selection. Therefore, structures may be morphologically similar even among unrelated species. Sharks, tunas, ichthyosaurs, and dolphins share similar lifestyles and habitats and have similar shapes. Worms, caecilians, cacti, and spurges are other examples of organisms that resemble one another but have evolved from different ancestries.

20.6 Interpreting Evolutionary Linages

- The evolution and adaptive radiation of horses demonstrate that many species arise and disappear, revealing that the evolution of a species is not a linear process. Possession of intermediate traits may not be evidence of direct ancestry.
- In anagenesis, evolutionary changes in one species gradually change that species until it is distinct enough from the original to be considered a novel species.
- The gradualist hypothesis proposes that large changes result from small changes over time. The punctuated equilibrium hypothesis proposes that speciation occurs rapidly during cladogenesis. Evolutionary biologists must consider both hypotheses because both may be involved in the evolution of the group they study.

20.7 Macroevolutionary Trends in Morphology

- A preadaptated trait evolved under pressures for one function and later was coopted for another.
- Allometric growth occurs when there are differential growth rates of different parts of the body during development. In closely related species, allometric growth can lead to significant morphological changes. The same body part may be much larger in one species than in another.
- Pedomorphosis (neoteny) is the retention of the juvenile traits in the adult. Pedomorphosis is an example of heterochrony, changes in developmental timing that can lead to novel species.

20.8 Evolutionary Developmental Biology

- *Hox* and *Pax* genes are examples of tool-kit genes. Tool-kit genes control the development of the body plan through regulation of the timing and amount of expression of many other genes important in the development of particular structures. Tool-kit genes may have different levels of activity at different times, leading to a different sequence of development and different morphology.

20.9 Evolutionary Biology since Darwin

- Many spiders use webs to catch flying insects. To attribute the function of modern spider webs to capturing insects, the flying insects would have to have been present and sufficiently abundant during the period of spider diversification. Spider silk could have been a preadaptation, originally serving some other purpose, such as defence, and been coopted for insect capture with the diversification of flying insects.
- New discoveries change our view of evolution and the history of the world, such as the discovery that the rise of dinosaurs spanned 15 to 20 million years.

Questions

Self-Test Questions

1. Which of the following statements about evolutionary studies is INCORRECT?
   a. Biologists study the products of evolution to understand processes causing it.
   b. Biologists design molecular experiments to examine evolutionary processes operating over short time periods.
   c. Biologists study inheritance of characteristics a parent acquired during its lifetime.
   d. Biologists study variation in homologous structures among related organisms.
   e. Biologists examine why a huge variety of species may inhabit a small island.
2. Which of the following ideas is NOT included in Darwin's theory?
   a. All organisms that ever existed arose through evolutionary modifications of ancestral species.
   b. Most species alive today resulted from the diversification of ancestral species.
   c. Natural selection drives some evolutionary change.
   d. Natural selection preserves favourable traits.
   e. Natural selection eliminates adaptive traits.
3. The father of taxonomy was
   a. Charles Darwin.
   b. Charles Lyell.
   c. Alfred Wallace.
   d. Carolus Linnaeus.
   e. Jean Baptiste de Lamarck.
4. The wings of birds, the forelegs of pigs, and the flippers of whales are examples of
   a. vestigial structures.
   b. homologous structures.
   c. acquired characteristics.
   d. artificial selection.
   e. uniformitarianism.
5. Which of the following statements is NOT compatible with Darwin's theory?
   a. All organisms have arisen by descent with modification.
   b. Evolution has altered and diversified ancestral species.
   c. Evolution occurs in individuals rather than in groups.
   d. Natural selection eliminates unsuccessful variations.
   e. Evolution occurs because some individuals function better than others in a particular environment.
6. Which of the following does NOT contribute to the study of evolution?
   a. population genetics
   b. inheritance of acquired characteristics
   c. the fossil record
   d. DNA sequencing
   e. comparative morphology
7. Which of the following could be an example of microevolution?
   a. a slight change in a bird population's song arising from a small genetic change in the population
   b. the evolution of many species of finch from a common ancestor
   c. the sudden disappearance of an entire genus
   d. the direct evolutionary link between living primates and humans
   e. a flood that drowns all members of a population
8. Which of the following ideas proposed by Lamarck was NOT included in Darwin's theory?
   a. Organisms change in response to their environments.
   b. Changes that an organism acquires during its lifetime are passed to its offspring.
   c. All species change with time.
   d. Changes are passed from one generation to the next.
   e. Specific mechanisms cause evolutionary change.
9. Medical advances now allow many people who suffer from genetic diseases to survive and reproduce. These advances
   a. refute Darwin's theory.
   b. support Lamarck's theory.
   c. disprove descent with modification.
   d. reduce the effects of natural selection.
   e. eliminate adaptive traits.
10. The belief that evolution is progressive or goal oriented is called
    a. gradualism.
    b. uniformitarianism.
    c. taxonomy.
    d. orthogenesis.
    e. the modern synthesis.

Questions for Discussion

1. Would Charles Darwin have had the same inspiration about natural selection and evolution had he visited other islands? Think of the situation on Hawaii, on Easter Island, or on Tristan da Cunha. Why would the island matter?
2. Recognizing the diversity of life means at least appreciating the nature of the organisms you encounter. Do you think that the fauna of the Burgess Shales (Cambrian rocks from British Columbia) is so unusual as to conceal the adaptive radiation that it represents? What is so unusual about the Burgess Shales fauna?
3. Explain why the characteristics we see in living organisms adapt them to the environments in which their ancestors lived rather than to the environments in which they live today. What are examples of this situation?

The bacterium *Escherichia coli*

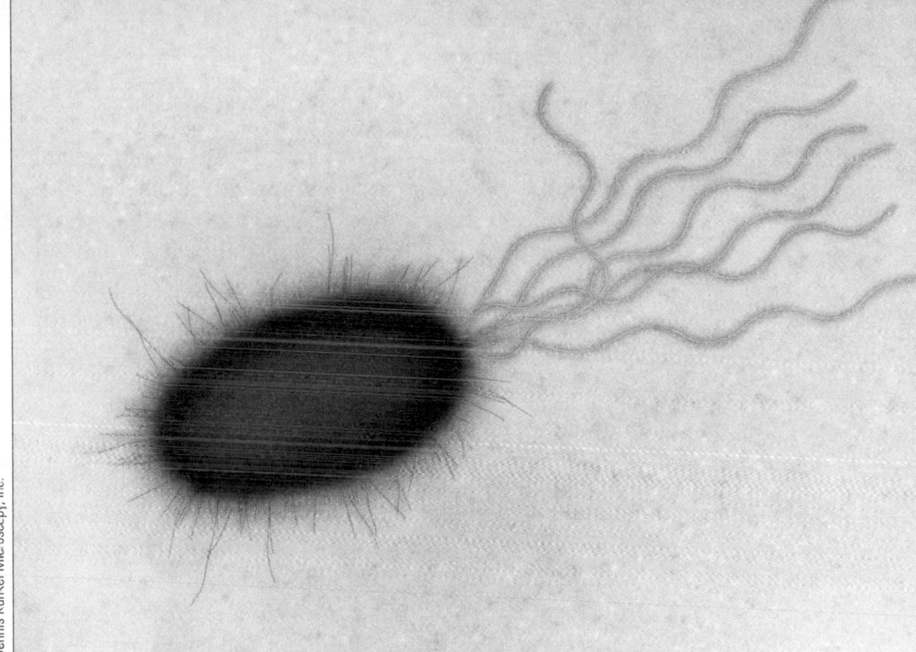

Dennis Kunkel Microscopy, Inc.

21 Prokaryotes

Study Plan

Why It Matters

In the spring of 2000, seven people, including a small child, in the town of Walkerton, Ontario, died and hundreds of others became ill when the town's drinking water supply was contaminated by a strain of *Escherichia coli* bacteria, known as *E. coli* O157:H7 (the letters indicate the location of bacterial **antigens**, substances that stimulate antibody production by the immune system; "O" refers to the cell wall antigen, and "H" is the flagellar antigen). This strain has been found in the intestines of healthy livestock animals such as cattle, sheep, and goats and can be passed on to humans if they eat meat from those animals that is not sufficiently cooked or if manure from infected animals contaminates groundwater that feeds into drinking water supplies, as was the case in Walkerton. Once cells of this strain colonize our intestinal tracts, they multiply and produce a toxin that kills intestinal epithelial cells, causing hemorrhaging. In some people, infection also results in hemolytic–uremic syndrome, in which red blood cells are destroyed and kidney function is compromised. Complications from this syndrome can last for the rest of the victim's life. Brett Finlay of the University of British Columbia, in collaboration with researchers from the University of Saskatchewan, has developed a vaccine against *E. coli* O157:H7 for cattle. Field trials of this vaccine are now under way; if successful, we may be able to stop our livestock from acting as carriers of this deadly strain.

But *E. coli* is also a normal and necessary inhabitant of healthy intestinal tracts because it provides us with vitamin K. In fact, without *E. coli*, our intestines would be overrun by harmful bacteria. So how did "friendly" *E. coli* become pathogenic? And why aren't antibiotics effective against the pathogenic strain of *E. coli* or against many other pathogenic bacteria? In this chapter, we explore these questions as we investigate the biology of bacteria and other prokaryotes. But don't think that all or even most prokaryotes are harmful! Nothing could be further from the truth: most known prokaryotes play a crucial role in ecosystems, recycling nutrients and breaking down compounds that no other organisms can. Others carry out reactions important in food production, in industry (e.g., production of pharmaceutical products), or in bioremediation of polluted sites.

In this chapter, we first look at the structure and function of prokaryotes, emphasizing the features that differentiate them from other organisms, and conclude with a look at the diversity of this group of fascinating organisms.

21.1 The Full Extent of Prokaryote Diversity Is Unknown

While reading this chapter, keep in mind that everything we know so far about prokaryotes is based on a tiny fraction of the total number of species. We have isolated and identified only about 6000 species, which may be as low as 1% of the total number. There are entire habitats—such as the oceans, which make up 70% of Earth's surface—for which we know almost nothing about the prokaryote inhabitants (see *Unanswered Questions* at the end of the chapter). Why have we only identified so few, and why are we not even sure how many prokaryotes there might be? We have been able to make detailed studies only of prokaryotes that we can grow in culture, and the vast majority of prokaryotes cannot grow on the media and conditions we can provide. As you will see later in the chapter, many prokaryotes live in very extreme conditions, and we cannot yet create favourable growth conditions in our labs. Estimates of prokaryote diversity from many habitats are thus based solely on molecular data, that is, DNA samples isolated from various habitats.

21.1a Prokaryotes Make Up Two of the Three Domains of Life

Two domains of living organisms, **Archaea** and **Bacteria**, consist of prokaryotes (the third domain, **Eukarya**, includes all eukaryotes). Bacteria are the prokaryotic organisms most familiar to us, including those responsible for diseases of humans and other animals. Archaea are not as well known as they were only discovered about 40 years ago. As you will see in this chapter, Archaea share some cellular features with eukaryotes and some with bacteria but have still other features that are unique. Many of the Archaea live under very extreme conditions that no other organisms, including bacteria, can survive.

21.2 Prokaryote Structure and Function

We begin our survey of prokaryotes by examining their cellular structure, their mode of reproduction, and how they obtain energy and nutrients.

Prokaryotes are the smallest organisms in the world **(Figure 21.1)**. Few species are more than 1 to 2 μm long; from 500 to 1000 of them would fit side

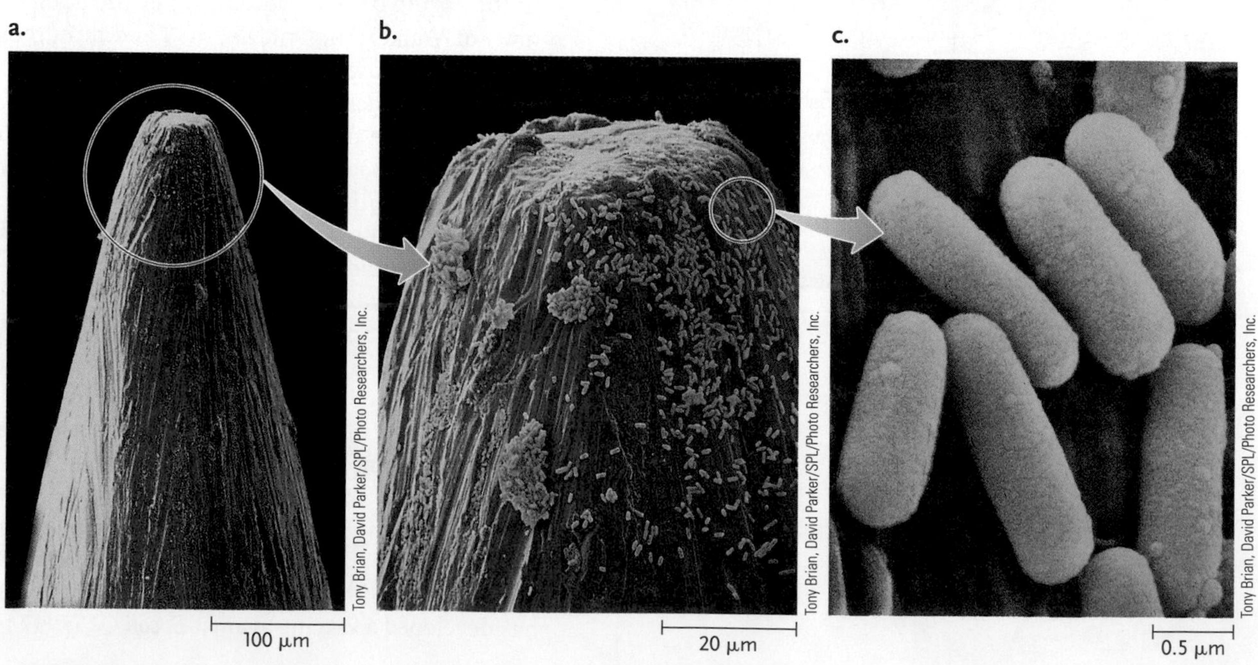

Figure 21.1
Bacillus bacteria on the point of a pin. Cells magnified **(a)** 70 times, **(b)** 350 times, and **(c)** 14 000 times.

by side across the dot above this letter "i." Despite the small size of prokaryotes, they dominate life on Earth: current estimates of total prokaryote diversity are in the billions of species, and their total collective mass (their **biomass**) on Earth exceeds that of animals and may be greater than that of all plant life. Prokaryotes colonize every niche on Earth that supports life—for example, huge numbers of bacteria inhabit the surfaces and cavities of a healthy human body, including the skin, mouth and nasal passages, and large intestine. Collectively, the bacteria in and on your body outnumber all the other cells in your body. It is not surprising that prokaryote diversity should be so much greater than that of eukaryotes because for about 3 billion years they were the only forms of life on Earth and so had time to diversify and expand into every habitat on Earth before the first eukaryotes appeared on the scene (see Chapter 2).

21.2a Prokaryotic Cells Appear Simple in Structure Compared with Eukaryotic Cells

Three cell shapes are common among prokaryotes: spiral, spherical (or **coccoid**; *coccus* = berry), and cylindrical (known as **rods**), but some Archaea even have square cells **(Figure 21.2)**.

At first glance, a typical prokaryotic cell seems much more simple than a eukaryotic cell **(Figure 21.3, p. 468)**: images taken with standard electron microscopy typically reveal little more than a cell wall and plasma membrane surrounding a cytoplasm with DNA concentrated in one region and ribosomes scattered throughout. The chromosome is not contained in a membrane-bound nucleus but is packed into an area of the cell called the **nucleoid**. Prokaryotic cells have no cytoplasmic organelles equivalent to the mitochondria, endoplasmic reticulum, or Golgi complex of eukaryotic cells (see Chapter 2). With few exceptions, the reactions carried out by these organelles in eukaryotes are distributed between the cytoplasmic solution and the plasma membrane in prokaryotes. This evident simplicity led people to regard prokaryote cells as featureless and disorganized. However, the apparent simplicity of these cells is misleading: new microscopic techniques reveal that prokaryote cells do have a cytoskeleton—not homologous to that of a eukaryote but serving some of the same functions—and have more sophisticated organization than was previously thought.

Internal Structures. The genome of most prokaryotes consists of a single, circular DNA molecule, although some, such as the causative agent of Lyme disease

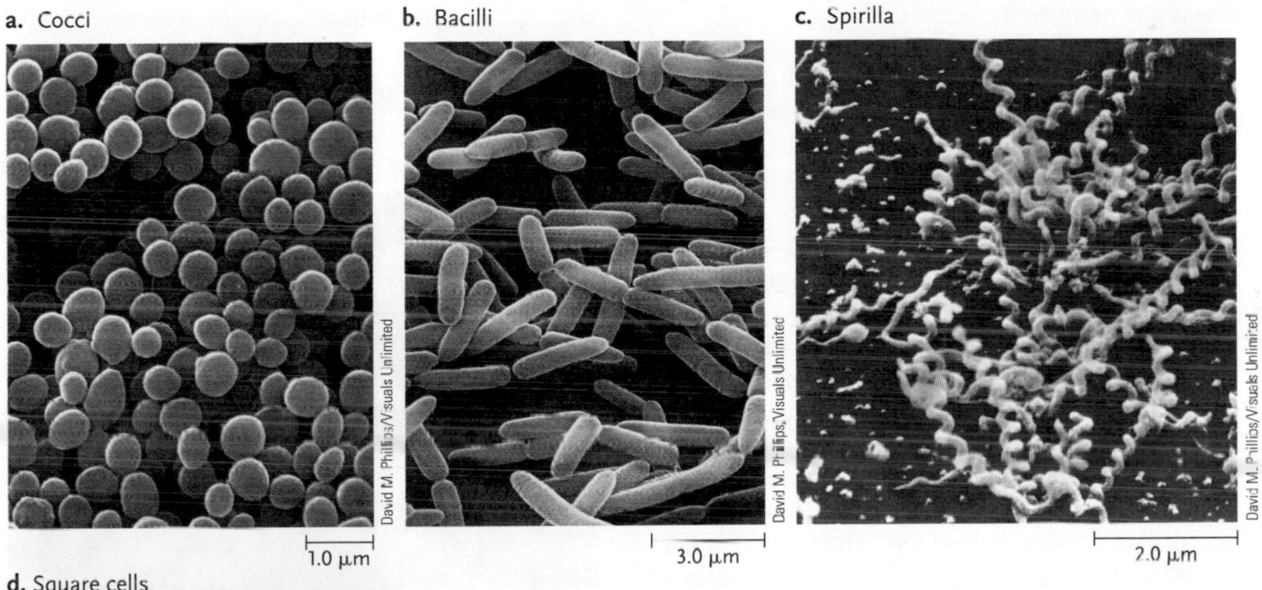

Figure 21.2
Common shapes among prokaryotes. **(a)** Scanning electron microscope (SEM) image of *Micrococcus*, a coccoid bacterium. **(b)** SEM image of *Salmonella*, a rod bacterium. **(c)** SEM image of *Spiroplasma*, a spiral bacterium. **(d)** SEM image of *Haloquadratum walsbyi*, a square archaeon.

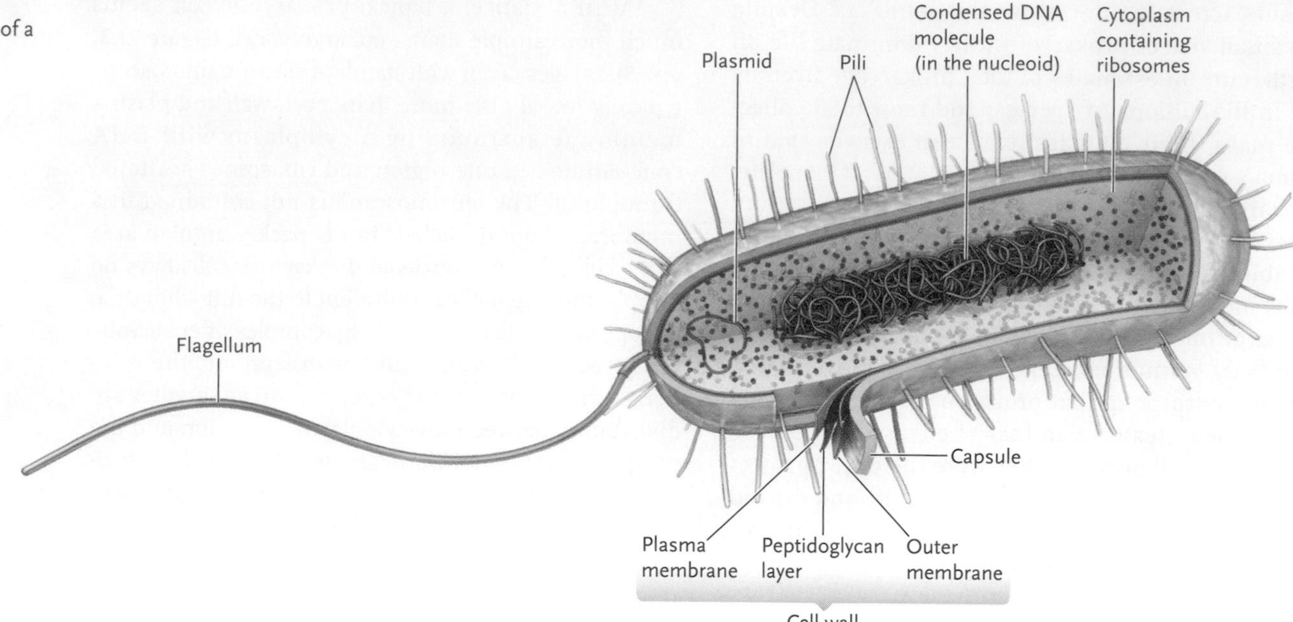

Figure 21.3
The structure of a bacterial cell.

(*Borrelia burgdorferi*), have a linear chromosome. Many prokaryotes also contain small circles of DNA called **plasmids (Figure 21.4)**, which generally contain genes for nonessential but beneficial functions such as antibiotic resistance. Plasmids replicate independently of the cell's chromosomes and can be transferred from one cell to another, meaning that genes for antibiotic resistance are readily shared among prokaryotic cells, even among cells of different species. This *horizontal gene transfer* allows antibiotic resistance and other traits to spread very quickly in bacterial populations. Horizontal gene transfer also occurs when bacterial cells take up DNA from their environment (e.g., from other cells that have lysed) or when viruses transfer DNA from one bacterium to another (see Chapter 22). Evidence indicates that a virus transferred toxin-encoding genes from *Shigella dysenteriae* (which causes bloody diarrhea) to *E. coli*, resulting in the deadly O157:H7 strain.

Like eukaryotic cells, prokaryotic cells contain ribosomes. Bacterial ribosomes are smaller than eukaryotic ribosomes but carry out protein synthesis by essentially the same mechanisms as those of eukaryotes (see Chapter 14). Archaeal ribosomes resemble those of bacteria in size but differ in structure; protein synthesis in Archaea is a combination of bacterial and eukaryotic processes, with some unique archaeal features. As a result, antibiotics that stop bacterial infections by targeting ribosome activity do not interfere with archaeal protein synthesis.

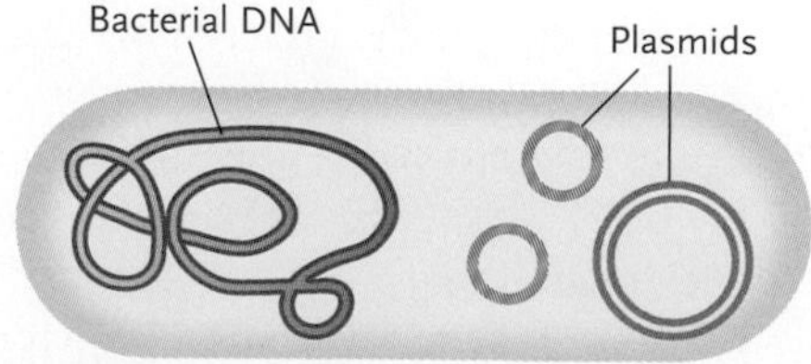

Figure 21.4
Plasmids inside a prokaryote cell.

Prokaryotic Cell Walls. Most prokaryotes have a cell wall that lies outside their plasma membrane. The primary component of bacterial cell walls is **peptidoglycan**, a polymer of sugars and amino acids, which forms linear chains. Peptide cross-linkages between the chains give the cell wall great strength and rigidity. The antibiotic penicillin prevents the formation of these cross-linkages, resulting in a weak cell wall that is easily ruptured, killing the cell **(Figure 21.5)**.

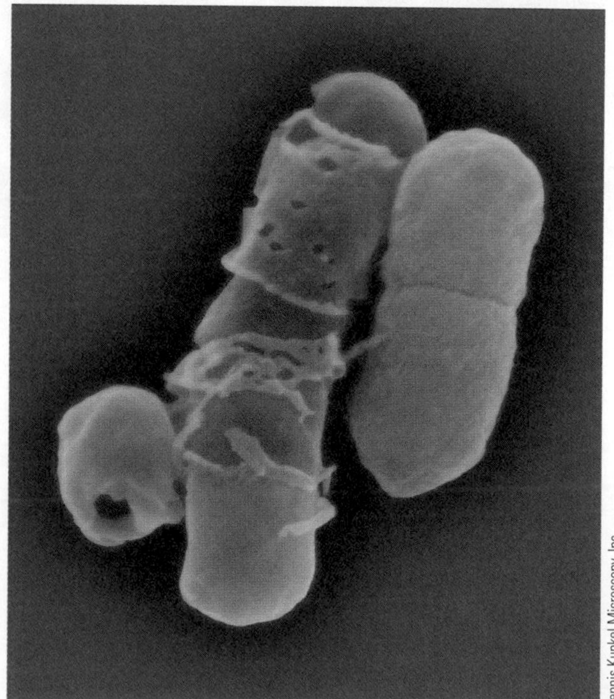

Dennis Kunkel Microscopy, Inc.

Figure 21.5
The cell on the left shows degradation of the cell wall following antibiotic treatment. The cell will eventually lyse, killing the bacterium. A cell with an intact cell wall is shown on the right.

Bacteria can be divided into two broad groups, Gram-positive and Gram-negative cells, based on their reaction to the Gram stain procedure, traditionally used as the first step in identification of an unknown bacterium. Cells are first stained with crystal violet, rinsed with ethanol, and then counterstained with safranin. Some cells retain the crystal violet and thus appear purple when viewed under the microscope; these are termed Gram-positive cells. In other bacteria, ethanol washes the crystal violet out of the cells, which are colourless until counterstained with safranin; these Gram-negative cells appear pink under the microscope. The differential response to staining is related to differences in cell wall structure: Gram-positive bacteria have cell walls composed almost entirely of a single, relatively thick peptidoglycan layer **(Figure 21.6a).** In contrast, the cell wall of Gram-negative bacteria has two distinct layers **(Figure 21.6b and c),** a thin peptidoglycan layer just outside the plasma membrane and an **outer membrane** external to the peptidoglycan layer. This outer membrane contains **lipopolysaccharides (LPS)** and thus is very different from the plasma membrane (Figure 21.6c). The outer membrane protects Gram-negative bacteria from potentially harmful substances in the environment; for example, it inhibits entry of penicillin. Therefore, Gram-negative cells are less sensitive to penicillin than are Gram-positive cells.

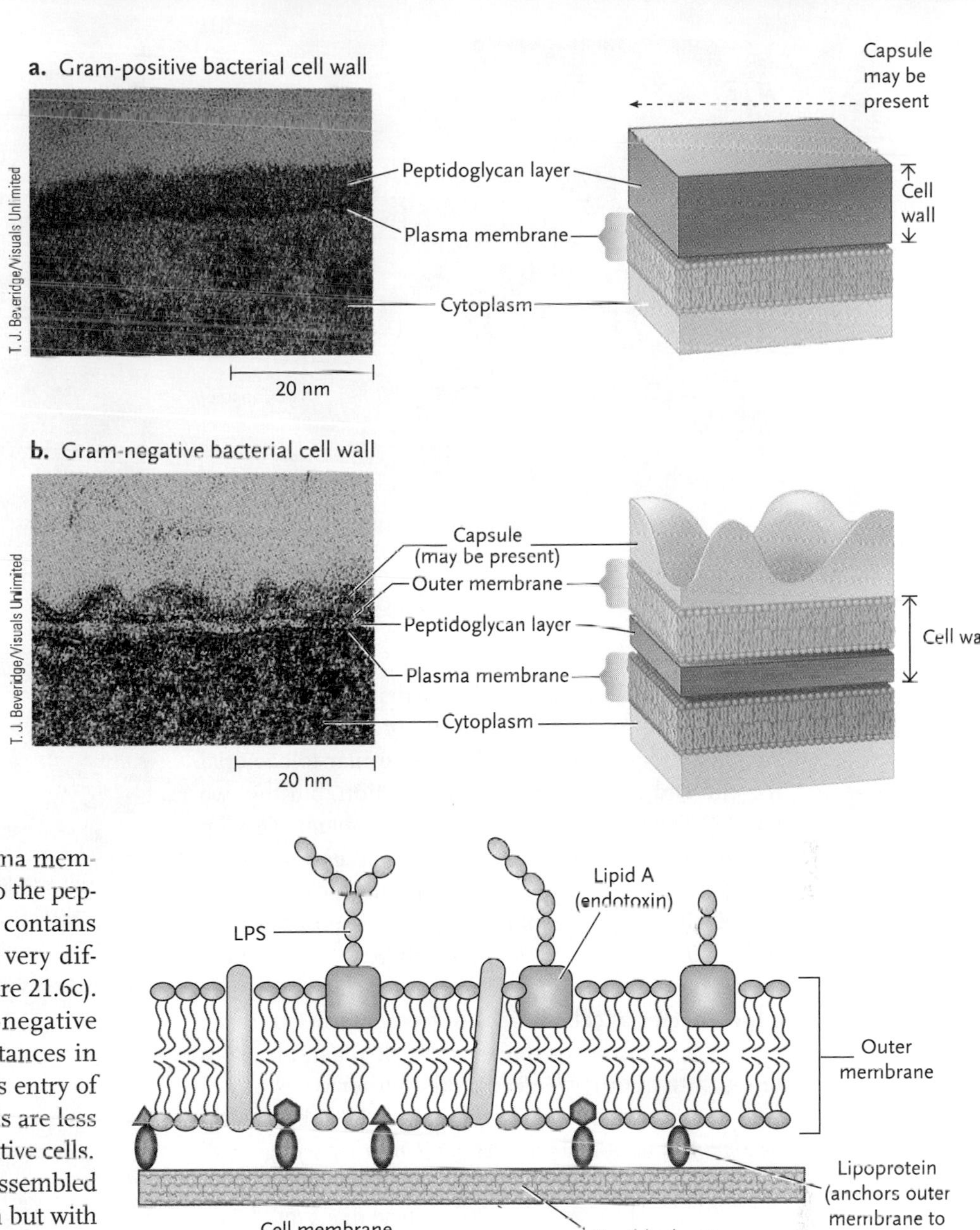

Figure 21.6
Cell wall structure in Gram-positive and Gram-negative bacteria. **(a)** The thick cell wall in Gram-positive bacteria. **(b)** The thin cell wall of Gram-negative bacteria. **(c)** detail of Gram-negative cell wall, showing thin peptidoglycan layer and outer membrane with lipopolysaccharides (LPS).

The cell walls of some Archaea are assembled from a molecule related to peptidoglycan but with different molecular components and bonding structure. Others have walls assembled from proteins or polysaccharides instead of peptidoglycan. Archaea have a variable response to the Gram stain, so this procedure is not useful in identification of Archaea.

The cell wall of many prokaryotes is surrounded by a layer of polysaccharides known as a **capsule (Figure 21.7, p. 470;** see also Figure 21.6). Capsules are "sticky" and play important roles in protecting cells in different environments. Cells with capsules are protected to some extent from desiccation, extreme temperatures, bacterial viruses, and harmful molecules such as antibiotics and antibodies. In many pathogenic bacteria, the presence or absence of the protective capsule differentiates infective from noninfective forms. For example, normal *Streptococcus pneumoniae* bacteria are capsulated and virulent, causing severe pneumonia in humans and other mammals. Mutant *S. pneumoniae* without capsules are nonvirulent and can easily be eliminated by the body's immune system if they are injected into mice or other animals.

Flagella and Pili. Many prokaryotes can move actively through liquids and across wet surfaces, most commonly via **flagella** (singular, *flagellum* = whip) extending from the cell wall (see Figure 21.3). As outlined in Chapter 2, prokaryotic flagella are very different from eukaryotic flagella in both structure and pattern of

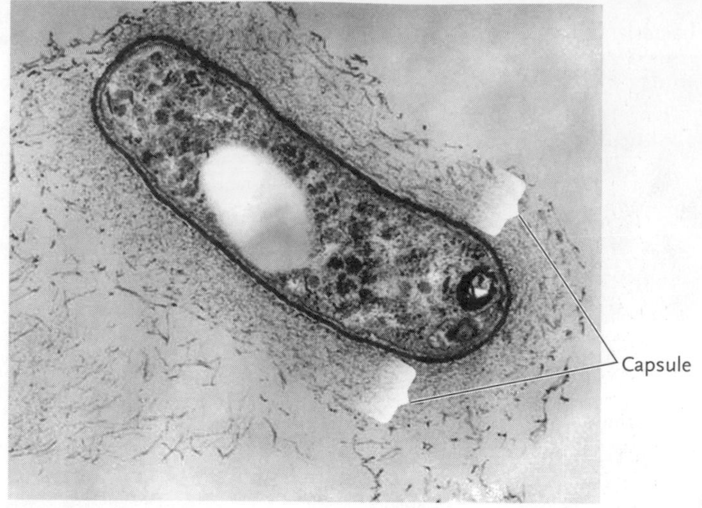

Figure 21.7
The capsule surrounding the cell wall of *Rhizobium*, a Gram-negative soil bacterium.

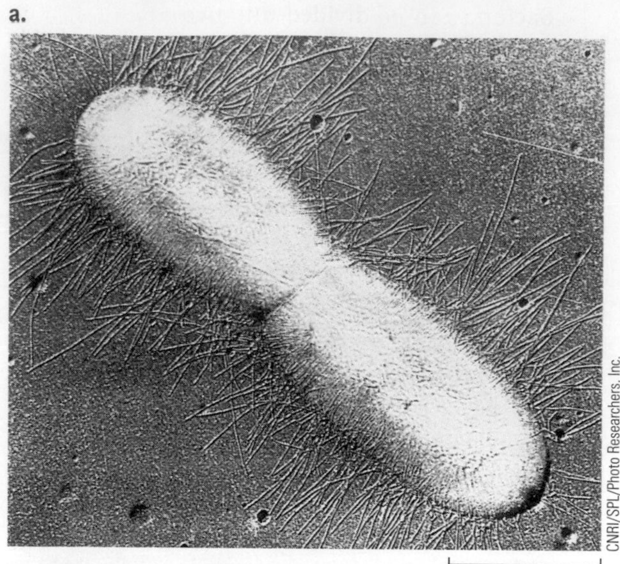

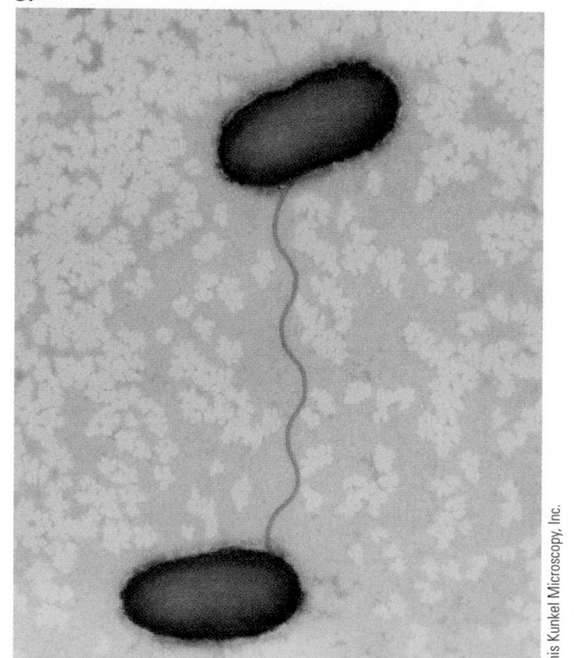

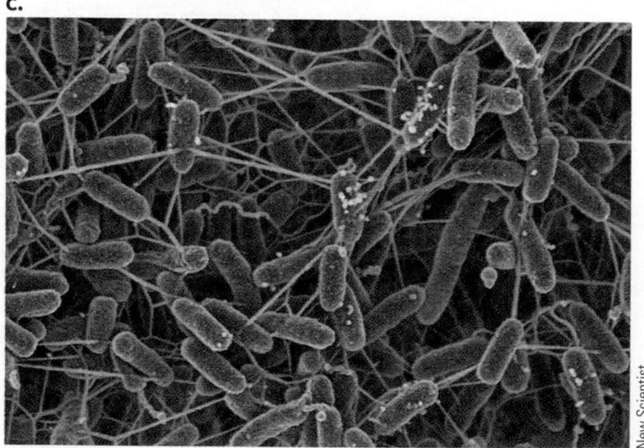

Figure 21.8
(a) Pili extending from the surface of a dividing *E. coli* bacterium. **(b)** Sex pilus connecting two bacterial cells. **(c)** Nanowires (pili that conduct electricity) on *Shewanella oneidensis*. Note that these nanowires are much longer than the cells.

movement. Prokaryotic flagella are made of rigid helical proteins and rotate much like the propeller of a boat. Archaean flagella are superficially similar to bacterial flagella and carry out the same function, but the two types of flagella contain different components, develop differently, and are coded for by different genes.

Some prokaryotes have rigid shafts of protein called **pili** (singular, *pilus* = "hair") extending from their cell walls **(Figure 21.8a),** which help them adhere to other cells. One type, called a *sex pilus,* not only allows bacterial cells to adhere to each other but also acts as a conduit for the transfer of plasmids from one cell to another **(Figure 21.8b).** Other types of pili enable bacteria to bind to animal cells. The bacterium that causes gonorrhea (*Neisseria gonorrhoeae*) uses pili to adhere to cells of the throat, eye, urogenital tract, or rectum in humans. In 2005, it was discovered that the pili of some bacteria (e.g., species of *Geobacter* and *Shewanella*) conduct electricity; these "nanowires" transfer electrons out of the cell onto minerals such as iron oxides in their environment **(Figure 21.8c).** Such electricity-generating bacteria hold promise for the development of microbial fuel cells as an alternative energy source (see *Unanswered Questions*).

Even though prokaryotes are simpler and less structurally diverse than eukaryotic cells, they are much more diverse metabolically, as we will now explore.

21.2b Prokaryotes Have the Greatest Metabolic Diversity of All Organisms

As outlined in Chapter 3, organisms can be grouped into four modes of nutrition based on sources of energy and carbon (see Table 3.1). From reading the chapters on photosynthesis and respiration, you are familiar with photoautotrophs such as green plants, which use light as their energy source and CO_2 as their carbon source, and chemoheterotrophs, which use organic molecules as sources of both energy and carbon. Humans and other animals are chemoheterotrophs, as are fungi. Two other modes of nutrition are found only in prokaryotes. **Photoheterotrophs** use light as an energy source and obtain carbon from organic molecules rather than from CO_2. **Chemoautotrophs** are commonly referred to as "lithotrophs" (*lithos* = rock, thus "rock-eaters"). As this name suggests, chemoautotrophs obtain energy by oxidizing inorganic substances such as hydrogen, iron, sulphur, ammonia, and nitrites and use CO_2 as their carbon source. Chemolithotrophs thrive in habitats such as the deep-sea hydrothermal vents **(Figure 21.9)**, where reduced inorganic compounds are abundant; their ability to harness energy from these compounds makes them the foundation upon which the rest of the vent community ultimately depends, just as terrestrial organisms rely on the ability of plants and other photoautotrophs to capture light energy.

We breathe oxygen to provide the final electron acceptor for the electrons we remove from our food and pass down an electron transport chain to make ATP via aerobic respiration (Chapter 6). Some prokaryotes also use oxygen as a final electron acceptor; like us, these are aerobic organisms or **aerobes**. Aerobes may be **obligate**, that is, they cannot survive without oxygen. But some prokaryotes "breathe" metals, using metals as the final electron acceptor for electrons; these organisms obtain energy via anaerobic respiration. **Anaerobic respiration** can also involve other inorganic molecules, such as nitrate or sulphate, as the final electron acceptors. Only prokaryotes are capable of this type of respiration. **Obligate anaerobes** are poisoned by oxygen and survive either by fermentation, in which organic molecules are the final electron acceptors, or by anaerobic respiration. **Facultative anaerobes** use O_2 when it is present, but under anaerobic conditions, they live by fermentation or anaerobic respiration. As you learned in Chapter 6, prokaryotes carry out a wider range of fermentation reactions than do eukaryotes; many of these fermentations are economically important to humans, for example, in the production of foods such as cheese, yogurt, and chocolate.

21.2c Prokaryotes Play Key Roles in Biogeochemical Cycles

The ability of prokaryotes to metabolize such a wide range of substrates makes them key players in the life-sustaining recycling of elements such as carbon, oxygen, and nitrogen, among others. The pathway by which a chemical element moves through an ecosystem is known as a **biogeochemical cycle.** As an element flows through its cycle, it is transformed from one form to another; prokaryotes are crucial in many of these transformations. We will look at the nitrogen cycle as an example of the key role prokaryotes play in biogeochemical cycles.

Nitrogen is a component of proteins and nucleotides and so is of vital importance for all organisms. The largest source of nitrogen on Earth is the atmosphere, which is almost 80% nitrogen. Why can't we just use this atmospheric nitrogen since it is so abundant? Most organisms cannot make use of this nitrogen because they cannot break the strong triple bond between the two nitrogen atoms. Prokaryotes are the only organisms that can break this bond and convert N_2 into forms that can be used by other organisms. In this conversion process, known as **nitrogen fixation**, N_2 is reduced to ammonia (NH_3). Ammonia is quickly ionized to ammonium (NH_4^+), which prokaryote cells then use to produce nitrogen-containing molecules such as amino acids and nucleic acids. Nitrogen fixation is the only means of replenishing the nitrogen sources used by most organisms—in other words, all organisms rely on nitrogen fixed by bacteria. Examples of nitrogen-fixing bacteria include cyanobacteria and *Rhizobium* (which is symbiotic with plants; see Chapter 41).

Not all bacteria convert fixed nitrogen directly into organic molecules. Some bacteria carry out **nitrification**, the conversion of ammonium (NH_4^+) to nitrate (NO_3^-). This is carried out in two steps by two types of *nitrifying bacteria* present in soil and water, one of which converts ammonium to nitrite (NO_2^-), whereas the other converts nitrite to nitrate. Nitrate is then taken up by plants and fungi and incorporated into their organic molecules. Animals obtain

Figure 21.9
Hydrothermal vents on the ocean floor.

nitrogen in organic form by eating other organisms or each other.

In sum, nitrification makes nitrogen available to many other organisms, including plants, animals, and bacteria that cannot metabolize ammonia. The metabolic versatility of the prokaryotes is one factor that accounts for their abundance and persistence on the planet; another factor is their impressive reproductive capacity.

21.2d Asexual Reproduction Can Result in Rapid Population Growth

In prokaryotes, asexual reproduction is the normal mode of reproduction. In this process, a parent cell divides by binary fission into two daughter cells that are exact genetic copies of the parent **(Figure 21.10)**. Reproducing by binary fission means that, under favourable conditions, populations of prokaryotes can have very rapid exponential growth as one cell becomes two, two become four, and so on. Some prokaryotes can double their population size in only 20 minutes; thus, one cell, given ideal conditions, can produce millions of cells in only a few hours.

These short generation times, combined with the small genomes (roughly 1000 times smaller than an average eukaryote), mean that prokaryotes have higher mutation rates than do eukaryotes. This translates to roughly 1000 times more mutations per gene, per unit time, per individual than for eukaryotes. Genetic variability in prokaryotic populations, the basis for their diversity, derives largely from mutation and to a lesser degree from horizontal gene transfer (see Chapter 10). Further, the typically much larger populations of prokaryotes compared with eukaryotes contribute to the much greater genetic variability in prokaryotes. In short, prokaryotes have an enormous capacity to adapt, which is one reason for their evolutionary success.

Figure 21.10
E. coli cell dividing by binary fission.

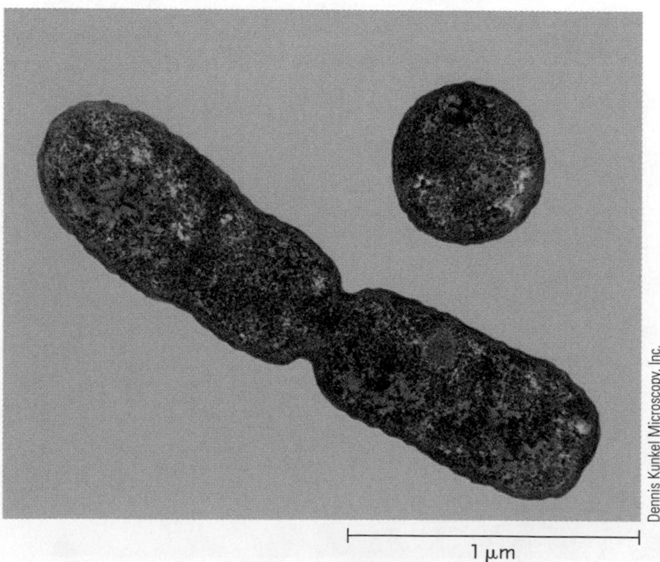

As we have seen, the success of bacteria is beneficial to humans in many ways but can also be detrimental to us when dealing with successful pathogenic bacteria. In the next section, we investigate how some bacteria cause disease and how they are able to resist treatment with antibiotics.

21.2e Pathogenic Bacteria Cause Diseases by Different Mechanisms

Some bacteria produce **exotoxins**, toxic proteins that leak from or are secreted from the bacterium. For example, botulism food poisoning is caused by the exotoxin of the Gram-positive bacterium *Clostridium botulinum*, which grows in poorly preserved foods **(Figure 21.11)**. The botulism exotoxin, botulin, is one of the most poisonous substances known: just a few nanograms can cause severe illness. What makes botulin so toxic? It produces muscle paralysis that can be fatal if the muscles that control breathing are affected. Interestingly, botulin is used under the brand name Botox for the cosmetic removal of wrinkles and in the treatment of migraine headaches and some other medical conditions. Exotoxins produced by certain strains of *Streptococcus pyogenes* have "superantigen properties" (i.e., overactivation of the immune system) that cause necrotizing fasciitis ("flesh-eating disease"). In 1994, Lucien Bouchard, who was then premier of Quebec, lost a leg to this disease.

Other bacteria cause disease through **endotoxins.** Endotoxins are natural components of the outer membrane of Gram-negative bacteria such as *E. coli*, *Salmonella*, and *Shigella*. When a Gram-negative cell lyses, the lipopolysaccharides of the outer membrane are released; exposure to a specific component of this layer, known as lipid A, causes endotoxic shock. The endotoxin overstimulates the host's immune system, triggering inflammation and an often lethal immune response. Endotoxins have different effects depending on the bacterial species and the site of infection, which include typhoid or other fevers, diarrhea, and, in severe cases, organ failure and death.

21.2f Pathogenic Bacteria Commonly Develop Resistance to Antibiotics

An **antibiotic** is a natural or synthetic substance that kills or inhibits the growth of bacteria and other microorganisms. Prokaryotes and fungi produce these substances naturally as defensive molecules, and we have also developed ways to synthesize several types of antibiotics. Different types of antibiotics have different modes of action: for example, streptomycins, produced by soil bacteria, block protein synthesis in their targets whereas penicillins, produced by fungi, target the peptide cross-linkages in peptidoglycan, as described above.

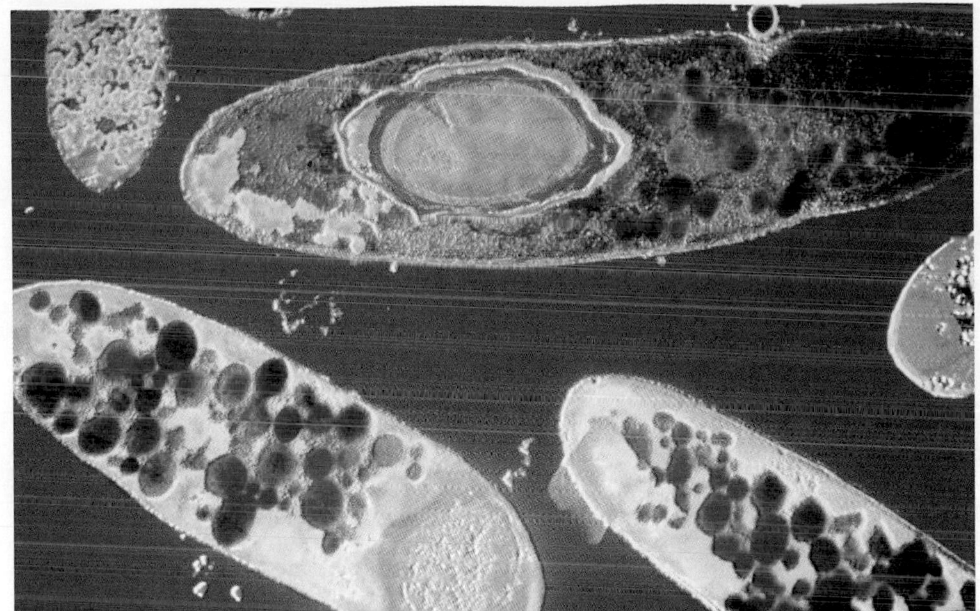

Figure 21.11
The bacterium *Clostridium butyricum*, one of the *Clostridium* species that produces the toxin botulin (colourized TEM). The large stained structure in the cells is a spore (a survival structure).

How are bacteria able to block the actions of antibiotics? There are various mechanisms by which bacteria resist antibiotics **(Figure 21.12).** For example, some bacteria are able to pump antibiotics out of the cell using membrane-bound pumps. They can also produce molecules that bind to the antibiotic or enzymes that break down the antibiotic, rendering it ineffective against its target. Alternatively, a simple mutation can result in a change in the structure of the antibiotic's target, so that the antibiotic cannot bind to it. Finally, bacteria can develop new enzymes or pathways that are not inhibited by the antibiotic.

Bacteria can develop resistance through mutations, but they can also acquire resistance via horizontal gene transfer (e.g., plasmid transfer). Taking antibiotics routinely in mild doses, or failing to complete a prescribed dosage, contributes to the development of resistance by selecting strains that can survive in the presence of the drug. Prescription of antibiotics for colds and other virus-caused diseases can also promote bacterial resistance because viruses are unaffected by antibiotics, but the presence of antibiotics in your system can lead to resistance. Antibacterial agents that may promote resistance are also commonly included in such commercial products as soaps, detergents, and deodorants. Resistance is a form of evolutionary adaptation; antibiotics alter the bacterium's environment, conferring a reproductive advantage on those strains best adapted to the altered conditions.

The development of resistant strains has made tuberculosis, cholera, typhoid fever, gonorrhea, and other bacterial diseases difficult to treat with antibiotics. For example, as recently as 1988, drug-resistant strains of *Streptococcus pneumoniae*, which causes pneumonia, meningitis, and middle-ear infections, were practically unknown. Now, resistant strains of *S. pneumoniae* are common and increasingly difficult to treat.

21.2g In Nature, Prokaryotes May Live in Communities Attached to a Surface

Researchers grow prokaryotes as individuals in pure cultures. We have learned a lot about prokaryotes from studies using pure cultures, but in nature, prokaryotes rarely exist as individuals or as pure cultures. Instead, many prokaryotes live in communities where they interact in a variety of ways. One important type of prokaryotic community is known

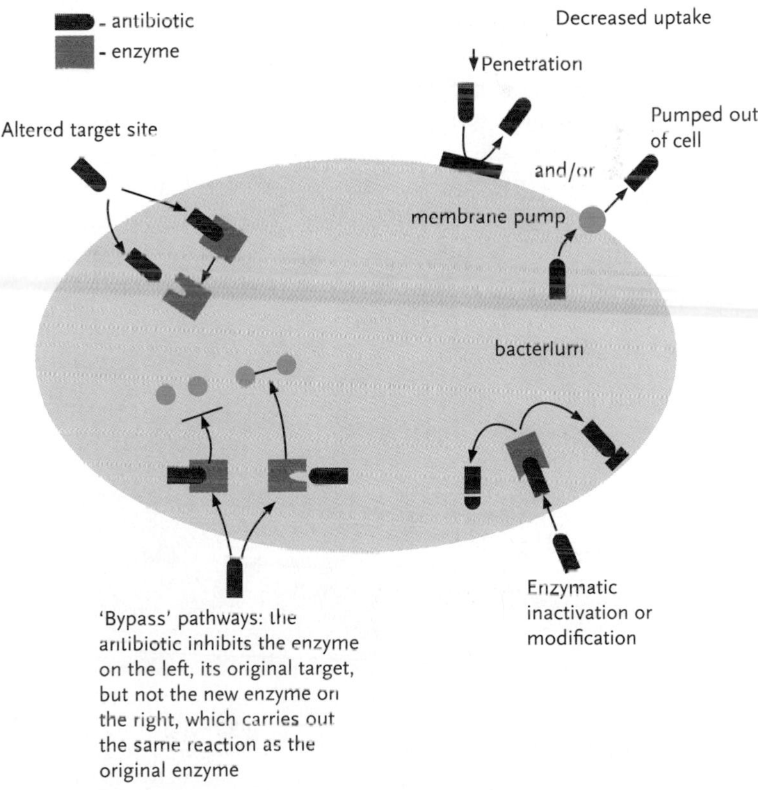

Figure 21.12
Four major mechanisms of antibiotic resistance.

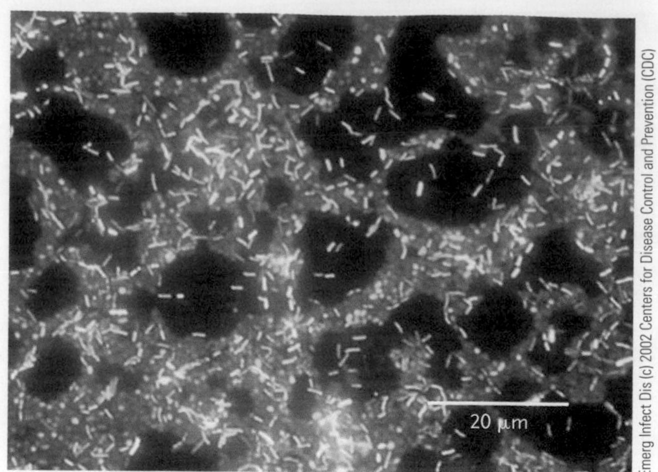

Figure 21.13
Biofilm grown on a stainless steel surface.

as a **biofilm**, which consists of a complex aggregation of microorganisms attached to a surface and surrounded by a film of polymers **(Figure 21.13).** Life in a biofilm offers several benefits: organisms can adhere to hospitable surfaces, they can live on the products of other cells, conditions within the biofilm promote gene transfer between species, and the biofilm protects cells from harmful environmental conditions. Biofilms form on any surface with sufficient water and nutrients. For example, you're probably familiar with how slippery rocks in a stream can be when you try to step from one to the next; the slipperiness is due to biofilms on the rocks. Dental plaque is also a biofilm; if this biofilm spreads below the gumline, it causes inflammation of the gums (gingivitis). Regular removal of plaque by brushing, flossing, and dental checkups helps prevent gingivitis.

Biofilms have practical consequences for humans, both beneficial and detrimental. On the beneficial side, for example, biofilms on solid supports are used in sewage treatment plants for processing organic matter before the water is discharged, and they can be effective in bioremediation of toxic organic molecules contaminating groundwater. But biofilms can also be harmful to human health. Biofilms adhere to many kinds of surgical equipment and supplies, including catheters, pacemakers, and artificial joints. Even if the bacteria colonizing these devices are not pathogenic, their presence is obviously not desirable given that these devices should be sterile. As well, many heterotrophic bacteria will become opportunistic pathogens, given the right conditions. Biofilm infections are difficult to treat because bacteria in a biofilm are up to 1000 times more resistant to antibiotics than are the same bacteria in liquid cultures.

How does a biofilm form? Imagine a surface, such as a rock in a stream, over which water is flowing **(Figure 21.14).** Due to the nutrients in the water, the surface rapidly becomes coated with polymeric organic molecules, such as polysaccharides or glycoproteins. Once the surface is conditioned with organic molecules, free prokaryotes attach in a reversible manner in a matter of seconds (see Figure 21.14, step 1). If the cells remain attached, the association may become irreversible (step 2), at which point, the prokaryotes grow and divide on the surface (step 3). Next, the physiology of the cells changes, and they begin to secrete *extracellular polymeric substances* (EPS), a slimy, gluelike substance similar to the molecules found in bacterial capsules. EPS extends between cells in the mixture, forming a matrix that binds cells to each other and anchors the complex to the surface, thereby establishing the biofilm (step 4). The slime layer entraps a variety of materials, such as dead cells and insoluble minerals. The physiological change accompanying the formation of a biofilm results from marked changes in a prokaryote's gene expression pattern—in effect, the prokaryotes in a biofilm become very different organisms. Over time, other organisms are attracted to and join the biofilm; depending on the environment, these may include other bacterial species, algae, fungi, or protozoa producing diverse microbial communities (step 5). As described in the *Molecule Behind Biology* box on page 475, prokaryotes in a biofilm communicate with each other via

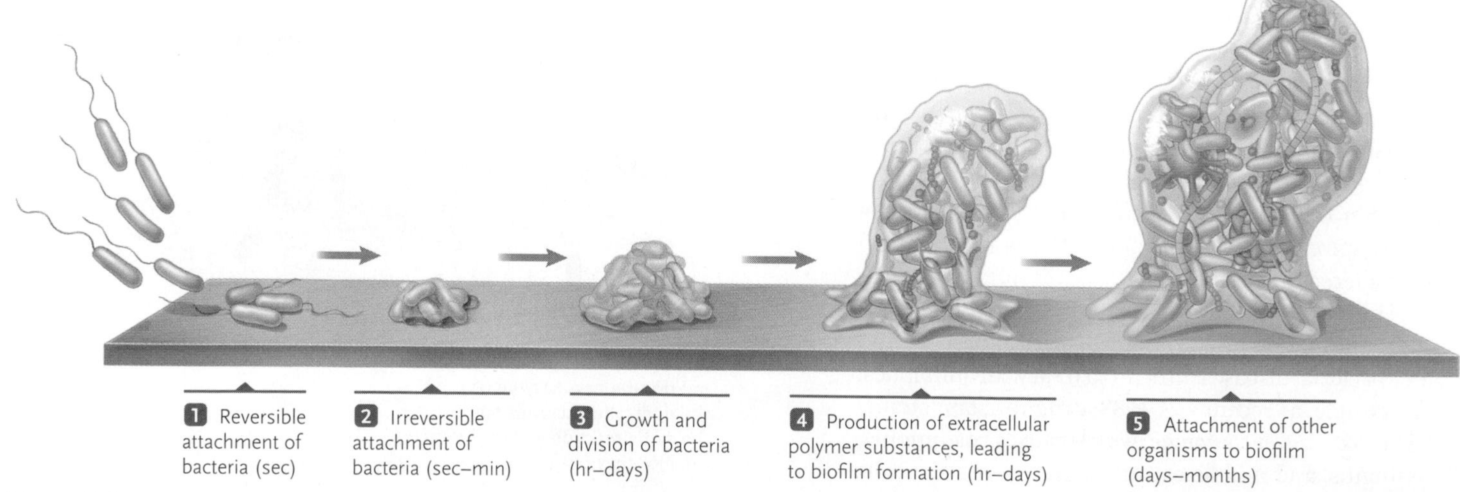

Figure 21.14
Steps in the formation of a biofilm.

MOLECULE BEHIND BIOLOGY

N-Acyl-l-Homoserine Lactone

Most bacteria are social organisms that interact in many ways and display social behaviours, such as hunting for food in swarms, bioluminescence (see Chapter 1), biofilm formation, and virulence in pathogenic bacteria. These behaviours happen only when a critical population density is reached, meaning that bacteria must be able to sense the presence of other cells. How does a bacterial cell know that it is not alone? Bacteria use quorum sensing to communicate; this mechanism involves the release of signalling molecules into the environment. Accumulation of signalling molecules enables the cell to determine the density of other cells around it and respond accordingly; the response occurs after the signalling molecule is perceived by specific receptors on the cell's membrane and triggers activation of specific genes. Different bacterial species use different signalling molecules, for example, many Gram-negative bacteria use *N*-acyl-l-homoserine lactones (a lactone is a type of cyclic ester) such as that shown in **Figure 1.** Gram positive cells also signal each other but use small peptides rather than lactones. If we can learn to "speak" or "translate" these bacterial languages, could we interfere with the social behaviours they control? The possibility has important implications for medical science given the role of these signals in processes such as the onset of virulence in pathogenic bacteria and communication within biofilms such as those that form on medical devices implanted in patients.

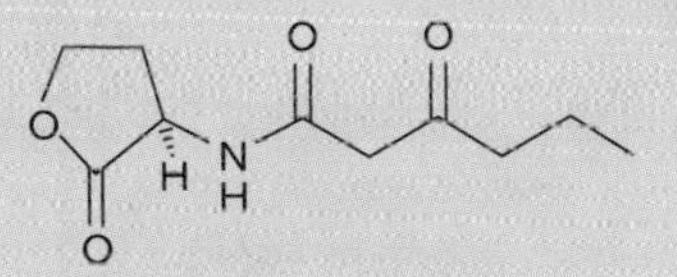

Figure 1
N-Acyl-l-homoserine lactone from *Vibrio fischeri.*

quorum sensing; in fact, this communication is part of biofilm formation—it allows cells to start secreting EPS when a high enough cell density is reached.

Much remains to be learned about how bacteria form a biofilm, how the change in gene expression during the transition is regulated, and how bacteria interact within a biofilm.

In the next two sections, we describe the major groups of prokaryotes.

STUDY BREAK

1. What distinguishes a prokaryotic cell from a eukaryotic cell?
2. What is the difference between a chemoheterotroph and a photoautotroph?
3. What is the difference between an obligate anaerobe and a facultative anaerobe?
4. What is the difference between nitrogen fixation and nitrification? Why are nitrogen-fixing prokaryotes important?
5. What is binary fission?
6. What is the difference between an endotoxin and an exotoxin? Explain how they differ with respect to how they cause disease.
7. Explain four mechanisms by which bacteria protect themselves from antibiotics.
8. What is a biofilm? Give an example of a biofilm that is beneficial to humans and one that is harmful.
9. What is quorum sensing?

21.3 The Domain Bacteria

As for other organisms, prokaryote classification has been revolutionized by molecular techniques that allow researchers to compare nucleic acid and protein sequences as tests of evolutionary relatedness. Ribosomal RNA (rRNA) sequences have been most widely used in the evolutionary studies of prokaryotes. Researchers have identified several evolutionary branches within each prokaryote domain **(Figure 21.15, p. 476)**, but these classifications will likely change in the future when full genomic sequences can be compared. We discuss the major groups of the domain Bacteria in this section, and of the domain Archaea in the next section.

21.3a Molecular Studies Reveal More than a Dozen Evolutionary Branches in the Bacteria

Sequencing studies reveal that bacteria have more than 12 distinct and separate evolutionary branches. We restrict our discussion to six particularly important groups: proteobacteria, green bacteria, cyanobacteria, Gram-positive bacteria, spirochetes, and chlamydias (see Figure 21.15).

Proteobacteria: The Purple Bacteria and Their Relatives. This highly diverse group of Gram-negative bacteria likely evolved from a purple, photosynthetic ancestor. Their purple colour comes from their photosynthetic pigment, a type

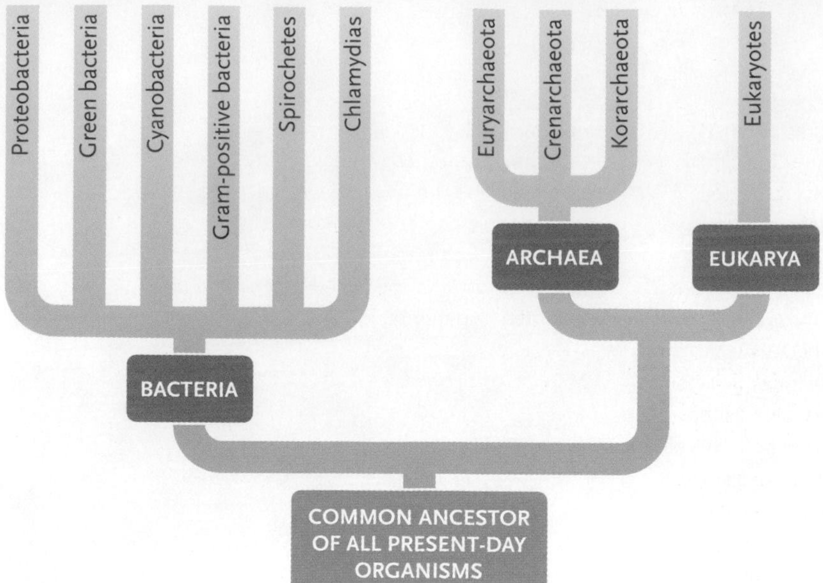

Figure 21.15
An abbreviated phylogenetic tree of prokaryotes.

Hans Reichenbach, Gesellschaft for Biotechnologische Forschung, Braunsweig, Germany
100 μm

Figure 21.16
The fruiting body of *Chondromyces crocatus*, a myxobacterium. Cells of this species collect together to form the fruiting body.

of chlorophyll distinct from that of plants. Many present-day species are either photoautotrophs (the purple sulphur bacteria) or photoheterotrophs (the purple nonsulphur bacteria); both groups carry out a type of photosynthesis that does not use water as an electron donor and does not release oxygen as a by-product.

Other present-day proteobacteria are chemoheterotrophs that are thought to have evolved as an evolutionary branch following the loss of photosynthetic capabilities in an early proteobacterium. The evolutionary ancestors of mitochondria are considered likely to have been ancient non-photosynthetic proteobacteria.

Among the chemoheterotrophs classified with the proteobacteria are *E. coli*, plant pathogenic bacteria, and bacteria that cause human diseases such as bubonic plague, gonorrhea, and various forms of gastroenteritis and dysentery. The proteobacteria also include both free-living and symbiotic nitrogen-fixing bacteria.

Myxobacteria are an unusual group of non-photosynthetic proteobacteria, which form colonies held together by the slime they produce. Enzymes secreted by the colonies digest "prey"—other bacteria, primarily—that become stuck in the slime. When environmental conditions become unfavourable, as when soil nutrients or water are depleted, myxobacteria form a fruiting body, a differentiated multicellular stage large enough to be visible to the naked eye **(Figure 21.16).** The fruiting body contains clusters of spores that are dispersed to form new colonies when the fruiting body bursts. Quorum sensing is involved in spore formation.

Helicobacter pylori, the cause of many gastric ulcers (see *People Behind Biology* box on page 477), is also a proteobacterium.

Green Bacteria. This diverse group of photosynthetic Gram-negative bacteria is named for the chlorophyll pigments that give the cells their green colour (a different form of chlorophyll than that found in plants). Like the purple bacteria, they do not release oxygen as a by-product of photosynthesis. Also like the purple bacteria, some are photoautotrophs, whereas others are photoheterotrophs. The photoautotrophic green bacteria are fairly closely related to the Archaea and are usually found in hot springs, whereas the photoheterotrophic type is found typically in marine and high-salt environments.

Cyanobacteria. These Gram-negative photoautotrophs are blue-green in colour (**Figure 21.17**) and carry out photosynthesis by the same pathways and using the same chlorophyll as eukaryotic algae and plants. Like plants and algae, they release oxygen as a by-product of photosynthesis.

The direct ancestors of present-day cyanobacteria were the first organisms to use the water-splitting reactions of photosynthesis. As such, they were critical to the accumulation of oxygen in the atmosphere, which allowed the evolutionary development of aerobic organisms. Chloroplasts probably

People Behind Biology
Barry Marshall and Robin Warren

A few hours after you eat, you go to your doctor complaining of stomach pain, abdominal bloating and nausea; most worryingly, you have started to vomit blood. Your doctor tells you that you have a gastric ulcer, a lesion in your stomach lining. If this visit to your doctor had occurred prior to the mid-1980s, your doctor would have explained that ulcers are caused by increased stomach acidity due to stress. The treatment? Drink lots of milk, take antacids, and give up alcohol and your favourite spicy foods—no more curries or chili—that would aggravate your ulcer. This view of ulcers was accepted for years until two Australian physicians, Barry Marshall and Robin Warren, demonstrated that most ulcers are caused by a bacterial infection. Marshall and Warren observed that biopsies from patients with ulcers revealed large numbers of spiral-shaped bacterial cells in inflamed tissues. Together the two physicians carried out a series of studies that demonstrated the link between ulcers and the presence of the bacterium (later named *Helicobacter pylori*) **(Figure 1).** But despite having research published in respected medical journals, the medical community did not believe Marshall and Warren's findings—how could bacteria possibly survive in the very acidic conditions of the stomach? Out of frustration, and anxious to get proper treatment for his patients, Marshall drank a culture of *H. pylori*! After about a week, he developed severe abdominal pain and vomiting, and endoscopic examination of his stomach showed regions of inflammation teeming with *H. pylori*. Much to his disappointment, he did not develop ulcers, but he had made the point that *H. pylori* is pathogenic. Marshall and Warren also showed that antibiotics were effective in treating ulcers, and in 2005, they were awarded the Nobel Prize in Medicine. So how is *H. pylori* able to survive in a stomach? It is able to burrow deep into the mucus lining the stomach by means of its numerous flagella, and it produces urease, which converts urea into CO_2 and ammonia, making the region around its cells more basic.

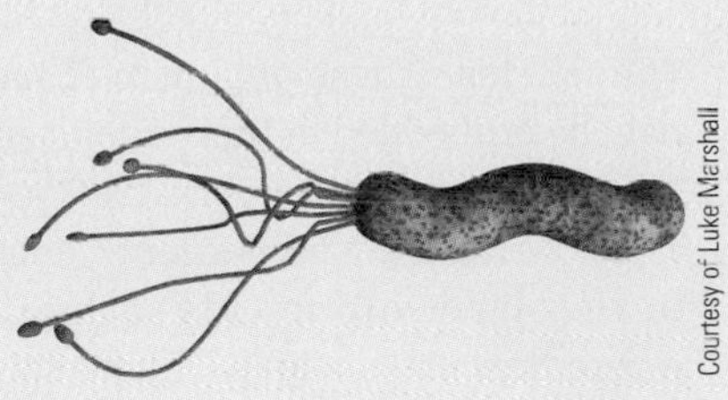

Courtesy of Luke Marshall

Figure 1
A high-resolution image of *Helicobacter pylori*, a causative agent of ulcers.

evolved from early cyanobacteria that were incorporated into the cytoplasm of primitive eukaryotes, which eventually gave rise to the algae and higher plants as discussed in Chapter 25. Besides releasing oxygen, present-day cyanobacteria help fix nitrogen into organic compounds in aquatic habitats and as symbiotic partners with fungi in lichens (see Chapter 24).

a.

Dr. Jeremy Burgess/SPL/Photo Researchers, Inc.

b.

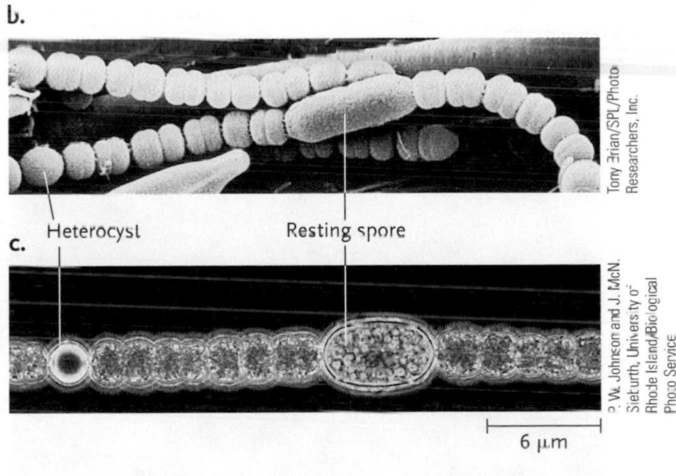

Tony Brian/SPL/Photo Researchers, Inc.

P. W. Johnson and J. McN. Sieburth, University of Rhode Island/Biological Photo Service

Figure 21.17
Cyanobacteria. **(a)** A population of cyanobacteria covering the surface of a pond. **(b)** and **(c)** Chains of cyanobacterial cells. Some cells in the chains form spores. The heterocyst is a specialized cell that fixes nitrogen.

Gram-Positive Bacteria. This large group contains many species that live primarily as chemoheterotrophs. Some cause human diseases, including *Bacillus anthracis*, the causal agent of anthrax; *Staphylococcus*, which causes some forms of food poisoning, toxic shock syndrome, pneumonia, and meningitis; and *Streptococcus* **(Figure 21.18)**, which causes strep throat, necrotizing fasciitis, and some forms of pneumonia. However, some Gram-positive bacteria are beneficial to humans; *Lactobacillus*, for example, carries out the lactic acid fermentation used in the production of pickles, sauerkraut, and yogurt. One unusual group of bacteria, the mycoplasmas, is placed among the Gram-positive bacteria by molecular studies even though they show a Gram-negative staining reaction. This staining reaction results because they are naked cells that secondarily lost their cell walls in evolution. Some mycoplasmas, with diameters from 0.1 to 0.2 μm, are the smallest known cells.

Spirochetes. These organisms have helically spiralled flagella embedded in their cytoplasm, causing the cells to move in a twisting, corkscrew pattern **(Figure 21.19)**. Their corkscrew movements enable them to move in viscous environments such as mud and sewage, where they are common. Some spirochetes are harmless inhabitants of the human mouth; another species, *Treponema pallidum*, is the cause of syphilis. Termites have symbiotic spirochetes in their intestines that enable them to digest cellulose.

Chlamydias. These bacteria are unusual because although they are Gram-negative and have cell walls with an outer membrane, they lack peptidoglycan. All the known chlamydias are intracellular parasites that cause various diseases in animals. One bacterium of this group, *Chlamydia trachomatis*, is responsible for one of the most common sexually transmitted infections of the urinary and reproductive tracts of humans and also causes trachoma, an infection of the cornea that is the leading cause of blindness in humans.

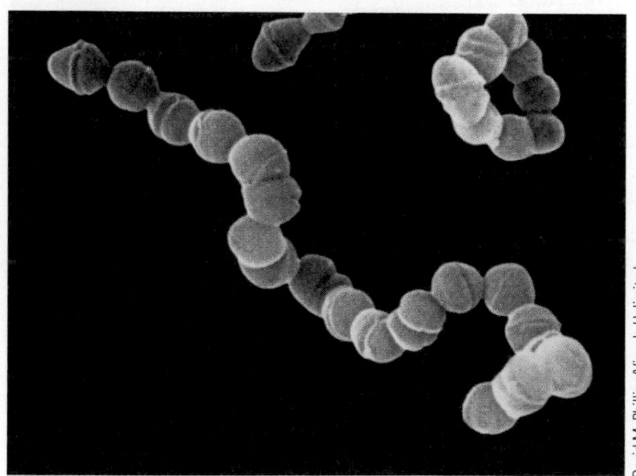
David M. Phillips/Visuals Unlimited

Figure 21.18
Streptococcus bacteria forming the long chains of cells typical of many species in this genus.

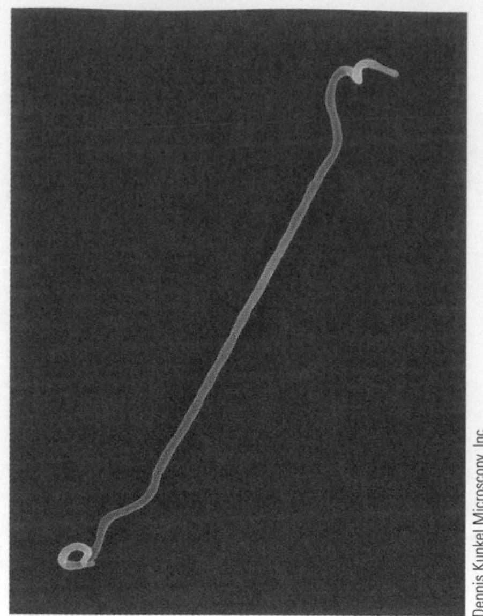
Dennis Kunkel Microscopy, Inc.

Figure 21.19
Treponema pallidum, a spirochete bacterium that is a causal agent of syphilis (scanning electron microscope image).

In this section, you have seen that bacteria thrive in nearly every habitat on Earth. However, some members of the second prokaryotic domain, the Archaea, the subject of the next section, live in habitats that are too forbidding even for the bacteria.

Study Break

1. What methodologies have been used to classify prokaryotes?
2. What were the likely characteristics of the evolutionary ancestor of present-day proteobacteria?
3. What are the differences between the way photosynthesis is carried out by photosynthetic proteobacteria and by cyanobacteria?

21.4 The Domain Archaea

The first Archaea were isolated from extreme environments, such as hot springs, hydrothermal vents on the ocean floor, and salt lakes **(Figure 21.20)**. For that reason, these prokaryotes were called *extremophiles* ("extreme lovers"). Subsequently, Archaea have also been found living in less extreme environments.

Archaea share some cellular features with eukaryotes and some with bacteria and have other features that are unique **(Table 21.1)**.

21.4a Archaea Have Some Unique Characteristics

Among their unique characteristics are certain features of their plasma membranes and cell walls. The lipid molecules in archaeal plasma membranes

Figure 21.20
Typically extreme archaeal habitats. **(a)** Highly saline water in Great Salt Lake, Utah, coloured red purple by archaea. **(b)** Hot, sulphur-rich water in Emerald Pool, Yellowstone National Park, coloured brightly by the oxidative activity of archaea, which convert H_2S to elemental sulphur.

are unlike those in the plasma membranes of all other organisms: there is a different linkage between glycerol and the hydrophobic tails, and the tails are isoprenes rather than fatty acids (see Chapter 5). Also, some lipids have polar head groups at both ends. Why would such seemingly minor differences be significant? These unique lipids are more resistant to disruption, making the plasma membranes better suited to extreme environments. Similarly, the unique cell walls of Archaea are more resistant to extremes than those of bacteria; some Archaea can even survive being boiled in strong detergents!

Many Archaea are chemoautotrophs, whereas others are chemoheterotrophs. No known member of the Archaea has been shown to be pathogenic.

21.4b Molecular Studies Reveal Three Evolutionary Branches in the Archaea

Based on differences in rRNA sequence data, the domain Archaea is divided into three groups (see Figure 21.15). Two major groups, the **Euryarchaeota** and the **Crenarchaeota**, contain Archaea that have been cultured in the laboratory. The third group, the

Table 21.1 Characteristics of the Bacteria, Archaea, and Eukarya

Characteristic	Bacteria	Archaea*	Eukarya
DNA arrangement	Single, circular in most, but some linear and/or multiple	Single, circular	Multiple linear molecules
Chromosomal proteins	Prokaryotic histonelike proteins	Five eukaryotic histones	Five eukaryotic histones
Genes arranged in operons	Yes	Yes	No
Nuclear envelope	No	No	Yes
Mitochondria	No	No	Yes
Chloroplasts	No	No	Yes
Peptidoglycan in cell wall	Present	Absent; some have pseudopeptidoglycan	Absent
Membrane lipids	Unbranched; linked by ester linkages	Branched; linked by ether linkage; may have polar heads at both ends	Unbranched; linked by ester linkages
RNA polymerase	Limited variations	Multiple types	Multiple types
Ribosomal proteins	Prokaryotic	Some prokaryotic, some eukaryotic	Eukaryotic
First amino acid placed in proteins	Formylmethionine	Methionine	Methionine
Aminoacyl–tRNA synthetases	Prokaryotic	Eukaryotic	Eukaryotic
Cell division proteins	Prokaryotic	Prokaryotic	Eukaryotic
Proteins of energy metabolism	Prokaryotic	Prokaryotic	Eukaryotic

*Given that very few Archaea have been identified or cultured, the information in this table is based on an extremely small data set.

Korarchaeota, has been recognized solely on the basis of DNA taken from environmental samples.

Euryarchaeota. These organisms are found in various extreme environments. They include methanogens, extreme halophiles, and some extreme thermophiles, as described below.

Methanogens (methane generators) live in low-oxygen environments **(Figure 21.21)** and represent about one half of all known species of Archaea. Methanogens are obligate anaerobes that live in the anoxic (oxygen-lacking) sediments of swamps, lakes, marshes, and sewage works, as well as in more moderate environments, such as the rumen of cattle and sheep, the large intestine of dogs and humans, and the hindguts of insects such as termites and cockroaches. Methanogens generate energy by converting various substrates such as carbon dioxide and hydrogen gas or acetate into methane gas, which is released into the atmosphere.

Halophiles are salt-loving organisms. Extreme halophilic Archaea live in highly saline environments such as the Dead Sea and on foods preserved by salting. They require a minimum NaCl concentration of about 1.5 M (about 9% solution) to survive and can live in a fully saturated solution (5.5 M, or 32%). Most are aerobic chemoheterotrophs, which obtain energy from sugars, alcohols, and amino acids using pathways similar to those of bacteria. Many extreme halophiles use light as a secondary energy source, supplementing the oxidations that are their primary source of energy.

Extreme thermophiles live in extremely hot environments such as hot springs and ocean floor hydrothermal vents. Their optimal temperature range for growth is 70° to 95°C, close to the boiling point of water. By comparison, no eukaryotic organism is known to live at a temperature higher than 60°C. Some extreme thermophiles are members of the Euryarchaeota, but most belong to the Crenarchaeota, the next group that we discuss.

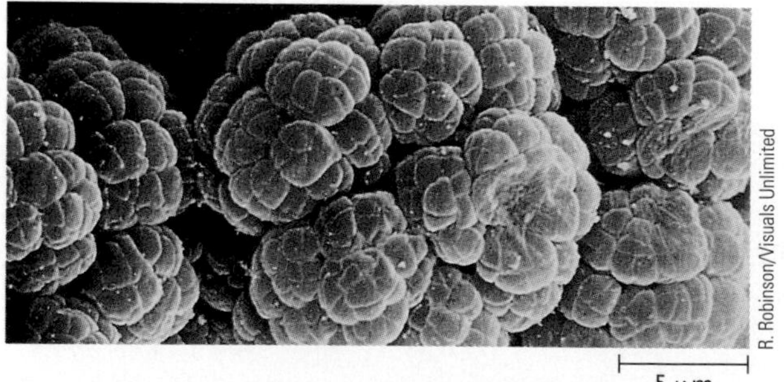

Figure 21.21
A colony of the methanogenic archaeon *Methanosarcina*, which lives in the sulphurous, waterlogged soils of marshes and swamps.

Crenarchaeota. This group includes most of the extreme thermophiles, which have a higher optimal temperature range than those belonging to the Euryarchaeota. For example, the most thermophilic member of this group, *Pyrobolus*, dies below 90°C, grows optimally at 106°C, and can survive an hour of autoclaving at 121°C! *Pyrobolus* lives in ocean floor hydrothermal vents, where the pressure creates water temperatures greater than the boiling point of water on Earth's surface.

Also in this group are **psychrophiles** ("cold loving"), organisms that grow optimally in cold temperatures in the range from −10 to −20°C. These organisms are found mostly in the Antarctic and Arctic oceans, which are frozen most of the year, and in the intense cold at ocean depths.

Mesophilic members of the Crenarchaeota comprise a large part of plankton found in cool, marine waters, where they are food sources for other marine organisms.

Korarchaeota. This group has been recognized solely on the basis of DNA samples obtained from marine and terrestrial hydrothermal environments. To date, no members of this group have been isolated and cultivated in the lab, and nothing is known about their physiology. Molecular data indicate that they are the oldest archaeal lineage.

Thermophilic Archaea are important commercially. For example, the thermostable DNA polymerase required for the polymerase chain reaction (PCR; you read about PCR in Chapter 16) comes from the thermophile *Thermus aquaticus*.

We began this chapter with prokaryotes, whose metabolic diversity and environmental range and ecological importance belie their structural simplicity. In the next chapter, we look at still simpler entities: viruses, viroids, and prions, which are derived from living organisms and retain only some of the properties of life.

Study Break

1. What distinguishes members of the Archaea from members of the Bacteria and Eukarya?
2. How does a methanogen obtain its energy? In which group or groups of Archaea are methanogens found?
3. Where do extreme halophilic Archaea live? How do they obtain energy? In which group or groups of Archaea are the extreme halophiles found?
4. What are extreme thermophiles and psychrophiles?

Unanswered Questions

What prokaryotes live in the world's oceans and what are their ecological roles?

Of the billions of prokaryotes on Earth, a vast number live in the open ocean and even more in the ocean sediments—these deeply buried prokaryotes may make up between a tenth to a third of all of Earth's biomass. So far, we have not been able to culture most of these organisms, so their physiology remains a mystery. Why should we care about identifying them and understanding their physiology and ecology? Aside from wanting to understand the full range of prokaryotic diversity on Earth as a goal in and of itself, there is also some urgency to understand the role these unknown organisms play in biogeochemical cycles of the ocean. As elsewhere on Earth, these prokaryotes drive the cycles of carbon and other elements in the ocean, but until we gain a clearer picture of which prokaryotes are doing what, we won't really understand these cycles, nor are we able to predict the effects of perturbations. For example, it has been proposed that one way to reduce carbon dioxide concentration in the atmosphere would be to capture CO_2 emissions and sequester them in the ocean. Without an understanding of the ocean-dwelling prokaryotes and their carbon metabolism, how can we accurately predict whether this plan will be successful or if it will lead to unforeseen problems?

Can we harness microbial reactions as a source of electricity?

If we could capture the electron flow from bacterial cells to the terminal electron acceptor, we would have a source of electricity (an electric current is just a stream of electrons). This is the theory behind a microbial fuel cell (MFC), which harnesses the power of prokaryotes to convert chemical energy into electrical energy **(Figure 1).** MFCs have been studied for almost 100 years, but inefficiencies of the systems, such as incomplete oxidation of substrates and the requirement for electron shuttles to carry electrons from the bacteria to the electrode, meant that very little current was produced. MFCs seemed doomed to be little more than novelties, with no practical use. The discovery that some bacteria such as *Geobacter* can completely oxidize organic compounds and transfer electrons directly to an electrode means that much more efficient fuel cells are possible. Many challenges must be overcome before this technology is commercially viable, but with our pressing need for alternative sources of energy, the MFC is currently a very active area of research in both biology and engineering.

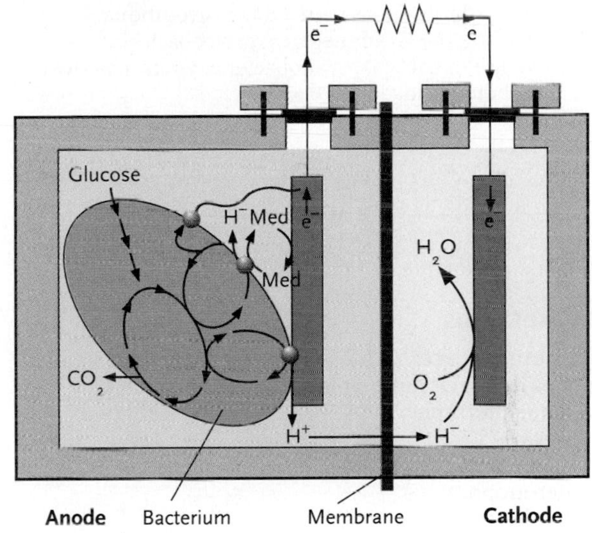

Figure 1
Schematic diagram of a microbial fuel cell.

Review

Go to CENGAGENOW at http://hed.nelson.com/ to access quizzing, animations, exercises, articles, and personalized homework help.

21.1 The Full Extent of Prokaryote Diversity Is Unknown

- Prokaryotes are the most abundant and diverse organisms on Earth; however, the vast majority of prokaryotes have not been described because they cannot be cultured using standard techniques.
- Prokaryotes comprise two of the three domains of life, the Archaea and the Bacteria.

21.2 Prokaryote Structure and Function

- Prokaryotic genomes typically consist of a single, circular DNA molecule packaged into the nucleoid. Many prokaryotic species also contain plasmids, which replicate independently of the chromosome and can be passed to other cells.
- Gram-positive bacterial cell walls consist of a single, relatively thick peptidoglycan layer. Gram-negative bacteria have walls consisting of a relatively thin peptidoglycan sheath surrounded by an outer lipopolysaccharide membrane.
- A polysaccharide capsule surrounds many bacteria, protecting them and helping them adhere to surfaces.
- Prokaryotes show great diversity in their modes of obtaining energy and carbon. Two of the modes of nutrition found among eukaryotes are also found in prokaryotes (chemoheterotrophy and photoautotrophy), but two other modes are unique to prokaryotes: chemoautotrophs obtain energy by oxidizing inorganic substrates and use carbon dioxide as their carbon source, and photoheterotrophs use light as a source of energy and obtain their carbon from organic molecules.
- As a group, prokaryotes can obtain energy via aerobic respiration, anaerobic respiration, and/or various forms of fermentation.

- Some prokaryotes are capable of nitrogen fixation, the conversion of atmospheric nitrogen to ammonia; others are responsible for nitrification, the conversion of ammonium to nitrate.
- Prokaryotes normally reproduce asexually by binary fission, which can result in very rapid population growth under favourable conditions.
- In nature, prokaryotes may live in an interacting community, such as a biofilm.
- Pathogenic bacteria cause disease via exotoxins and endotoxins.
- Bacteria may develop resistance to antibiotics through mutation of their own genes or by acquiring resistance genes from other bacteria.

21.3 The Domain Bacteria

- Bacteria are divided into more than a dozen evolutionary branches, including the Gram-negative proteobacteria, Gram-negative green bacteria, cyanobacteria, Gram-positive bacteria, spirochetes, and chlamydias.

21.4 The Domain Archaea

- Archaea have some features that are like those of bacteria, other features that are eukaryotic, and some that are unique (see Table 21.1).
- Archaea are classified into three groups: the Euryarchaeota (methanogens, extreme halophiles, and some extreme thermophiles); the Crenarchaeota (most of the extreme thermophiles, as well as psychrophiles and mesophiles); and the Korarchaeota, known only from DNA samples.

Questions

Self-Test Questions

1. A bacterium that uses nitrites as its only energy source was found in a deep salt mine. It is a
   a. chemoautotroph.
   b. parasite.
   c. photoautotroph.
   d. heterotroph.
   e. photoheterotroph.
2. The ________ are all oxygen-producing photoautotrophs.
   a. spirochetes
   b. chlamydias
   c. Gram-positive bacteria
   d. cyanobacteria
   e. proteobacteria
3. You would find an endotoxin associated with
   a. Gram-positive bacteria.
   b. Gram-negative bacteria.
   c. the cell wall.
   d. Both a and c are correct.
   e. Both b and c are correct.
4. Which of the following is not a property of an endospore?
   a. Resistant to boiling—must be autoclaved to be killed
   b. Metabolically inactive
   c. Can survive millions of years
   d. Provides a method to preserve bacterial DNA under harsh conditions
   e. Is a means that bacterial cells use to multiply
5. Which of the following statements about Gram-positive bacterial cell walls is true?
   1. More sensitive to effects of penicillium than are Gram-negative cell walls
   2. Are the only type of cell wall that contain peptidoglycan
   3. Have a thick peptidoglycan layer comprising about 90% of the cell wall
   4. Are quite complex relative to Gram-negative cell walls
      a. 1,2
      b. 1,3
      c. 3,4
      d. 2,4
      e. 1,4
6. Which of the following structures is not found in prokaryotic cells?
   a. chromosome
   b. cell wall
   c. ribosomes
   d. mitochondria
   e. plasma membrane

Questions for Discussion

1. You have isolated an unknown prokaryote from a soil sample. What features could you look for to help you determine if this prokaryote was a bacterium or an archaeon? Indicate how each feature would differ in an archaeon and a bacterium.
2. Some manufacturers have produced cleaning products that contain a compound that they claim can kill "99.9% of bacteria" on contact. Briefly explain to the manufacturer why this achievement is not necessarily good news.
3. In the lab, you have isolated some prokaryotic cells that belong either to a Gram-positive bacterium or an archaeon. What cellular (structural) features could you look for in order to determine which type of organism you have isolated? Indicate how that feature would differ between the two kinds of organism (assume that you have the necessary equipment to test for any cellular feature you want).

Influenza virus.

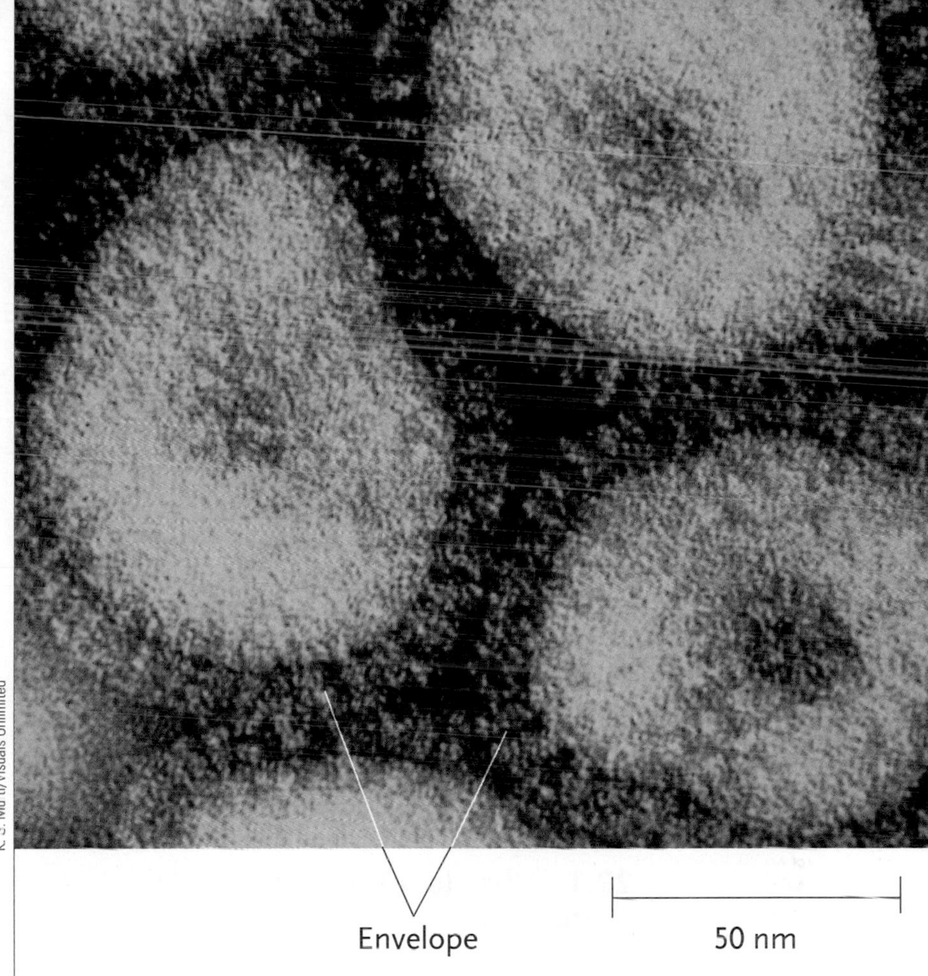

K. G. Murti/Visuals Unlimited

Study Plan

22 Viruses, Viroids, and Prions: Infectious Biological Particles

Why It Matters

Each winter in Canada, people line up for their annual flu shot. For many of us, this shot represents a gamble that we will be protected against the strains of the influenza virus (shown in the micrograph above) making the rounds that winter. Influenza is a respiratory illness that causes high fever, chills and muscle aches, sore throat, and a cough, among other symptoms. The specific strains of influenza circulating around the world change from year to year, so each year, the World Health Organization determines which strains are most likely to be prevalent during the winter flu season. A flu vaccine is then prepared containing killed viruses of those strains. Because the vaccine itself contains only killed viruses, you won't develop influenza, but your body will produce **antibodies** against the virus, protecting you against subsequent infection by any of those specific strains. (Antibodies are highly specific protein molecules, produced by the immune system, that recognize and bind to specific proteins of a pathogen, such as proteins in a virus' coat).

For most people, getting the flu means feeling awful for a few days, but for the very young, the elderly, and people with weakened immune systems, the stakes are higher: a bout of flu can be lethal. Some flu outbreaks have been devastatingly lethal to a greater proportion of the population. The worst recorded example is the flu *pandemic* (an outbreak or epidemic that spreads around the world) of 1918. A strain of influenza virus known as the Spanish flu infected almost half of the world's population, killing about 1 in every 20 people. Why was the Spanish flu so deadly? And why do we need to develop new flu vaccines so often? We investigate these questions later in this chapter. We also look at the beneficial roles played by viruses—not all are pathogenic—and investigate ways in which we may be able to harness the infective abilities of viruses for our own uses. For example, can we use viruses as vectors for gene therapy to fight diseases? We start with a look at the defining characteristics of viruses: how they are able to enter cells and take over the cell's machinery to make more copies of themselves. We also compare viruses with viroids and prions, other infectious particles.

22.1 What Is a Virus? Characteristics of Viruses

The structure of a virus is reduced to the minimum necessary to transmit its genome from one host cell to another. A virus is simply one or more nucleic acid molecules surrounded by a protein coat or **capsid** **(Figure 22.1a, b)**. Some capsids may be enclosed within a membrane or **envelope** derived from their host cell's membrane **(Figure 22.1c)**. So a virus is not a cell—it does not have a cytoplasm enclosed by a plasma membrane, as do all known living organisms. Viruses also lack many of the properties of life shared by all other organisms (see Chapter 2). For example, they lack a metabolic system to provide energy for their life cycles and cannot reproduce on their own; instead, they are dependent on the host cells they infect for these functions. Many biologists do not consider viruses living organisms; instead, they are referred to as infectious biological particles.

The nucleic acid genome of a virus may be either DNA or RNA and can be composed of either a single strand or a double strand of RNA or DNA. Viral genomes range from just a few genes to over a hundred genes; all viruses have genes that encode at least their coat proteins and the enzymes required for nucleic acid replication. Many viruses also have genes that encode *recognition proteins* that become implanted in the coat surface. These coat proteins recognize and bind to the host cell, promoting entry of the virus particle or its nucleic acid core into that cell.

Most viruses take one of two basic structural forms, helical or polyhedral. In **helical viruses**, the protein subunits assemble in a rodlike spiral around the genome (see Figure 22.1a). A number of viruses that infect plant cells are helical. In **polyhedral viruses,** the coat proteins form triangular units that fit together like the parts of a geodesic sphere (see Figure 22.1b). The polyhedral viruses include forms that infect animals, plants, and bacteria. In some polyhedral viruses, protein spikes that provide host cell recognition extend from the corners, where the facets fit together. Both helical and polyhedral viruses can be enveloped in a membrane derived from the host's membrane (see Figure 22.1c and **Figure 22.2**). Recognition protein spikes extend through the membrane, allowing the virus to recognize and bind to host cells.

Although they are not considered to be alive, viruses are classified into orders, families, genera,

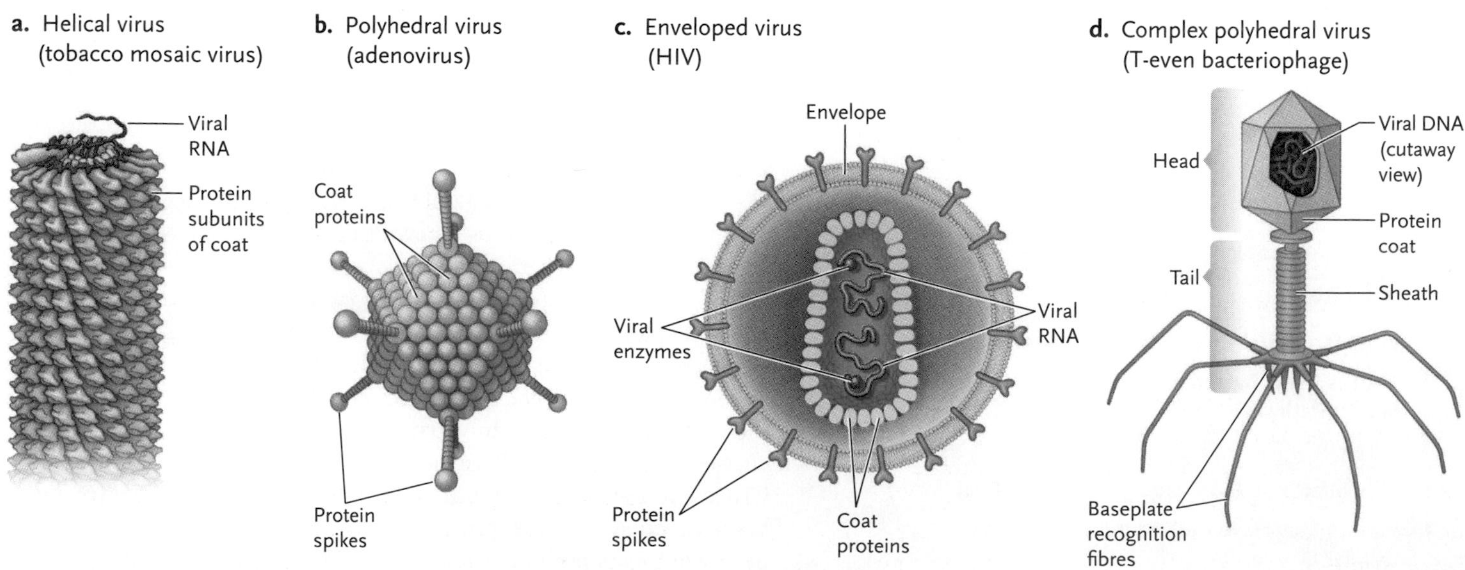

Figure 22.1
Viral structure. The tobacco mosaic virus in **(a)** assembles from more than 2000 identical protein subunits.

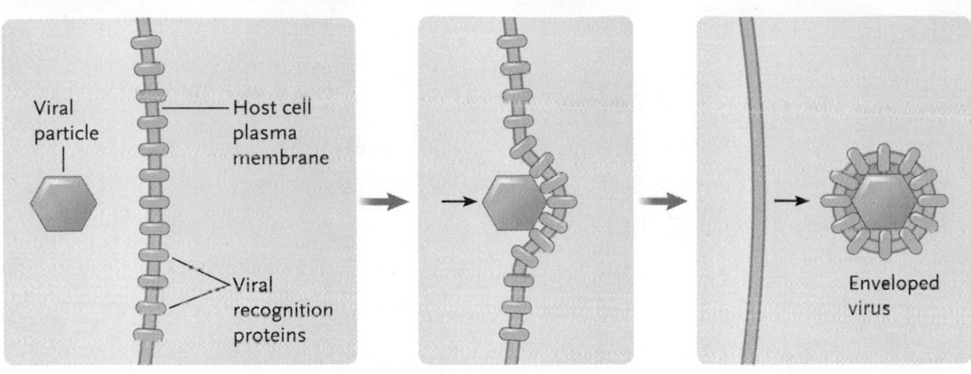

Figure 22.2
How enveloped viruses acquire their envelope.

and species using several criteria, including virus size and structure, genome structure (RNA or DNA, single stranded or double stranded), and how their nucleic acid is replicated. More than 4000 species of viruses have been classified into more than 80 families. The family names end in *-viridae* and may refer either to the geographic region where the virus was first discovered or to the structure of the virus. For example, Coronaviridae, the family to which influenza virus belongs, is named for the "crown" of protein spikes on the capsid, as shown in the photomicrograph at the start of this chapter (*corona* = crown). Unlike the species names of living organisms, a virus' species name is the name of the disease it causes and can be one or two words, for example, herpesvirus or Ebola virus.

As was the case for our look at prokaryotes in the previous chapter, we have just scratched the surface of viral diversity in this chapter; for example, there are millions of viruses in every millilitre of ocean water, most of which have not been identified. As we learn more about viruses, their classification will likely change.

Every living organism is likely permanently infected by one or more kinds of viruses. Usually, a virus infects only a single species or a few closely related species. A virus may even infect only one organ system or a single tissue or cell type in its host. However, some viruses are able to infect unrelated species, either naturally or after mutating.

Of the roughly 80 viral families described to date, 21 include viruses that cause human diseases. Viruses also cause diseases of wild and domestic animals. Plant viruses cause annual losses of millions of tonnes of crops, especially cereals, potatoes, sugar beets, and sugar cane. (**Table 22.1** lists some important viral families of viruses that infect animals.) The effects of viruses on the organisms they infect range from undetectable, to merely bothersome, to seriously debilitating or lethal. For instance, some viral infections of humans, such as those causing cold sores, chickenpox, and the common cold, are usually little more than a nuisance to healthy adults. Others cause some of the most severe and deadly human diseases, including AIDS, encephalitis, and Ebola hemorrhagic fever.

However, not all viruses are harmful to people. For example, one of the primary reasons why bacteria do not completely overrun this planet is that they are destroyed in incredibly huge numbers by viruses known as **bacteriophages**, or **phages** for short (*phagein* = to eat) (see Figure 22.1d). Viruses also provide a natural means to control some insect pests, such as spruce budworm.

Viruses are vital components of ecosystems and may be the dominant "entity" in some ecosystems, such as the oceans. We don't yet fully understand their roles in these ecosystems, but it is clear that they affect nutrient cycling through their effects on prokaryotes. For example, in certain regions of the ocean, a few genera of cyanobacteria dominate the marine phytoplankton, making major contributions to global photosynthesis. Bacteriophages infect these cyanobacteria, causing high levels of mortality, thus influencing cyanobacterial population dynamics well as the release of nutrients from bacterial cells. But these viruses also help keep photosynthesis going in their cyanobacterial hosts, as recently discovered by Nicholas Mann and colleagues at the Univeristy of Warwick. As you read in Chapter 7, one of the proteins that makes up photosystem II is very susceptible to light-induced damage and so is constantly being replaced by newly synthesized molecules. As long as the cell can make new protein fast enough to keep up with damage, photosynthesis can continue; but if the rate of damage exceeds the repair rate, the rate of photosynthesis will drop. When these bacteriophages infect cyanobacteria, they shut down their host's protein synthesis. Without continued synthesis of the photosystem protein, photosynthesis should slow down following infection—but it doesn't. How is the photosynthetic rate maintained? Mann and his colleagues found that the virus' genome includes genes for this protein; expression of these viral proteins enables the repair rate to keep up with light-induced damage, allowing the cell to photosynthesize. Although the virus is doing this for "selfish" reasons (i.e., to ensure that its host has sufficient resources for the virus to complete its life cycle), the outcome of this association is that much

Table 22.1 Major Animal Viruses

Viral Family	Envelope	Nucleic Acid	Diseases
Adenovirus	No	ds DNA	Respiratory infections, tumours
Flavivirus	Yes	ss RNA	Yellow fever, dengue, hepatitis C
Hepadnavirus	Yes	ds DNA	Hepatitis B
Human herpesvirus	Yes	ds DNA	
Herpes simplex I			Oral herpes, cold sores
Herpes simplex II			Genital herpes
Varicella-zoster virus			Chickenpox, shingles
Herpesvirus 4 (Epstein-Barr virus)			Infectious mononucleosis
Orthomyxovirus	Yes	ss RNA	Influenza
Papovavirus	No	ds DNA	Benign and malignant warts
Papillomavirus			Human papillomavirus (genital warts)
Paramyxovirus	Yes	ss RNA	Measles, mumps, pneumonia
Picornavirus	No	ss RNA	
Enterovirus			Polio, hemorrhagic eye disease, gastroenteritis
Rhinovirus			Common cold
Hepatitis A virus			Hepatitis A
Apthovirus			Foot-and-mouth disease in livestock
Poxvirus	Yes	ds DNA	Smallpox, cowpox
Retrovirus	Yes	ss RNA	
HTLV I, II			T-cell leukemia
HIV			AIDS
Rhabdovirus	Yes	ss RNA	Rabies, other animal diseases

ds = double-stranded; HTLV = human T lymphotropic virus; ss = single-stranded.

of the carbon fixed on Earth may be facilitated by virus-controlled photosynthesis.

Study Break

1. What is a virus?
2. List three features of viruses that distinguish them from living organisms.

22.2 Viruses Infect Bacterial, Animal, and Plant Cells by Similar Pathways

Viral particles move by random molecular motions until they contact the surface of a host cell. For infection to occur, the virus or the viral genome must then enter the cell. Inside the cell, the viral genes are expressed, leading to replication of the viral genome and assembly of progeny viruses. The viruses are then released from the host cell, a process that often ruptures the host cell, killing it.

22.2a Infection of Bacterial Cells

We have learned a great deal about the infective cycles of viruses, as well as the genetics of both viruses and bacteria, from studies of the bacteriophages infecting *Escherichia coli (E. coli)*. Some of these are **virulent bacteriophages**, which kill their host cells during each cycle of infection, whereas others are **temperate**. Temperate bacteriophages enter an inactive phase inside the host cell and can be passed on to several generations of daughter cells before becoming active and killing their host.

Virulent Bacteriophages. Among the virulent bacteriophages infecting *E. coli*, the **T-even bacteriophages** T2, T4, and T6 have been the most valuable in genetic studies. The coats of these phages are divided into a *head* and a *tail* (see Figure 22.1d). A double-stranded linear molecule of DNA is packed into the head. The tail, assembled from several different proteins, has recognition proteins at its tip that can bind to the surface of the host cell. Once the tail is attached, it functions as a sort of syringe that injects the DNA genome into the cell **(Figure 22.3).**

Infection begins when a T-even phage collides randomly with the surface of an *E. coli* cell and the tail attaches to the host cell wall (**Figure 22.4,** step 1). An enzyme present in the viral coat, *lysozyme*, then digests a hole in the cell wall through which the tail injects the DNA of the phage (step 2). The proteins of the viral coat remain outside. Throughout its life cycle within the bacterial cell, the phage uses host cell machinery to express its genes. One of the proteins produced early in the infection is an enzyme that breaks down the bacterial chromosome. The phage gene for a DNA polymerase that replicates the phage's DNA is also expressed early on. Eventually, 100 to 200 new viral DNA molecules are synthesized (step 3). Later in the infection, the host cell machinery transcribes the phage genes for the viral coat proteins (step 4). As the head and tail proteins assemble, the replicated viral DNA is packed into the heads (step 5).

When viral assembly is complete, the cell synthesizes a phage-encoded lysozyme that lyses the bacterial cell wall, causing the cell to rupture and releasing viral particles that can infect other *E. coli* cells (step 6). This whole series of events, from infection of a cell through to the release of progeny phages from the ruptured (or **lysed**) cell, is called the **lytic cycle.**

Some virulent phages (although not T-even phages) may package fragments of the host cell's

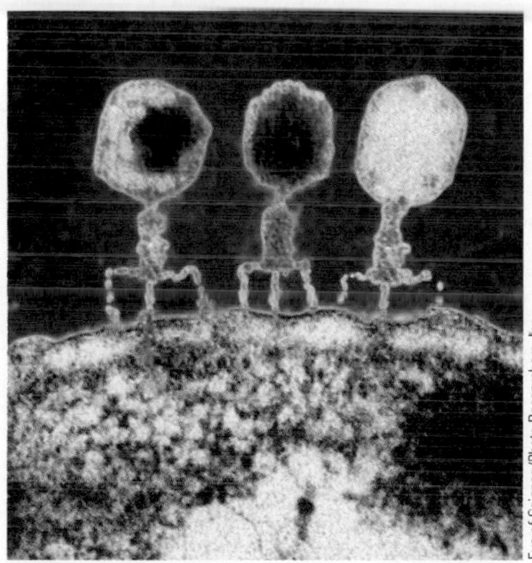

Figure 22.3
Bacteriophages injecting their DNA into *E. coli*.

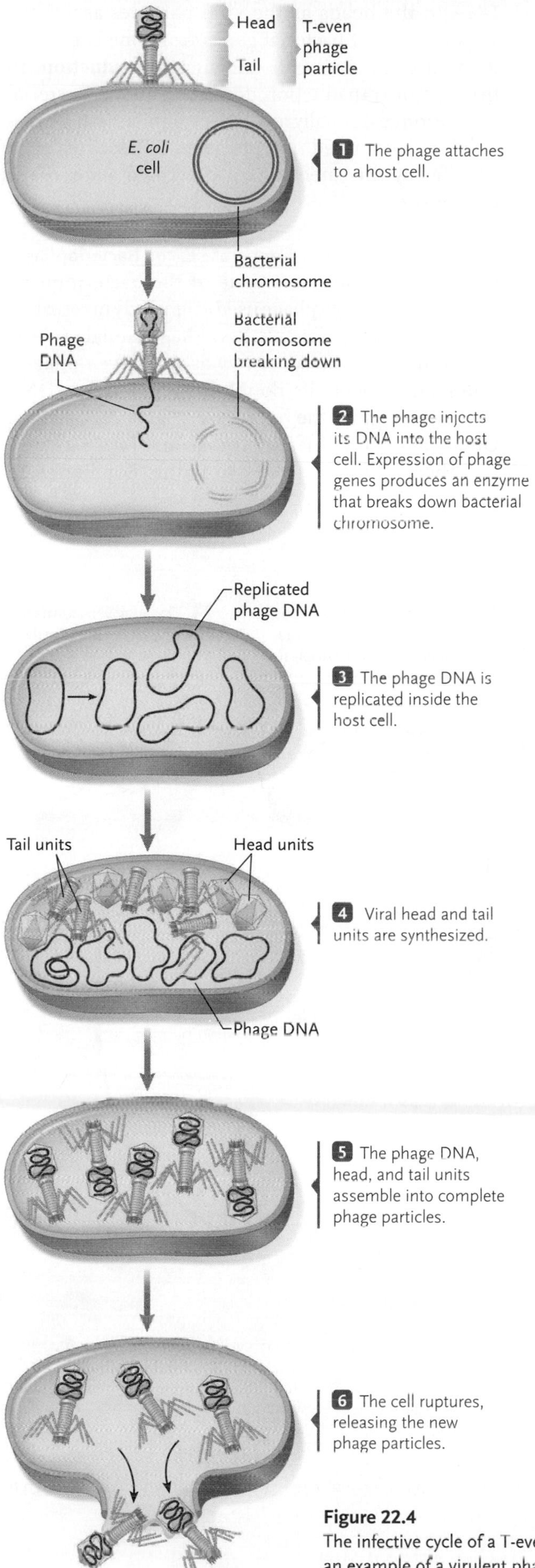

Head
Tail
T-even phage particle
E. coli cell
Bacterial chromosome

1 The phage attaches to a host cell.

Phage DNA
Bacterial chromosome breaking down

2 The phage injects its DNA into the host cell. Expression of phage genes produces an enzyme that breaks down bacterial chromosome.

Replicated phage DNA

3 The phage DNA is replicated inside the host cell.

Tail units
Head units
Phage DNA

4 Viral head and tail units are synthesized.

5 The phage DNA, head, and tail units assemble into complete phage particles.

6 The cell ruptures, releasing the new phage particles.

Figure 22.4
The infective cycle of a T-even bacteriophage, an example of a virulent phage.

DNA in the heads as the viral particles assemble. This transfer of bacterial genes from one bacterium to another via a virus is known as **transduction.** In the type of transduction described above, bacterial genes from essentially any DNA fragment can be randomly incorporated into phage particles; thus, gene transfer by this mechanism is termed **generalized transduction.**

A Scientist's Favourite Temperate *E. coli* Bacteriophage, Lambda. The infective cycle of the bacteriophage *lambda* (λ), an *E. coli* phage used extensively in research, is typical of temperate phages. Phage lambda infects *E. coli* in much the same way as the T-even phages. The phage injects its double-stranded linear DNA chromosome into the bacterium (**Figure 22.5,** step 1). Once inside, the linear chromosome forms a circle and then follows one of two paths. Sophisticated molecular switches govern which path is followed at the time of infection.

One path is the lytic cycle, which is like the lytic cycles of virulent phages. The lytic cycle (see Figure 22.5, left side) starts with steps 1 to 2 (infection) and then goes directly to steps 7 through 9 (production and release of progeny virus) and back to step 1. A second and more common path is the **lysogenic cycle** (see Figure 22.5, right side). This cycle begins when the viral chromosome integrates into the host cell's DNA by recombination (see Figure 22.5, steps 1 through 3). The DNA of a temperate phage typically inserts at one or possibly a few specific sites in the bacterial chromosome through the action of a phage-encoded enzyme that recognizes certain sequences in the host DNA. Once integrated, the lambda genes are mostly inactive, so no phage components are made. While inserted in the host cell

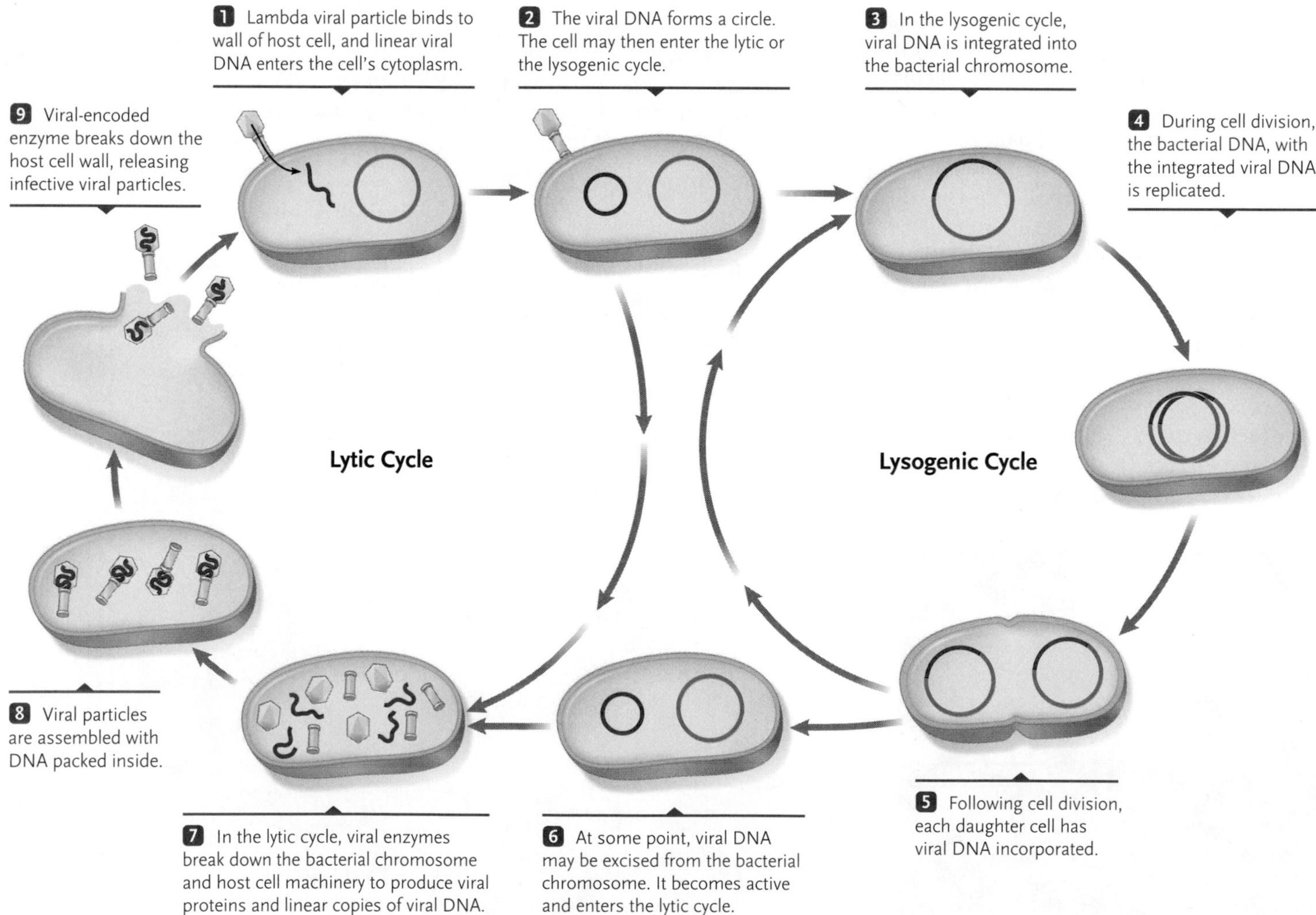

1 Lambda viral particle binds to wall of host cell, and linear viral DNA enters the cell's cytoplasm.
2 The viral DNA forms a circle. The cell may then enter the lytic or the lysogenic cycle.
3 In the lysogenic cycle, viral DNA is integrated into the bacterial chromosome.
4 During cell division, the bacterial DNA, with the integrated viral DNA, is replicated.
5 Following cell division, each daughter cell has viral DNA incorporated.
6 At some point, viral DNA may be excised from the bacterial chromosome. It becomes active and enters the lytic cycle.
7 In the lytic cycle, viral enzymes break down the bacterial chromosome and host cell machinery to produce viral proteins and linear copies of viral DNA.
8 Viral particles are assembled with DNA packed inside.
9 Viral-encoded enzyme breaks down the host cell wall, releasing infective viral particles.
Lytic Cycle
Lysogenic Cycle

Figure 22.5
The infective cycle of lambda, an example of a temperate phage, which can go through the lytic cycle or the lysogenic cycle.

DNA, the virus is known as a **prophage** (*pro* = before). When the host cell DNA replicates, so does the integrated viral DNA, which is passed on to daughter cells along with the host cell DNA (see Figure 22.5, steps 4 and 5).

What triggers the integrated prophage to become active (step 6)? Certain environmental signals, such as ultraviolet irradiation, stimulate this change, causing the prophage to enter the lytic cycle (see Figure 22.5, steps 6 through 9). Genes that were inactive in the prophage are now transcribed. Among the first viral proteins synthesized are enzymes that excise the lambda chromosome from the host chromosome. The result is a circular lambda chromosome that replicates itself and directs the production of viral DNA and coat proteins. This active stage culminates in the lysis of the host cell and the release of infective viral particles.

The excision of the prophage from its host's DNA is not always precise, resulting in the inclusion of one or more host cell genes with the viral DNA. These genes are replicated with the viral DNA and packed into the coats, and may be carried to a new host cell in the next cycle of infection. Clearly, only genes that are adjacent to the integration site(s) of a temperate phage can be cut out with the viral DNA, included in phage particles during the lytic stage, and undergo transduction. Accordingly, this mechanism of gene transfer is termed **specialized transduction.**

Infection of Animal Cells. Viruses infecting animal cells follow a pattern similar to that for bacterial cells, except that both the viral coat and the genome enter a host cell. Depending on the virus, removal of the coat to release the genome occurs during or after cell entry; the envelope does not enter the cell.

Viruses without an envelope, such as poliovirus, bind by their recognition proteins to the plasma membrane and are then taken into the host cell by endocytosis. The virus coat and genome of enveloped viruses, such as herpesvirus, influenza virus, and the virus causing rabies, enter the host cell by fusion of their envelope with the host cell plasma membrane.

Once inside the host cell, the genome directs the synthesis of additional viral particles by basically the same pathways as bacterial viruses. Some animal viruses, however, replicate themselves in very complex ways; one example is HIV, the virus that causes AIDS (see *Molecule Behind Biology*). Newly completed viruses that do not acquire an envelope are released by rupture of the host cell's plasma membrane, typically killing the cell. In contrast, most enveloped viruses receive their envelope as they pass through the plasma membrane, usually without breaking the membrane (see Figure 22.2). This pattern of viral release typically does not cause immediate damage to the host cell unless very high numbers of virus particles are released.

The vast majority of animal virus infections are asymptomatic because causing disease is of no benefit to the virus. However, a number of pathogenic viruses cause diseases in a variety of ways. Some viruses (e.g., herpesvirus) cause cell death when progeny viruses are released from the cell. This can lead to massive cell death, destroying vital tissues such as nervous tissue or white or red blood cells, or causing lesions in skin and mucous membranes. Other viruses release cellular molecules when infected cells break down, which can induce fever and inflammation (e.g., influenza virus). Yet other viruses alter gene function when they insert into the host cell DNA, leading to cancer and other abnormalities.

Some animal viruses enter a **latent phase**, similar to the lysogenic cycle for bacteriophages, in which the virus remains in the cell in an inactive form. The herpesviruses that cause oral and genital ulcers in humans remain in a latent phase in the cytoplasm of some body cells for the life of the individual. At times, particularly during periods of stress, the virus becomes active in some cells, directing viral replication and causing ulcers to form as cells break down during viral release.

Plant Viruses. Plant viruses may be rodlike or polyhedral. Although most include RNA as their nucleic acid, some contain DNA. None of the known plant viruses have envelopes. They enter cells through mechanical injuries to leaves and stems; they can also be transmitted from one plant to another during pollination or via herbivorous animals such as leafhoppers, aphids, and nematodes. Plant viruses can also be transmitted from one generation to the next in seeds. Once inside a cell, plant viruses replicate via the same processes as animal viruses. However, within plants, virus particles can pass from infected to healthy cells through plasmodesmata, the openings in cell walls that interconnect the cytoplasm of plant cells, and through the vascular system.

Plant viruses are generally named and classified by the type of plant they infect and their most visible effects. *Tomato bushy stunt virus,* for example, causes dwarfing and overgrowth of leaves and stems of tomato plants, and *tobacco mosaic virus* causes a mosaic-like pattern of spots on the leaves of tobacco plants. Most species of crop plants can be infected by at least one destructive virus.

The tobacco mosaic virus was the first virus to be isolated, disassembled, and reassembled in a test tube (see Figure 22.1a).

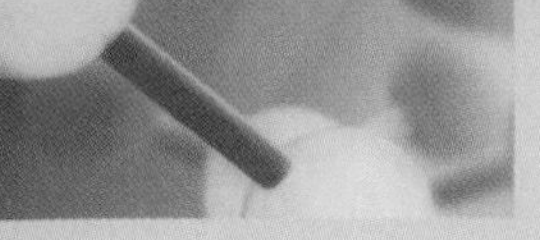

Reverse Transcriptase

Acquired immune deficiency syndrome (AIDS) is a disease caused by the human immunodeficiency virus (HIV). This disease has likely already killed about 25 million people worldwide, and the epidemic continues to grow, with infection rates in some areas of Africa as high as one in three adults. Even more concerning, infection rates are increasing in south and east Asia, some of the most densely populated regions of the world. If the epidemic continues to spread at current rates, the World Health Organization has projected AIDS as the fourth leading cause of death by 2030 (behind heart disease, other chronic diseases and car accidents). Although drug treatments to hold AIDS in check do exist, they are very expensive, and most people in developing countries cannot afford them. There is no cure for AIDS, so the millions of people currently infected will die prematurely.

HIV is a retrovirus that contains two copies of single-stranded RNA. It also carries several molecules of an enzyme, reverse transcriptase in its capsid. Replication of retroviruses is unusual: the virus' genome enters the host cell along with reverse transcriptase, which copies the viral RNA onto a complementary strand of DNA **(Figure 1).** A second strand of DNA is then synthesized, using the first strand as a template. The resulting double-stranded DNA integrates into the host cell's DNA as a provirus (comparable to the prophage described above). It is transcribed by the host cell into mRNA, which is translated to produce viral proteins, including capsid proteins and reverse transcriptase molecules. New virus particles are released from the cell to infect other cells or be passed to new hosts.

Why is HIV so lethal? The cells targeted by HIV include intestinal epithelial cells, brain cells, and cells of the immune system, including cells that produce antibodies. Obviously,

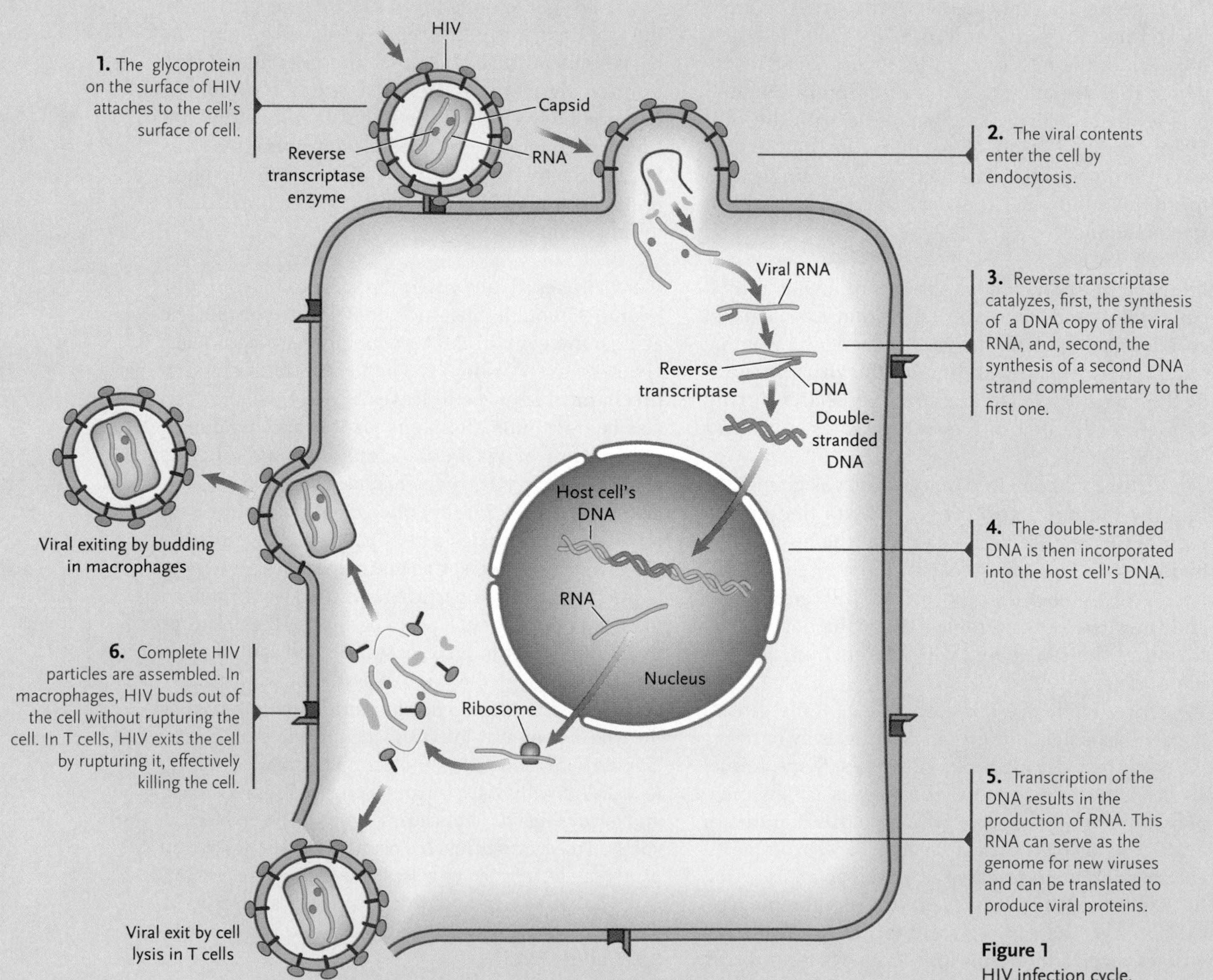

1. The glycoprotein on the surface of HIV attaches to the cell's surface of cell.

2. The viral contents enter the cell by endocytosis.

3. Reverse transcriptase catalyzes, first, the synthesis of a DNA copy of the viral RNA, and, second, the synthesis of a second DNA strand complementary to the first one.

4. The double-stranded DNA is then incorporated into the host cell's DNA.

5. Transcription of the DNA results in the production of RNA. This RNA can serve as the genome for new viruses and can be translated to produce viral proteins.

6. Complete HIV particles are assembled. In macrophages, HIV buds out of the cell without rupturing the cell. In T cells, HIV exits the cell by rupturing it, effectively killing the cell.

Figure 1
HIV infection cycle.

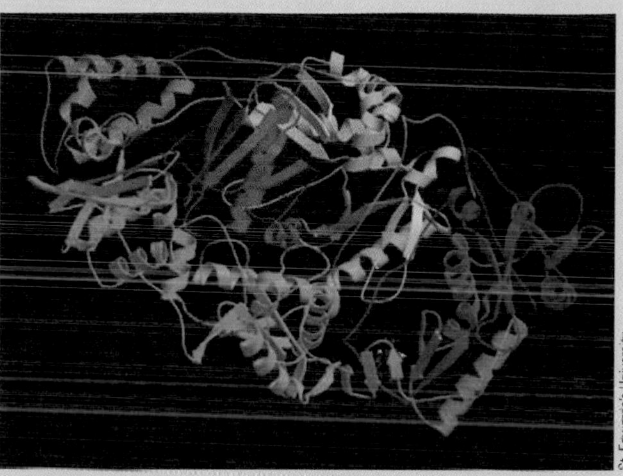

Figure 2
Reverse transcriptase.

infection of these cells compromises the body's ability to fight off the virus. Some of the immune system cells are not killed by the virus but instead act as a continuing source of infection.

Because reverse transcriptase **(Figure 2)** is a unique feature of HIV, it makes a good target for drug treatment (if the drugs affect only this enzyme, they will not harm the human host). Several anti-retroviral drugs have been developed, although HIV has become resistant to some of these drugs. The search continues for a vaccine that would prevent HIV infection, but despitea years of research, no vaccine exists yet.

Why is there no vaccine, and how does HIV become resistant so quickly to drugs? The answer to both questions is that HIV mutates quickly and extensively. In a cell's normal DNA replication process, DNA polymerase has proofreading capabilities, so the replicated DNA contains few errors. Reverse transcriptase does not have any proofreading ability, so any errors made when it catalyzes the synthesis of DNA from RNA (and there are a lot of such errors) persist. Proteins encoded by this mutated DNA will be different from those of the original virus; for example, the proteins of the viral coat will be different and so are not recognized by existing antibodies.

However, reverse transcriptase has also made important positive contributions to biomedical research. For example, retroviruses play an important role in gene therapy, in which new diseases are treated by introducing new genes into the body. Viruses are very effective vectors for introducing genes into cells. The desired genes are cloned into the viral genome, and once the virus is taken up by the cell, those genes are introduced into all cells infected by the virus. Retroviruses are particularly useful in gene therapy since the genetic material they carry is integrated into the host cell genome.

Study Break

1. What is the difference between a virulent phage and a temperate phage?
2. What are the two types of transduction? How do they differ from each other?
3. How do plant viruses differ from animal viruses?

22.3 Viral Infections Are Typically Difficult to Treat

Viral infections are unaffected by antibiotics and other treatment methods used for bacterial infections. As a result, many viral infections are allowed to run their course, with treatment limited to relieving the symptoms while the natural immune defenses of the patient attack the virus. Some viruses, however, cause serious and sometimes deadly symptoms on infection; consequently, researchers have spent considerable effort in developing antiviral drugs to treat them. Many of these drugs fight the virus directly by targeting a stage of the viral life cycle; for example, the drug zanamivir inhibits release of influenza virus particles from cells.

The influenza virus illustrates the difficulties inherent in treating viral diseases. As mentioned at the start of the chapter, the influenza type A virus causes flu epidemics that sweep over the world each year. Why does a new vaccine have to be developed each year? One reason for the success of this virus is that its genome consists of eight separate pieces of RNA. When two different influenza viruses infect the same individual, these RNA pieces can assemble in random combinations derived from either parent virus. The new combinations can change the protein coat of the virus, making it unrecognizable to antibodies developed against either parent virus. Being "invisible" to these antibodies means that new virus strains can infect people who have already had the flu caused by a different strain or who had flu shots effective only against the parent strains of the virus. Random mutations in the RNA genome of the virus add to the variations in the coat proteins that make previously formed antibodies ineffective.

In the opening to this chapter, we learned that the 1918 influenza virus killed many of its hosts. Why was this strain so virulent? Researchers have learned that the 1918 influenza virus had mutations in the polymerase genes that replicated the viral genome in host cells, likely making this strain capable of replicating more efficiently.

Other viruses are also considered to have evolved from a virus that previously infected other animals. HIV is one of these; until the second half of the twentieth century, infections of this virus were apparently restricted almost entirely to chimpanzees and gorillas in Africa. Now the virus infects nearly 40 million people worldwide, with the greatest concentration of infected individuals in sub-Saharan Africa.

Study Break

What makes a viral infection often more difficult to treat than a bacterial infection?

22.4 Viruses May Have Evolved from Fragments of Cellular DNA or RNA

Where did viruses come from? Several different hypotheses have been proposed to explain the origin of viruses. Some biologists have suggested that because viruses can duplicate only by infecting a host cell, they probably evolved after cells appeared. They may represent "escaped" fragments of DNA molecules that once formed part of the genetic material of living cells or an RNA copy of such a fragment. In some way, the fragments became surrounded by a protective layer of protein with recognition functions and escaped from their parent cells. As viruses evolved, the information encoded in the core of the virus became reduced to a set of directions for producing more viral particles of the same kind.

More recent hypotheses suggest that viruses are very ancient, with virus-like particles predating the first cells. The first viruses originated from the "primordial gene pool"—the pool of RNA that is thought to have been the first genetic material (see Chapter 2).

Regardless of their origin, viruses have played an important role in the evolution of cellular life because of their ability to integrate their genes into their hosts and to acquire genes from their hosts, as described above. In this way, viruses can be a source of new cellular genetic material, providing new enzymes and other proteins to a cell. Viruses may also have played a more direct role in the evolution of eukaryotic cells: some biologists have suggested that the nucleus originated from a large, double-stranded DNA virus that infected prokaryote cells, resulting in the first eukaryotic cell.

Study Break

Why do some biologists think viruses must have originated after cells evolved, rather than predating cells?

22.5 Viroids and Prions Are Infective Agents Even Simpler in Structure Than Viruses

Viroids, first discovered in 1971, are small, infectious pieces of RNA. Although the RNA is single-stranded, bonding within the molecule causes it to become circular. Viroids are smaller than any virus and lack a protein coat. They also differ from viruses in that their RNA genome does not code for any proteins. Viroids are plant pathogens that can rapidly destroy entire fields of citrus, potatoes, tomatoes, coconut palms, and other crop plants. How do viroids cause such devastating diseases without synthesizing any proteins?

The manner in which viroids cause disease remains unknown. In fact, researchers believe that there is more than one mechanism. Recent research indicates that the viroid may disrupt normal RNA processing of the host cell: if the viroid's RNA sequence is complementary to mRNA of the host cell, it can bind to the host's mRNA, thus preventing normal protein synthesis and causing disease.

Prions, a loose acronym for *pro*tineaceous *in*fectious particles, cause spongiform encephalopathies (SEs), degenerate diseases of the nervous system in mammals characterized by loss of motor control and erratic behaviour. The brains of affected animals are full of spongy holes **(Figure 22.6)** (hence the "spongiform" designation) and deposits of proteinaceous material. Under the microscope, aggregates of misfolded proteins, called amyloid fibres, are seen in brain tissues; the accumulation of these proteins is the likely cause of the brain damage. SEs progress slowly, meaning that animals may be sick for a long time before their symptoms become obvious, but death is inevitable.

One SE disease is *scrapie*, a brain disease that causes sheep to rub against fences, rocks, or trees until they scrape off most of their wool. In cattle, a similar disease is bovine spongiform encephalopathy (BSE), also known as "mad cow disease." Humans also have SE diseases, such as *kuru*, found among

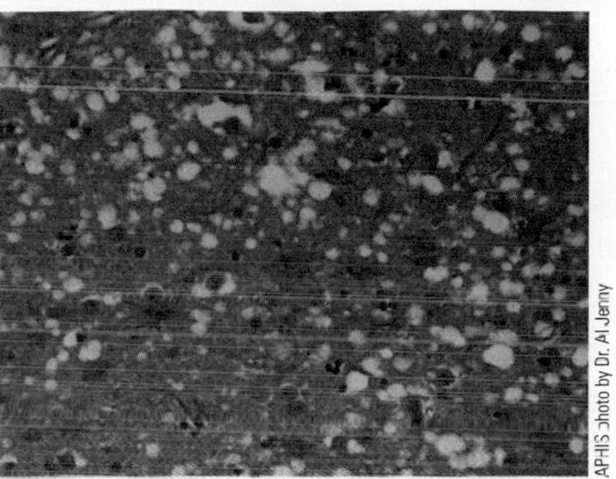

Figure 22.6
Bovine spongiform encephalopathy (BSE). The light-coloured patches in this section from a brain damaged by BSE are areas where tissue has been destroyed.

cannibals in New Guinea, who became infected by eating raw human brain during ritual feasts following the death of an individual. *Creutzfeldt-Jakob disease (CJD)* is a very rare SE disease that affects about one person in a million per year, globally. The symptoms of CJD include rapid mental deterioration, loss of vision and speech, and paralysis; autopsies show spongy holes and deposits in brain tissue similar to those of cattle with BSE. We don't know how CJD is transmitted naturally, but we know it can be transmitted inadvertently, for example, with corneal transplants.

SE diseases hit the headlines worldwide in the late 1980s when farmers in the United Kingdom reported a new disease, later determined to be BSE, spreading among their cattle. It is estimated that over 900 000 cows in the United Kingdom were affected, many of which entered the human food chain before developing symptoms. Where did BSE come from? The source was determined to be meat and bone meal fed to the cows; this meal came from the carcasses of sheep and cattle. The practice of feeding animal meal to cattle had been followed for years, but a money-saving change in processing in the early 1980s (a reduction in how long rendered material was held at high temperature) allowed the infectious agent—maybe from scrapie-infected sheep—to survive in the meat and bone meal. Worse was to come when it became evident that BSE had spread to humans who had eaten contaminated beef. This new human disease, known as variant CJD, is linked to eating meat products from cattle with BSE. Between 1996, when variant CJD was first described, and 2007, there were 208 cases from 11 countries, with the vast majority of these in the United Kingdom. Evidence from studies of kuru suggests that it may take more than 50 years for prion diseases to develop, so there is some concern that a spike in variant CJD cases is still to come.

Concern about variant CJD explains why the discovery of even one cow with BSE can wreak havoc on a country's beef exports, as happened in Alberta in 2003. The United States closed its border to all beef from Canada within a day, followed shortly by border closings of 40 other countries. Loss of these markets caused serious economic hardship for Canadian ranchers and farmers.

What is the cause of BSE and other SE diseases, and how does this causative agent spread? As explained in *People Behind Biology*, Stanley Prusiner demonstrated that infectious proteins cause these diseases. Prions are the only known infectious agents that do not include a nucleic acid molecule, and their discovery changed some fundamental views of biology.

Our current understanding of prion infection is that prion proteins are able to survive passage through the stomach of an animal consuming them; they then enter that animal's bloodstream and proceed to the brain where they somehow interact with normal prion proteins, causing these proteins to change shape to become abnormal and infectious. As the infection spreads, neural functioning is impaired and protein fibrils accumulate, leading to the SE characteristic of these diseases.

What is the function of "normal" prion proteins? We don't know yet, but there is some evidence that normal prions may protect neurons from overactivity. In recent research, mice lacking normal prion proteins were found to have "hyperactive" neurons, which responded longer and more vigorously to stimulation, compared with neurons of mice with the normal form of prion proteins. This hyperactivity ultimately led to the destruction of the neurons. Perhaps the inability of the misfolded prion proteins to carry out their normal protective function results in dementia and the other symptoms of BSE.

In this chapter, we focused on the simplest biological entities: viruses, viroids, and prions, which possess only some of the properties of life. In the next five chapters, we investigate more structurally complex organisms: the eukaryotic kingdoms of protists, fungi, plants, and animals.

Study Break

How do viroids and prions differ from viruses? How do they differ from each other?

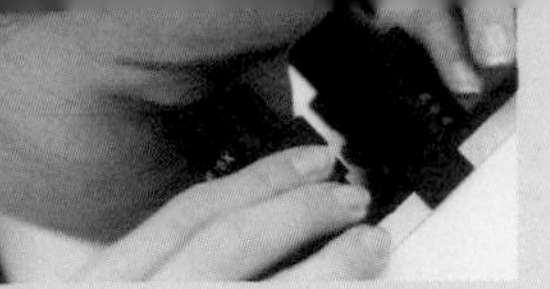

People Behind Biology

Stanley Prusiner

For several decades, scientists had hypothesized that a slow virus—a disease-causing virus with a long incubation period and gradual onset of pathogenicity—was responsible for scrapie and other spongiform encephalopathies. However, scientists had repeatedly examined the brains of infected animals and not found any evidence of viral infection. In 1982, Stanley Prusiner, a researcher at University of California, San Francisco, determined that the infectious agent was a protein. He pointed to the accumulation of protein fibrils in the brains of infected animals and termed this protein the prion protein (PrP). The research community mostly rejected this hypothesis because it went against all the accepted dogma of biology—genes in the form of DNA or RNA were necessary to cause disease. How could a protein make copies of itself? Prusiner located the gene for PrP and then found that prion proteins are naturally occurring membrane proteins in many types of cells, including neurons. In sheep infected with scrapie, Prusiner found "rogue" forms of the prion proteins that were abnormally folded. He proposed that these infectious prion proteins somehow interacted with "normal" prion proteins to cause misfolding of these proteins; thus, the abnormal protein structure is "infectious." The misfolded prion proteins aggregate, forming the masses of fibrils characteristic of SE diseases. In 1997, Prusiner received a Nobel Prize for his discovery of prions.

Unanswered Questions

Do viruses infect extremophile organisms?

As you learned in Chapter 21, prokaryotic organisms have been able to colonize every habitat on Earth, from frozen valleys of Antarctica to hydrothermal vents in deep ocean and hot springs. They can even live at depths of more than 1 kilometre in Earth's crust. So when we think of *extremophiles*—organisms that can live in conditions of extreme pH, temperature, salinity, desiccation, etc.—we usually think of prokaryotes. But there are some eukaryotic extremophiles too, such as the algae that live in Spain's Rio Tinto, a river with a pH of 2 and elevated levels of iron and copper. Do viruses infect extremophiles? If so, what type of viruses are they? What role do they play in these extreme environments?

Several lines of research indicate that viruses infect organisms living in extreme saline environments, in polar environments, at ocean depths, and in extremely hot environments. It is thought that early life forms might have been prokaryotic thermophiles, so studying the viruses that infect thermophilic archaea and bacteria might shed light on the evolution of cellular life and the origin of viruses. Recently, viruses have been found in archaea living in hot springs. Some of these viruses have morphological and molecular features unrelated to those of any other known viruses. They also show incredible genetic diversity—their genetic sequences do not match those of known viruses, and we don't yet know what most of their genes encode. Although some of these unknown proteins may carry out the same functions as known proteins, we may discover proteins with new functions.

The thermophilic viruses do not lyse their host cells and appear to persist inside their hosts in a stable state. Perhaps, like the phages that infect marine cyanobacteria, these viruses assist their hosts' survival in extreme environments.

How do prion proteins move within the brain?

The brain-wasting diseases caused by prions are not well understood, despite much research. We know that prion proteins invade nerve cells and ultimately lead to fatal degeneration of the nervous system. To understand disease progression, scientists have investigated how prion proteins move through the nervous system. Using labelled-protein techniques, researchers have tracked infectious prion proteins from sites of infection up to the brain. In mice, prion proteins move via the projections of nerve cells to points of contact with other cells. Perhaps prion proteins are able to cross into the adjacent cell. An understanding of how prions invade cells and replicate are crucial if we are to develop therapies to stop the spread of brain-wasting diseases.

Review

Go to CENGAGENOW™ at http://hed.nelson.com/ to access quizzing, animations, exercises, articles, and personalized homework help.

22.1 What Is a Virus? Characteristics of Viruses

- Viruses are non-living infective agents. A free virus particle consists of a nucleic acid genome enclosed in a protein coat. Recognition proteins enabling the virus to attach to host cells extend from the surface of infectious viruses.

22.2 Viruses Infect Bacterial, Animal, and Plant Cells by Similar Pathways

- Viruses reproduce by entering a host cell and directing the cellular machinery to make new particles of the same kind.

22.3 Viral Infections Are Typically Difficult to Treat

- Viruses are unaffected by antibiotics and most other treatment methods. As well, many viruses have great genetic variability. For these reasons, viral infections are difficult to treat.

22.4 Viruses May Have Evolved from Fragments of Cellular DNA or RNA

- There are several hypotheses about the origin of viruses. Viruses may have evolved after cells did and may have descended from nucleic acid fragments that "escaped" from a cell. Evidence for this hypothesis comes from the fact that viruses can duplicate only by infecting a host cell. On the other hand, a competing hypothesis suggests that viruses evolved before the first cells, with the first virus-like particles originating from the pool of RNA that was the first genetic material.

22.5 Viroids and Prions Are Infective Agents Even Simpler in Structure Than Viruses

- Viroids, which infect crop plants, consist of only a very small, single-stranded RNA molecule. Prions, which cause brain diseases in some animals, are infectious proteins with no associated nucleic acid. Prions are misfolded versions of normal cellular proteins, which can induce other normal proteins to misfold.

Questions

Self-Test Questions

1. Which of the following best defines a virus?
   a. A non-cellular entity containing a nucleoid region.
   b. An entity composed of proteins, nucleic acids and ribosomes.
   c. An entity composed of proteins and nucleic acids that can't replicate outside a host.
   d. A naked fragment of nucleic acid
   e. A disease-causing group of proteins
2. Most viruses form a capsid around their nucleic acid core. This capsid is composed of:
   a. protein
   b. polysaccharides
   c. antigens
   d. glycoprotein
   e. lipoprotein
3. Viral envelopes generally _____.
   a. are composed of a lipid bilayer, derived from the host cell's membrane.
   b. contain glycoproteins of viral origin.
   c. are located between virus's capsid and its nucleic acid.
   d. Both A and B are correct.
   e. A, B and C are all correct.
4. Plant viruses are different from animal viruses in that they _____________.
   a. lack the ability to actively infect a host cell.
   b. lack the ability to replicate their RNA genome.
   c. are covered by a membrane envelope.
   d. are easily curable.
   e. There are NO differences between animal and plant viruses.
5. When a bacteriophage enters the lysogenic stage,
   a. the viral DNA is replicated outside the host cell.
   b. it enters the host cell and kills it immediately.
   c. it enters the host cell, picks up host DNA, and leaves the cell unharmed.
   d. it sits on the host cell plasma membrane, with which it covers itself, and then leaves the cell.
   e. it injects its DNA into the host cell DNA, and the host DNA integrates viral DNA into the host genome.
6. Reverse transcriptase synthesizes
   a. RNA from DNA.
   b. DNA from RNA.
   c. proteins from DNA.
   d. proteins from RNA.
7. Which of the following statements about prions is FALSE?
   a. Prions can only be transmitted from animals to humans.
   b. Prions contain no nucleic acids and have the same amino acid sequence as the normal protein.
   c. Prions have a different three-dimensional structure from their natural protein.
   d. Prion proteins reproduce by converting a normal protein to an infectious prion protein by misfolding it.
   e. All evidence to date indicates that prions infect mammals but not other animals.

Questions for Discussion

1. From what you have read in this chapter, would you consider viruses to be alive? Why or why not?
2. Why do animal viruses have envelopes, whereas bacteriophages do not?
3. Why is it difficult to design an effective, long-lasting vaccine for the flu virus and the HIV virus?

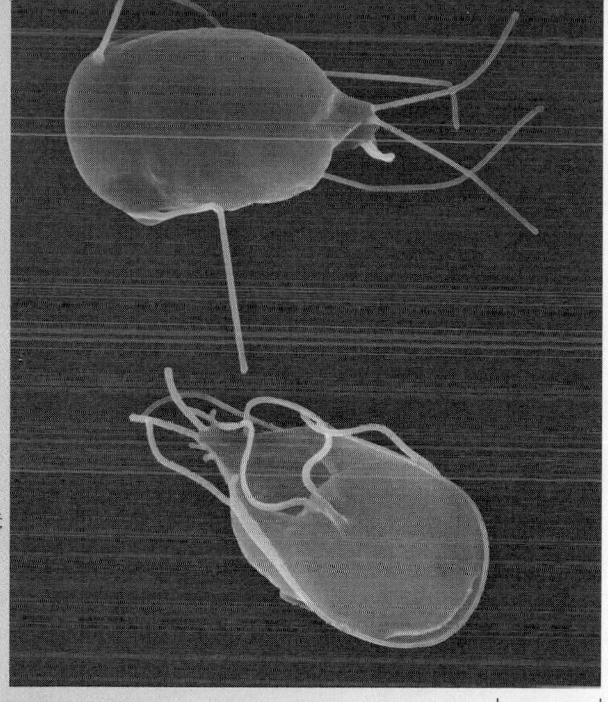

a.

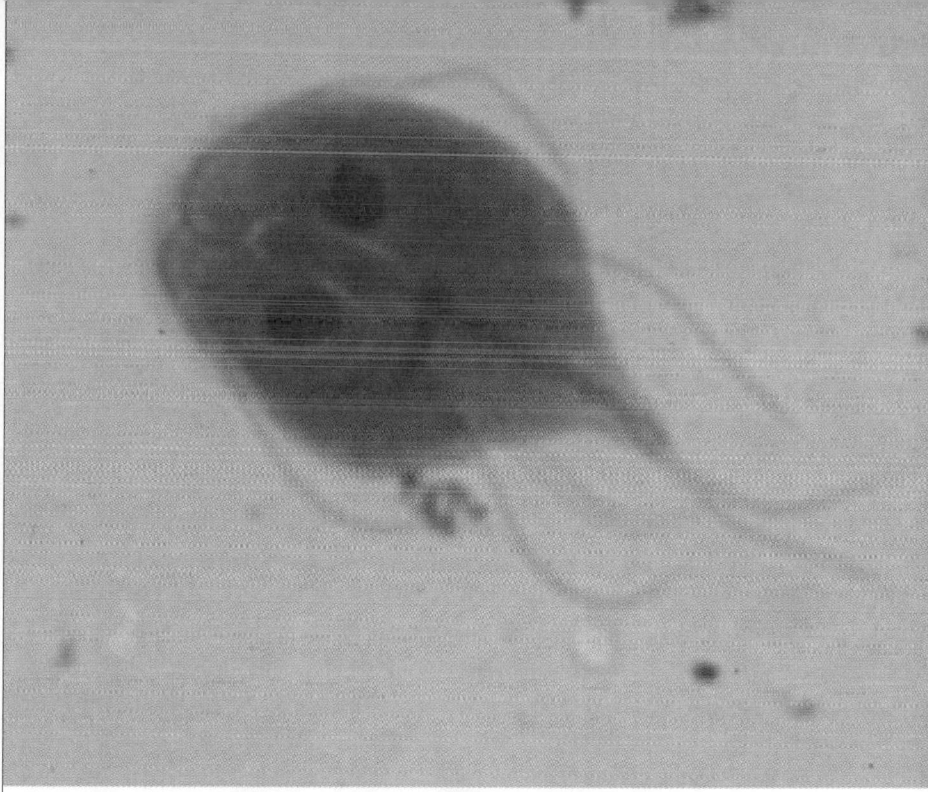

b.

Giardia lamblia **(a)** Scanning electron microscope image; **(b)** light microscope image.

23 Protists

Study Plan

Why It Matters

You are on a backpacking trip in your favourite wilderness area on a hot and sunny day. You pause to take a drink of water from your water bottle but discover it is almost empty. You are very thirsty, so you refill your bottle from a nearby stream: the water is clear and cold and looks clean, and, besides, you're out in the middle of nowhere, so it must be safe to drink, right? You continue on the hike and feel fine. But a few days after you get home, you don't feel so great: you have abdominal pain, cramps, and diarrhea. Your doctor says that you have giardiasis, or "beaver fever," caused by *Giardia lamblia,* the most common intestinal parasite in North America (it is very prevalent in water bodies formed by beaver dams). What is *Giardia,* and how does it make you sick?

Giardia is a single-celled eukaryote that can exist in two forms: a dormant cyst and a motile feeding stage. When you drank from that seemingly clean stream, you ingested some cysts. The cysts can survive for months, so it is important to boil or filter water when you are out hiking or camping. As the swallowed cysts moved from your stomach into your small intestine, the cysts released the motile feeding stage, **trophozoites** (*troph* = food; *zoon* = animal), shown in the photographs at the start of this chapter. Using their multiple flagella, the trophozoites were able to swim about in your intestinal space and attach themselves to the epithelial cells of your intestine. Infection with *Giardia* can become chronic, causing inflammation and reduction of the absorptive capacity of the gut. So why doesn't your immune system detect the presence of *Giardia* and get rid of the parasite? *Giardia* can alter the proteins on its surface that your immune system relies on to recognize an invader and so escapes recognition; thus, *Giardia* infections can be persistent or recur.

Giardia is a **protist** (Greek *protistos* = the very first). Protists are a very heterogeneous collection of about 200 000 eukaryotes that are not actually closely related to each other; that is, they did not all arise from a common ancestor. Most are unicellular and microscopic, but some are large, muticellular organisms. Like their most ancient ancestors, almost all of these eukaryotic species are aquatic. **Figure 23.1** shows a number of protists, illustrating their great diversity. Traditionally, protists are grouped together into the kingdom Protista (sometimes called "Protoctista"). This kingdom has traditionally been a catch-all group that consists of those eukaryotes that are not animals, fungi, or plants.

23.1 Evolution of Protists Involved Endosymbiosis

Protists likely evolved about 1.5 to 2 billion years ago. We don't fully understand how they evolved, although we know that endosymbiosis played an important role in the process. As eukaryotes, protists contain mitochondria

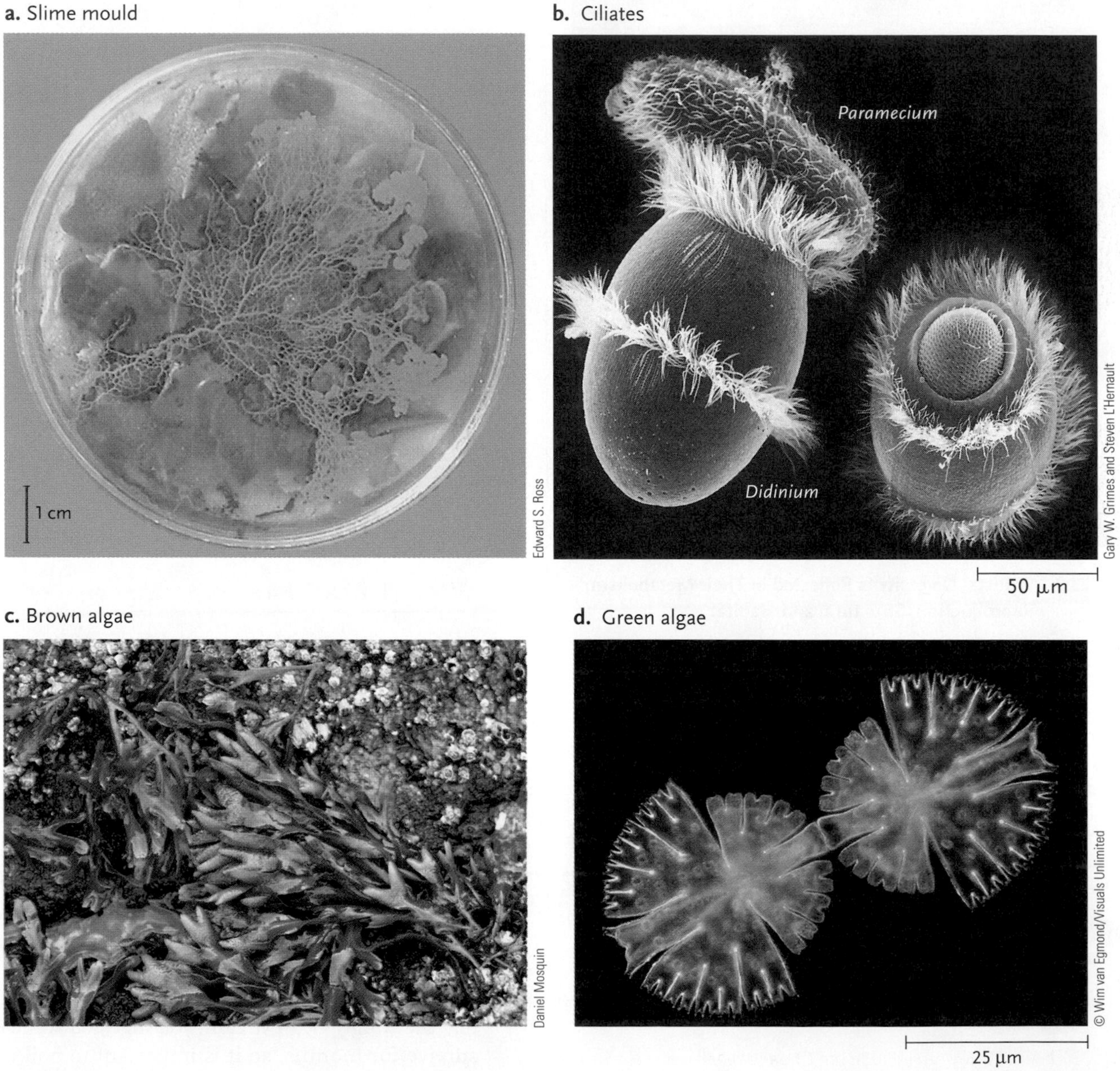

a. Slime mould

1 cm

Edward S. Ross

b. Ciliates

Paramecium

Didinium

50 μm

Gary W. Grimes and Steven L'Hernault

c. Brown algae

Daniel Mosquin

d. Green algae

25 μm

© Wim van Egmond/Visuals Unlimited

Figure 23.1
A sampling of protist diversity. **(a)** *Physarum*, a plasmodial slime mould grown in organic debris in a Petri dish. **(b)** *Didinium*, a ciliate, consuming another ciliate, *Paramecium*. **(c)** *Fucus gardneri* (common rockweed), a brown alga growing in rocky intertidal zones. **(d)** *Micrasterias*, a single-celled green alga, here shown dividing in two.

(although some have very reduced versions of this organelle), and many also contain chloroplasts. As outlined in Chapter 2, mitochondria and chloroplasts are the descendants of free-living prokaryotes that, over evolutionary time, became organelles. All mitochondria are thought to have arisen from a single endosymbiotic event, but the history of chloroplasts is more complex.

The first chloroplasts evolved from free-living photosynthetic prokaryotes (cyanobacteria) ingested by eukaryote cells that had already acquired mitochondria (see Chapter 2). In some cells, the cyanobacterium was not digested but instead formed a symbiotic relationship with the engulfing host cell—it became an endosymbiont, an independent organism living inside another organism (see Figure 2.22). Over evolutionary time, the prokaryote lost genes no longer required for independent existence and transferred most of its genes to the host's nuclear genome. As explained in Chapter 2, moving some of the genes to the nucleus is thought to have given the host cell better control of overall cell function. The prokaryote had become an organelle, part of the eukaryote cell. As we'll see, some photosynthetic protists originated from this endosymbiotic event, whereas other protists were formed when a eukaryote engulfed a photosynthetic eukaryote that eventually became a chloroplast. We will return to this topic at the end of the chapter.

Study Break

How did the first chloroplasts evolve?

23.2 What Is a Protist? Characteristics of Protists

Because protists are eukaryotes, the boundary between them and prokaryotes is clear and obvious. Unlike prokaryotes, protists have a membrane-bound nucleus, with multiple, linear chromosomes. In addition to cytoplasmic organelles, including mitochondria and chloroplasts (in some species), protists have microtubules and microfilaments, which provide motility and cytoskeletal support. As well, they share characteristics of transcription and translation with other eukaryotes.

The phylogenetic relationship between protists and other eukaryotes is more complex **(Figure 23.2)**.

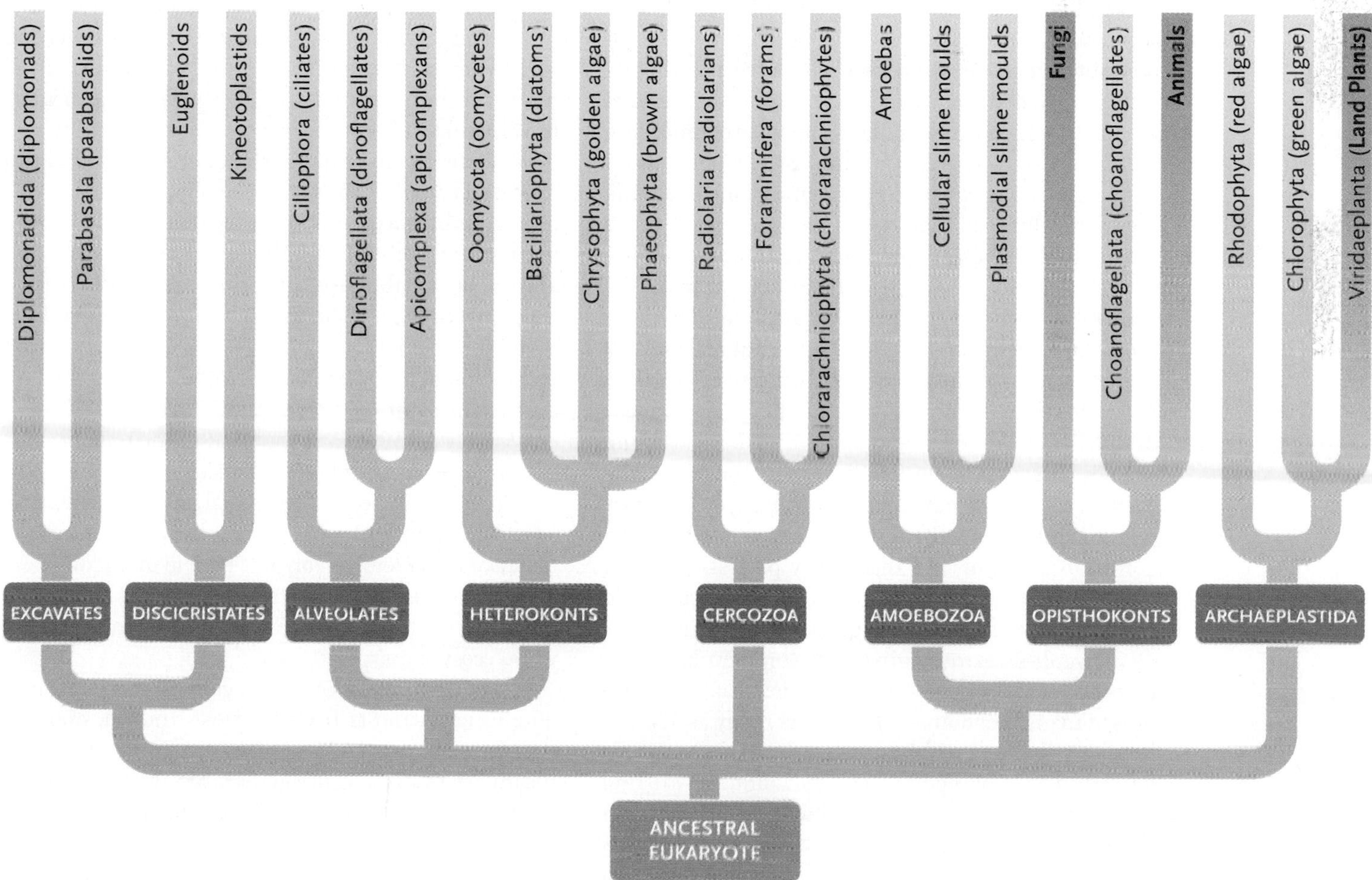

Figure 23.2
The phylogenetic relationship between the evolutionary groups within the kingdom Protista and the other eukaryotes. The Archaeplastida (boxed) include the land plants of the kingdom Plantae, and the Opisthokonts (boxed) include the animals of the kingdom Animalia and the fungi of the kingdom Fungi. The tree was constructed based on a consensus of molecular and ultrastructural data.

Over evolutionary time, the eukaryotic family tree branched out in many directions. All of the organisms in the eukaryotic lineages consist of protists except for three groups, the animals, land plants, and fungi, which arose from protist ancestors. Although some protists have features that resemble those of the fungi, plants, or animals, several characteristics are distinctive. In contrast to fungi, most protists are motile or have motile stages in their life cycles, and their cell walls are made of cellulose, not chitin.

How do photosynthesizing protists differ from plants? Unlike plants, many photoautotrophic protists can also live as heterotrophs, and some regularly combine both modes of nutrition. Protists do not retain developing embryos in parental tissue, as plants do, nor do they have highly differentiated structures equivalent to roots, stems, and leaves. Photosynthetic protists are sometimes referred to as "algae"; these protists are generally aquatic and often unicellular and microscopic (although many are multicellular). However, the different groups of algae are not closely related to each other (see Figure 23.2), so the term "algae" does not indicate any sort of relatedness among organisms referred to by that term.

How do protists differ from animals? Unlike protists, all animals are multicellular and have features such as an internal digestive tract and complex developmental stages. Protists also lack nerve cells, highly differentiated structures such as limbs and a heart, and collagen, an extracellular support protein. These features characterize many animals. The one reasonable certainty about protist classification is that the organisms lumped together in the kingdom Protista are not prokaryotes, fungi, plants, or animals.

The extreme diversity of the group has made the protists so difficult to classify that their status as a kingdom remains highly unsettled. Until recently, the protists were classified into phyla within the kingdom Protista according to criteria such as body form, modes of nutrition and movement, and forms of meiosis and mitosis. However, molecular data, now considered the most informative method for determining evolutionary relationships, show that most protists do not share a common ancestor and that many protists grouped together in a phylum are no more closely related to each other than they are to the fungi, plants, or animals.

Given this extreme diversity, some evolutionists maintain that the kingdom Protista is actually a collection of many kingdoms—perhaps as many as 30! Evolutionary lineages within the kingdoms are variously described as subkingdoms or phyla, and the existing schemes are constantly revised as new information is obtained. The tree shown in Figure 23.2 represents a current consensus, based on both structural and molecular data. Remember that such a tree represents one hypothesis about relationships among organisms; there are numerous other trees, representing alternative hypotheses.

For simplicity, we retain the Protista as a single kingdom in this book, with the understanding that it is a collection of largely unrelated organisms placed together for convenience. We refer to the major evolutionary clusterings indicated by molecular and structural comparisons as "groups" (see Figure 23.2).

Study Break

What features distinguish protists from prokaryotes? What distinguish them from fungi, plants, and animals?

23.3 Protists' Diversity Is Reflected in Their Metabolism, Reproduction, Structure, and Habitat

As you might expect from the broad range of organisms included in this kingdom, protists are highly diverse in metabolism, reproduction, structure, and habitat.

Habitat. Protists live in aqueous habitats, including aquatic or moist terrestrial locations such as oceans, freshwater lakes, ponds, streams, and moist soils and within host organisms. In bodies of water, small photosynthetic protists collectively make up the **phytoplankton** (*phytos* = plant; *planktos* = drifting), the organisms that capture the energy of sunlight in nearly all aquatic habitats. These phototrophs provide organic substances and oxygen for heterotrophic bacteria, other protists, and the small crustaceans and animal larvae that are the primary constituents of **zooplankton** (*zoe* = life, usually meaning animal life). Although protists are not animals, biologists often include them among the zooplankton. Phytoplankton and larger multicellular protists forming seaweeds collectively account for about half of the total organic matter produced by photosynthesis.

In the moist soils of terrestrial environments, protists play important roles among the detritus feeders that recycle matter from organic back to inorganic form. In their roles in phytoplankton, in zooplankton, and as detritus feeders, protists are enormously important in world ecosystems.

Protists that live in host organisms are parasites, obtaining nutrients from the host. Indeed, many of the parasites that have significant effects on human health are protists, causing diseases such as malaria, sleeping sickness, and amoebic dysentery.

Structure. Whereas most protists are single cells, others live as **colonies (Figure 23.3)** in which individual cells show little or no differentiation and are potentially independent. Within colonies, individuals use cell signalling to cooperate on tasks such as feeding or

Figure 23.3
Colonial protist (*Dinobryon*).

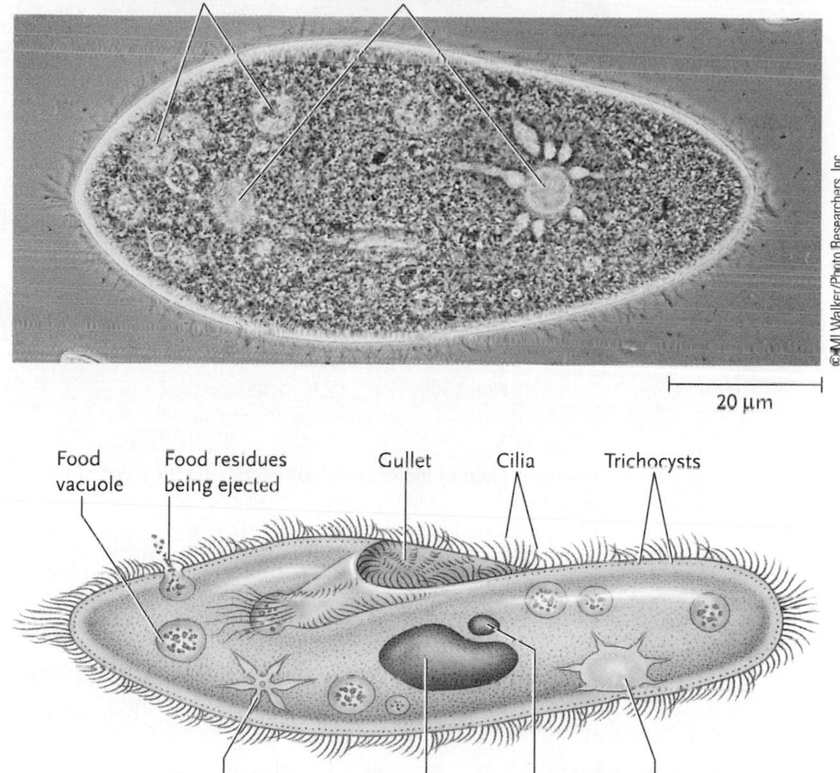

Figure 23.4
A ciliate, *Paramecium*, showing the cytoplasmic structures typical of many protists.

movement. Some protists are large multicellular organisms; for example, the giant kelp of coastal waters can rival forest trees in size.

Many single-celled and colonial protists have complex intracellular structures, some found nowhere else among living organisms **(Figure 23.4)**. These unique structures reflect key aspects of the habitats in which protists live. For example, consider a single-celled protist living in a freshwater pond. Its cytoplasm is hypertonic to the water surrounding it, meaning that water flows into the cell by osmosis (see Section 5.5). How can the protist prevent itself from bursting? A specialized cytoplasmic organelle, the **contractile vacuole**, gradually fills with fluid. When this vacuole reaches its maximum size, it moves to the plasma membrane and forcibly contracts, expelling the fluid to the outside through a pore in the membrane.

The cells of some protists are supported by an external cell wall or by an internal or external shell built up from organic or mineral matter; in some, the shell takes on highly elaborate forms. Instead of a cell wall, other protists have a **pellicle**, a layer of supportive protein fibres located inside the cell just under the plasma membrane, providing strength and flexibility **(Figure 23.5)**.

At some time during their lives, almost all protists move. Some move by amoeboid motion, in which the cell extends one or more lobes of cytoplasm called **pseudopodia** ("false feet"; see **Figure 23.6, p. 502**). The rest of the cytoplasm and the nucleus then flow into the pseudopodium, completing the movement. Other protists move by the beating of flagella or cilia. In some protists, cilia are arranged in complex patterns, with an equally complex network of microtubules and other cytoskeletal fibres supporting the cilia under the plasma membrane.

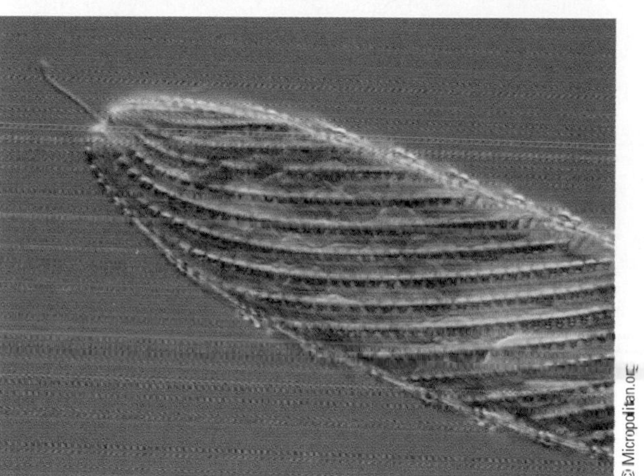

Figure 23.5
Euglena spirogyra, showing pellicle (strips of protein fibres).

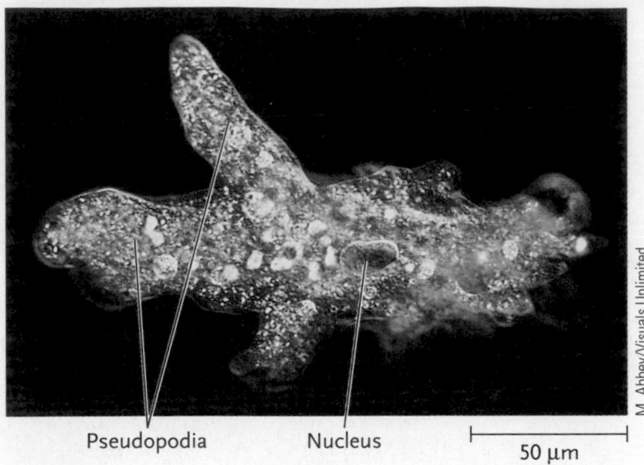

Figure 23.6
Amoeba proteus of the Amoebozoa is perhaps the most familiar protist of all.

Many protists can exist in more than one form, for example, as a motile form and as a nonmotile cyst that can survive unfavourable conditions. This morphological variability allows the species to live in different habitats at different stages in its life.

Metabolism. Almost all protists are aerobic organisms that live either as heterotrophs—obtaining carbon from organic molecules produced by other organisms—or as photoautotrophs, by producing organic molecules for themselves by photosynthesis (see Chapter 3). Some heterotrophic protists obtain organic molecules by engulfing part or all of other organisms (*phagocytosis*) and digesting them internally. Others absorb small organic molecules from their environment by diffusion. Some protists can live as either heterotrophs or autotrophs.

Reproduction. Reproduction may be asexual, by mitosis, or sexual, through meiotic cell division and formation of gametes. In protists that reproduce by both mitosis and meiosis, the two modes of cell division are often combined into a **life cycle** that is highly distinctive among the different protist groups. We do not yet have a complete understanding of how many protists reproduce.

Study Break

Define each of the following terms in your own words and indicate the role each plays in the life of a protist: pellicle, pseudopodia, contractile vacuole.

23.4 The Protist Groups

In this section, we look at the biological features of the groups included in Figure 23.2. Our focus is the ecological or economic importance of each group, the habitats in which you would find those organisms, and key features that differentiate the group from other protists. As you read through the information on each group, think about how the structural features of a group relate to its habitat and lifestyle.

23.4a Excavates Lack "Typical" Mitochondria

This group takes its name from the hollow (excavated) ventral feeding groove found in most members. All Excavates are single-celled animal parasites that lack mitochondria and move by means of flagella. Because they lack mitochondria, they are limited to glycolysis as an ATP source (see Chapter 6). Originally, the lack of mitochondria led biologists to consider this group as the most ancient line of protists; however, it now appears that the ancestor of this group did have mitochondria. The nuclei of Excavates contain genes derived from mitochondria, and they also have organelles that likely evolved from mitochondria. Excavates may have lost their mitochondria as an adaptation to the parasitic way of life, in which oxygen is in short supply. We consider two subgroups here, the Diplomonadida and the Parabasala.

Diplomonadida. Diplomonad means "double cell," and these organisms do look like two cells together (see the figure at the beginning of the chapter), with their two apparently identical, functional nuclei and multiple flagella arranged symmetrically around the cell's longitudinal axis. The best-known diplomonad is *Giardia lamblia,* profiled at the beginning of this chapter. Some are free-living, but many live in animal intestines; some diplomonads do not cause harm to the host, whereas others, like *Giardia,* live as parasites.

Parabasala. The sexually transmitted disease trichomoniasis is caused by the parabasalid *Trichomonas vaginalis* **(Figure 23.7a).** The infection is usually symptomless in men, but in women, *T. vaginalis* can cause severe inflammation and irritation of the vagina and vulva. If untreated, trichomoniasis can cause infection of the uterus and fallopian tubes that can result in infertility. Luckily, drugs can easily cure the infection.

Parabasalids take their names from cytoplasmic structures associated with the nucleus, *parabasal bodies;* some biologists consider these structures to be the Golgi apparatus of these cells. Parabasalids are also characterized by a sort of fin called an **undulating membrane**, formed by a flagellum buried in a fold of the cytoplasm, in addition to freely beating flagella. The buried flagellum allows parabasalids to move through thick, viscous fluids, such as those lining human reproductive tracts.

Other parabasalids (e.g., *Trichonympha;* **Figure 23.7b**) are symbionts that live in the guts of termites

a. *Trichomonas vaginalis*

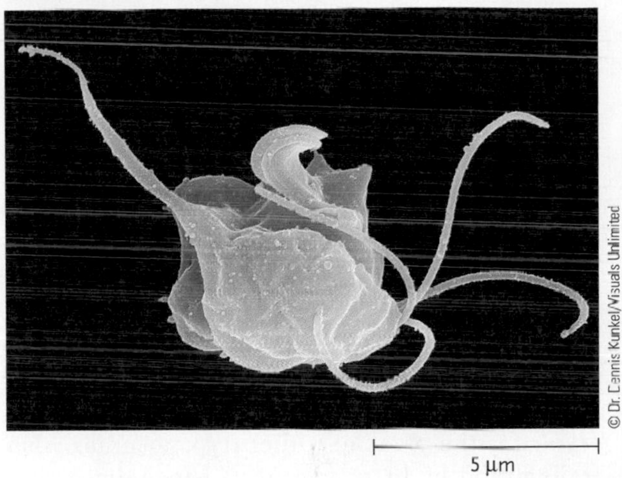

b. Trichonympha

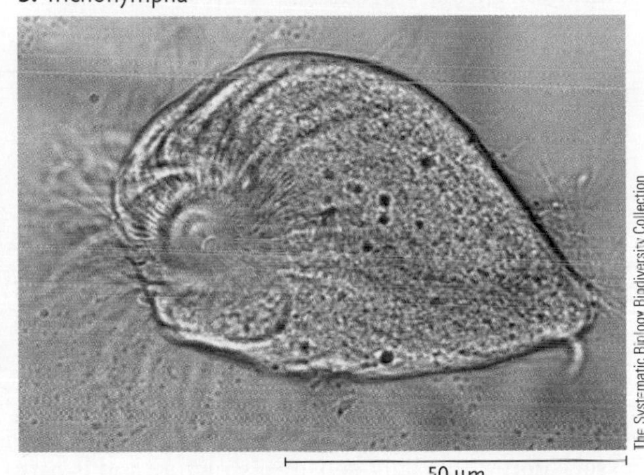

Figure 23.7
Examples of parabasalids (Excavates). **(a)** A parabasalid, *Trichomonas vaginalis,* that causes a sexually transmitted disease, trichomoniasis; **(b)** *Trichonympha,* a parabasalid that lives in the guts of termites.

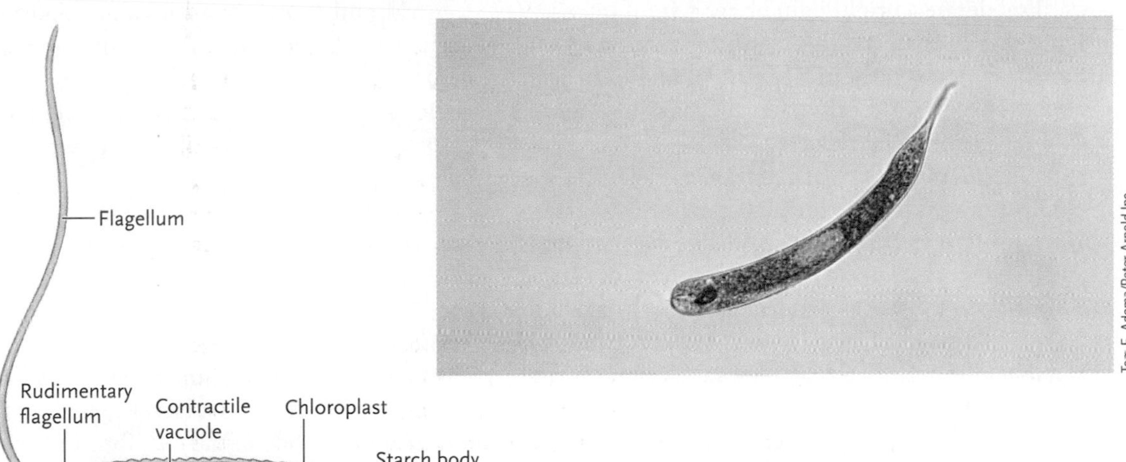

Figure 23.8
Body plan and a colour photo of *Euglena gracilis.*

and other wood-eating insects, digesting the cellulose in the wood for their hosts. As if this endosymbiotic relationship were not complex enough, biologists recently discovered that the protists themselves cannot produce the enzymes necessary to break down cellulose but instead rely on bacterial symbionts to break down the cellulose.

23.4b Discicristates Include the Euglenoids and Kinetoplastids: Highly Motile Protists

Protists of this group are sometimes referred to as *protozoa* (*proto* = first; *zoon* = animal) because they are similar to animals in that they ingest food and move by themselves. The **Discicristates** are named for their disk-shaped mitochondrial cristae (folds of the inner mitochondrial membrane). The group includes about 1800 species, almost all single-celled, highly motile cells that swim by means of flagella. Although most are photosynthetic, some can also live as heterotrophs, and some even alternate between photosynthesis and life as a heterotroph. Other organisms in this group are parasitic.

Euglenoids. You have probably seen an example of one genus of euglenoids, *Euglena,* in your earlier biology classes **(Figure 23.8, p.504)** as they are often used to illustrate how some protists have plantlike features (photosynthesis) combined with features that we consider animal-like (movement). Euglenoids are important primary producers in freshwater ponds, streams, and lakes, and even some marine habitats. Most are autotrophs that carry out photosynthesis using the same photosynthetic pigments and mechanisms as plants. If light is not available, many of the photosynthetic euglenoids can also live as heterotrophs by absorbing organic molecules through the plasma membrane or by engulfing small particles. Other euglenoids lack chloroplasts and live entirely as heterotrophs.

The name *Euglena* roughly translates as "eyeball organism," a reference to the large *eyespot* that is an obvious feature of photosynthetic euglenoids (see Figure 23.8). The *eyespot* contains pigment granules in association with a light-sensitive structure and is part of a sensory mechanism that stimulates cells to swim toward moderately bright light or away from intensely bright light so that the organism finds optimal conditions for photosynthetic activity. In addition to an eyespot, euglenoids contain numerous organelles, including a contractile vacuole.

Rather than an external cell wall, euglenoids have a spirally grooved pellicle formed from strips of transparent, protein-rich material underneath the membrane (see Figure 23.5). In some euglenoids, the strips are arranged in a spiral pattern, allowing the cell to change its shape in a wriggling sort of motion (known as euglenoid movement) that allows the cell to change direction. Euglenoids can also swim by whiplike movements of flagella that extend from one end of the cell. Most have two flagella: one rudimentary and short, the other long.

Kinetoplastids. Sleeping sickness is a fatal disease endemic to sub-Saharan Africa. Although the disease was almost eradicated about 40 years ago, it has been making a comeback due to wars and the subsequent refugee movement and damage to health care systems. Sleeping sickness is caused by various subspecies of *Trypanosoma brucei* **(Figure 23.9)** that are transmitted from one host to another by bites of the tsetse fly. Early symptoms include fever, headaches, rashes, and anemia. Untreated, the disease damages the central nervous system, leading to a sleeplike coma and eventual death. The disease has proved difficult to control because the same trypanosomes infect wild mammals, providing an inexhaustible reservoir for the parasite. Other trypanosomes, also transmitted by insects, cause Chagas disease in Central and South America and leishmaniasis in many tropical countries. Humans with Chagas disease have an enlarged liver and spleen and may experience severe brain and heart damage; leishmaniasis causes skin sores and ulcers, as well as liver and spleen damage.

Like trypanosomes, other kinetoplastids are heterotrophs that live as animal parasites. Kinetoplastid cells are characterized by a single mitochondrion that contains a large DNA-protein deposit called a *kinetoplast* (see Figure 23.9). Most kinetoplastids also have a leading and a trailing flagellum, which are used for movement. In some cases, the trailing flagellum is attached to the side of the cell, forming an undulating membrane that allows the organism to glide along or attach to surfaces.

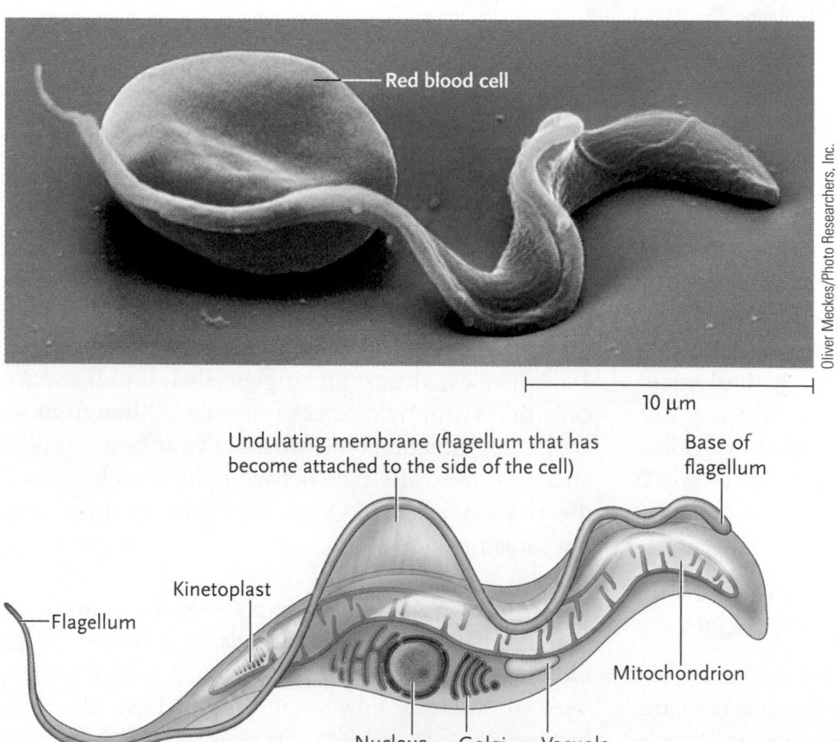

Figure 23.9
Trypansoma brucei, the parasitic kinetoplastid that causes African sleeping sickness.

23.4c Alveolates Have Complex Cytoplasmic Structures and Move via Flagella or Cilia

This group is named for the small, membrane-bound vesicles called *alveoli* (*alvus* = belly) in a layer just under the plasma membrane. The Alveolates include two motile, primarily free-living groups, the Ciliophora and Dinoflagellata, and a nonmotile, parasitic group, the Apicomplexa.

Ciliophora: The Ciliates. Have you ever wondered how we know what we know about the details of cellular functioning? For example, how did we find out about the existence of telomeres at the ends of eukaryotic chromosomes and the function of telomerase? An important tool in these discoveries has been the use of model organisms—organisms that are easily manipulated and easily raised in the lab and for which we have abundant data, for example, genome sequences (see *The Chemical and Physical Foundations of Biology* pages). Several protists are ideal model organisms because even though they are single celled, the complexity of their structures and functions is comparable to that of humans and other animals. One ciliate, *Tetrahymena* **(Figure 23.10)**, was the organism in which telomeres and telomerase were discovered; it was also the cell in which the first motor protein was identified, cell cycle control mechanisms were first described, and ribozymes were discovered. The involvement of ciliates with scientific research dates back several centuries as they were among the first organisms observed in the seventeenth century by the pioneering microscopist Anton van Leeuwenhoek.

Ciliophora is a large group, with nearly 10 000 known species of primarily single-celled but highly complex heterotrophic organisms that swim by means of cilia (see Figures 23.4 and 23.10). Any sample of pond water or bottom mud contains a wealth of these creatures. Some ciliates live individually, whereas others are colonial. Certain ciliates are animal parasites; others live and reproduce in their hosts as mutually beneficial symbionts. A compartment of the stomach of cattle and other grazing animals contains large numbers of symbiotic ciliates that digest the cellulose in their hosts' plant diet. The host animals then digest the excess ciliates.

The organisms in the Ciliophora have many highly developed organelles, including a mouthlike gullet lined with cilia, structures that exude toxins and other defensive materials from the cell surface, contractile vacuoles, and a complex systems of food vacuoles. A pellicle reinforces the cell's shape. A complex cytoskeleton anchors the cilia just below the pellicle and coordinates the ciliary beating. The cilia can stop and reverse their beating in synchrony, allowing ciliates to stop, back up, and turn if they encounter negative stimuli.

The ciliates are the only eukaryotes that have two types of nuclei in each cell: one or more small nuclei called *micronuclei* and a single larger *macronucleus* (see Figure 23.4). A **micronucleus** is a diploid nucleus that contains a complete complement of genes. It functions primarily in cellular reproduction, which may be asexual or sexual. The number of micronuclei present depends on the species. The **macronucleus** develops from a micronucleus but loses all genes except those required for basic functions (e.g., feeding,

a. Cilate

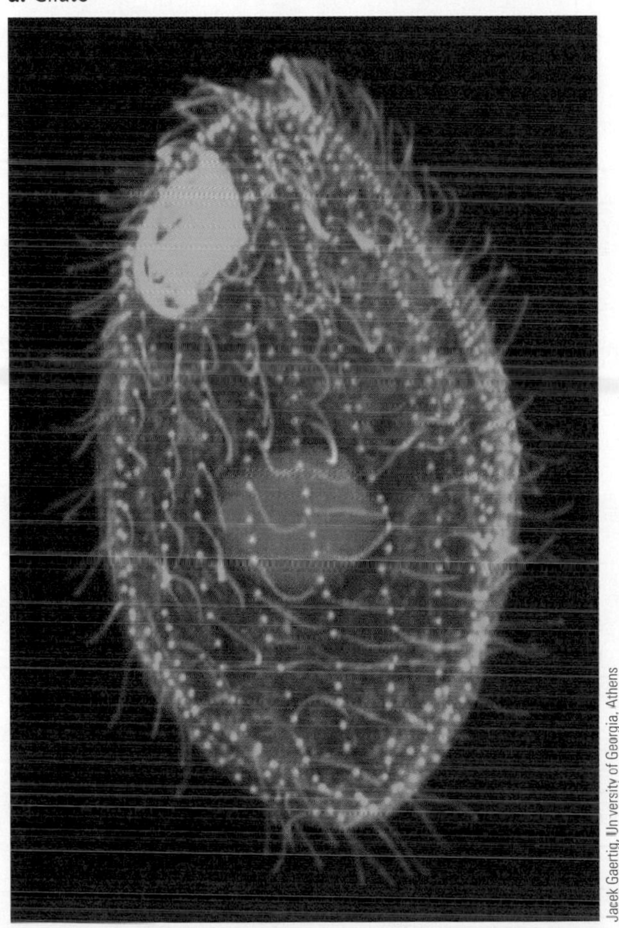

b. Cilia

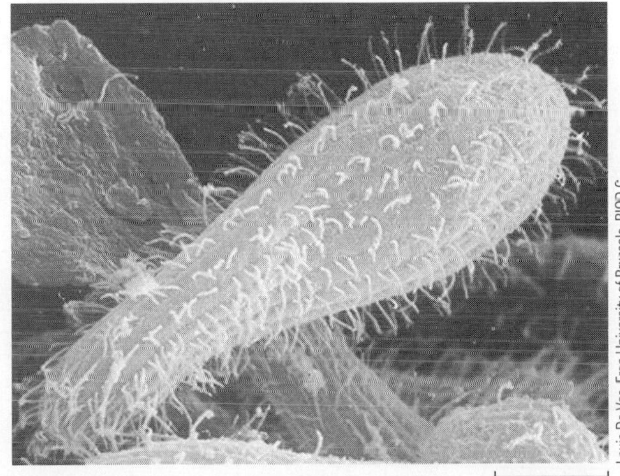

Figure 23.10 *Tetrahymena*, a ciliate **(a)** stained with fluorescent dye to show cilia and microtubules; **(b)** SEM image showing cilia.

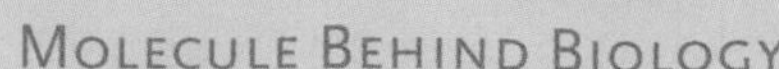

Molecule Behind Biology

Saxitoxin

Some dinoflagellates that cause red tides also produce neurotoxins. Fish that feed on the dinoflagellates and birds that feed on the fish may be killed in huge numbers by the toxins. Dinoflagellate toxins do not noticeably affect clams, oysters, and other molluscs but become concentrated in their tissues. Eating the tainted molluscs can cause paralytic shellfish poisoning in humans and other animals, characterized by nausea, vomiting, shortness of breath, and a choking feeling. The main toxin responsible is saxitoxin **(Figure 1),** a neurotoxic alkaloid that is the most lethal non-protein toxin known—a dose of just 0.2 mg is enough to kill an average-weight person.

Figure 1
Saxitoxin, one of the neurotoxins produced by dinoflagellates.

Saxitoxin acts by binding to sodium channels of nerve cells, thus preventing the normal movement of sodium ions through the channel and blocking the transmission of nerve impulses.

Saxitoxin is especially deadly for mammals because it paralyzes the diaphragm and other muscles required for breathing. There is no cure, and death can occur within minutes if the person is not treated quickly; treatment involves artificial respiration to support breathing. Saxitoxin has been experimented with as a chemical weapon but also has more constructive uses. For example, it has been used to determine the components of sodium channels in cell membranes and in studies of various nerve disorders.

Other photosynthetic protists also produce blooms, and some of these also produce toxins.

metabolism) of the cell and for synthesis of ribosomal RNA. The macronucleus contains numerous copies of these genes, allowing it to synthesize large quantities of proteins and rRNA.

Ciliates abound in freshwater and marine habitats, where they feed voraciously on bacteria, algae, and each other. *Paramecium* and *Tetrahymena* are typical of the group (see Figures 23.4 and 23.10). Their rows of cilia drive them through their watery habitat, rotating the cell on its long axis while it moves forward or back and turns. The cilia also sweep water laden with prey and food particles into the gullet, where food vacuoles form. The ciliate digests food in the vacuoles and eliminates indigestible material through an anal pore. Contractile vacuoles with elaborate, raylike extensions remove excess water from the cytoplasm and expel it to the outside. When under attack or otherwise stressed, *Paramecium* discharges many dartlike protein threads from surface organelles called **trichocysts.**

a.

Hong Kong Red Tide Information Network/ The Agriculture, Fisheries and Conservation Department

b.

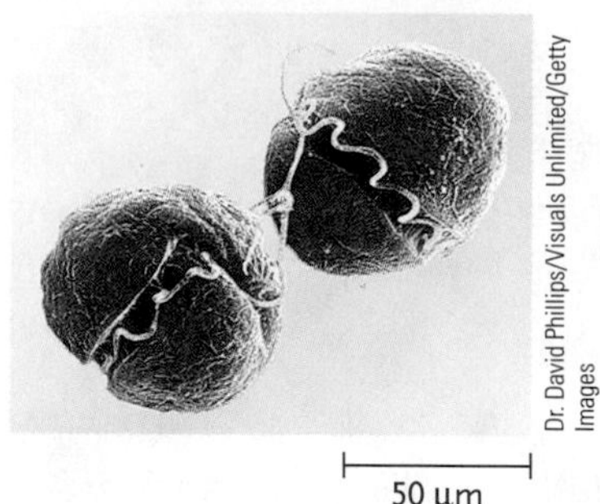

Dr. David Phillips/Visuals Unlimited/Getty Images

Figure 23.11
(a) Red tide caused by dinoflagellate bloom.
(b) *Karenia brevis,* a toxin-producing dinoflagellate.

Dinoflagellata: The Dinoflagellates. In spring and summer, the coastal waters of Canada sometimes turn reddish in colour **(Figure 23.11a).** These *red tides* are caused by a population explosion, or *bloom,* of certain **dinoflagellates** that make up a large proportion of marine phytoplankton. These protists typically have a shell formed from cellulose plates **(Figure 23.11b).** The beating of flagella, which fit into grooves in the plates, makes dinoflagellates spin like a top (*dinos* = spinning) as they swim.

Red tides are caused by conditions such as increased nutrient runoff into coastal waters (particularly from farms and industrial areas), warm ocean surface temperatures, and calm water. Red tides occur in the waters of many other countries besides Canada and are more common in warmer waters. Some red tide dinoflagellates produce a toxin that interferes with nerve function in animals that ingest them (see *Molecule Behind Biology*).

More than 4000 dinoflagellate species are known, and most, like those that cause red tides, are single-celled organisms in marine phytoplankton. Their abundance in phytoplankton makes dinoflagellates a major primary producer of ocean ecosystems. You can sometimes see their abundance because some are **bioluminescent,** that is, they glow or release a

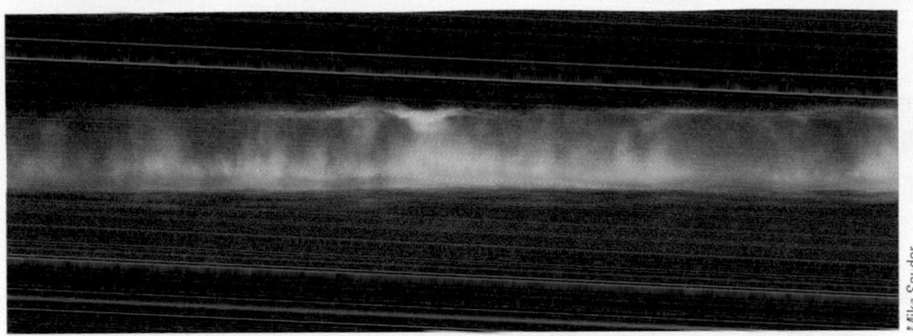

Figure 23.12
Bioluminescent dinoflagellates (*Lingulodinium polyedrum*) lighting a breaking wave at midnight.

Figure 23.13
Bleached elkhorn coral (*Acropora palmata*).

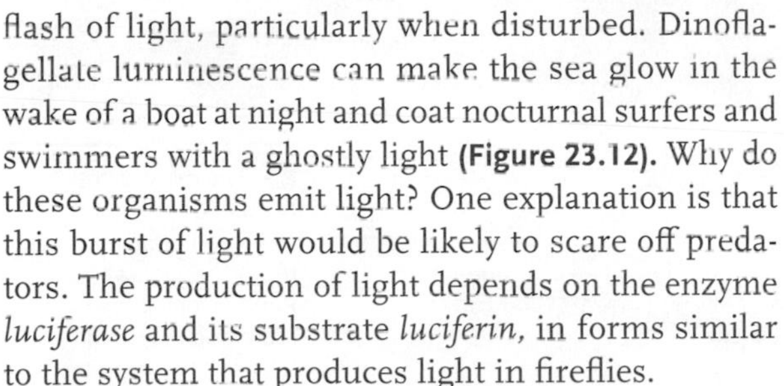

flash of light, particularly when disturbed. Dinoflagellate luminescence can make the sea glow in the wake of a boat at night and coat nocturnal surfers and swimmers with a ghostly light **(Figure 23.12)**. Why do these organisms emit light? One explanation is that this burst of light would be likely to scare off predators. The production of light depends on the enzyme *luciferase* and its substrate *luciferin*, in forms similar to the system that produces light in fireflies.

Dinoflagellates live as heterotrophs or autotrophs; many can carry out both modes of nutrition. Some dinoflagellates live as symbionts in the tissues of other marine organisms such as jellyfish, sea anemones, corals, and molluscs and give these organisms their distinctive colours. Dinoflagellates in coral use the coral's carbon dioxide and nitrogenous waste while supplying 90% of the coral's carbon. The vast numbers of dinoflagellates living as photosynthetic symbionts in tropical coral reefs allow the reefs to reach massive sizes; without dinoflagellates, many coral species would die. When stressed, corals eject their endosymbionts, a phenomenon known as coral bleaching because the absence of the pigmented dinoflagellates allows the coral's calcareous skeleton to be visible **(Figure 23.13)**. What causes the coral to become stressed? Increased water temperatures appear to be the main cause, although exposure to contaminants such as oil can also cause bleaching. If the stress causing the bleaching is transient, the coral usually regains its endosymbionts, but if the stress persists, the coral will die.

Apicomplexa. Apicomplexans are nonmotile parasites of animals. They take their name from the *apical complex*, a group of organelles at one end of a cell, which helps the cell attach to and invade host cells. Apicomplexans absorb nutrients through their plasma membranes (rather than by engulfing food particles) and lack food vacuoles. One genus, *Plasmodium*, is responsible for malaria, one of the most widespread and debilitating human diseases. About 500 million people are infected with malaria in tropical regions, including Africa, India, Southeast Asia, the Middle East, Oceania, and Central and South America. Malaria kills about 2 million people each year, twice as many as are killed by AIDS worldwide. It is particularly deadly for children younger than six. In many countries where malaria is common, people are often infected repeatedly, with new infections occurring alongside preexisting infections.

Plasmodium is transmitted by 60 different species of mosquitoes, all members of the genus *Anopheles*. Infective cells develop inside the female mosquito, which transfers the cells to human or bird hosts **(Figure 23.14, p. 508)**. The infecting parasites divide repeatedly by asexual reproduction in their hosts, initially in liver cells and then in red blood cells. Their growth causes red blood cells to rupture in regular cycles every 48 or *72 hours*, depending on the *Plasmodium* species. The ruptured red blood cells clog vessels and release the parasite's metabolic wastes, causing cycles of chills and fever.

The victim's immune system is ineffective because during most of the infective cycle, the parasite is inside body cells and thus "hidden" from antibodies. Furthermore, like *Giardia*, *Plasmodium* regularly changes its surface molecules, continually producing new forms that are not recognized by antibodies developed against a previous form. In this way, the parasite keeps one step ahead of the immune system, often making malarial infections essentially permanent. For a time, malaria was controlled in many countries by insecticides such as DDT. However, the mosquitoes developed resistance against the insecticides and have returned in even greater numbers than before the spraying began.

In addition to the asexual reproduction described above for *Plasmodium*, apicomplexans also reproduce sexually, forming gametes that fuse to produce cysts. As in *Giardia*, when a host organism ingests the cysts, they divide to produce infective cells. Many apicomplexans use more than one host species for different stages of their life cycle. For example, another organism in this group, *Toxoplasma*, has the sexual phase of its life cycle in cats and the asexual phases in humans, cattle, pigs, and other animals. Feces of infected cats contain cysts; humans ingesting or

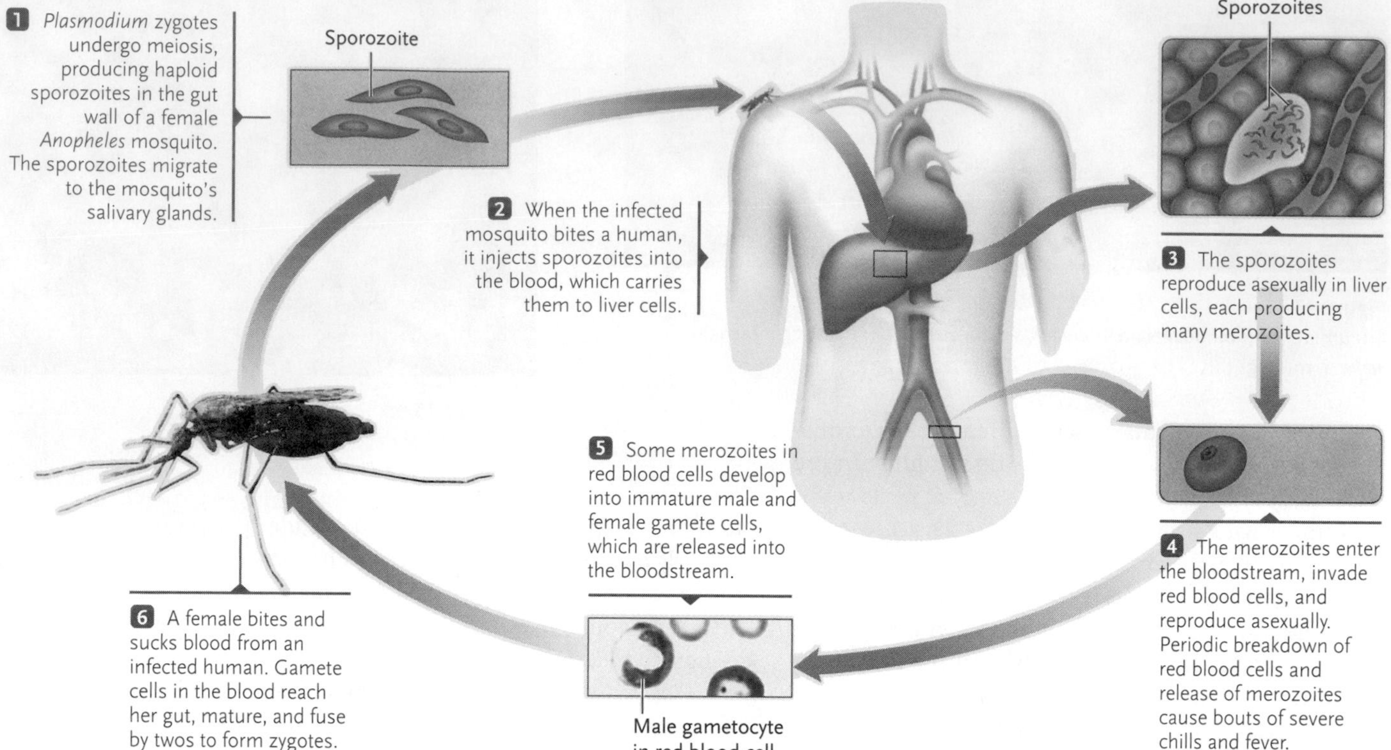

1 Plasmodium zygotes undergo meiosis, producing haploid sporozoites in the gut wall of a female Anopheles mosquito. The sporozoites migrate to the mosquito's salivary glands.
Sporozoite
2 When the infected mosquito bites a human, it injects sporozoites into the blood, which carries them to liver cells.
Sporozoites
3 The sporozoites reproduce asexually in liver cells, each producing many merozoites.
4 The merozoites enter the bloodstream, invade red blood cells, and reproduce asexually. Periodic breakdown of red blood cells and release of merozoites cause bouts of severe chills and fever.
5 Some merozoites in red blood cells develop into immature male and female gamete cells, which are released into the bloodstream.
Male gametocyte in red blood cell
6 A female bites and sucks blood from an infected human. Gamete cells in the blood reach her gut, mature, and fuse by twos to form zygotes.

Figure 23.14
Life cycle of a *Plasmodium* species that causes malaria.

inhaling the cysts develop toxoplasmosis, a disease that is usually mild in adults but can cause severe brain damage or even death to a fetus. Because of the danger of toxoplasmosis, pregnant women should avoid emptying litter boxes or otherwise cleaning up after a cat.

23.4d Heterokonts Have Two Dissimilar Flagella at Some Stage of Their Life Cycles

The Heterokonts (*hetero* = different; *kontos* = pole, referring to the flagellum) are named for their two different flagella: one smooth and a second covered with bristles, giving it a "hairy" appearance **(Figure 23.15)**. In most heterokonts, the flagella occur only on reproductive cells such as eggs and sperm. The heterokonts include the Oomycota (water moulds), Bacillariophyta (diatoms), Chrysophyta (golden algae), and Phaeophyta (brown algae). Recall that "algae" is a general term for photosynthetic protists, but the different groups of algae are not closely related to each other, so the term does not imply a phylogenetic grouping.

Hairy flagellum

Smooth flagellum

Figure 23.15
Heterokont protist, with smooth and "hairy" flagella.

Oomycota: Water Moulds and Downy Mildews. In Ireland, the summer of 1846 started off warm and sunny. This was a welcome change as the previous summer had been cool and damp, causing the potato crop to fail. But then the weather turned wet and cold again and within one week at the end of July, the entire potato crop was destroyed—the leaves rotting and the tubers turning to black, putrid mush **(Figure 23.16)**. Worse was to come: the unseasonably cool and damp growing seasons persisted until 1860, causing the potato crops to fail year after year. These crop failures were catastrophic because potatoes were virtually the only food source for most people. Altogether, about one-third of the Irish population died or emigrated (to Canada and the United States among other countries) due to the potato famines.

Figure 23.16
Blight caused by *Phytophthora infestans* in a potato crop.

In 1861, the organism that caused the blight was identified as a water mould, *Phytophthora infestans*. Originally thought to be a fungus, *P. infestans* produces infective cells that are easily dispersed by wind and water. The blight caused by this organism has recently reemerged as a serious disease in potato-growing regions of Canada and the United States due to the migration of new strains from Mexico that are resistant to existing pesticides.

Water moulds are not fungi; they are oomycetes **(Figures 23.17a)**, but they do share some features with fungi. Like fungi, oomycetes grow as microscopic, nonmotile filaments called **hyphae** (singular, hypha), forming a network called a **mycelium (Figure 23.17b)**. Also like fungi, they are heterotrophs, which secrete enzymes that digest the complex molecules of surrounding organic matter or living tissue into simpler molecules that are small enough to be absorbed into their cells. Other features, however, set the Oomycota apart from the fungi; chief among them are differences in nucleotide sequence, which clearly indicate close evolutionary relationships to other heterokonts rather than to the fungi.

The water moulds live almost exclusively in freshwater lakes and streams or moist terrestrial habitats, where they are key decomposers. Dead animal or plant material immersed in water commonly becomes coated with cottony water moulds. Other water moulds parasitize living aquatic animals, such as the mould growing on the fish shown in Figure 23.17b. The downy mildews are parasites of land plants **(Figure 23.17c)**. Oomycetes may reproduce asexually or sexually.

Bacillariophyta: Diatoms. When you look at the organisms shown in **Figure 23.18,** they may not look like living organisms at all but instead like artwork or jewels. These are bacillariophytes or **diatoms**, single-celled organisms with a glassy silica shell, which is intricately formed and beautiful in many species. The two halves of the shell fit together like the top and bottom of a Petri dish or box of chocolates (see Figure 23.18). Substances move in and out of the cell through elaborately patterned perforations in the shell. Diatom shells are common in fossil deposits. In fact, more diatoms are known as fossils than as living species—some 35 000 extinct species have been described compared with 7000 living species. For about 180 million years, diatom shells have been accumulating into thick layers of sediment at the bottom of lakes and seas.

In fact, you probably use diatoms—or their remnants—a couple of times a day when you brush your teeth. Most toothpaste contains a mild abrasive to assist in removing plaque, a bacterial biofilm that forms on your teeth. This abrasive is commonly made from grinding the fossilized shells of diatoms into a fine powder, called *diatomaceous earth*. In addition to toothpaste, diatomaceous earth is used in filters, as an insulating material, and as a pesticide. Diatomaceous earth kills crawling insects and insect larvae by abrading their exoskeleton, causing them to dehydrate and die. Insects also die when they eat the powder, but larger animals, including humans, are unaffected by it.

a. Water mould

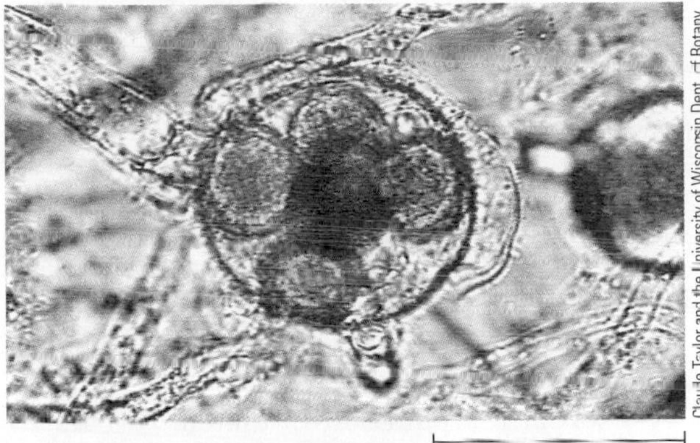

b. Water mould infecting fish

c. Downy mildew

Figure 23.17
Oomycota. **(a)** The water mould *Saprolegnia parasitica* **(b)** *S. parasitica* growing as cottony white fibres on the tail of an aquarium fish. **(c)** Downy mildew *Plasmopara viticola* growing on grapes. At times, it has nearly destroyed vineyards in Europe and North America.

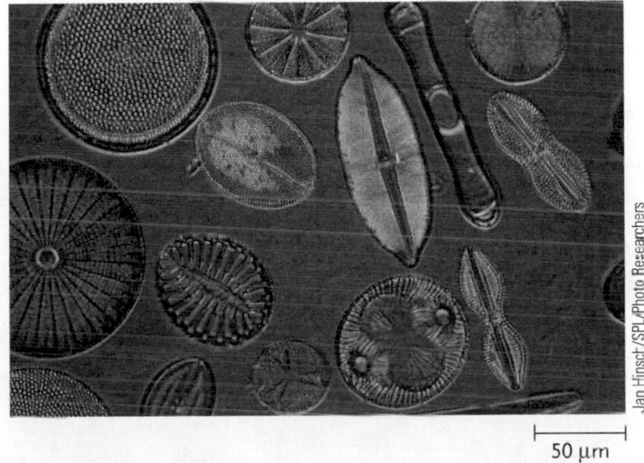

Figure 23.18
Diatoms. Depending on the species, the shells are either radially or bilaterally symmetrical, as seen in this sample.

Diatoms are photoautotrophs that carry out photosynthesis by pathways similar to those of plants. They are among the primary photosynthetic organisms in marine plankton and are also abundant in freshwater habitats as both phytoplankton and bottom-dwelling species. Although most diatoms are free living, some are symbionts inside other marine protists. One diatom, *Pseudonitzschia*, produces a toxic amino acid that can accumulate in shellfish. The amino acid, which acts as a nerve poison, causes amnesic shellfish poisoning when ingested by humans; the poisoning can be fatal.

Asexual reproduction in diatoms occurs by mitosis followed by a form of cytoplasmic division in which each daughter cell receives either the top or bottom half of the parent shell. The daughter cell then secretes the missing half, which becomes the smaller, inside shell of the box. The daughter cell receiving the larger top half grows to the same size as the parent shell, but the cell receiving the smaller bottom half is limited to the size of this shell. As asexual divisions continue, the cells receiving bottom halves become progressively smaller. When a minimum size is reached, sexual reproduction is triggered. The cells produce flagellated gametes, which fuse to form a zygote. The zygote grows to normal size before secreting a completely new shell with full-sized top and bottom halves.

Although flagella are present only in gametes, many diatoms move by an unusual mechanism in which a secretion released through grooves in the shell propels them in a gliding motion.

Chrysophyta: Golden Algae. Nearly all chrysophytes are autotrophs and carry out photosynthesis using pathways similar to those of plants. Their colour is due to a brownish carotenoid pigment, fucoxanthin, which masks the green colour of the chlorophylls **(Figure 23.19a)**. However, most chrysophytes can also live as heterotrophs if there is not sufficient light for photosynthesis. They switch to feeding on dissolved organic molecules or preying on bacteria and diatoms. Golden algae are important in freshwater habitats and in "nanoplankton," a community of marine phytoplankton composed of huge numbers of extremely small cells. During the spring and fall, "blooms" of golden algae are responsible for the fishy taste of many cities' drinking water.

Most golden algae are colonial forms (see Figures 23.3 and 23.20a) in which each cell of the colony bears a pair of flagella. The golden algae have glassy shells, but in the form of plates or scales rather than in the Petri dish form of the diatoms.

Phaeophyta: Brown Algae. If you were asked where in Canada you'd find forests of giant trees, you'd likely think of the temperate rain forests of the British Columbia coast. But there are also vast underwater forests in the waters off the B.C. coast, formed not by trees but by a type of brown algae known as kelp (*Macrocystis integrifolia*), which can grow to lengths of 30 m. A related species, giant kelp (*M. pyrifera*) **(Figure 23.19b)**, can grow up to 60 m long. Kelps are the largest and most complex of all protists. Their tissues are differentiated into leaflike *blades*, stalklike *stipes*, and rootlike *holdfasts* that anchor them to the bottom. Hollow, gas-filled bladders give buoyancy to the stipes and blades and help keep them upright and oriented toward the sunlit upper layers of water **(Figure 23.19c)**. The stipes of some kelps contain tubelike vessels, similar to the vascular elements of plants, which rapidly distribute the products of photosynthesis throughout the body of the alga. Kelps have an astonishingly fast growth rate—giant kelp can grow up to 30 cm per day!

Just as for terrestrial forests, kelp forests provide food and habitat for many marine organisms. Herds of sea otters (*Enhydra lutris*), for example, tend to live in and near kelp forests. When sea otters sleep at sea, they wrap kelp around themselves to keep from drifting away **(Figure 23.20)**. Although the forest is an important habitat for the sea otters, the otters, in turn, are critical for the survival of these forests. Sea otters are one of the few predators of sea urchins, which graze on the kelp and can cause deforestation if their populations get very large. Predation by sea otters keeps sea urchin populations in control, preventing destruction of kelp forests.

a. Golden alga

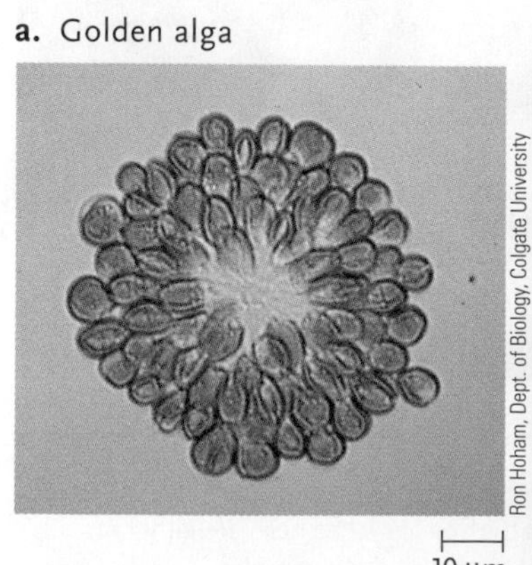

Ron Hoham, Dept. of Biology, Colgate University

b. Giant kelp

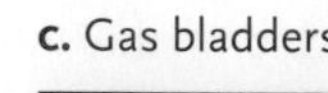

© Phillip Colla

c. Gas bladders

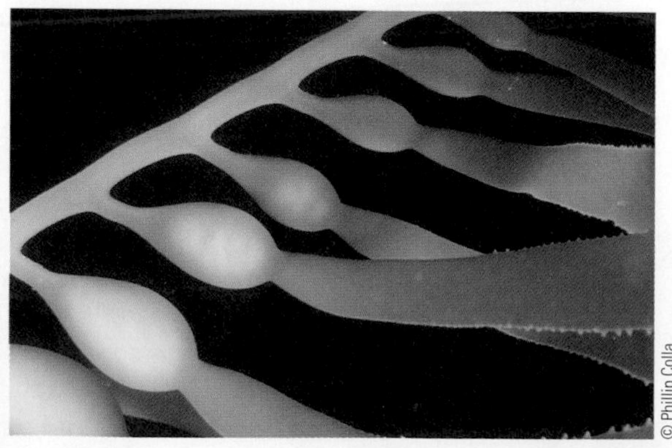

© Phillip Colla

Figure 23.19 Golden and brown algae. **(a)** A microscopic swimming colony of *Synura*, a golden alga. Each cell bears two flagellae, which are not visible in this light micrograph. **(b)** A forest of *Macrocystis pyrifera* (giant kelp). **(c)** Gas bladders connect kelp's stipes ("stems") to its blades ("leaves").

Figure 23.20
A sea otter (*Enhydra lutris*) wrapped in kelp.

All phaeophytes (brown algae, *phaios* = brown) are photoautotrophs, but not all are as large as kelps. Nearly all of the 1500 known species inhabit temperate or cool coastal marine waters. Like golden algae, phaeophytes contain fucoxanthin, which gives them their characteristic colour. Their cell walls contain cellulose and a mucilaginous polysaccharide, alginic acid. This alginic acid, called **algin** when extracted, is an essentially tasteless substance used to thicken such diverse products as ice cream, salad dressing, jellybeans, cosmetics, and floor polish. Brown algae are also harvested as food crops and fertilizer.

Life cycles among the brown algae are typically complex and in many species consist of alternating haploid and diploid generations **(Figure 23.21).** The large structures that we recognize as kelps and other brown seaweeds are diploid **sporophytes**, so called because they give rise to haploid spores by meiosis. The spores, which are flagellated swimming cells, germinate and divide by mitosis to form an independent, haploid **gametophyte** generation. The gametophytes give rise to haploid gametes, the egg and sperm cells. Most brown algal gametophytes are multicellular structures only a few centimetres in diameter. Cells in the gametophyte, produced by mitosis, differentiate to form nonmotile eggs or flagellated, swimming sperm cells. The sperm cells have the two different types of flagella characteristic of the heterokont protists. Fusion of egg and sperm produces a diploid zygote that grows by mitotic divisions into the sporophyte generation. This complex life cycle is very similar to that of land plants (see Chapter 25).

23.4e Cercozoa Are Amoebas with Filamentous Pseudopods

Amoeba (*amoibe* = change) is a descriptive term for a single-celled protist that moves by means of pseudopodia, as described earlier in this chapter (see Figure 23.6). Several major groups of protists contain

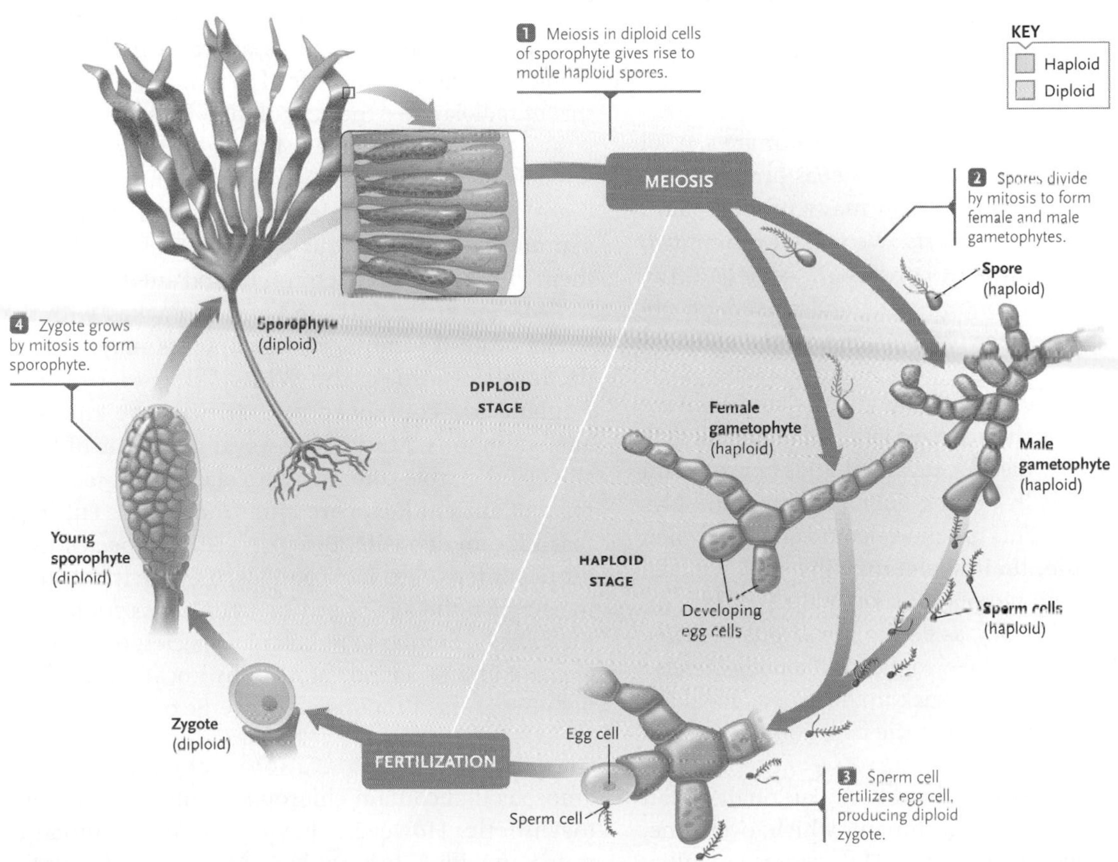

Figure 23.21
The life cycle of the brown alga *Laminaria*, which alternates between a diploid sporophyte stage and a haploid gametophyte stage.

a. Radiolarian

10 um

Manfred Kage/Peter Arnold Inc.

b. Radiolarian skeletons

Wim van Egmond/Visuals Unlimited

c. Living foram

10 µm

Courtesy of Allen W. H. Be and David A. Caron

d. Foram shells

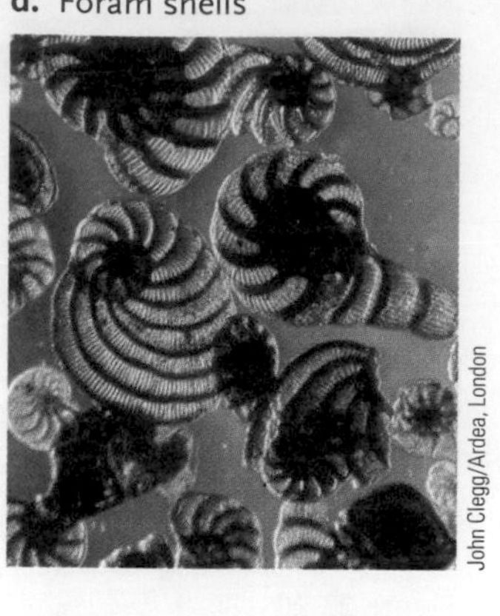

John Clegg/Ardea, London

Figure 23.22
(a) A living radiolarian. **(b)** The internal skeletons of two radiolarian species, possibly *Pterocorys* and *Stylosphaera*. Bundles of microtubules support the cytoplasmic extensions of the radiolarians. **(c)** A living foram, showing the cytoplasmic strands extending from its shelf. **(d)** Empty foram shells. **(e)** The body plan of a foram. Needlelike, glassy spines support the cytoplasmic extensions of the forams.

e. Foram body plan

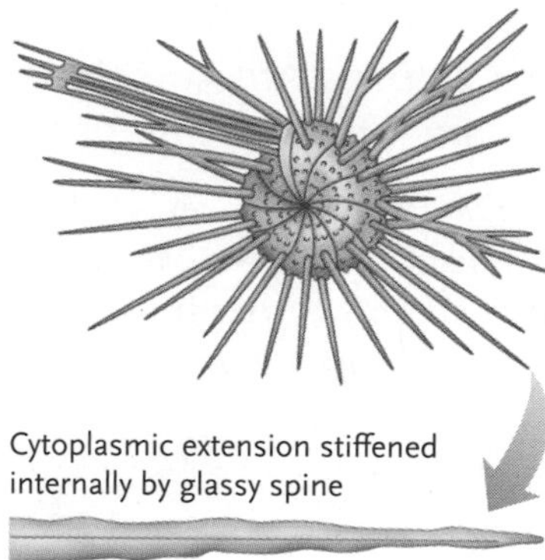

amoebas, which are similar in form but are not all closely related. The cercozoan amoebas produce stiff, filamentous pseudopodia, and many produce hard outer shells, also called *tests*. We consider here two heterotrophic groups of cercozoan amoebae, the Radiolaria and the Foraminifera, and a third, photosynthesizing group, the Chlorarachniophyta.

Radiolaria. Radiolarians (*radiolus* = small sunbeam) are marine organisms characterized by a glassy internal skeleton and **axopods**, slender, raylike strands of cytoplasm supported internally by long bundles of microtubules **(Figure 23.22a, b)**. This glassy skeleton is heavy—when radiolarians die, their skeletons sink to the ocean floor—so how do radiolarians keep afloat? The axopods provide buoyancy, as do the numerous vacuoles and lipid droplets in the cytoplasm. Axopods are also involved in feeding: prey stick to the axopods and are then engulfed, brought into the cell, and digested in food vacuoles.

Radiolarian skeletons that accumulate on the ocean floor become part of the sediment, which, over time, hardens into sedimentary rock. The presence of radiolarians in such rocks is very useful to the oil industry as indicators of oil-bearing strata.

Foraminifera: Forams. These organisms take their name from the perforations in their shells (*foramen* = little hole), through which extend long, slender strands of cytoplasm supported internally by a network of needlelike spines. Their shells consist of organic matter reinforced by calcium carbonate **(Figure 23.22c–e)**. Most foram shells are chambered, spiral structures that, although microscopic, resemble those of molluscs.

Like radiolarians, forams live in marine environments. Some species are planktonic, but they are most abundant on sandy bottoms and attached to rocks along the coasts. Forams feed in a manner similar to that of radiolarians: they engulf prey that adhere to the strands and conduct them through the holes in the shell into the central cytoplasm, where they are digested in food vacuoles. Some forams have algal symbionts that carry out photosynthesis, allowing them to live as both heterotrophs and autotrophs.

Marine sediments are typically packed with the shells of dead forams. The sediments may be hundreds of feet thick: the White Cliffs of Dover in England are composed primarily of the shells of ancient forams. Most of the world's deposits of limestone and marble contain foram shells; the great pyramids of ancient Egypt are built from blocks cut from fossil foram deposits. Because distinct species lived during different geologic periods, they are widely used to establish the age of sedimentary rocks containing their shells. Similar to radiolarian species, oil prospectors use forams as indicators of hydrocarbon deposits because layers of forams often overlie oil deposits.

Chlorarachniophyta. Chlorarachniophytes are amoebas that contain chloroplasts and thus are photosynthetic. However, they combine this mode of nutrition with heterotrophy, engulfing food with the many filamentous pseudopodia that extend from the cell surface.

23.4f Amoebozoa Includes Slime Moulds and Most Amoebas

The Amoebozoa includes most of the amoebas (others are in the Cercozoa) as well as the cellular and plasmodial slime moulds. All members of this group use pseudopods for locomotion and feeding for all or part of their life cycles.

Amoebas. Amoebas of the Amoebozoa are single-celled organisms that are abundant in marine and freshwater environments and in the soil. All amoebas are microscopic, although some species can grow up to 5 mm in size and so are visible with the naked eye. Some amoebas are parasitic, such as the 45 species that infect the human digestive tract. One of these parasites, *Entamoeba histolytica*, causes amoebic dysentery. Cysts of this amoeba contaminate water supplies and soil in regions with inadequate sewage treatment. When ingested, a cyst breaks open to release an amoeba that feeds and divides rapidly in the digestive tract. Enzymes released by the amoebas destroy cells lining the intestine, producing the ulcerations, painful cramps, and debilitating diarrhea characteristic of the disease. Amoebic dysentery afflicts millions of people worldwide; in less developed countries, it is a leading cause of death among infants and small children.

However, most amoebas are heterotrophs that feed on bacteria, other protists, and bits of organic matter. Unlike the stiff, supported pseudopodia of cercozoans, pseudopods of amoebas extend and retract at any point on their body surface and are unsupported by any internal cellular organization—amoebas are thus "shape-shifters." How can an amoeba capture a fast-moving organism? As an amoeba moves, its cytoplasm doesn't just move but also changes state, from a more liquid state to a more solid state and back again, allowing the amoeba to send out pseudopodia in different directions very quickly. These fast-moving pseudopods can capture even fast-swimming prey such as ciliates **(Figure 23.23)**.

Amoebas reproduce only asexually, via binary fission. In unfavourable environmental conditions, some amoebas can form a cyst, essentially by rolling up and secreting a protective membrane. They survive as cysts until favourable conditions return.

Slime Moulds. After a very wet spring in 1973, residents of Dallas, Texas, were alarmed to see large, yellow blobs that resembled scrambled eggs *crawling* on their lawns. People thought it was an alien invasion. Luckily, a local biologist was able to prevent mass panic by identifying the blobs as slime moulds, unusual heterotrophic protists. Slime moulds exist for part of their lives as individuals that move by amoeboid motion but then come together in a coordinated mass—essentially, a large amoeba—that ultimately differentiates into a stalked structure called a **fruiting body**, in which spores are formed.

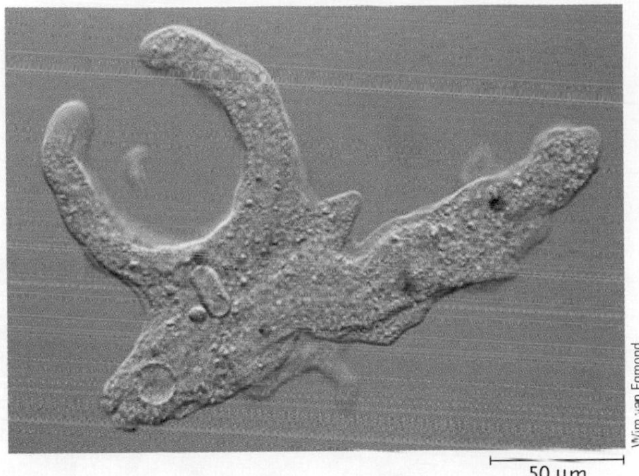

Figure 23.23
An amoeba capturing prey with pseudopods.

There are two major evolutionary lineages of slime moulds: the cellular slime moulds and the plasmodial slime moulds, which differ in cellular organization. Both types of slime moulds have been of great interest to scientists because of their ability to differentiate into fruiting bodies with stalks and spore-bearing structures. This differentiation is much simpler than the complex developmental pathways of other eukaryotes, providing a unique opportunity to study cell differentiation at its most fundamental level. Slime moulds also respond to stimuli in their environment, moving away from bright light and toward food. We have learned a great deal about eukaryotic signalling pathways, cell differentiation, and cell movement from studies of slime moulds.

Slime moulds live on moist, rotting plant material such as decaying leaves and bark. The cells engulf particles of dead organic matter, along with bacteria, yeasts, and other microorganisms, and digest them internally. They can be a range of colours: brown, yellow, green, red, and even violet or blue.

These organisms exist primarily as individual cells, either separately or as a coordinated mass. Among the 70 or so species of cellular slime moulds, *Dictyostelium discoideum* is best known. Its life cycle begins when a haploid spore lands in a suitably moist environment containing decaying organic matter **(Figure 23.24, p. 514)**. The spore germinates into an amoeboid cell that grows and divides mitotically into separate haploid cells as long as the food source lasts. When the food supply dwindles, some of the cells release a chemical signal in pulses; in response, the amoebas move together and form a sausage-shaped mass that crawls in coordinated fashion like a slug. Some "slugs," although not much more than a millimetre in length, contain more than 100 000 individual

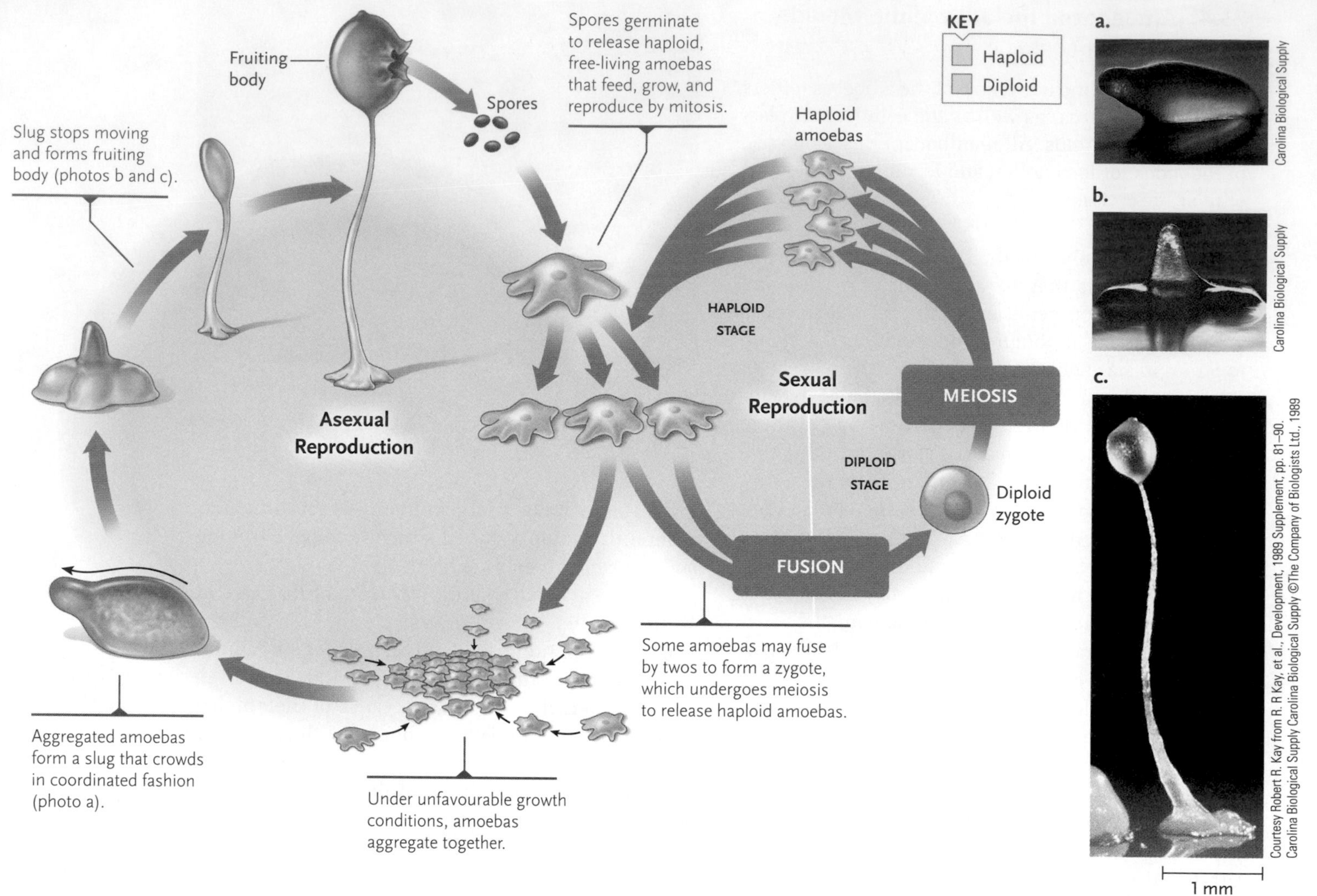
Fruiting body
Spores
Spores germinate to release haploid, free-living amoebas that feed, grow, and reproduce by mitosis.
KEY
Haploid
Diploid
Slug stops moving and forms fruiting body (photos b and c).
Haploid amoebas
HAPLOID STAGE
Asexual Reproduction
Sexual Reproduction
MEIOSIS
DIPLOID STAGE
Diploid zygote
FUSION
Some amoebas may fuse by twos to form a zygote, which undergoes meiosis to release haploid amoebas.
Aggregated amoebas form a slug that crowds in coordinated fashion (photo a).
Under unfavourable growth conditions, amoebas aggregate together.
a.
b.
c.
1 mm
Carolina Biological Supply
Carolina Biological Supply
Courtesy Robert R. Kay from R. R Kay, et al., Development, 1989 Supplement, pp. 81–90. Carolina Biological Supply Carolina Biological Supply ©The Company of Biologists Ltd., 1989

Figure 23.24
Life cycle of the cellular slime mould *Dictyostelium discoideum*. The light micrographs show **(a)** a migrating slug, **(b)** an early stage in fruiting body formation, and **(c)** a mature fruiting body.

cells. At some point, the "slug" stops moving and differentiates into a stalked fruiting body, with some cells becoming spores, whereas others form the stalk. The cells that form the stalk die in the process, essentially sacrificing themselves so that a stalk can form. Why is formation of a stalk so crucial? Raising the spore-forming cells higher up in the air improves the likelihood that spores will be carried away by air currents and dispersed farther away from the parent. Because the cells forming the "slug" and fruiting body are all products of mitosis, this is asexual reproduction.

Cellular slime moulds also reproduce sexually: two haploid cells fuse to form a diploid zygote (also shown in Figure 26.16) that enters a dormant stage. Eventually, the zygote undergoes meiosis, producing four haploid cells that may multiply inside the spore by mitosis. When conditions are favourable, the spore wall breaks down, releasing the cells. These grow and divide into separate amoeboid cells.

Plasmodial Slime Moulds. Plasmodial slime moulds exist primarily as a multinucleate **plasmodium,** in which individual nuclei are suspended in a common cytoplasm surrounded by a single plasma membrane. (This is not to be confused with *Plasmodium,* the genus of apicomplexans that causes malaria.) There are about 500 known species of plasmodial slime moulds. The plasmodium **(Figure 23.25a)** flows and feeds by phagocytosis like a single huge amoeba—a single cell that contains thousands to millions or even billions of diploid nuclei surrounded by a single plasma membrane. The plasmodium, which may range in size from a few centimetres to more than a metre in diameter, moves typically in thick, branching strands connected by thin sheets. The movements occur by cytoplasmic streaming, driven by actin microfilaments and myosin. These plasmodia are what the people in Dallas thought were aliens invading; after a period of heavy rain, plasmodia will sometimes crawl

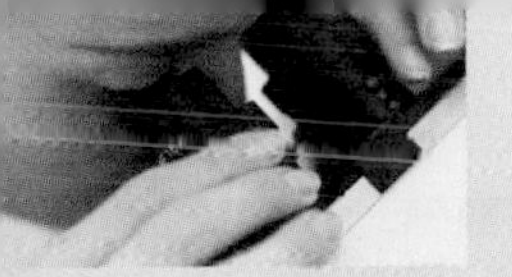

PEOPLE BEHIND BIOLOGY

Klaus-Peter Zauner, Soichiro Tsuda, and Yukio Pegio Gunjia

Robots controlled by slime moulds? Far from being a bizarre science fiction story, slime moulds may be the future of robotics, as demonstrated in research carried out by Klaus-Peter Zauner (University of Southampton, UK) and his collaborators at Kobe University in Japan, Soichiro Tsuda and Yukio-Pegio Gunjia. Zauner and colleagues grew *Physarum polycephalum* in a six-pointed star shape on an electrical circuit and connected the circuit to a six-legged robot with a computer interface. Each point of the *Physarum* plasmodium star corresponded to one leg of the robot **(Figure 1)**. When light was shone on certain parts of the robot, sensors mounted on the robot detected the light and illuminated the corresponding part of the plasmodium, which responded by moving away from the light, sending the robot scuttling into dark corners. One goal of Zauner's research in molecular computing is to incorporate this biological control right into the robot. Harnessing the capacity of living organisms to sense and respond to complex environments would give robots greater autonomy than is possible with control by computer programs.

New Scientist

Figure 1
A slime mould (image on screen) is able to direct the movement of a robot (in the foreground).

out of the woods to appear on lawns or the mulch of flowerbeds.

At some point, often in response to unfavourable environmental conditions, fruiting bodies form on the plasmodium. At the tips of the fruiting bodies, nuclei become enclosed in separate cells. These cells undergo meiosis, forming haploid, resistant spores that are released from the fruiting bodies and carried by water or wind **(Figure 23.25b)**. If they reach a favourable environment, the spores germinate to form gametes that fuse to form a diploid zygote. The zygote nucleus then divides repeatedly without an accompanying division of the cytoplasm, forming many diploid nuclei suspended in the common cytoplasm of a new plasmodium.

Plasmodial slime moulds are particularly useful in research because they become large enough to provide ample material for biochemical and molecular analyses. Actin and myosin extracted from *Physarum polycephalum*, for example, have been much used in studies of actin-based motility. A further advantage of plasmodial slime moulds is that the many nuclei of a plasmodium usually replicate and pass through mitosis in synchrony, making them useful in research that tracks the changes that take place in the cell cycle. More recently, slime moulds have been used in robotics research, as outlined in *People Behind Biology.*

23.4g Archaeplastida Include the Red and Green Algae and Land Plants

The Archaeplastida group consists of the red and green algae, which are protists, and the land plants (the *Viridaeplantae*, or "true plants"), which comprise the kingdom Plantae. These three groups of photoautotrophs share a common evolutionary origin. Here we describe the two types of algae; we discuss land plants and how they evolved from green algae in Chapter 25.

a.

George Barron

b.

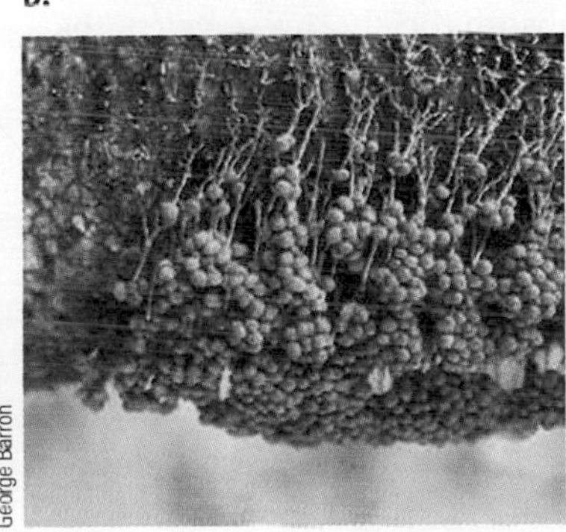
Greg Thorn

Figure 23.25
(a) Plasmodium of slime mould. **(b)** Fruiting bodies of slime mould.

a. Filamentous red alga

© Wim van Egmond/Visuals Unlimited

b. Sheetlike red alga

Douglas Faulkner/Sally Faulkner Collection

Figure 23.26
Red algae. **(a)** *Antithamnion plumula*, showing the filamentous and branched body form most common among red algae. **(b)** A sheetlike red alga growing on a tropical reef.

Rhodophyta: The Red Algae. Nearly all of the 4000 known species of red algae, which are also known as the Rhodophyta (*rhodon* = rose), are small marine seaweeds **(Figure 23.26).** Fewer than 200 species are found in freshwater lakes and streams or in soils. If you have had sushi, then you have eaten red algae: *Porphyra* is harvested for use as the *nori* wrapped around fish and rice.

Rhodophyte cell walls contain cellulose and mucilaginous pectins that give red algae a slippery texture. These pectins are widely used in industry and science. Extracted **agar** is used as a culture medium in the laboratory and as a setting agent for jellies and desserts. Carrageenan is used to thicken and stabilize paints, dairy products such as ice cream, and many other emulsions.

Some species secrete calcium carbonate into their cell walls; these coralline algae are important in building coral reefs—in some places, they play a bigger role in reef building than do corals.

Red algae are typically multicellular organisms, with diverse morphologies, although many have plantlike bodies composed of stalks bearing leaflike blades. Although most are free-living autotrophs, some are parasites that attach to other algae or plants.

Although most red algae are reddish in colour, some are greenish purple or black. The colour differences are produced by accessory pigments, *phycobilins*, which mask the green colour of their chlorophylls. Phycobilins absorb the shorter wavelengths of light (green and blue-green light) that penetrate to the ocean depths, allowing red algae to grow at deeper levels than any other algae. Some red algae live at depths up to 260 m if the water is clear enough to transmit light to these levels.

Red algae have complex reproductive cycles involving alternation between diploid sporophytes and haploid gametophytes. No flagellated cells occur in the red algae; instead, gametes are released into the water to be brought together by random collisions in currents.

Chlorophyta: The Green Algae. The green algae or Chlorophyta (*chloros* = green) carry out photosynthesis using the same pigments as plants, whereas other photosynthetic protists contain pigment combinations that are very different from those of land plants. This shared pigment composition is one line of evidence that one lineage of green algae was the ancestor of land plants. With at least 16 000 species, green algae show more diversity than any other algal group. They also have very diverse morphologies, including single-celled, colonial, and multicellular species (**Figure 23.27;** see also Figure 23.1d). Multicellular forms have a range of morphologies, including filamentous, tubular, and leaflike forms. Most green algae are microscopic, but some range upward to the size of small seaweeds.

Most green algae live in freshwater aquatic habitats, but some are marine, whereas others live on rocks, soil surfaces, or tree bark, or even in snow. Other organisms rely on green algae to photosynthesize for them by forming symbiotic relationships. For example, lichens are symbioses between green algae and fungi (see Chapter 24), and many animals, such as the sea slugs described in Chapter 3, contain green algal chloroplasts, or entire green algae, as symbionts in their cells.

Life cycles among the green algae are as diverse as their body forms. Many can reproduce either sexually or asexually, and some alternate between haploid and diploid generations. Gametes in different species may be undifferentiated flagellated cells or differentiated as a flagellated sperm cell and a nonmotile egg cell. Most common is a life cycle with a multicellular haploid phase and a single-celled diploid phase **(Figure 23.28).**

Among all the algae, the green algae are the most closely related to land plants, based on molecular, biochemical, and morphological data. Evidence of this close relationship includes not only the shared photosynthetic pigments, but also the use of starch as storage reserve, and the same cell wall composition.

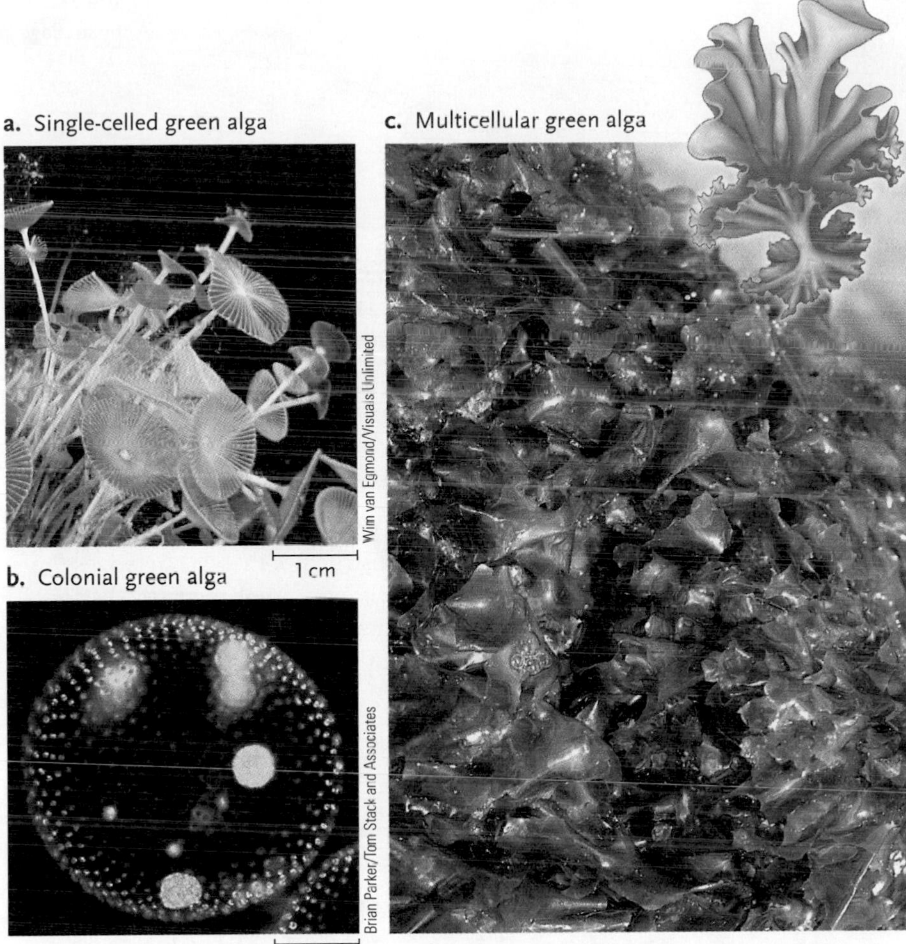

Figure 23.27
Green algae. **(a)** A single-celled green alga, *Acetabularia,* which grows in marine environments. Each individual in the cluster is a large single cell with a rootlike base, stalk, and cap. **(b)** A colonial green alga, *Volvox.* Each green dot in the spherical wall of the colony is a potentially independent, flagellated cell. Daughter colonies can be seen within the parent colony. **(c)** A multicellular green alga, *Ulva,* common to shallow seas around the world.

Which green alga might have been the ancestor of modern land plants? The evidence points to a group known as the **charophytes** as being most similar to the algal ancestors of land plants. This does not mean that modern-day charophytes are the ancestors of land plants but rather that the two groups share a common ancestor. Charophytes, including *Chara* (**Figure 23.29**, **p. 518**), *Spirogyra, Nitella,* and *Coleochaete,* live in freshwater ponds and lakes. Their ribosomal RNA and chloroplast DNA sequences are more closely related to plant sequences than those of any other green alga. We discuss the evolution of land plants from an algal ancestor more thoroughly in Chapter 25.

23.4h Opisthokonts Include the Choanoflagellates, Which May Be the Ancestors of Animals

Opisthokonts (*opistho* = posterior; *kontos* = flagellum) are named for the single, posterior flagellum found at some stage in the life cycle of these organisms. This

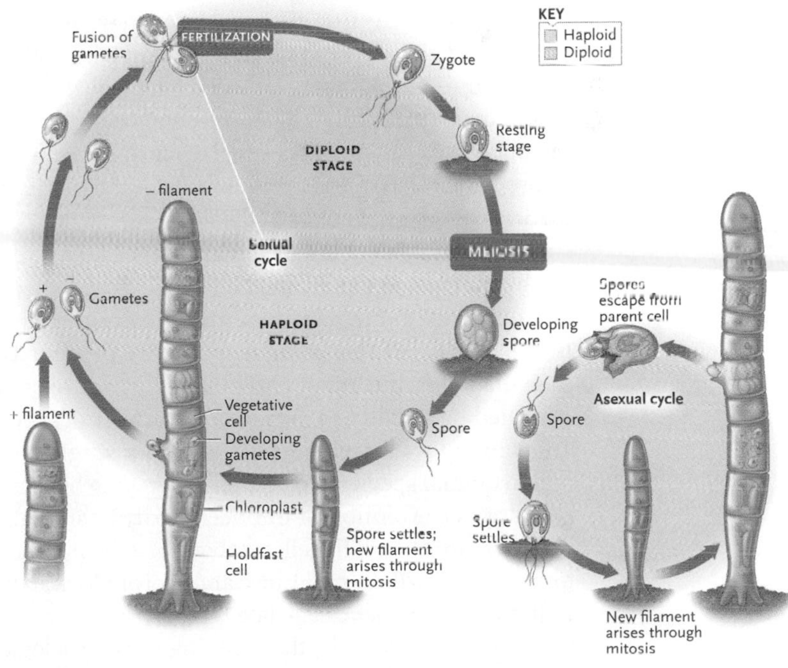

Figure 23.28
The life cycle of the green alga *Ulothrix,* in which the haploid stage is multicellular and the diploid stage is a single cell, the zygote. "+" and "−" are morphologically identical mating types ("sexes") of the alga.

Reproductive structures
Dr. John Clayton, National Institute of Water and Atmospheric Research, New Zealand

Figure 23.29
The charophyte *Chara,* representative of a group of green algae that may have given rise to the plant kingdom.

Figure 23.30
A choanoflagellate.

diverse group includes the choanoflagellates, protists thought to be the ancestors of fungi and animals.

Choanoflagellata (*choanos* = collar) are named for the collar surrounding the flagellum that the protist uses to feed and, in some species, to swim **(Figure 23.30).** The collar resembles an upside-down lampshade and is made up of small, fingerlike projections (microvilli) of the plasma membrane. As the flagellum moves water through the collar, these projections engulf bacteria and particles of organic matter in the water.

About 150 species of choanoflagellates live in either marine or freshwater habitats. Some species are mobile, with the flagellum pushing the cells along (in the same way that animal sperm are propelled by their flagella), but most choanoflagellates are *sessile* (attached by a stalk to a surface). A number of species are colonial with a cluster of cells on a single stalk; these colonial species are of great interest to biologists studying the evolution of multicellularity in animals.

Why are choanoflagellates thought to be the ancestor of animals? Both molecular and morphological data indicate that a choanoflagellate type of protist gave rise to animals: for example, there are many morphological similarities between choanoflagellates and the collar cells (choanocytes) of sponges as well as the cells that act as excretory organisms in flatworms and rotifers (see Chapter 26). Comparisons of nucleic acid sequences done to date also support the hypothesis that choanoflagellates are the closest living relatives to animals. Molecular data also indicate that a choanoflagellate-like organism was also likely the ancestor of the fungi (see Ch. 24).

Study Break

1. For each of the protist groups listed below, indicate the cell structure that characterizes the group: apicomplexans, dinoflagellates, discicristates, radiolarians.
2. Which groups of protists contain amoeboid forms?
3. What is the major difference between cellular slime moulds and plasmodial slime moulds?

23.5 Some Protist Groups Arose from Primary Endosymbiosis and Others from Secondary Endosymbiosis

We have encountered chloroplasts in a number of eukaryotic organisms in this chapter: red and green algae, euglenoids, dinoflagellates, heterokonts, chlorarachniophytes, and land plants. How did these chloroplasts evolve? Unlike the endosymbiotic event that gave rise to mitochondria, endosymbiosis involving photoautotrophs happened more than once, resulting in the formation of a wide range of photosynthetic eukaryotes.

The chloroplasts of the Archaeplastida—the red algae, green algae, and land plants—result from evolutionary divergence of the photosynthetic eukaryotes formed via a single primary endosymbiotic event (as shown in the top part of **Figure 23.31**) that happened about 1 billion years ago. In primary endosymbiosis, a eukaryotic cell engulfed a photosynthetic cyanobacterium but did not digest it. Organisms that originated from this event have chloroplasts with two membranes, one from the plasma membrane of the engulfing eukaryote and the other from the plasma membrane of the cyanobacterium.

This primary endosymbiotic event, which produced the first eukaryotic photoautorophs, was followed by at least three **secondary endosymbiosis** events, each time involving different heterotrophic

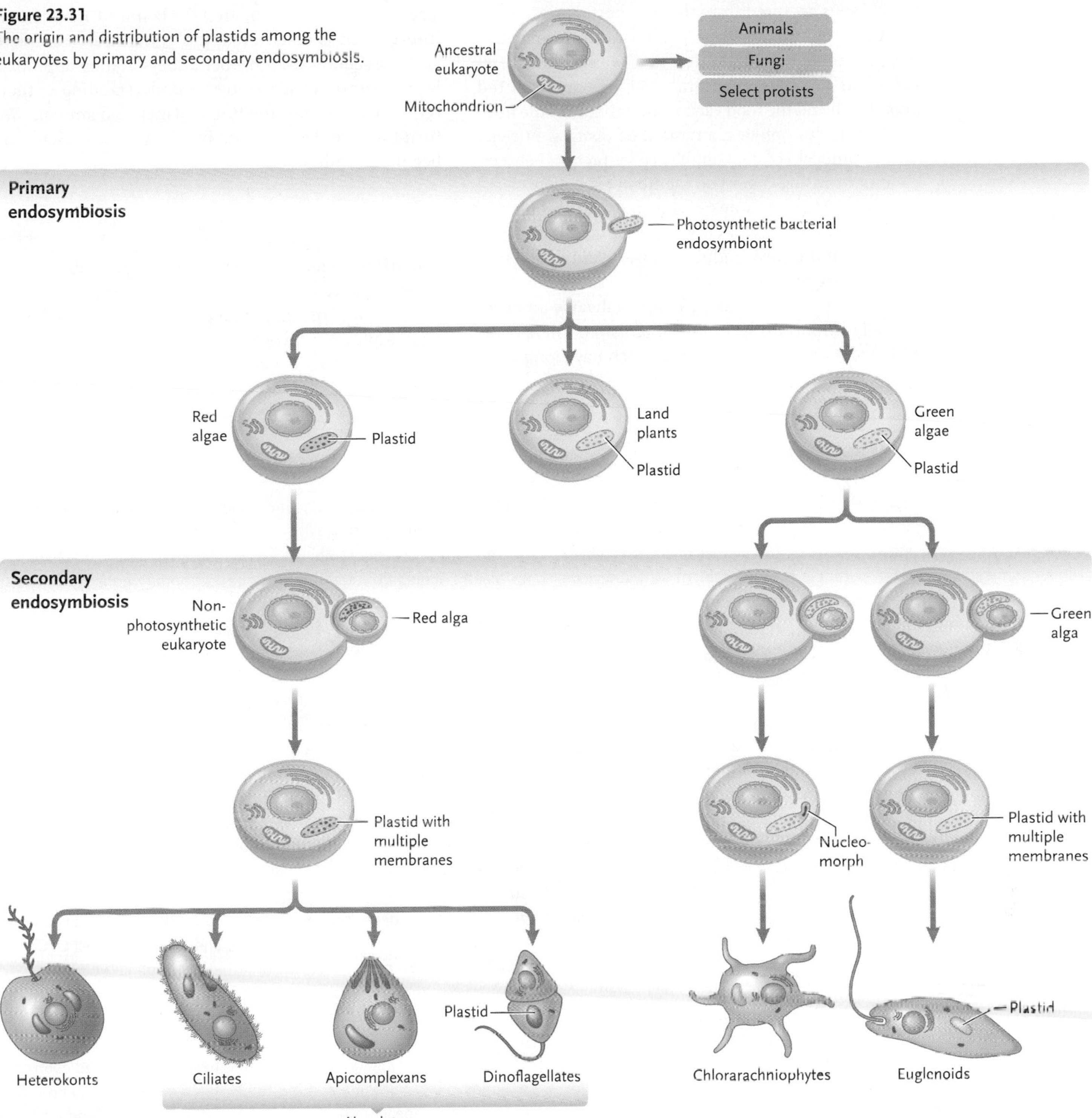

Figure 23.31
The origin and distribution of plastids among the eukaryotes by primary and secondary endosymbiosis.

eukaryotes engulfing a photosynthetic eukaryote, producing new evolutionary lineages (see Figure 23.31). In one of these events, red algal ancestors were engulfed. Over evolutionary time, these became the chloroplasts of the heterokonts and the dinoflagellates. From the same photosynthetic ancestor, loss of chloroplast functions occurred in the lineage of the Apicomplexa, which have a remnant plastid.

In an independent endosymbiotic event, a nonphotosynthetic eukaryote engulfed a green algal ancestor. Subsequent evolution in this case produced the euglenoids. In yet another event, a similar endosymbiosis involving a green alga led to the chlorarachniophytes. In these protists, the chloroplast is still contained within the remnants of the original symbiont cell.

Organisms that formed via secondary endosymbiosis have chloroplasts surrounded by additional membranes acquired from the new host. For example, chlorarachniophytes have plastids with four membranes (see Figure 23.31). The new membranes correspond to the plasma membrane of the engulfed phototroph and the food vacuole membrane of the host. In chlorarachniophytes, a remant or vestigial nucleus (a nucleomorph) of the engulfed cell is present between the inner two and outer two membranes. Biologists are sequencing the genomes of the chlorarachniophyte's nucleus, chloroplast, and vestigial nucleus to learn more about the early endosymbiosis event that generated these organisms.

In sum, the protists are a highly diverse and ecologically important group of organisms. Their complex evolutionary relationships, which have long been a subject of contention, are now being revised as new information is discovered, including more complete genome sequences. A deeper understanding of protists is also contributing to a better understanding of their recent descendants, the fungi, plants, and animals. We turn to these descendants in the next four chapters, beginning with the fungi.

Study Break

In primary endosymbiosis, a nonphotosynthetic eukaryotic cell engulfed a photosynthetic cyanobacterium. How many membranes surround the chloroplast that evolved?

Unanswered Questions

What was the first eukaryote?

Since prokaryotes precede eukaryotes in the fossil record, we assume that eukaryotes arose after prokaryotes. The first eukaryote would have been some sort of protist—a single-celled organism with a nucleus and some rudimentary organelles, perhaps even a half-tamed mitochondrion. One approach to identifying which of the surviving protists is the most ancient has been to infer evolutionary trees from gene sequence data. To determine the earliest branching eukaryote, these trees need to include the prokaryotes. But herein lies the problem—prokaryotes are very distant, evolutionarily speaking, from even the simplest eukaryotes, and the mathematical models used to construct evolutionary trees are not yet up to the job. Initially, these models suggested that some protist parasites, like the excavates ***Giardia*** and ***Trichomonas***, might be the most ancient eukaryotes, and this idea fit nicely with the fact that these protists lacked mitochondria. Indeed, for a time it was thought that the excavates might actually have diverged from the eukaryotic branch of life before the establishment of mitochondria. Nowadays, we know that ***Giardia*** and ***Trichomonas*** did initially have mitochondria. The latest research shows that they even have a tiny relic of the mitochondrion, although exactly what it does in these oxygen-shunning parasites remains to be figured out. Thus, trees depicting ***Giardia*** and ***Trichomonas*** at the base of the great expansion of eukaryotic life must be viewed with some caution—these protists might be the surviving representatives of the earliest cells with a nucleus, but they might not be. We simply need better methods for identifying what the first eukaryotes were like.

How many times did plastids arise by endosymbioses?

For many years, researchers thought that the green algae, plants, and red algae were the only organisms to have primary endosymbiosis–derived plastids. However, a second, independent primary endosymbiosis was recently discovered in which a shelled amoeba captured and partially domesticated a cyanobacterium. This organism, known as *Paulinella*, is a vital window into the process by which autotrophic eukaryotes first arose some 600 million years ago. *Paulinella* has tamed the cyanobacterium sufficiently to have it divide and segregate in coordination with host cell division, but the endosymbiont is still very much a cyanobacterium and has undergone little of the modification and streamlining we see in the red or green algal plastids.

After a primary endosymbiosis was established, the second chapter in plastid acquisition could take place. Secondary endosymbiosis involves a eukaryotic host engulfing and retaining a eukaryotic alga. Essentially, secondary endosymbiosis can convert a heterotrophic organism into an autotroph by hijacking a photosynthetic cell and putting it to work as a solar-powered food factory. Secondary endosymbiosis results in plastids with three or four membranes, and we know that it occurred at least three times—once for the euglenoids, once for the chlorarachniophytes, and once for the chromalveolates (a proposed grouping of heterokonts and alveolates). We can even tell what kind of endosymbiont was involved by the biochemistry and genetic makeup of the plastid: a green alga for euglenoids and chlorarachniophytes and a red alga for chromalveolates. The number of secondary endosymbioses is hotly debated, largely because not all protistologists support the existence of chromalveolates. Some contend that there were multiple, independent enslavements of different red algae to produce the dinoflagellates, heterokonts, and apicomplexans. Understanding these events is crucial to confirming or refuting the proposed chromalveolate "supergroup."

A nice example of secondary endosymbiosis in action was recently discovered by Japanese scientists who found a flagellate, *Hatena*, with a green algal endosymbiont. *Hatena* hasn't yet assumed control of endosymbiont division and has to get new symbionts each time it divides, so it appears to be at a very early stage in establishing a relationship. We also want to know how secondary endosymbioses proceed because they have been a major driver in eukaryotic evolution. The heterokonts, for instance, are the most important ocean phytoplankton and are key to ocean productivity and global carbon cycling. Knowing exactly how they got to be autotrophs in the first place is fundamental to understanding the world we live in.

Dr. Geoff McFadden is a professor of botany at the University of Melbourne. He studies the early evolution of eukaryotes, especially the origin and evolution of plastids and mitochondria. You can learn more about his research by visiting http://homepage.mac.com/fad1/McFaddenLab.html.

Review

Go to CENGAGENOW™ at http://hed.nelson.com/ to access quizzing, animations, exercises, articles, and personalized homework help.

23.1 Evolution of Protists Involved Endosymbiosis

- As eukaryotes, protists contain organelles including mitochondria and, sometimes, chloroplasts. Mitochondria evolved once via primary endosymbiosis, the engulfing of a free-living prokaryote that became an organelle over evolutionary time. Some photosynthetic protists were formed via primary endosymbiosis involving a photosynthetic prokaryote; others arose via more complex endosymbiotic events (see Section 23.5).

23.2 What Is a Protist? Characteristics of Protists

- Protists are eukaryotes that differ from fungi in having motile stages in their life cycles and cellulose cell walls. Unlike plants, they lack roots, stems, and leaves and do not retain embryos in parental tissue. Unlike animals, protists are often unicellular; they lack collagen, nerve cells, and an internal digestive tract.

23.3 Protists' Diversity Is Reflected in Their Metabolism, Reproduction, Structure, and Habitat

- Protists are aerobic organisms that live as autotrophs or as heterotrophs or by a combination of both nutritional modes. Some are symbionts living in or among the cells of other organisms.
- Protists live in aquatic or moist terrestrial habitats or as parasites within animals. They may be single-celled, colonial, or multicellular organisms, and they range in size from microscopic to some of Earth's largest organisms.
- Some protists are the most complex single cells known because of the wide variety of cytoplasmic structures they have; most are able to move by means of flagella, cilia, or pseudopodia.
- Reproduction may be asexual by mitotic divisions or sexual, involving meiosis and the union of gametes in fertilization.

23.4 The Protist Groups

- Excavates, exemplified by the Diplomonadida and Parabasala, are flagellated, single cells that lack "typical" mitochondria but often have organelles derived from mitochondria.
- Discicristates are almost all single-celled, autotrophic, and/or heterotrophic protists that swim using flagella.
- Alveolates include ciliates, which swim using cilia and have complex cytoplasmic structures, including both micronuclei and macronuclei, apicomplexans, nonmotile parasites of animals; and dinoflagellates, which have two flagella that propel them in a "whirling" motion and are primarily marine organisms. Many alveolates are photosynthetic.
- Heterokonts include diatoms, photosynthetic single-celled organisms covered by a glassy silica shell; golden algae, photosynthetic, mostly colonial forms; brown algae, primarily multicellular marine forms that include large seaweeds; and the funguslike Oomycota, which often grow as masses of microscopic filaments and live as saprophytes or parasites, secreting enzymes that digest organic matter in their surroundings. Most heterokonts have flagella only on reproductive cells.
- Cercozoa are amoebas with filamentous pseudopods supported by internal cellular structures. Many produce hard outer shells. Radiolarians are primarily marine organisms that secrete a glassy internal skeleton. Foraminifera are marine, single celled organisms that form chambered, spiral shells containing calcium. Both groups engulf prey that adhere to thin extensions of their cells. Chlorarachniophytes engulf food using their pseudopodia.
- Amoebozoa includes most amoebas and two types of slime moulds, cellular (which move as individual cells) and plasmodial (which move as large masses of nuclei sharing a common cytoplasm). Amoebas in this group are heterotrophs abundant in marine and freshwater environments and in the soil. They move by extending pseudopodia.
- Archaeplastida include the red and green algae, as well as the land plants that comprise the kingdom Plantae. Red algae are typically multicellular, primarily photosynthetic organisms of marine environments with complex life cycles. The green algae are single-celled, colonial, and multicellular species that live primarily in freshwater habitats and carry out photosynthesis by mechanisms similar to those of plants.
- Opisthokonts are a broad group of eukaryotes that includes the choanoflagellates, which have a single flagellum surrounded by a collar of fingerlike membrane projections. A choanoflagellate type of protist was likely the ancestor of animals.
- Several groups of protists, as well as land plants, contain chloroplasts, which arose via endosymbiosis events. In a primary endosymbiosis event, a eukaryotic cell engulfed a cyanobacterium, which became an organelle, the chloroplast. Evolutionary divergence from this ancestral phototrophic organism produced the red algae, green algae, and land plants. Other photosynthetic protists were produced by secondary endosymbiosis, in which a nonphotosynthetic eukaryote engulfed a photosynthetic eukaryote.

Questions

Self-Test Questions

1. Freely beating flagella buried in a fold of cytoplasm moving through viscous fluids of humans and commonly found as an infective agent in university health centres describes a member of
   a. Ciliophora.
   b. Discicristates.
   c. Diplomonadida.
   d. Parabasala.
   e. Alveolates.
2. The protist group Diplomonadida is characterized by
   a. a mouthlike gullet and a hairlike surface. *Paramecium* is an example.
   b. flagella and a lack of mitochondria. *Giardia* is an example.
   c. nonmotility, parasitism, and sporelike infective stages. *Toxoplasma* is an example.
   d. switching between autotrophic and heterotrophic life styles. *Euglena* is an example.
   e. large protein deposits. Movement is by two flagella, which are part of an undulating membrane. *Trypanosoma* is an example.
3. The greatest contributors to protist fossil deposits are
   a. Oomycota.
   b. Chrysophyta.
   c. Bacillariophyta.
   d. Sporophyta.
   e. Alveolates.

4. The group with the distinguishing characteristic of gas-filled bladders and a cell wall composed of alginic acid is
   a. Chrysophyta.
   b. Phaeophyta.
   c. Oomycota.
   d. Bacillariophyta.
   e. none of the above.
5. *Plasmodium* is transmitted to humans by the bite of a mosquito (*Anopheles*) and engages in a life cycle with infective spores, gametes, and cysts. This infective protist belongs to the group
   a. Apicomplexa.
   b. Heterokonts.
   c. Dinoflagellata.
   d. Oomycota.
   e. Ciliophora.
6. The latest stage for evolving the double membrane seen in modern-day algal chloroplasts is thought to be the combining of
   a. two ancestral nonphotosynthetic prokaryotes.
   b. two ancestral photosynthetic prokaryotes.
   c. a nonphotosynthetic eukaryote with a photosynthetic eukaryote.
   d. a photosynthetic prokaryote with a nonphotosynthetic eukaryote.
   e. mitochondria with an already established plastid.

Questions for Discussion

1. We have seen that, as a group, protists use three kinds of motility: flagella, cilia, and amoeboid movement. Cells in your body use these same three forms of motility. Name an example of cells that use each form.
2. Photosynthetic protists (sometimes referred to as "algae") are often thought of as single-celled plants. Why is it not correct to consider them as plants? What features differentiate these protists from plants? Would it be correct to consider the protists known as "protozoa" as single-celled animals? Explain why or why not.
3. Why is it harder to treat human diseases caused by protists, such as *Giardia*, than diseases caused by bacteria?
4. Many protists are able to produce cysts or other resting stages in their life cycle. What is the advantage of producing these resting structures?

The mushroom-forming fungus *Inocybe fastigiata*, a forest-dwelling species that commonly lives in close association with conifers and hardwood trees.

Fritz Polking/Peter Arnold, Inc.

Study Plan

24 Fungi

Why It Matters

If you were asked what the first crop on Earth was and which organisms grew it, you would probably think of corn, wheat, or some other crop plant grown by humans. But you'd be wrong—the first domesticated crop was a fungus, and the first farmers were a certain group of ants over 50 million years ago, whereas humans did not start farming until about 10 000 years ago. Researchers have used molecular data combined with fossil evidence to determine when ants first domesticated their fungal crop. Today, these leafcutter ants (Tribe Attini) of Central and South America **(Figure 24.1a, p. 524)** still grow certain fungi in gardens. Just as humans do, the ants plant their crop of fungus, fertilize it, weed it, and then feed on it. The ants harvest leaves, flowers, and other plant parts and carry these back to their nests, where the fungal gardens are grown **(Figure 24.1b, p. 524)**.

The ants plant small pieces of the plant material in the garden, placing bits of the fungus on each piece. They fertilize the garden with their excrement and graze on the fungal filaments. In fact, although the ants collect a wide range of plant matter, they never eat any of it directly—their sole food source is the fungus. When a

Figure 24.1
(a) Leaf-cutter ants.
(b) Fungal garden of leaf-cutter ants.

queen ant leaves her birth nest to start a new nest, she carries a bit of fungus in her mouth and uses it to start a garden in the new nest. The ants' habitat contains ample supplies of other foods, so why have these ants developed this complex and rather bizarre lifestyle? What benefit do they gain by devoting their lives to looking after a fungus? The answer lies in the ability of the fungus to unlock the nutrients tied up in plant tissue. Cellulose is the most abundant organic molecule on earth, but most organisms cannot get at the carbon it contains as they lack the enzymes needed to break apart the bonds in this molecule. Fungi are among the few organisms that can digest cellulose, so by forming a partnership with fungi, these ants gain access to a continuous source of carbon. In return, the fungus gains a secure habitat in which it doesn't have to compete with other organisms for a food source. Recent research has revealed that this ancient symbiosis is more complex than previously known (see *People Behind Biology*).

Although we often associate fungi with decay and decomposition, many fungi, such as those cultivated by leaf-cutter ants, instead live by forming symbiotic associations with other organisms. The vast majority of plants obtain soil minerals via a symbiotic relationship with soil fungi. Humans also have harnessed the metabolic activities of certain fungi to obtain substances ranging from flavourful cheeses and wine to bread and therapeutic drugs such as penicillin and the immunosuppressant cyclosporine. And, as you know from previous chapters, species such as the yeast *Saccharomyces cerevisiae* and the mould *Neurospora crassa* have long been pivotal model organisms in studies of DNA structure and function and in the development of genetic engineering methods. On the other hand, fungi collectively are the single greatest cause of plant diseases, and many species cause disease in humans and other animals. Some even produce carcinogenic toxins.

Evidence suggests that fungi were present on land at least 500 million years ago and possibly much earlier. Their presence on land was likely crucial for the successful colonization of land by plants, which relied on symbiotic associations with the fungi to obtain nutrients from the nutrient-poor soils of early land environments. In the course of the intervening millennia, evolution equipped fungi with a remarkable ability to break down a wide range of compounds, ranging from living and dead organisms and animal wastes to groceries, clothing, paper, and wood—even photographic film. Along with heterotrophic bacteria, they have become Earth's premier decomposers **(Figure 24.2)**. Despite their profound impact on ecosystems and other life forms, most of us have only a passing acquaintance with the fungi—perhaps limited to the mushrooms on our pizza or the invisible but annoying types that cause skin infections, such as athlete's foot. This chapter provides you with an overview of fungal biology. We begin with the features that set fungi apart from all other organisms and discuss the diversity of fungi existing today before revisiting associations between fungi and other organisms.

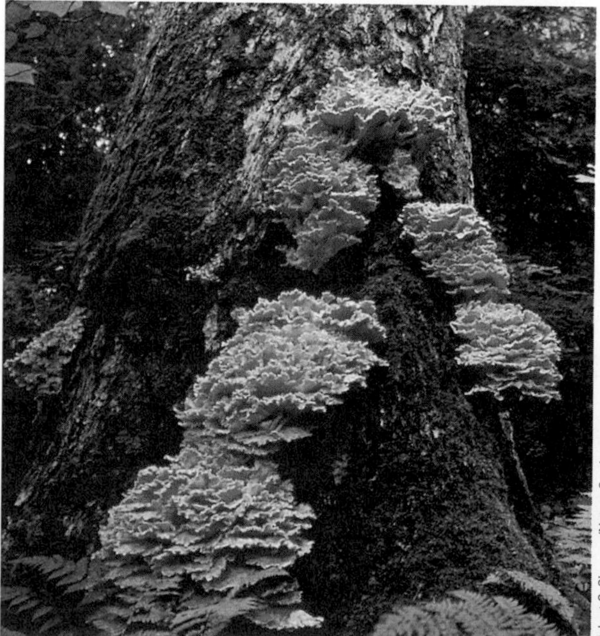

Figure 24.2
Example of a wood decay fungus: sulphur shelf fungus (*Polyporus*).

People Behind Biology
Cameron Currie

Discovery has been defined as "seeing what everyone else has seen and thinking what no one else has thought." Even though ant-fungal mutualism has been studied since 1874, in 1999 a graduate student at the University of Toronto, Cameron Currie, discovered a whole new dimension to this mutualism. For years, researchers studying this symbiosis had wondered how the ants kept their gardens free of competing fungi. The conditions created by the ants are ideal for many other fungi besides the garden fungus, and, as you know, fungal spores are everywhere—yet the ant gardens are pure monocultures of a single fungus. What prevents other fungi from invading the gardens? Biologists had thought that the ants kept other fungi out simply by weeding the gardens, removing all traces of invading fungi, and so keeping fungal competitors at bay. But Currie discovered that there is a third symbiont at work, and this organism keeps out other fungi. Currie noticed that ants had a whitish substance on their abdomens; other researchers had previously noticed this crust as well but assumed it was just part of the ant's exoskeleton **(Figure 1a).** When Currie took a closer look, he discovered that the crust was actually a bacterium of the genus *Pseudonocardia*; these bacteria are actinomycetes, which are known to produce antibiotics (e.g., streptomycin). On further exploration, Currie found that this bacterium produced an antibiotic that specifically and completely inhibited growth of a parasitic fungus, *Escovopsis*, which is the greatest threat to the gardens. If *Escovopsis* isn't stopped, it will overgrow the desirable fungus and take over the garden. This groundbreaking research, demonstrating that mutualisms do not necessarily involve just two species, was done while Currie was still a student. Since finishing his Ph.D., Currie has gone on to show that the ants' bodies have changed over evolutionary time to create and maintain a favourable environment for their bacteria. The bacteria live in specialized crevices on the ant's body that are associated with glands; secretions from these glands provide nutrients for the bacteria **(Figure 1b, c).** So not only did ants invent agriculture long before humans, they also used microbes to produce antibiotics, long before we thought of doing so. An interesting aspect of antibiotic use by the ants is that even though the parasitic fungus has been exposed to the antibiotic produced by the bacterium for a very long time, it has not become resistant to the antibiotic. Perhaps we can learn something from the ants about preventing antibiotic resistance, which has rendered many of the antibiotics we rely on ineffective (you read about antibiotic resistance in Chapter 21).

a.

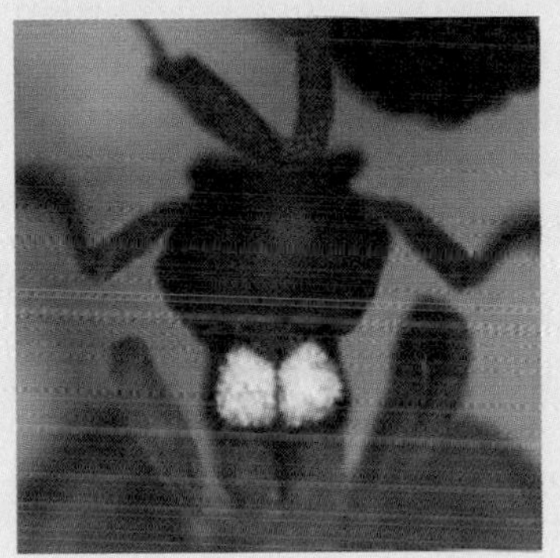

b.

c.

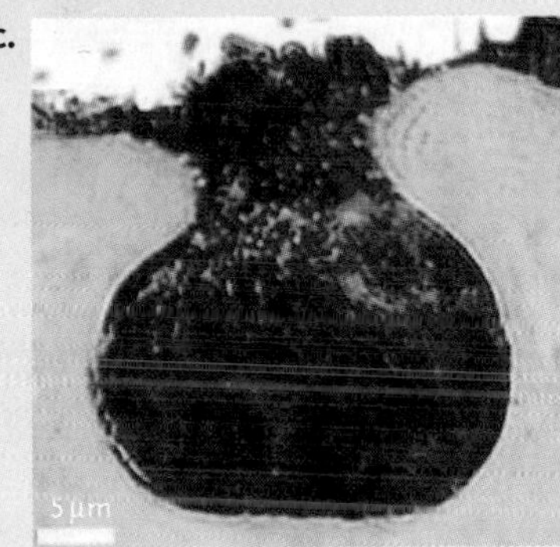

Figure 1
(a) Leaf-cutter ant showing bacterial "crust." **(b)** crypts (white spots) on ant's body house bacteria; **(c)** Crypt on the body of a leaf-cutter ant. From Cameron R. Currie, Michael Poulsen, John Mendenhall, Jacobus J. Boomsma, Johan Billen, "Coevolved crypts and exocrine glands support mutualistic bacteria in fungus-growing ants", Science, Vol. 311, 6 January 2006, pp. 81–83. Reprinted with permission from AAAS.

24.1 What Is a Fungus? General Characteristics of Fungi

We begin our survey of fungi by examining the features that distinguish fungi from other forms of life, how fungi obtain nutrients, and adaptations for reproduction and growth that enable fungi to spread far and wide through the environment.

Fungi are heterotrophic eukaryotes that obtain carbon by breaking down organic molecules synthesized by other organisms. Although all fungi are heterotrophs, fungi can be divided into two broad groups based on how they obtain carbon. If a fungus obtains carbon from nonliving material, it is a **saprotroph.** Fungi that decompose dead plant and animal tissues, for example, are saprotrophs. If a fungus obtains carbon from living organisms, it is a **symbiont.** Symbiosis is the living together of two (or sometimes more) organisms for extended periods; symbiotic relationships range along a continuum from **parasitism,** in which one organism benefits at the expense of the other, to **mutualism,** in which both organisms benefit. Although we often think of fungi as decomposers, fully half of all identified fungi live as symbionts with another organism.

Regardless of their nutrient source, fungi feed by **absorptive nutrition:** they secrete enzymes into their environment, breaking down large molecules into smaller molecules that can then be absorbed into their cells. This mode of nutrition means that fungi cannot be stationary as they would then deplete all of the food in their immediate environment. Instead, fungi have evolved the ability to proliferate quickly through their environment, digesting nutrients as they grow. How can fungi proliferate so quickly? Although some fungi are unicellular, most are composed of **hyphae** ("web"; singular = hypha) **(Figure 24.3a)**, fine filaments that spread through whatever substrate the fungus is growing in—soil, decomposing wood, your skin—forming a network or **mycelium (Figure 24.3b, c)**. Hyphae are essentially tubes of cytoplasm surrounded by cell walls made of chitin, a polysaccharide also found in the exoskeletons of insects and other arthropods.

Hyphae grow only at their tips, but because a single mycelium contains many, many tips, the entire mycelium grows outward very quickly. Together, this **apical growth** and absorptive nutrition account for much of the success of fungi. As the hyphal tips extend, they exert a mechanical force, allowing them to push through their substrate, releasing enzymes and absorbing nutrients as they go. Fungal species differ in the particular digestive enzymes they synthesize, so a substrate that is a suitable food source for one species may be unavailable to another. Although there are exceptions, fungi typically thrive only in moist environments, where they can directly absorb water, dissolved ions, simple sugars, amino acids, and other small molecules. When some of a mycelium's hyphal filaments contact a source of food, growth is channelled in the direction of the food source.

Nutrients are absorbed at the porous tips of hyphae; small atoms and molecules pass readily through these tips, and then transport mechanisms move them through the underlying plasma membrane. Some hyphae have regular cross-walls or **septa** ("fence" or "wall"; singular = septum), whereas others lack septa and are effectively one large cell **(Figure 24.4)**. But even septate hyphae should be thought of as interconnected compartments rather than separate cells as all septa have pores that allow cytoplasm and, in some fungi, even nuclei and other large organelles to flow through the mycelium. By a mechanism called *cytoplasmic streaming*, nutrients obtained by one part of a mycelium can be translocated to other nonabsorptive regions, such as reproductive structures.

When a fungus releases enzymes into its substrate, it faces competition from bacteria and other organisms for the nutrients that are now available. How can a fungus prevent these competitors from stealing the nutrients that it has just expended energy and resources to obtain? Many fungi produce antibacterial compounds and toxins that inhibit the growth of competing organisms. Many of these compounds are **secondary metabolites**, which are not required for day-to-day survival but are beneficial to the fungus. As we will see, many of these compounds are not only important in the life of a fungus but also benefit organisms associated with the fungus. Many are also of commercial or medical importance to humans; for example, the antibiotic penicillin is a secondary metabolite produced by species of *Penicillium*.

a. Fungal hyphae

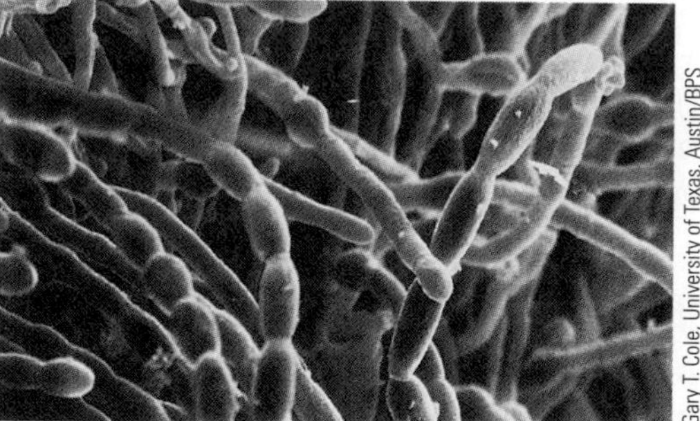

Gary T. Cole, University of Texas, Austin/BPS

b. Multicellular fungus

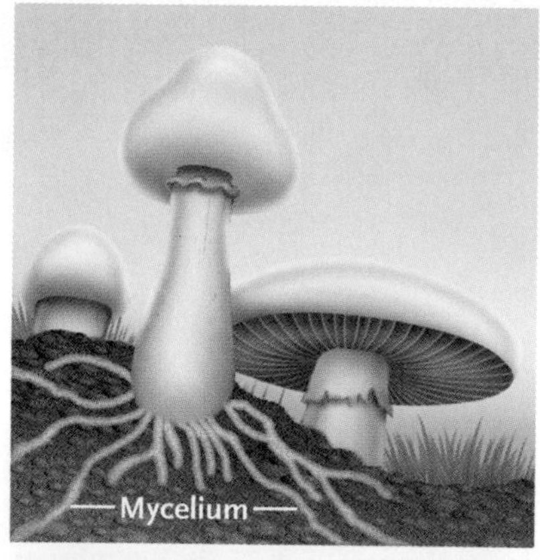

c. Mycelium on leaf litter

Dr. George Knaphus

Figure 24.3
(a) Micrograph of fungal hyphae. **(b)** Sketch of the mycelium of a mushroom-forming fungus, which consists of branching septate hyphae. **(c)** Mycelium on leaf litter.

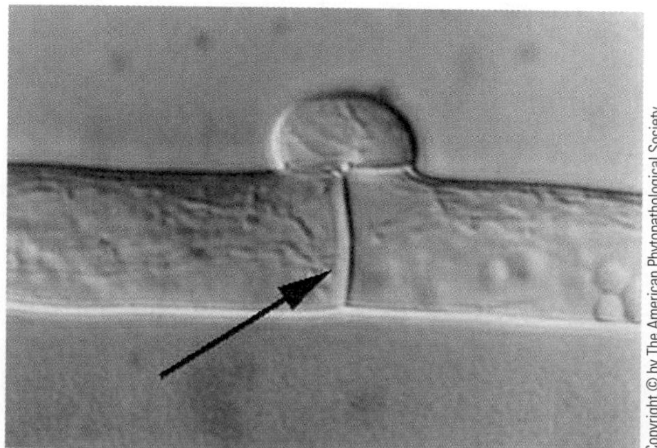

Figure 24.4
Septum in fungal hypha (the arrow is pointing to the septum between two hyphal compartments).

Fungi reproduce by spores, and this spore production can be amazingly prolific, with some species of fungi producing billions of spores per day (**Figure 24.5**). These spores are microscopic, featherlight, and able to survive in the environment for extended periods after they are released. Reproducing via such spores allows fungi to be opportunists, germinating only when favourable conditions exist and quickly exploiting food sources that occur unpredictably in the environment. Releasing vast numbers of spores, as some fungi do, improves the odds that the spores will germinate and produce a new individual.

Spores can be produced asexually or sexually; some fungi produce both asexual and sexual spores at different stages of their lives. Sexual reproduction in fungi is quite complex. In all organisms, sexual reproduction involves three stages: the fusion of two haploid cells (**plasmogamy**), bringing together their two nuclei in one common cytoplasm; this cytoplasmic fusion is usually quickly followed by nuclear fusion (**karyogamy**) in most organisms; nuclear fusion is followed by meiosis to produce genetically distinct haploid cells. As we will see, fungi are unique in that these events can be separated in time for durations ranging from seconds to many years.

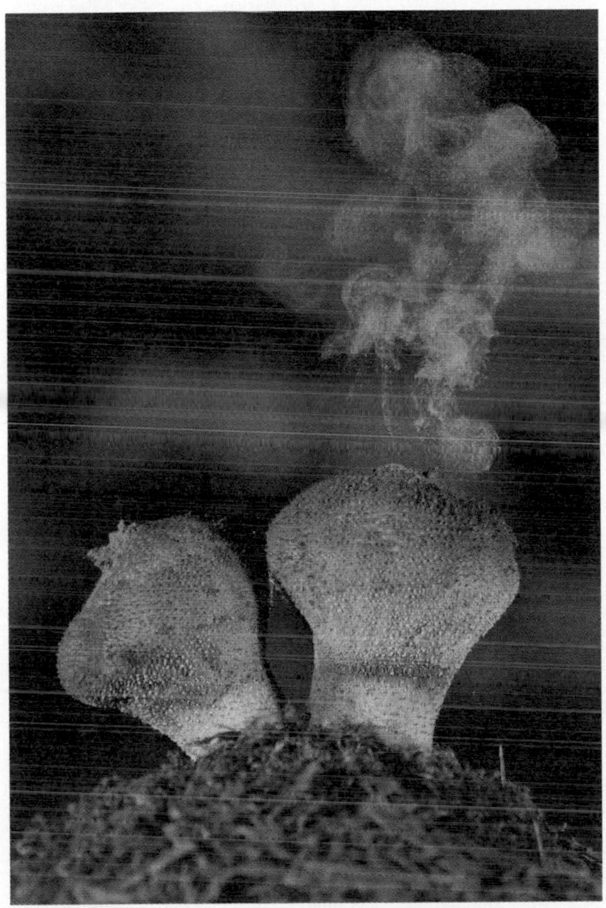
© Andrew Darrington / Alamy

Figure 24.5
Spores galore! Spore production by fungal fruiting bodies. Some fruiting bodies can release billions of spores per day.

Study Break

1. What physical features distinguish fungi from other organisms?
2. How do fungi reduce competition for resources?
3. By what means do fungi reproduce? Why is this mode of reproduction advantageous?

24.2 Evolution and Diversity of Fungi

24.2a Fungi Were Present on Earth by at Least 500 Million Years Ago

For many years, fungi were classified as plants because the earliest classification schemes had only two kingdoms, plants and animals. Fungi, like plants, have cell walls and did not move as animals did, so they were grouped with plants. As biologists learned more about the distinctive characteristics of fungi, however, it became clear that fungi should be treated as a separate kingdom. The discovery of chitin in fungal cells and recent comparisons of DNA and RNA sequences all indicate that fungi and animals are more closely related to each other than they are to other eukaryotes. The close biochemical relationship between fungi and animals may explain why fungal infections are typically so resistant to treatment and why it has proven rather difficult to develop drugs that kill fungi without damaging their human or other animal hosts.

Analysis of the sequences of several genes suggests that the lineages leading to animals and fungi may have diverged around 965 million years ago. What were the first fungi like? We do not know for certain: phylogenetic studies indicate that fungi first arose from a single-celled, flagellated protist similar to choanoflagellates (see Ch. 23)—the sort of organism that does not fossilize well. Although traces of what may be fossil fungi exist in rock formations nearly 1 billion years old, the oldest fossils that we can confidently assign to the modern kingdom Fungi appear in rock strata laid down about 500 million years ago.

24.2b Once They Appeared, Fungi Radiated into Several Major Lineages

Most likely, the first fungi were aquatic. When other kinds of organisms began to colonize land, they may well have brought fungi along with them. For example, researchers have discovered what appear to be mycorrhizas—symbiotic associations of a fungus and a plant—in fossils of some of the earliest known land plants. The final section of this chapter examines mycorrhizas more fully.

Over time, fungi diverged into the strikingly diverse lineages that we consider in the rest of this section **(Table 24.1).** Today, there are over 60 000 described species of fungi, with at least 1.6 million more that have not yet been described.

As the lineages diversified, different adaptations associated with reproduction arose. For example, you'll notice that the structures in which sexual spores are formed and mechanisms by which spores are dispersed become larger and more elaborate over evolutionary time. Traditionally, therefore, biologists have classified fungi primarily by the distinctive structures produced in sexual reproduction. These features are still useful indicators of the phylogenetic standing of a fungus, but the powerful tools of molecular analysis are bringing many revisions to our understanding of the evolutionary journey of fungi.

The evolutionary origins and lineages of fungi have been obscure ever since biologists began puzzling over the characteristics of this group. With the advent of molecular techniques for research, these topics have become extremely active and exciting areas of biological research that may shed light on fundamental events in the evolution of all eukaryotes. Not surprisingly, when so much new information is coming to light, biologists hold a wide range of views on how various groups arose and may be related. Currently, we recognize five phyla of fungi, known formally as the Chytridiomycota, Zygomycota, Glomeromycota, Ascomycota, and Basidiomycota **(Figure 24.6).** However, we know now that two of these phyla, the chytridiomycota and the zygomycota, are not monophyletic (i.e., they are taxa that do not contain only an ancestor and all of its descendants; see Chapter 19), so the classification scheme presented in Figure 24.4 will soon change to reflect this new information. Why do classifications of organisms change so often? Bear in mind that classification schemes such as those presented here are hypotheses that explain our best understanding of evolutionary relationships among organisms at any one time; like any other hypotheses, classification schemes are open to revision as we find out more about the organisms. Even through fungal classification will change greatly over the next few years, we summarize the major phyla recognized today as a way of illustrating the diversity of this group of organisms.

Table 24.1 Summary of Fungal Phyla

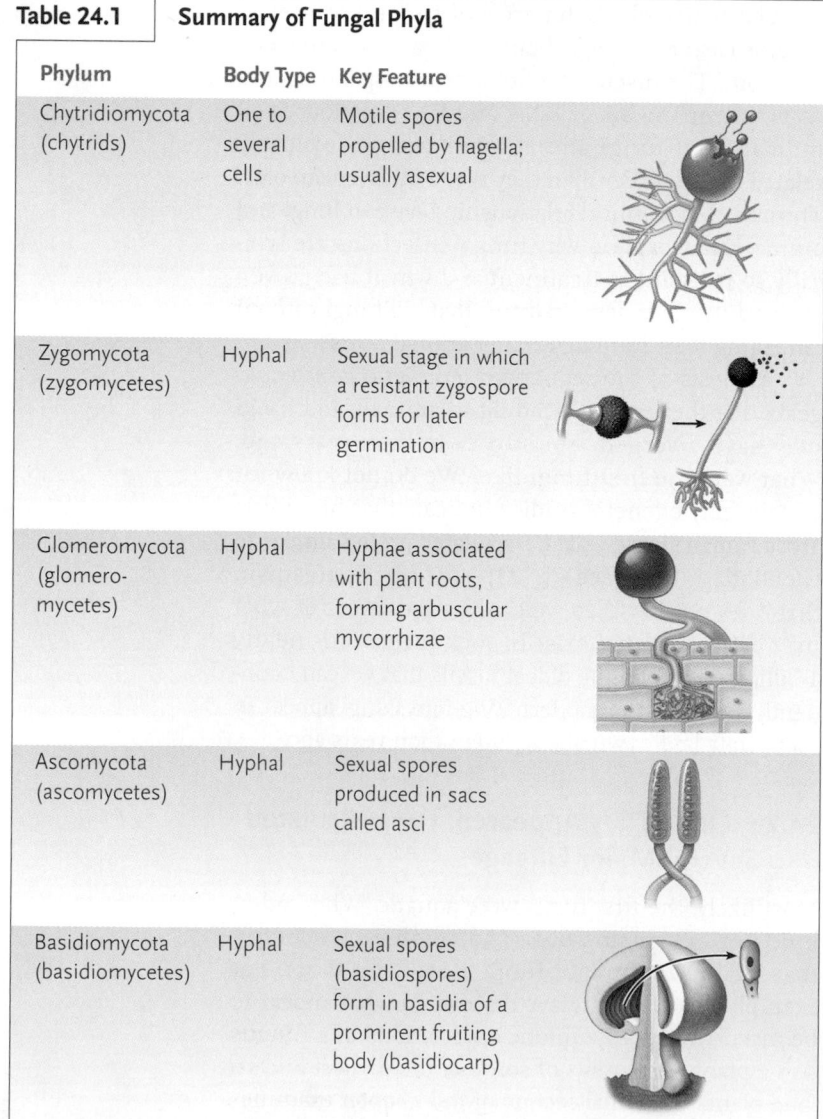

Phylum	Body Type	Key Feature
Chytridiomycota (chytrids)	One to several cells	Motile spores propelled by flagella; usually asexual
Zygomycota (zygomycetes)	Hyphal	Sexual stage in which a resistant zygospore forms for later germination
Glomeromycota (glomero-mycetes)	Hyphal	Hyphae associated with plant roots, forming arbuscular mycorrhizae
Ascomycota (ascomycetes)	Hyphal	Sexual spores produced in sacs called asci
Basidiomycota (basidiomycetes)	Hyphal	Sexual spores (basidiospores) form in basidia of a prominent fruiting body (basidiocarp)

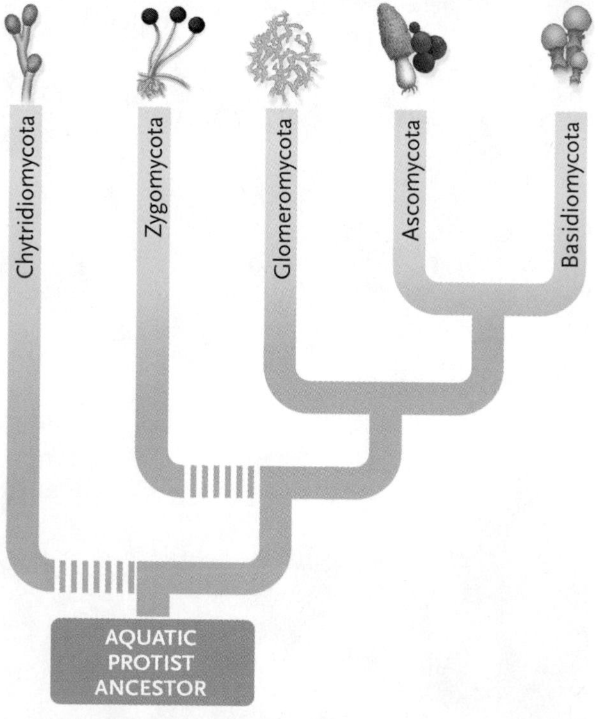

Figure 24.6
A phylogeny of fungi. This scheme represents a widely accepted view of the general relationships between major groups of fungi, but it may well be revised as new molecular findings provide more information. The dashed lines indicate that two groups, the chytrids and the zygomycetes, are probably paraphyletic—they include subgroups that are not all descended from a single ancestor.

a. *Chytriomyces hyalinus*

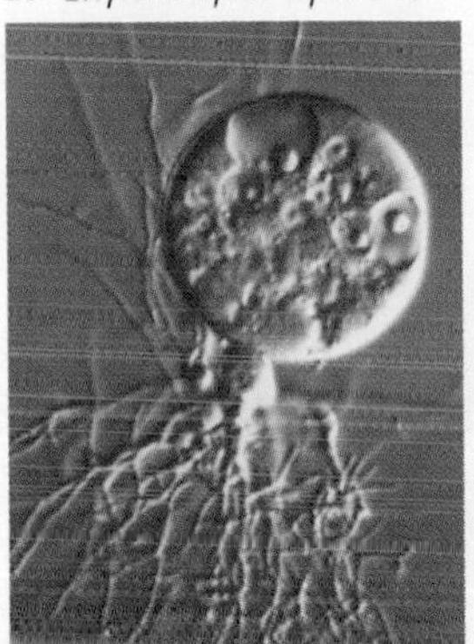

John Taylor/Visuals Unlimited

b. Chytridiomycosis in a frog

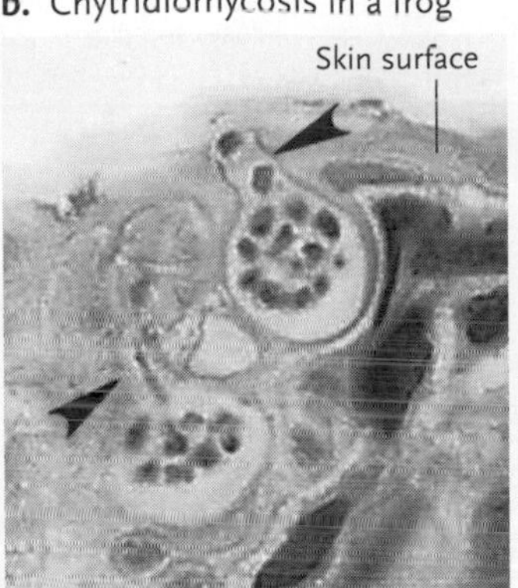

Center for Disease Control

c. Harlequin frog

Courtesy Ken Nemuras

Figure 24.7
Chytrids. **(a)** *Chytriomyces hyalinus*, one of the few chytrids that reproduce sexually. **(b)** Chytridiomycosis, a fungal infection, shown here in the skin of a frog. The two arrows point to flask-shaped cells of the parasitic chytrid *Batrachochytrium dendrobatis*, which has devastated populations of harlequin frogs **(c)**.

Phylum Chytridiomycota The Chytridiomycota are likely the most ancient group of fungi as they retain several traits characteristic of an aquatic lifestyle. For example, chytrids (as they are commonly called) are the only fungi that produce flagellated, motile spores **(Figure 24.7a)**; these spores use chemotaxis (movement in response to a chemical gradient) to locate suitable substrates. Chytrids live in soil or freshwater habitats, wherever there is at least a film of water through which their motile spores can swim.

Most chytrids are saprotrophs, organisms that obtain nutrients by breaking down dead organic matter, although some are symbionts in the gut of cattle and other herbivores, where they break down cellulose to provide carbon for their hosts, and still others are parasites of animals, plants, algae, or other fungi. These tiny fungi also cause a disease, chytridiomycosis, that is one cause of the decline in amphibian species worldwide. Globally, at least 43% of all amphibian species are declining in population, and nearly 33% are threatened with extinction. Although many factors contribute to amphibian decline, including habitat loss, fragmentation, and increasing levels of environmental pollutants, chytridiomycosis has been linked to the decline of amphibian populations in Australia, New Zealand, central and South America, and parts of Europe. This disease has wiped out an estimated two-thirds of the species of harlequin frogs (*Atelopus*) in the American tropics **(Figure 24.7b)**. The epidemic has correlated with the rising average temperature in the frogs' habitats, an increase credited to global warming. Studies show that the warmer environment provides optimal growing temperatures for the chytrid pathogen. How does infection by a chytrid kill these animals? We don't yet fully understand why chytridiomycosis is so lethal. The fungus colonizes the skin of these animals **(Figure 24.7c)** and may release toxins that are absorbed through the animal's skin, or, given that amphibians take up water and breathe through their skin, the fungus may directly affect water uptake and respiration.

Although most chytrids are unicellular, some live as chains of cells and have rhizoids that anchor the fungus to its substrate and that may also absorb nutrients from the substrate. The vegetative stage of most chytrids is haploid; asexual reproduction involves the formation of a **sporangium**, in which motile spores are formed. A few chytrids reproduce sexually, via male and female gametes that fuse, to form a diploid zygote. This cell may form a mycelium that gives rise to sporangia, or it may directly give rise to either asexual or sexual spores.

Zygomycota This group of fungi includes the moulds on fruit and bread familiar to many of us and takes its name from the structure formed in sexual reproduction, the zygospore **(Figure 24.8, p. 530)**. Many zygomycetes are saprotrophs that live in soil, feeding on organic matter. Their metabolic activities release mineral nutrients in forms that plant roots can take up. Some zygomycetes are parasites of insects (and even other zygomycetes), and some wreak havoc on human food supplies, spoiling stored grains, bread, fruits, and vegetables **(Figure 24.9, p. 530)**. Others, however, have become major players in commercial enterprises, where they are used in manufacturing products that range from industrial pigments to pharmaceuticals, such as production of steroids (e.g., anti-inflammatory drugs). Zygomycetes are also used in the production of fermented foods such as tempeh.

Most zygomycetes consist of a haploid mycelium that lacks regular septa, although some groups have septa, and in others, septa form to wall off reproductive structures and aging regions of the mycelium. Sexual reproduction occurs when mycelia of different mating types (known as + and − types, rather than male and female) produce specialized hyphae that grow toward each other and form sex organs (**gametangia**) at their tips (see Figure 24.8, steps 1 and 2). How do the gametangia find each other? Pheromones secreted by each mycelium stimulate the development of sexual structures in the complementary strain and cause gametangia to grow toward each other. The gametangia fuse, forming a thick-walled spore, a **zygospore** (see Figure 24.8, step 3), which can remain dormant for months or years, allowing the

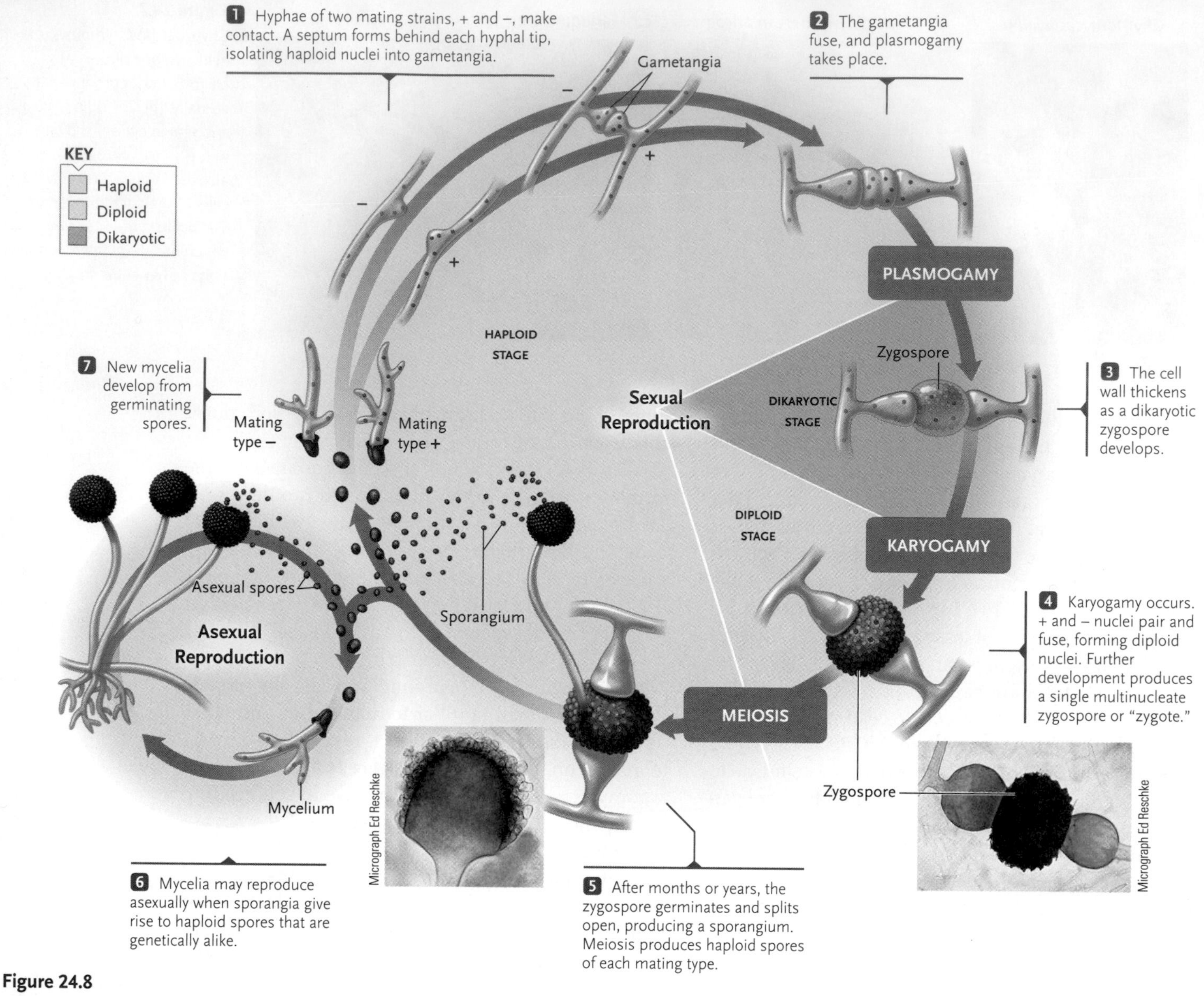

1 Hyphae of two mating strains, + and –, make contact. A septum forms behind each hyphal tip, isolating haploid nuclei into gametangia.

Gametangia

2 The gametangia fuse, and plasmogamy takes place.

KEY
Haploid
Diploid
Dikaryotic

PLASMOGAMY

HAPLOID STAGE

Zygospore

Sexual Reproduction

DIKARYOTIC STAGE

3 The cell wall thickens as a dikaryotic zygospore develops.

7 New mycelia develop from germinating spores.

Mating type –

Mating type +

DIPLOID STAGE

KARYOGAMY

Asexual spores

Sporangium

Asexual Reproduction

4 Karyogamy occurs. + and – nuclei pair and fuse, forming diploid nuclei. Further development produces a single multinucleate zygospore or "zygote."

MEIOSIS

Mycelium

Micrograph Ed Reschke

Zygospore

Micrograph Ed Reschke

6 Mycelia may reproduce asexually when sporangia give rise to haploid spores that are genetically alike.

5 After months or years, the zygospore germinates and splits open, producing a sporangium. Meiosis produces haploid spores of each mating type.

Figure 24.8
Life cycle of the bread mould *Rhizopus stolonifer,* a zygomycete. Asexual reproduction is common, but different mating types (+ and –) also reproduce sexually. In both cases, haploid spores are formed and give rise to new mycelia.

zygomycete to survive unfavourable environmental conditions. Eventually, meiosis occurs in the zygospore, forming a sporangium that will produce haploid spores (see Figure 24.8, step 5). Note that meiosis does not always produce gametes! We often tend to characterize meiosis as the formation of gametes, probably because we are so familiar with how sexual reproduction occurs in humans and other animals. But in many organisms, such as fungi and plants, meiosis results in the formation of haploid spores.

Like other fungi, however, zygomycetes also reproduce asexually, as shown in steps 6 and 7 of Figure 24.8. When a haploid spore lands on a favourable substrate, it germinates and gives rise to a branching mycelium. Some of the hyphae grow upward, and saclike sporangia form at the tips of these aerial hyphae. Inside the sporangia, the asexual cycle comes full circle as new haploid spores arise through mitosis and are released.

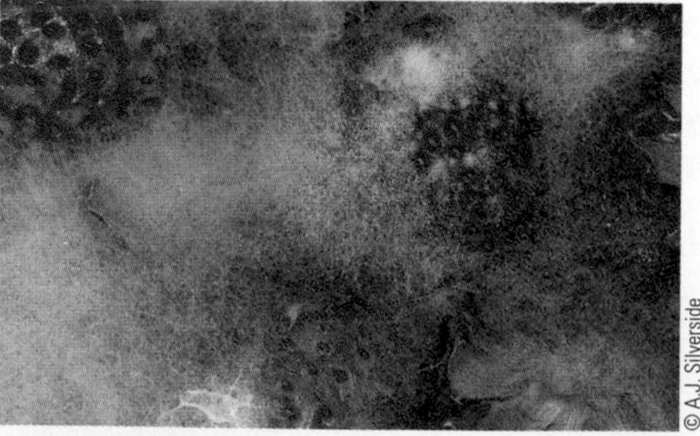

© A.J. Silverside

Figure 24.9
Zygomycete fungus growing on strawberries.

The black bread mould *Rhizopus stolonifer* may produce so many charcoal-coloured sporangia in asexual reproduction **(Figure 24.10a)** that mouldy bread looks black. The spores released are lightweight, dry, and readily wafted away by air currents. In fact, winds have dispersed *R. stolonifer* spores just about everywhere on Earth, including the Arctic. Another zygomycete, *Pilobolus* **(Figure 24.10b),** forcefully spews its sporangia away from the dung in which it grows. A grazing animal may eat a sporangium on a blade of grass; the spores then pass through the animal's gut unharmed and begin the life cycle again in a new dung pile.

a. Sporangia of *Rhizopus stolonifer*

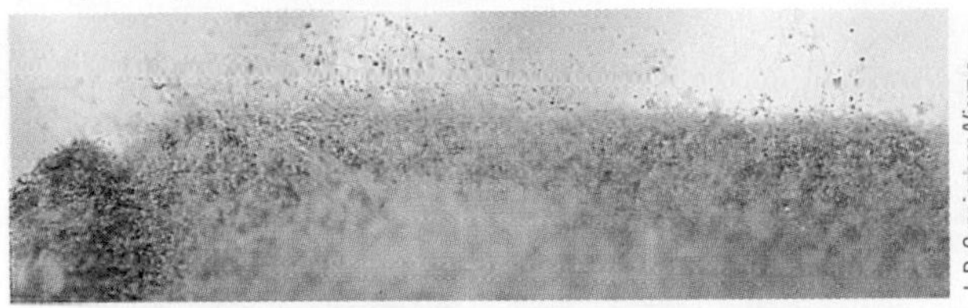

b. Sporangia (dark sacs) of *Pilobolus*

Figure 24.10
Two of the numerous strategies for spore dispersal by zygomycetes. **(a)** The sporangia of *Rhizopus stolonifer*, shown here on a slice of bread, release powdery spores that are easily dispersed by air currents. **(b)** In *Pilobolus*, the spores are contained in a sporangium (the dark sac) at the end of a stalked structure. When incoming rays of sunlight strike a light-sensitive portion of the stalk, turgor pressure (pressure against a cell wall due to the movement of water into the cell) inside a vacuole in the swollen portion becomes so great that the entire sporangium may be ejected outward as far as 2 m—a remarkable feat given that the stalk is only 5 to 10 mm tall.

Glomeromycota Until recently, fungi in the phylum Glomeromycota were classified as zygomycetes based on morphological similarities such as the lack of regular septa. However, these fungi are quite dissimilar from zygomycetes in many ways—for example, sexual reproduction is unknown in this group of fungi, with spores usually forming asexually simply by walling off a section of a hypha **(Figure 24.11)**—causing many researchers to question the inclusion of these fungi in the phylum Zygomycota. Recent evidence from molecular studies resulted in these fungi being placed in their own phylum.

The 160 known members of this phylum are all specialized to form **mycorrhizas**, or symbiotic associations with plant roots. This group of fungi has a tremendous ecological importance as they collectively make up roughly half of the fungi in soil and form mycorrhizas with many land plants, including most major crop species, such as wheat and maize. Mycelia of these fungi colonize the roots of host plants and also proliferate in the soil around the plants. Inside the roots, hyphae penetrate through cell walls and branch repeatedly to form arbuscules ("little trees") (see Figure 24.11). The branches of each arbuscule are enfolded by the cell's plasma membrane, forming an interface with a large surface area through which nutrients are exchanged between the plant and the fungus. Some glomeromycetes also form vesicles inside roots, which store nutrients and can also act as spores. The fungus obtains sugars from the plant and in return provides the plant with a steady supply of dissolved minerals that it has obtained from the surrounding soil. We take a closer look at mycorrhizas in Section 24.3.

Ascomycota The phylum Ascomycota takes its name from the saclike structures (**asci**; singular, ascus) in which spores are formed in sexual reproduction. These asci are often enclosed in a fruiting body

a. Arbuscules (black) in leek root colonized by arbuscular mycorrhizal fungus

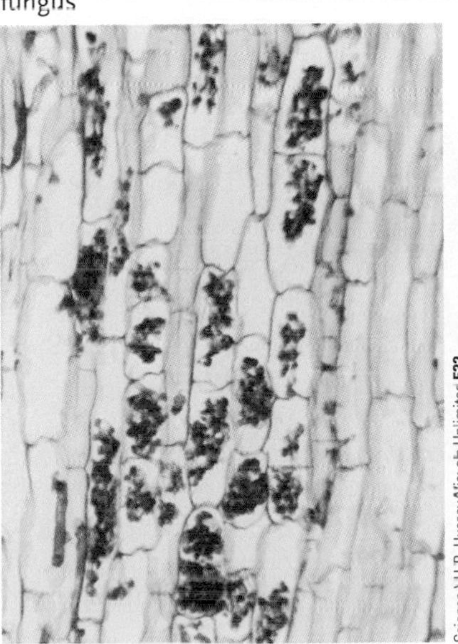

b. Arbuscule

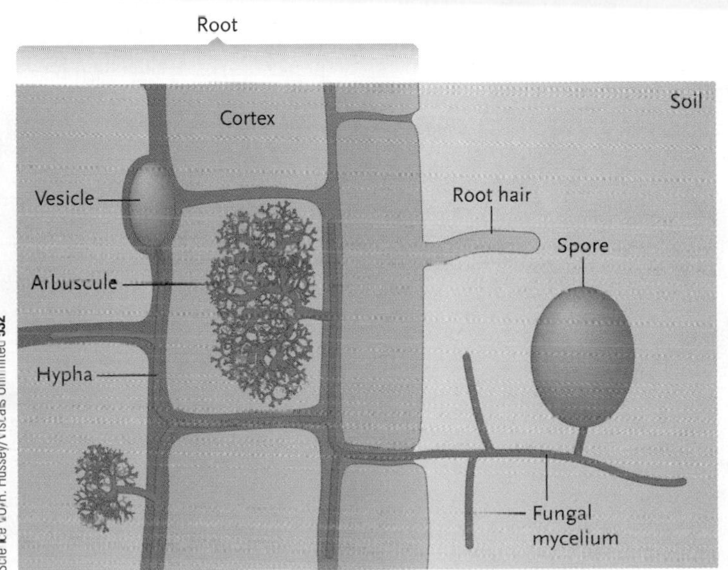

Figure 24.11
Glomeromycete fungus forming a mycorrhiza. **(a)** In this instance, the roots of leeks are growing in association with the glomeromycete fungus *Glomus versiforme* (longitudinal section). Notice the arbuscules that have formed as fungal hyphae branch after entering the root **(b)**.

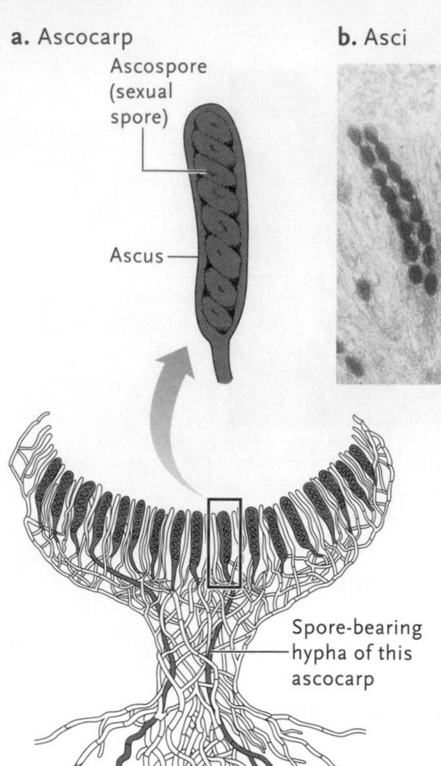

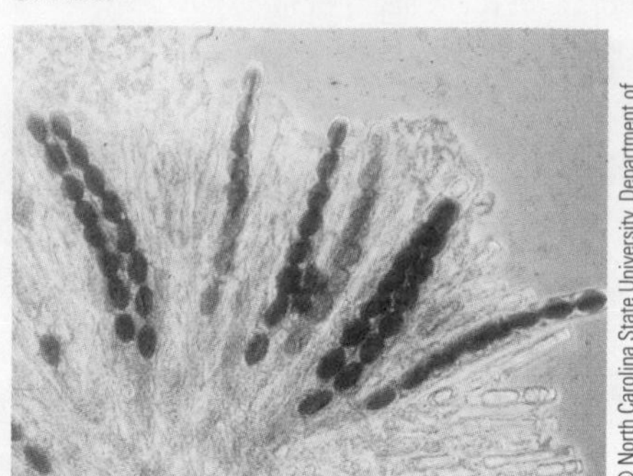

b. Asci
© North Carolina State University, Department of Plant Pathology

Figure 24.12
A few of the ascomycetes, or sac fungi. The examples shown are species that form multicellular fruiting bodies as reproductive structures. **(a)** A cup-shaped ascocarp, composed of tightly interwoven hyphae. The spore-producing asci occur inside the cup. **(b)** Asci on the inner surface of an ascocarp. **(c)** Scarlet cup fungus (*Sarcoscypha*).**(d)** A true morel (*Morchella esculenta*), a prized edible fungus.

(**ascocarp**) **(Figure 24.12a, b, c)**. Ascomycetes are much more numerous than chytrids, zygomycetes, or glomeromycetes, with more than 30 000 identified species.

Some ascomycetes are very useful to humans. One species, the orange bread mould *Neurospora crassa*, has been important in genetic research, including the elucidation of the one gene–one enzyme hypothesis (see Chapter 13). *Saccharomyces cerevisiae*, which produces the ethanol in alcoholic beverages and the carbon dioxide that leavens bread, is also a model organism used in genetic research. By one estimate, it has been the subject of more genetic experiments than any other eukaryotic microorganism. This multifaceted phylum also includes gourmet delicacies such as truffles (*Tuber melanosporum*) and the succulent morel *Morchella esculenta* **(Figure 24.12d)**.

Many ascomycetes are saprotrophs, playing a key role in the breakdown of cellulose and other polymers. Ascomycetes are also common in symbiotic associations, forming mycorrhizas and lichens (see Section 24.3). A few ascomycetes prey on various agricultural insect pests—some are even carnivores that trap their prey in nooses **(Figure 24.13a)**—and thus have potential for use as "biological pesticides."

However, other ascomycetes are devastating plant pathogens, including the blue-stain fungi that are associated with mountain pine beetles and contribute to the death of beetle-infested trees **(Figure 24.13b;** see also Chapter 3). Several ascomycetes can be serious pathogens of humans. The yeast *Candida albicans* **(Figure 24.14)** infects mucous membranes, especially of the vagina and mouth, causing a condition called thrush. Another yeast, *Pneumocystis carinii*, causes virulent pneumonia in AIDS patients and other immunocompromised people.

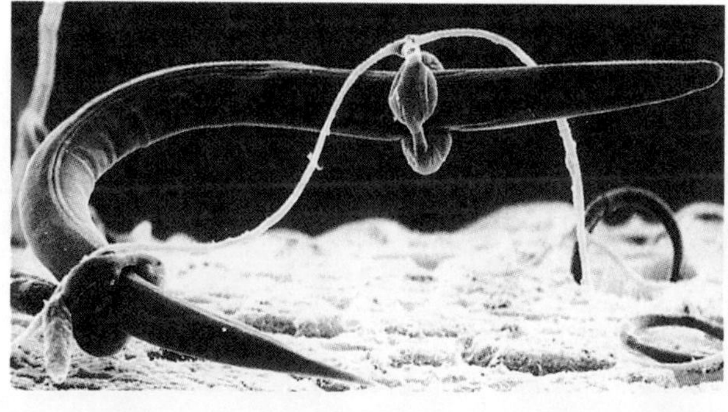

b. Stump of pine tree infected with blue-stain fungus
Reproduced with the permission of the Minister of Public Works and Government Services Canada, 2009.

Figure 24.13
(a) Nematode-trapping fungus. Hyphae of this ascomycete (*Arthobotrys*) form nooselike rings. When a prey organism enters the loop, rapid changes in ion concentration draw water into the loop by osmosis. The increased turgour pressure causes the noose to tighten, trapping its prey. Enzymes produced by the fungus then break down the nematode's tissues. **(b)** Stump of a pine tree infected with blue-stain fungus; the fungus grows into the tree's water-conducting tissue, blocking the flow of water.

Yeast cells

Gary T. Cole, University of Texas, Austin/BPS

Figure 24.14
Candida albicans, the cause of yeast infections of the mouth and vagina.

Claviceps purpurea, a parasite on rye and other grains, causes ergotism, a disease marked by vomiting, hallucinations, convulsions, and, in severe cases, gangrene and even death. It has even been suggested that this fungus was the cause of the Salem witch hunts of seventeenth century New England, as discussed in *Molecule Behind Biology*. Other ascomycetes cause nuisance infections, such as athlete's foot and ringworm.

Most ascomycetes grow as haploid mycelia with regular septa; large pores in the septa allow organelles, including nuclei, to move with cytoplasm through the mycelium. Some ascomycetes are **yeasts** or filamentous fungi with a yeast stage; a yeast is a unicellular growth form that reproduces asexually by **budding** or binary fission (see Figure 24.14). Sexual reproduction generally involves fusion of hyphae from mycelia of + and − mating types **(Figure 24.15)**. The cytoplasm of the two hyphae fuses, but fusion of the nuclei is delayed, resulting in the formation of **dikaryotic hyphae** that contain two separate nuclei and thus are

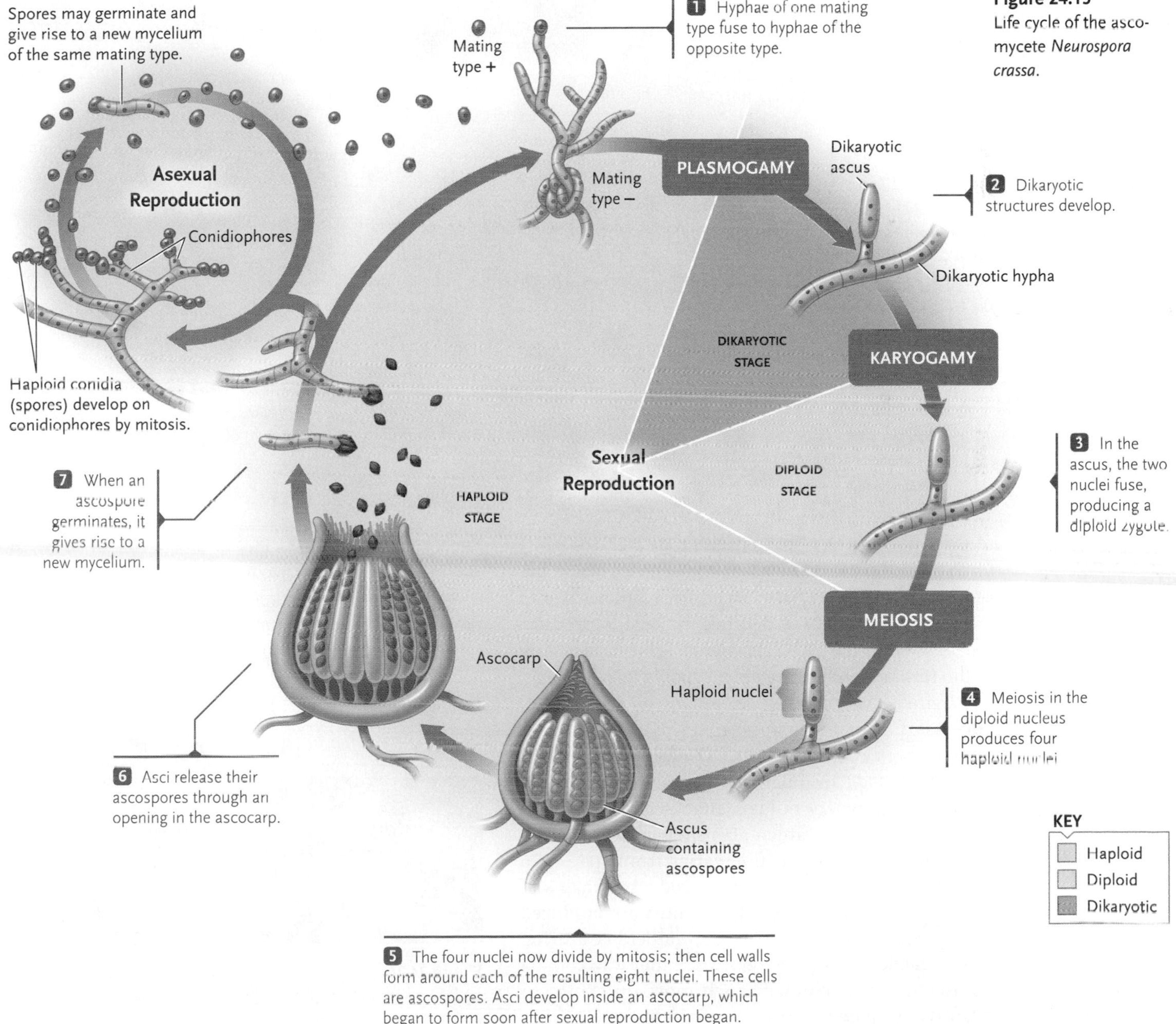
Spores may germinate and give rise to a new mycelium of the same mating type.
Mating type +
1 Hyphae of one mating type fuse to hyphae of the opposite type.
Asexual Reproduction
Conidiophores
Mating type −
PLASMOGAMY
Dikaryotic ascus
2 Dikaryotic structures develop.
Dikaryotic hypha
Haploid conidia (spores) develop on conidiophores by mitosis.
DIKARYOTIC STAGE
KARYOGAMY
Sexual Reproduction
DIPLOID STAGE
HAPLOID STAGE
3 In the ascus, the two nuclei fuse, producing a diploid zygote.
7 When an ascospore germinates, it gives rise to a new mycelium.
MEIOSIS
Ascocarp
Haploid nuclei
4 Meiosis in the diploid nucleus produces four haploid nuclei
6 Asci release their ascospores through an opening in the ascocarp.
Ascus containing ascospores
KEY
Haploid
Diploid
Dikaryotic
5 The four nuclei now divide by mitosis; then cell walls form around each of the resulting eight nuclei. These cells are ascospores. Asci develop inside an ascocarp, which began to form soon after sexual reproduction began.

Figure 24.15
Life cycle of the ascomycete *Neurospora crassa*.

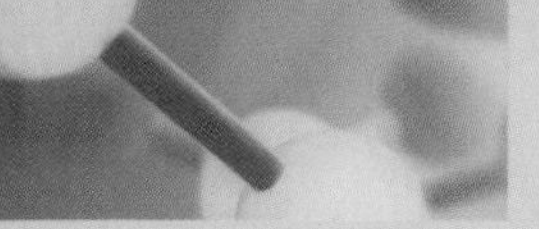

Molecule Behind Biology

Lysergic Acid

Was a fungus responsible for the Salem witch trials? In Salem, Massachusetts, in the 1700s, several women were tried and found guilty of witchcraft. Their accusers were young women who had been experiencing bizarre symptoms: hallucinations, convulsions, a sensation of "prickling" of the skin, and even paralysis. Further evidence of witchcraft was the fact that cattle and other animals also suffered these symptoms. What was the real cause of these symptoms? Were they an example of mass hysteria? Or is there a biological explanation?

The symptoms reported by the "bewitched" girls match those of someone who has eaten flour made from wheat infected by the ascomycete fungus *Claviceps purpurea*. Ascospores of this fungus germinate when they land on the flower of a grass plant, such as wheat. The fungus grows quickly and, by the end of the growing season, forms a tough mass of hyphae known as a sclerotium in the seed head of the grass **(Figure 1)**. If the seed head isn't harvested, the sclerotia will fall to the ground, where they remain over winter. In the spring, the sclerotia will germinate, producing numerous asci borne on stalks. However, if the fungus has infected a commercial grain crop, such as wheat, sclerotia are easily harvested along with the plants' seed heads and often end up being ground into flour along with the grain. In medieval times, if the weather favoured development of the fungus, up to 30% of some grain harvests were evidently not grain but sclerotia!

Figure 1
Sclerotium of *Claviceps purpurea* in a grass seed head.

Sclerotia produce many alkaloids, including lysergic acid **(Figure 2)**, which causes a range of symptoms, including hallucinations, convulsions, a sensation of ants crawling over the body, limb distortions, and dementia. These symptoms match those of the supposedly "bewitched" people of Salem in 1692. Further support for ergotism being the cause of the bewitching is the fact that most of the victims were adolescents, who are most suspectible to the effects of ergot alkaloids. Furthermore, the fact that cattle and other domestic animals would also have eaten infected grain and also presented the same symptoms as the "victims" suggests that ergot, not mass hysteria, was involved. Lysergic acid was purified in 1943 by a chemist (Albert Hoffman) to produce the psychoactive drug LSD. Researchers hoped that this drug would be useful psychotherapy, but its negative effects outweighed the benefits, and this line of research was dropped. However, other ergot alkaloids offer promise as treatment for migraine headaches.

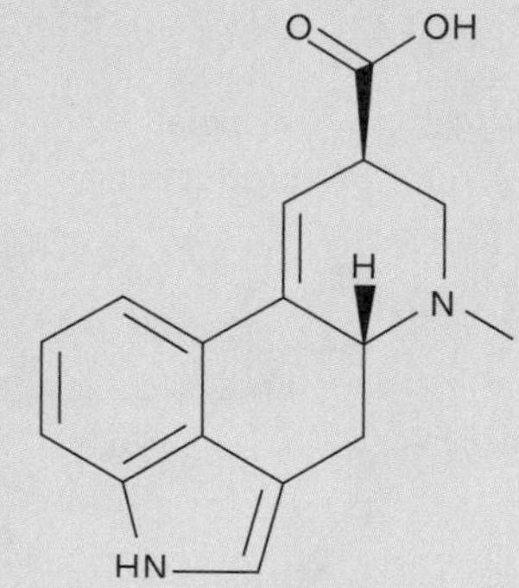

Figure 2
Structure of lysergic acid.

referred to as "$n + n$" rather than n or $2n$. Sacs (asci) form at the tips of these dikaryotic hyphae; inside the asci, the two nuclei fuse, forming a diploid zygote nucleus, which then undergoes meiosis to produce four haploid nuclei. Mitosis usually follows, resulting in the formation of eight haploid spores (**ascospores**).

Unlike zygomycetes, ascomycetes do not produce asexual spores in sporangia. Instead, modified hyphae produce numerous asexual spores called **conidia** ("dust"; singular, *conidium*), such as those seen when powdery mildew attacks grasses, roses, and other common garden plants **(Figure 24.16a)**. The mode of conidial production varies from species to species, with some ascomycetes producing chains of conidia, whereas in others, the conidia are produced on a hypha in a series of "bubbles," rather like a string of detachable beads **(Figure 24.16b)**. Either way, conidia are formed and released much more quickly than zygomycete spores.

Basidiomycota The 24 000 or so species of fungi in the phylum Basidiomycota include the mushroom-forming species, bracket fungi, stinkhorns, smuts, rusts, and puffballs **(Figure 24.17)**. The common name for this group is club fungi, due to the club-shaped

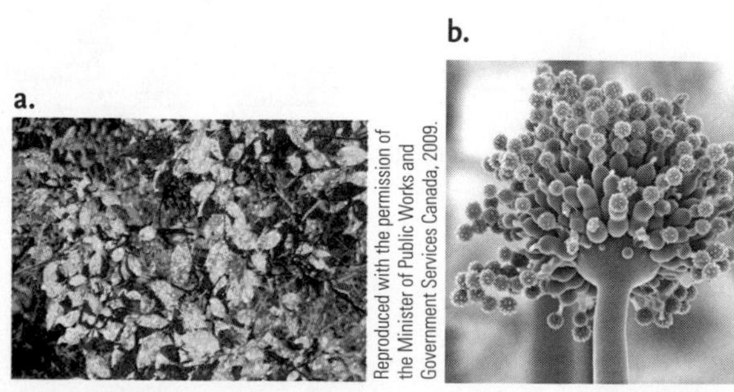

Figure 24.16
(a) Powdery mildew on leaves. **(b)** Conidia produced in asexual reproduction by ascomycete fungi.

a. Coral fungus

Robert C. Simpson/Nature Stock

b. Shelf fungus

Robert C. Simpson/Nature Stock

c. White-egg bird's nest fungus

Jeffrey Lepore/Photo Researchers, Inc.

d. Fly agaric mushroom

Jane Burton/Bruce Coleman Ltd.

e. Scarlet hood

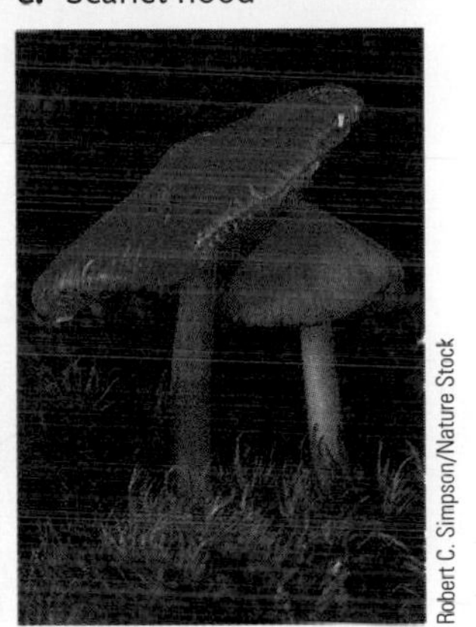

Robert C. Simpson/Nature Stock

Figure 24.17
Examples of basidiomycetes, or club fungi. **(a)** The light red coral fungus *Ramaria*. **(b)** The shelf fungus *Polyporus*. **(c)** The white-egg bird's nest fungus *Crucibulum laeve*. Each tiny "egg" contains spores. Raindrops splashing into the "nest" can cause "eggs" to be ejected, thereby spreading spores into the surrounding environment. **(d)** The fly agaric mushroom *Amanita muscaria*, which causes hallucinations. **(e)** The scarlet hood *Hygrophorus*.

cells (**basidia**; singular, basidium) in which sexual spores are produced.

Many basidiomycetes produce enzymes for digesting cellulose and lignin and are important decomposers of woody plant debris. Very few organisms can degrade lignin due to its very complex, irregular structure (**Figure 24.18, p. 536**). The ability to degrade lignin also enables some basidiomycetes to break down complex organic compounds such as DDT, PCBs, and other persistent environmental pollutants that are structurally similar to lignin. Bioremediation of contaminated sites by these fungi is a very active research area.

A surprising number of basidiomycetes, including the prized edible oyster mushrooms (*Pleurotus ostreatus*), also can trap and consume small animals such as rotifers and nematodes by secreting paralyzing toxins or gluey substances that immobilize the prey, in a manner similar to that shown earlier for ascomycetes (see Figure 24.13). As is the case for insectivorous plants, such as the Venus flytrap (*Dionaea muscipula*), discussed in Chapter 47, this adaptation gives the fungus access to a rich source of molecular nitrogen, an essential nutrient that often is scarce in terrestrial habitats. For example, the wood that is the substrate for many basidiomycetes is high in carbon but low in nitrogen; many wood-decay fungi have been found to be carnivorous, obtaining supplemental nitrogen from various invertebrates.

Some basidiomycetes form mycorrhizas with the roots of forest trees, as discussed later in this chapter. Recent research has shown that these mycorrhizas can be drawn into associations with achlorophyllous plants (plants that lack chlorophyll and so cannot carry out photosynthesis), which thus obtain nutrients from the trees via shared mycorrhizal fungi. Other basidiomycetes, the rusts and smuts, are parasites that cause serious diseases in wheat, rice, and other plants. Still others produce millions of dollars worth of the common edible button mushroom (*Agaricus bisporus*) sold in grocery stores. *Amanita muscaria* (see Figure 24.17d) has been used in the religious rituals of ancient societies in Central America, Russia, and India. Other species of this genus, including the death cap mushroom *Amanita phalloides*, produce deadly toxins. The *A. phalloides* toxin, called α-amanitin, halts gene transcription, and hence protein synthesis, by inhibiting the activity of RNA polymerase. Within 8 to 24 hours of ingesting as little as 5 mg of the mushroom, vomiting and diarrhea begin. Later, kidney and liver cells start to degenerate; without intensive

Figure 24.18
Structure of lignin.

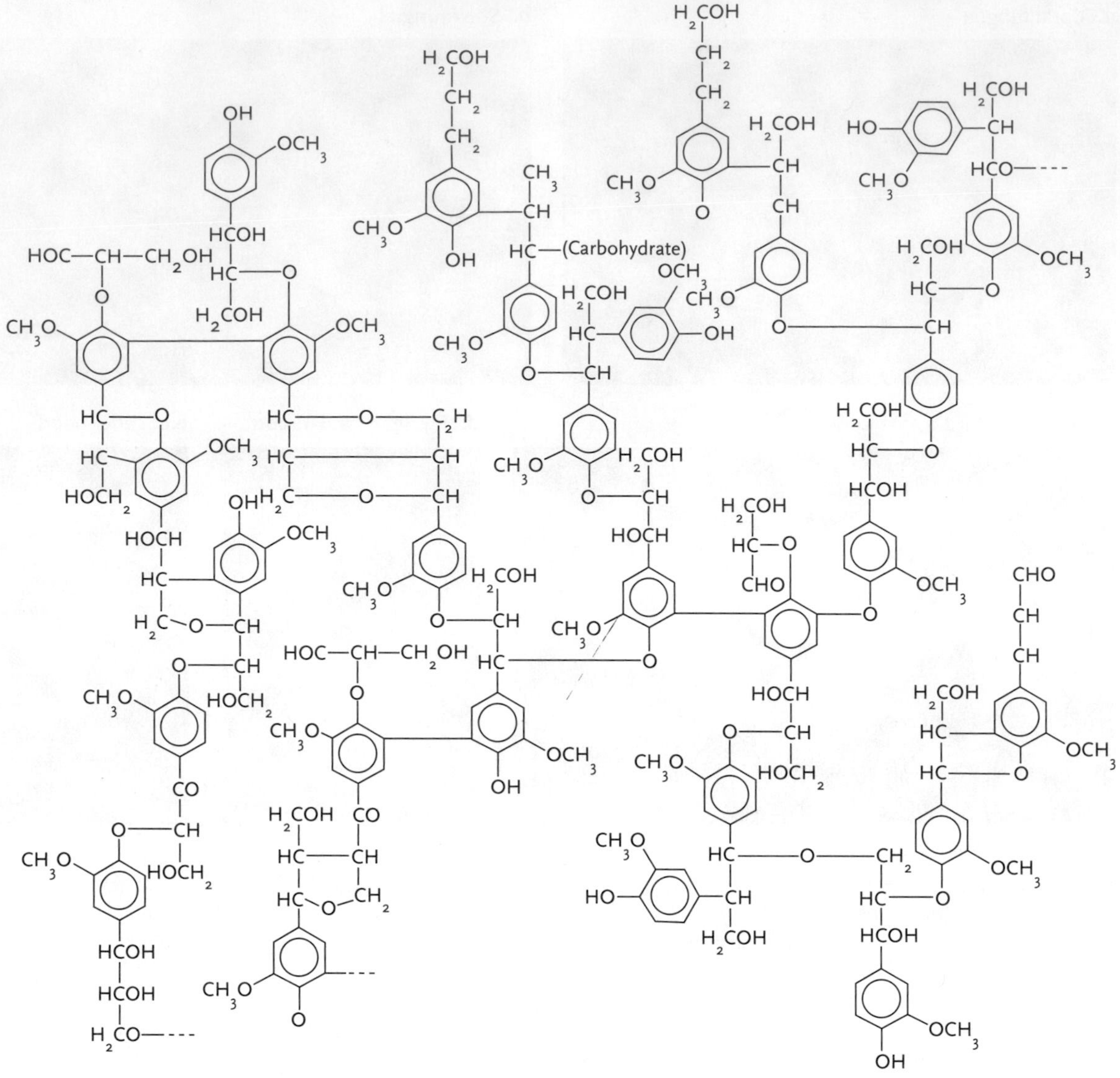

medical care, death can follow within a few days. You can read more about the effect of amanitin on gene expression in Chapter 14.

Most basidiomycetes are mycelial, although some grow as yeasts. The mycelium of many basidiomycetes contains two different, separate nuclei as a result of fusion between two different haploid mycelia and is termed a **dikaryon** ($n + n$) **(Figure 24.19).** A dikaryotic mycelium is formed following fusion of the two haploid mycelia when both types of nuclei divide and migrate through the mycelium such that each hyphal compartment contains two dissimilar nuclei.

Basidiomycete fungi can grow for most of their lives as dikaryon mycelia—a major departure from an ascomycete's short-lived dikaryotic stage. After an extensive mycelium develops, favourable environmental conditions trigger the formation of fruiting bodies (**basidiocarps**), in which basidia develop. A basidiocarp consists of tight clusters of hyphae; the feeding mycelium is buried in the substrate. The shelflike bracket fungi visible on trees are basidiocarps, as are the structures we call mushrooms and toadstools. Each mushroom is a short-lived reproductive body consisting of a stalk and a cap; basidia develop on "gills," the sheets of tissue on the underside of the cap. Inside each basidium, the two nuclei fuse; meiosis follows, resulting in the formation of four haploid basidiospores on the outside of the basidium (see Figure 24.19). Why does the fungus expend energy and resources on such elaborate spore dispersal structures? A layer of still air occurs just above the ground (and any other surface); by elevating the basidia above this layer, the fungus increases the likelihood that its spores will be carried away by the wind.

The prolonged dikaryon stage in basidiomycetes allows them many more opportunities for producing sexual spores than in ascomycetes, in which the dikaryon state is short-lived. Basidia can produce huge numbers of spores—some species can produce 100 million spores *per hour* during reproductive periods, day after day! Basidiomycete mycelia can live for many years and spread over large areas. The largest organism on Earth could be the mycelium of a single individual of the basidiomycete *Armillaria ostoyae*, which spreads over 8.9 km^2 of land in eastern Oregon. This organism

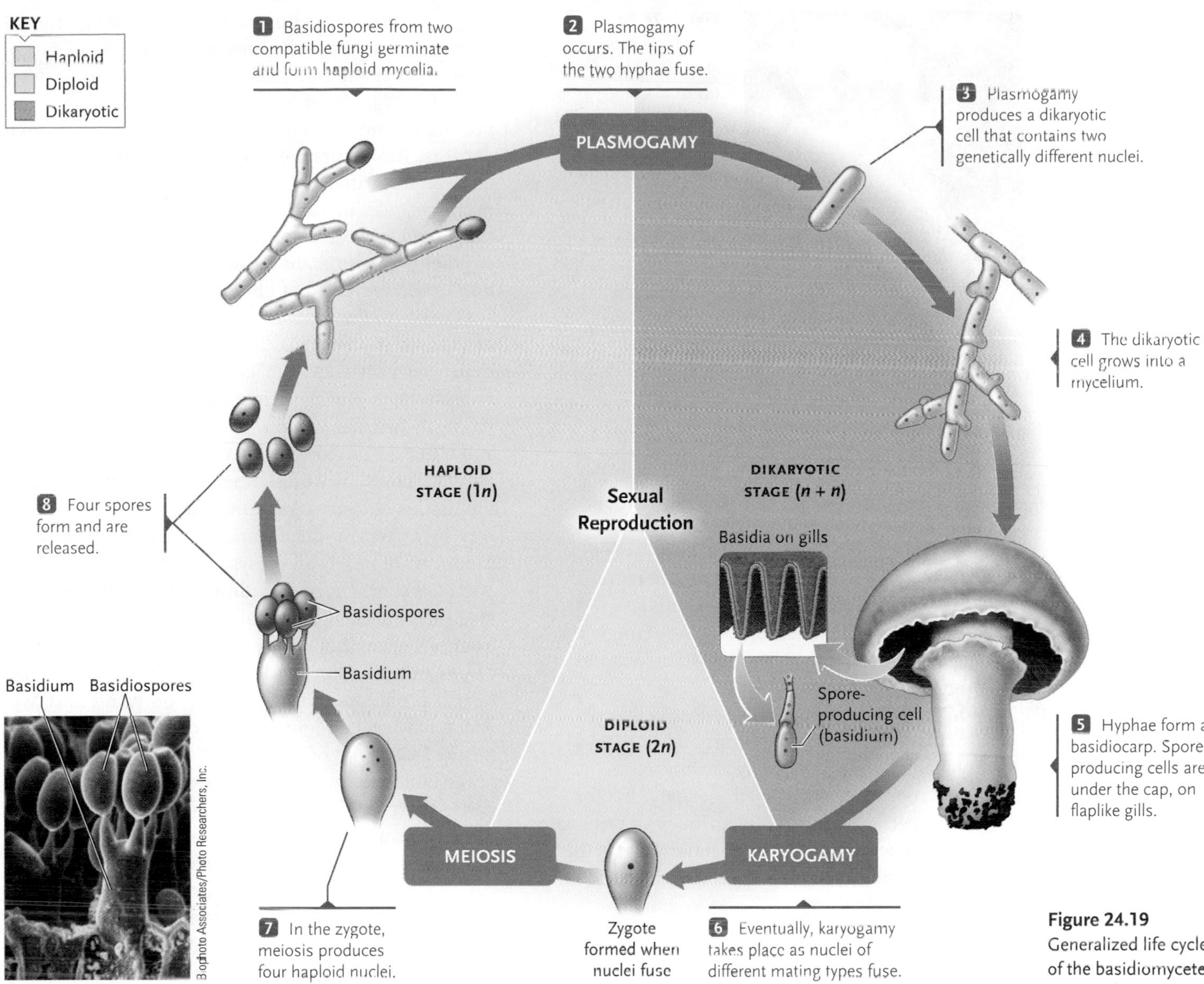
KEY
Haploid
Diploid
Dikaryotic
1 Basidiospores from two compatible fungi germinate and form haploid mycelia.
2 Plasmogamy occurs. The tips of the two hyphae fuse.
PLASMOGAMY
3 Plasmogamy produces a dikaryotic cell that contains two genetically different nuclei.
4 The dikaryotic cell grows into a mycelium.
HAPLOID STAGE (1n)
Sexual Reproduction
DIKARYOTIC STAGE (n + n)
Basidia on gills
8 Four spores form and are released.
Basidiospores
Basidium
Basidium Basidiospores
Spore-producing cell (basidium)
DIPLOID STAGE (2n)
5 Hyphae form a basidiocarp. Spore-producing cells are under the cap, on flaplike gills.
MEIOSIS
KARYOGAMY
7 In the zygote, meiosis produces four haploid nuclei.
Zygote formed when nuclei fuse
6 Eventually, karyogamy takes place as nuclei of different mating types fuse.
Biophoto Associates/Photo Researchers, Inc.

Figure 24.19 Generalized life cycle of the basidiomycete *Agaricus bisporus*, a species known commonly as the button mushroom. During the dikaryotic stage, cells contain two genetically different nuclei, shown here in different colours. Inset: Micrograph showing basidia and basidiospores.

weighs at least 150 tonnes and is likely at least 2400 years old, making it not only the largest but also one of the heaviest and oldest organisms on earth.

As for ascomycetes, asexual reproduction in basidiomycetes involves formation of conidia or budding, in yeast forms such as *Cryptococcus neoformans*, which causes a form of meningitis in humans.

Deuteromycota In the past, when biologists isolated fungi and tried to grow them in the lab, they found that many species did not produce a sexual stage. Since fungal classification traditionally relied on features produced in sexual reproduction, these fungi could not be placed in any of the phyla described above. Instead, researchers grouped them together in an artificial group called the Deuteromycota (also known as Fungi Imperfecti, or the "imperfect fungi"—imperfect meaning that a sexual stage is absent). This group is not a true phylum but serves as a "holding pen" for fungal species that cannot yet be identified. With the development of molecular sequencing techniques, we have been able to identify many fungi classified as deuteromycetes and place them in the proper phylum. Others, however, defy classification—some of these fungi may not have any sexual stage or perhaps do not form sexual structures when cultured in the lab. When researchers discover a sexual phase for a conidial fungus, or when molecular studies establish a clear relationship to a sexual species, the conidial fungus is reassigned to the appropriate phylum. Thus far, some have been classified as basidiomycetes, but most conidial fungi have turned out to be ascomycetes.

Well-known examples of deuteromycetes are *Penicillium* and *Aspergillus*. Certain species of *Penicillium* **(Figure 24.20, p. 538)** are the source of the penicillin family of antibiotics, whereas others produce the aroma and distinctive flavours of Camembert and Roquefort cheeses. Strains of *Aspergillus* grow in damp

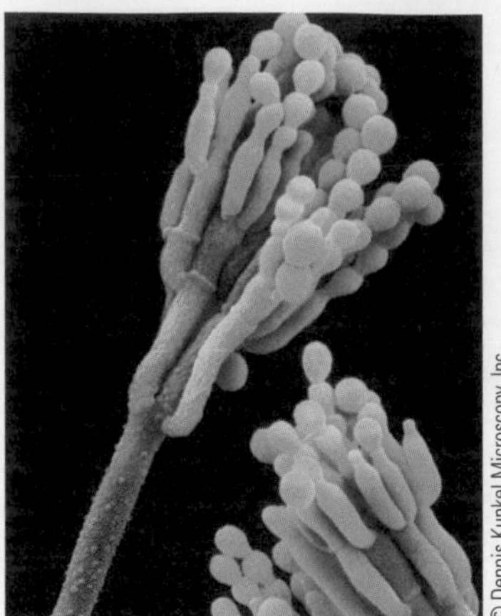

Figure 24.20
Conidia of *Penicillium*. Note the rows of conidia (asexual spores) atop the elongate cells that produce them.

© Dennis Kunkel Microscopy, Inc.

grain or peanuts. Their metabolic wastes, known as aflatoxins, can cause cancer in humans who eat the poisoned food over an extended period.

Study Break

1. What evidence is there that fungi are more closely related to animals than plants?
2. Name the five phyla of the kingdom Fungi and describe the reproductive adaptations that distinguish each one.
3. What are the two main differences between asexual spores produced by zygomycetes and asexual spores produced by ascomycetes?
4. Fungi reproduce sexually or asexually, but for many species, the life cycle includes an unusual stage not seen in other organisms. What is this genetic condition, and what is its role in the life cycle?

24.3 Fungal Lifestyles

As mentioned earlier, fungi can be categorized as saprotrophs or symbionts, depending on whether they obtain nutrients from living organisms or from dead organic matter. It is important to remember that the categories of "saptrotoph" and "symbiont" are "boxes" that we have created to classify fungi, but fungi are very versatile organisms, and many fungi are capable of acting as both symbionts and saprotrophs at different times or under different conditions. Most people are more familiar with the role of fungi as saprotrophs (decomposers) rather than as symbionts, so in this section, we take a brief look at saprotrophy and then spend more time looking at fungal symbioses.

24.3a Fungi as Saprotrophs

With their adaptations for efficient extracellular digestion, fungi are masters of the decay so vital to terrestrial ecosystems (see Figure 24.2). For instance, in a single autumn, one elm tree can shed 200 kg of withered leaves! Without the metabolic activities of saprotrophic fungi and other decomposers such as bacteria and other organisms (e.g., earthworms), natural communities would rapidly become buried in their own detritus. Even worse, without decomposers to break down this detritus, the soil would become depleted of nutrients, making further plant growth impossible. As fungi (and other decomposers) digest the dead tissues of other organisms, they also make a major contribution to the recycling of chemical elements those tissues contain. For instance, over time, the degradation of organic compounds by saprotrophic fungi helps return key nutrients such as nitrogen and phosphorus to ecosystems. But the prime example of this recycling virtuosity involves carbon. The respiring cells of fungi and other decomposers give off carbon dioxide, liberating carbon that would otherwise remain locked in the tissues of dead organisms. Each year, this activity recycles a vast amount of carbon to plants, the primary producers of nearly all ecosystems on Earth.

However, there is a downside to the impressive enzymatic abilities of saprotrophic fungi: for example, when they decompose materials that are part of our houses, they can cause major economic and health problems. Fungi growing on wood and drywall following flooding or water damage to a building **(Figure 24.21a)** not only weaken the structural integrity of the building but also can be health hazards. The airborne spores of these fungi act as allergens, and some can also cause more serious health problems—for example, some fungi can colonize and grow in sinus cavities. Another example is dry rot, which causes millions of dollars in damage to buildings in Europe, Asia, and Australia **(Figure 24.21b)**. Dry rot is notorious not only because it causes widespread and costly damage but also because the fungus responsible, *Serpula lacrymans,* seems to have the mysterious ability to break down dry wood completely, which should not be possible—as described above, wood decay usually happens once wood becomes wet. Does this fungus really have the amazing ability to break down dry wood? In fact, this fungus is as dependent on water for growth as any other, but it can form specialized mycelial cords, which very efficiently transport water and nutrients over long distances through concrete, bricks, and other unfavourable substrates until the fungus at last finds wood. Then the mycelial cords release water into the substrate, allowing the fungus to spread through the wood and begin the process of decay.

24.3b Fungi as Symbionts

Many fungi are partners in mutually beneficial interactions with animals or photosynthetic organisms; some of these associations shaped the evolution of life on earth and still play major roles in the functioning of ecosystems today. Chapter 46 discusses the general

a.

U.S. Environmental Protection Agency

b.

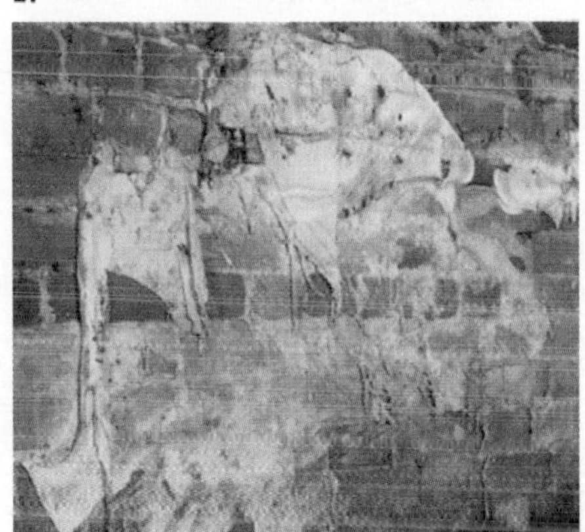

Figure 24.21
(a) Mould growth following flooding.
(b) Dry rot (*Serpula lacrymans*).

features of symbiotic associations more fully; here we are interested in some examples of the symbioses fungi form with other organisms.

Lichens Are Associations Between a Fungus and One or More Photosynthetic Organisms A **lichen** is a compound organism formed by an association between a fungus, an ascomycete or sometimes a basidiomycete, and a green alga and/or a cyanobacterium. Lichens may grow as crusts on rocks, bark, or soil; as flattened leaflike forms; or as radially symmetrical cups, treelike structures, or hairlike strands **(Figure 24.22).** Lichens have vital ecological roles and important human uses. Lichens secrete acids that eat away at rock, breaking it down and converting it to soil that can support plants. Many animals, such as caribou (*Rangifer tarandus*), rely on lichens for their winter forage. Some environmental chemists monitor air pollution by monitoring lichens, most of which cannot grow in heavily polluted air. Humans use lichens as sources of dyes and perfumes, as well as medicines. Lichen chemicals are currently being explored as a source of natural pesticides.

The fungus (called the **mycobiont**) makes up most of the body **(thallus)** of the lichen, with the photosynthetic partner **(photobiont)** usually confined to a thin layer inside the lichen thallus (see **Figure 24.22a**). Some lichens have a green algal photobiont inside the thallus and a cyanobacterial photobiont contained in "pockets" on or in the thallus. Because lichens are composite organisms, it may seem odd to talk of

a. Thallus cross section

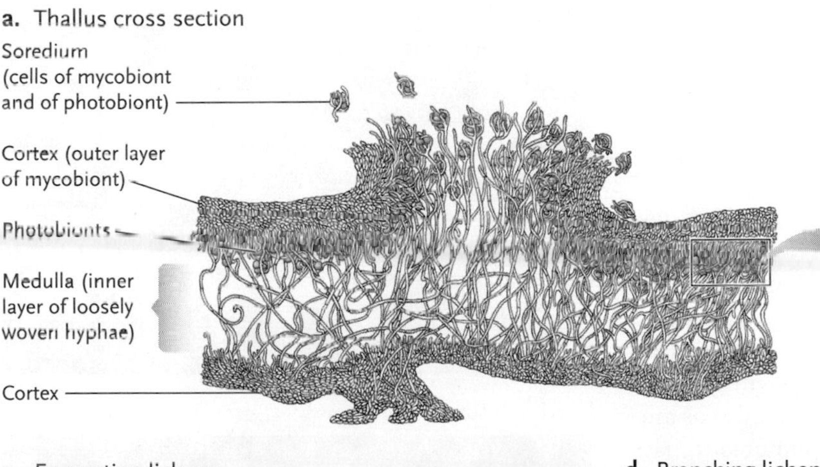

b. Soredia

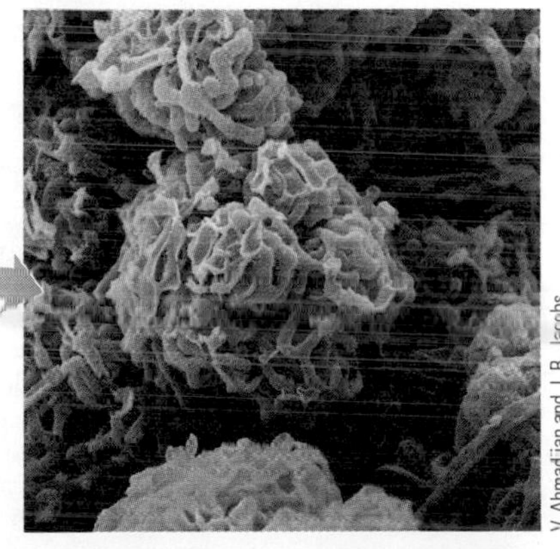

c. Encrusting lichens

Jane Burton/Bruce Coleman Ltd.

d. Branching lichen

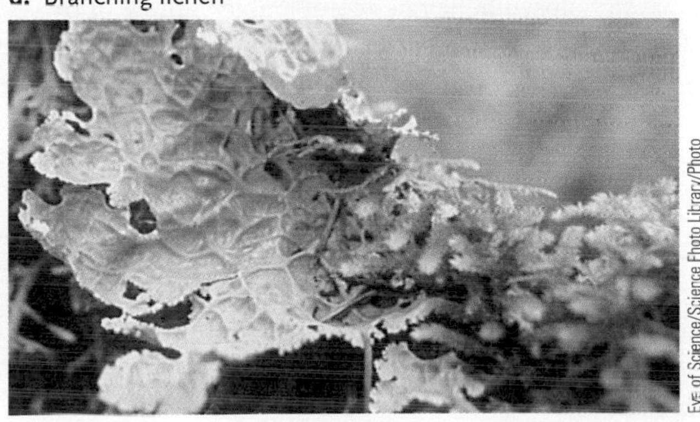

Figure 24.22
Lichens. **(a)** Sketch of a cross section through the thallus of the lichen *Lobaria verrucosa*. The soredia **(b)**, which contain both hyphae and algal cells, are a type of dispersal fragment by which lichens reproduce asexually. **(c)** Encrusting lichens. **(d)** *Peltigera*, a flattened, leaf-like lichen.

lichen "species," but biologists do give lichens binomial names, based on the mycobiont. More than 13 500 different lichen species are recognized, each a unique combination of a particular species of fungus and one or more species of photobiont. As you might expect for a compound organism made up of two (or even three) organisms, reproduction can be complicated: it is not enough for each organism to reproduce itself because formation of a new lichen requires that both partners be dispersed and end up together. Many lichens reproduce asexually, by specialized fragments such as the **soredia** (singular, soredium), shown in Figure 24.22. Each soredium consists of photobiont cells wrapped in hypae; the soredia can be dispersed by water, wind, or passing animals.

Inside the thallus, specialized hyphae wrap around and sometimes penetrate photobiont cells, which become the fungus' sole source of carbon. Often the mycobiont absorbs up to 80% of the carbohydrates produced by the photobiont. Benefits for the photobiont are less clear-cut, in part because the drain on nutrients hampers its growth and because the mycobiont often controls reproduction of the photobiont. In one view, many and possibly most lichens are parasitic symbioses, with the fungus enslaving the photobiont. On the other hand, although it is relatively rare to find a lichen photobiont species living independently in the same conditions under which the lichen survives, it may eke out an enduring existence as part of a lichen; some lichens have been dated as being more than 4000 years old! Studies have also revealed that at least some green algae clearly benefit from the relationship. Such algae are sensitive to desiccation and intense ultraviolet radiation. Sheltered by the lichen's fungal tissues, a green alga can thrive in locales where alone it would perish. Clearly, we still have much to learn about the physiological interactions between lichen partners.

Lichens often live in harsh, dry microenvironments, including on bare rock and wind-whipped tree trunks. Some lichens actually live *inside* rocks (see *Life on the Edge*). Unlike plants, lichens do not control water loss from their tissues; instead, their water status reflects that of their environment, and some lichens may dry out and rewet several times a day. Lichens are very slow growing, even though the photobiont may have photosynthetic rates comparable to those of free-living species. What happens to all of the carbohydrates made in photosynthesis if they are not used to fuel growth? The mycobiont takes much of the carbohydrate made by the photobiont and uses it to synthesize secondary metabolites and other compounds that allow the lichen to survive repeated wet–dry cycles and extreme temperatures common in their habitats. These compounds give lichens their vibrant colours and may also inhibit grazing on lichens by slugs and other invertebrates. The mycobiont uses other lichen chemicals to control the photobiont; some chemicals regulate photobiont reproduction, whereas others cause photobiont cells to "leak" carbohydrates to the mycobiont.

Mycorrhizas Are Symbiotic Associations Between Fungi and Plant Roots You might have learned in previous courses that plant roots are responsible for taking up soil nutrients. For most plants, however, this is not true: the roots of most plants are colonized by mycorrhizal fungi, which have mycelia that extend out into the soil far beyond the root zone of the plant and which take up most of the nutrients used by the plant **(Figure 24.23).** Mycorrhizas, or "fungus roots," are mutualistic symbioses between certain soil-dwelling fungi and plant roots. Mycorrhizal plants greatly enhance the uptake of various nutrients, especially phosphorus and nitrogen, from soil (as discussed in Chapter 41) because the fungal mycelium has a tremendous surface area for

a. Lodgepole pine

Prof. D. J. Read, University of Sheffield

b. Mycorrhiza

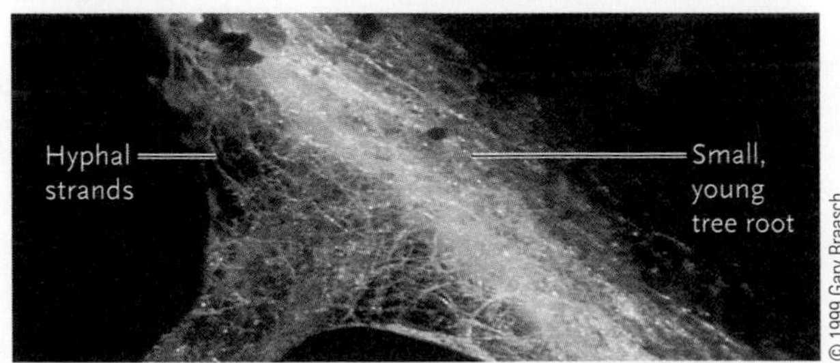

© 1999 Gary Braasch

Figure 24.23
Ectomycorrhizas. **(a)** Lodgepole pine, *Pinus contorta*, seedling, longitudinal section. Notice the extent of the mycorrhiza compared with the above-ground portion of the seedling, which is only about 4 cm tall. **(b)** Mycorrhiza of a hemlock tree.

Life on the Edge

Cryptoendolithic Lichens

We tend to think of Antarctica as completely covered in ice, but some valleys of this continent are completely lacking in ice **(Figure 1a).** These dry valleys may look barren, but they are home to many endoliths—organisms that live in a narrow band under the surface of porous rocks. Predominant among these endoliths are cryptoendolithic lichens ("crypto" = hidden; "endo" = inside; "lith" = rock) **(Figure 1b).** These lichens lack the stratified layers typical of most other lichens; instead, hyphae and clusters of photobiont cells grow around and between the rock crystals, and the lichen that forms is embedded inside the rock. Enough light penetrates through the translucent surface layer of rock to allow photosynthesis. Studying endolithic organisms not only helps us understand the diversity of life on Earth but may also be a model for life on other planets. If some organisms can live in such extreme conditions here on Earth, could similar kinds of organisms also exist elsewhere in the universe?

a.

© University of Canterbury–Christchurch, New Zealand

b.

Photo courtesy of NASA

Figure 1
(a) Antarctic dry valley. **(b)** Cryptoendolithic lichen.

absorbing mineral ions from a large volume of the surrounding soil.

As well, some mycorrhizal fungi can access sources of nutrients that are not available to plants: for example, certain basidiomycete fungi can penetrate directly into rocks and extract nutrients, which are then transported to their plant hosts. Other mycorrhizal associations involve the carnivorous basidiomycetes described above, which can obtain nitrogen by trapping and killing soil invertebrates and then transferring nitrogen from their prey to their host plants. By forming partnerships with these fungi, mycorrhizal plants gain access to nutrient sources that nonmycorrhizal plants do not. In exchange for soil nutrients, the plants provide the mycorrhizal fungi with sugars produced through photosynthesis. Mycorrhizas are generally mutualisms, representing a "win–win" situation for the partners. For plants that inhabit soils poor in mineral ions, such as in tropical rain forests, mycorrhizal associations are crucial for survival. Likewise, in temperate forests, species of spruce, oak, pine, and some other trees die unless mycorrhizal fungi are present **(Figure 24.24).** There are at least seven different types of mycorrhizas, but the most common types are ectomycorrhizas and arbuscular mycorrhizas.

Arbuscular mycorrhizas are the oldest and most abundant type of mycorrhiza, formed by glomeromycete fungi and a wide range of plants, including nonseed plants and most flowering plants. In this type of mycorrhiza, fungal hyphae penetrate the cells of the root, forming arbuscules as described above (see Figure 24.11). Fossils show that arbuscular mycorrhizas were common among ancient land plants, and some biologists have speculated that they might have been crucial for the colonization of land by plants by enhancing the transport of water and minerals to the plants.

Ectomycorrhizas evolved more recently and involve basidiomycetes and some ascomycetes. In these mycorrhizas, fungal hyphae form a sheath or mantle around a root (see Figure 24.20) and also grow between, but not inside, the root cells of their plant hosts. Ectomycorrhizal associations are very common with trees, such as the conifers of Canada's boreal forest and coastal rain forests. The extensive root system of a single mature pine may be studded with ectomycorrhizas involving dozens of fungal species. The musky-flavoured truffles (*Tuber melanosporum*) prized by gourmets are ascomycetes that form ectomycorrhizal associations with oak trees (*Quercus* spp.).

For plants, the benefits of being mycorrhizal extend beyond enhanced uptake of soil nutrients. In some cases, mycorrhizal fungi enhance a plant's

F.B. Reeves

Figure 24.24 **Effect of mycorrhizal fungi on plant growth.** The six-month-old juniper seedlings on the left were grown in sterilized low-phosphorus soil inoculated with a mycorrhizal fungus. The seedlings on the right were grown under the same conditions but without the fungus.

defences against pathogens, and nutrients can be transferred among mycorrhizal plants via shared mycorrhizal fungal hyphae. Mycorrhizal fungi may, in fact, play a major role in shaping plant communities and ecosystems.

Endophytes Are Fungi Living in the Above-Ground Tissues of Plants Just as the roots of many plants are colonized by fungi, so too are leaves and shoots **(Figure 24.25)**. Although some of these fungi are pathogens, many others are evidently peacefully coexisting with their plant hosts.

Biologists have known about the presence of these leaf endophytes for some time, but recent discoveries have revealed a startling diversity of these fungi, sometimes within a single plant. Samples of plants from temperate regions have been revealed to have tens of different species of endophytes in a single plant, but tropical plants are truly impressive, with several reports of hundreds of different types of endophytes being isolated from a single plant. Most of these endophytes have not yet been identified to species as researchers have not yet observed sexual stages, so it is difficult to know how many species of endophytes are really living in these tropical plants. A bigger question is what are these endophytes doing in these leaves? Are they mutualists, like mycorrhizal fungi? In many cases, we simply don't know enough about the interaction between the fungus and its host to answer these questions, but in some cases, the fungi do benefit their plant hosts by producing toxins that deter herbivores. Synthesis of toxins and other secondary metabolites has made these endophytes of great potential importance to humans. For example, the anticancer drug taxol (sold under the tradename Taxol) was originally isolated from the bark of the Pacific yew tree (*Taxus brevifolia*). Production of taxol from this source was limited since the tree is quite rare and makes only a small amount of taxol. However, researchers later discovered that a fungal endophyte living in the needles of the Pacific yew also makes taxol—as do other endophytes living in completely different tree species. Evidence indicates that taxol inhibits the growth of other fungi, so these endophytes may be producing it to protect themselves. Unlike the yew trees that were the original source of taxol, these endophytic fungi can be grown very easily in the lab, so we may be able to produce large amounts of this promising anticancer drug very easily. What other sources of medicines are out there, hiding inside plants? The possibility of finding new antibiotics and medicinal compounds makes saving rain forests even more urgent as not only the trees are disappearing but the endophytes inside them as well.

Even though fungi are not closely related to plants in an evolutionary sense, you can see that relationships between fungi and plants play important roles in the lives of both types of organisms. Many saprotrophic and parasitic fungi depend on plants or their products as a source of carbon. Plants rely on fungi for nutrients, either directly, through mycorrhizal relationships, or indirectly, through the role of fungi as decomposers. The very first land plants likely relied on mycorrhizal associations to survive in the new harsh environments they faced. In the next chapter, we look at how land plants evolved and diversified.

Study Break

1. Describe the difference between a saprotroph and a symbiont.
2. What is a lichen? Explain how each partner contributes to the whole organism.
3. What benefit does a plant derive from being mycorrhizal?
4. What are the two most common types of mycorrhizas? How do they differ?
5. What is an endophyte? Why is their relationship with their plant hosts of interest to medical researchers?

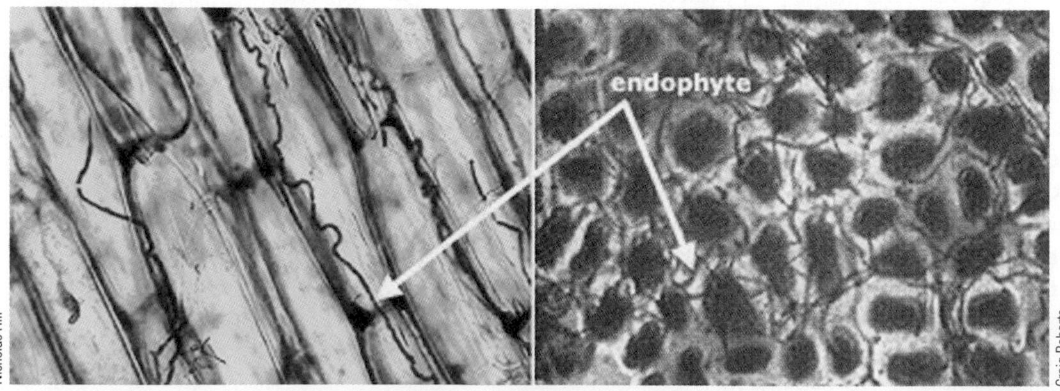

Figure 24.25
Leaf endophytes growing inside plant leaves.

Unanswered Questions

How is hyphal tip growth maintained?

In this chapter, we learned that fungi grow only at the tips of their hyphae. This pattern of growth requires that a fungus establishes and maintains polarized growth of hyphae, that is, that one end of a hypha is the tip, and growth occurs only at this end of a hypha. We know that both actin filaments and microtubules (components of the cytoskeleton, the matrix of protein fibres and tubes that maintains the shape and organization of eukaryotic cells; see Chapter 2) play a major role in the establishment and maintenance of polar growth in hyphae. In particular, microtubules (hollow tubes made of protein that can change length very quickly) are required for rapid tip growth of hyphae. Microtubules run the length of a hypha, and their ends extend into the hyphal tip; molecular motors (motor proteins; see Chapter 2) carry organelles and growth supplies along these microtubule "tracks" to the hyphal tip. In a surprise twist, it was recently found that the motors are involved in organizing the microtubules—this relationship is analogous to a train being involved in building its own railway. How do the motors organize the microtubules? We do not yet understand how these motor proteins regulate the stability and turnover of the microtubule system. Answering this question will not only give us a better understanding of fungal growth—which has practical implications, such as aiding in the development of fungicides for plant pathogenic fungi or enhancing growth of economically useful fungi—but will also clarify the role of cytoskeleton and motors in other eukaryotic cells.

How do fungi communicate with potential symbiotic partners?

For all of the symbiotic associations we have investigated in this chapter—mycorrhizas, endophytes, lichens—we still don't know how a fungus determines that it has the "right" partner. Establishment of these symbioses, especially mycorrhizas, requires coordinated development, which means the partners must be communicating with each other. Despite the ecological importance of these associations, we know very little about the signals through which the partners talk to each other. For mycorrhizas and other plant–microbe associations, we do know that secondary metabolites produced by the plant and exuded from the roots can act as branching factors, which stimulate branching of mycorrhizal hyphae near the roots, and may also induce expression of fungal genes necessary for establishment of the symbiosis. But the identity of which metabolite sends which signal and at what point in the establishment of a mycorrhiza is still unknown. In two recent studies, researchers in Japan and France identified a strigolactone as the active component of the branching factor. The strigolactone acts as a "metabolic switch," activating mitochondria and thus ramping up the respiration rate of fungus, providing the energy needed for increased branching. Other types of plant secondary metabolites known as flavonoids may also be involved in communication between a mycorrhizal fungus and its plant partner; flavonoids are known to be important signalling molecules in symbiosis between legumes and nitrogen-fixing bacteria (you will read more about this symbiosis in Chapter 41).

Do strigolactones play other roles in the development of mycorrhizas? For example, are they involved in the formation of arbuscules (see Figure 24.11), which involves prolific hyphal branching? Is the plant stimulated to produce strigolactones or other signalling molecules by the presence of the "right" mycorrhizal fungus? Many questions remain to be answered about how fungi communicate with plants and other symbiotic partners.

Review

Go to CENGAGENOW™ at http://hed.nelson.com/ to access quizzing, animations, exercises, articles, and personalized homework help.

24.1 What Is a Fungus? General Characteristics of Fungi

- Fungi can occur as single-celled yeasts or as multicellular filamentous organisms.
- A fungal mycelium consists of filamentous hyphae that grow throughout the substrate on which the fungus feeds (see Figure 24.3). A cell wall of chitin surrounds the plasma membrane, and in most species, septa partition the hyphae into cell-like compartments. Pores in septa permit cytoplasm and sometimes organelles to move between hyphal cells.
- Fungi gain nutrients by extracellular digestion and absorption at hyphal tips. Saprotrophic species feed on nonliving organic matter and are key decomposers contributing to the recycling of carbon and other nutrients in ecosystems. Many fungi are symbionts, obtaining nutrients from organic matter of living hosts; these symbioses range from parasitism, in which the fungus benefits at the expense of its host, to mutualism, in which both the fungus and its host benefit.
- All fungi reproduce via spores generated either asexually or sexually (see Figure 24.4). Some types also may reproduce asexually by budding or fragmentation of the parent body. Sexual reproduction usually has two stages. First, in plasmogamy, the cytoplasm of two haploid cells fuses, producing a cell that contains a haploid nucleus from each parent. In karyogamy, the nuclei fuse and form a diploid zygote; this stage is delayed in some phyla, resulting in a prolonged dikaryon ($n + n$) condition. Meiosis then generates haploid spores.

24.2 Evolution and Diversity of Fungi

- Fungi have traditionally been classified mainly on the basis of the structures formed in sexual reproduction. When a sexual phase cannot be detected, or is absent from the life cycle, the specimen is assigned to an informal grouping, the Deuteromycete fungi. Currently, five main phyla of fungi are recognized (see Figure 24.6):
- Chytridomycetes are the only fungi that produce motile, flagellated spores. Many are parasites, including the species responsible for chytridomycosis, a disease contributing to the worldwide decline in amphibian populations (see Figure 24.7).
- Zygomycetes have aseptate hyphae. Asexual reproduction involves production of spores by sporangia. Sexual reproduction occurs by way of hyphae that occur in + and − mating types; haploid nuclei in the hyphae function as gametes. Further development produces the zygospore, which may remain dormant for a time. When the zygospore breaks dormancy, it produces a stalked sporangium containing haploid spores of each mating type, which are released (see Figure 24.8).
- Glomeromycetes form arbuscular mycorrhizas, the most widespread type of mycorrhiza (see Figure 24.11). They reproduce asexually, by way of spores formed from hyphae.
- Ascomycetes reproduce both asexually, via chains of haploid asexual spores called conidia, and sexually, via production of haploid ascospores in saclike cells called asci. In the most complex species, asci are produced in reproductive bodies called ascocarps (see Figure 24.12).
- Most Basidiomycete species reproduce only sexually. Club-shaped basidia develop on a basidiocarp (the fruiting body or mushroom) and bear sexual spores on their surface. When dispersed, these basidiospores may germinate and give rise to a haploid mycelium (see Figure 24.19).

24.3 Fungal Lifestyles

- All fungi are heterotrophs but can obtain carbon by degrading dead organic matter (as saptrotrophs) or from living hosts (as symbionts). The two lifestyles are not mutually exclusive, with many fungi—such as the mycorrhizal fungi that also prey on invertebrates—combining these two modes of nutrition.
- Some basidiomycete fungi form a mutualistic symbiosis with leaf-cutter ants (see Figure 1 and Figure 2, *People Behind Biology*); the ants raise the fungi, which is the sole crop on which they feed. Recently, it was discovered that there is another partner in this ancient symbiosis, an actinomycete bacterium that lives on the ants' bodies and contributes to keeping parasitic fungi out of their fungal gardens.
- Many ascomycetes and a few basidiomycetes enter into symbioses with green algae and/or cyanobacteria to produce a compound organism known as a lichen. Fungal hyphae form the bulk of the lichen body (thallus); the hyphae entwine the algal cells that supply the lichen's carbohydrates, most of which are absorbed by the fungus (see Figure 24.22).
- Fungi in the Glomeromycota, Ascomycota, and Basidiomycota form symbiotic associations known as mycorrhizas with plant roots. Hyphae of mycorrhizal fungi proliferate in the soil beyond plant roots and make mineral ions and, in some cases, organic forms of nutrients available to the plant. Some mycorrhizal associations also increase plant defences against pathogens. In turn, the fungus obtains carbohydrates and possibly other growth-enhancing substances from the plant (see Figures 24.14 and 24.25).
- Endophytic fungi occur in the above-ground parts of many plants (see Figure 24.22); this type of plant–fungus symbiosis is not as well understood as are mycorrhizas, but at least some endophytic fungi are known to produce toxins that deter herbivores.

Questions

Self-Test Questions

1. A trait common to all fungi is
   a. reproduction via spores.
   b. parasitism.
   c. septate hyphae.
   d. a dikaryotic phase inside a zygospore.
   e. plasmogamy when an ascogonium fuses with an antheridium.
2. The chief characteristic(s) used to classify fungi into the major fungal phyla is/are
   a. nutritional dependence on nonliving organic matter.
   b. recycling of nutrients in terrestrial ecosystems.
   c. adaptations for obtaining water.
   d. features of reproduction.
   e. cell wall metabolism.
3. At lunch, you eat a mushroom, some truffles, a little Camembert cheese, and a bit of mouldy bread. This meal includes fungi from all the following groups *except*
   a. Basidiomycota.
   b. Ascomycota.
   c. Deuteromycetes.
   d. Glomeromycota.
   e. Zygomycota.
4. Which of the following fungal reproductive structures is diploid?
   a. Basidiocarp
   b. Ascospore
   c. Conidium
   d. Gametangium
   e. Zygospore
5. A mushroom is
   a. the food-absorbing region of an ascomycete.
   b. the food-absorbing region of a basidiomycete.
   c. a reproductive structure formed only by basidiomycetes.
   d. a specialized form of mycelium not constructed of hyphae.
   e. a collection of saclike cells called asci.
6. A zygomycete is characterized by
   a. septate hyphae.
   b. mostly sexual reproduction.
   c. + and − mating strains.
   d. the tendency to form mycorrhizal associations with plant roots.
   e. a life cycle in which karyogamy does not occur.
7. Which of the following best describes a lichen? It is
   a. a fungus that breaks down rock to provide nutrients for an alga.
   b. the last organisms(s) to colonize bare rocks and convert them to soil.
   c. an organism that spends part of the life cycle as a photosymbiont and part as a mycobiont.
   d. an association between a basidiomycete and an ascomycete.
   e. an association between a green alga and a fungus.

Questions for Discussion

1. A mycologist wants to classify a specimen that appears to be a new species of fungus. To begin the classification process, what kinds of information on structures and/or functions must the researcher obtain to assign the fungus to one of the major fungal groups?
2. In a natural setting—a pile of horse manure in a field, for example—the sequence in which various fungi appear illustrates ecological succession, the replacement of one species by another in a community. The earliest fungi are the most efficient opportunists because they can form and disperse spores most rapidly. In what order would you expect representatives from each phylum of fungi to appear on the manure pile? Why?
3. As the text noted, conifers and some other types of plants cannot grow properly if their roots do not form associations with fungi. These associations provide the plant with minerals such as nitrogen and phosphate and in return fungi receive carbohydrates synthesized by the plant. In some instances, however, the plant receives proportionately more nutrients than the fungus does. Would you still classify such associations as mutualisms?
4. What evidence would you look for to determine whether the association between a plant and an endophyte was mutualistic?
5. Why is it more difficult to develop drugs against fungal infections of humans than bacterial infections?

Monotropa uniflora, a heterotrophic plant that lacks chlorophyll.

© Peter F Zika/Visuals Unlimited

Study Plan

25 Plants

Why It Matters

You are out for a walk in a forest near your home; you are busy thinking about other things and so are not paying close attention to the plants that you're walking by—they are just a pleasing green background for your walk. Suddenly, your eye is caught by a small, glaringly white plant, like the one shown in the photo above—at least you think it's a plant. But aren't all plants green? How can there be a completely white plant?

What you have found is a plant known as ghost flower or Indian pipe (*Monotropa uniflora*), an achlorophyllous plant that does not produce chlorophyll and so cannot photosynthesize. Achlorophyllous plants like this are not photoautotrophs like most plants but instead are heterotrophs, living on organic carbon obtained from other plants. How do they get this carbon? They feed on neighbouring trees through shared root-colonizing fungi (mycorrhizal fungi; see Chapter 24).

What features could you look for to determine whether this *Monotropa* is a plant? What characteristics set plants apart from other organisms? And how did plants evolve? In this chapter, we investigate these questions and look at the adaptations to terrestrial life that have made plants so successful. And they are very successful organisms: they can thrive in habitats where no animal can survive for long and are able to grow much larger and live much longer than do animals. Together with photosynthetic bacteria and protists, plant tissues provide the nutritional foundation for nearly all communities of life. Humans also use plants as sources of medicinal drugs, wood for building, fibres used in paper and clothing, and a wealth of other products. The partnership between humans and plants goes back at least 9000 years, when we first domesticated cereal plants for crops.

Despite the long history between plants and humans, there is still much about their biology that we don't understand and many questions that remain to be answered.

We start by considering the defining characteristics of plants and then look at the evolution of plants and their adaptations to life on land; we conclude by looking at the diversity of land plants.

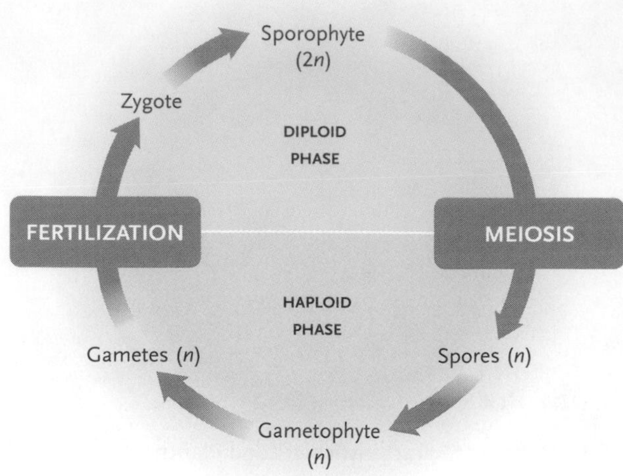

Figure 25.1
Overview of the alternation of generations, the basic pattern of the plant life cycle. The relative dominance of haploid and diploid phases is different for different plant groups.

25.1 Defining Characteristics of Land Plants

Land plants are eukaryotes; as we learned from the *Monotropa* example, not all are capable of photosynthesizing, but almost all plants are photoautotrophs. Like animals, they are all multicellular, but if you'd taken a piece of tissue from the *Monotropa* and looked at it under the microscope, you'd see that, unlike animal cells, the cells have walls, which are made of cellulose. All plants are sessile or stationary (not able to move around); no terrestrial animals are sessile, although some aquatic ones are. Plants also have a very different life cycle from animals, known as an **alternation of generations** life cycle.

For sexually reproducing organisms, meiosis in diploid cells produces haploid (*n*) cells (see Chapter 10). In animals, the cells produced by meiosis are gametes—sperm or eggs—but in plants (and fungi), meiosis gives rise to **spores,** which can give rise to a new haploid individual asexually, without mating.

In most animals, the diploid stage dominates the life cycle, with single-celled gametes as the only haploid stage, which is short-lived: fusion of gametes produces a new diploid stage (some animals, e.g., social insects such as bees and wasps, have a different life cycle). In other organisms, such as many green algae, the haploid stage dominates the life cycle; the haploid alga spends much of its life producing and releasing gametes into the surrounding water. The single-celled zygote is the only diploid stage and divides by meiosis to produce spores that give rise to the haploid stage again.

In contrast, land plants have two multicellular stages in their life cycles, one diploid and one haploid (**Figure 25.1**). The diploid generation produces spores and is called a **sporophyte** ("*phyte* = plant," hence "spore-producing plant"). The haploid generation produces gametes and is called a **gametophyte** ("gamete-producing plant"). The haploid phase of the plant life cycle begins in specialized cells of the sporophyte, where haploid spores are produced by meiosis. When a spore germinates, it divides by mitosis to produce a multicellular haploid gametophyte. A gametophyte's function is to nourish and protect the forthcoming sporophyte generation. Each generation gives rise to the other—hence the name *alternation of generations* for this life cycle.

The final defining feature of land plants is that the embryo (new sporophyte generation) is retained inside gametophyte tissue. The reason for retention of embryos in parental tissue and for the rather complex life cycle will become clearer after we've looked at the evolution of plants and their transition onto land.

Study Break

1. What features of land plants differentiate them from other eukaryotes, for example, from fungi? From animals?
2. What is an alternation of generations life cycle? How does this differ from the life cycle of most animals?
3. What does meiosis produce in plants?

25.2 The Transition to Life on Land

Ages ago, along the shores of the ancient ocean, the only sound was the rhythmic muffled crash of waves breaking in the distance. There were no birds or other animals, no plants with leaves rustling in the breeze. In the preceding eons, oxygen-producing photosynthetic cells had come into being and had gradually changed the atmosphere. Solar radiation had converted much of the oxygen into a dense ozone layer—a shield against lethal doses of ultraviolet radiation, which had kept early organisms below the water's surface. Now, they could populate the land.

Cyanobacteria were probably the first to adapt to intertidal zones and then to spread into shallow, coastal streams. Later, green algae and fungi made the same journey. Around 480 million years ago, one group of green algae, living near the water's edge, or perhaps in a moist terrestrial environment, became the ancestors of modern plants. Several lines of evidence indicate that these algae were charophytes (a group discussed in Chapter 23): both groups have cellulose cell walls, they store energy captured during photosynthesis as starch, and their light-absorbing pigments include both chlorophyll *a* and chlorophyll *b*. Molecular data also support the relationship between the charophytes and land plants. Like other green algae, the charophyte lineage that produced the ancestor of land plants arose in water and has aquatic descendants today **(Figure 25.2)**. Yet because terrestrial environments pose very different challenges than aquatic environments, evolution in land plants produced a range of adaptations crucial to survival on dry land.

The algal ancestors of plants probably invaded land about 450 million years ago (mya). We say "probably" because the fossil record is sketchy in pinpointing when the first truly terrestrial plants appeared, and many important stages in evolution are not represented in the fossil record. Even in more recent deposits, the most common finds of possible plant parts are microscopic bits and pieces; easily identifiable parts such as leaves, stems, roots, and reproductive parts seldom occur together, and even if they do, it can be difficult to determine whether the fossilized bits all belong to the same individual. Whole plants are extremely rare. Adding to the challenge, some chemical and structural adaptations to life on land arose independently in several plant lineages. Despite these problems, botanists have been able to gain insight into several innovations and overall trends in plant evolution.

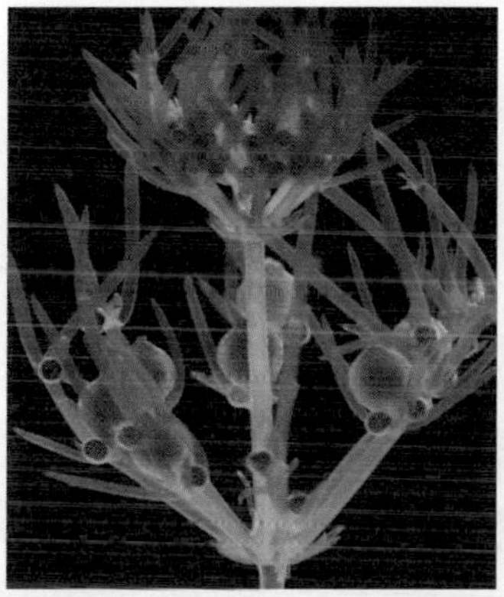

While the ancestors of land plants were making the transition to a fully terrestrial life, some remarkable adaptive changes unfolded. Eons of natural selection sorted out solutions to fundamental problems, among them avoiding desiccation, physically supporting the plant body in air, obtaining nutrients from soil, and reproducing sexually in environments where water would not be available for dispersal of eggs and sperm. With time, plants evolved features that not only addressed these problems but also provided access to a wide range of terrestrial environments. Those ecological opportunities opened the way for a dramatic radiation of varied plant species—and for the survival of plant-dependent organisms such as ourselves. Today the **kingdom Plantae** encompasses more than 300 000 living species, organized in this textbook into 10 phyla. These modern plants range from mosses, horsetails, and ferns, to conifers and flowering plants **(Figure 25.3, p. 550)**.

© Courtesy Microbial Culture Collection, National Institute for Environmental Studies, Japan

Figure 25.2
Chara, a stonewort. This representative of the charophyte lineage is known commonly as a stonewort due to the calcium carbonate that accumulates on its surface.

25.2a Early Biochemical and Structural Adaptations Enhanced Plant Survival on Land

The greatest challenge plants had to overcome to survive on land was how to survive in the dry terrestrial conditions. Unlike most modern-day plants, the earliest land plants lacked a waterproof **cuticle** (a outer waxy layer that prevents water loss from plant tissues) and specialized tissues to transport water from the soil through the plant body. These limitations restricted these early plants to moist habitats and made it necessary for them to stay small and grow close to the ground so that they could obtain water via diffusion. Like modern-day mosses, these plants were **poikilohydric** (*poikilo* = variable; *hydric* = relating to water), meaning that they have little control over their internal water content. Instead, their water content fluctuates with moisture levels in their environment: as their habitat dries out, so do their tissues, and their metabolic activities virtually cease. When external moisture levels rise, they quickly rehydrate and become metabolically active. How are poikilohydric plants able to survive prolonged dehydration that would be lethal to most plants? This question is explored further in *Life on the Edge*. Later-evolving plants were able to regulate water content and restrict water loss because they had cuticles covering their outer surfaces **(Figure 25.4a, p. 550)**, as well as **stomata** (singular, stoma; *stoma* = mouth), pores in the cuticle-covered surfaces **(Figure 25.4b)** that open and

a. Mosses growing on rocks

c. An orchid

b. A jack pine

Figure 25.3
Representatives of the kingdom Plantae. **(a)** Mosses growing on rocks. Mosses evolved relatively soon after plants made the transition to land. **(b)** A jack pine (*Pinus banksiana*). This species and other conifers belonging to the phylum Coniferophyta represent the gymnosperms. **(c)** An orchid, *Calypso bulbosa*, a showy example of a flowering plant.

close to regulate water loss (and are the main route for carbon dioxide to enter leaves; see Chapter 29). These plants also had specialized water-transport tissues, described further in the next section.

a. Cuticle on the surface of a leaf

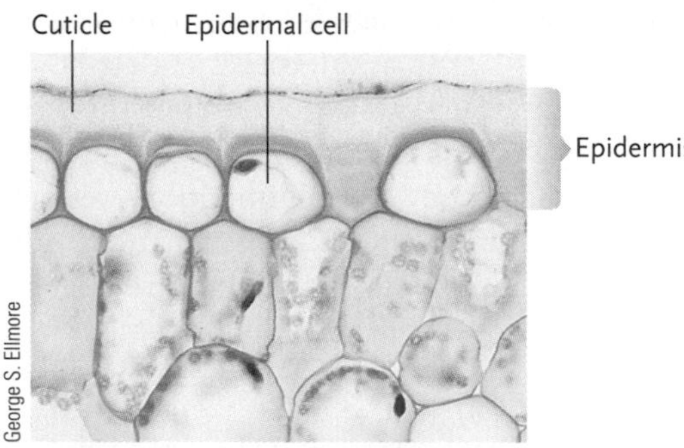

b. Stomata

Figure 25.4
Adaptations for limiting water loss. **(a)** A waxy cuticle, which covers the epidermis of land plants and helps reduce water loss. **(b)** Surface view of stomata in the epidermis (surface layer of cells) of a leaf. Stomata allow carbon dioxide to enter plant tissues and oxygen and water to leave.

25.2b Symbiotic Associations with Fungi Were Likely Required for Evolution of Land Plants

The ancestor of land plants was not the first organism to colonize terrestrial habitats; certain bacteria, protists, and fungi had been present since the late Proterozoic (around 540 mya). Almost all modern-day plants form symbiotic associations, known as mycorrhizas, with certain soil fungi (see Chapter 24). In these associations, the fungus colonizes the plant's roots and grows prolifically in the soil beyond the root system **(Figure 25.5)**. Both partners generally benefit by a two-way exchange of nutrients: the plant provides the fun-gus with carbon, and the fungus increases the plant's supply of soil nutrients, which it is able to obtain much more efficiently than do the plant's own roots. Such mutually beneficial relationships may have been essential to the evolution of land plants and to their success in terrestrial habitats (see *People Behind Biology*).

25.2c Vascular Tissue Was an Innovation for Transporting Substances within a Large Plant Body

As mentioned above, the earliest land plants did not have specialized water-conducting tissue. Growing low to the ground helped them stay moist but was not very effective in capturing light; since all early land plants were low growing, there would have been intense competition for light. If any plant were able to grow taller than its neighbours, it would have had a major advantage. But how could a plant support upright growth against the force of gravity? Plants require strengthening tissue to grow upright. And growing up and away from the ground surface also requires an internal water circulation system since diffusion is not effective over larger differences. Both

Figure 25.5
Mycorrhizal fungus colonizing plant root and soil around the root.

People Behind Biology
Kris Pirozynski and David Malloch

If almost all land plants today are dependent to some extent on mutually beneficial relationships with mycorrhizal fungi, would the first land plants have been any different? The hypothesis that mutualisms with fungi were required for the evolution of land plants was first put forward in 1975 by two researchers at the Biosystematics Research Institute of Agriculture Canada and has since received strong support from both fossil and molecular data.

In their 1975 paper outlining their hypothesis, Kris Pirozynski and David Malloch pointed out that associations with fungi would have helped the earliest land plants avoid starvation: early soils would not have been as fertile as most modern-day soils, and nutrients would certainly not have been as abundant as in the aquatic environments in which the algal ancestor of land plants lived. Fungi are very adept at proliferating in their substrates and foraging for nutrients, which they take up via extracellular enzymatic digestion (see Chapter 24). The earliest plants did not have roots, so forming a partnership with fungi would greatly have enhanced their uptake of nutrients. The fungi might also have protected the roots of its plant partner from root pathogens, as do modern-day mycorrhizal fungi.

Pirozynski and Malloch's hypothesis has since received strong support from both the fossil record and molecular data.

challenges were solved by the evolution of **xylem,** specialized tissue that transports water through the plant body and is made up of cells whose walls are reinforced with **lignin,** a tough complex polymer that strengthens the cell wall and allows for upright growth (see *Molecule Behind Biology*).

Xylem is one type of **vascular tissue** (*vas* = duct or vessel). Plants with this tissue (and the other type of vascular tissue, **phloem,** which conducts sugars through the plant body) are known as **vascular plants.** Chapter 29 explains how xylem and phloem perform these key internal transport functions.

Ferns, conifers, and flowering plants—most of the plants you are familiar with—are vascular plants. Supported by lignin and with a well-developed vascular system, the body of a plant can grow very large. Extreme examples are the giant redwood trees of the northern California coast, some of which are more than 90 m tall. By contrast, nonvascular plants lack lignin, have very simple internal transport systems or none at all, and are generally small **(Table 25.1).**

Vascular plants also have **apical meristems,** regions of constantly dividing cells near the tips of shoots and roots that produce all tissues of the plant body. Meristem tissue is the foundation for a vascular plant's extensively branching stem and root systems and is a central topic of Chapter 28.

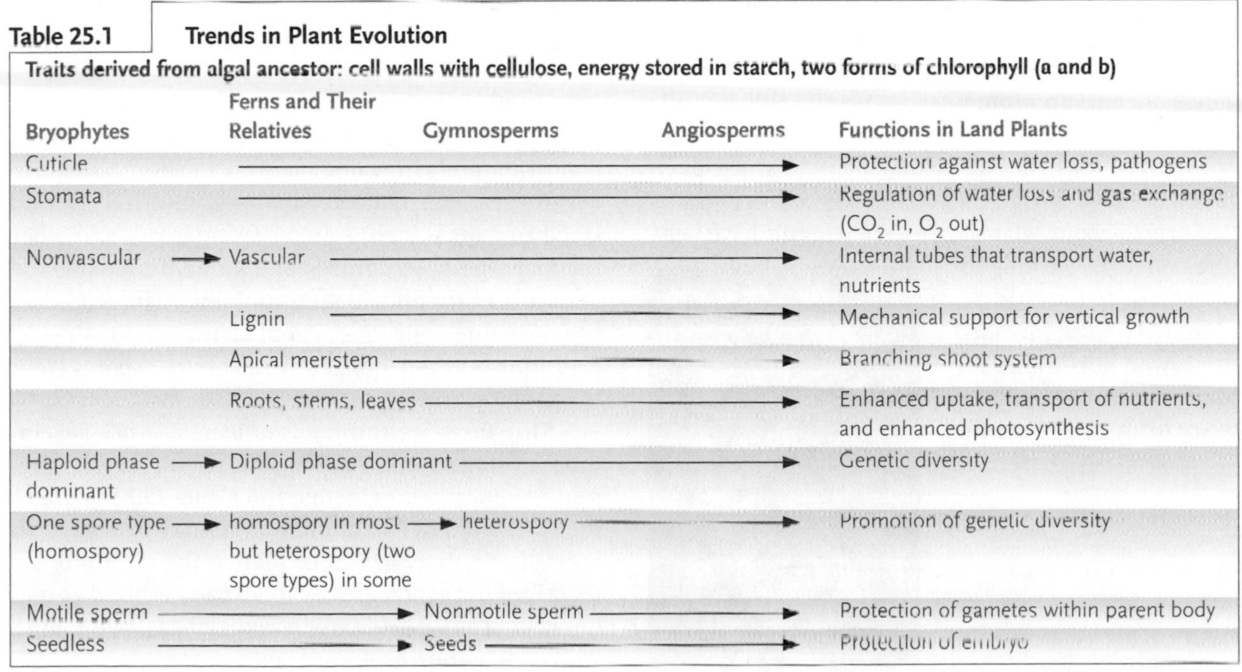

Table 25.1 Trends in Plant Evolution

Traits derived from algal ancestor: cell walls with cellulose, energy stored in starch, two forms of chlorophyll (a and b)

Bryophytes	Ferns and Their Relatives	Gymnosperms	Angiosperms	Functions in Land Plants
Cuticle	→	→	→	Protection against water loss, pathogens
Stomata	→	→	→	Regulation of water loss and gas exchange (CO_2 in, O_2 out)
Nonvascular →	Vascular →	→	→	Internal tubes that transport water, nutrients
	Lignin →	→	→	Mechanical support for vertical growth
	Apical meristem →	→	→	Branching shoot system
	Roots, stems, leaves →	→	→	Enhanced uptake, transport of nutrients, and enhanced photosynthesis
Haploid phase dominant →	Diploid phase dominant →	→	→	Genetic diversity
One spore type (homospory) →	homospory in most but heterospory (two spore types) in some →	heterospory →	→	Promotion of genetic diversity
Motile sperm →	→	Nonmotile sperm →	→	Protection of gametes within parent body
Seedless →	→	Seeds →	→	Protection of embryo

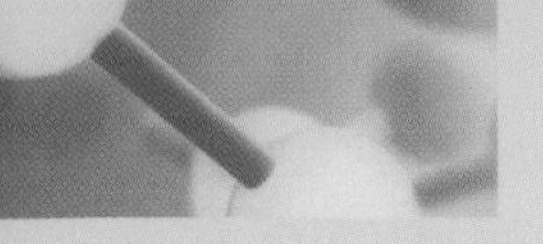

MOLECULE BEHIND BIOLOGY

Coniferyl Alcohol, a Building Block of Lignin

How is lignin formed, and how did it first evolve? Lignin is a polymer of several different monomers, including coniferyl alcohol **(Figure 1).** These molecules are synthesized from the amino acid phenylalanine in a series of reactions in the cytoplasm. The monomers are then transported through the cell membrane, where polymerization happens. We still do not fully understand how lignin is formed from monomers, but we do know that oxidative enzymes are involved in polymerization; thus, oxygen is required for the process. Lignin is thought to have evolved due to the high oxygen levels in the atmosphere around 430 million years ago, which would have favoured the polymerization reaction.

Lignin is very difficult to degrade, with only a few fungi and bacteria able to break it down (see Chapter 24). Its accumulation in plant tissues would have meant that dead vascular plants, especially if large, would have decomposed more slowly than the earlier land plants, contributing to the formation of coal, one of today's fossil fuels. The forests of the Carboniferous period were dominated by large vascular seedless plants, which were abundant in lignin. When these plants died and fell to the ground, they became buried in anaerobic sediments; even those that were not buried in such sediments would have been fairly slow to decompose due to their lignin content. Over geologic time, these buried remains became compressed and fossilized; today they form much of the world's coal reserves. This is why coal is called a "fossil fuel" and the Carboniferous period is called the Coal Age. Characterized by a moist climate over much of the planet and by the dominance of seedless vascular plants, the Carboniferous period continued for 150 million years, ending when climate patterns changed during the Paleozoic era.

Figure 1
Coniferyl alcohol, one of the monomers of lignin.

25.2d Root and Shoot Systems Were Adaptations for Nutrition and Support

The body of a nonvascular plant is not differentiated into true roots and stems—structures that are fundamental adaptations for absorbing nutrients from soil and for support of an erect plant body. The evolution of sturdy stems—the basis of an aerial *shoot system*—went hand in hand with the capacity to synthesize lignin. To become large, land plants also require a means of anchoring aerial parts in the soil, as well as effective strategies for obtaining soil nutrients. **Roots**—anchoring structures that also absorb water and nutrients in association with mycorrhizal fungi—were the eventual solution to these problems. The earliest fossils showing clear evidence of roots are from vascular plants, although the exact timing of this change is uncertain. The first unquestioned fossils of a vascular plant, a small plant called *Cooksonia* **(Figure 25.6),** were found in deposits that date to about 420 mya. *Cooksonia* fossils have been unearthed in various locales, but, frustratingly, none have ever included the lower portion of the plant—only its leafless, branching upper stems.

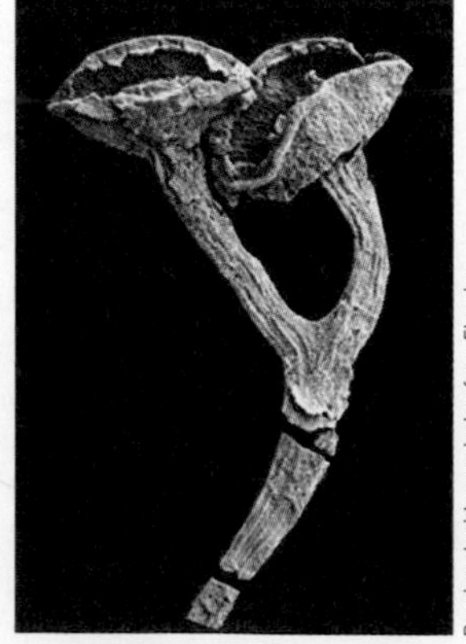

Figure 25.6
Fossil of one of the earliest vascular plants, *Cooksonia*, which dates to about 420 mya. *Cooksonia* was small, and as this image shows, its stems lacked leaves and probably were less than 3 cm long. The cup-shaped structures at the top of the stems produced reproductive spores.

Cooksonia probably was supported physically only by a **rhizome**—a horizontal, modified stem that can penetrate a substrate and anchor the plant. At some point, however, ancestral forms of vascular plants did come to have true roots. Ultimately, vascular plants developed specialized **root systems,** which generally consist of underground, cylindrical absorptive structures with a large surface area that favours the rapid uptake of soil water and dissolved mineral ions.

Above ground, the simple stems of early land plants also became more specialized, evolving into **shoot systems** in vascular plants. Shoot systems have stems and leaves that arise from apical meristems and that function in the absorption of light energy from the sun and carbon dioxide from the air. Stems grew larger and branched extensively after the evolution of lignin. The mechanical strength of lignified tissues almost certainly provided plants with several adaptive advantages. For instance, a strong, internal scaffold could support upright stems bearing leaves and other photosynthetic structures and so help increase the surface area for intercepting sunlight. Also, reproductive structures borne on aerial stems might serve as platforms for more efficient launching of spores from the parent plant.

Structures we think of as "leaves" arose several times during plant evolution. In general, leaves represent modifications of stems, and **Figure 25.7** illustrates the basic steps of two main evolutionary pathways. In at least one early group of plants, the club mosses described in Section 25.4, leaflike parts evolved as outgrowths of the plant's main vertical axis (see Figure 25.7a). In other groups, leaves arose when small,

a. Leaf development as an offshoot of the main vertical axis

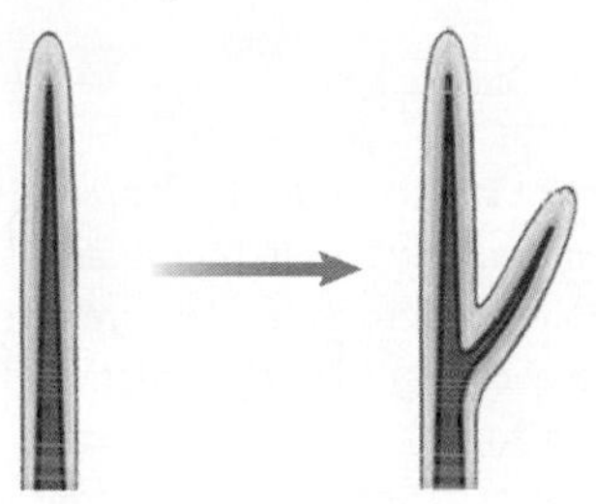

b. Development of leaves in a branching pattern

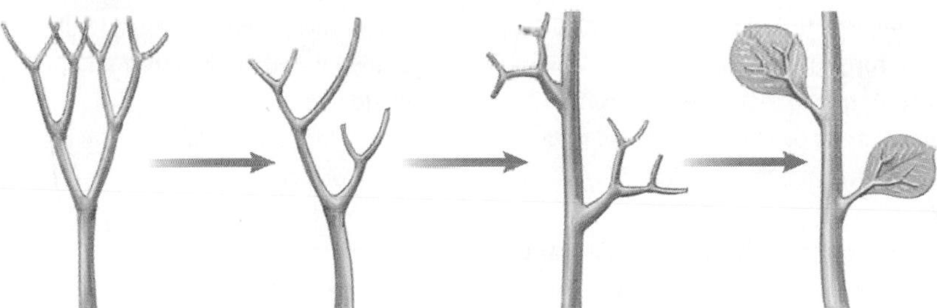

Figure 25.7
Evolution of leaves. **(a)** One type of early leaflike structure may have evolved as offshoots of the plant's main vertical axis; there was only one vein (transport vessel) in each leaf. Today, the seedless vascular plants known as lycophytes (club mosses) have this type of leaf.
(b) In other groups of seedless vascular plants, leaves arose in a series of steps that began when the main stem evolved a branching growth pattern. Small side branches then fanned out and photosynthetic tissue filled the space between them, becoming the leaf blade. With time, the small branches became modified into veins.

neighbouring stem branches became joined by thin, weblike tissue containing cells that had chloroplasts (see Figure 25.7b).

Other land plant adaptations were related to the demands of reproduction in a dry environment. As described in more detail shortly, these adaptations included multicellular chambers that protect developing gametes and a dependent, multicellular embryo that is sheltered inside the tissues of a parent plant.

25.2e In the Plant Life Cycle, the Diploid Phase Became Dominant

As early plants moved into drier habitats, their life cycles also were modified considerably. As plants evolved on land, the haploid gametophyte phase became physically smaller and less complex and had a shorter life span, whereas the opposite occurred with the diploid sporophyte phase. In mosses and other nonvascular plants, the sporophyte is a little larger and long-lived than in green algae, and in vascular plants, the sporophyte clearly is larger and more complex and lives much longer than the gametophyte **(Figure 25.8).** When you look at a pine tree, for example, you see a large, long-lived sporophyte. The sporophyte generation begins after fertilization, when the zygote divides by mitosis to produce a multicellular diploid organism. Its body will eventually develop capsules called **sporangia** (*angium* = vessel or chamber," hence, "spore-producing chambers"; singular, sporangium), which produce spores by meiosis.

Why did the diploid phase become dominant over evolutionary time? Many botanists hypothesize that the trend toward "diploid dominance" reflects the advantage of being diploid in land environments; if there is only one copy of DNA, as in a haploid plant, and if a deleterious mutation occurs or if the DNA is damaged (e.g., by ultraviolet radiation, which is a greater problem on land than in aquatic habitats), the consequences could well be fatal. In contrast, the sporophyte phase of that plant is diploid and so has a

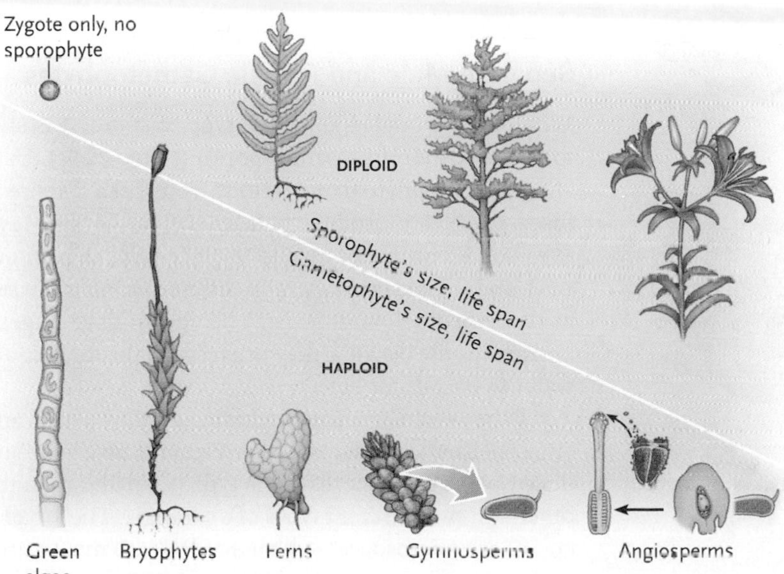

Figure 25.8
Evolutionary trend from dominance of the gametophyte (haploid) generation to dominance of the sporophyte (diploid) generation, represented here by existing species ranging from a green alga (*Ulothrix*) to a flowering plant. This trend developed as early plants were colonizing habitats on land. In general, the sporophytes of vascular plants are larger and more complex than those of bryophytes, and their gametophytes are reduced in size and complexity. In this diagram, the fern represents seedless vascular plants.

LIFE ON THE EDGE

Poikilohydric Plants

Most land plants, including our major crops, are killed if they dry out to the point of equilibrium with the water content of the air around them; this point is all too clearly illustrated by the terrible famines in Africa and other regions of the world that result from drought. But some plants are able to survive drying out to 10% absolute water content or less for months, and even years, in some cases **(Figure 1).**

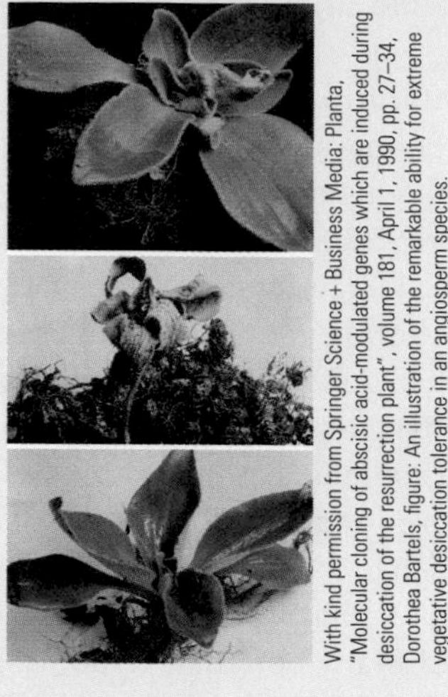

Figure 1
Desiccation-tolerant plant shown in a dehydrated state and following rewetting.

This ability is widespread among bryophytes but much less common in vascular plants: only about 50 species of seedless vascular plants have this ability in their sporophyte stage, along with about 300 species of angiosperms. Most of these desiccation-tolerant vascular plants, known as resurrection plants, live on rock outcrops in regions of southern Africa and Australia that receive only seasonal and sporadic rainfall. As far as we know, no gymnosperms have this ability.

How does dehydration kill a plant? Cellular water maintains membrane structure as well as the shapes of macromolecules such as enzymes and other proteins. Dehydration thus results in lethal changes to both membrane structure and macromolecular shape. A cell's metabolism also relies on water; as a cell dries out, metabolism first decreases and then ceases altogether. How do poikilohydric plants survive these changes that kill all other plants? We don't understand all of the mechanisms at play, but we do know that part of the answer is accumulation of sugars (e.g., sucrose) in cells. These sugars and certain proteins replace the water in membranes and around macromolecules, preventing lethal changes in conformation. The high sugar content also converts the cytoplasm from its normal consistency to a thick, slow-moving liquid known as glass, immobilizing the cytoplasm. The cells are able to survive in a dehydrated state with metabolism slowed to a state of dormancy or "suspended animation." The cell walls of desiccation-tolerant plants are also more flexible, able to fold as the cell dries, allowing the entire cell to contract as it dries out.

These mechanisms come at a cost to the plant, limiting their growth and reproduction. We don't yet understand how tolerance restricts growth; once we have a better understanding of this relationship, might we be able to uncouple tolerance from slow growth and develop drought-tolerant plants with a higher productivity? This very active area of research clearly has practical applications in maintaining our food supply in the face of droughts and climate change.

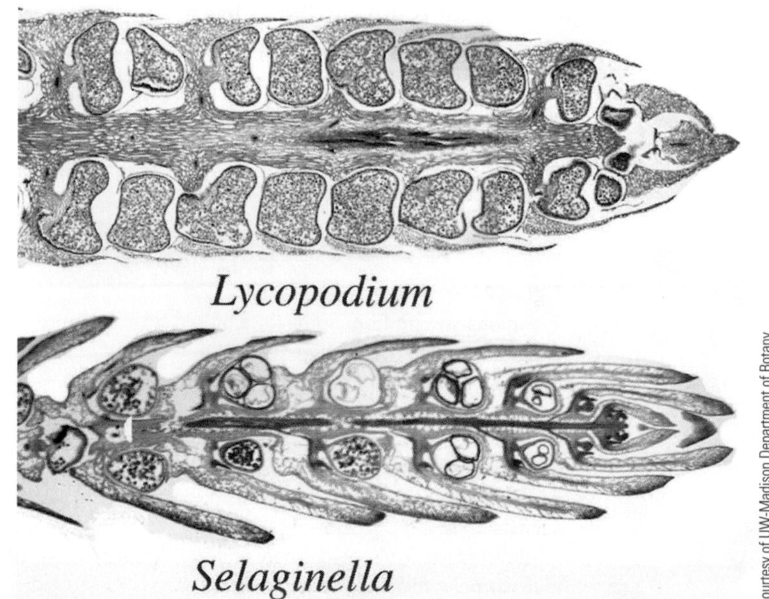

Figure 25.9
Comparison of **(a)** homospory and **(b)** heterospory.

"backup" copy of the DNA that can continue to function normally even if one strand is damaged.

25.2f Some Vascular Plants Evolved Separate Male and Female Gametophytes

When a plant makes only one type of spore, it is said to be **homosporous** ("same spore") **(Figure 25.9a).** Usually, a gametophyte that develops from such a spore is bisexual—it can produce both sperm and eggs. However, some homosporous plants have ways to produce male and female sex organs on different gametophytes, as described below in ferns. The sperm have flagella and are motile because they must swim through liquid water to encounter eggs.

Other vascular plants, including gymnosperms and angiosperms, are **heterosporous (Figure 25.9b).** They produce two types of spores—one type is smaller than the other—in two different types of sporangia. The smaller spores are **microspores**, which develop into male gametophytes, and the larger **megaspores** will develop into female gametophytes. Heterospory and the development of gametophytes inside spore walls are important steps in the evolution of the seed, as we will see further on.

As you will read in a later section, the evolution of seeds and related innovations, such as pollen grains and pollination, helped spark the rapid diversification of plants in the Devonian period, 408 to 360 mya. In fact, so many new fossils appear in Devonian rocks that paleobotanists—scientists who specialize in the study of fossil plants—have thus far been unable to determine which fossil lineages gave rise to the modern plant phyla. Clearly, however, as each major lineage came into being, its characteristic adaptations included major modifications of existing structures and functions **(Figure 25.10).**

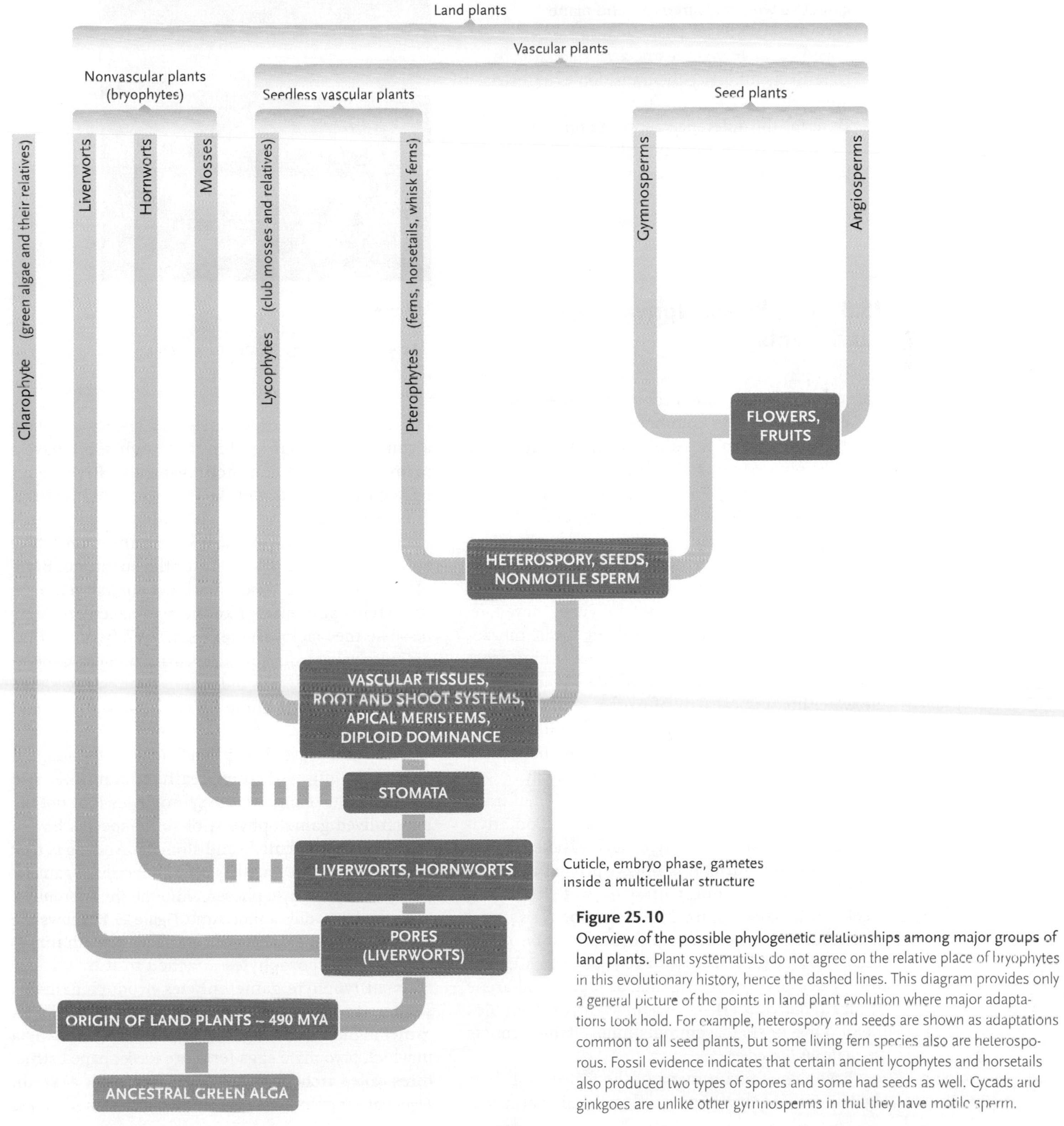

Figure 25.10
Overview of the possible phylogenetic relationships among major groups of land plants. Plant systematists do not agree on the relative place of bryophytes in this evolutionary history, hence the dashed lines. This diagram provides only a general picture of the points in land plant evolution where major adaptations took hold. For example, heterospory and seeds are shown as adaptations common to all seed plants, but some living fern species also are heterosporous. Fossil evidence indicates that certain ancient lycophytes and horsetails also produced two types of spores and some had seeds as well. Cycads and ginkgoes are unlike other gymnosperms in that they have motile sperm.

The next sections fill out this general picture, beginning with the plants that are the living representatives of the earliest land plants.

Study Break

1. What features do land plants share with their closest living relatives, the charophyte algae? What features differentiate the two groups?
2. How did mycorrhizal fungi fulfill the role we associate with roots in early land plants?
3. How did plant adaptations such as a root system, a shoot system, and a vascular system collectively influence the transition to terrestrial life?
4. Describe the difference between homospory and heterospory and explain how heterospory paved the way for other reproductive adaptations in land plants.

a.

b.

Figure 25.11
Bryophytes of arid habitats: **(a)** moss growing on exposed rock; **(b)** mosses and other plants in alpine tundra.

25.3 Bryophytes: Nonvascular Land Plants

The **bryophytes** (*bryon* = moss)—liverworts, hornworts, and mosses—are important both ecologically and economically. As colonizers of bare land, their small bodies trap particles of organic and inorganic matter, helping to build soil on bare rock and stabilizing soil surfaces with a biological crust in harsh places such as coastal dunes, inland deserts, and embankments created by road construction. In arctic tundras, bryophytes constitute as much as half of the biomass, and they are crucial components of the food web that supports animals in that ecosystem. People have long used *Sphagnum* and other absorbent "peat" mosses (which typically grow in bogs) for everything from primitive diapers and filtering whiskey to increasing the water-holding capacity of garden soil. Peat moss also has found use as a fuel; each day, the Rhode generating station in Ireland, one of several in that nation, burns 2000 tonnes of peat to produce electricity.

Bryophytes have a curious combination of traits that allow them to bridge aquatic and land environments. Because bryophytes lack vascular tissue and are poikilohydric, it is not surprising that they are small and commonly grow on wet sites along creek banks (see Figure 25.3a); in bogs, swamps, or the dense shade of damp forests; and on moist tree trunks or rooftops. However, some mosses live in very dry environments, such as alpine and arctic tundra **(Figure 25.11)**. Being poikilohydric enables them to live in such seemingly inhospitable habitats (see *Life on the Edge*).

Bryophytes retain many of the features of their algal ancestors: they produce flagellated sperm that must swim through water to reach eggs and lack a complex vascular system (although some have a primitive type of conducting tissue). Bryophytes have parts that are rootlike, stemlike, and leaflike. However, the "roots" are **rhizoids** that serve only to anchor the plant to its substrate and do not take up any water or nutrients from the substrate. Bryophyte "stems" and "leaves" are not considered to be true stems and leaves like those of vascular plants because they lack vascular tissue and because they did not evolve from the same structures as vascular plant stems and leaves did. (Said another way, stems and leaves are not homologous in bryophytes and vascular plants.)

In other ways, bryophytes are clearly adapted to land. Along with their leaflike, stemlike, and fibrous, rootlike organs, the sporophytes (but not the longer-lived gametophytes) of some species have a water-conserving cuticle and stomata. And, as is true of all plants, the life cycle has both multicellular gametophyte and sporophyte phases, although the sporophyte is tiny and lives only a short time. **Figure 25.12** shows the green, leafy gametophyte of a moss plant, with miniscule diploid sporophytes attached to it by slender stalks. Bryophyte gametophytes produce gametes sheltered within a layer of protective cells called a **gametangium** (plural, gametangia). The gametangia in which bryophyte eggs form are flask-shaped structures called **archegonia** (*archi* = first; *gonos* = seed). Flagellated sperm form in rounded gametangia called

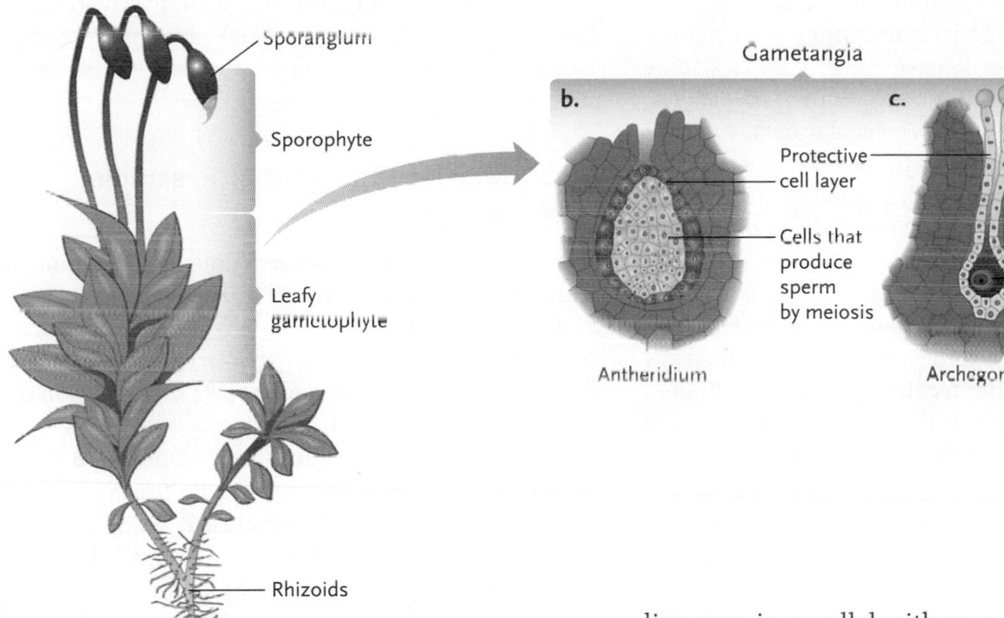

Figure 25.12
Multicellular structures enclosing plant gametes, a bryophyte innovation.
(a) The gametophyte and sporophyte phases of the moss *Mnium*. In this species, the gametangia are embedded in tissue of the gametophyte. In some other bryophytes, the gametangia are attached on the gametophyte's surface. The two types of moss gametangia are the **(b)** antheridium, containing cells from which sperm arise, and the **(c)** archegonium, containing an egg cell. The zygote that results from fertilization of an egg cell gives rise to a sporophyte.

antheridia (*antheros* = flowerlike; singular, antheridium). The sperm swim through a film of water to the archegonia and fertilize eggs. Each fertilized egg gives rise to a diploid embryo sporophyte, which stays attached to the gametophyte and produces spores—and the cycle repeats.

Despite these similarities with more complex plants, bryophytes are unique in several ways. Unlike vascular plants, the gametophyte is much larger and longer-lived than the sporophyte and is photosynthetic, whereas the comparatively tiny sporophyte remains attached to the gametophyte and depends on the gametophyte for much of its nutrition.

Bryophytes are not a monophyletic group (i.e., they did not all evolve from a common ancestor); instead, the various bryophytes evolved as separate lineages, in parallel with vascular plants. There is still debate as to which type of bryophyte was the first to evolve. Our survey of nonvascular plants begins with the liverworts and hornworts, the simplest of the group, and concludes with mosses—plants that not only are more familiar to most of us but whose structure and physiology more closely resemble those of vascular plants.

25.3a Liverworts May Have Been the First Land Plants

Liverworts make up the phylum **Hepatophyta**, so called because early herbalists thought that these small plants were shaped like the lobes of the human liver (*hepat* = liver; *wort* = herb). The resemblance might be a little vague to modern eyes: many of the 6000 species of liverworts consist of a flat, branching, ribbonlike plate of tissue closely pressed against damp soil **(Figure 25.13a)**. This simple body, called a **thallus** (plural, thalli), is the gametophyte generation.

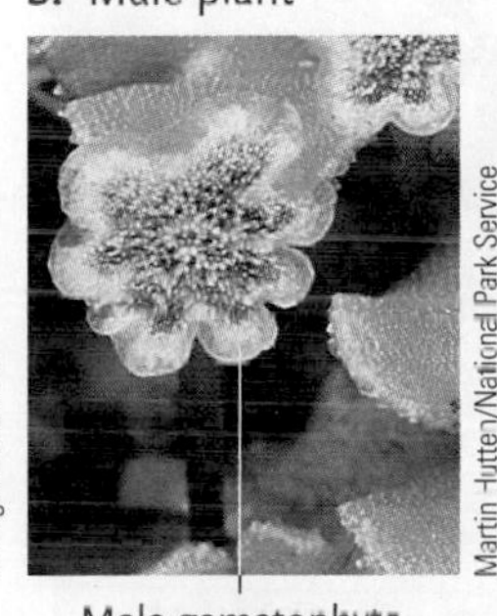

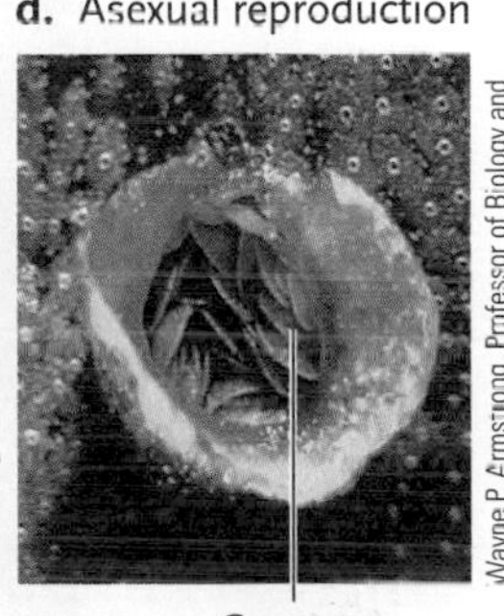

Figure 25.13
The bryophyte *Marchantia*; **(a)** thallus of *Marchantia*, the only liverwort to produce **(b)** male and **(c)** female gametophytes on separate plants. *Marchantia* also reproduces sexually by way of **(d)** gemmae, multicellular vegetative bodies that develop in tiny cups on the plant body. Gemmae can grow into new plants when splashing raindrops transport them to suitable sites.

Threadlike rhizoids anchor the gametophytes to their substrate. None have true stomata, the openings that regulate gas exchange in most other land plants, although some species do have pores. They lack some features present in the other two groups of bryophytes; this evidence, together with molecular data, suggests that liverworts were probably the first land plants.

We will look at one genus, *Marchantia* (see Figure 25.13), as an example of liverwort reproduction. Separate male and female gametophytes produce sexual organs (antheridia and archegonia) on tall stalks **(Figure 25.13b, c).** The motile sperm released from antheridia swim through surface water to reach the eggs inside archegonia. After fertilization, a small, diploid sporophyte develops inside the archegonium, matures there, and produces haploid spores by meiosis. During meiosis, sex chromosomes segregate, so some spores have the male genotype and others the female genotype. As in other liverworts, the spores develop inside jacketed sporangia that split open to release the spores. A spore that is carried by air currents to a suitable location germinates and gives rise to a haploid gametophyte, which is either male or female. *Marchantia* also can reproduce asexually by way of **gemmae** (*gem* = bud; singular, gemma), small cell masses that form in cuplike growths on a thallus **(Figure 25.13d).** Gemmae can grow into new thalli when rainwater splashes them out of the cups and onto an appropriately moist substrate.

25.3b Hornworts Have Both Plantlike and Algalike Features

Roughly 100 species of hornworts make up the phylum **Anthocerophyta.** Like some liverworts, a hornwort gametophyte has a flat thallus, but the sporangium of the sporophyte phase is long and pointed, like a horn **(Figure 25.14),** and splits into two or three ribbonlike sections when it releases spores. Sexual reproduction occurs in basically the same way as in liverworts, and hornworts also reproduce asexually by fragmentation as pieces of a thallus break off and develop into new individuals.

Figure 25.14
The hornwort *Anthoceros*. The base of each long, slender sporophyte is embedded into the flattened, leafy gametophyte.

25.3c Mosses Most Closely Resemble Vascular Plants

Chances are that you have seen, touched, or sat on at least some of the approximately 10 000 species of mosses, and the use of the name **Bryophyta** for this phylum underscores the fact that mosses are the best-known bryophytes, forming tufts or carpets of vegetation on the surface of rocks, soil, or bark.

The moss life cycle, diagrammed in **Figure 25.15,** begins when a haploid (n) spore lands on a wet soil surface. After the spore germinates, it elongates and branches into a filamentous web of tissue called a **protonema** ("first thread"), which can become dense enough to colour the surface of soil, rocks, or bark visibly green. After several weeks of growth, the budlike cell masses on a protonema develop into leafy, green gametophytes anchored by rhizoids. A single protonema can be extremely prolific, producing bud after bud, thus giving rise to a dense clone of genetically identical gametophytes. Leafy mosses also may reproduce asexually by gemmae produced at the surface of rhizoids and on aboveground parts.

Antheridia and archegonia are produced at the tips of male and female gametophytes, respectively. Propelled by flagella, sperm released from antheridia swim through a film of dew or rainwater and down a channel in the neck of the archegonium, attracted by a chemical gradient secreted by each egg. Fertilization produces the new sporophyte generation inside the archegonium, in the form of diploid zygotes that develop into small, mature sporophytes, each consisting of a sporangium on a stalk. Moss sporophytes may eventually develop chloroplasts and nourish themselves photosynthetically, but initially they depend on the gametophytes for food. Even after a moss sporophyte begins photosynthesis, it still must obtain water, carbohydrates, and some other nutrients from the gametophyte.

Certain moss gametophytes are structurally complex, with features similar to those of higher plants. For example, some species have a central strand of primitive conducting tissue. One kind of tissue is made up of elongated, thin-walled, dead and empty cells that conduct water. In a few mosses, the water-conducting cells are surrounded by sugar-conducting tissue resembling the phloem of vascular plants. These tissues did not give rise to the xylem and phloem of vascular plants, however.

In the next section, we turn to the vascular plants, which have specialized tissues that can transport

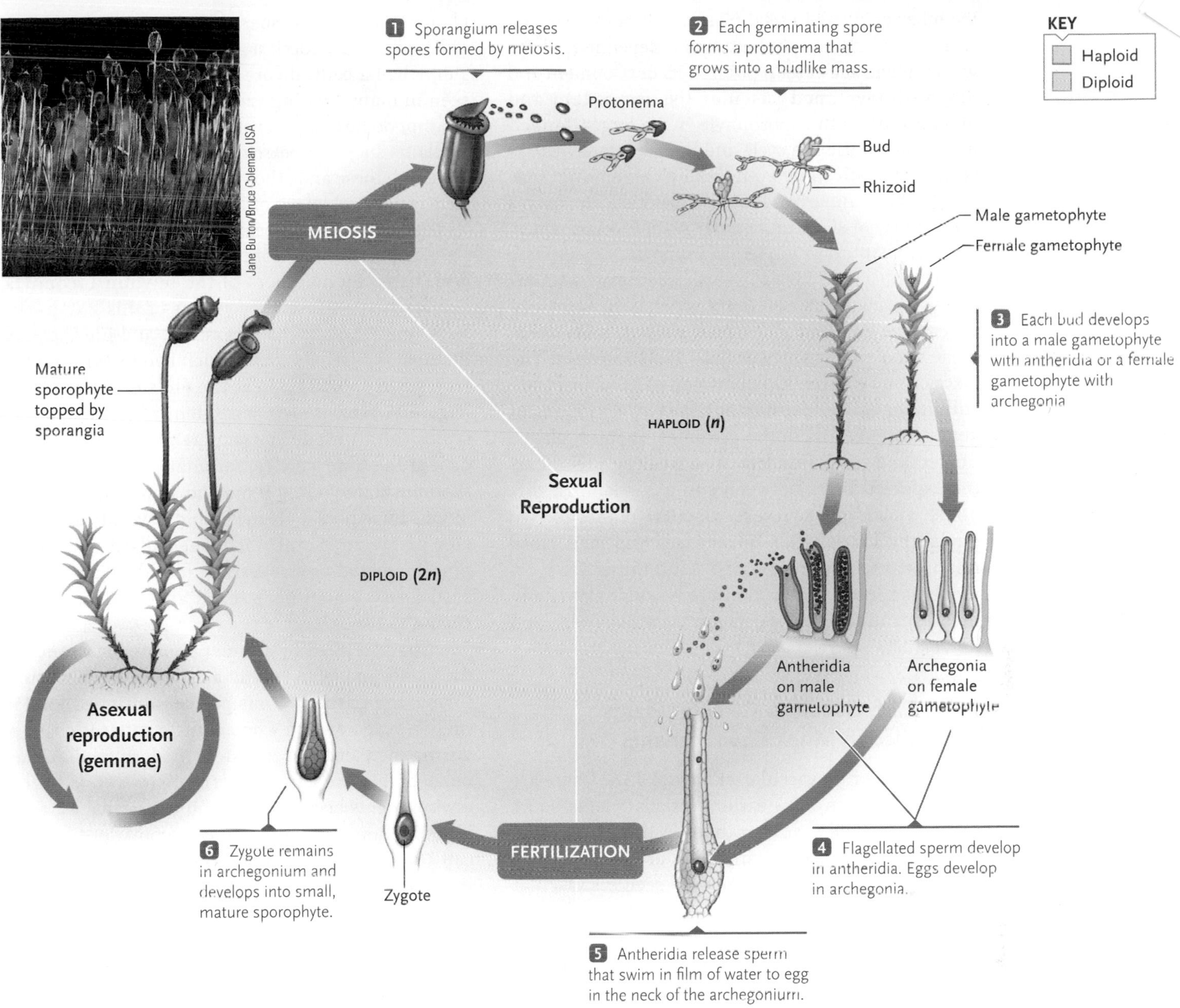

Jane Burton/Bruce Coleman USA
1 Sporangium releases spores formed by meiosis.
2 Each germinating spore forms a protonema that grows into a budlike mass.
KEY
Haploid
Diploid
Protonema
Bud
Rhizoid
Male gametophyte
Female gametophyte
MEIOSIS
3 Each bud develops into a male gametophyte with antheridia or a female gametophyte with archegonia
Mature sporophyte topped by sporangia
HAPLOID (n)
Sexual Reproduction
DIPLOID (2n)
Antheridia on male gametophyte
Archegonia on female gametophyte
Asexual reproduction (gemmae)
6 Zygote remains in archegonium and develops into small, mature sporophyte.
Zygote
FERTILIZATION
4 Flagellated sperm develop in antheridia. Eggs develop in archegonia.
5 Antheridia release sperm that swim in film of water to egg in the neck of the archegonium.

Figure 25.15
Life cycle of the moss *Polytrichum*.

water, minerals, and sugars. Without the capacity to move these substances efficiently throughout the plant body, large sporophytes could not have survived on land. Unlike bryophytes, modern vascular plants are monophyletic—all groups are descended from a common ancestor.

Study Break

1. Give some examples of bryophyte features that bridge aquatic and terrestrial environments.
2. How do specific aspects of a moss plant's anatomy resemble those of vascular plants?

25.4 Seedless Vascular Plants

The first vascular plants, which did not produce seeds, were the dominant plants on Earth for almost 200 million years, until seed plants became abundant. The fossil record shows that seedless vascular plants were well established by the late Silurian, about 428 mya, and they flourished until the end of the Carboniferous, about 250 mya. Some living seedless vascular plants have certain bryophyte-like traits, whereas others have some characteristics of seed plants. On the one hand, like bryophytes, seedless vascular plants disperse themselves by releasing spores, and they have swimming sperm that require free water to reach eggs. On the other hand, as in seed plants, the sporophyte of a seedless vascular plant becomes independent of the gametophyte at a certain point in its development and has well-developed vascular tissues (xylem and phloem). Also, the sporophyte is the larger, longer-lived stage of the life cycle and the gametophytes are very small, with some even lacking chlorophyll. **Table 25.2, p. 573** summarizes these characteristics and gives an overview of seedless vascular plant features within the larger context of modern plant phyla.

In the late Paleozoic era, seedless vascular plants were Earth's dominant vegetation. Some lineages have endured to the present, but, collectively, these survivors total fewer than 14 000 species. The taxonomic relationships between various lines are still under active investigation, and comparisons of gene sequences from the genomes in chloroplasts, nuclei, and mitochondria are revealing previously unsuspected links between some of them. In this book, we assign seedless vascular plants to two phyla, the Lycophyta (club mosses and their close relatives; the common name "club moss" for lycophytes is misleading, as they are vascular plants, not mosses) and the Pterophyta (ferns, whisk ferns, and horsetails).

25.4a Early Seedless Vascular Plants Flourished in Moist Environments

What did the first vascular plant look like? There are no living relatives of the earliest vascular plants, so we rely on fossil data to answer this question. The extinct genus *Cooksonia* (see Figure 25.6) probably was one of the earliest ancestors of modern seedless vascular plants. Like other members of its extinct phylum, *Cooksonia* was small, rootless, and leafless, but its simple stems had a central core of xylem, an arrangement seen in many existing vascular plants. Mudflats and swamps of the damp Devonian period were dominated by plants such as *Cooksonia* and *Rhynia* **(Figure 25.16)**. Although these and other now-extinct phyla came and went, ancestral forms of both modern phyla of seedless vascular plants appeared.

Carboniferous forests were swampy places dominated by members of the phylum **Lycophyta**, and fascinating fossil specimens of this group have been unearthed in North America and Europe. One example is *Lepidodendron*, which had broad, straplike leaves and sporangia near the ends of the branches **(Figure 25.17b)**. It also had xylem and other tissues typical of all modern vascular plants. Also abundant at the time were representatives of the phylum **Pterophyta**, including ferns and giants such as *Calamites*—huge horsetails that could have a trunk diameter of 30 cm. Some early seed plants also were present, including now-extinct fernlike plants, called seed ferns, which bore seeds at the tips of leaves **(Figure 25.16b)**.

Characterized by a moist climate over much of the planet and by the dominance of seedless vascular plants, the Carboniferous period continued for 150 million years, ending when climate patterns changed during the Paleozoic era. Most modern seedless vascular plants are confined largely to wet or humid environments because they require external water for reproduction. However, some are poikilohydric and can survive in a dehydrated state for long periods of time (see *Life on the Edge*).

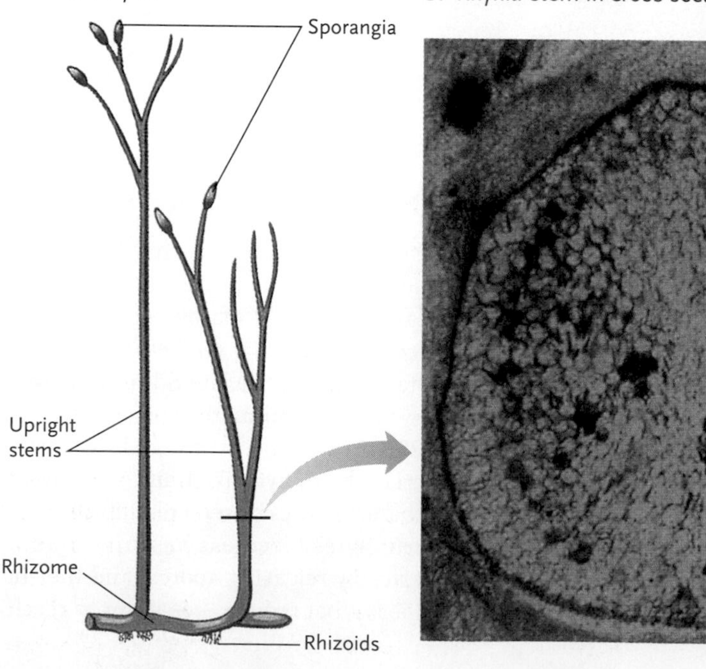

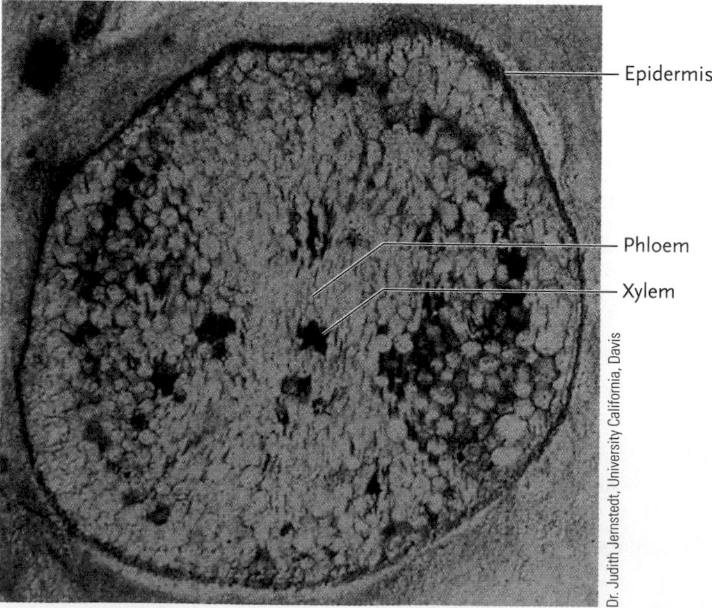

Figure 25.16
Rhynia, an early seedless vascular plant. **(a)** Fossil-based reconstruction of the entire plant, about 30 cm tall. **(b)** Cross section of the stem, approximately 3 mm in diameter. This fossil was embedded in chert approximately 400 million years ago. Still visible in it are traces of the transport tissues xylem and phloem, along with other specialized tissues.

a. The lycophyte tree *(Lepidodendron)*

Stem of a giant lycophyte *(Lepidodendron)*

Figure 25.17
Reconstruction of the lycophyte tree (*Lepidodendron*) and its environment. **(a)** Fossil evidence suggests that *Lepidodendron* grew to be about 35 m tall with a trunk 1 m in diameter. **(b)** Artist's depiction of a Coal Age forest.

25.4b Modern Lycophytes Are Small and Have Simple Vascular Tissues

Lycophytes were highly diverse 350 mya, when some tree-sized forms inhabited lush swamp forests. Today, however, such giants are no more. The most familiar of the 1000 or so living species of lycophytes are club mosses (e.g., species of *Lycopodium* and *Selaginella*), which grow on forest floors **(Figure 25.18).** Club moss sporophytes have upright or horizontal stems that contain xylem and bear small green leaves and roots. Sporangia are clustered at the bases of specialized leaves, called **sporophylls** (*phyll* = leaf; thus, sporophyll = "spore-bearing leaf"). Sporophylls are clustered into a **cone** or **strobilus** (plural = strobili) at the tips of stems. Most lycophytes are homosporous, but some are heterosporous, producing two types of spores that will in turn produce separate male and female gametophytes.

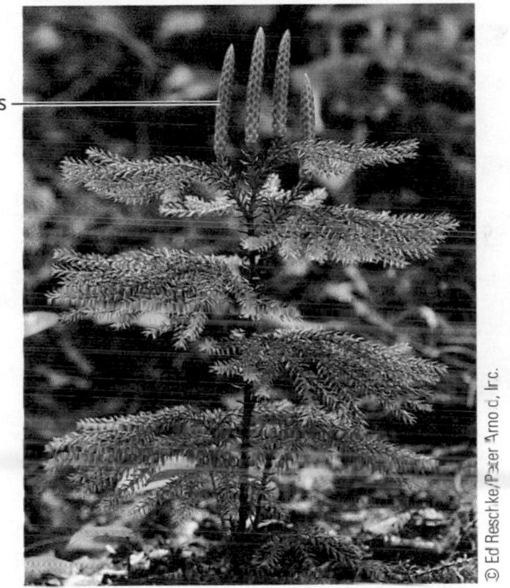

Figure 25.18
Lycophytes. *Lycopodium* sporophyte, showing the conelike strobili in which spores are produced.

25.4c Ferns, Whisk Ferns, Horsetails, and Their Relatives Make Up the Diverse Phylum Pterophyta

Second in size only to the flowering plants, the phylum Pterophyta (*pteron* = wing) contains a large and diverse group of vascular plants—the 13 000 or so species of ferns, whisk ferns, and horsetails. Most ferns, including some that are popular houseplants, are native to tropical and temperate regions. Some floating species are less than 1 cm across, whereas some tropical tree ferns grow to 25 m tall. Other species are adapted to life in arctic and alpine tundras, salty mangrove swamps, and semi-arid deserts.

Features of Ferns. The familiar plant body of a fern is the sporophyte phase **(Figure 25.19, p. 562),** which produces an aboveground clump of leaves. Young leaves are tightly coiled, and as they emerge above the soil, these "fiddleheads" (so named because they resemble the scrolled pegheads of violins) unroll

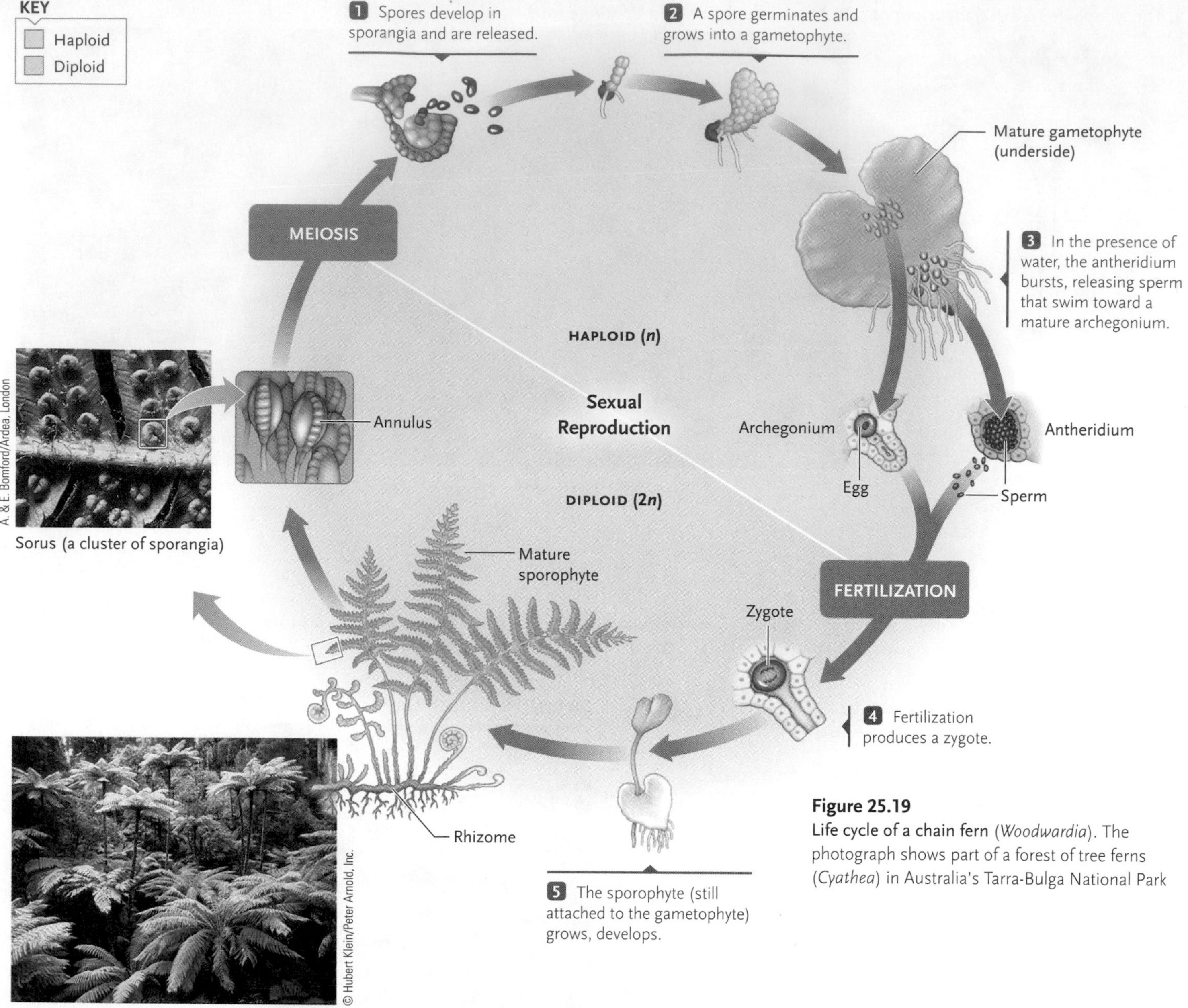
KEY
Haploid
Diploid
1 Spores develop in sporangia and are released.
2 A spore germinates and grows into a gametophyte.
Mature gametophyte (underside)
3 In the presence of water, the antheridium bursts, releasing sperm that swim toward a mature archegonium.
MEIOSIS
HAPLOID (n)
Sexual Reproduction
DIPLOID (2n)
Annulus
Archegonium
Antheridium
Egg
Sperm
A. & E. Bomford/Ardea, London
Sorus (a cluster of sporangia)
Mature sporophyte
FERTILIZATION
Zygote
4 Fertilization produces a zygote.
Rhizome
5 The sporophyte (still attached to the gametophyte) grows, develops.
© Hubert Klein/Peter Arnold, Inc.

Figure 25.19
Life cycle of a chain fern (*Woodwardia*). The photograph shows part of a forest of tree ferns (*Cyathea*) in Australia's Tarra-Bulga National Park

and expand. The fiddleheads of some species are edible when cooked, tasting similar to fresh asparagus, but be sure you have collected the right type of fiddlehead—some species contain a carcinogen.

Sporangia are produced on the lower surface or margins of leaves. Often several sporangia are clustered into a rust-coloured **sorus** ("heap"; plural, sori) (see Figure 25.18). Spores released from sporangia develop into gametophytes, which are typically small, heart-shaped plants anchored to the soil by rhizoids. Antheridia and archegonia develop on the underside of gametophytes, where moisture is trapped. Inside an antheridium is a globular packet of haploid cells, each of which develops into a helical sperm with many flagella. When water is present, the antheridium bursts, releasing the sperm. If mature archegonia are nearby, the sperm swim toward them, drawn by a chemical attractant that diffuses from the neck of the archegonium, which is open when free water is present.

In some ferns, antheridia and archegonia are produced on a single bisexual gametophyte. In other ferns, the first spores to germinate develop into bisexual gametophytes, which produce a chemical (antheridiogen) that diffuses through the substrate and causes all later-germinating spores to develop into male gametophytes. What is the advantage of producing a few bisexual gametophytes followed by many male gametophytes? If a bisexual gametophyte is surrounded by several male gametophytes that developed from other spores, it is more likely that eggs will be fertilized by sperm from one of the male gametophytes rather than by its own sperm, thus increasing the genetic diversity of the resulting zygote.

An embryo is retained on and nourished by the gametophyte for the first part of its life but soon develops into a young sporophyte larger than the gametophyte, with its own green leaf and root system. Once the sporophyte is nutritionally independent, the parent gametophyte degenerates and dies.

Features of Whisk Ferns. The whisk ferns and their relatives are represented by only 2 genera, with about 10 species in total; we look at just one genus, *Psilotum* (pronounced si-lo′-tum) **(Figure 25.20)**. Whisk ferns grow in tropical and subtropical regions, often as epiphytes.

The sporophytes of *Psilotum* resemble the extinct vascular plants in that they lack true roots and leaves. Instead, small, leaflike scales adorn an upright, green, branching stem, which arises from a horizontal rhizome system anchored by rhizoids. Symbiotic fungi colonize the rhizoids, increasing the plant's uptake of soil nutrients (read more about these mycorrhizal fungi in Chapter 24). The stem is photosynthetic and bears sporangia above the small scales. Gametophytes of *Psilotum* are nonphotosynthetic and live underground **(Figure 25.21)**; like the sporophyte, they obtain nutrients via symbioses with mycorrhizal fungi.

Features of Horsetails. The ancient relatives of modern-day horsetails included treelike forms taller than a two-storey building. Only 15 species in a single genus, *Equisetum*, have survived to the present **(Figure 25.22)**. Horsetails grow in moist soil along streams and in disturbed habitats, such as roadsides and beds of railway tracks. Their sporophytes typically have underground rhizomes and roots that anchor the rhizome to the soil. Small, scalelike leaves are arranged in whorls about a photosynthetic stem that is stiff and gritty because horsetails accumulate silica in their tissues. Pioneers used them to scrub out pots and pans—hence their other common name, "scouring rushes."

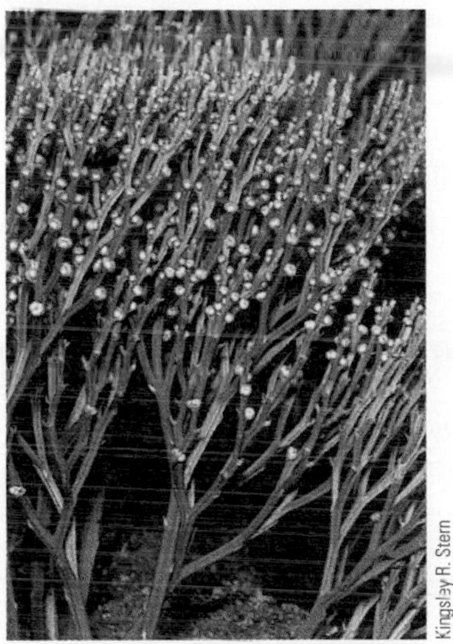

Figure 25.20
Sporophytes of a whisk fern (*Psilotum*), a seedless vascular plant. Three-lobed sporangia occur at the ends of stubby branchlets; inside the sporangia, meiosis gives rise to haploid spores.

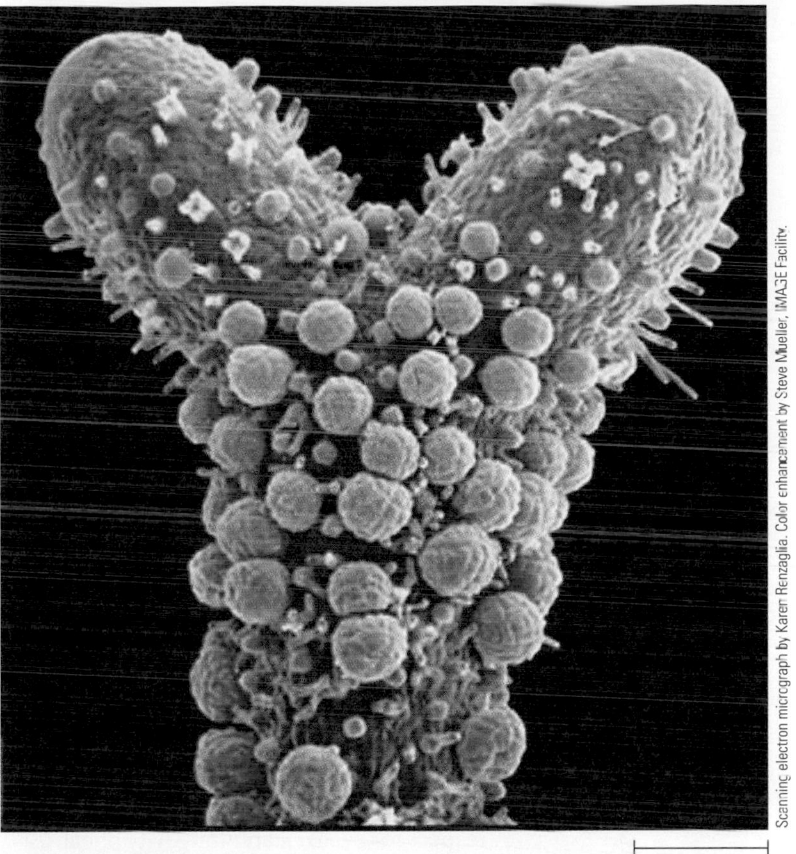

Scanning electron micrograph by Karen Renzaglia. Color enhancement by Steve Mueller, IMAGE Facility.
0.5 mm

Figure 25.21
Scanning electron micrograph image of the subterranean gametophyte of *Psilotum*. Antheridia have been coloured blue, and the smaller archegonia have been coloured pink.

a. Sporophyte stem
b. Sporangia
Strobilus, an aggregation of sporangia and sporophylls at the tip of the horsetail sporophyte
c. Each petal-shaped sporangium of a strobilus contains spores that are formed by meiosis.
William Ferguson
W. H. Hodges
© Kratz/Zefa/CORBIS

Figure 25.22
A species of *Equisetum*, the horsetails. **(a)** Vegetative stem. **(b)** Strobili, which bear sporangia. **(c)** Close up of sporangium and associated structures on a strobilus.

As in lycophytes, *Equisetum* sporangia are borne in strobili. Haploid spores germinate within a few days to produce gametophytes, which are free-living plants about the size of a small pea.

25.4d Some Seedless Vascular Plants Are Heterosporous

Most seedless vascular plants are homosporous, but some (e.g., some lycophytes and some ferns) are heterosporous, producing microspores and megaspores in separate sporangia (see Figure 25.8). Both types of spores are usually shed from sporangia and germinate on the ground some distance from the parent plant. In many heterosporous plants, the gametophytes produced by the spores develop inside the spore wall; this **endosporous** development provides increased protection for the gametes and, later, for the developing embryo. The microspore gives rise to a male gametophyte, which produces motile sperm. At maturity, the microspore wall will rupture, releasing the sperm, which swim to the female gametophyte; water is thus still required for fertilization in these plants. The megaspore produces a female gametophyte inside the spore wall; archegonia of this gametophyte produce eggs as in other seedless plants.

Study Break

1. Compare the lycophyte and bryophyte life cycles with respect to the sizes and longevity of gametophyte and sporophyte phases.
2. How does the life cycle of a horsetail differ from that of a fern?

25.5 Gymnosperms: The First Seed Plants

Gymnosperms are the conifers and their relatives. The earliest fossils identified as gymnosperms are found in Devonian rocks. By the Carboniferous, when nonvascular plants were dominant, many lines of gymnosperms, including conifers, had also evolved. These radiated during the Permian period; the Mesozoic era that followed, 248 to 65 mya, was the age not only of the dinosaurs but of the gymnosperms as well.

The evolution of gymnosperms marked sweeping changes in plant structures related to reproduction. The evolution of gymnosperms included important reproductive adaptations—pollen and pollination, the ovule, and the seed. The fossil record has not revealed the sequence in which these changes arose, but all of them contributed to the radiation of gymnosperms into land environments.

As a prelude to our survey of modern gymnosperms, we begin by considering some of these innovations.

25.5a Major Reproductive Adaptations Occurred as Gymnosperms Evolved

The word *gymnosperm* is derived from the Greek *gymnos,* meaning naked, and *sperma,* meaning seed. As this name indicates, gymnosperms produce seeds that are exposed, not enclosed in fruit as are the seeds of other seed plants.

Ovules: Increased Protection for Female Gametophyte and Egg. How did seeds first arise? Think about the heterosporous plants described in the previous section and picture two steps that would lead us toward the development of a seed. In the first step, spores are not shed from the plant but instead are retained inside sporangia on the sporophyte. In the second step, the number of megaspores is reduced to just one per sporangium (i.e., four megaspores are produced by meiosis, but only one survives). These two steps result in retention of a single megaspore inside a megasporangium on a plant **(Figure 25.23).** As in all land plants, the megaspore will give rise to a female gametophyte; because this is a heterosporous plant, the gametophyte will develop inside the megaspore wall and inside the megasporangium. Physically connected to the sporophyte and surrounded by protective layers, a female gametophyte no longer faces the same risks of predation or environmental assault that can threaten a free-living gametophyte.

This new structure, of an egg developing inside a gametophyte that is retained not only inside the spore wall but also inside megasporangial tissue, is an **ovule.** When fertilized, an ovule becomes a **seed:** the

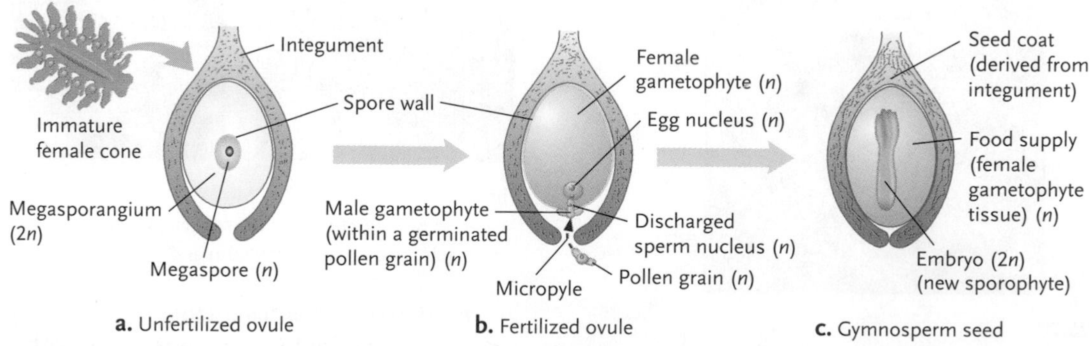

Figure 25.23
Structure of an ovule.

fertilized egg will produce an embryo surrounded by nutritive tissue, all encased in sporangial tissue that has become a seed coat.

When you look at Figure 25.23, you can see that the megasporangium is surrounded by extra layers of sporophyte tissue, which would add additional protection for gametes and embryos, but this tissue, along with that of the megasporangium, has also created a problem: how can sperm get to the egg now that the gametophyte is enclosed inside these layers of tissue? The solution is similar to that of internal fertilization in animals: there needs to be a male structure that can penetrate through sporophyte tissue and release sperm inside the female gametophyte. In the next section, we look at the male gametophyte in seed plants.

Pollen: Eliminating the Need for Water in Reproduction. As for megaspores, the microspores of gymnosperms (and other seed plants) are not dispersed. Instead, they are retained inside microsporangia and are enveloped in additional layers of sporophyte tissue. As in other heterosporous plants, each microspore produces a male gametophyte, which develops inside the microspore wall. This male gametophyte is very small relative to those of nonseed plants—it is made of only a few cells—and is called a **pollen grain.** Pollen grains are transferred to female reproductive parts via air currents or on the bodies of animal pollinators; this transfer is known as **pollination.** When the pollen grain lands on female tissue, the pollen grain germinates to produce a **pollen tube (Figure 25.24),** a cell that grows through female gametophyte tissue by invasive growth and carries the nonmotile sperm to the egg.

Pollen and pollination were enormously important adaptations for gymnosperms because the shift to nonswimming sperm, along with a means for delivering them to female gametes, meant that reproduction no longer required liquid water. The only gymnosperms that have retained swimming sperm are the cycads and ginkgoes described shortly, which have relatively few living species and are restricted to just a few native habitats.

Seeds: Protecting and Nourishing Plant Embryos. As described above, a seed is the structure that forms when an ovule matures, after a pollen grain reaches it and a sperm fertilizes the egg. Seeds consist of three basic parts: (1) the embryo sporophyte, (2) tissues around it containing nutrients that nourish the embryo until it becomes established as a plantlet with leaves and roots, and (3) a tough, protective outer seed coat **(Figure 25.25).** This complex structure makes seeds ideal packages for sheltering an embryo from drought, cold, or other adverse conditions. As a result, seed plants enjoy a tremendous survival advantage over species that simply release spores to the environment. Encased in a seed, the embryo also can be transported far from its parent, as when ocean currents carry coconut seeds ("coconuts" protected in large, buoyant fruits) hundreds of kilometres across the sea. As discussed in Chapter 30, some plant embryos housed in seeds can remain dormant for months or years before environmental conditions finally prompt them to germinate and grow.

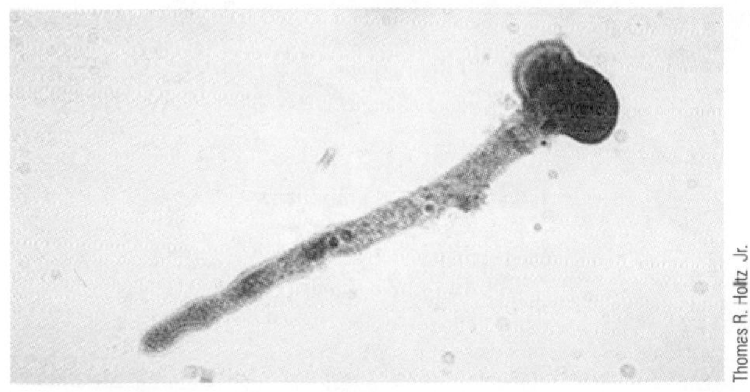
Thomes R. Holtz Jr.

Figure 25.24
Pollen tube growth.

25.5b Modern Gymnosperms Include Conifers and a Few Other Groups Represented by Relatively Few Species That Tend to Be Restricted to Certain Climates

Today there are about 800 gymnosperm species. The sporophytes of nearly all are large trees or shrubs, although a few are woody vines.

Economically, gymnosperms, particularly conifers, are vital to human societies. They are sources of lumber, paper pulp, turpentine, and resins, among other products. They also have huge ecological importance. Their habitats range from tropical forests to deserts, but gymnosperms are most dominant in the cool-temperate zones of the Northern and Southern Hemispheres. They flourish in poor soils, where flowering plants don't compete as well. In Canada, for example, gymnosperms make up most of the boreal forests that cover about one-third of the country's landmass. Our survey of gymnosperms begins with the conifers and then we will look at the cycads, ginkgoes, and gnetophytes—the latter two groups are remnants of lineages that have all but vanished from the modern scene.

Conifers Are the Most Common Gymnosperms. About 80% of all living gymnosperm species are members of one phylum, the **Coniferophyta**, or conifers ("cone-bearers") such as pines, spruces, and firs. Coniferous trees and shrubs are longer-lived, and anatomically and

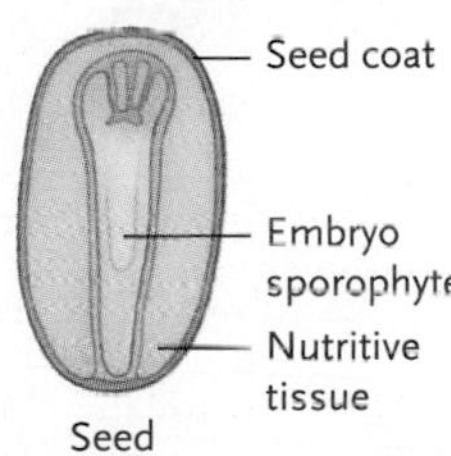

Figure 25.25
Generalized view of the seed of a pine, a gymnosperm.

morphologically more complex, than any sporophyte phase we have discussed so far. Characteristically, they form woody cones, and most have needlelike leaves that are adapted to dry environments. For instance, needles have a thick cuticle, sunken stomata, and a fibrous epidermis, all traits that reduce the loss of water vapour.

Pines and many other gymnosperms produce resins, a mix of organic compounds that are by-products of metabolism. Resin accumulates and flows in long resin ducts through the wood, inhibiting the activity of wood-boring insects and certain microbes. Pine resin extracts are the raw material of turpentine and (minus the volatile terpenes), the sticky rosin used to treat violin bows. Fossil resin is known as amber and is commonly used in jewellery; often amber contains fossilized insects or even small animals.

We know a great deal about the pine life cycle **(Figure 25.26)**, so it is a convenient model for gymnosperms.

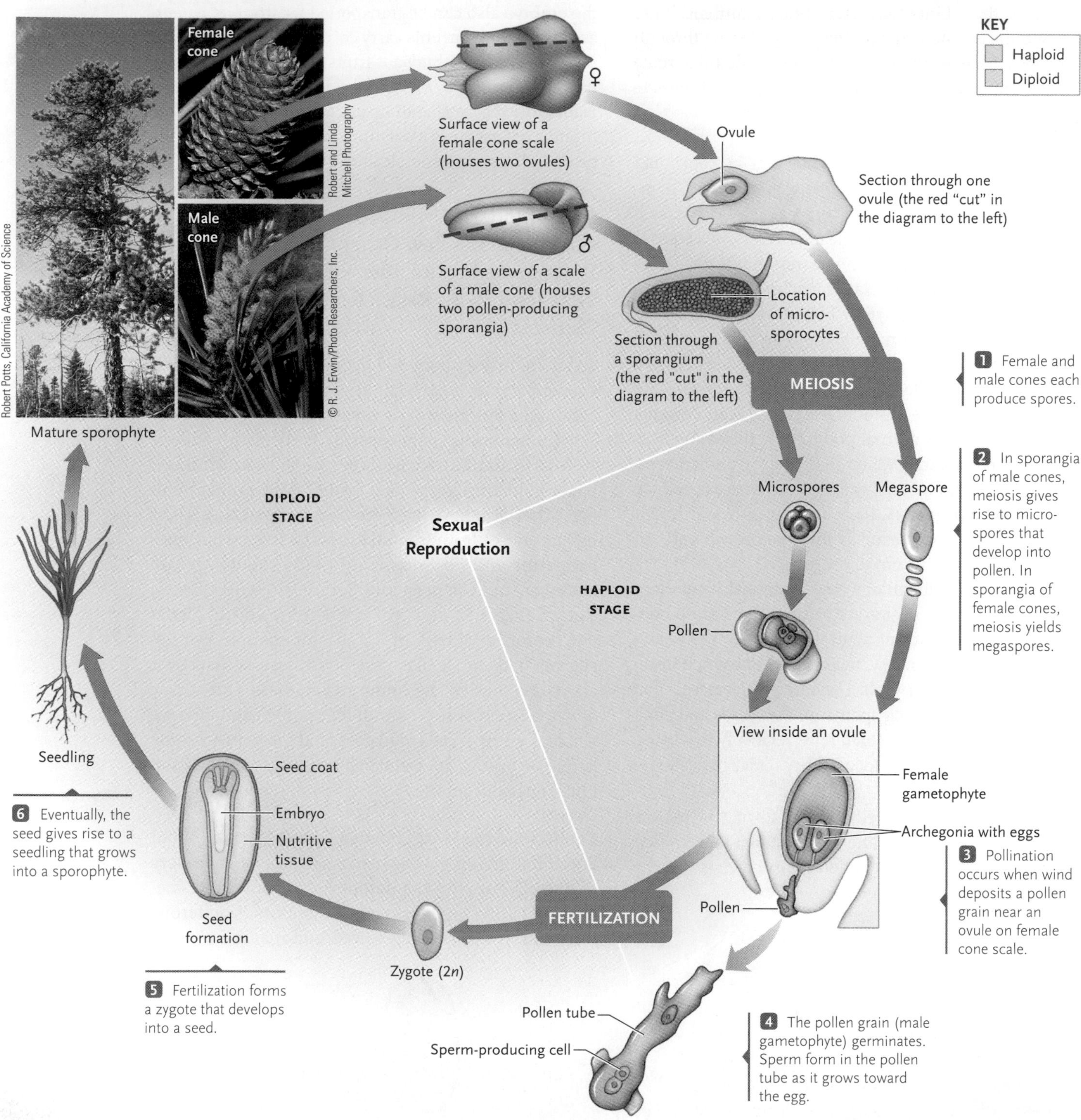

Figure 25.26
Life cycle of a representative conifer, a ponderosa pine (*Pinus ponderosa*). Pines are the dominant conifers in the Northern Hemisphere, and their large sporophytes provide a heavily exploited source of wood.

Male cones are relatively small and delicate (about 1 cm long) and are borne on the lower branches. Each cone consists of many sporophylls with two microsporangia on their undersides. Inside the microsporangia, **microspores** are produced by meiosis. Each microspore then undergoes mitosis to develop into a winged pollen grain—an immature male gametophyte. At this stage, the pollen grain consists of four cells, two that will degenerate and two that will function later in reproduction.

Young female cones develop higher in the tree, at the tips of upper branches. Ovules are produced on modified sporophylls. Inside each ovule, four megaspores are produced by meiosis, but only one survives to develop into a megagametophyte. This female gametophyte develops slowly, becoming mature only when pollination is under way; in a pine, this process takes well over a year. The mature female gametophyte is a small oval mass of cells with several archegonia at one end, each containing an egg.

Each spring, air currents release vast numbers of pollen grains from male cones—by some estimates, billions may be released from a single pine tree. The extravagant numbers ensure that at least some pollen grains will land on female cones. The process is not as random as it might seem: studies have shown that the contours of female cones create air currents that can favour the "delivery" of pollen grains near the cone scales. After pollination, the two remaining cells of the pollen grain divide, one producing sperm by mitosis, the other producing the pollen tube that grows toward the developing gametophyte. When a pollen tube reaches an egg, the stage is set for fertilization, the formation of a zygote, and early development of the plant embryo. Often fertilization occurs months to a year after pollination. Once an embryo forms, a pine seed—which, recall, includes the embryo, female gametophyte tissue, and seed coat—eventually is shed from the cone. The seed coat protects the embryo from drying out, and the female gametophyte tissue serves as its food reserve. This tissue makes up the bulk of a "pine nut."

Cycads Are Restricted to Warmer Climates. During the Mesozoic era, the **Cycadophyta** (*kykas* = palm), or cycads, flourished along with the dinosaurs. About 185 species have survived to the present, but they are confined to the tropics and subtropics.

At first glance, you might mistake a cycad for a small palm tree **(Figure 25.27)**. Some cycads have massive cones that bear either pollen or ovules. Air currents or crawling insects transfer pollen from male plants to the developing gametophyte on female plants. Poisonous alkaloids that may help deter insect predators occur in various cycad tissues. In tropical Asia, some people consume cycad seeds and flour made from cycad trunks, but only after rinsing away the toxic compounds. Much in demand from fanciers of unusual plants, cycads in some countries are uprooted and sold in what amounts to a black-market trade—greatly diminishing their numbers in the wild.

Carlton Ray/Science Photo Library/Photo Researchers, Inc.

Figure 25.27
The cycad *Zamia* showing a large, terminal female cone and fernlike leaves.

Ginkgoes Are Limited to a Single Living Species The phylum **Ginkgophyta** has only one living species, the ginkgo (or maidenhair) tree (*Ginkgo biloba*), which grows wild today only in warm-temperate forests of central China. Ginkgo trees are large, diffusely branching trees with characteristic fan-shaped leaves **(Figure 25.28)** that turn a brilliant yellow in autumn. Nursery-propagated male trees often are planted in cities because they are resistant to insects, disease, and air pollutants. The female trees are equally pollution resistant, but gardeners shy away from them because their seeds produce a foul odour that only a ginkgo could love. The

Figure 25.28
Ginkgo biloba. **(a)** A ginkgo tree. **(b)** A fossilized ginkgo leaf compared with a leaf from a living tree. The fossil formed at the Cretaceous–Tertiary boundary. Even though 65 million years have passed, the leaf structure has not changed much. **(c)** Pollen-bearing cones and **(d)** fleshy-coated seeds of the *Ginkgo*.

a. Ginkgo tree

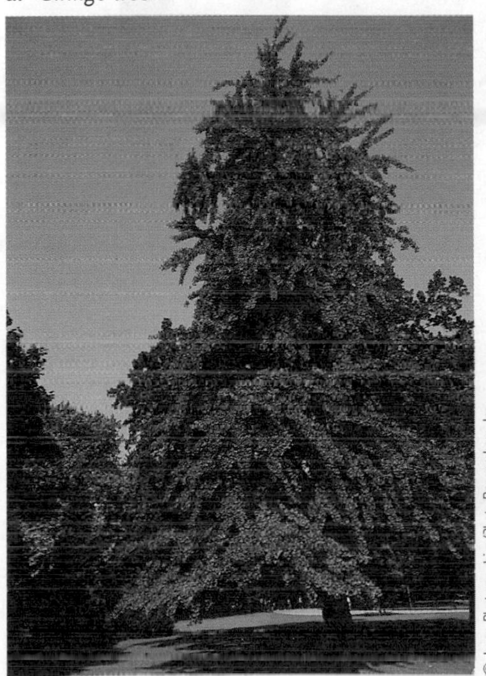
© Joyce Photographics/Photo Researchers, Inc.

b. Fossil and modern ginkgo leaves

Runk/Schoenberger/Grant Heilman

c. Male cone

William Ferguson

d. Ginkgo seeds

Kingsley R. Stern

leaves and seeds have been used in traditional Chinese medicine for centuries. The extract of the leaves is one of the most intensely investigated herbal medicines; although studies have not found any conclusive evidence for claims that the extract improves memory, there is some evidence that it does assist in blood flow and so may be effective in treatment of circulatory disorders.

Gnetophytes Include Simple Seed Plants with Intriguing Features. The phylum Gnetophyta contains three genera—*Gnetum, Ephedra,* and *Welwitschia*—that together include about 70 species. Moist, tropical regions are home to about 30 species of *Gnetum,* which includes both trees and leathery-leafed vines (lianas). About 35 species of *Ephedra* grow in desert regions of the world **(Figure 25.29a–c).**

Of all the gymnosperms, *Welwitschia* is the most bizarre. This seed-producing plant grows in the hot deserts of southwest Africa. The bulk of the plant is a deep-reaching taproot. The only exposed part is a woody, disk-shaped stem that bears cone-shaped strobili and leaves. The plant never produces more than two strap-shaped leaves, which split lengthwise repeatedly as the plant grows older, producing a rather scraggly pile **(Figure 25.29d).**

a. *Ephedra* plant

Edward S. Ross

b. *Ephedra* male cone

William Ferguson

c. *Ephedra* female cone

Robert & Linda Mitchell Photography

d. *Welwitschia* plant with female cones

© Fletcher and Baylis/Photo Researchers, Inc.

Figure 25.29
Gnetophytes. **(a)** Sporophyte of *Ephedra*, with close-ups of **(b)** its pollen-bearing cones and **(c)** seed-bearing cone, which develop on separate plants. **(d)** Sporophyte of *Welwitschia mirabilis*, with seed-bearing cones.

Study Break

1. What are the four major reproductive adaptations that evolved in gymnosperms?
2. What are the basic parts of a seed, and how is each one adaptive?
3. Describe some features that make conifers structurally more complex than other gymnosperms.

25.6 Angiosperms: Flowering Plants

Of all plant phyla, the flowering plants, or **angiosperms**, are the most successful today. At least 260 000 species are known (**Figure 25.30,** shows a few examples), and botanists regularly discover new ones in previously unexplored regions of the tropics. The word *angiosperm* is derived from the Greek *angeion* ("vessel") and *sperma* ("seed"). The "vessel" refers to the modified sporophyll, called a *carpel,* which surrounds and protects the ovules. Carpels are located in the centre of **flowers,** reproductive structures that are a defining feature of angiosperms. Another defining feature is the **fruit**—botanically speaking, a structure that helps protect and disperse seeds.

In addition to having flowers and fruits, angiosperms are the most ecologically diverse plants on Earth, growing on dry land and in wetlands, freshwater, and the seas. Angiosperms range in size from tiny duckweeds that are about 1 mm long to towering *Eucalyptus* trees more than 100 m tall.

25.6a The Fossil Record Provides Little Information about the Origin of Flowering Plants

The evolutionary origin of angiosperms has confounded plant biologists for well over a hundred years. Charles Darwin called it the "abominable mystery" because flowering plants appear suddenly in the fossil record, without a fossil sequence that links them to any other plant groups. As with gymnosperms, attempts to reconstruct the earliest flowering plant lineages have produced several conflicting classifications and family trees. Some paleobotanists hypothesize that flowering plants arose in the Jurassic period; others propose that they evolved in the Triassic from now-extinct gymnosperms or from seed ferns. However, progress in this area does not rely solely on fossil evidence; molecular data can be used to test hypotheses, and the combination of molecular, morphological, and fossil evidence offers great promise (see *Unanswered Questions*).

a. Flowering plants in a desert

© Bob Rowan, Progressive Image/Corbis

b. Alpine angiosperms

Bill Coster/Peter Arnold, Inc.

c. Triticale, a grass

© John Mason/Ardea, London

d. The carnivorous plant Venus flytrap

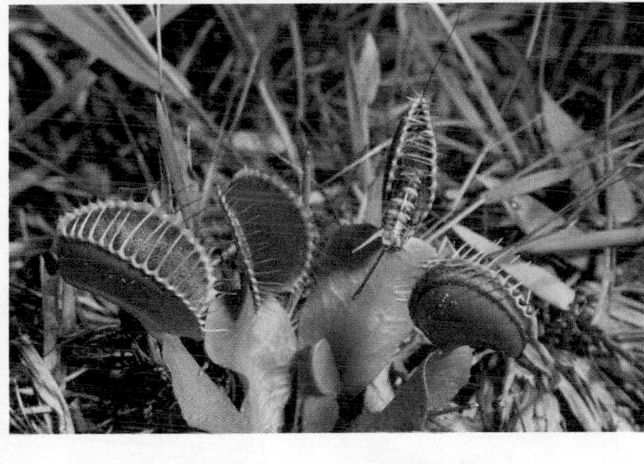

Howard Miller/Photo Researchers, Inc.

Figure 25.30
Flowering plants. Diverse photosynthetic species are adapted to nearly all environments, ranging from **(a)** deserts to **(b)** snowlines of high mountains. **(c)** Triticale, a hybrid grain derived from parental stocks of wheat (*Triticum*) and rye (*Secale*), is one example of the various grasses used by humans. **(d)** The carnivorous plant Venus flytrap (*Dionaea muscipula*) grows in nitrogen-poor soils and traps insects as an additional source of nitrogen.

The fossil record has yet to reveal obvious transitional organisms between flowering plants and either gymnosperms or seedless vascular plants. As the Mesozoic era ended and the modern Cenozoic era began, great extinctions occurred among both plant and animal kingdoms. Gymnosperms declined, and dinosaurs disappeared. Flowering plants, mammals, and social insects flourished, radiating into new environments. Today we live in what has been called "the age of flowering plants."

25.6b Angiosperms Are Subdivided into Several Groups, Including Monocots and Eudicots

Angiosperms are assigned to the phylum **Anthophyta,** a name that derives from the Greek *anthos,* meaning flower. The great majority of angiosperms are classified either as monocots or eudicots, which are differentiated on the basis of morphological features such as the number of flower parts and the pattern of vascular tissue in stems and leaves. The two groups also differ in terms of the morphology of their embryos: **monocot** embryos have a single seed leaf called a cotyledon, whereas **eudicots** ("true dicots") generally have two cotyledons **(Figure 25.31, p. 570).**

Botanists currently recognize several other groups of plants in addition to eudicots and monocots, but figuring out the appropriate classification for and relationships among these other groups is an ongoing challenge and an extremely active area of plant research. In this chapter, we focus only on monocots and eudicots.

There are at least 60 000 species of monocots, including 10 000 grasses and 20 000 orchids. **Figure 25.32a, p. 570** gives some idea of the variety of living monocots, which include grasses, palms, lilies, and orchids. The world's major crop plants (wheat, corn, rice, rye, sugarcane, and barley) are all monocots and are all domesticated grasses. Eudicots are even more diverse, with nearly 200 000 species **(Figure 25.32b).** They include flowering shrubs and trees, most non-woody (herbaceous) plants, and cacti. **Figure 25.33, p. 571** shows the life cycle of a lily, a monocot. The life cycle of a typical eudicot is described in detail in the next unit, which focuses on the structure and function of flowering plants.

Figure 25.31 Comparison of monocots and dicots.

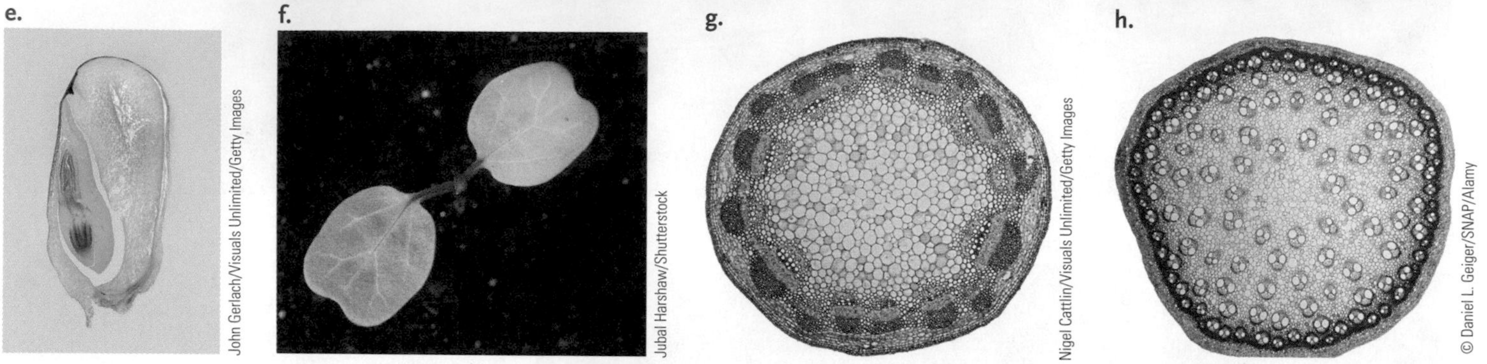

a. Dorling Kindersley/Getty Images

b. Ed Reschke/Peter Arnold Inc.

c. Ed Reschke/Peter Arnold Inc.

d. Jerome Wexler/Visuals Unlimited/Getty Images

e. John Gerlach/Visuals Unlimited/Getty Images

f. Jubal Harshaw/Shutterstock

g. Nigel Cattlin/Visuals Unlimited/Getty Images

h. © Daniel L. Geiger/SNAP/Alamy

a. Representative monocots

Wheat (*Triticum*) Triff/Shutterstock

Trillium (*Trillium*) Joel Blit/Shutterstock

Western wood lily (*Lilium philadelphicum*) © Louise Heusinkveld/Alamy

b. Representative eudicots

Wild rose (*Rosa acicularis*) © Organica/Alamy

Twinflower (*Linnaea borealis*) © Bob Gibbons/Alamy

Claret cup cactus (*Echinocereus triglochidratus*) John M. Roberts/Corbis

Figure 25.32
Examples of monocots and eudicots: **(a)** representative monocots: wheat (*Triticum*); trillium (*Trillium*), and Western wood lily (*Lilium philadelphicum;* **(b)** representative eudicots: wild rose (*Rosa acicularis*); twinflower (*Linnaea borealis*); cherry (*Prunus*); cactus (*Echinocereus triglochidiatus*).

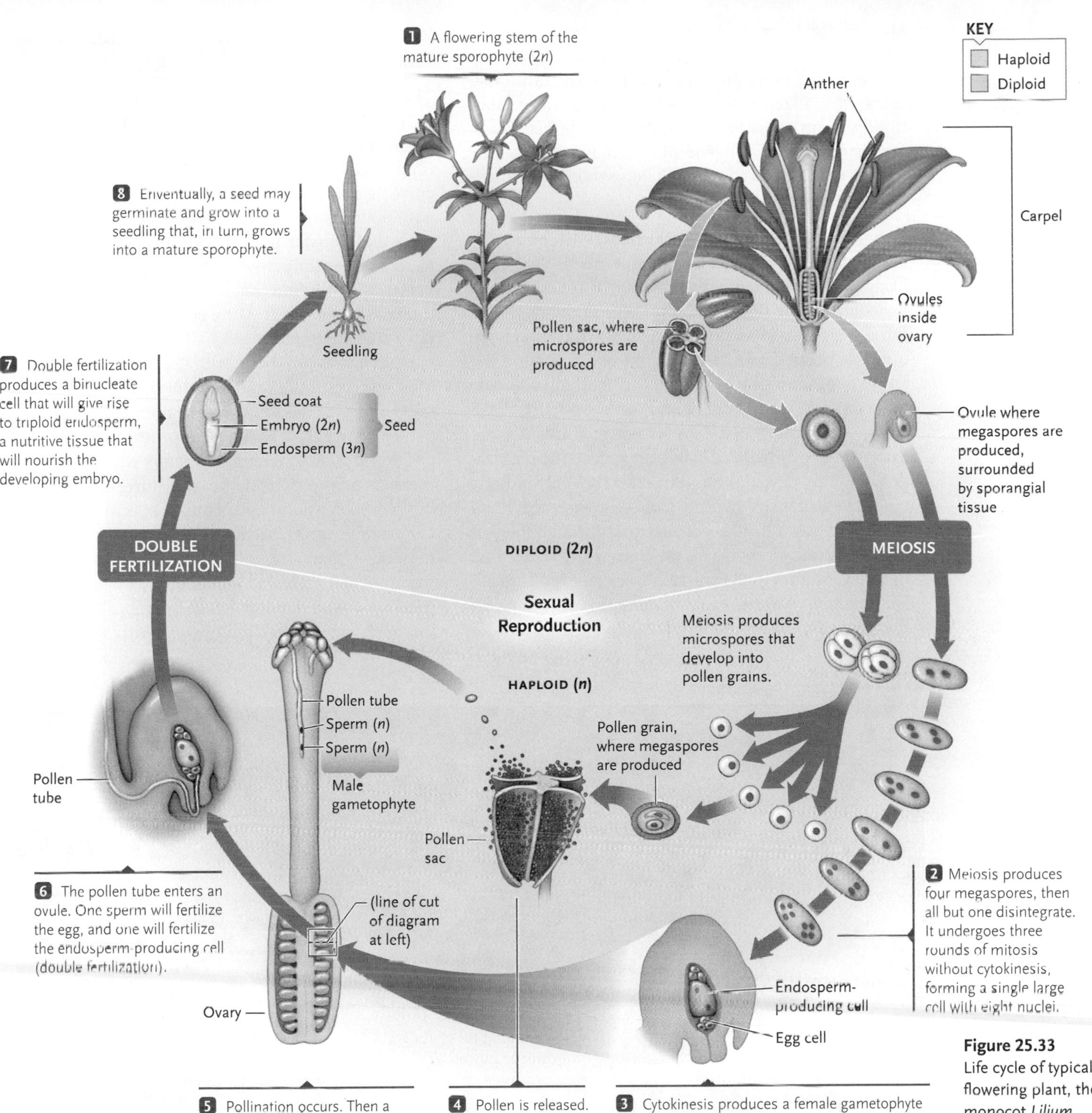

KEY
Haploid
Diploid
1 A flowering stem of the mature sporophyte (2n)
Anther
Carpel
Ovules inside ovary
Pollen sac, where microspores are produced
Ovule where megaspores are produced, surrounded by sporangial tissue
8 Eventually, a seed may germinate and grow into a seedling that, in turn, grows into a mature sporophyte.
Seedling
7 Double fertilization produces a binucleate cell that will give rise to triploid endosperm, a nutritive tissue that will nourish the developing embryo.
Seed coat
Embryo (2n)
Endosperm (3n)
Seed
DOUBLE FERTILIZATION
DIPLOID (2n)
MEIOSIS
Sexual Reproduction
HAPLOID (n)
Meiosis produces microspores that develop into pollen grains.
Pollen tube
Sperm (n)
Sperm (n)
Male gametophyte
Pollen grain, where megaspores are produced
Pollen sac
Pollen tube
6 The pollen tube enters an ovule. One sperm will fertilize the egg, and one will fertilize the endosperm-producing cell (double fertilization).
(line of cut of diagram at left)
Ovary
Endosperm-producing cell
Egg cell
2 Meiosis produces four megaspores, then all but one disintegrate. It undergoes three rounds of mitosis without cytokinesis, forming a single large cell with eight nuclei.
5 Pollination occurs. Then a pollen grain develops into a pollen tube that grows toward the ovary. The tube contains two sperm. It is the mature male gametophyte.
4 Pollen is released.
3 Cytokinesis produces a female gametophyte that consists of seven cells. One cell becomes the egg. Another large cell (with two nuclei) forms a nutritive tissue called endosperm. The remaining cells also have brief reproductive roles, but they eventually disintegrate. The large central cell contains two nuclei and will produce endosperm after fertilization.

Figure 25.33
Life cycle of typical flowering plant, the monocot *Lilium*. Double fertilization is a notable feature of the cycle. The male gametophyte delivers two sperm to an ovule. One sperm fertilizes the egg, forming the embryo, and the other fertilizes the endosperm-producing cell, which nourishes the embryo.

25.6c Many Factors Contributed to the Adaptive Success of Angiosperms

Flowering plants likely originated about 140 mya. It took only about 40 million years—a short span in geologic time—for angiosperms to eclipse gymnosperms as the prevailing form of plant life on land. Several factors fuelled this adaptive success. As with other seed plants, the large, diploid sporophyte phase dominates a flowering plant's life cycle, and the sporophyte retains and nourishes the much smaller gametophytes. But flowering plants also show some evolutionary innovations not seen in gymnosperms.

More Efficient Transport of Water and Nutrients. Where gymnosperms have only one type of water-conducting cell in their xylem, angiosperms have an additional, more specialized type of cell that moves water more rapidly from roots to shoots. Also, modifications in angiosperm phloem tissue allow it to more efficiently transport sugars produced in photosynthesis through the plant body.

Enhanced Nutrition and Physical Protection for Embryos. Other changes in angiosperms made it more likely that reproduction would succeed. For example, a two-step double-fertilization process in the ovules of flowering plants produces both an embryo and a unique nutritive tissue (called endosperm) that nourishes the embryonic sporophyte. The ovule containing a female gametophyte is enclosed within an ovary, part of the carpel, which shelters the ovule against desiccation and against attack by herbivores or pathogens. After fertilization, an ovary develops into a fruit that not only protects seeds but also helps disperse them—for instance, when an animal eats a fruit, seeds may pass through the animal's gut none the worse for the journey and be released in a new location in the animal's feces. Above all, angiosperms have flowers, the unique reproductive organs that you will read much more about in the next unit.

25.6d Angiosperms Coevolved with Animal Pollinators

The evolutionary success of angiosperms is due not only to the adaptations just described but also to the efficient mechanisms of transferring pollen to female reproductive parts. Whereas a conifer depends on air currents to disperse its pollen, angiosperms coevolved with pollinators—insects, bats, birds, and other animals that transfer pollen from male floral structures to female reproductive parts (often while obtaining nectar). **Coevolution** occurs when two or more species interact closely in the same ecological setting. A heritable change in one species affects selection pressure operating between them, with the result being that the other species evolves as well. Over time, plants have coevolved with their pollinating animals.

In general, a flower's reproductive parts are positioned so that visiting pollinators will brush against them. In addition, many floral features correlate with the morphology and behaviour of specific pollinators. For example, reproductive parts may be located above nectar-filled floral tubes the same length as the feeding structure of a preferred pollinator. Nectar-sipping bats **(Figure 25.34a)** and moths forage by night. They pollinate intensely sweet-smelling flowers with white or pale

a. Bat pollinating a giant saguaro

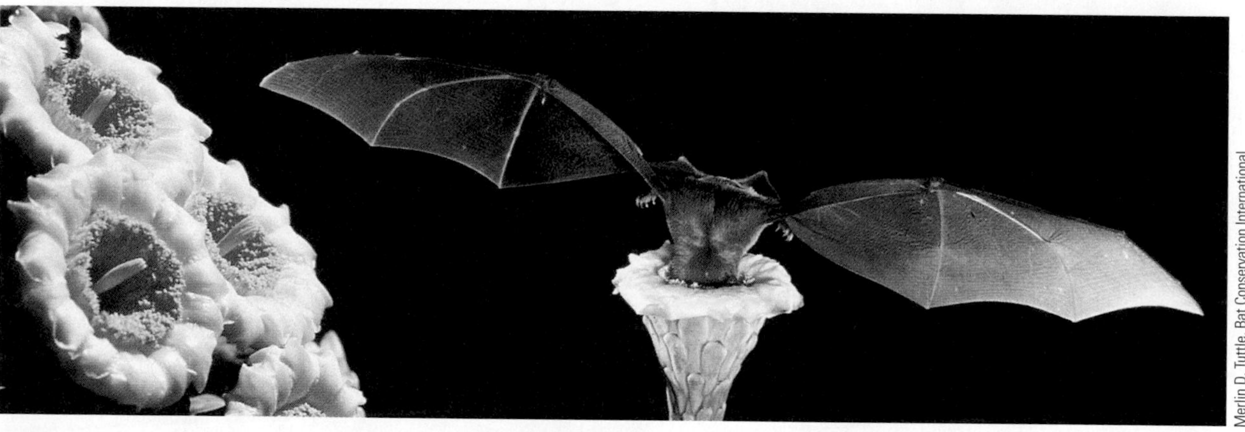
Merlin D. Tuttle, Bat Conservation International

b. Hawkmoth pollinating an orchid

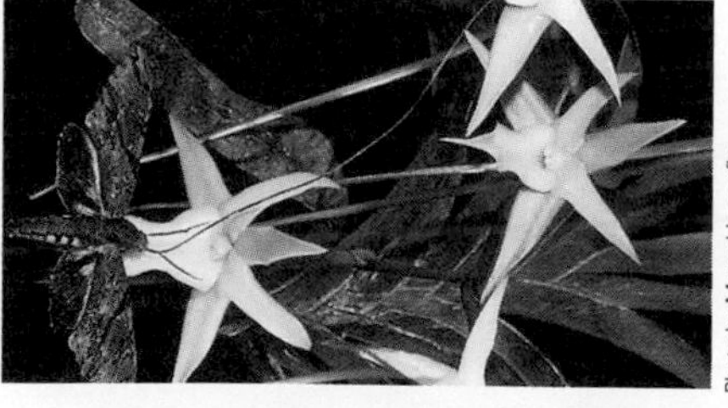
Photo by Marcel Lecoufle

c. Hummingbird visiting a hibiscus flower

Robert A. Tyrrell

d. Bee-attracting pattern of a marsh marigold

Thomas Eisner/Cornell University

Figure 25.34
Coevolution of flowering plants and animal pollinators. The colours and configurations of some flowers, and the production of nectar or odours, have coevolved with specific animal pollinators. **(a)** At night, nectar-feeding bats sip nectar from flowers of the giant saguaro cactus (*Carnegia gigantea*), transferring pollen from flower to flower in the process. **(b)** The hawkmoth *Xanthopan morgani praedicta* has a proboscis long enough to reach nectar at the base of the equally long floral spur of the orchid *Angraecum sesquipedale.* **(c)** A Bahama woodstar hummingbird (*Calliphlox evelynae*) sipping nectar from a hibiscus blossom (*Hibiscus*). The long, narrow bill of hummingbirds coevolved with long, narrow floral tubes. **(d)** Under ultraviolet light, the bee-attracting pattern of a gold-petalled marsh marigold becomes visible to human eyes.

petals that are more visible than coloured petals in the dark. Long, thin mouthparts of moths and butterflies reach nectar in narrow floral tubes or floral spurs. The Madagascar hawkmoth uncoils a mouthpart the same length—an astonishing 22 cm—as the narrow flower of the orchid it pollinates, *Angraecum sesquipedale* **(Figure 25.34b).** Red and yellow flowers attract birds **(Figure 25.34c),** which have good daytime vision but a poor sense of smell. Hence, bird-pollinated plants do not squander metabolic resources to make fragrances. By contrast, flowers of species that are pollinated by beetles or flies may smell like rotten meat, dung, or decaying matter. Daisies and other fragrant flowers with distinctive patterns, shapes, and red or orange components attract butterflies, which forage by day.

Bees see ultraviolet light and visit flowers with sweet odours and parts that appear to humans as yellow, blue, or purple **(Figure 25.34d).** Produced by pigments that absorb ultraviolet light, the colours form patterns called "nectar guides" that attract bees—which may pick up or drop off pollen during the visit. Here, as in our other examples, flowers contribute to the reproductive success of plants that bear them.

In this chapter, we have introduced some of the strategies that plants use to meet challenges of life on Earth; they face the same challenges as

Table 25.2 Plant Phyla and Major Characteristics

Phylum	Common Name	Number of Species	Common General Characteristics
Bryophytes: nonvascular plants. Gametophyte dominant, free water required for fertilization, cuticle and stomata present in some.			
Hepatophyta	Liverworts	6000	Leafy or simple flattened thallus, rhizoids; spores in capsules. Moist, humid habitats.
Anthocerophyta	Hornworts	100	Simple flattened thallus, rhizoids; hornlike sporangia. Moist, humid habitats.
Bryophyta	Mosses	10 000	Feathery or cushiony thallus; some have hydroids; spores in capsules. Moist, humid habitats; colonizes bare rock, soil, or bark.
Seedless vascular plants: sporophyte dominant, free water required for fertilization, cuticle and stomata present.			
Lycophyta	Club mosses	1000	Simple leaves, true roots; most species have sporangia on sporophylls. Mostly wet or shady habitats.
Pterophyta	Ferns, whisk ferns, horsetails	13 000	*Ferns:* Finely divided leaves, sporangia often in sori. Habitats from wet to arid. *Whisk ferns:* Branching stem from rhizomes; sporangia on stem scales. Tropical to subtropical habitats. *Horsetails:* Hollow photosynthetic stem, scalelike leaves, sporangia in strobili. Swamps, disturbed habitats.
Gymnosperms: vascular plants with "naked" seeds. Sporophyte dominant, fertilization by pollination, cuticle and stomata present.			
Cycadophyta	Cycads	185	Shrubby or treelike with palmlike leaves, pithy stems; male and female strobili on separate plants. Widespread distribution.
Ginkgophyta	Ginkgo	1	Woody-stemmed tree, deciduous fan-shaped leaves. Male, female structures on separate plants. Temperate areas of China.
Gnetophyta	Gnetophytes	70	Shrubs or woody vines; one has strappy leaves. Male and female strobili on separate plants. Limited to deserts, tropics.
Coniferophyta	Conifers	550	Mostly evergreen, woody trees and shrubs with needlelike or scalelike leaves; male and female cones usually on same plant.
Angiosperms: plants with flowers and seeds protected inside fruits. Sporophyte dominant, fertilization by pollination, cuticle and stomata present. Major groups: monocots, eudicots.			
Anthophyta	Flowering plants	268 500+ (including magnoliids, other basal angiosperms)	Wood and herbaceous plants. Nearly all land habitats, some aquatic.
Monocots	Grasses, palms, lilies, orchids, and others	60 000	One cotyledon; parallel-veined leaves common; bundles of vascular tissue scattered in stem.
Eudicots	Most fruit trees, roses, beans, potatoes, and others	200 000	Most species have two cotyledons; net-veined leaves common; central core of vascular tissue in stem.

animals and other terrestrial organisms (attract a mate, reproduce, disperse offspring, survive unfavourable conditions) but have had to find ways to do all of these without being able to move around (they are sessile). Many of these topics are followed up in more detail in the chapters dealing with plant biology (Chapters 28 to 31).

The next two chapters introduce animals. As you read those chapters, look for similarities and differences in how they have addressed the challenges of life compared to plants.

Study Break

List at least three adaptations that have contributed to the evolutionary success of angiosperms as a group.

Unanswered Questions

Where did flowering plants come from?

Flowers are a unique feature of the angiosperms, yet botanists still understand little of their evolutionary origin. When flowering plants appear in the Cretaceous fossil record, they appear suddenly and diversify immediately, a situation Darwin famously referred to as an "abominable mystery." What did the first angiosperms and the first flower look like? And where did they arise?

As described in this chapter, recent molecular analyses have converged on *Amborella trichopoda* as the living representative of the most ancient lineage in the angiosperm family tree. This research has shed light on many questions. For example, *Amborella* flowers have some features considered evolutionarily primitive, such as petals and sepals that are not distinctly different in form. This observation supports the hypothesis that two other types of flower parts, the calyx and corolla, arose later in angiosperm evolution. But *Amborella* also has some features thought to have evolved much more recently, such as single-sex flowers that have either male or female reproductive parts (but never both). Should we be surprised to find both primitive and advanced traits in this ancient lineage? Not at all. *Amborella* has existed on Earth for millions of years, and its flowers may have evolved new features over that time.

The puzzle of where angiosperms came from and what the first flowering plants looked like has not been solved by fossil studies either. The fossil species *Archaefructus* might be the oldest known fossil flower. It consists of an elongated axis with what its discoverers described as stamens (male reproductive structures) toward the base, carpels (female reproductive structures) toward the apex, and no sepals and petals. This elongated flower is unlike the flowers of any modern angiosperm, and its structure suggests that the earliest flowers may have been very different from what we see today. However, some paleobotanists have reinterpreted the *Archaefructus* "flower" as an inflorescence (a flower cluster), with male flowers at the base and female flowers toward the apex. In addition, radiometric dating places *Archaefructus* in the early to mid-Cretaceous, a period from which other early angiosperm fossils are known. Thus, *Archaefructus* may not be the oldest flower, and the fossil specimen may represent a cluster of flowers instead of a single flower. This debate continues.

Botanists also disagree about the ancestors of angiosperms. Some gnetophytes—gymnosperms that include *Welwitschia* and *Ephedra* species (refer to Figure 25.28ə)—have features similar to those of angiosperms. Botanists long speculated that the two groups were closely related, with a common ancestor that had flowerlike features. However, recent analyses based on DNA sequence data suggest that gnetophytes are not closely related to angiosperms after all. There are also fossil gymnosperm taxa with features that might be forerunners of carpels or other flower parts, but paleobotanists disagree on these interpretations as well. Thus, examinations of fossils and extant species have yet to resolve key questions about the evolution of angiosperms.

What, then, can molecular data tell us? Studies of the genetic mechanisms that guide the development of flower parts have provided a framework for understanding how genes control flower formation. This research has also given us insight into what kinds of molecular changes may have led to the evolution of flowers. For instance, certain genes that encode transcription factors required for the formation of reproductive organs in flowers are also found in gymnosperms. This finding is not surprising because gymnosperms also form male and female reproductive structures; the most logical hypothesis is that angiosperms retained the gymnosperm developmental program for these organs. Yet genes for other transcription factors active in flower formation are not found in gymnosperms. We know that transcription factors may turn on and off entire developmental pathways, such as those that cause undifferentiated tissue (called meristem tissue) to form a flower. One hypothesis is that in an ancient gymnosperm ancestor, duplications in a particular gene family gave rise to genes that, in turn, accumulated mutations, allowing them to perform new functions that resulted in the formation of the first flowers.

As much insight as these molecular studies give us into events that might have resulted in the evolution of flowers, they have not brought us any closer to understanding the fundamental question of where angiosperms arose. Additional fossil data may help provide the answer, but it is also possible that the earliest angiosperms, or their direct ancestors, lived in habitats where fossils do not readily form. Additional molecular data may deepen our understanding of how changes in genes produced the first flower. But molecular data based on contemporary species will not help decipher what the first angiosperm and the first flower looked like. Thus, it is possible that the abominable mystery will live on.

Amy Litt is director of plant genomics and Cullman curator at the New York Botanical Garden, where she also earned her Ph.D. Her main interests lie in the evolution of plant form and how changes in gene function during the course of plant evolution have produced novel plant forms and functions—particularly new flower and fruit morphologies. Learn more about her work at http://sciweb.nybg.org/science2/Profile_106.asp.

Review

Go to CENGAGENOW™ at http://hed.nelson.com/ to access quizzing, animations, exercises, articles, and personalized homework help.

25.1 Defining Characteristics of Land Plants

- Land plants are multicellular eukaryotes with cellulose cell walls. Most, but not all, are photoautotrophs. All have an alternation of generations life cycle, although which generation is dominant varies among groups of plants, and all retain embryos inside parental tissue.

25.2 The Transition to Life on Land

- Plants are thought to have evolved from charophyte green algae between 425 and 490 million years ago.
- Adaptations to terrestrial life in the earliest land plants include poikilohydry, multicellular chambers that protect developing gametes, and an embryo sheltered inside a parent plant.
- Other key evolutionary trends among land plants included symbiotic associations with fungi; the development of vascular tissues, root systems, and shoot systems; lignified stems and leaves equipped with stomata; increasing dominance by the diploid sporophyte generation; and a shift from homospory to heterospory.
- Gametophytes became reduced in size; male gametophytes (pollen) became specialized for dispersal without liquid water, and female gametophytes are increasingly protected inside sporophyte tissues.

25.3 Bryophytes: Nonvascular Land Plants

- Existing nonvascular land plants, or bryophytes, include the liverworts, hornworts, and mosses. Liverworts may have been the first land plants.
- Bryophytes produce flagellated sperm that swim through free water to reach eggs. They lack a vascular system, roots, stems, and leaves. The gametophyte phase is dominant.

25.4 Seedless Vascular Plants

- Existing seedless vascular land plants include the lycophytes (club mosses), whisk ferns, horsetails, and ferns. Like bryophytes, they release spores and have swimming sperm. Unlike bryophytes, they have well-developed vascular tissues. The sporophyte generation is dominant and independent of the gametophyte.
- Most seedless vascular plants are homosporous, but some are heterosporous.

25.5 Gymnosperms: The First Seed Plants

- Gymnosperms (conifers and their relatives), together with angiosperms (flowering plants), are the seed-bearing vascular plants. Reproductive innovations include pollination, the ovule, and the seed. Liquid water is not required for reproduction.
- During the Mesozoic, gymnosperms were the dominant land plants. Today conifers are the primary vegetation of forests at higher latitudes and elevations and have important economic uses as sources of lumber and other products.

25.6 Angiosperms: Flowering Plants

- Angiosperms (Anthophyta) have dominated the land for more than 100 million years and currently are the most diverse plant group.
- The angiosperm vascular system moves water and sugars through the plant body more efficiently than that of gymnosperms. Reproductive adaptations include a protective ovary around the ovule, endosperm, flowers that attract pollinators, and fruits that protect and disperse seeds.

Questions

Self-Test Questions

1. Which of the following is not an evolutionary trend among plants?
   a. developing vascular tissues
   b. becoming seedless
   c. having a dominant diploid generation
   d. producing nonmotile gametes
   e. producing two types of spores
2. As plants made the evolutionary transition to a terrestrial existence, they benefited from adaptations that
   a. increased the motility of their gametes on dry land.
   b. flattened the plant body to expose it to the sun.
   c. reduced the number and distribution of roots to prevent drying.
   d. provided mechanisms for gaining access to nutrients in soil.
   e. allowed stems and leaves to absorb water from the atmosphere.
3. Land plants no longer required water as a medium for reproduction with the evolution of
   a. fruits and roots.
   b. flowers and leaves.
   c. cell walls and rhizoids.
   d. lignified stems.
   e. seeds and pollen.
4. Which is the correct matching of phylum and plant group?
   a. Anthophyta: pines
   b. Bryophyta: gnetophytes
   c. Coniferophyta: angiosperms
   d. Hepatophyta: cycads
   e. Pterophyta: horsetails
5. A homeowner noticed moss growing between bricks on his patio. Closer examination revealed tiny brown stalks with cup-like tops emerging from green leaflets. These brown structures were
   a. the sporophyte generation.
   b. the gametophyte generation.
   c. elongated haploid reproductive cells.
   d. archegonia.
   e. antheridia.
6. Horsetails are most closely related to
   a. mosses and whisk ferns.
   b. liverworts and hornworts.
   c. cycads and ginkgoes.
   d. club mosses and ferns.
   e. gnetophytes and gymnosperms.

7. The evolution of true roots is first seen in
   a. liverworts.
   b. seedless vascular plants.
   c. mosses.
   d. flowering plants.
   e. conifers.
8. Based solely on numbers of species, the most successful plants today are
   a. angiosperms.
   b. ferns.
   c. gymnosperms.
   d. mosses.
   e. the bryophytes as a group.

Questions for Discussion

1. Working in the field, you discover a fossil of a previously undescribed plant species. The specimen is small and may not be complete; the parts you have do not include any floral organs. What sorts of observations would you need to classify the fossil as a seedless vascular plant with reasonable accuracy? What evidence would you need to distinguish between a fossil lycopod and a fern?
2. Compare the size, anatomical complexity, and degree of independence of a moss gametophyte, a fern gametophyte, a Douglas fir female gametophyte, and a dogwood female gametophyte. Which one is the most protected from the external environment? Which trends in plant evolution does your work on this question bring to mind?
3. How has the relative lack of fossil early angiosperms affected our understanding of this group?

Workers of the weaver ant, *Oecophylla*, engaged in the construction of their nest, which is formed from living leaves, curled or folded to form an envelope held together by silk secreted by the larvae.

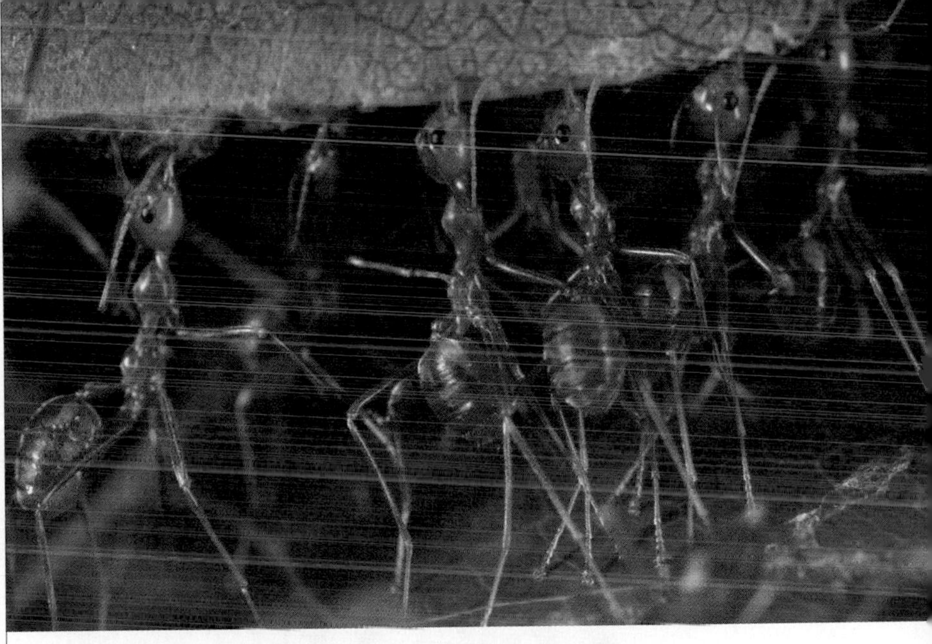

Mark Moffett/Mincen Pictures

Study Plan

26 Protostomes

Why It Matters

During the early Cambrian, beginning about 540 million years ago, conditions were ripe for rapid development of the marine fauna and an explosion of new forms appeared, particularly in the warm and shallow seas bordering the continents. About 505 million years ago, a series of mud slides carried the animals that lived at the edge of a submarine cliff, the Cathedral Escarpment, over its edge, and buried them in fine silt. That mud and its contained fossils formed shale, a sedimentary rock that has layers that are easily split. During continent and mountain building, the shale beds, now known as the Burgess Shale, came to lie in the Canadian Rocky Mountains of eastern British Columbia in what is now Yoho National Park.

Charles Walcott, an American palaeontologist working in the Burgess Shale area in 1909, located a rich bed of very strange fossils that were exquisitely preserved, including the soft parts. Reconstructions have revealed not only familiar trilobites and sponges but also many truly bizarre animals (**Figure 26.1, p. 578**). For example, *Opabinia* was about as long as a tube of lipstick and had five eyes on its head and a single anterior grasping organ, which was probably used to catch prey. The smaller *Hallucigenia* had seven pairs of hard spines on its

Opabinia
Dr. Chip Clark, National Museum of Natural History, Smithsonian Institution
Hallucigenia
Dr. Chip Clark, National Museum of Natural History, Smithsonian Institution

Figure 26.1
Animals of the Burgess Shale. *Opabinia* had five eyes and a grasping organ on its head. *Hallucigenia* had seven pairs of spines and soft protuberances.

back and what appear to be seven pairs of softer ventral protuberances that probably functioned for locomotion. Some organisms look like early chordates, but many do not resemble any living animals and may represent phyla that have never been described.

The Burgess Shale and other similar sites provide us with a snapshot of some of the animals that inhabited the coastal waters at the time of the "Cambrian Explosion." Most of the bizarre forms did not survive the extinctions that were to come. Without those extinctions, some of the forms might have survived to found lineages completely different from those living today.

In this chapter, we introduce the general characteristics of animals and a phylogenetic hypothesis about their evolutionary history and classification. We also survey the major invertebrate phyla belonging to one lineage, the Protostomia. In Chapter 19, we defined the various levels used in the Linnaen system of classifying animals. In Chapter 27, we examine the other major animal lineage, the Deuterostomia, which includes the phylum Chordata and their nearest invertebrate relatives.

26.1 What Is an Animal?

Biologists recognize the kingdom Animalia as a monophyletic group that is easily distinguished from the other kingdoms.

26.1a All Animals Share Certain Structural and Behavioural Characteristics

Animals are eukaryotic, multicellular organisms. The cell membranes of adjacent animal cells are in direct contact. This is different from plants and fungi, which have cell walls around the cells. Animal cells may be organized into different morphological types to reflect their role in the functioning of the animal as a single unit.

All animals are **heterotrophs:** they depend on other life forms for their food, either by eating them directly or living in a parasitic association with them. They use oxygen to metabolize their food through aerobic respiration, and most store excess energy as glycogen, oil, or fat.

All animals are **motile** (able to move from place to place) at some time in their lives. Most familiar animals are motile as adults. However, in some species, such as mussels and barnacles, only the young are motile; they eventually settle down as **sessile** (unable to move from one place to another) adults. All animals are able to perceive and respond to information about the environment in which they live.

Animals reproduce either asexually or sexually; in many groups, they switch from one mode to the other. Sexually reproducing species produce haploid **gametes** (eggs and sperm) that fuse to form diploid **zygotes** (fertilized eggs). For many invertebrates, development to the adult involves one or more **larval forms.** This

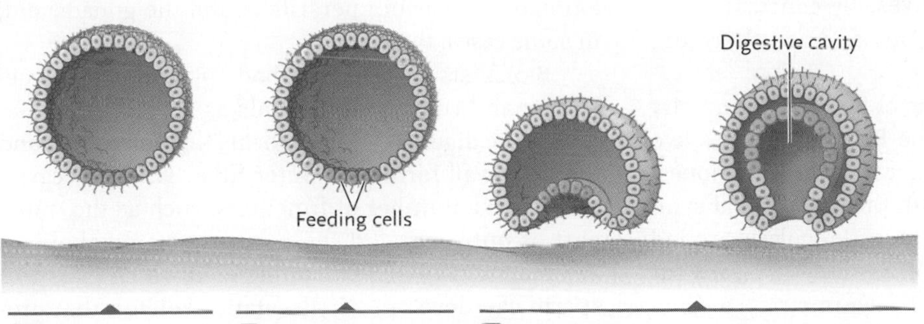
Digestive cavity
Feeding cells
1 Colonial flagellated protist with unspecialized cells
2 Certain cells became specialized for feeding and other functions.
3 A developmental reorganization produced a two-layered animal with a sac-within-a-sac body plan.

Figure 26.2
Animal origins. Many biologists believe that animals arose from a colonial, flagellated protist in which cells became specialized for specific functions and a developmental reorganization produced two cell layers. The cell movements illustrated here are similar to those that occur during the development of many animals, as described in Chapter 48.

pattern of development, in which a species can exist during development in two or more distinct forms, is referred to as **polymorphic development.** This developmental strategy is important for the success of many of the invertebrate groups.

26.1b The Animal Lineage Probably Arose from a Colonial Choanoflagellate Ancestor

Most biologists agree that the common ancestor of all animals was probably a colonial, flagellated protist that lived at least 700 million years ago, during the Precambrian. It may have resembled the minute, sessile choanoflagellates (see Chapter 23) that live in both freshwater and marine habitats today. The German embryologist Ernst Haeckel proposed a colonial, flagellated ancestor in 1874, suggesting that it was a hollow, ball-shaped organism with unspecialized cells. Its cells became specialized for particular functions, and a developmental reorganization produced a double-layered, sac-within-a-sac body plan (**Figure 26.2**). The embryology of many living animals roughly parallels this hypothetical evolutionary transformation (see Chapter 39). He included this hypothetical organism among what he called the Metazoa (*meta* = more developed; *zoon* = animal) to distinguish them from the protozoa.

Study Break

1. What characteristics distinguish animals from plants?
2. What early steps may have led to the first metazoans?

26.2 Key Innovations in Animal Evolution

Once established, the animal lineage diversified quickly into an amazing array of body plans. Biologists have used several key morphological innovations to unravel the evolutionary relationships of the major animal groups.

26.2a Tissues and Tissue Layers Appeared Early in Animal Evolution

In most Metazoans, the process of development gives rise to two or three layers that eventually form **tissues,** groups of similar differentiated cells that are specialized for particular functions.

In most metazoans, embryonic tissues form as either two or three concentric **germ layers** (see Chapter 39). The innermost layer, the **endoderm,** eventually develops into the lining of the gut (digestive system) and, in some animals, respiratory organs. The outermost layer, the **ectoderm,** forms the external covering and nervous system. Between the two, the **mesoderm** forms the muscles of the body wall and most other structures between the gut and the external covering. Some animals have a **diploblastic** body plan that includes only two embryonic layers, endoderm and ectoderm, but most are **triploblastic,** having all three germ layers.

26.2b Most Animals Exhibit Either Radial or Bilateral Symmetry

The most obvious feature of an animal's body plan is its shape (**Figure 26.3**). Most animals are **symmetrical;** in other words, their bodies can be divided by a

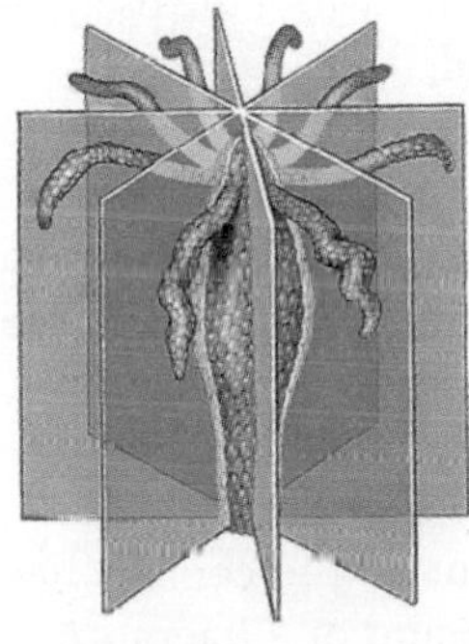

Radial symmetry

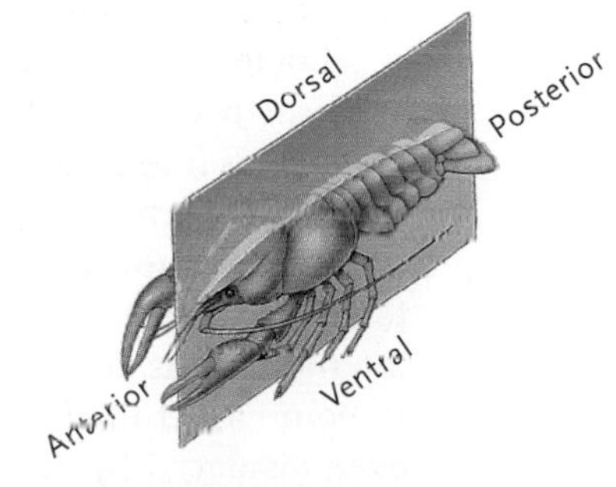
Dorsal
Posterior
Anterior
Ventral

Bilateral symmetry

Figure 26.3
Patterns of body symmetry. Most animals have either radial or bilateral symmetry.

plane into mirror-image halves. By contrast, most sponges have irregular shapes and are therefore **asymmetrical.**

All other phyla exhibit one of two body symmetry patterns (see Figure 26.3). The Radiata includes two phyla, Cnidaria (hydras, jellyfishes, and sea anemones) and Ctenophora (comb jellies), that have **radial symmetry.** Their body parts are arranged regularly around a central axis, like the spokes on a wheel. Thus, any cut down the long axis of a radially symmetrical animal divides it into matching halves.

All other metazoan phyla fall within the Bilateria, animals that have **bilateral symmetry.** In other words, they have left and right sides that are mirror images of each other on either side of the body's midline. Bilaterally symmetrical animals also have front (**anterior**) and back (**posterior**) ends, as well as upper (**dorsal**) and lower (**ventral**) surfaces. As they move through the environment, the anterior end encounters food, shelter, or enemies first. In bilaterally symmetrical animals, natural selection favoured **cephalization,** the development of an anterior head where sensory organs and nerve tissue are concentrated.

26.2c Many Animals Have Body Cavities That Surround Their Internal Organs

The body plans of many bilaterally symmetrical animals include a body cavity that separates the gut from the muscles of the body wall. **Acoelomate** animals (*a* = without; *koiloma* = cavity), such as flatworms (phylum Platyhelminthes), do not have such a cavity; instead, a mass of cells, derived largely from mesoderm, packs the region between the gut and the body wall **(Figure 26.4a).**

Pseudocoelomate animals (*pseudo* = false), including the roundworms (phylum Nematoda) and wheel animals (phylum Rotifera), have a **pseudocoelom,** a fluid-filled space between the gut and the muscles of the body wall that has no mesodermal lining around the endoderm **(Figure 26.4b).** The muscles of the body wall, derived from mesoderm, form the outer lining of the pseudocoelom, and its inner lining is the gut, which has no muscles. Internal organs lie within the pseudocoelom and are bathed by its fluid.

Coelomate animals have a **coelom,** a fluid-filled body cavity completely lined by mesoderm. In vertebrates, this lining takes the form of the **peritoneum,** a thin tissue derived from mesoderm **(Figure 26.4c).** The inner and outer layers of the peritoneum connect, forming **mesenteries,** membranes that surround the internal organs and suspend them within the coelom. In some arthropods and molluscs, the coelom has been displaced by the development of a haemocoel, resulting from an open circulatory system. This can be envisaged as consisting of a single large blood vessel that has expanded to fill the coelom. In these animals, the coelom persists aound the gonads and, in some cases, the heart.

Biologists describe the body plan of pseudocoelomate and coelomate animals as a "tube-within-a-tube." The digestive system forms the inner tube, and the body wall forms the outer tube. The body cavity may serve a number of functions, such as the transport of nutrients and the products of metabolism, the provision of an environment in which eggs and sperm can develop, a **hydrostatic skeleton** that provides a basis for locomotion (see Chapter 36), and an appropriate environment for the functioning of internal organs.

26.2d Developmental Patterns Mark a Major Divergence in Animal Ancestry

Embryological evidence suggests that bilaterally symmetrical animals are divided into two lineages, the **protostomes** and the **deuterostomes,** that differ in several developmental characteristics **(Figure 26.5, p. 582).**

Shortly after fertilization, an egg undergoes a series of cell divisions called **cleavage.** The first two cell divisions divide a zygote as you might slice an apple, cutting it into four wedges from top to bottom. In some animals, subsequent cell divisions occur at oblique angles to the vertical axis of the embryo, ultimately producing a mass in which each cell at the top of the embryo lies in the groove between the pair of cells below it (see the left side of Figure 26.5a). This pattern is called **spiral cleavage.** It is generally characteristic of most protostomes, although cleavage patterns in arthropods and some other groups are highly specialized. In deuterostomes, by contrast, the third cell division is perpendicular to the vertical axis of the embryo, cutting each of the four cells near its midsection. The fourth cell division is vertical, producing a mass of cells that are stacked directly above and below one another (see the right side of Figure 26.5a). This pattern is called **radial cleavage.**

Protostomes and deuterostomes often differ in the timing of important developmental events. During cleavage, certain genes are activated at specific times, determining a cell's developmental path and ultimate fate. Many protostomes undergo **determinate cleavage:** each cell's developmental path is determined as the cell is produced. Thus, one cell isolated from a two- or four-cell protostome embryo cannot develop into a functional embryo or larva. By contrast, many deuterostomes have **indeterminate cleavage:** the developmental fates of cells are determined later. A cell isolated from a four-cell deuterostome embryo will develop into a functional embryo. In humans, the two cells produced by the first cleavage division sometimes separate and develop into identical twins.

As development proceeds, an opening on the surface of the embryo eventually connects the

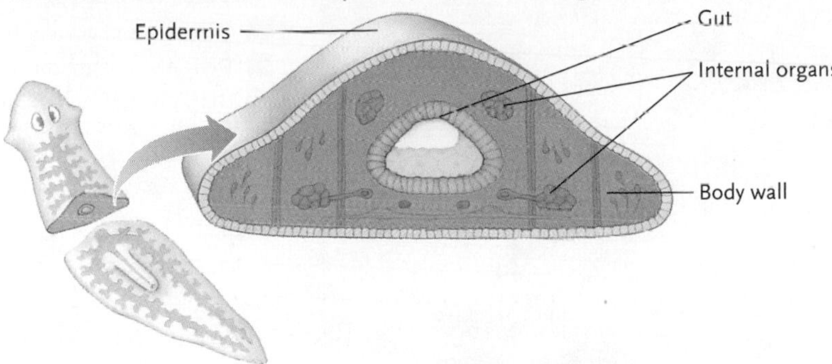
a. In acoelomate animals, no body cavity separates the gut and body wall.
Epidermis
Gut
Internal organs
Body wall

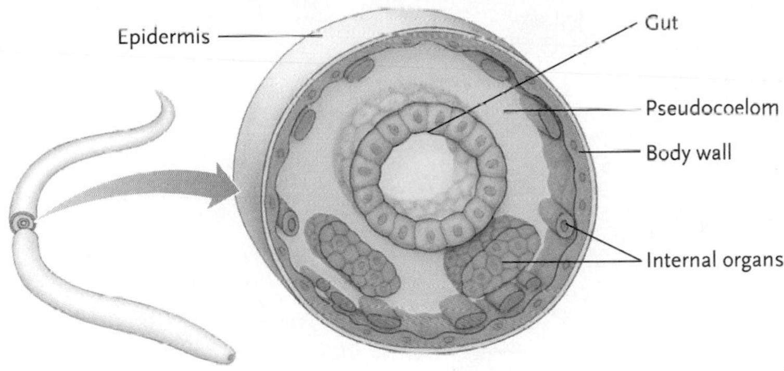
b. In pseudocoelomate animals, the pseudocoelom forms between the gut (a derivative of endoderm) and the body wall (a derivative of mesoderm).
Epidermis
Gut
Pseudocoelom
Body wall
Internal organs

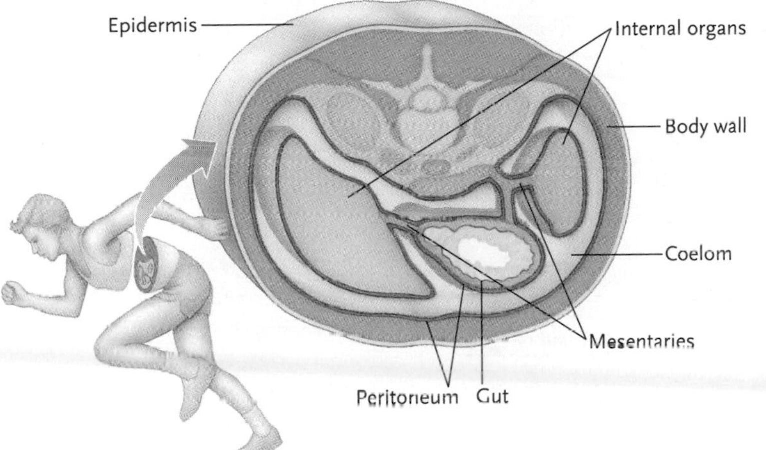
c. In coelomate animals, the coelom is completely lined by peritoneum (a derivative of mesoderm).
Epidermis
Internal organs
Body wall
Coelom
Mesentaries
Peritoneum
Gut
KEY
Derivatives of ectoderm
Derivatives of mesoderm
Derivatives of endoderm
Body cavity

Figure 26.4
Body plans of triploblastic animals. Derivatives of endoderm are yellow, those of mesoderm are red, and those of ectoderm are blue.

developing gut, called the **archenteron,** to the outside environment. This opening is called the **blastopore** (see Figure 26.5b). Later in development, a second opening at the opposite end of the embryo transforms the pouchlike gut into a digestive tube (see Figure 26.5c). In protostomes (*proto* = first; *stoma* = mouth), the blastopore develops into the mouth and the second opening forms the anus. In deuterostomes (*deuteros* = second), the blastopore develops into the anus and the second opening becomes the mouth.

Protostomes and deuterostomes differ in the origin of mesoderm and the coelom (see Figure 26.5b). In most protostomes, mesoderm originates from a few specific cells near the blastopore. As the mesoderm grows and develops, it splits into inner and outer layers. The space between the layers forms a **schizocoelom** (*schizo* = split). In deuterostomes, mesoderm forms from outpocketings of the archenteron. The space pinched off by the outpocketings forms an **enterocoelom** (*entero* = intestine).

Several other characteristics differ in protostomes and deuterostomes. For example, the nervous system of protostomes is positioned on the ventral side of the body, and their brain surrounds the opening of the

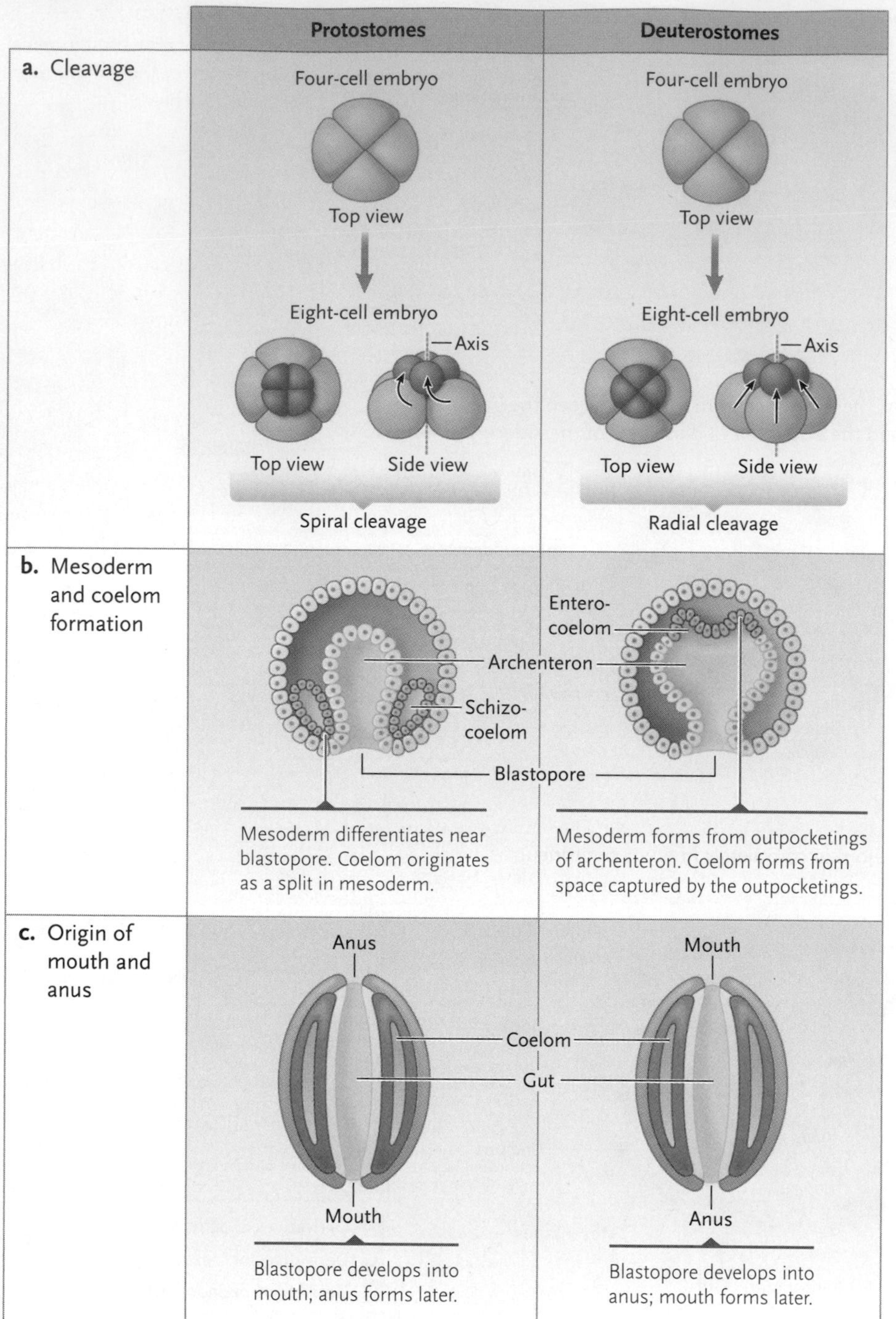

Figure 26.5
Protostomes and deuterostomes. The two lineages of coelomate animals differ in **(a)** cleavage patterns, **(b)** the origin of mesoderm and the coelom, and **(c)** the polarity of the digestive system.

digestive tract. By contrast, the nervous system and brain of deuterostomes lie on the dorsal side of the body.

26.2e Segmentation Divides the Bodies of Some Animals into Repeating Units

Some phyla in both the protostome and deuterostome lineages exhibit varying degrees of **segmentation**, the production of body parts as repeating units. During development, segmentation first arises in the mesoderm, the middle tissue layer that produces most of the body's bulk. In vertebrates, segmentation is obvious in the embryo, and in the adult there is evidence of segmentation in the vertebral column (backbone), ribs, and associated muscles, as well as the nervous system. Among invertebrates, segmentation is pronounced in annelids (earthworms and their relatives), where each segment, visible externally as a ring, has its own set of muscles, ganglion (collection of nerve cells), and excretory structures. Arthropods (insects and their relatives) are also segmented, although some segments may be specialized, bearing, for example, wings or reproductive structures.

The advantages of segmentation lie principally in movement, but to different degrees. In vertebrates, with their articulated backbone and each segment with its own muscles, segmentation permits the S-shaped side-to-side motion—think of fish or snakes. Annelids are capable of similar motion, but many of them live in burrows or tubes. The ability to expand segments by contracting muscles of adjacent segments assists this lifestyle. Arthropods, with their articulated stiffened cuticle to which their muscles are attached, gain significant leverage and strength (see Chapter 36). They have taken advantage of the existence of segmental appendages to assign special functions such as locomotion, reproduction, or gas exchange to particular appendages.

Study Break

1. What is a tissue, and what three primary tissue layers are present in the embryos of most animals? Explain the function of each layer.
2. What kind of symmetry does an earthworm have?
3. What is the function of the coelom, and what is the importance of the fluid?

26.3 An Overview of Animal Phylogeny and Classification

For many years, biologists used the morphological innovations and embryological patterns described above, together with evidence from the fossil record, to trace the phylogenetic history of animals (see Chapter 19). That evidence led to the construction of phylogenetic trees that were broadly accepted as reasonable hypotheses about the relatedness of various phyla. Thus, phyla with similar developmental and morphological patterns were regarded as sharing common ancestries. For example, annelids and arthropods, both schizocoelous, segmented coelomates, were seen as sharing a common ancestor, a view that was supported by the fossil record and by the existence of the Phylum Onychophora, which has some of the characteristics of both phyla. Increasingly, however, biologists are using molecular sequence data to reanalyze animal relationships.

26.3a Molecular Analyses Have Refined Our Understanding of Animal Phylogeny

Molecular analyses of animal relationships are often based on nucleotide sequences in small subunit ribosomal RNA and mitochondrial DNA, and, more recently, the sequences of specific genes. These analyses are used to construct molecular cladograms (see Chapter 19). **Figure 26.6, p. 584,** is a phylogenetic tree developed from a number of cladograms based on molecular sequences. It represents, as do all such trees, a working hypothesis that explains the information that is now available.

The phylogenetic tree based on molecular characters includes the major lineages that biologists had defined using the morphological innovations and embryological characters described above. For example, molecular data confirm the distinctions between the Radiata and the Bilateria. They also confirm the separation of the deuterostome phyla from all others within the Bilateria.

The sponges are to some degree a special case. Because the way that the tissues are formed during embryology in the most primitive sponges differs from the other Metazoa, sponges have in the past been regarded as lacking "true" tissues and were placed in a separate subkingdom, the Parazoa, distinct from the remaining metazoans in the Eumetazoa. But the most recent molecular evidence includes them with the other Metazoa in a single monophyletic lineage. They do not form distinct nervous tissue, and that, together with absence of symmetry, separates them from all other Metazoans. However, molecular studies confirm that sponges and other Metazoa share a common ancestor.

Molecular phylogeny confirms the Protostomia and Deuterostomia as separate lineages within the Metazoa. Protostomia is, in turn, subdivided into two major lineages, the Lophotrochozoa and the Ecdysozoa, groupings that were not previously recognized. The name Lophotrochozoa (*lophos* = crest; *troch* = wheel; *zoa* = animals, plural of *zoon*) refers to both the "lophophore," a feeding structure found in three phyla (illustrated in Figure 26.15), and the "trochophore," a type of larva found in annelids and molluscs (illustrated in Figure 26.23). The name Ecdysozoa (*ekdero* = strip off the skin) refers to the cuticle that these species secrete and periodically replace; the shedding of the cuticle is called **ecdysis**.

26.3b Molecular Phylogeny Reveals Surprising Patterns in the Evolution of Key Morphological Innovations

Molecular phylogeny has forced biologists to reevaluate the evolution of several important morphological innovations. Traditional phylogenies based on morphology and embryology implied that the absence of a body cavity, the acoelomate condition, was ancestral and that the presence of a body cavity, the pseudocoelomate or coelomate condition, was derived. But the molecular tree provides a very different view. It suggests that the schizocoelomate condition is ancestral, having evolved in the common ancestor of the lineage. If that hypothesis is correct, then the acoelomate condition of flatworms may represent the evolutionary *loss* of the schizocoelom, *not* an ancestral condition. Similarly, the molecular tree hypothesizes that the pseudocoelom

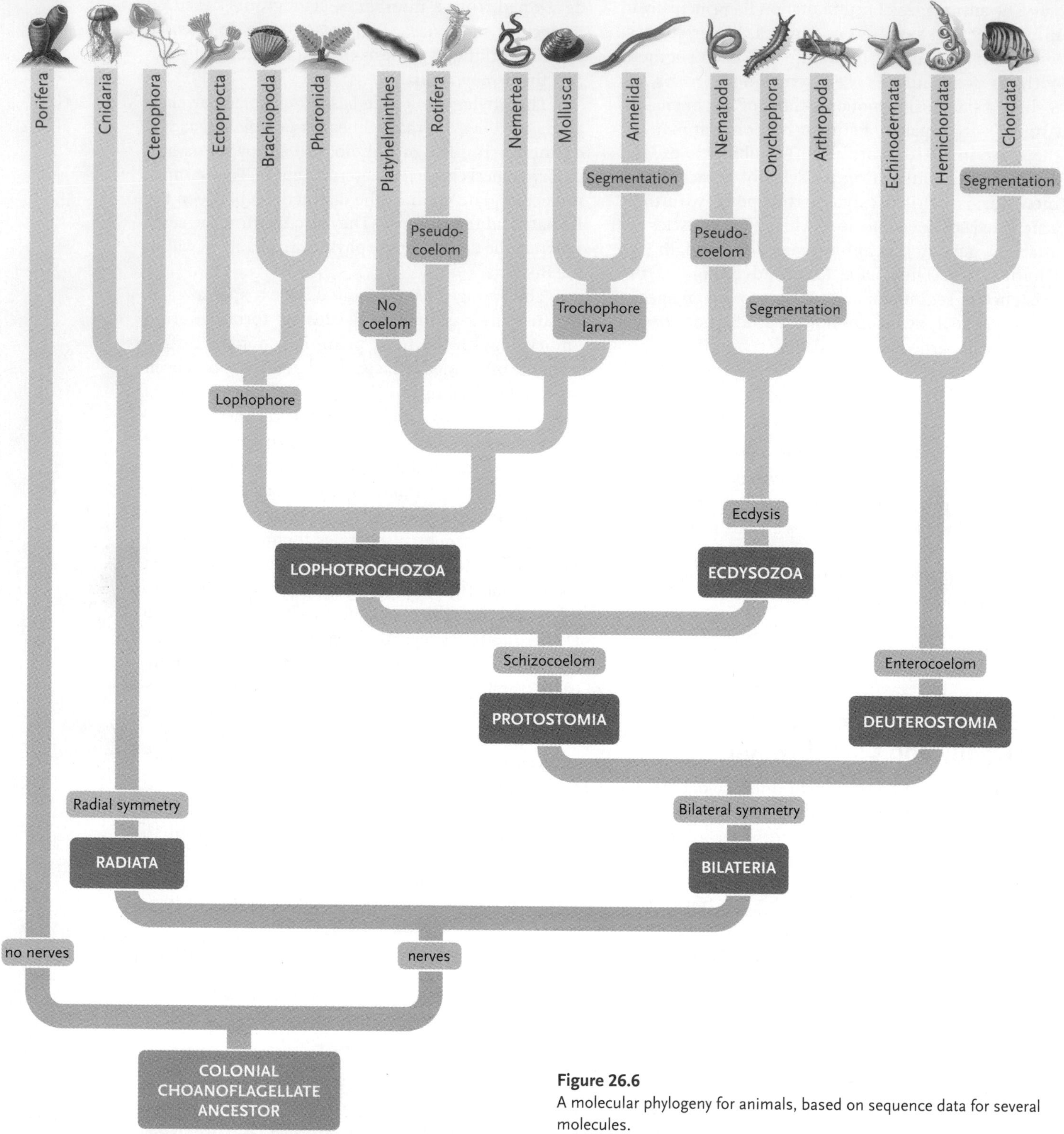

Figure 26.6
A molecular phylogeny for animals, based on sequence data for several molecules.

evolved independently in rotifers (Lophotrochozoa, phylum Rotifera) and in roundworms (Ecdysozoa, phylum Nematoda) as modifications of the ancestral schizocoelom.

Traditional phylogenies also suggested that the segmented body plan of several protostome phyla was inherited from a segmented common ancestor and that segmentation arose independently in the chordates by convergent evolution. The molecular tree, by contrast, suggests that segmentation evolved independently in *three* lineages: segmented worms (Lophotrochozoa, phylum Annelida), arthropods and velvet worms (Ecdysozoa, phyla Arthropoda and Onychophora), and chordates (Deuterostomia, phylum Chordata).

The hypothesis based on molecular studies and represented in Figure 26.6 is the framework that we use for our consideration of the major invertebrate phyla. It is important to recognize, however, that phylogenetic trees are always provisional. In the future, new data may lead to revisions of the phylogeny.

Figure 26.7
Asymmetry in sponges. The shapes of sponges vary with their habitats. Those that occupy calm waters, such as this stinker vase sponge (*Ircinia campana*), may be lobed, tubular, cuplike, or vaselike.

Study Break

1. How is molecular analysis used in creating phylogenetic trees?
2. Describe the way molecular phylogeny has changed how biologists view the absence of the coelom.

26.4 Phylum Porifera

Sponges **(Figure 26.7)** are mostly marine, with a small number of species living in fresh water. They have no particular symmetry, are completely sessile as adults, and obtain their food by filtering it from the water. Sponges have been abundant since the Cambrian, and about 8000 living species are known. They range in size from 1 cm to 2 m.

Their body plan **(Figure 26.8)** is simple: sponges can be regarded as sacs with a cavity, the spongocoel, opening to the environment via an osteopore. There are two layers of organized cells. The cells on the outside of the sponge, the pinacocytes, form an epithelium. The inner layer of cells, lining the cavity, are choanocytes, each with a flagellum surrounded by microvilli. The two layers are separated by a gelatinous matrix, the mesohyl. The mesohyl contains archaeocytes, amoebalike cells that move throughout the mesohyl by typical amoeboid movement. The wall of the bag is perforated by a number of pores lined by porocytes, specialized derivatives of the pinacocytes.

Almost all sponges are filter feeders. The action of the choanocytes sets up a unidirectional current by which water enters the spongocoel through the porocytes and leaves via the osteopore. Flow rates can be adjusted by the porocytes, which are capable of contraction, suggesting communication among the cells in spite of the absence of nerves. Particles of food are captured by the choanocytes and passed to the mesohyl, where they are ingested and digested by the archaeocytes, which may also store reserves.

Some archaeocytes may become specialized to form extracellular rigid supporting structures that give shape to the sponge. These are microscopic rigid structures of various shapes (depending on the species) composed of a calcareous or siliceous (silicon) material. Collagen is also found in the mesohyl, as is a collagen-like protein, spongin. These are products of the

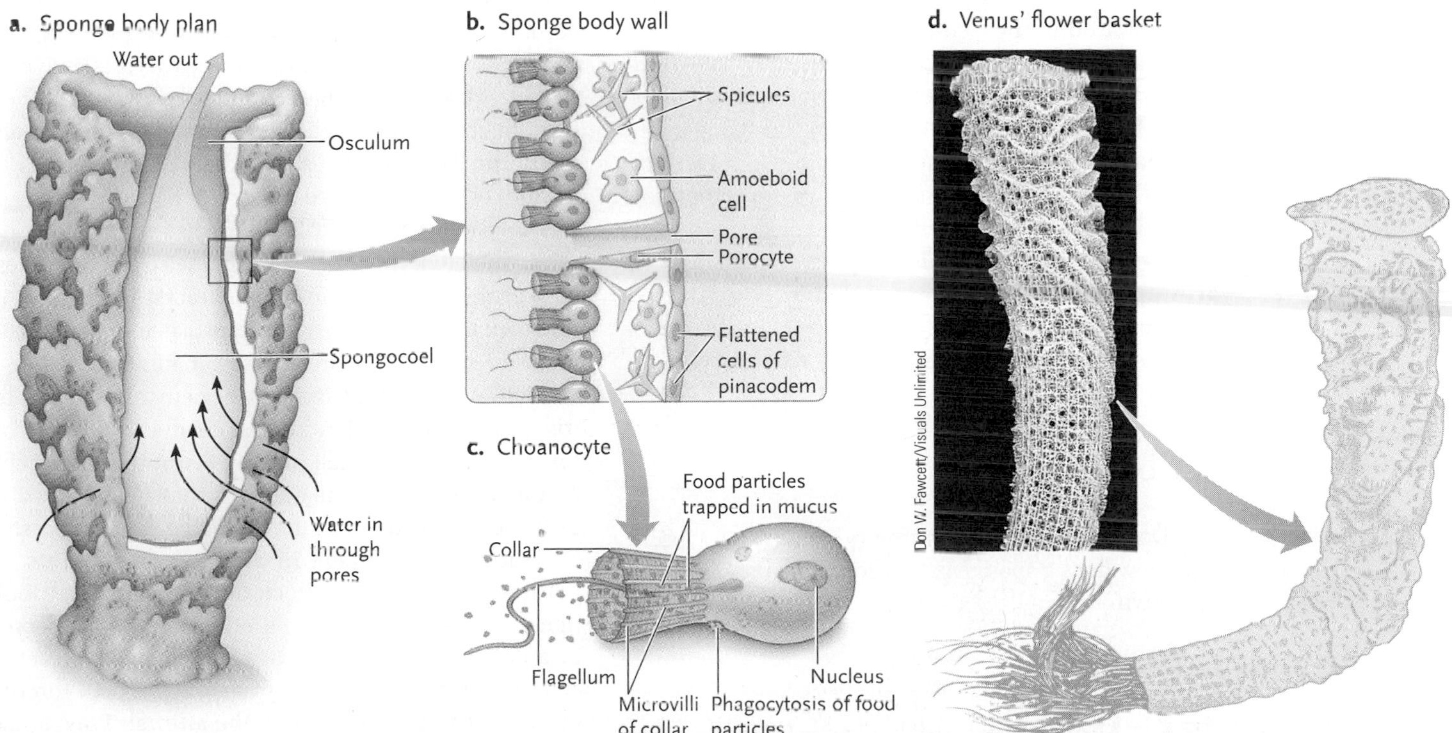

Figure 26.8
The body plan of sponges. Most sponges have **(a)** simple body plans and **(b)** relatively few cell types. **(c)** Beating flagella on the choanocytes create a flow of water through incurrent pores, into the spongocoel, and out through the osculum. **(d)** Venus flower basket (*Euplectella* species), a marine sponge, has spicules of silica fused into a rigid framework.

archaeocytes. The archaeocytes are "totipotent"—like stem cells, they have the capacity to differentiate into any of the cell types, including eggs and sperm.

Most sponges are monoecious: individuals produce both sperm and eggs. Sperm are released into the spongocoel and then out into the environment; eggs (oocytes) remain in the mesohyl, where sperm from other sponges, drawn in with water, are captured by choanocytes and carried to oocytes. Early development occurs within the sponge and produces a ciliated larva that permits the distribution of the species within the habitat. The larvae are of various types: many are free swimming, whereas some use their cilia to crawl over the substrate. There is evidence that some larvae avoid light to select a location to settle, where they undergo **metamorphosis** (a reorganization of form) into sessile adults. Some sponges also reproduce asexually; small fragments break off an adult and grow into new sponges. Many species, particularly those in fresh water, also produce **gemmules**, clusters of cells with a resistant covering that allows them to survive unfavourable conditions. Gemmules germinate into new sponges when conditions improve.

Even with a very simple basic body plan, sponges have achieved remarkable diversity. Sponges formed very large reefs during the Mesozoic, and a modern reef, originating at the end of the last ice age, has been found off the west coast of Canada. It is being studied by Verena Tunnicliffes lab at the University of Victoria.

Many sponges serve as refuges for other species. Blue-green algae and cyanobacteria can be found in the mesohyl and, in some species, within the archaeocytes. A curious relationship with another species can be found in the Venus flower basket, *Euplectella aspergillum* (see Figure 26.8d). Male and female shrimp (*Spongicola* species) may enter the spongocoel when small, feed on material brought in by the sponge, and grow large enough that they are unable to leave. The pair of shrimp spend their entire lives in the prison formed by the elaborate basket of spicules.

One species, *Asbestopluma hypogea*, catches small arthropods that become entangled in hook-shaped spicules on the surface. The prey are then encased in filamentous structures and digested. Choanocytes are absent in this sponge.

Study Break

1. Do sponges exhibit symmetry? If so, what type?
2. How does a sponge gather food from its environment?

26.5 Metazoans with Radial Symmetry

Unlike sponges, the remaining metazoans have some form of symmetry and well-differentiated tissues, including nerves, that develop from distinct layers in the embryo. In this section, we describe metazoans with radial symmetry, a body plan that permits the detection of stimuli from all directions. This is an effective adaptation for life in open water.

Two phyla of soft-bodied organisms, Cnidaria and Ctenophora, have radial symmetry and nerves. Both phyla possess a **gastrovascular cavity** with a single opening, the mouth. Gas exchange and excretion can occur by diffusion because no cell is far from a body surface.

The radiate phyla have a diploblastic body plan with only inner and outer tissue layers, the **gastrodermis** (an endoderm derivative) and the **epidermis** (an ectoderm derivative), respectively. Most species also possess a gelatinous **mesoglea** (*meso* = middle; *glea* = glue) between the two layers. The mesoglea contains widely dispersed fibrous and amoeboid cells, recalling the organization of the mesohyl in sponges.

26.5a Phylum Cnidaria

Nearly all of the 8900 species in the phylum Cnidaria (*cnid* = stinging nettle, a plant with irritating hairs) live in the sea. Their body plan is organized around a saclike gastrovascular cavity and the mouth is ringed with tentacles, which push food into it. Cnidarians may be vase-shaped, upward-pointing **polyps** or bell-shaped, downward-pointing **medusae (Figure 26.9).** Most polyps attach to a substrate at the *aboral* (opposite the mouth) end; medusae are unattached and float.

Cnidarians are the simplest animals that exhibit a division of labour among irreversibly specialized tissues (see Figure 26.9c) and that have nerve cells. The gastrodermis includes sensory receptor cells, gland cells, and phagocytic nutritive cells. Gland cells secrete enzymes for the **extracellular digestion** of food, which is then engulfed by nutritive cells and exposed to **intracellular digestion.** The epidermis includes sensory cells, contractile cells, and cells specialized for prey capture.

Cnidarians prey on crustaceans, fishes, and other animals. The epidermis includes unique cells, **cnidocytes,** each armed with a stinging **nematocyst (Figure 26.10).** The nematocyst contains an encapsulated, coiled thread that is fired at prey or predators, sometimes releasing a toxin through its tip. Discharge of nematocysts may be triggered by touch, vibrations, or chemical stimuli. The toxin can paralyze small prey by disrupting nerve cell membranes. The painful stings of some jellyfishes and certain corals result from the discharge of nematocysts.

Cnidarians engage in directed movements by contracting specialized ectodermal cells that look like muscles. In medusae, the mesogleal jelly serves as a deformable skeleton against which contractile cells act. Rapid contractions narrow the bell, forcing out jets of water that propel the animal. Polyps use their water-filled gastrovascular cavity as a hydrostatic skeleton. When some cells contract, fluid within the chamber is shunted about, changing the body's shape and moving it in a particular direction.

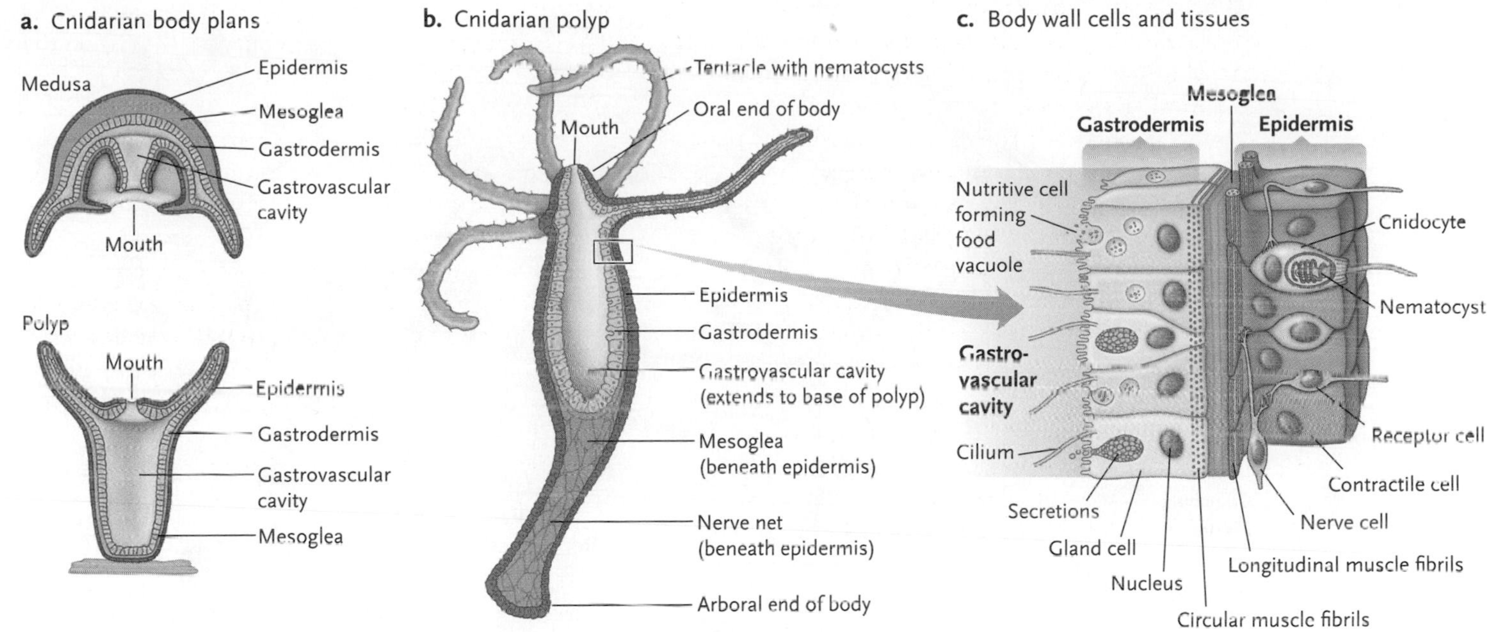

Figure 26.9
The cnidarian body plan. (a) Cnidarians exist as either polyps or medusae. **(b)** The body of both forms is organized around a gastrovascular cavity, which extends all the way to the aboral end of the animal. **(c)** The two tissue layers in the body wall, the gastrodermis and the epidermis, include a variety of cell types.

The **nerve net**, which threads through both tissue layers, is a simple nervous system that coordinates responses to stimuli (see Chapter 33). Although there is no recognizable "brain," there are control and coordination centres, particularly in a ring of nerves encircling the mouth. In spite of its structural simplicity, the nerve net permits directed swimming movements so the animal can escape predators.

Many cnidarians exist in only the polyp or the medusa form, but some have a life cycle that alternates between them **(Figure 26.11, p. 588).** In the alternating type, the polyp often produces new individuals asexually from buds that break free of the parent (see Chapter 40). The medusa is often the sexual stage, producing sperm and eggs, which are released into the water. Sexual reproduction results in a ciliated, nonfeeding larval stage, the planula, that eventually settles and undergoes metamorphosis into the polyp form. The four classes of Cnidaria differ in the form that predominates in the life cycle.

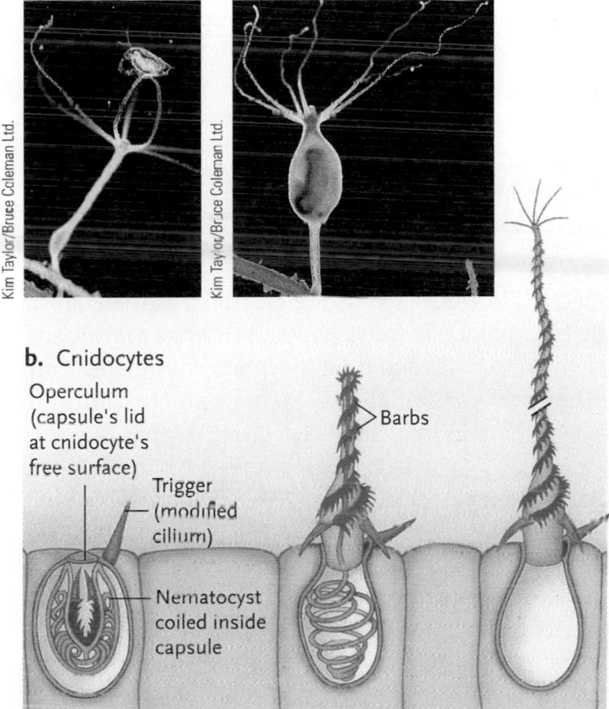

Figure 26.10
Predation by cnidarians. (a) A polyp of a freshwater *Hydra* captures a small crustacean with its tentacles and swallows it whole. **(b)** Cnidocytes, special cells on the tentacles, encapsulate nematocysts, which are discharged at prey.

Class Hydrozoa. Most of the 2700 species in the class Hydrozoa have both polyp and medusa stages in their life cycles (see Figure 26.11). The polyps form sessile colonies that develop asexually from one individual. A colony can include thousands of polyps, which may be specialized for feeding, defence, or reproduction. They share food through their connected gastrovascular cavities. A few warm-water species secrete a calcareous skeleton and form large colonies. These hydrocorals are different from the anthozoans that form coral reefs (see Class Anthozoa, below).

Some pelagic hydrozoans have both polyp and medusoid forms present in the same colony, which functions as an individual organism. The majestic Portuguese man-of-war jellyfish, for example, has the medusoid bell modified to form a gas-filled sail.

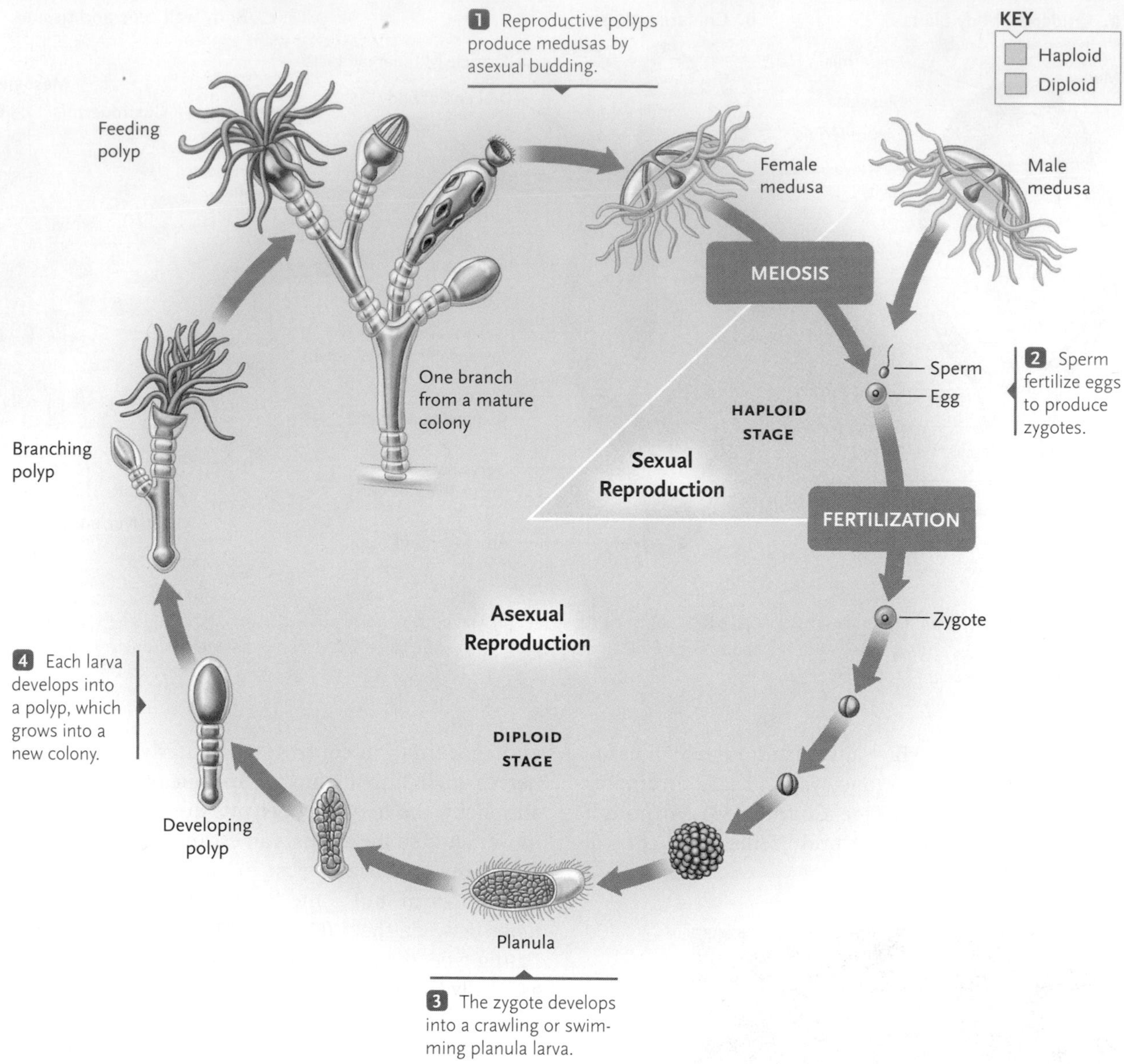
1 Reproductive polyps produce medusas by asexual budding.
KEY
Haploid
Diploid
Feeding polyp
Female medusa
Male medusa
MEIOSIS
One branch from a mature colony
Sperm
Egg
2 Sperm fertilize eggs to produce zygotes.
HAPLOID STAGE
Branching polyp
Sexual Reproduction
FERTILIZATION
Zygote
Asexual Reproduction
4 Each larva develops into a polyp, which grows into a new colony.
DIPLOID STAGE
Developing polyp
Planula
3 The zygote develops into a crawling or swimming planula larva.

Figure 26.11
Life cycle of *Obelia*. The life cycle of *Obelia*, a colonial hydrozoan, includes both polyp and medusa stages.

The hydroid form is represented by feeding and reproductive polyps dangling from the sail (see Chapter 46).

Unlike most Hydrozoa, freshwater species of *Hydra* (see Figure 26.10a) live as solitary polyps that attach temporarily to rocks, twigs, and leaves. Under favourable conditions, hydras reproduce by budding. Under adverse conditions, they produce eggs and sperm. Zygotes, formed by fertilization, are encapsulated in a protective coating but develop and grow when conditions improve. There is no larval stage; the eggs hatch into small *Hydra*.

Class Scyphozoa. The medusa stage predominates in the 200 species of the class Scyphozoa or jellyfish **(Figure 26.12a).** They range from 2 cm to more than 2 m in diameter. Nerve cells near the margin of the bell control their tentacles and coordinate the rhythmic activity of contractile cells, which move the animal. Specialized sensory cells are clustered at the edge of the bell: statocysts (see Chapter 34) sense gravity, and ocelli are sensitive to light. Scyphozoan medusae are either male or female, releasing gametes into the water, where fertilization takes place.

Class Cubozoa. Most of the 20 known species of box jellyfish, the Cubozoa **(Figure 26.12b),** exist as cube-shaped medusae only a few centimetres tall; the largest species grows to 25 cm in height. Nematocyst-rich tentacles grow in clusters from the four corners of the boxlike medusa, and groups of light receptors and image-forming eyes occur on the four sides of the bell. The eyes have lenses and retinas and are used in actively pursuing prey. Unlike the scyphozoan jellyfish, cubozoans are active swimmers. They eat small fish and invertebrates, immobilizing their prey with one of the deadliest toxins produced by animals.

a. Scyphozoan

b. Cubozoan

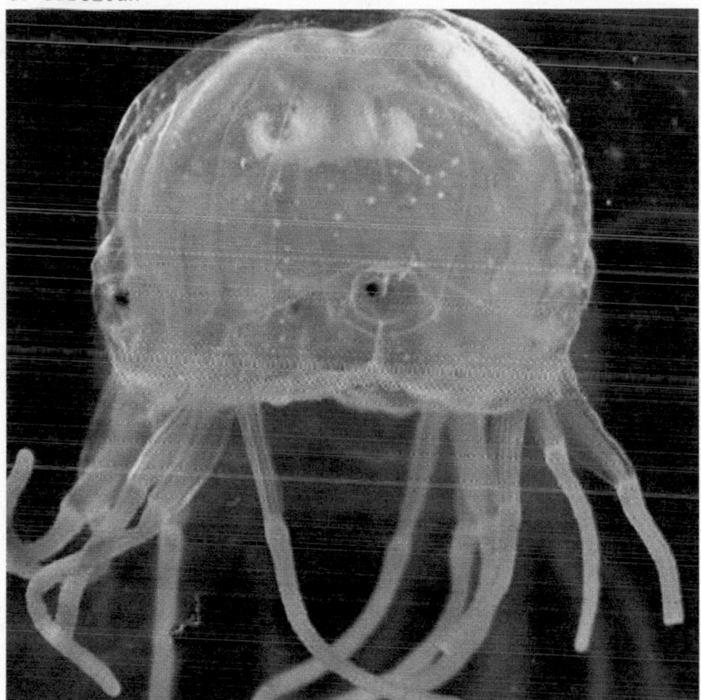

Figure 26.12

Scyphozoans and cubozoans. **(a)** Most scyphozoans, like the sea nettle (*Chrysaora* species), live as floating medusae. Their tentacles trap prey, and the long oral arms transfer it to the mouth on the underside of the bell. **(b)** Cubozoans, unlike most jelly fish, are active swimmers and can change direction abruptly in their pursuit of prey. They have several light-sensitive organs, but only four of them, two of which are clearly visible here, form images.

Cubozoans live in tropical and subtropical coastal waters, where they sometimes pose a serious threat to swimmers: the nematocysts of some species can inflict considerable pain to, and may kill, humans.

Class Anthozoa. The Anthozoa includes 6000 species of corals and sea anemones **(Figure 26.13, p. 590)**. Anthozoans exist only as polyps, which have a more complex structure than the Hydrozoa. A muscular pharynx leads into the gastrovascular cavity, and the body often consists of compartments partially separated by vertical membranes called septa. They reproduce by budding or fission. Most also reproduce sexually, producing eggs that develop into ciliated larvae. Corals (see Figure 26.13a) are always sessile and colonial. Their ciliated larvae settle and metamorphose into polyps that produce colonies by budding. Most species of corals build calcium carbonate skeletons that sometimes accumulate into gigantic underwater reefs. A coral reef usually contains more than one species of anthozoan. The energy needs of corals are partly fulfilled by the photosynthetic activity of symbiotic protists that live within the anthozoans. For this reason, corals are restricted to shallow water, where sunlight can penetrate.

Sea anemones (see Figure 26.13b), by contrast, are soft-bodied, solitary polyps, ranging from 1 to 10 cm in diameter. They occupy shallow coastal waters. Most species are sessile, but some move by crawling slowly or by using the gastrovascular cavity as a hydrostatic skeleton.

26.5b Phylum Ctenophora

The 100 species of comb jellies in the marine phylum Ctenophora (*ctenos* = comb; *phor* = to carry) also have radial symmetry, mesoglea, and feeding tentacles. However, they differ from Cnidaria in significant ways. They lack nematocysts, they expel some waste through anal pores at the other end of the body from the mouth, and certain tissues appear to be of mesodermal origin. These transparent and often luminescent (light producing) animals range in size from a few millimetres to 30 cm in diameter, with tentacles up to 1 m or more in length **(Figure 26.14, p. 590)**.

Ctenophores move by beating cilia arranged on eight longitudinal plates that resemble combs. They are the largest animals to use cilia for locomotion, but they are feeble swimmers. Nerve cells coordinate the animals' movements, and a gravity-sensing statocyst helps them maintain an upright position. Most species have two tentacles with specialized cells that discharge sticky filaments to entrap small animals floating in the sea, particularly small crustaceans. The food-laden

a. Coral

b. Sea anemone escape behaviour

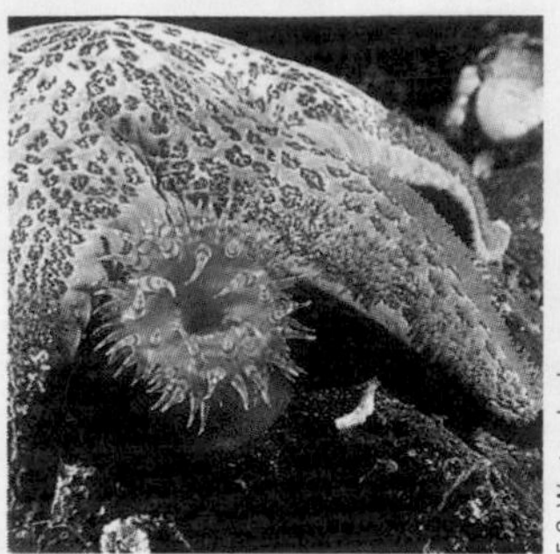

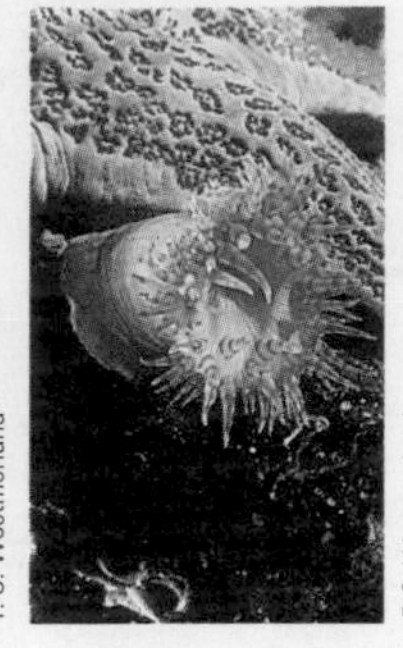

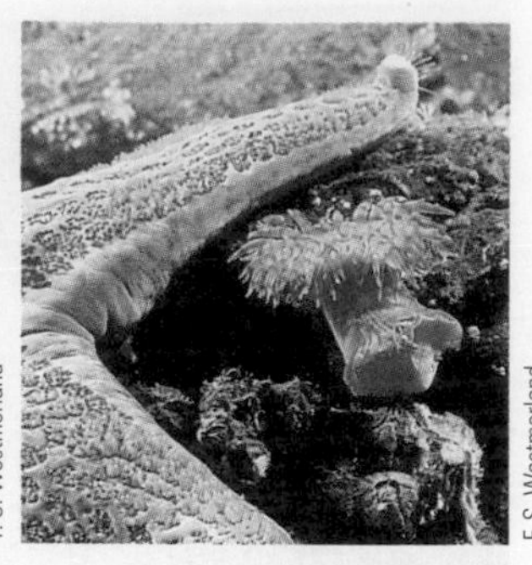

Figure 26.13
Anthozoans. **(a)** Many corals are colonial, and their polyps build a hard skeleton of calcium carbonate. The skeletons accumulate to form coral reefs in shallow tropical waters. **(b)** A sea anemone detaches from its substrate to escape from a predatory sea star.

tentacles are drawn across the mouth. Others lack tentacles and take large prey by a single gulp of the mouth. Some species that attack Cnidaria incorporate the nematocysts from the prey and use them in feeding (see Chapter 46). Ctenophores are hermaphroditic, producing gametes in cells that line the gastrovascular cavity. Eggs and sperm are expelled through the mouth or from special pores, and fertilization occurs in the open water.

Study Break

1. How do cnidarians capture, consume, and digest their prey?
2. Describe the differences between a polyp and a medusa.
3. Which group of cnidarians has only a polyp stage in its life cycle?
4. What do ctenophores eat, and how do they collect their food?

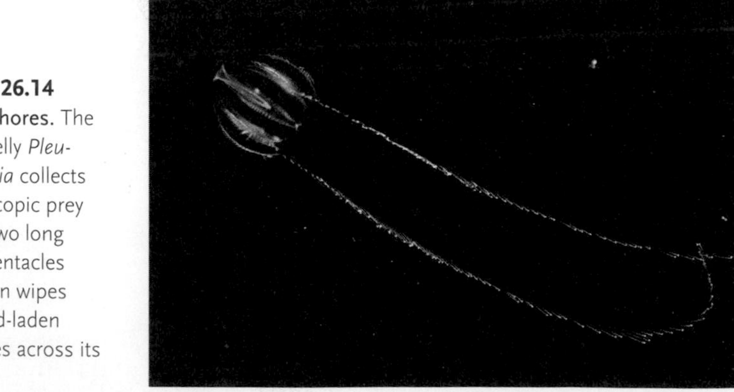

Figure 26.14
Ctenophores. The comb jelly *Pleurobrachia* collects microscopic prey on its two long sticky tentacles and then wipes the food-laden tentacles across its mouth.

26.6 Lophotrochozoan Protostomes

The remaining organisms described in this chapter are in the group Bilateria because of their bilateral symmetry. They have a greater variety of tissues, some of which are developed into organ systems. Most of the phyla have a coelom or pseudocoelom. With bilateral symmetry and sensory organs that are concentrated at the anterior end of the body, most bilaterians can make directed movements in pursuit of food or mates or to escape danger. Organ systems can operate more efficiently than simple tissues. For example, animals that have a tubular digestive system surrounded by a space (the coelom) use muscular contractions of the digestive system to move ingested food past specialized epithelial cells that break it down and absorb the breakdown products.

Molecular analyses group eight of the Bilateria phyla into the Lophotrochozoa, one of the two main protostome lineages (see Figure 26.6).

26.6a Three Lophophorate Phyla Share a Distinctive Feeding Structure

Three small groups of mostly marine (a few are aquatic), coelomate animals, the phyla Brachiopoda, Ectoprocta, and Phoronida, possess a **lophophore**, a circular or U-shaped fold with one or two rows of hollow, ciliated tentacles surrounding the mouth **(Figure 26.15)**. Molecular sequence data and the lophophore suggest that these phyla share a common ancestry.

The coelomic cavity extends into the lophophore, which looks like a crown of tentacles at the anterior end of the animal. The lophophore is involved in the capture of food and serves as a site for gas exchange. Most lophophorates are sessile suspension-feeders as adults. Movement of cilia on the tentacles brings food-laden water toward the lophophore, where the tentacles capture small organisms and debris, and the cilia transport

a. Ectoprocta (*Plumatella repens*)

b. Brachiopoda (*Terebraulina septentrionalis*)

© Andrew J. Martinez/Photo Researchers, Inc.

c. Phoronida (*Phoronis*)

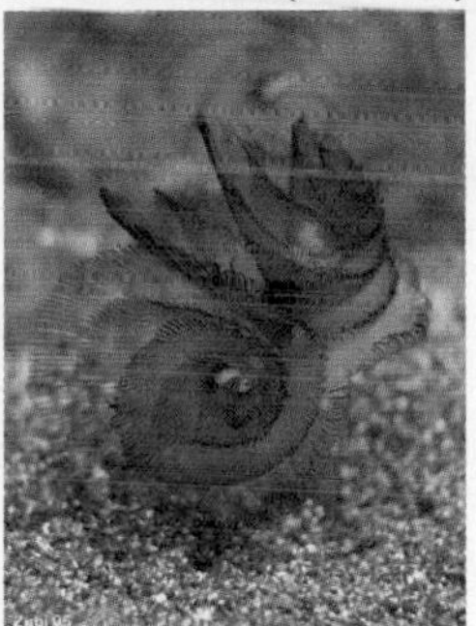

© blickwinkel/Hecker/Alamy

© Lawrence Naylor/Photo Researchers, Inc.

Figure 26.15
Lophophorate animals. Although the lophophorate animals differ markedly in appearance, they all use a lophophore to acquire food.

them to the mouth. The lophophorates have a complete digestive system, which is U-shaped in most species, with the anus lying outside the ring of tentacles.

Phylum Ectoprocta. The Ectoprocta (sometimes called Bryozoa or Polyzoa) are tiny colonial animals that occupy mainly marine habitats (see Figure 26.15a). They secrete a hard covering over their soft bodies. The lophophore is normally retracted into a chamber at the anterior end of the animal and extended when the animal feeds. Each colony, which may include more than a million individuals, is produced asexually by a single animal. Ectoproct colonies are permanently attached to solid substrates, where they form encrusting mats, bushy upright growths, or jellylike blobs. Sexual reproduction involves the production of eggs and sperm in the coelom. The sperm are shed through special pores. Fertilization may be internal or external, and the zygote gives rise to a ciliated larva that eventually settles and undergoes metamorphosis. Nearly 5000 living species are known, and about 50 of those live in fresh water.

Phylum Brachiopoda. The brachiopods, or lampshells, have two calcified shells that are secreted on the animal's dorsal and ventral sides (see Figure 26.15b). Most species attach to substrates with a stalk that protrudes through one of the shells. The lophophore is held within the two shells, and the animal feeds by opening its shell and drawing water over its tentacles. The animal has well-developed organs, such as a heart that propels blood through a number of interconnected sinuses and specialized excretory organs. Eggs and sperm are produced in different individuals (dioecious), and fertilization is external. The zygote gives rise to a ciliated larva.

Phylum Phoronida. The 18 or so species of phoronid worms vary in length from a few millimetres to 25 cm (see Figure 26.15c). They usually build tubes of chitin, a polymer of N-acetylglucosamine (see *Molecule Behind Biology*, Chapter 36), in soft ocean sediments or on hard substrates and feed by protruding the lophophore from the top of the tube. Phoronids reproduce both sexually and by budding. The animals are monoecious (both eggs and sperm produced by one individual). A ciliated feeding larva is produced that settles, undergoes metamorphosis, secretes a tube, and develops into an adult.

26.6b Phylum Platyhelminthes

The 13 000 flatworm species in the phylum Platyhelminthes (*plat* = flat; *helminth* = worm) live in aquatic and moist terrestrial habitats. Some are parasitic. Like cnidarians, flatworms can swim or float in water, but they are also able to crawl over surfaces. They range from less than 1 mm to more than 20 m in length, and most are just a few millimetres thick. Free-living species eat live prey or decomposing carcasses, whereas parasitic species derive their nutrition from the tissues of living hosts.

Like the radiate phyla, flatworms are acoelomate, but they have a complex structural organization that reflects their triploblastic construction **(Figure 26.16, p. 592).** In those with a gut (some parasitic forms lack this organ), endoderm lines the digestive cavity with cells specialized for the chemical breakdown and absorption of ingested food. A single opening serves as both mouth and anus. Mesoderm, the middle tissue layer, produces muscles and reproductive organs. Ectoderm produces a ciliated epidermis, the nervous system, and the **flame cell** system, a simple excretory system (see Chapter 43). Flatworms lack circulatory or respiratory systems, but because all cells of their dorsoventrally (top-to-bottom) flattened bodies are near an interior or exterior surface, diffusion supplies them with nutrients and oxygen.

The flatworm nervous system includes two or more longitudinal ventral nerve cords interconnected

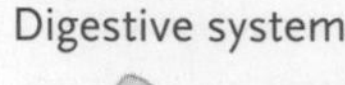

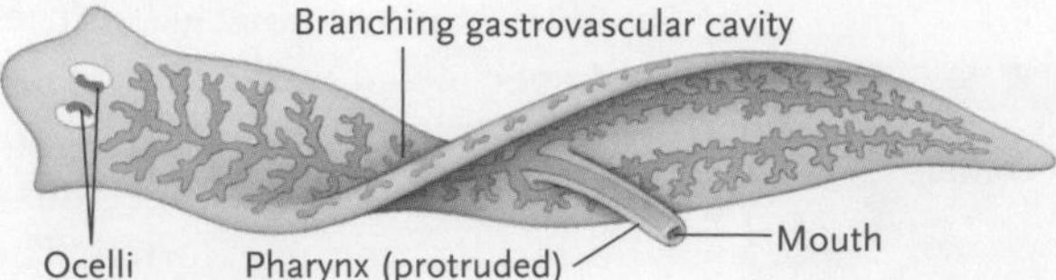

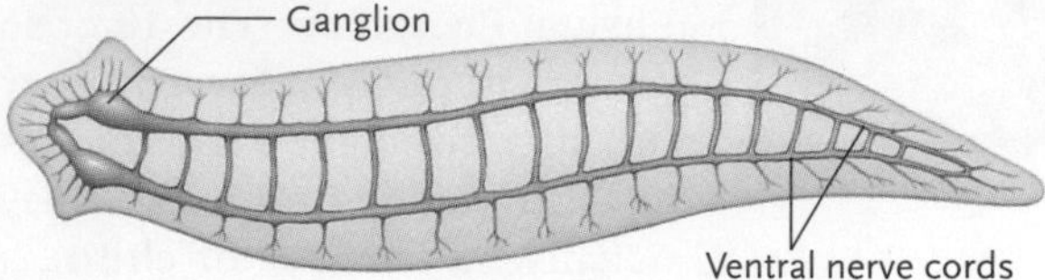

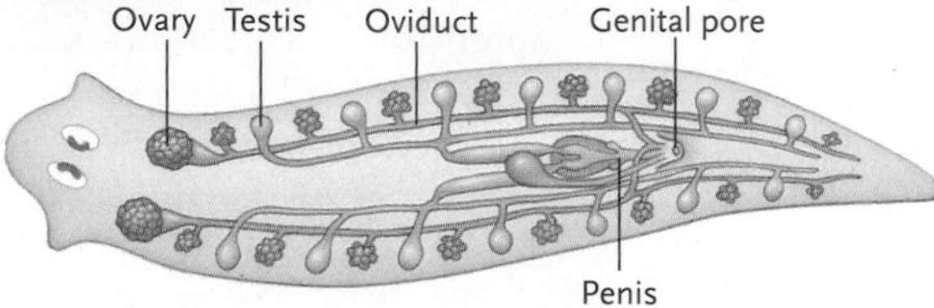

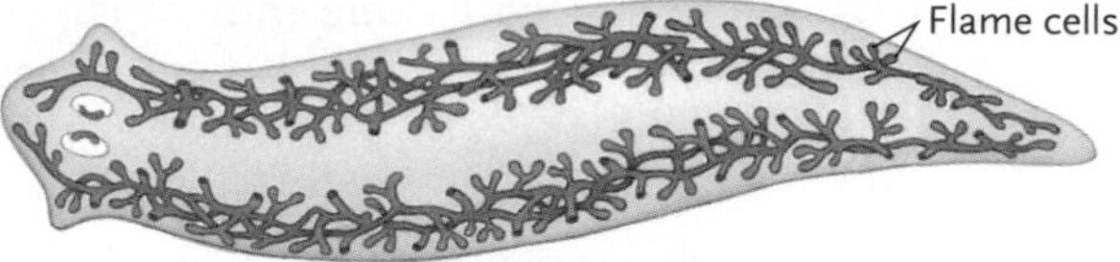

Figure 26.16
Flatworms. The phylum Platyhelminthes, exemplified by a freshwater planarian, have well-developed digestive, excretory, nervous, and reproductive systems. Because flatworms are acoelomate, their organ systems are embedded in a solid mass of tissue between the gut and the epidermis.

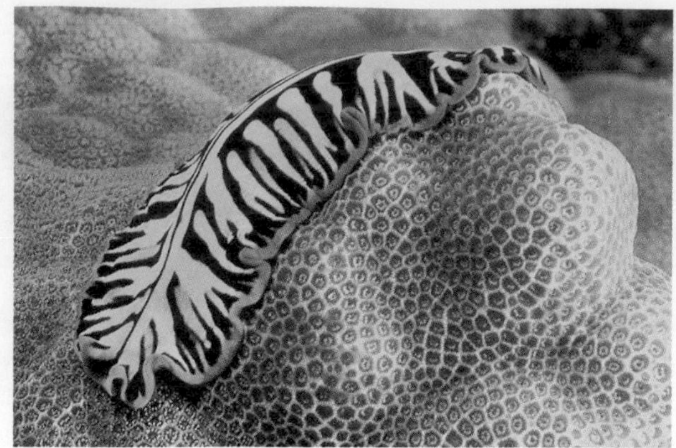

Figure 26.17
Turbellaria. A few turbellarians, such as *Pseudoceros dimidiatus*, are colourful marine worms.

by numerous smaller nerve fibres, like rungs on a ladder. An anterior **ganglion**, a concentration of nervous system tissue that serves as a primitive "brain," integrates their behaviour (see Chapter 33). Most free-living species have ocelli or "eye spots" that distinguish light from dark and chemoreceptor organs that sense chemical cues.

The phylum Platyhelminthes includes four classes, defined largely by their anatomical adaptations to free-living or parasitic habits. One class, Turbellaria, is free-living, whereas the remaining three classes are parasitic, obtaining their nutrition from the tissues of another animal, the host.

Class Turbellaria. Most free-living flatworms (class Turbellaria) live in the sea **(Figure 26.17),** where they may be brightly coloured. The familiar planarians and a few others live in fresh water or on land and are drab. Turbellarians swim by undulating the body wall musculature or crawl across surfaces by using muscles and cilia to glide on mucus trails produced by the ventral epidermis. Some terrestrial turbellarians are relatively large and prey on other invertebrates. For example, *Microplana termitophaga* waits at the entrance to termite colonies in Africa and entangles the prey in the slime that they produce. Other species may gang up on large snails.

The gastrovascular cavity in free-living flatworms is similar to that in cnidarians. Food is ingested and wastes are eliminated through a single opening, the mouth, located on the ventral surface. Most turbellarians acquire food with a muscular **pharynx** that connects the mouth to the digestive cavity (see Figure 26.16a). Chemicals secreted into the saclike cavity digest ingested items, after which cells throughout the gastrovascular surface engulf food particles and subject them to intracellular digestion. In some species, the digestive cavity is highly branched, increasing the surface area for digestion and absorption.

Nearly all turbellarians are hermaphroditic, with complex reproductive systems (see Figure 26.16c). When they mate, each partner functions simultaneously as a male and a female. The eggs of most species hatch directly into small worms, but ciliated larvae occur in a few marine turbellarians. Many free-living species also reproduce asexually by simply separating the anterior half of the animal from the posterior half. Both halves subsequently regenerate the missing parts.

Class Monogenea. Flukes (classes Trematoda and Monogenea) are parasites that obtain nutrients from host tissues. Monogenea flukes are ectoparasites that attach to the gills or skin of aquatic vertebrates. They have an anterior sucker surrounding the mouth and a more posterior sucker. The suckers may be equipped with hooks.

Reproduction occurs by internal fertilization. The eggs are released into water and hatch as ciliated larvae. The larvae attach to a new host and undergo metamorphosis.

Class Trematoda. Adult trematodes **(Figure 26.18)** are all internal parasites of vertebrates, but their development involves two or more host species in their life cycle. They are sometimes called digenean (two hosts) flukes. The host species in which sexual reproduction occurs is

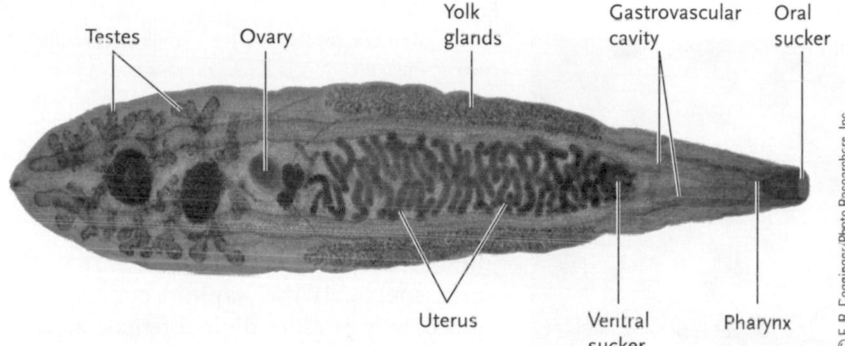

Figure 26.18
Trematoda. The hermaphroditic Chinese liver fluke (*Opisthorchis sinensis*) uses a well-developed reproductive system to produce thousands of eggs.

the primary host, and other hosts, usually invertebrates, are secondary hosts. Thus, the same individual will encounter very different environments during its life and may have two or more very different larval stages during development (see Polymorphic Development). Like the monogeneans, trematodes normally have two suckers, one of which is around the mouth. The unciliated epidermis is a syncytium (the cells are interconnected without separating membranes). Trematodes can be found in many vertebrates, including humans, where they may cause some serious diseases.

Class Cestoda. Tapeworms **(Figure 26.19)** are parasitic in the intestines of vertebrates, their primary host. They lack a mouth or digestive system and absorb nutrients from the host's intestinal contents across the syncytial epithelium. The anterior end is modified as a scolex, consisting of hooks and/or suckers that allow it to attach to the wall of the intestine. The remainder of the worm consists of a series of identical units, proglottids, each with its own reproductive system. Proglottids are generated just posterior to the scolex and become progressively more mature near the tail. The posterior, fully mature units break off or burst and are passed out with the feces. Worms may consist of only a few proglottids, but many species have 2000 to 3000, and such worms may be 10 m in length, occupying the entire length of the human small intestine.

Each proglottid contains a complete set of reproductive organs producing both sperm and eggs. Fertilization is internal and may involve a neighbouring worm, or the worm may be self-fertilizing. Each proglottid may contain as many as 50 000 eggs. Further development varies with the species, but, typically, the eggs must be eaten by an appropriate intermediate host, usually an arthropod, in which it undergoes development into a series of larval stages. The life cycle is completed when an appropriate primary host eats an infected intermediate host. For example, the adult tapeworm *Hymenolepis diminuta* lives in rat intestines. The eggs in rat feces are eaten by flour beetles, where larvae develop and form cysts. Rats become infected when they eat the beetles. Humans can also become infected by unwittingly consuming infected beetles that may live in dry breakfast cereals.

26.6c Phylum Rotifera

Most of the 1800 species in the pseudocoelomate phylum Rotifera (*rota* = wheel; *fera* = to bear) live in fresh water, and a few are marine **(Figure 26.20, p. 594)**. Most are less than 0.5 mm long, but a few range up to 3 mm. They exhibit *eutely*, a mode of development in which cell division ceases early and subsequent growth is by cell enlargement. In spite of their size, they have well-developed digestive, reproductive, excretory, and nervous systems. In some habitats, rotifers make up a large part of the zooplankton (tiny animals that float in open water). Some species, however, are attached to the substrate and move only a little. Others may form colonies, and some live in pitcher plants (see Chapter 47).

Rotifers use coordinated movements of cilia, arranged in a wheel-like **corona** around the head, to propel themselves in the environment. Cilia also bring food-laden water to their mouths. Ingested

a. Tapeworm

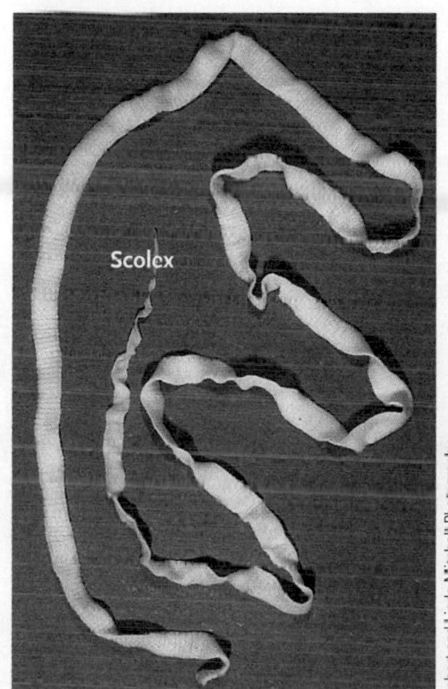

b. Scolex

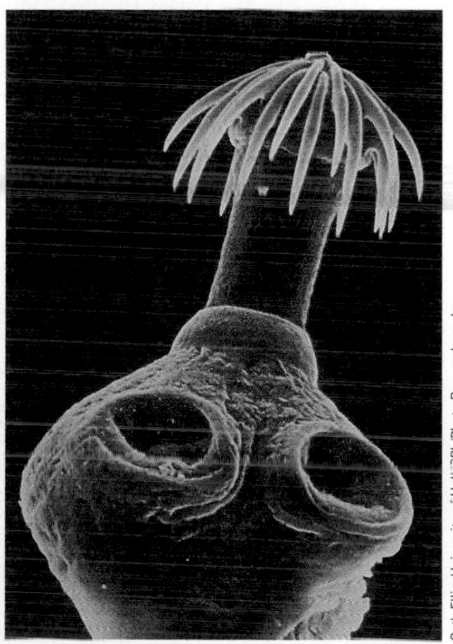

Figure 26.19
Cestoda. **(a)** Tapeworms have long bodies composed of a series of proglottids, each of which produces thousands of fertilized eggs. **(b)** The anterior end is a scolex with hooks and suckers that attach to the host's intestinal wall.

a. Rotifer body plan

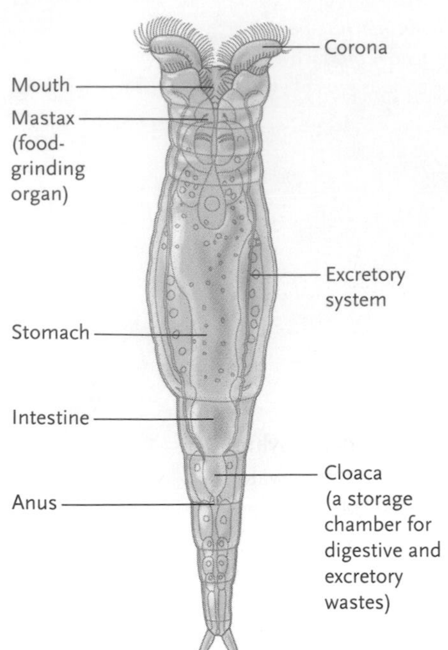

b. Rotifer laying eggs

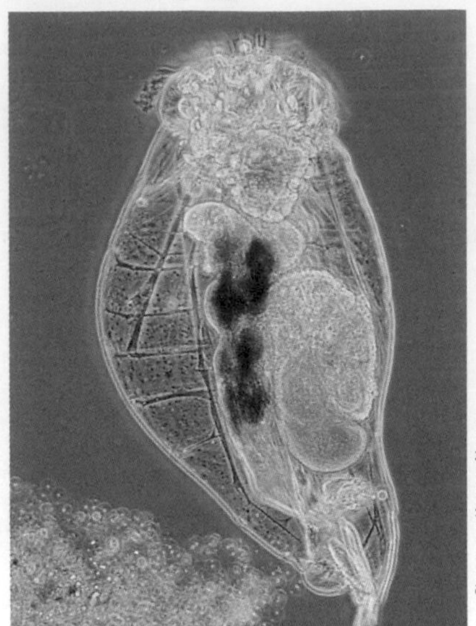

Figure 26.20
Phylum Rotifera. **(a)** Despite their small size, rotifers such as *Philodina roseola* have complex body plans and organ systems. **(b)** This rotifer, another *Philodina* species, is laying eggs.

microorganisms are conveyed to the **mastax**, a toothed grinding organ, and then passed to the stomach and intestine. Rotifers have a **complete digestive tract**: food enters through the mouth, and undigested waste is voided through a separate anus.

The life history patterns of some rotifers are adapted to the ever-changing environments in small bodies of water. During most months, rotifer populations of these species include only females that reproduce by **parthenogenesis** (the development of unfertilized eggs; see Chapter 39). In this particular form of parthenogenesis, females produce diploid eggs by mitosis that develop into females. When environmental conditions deteriorate, females produce eggs by meiosis. If these eggs remain unfertilized, they develop into haploid males that produce sperm. If the haploid eggs are fertilized, they produce diploid female zygotes. The fertilized eggs have durable shells and food reserves to survive drying or freezing.

26.6d Phylum Nemertea

The 650 species of ribbon worms or proboscis worms vary from less than 1 cm to 30 m in length **(Figure 26.21)**. Most species are marine, but a few occupy moist terrestrial habitats. The often brightly coloured ribbon worms have no obvious coelom and use a ciliated epidermis to glide over a film of secreted mucus. Ribbon worms have a complete digestive tract with a mouth and an anus. They have a circulatory system in which fluid flows through **circulatory vessels** that carry nutrients and oxygen to tissues and remove wastes. They have a muscular, mucus-covered proboscis, a tube that can be everted (turned inside out) through a separate pore to capture prey. The proboscis is housed within a chamber, the **rhynchocoel**, which is unique to this phylum (see Figure 26.21b).

Nemerteans are aggressive predators. The proboscis may have a barb that is used to impale the prey, or the proboscis may wrap around the prey in a form of stranglehold. Many nemerteans are burrowing animals, living in tubes that protect them from predators. The life cycle includes a microscopic ciliated larva.

a. Ribbon worm

b. Ribbon worm anatomy

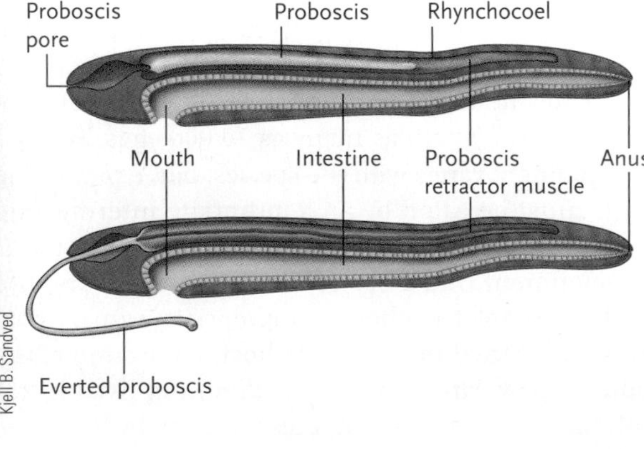

Figure 26.21
(a) The flattened, elongated bodies of ribbon worms, such as genus *Lineus*, are often brightly coloured. **(b)** Ribbon worms have a complete digestive system and a specialized cavity, the rhynchocoel, that houses a protrusible proboscis.

Polymorphic Development

Most of the protostomes share a capacity for developmental polymorphism. During development from egg to adult, the organism may assume different morphologies. Most commonly, the immature form is referred to as a larva. In insects, for example, the caterpillar that hatches from the egg and that grows through a number of moults is a feeding stage very different from the adult butterfly, the distributive and reproductive stage. The transformation from larva to adult stage is accomplished by metamorphosis.

In other cases, particularly in sessile marine animals, the larval stage functions in distribution. Often this is an inconspicuous ciliated stage, such as the trochophore larva of molluscs and marine annelids (see Figure 26.23), that drifts with ocean currents. It settles to the ocean floor in response to some signal and metamorphoses into the form that will eventually become the adult. Some of the Cnidaria may have three distinct forms (see Figure 26.11). This capacity for assuming different forms during development is particularly important for two lifestyles, parasitism and social insects.

Populations of animals that live in other organisms are faced with a particular challenge. The environment in which they live, the host, is discontinuous in space: one host is not connected to another. It is also discontinuous in time: the host eventually dies. It is thus essential for a parasite to move from one part of this discontinuous environment to another if the parasitc population is to survive. Moving to another host may involve a period as a free-living form or further development in an alternate host. During its life cycle, the parasite is thus obliged to experience two or more different environments. These different environments have favoured different developmental stages, often a series of morphologically distinct larvae. In the Chinese liver fluke (*Opisthorchis sinensis*), for example **(Figure 1),** the egg is eaten by a snail and hatches into a ciliated larva, the miracidium.

Almost immediately, metamorphosis occurs involving extensive reorganization

(continued on page 596)

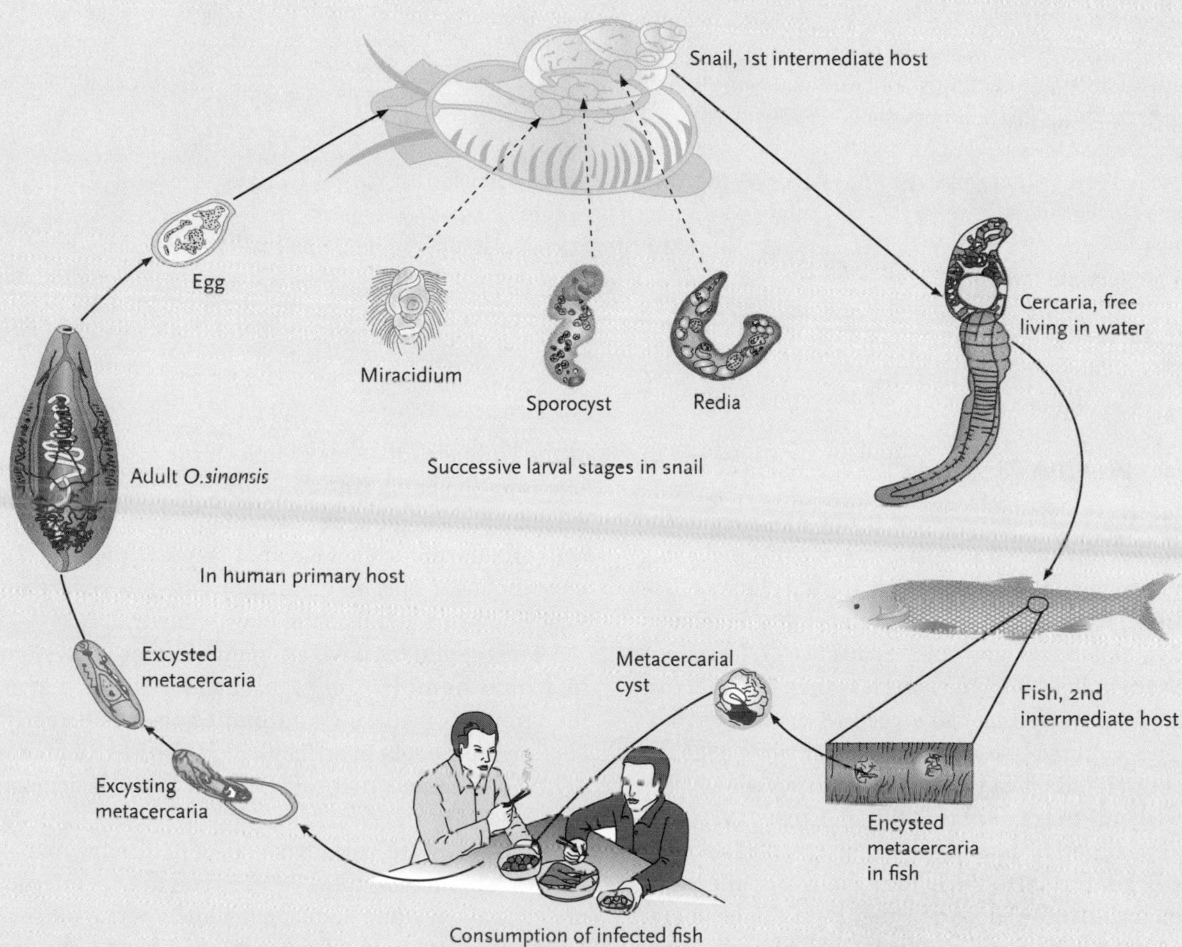

Figure 1
The life cycle of the liver fluke *Opisthorchis sinensis*. Humans become infected by eating raw fish, and the adult fluke lives in the liver and bile duct. Estimates of the number of persons infected range up to 30 000 000.

(continued from page 595)

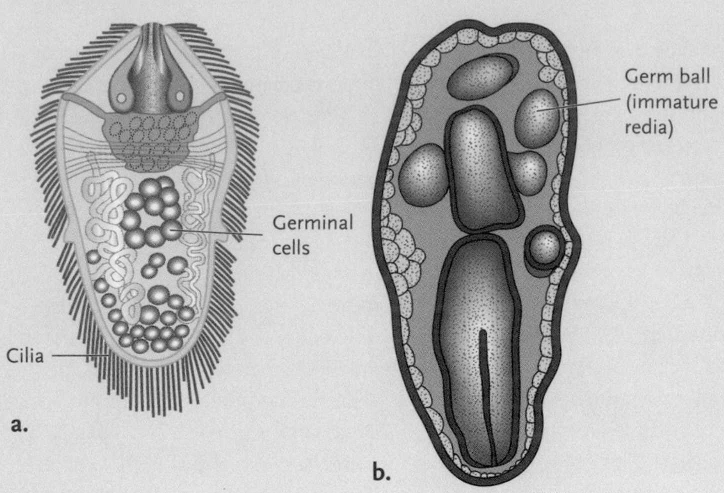

Figure 2
The transformation of a miracidium **(a)** into a sporocyst **(b)**, involving the development of totipotent germ cells (stem cells) into germ balls that will form several copies of the next larval stage.

of the larva. This produces the sporocyst. Groups of embryonic cells, called "germ balls" **(Figure 2),** within the body cavity of the larva develop to produce additional larval stages, which are morphologically distinct from the sporocyst. In each stage, groups of embryonic germ balls are reserved to give rise to increased numbers of the next stage. The snail eventually releases enormous numbers of another larval form, the free-swimming cercaria, that enters another intermediate host, a fish, where it forms a cyst in the muscle. This cyst will develop into the adult fluke if it is consumed by a human. The existence of populations of totipotent stem cells in flatworms has made possible the developmental polymorphism on which parasitism depends. The development of the cells is directed into different pathways appropriate for each parasitic stage.

Developmental polymorphism is also a feature of social insects. Social insects live in colonies and are characterized by different castes (individuals that perform particular tasks on behalf of the entire colony), which usually differ in morphology. The difference among the castes is particularly pronounced in termites **(Figure 3).**

Figure 3
Termite castes. The queen termite in the centre of the photograph is surrounded by workers, called "pseudergates." One soldier, with an enlarged head and mandibles, is also visible. At each moult, depending on the conditions in the colony, a pseudergate may develop into another pseudergate, embark on development to a soldier, or develop into a winged supplementary reproductive caste that will leave the colony to found a new one.

26.6e Phylum Mollusca

Most of the 100 000 species of fleshy molluscs in the coelomate phylum Mollusca (*moll* = soft), including clams, snails, octopuses, and their relatives, are marine. However, many clams and snails occupy freshwater habitats, and some snails live on land. Molluscs vary in length from clams less than 1 mm across to the giant squids that can exceed 18 m in length.

The mollusc body is divided into three regions: the visceral mass, head–foot, and mantle **(Figure 26.22).** The **visceral mass** contains the digestive, excretory, and reproductive systems and the heart. The muscular **head–foot** often provides the major means of locomotion. In the more active groups, the head area of the head–foot region is well defined and carries sensory organs and a brain. The mouth often includes a toothed **radula,** which scrapes food into small particles or drills through the shells of prey.

Many molluscs are covered by a protective shell of calcium carbonate secreted by the **mantle,** a folding of the body wall that may enclose the visceral mass. The mantle also defines a space, the **mantle cavity,** that houses the **gills,** delicate respiratory structures with an enormous surface area (see Chapter 42). In most molluscs, cilia on the mantle and gills generate a steady flow of water into the mantle cavity.

Most molluscs have an **open circulatory system** in which **hemolymph,** a bloodlike fluid, leaves the circulatory vessels and bathes tissues directly. Hemolymph pools in spaces called **sinuses** and then drains into vessels that carry it back to the heart (see Figure 26.25).

The sexes are usually separate, although many snails are hermaphroditic. Fertilization may be internal or external. In some snails, eggs and sperm are produced simultaneously in the same organ, an ovotestis. In others, the hermaphroditism is serial, with younger snails producing sperm and older individuals switching to egg production. Fertilization is often internal in these organisms, and in simultaneous hermaphrodites, there is a mutual exchange of sperm during

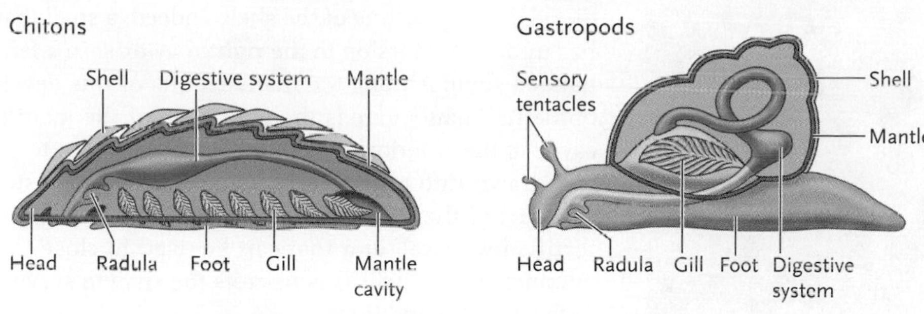

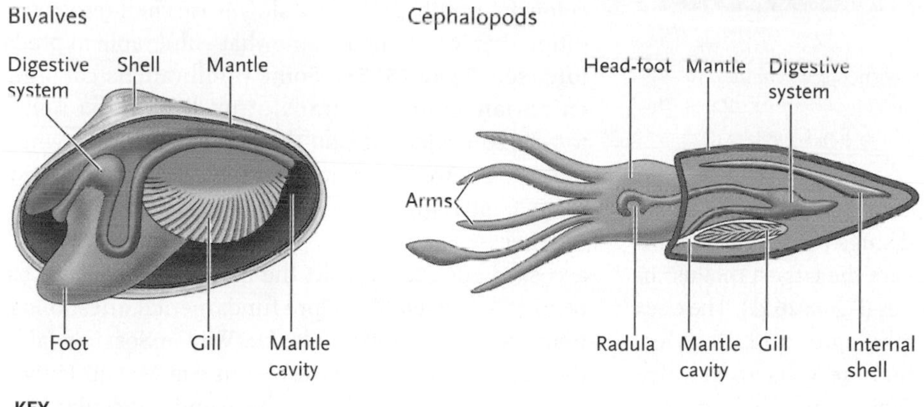

KEY

- Head-foot
- Visceral mass
- Mantle

Figure 26.22
Molluscan body plans. The bilaterally symmetrical body plans of molluscs include a muscular head–foot, a visceral mass, and a mantle.

copulation. Sperm may be stored for long periods before being used. In some terrestrial snails, a calcium "love dart" may be fired into one of the partners preceding a mutual exchange of sperm. Dr. Ron Chase of McGill University has shown that mucus coating the dart makes it more likely that the shooter's sperm will be used to fertilize the eggs.

Apical tuft of cilia

Band of cilia

Stomach

Mouth

Anus

Figure 26.23
Trochophore larva. At the conclusion of their embryological development, both molluscs and annelids typically pass through a trochophore stage. The top-shaped trochophore larva has a band of cilia just anterior to its mouth.

The zygotes of marine species often develop into free-swimming, ciliated **trochophore** larvae **(Figure 26.23)**, typical of both this phylum and the phylum Annelida, which we describe next. In some molluscs, the trochophore develops into a second larval stage, called a **veliger**, before metamorphosing into an adult. In some snails, the larval stage may occur only within the egg. Squids and octopuses have no larval stage, and eggs hatch into miniature replicas of the adult. Although members of the phylum share common characteristics, they have evolved an extraordinary diversity in form and lifestyle, ranging from sessile clams to the agile octopus capable of learned behaviour. The phylum includes seven classes. We examine the four most commonly encountered classes below.

Class Polyplacophora. The 600 species of chitons (Polyplacophora, from *poly* = many and *plak* = plate) are sedentary molluscs that graze on algae along rocky marine coasts. The oval, bilaterally symmetrical body has a dorsal shell divided into eight plates that allow it to conform to irregularly shaped surfaces **(Figure 26.24, p. 598)**. When a chiton is disturbed or exposed to strong wave action, the muscles of its broad foot maintain a tenacious grip, and the mantle's edge functions like a suction cup to hold fast to the substrate.

Figure 26.24
Polyplacophora. Chitons live on rocky shores, where they use their foot and mantle to grip rocks and other hard substrates. This chiton (*Mopalia ciliata*) lives in Monterey Bay, California.

Class Gastropoda. Snails and slugs (Gastropoda, from *gaster* = belly and *pod* = foot) are the largest molluscan group, numbering 40 000 species **(Figure 26.25)**. The class exhibits a wide range of morphologies and lifestyles. Aquatic and marine species use gills to acquire oxygen, but in terrestrial species, a modified mantle cavity functions as an air-breathing lung. Some snails have the opening into the mantle cavity extended as a tubular siphon. Gastropods feed on algae, vascular plants, or animal prey. Some are scavengers, and a few are parasites.

The visceral mass of most snails is housed in a coiled or cone-shaped shell that is balanced above the rest of the body, much as you balance a backpack full of books (see **Figure 26.25a, b**). Most shelled species undergo **torsion** during development. Differential growth rates and muscle contractions twist the developing visceral mass and mantle a full 180° relative to the head and foot. These events begin in the larva before the shell is established and thus are not dictated by the coiling of the shell. Indeed, a snail that has undergone torsion to the right may exist in a left-handed shell. Among the many results of this developmental manoeuvre is the relocation of the mantle cavity to the anterior, allowing the head and foot to be withdrawn into the shell. In some snails, the posterior part of the foot carries an ovoid disk of protein fortified with calcium that can be used to close the entrance to the shell. This permits the snail to survive unfavourable conditions.

Some gastropods, including terrestrial slugs and colourful nudibranchs (sea slugs), are shell-less, a condition that leaves them somewhat vulnerable to predators (see **Figure 26.25c**). Some nudibranchs consume cnidarians and then transfer undischarged nematocysts to projections on their dorsal surface, where these "borrowed" stinging capsules provide protection (see Chapter 46).

Because many of its neurons are large and easily accessed and identifiable, the nudibranch *Aplysia* has been widely used to explore fundamental questions in neurobiology. For example, Dr. Wayne Sossin's lab at the Montreal Neurological Institute at McGill University is examining the biochemical and molecular basis of memory and learning in *Aplysia*.

The nervous and sensory systems of gastropods are well developed. Tentacles on the head include chemical and touch receptors; the eyes detect changes in light intensity but do not form images. The importance and relative sophistication of the nervous system is well illustrated by some limpets. *Patella vulgaris* is a gastropod with a conical shell **(Figure 26.26)** that lives on rocks in the intertidal zone. During low tide, it is exposed to the air and its foot and mucus secretion combine to fasten it closely to the rock. During development, the edges of its shell grow to conform to irregularities in the rock, increasing the protection against drying. As the rising tide covers the limpet, it moves

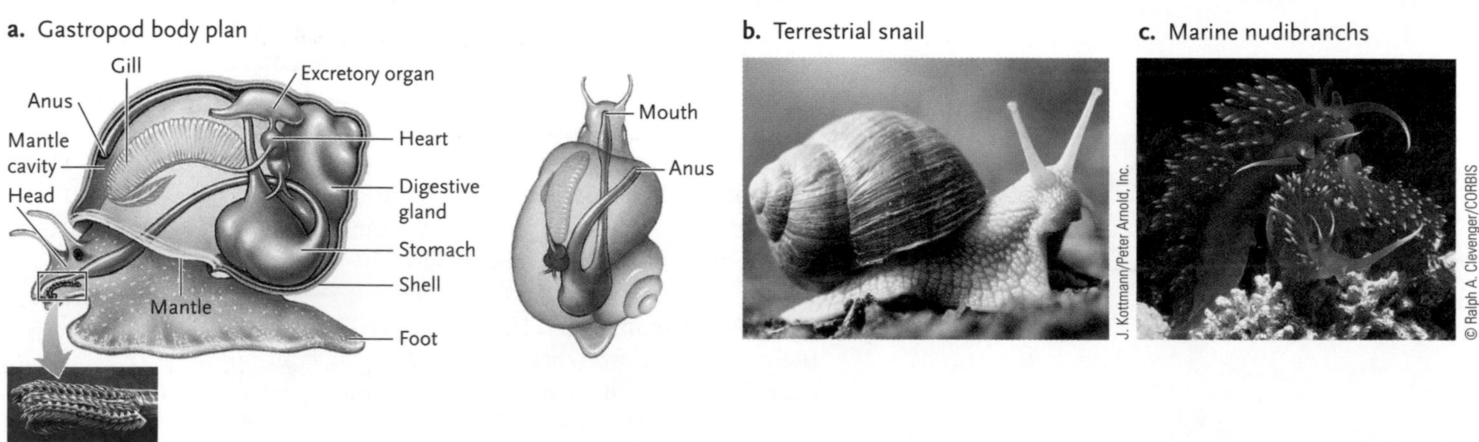

Figure 26.25
Gastropoda. (a) Most gastropods have a coiled shell that houses the visceral mass. A developmental process called torsion causes the digestive and excretory systems to eliminate wastes into the mantle cavity, near the animal's head. **(b)** The terrestial snail (*Helix pomatia*) is a typical terrestrial gastropod. **(c)** Nudibranchs, like this pair of Spanish shawl nudibranchs (*Flabellina iodinea*), are shell-less marine snails. Photo: Herve Chaumeton/Agence Nature

Figure 26.26
The common limpet, *Patella vulgata*.

about, foraging and feeding on algae. About an hour before the falling tide would once again expose it to desiccation, it returns to its precise location so that it can seal itself against exposure to air. This involves not only precise navigation but also a sense of time attuned to the tides.

Class Bivalvia. The 8000 species of clams, scallops, oysters, and mussels (Bivalvia, from *bi* = two and *valv* = folding door) are restricted to aquatic habitats. They are enclosed within a pair of shells, hinged together dorsally by an elastic ligament. Contraction of the adductor muscles closes the shell and stretches the ligament. When the muscles relax, the stretched ligament opens the shell **(Figure 26.27)**. Although some bivalves are tiny, the giant clams of the South Pacific can be more than 1 m across and weigh 225 kg.

Adult mussels and oysters are sessile and permanently attached to hard substrates. However, many clams are mobile and use their muscular foot to burrow in sand or mud. Some bivalves, such as young scallops, swim by rhythmically clapping their valves together, forcing a current of water out of the mantle cavity (see Figure 26.27b). The "scallops" that we eat are their well-developed adductor muscles.

Bivalves have a reduced head and lack a radula. Part of the mantle forms two tubes called *siphons* (see Figure 26.27c). Beating of cilia on the gills and mantle carries water into the mantle cavity through the incurrent siphon and out through the excurrent siphon. Incurrent water carries dissolved oxygen and particulate food to the gills, where oxygen is absorbed. Mucus strands on the gills trap food, which is then transported by cilia to *palps*, where final sorting takes place; acceptable bits are carried to the mouth. The excurrent water carries away metabolic wastes and feces.

Despite their sedentary existence, bivalves have moderately well-developed nervous systems: sensory organs that detect chemicals, touch, and light and statocysts to sense their orientation. When they encounter pollutants, many bivalves stop pumping water and close their shells. When confronted by a predator, some burrow into sediments or swim away.

Class Cephalopoda. The 600 species of octopuses, squids, and nautiluses constituting the class Cephalopoda (*cephal* = head; *pod* = foot) are active marine predators and include the fastest and most intelligent invertebrates **(Figure 26.28, p. 600)**. They vary in length from a few centimetres to 18 m.

The cephalopod body has a fused head and foot. The head comprises the mouth and eyes. The ancestral "foot" forms a set of arms, which are equipped with suction pads, adhesive structures, or hooks. Cephalopods use their arms to capture prey and a pair of beaklike jaws to bite or crush it. Venomous secretions often speed the captive's death. Some species use their radula to drill through the shells of other molluscs.

Cephalopods have a highly modified shell. Octopuses have no remnant of a shell at all. In squids and

a. Bivalve body plan

Ligament (connects to opposite shell)
Mouth
Anterior adductor muscle
Left mantle
Posterior adductor muscle
Water flows out through excurrent siphon
Water flows in through incurrent siphon
Foot
Palps
Left gill
Right shell

b. Bivalve locomotion

c. Geoduck

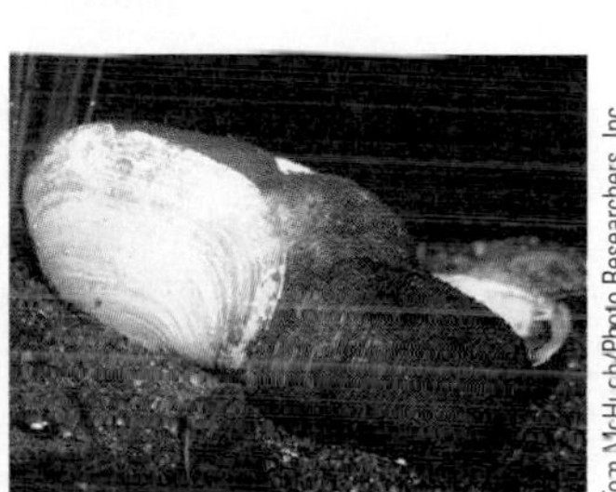

Figure 26.27
Bivalvia. **(a)** Bivalves are enclosed in a hinged two-part shell. Part of the mantle forms a pair of water-transporting siphons. **(b)** When threatened by a predator (in this case, a sea star), some scallops clap their shells together rapidly, propelling the animal away from danger. **(c)** The geoduck (*Panope generosa*) is a clam with enormous muscular siphons.

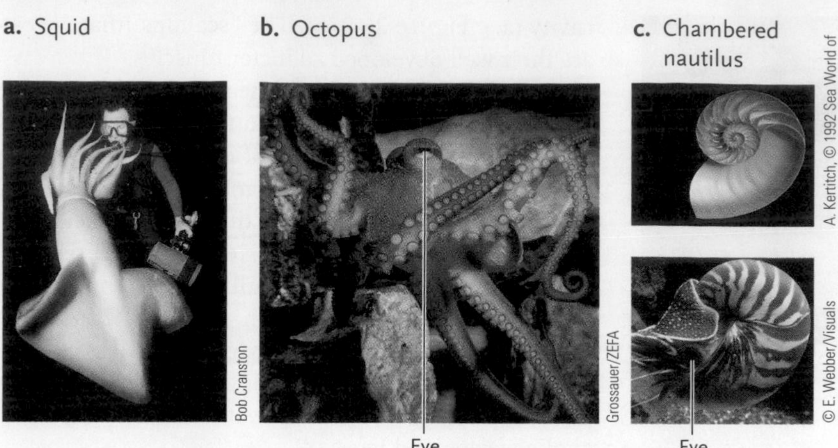

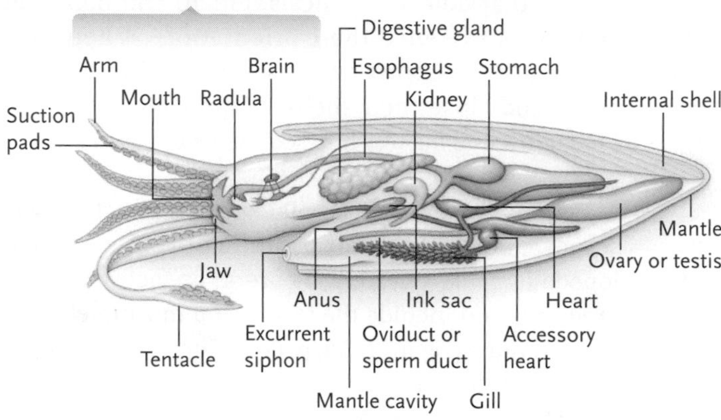

Figure 26.28

Cephalopoda. **(a)** Squids, such as *Dosidicus gigas*, and **(b)** octopuses, such as *Octopus vulgaris*, are the most familiar cephalopods. **(c)** The chambered nautilus (*Nautilus macromphalus*) and its relatives retain an external shell. **(d)** Like other cephalopods, the squid body includes a fused head and foot; most organ systems are enclosed by the mantle.

cuttlefishes, the shell is reduced to a stiff internal support. Only the chambered nautilus (see Figure 26.28c) and its relatives retain an external shell; spaces (chambers) in the shell regulate the animal's buoyancy. Species in the genus *Nautilus* are clearly cephalopods because the foot is modified in a way that is characteristic of that class. But they have retained an elegant, chambered shell, a body plan that is very successful, since essentially identical animals can be found among the Cambrian fossils.

Squids (see Figure 26.28a, d) move by a kind of jet propulsion. When muscles in the mantle relax, water enters the mantle cavity. When they contract, a jet of water is squeezed out through a funnel. By manipulating the position of the mantle and funnel, the animal can control the rate and direction of its locomotion. While escaping, many species simultaneously release a dark fluid ("ink") that obscures their direction of movement. Octopuses and squids are able to change colour rapidly by the migration of various pigments in special pigment cells called chromatophores. Many squids have light-emitting cells called photophores.

Cephalopods are the only molluscs to have a **closed circulatory system.** The heart and accessory hearts speed the flow of hemolymph through blood vessels and gills, enhancing the uptake of oxygen and release of carbon dioxide.

Cephalopods have larger brains than other molluscs, and their brains are more complex than any other invertebrate. Giant nerve fibres connect the brain with the muscles of the mantle, enabling quick responses to food or danger (see Chapter 33).

The image-forming eyes of cephalopods, complete with lens and retina, are similar to those of vertebrates (see Chapter 34). The same basic plan for an eye has arisen independently in the cubozoan Cnidaria, the cephalopods, and the vertebrates, and represents an example of convergent evolution. Cephalopods are also highly intelligent. Octopuses, for example, learn to recognize objects with distinctive shapes or colours and can be trained to approach or avoid them.

Cephalopods have separate sexes and elaborate courtship rituals. Males store sperm within the mantle cavity and use a specialized tentacle to transfer packets of sperm into the female's mantle cavity, where fertilization occurs. The young hatch with an adult body form.

26.6f Phylum Annelida

The 15 000 species of segmented worms in the phylum Annelida (*annelis* = ring) occupy marine, freshwater, and moist terrestrial habitats. They range from a few millimetres to as much as 3 m in length. Terrestrial annelids eat organic debris, whereas aquatic species consume algae, microscopic organisms, detritus, or other animals. They have a complete digestive system, with the mouth at the front end and the anus at the rear.

The annelid body is highly segmented: the body wall muscles and some organs, including respiratory surfaces; parts of the nervous, circulatory, and excretory systems; and the coelom, are divided into similar repeating units **(Figure 26.29).** Body segments are separated by transverse partitions called **septa** (singular, septum). The digestive system and major blood vessels are not segmented and run the length of the animal.

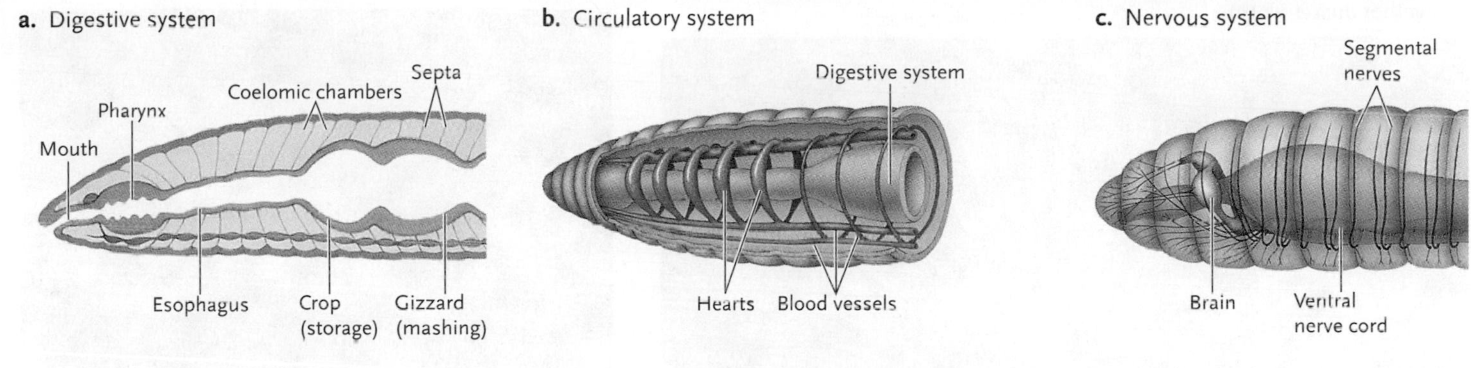

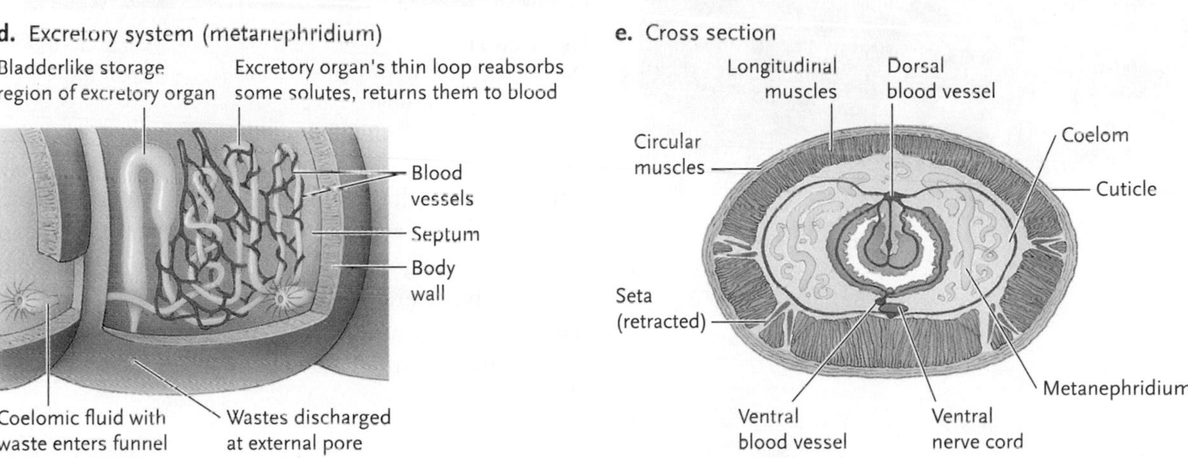

Figure 26.29
Segmentation in the phylum Annelida. Although the digestive system **(a)**, the longitudinal blood vessels **(b)**, and the ventral nerve cord **(c)** form continuous structures, the coelom **(a)**, blood vessels **(b)**, nerves **(c)**, and excretory organs **(d)** appear as repeating structures in most segments. The body musculature **(e)** includes both circular and longitudinal layers that allow these animals to use the coelomic chambers as a hydrostatic skeleton.

The body wall muscles of annelids have both circular and longitudinal layers. Alternate contractions of these muscle groups allow annelids to make directed movements, using the coelom as a hydrostatic skeleton. The outer covering of annelids is a flexible cuticle that grows with the animal; it is not moulted. All annelids except leeches also have chitin-reinforced bristles, called **setae** (sometimes written *chaetae*; singular, seta), which protrude outward from the body wall. Setae anchor the worm against the substrate, providing traction.

Annelids have a closed circulatory system. The blood of most annelids contains haemoglobin or another oxygen-binding pigment. Oxygen diffusing across the cuticle may be picked up by capillaries in the skin to be transported to the tissues.

The excretory system is composed of paired **metanephridia** (singular, metanephridium) (see Figure 26.29d and Chapter 43), which usually occur in all body segments posterior to the head. The nervous system is well developed, with local control centres (ganglia) in every segment, a simple brain in the head, and sensory organs that detect chemicals, moisture, light, and touch.

Most freshwater and terrestrial annelids are hermaphroditic, and worms exchange sperm when they mate. Newly hatched worms have an adult morphology. Some terrestrial annelids also reproduce asexually by fragmenting and regenerating missing parts. Marine annelids usually have separate sexes and release gametes into the sea for fertilization. The zygotes develop into trochophore larvae that add segments, gradually assuming an adult form.

Annelids are divided into three classes.

Class Polychaeta. The 10 000 species of bristle worms (Polychaeta, from *poly* = many and *chaeta* = bristles) are primarily marine **(Figure 26.30, p. 602)**. Many live under rocks or in tubes constructed from mucus, calcium carbonate secretions, grains of sand, and small shell fragments. Their setae project from well-developed parapodia (singular parapodium = closely resembling a foot), fleshy lateral extensions of the body wall used for locomotion and gas exchange. Sense organs are concentrated on a well-developed head.

Many crawling or swimming polychaetes are predatory, using sharp jaws in a protrusible muscular

a. Feather duster worm

Kjell B. Sandved@sandved.com

b. Polychaete feeding structures

c. Polychaete setae

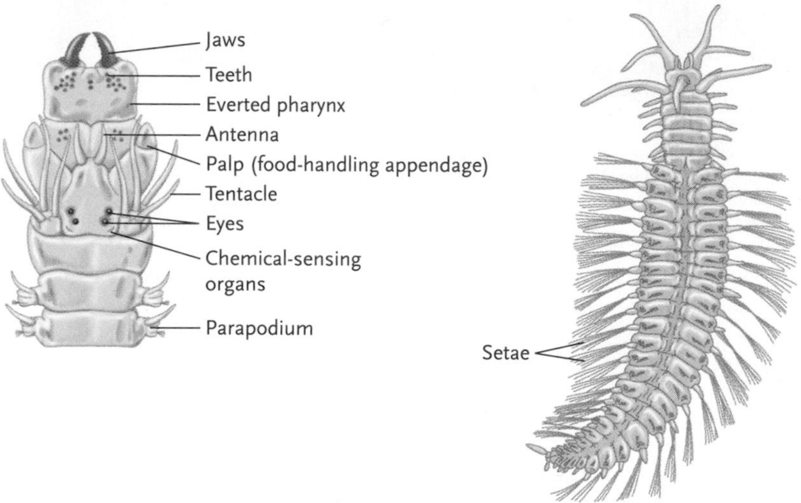

Figure 26.30
Polychaeta. **(a)** The tube-dwelling feather duster worm (*Sabella melanostigma*) has mucus-covered tentacles that trap small food particles. **(b)** Some polychaetes, such as *Nereis*, actively seek food; when they encounter a suitable tidbit, they evert their pharynx, exposing sharp jaws that grab the prey and pull it into the digestive system. **(c)** Many marine polychaetes (such as *Proceraea cornuta*, shown here) have numerous setae, which they use for locomotion.

pharynx to grab small invertebrate prey. Other species graze on algae or scavenge organic matter. A few tube dwellers draw food-laden water into the tube by beating their parapodia; most others collect food by extending feathery, ciliated, mucus-coated tentacles.

Class Oligochaeta. Most of the 3500 species of oligochaete worms (*oligo* = few) are terrestrial **(Figure 26.31),** but they are restricted to moist habitats because they quickly dehydrate in dry air or soil. They range in length from a few millimetres to more than 3 m. Terrestrial oligochaetes, the earthworms, are nocturnal, spending their days in burrows that they excavate. They are important scavengers, assisting in mixing and aerating soil and the conversion of plant and animal debris to nutrients useful to plants.

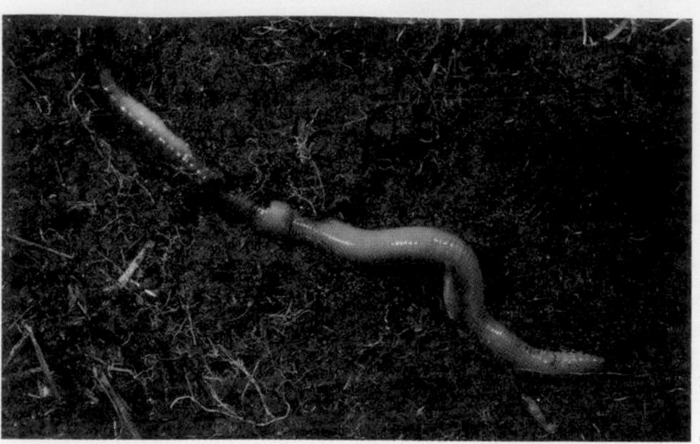

Duncan Mcewan/npl/Minden Pictures

Figure 26.31
Oligochaeta. Earthworms (genus *Lumbricus*) generally move across the ground surface at night.

Aquatic species live in mud or detritus at the bottom of lakes and rivers. Earthworms have complex organ systems (see Figure 26.29), and they sense light and touch at both ends of the body. In addition, they have moisture receptors, an important adaptation in organisms that must stay wet to allow gas exchange across the skin.

Class Hirudinea. Most of the 500 species of leeches (*hirudo* = leech) live in fresh water and suck the blood of vertebrates. These blood feeders have dorsoventrally flattened, tapered bodies with a sucker at each end. Although the body wall is segmented, the coelom is reduced and not partitioned. About a quarter of the known species are not blood feeders but prey on other invertebrates. Almost all of the leeches live in fresh water, but a few marine species are known. Some leeches are terrestrial, living in the moist tropics and feeding on warm-blooded vertebrates.

Blood-feeding leeches attach to the host with the posterior sucker and use their sharp jaws on the anterior sucker to make a small, often painless, triangular incision. A sucking apparatus draws blood from the prey, and a special secretion prevents the host's blood from coagulating. Leeches have a highly branched gut that allows them to consume huge blood meals **(Figure 26.32).** For centuries, doctors used medicinal

Leech before feeding

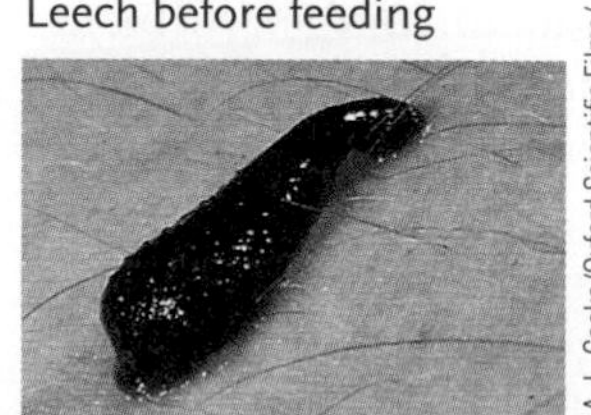

J. A. L. Cooke/Oxford Scientific Films/ Photolibrary.com

Leech after feeding

J. A. L. Cooke/Oxford Scientific Films/ Photolibrary.com

Figure 26.32
Hirudinea. Parasitic leeches consume huge blood meals, as shown by these before and after photos of a medicinal leech (*Hirudo medicinalis*). Because suitable hosts are often hard to locate, gorging allows a leech to take advantage of any host it finds.

Life on the Edge

Hydrothermal Vents

Hydrothermal vents on the sea bed, discovered in 1970, are equivalent to miniature undersea volcanoes. Superheated water emerges from them at temperatures up to 400°C, laden with sulphides **(Figure 1)**. The Endeavour Hot Vent Area, over 2000 m deep, lies 250 km off the coast of Vancouver Island. It has been explored by Verena Tunnicliffe at the University of Victoria and was declared a Marine Protected Area by the Canadian government in 2003. A range of invertebrates, particularly molluscs and annelids, flourish near the vents. Many of these species are new to science, and they are larger and more numerous than the fauna nearby. They experience at least brief exposure to temperatures as high as 50°C. More important, however, is the absence of sunlight, which deprives them of a source of food from plants, and the presence of sulphides. Sulphide is normally toxic, but associated with the vents are mats of bacteria that utilize sulphide for energy production and growth. The metazoans feed on these, and some of the invertebrates have symbiotic bacteria that rely on the sulphides.

Canadian Scientific Submersible Facility

Figure 1
A hot vent "smoker," surrounded by organisms specific to the environment. Inset "Tube worms," originally placed in a separate Phylum Vestimentifera. Molecular analysis places them among the annelids.

leeches (*Hirudo medicinalis*) to "bleed" patients; today, surgeons still use them to drain excess fluid from tissues after reconstructive surgery, reducing swelling until the patient's blood vessels regenerate and resume this function.

Study Break

1. What characteristic reveals the close evolutionary relationship of ectoprocts, brachiopods, and phoronid worms?
2. Describe the three regions of the mollusc body.
3. Which organ systems exhibit segmentation in most annelid worms?

26.7 Ecdysozoan Protostomes

The three phyla in the protostome group Ecdysozoa all have an external cuticle secreted by epidermal cells. The cuticle serves as protection from harsh environmental conditions and helps parasitic species resist host defences. It also permits these animals to change the nature of the covering, which is important if the life stages live in different environments. Although many of these animals live in aquatic or moist terrestrial habitats, a tough exoskeleton allows many, particularly the insects, to thrive on dry land.

26.7a Phylum Nematoda

Members of the phylum Nematoda (*nemata* = thread) are round worms, often tapered at each end. The numerous species of free-living worms are microscopic, reaching a size of at most a few millimetres. Some parasitic species, however, are larger **(Figure 26.33)**, and some are very large. The record is held by *Placentonema gigantissima*, a parasite of the placenta of the sperm whale: it may reach 9 m in length! Although superficially very similar in morphology, nematodes have achieved remarkable diversity. One species lives only in vinegar, and another is found in beer vats. In marine sediments, concentrations of a million or more worms per square metre have been reported.

Figure 26.33
Phylum Nematoda. Many roundworms are animal parasites, like these *Anguillicola crassus*, shown here inside the swim bladder of an eel.

A hectare of farm soil may contain a billion or more nematodes. A single rotting fruit on the ground will contain tens of thousands of worms. Many species are parasitic in plants and animals, and some cause serious diseases in humans. Although fewer than 20 000 species have been described, it is generally agreed that the number of living species is at least 100 000.

The nematode cuticle, often complex in structure, is composed of collagen-like proteins secreted by an epidermis that is often syncytial **(Figure 26.34)**. The cuticle is replaced four times during the life of the nematode, and in some cases, the characteristics of each of the cuticles differ. Moulting of the cuticle is not necessary for the worms to increase in size, and growth usually occurs between moults. *Ascaris lumbricoides*, a common intestinal parasite in humans, represents an extreme case, growing in length from about 6 mm after the final moult to an adult of more than 20 cm. Nematodes, like rotifers, exhibit eutely, having few or no cell divisions in somatic cells after hatching.

This characteristic, together with a transparent cuticle, has made *Caenorhabditis elegans*, which has fewer than 1000 cells, such a useful model for studying development. It eats bacteria such as *E. coli* and can be reared in the lab easily. Because the number of cells is so small, the developmental fate of each cell in the embryo has been documented using techniques such as microinjection or laser microsurgery. The genome is small and has been completely sequenced, yielding about 17 000 genes. *C. elegans* is widely used as a model to explore general questions in developmental biology. For example, Dr. David Bailey at Simon Fraser University in Vancouver uses *C. elegans* to ask questions such as how many of the genes are essential to normal development. He has determined which mutations are lethal and estimates that about 4000 to 5000 genes of the 17 000 are essential for development in *C. elegans*.

Growth in nematodes occurs by an increase in cell size, and in a large nematode such as *Ascaris*, a muscle cell may be more than a centimetre in length.

Figure 26.34
Cross section of a typical nematode.

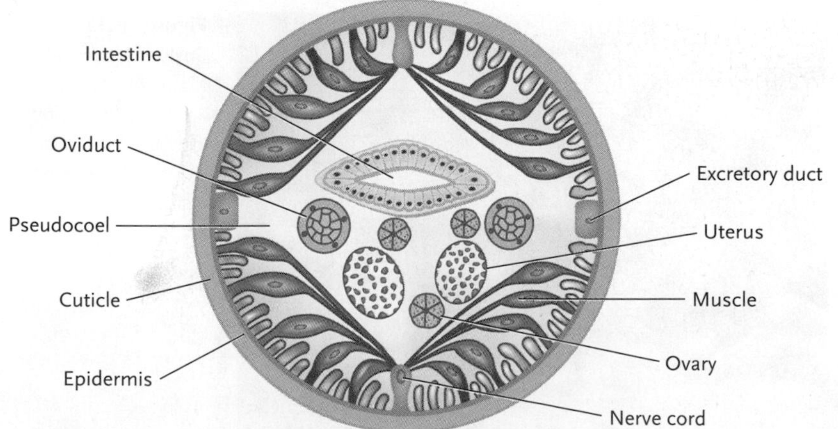

There are no cilia or flagella in nematodes; the spermatozoa move by amoeboid motion. A single layer of muscles forms part of the body wall. These muscles, like those of flatworms, do not receive nerves but make contact with the ventral, dorsal, or lateral nerve cords by long extensions of the muscle (see Figure 26.34).

The nervous system consists of dorsal, lateral, and particularly prominent ventral nerve cords, with a nerve ring surrounding the pharynx at the anterior. Nematodes respond to various chemicals, likely through sense organs located in pits at the anterior end. Some are sensitive to light, possibly through a general sensitivity of their nerves, but others have pigmented eye spots.

The gut of nematodes is a simple tube consisting of a single layer of epithelial cells. There are no muscles surrounding the gut, and food is propelled through the digestive system by a muscular pharynx. The pumping action of the pharynx is also responsible for maintaining pressure in the pseudocoelom. The resulting stiffness produces a hydrostatic skeleton. The cuticle has some elasticity, so that a contraction of muscles in the dorsal part of the worm results in an expansion on the ventral side. Alternate contraction and relaxation produces the dorsoventral wave that characterizes the movement of most nematodes.

The sexes of most nematodes are separate, and fertilization is internal. A few nematodes are hermaphroditic and may be self-fertilizing. Others may be parthenogenetic. Fertilized females, particularly those of parasitic species, produce huge numbers of eggs. The intestinal parasite *A. lumbricoides* may produce 200 000 eggs per day for about 10 months.

Nematodes are particularly successful as parasites and have invaded representatives of most other phyla. *A. lumbricoides* infects about a billion people, or about a sixth of the entire human population. Most wild vertebrates harbour one or more species of nematode parasites. The replaceable cuticle contributes to this success for it allows the worm to produce a different cuticle in each different environment that it encounters as it moves from a free-living form to a parasitic form or from one host to another.

26.7b Phylum Onychophora

The 65 living species of velvet worms (Onychophora, from *onux* = claw and *phor* = to bear) live under stones, logs, and forest litter in moist temperate and tropical habitats in the southern hemisphere. They range in size from 15 mm to 15 cm and feed on small invertebrates and plants. Living onychophorans are all terrestrial, but fossils are known from marine environments.

Onychophorans have a flexible cuticle, superficially segmented bodies, and numerous pairs of unjointed legs **(Figure 26.35)**. Like annelids, they have pairs of excretory organs in most segments. But unlike

Figure 26.35
Phylum Onychophora. Members of the small phylum Onychophora, such as species in the genus *Dnycophor*, have segmented bodies and unjointed appendages.

annelids, no internal septa separate the segments; they have an open circulatory system, a specialized respiratory system similar to that of insects, and relatively large brains, jaws, and tiny claws on their feet. Many produce live young, which, in some species, are nourished within a uterus (see Chapter 40). The sexes are separate, and fertilization is internal.

Fossil onychophorans are known from the Cambrian (they are represented in the Burgess Shale), and the body plan has not changed much since then, suggesting that this highly specialized group of animals represented one of the successes in the experiments of the Cambrian speciation.

26.7c Phylum Arthropoda

If the Mesozoic was the age of the dinosaurs, we are living in the age of the arthropods (*arthros* = joint; *poda* = feet). About three-quarters of all living species of animals are arthropods, a phylum that includes insects, spiders, scorpions, crustaceans, centipedes, millipedes, and the extinct trilobites.

Arthropods have a segmented body encased in a rigid **exoskeleton.** This external covering is a complex of chitin (see *Molecule Behind Biology*) and glycoproteins. In some marine and freshwater groups, such as crabs and lobsters, the cuticle is hardened with calcium carbonate. In terrestrial forms, such as insects, a surface layer of wax provides protection from dehydration. The exoskeleton is thin and flexible at the joints between body segments and at the joints of appendages. Contractions of muscles attached to the exoskeleton move individual body parts like levers, allowing highly coordinated movements and patterns of locomotion.

Although the exoskeleton has obvious advantages, it is nonexpandable and could limit the growth of the animal. Arthropods periodically develop a new cuticle beneath the old one, which they shed in the complex process of ecdysis **(Figure 26.36).** The new cuticle is soft and usually pleated, allowing for expansion after ecdysis. After shedding the old cuticle, arthropods swell with water or air before the new one hardens. They are especially vulnerable to predators at these times.

Primitively, each segment had a pair of lateral appendages, often specialized for locomotion, gas exchange, eating, or reproduction. As arthropods evolved, however, body segments became grouped in various ways. Each region, along with its highly modified paired appendages, is specialized, and the structure and function of the regions vary greatly among groups.

The coelom of arthropods is greatly reduced, and another cavity, the **haemocoel,** is filled with bloodlike **haemolymph.** The heart pumps the haemolymph through an open circulatory system, bathing tissues directly.

Because the hardened cuticle does not permit the easy passage of O_2 and CO_2, arthropods have specialized mechanisms for gas exchange. Marine and freshwater species, such as crabs and lobsters, rely on diffusion across gills that are specialized appendages, usually assisted by currents established by the appendages. The terrestrial groups have developed unique respiratory systems (see Chapter 42).

Many arthropods are equipped with a highly organized central nervous system, touch receptors, chemical

Figure 26.36
Ecdysis in insects. Like all other arthropods, this cicada (*Graptopsaltria nigrofuscata*) sheds its old exoskeleton as it grows.

sensors, image-forming **compound eyes**, and, in some, hearing organs. These are described in Chapters 33 and 34.

The phylogeny of this huge and diverse phylum has been a difficult and disputed subject for many years. Hexapods, and specifically insects, have been regarded by some as most closely related to myriapods, based largely on shared anatomical characters such as Malpighian tubules for excretion and one pair of antennae. Others, however, relate insects more closely to Crustacea, based on other morphological characteristics such as similarities in mouthparts and walking appendages. Molecular studies, including analysis of mitochondrial DNA and *Hox* genes, support the view that hexapods and crustacea are paraphyletic (see Chapter 19 for a definition of paraphyletic) and that myriapods and chelicerates form a separate paraphyletic grouping. This is an active area in research, and other hypotheses may be developed.

We follow the traditional definition of five *subphyla*, partly because this classification adequately reflects arthropod diversity and partly because no alternative hypothesis has been widely adopted by experts.

Subphylum Trilobita. The trilobites (*tri* = three; *lob* = lobed), now extinct, were among the most numerous animals in the shallow Paleozoic seas. Most were ovoid, dorsoventrally flattened, and heavily armoured, with two deep longitudinal grooves that divided the body into one median and two lateral lobes **(Figure 26.37).** The head included a pair of sensory antennae (singular, antenna) and compound eyes, and the segmented thorax and abdomen had pairs of identical appendages, each with two branches. The inner branch was used for locomotion, and the outer, consisting of a number of fine filaments, was used as a gill or in filter feeding.

The position of trilobites in the fossil record indicates that they were among the earliest arthropods. Thus, biologists are confident that their three body regions and unspecialized appendages represent ancestral traits in the phylum. Although there were numerous species, indicating a high degree of success, trilobites disappeared in the Permian mass extinction.

Figure 26.37
Subphylum Trilobita. Trilobites, such as the *Olenellus gilberti*, bore many pairs of relatively undifferentiated appendages.

Subphylum Chelicerata. In spiders, ticks, mites, scorpions, and horseshoe crabs (subphylum Chelicerata, from *cheol* = claw and *cera* = horn), the first pair of appendages, the chelicerae, are fanglike structures used for biting prey. The second pair of appendages, the pedipalps, serve as grasping organs, sensory organs, or walking legs. All chelicerates have two major body regions, the cephalothorax (a fused head–thorax) and the abdomen. The group originated in shallow Paleozoic seas, but most living species are terrestrial. They vary in size from less than a millimetre to 20 cm; all are predators or parasites.

The 60 000 species of spiders, scorpions, mites, and ticks (class Arachnida) represent the vast majority of chelicerates **(Figure 26.38).** Arachnids have four pairs of walking legs on the cephalothorax and highly modified chelicerae and pedipalps. In some spiders, males use their pedipalps to transfer packets of sperm to females. Scorpions use them (the "claws") to shred food and to grasp one another during courtship. Many predatory arachnids have excellent vision, provided by up to four pairs of simple eyes on the cephalothorax. Scorpions and some spiders also have unique pocket-like respiratory organs called **book lungs** (see Chapter 42), derived from abdominal appendages.

Like most other arachnids, spiders subsist on a liquid diet. They use their chelicerae to inject paralyzing poisons and digestive enzymes into prey and then suck up the partly digested tissues. Many spiders are economically important predators, helping to control insect pests. Only a few are a threat to humans. The toxin of a black widow (*Latrodectus mactans*) causes paralysis, and the toxin of the brown recluse (*Loxosceles reclusa*) destroys tissues around the site of the bite.

Although many spiders hunt actively, others capture prey on silken threads secreted by **spinnerets,** which are modified abdominal appendages. Some species weave the threads into complex, netlike webs. The silk is secreted as a liquid protein but quickly polymerizes. Spiders also use silk to make nests, to protect their egg masses, as a safety line when moving through the environment, and to wrap prey for later consumption. Spider silk is extremely tough, and the material from some spiders exceeds the tensile strength of steel. It is also highly elastic. These properties have led to proposals for its use in fabrics. A Canadian company has developed transgenic goats that produce spider silk in their milk.

Most mites are tiny, but they have a big impact. Some are serious agricultural pests that feed on plant sap. Others cause mange (patchy hair loss) or painful

a. Wolf spider

P. J. Bryand, University of California–Irvine/BPS

b. Spider anatomy

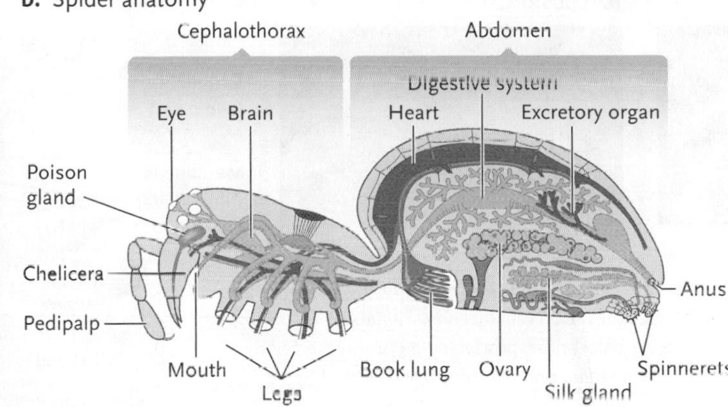

c. Scorpion

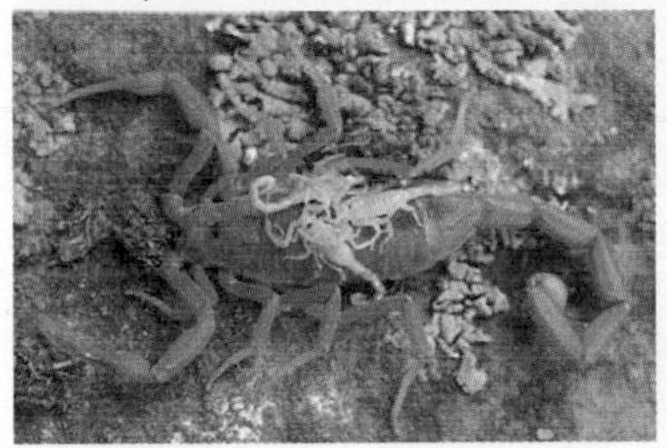

P. J. Bryand, Univ. of California–Irvine/BPS

d. House dust mite

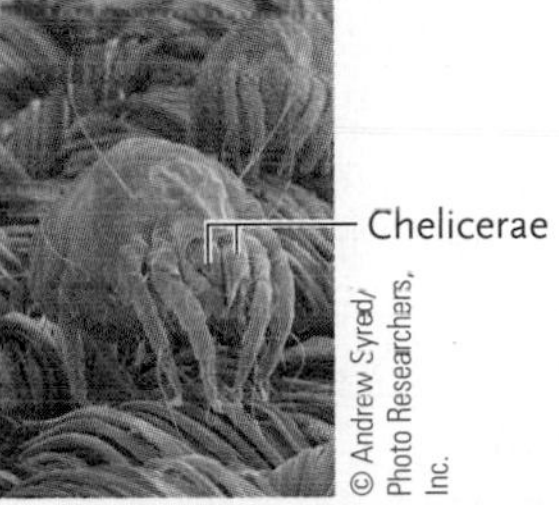

© Andrew Syred/ Photo Researchers, Inc.

Figure 26.38
Subphylum Chelicerata, Class Arachnida. **(a)** The wolf spider (*Lycosa* species) is harmless to humans. **(b)** The arachnid body plan includes a cephalothorax and an abdomen. **(c)** Scorpions have a stinger at the tip of the segmented abdomen. Many, such as *Centruroides sculpuratus*, protect their eggs and young. **(d)** House dust mites (*Dermatophagoides pteronyssinus*), shown in a scanning electron micrograph, feed on microscopic debris.

and itchy welts on animals. House dust mites, which feed on the dried skin cast off by humans, cause allergic reactions in many people. Ticks, which are generally larger than mites, are blood feeders that often transmit pathogens, such as those causing Rocky Mountain spotted fever and Lyme disease.

The subphylum Chelicerata also includes five species of horseshoe crabs (class Merostomata), an ancient lineage that has not changed much over its 350 million-year history **(Figure 26.39)**. Horseshoe crabs are carnivorous bottom feeders in shallow coastal waters. Beneath their characteristic shell, they have one pair of chelicerae, a pair of pedipalps, four pairs of walking legs, and a set of paperlike gills, derived from ancestral walking legs. A component of horseshoe crab blood is important to the pharmaceutical industry, where it is used to test for the presence of endotoxins resulting from bacterial contamination during manufacture.

Jane Burton/Bruce Coleman Inc.

Figure 26.39
Marine chelicerates. Horseshoe crabs, such as *Limulus polyphemus*, are included in the Merostomata.

Subphylum Crustacea. The 35 000 species of shrimps, lobsters, crabs, and their relatives in the subphylum Crustacea (*crusta* = shell) represent a lineage that emerged more than 500 million years ago **(Figure 26.40, p. 608)**. They are abundant in marine and freshwater habitats. A few species, such as sowbugs and pillbugs, live in moist, sheltered terrestrial environments. In many crustaceans, two and, in some cases, all three of the arthropod body regions (head, thorax, and abdomen) may be fused. Fusion of the head and thorax into a cephalothorax is a common pattern. In some, the exoskeleton forms a carapace, a protective covering that extends backward from the head. Crustaceans vary in size from water fleas less than 1 mm long to lobsters that can grow to 60 cm in length and weigh as much as 20 kg.

Crustaceans generally have five characteristic pairs of appendages on the head (see Figure 26.40c). Most have two pairs of sensory antennae and three pairs of mouthparts. The latter include one pair of **mandibles**, which move laterally to bite and chew, and two pairs of **maxillae** (singular, maxilla), which hold and manipulate food. Numerous paired appendages posterior to the mouthparts vary among groups. Ancestrally, crustacean appendages were divided into two branches at the base, but many living species have unbranched appendages.

Most crustaceans are active animals that exhibit complex movements during locomotion and in the

Figure 26.40
Decapod crustaceans. **(a)** Crabs, such as this ghost crab in the genus *Ocypode*, and **(b)** lobsters (*Homarus americanus*) are typical decapod crustaceans. The abdomen of a crab is shortened and wrapped under the cephalothorax, producing a compressed body. **(c)** Lobsters bear 19 pairs of distinctive appendages; one pair of mandibles and two pairs of maxillae are not illustrated in this lateral view.

performance of other behaviours. These activities are coordinated by elaborate sensory and nervous systems, including chemical and touch receptors in the antennae, compound eyes, statocysts on the head, and sensory hairs embedded in the exoskeleton throughout the body. The nervous system is similar to that in annelids, but the ganglia, particularly those forming the brain, are larger and more complex. Larger species have complex, feathery gills derived from appendages tucked beneath the carapace. Metabolic wastes such as ammonia are excreted by diffusion across the gills or, in larger species, by **antennal glands**, located in the head.

The sexes are typically separate, and courtship rituals are often complex. Eggs are usually brooded on the surface of the female's body or beneath the carapace. Many have free-swimming larvae that, after undergoing a series of moults, gradually assume an adult form.

The subphylum includes so many different body plans that it is usually divided into six classes with numerous subclasses and orders. The crabs, lobsters, and shrimps (class Malacostraca, order Decapoda, *deka* = 10 + *poda* = foot) number more than 10 000 species. The vast majority of decapods are marine, but a few shrimps, crabs, and crayfishes occupy freshwater habitats. Some crabs also live in moist terrestrial habitats, where they scavenge dead vegetation, clearing the forest floor of debris.

All decapods exhibit extreme specialization of their appendages. In the American lobster, for example, each of the 19 pairs of appendages is different (see Figure 26.40c). Behind the antennae, mandibles, and maxillae, the thoracic segments have three pairs of maxillipeds, which shred food and pass it up to the mouth, a pair of large chelipeds (pinching claws), and four pairs of walking legs. The abdominal appendages include a pair specialized for sperm transfer (in males only), swimmerets for locomotion and for brooding eggs, and uropods, which, in combination with the telson (the tip of the abdomen), make a fan-shaped tail.

Representatives of several crustacean classes—fairy shrimps, amphipods, water fleas, ostracods, and copepods **(Figure 26.41)**—live as plankton in the upper waters of oceans and lakes. Most are only a few millimetres long but are present in huge numbers. They feed on microscopic algae or detritus and are themselves food for larger invertebrates, fishes, and some suspension-feeding marine mammals such as the baleen whales. Planktonic crustaceans are among the most abundant animals on Earth. The total biomass of a single species, *Euphausia superba*, is estimated at 500 000 000 tonnes, more than the total mass of humans.

Adult barnacles (class Maxillopoda, subclass Cirripedia, *cirrus* = curl of hair and *poda* = foot) are sessile marine crustaceans that live within a strong, calcified, cup-shaped shell **(Figure 26.42)**. Their free-swimming larvae attach permanently to substrates—rocks, wooden pilings, the hulls of ships, the shells of

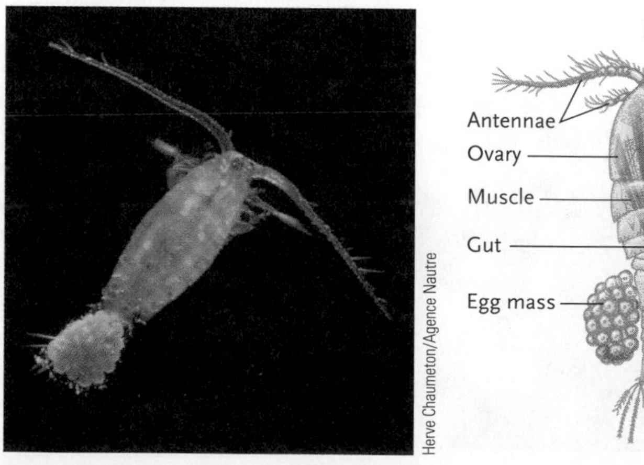

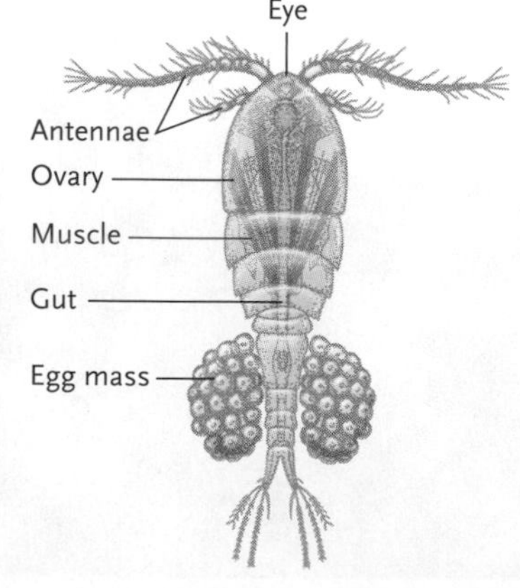

Figure 26.41
Copepods. Tiny crustaceans, such as this copepod (*Calanus* species on the left, *Cyclops* species on the right), occur by the billions in freshwater and marine plankton.

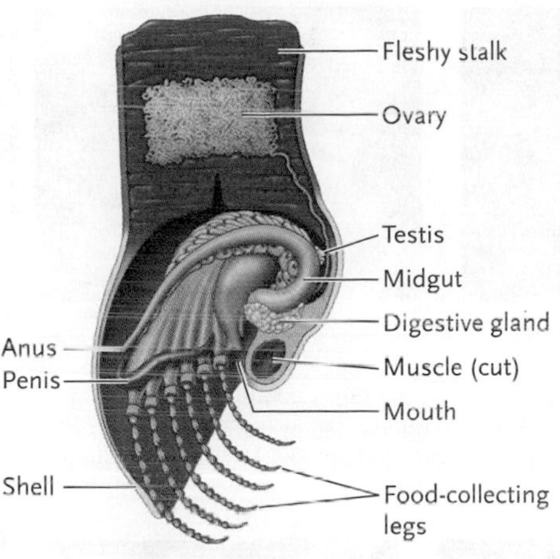

Figure 26.42
Barnacles. Gooseneck barnacles (*Lepas anatifera*) attach to the underside of floating debris. Like other barnacles, they open their shells and extend their feathery legs to collect particulate food from seawater.

molluscs, and even the skin of whales—and secrete the shell, which is a modified exoskeleton. To feed, barnacles open the shell and extend six pairs of feathery legs. The beating legs capture microscopic plankton and transfer it to the mouth. Unlike most crustaceans, barnacles are hermaphroditic.

Subphylum Myriapoda. The 3000 species of centipedes (class Chilopoda) and 10 000 species of millipedes (class Diplopoda) are classified together in the subphylum Myriapoda (murias = 10 000; poda = foot). Myriapods have two body regions, a head and a segmented trunk **(Figure 26.43)**. The head bears one pair of antennae, and the trunk bears one (centipedes) or two (millipedes) pairs of walking legs on most of its many segments. Myriapods are terrestrial, and many species live under rocks or dead leaves. Centipedes are fast and voracious predators; they generally feed on invertebrates, but some eat small vertebrates. Although most species are less than 10 cm long, some grow to 25 cm. The millipedes are slow but powerful herbivores or scavengers. The largest species attain a length of nearly 30 cm.

Subphylum Hexapoda. The subphylum Hexapoda (hex = six) includes the class Insecta, as well as some other smaller classes. In terms of sheer numbers and diversity, the approximately 1 000 000 species of insects are the most successful animals on Earth, occupying virtually every terrestrial and aquatic habitat. They were among the first animals to colonize terrestrial habitats, where most species still live. The oldest Hexapod fossils date from the Devonian, about 400 million years ago, and the first insect fossils appeared shortly after. Insects are generally small, ranging from 0.1 mm to 30 cm in length. The class is divided into about 30 orders **(Figure 26.44, p. 610)**.

The insect body plan always includes a head, a thorax, and an abdomen **(Figure 26.45, p. 611)**. The head is equipped with multiple mouthparts, a pair of compound eyes, and one pair of sensory antennae. The thorax has three pairs of walking legs and often one or two pairs of wings. Adult insects are the only invertebrates capable of flight. The origin of wings is uncertain. The traditional view holds that they are new structures arising as outgrowths of the body wall. However, on the basis of both fossil and molecular evidence, one of the foremost researchers in the field, Jarmila Kukalova-Peck of Carleton University in Ottawa, maintains that wings are derived from branches of a proximal (near the body) segment of the leg.

Insects exchange gases through a specialized **tracheal system** (see Chapter 42), a branching network of tubes that carries oxygen from small openings in the exoskeleton to individual cells throughout the body. Insects excrete nitrogenous wastes through

a.

b.

Figure 26.43
Millipedes and centipedes. (a) Millipedes, such as *Spirobolus* species, feed on living and decaying vegetation. They have two pairs of walking legs on most segments. **(b)** Like all centipedes, this Southeast Asian species (*Scolopendra subspinipes*), shown feeding on a small frog, is a voracious predator. Centipedes have one pair of walking legs per segment.

© Arthur Evans/Animals, Animals—Earth Scenes

a. Silverfish (Thysanura, *Ctenolepisma longicaudata*) are primitive wingless insects.

Edward S. Ross

b. Dragonflies, like the flame skimmer (Odonata, *Libellula saturata*), have aquatic larvae that are active predators; adults capture other insects in mid-air.

BIOS Borrell Bartomeu/Peter Arnold, Inc.

c. Male praying mantids (Mantodea, *Mantis religiosa*) are often eaten by the larger females during or immediately after mating.

Edward S. Ross

d. This rhinoceros beetle (Coleoptera, *Dynastes granti*) is one of more than 250,000 beetle species that have been described.

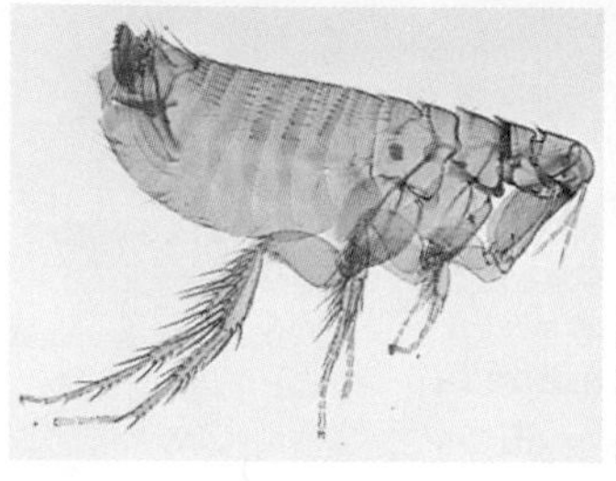

Edward S. Ross

e. Fleas (Siphonoptera, *Hystrichopsylla dippiei*) have strong legs with an elastic ligament that allows these parasites to jump on and off their animal hosts.

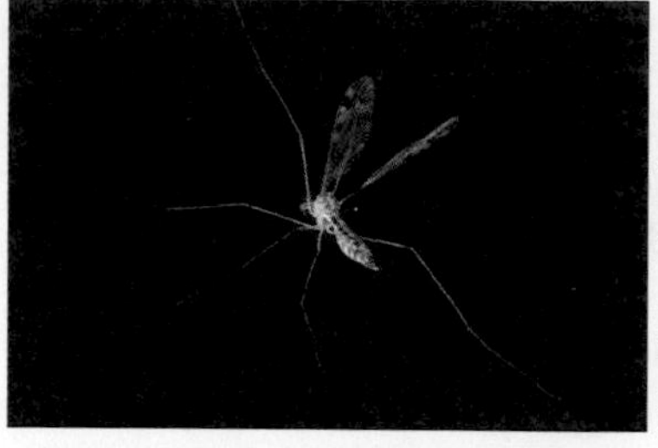

Michael Durham/Minden Pictures

f. Crane flies (Diptera, *Tipula* species) look like giant mosquitoes, but their mouthparts are not useful for biting other animals; the adults of most species live only a few days and do not feed at all.

C. P. Hickman, Jr.

g. The luna moth (Lepidoptera, *Actias luna*), like other butterflies and moths, has wings that are covered with colorful microscopic scales.

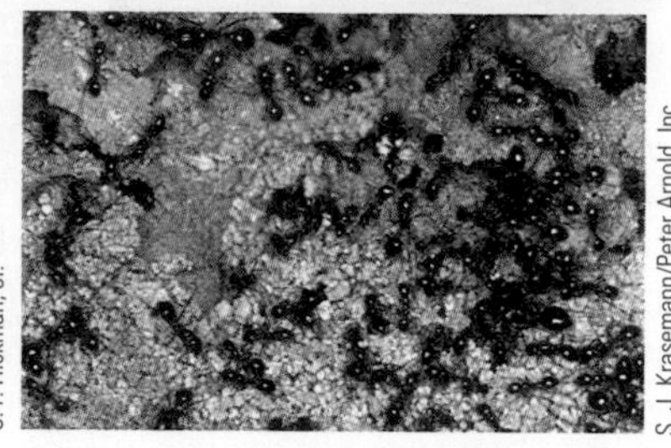

S. J. Krasemann/Peter Arnold, Inc.

h. Like many other ant species, fire ants (Hymenoptera, *Solenopsis invicta*) live in large cooperative colonies. Fire ants—named for their painful sting—were introduced into southeastern North America, where they are now serious pests.

Figure 26.44
Insect diversity. Insects are grouped into about 30 orders, 8 of which are illustrated here.

specialized **Malpighian tubules** (see Chapter 43) that transport wastes to the digestive system for disposal with the feces. These two organ systems also appear in some of the terrestrial chelicerates. Since these are not paraphyletic with hexapods, this is another example of convergent evolution.

Insect sensory systems are diverse and complex. Besides a pair of image-forming compound eyes, many insects have light-sensing ocelli on their heads. Many also have hairs, sensitive to touch, on their antennae, legs, and other regions of the body. Chemical receptors are particularly common on the legs and feet, allowing the identification of food. Many groups of insects have sound receptors to detect predators and potential mates. The familiar chirping of crickets, for example, is a mating call emitted by males that may repel other males and attract females. The beetles of the family Lampyridae emit light signals from their abdomens to attract mates (see Chapter 33).

As a group, insects use an enormous variety of materials as food, and their mouthparts may be modified to reflect the nature of the food source **(Figure 26.46)**. The basic plan is reflected in a plant feeder such as a locust or a generalized feeder such as a cockroach. The *labrum* is an anterior flaplike extension of the front of the head that covers the mouthparts and has sensory structures. The mouthparts themselves are modified appendages. The paired mandibles are chewing organs, and behind those are paired maxillae abundantly supplied with sense organs, particularly on its *palps* (jointed projections), which act to scoop the food. The most posterior is the *labium*, representing a fused pair of appendages, is well supplied with sensory structures and palps. This ancestral mandibulate pattern, with mouthparts representing three of the six segments that form the insect head, is modified in various ways to accommodate different modes of feeding. In some biting flies, such as mosquitoes, the mouthparts are piercing structures, with a narrow channel to suck up blood. In butterflies and moths, the mouthparts include a long proboscis to drink nectar. In houseflies, the mouthparts are adapted for sopping up food that has been moistened by its saliva.

Life on land requires internal fertilization (see Chapter 38). In insects, males may produce packets of sperm enclosed in spermatophores and insert them into the female ducts, or sperm transfer may be direct via a penis. Sperm are stored in the female until used to fertilize eggs at the time of egg laying. The eggs of most insects are covered with a waterproof shell before they are fertilized and have one or more minute pores to permit the entry of sperm.

Parthenogenesis occurs in a number of species. In aphids, not only are the females parthenogenetic at

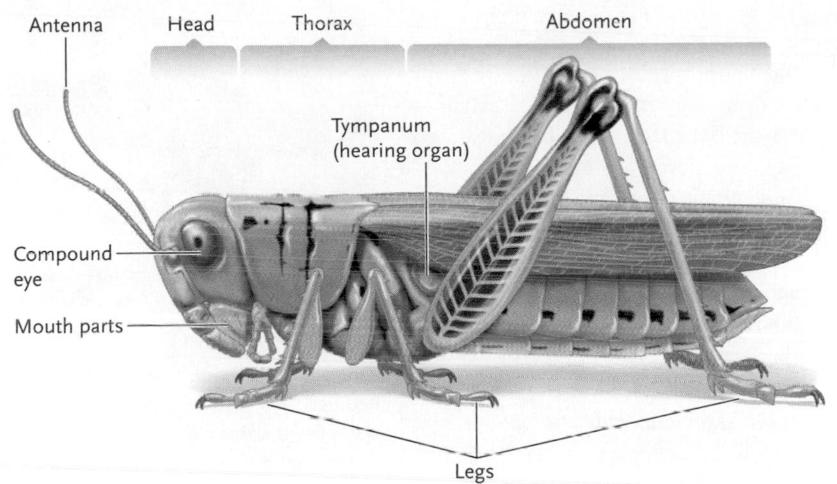

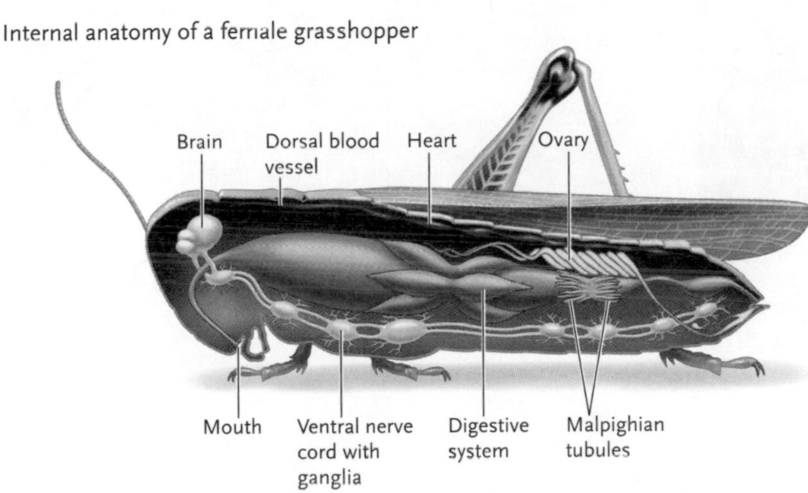

Figure 26.45
The insect body plan. Insects have a distinct head, thorax, and abdomen. Of all the internal organ systems, only the dorsal blood vessel, ventral nerve cord, and some muscles are strongly segmented.

times when food plants are abundant, they also produce live young, and development is so telescoped that embryos within the mother already have embryos within their ovaries. This results in an enormously rapid increase in population when conditions are favourable. Under less favourable conditions, normal sexual reproduction occurs. In a few species, parthenogenesis is the only mode of reproduction and males are unknown.

After it hatches from an egg, an insect passes through a series of developmental stages called **instars.** Several hormones control development and ecdysis, which marks the passage from one instar to the next. Insects exhibit one of three basic patterns of postembryonic development **(Figure 26.47, p. 612).** Primitive, wingless species (order Thysanura) simply grow and shed their exoskeleton, undergoing only minimal changes in morphology. Early instars lack scales on their cuticle, and the appearance of scales corresponds with reproductive maturity. Moulting cycles may continue after reproductive maturity.

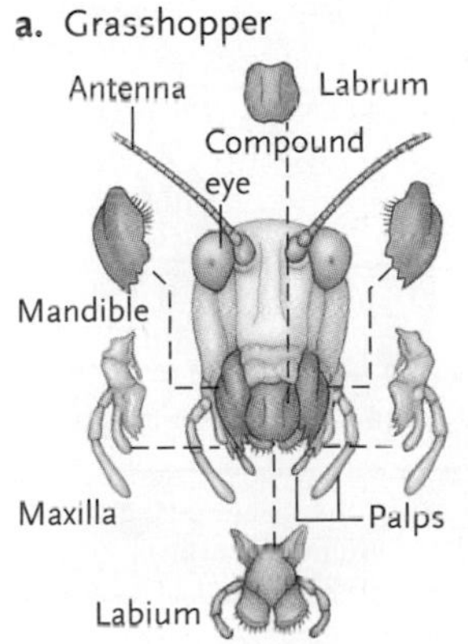

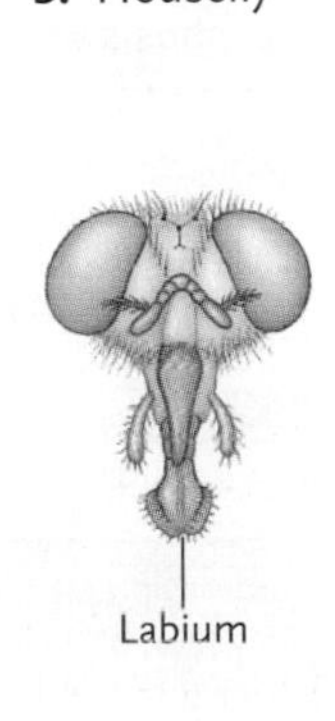

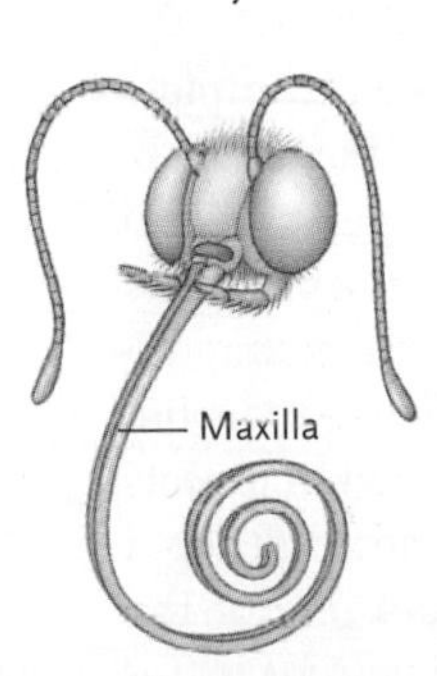

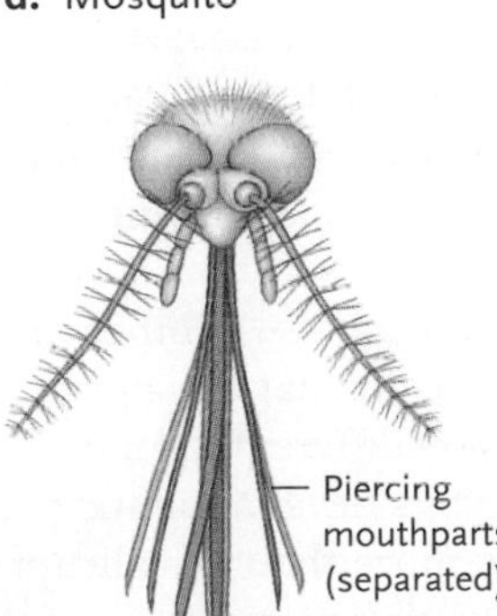

Figure 26.46
Specialized insect mouthparts. The **(a)** ancestral chewing mouthparts have been modified during evolution, allowing different insects to **(b)** sponge up food, **(c)** drink nectar, and **(d)** pierce skin to drink blood.

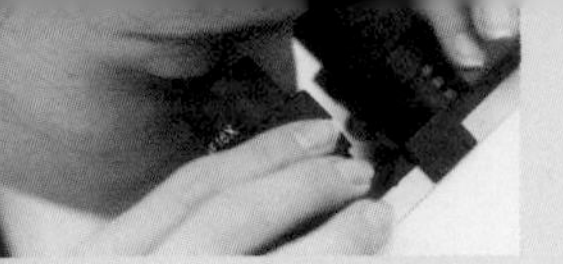

People Behind Biology

V.B. Wigglesworth

V.B. Wigglesworth was a British researcher who founded the subject of insect physiology. He had an active research career that spanned seven decades, from 1928 to 1991. He discovered the utility of the blood-sucking bug *Rhodnius prolixus* **(Figure 1)** for experimental work. Unfed, the insect remains in a state of suspended development. However, when it takes a blood meal, development to the next stage begins, and Wigglesworth used this signal, together with clever surgical approaches **(Figure 2),** to establish the basic facts of the hormonal control of development in insects. Although he is perhaps best known for this work, he also established the basic facts of insect digestion, excretion and the operation of the Malpighian tubules, the operation of the tracheal system, and the properties of the cuticle. He used a keen sense of observation to identify appropriate experimental questions, and devised and carried out clever experimental approaches to answer the questions he investigated.

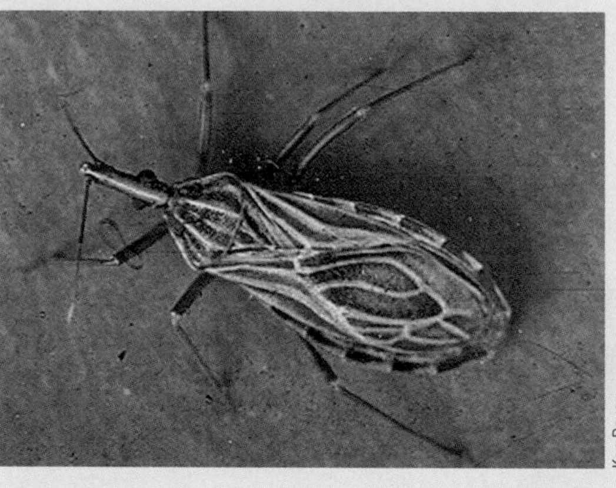

Ken Davey

Figure 1
The adult female of *Rhodnius prolixus.*

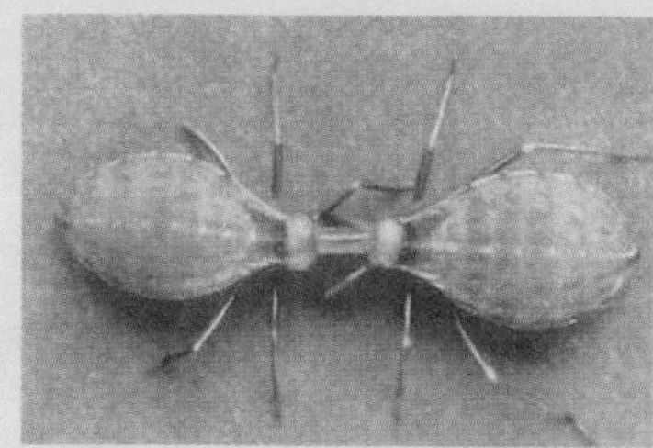

From: Plate II a opposite p 45 of the "Physiology of Insect Metamorphosis" by VB Wigglesworth. Cambridge University Press 1954

Figure 2
One of Wigglesworth's surgical procedures. The nymph on the right was decapitated within a day of feeding, before the hormones from the head governing moulting were secreted; therefore, it will not develop. The insect on the left was decapitated after the hormones were released and will develop normally. The two are joined so that their hemocoels are connected (a procedure called parabiosis). They will both initiate the formation of a new cuticle driven by hormones from the insect on the left.

Figure 26.47
Patterns of postembryonic development in insects.

a. Limited metamorphosis

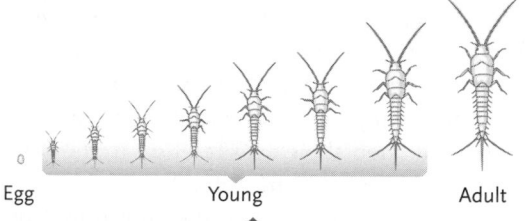

Egg Young Adult

Some wingless insects, like silverfish (order Thysanura), do not undergo a dramatic change in form as they grow.

b. Metamorphosis without a pupa

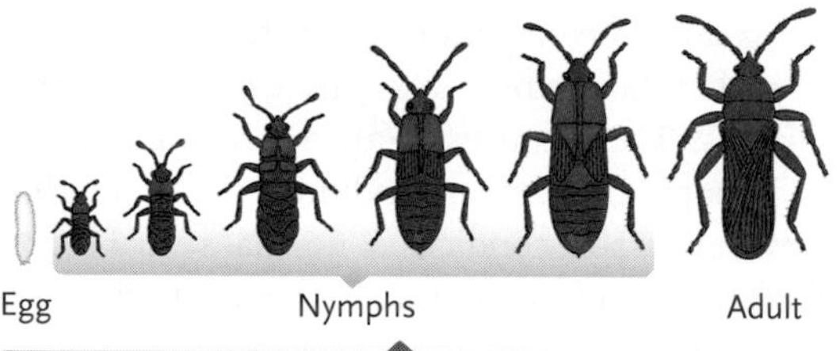

Some insects, such as the Order Hemiptera, undergo a metamorphosis that involves no major reorganisation in form apart from the development of wings.

c. Metamorphosis with a pupa

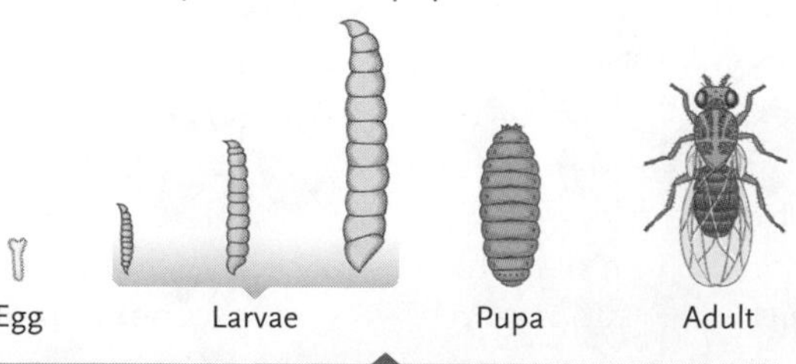

Fruit flies (order Diptera) and many other insects undergo a total reorganization of their internal and external anatomy when they pass through the pupal stage of the life cycle.

Other species undergo what is often called **incomplete metamorphosis.** They hatch from the egg as a nymph, which lacks functional wings. In many species, such as grasshoppers (order Orthoptera), the nymphs resemble the adults. In other insects, such as dragonflies (order Odonata), the aquatic nymphs are morphologically very different from the adults. Even in insects following this developmental pattern, the adult form differs by more than the abrupt development of the wings. The nature or colour of the cuticle may differ

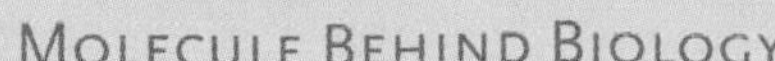

MOLECULE BEHIND BIOLOGY

Insect Juvenile Hormone

The juvenile hormone of insects is a family of hormones, each differing only slightly in structure **(Figure 1).** Its existence was first demonstrated by the English researcher V.B. Wigglesworth (see People Behind Biology) in 1948. Using surgical procedures, he showed that the corpus allatum, an endocrine organ just behind the brain, was the source of a factor governing metamorphosis. In the presence of the factor, the insect remained larval, and in its absence, metamorphosis occurred, leading to the adult insect. In the adult, the hormone governs egg production and other elements of reproduction. The precise structure of the first member of the family of molecules was not elucidated until 1967. Because juvenile hormone is an oil, it passes easily through the cuticle of insects **(Figure 2).** This raised the possibility that mimics of the hormone might be useful as insecticides. Since the hormone has no obvious counterpart in other animals, it was argued that insecticides based on the hormone should be safe. Some compounds have emerged as useful pesticides and have been particularly useful in controlling mosquito larvae in water bodies and fleas on pets.

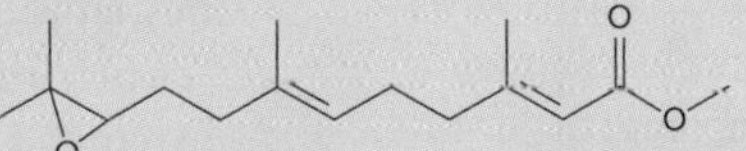

Figure 1
JH III, the most common of the family of molecules used as juvenile hormone in insects.

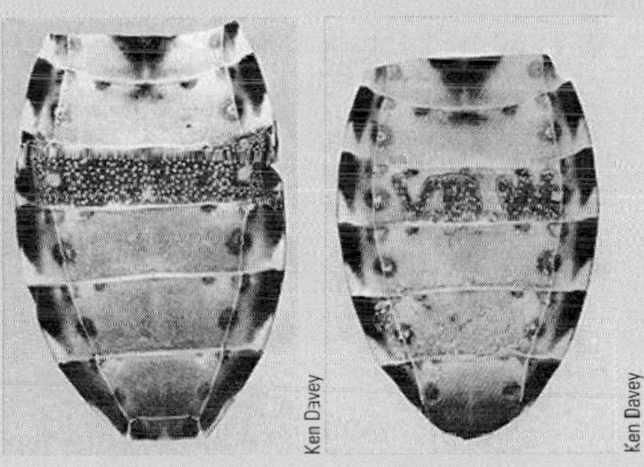

Figure 2
Juvenile hormone passes easily through the cuticle. In this experiment, V.B. Wigglesworth applied the appropriate concentration of the hormone to a localized area on the dorsal surface of a last-stage larva of *Rhodnius prolixus* during the process of forming the adult cuticle. On the left, he applied the hormone to a single segment, and on the right, he applied it in the form of his initials. When the insects moulted to the adult, the new cuticle in the treated portions retained the characteristics of the larval cuticle, whereas the rest of the insect exhibited normal adult cuticle. This photo also shows that in some insects with "incomplete metamorphosis," the changes in morphology may be very great.

(see *Molecule Behind Biology*). The terminal segments are reorganized to produce the external genitalia. In general, however, the descendants of the cells present in the first instar produce these changes.

Most insects undergo **complete metamorphosis:** the larva that hatches from the egg differs greatly from the adult. Larvae and adults often occupy different habitats and consume different food. The larvae (caterpillars, grubs, or maggots) are often worm-shaped, with chewing mouthparts. They grow and moult several times, retaining their larval morphology. Before they transform into sexually mature adults, they spend a period of time as a sessile pupa. During this stage, most of the larval tissues are destroyed and replaced by groups of embryonic cells, called "disks," that have been in place since hatching. Although these cells are not obviously differentiated, their developmental fate is determined. Thus, there are antennal disks, eye disks, wing disks, and so on. The process is fundamentally different from that in insects with incomplete metamorphosis. In the latter, existing cells are reprogrammed at the last moult to produce the adult form, whereas in insects with complete metamorphosis, entirely new cells, programmed during embryogenesis to produce adult tissues, are involved.

Moths, butterflies, beetles, wasps, and flies are examples of insects with complete metamorphosis. Their larval stages specialize in feeding and growth, whereas the adults are adapted for dispersal and reproduction. In some species, the adults never feed, relying on the energy stores accumulated during the larval stage. This mode of development has been highly successful. The four principal orders with a pupa—the Lepidoptera, Coleoptera, Hymenoptera, and Diptera—account for about two-thirds of all known species of animals.

The evolution of insects has been characterized by innovations in morphology, life cycle patterns, locomotion, feeding, and habitat use. Insects' well-developed nervous systems govern exceptionally complex patterns of behaviour, including parental care, a habit that reaches its zenith in the colonial social insects, the termites, ants, bees, and wasps (see *Polymorphic Development*). The factors that contribute to the insects' success also make them our most aggressive competitors. They destroy agricultural crops, stored food, wool, paper, and timber. They feed on blood from humans and domesticated animals, sometimes transmitting disease-causing pathogens such as malaria as they do so. Nevertheless, insects are essential members of terrestrial ecological communities. Many species pollinate flowering plants, including important crops. Many others attack or parasitize species that are harmful to human activities. Most insects are a primary source of food for other animals. Some make useful products, such as honey, shellac, beeswax, and silk, and many human cultures use them for food.

Study Break

1. What are the advantages of moulting in nematodes?
2. If an arthropod's rigid exoskeleton cannot be expanded, how does the animal grow?
3. How do the number of body regions differ among the four subphyla of living arthropods?
4. How do the life stages differ between insects that have incomplete metamorphosis and those that have complete metamorphosis?

Unanswered Questions

How many species of animals are there? Most scientists agree that we have only begun to document the diversity of life. A little over a million species of animals have been described so far, and the number increases every day, but estimates of the total differ widely. Some estimates, based on sampling from single trees in a tropical rain forest, place the number of insect species alone at between 5 and 10 million. Recently, more concerted international efforts to document the diversity of life have begun to emerge. For example, the Census of Marine Life is an international consortium dedicated to exploring marine diversity. Directed by Ron O'Dor, on leave from Dalhousie University, it coordinates the efforts from all of the major countries and regions of the world. One of the major tools for management of the enormous amount of data is the Barcode of Life, a concept originated by Paul Hebert at the University of Guelph in 2003 (see Chapter 3). This initiative has grown to a major international consortium involving more than 45 countries.

Review

Go to CENGAGENOW™ at http://hed.nelson.com/ to access quizzing, animations, exercises, articles, and personalized homework help.

26.1 What Is an Animal?

- Animals are eukaryotic, multicellular organisms that are differentiated from plants by heterotrophy, motility, and direct contact between adjacent cells.
- Animals probably arose in the Precambrian from a hollow sphere of colonial flagellates that reorganized as a double-layered sac-within-a-sac.

26.2 Key Innovations in Animal Evolution

- Tissues, groupings of identical cells specialized to perform specific functions, are organized into two or three tissue layers, ectoderm, endoderm, and, in those animals with three layers, mesoderm. In some sponges, the specialized cells may be capable of dedifferentiation.
- Some animals exhibit radial symmetry; most exhibit bilateral symmetry. Bilaterally symmetrical animals have left and right sides, dorsal and ventral sides, and anterior and posterior ends.
- Acoelomate animals have no body cavity. Pseudocoelomate animals have a body cavity between the derivatives of endoderm and of mesoderm. Coelomate animals have a body cavity that is entirely lined by derivatives of mesoderm. The cavities are filled with fluid that separates and protects the organs and in some cases functions as hydrostatic skeleton.
- Two lineages of animals differ in developmental patterns. Most protostomes exhibit spiral, determinate cleavage; the coelom (when present) is a schizocoelom; and the blastopore develops into the mouth. Deuterostomes have radial symmetry, indeterminate cleavage, an enterocoelom, and their blastopore becomes the anus.
- The development of many protostomes includes a larval stage. This polymorphic development allows sessile animals to be distributed, permits parasitic forms to exist in widely different environments, and avoids competition between the young and the adults.
- Four animal phyla exhibit segmentation.

26.3 An Overview of Animal Phylogeny and Classification

- Sequence analyses of highly conserved structures such as rRNA, mitochondrial DNA, and DNA coding for specific proteins can be compared in various species. The closer the similarity, the more closely related the species are assumed to be. Phylogenetic trees based on such data have confirmed some relationships based on developmental and morphological data and challenged others.
- The Radiata includes animals with two tissue layers and radial symmetry, and the Bilateria includes animals with three tissue layers and bilateral symmetry.

- Bilateria is further subdivided into Protostomia and Deuterostomia. The phylogeny based on molecular evidence divides the Protostomia into the Lophotrochozoa and the Ecdysozoa.
- Molecular phylogeny suggests that ancestral protostomes had a coelom and that acoelomate and pseudocoelomate conditions were derived from the coelomate.
- Segmentation arose independently in three lineages: the annelids, the Onychophora/Arthropoda, and the Chordata.

26.4 Phylum Porifera

- Sponges (phylum Porifera) are asymmetrical animals, many with limited integration of cells in their bodies.
- The body of many sponges is a water-filtering system with incurrent pores, a spongocoel, and an osculum, through which water exits the body. Flagellated choanocytes draw water into the body and capture particulate food.

26.5 Metazoans with Radial Symmetry

- The two major radiate phyla have two well-developed tissue layers with a gelatinous mesoglea between them. They lack organ systems but have well-developed nerve nets. All are aquatic or marine.
- The hydrozoans, jellyfishes, sea anemones, and corals (phylum Cnidaria) are predators that capture prey with tentacles and stinging nematocysts.
- The life cycles of cnidarians may include polyps, medusae, or both. Anthozoans lack a medusa stage, whereas in jellyfish (Scyphozoa and Cubozoa), medusae are prominent and hydroids may be absent, and both are present in Hydrozoa.
- The small, translucent comb jellies (phylum Ctenophora) use long, sticky tentacles to capture particulate food. They are weak swimmers that use rows of cilia for locomotion.

26.6 Lophotrochozoan Protostomes

- The taxon Lophotrochozoa includes eight phyla that share either a characteristic type of larva or a specialized feeding structure.
- Flatworms (phylum Platyhelminthes) are either free-living or parasitic. Free-living species have well-developed digestive, excretory, reproductive, and nervous systems. Parasitic flukes and tapeworms live within or upon animal hosts. They attach to hosts with suckers or hooks, and they produce numerous eggs. Some organ systems may be greatly reduced in parasitic species.
- The wheel animals (phylum Rotifera) are tiny and abundant inhabitants of freshwater and marine ecosystems. Movements of cilia in the corona control their locomotion and bring food to their mouths. Many are parthenogenetic.
- Three small phyla (Ectoprocta, Brachiopoda, and Phoronida) all use a lophophore to feed on particulate matter. Brachiopods live within a two-part shell; ectoprocts form flattened or branching colonies; and phoronids are small, usually tube-dwelling worms.
- The ribbon worms (phylum Nemertea) are elongate and often colourful animals with a proboscis housed in a unique structure, the rhynchocoel.
- Chitons, snails, clams, octopuses, and their relatives (phylum Mollusca) have fleshy bodies that are often enclosed in a hard shell. The molluscan body plan includes a head–foot, a visceral mass, and a mantle.
- Segmented worms (phylum Annelida) generally exhibit segmentation of the coelom and of the muscular, circulatory, excretory, respiratory, and nervous systems. Polychaetes have segmental appendages used in locomotion and gas exchange. Leeches have reduced segmentation.

26.7 Ecdysozoan Protostomes

- The taxon Ecdysozoa includes three phyla that periodically shed their cuticle.
- Roundworms (phylum Nematoda) feed on decaying organic matter or parasitize plants or animals. Locomotion depends on muscles contracting against a hydrostatic skeleton provided by a fluid-filled pseudocoel. Moulting is not essential for growth, but it permits changing the nature of the cuticle to accommodate different environments.
- The velvet worms (phylum Onychophora) have segmented bodies and unjointed legs. Some species bear live young, which develop in a uterus.
- The arthropods (phylum Arthropoda) are the most diverse animals on Earth. Their segmented bodies are often differentiated into distinct regions, and their jointed appendages are specialized for feeding, locomotion, or reproduction. They shed their firm, water-resistant exoskeleton to accommodate growth or when they begin a new stage of the life cycle. Arthropods have an open circulatory system, numerous sense organs that provide input to a complex nervous system, and, in some groups, highly specialized respiratory and excretory systems.
- Arthropods are divided into five subphyla. The extinct trilobites (subphylum Trilobita), with three-lobed bodies and relatively undifferentiated appendages, were abundant in Paleozoic seas.
- Spiders, ticks, mites, scorpions, and horseshoe crabs (subphylum Chelicerata) have a cephalothorax and an abdomen; two pairs of appendages on the head serve in feeding.
- Lobsters, crabs, and their relatives (subphylum Crustacea) have a carapace that covers the cephalothorax as well as highly modified appendages, including five pairs on the head.
- The centipedes and millipedes (subphylum Myriapoda) are largely terrestrial. They have a head and an elongate, segmented trunk.
- Insects and their relatives (subphylum Hexapoda) are also largely terrestrial. Insects have three body regions, three pairs of walking legs on the thorax, and a pair of antennae and three pairs of feeding appendages on the head.
- Most insects undergo metamorphosis. In incomplete metamorphosis, the cells of the nymph are reprogrammed to produce adult structures. In complete metamorphosis, an additional stage, the pupa, permits entirely new adult structures to replace larval cells.

Questions

Self-Test Questions

1. Which of the following characteristics is *not* typical of most animals?
   a. heterotrophic
   b. sessile
   c. radially symmetrical
   d. multicellular
   e. motile at some stage of life cycle
2. A body cavity that separates the digestive system from the body wall but is *not* completely lined with mesoderm is called a
   a. schizocoelom.
   b. mesentery.
   c. peritoneum.
   d. pseudocoelom.
   e. hydrostatic skeleton.
3. Which part of a mollusc secretes the shell?
   a. visceral mass
   b. radula
   c. trochophore
   d. head–foot
   e. mantle
4. Which of the following is not a result of polymorphic development?
   a. castes in social insects
   b. alternation of generations in Cnidaria
   c. the pupal stage in insects
   d. the adult octopus
   e. the trochophore larva
5. Ecdysis refers to a process in which
   a. bivalves use siphons to pass water across their gills.
   b. arthropods and nematodes shed their cuticles.
   c. cnidarians build skeletons of calcium carbonate.
   d. rotifers produce unfertilized eggs.
   e. squids escape from predators in a cloud of ink.

Questions for Discussion

1. Many invertebrate species are hermaphroditic. What selective advantages might this characteristic offer? In what kinds of environments might it be most useful?
2. In terms of numbers of species, insects are the dominant life form on Earth, but the individuals are also smaller in size than many other groups. What has contributed to their success, and why are they not larger?
3. The egg of the human parasite *A. lumbricoides* hatches in the small intestine. What experiments would you do to test whether this is a result of the egg shell being digested by the intestinal enzymes?

The molar tooth of a an extinct mammal *(Desmostylus)* was used to crush and grind marine plants. Paleontologists discovered that *Desmostylus* was more walrus than seacowlike only when they found almost-complete skeletons. You may remember this as Figure 3.22c.

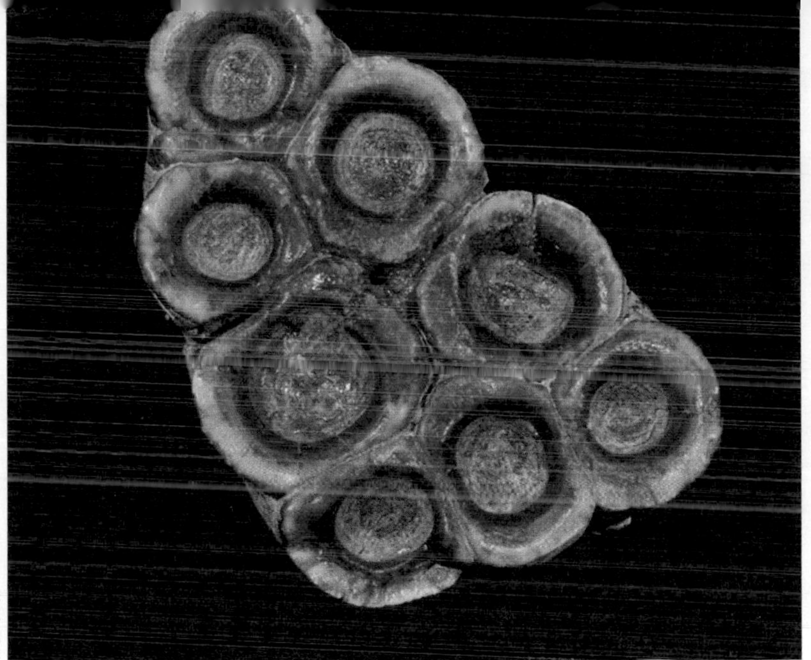

M. B. Fenton

Study Plan

27 Deuterostomes: Vertebrates and Their Closest Relatives

Why It Matters

Based on molecular evidence, Xenoturbellida was identified as a new phylum in November 2006. This new phylum is closely related to the Chordata (traditional phylogeny in **Figure 27.1a, p. 618**), which includes vertebrates, among them *Homo sapiens*. Specifically, a phylogenetic analysis of 170 nuclear proteins and 13 mitochondrial proteins was used to derive the phylogeny that placed Xenoturbellida among the Deuterostomes **(Figure 27.1b, p. 619)**. Look at some of the organisms **(Figure 27.2, p. 620)** arranged in the phylogeny.

Xenoturbellida (such as *Xenoturbella bocki*; see Figure 27.2f) was originally described in 1949. They are delicate, ciliated marine worms with simple body plans. They lack a gut wih two openings, organized gonads, excretory structures, and a coelom. The nervous system is a diffuse net with no brain. Until 2006, there were more questions than answers about their phylogenetic position, even to what phylum they should belong. At first, *X. bocki* was thought to be a turbellarian flatworm (Platyhelminthes), but it also was identified as a possible hemichordate or echinoderm (based on similarities in the nerve net). The details of *Xenoturbella*'s cilia are like those of hemichordates,

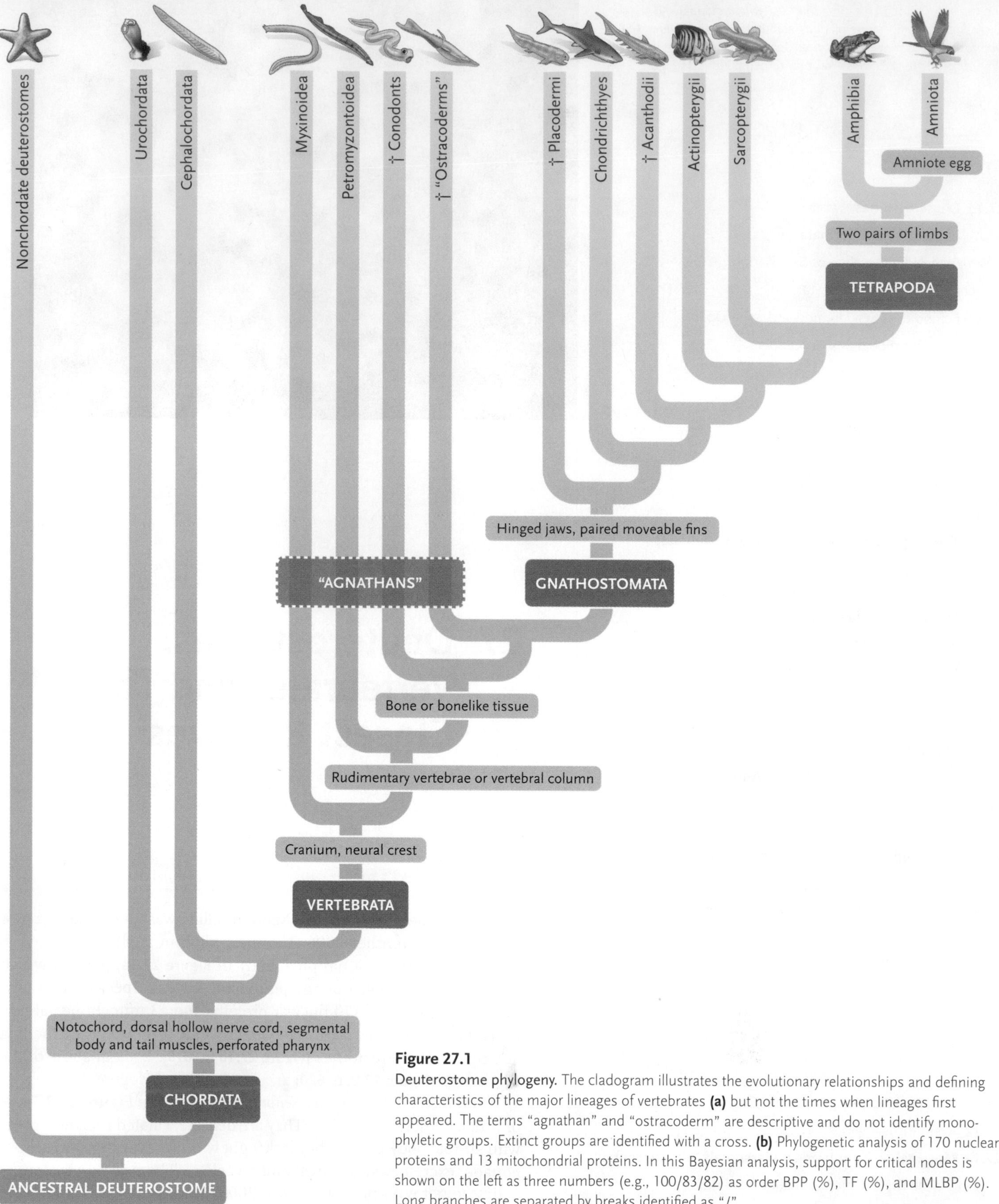

Figure 27.1
Deuterostome phylogeny. The cladogram illustrates the evolutionary relationships and defining characteristics of the major lineages of vertebrates **(a)** but not the times when lineages first appeared. The terms "agnathan" and "ostracoderm" are descriptive and do not identify monophyletic groups. Extinct groups are identified with a cross. **(b)** Phylogenetic analysis of 170 nuclear proteins and 13 mitochondrial proteins. In this Bayesian analysis, support for critical nodes is shown on the left as three numbers (e.g., 100/83/82) as order BPP (%), TF (%), and MLBP (%). Long branches are separated by breaks identified as "/".

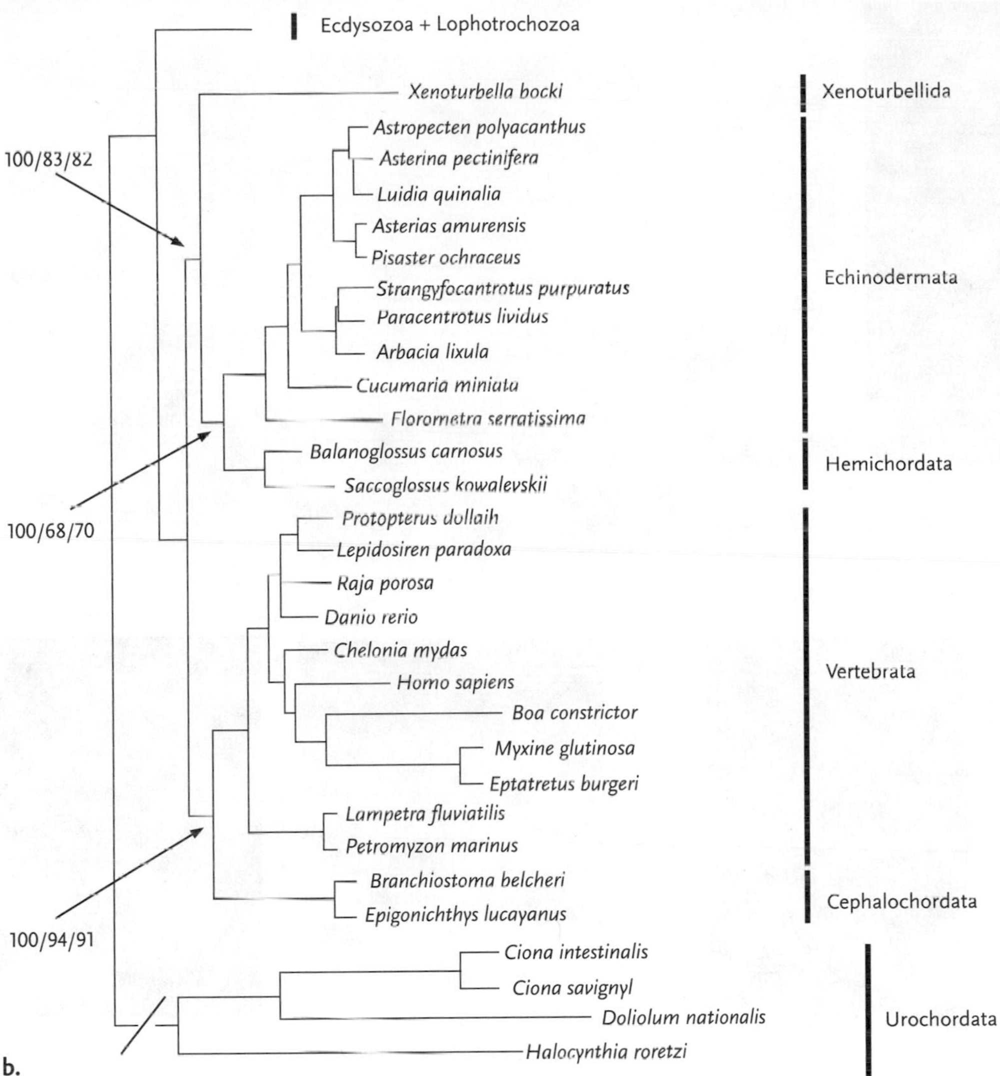

which could indicate that it is really an acoelomorph flatworm.

In 1997, analysis of molecular phylogenetic data was used to place *Xenoturbella* in the Mollusca, specifically among the bivalves. This arrangement was supported by the discovery of bivalvelike eggs and larvae within specimens of *Xenoturbella*. In 1997, it was easy to believe the molecular argument.

How can molecular data be challenged? In 1998, an alternative explanation was offered: the mollusc genetic information appeared inside *Xenoturbella* because it eats molluscs. When the molluscan genetic information is ignored, *Xenoturbella* is clearly a deuterostome, most closely related to Echinodermata (see Figure 27.1).

Thus, making correct choices about classification (see Chapter 19) means looking beyond appearance and may also require careful consideration of molecular data.

27.1 Deuterostomes

Membership in the Deuterostomia (Greek, *deutero* = second; *stomia* = opening) is restricted to animals in which the anus develops from the blastopore and the mouth from a second opening. At first glance, deuterostome animals—such as echinoderms, chordates, and hemichordates, let alone *Xenoturbella*—are not obviously similar, reflecting modifications of their bodies that mask underlying developmental and genetic features.

Study Break

What is the difference between protostomes and deuterostomes?

27.2 Phylum Echinodermata

The phylum Echinodermata (*echino* = spiny; *derm* = skin) includes 6500 species of sea stars, sea urchins, sea cucumbers, brittle stars, and sea lilies. These slow-moving or sessile, bottom-dwelling animals are important herbivores and predators living in oceans from the shallow coastal waters to the oceans' depths. The phylum was diverse in the Paleozoic, but only a

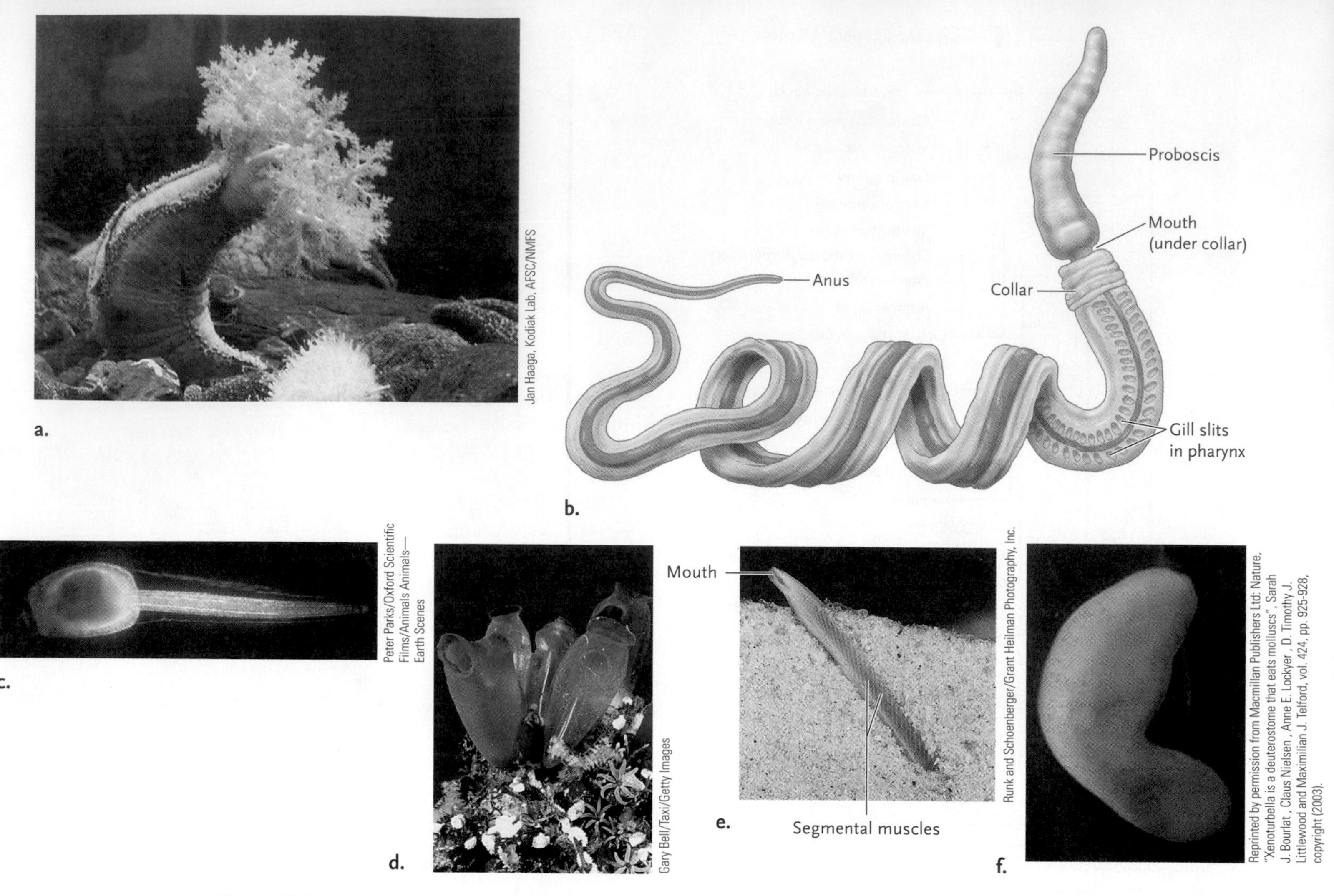

Figure 27.2

Deuterostomes. **(a)** Holothuroidea. A sea cucumber (*Cucumaraia miniata*) extends its tentacles, which are modified tube feet. **(b)** Phylum Hemichordata. Acorn worms draw food- and oxygen-laden water in through the mouth and expel it through gill slits in the anterior region of the trunk. **(c)** Urochordates. A tadpole-like tunicate larva will metamorphose into a sessile adult. **(d and e)** Cephalochordates. The unpigmented skin of an adult lancet (*Brachiostoma* species) reveals their segmented body wall muscles. **(f)** A *Xenoturbella bocki* does not look very similar to any of the other animals illustrated here.

remnant of that fauna remains. Echinoderms vary in size from less than 1 cm in diameter to more than 50 cm long. Adult echinoderms develop from bilaterally symmetrical, free-swimming larvae. As the larvae develop, they assume a secondary radial symmetry, often organized around five rays or "arms" **(Figure 27.3).** Many echinoderms have an *oral surface,* with the mouth facing the substrate, and an *aboral surface* facing in the opposite direction. Virtually all echinoderms have an internal skeleton made of calcium-stiffened *ossicles* that develop from mesoderm. In some groups, fused ossicles form a rigid container called a *test.* In most, spines or bumps project from the ossicles.

The internal anatomy of echinoderms is unique among animals (see Figure 27.3). They have a well-defined coelom and a complete digestive system (see Figure 27.3e) but no excretory or respiratory systems, and most have only a minimal circulatory system. In many, gases are exchanged and metabolic wastes eliminated through projections of the epidermis and peritoneum near the base of the spines. Given their radial symmetry, there is no head or central brain; the nervous system is organized around nerve cords that encircle the mouth and branch into the radii. Sensory cells are abundant in the skin.

Echinoderms move using a system of fluid-filled canals, the *water vascular system* (see Figure 27.3f). In a sea star, for example, water enters the system through the *madreporite,* a sievelike plate on the aboral surface. A short tube connects it to the *ring canal,* which surrounds the esophagus. The ring canal branches into five *radial canals* that extend into the arms. Each radial canal is connected to numerous *tube feet* that protrude through holes in the plates. Each tube foot has a mucus-covered, suckerlike tip and a small muscular

a. Asteroidea: This sea star (*Fromia milleporella*) lives in the intertidal zone.

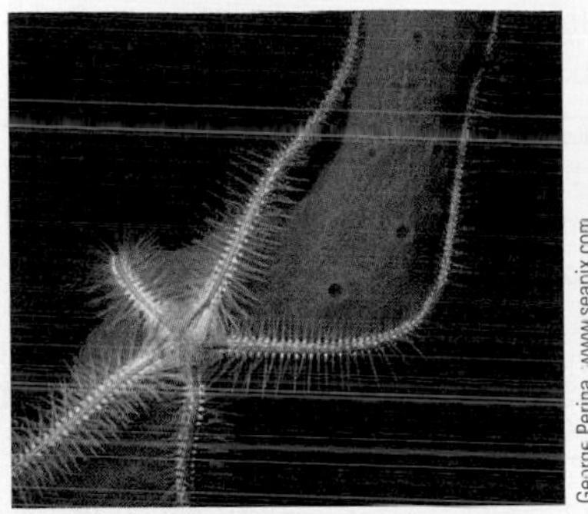

b. Ophiuroidea: A brittle star (*Ophiothrix swensonii*) perches on a coral branch.

c. Echinoidea: A sea urchin (*Strongylocentrotus purpuratus*) grazes on algae.

d. Crinoidea: A feather star (*Himerometra robustipinna*) feeds by catching small particles with its numerous arms

Figure 27.3

Echinoderm diversity. **(a)–(d)** Echinoderms exhibit secondary radial symmetry, usually organized as five rays around an oral–aboral axis. Internal anatomy of a sea star. The coelom **(e)** is well developed in echinoderms, as illustrated by this cutaway diagram of a sea star. The water vascular system **(f)**, unique in the animal kingdom, operates the tube feet. Tube feet **(g)** are responsible for locomotion. Note the pedicillariae on the upper surface of the star's arm.

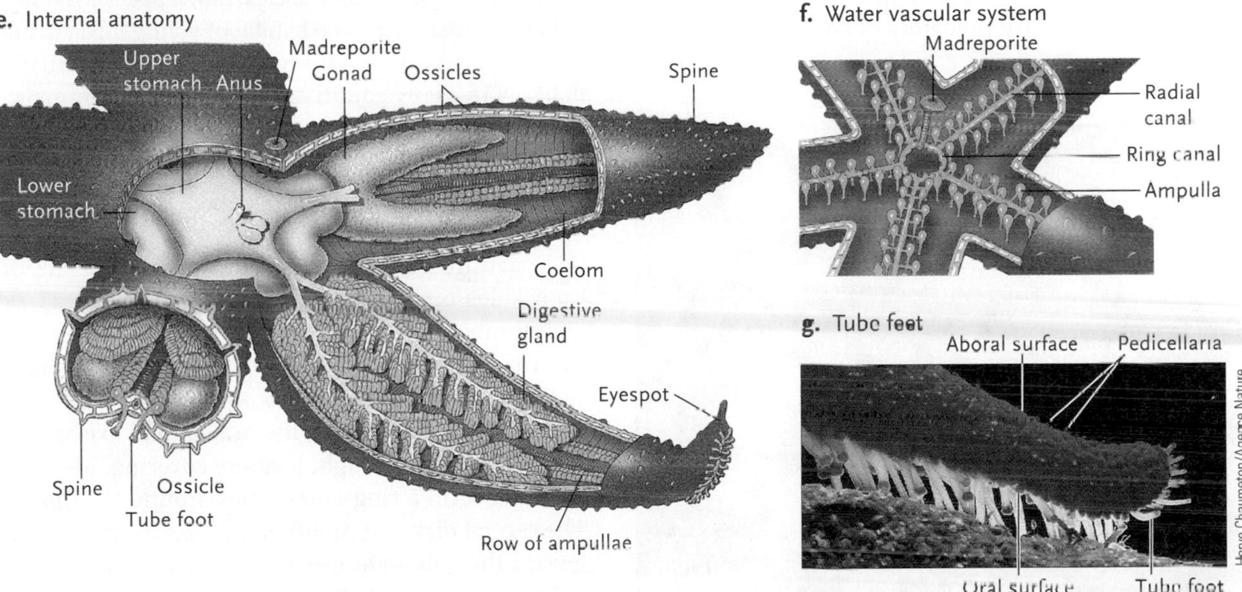

bulb, the *ampulla*, that lies inside the body. When an ampulla contracts, fluid is forced into the tube foot, causing it to lengthen and attach to the substrate (see Figure 27.3g). The tube foot then contracts, pulling the animal along. As the tube foot shortens, water is forced back into the ampulla, and the tube foot releases its grip on the substrate. The tube foot can then take another step forward, reattaching to the substrate. Although each tube foot has limited strength, the coordinated action of hundreds or even thousands of them is so strong that they can hold an echinoderm to a substrate even against strong wave action.

Echinoderms have separate sexes, and most reproduce by releasing gametes into the water. Radial cleavage is so clearly apparent in the transparent eggs of some sea urchins that they are commonly used to demonstrate cleavage in introductory biology laboratories. A few echinoderms reproduce asexually by splitting in half and regenerating the missing parts. Other echinoderms regenerate body parts lost to predators. Four-day-old sand dollars (*Dendraster excentricus*) asexually clone themselves in response to the odour of fish (in mucus), apparently a defensive response.

Echinoderms are divided into six groups, the most recently described (1986) being the sea daisies (Concentricycloidea). These small, medusa-shaped animals occupy sunken, waterlogged wood in the deep sea. Sunken ships often are important habitats for marine organisms. The five other groups, described below, are more diverse and better known.

27.2a Asteroidea: Starfish or Sea Stars

Sea stars live on rocky shorelines to depths of 10 000 m. Many are brightly coloured. The body consists of a central disk surrounded by 5 to 20 radiating "arms" (see Figure 27.3a), with the mouth centred on the oral surface. The ossicles of the endoskeleton are not fused, permitting flexibility of the arms and disk. Pedicellariae are small pincers at the base of short spines. They are used to remove debris that falls onto the animal's aboral (see Figure 27.3c). Many sea stars eat invertebrates and small fishes. Species that consume bivalve molluscs grasp the two valves with tube feet and slip their everted stomachs between the bivalve's shells **(Figure 27.4)**. The stomach secretes digestive enzymes that dissolve the mollusc's tissues. Some sea stars are destructive predators of corals, endangering many reefs.

Figure 27.4
Starfish feeding on a mussel. Even when the tide is out in the Queen Charlotte Islands, starfish hunt mussels.

27.2b Ophiuroidea: Brittle Stars

The 2000 species of brittle stars and basket stars occupy roughly the same range of habitats as sea stars. Their bodies have a well-defined central disk and slender, elongated arms that are sometimes branched (see Figure 27.3b). Ophiuroids can crawl fairly swiftly across substrates by moving their arms in a coordinated fashion. As their common name implies, the arms are delicate and easily broken, an adaptation allowing them to escape from predators with only minor damage. Brittle stars feed on small prey, suspended plankton, or detritus that they extract from muddy deposits.

27.2c Echinoidea: Sea Urchins and Sand Dollars

The 950 species of sea urchins and sand dollars lack arms (see Figure 27.3c). Their ossicles are fused into solid tests that provide excellent protection but restrict flexibility. The test is spherical in sea urchins and flattened in sand dollars. These animals use tube feet in locomotion. Five rows of tube feet emerge through pores in the test. Most echinoids have movable spines, some with poison glands. A jab from some tropical species can cause a careless swimmer severe pain and inflammation. Echinoids graze on algae and other organisms that cling to surfaces. In the centre of an urchin's oral surface is a five-part nipping jaw that is controlled by powerful muscles. Some species damage kelp beds, disrupting the habitat of young lobsters and other crustaceans. Echinoid ovaries are a gourmet delicacy in many countries, making these animals a prized natural resource.

27.2d Holothuroidea: Sea Cucumbers

Sea cucumbers are elongated animals that lie on their sides on the ocean bottom (see Figure 27.2a) and number about 1500 species. Although they have five rows of tube feet, their endoskeleton is reduced to widely separated microscopic plates. The body, which is elongated along the oral–aboral axis, is soft and fleshy, with a tough, leathery covering. Modified tube feet form a ring of tentacles around the mouth. The central disk and mouth point upward rather than toward the substrate. Some species secrete a mucus net that traps plankton or other food particles. The net and tentacles are inserted into the mouth, where the net and trapped food are ingested. Other species extract food from bottom sediments. Many sea cucumbers exchange gases through an extensively branched *respiratory tree* arising from the rectum, the part of the digestive system just inside the anus at the aboral end of the animal. A well-developed circulatory system distributes oxygen and nutrients to tissues throughout the body.

Sea cucumbers actually are home for specialized symbiotic fish. *Carapus bermudensis*, the pearl fish, enters sea cucumbers' cloacal opening tail first. The cloaca is the chamber receiving urine, feces, and reproductive products. Pearl fish are members of a group that usually live in the tubes of other animals, including the cavities of bivalves. These fish have elongated, thin bodies. They have lost pelvic fins and scales, and the anal opening has moved forward to a position under the head. This adaptation ensures that the fish defecates outside the body of the sea cucumber. These fishes use olfactory cues to find the "correct" host.

27.2e Crinoidea: Sea Lilies and Feather Stars

The 600 living species of sea lilies and feather stars are the surviving remnants of a diverse and abundant fauna 500 million years ago (see Figure 27.3d). Most species occupy marine waters of medium depth. Between five and several hundred branched arms surround the disk that contains the mouth. New arms are added as a crinoid grows larger. The branches of the arms are covered with tiny, mucus-coated tube feet that trap suspended microscopic organisms. Sessile sea lilies have the central disk attached to a flexible stalk that can reach 1 m in length. By contrast, adult feather stars can swim or crawl weakly, attaching temporarily to substrates. The disks comprising sea lily stalks, called ossicles, are common fossils in many deposits **(Figure 27.5)**.

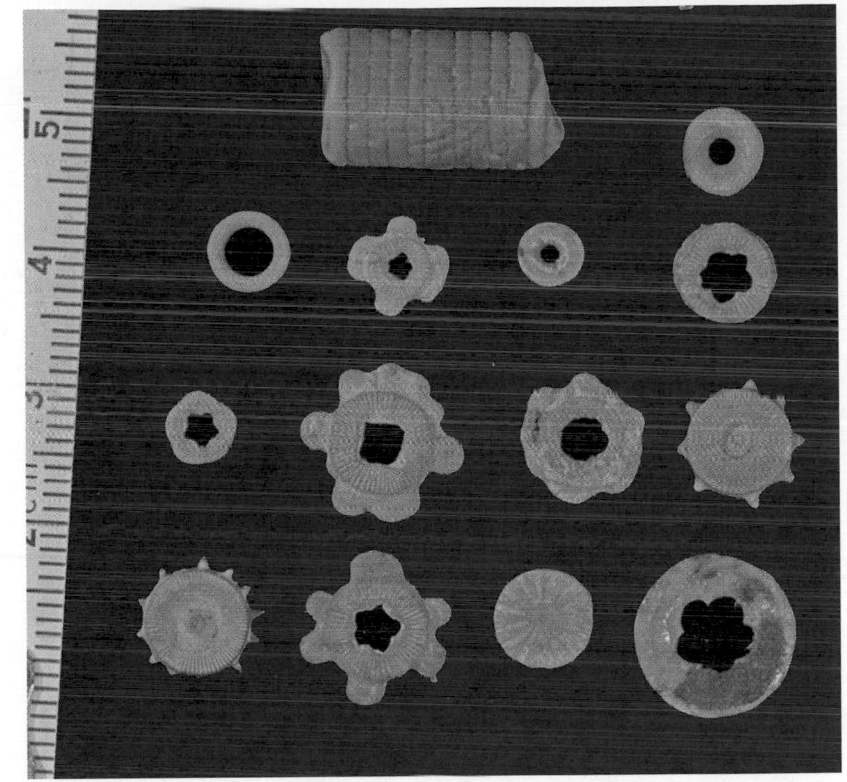

Figure 27.5
Fossil crinoid stems. Ossicles comprising the stems of crinoids are commonly fossilized. The individual ossicles are from the Devonian of Ontario. The section of complete stem is *Encrinus liliiformis* from the Triassic of Germany. Scale is in mm.

Study Break

1. What are echinoderms? How do adult echinoderms develop?
2. Use a table to compare an echinoderm and a human by system: (a) digestive, (b) excretory, (c) respiratory, (d) circulatory, and (e) nervous.
3. Using a sea star as an example, describe how echinoderms move.

27.3 Phylum Hemichordata

The 80 species of **acorn worms** comprising this phylum take their name from *hemi*, meaning half, and *chord*, referring to the phylum Chordata. Acorn worms are sedentary marine animals living in U-shaped tubes or burrows in coastal sand or mud. Their soft bodies range in length from 2 cm to 2 m and are organized into an anterior proboscis, a tentacled collar, and an elongate trunk (see Figure 27.2b). They use the muscular, mucus-coated proboscis to construct burrows and trap food particles. Acorn worms also have pairs of gill slits in the pharynx, the part of the digestive system just posterior to the mouth. Beating cilia create a flow of water, which enters the pharynx through the mouth and exits through the gill slits. As water passes through, suspended food particles are trapped and shunted into the digestive system, and gases are exchanged across the partitions between gill slits. The dorsal nerve cord, coupled with feeding and respiration, reflects a close evolutionary relationship between hemichordates and chordates.

Study Break

How do hemichordates feed?

27.4 Phylum Chordata

This phylum includes evolutionary lines of invertebrates, the Urochordata and Cephalochordata, as well as the more diverse line, the Vertebrata. A *notochord*, a *dorsal hollow nerve cord*, and *gill slits* (a perforated pharynx) are key morphological features distinguishing chordates from all other Deuterostomes. These features occur during at least some time in a chordate's life cycle. Chordates also have segmental muscles in the body wall and tail **(Figure 27.6, p. 624)**. Collectively, these structures enable higher levels of

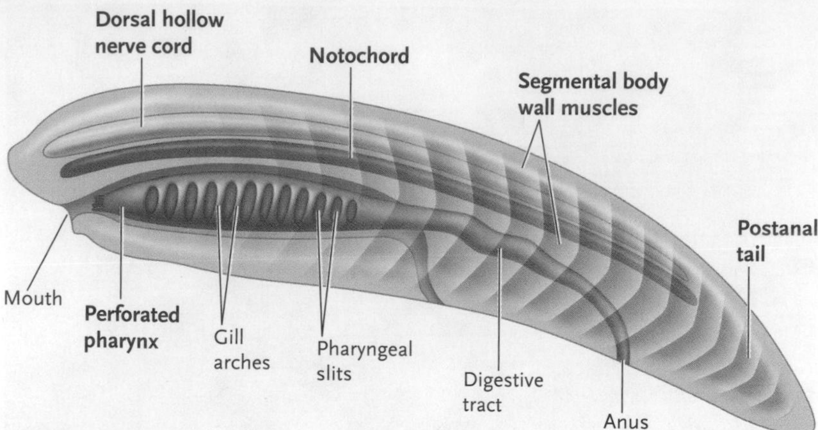

Figure 27.6 Diagnostic chordate characteristics. Chordates have a notochord, a dorsal hollow nerve cord, gill slits (a perforated pharynx), and a muscular postanal tail with segmental body wall and tail muscles.

activity and unique modes of aquatic locomotion, as well as more efficient feeding and oxygen acquisition.

Early in chordate embryonic development, the **notochord** (*noto* = back; *chord* = string), a flexible rod, develops from mesoderm dorsal to the developing digestive system. The notochord is constructed of fluid-filled cells surrounded by tough connective tissue. It supports the embryo from head to tail. The notochord is the skeleton of invertebrate chordates, serving as an anchor for body wall muscles. When these muscles contract, the notochord bends but does not shorten. Waves of contractions pass down one side of the animal and then down the other, sweeping the body and tail back and forth in a smooth and continuous movement. Thus, the chordate body swings left and right during locomotion, propelling the animal forward. The chordate tail, which is posterior to the anus, provides most of the propulsion in some aquatic species. Segmentation allows each muscle block to contract independently. Unlike the bodies of annelids and other nonchordate invertebrates, the chordate body does not shorten when the animal is moving. Remnants of the notochord persist as gelatinous disks between the vertebrae of some adult vertebrates.

The central nervous system of chordates is a hollow nerve cord on the dorsal side of the embryo (see Chapter 39). Most nonchordate invertebrates have ventral, solid nerve cords. In vertebrates, an anterior enlargement of the nerve cord forms the brain. In invertebrates, an anterior concentration of nervous system tissue is a *ganglion* and may be referred to as a "brain."

Gill slits mean that the chordate pharynx is perforated. The pharynx is the part of the digestive system just behind the mouth. **Gill slits** are paired openings originating as exit holes for water that carried particulate food into the mouth, allowing chordates to gather food by filtration. Invertebrate chordates also collect oxygen and release carbon dioxide across the walls of the pharynx. In fishes, gill arches have evolved as supporting structures between the slits in the pharynx. Invertebrate chordates and fishes retain a perforated pharynx throughout their lives. In most air-breathing vertebrates, the slits are present only during embryonic development and in some larvae (see Chapter 34).

27.4a Subphylum Urochordata: Sea Squirts and Tunicates

The 2500 species of urochordates (*uro* = tail) float in surface waters or attach to substrates in shallow marine habitats. Sessile adults of many species secrete a gelatinous or leathery "tunic" around their bodies and squirt water through a siphon when disturbed. Adults can attain lengths of several centimetres (**Figure 27.7**; see also Figure 27.2c, d). In the most common group of sea squirts (Ascidiacea), swimming larvae have notochords, dorsal hollow nerve cords, and gill slits, features lacking in the sessile adults. Larvae eventually attach to substrates and transform into sessile adults. During metamorphosis, larvae lose most traces of the notochord, dorsal nerve cord, and tail, and their basket-like pharynx enlarges. In adults, beating cilia pull water into the pharynx through an *incurrent siphon*. A mucus net traps particulate food, which is carried with the mucus to the gut. Water passes through the pharyngeal slits, enters a chamber called the *atrium*, and is expelled through the atrial siphon along with digestive wastes and carbon dioxide. Oxygen is absorbed across the walls of the pharynx. In some urochordates, the larvae are neotenous (see Chapters 19 and 26), acquiring the ability to reproduce and remaining active throughout their life cycles.

a.

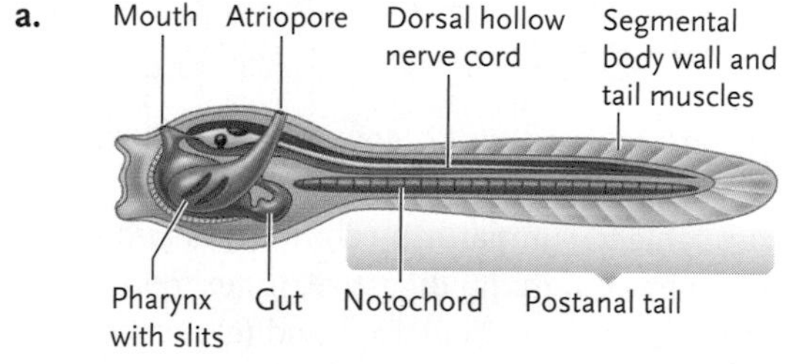

b.

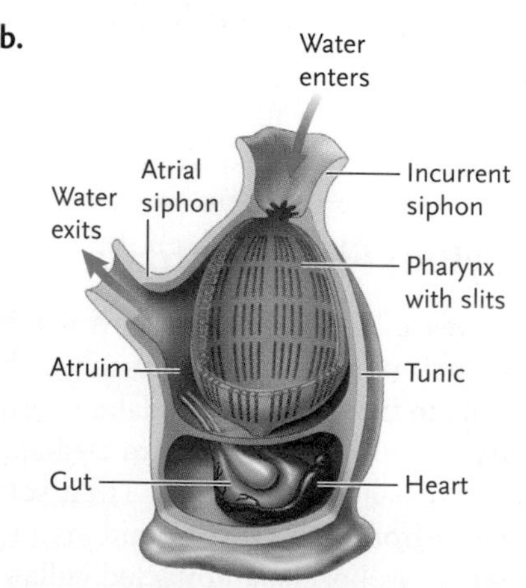

Figure 27.7 Diagrams of urochordates. The tadpole-like tunicate larva **(a)** metamorphoses into an adult, a sessile filter-feeder. **(b)** In the adult, the atriopore becomes the atrial siphon.

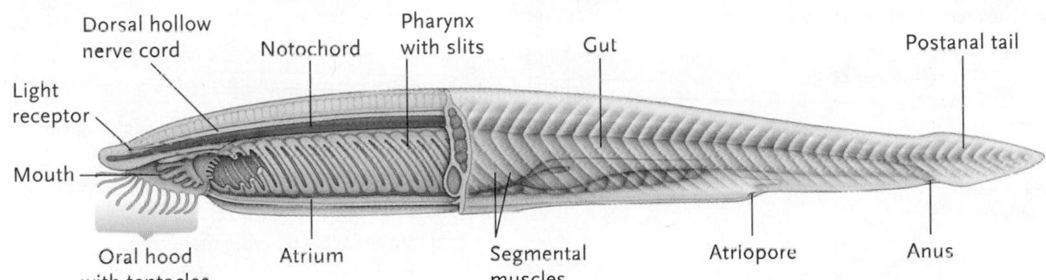

Figure 27.8
A drawing of the internal anatomy of an adult lancet (*Brachiostoma*).

27.4b Subphylum Cephalochordata: Lancelets

All 28 species of cephalochordates (*cephalo* = head) live in warm, shallow marine habitats, where they lie mostly buried in sand (see Figure 27.2e). Although generally sedentary, they have well-developed body wall muscles and a prominent notochord. Most species are included in the genus *Branchiostoma* (formerly *Amphioxus*). Lancelet bodies, which are 5 to 10 cm long, are pointed at both ends like the double-edged surgical tools for which they are named **(Figure 27.8).** Adults have light receptors on the head as well as chemical sense organs on tentacles that grow from the *oral hood*. Lancelets use cilia to draw food-laden water through hundreds of pharyngeal slits; water flows into the atrium and is expelled through the *atriopore*. Most gas exchange occurs across the skin.

27.4c Subphylum Vertebrata: Vertebrates

Species in this subphylum have a distinct head (they are craniate), and most have a backbone (spine) made up of individual bony vertebrae (see Chapters 19 and 39). This internal skeletal feature provides structural support for muscles and protects the nervous system and other organs. In addition, the internal skeleton and attached muscles allow most vertebrates to move rapidly. Vertebrates are the only animals that have bone, a connective tissue in which cells secrete the mineralized matrix that surrounds them (see Chapter 36). One vertebrate lineage, cartilaginous fishes (class Chondrichthyes), may have lost its bone over evolutionary time. These animals, mostly sharks and rays, have skeletons of cartilage, a dense, flexible connective tissue that can be a developmental precursor of bone (see Chapters 36 and 39).

At the anterior end of the vertebral column, the head is usually protected by a bony cranium or skull. The backbone surrounds and protects the dorsal nerve cord, and the bony cranium surrounds the brain. The cranium, vertebral column, ribs, and sternum (breastbone) comprise the axial skeleton. Most vertebrates also have a pectoral girdle anteriorly and a pelvic girdle posteriorly that attach bones in the fins or limbs to the axial skeleton. The bones of the two girdles and the appendages constitute the appendicular skeleton.

Vertebrates have neural crest cells (see Chapter 39), a unique cell type distinct from endoderm, mesoderm, and ectoderm. Neural crest cells arise next to the developing nervous system but migrate throughout the body. Neural crest cells ultimately contribute to uniquely vertebrate structures such as parts of the cranium, teeth, sensory organs, cranial nerves, and the medulla (the interior part) of the adrenal glands.

The brains of vertebrates are larger and more complex than those of invertebrate chordates. Moreover, the vertebrate brain is divided into three regions, the forebrain, midbrain, and hindbrain, each govering distinct nervous system functions (see Chapter 33).

Study Break

1. List four morphological features distinguishing chordates from other deuterostomes.
2. Explain the purpose and structure of gill slits.
3. What are tunicates and lancelets? To which subphyla do they belong? What characteristics of swimming tunicate larvae are missing from the sessile adults?

27.5 The Origin and Diversification of Vertebrates

Biologists have used embryological, molecular, and fossil evidence to trace the origin of vertebrates and to chronicle the evolutionary diversification of the group to which humans belong. We suspect that vertebrates arose from a cephalochordate-like ancestor through duplication of genes that regulate development. Vertebrates appear to be more closely related to cephalochordates than to urochordates (see Figure 27.1). The change from cephalochordate-like creature to vertebrate was marked by the emergence of neural crest, bone, and other vertebrate traits. Biologists hypothesize that an increase in the number of genes that control the expression of other genes (homeotic) may have facilitated the development of more complex anatomy. (For more about homeotic genes, see Chapters 14 and 20.) When it comes to organization, there is no

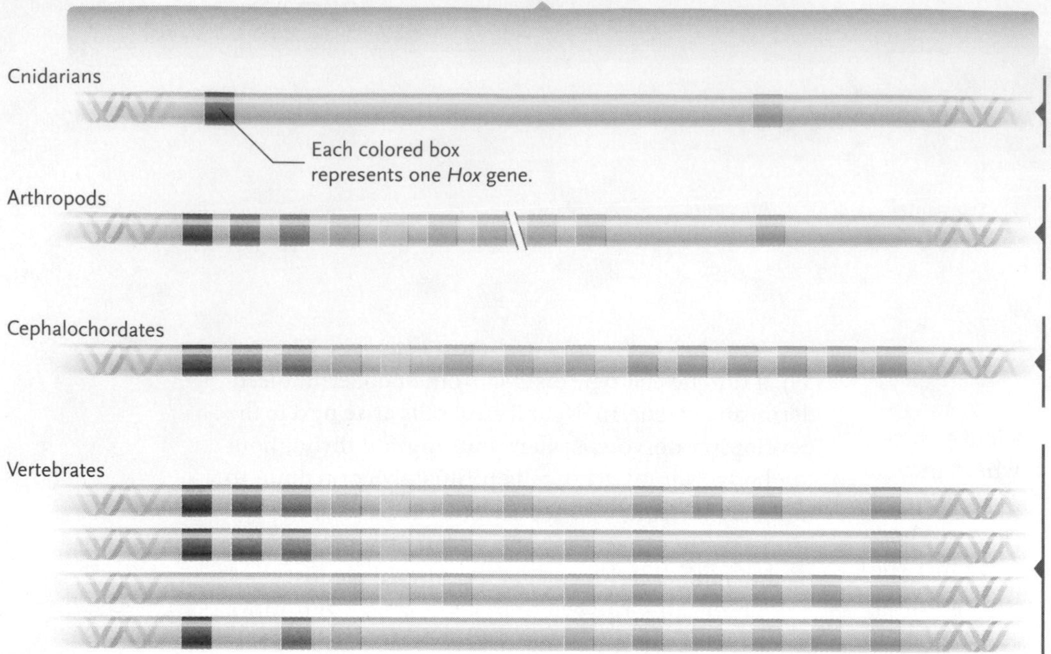

Each row of colored boxes represents one Hox gene complex.
Cnidarians
Each colored box represents one Hox gene.
Arthropods
Cephalochordates
Vertebrates
a. Invertebrates with simple anatomy, such as cnidarians, have a single Hox gene complex that includes just a few Hox genes.
b. Invertebrates with more complicated anatomy, such as arthropods, have a single Hox gene complex, but with a larger number of Hox genes.
c. Invertebrate chordates, such as cephalochordates, also have a single Hox gene complex, but with even more Hox genes than are found in nonchordate invertebrates.
d. Vertebrates, such as the laboratory mouse, have numerous Hox genes, arranged in two to seven Hox gene complexes. The additional Hox gene complexes are products of wholesale duplications of the ancestral Hox gene complex. The additional copies of Hox genes specify the development of uniquely vertebrate characteristics, such as the cranium, vertebral column, and neural crest cells.

Figure 27.9
***Hox* genes and the evolution of vertebrates.** The *Hox* genes in different animals appear to be homologous, indicated here by their colour and position in the complex. Vertebrates have many more individual *Hox* genes than invertebrates, and the entire *Hox* gene complex was duplicated in the vertebrate lineage.

compelling reason to believe that "more complex" is superior to "simple."

Hox genes are homeotic genes that influence the three-dimensional shape of the animal and the locations of important structures such as eyes, wings, or legs, particularly along the head-to-tail axis of the body. *Hox* genes are arranged on chromosomes in a particular order, forming the *Hox* gene complex. Each gene in the complex governs the development of particular structures. Animal groups with the simplest structure, such as cnidarians, have two *Hox* genes. Those with more complex anatomy, such as insects, have 10. Chordates typically have up to 13 or 14. Lineages with many *Hox* genes generally have more complex anatomy than those with fewer *Hox* genes.

Molecular analyses reveal that the entire *Hox* gene complex was duplicated several times in the evolution of vertebrates, producing multiple copies of all the genes in the *Hox* complex **(Figure 27.9)**. The cephalochordate *Branchiostoma* has one *Hox* gene complex, whereas hagfish, the most ancestral living vertebrate, has two. All vertebrates with jaws have at least four sets of *Hox* genes, and some fishes have seven. Evolutionary biologists who study development hypothesize that the duplication of *Hox* genes and other tool-kit genes allowed the evolution of new structures. Although original copies of these genes maintained their ancestral functions, duplicate copies were available to assume *new* functions, leading to the development of novel structures, such as the vertebral column and jaws. These changes coincided with the adaptive radiation of vertebrates.

The oldest known vertebrate fossils are from the early Cambrian (about 550 million years ago) in China. Both *Myllokunmingia* and *Haikouichthys* were fish-shaped animals about 3 cm long **(Figures 27.10** and **27.11)**. In both species, the brain was surrounded by a cranium of fibrous connective tissue or cartilage. They also had segmental body wall muscles and fairly well-developed fins, but neither shows any evidence of bone.

The early vertebrates gave rise to numerous descendants (see Figure 27.1a), which varied greatly in anatomy, physiology, and ecology. New feeding mechanisms and locomotor structures were correlated with their success. Today, vertebrates occupy nearly every habitat on Earth and eat virtually all other organisms. Although biologists identify vertebrates from four key morphological innovations (cranium, vertebrae, bone, and neural crest cells), these structures did not evolve spontaneously. Important biological changes during the evolution of vertebrates included improved access to energy (food), which involved mobility and jaws, combined with effective aerobic metabolism (access to oxygen).

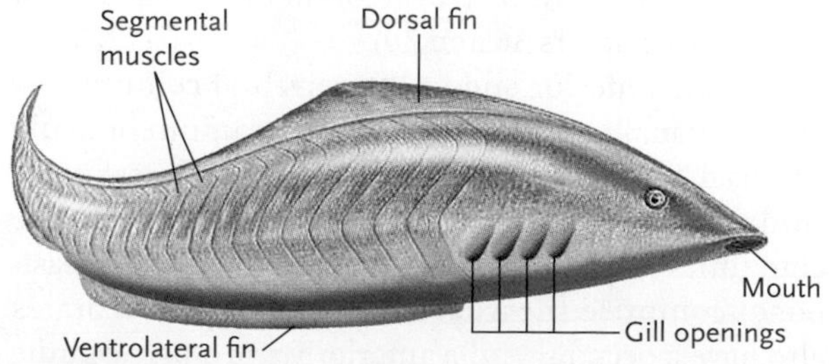

Figure 27.10
Cambrian agnathan, *Haikouichthys*, was more like a hagfish than a lamprey but generally similar to an ammocoetes larva.

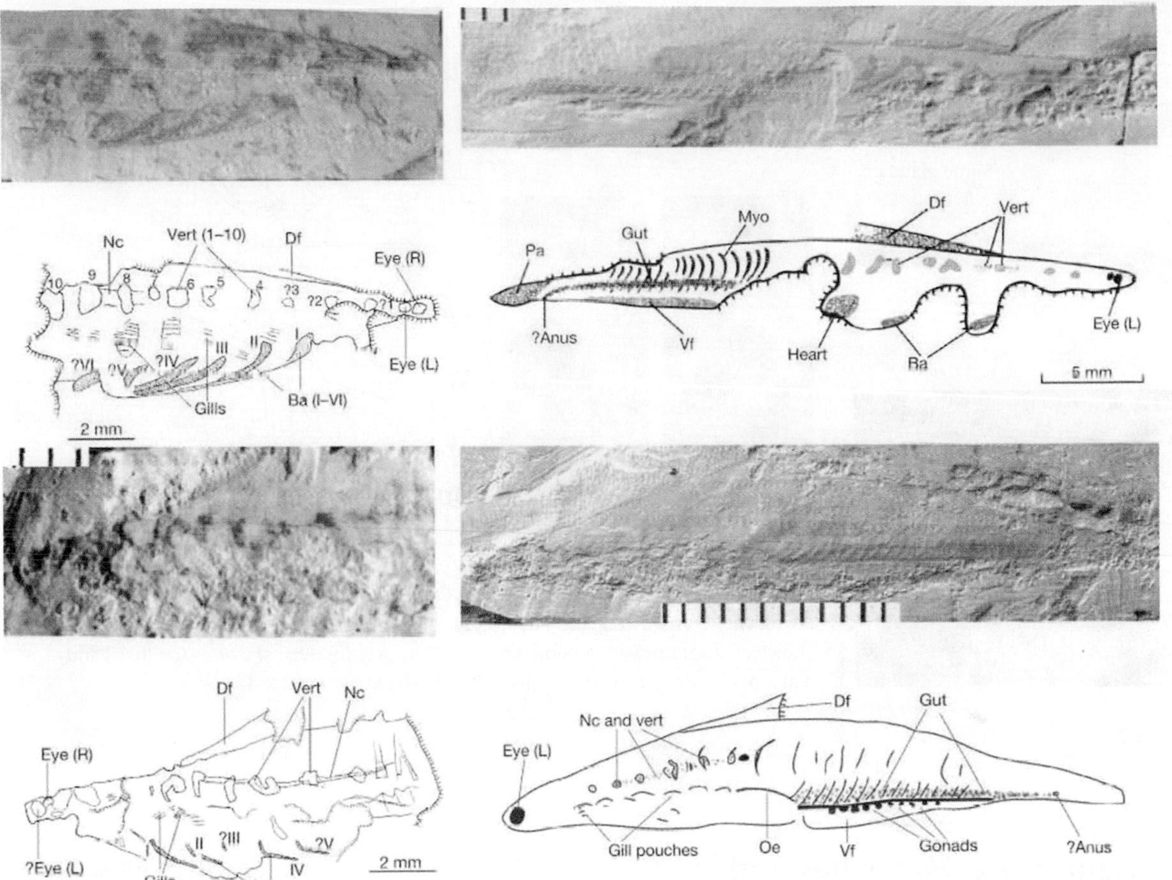

Figure 27.11

A diagram showing an early vertebrate. *Myllokunmingia* is one of the earliest vertebrates yet discovered. This species has no bones and was about 30 cm long. The labels identify features, some with abbreviations, including the following: Ap – anterior plates; Ba – branchial arches; Df – dorsal fin; Myo – myosepta; Nc – notochord; Nc and Vert – notochord with vertebral elements; Nos – nostril; Ns – nasal sacs; Oc – otic capsule; Oe – oesophagus; Pa – post anal tail; Vert – vertebral elements; Vf – ventral fin fold; l – left; R – right. Reprinted by permission from Macmillan Publishers Ltd: Nature, "A role for the immunological synapse in lineage commitment of CD4 lymphocytes", Roberto A. Maldonado, Darrell J. Irvine, Robert Schreiber and Laurie H. Glimcher, vol. 431, pp. 527-532, copyright (2004).

The earliest vertebrates lacked jaws (Agnatha, from *a* = not and *gnath* = jawed), but Agnatha is not a monophyletic group. Although most became extinct by the end of the Paleozoic, two ancestral lineages, Myxinoidea (hagfishes) and Petromyzontoidea (lampreys), survive today. All other vertebrates have movable jaws and form a monophyletic lineage Gnathostomata (*gnath* = jawed; *stoma* = mouth). The first jawed fishes, the Acanthodii and Placodermi, are now extinct, but several other lineages of jawed fishes are still abundant. Included are Chondrichthyes, fishes with cartilaginous skeletons (sharks, skates, chimaeras), and Teleostei (actinopterygians and sarcopterygians) with bony endoskeletons. Although all jawless vertebrates and most jawed fishes are restricted to aquatic habitats, mudskippers (*Periophthalmus* species) and climbing perch (*Anabas* species) regularly venture onto land. Many fish have developed lunglike structures for breathing atmospheric oxygen, but most use gills to extract dissolved oxygen from water. Lungs may be an ancestral trait in vertebrates.

Gnathostomata also includes the monophyletic lineage Tetrapoda (*tetra* = four; *pod* = foot), most of which use four limbs for locomotion. Many tetrapods are amphibious, semiterrestrial, or terrestrial, although some, such as sea turtles and porpoises, have secondarily returned to aquatic habitats. Adult tetrapods generally use lungs to breathe atmospheric oxygen. Within the Tetrapoda, one lineage, the Amphibia (such as frogs and salamanders), typically needs standing water to complete its life cycle. Another lineage, the Amniota, comprises animals with specialized eggs that can develop on land. Shortly after their appearance, amniotes diversified into three lineages, one ancestral to living mammals, another to living turtles, and a third to lizards, snakes, alligators, and birds.

Study Break

1. What is the advantage of a backbone?
2. What marked the change from a cephalochordate-like creature to a vertebrate?
3. What is a *Hox* gene, and how does it influence the diversity of vertebrates?

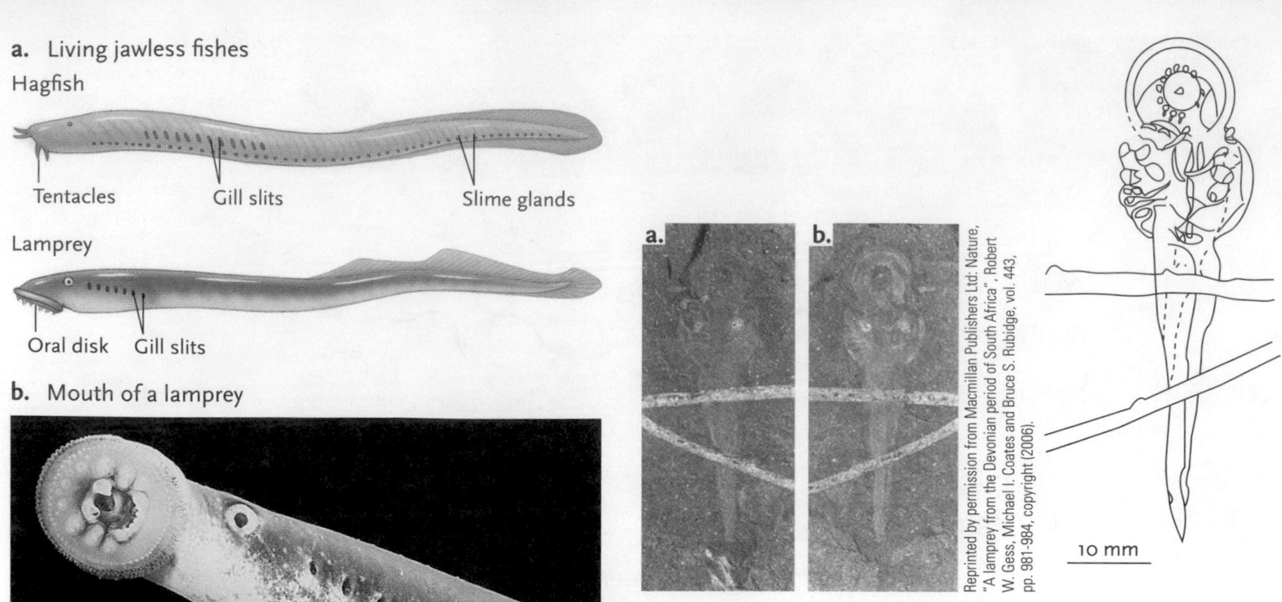

Figure 27.12

Living agnathans. Two groups of jawless fishes, the hagfishes and the lampreys **(a),** are shown as diagrams with a photograph of a lamprey **(b).** Also shown is the fossil and diagram of a Devonian lamprey from South Africa.

27.6 Agnathans: Hagfishes and Lampreys, Conodonts, and Ostracoderms

Lacking jaws, the earliest vertebrates used a muscular pharynx to suck water containing food particles into the mouth, and used gills both to acquire dissolved oxygen and to filter food from the water. The aganthans that flourished in the Paleozoic varied greatly in size and shape and possessed different combinations of vertebrate characters.

Lampreys and hagfishes, the two living groups of agnathans, have skeletons composed entirely of cartilage. Although as yet no fossilized lampreys or hagfishes have been found in early Paleozoic strata, the absence of bone in their living descendants suggests that they arose early in vertebrate history, before the evolution of bone. The first fossil lamprey is known from the Devonian of South Africa **(Figure 27.12).** Hagfishes and lampreys have a well-developed notochord but no true vertebrae or paired fins. Their skin lacks scales. Individuals grow to a maximum length of about 1 m (see Figure 27.12). Two possible phylogenies for hagfishes and other vertebrates are presented **(Figure 27.13),** but at this time, there are too few data to decide which is most likely to be correct.

The axial skeletons of the 60 living species of hagfishes include only a cranium and a notochord. No specialized structures surround the dorsal nerve cord. Hagfishes are marine scavengers that burrow in sediments on continental shelves. They feed on invertebrate prey and on dead or dying fishes. In response to

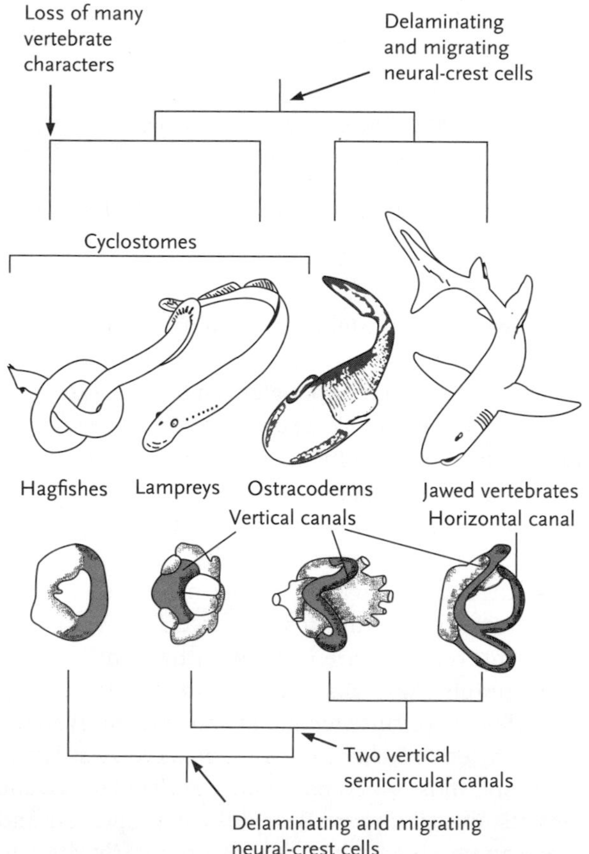

Figure 27.13

Two alternatives for hagfishes. The top tree implies that they are vertebrates that have lost features and the bottom one that they are a sister group of all other vertebrates. One striking difference is the presence of one semicircular canal in hagfishes and at least two in all other vertebrates. The "truth" remains elusive.

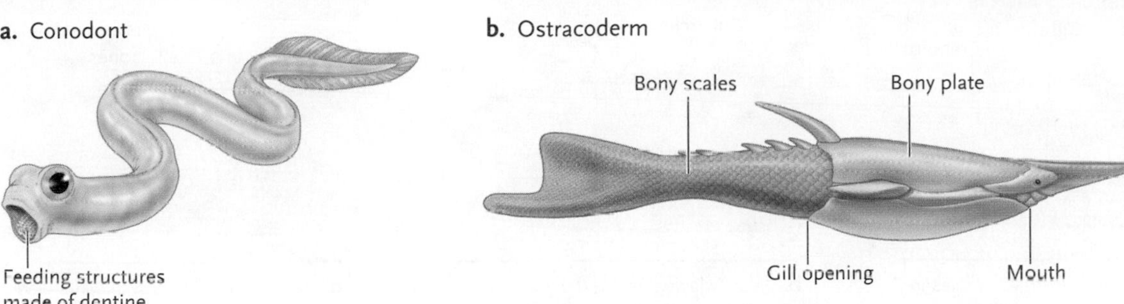

Figure 27.14
Extinct agnathans. **(a)** Conodonts were elaborate, soft-bodied animals with bonelike feeding structures in the mouth and pharynx. **(b)** *Pteropsis*, an ostracoderm, had large bony plates on its head and small body scales on the rest of its body. It was about 6 cm long.

predators, they secrete an immense quantity of sticky, noxious slime. When no longer threatened, a hagfish ties itself into a knot and wipes the slime from its body. The life cycle of a hagfish lacks a larval stage.

The 38 living species of lamprey have a more specialized axial skeleton than hagfishes do. Their notochord is surrounded by dorsally pointing cartilage that partially covers the nerve cord, perhaps representing an early stage in the evolution of the vertebral column. About half of the living lamprey species are parasitic as adults and use the sucking disk around their mouths to attach to the bodies of fish (or other prey), rasp a hole in the host's body, and ingest body fluids. In most species, sexually mature adults migrate from the ocean or a lake to the headwaters of a stream, where they reproduce and then die. The suspension-feeding ammocoetes larvae of lampreys resemble adult cephalochordates. They burrow into mud and develop for as long as seven years before metamorphosing and migrating to the sea or a lake to live as adults.

Conodonts and ostracoderms were early jawless vertebrates with bony structures. Conodonts are mysterious bonelike fossils, most less than 1 mm long, occurring in oceanic rocks from the early Paleozoic through the early Mesozoic. Called **conodont** elements, these abundant fossils were originally described as supporting structures of marine algae or feeding structures of ancient invertebrates. Recent analyses of their mineral composition reveal that they were made of dentine, a bonelike component of vertebrate teeth. In the 1980s and 1990s, fossils of intact conodont animals with these elements in place were discovered.

Now it is clear that conodonts were elongate, soft-bodied animals, 3 to 10 cm long. They had a notochord, a cranium, segmental body wall muscles, and large, movable eyes **(Figure 27.14a)**. The conodont elements at the front of the mouth were forward-pointing, hook-shaped structures (the original fossils) that apparently were used in the collection of food. Conodont elements in the pharynx were stouter, suitable for crushing food. Paleontologists now classify conodonts as vertebrates, the earliest ones with bonelike structures.

Ostracoderms (*ostrac* = shell; *derm* = skin) include an assortment of jawless fishes representing several evolutionary lines that lived from the Ordovician through the Devonian **(Figure 27.14b)**. Like their invertebrate chordate ancestors, ostracoderms probably used their pharynx to draw water with food particles into their mouths and used gills to filter food from water. The muscular pharynx was more efficient than that of agnathans that used currents generated by cilia. Greater flow rates allowed ostracoderms to collect food more rapidly and achieve larger body sizes. Although most ostracoderms were much smaller, some were 2 m long.

The skin of ostracoderms was heavily armoured with bony plates and scales. Although some had paired lateral extensions of their bony armour, they could not move them in the way living fishes move paired fins. Ostracoderms lacked a true vertebral column, but they had rudimentary support structures surrounding the nerve cord. Ostracoderms had other distinctly vertebrate-like characteristics. Their head shields indicate that their brains had the three regions (forebrain, midbrain, and hindbrain) typical of all later vertebrates (see Chapter 33).

Study Break

1. How did the earliest vertebrates feed without jaws?
2. Compare the hagfish and the lamprey based on their body structure, feeding habits, and life cycles.

27.7 Jawed Fishes: Jaws Expanded the Feeding Opportunities for Vertebrates

The first gnathostomes were jawed fishes. Jaws meant that they could eat more than just filtered food particles and take larger food items with higher energy content. The renowned anatomist and paleontologist A.S. Romer (see Chapter 19, *People Behind Biology*) described the evolution of jaws as "perhaps the greatest of all advances in vertebrate history." Hinged jaws allow vertebrates to grasp, kill, shred, and crush large food items. Some species also use their jaws for defence, for grooming, to construct nests, and to transport young.

Embryological evidence suggests that jaws evolved from paired gill arches in the pharynx of a jawless ancestor **(Figure 27.15, p. 630)**. One pair of ancestral **gill arches** formed bones in the upper and lower

Figure 27.15 The evolution of jaws.

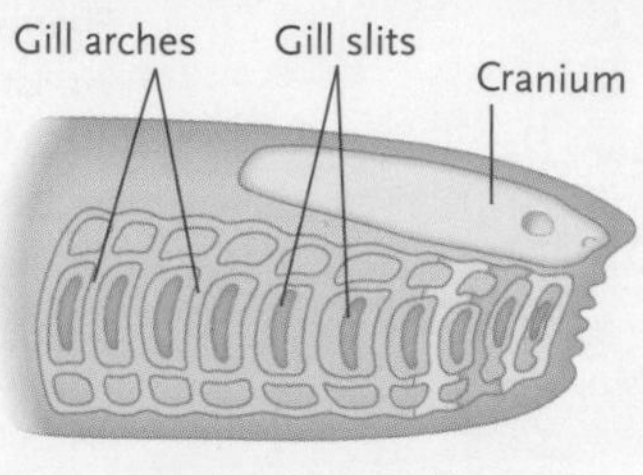

a. Jaws evolved from gill arches in the pharynx of jawless fishes.

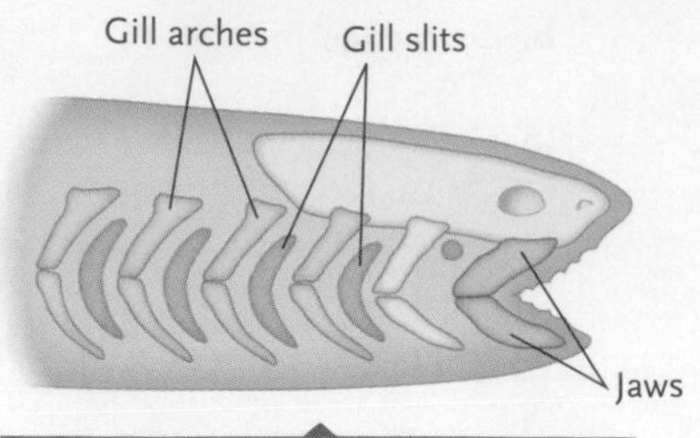

b. In early jawed fishes, the upper jaw was firmly attached to the cranium.

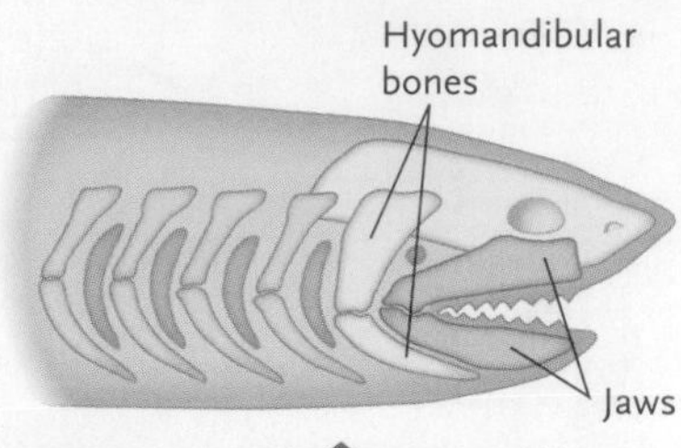

c. In later jawed fishes, the jaws were supported by the hyomandibular bones, which were derived from a second pair of gill arches.

jaws, whereas a second pair was transformed into the **hyomandibular bones** that braced the jaws against the cranium. Nerves and muscles of the ancestral suspension-feeding pharynx control the movement and actions of jaws. Jawed fishes also had fins, first appearing as folds of skin and movable spines that stabilized locomotion and deterred predators. Movable fins appeared independently in several lineages, and by the Devonian, most jawed fishes had unpaired (dorsal, anal, and caudal) and paired (pectoral and pelvic) fins **(Figure 27.16)**.

In two early lineages of jawed fishes (Acanthodii and Placodermi), the upper jaw was firmly attached to the cranium. This meant an inflexible mouth that simply snapped open and shut. Acanthodians and placoderms had internal skeletons.

27.7a Class Acanthodii

The spiny "sharks" (*acanth* = spine) persisted from the late Ordovician through the Permian. Most of these sharklike fishes were less than 20 cm long, with small, light scales, streamlined bodies, well-developed eyes, large jaws, and numerous teeth **(Figure 27.17a)**. Although acanthodians were not true sharks, they probably were fast swimmers and efficient predators. Many of them lived in fresh water. Most had a row of ventral spines and fins with internal skeletal support on each side of the body. The anatomy of acanthodians suggests a close relationship to bony fishes of today.

27.7b Class Placodermi

The placoderms (*plac* = plate; *derm* = skin) appeared in the Silurian and diversified in the Devonian and Carboniferous but left no direct descendants. Some, such as *Dunkleosteus* species **(Figure 27.17b and c)**, reached lengths of 10 m. The bodies of placoderms were covered with large, heavy plates of bone anteriorly and smaller scales posteriorly. Their jaws had sharp cutting edges but no separate teeth, and their paired fins had internal skeletons and powerful muscles.

27.7c Class Chondrichthyes

The cartilaginous fishes (*chondr* = cartilage; *ichthy* = fish) are represented today by about 850 living species of sharks, skates and rays, and chimeras. As the name implies, their skeletons are entirely cartilaginous. However, the absence of bone is a derived trait because

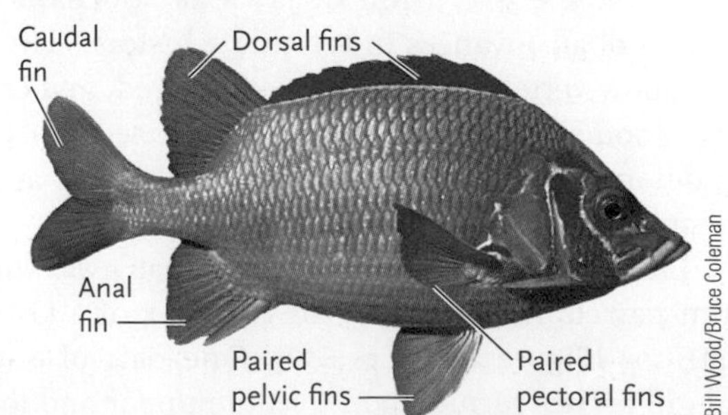

Figure 27.16 Fish fins. Most fishes have both paired and unpaired fins.

a. Spiny shark

b. Placoderm

c.

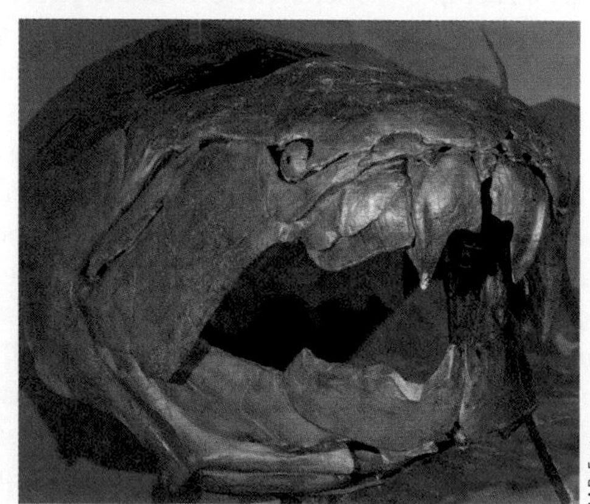

Figure 27.17 Early gnathostomes. *Climatius*, an acanthodian **(a)** (spiny shark), was small, about 8 cm long. The placoderm **(b)** *Dunkleosteus* was gigantic, growing to 10 m in length. Although some acanthodians had teeth, placoderms had only sharp cutting edges. The 10 m long skull of a *Dunkleosteus* **(c)** demonstrates how impressive placoderms could be.

a. Manta ray

b. Galápagos shark

© Gido Braase/Deep Blue Productions

Jonathan Bird/Oceanic Research Group, Inc.

c. Swell shark egg case

Alex Kerstitch/Visuals Unlimited

Figure 27.18
Chondricthyes. **(a)** Skates and rays, such as the manta ray (*Manta birostris*), as well as **(b)** sharks, such as the Galapagos shark (*Carcharhinus galapagensis*), are grouped in the Elasmobranchii. The eggs of many sharks **(c)** include a large yolk that nourishes the developing embryo.

all earlier fishes had bony armour or bony endoskeletons. Most living chondrichthyans are grouped into two subclasses, the **Elasmobranchii** (skates, rays, and sharks; **Figure 27.18**) and the **Holocephali** (chimeras). Most are marine predators. With about 40 living species, holocephalians are the only cartilaginous fishes with an operculum (gill cover).

Skates and rays are dorsoventrally flattened (see Figure 27.18a) and swim by undulating their enlarged pectoral fins. Most are bottom dwellers that often lie partly buried in sand. They eat hard-shelled invertebrates (see Chapter 26), which they crush with rows of flattened teeth (see Figure 27.18). The largest species, the manta ray (*Manta birostris*), measures 6 m across and eats plankton in the open ocean. Some rays have electric organs that stun prey with shocks of as much as 200 volts. There are species of freshwater skates and rays in some rivers in the tropics; for example, in the Mekong River basin, some *Himantura chaophraya* are 2 m across.

Sharks (see Figure 27.18b) are among the oceans' dominant predators. Flexible fins, lightweight skeletons, streamlined bodies, and the absence of heavy body armour allow most sharks to rapidly pursue prey. Their livers often contain squalene, an oil that is lighter than water, which increases their buoyancy. The great white shark (*Carcharodon carcharias*), the largest living predatory species of shark, can be 10 m long. At 18 m, the whale shark (*Rhincodon typus*) is the world's largest fish, and it eats only plankton. Sharks' teeth are designed for cutting. *Isisius plutodus*, the cookie-cutter shark, uses piercing teeth in its upper jaw to attach to a prey, biting with the lower jaw and its cutting teeth while rotating its body (see Figure 3.22h). The feeding process removes a disk of flesh from its prey. The combination of serrated teeth and flexible extensible jaws makes the effects of shark bites awesome.

Elasmobranchs have remarkable adaptations for acquiring and processing food. Their teeth develop in whorls under the fleshy parts of the mouth. New teeth migrate forward as old, worn teeth break free (**Figure 27.19, p. 632;** see also Figure 3.22h). In many sharks, the upper jaw is loosely attached to the cranium, and it swings down during feeding. As the jaws open, the mouth spreads widely, sucking in large, hard-to-digest chunks of prey, which are swallowed intact allowing hurried eating. Although the elasmobranch digestive system is short, it includes a corkscrew-shaped **spiral valve**, which slows the passage of material and increases the surface area available for digestion and absorption.

Elasmobranchs also have well-developed sensory systems. In addition to vision and olfaction, they use **electroreceptors** to detect weak electric currents produced by other animals. Their **lateral line system**, a row of tiny sensors in canals along both sides of the body, detects vibrations in water (see Figure 35.8). They use urea as a metabolite, meaning that their body fluids are more concentrated than sea water. Freshwater skates have much lower concentrations of urea in their blood than their saltwater relatives do.

Chondrichthyans have evolved numerous reproductive specializations. Males have a pair of organs, the **claspers**, on the pelvic fins, which help transfer sperm into the female's reproductive tract. Fertilization occurs internally. In many species, females produce yolky eggs with tough leathery shells (see Figure 27.18c). Others retain the eggs within the oviduct until the young hatch. A few species nourish young in utero (see Chapters 38 and 39).

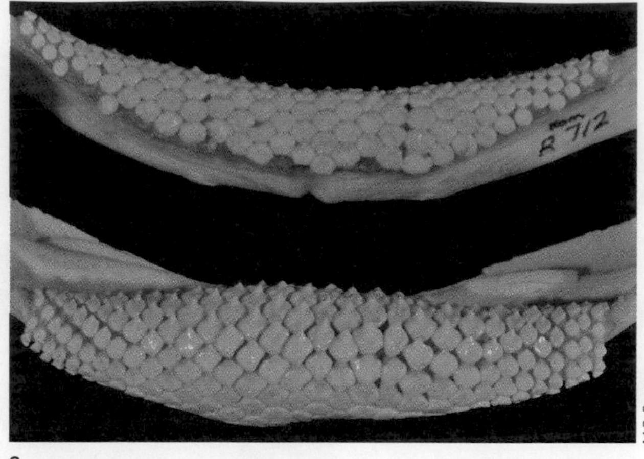

a.

b.

Figure 27.19
Elasmobranch teeth. Barndoor skates (b, *Dipturus laevis*; see Chapter 48) are specialized for crushing hard prey, such as bivalve molluscs. Cookie-cutter sharks (*Isistius plutodus*) have cutting teeth. In **(a)** and **(b)**, the replacement pattern of the teeth (from back to front of the jaws) is obvious.

27.7d The Bony Fishes

In terms of diversity (numbers of species) and sheer numbers of individuals, fishes with bony endoskeletons (cranium, vertebral column with ribs, and bones supporting their movable fins) are the most successful of all vertebrates. The endoskeleton provides lightweight support compared with the bony armour of ostracoderms and placoderms, enhancing their locomotor efficiency. Some "bony" fish have cartilaginous skeletons, but they are not chondrichthyeans.

Bony fishes have numerous adaptations that increase swimming efficiency. The scales of most bony fishes are small, smooth, and lightweight, and their bodies are covered with a protective coat of mucus that retards bacterial growth and minimizes drag as water flows past the body.

Bony fishes first appeared in the Silurian and rapidly diversified into two lineages, Actinopterygii and Sarcopterygii. The ray-finned fishes (Actinopterygii, from *acti* = ray and *ptery* = fin) have fins supported by thin and flexible bony rays, whereas the fleshy-finned fishes (Sarcopterygii, from *sarco* = flesh) have fins supported by muscles and an internal bony skeleton. Ray-finned fishes are more diverse as measured by numbers of species and today vastly outnumber fleshy-finned fishes. The ~30 000 living species of bony fishes occupy nearly every aquatic habitat and represent more than 95% of living fish species. Adults range from 1 cm to more than 6 m in length. In the Yangtze River basin, *Pseuphurus glodius*, the Chinese paddlefish, can weigh up to 500 kg.

Class Actinopterygii. Sturgeons **(Figure 27.20a)** and paddlefishes, the most ancestral members of this group, are characterized by mostly cartilaginous skeletons. These large fishes live in rivers and lakes of the Northern Hemisphere. Sturgeons eat detritus and invertebrates, whereas paddlefish eat plankton. Gars **(Figure 27.20b)** and bowfins are remnants of a more recent radiation. They occur in the eastern half of North America, where they eat fish and other prey. Gars are protected from predators by a heavy coat of bony scales.

The subclass Teleosteii represents the latest radiation of Actinopterygii, one that produced a wide range of body forms **(Figure 27.21).** Teleosts have an internal skeleton made almost entirely of bone. On either side of the head, the **operculum**, a flap of the body wall, covers a chamber that houses the gills. Sensory systems (see Chapter 34) generally include large eyes, a lateral line system, sound receptors, chemoreceptive nostrils, and taste buds.

Variations in jaw structure allow different teleosts to consume plankton, seaweed, invertebrates, or other vertebrates. Teleosts exhibit remarkable adaptations for feeding and locomotion. When some teleosts open their mouths, bones at the front of the jaws swing forward to create a circular opening. Folds of skin extend

a. Lake sturgeon

Ken Lucas/Visuals Unlimited

b. Long-nosed gar

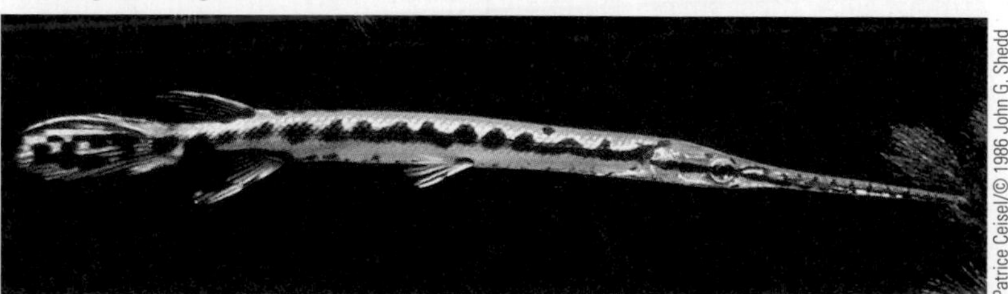

Patrice Ceisel/© 1986 John G. Shedd Aquarium

Figure 27.20
Ancestral actinopterygians (ray-finned bony fishes). Lake sturgeon (**a**, *Acipenser fulvescens*) and a long-nosed gar (**b**, *Lepidosteus sasteus*) are living representatives of early ray-finned fishes.

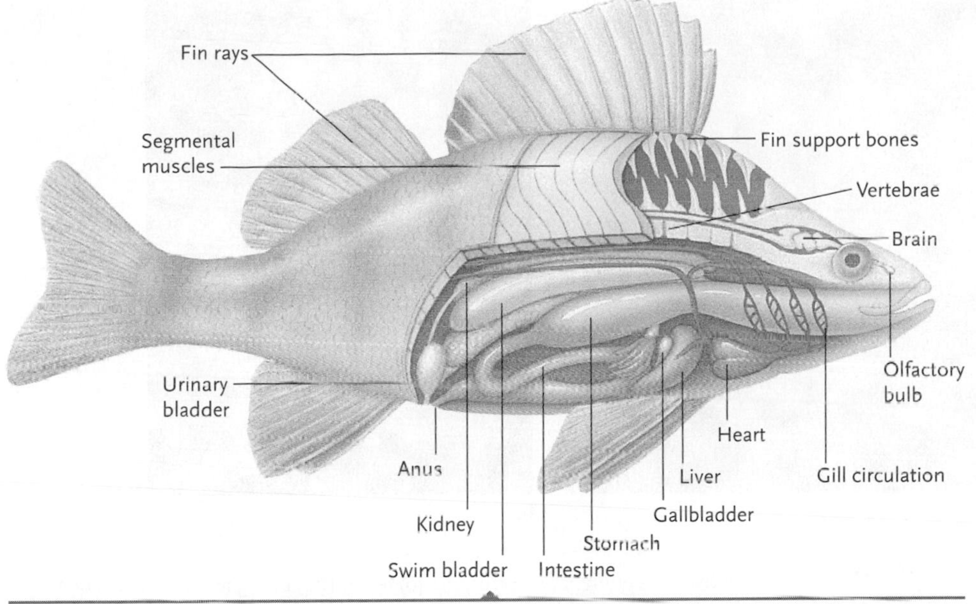

a. Teleost internal anatomy

b. Sea horses, like the northern sea horse (*Hippocampus hudsonius*), use a prehensile tail to hold on to substrates; they are weak swimmers.

c. The long, flexible body of a spotted moray eel (*Gymnothorax moringa*) can wiggle through the nooks and crannies of a reef.

d. Flatfishes, like this European flounder (*Platichthys flesus*), lie on one side and leap at passing prey.

e. Open ocean predators, like the yellowfin tuna (*Thunnus albacares*), have strong, torpedo-shaped bodies and powerful caudal fins.

f. Kissing Gouramis (*Helostoma temmincki*) extend their jaws into a tube that sucks food into the mouth.

Figure 27.21
Teleost diversity. Although all teleosts (bony fish) share similar internal features, their diverse shapes adapt them to different diets and types of swimming.

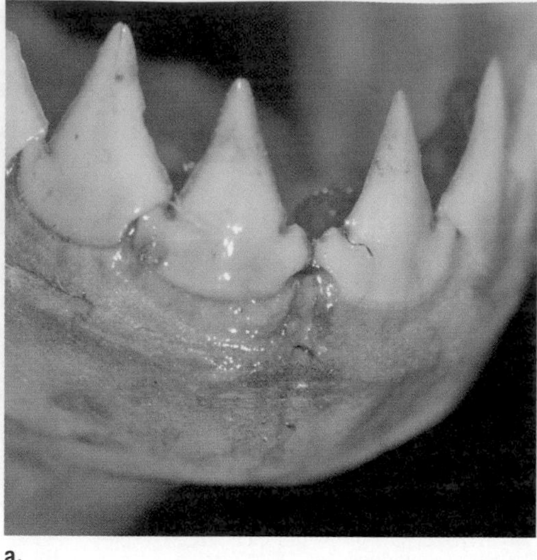

a.

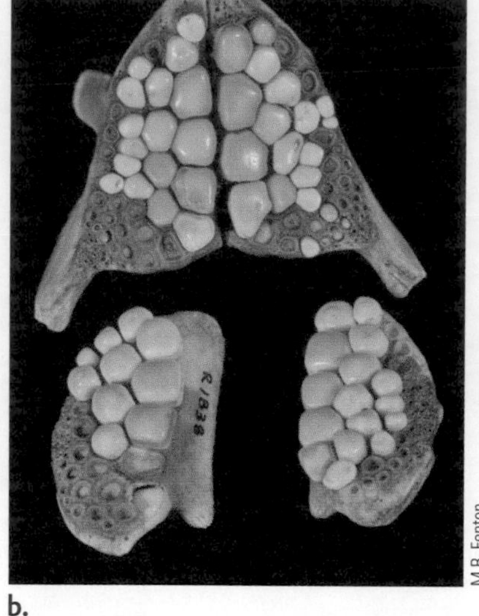

b.

Figure 27.22
Teleost teeth. Like Chrondricthyes, bony fish also have developed cutting **(a)** and crushing **(b)** teeth. The cutting teeth are those of a pirhana (*Sarrasalamus* species); the crushing teeth are from a black drum (*Pogones cromis*).

backward, forming a tube through which they suck food (see Figure 27.21f). Like Chondrichthyes, Actinopterygii exhibit great variation in tooth structure **(Figure 27.22).** Species such as pirhanas (*Sarrasalamus*) are notorious for their bites. Other species have teeth specialized for crushing hard prey, such as bivalve molluscs. Whereas the pirhana's teeth are on the premaxilla, maxilla, and mandible (as they are in mammals and many other vertebrates), the crushing teeth of ray-finned fishes often occur on the bones of the pharynx.

In many modern ray-finned fishes, a gas-filled **swim bladder** serves as a hydrostatic organ that increases buoyancy (see Figure 27.21). The swim bladder is derived from an ancestral air-breathing lung that allowed early actinopterygians to gulp air, supplementing gill respiration in aquatic habitats, where dissolved oxygen concentration is low.

Many have symmetrical tail fins posterior to the vertebral column that provide power for locomotion. Their pectoral fins often lie high on the sides of the body, providing fine control over swimming. Some species use pectoral fins for acquiring food, for courtship, and for care of eggs and young. Some teleosts use pectoral fins for crawling on land (e.g., mudskippers, *Periophthalmus* species, climbing perch, *Anabas* species) or gliding in air (flying fish, family Exocoetidae).

Most marine species produce small eggs that hatch into larvae that live among the plankton. Eggs of freshwater teleosts are generally larger and hatch into tiny versions of the adults. Parents often care for their eggs and young, fanning oxygen-rich water over them, removing fungal growths, and protecting them from predators. Some freshwater species, such as guppies, give birth to live young (see Box 38.3).

Class Sacropterygii. The two groups of fleshy-finned fishes—lobe-finned fishes and lungfishes—are represented by only eight living species **(Figure 27.23).** Although lobe-finned fishes were once thought to have been extinct for 65 million years, a living coelacanth (*Latimeria chalumnae*) was discovered in 1938 near the Comoros Islands, off the southeastern coast of Africa. A population of these metre-long fish live at depths of 70 to 600 m, feeding on fishes and squid. Remarkably, a second population of coelacanths was discovered in 1998, 10 000 km east of the Comoros, when a specimen

Figure 27.23
Sarcopterygians. The coelocanth (**a**, *Latimeria chalumnae*) is now one of two living species of lobe-finned fishes. The Australian lungfish (**b**, *Neoceratodus forsteri*) is one of six living lungfish species.

a. Coelacanth

b. Australian lungfish

was found in an Indonesian fish market. Analyses of the DNA of the Indonesian specimen indicated that it is a distinct species (*Latimeria menadoensis*).

Lungfishes have changed relatively little over the last 200 million years. Six living species are distributed on southern continents. Australian lungfishes live in rivers and pools, using their lungs to supplement gill respiration when dissolved oxygen concentration is low. South American and African species live in swamps and use their lungs for breathing during the annual dry season, which they spend encased in a mucus-lined burrow in the dry mud. When the rains begin, water fills the burrow and the fishes awaken from dormancy. During their periods of dormancy, these fishes excrete urea.

Study Break

1. What did the evolution of jaws mean for fish?
2. What physiological characteristics make sharks dominant ocean predators?
3. What is the lateral line system? What does it do?

27.8 Early Tetrapods and Modern Amphibians

The fossil record suggests that tetrapods evolved in the late Devonian from a group of fleshy-finned fishes, the Osteolepiformes. Osteolepiforms and early tetrapods shared several derived characteristics. Both had infoldings of their tooth surfaces, a trait of unknown function. The shapes and positions of bones on the dorsal side of their crania and in their appendages were similar.

Some problems of moving onto land were identified earlier (see Chapter 3). During dry periods in swampy, late Devonian habitats, drying pools may have forced osteolepiform ancestors to move overland to adjacent pools that still had water. During these excursions, the fish may have found that land plants, worms, and arthropods provided abundant food, and oxygen was more readily available in air than in water (see Table 3.1). Furthermore, there may well have been fewer terrestrial predators at that time, but this interpretation is open to question.

Osteolepiforms **(Figure 27.24a)** usually had strong, stout fins that allowed them to crawl on mud. Crescent-shaped bones in their vertebral columns provided good support. Their nostrils lead to sensory pits housing olfactory (odour) receptors (see Chapter 34). They almost certainly had lungs, allowing them to breathe atmospheric oxygen. Like living lungfishes, they also could have excreted urea or uric acid rather than ammonium, which is toxic.

The earliest tetrapod with nearly complete skeletal data is the semiterrestrial, metre-long *Ichthyostega* **(Figure 27.24b)**. Compared with its fleshy-finned ancestors, *Ichthyostega* had a more robust vertebral column, sturdier limb girdles and appendages, a rib cage that protected its internal organs (including lungs), and a neck. Fishes lack necks because the pectoral girdle is fused to the cranium. In *Ichthyostega*, several vertebrae separated the pectoral girdle and the cranium, allowing the animal to move its head to scan the environment and capture food. *Ichthyostega* retained a fishlike lateral line system, caudal fin, and scaly body covering.

Life on land also required changes in sensory systems. In fishes, the body wall picks up sound vibrations and transfers them directly to sensory receptors. Sound waves are harder to detect in air. Early tetrapods evolved a **tympanum** (ear drum), a specialized membrane on either side of the head that is vibrated by airborne sounds. The tympanum connects to the **stapes**, a bone homologous to the hyomandibula, which had supported the jaws of fishes (see Figure 19.10). The stapes, in turn, transfers vibrations to the sensory cells of an inner ear.

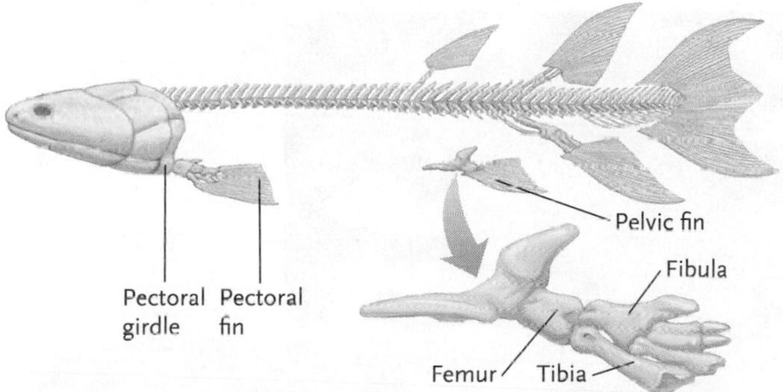

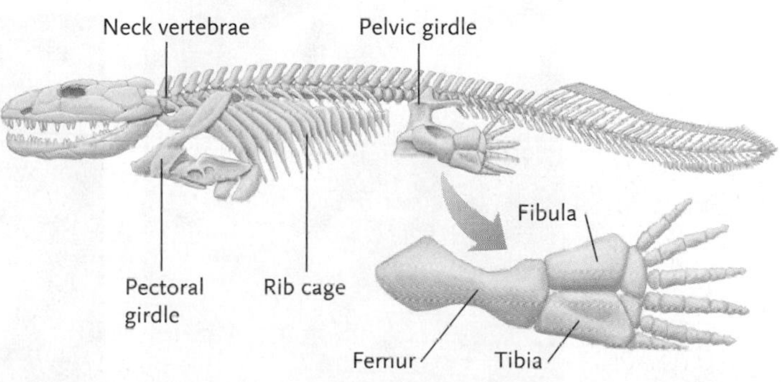

Figure 27.24
Evolution of tetrapod limbs. The limb skeleton of osteolepiform fishes such as **(a)** *Eusthenopteron* is homologous to that of early tetrapods, such as **(b)** *Ichthyostega*. Although *Ichthyostega* retained many fishlike characteristics, its pectoral girdle was completely freed from the cranium, and it had a heavy rib cage. Fossils of its forefoot have not yet been discovered.

Figure 27.25
A fossil amphibian. This amphibian, *Eryops*, from the Texas Permian, was about 1.8 m long. It is classified as a rhachitomus labryrinthodont of the order Temnospondyli.

27.8a Class Amphibia: Frogs and Toads, Salamanders, and Caecilians

Most of the 6000+ living species of amphibians (*amphi* = both; *bios* = life) are small, and their skeletons contain fewer bones than those of Paleozoic tetrapods such as *Ichthyostega*. All living amphibians are carnivorous as adults, but the aquatic larvae of some are herbivores. Fossil amphibians, such as *Eryops* **(Figure 27.25)**, were quite large and predatory.

The thin, scaleless skin of most living amphibians is well supplied with blood vessels and can be a major site of gas exchange. Because some oxygen and carbon dioxide enter the body across a thin layer of water, most amphibians have moist skin, restricting them to aquatic or humid terrestrial habitats. Adults of some species also breathe using saclike lungs. The evolution of lungs was accompanied by modifications of the heart and circulatory system that increase the efficiency with which oxygen is delivered to body tissues (see Chapter 39). Some adult anurans have a waxy coating on their skin, making them as waterproof as lizards **(Figure 27.26)**.

The life cycles of many amphibians include larval and adult stages. In frogs, larvae (tadpoles) hatch from fertilized eggs and eventually metamorphose into adults (see Chapter 39). The larvae of most frog species are aquatic, but adults may live their lives in water (be aquatic), move between land and water (be amphibious), and live entirely on land (be terrestrial). Some salamanders are pedomorphic (see Figure 20.19), which means that the larval stage attains sexual maturity without changing its form or moving to land. Some frogs and salamanders reproduce on land, omitting the larval stage altogether. In these speies, tiny adults emerge directly from fully developed eggs. However, the eggs of terrestrial breeders dry out quickly unless they are laid in moist places.

a.

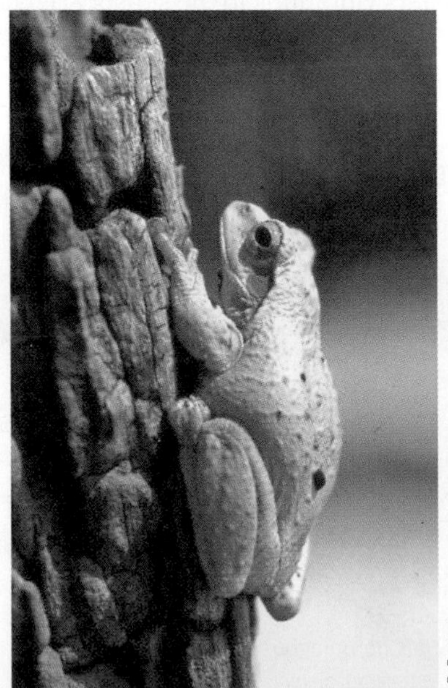

Figure 27.26
Waterproof frogs. (a) *Chiromantis xerampelina* from southern Africa and **(b)** *Phyllomedusa sauvagii* from South America make their skin waterproof with a waxy secretion. These frogs are as waterproof as chameleons. They also excrete uric acid to further conserve water.

b.

a. A frog

b. A salamander

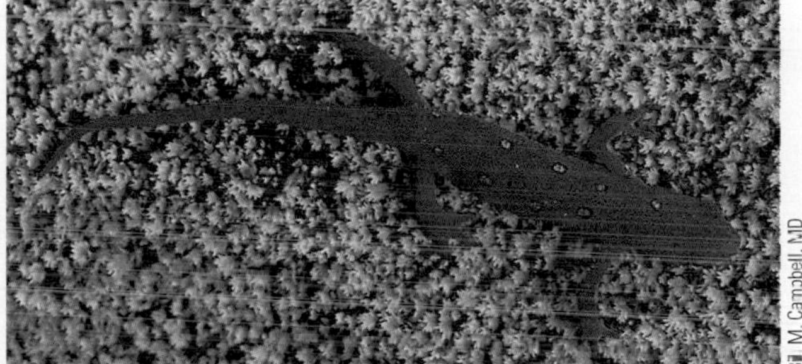

c. A caecelian

Stephen Dalton/Photo Researchers, Inc.

Bill M. Campbell, MD

Juan M. Renjifo/Animals Animals—Earth Scenes

Figure 27.27
Living amphibians. Anurans **(a),** such as the northern leopard frog (*Rana pipiens*), have compact bodies and long hind legs. Urodeles **(b),** such as the red-spotted newt (*Notophthalmus viridescens*), have an elongate body and four legs. Caecilians **(c),** such as *Caecelia nigricans* from Colombia, are legless burrowers.

Modern amphibians are represented by three lineages **(Figure 27.27),** but the evolutionary origin of frogs, salamanders, and caecilians has remained unresolved. The 2008 description of a small fossil from the Lower Permian of Texas suggests that frogs and salamanders share a relatively close common ancestor, whereas caecilians are distantly related to them.

Populations of practically all amphibians have declined rapidly in recent years. These declines are probably due to exposure to acid rain, high levels of ultraviolet B radiation, and fungal and parasitic infections. Another major factor in the decline of amphibians may be habitat splitting, the human-induced disconnection of habitats essential to the survival of amphibians. This aspect of habitat fragmentation (see Box 47.2) can cause adult amphibians to move across inhospitable habitat (roads, power line rights-of-way) to reach breeding habitats.

Anura. The 3700 species of frogs and toads (*an* = not; *ura* = tail) have short, compact bodies, and the adults lack tails. Their elongated hindlegs and webbed feet allow them to hop on land or to swim. A few species are adapted to dry habitats, encasing themselves in mucus cocoons to withstand periods of drought.

Urodela. The 400 species of salamanders (*uro* = tail; *del* = visible) have an elongate, tailed body and four legs. They walk by alternately contracting muscles on either side of the body, much the way fishes swim. Species in the most diverse group, the lungless salamanders, are fully terrestrial throughout their lives, using their skin and the lining of the throat for gas exchange.

Gymnophonia. The 200 species of caecelians (*gymno* = naked; *ophioneos* = snakelike) are legless, burrowing animals with wormlike bodies. They occupy tropical habitats throughout the world. Unlike other extant amphibians, caecelians have small bony scales embedded in their skin. Fertilization is internal, and females give birth to live young. In some species, the mother's skin produces a milklike substance for the young, which use specialized teeth to collect it from the mother's body (see Chapter 39).

Study Break

1. Present four lines of evidence suggesting that tetrapods arose from Osteolepiformes.
2. Why was the development of the tympanum important to life on land?
3. What characteristics allow amphibians to use their skin as a major site of gas exchange?

27.9 The Origin and Mesozoic Radiations of Amniotes

The amniote lineage arose during the Carboniferous, a time when seed plants and insects began to invade terrestrial habitats, providing additional food and cover for early terrestrial vertebrates. Amniotes take their name from the **amnion**, a fluid-filled sac that surrounds the embryo during development (see Chapter 39). Although the fossil record includes many skeletal remains of early amniotes, it provides little direct information about soft body parts and physiology. Three key features of living amniotes allow life on dry land and liberate them from reliance on standing water. The changes involve being waterproof and producing waterproof eggs.

- First, waterproof skin: keratin and lipids in the cells make skin relatively impermeable to water.
- Second, **amniote (amniotic) eggs** can survive and develop on dry land because they have four specialized membranes and a hard or leathery shell perforated by microscopic pores **(Figure 27.28).** Amniote eggs are resistant to desiccation. The membranes protect the developing embryo and facilitate gas exchange and excretion. The shell mediates the exchange of air and water between the egg and its environment. Developing amniote embryos can excrete uric acid, which is stored in the allantois of the embryo, which will later become the bladder. Generous supplies of **yolk** in the egg are the developing embryo's main energy source, whereas **albumin** supplies nutrients and water. There is no larval stage, and hatchling amniotes are miniature versions of the adult. Amniote eggs are the ancestral condition, but they are circumvented in most mammals (and some reptiles; see Chapter 19).
- Third, some amniotes produce *urea* and/or *uric acid* as a waste product of nitrogen metabolism (see Chapter 44). Although ammonium is less expensive (metabolically) to produce, it is toxic and must be flushed away with water. Urea and uric acid are not toxic, so they can be stored or voided without risk while conserving water.

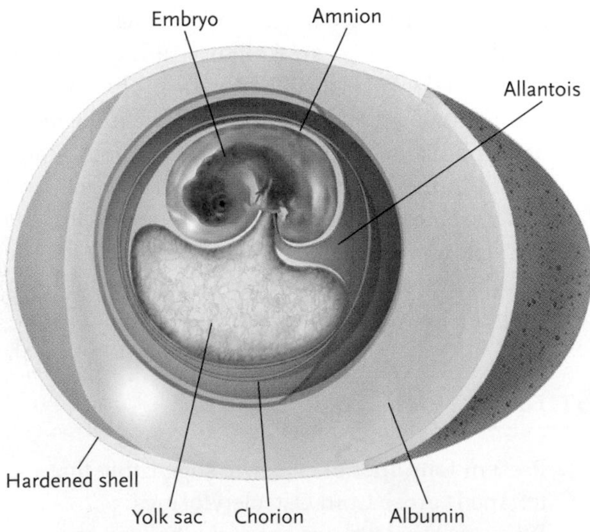

Figure 27.28
The amniote egg. A water-retaining egg with four specialized membranes surrounded by a hard or leathery shell allowed amniotes and their descendants to reproduce in dry environments.

The abundance and diversity of fossils of amniotes indicate that they were extremely successful, quickly replacing many nonamniote species in terrestrial habitats. During the Carboniferous and Permian, amniotes produced three major radiations: synapsids, anapsids, and diapsids **(Figure 27.29),** distinguishable by the numbers of bony arches in the temporal region of the skull (in addition to the openings for the eyes). The bony arches delimit fenestrae, openings in the skull that allow space for contraction (and expansion) of large and powerful jaw muscles.

Synapsids (Figure 27.30a, p. 640), a group of small predators, were the first offshoot from ancestral amniotes. Synapsids (*syn* = with; *apsid* = connection) had one temporal arch on each side of the head. They emerged late in the Permian, and mammals are their living descendants.

Anapsida (Figure 27.30b), the second lineage (*an* = not), had no temporal arches and no spaces on the sides of the skull. Turtles are living representatives of this group.

Diapsida (Figure 27.30c, d; *di* = two) comprise the third lineage and included most Mesozoic amniotes. Diapsids had two temporal arches, and their descendants include the dinosaurs, as well as extant lizards and snakes, crocodilians, and birds.

27.9a Extinct Diapsids

Early diapsids differentiated into two lineages, **Archosauromorpha** (*archo* = ruler + *sauro* = lizard + *morph* = form) and **Lepidosauromorpha** (*lepi* = scale), which differed in many skeletal characteristics. Archosaurs (archosauromorphs), or "ruling reptiles", include include crocodilians, pterosaurs, and dinosaurs. Crocodilians first appeared during the Triassic. They have bony armour and a laterally flattened tail, which is used to propel them through water. Pterosaurs, now extinct, were flying predators of the Jurassic and

Figure 27.29
Amniote ancestry. The early amniotes gave rise to three lineages (anapsids, synapsids, and diapsids) and numerous descendants. The lineages are distinguished by the number of bony arches in the temporal region of the skull (indicated on the small icons).

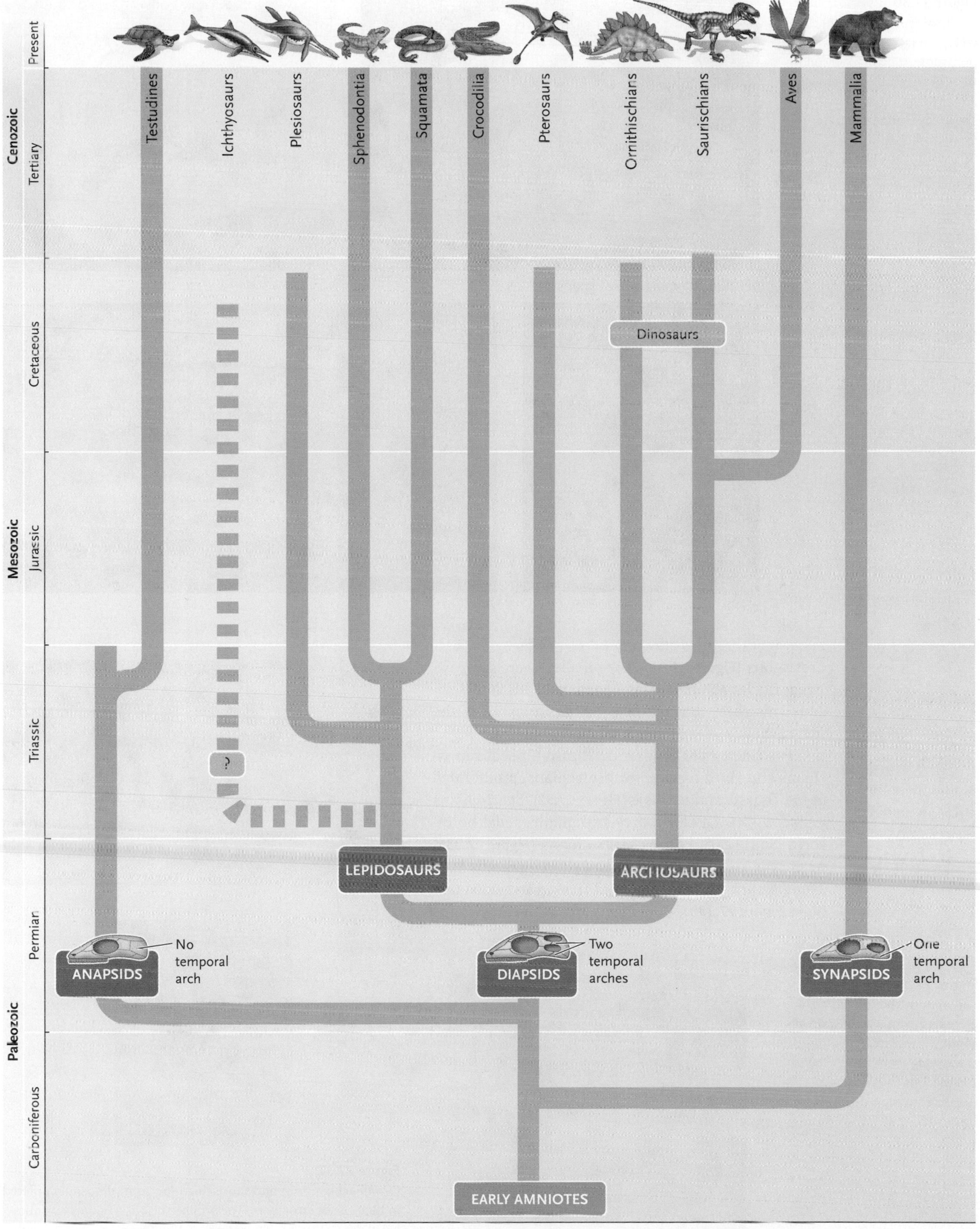
Present
Cenozoic
Tertiary
Cretaceous
Mesozoic
Jurassic
Triassic
Permian
Paleozoic
Carboniferous
Testudines
Ichthyosaurs
Plesiosaurs
Sphenodontia
Squamata
Crocodilia
Pterosaurs
Ornithischians
Saurischians
Aves
Mammalia
Dinosaurs
?
LEPIDOSAURS
ARCHOSAURS
No temporal arch
ANAPSIDS
Two temporal arches
DIAPSIDS
One temporal arch
SYNAPSIDS
EARLY AMNIOTES

Figure 27.30
Skulls of reptiles. The anapsid condition **(a)** shown by a snapping turtle, the synapsid condition **(b)** shown by *Dimetrodon*, and the diapsid conditions shown by *Camarosaurus* **(c)** and Champosaurus **(d)**.

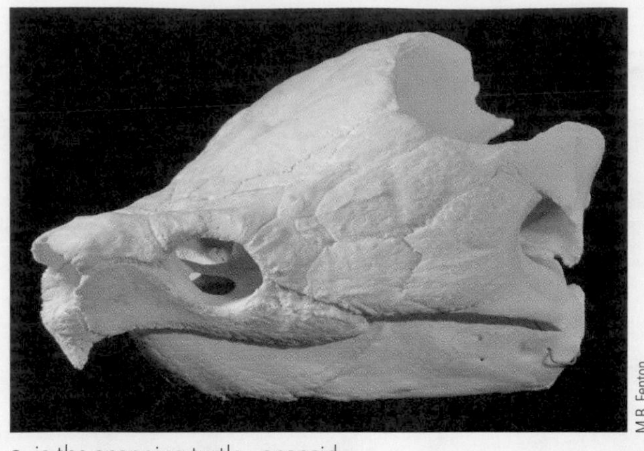

a. is the snapping turtle - anapsid

M.B. Fenton

b. is *Dimetrodon* a synapsid

c.

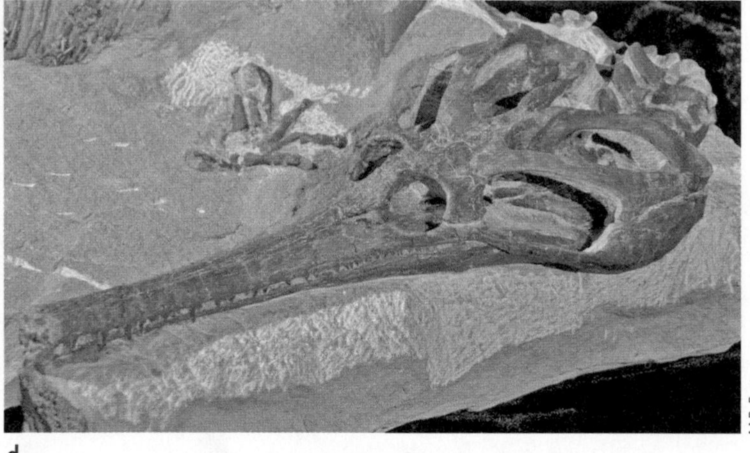

d.

Cretaceous **(Figure 27.31).** The smallest were sparrow-sized; the largest had wing spans of 11 m. Some evidence indicates that pterosaur wings attached to the side of their bodies at about the hips.

Two lineages of dinosaurs, "lizard-hipped" saurischians and "bird-hipped" ornithischians, proliferated in the Triassic and Jurassic **(Figure 27.32).** Saurischians included bipedal carnivores and quadrupedal herbivores. Some carnivorous saurischians **(Figure 27.33a)** were swift runners, and some had short forelimbs (e.g., *Tyrannosaurus rex*, which was 12 m long and stood 6 m high; **Figure 27.33b**). One group of small carnivorous

Figure 27.31
***Rhamphorynchus meunsteri*, a pterosaur with a wing span of about 1.7 m.** Note the impressions of the wing membranes, the teeth, and the long tail. This species is known from the Upper Jurassic of Germany.

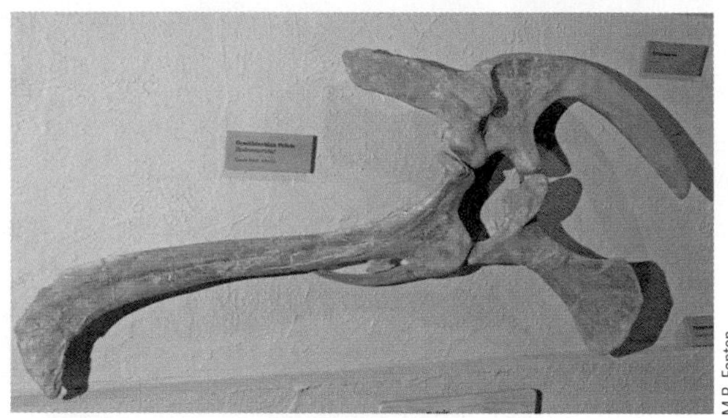

M.B. Fenton

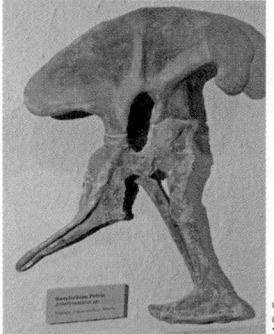

Figure 27.32
Ornithischian (top) and saurischian (bottom) dinosaurs differed in their pelvic structures. The ornithischian is a hadrasaur (duck-billed dinosaur), the saurischian an Albertosaurus. In each case, the acetabulum is the large elliptical area in the middle.

a.

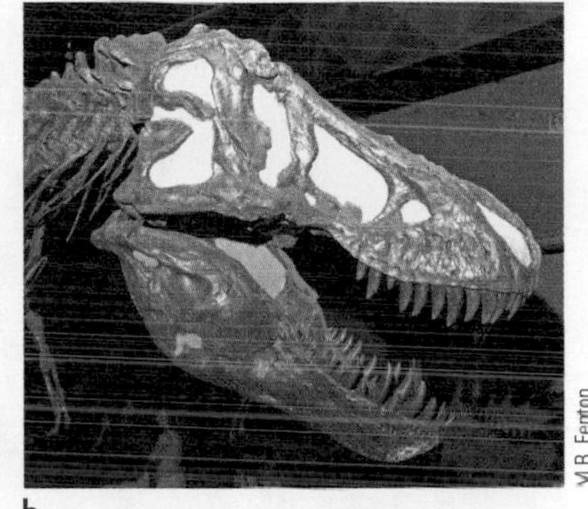

b.

Figure 27.33
Saurischian dinosaurs. Whereas *Ornitholestes hermanii* stood less than 1 m at the shoulder, the fearsome *Tyrannosaurus rex* was about 12 m long. Both were carnivores.

saurischians, the deinonychsaurs, is ancestral to birds (see Figure 27.33a).

By the Cretaceous, some herbivorous saurischians **(Figures 27.34** and **27.35)** were gigantic, and many had long, flexible necks. *Apatosaurus* (previously known as *Brontosaurus*) was 25 m long and may have weighed 50 000 kg. The largely herbivorous ornithischian dinosaurs had large, chunky bodies. This lineage included armoured or plated dinosaurs (*Ankylosaurus* and *Stegosaurus*), duck billed dinosaurs (*Hadrosaurus*), horned dinosaurs (*Styracosaurus*), and some with remarkably thick skulls (*Pachycephalosaurus*). Ornithischians were most abundant in the Jurassic and Cretaceous.

Lepidosaurs (Lepidosauromorpha) are the second major lineage of diapsids. This diverse group included both marine and terrestrial animals. Fossil lepidosaurs include champosaurs (see Figure 27.30d), which were freshwater fish eaters, and the marine, fish-eating **plesiosaurs**, with long, paddlelike limbs they used like oars **(Figure 27.36. p. 642)**. Fossil lepidosaurs also included ichthyosaurs (see Figure 19.1), porpoise-like animals with laterally flattened tails. Like today's whales, ichthyosaurs were highly specialized for marine life and gave birth to live young. Squamates, the living lizards and snakes, is the third important group within this lineage. *Sphenodon*, the tuatara, is the last living genus of a once diverse group of lizard-like squamates.

a. *Lambosaurus*

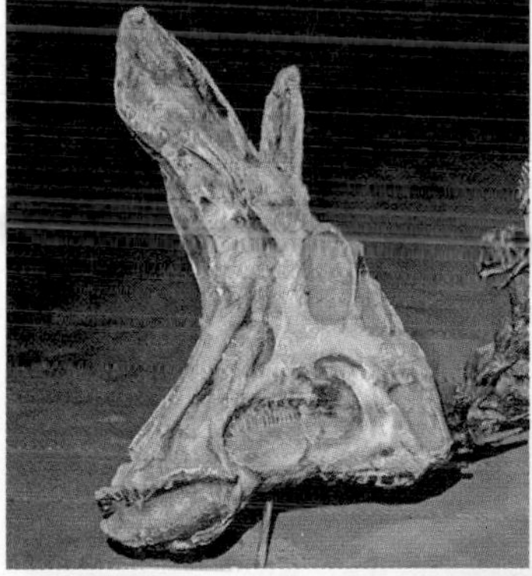

b. *Pachycephalosaurus*

c. *Triceratops*

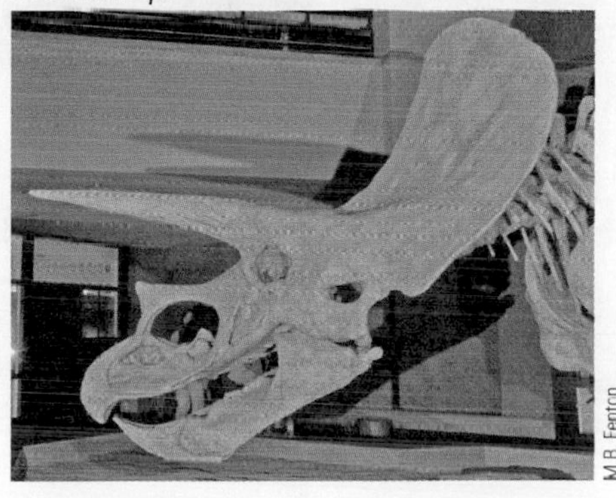

Figure 27.34
Ornithischian dinosaurs. These herbivores ranged in size from the 15-m long **(a)** *Lambeosaurus lambei*, a smaller, thick-skulled **(b)** *Pachycephalosaurus*, and the 10-m long **(c)** *Triceratops horridus*.

a.

b.

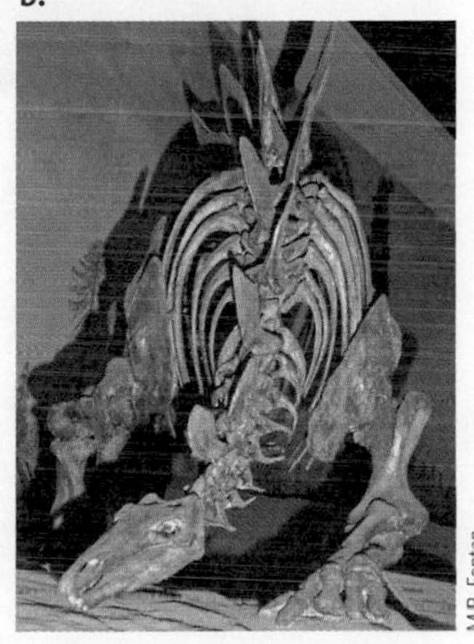

Figure 27.35
Large, lumbering herbivores. Other ornithischian dinosaurs included the 18-m long **(a)** *Camarasaurus supremus* and the 9-m long **(b)** *Stegosaurus armatus*. The latter had distinctive plates along its back.

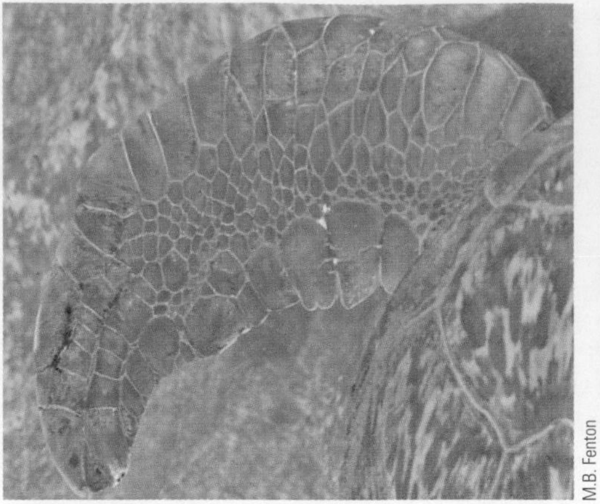

Figure 27.36
Paddles. Paddlelike forelimbs developed in sea turtles (left) and pleisiosaurs (right, *Trinacromerum bonneri*).

The teeth of reptiles provide important clues about their diets **(Figure 27.37)** and show interesting parallels with the teeth of other vertebrates.

Study Break

1. Where do amniotes get their name? Why are amniote eggs resistant to desiccation?
2. What three key features liberate living amniotes from reliance on standing water?
3. Name and describe three major radiations of amniotes during the Carboniferous and Permian.

27.10 Subclass Testudinata: Turtles and Tortoises

The turtle body plan, largely defined by a bony, boxlike shell, has changed little since the group first appeared during the Triassic **(Figure 27.38).** A turtle's ribs are fused to the inside of the shell, and in contrast to other tetrapods, the pectoral and pelvic girdles lie within the rib cage. The shell is formed from large keratinized scales covering the bony plates.

The 250 living species occupy terrestrial, freshwater, and marine habitats. They range from 8 cm to

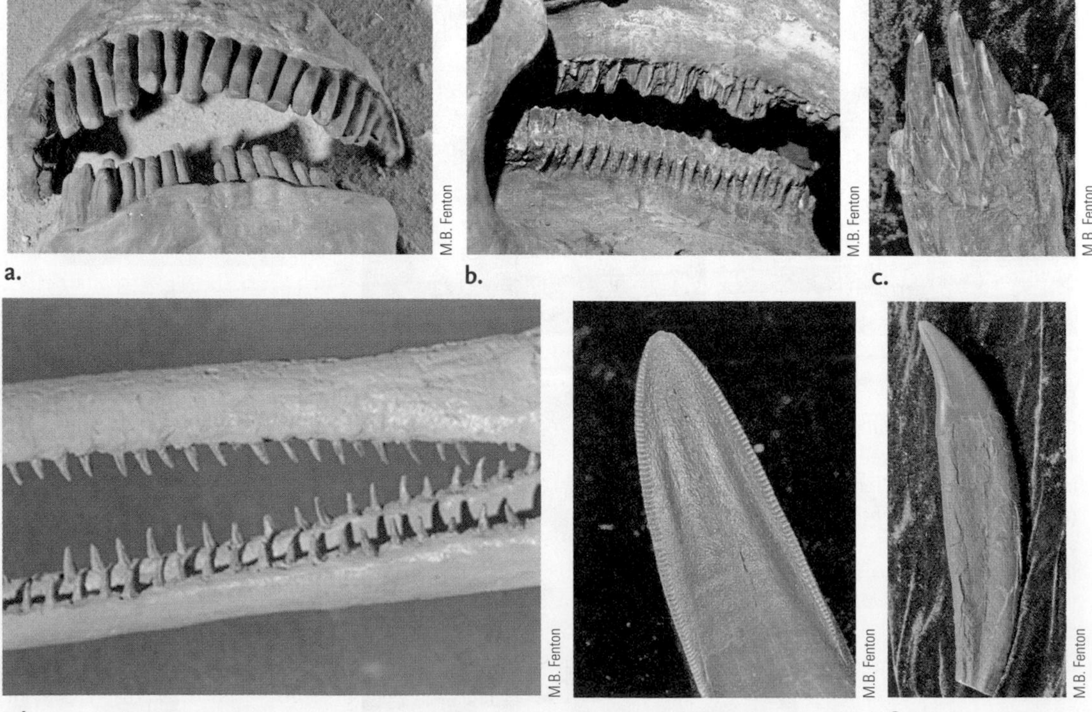

Figure 27.37
Reptile teeth. As usual, teeth reflect the dietary habits of vertebrates. Herbivorous dinosaurs (**a**, *Diplodocus longus*, and **b**, hadrasaur) had teeth adapted for gathering plant material **(a)** and grinding it **(b)**. They differ from those of a carnivorous dinosaur (**c**, *Daspletosaurus*) or a fish-eating reptile such as a camphosaur **(d)**. A tooth of a *Tyrannosaurus rex* changed distinctly over its length. The biting part of the tooth **(e)** had enamel and serrated edges. There was no enamel on the part of the tooth located within the socket of the skull **(e, f)**.

a. The turtle skeleton

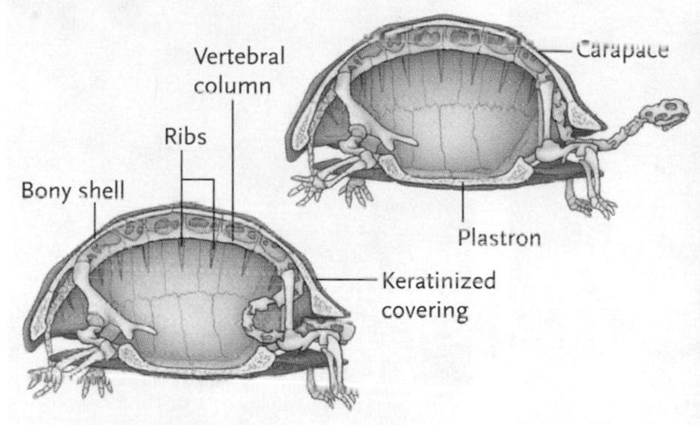

b. An aquatic turtle

Figure 27.38
Testudines. Most turtles **(a)** can withdraw their heads and legs into a bony shell. Aquatic turtles **(b)**, such as the eastern painted turtle (*Chrysmys picta*), often bask in the sun to warm up. The sunlight may help eliminate parasites that cling to the turtle's skin.

2 m in length. Turtles use a keratinized beak in feeding, whether they eat animal or plant material. When threatened, most species retract into their shells. Many species are now endangered because adults are hunted for meat and their eggs are eaten by humans and other predators. Young are often collected for the pet trade, and the beaches favoured as nesting sites by marine species are too often used as tourist attractions (see Chapter 48).

Study Break

Describe the body plan of a turtle.

27.11 Living Diapsids: Sphenodontids, Squamates, and Crocodilians

27.11a Infraclass Lepidosaura, Order Rhynchocephalia: The Tuatara

Sphenodon punctatus is one of two living species of sphenodontids (*sphen* = wedge; *dont* = tooth) or tuataras, a lineage that was diverse in the Mesozoic **(Figure 27.39a, p. 644)**. These lizardlike animals are best known for having a "third" or pineal eye. They survive on a few islands off the coast of New Zealand. Adults are about 60 cm long. They live in dense colonies, where males and females defend small territories. They often share underground burrows with seabirds and eat invertebrates and small vertebrates. They are primarily nocturnal and maintain low body temperatures during periods of activity. Their survival is threatened by two introduced predators, cats and rats.

27.11b Infraclass Lepidosaura, Order Squamata: Lizards and Snakes

Lizards and snakes are covered by overlapping, keratinized scales (*squam* = scale) that protect against dehydration. Squamates periodically shed their skin while growing, much the way arthropods shed their exoskeletons (see Chapter 26). Most squamates regulate their body temperature behaviourally (see Chapter 43), so they are active only when weather conditions are favourable. They shuttle between sunny and shady places to warm up or cool down as needed.

Most of the 3700 lizard species are less than 15 cm long, but Komodo dragons (*Varanus komodoensis*) grow to nearly 3 m in length (see Figure 34.16c). Lizards occupy a wide range of habitats and are especially common in deserts and the tropics. One species (*Lacerta vivipara*) occurs within the Arctic Circle. Most lizards eat insects, although some consume leaves or meat.

The 2300 species of snakes evolved from a lineage of lizards that lost their legs over evolutionary time. Streamlined bodies make snakes efficient burrowers or climbers **(Figure 27.39c)**. Many subterranean species are 10 or 15 cm long, whereas the giant constrictors may grow to 10 m. Unlike lizards, all snakes are predators that swallow prey whole. Compared with their lizard ancestors, snake skull bones are reduced in size and connected to each other by elastic ligaments. This gives snakes remarkable capacity to stretch their mouths. Some snakes can swallow food items that are larger than their heads (see Chapter 41). Snakes also have well-developed sensory systems for detecting prey. The flicking tongue carries airborne molecules to sensory receptors in the roof of the mouth (see Box 34.4). Most snakes can detect vibrations on the ground, and some, like rattlesnakes, have heat-sensing organs (see Figure 34.32). Many snakes kill by constriction, which suffocates prey, whereas several species produce venoms, toxins that immobilize, kill, and partially digest prey (see Box 46.1).

27.11c Infraclass Archosauria, Order Crocodylia: Crocodiles, Alligators, and Gavials

The 21 species of alligators and crocodiles (*crocodil* = crocodile), along with the birds, are the living remnants of the archosaurs **(Figure 27.39d)**. Australian saltwater

a. Sphenodontia includes the tuatara (*Sphenodon punctatus*) and one other species.

Stephen Dalton/Photo Researchers, Inc.

b. Basilisk lizards (*Basiliscus basiliscus*) escape from predators by running across the surface of streams.

c. A western diamondback rattlesnake (*Crotalus atrox*) of the American southwest bares its fangs with which it injects a powerful toxin into prey.

Mary Ann McDonald/Corbis

d. Crocodilia includes semiaquatic predators, like this resting African Nile crocodile (*Crocodylus niloticus*), that frequently bask in the sun.

Figure 27.39
Living nonfeathered diapsids.

crocodiles (*Crocodylus porosus*) are the largest, growing to 7 m in length. Crocodilians are aquatic predators that eat other vertebrates. Striking anatomical adaptations distinguish them from living lepidosaurs, including a four-chambered heart that is homologous to the heart in birds. In some crocodilians, muscles that originate on the pubis insert on the liver. When these muscles contract, the liver moves toward the tail, creating negative pressure in the chest cavity, a situation analogous to the role of the diaphragm in mammals.

American alligators (*Alligator mississippiensis*) exhibit strong maternal behaviour, perhaps reflecting their relationship to birds. Females guard their nests ferociously and, after the young hatch, free their offspring from the nest. The young stay close to the mother for about a year, feeding on scraps that fall from her mouth and living under her watchful protection.

Many species of alligators and crocodiles are endangered because their habitats have been disrupted by human activities. They have been hunted for meat and leather and because larger individuals are predators of humans. There is hope, however, as some populations of *A. mississippiensis* have recovered in the wake of efforts to protect them. In Africa and Australia, crocodiles are farmed for their meat and skin.

In the past, crocodilians were more diverse in body form than they are today. *Dakosaurus andiniensis*, a Jurassic–Cretaceous marine crocodilian from western South America, differed dramatically from "typical" crocodilians **(Figure 27.40).**

Study Break

1. How do snakes kill their prey?
2. What features of crocodilians are homologous to those of birds? Which ones are analogous to those of mammals?

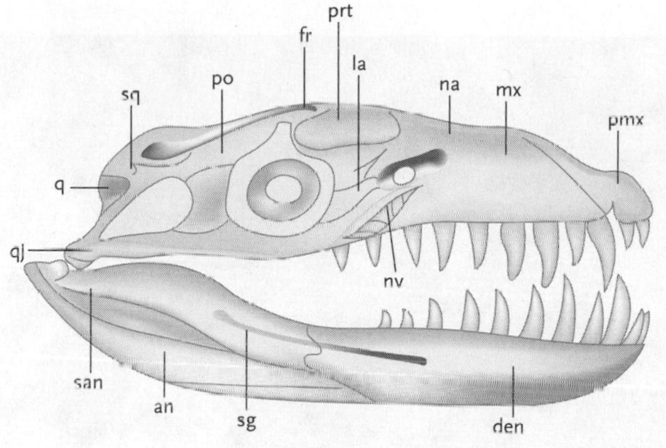

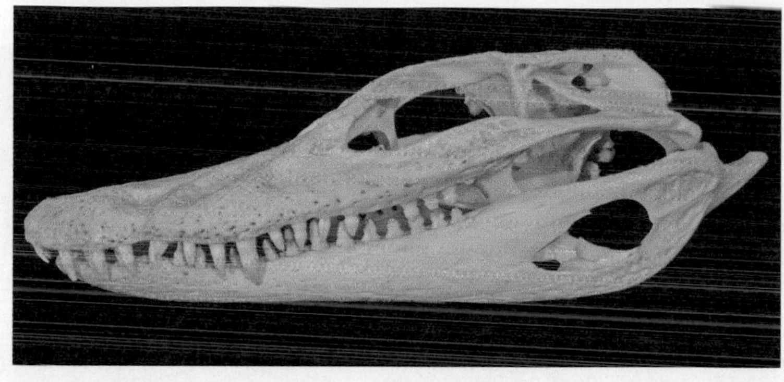

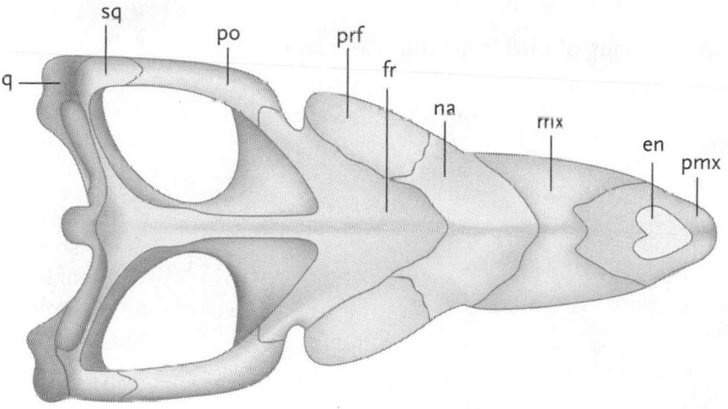

Figure 27.40
Crocodilians. *Dakosaurus andinensis*, a crocodile from the Jurassic–Cretaceous boundary in Patagonia (left), has a more robust skull and jaw than a more typical member of the group (above, *Alligator mississipiensis*). The skull of *Dakosaurus* is more rounded than the wedge-shaped skull of *Alligator*. Bones are abbreviated: an – angular; den – dentary; en – external nares; eoc – exoccipital; fr – frontal; ic – internal carotid formane; la – lacrimal; na – nasal; nv – neurovascular formina; pmx – premaxilla; po – postorbital; prf – prefrontal; pt – pterygoid; q – quadrate; qj – quadratojugal; san – surangular; sg – surangular groove; soc – supraoccipital; sq – squamosal.

27.12 Aves: Birds

Birds (Aves; *avis* = bird) appeared in the Jurassic as descendants of carnivorous, bipedal dinosaurs (see Figure 19.14). Birds belong to the archosaur lineage, and their evolutionary relationship to dinosaurs is evident in their skeletal anatomy and in the scales on their legs and feet. Powered flight gave birds access to new adaptive zones, likely contributing to their astounding evolutionary success **(Figure 27.41, p. 646)**. Some species of birds are flightless, and some of these are bipedal runners. Other birds are weak fliers.

Three skeletal features associated with flight in birds are the **keeled sternum** (breastbone), the furculum (wishbone), and the uncinate processes on the ribs **(Figure 27.42, p. 647)**. The keel on the sternum anchors the flight muscles (see Figure 27.41c), the furculum acts like a spring, and the uncinate processes, which effect overlap of adjoining ribs, give the rib cage strength. In flightless species, the sternum often lacks a keel (see Figure 27.42), an exception being penguins that "fly" through the water. However, flightless species often have uncinate processes.

Birds' skeletons are light and strong (see Figure 27.41b). The skeleton of a 1.5-kg frigate bird (*Fregata magnificens*) weighs just 100 g, far less than the weight of its feathers. Although the skeleton of a 20-g mammal weighs the same as that of a 20-g bird, the bird's bones are larger and lighter. Most birds have hollow limb bones with small supporting struts that criss-cross the internal cavities. Birds have reduced numbers of separate bony elements in the wings, skull, and vertebral column (especially the tail), so the skeleton is rigid. The bones associated with flight are generally large, and the wingbones are long (see Figure 27.41).

All extant birds **(Figure 27.43, p. 647)** use a keratinized bill for feeding rather than teeth, which are dense and heavy. Many species have a long, flexible neck that allows them to use their bills for feeding, grooming, nest building, and social interactions. Birds' soft internal organs are modified to reduce mass. Most birds lack a urinary bladder, so uric acid paste is eliminated with digestive wastes. Females have only one ovary and never carry more than one mature egg at a time. Eggs are laid as soon as they are shelled. Egg sizes give an indication of the range of size in birds **(Figure 27.44, p. 648)**. Birds range in size from a bee hummingbird (*Mellisuga helenae*) at 2 g to ostriches (*Struthio camelus*) at about 150 kg. The size spectrum is illustrated by a comparison of breast bones **(Figure 27.45, p. 648)**.

All birds have feathers (see Figure 27.42d), sturdy, lightweight structures derived from scales in the skin of their reptilian ancestors. Each feather has numerous barbs and barbules with tiny hooks and grooves that maintain the feathers' structures, even during vigorous activity. Flight feathers on the wings provide lift, whereas contour feathers streamline the surface of the body. Down feathers form an insulating cover close to the skin. Moulting replaces feathers once or twice each year. But not all animals with feathers are birds. Several extinct archosaurs had

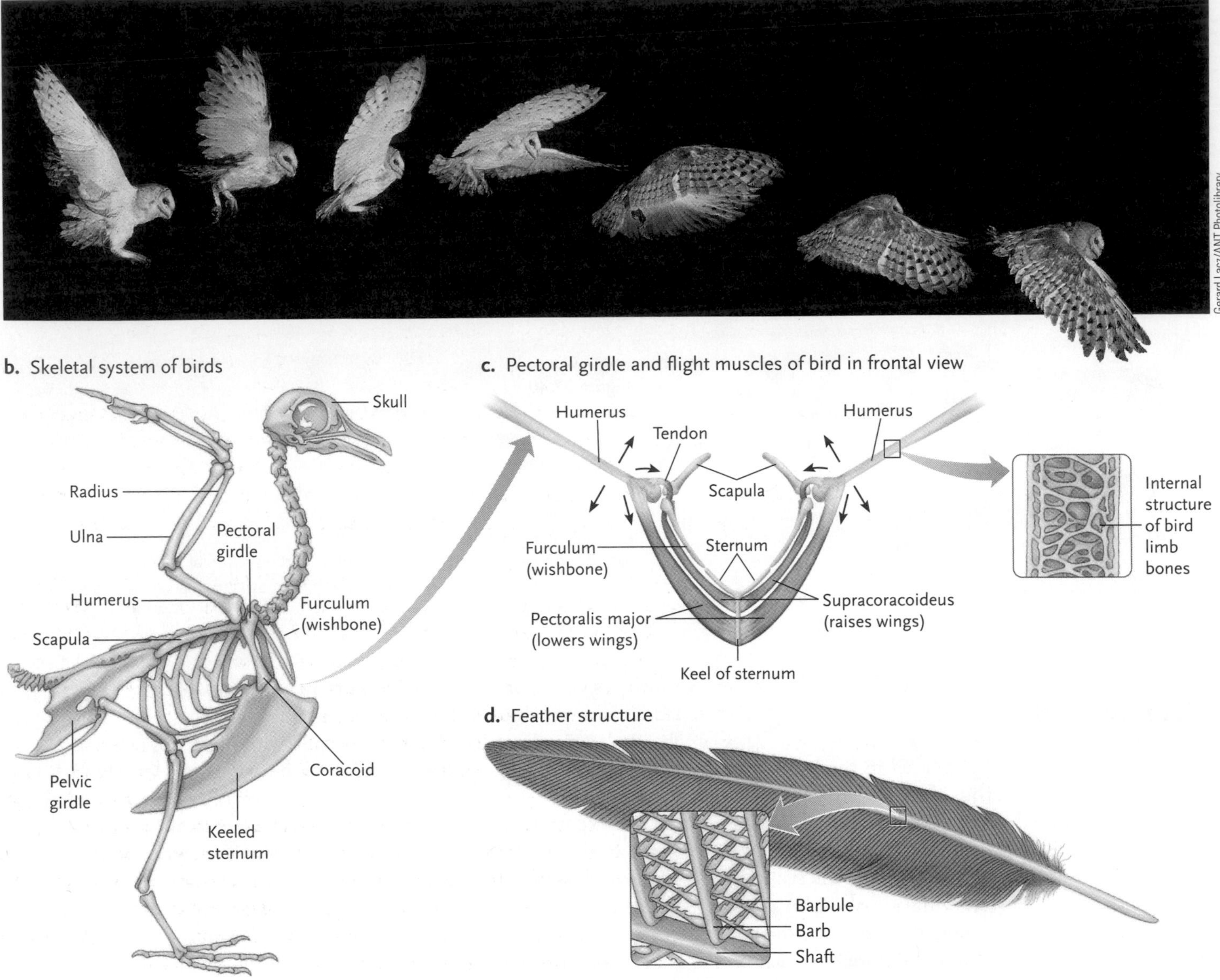

Figure 27.41
Adaptations for flight in birds. The flapping movements **(a)** of a bird's wing provide thrust for forward momentum and lift to counteract gravity. The bird skeleton **(b)** includes a boxlike trunk, short tail, long neck, lightweight skull and beak, and well-developed limbs. In large birds, limb bones are hollow. Two sets of flight muscles **(c)** originate on the keeled sternum; one set raises the wings, whereas the other lowers them. Flexible feathers **(d)** form an airfoil on the wing surface.

feathers but these animals had none of the adaptations for flight.

Other adaptations for flight allow birds to harness the energy needed to power their flight muscles. Their metabolic rates are 8 to 10 times higher than those of comparably sized reptiles, allowing them to process energy-rich food rapidly. A complex and efficient respiratory system (see Chapter 42) and a four-chambered heart (see Chapter 37) enable them to consume and distribute oxygen efficiently. As a consequence of high rates of metabolic heat production, most birds maintain a high and constant body temperature (see Chapter 43).

Flying birds were abundant by the Cretaceous. Even in the Jurassic, *Archaeopteryx* had a furculum and was capable of at least limited flight. Until 2008, two main theories purported to explain the evolution of flight in birds. Proponents of the "top-down" theory argued that ancestral birds lived in trees and glided down from them in pursuit of insect prey. Gliding and access to prey are key elements of this theory. Proponents of the "bottom-up" theory proposed that a protobird was a runner (cursorial) and ran in pursuit of prey and jumped up to catch it.

In 2008, Kenneth P. Dial and two colleagues proposed the "ontogenic–transitional wing" (OTW)

Figure 27.42
Bird skeletons and flight. Compared are the thoracic skeletons of Hudsonian curlew (**a**, *Numenius phaeopus*), kiwi (**b** and **d**, *Apteryx australis*), and a penguin **(c).** Note keels on the sterna of the curlew and the penguin but not on the kiwi. Neither the penguin nor the kiwi can fly, but the penguin "flies" in water. The wings of the kiwi are drastically reduced **(d),** and there is no furculum (wishbone), which is obvious in the penguin and the curlew. All three species have distinct uncinate processes on the ribs **(a, c, d).**

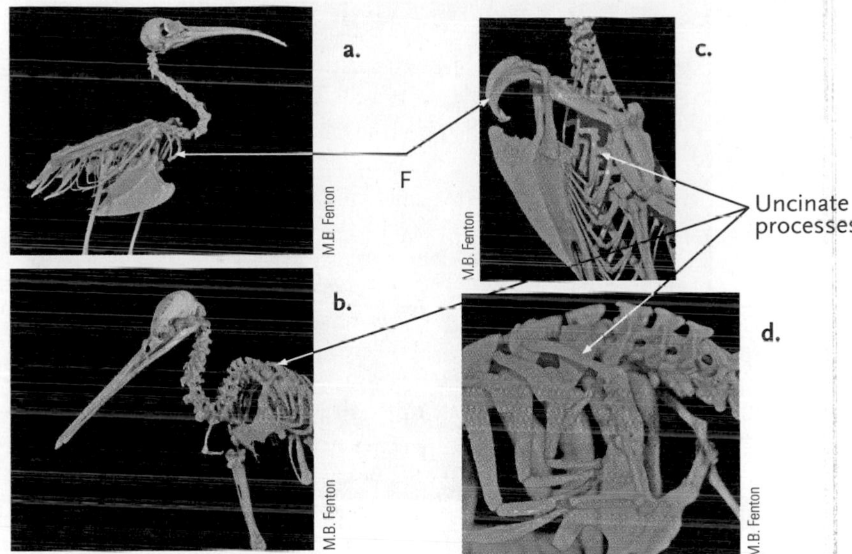

hypothesis to explain the evolution of flight in birds. They asserted that the transitional stages leading to the development of flight in modern birds corresponded to its evolutionary development. Key to the OTW theory is the observation that in developing from flightless hatchlings to flight-capable juveniles, individual birds move their protowings in the same ways as adults move fully developed wings. Dial and his colleagues noted that flap-running allows as yet flightless birds to move over obstacles. The OTW theory provides another look at the evolution of flight, and its predictions can be tested with fledglings of extant species. The combination of wings and bipedalism is central to the OTW hypothesis. Birds are bipedal, and pterosaurs may have been. Bats, however, are not bipedal, so the OTW hypothesis will not explain evolution of flight in that group.

The first known radiation of birds produced the enantiornithines ("opposite" birds), the dominant birds of the Jurassic and Cretaceous. Ornithurines

Figure 27.43
Bird diversity.

a. The Laysan albatross (Procellariiformes, *Phoebastria immutabilis*) has the long thin wings typical of birds that fly great distances.

b. The roseate spoonbill (Ciconiformes, *Ajaia ajuja*) uses its bill to strain food particles from water.

c. The bald eagle (Falconiformes, *Haliaeetus leucocephalus*) uses its sharp bill and talons to capture and tear apart prey.

d. A European nightjar (Caprimulgiformes, *Caprimulgus europaeus*) uses its wide mouth to capture flying insects.

e. A Bahama woodstar hummingbird (Apodiformes, *Calliphlox evelynae*) hovers before a hibiscus blossom to drink nectar from the base of the flower.

f. The chestnut-backed chickadee (Passeriformes, *Parus rufescens*) uses its thin bill to probe for insects in dense vegetation.

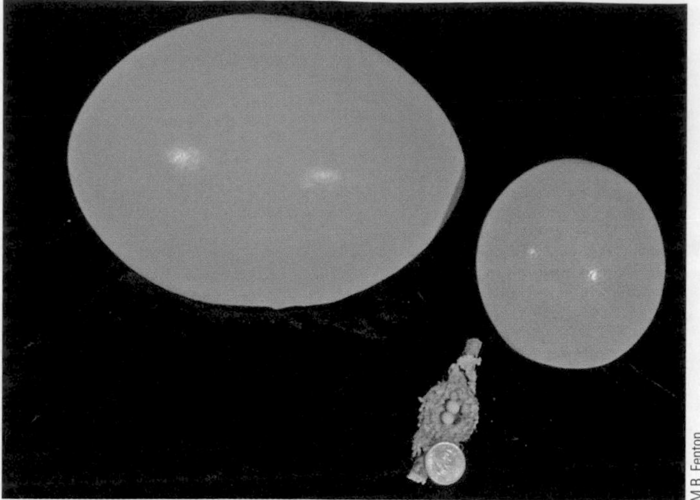

Figure 27.44
Bird eggs. Bird eggs range in size from those of elephant birds (left, *Aepyornis* of Madagascar) to ostriches (*Struthio camelus*, right) and a hummingbird (bottom). The scale, a Canadian $2 coin, is 2.8 cm in diameter.

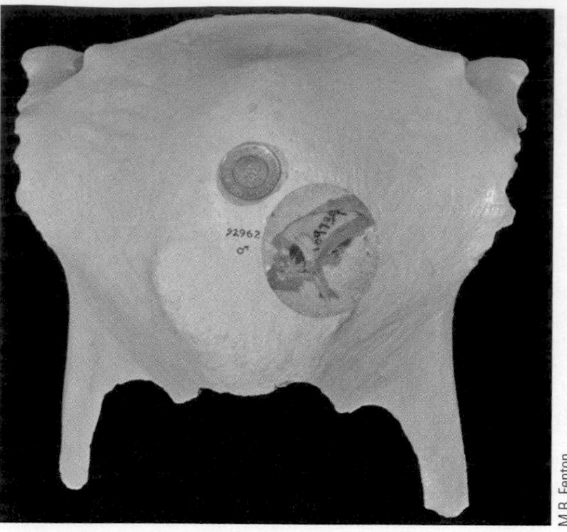

Figure 27.45
Breast bones of birds. Compared are the unkeeled breastbone of an ostrich (*Struthio camelus*) and a keeled breastbone of a hummingbird (*Trochilus polytmus*). A Canadian $2 coin (2.8 cm in diameter) is shown for scale.

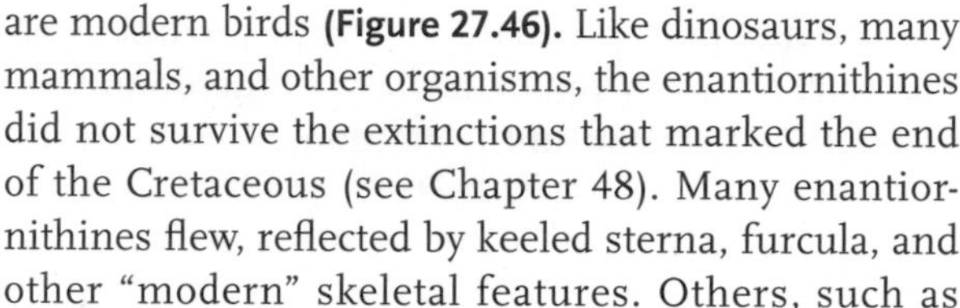

are modern birds **(Figure 27.46).** Like dinosaurs, many mammals, and other organisms, the enantiornithines did not survive the extinctions that marked the end of the Cretaceous (see Chapter 48). Many enantiornithines flew, reflected by keeled sterna, furcula, and other "modern" skeletal features. Others, such as Hesperornis, were swimmers that used their feet for propulsion and, unlike penguins, had keel-less sterna **(Figure 27.47).** Ornithurines include modern groups of wading birds and seabirds, first known from late Cretaceous rocks. Woodpeckers, perching birds, birds of prey, pigeons, swifts, the flightless ratites, penguins,

Figure 27.46
Evolution of birds. Enantiornithines, or opposite birds, were dominant in the Mesozoic but coexisted with ornithurine (more modern) birds in the early Cretaceous. The enantiornithines did not survive the extinctions at the end of the Cretaceoous. By the Miocene, passerine birds became the dominant landbirds.

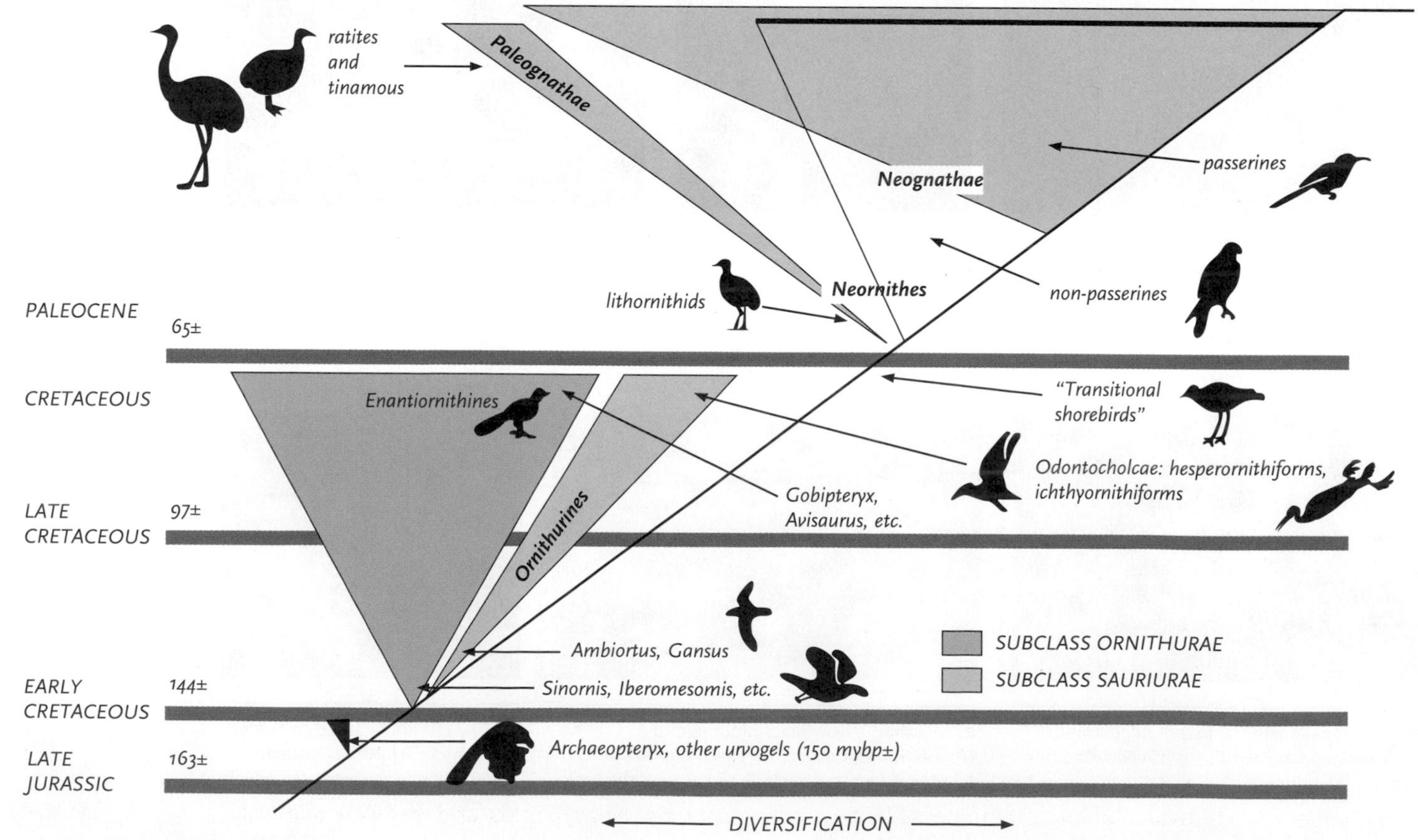

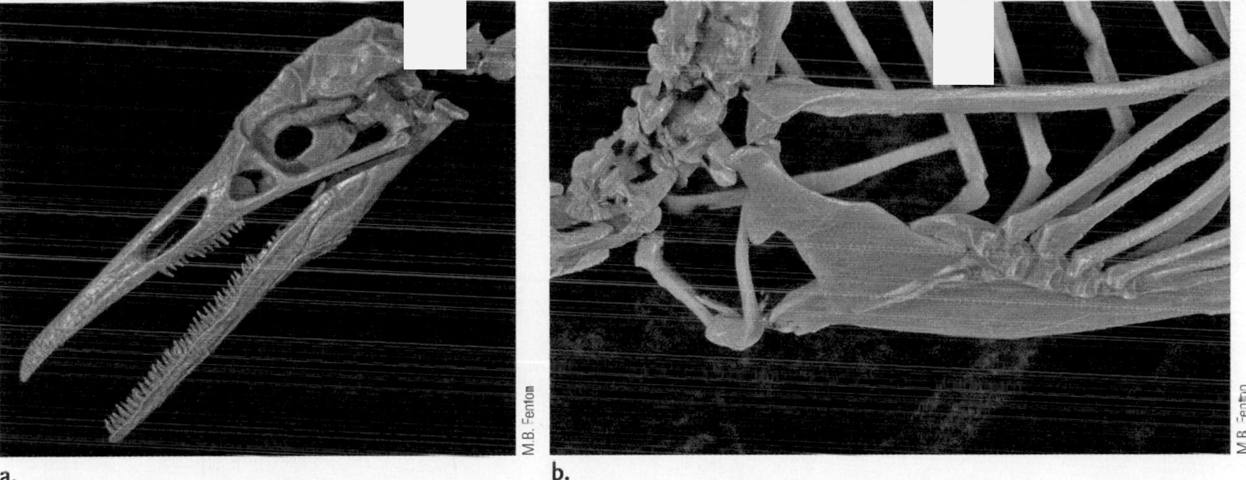

Figure 27.47
Skull **(a)** and sternum **(b)** of *Hesperornis*, a Cretaceous enantiornithine bird. Note the teeth, along with an unkeeled sternum and a furculum. This diving bird swam with its feet rather than its wings. The skull is 25 cm long.

and some other groups were all present by the end of the Oligocene. Birds continued to diversify through the Miocene.

The ~9000 living bird species show extraordinary ecological specializations built on the same body plan. Living birds are traditionally classified into nearly 30 orders. A bird's bill usually reflects its diet. Seed and nut eaters, such as finches and parrots, have deep, stout bills that crack hard shells. Carnivorous hawks and carrion-eating vultures have sharp beaks to rip flesh. Nectar-feeding hummingbirds and sunbirds have long slender bills to reach into flowers, although many perching birds also have slender bills to feed on insects. The bills of ducks are modified to extract particulate matter from water.

Birds also differ in the structure of their feet and wings. Predators have large, strong talons (claws), whereas ducks and other swimming birds have webbed feet that serve as paddles. Long-distance fliers such as albatrosses have narrow wings, whereas species that hover at flowers have short, broad wings. The wings of penguins and similar species are so specialized for swimming that they are incapable of aerial flight.

All birds have well-developed sensory and nervous systems, and their brains are proportionately larger than those of comparably sized diapsids. Large eyes provide sharp vision, and most species also have good hearing, which nocturnal hunters such as owls use to locate prey. Vultures and some other species have a good sense of smell, which they use to find food. Migrating birds use polarized light, changes in air pressure, and Earth's magnetic field for orientation (see Chapter 34).

Many birds exhibit complex social behaviour, including courtship, territoriality, and parental care. Many species use vocalizations and visual displays to challenge other individuals or attract mates. Most raise their young in nests, using body heat to incubate eggs. The nest may be a simple depression on a gravel beach, a cup woven from twigs and grasses, or a feather-lined hole in a tree.

Many bird species make semiannual long-distance migrations (see Chapters 3 and 40). Golden plovers (*Pluvialis dominica*) and the godwit (see *The Chemical and Physical Foundations of Biology* pages) migrate 20 000 km twice each year. Migrations are a response to seasonal changes in climate. Birds travel toward the tropics as winter approaches. In spring, they return to high latitudes to breed and to use seasonally abundant food sources.

Study Break

1. What three skeletal features are associated with bird flight? Which ones are missing in flightless birds?
2. What adaptations make flight possible in birds and pterosaurs?
3. What characteristics maintain the structure of feathers and make them important to flight in birds?

27.13 Mammalia: Monotremes, Marsupials, and Placentals

Mammals are part of the synapsid lineage, the first of the aminiotes to diversify. During the late Paleozoic, medium- to large-sized synapsids were the most abundant veretebrate predators in terrestrial habitats. Therapsids were one successful and persistent branch of synapids, and they were relatively

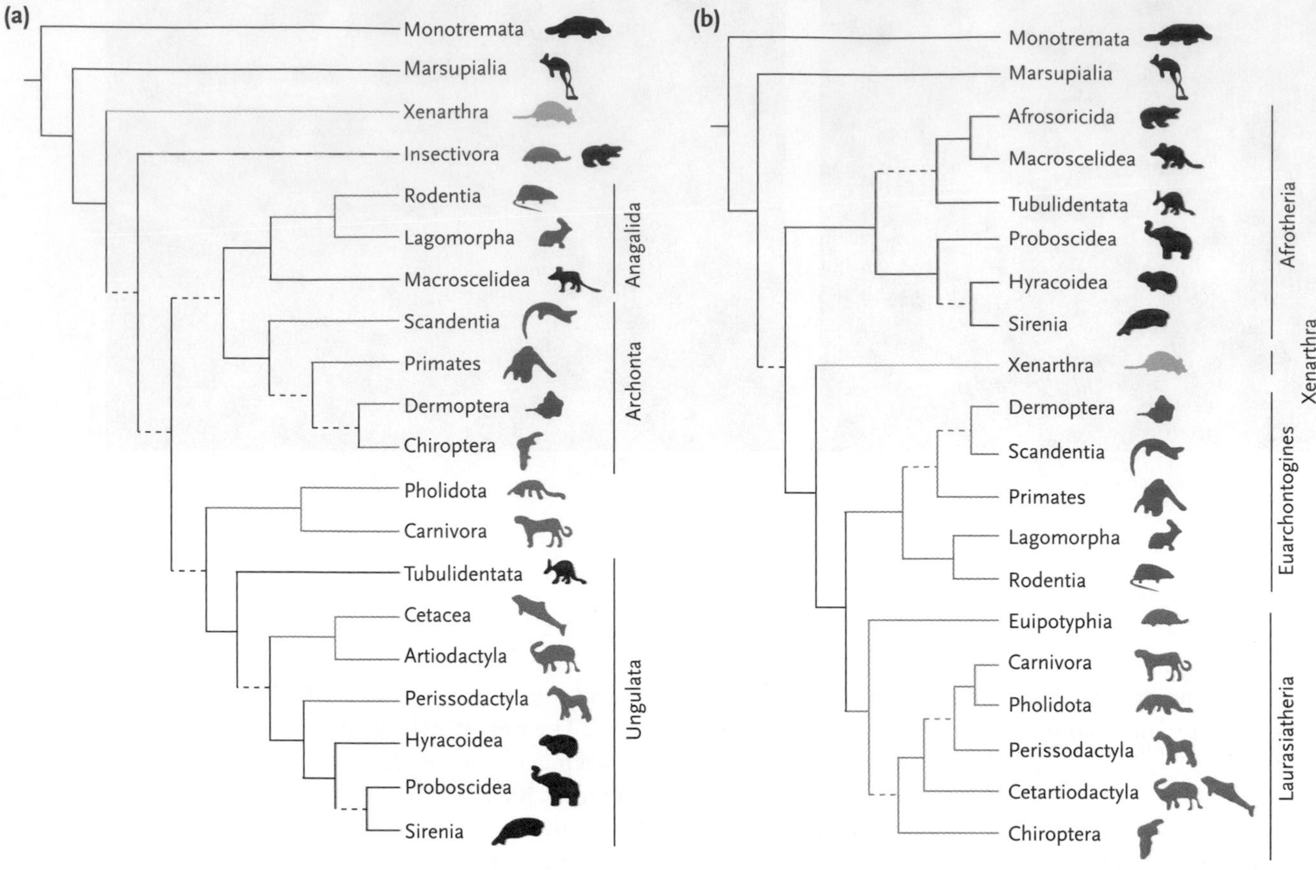

Figure 27.48
Modern mammals. In 2004, the prevailing phylogenies of mammals derived from **(a)** morphological and **(b)** molecular data.

mammal-like in their legs, skulls, jaws, and teeth. By the end of the Triassic, the earliest mammals (most of them no bigger than a rat) had appeared. Several lineages of early mammals, such as multituberculates (see Chapter 48) and the lineage that includes the Mesozoic beaver (see Figures 19.7 and 19.8), persisted and even flourished through much of the Mesozoic. These mammals coexisted with dinosaurs and other diapsids, as well as with the enantiornithine birds.

Paleontologists hypothesize that most Mesozoic mammals were nocturnal, perhaps to avoid diurnal predators and/or overheating. There are two living mammalian lineages **(Figure 27.48),** the egg-laying Prototheria (or Monotremata) and the live-bearing Theria (marsupials and placentals).

Several features distinguish mammals from other vertebrates, but mammalian diversity makes it difficult to generalize absolutely about definitive characteristics. Living mammals are relatively easy to recognize. They are usually furry and have a diaphragm (a sheet of muscle separating the chest cavity from the viscera); most are **homeothermic** (warm-blooded) and bear live young. In mammals, most blood leaves the heart through the left aortic arch (the main blood vessel leaving the heart). Mammals have two occipital condyles where the skull attaches to the neck, as well as a secondary palate (the plate of bones forming the roof of the mouth). They are *heterodont* and *diphyodont* **(Figure 27.49).** Heterodont means that different teeth are specialized for different jobs; diphyodont means that there are two generations of teeth (milk or deciduous teeth and adult teeth). But some mammals have no teeth, and others lay eggs. The secondary palate allows mammals to breathe while sucking, without releasing hold on the nipple—an essential part of nursing.

Homeothermy means that mammals typically maintain an elevated and stable body temperature so that they can be active under different environmental conditions. They can do this because of their metabolic rates and insulation. Heterodont teeth make mammals more efficient at mechanically dealing with their food (chewing), reducing the lag between the time food is consumed and when the energy in it is available to the consumer. Heterodont teeth are correlated with improved jaw articulation, in mammals between the dentary (lower jaw) and squamosal (bone on the skull). The diaphragm means that mammals are reasonably efficient at breathing, and the circulatory system with a four-chambered heart makes them efficient at internal circulation of resources or collection of wastes. Milk is a rich food source, and by feeding it to their young, female mammals

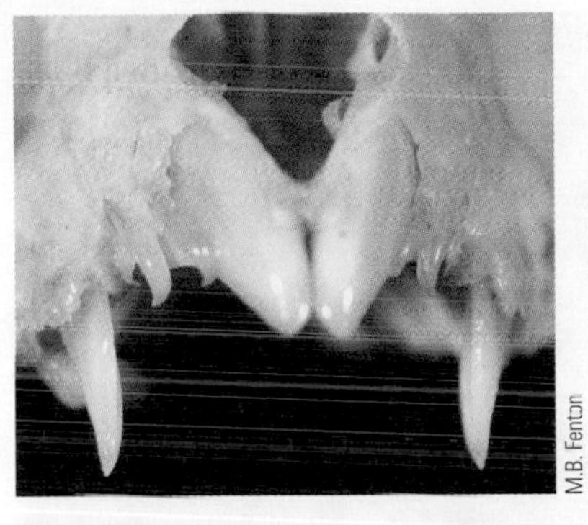

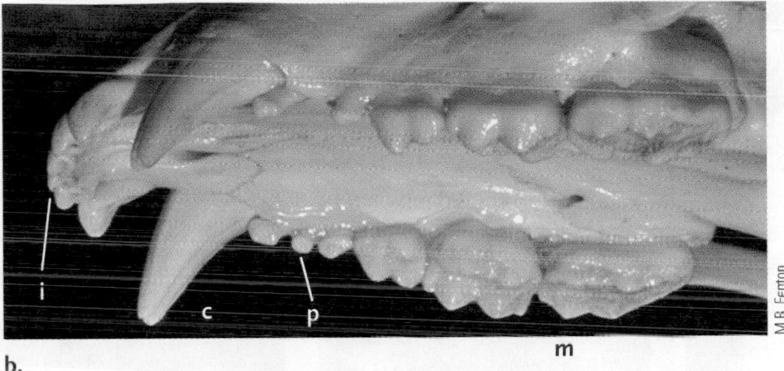

a. b.

Figure 27.49
Mammal teeth. In most mammals, the teeth are diphyodont, meaning that milk (deciduous) teeth are replaced by permanent teeth. The skull of a vampire bat (*Desmodus rotundus*) clearly shows four deciduous teeth, as well as permanent teeth **(a)**. The teeth of mammals are also heterodont **(b)**, meaning that different teeth are specialized to do different jobs. In this bear (*Ursus americana*), incisors (i), a canine (c), premolars (p), and molars (m) are obvious.

provide the best opportunity for growth and development. The cortex of the brain is central to information processing and learning. Mammals' brains are another key to their evolutionary success.

27.13a The Mammalian Radiation: Variation on Mammals

The egg-laying Prototheria (*proto* = first; *theri* = wild beast), also called Monotremata, and the live-bearing Theria are the two groups of living mammals. Among the Theria, the Metatheria (*meta* = between), also called marsupials, and the Eutheria (*eu* = good), or placentals, differ in their reproductive adaptations.

Monotremata. The monotremes (*mono* = one; *trema* = perforation) are represented by three living species that occur only in the Australian region. Females lay leathery-shelled eggs **(Figure 27.50),** and newly hatched young lap up milk secreted by modified sweat glands (mammary glands) on the mother's belly. The duck-billed platypus (*Ornithorhynchus anatinus*) lives in burrows along riverbanks and feeds on aquatic invertebrates. The two species of echidnas or spiny anteaters (*Tachyglossus aculeatus* and *Zaglossus bruijnii*) feed on ants or termites.

Marsupialia. Represented by 240 species, marsupials (*marsupion* = purse) (Metatheria) are characterized by short gestation periods. The young are briefly (as few as 8 to 10 days in some species and up to 30 days in others) nourished in the uterus via a placenta and are then born at an early stage of development. Newborns use their forelimbs to drag themselves from the vagina and across the mother's belly fur to her abdominal pouch, the marsupium, where they complete their development attached to a teat. Marsupials are prevalent among the native mammals of Australia and also

a. Short-nosed echidna

b. Duck-billed platypus

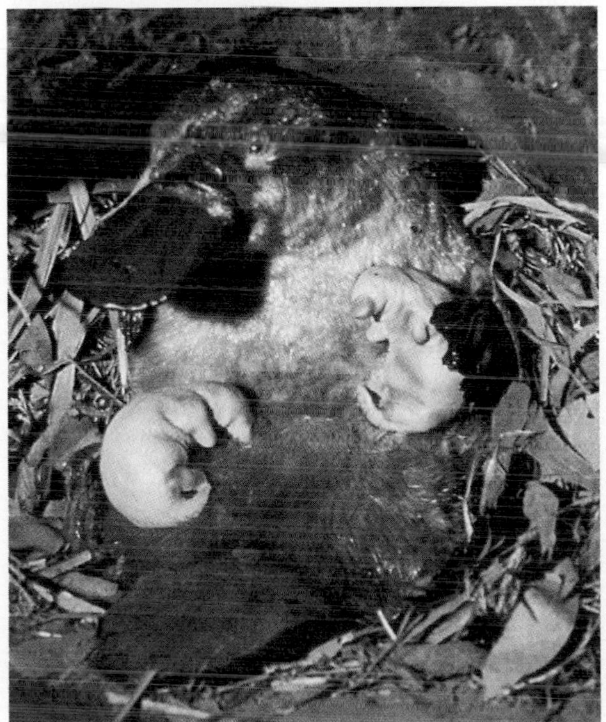

Figure 27.50
Monotremes. The short-nosed echidna (**a**, *Tachyglossus aculeatus*) is terrestrial. The duck-billed platypus (**b**, *Ornithorhynchus anatinus*) raises its young in a stream-side burrow.

Milise, T./Arco Images/Peter Arnold, Inc.

M.B. Fenton

M.B. Fenton

Figure 27.51
Marsupials. A kangaroo (*Macropus giganteus*) carries her "joey" in her pouch; a male koala (*Phascolarctos cinereus*) naps; and an opossum from Guyana (*Didelphis* species) emerges from its den after dark to feed.

are diverse in South America **(Figure 27.51).** One species, the opossum (*Didelphis virginiana*), occurs as far north as Canada. South America once had a diverse marsupial fauna, which declined after the Isthmus of Panama bridged the seaway between North and South America (see Chapter 18), allowing placental mammals to move southward.

Placental mammals (Eutheria) are represented by 4000 living species. They complete embryonic development in the mother's uterus, nourished through a **placenta** until they reach an advanced stage of development (**viviparous**). Some species, such as humans, are helpless at birth (**altricial**), but others, such as horses, are born with fur and are quickly mobile (**precocial**). Biologists divide the eutherians into about 18 orders, of which only 8 have more than 50 living species **(Figure 27.52).** Rodents (Rodentia) make up about 45% of eutherian species, and bats (Chiroptera) comprise another 22%. We belong to the primates, along with 169 other species, representing about 5% of the current mammalian diversity.

Some eutherians are obviously specialized for locomotion. Although whales and dolphins (order Cetacea) and manatees and dugongs (order Sirenia) are descended from terrestrial ancestors, they are aquatic (mainly marine) and can no longer function on land. By contrast, seals and walruses (order Carnivora) feed under water but rest and breed on land. Bats (order Chiroptera) use wings for powered flight.

Although early mammals appear to have been insectivorous, the diets of modern eutherians are diverse. Odd-toed ungulates (*ungula* = hoof) such as horses and rhinoceroses (order Perissodactyla), even-toed ungulates such as cows and camels (order Artiodactyla), and rabbits and hares (order Lagomorpha) all eat vegetation. Some of the vegetarians use fermentation to digest cellulose (see Chapter 41). Carnivores (order Carnivora) usually consume other animals, but some, such as the giant panda (*Ailuropoda melanoluca*), are vegetarians. Most bats eat insects, but some feed on flowers, fruit, or nectar, and some, the vampires, consume blood. Many whales and dolphins prey on fishes and other animals, but some eat plankton. Some groups, including rodents and primates, feed opportunistically on both plant and animal matter. Ants and termites are the preferred food of a variety of mammals, both prototherian and therian.

Study Break

1. How do monotremes differ from marsupials and placentals?
2. How do marsupials and placentals differ?
3. Are all mammals vivipārious?

27.14 Evolutionary Convergence and Mammalian Diversity: Tails to Teeth

In the discussion on the Mesozoic beaver (see Figures 19.6 and 19.7), we learned that a dorsoventrally flattened tail occurred in a Mesozoic mammal and today occurs in a monotreme (duck-billed platypus) and in beavers (*Castor* species). Evolutionary convergences in design features such as these are common in mammals. Other good examples are the development of protective spines (quills) from hairs. These occur in spiny anteaters (monotremes), porcupines (rodents), and hedgehogs and tenrecs (insectivores).

Thao Allofs/Photonica/Getty Images

a. The capybara (Rodentia, *Hydrochoerus hydrochaeris*), the largest rodent, feeds on vegetation in South American wetlands.

J. Scott Altenbach, University of New Mexico

b. Most bats, like the Yuma Myotis (Chiroptera, *Myotis yumanensis*), are nocturnal predators on insects.

Leonard Lee Rue III/FPG/Getty Images

c. Walruses (Carnivora, *Obodenus rosmarus*) feed primarily on marine invertebrates in frigid arctic waters.

Martin Harvey/Peter Arnold

d. The black rhinoceros (Perissodactyla, *Diceros bicornis*) feeds on grass in sub-Saharan Africa.

David Parker/SPL/Photo Researchers, Inc.

e. Arabian camels (Artiodactyla, *Camelus dromedarius*) use enlarged foot pads to cross hot desert sands.

Figure 27.52
Eutherian diversity.

Another striking example of convergence among mammals is provided by the teeth and lumbar vertebrae of the Mesozoic *Fruitafossor windscheffeli* **(Figure 27.53)** and some living edentates (armadillos and sloths). Like sloths and armadillos, *Fruitafossor* had round molars with open roots **(Figure 27.54, p. 654).** Also like sloths and armadillos, *Fruitafossor* had processes in its lumbar vertebrae known only from living edentates. An analysis of the morphological features of *Fruitafosser* was used with other data to establish its phylogenetic relationships with other mammals **(Figure 27.55, p. 654).** Although the teeth and vertebral structures converge between *Fruitafossor* and the edentates, *Fruitafossor* is not closely related to any living mammals. We do not even know if *Fruitafossor* had other features of mammals such as mammary glands, a diaphragm, and vivipary. But *Fruitafossor*'s bones, particularly its jaw joints and occipital condyles, make it a mammal.

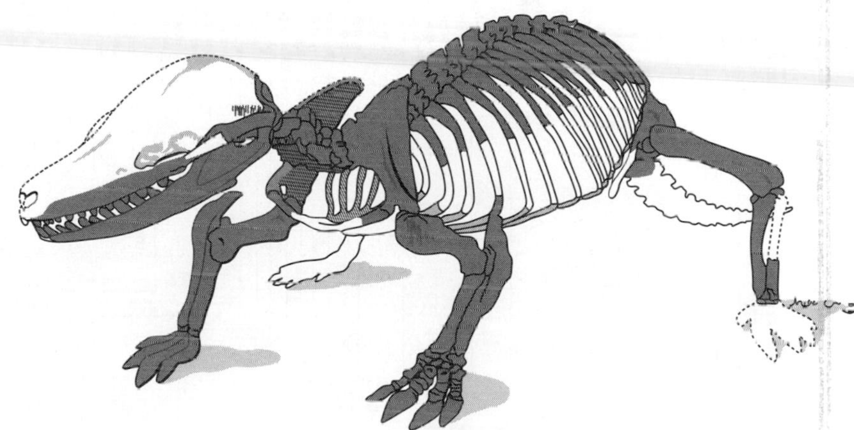

Figure 27.53
Fruitafossor, a mammal of the mid-Jurassic. Stippled bones are known as fossils, other bones presumed.

Figure 27.54
Convergences in Mammals. Round teeth with open roots are well known from edentate mammals like armadillos **(c),** and tubulidentates, the aardvark (see Figure 27.59a). They also appear in *Fruitafossor* **(a, b).**

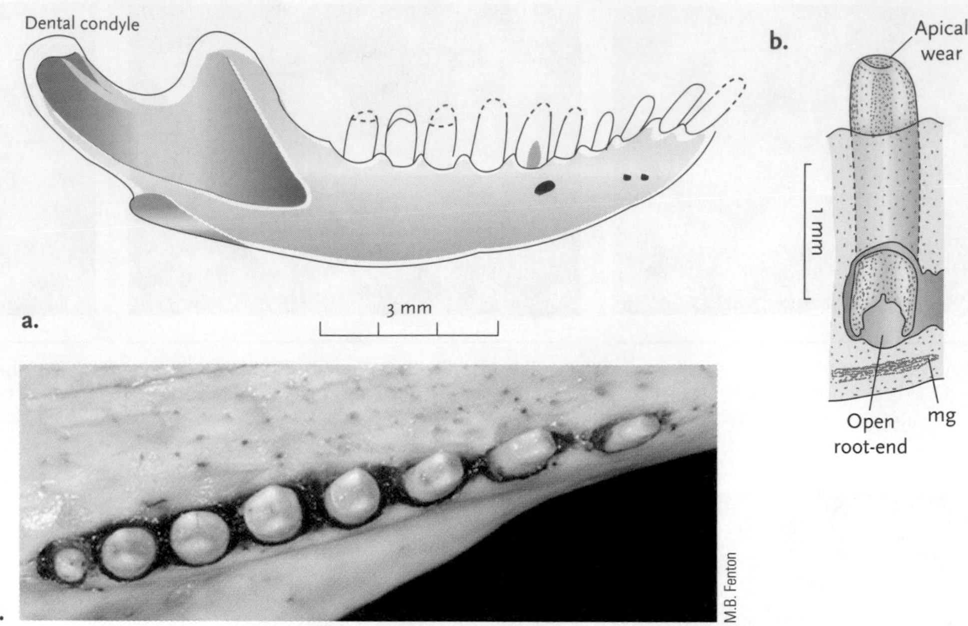

27.14a Mammalian Teeth: Diversity of Form and Function

As in other vertebrates, mammals' teeth provide a good indication of diet. Some molars (cheek teeth) with "W"-shaped cusps cut and crush food **(Figure 27.56a, b, c),** whereas others mainly crush **(Figure 27.56d, e).** Grinding teeth have appeared in a wide range of forms in mammals **(Figure 27.57)** and show considerable variation in the details of their design.

Animals such as the walrus **(Figure 27. 58a)** have tusks for digging and small flat molars for crushing the shells of bivalves (compare with Figures 27.19a and 27.21b). The molars of *Desmostylus* have an artistic circular pattern (see Figure 3.22c). These Miocene mammals were thought to have resembled Sirenia, the dugongs and manatees. Later discoveries

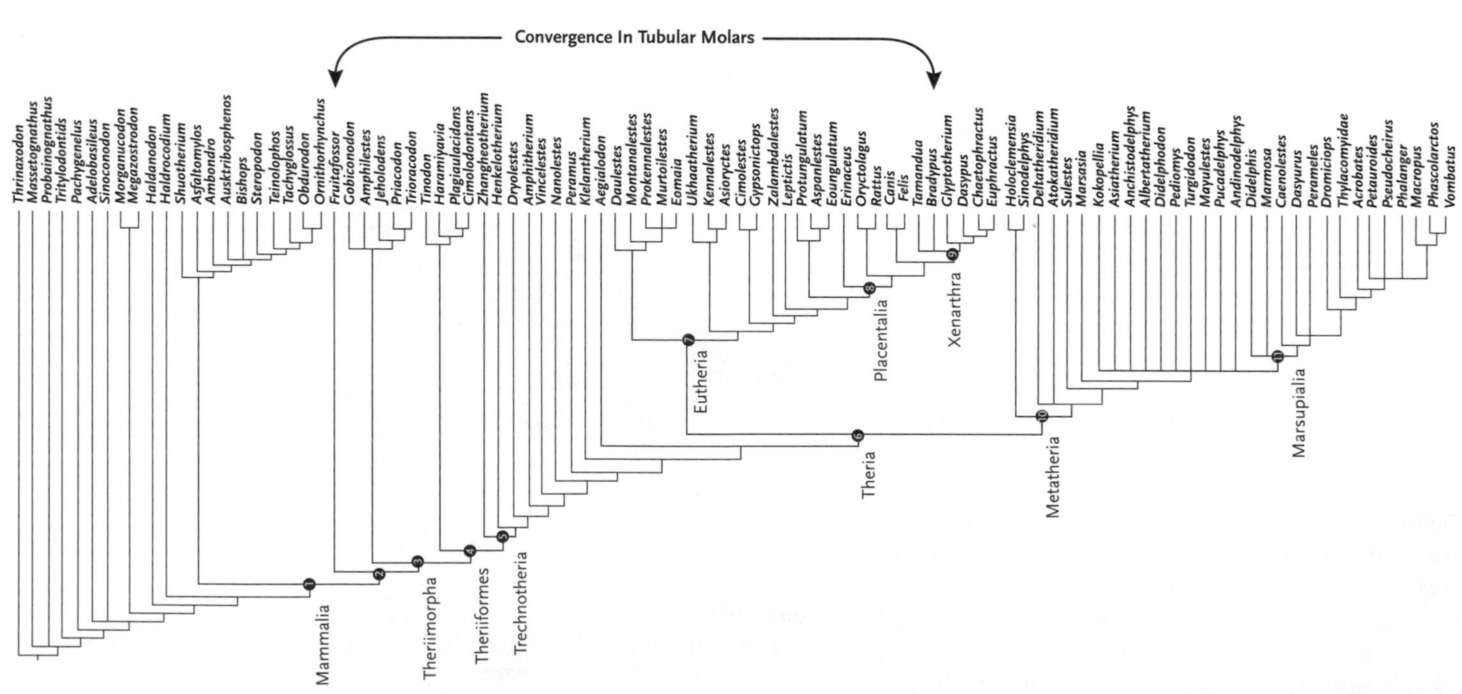

Figure 27.55
***Fruitafossor* as a mammal.** In a phylogeny of mammals based on morphological characters, this species is not a monotreme and does not appear to be closely related to any living mammals.

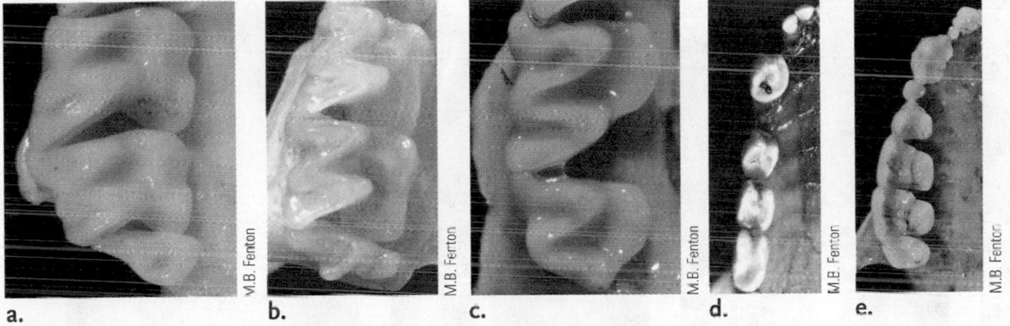

Figure 27.56
Teeth for cutting and crushing. The molar teeth of insectivores (shrews, moles, many bats) are "W" shaped, so they cut and crush at the same time. Bats that eat fruit have molars more specialized for crushing. Here *Suncus* **(a)** is a shrew, *Condylura* **(b)** a mole, and *Taphozous* **(c)** an insectivorous bat. *Pteropus* **(d)** and *Brachyphylla* **(e)** are fruit eating bats.

revealed that they had massive limbs and, in body form, looked more like modern hippos. They presumably used their teeth for crushing aquatic vegetation.

Mammals that eat mainly ants and termites (see **Figure 27.59, p. 656**) often lack teeth entirely. This adaptive zone has been exploited by mammals across the tropics. The South American examples (*Dasypus* and *Myrmecophaga*, order Edentata) are different evolutionary lines (see Figure 27.48) from the African ones (*Orycteropus*, order Tubulidantata, and *Manis*, order Pholidota). Australia has both monotreme and marsupial anteaters. The most astonishing anteater is the aardwolf, a variation on a hyena **(Figure 27.60, p. 656)**; both of these species belong to the order Carnivora.

Whereas reptiles, amphibians, fish, and sharks can replace teeth many times (e.g., Figure 27.19), mammals replace them only once. Teeth wear with age **(Figure 27.61a and b, p. 656)**. When the teeth are worn out, the animal can no longer feed

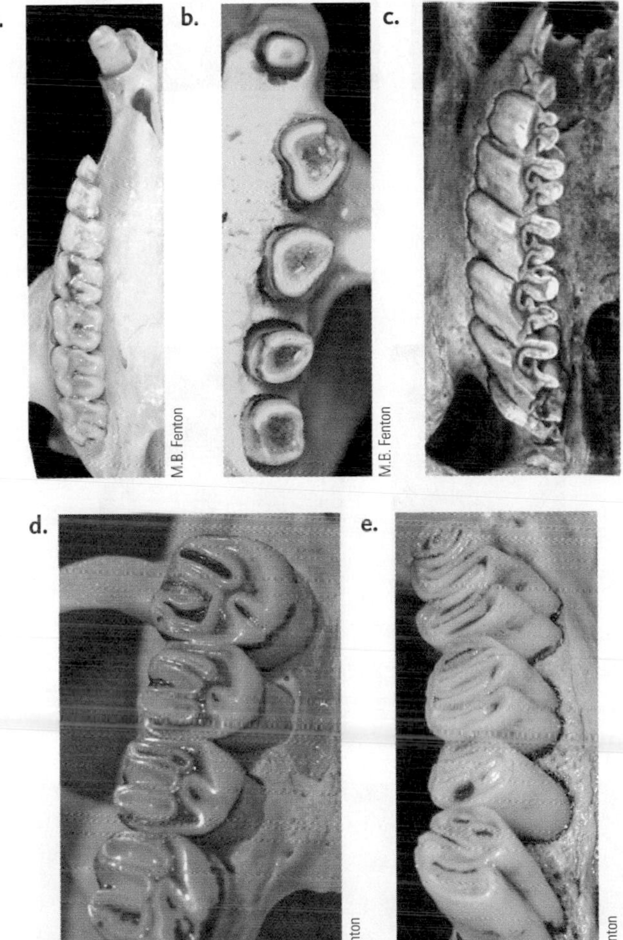

Figure 27.57
Molar teeth for crushing plant material. This selection of herbivores includes a hyrax (**a**, *Heterohyrax brucei* from Africa), a three-toed sloth (**b**, *Bradypus tridactylus* from South America), a black rhino (**c**, *Diceros bicornis* from Africa), a porcupine (**d**, *Erethizon dorsatum* from North America), and a paca (**e**, *Cuniculus paca* from South America). The hyrax belongs to the order Hyracoidea, the sloth to the order Edentata, the rhino to the order Persissodactyla, and the porcupine and the paca tothe order Rodentia.

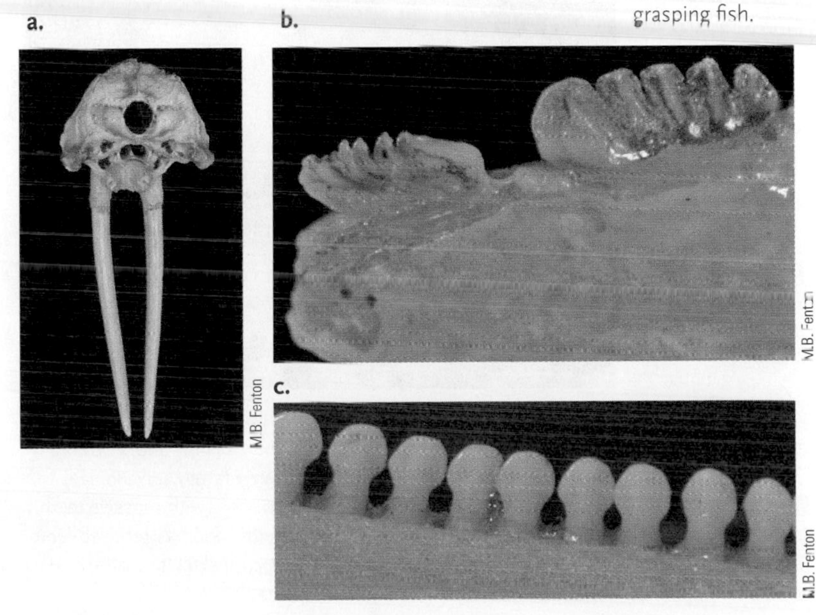

Figure 27.58
Teeth for different jobs. Whereas walrus (**a**, *Odobenus rosmarus*) use tusks for digging clams, which they crush with their molars, flying lemurs (**b**, *Cynocephalus*) use comblike lower incisor teeth to comb their fur, and dolphins (**c**, *Tursiops*) have rows of similar teeth (homodont) for grasping fish.

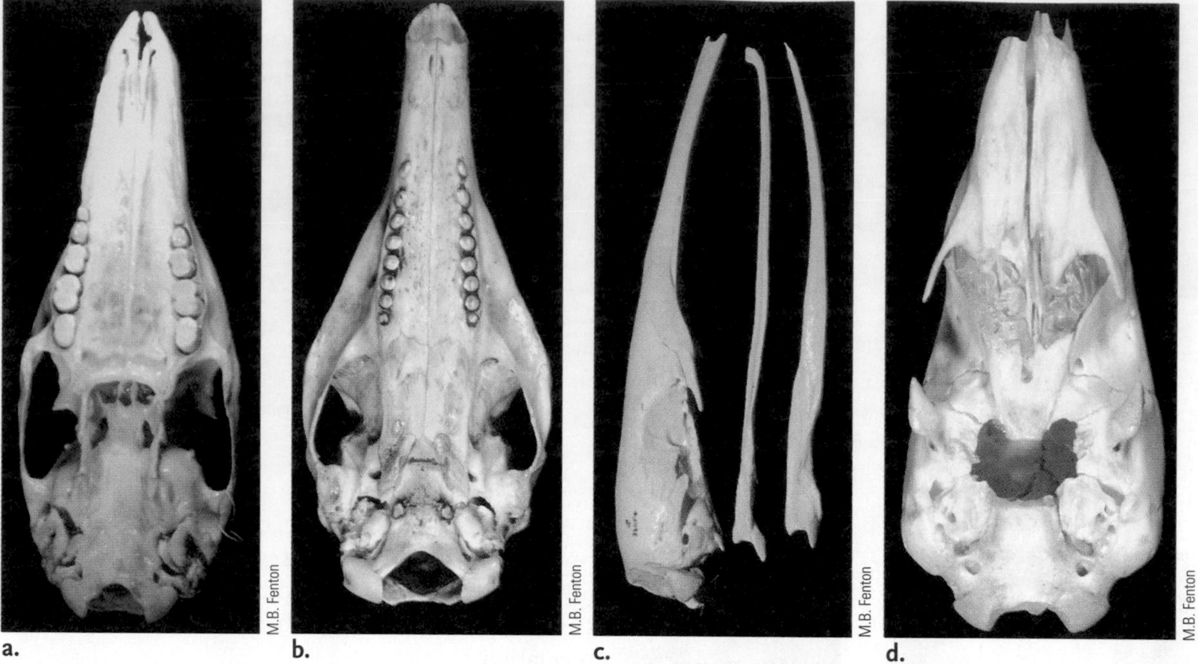

Figure 27.59
Ant- and termite-eating mammals, some with and some without teeth. The aardvark (**a,** *Orycteropus afer*) is from Africa and the armadillo (**b,** *Dasypus*) and giant anteater (**c,** *Myrmecophaga*) are from South America. Scaly anteaters (*Manis* species) occur from Africa to southeast Asia. The aardvark belongs to the order Tubulidentata, the armadillo and the giant anteater to the order Edentata, and the scaly anteater to the order Pholidota.

itself properly and dies. Elephants deal with this problem by having only four active molars in the jaw at any one time. The new molar grows in from the back **(Figure 27.61c)**, replacing the worn one. In rodents and some other mammals (and also in hydrasaur dinosaurs), molar (and for rodents and lagomorphs incisor) teeth grow continuously. Here the teeth are curved so that pressure during biting

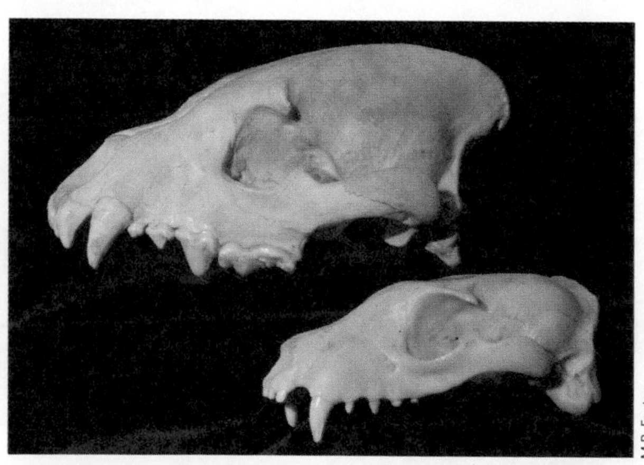

Figure 27.60
Divergence! Spotted hyena (top, *Crocuta crocuta*) and aardwolf (bottom, *Proteles capensis*) are in the same family (Hyaenidae). The spotted hyena is a carnivorous scavenger with massive teeth. The aardwolf eats mainly ants and termites and has reduced teeth (and a differently shaped skull). The *Crocuta* skull is about 30 cm long. Both belong to the order Carnivora.

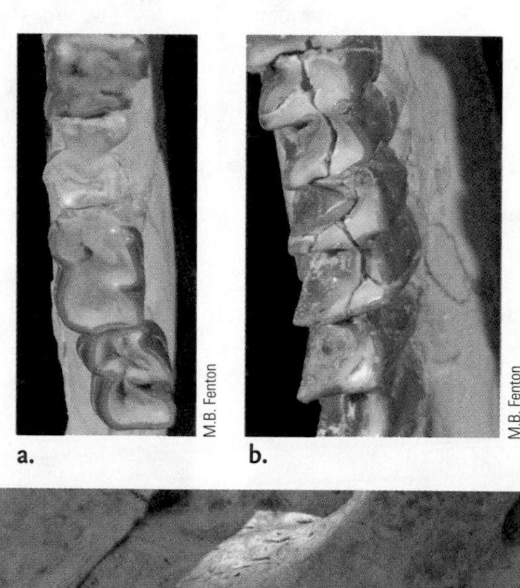

Figure 27.61
Tooth wear. The teeth of a fossil rhino. First, the worn teeth of an old *Hyracodon nebraskensis* are compared with those of a young one (**a** and **b**, respectively). Elephants (**c**, *Loxodonta africana*) have four functional molars in the mouth at any one time (one in each jaw quadrant). New molars push into the tooth row from the back.

Molecule Behind Biology

Geckel®

Geckos **(Figure 1)** can cling to vertical and even inverted smooth surfaces such as window glass. They do this using specialized keratinous setae (fine hairs) on their feet. There are spatulate extensions at the end of each seta. The other element in the adhesive ability of geckos is an adhesive.

Figure 1
Geckos, such as this one, can walk on (stick to) glass.

But the remarkable feature of geckos is that the system allows rapid detachment of the foot. As many people have learned using Crazy Glue® and its equivalents, getting stuck to something is easy; getting unstuck is a different story.

As remarkable as geckos, some mussels (see Chapter 26) secrete a specialized adhesive with a high concentraton of catecholic amino acid 3,4-dihydroxy-l-phenlalanine (DOPA). DOPA allows the mussels to cling firmly to wet surfaces. In contrast, the adhesive ability of geckos is diminished by full immersion in water.

Geckel® is a new hybrid adhesive **(Figure 2)** combining the adhesive features of those used by geckos and mussels. Geckel® is a thin layer of a synthetic polymer that retains its adhesive properties in dry and wet environments for more than 1000 contact cycles.

Work with geckos (probably ***Rhoptropus biporosus***) from the Namib desert sheds light on the evolutionary background of their extraordinary clinging power. These small geckos weigh about 2 g and show great mobility on the variety of substrates they encounter—rough, undulant, and unpredictable, often providing few points of adhesion. The adhesive pads under the geckos' toes allow them to cling to the full spectrum of surfaces, and their ability to stick to glass is coincidental.

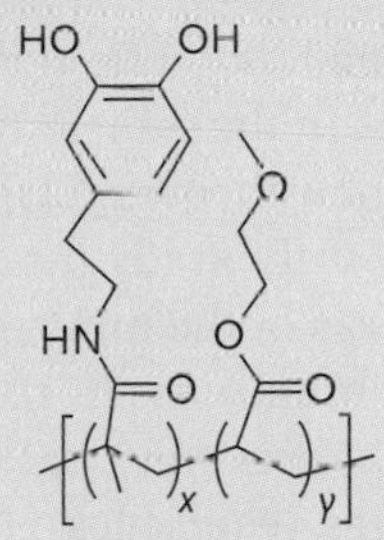

p(DMA-MEA)

Figure 2
Geckel®, a fabricated adhesive that mimics those produced and used by geckos and mussels.

is not directed at the points of growth (see Figures 19.8b and 48.4).

Study Break

1. What features are found in most mammals and distinguish them from other vertebrates?
2. How is heterodont different from diphyodont?
3. Distinguish among monotremes, marsupials, and placentals.

27.15 The Evolution of Humans

Genetic analyses of living hominoid species indicate that African hominoids diverged into several lineages between 10 and 5 million years ago. One lineage, the **hominids**, includes modern humans and our bipedal ancestors. Upright posture and bipedal locomotion are adaptations that distinguish hominids from apes. Bipedal locomotion largely freed the hands from locomotor functions, allowing them to become specialized for other activities, such as tool use. Evolutionary refinements in grasping ability allow hominids to hold objects tightly with a *power grip* or manipulate them precisely with a *precision grip* **(Figure 27.62)**.

Female hominids suffer at least one consequence of being bipedal, namely the shift in the body's centre of mass during pregnancy. In humans, specialized adaptations of the axial skeleton include an increase in the number of lumbar vertebrae and the lengths of individual vertebra. There also is a marked posterior concavity of individual lumbar vertebrae (lordosis), which stabilizes the centre of mass of the upper body over the hips. Females have a derived curvature of the

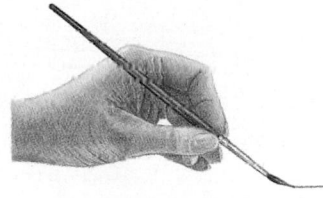

a. Power grip

b. Precision grip

Figure 27.62
Power grip versus precision grip. Hominids grasp objects in two distinct ways. The power grip **(a)** allows us to grasp an object firmly, whereas the precision grip **(b)** allows us to manipulate objects by fine movements.

lumbar area and reinforcement of those vertebrae to compensate for the additional load associated with pregnancy. Evidence from *Australopithecus* fossils suggests that these adaptations to bipedalism preceded the evolution of species in the genus *Homo*.

In 2007, S.K.S. Thorpe, R.L. Holder, and R.H. Crompton proposed that bipedalism arose in an arboreal setting. Specifically, they asserted that hand-assisted bipedalism allowed the ancestors of humans and great apes to move on flexible supports (branches) that otherwise would be too small. Thorpe et al. compared human and orangutan (*Pongo abelii*) locomotion and found that organutans walking on flexible branches increase knee and hip extension, just like humans do when running on a springy track. In a bipedal gait, humans and orangutans do not flex the hind limbs in the same way as gorillas and chimps do.

This new theory explains the morphological adaptations to orthogrady (upright posture), such as lateral stiffness of the lumbar spine; both occur in more advanced hominids. In six-million-year-old fossils of *Orrorin tugensis*, the head of the femur suggests that this species resembles *Homo* and *Australopithecus*. Although *O. tugensis* is not more closely related to *Homo* than to *Australopithecus* **(Figure 27.63),** its gait would have been more like that of *Australopithecus*.

Paleontologists have uncovered fossil remains of numerous hominids that lived in East Africa and South Africa from roughly 6 million to 1 million years ago (see Figure 27.63). In 2000, researchers found 13 fossils of *O. tugenensis* ("first man" in a local African language), a species that lived about 6 million years ago in East African forests. The best-studied early hominid fossils, the remains of 50 individuals discovered in the East African Rift Valley, date from about 5 million years ago. Named *Ardipithecus ramidus*, these hominids stood 120 cm tall and had apelike teeth. Other *Ardipithecus* fossils, recently discovered at a different site, appear to be much older (5.8 million years) and show evidence of bipedal locomotion.

Hominid fossils from 4.2 to 1.2 million years ago are known from many sites in East, Central, and South Africa. They are currently assigned to the genera *Australopithecus* (*australo* = southern; *pithecus* = ape) and *Paranthropus* (*para* = beside; *anthropus* = man). With their large faces, protruding jaws, and small skulls and brains, most of these hominids had an apelike appearance. *Australopithecus anamensis*, which lived in East Africa around 4 million years ago, is the oldest known species. It had thick enamel on its teeth, a derived hominid characteristic. A fossilized leg bone suggests that it was bipedal.

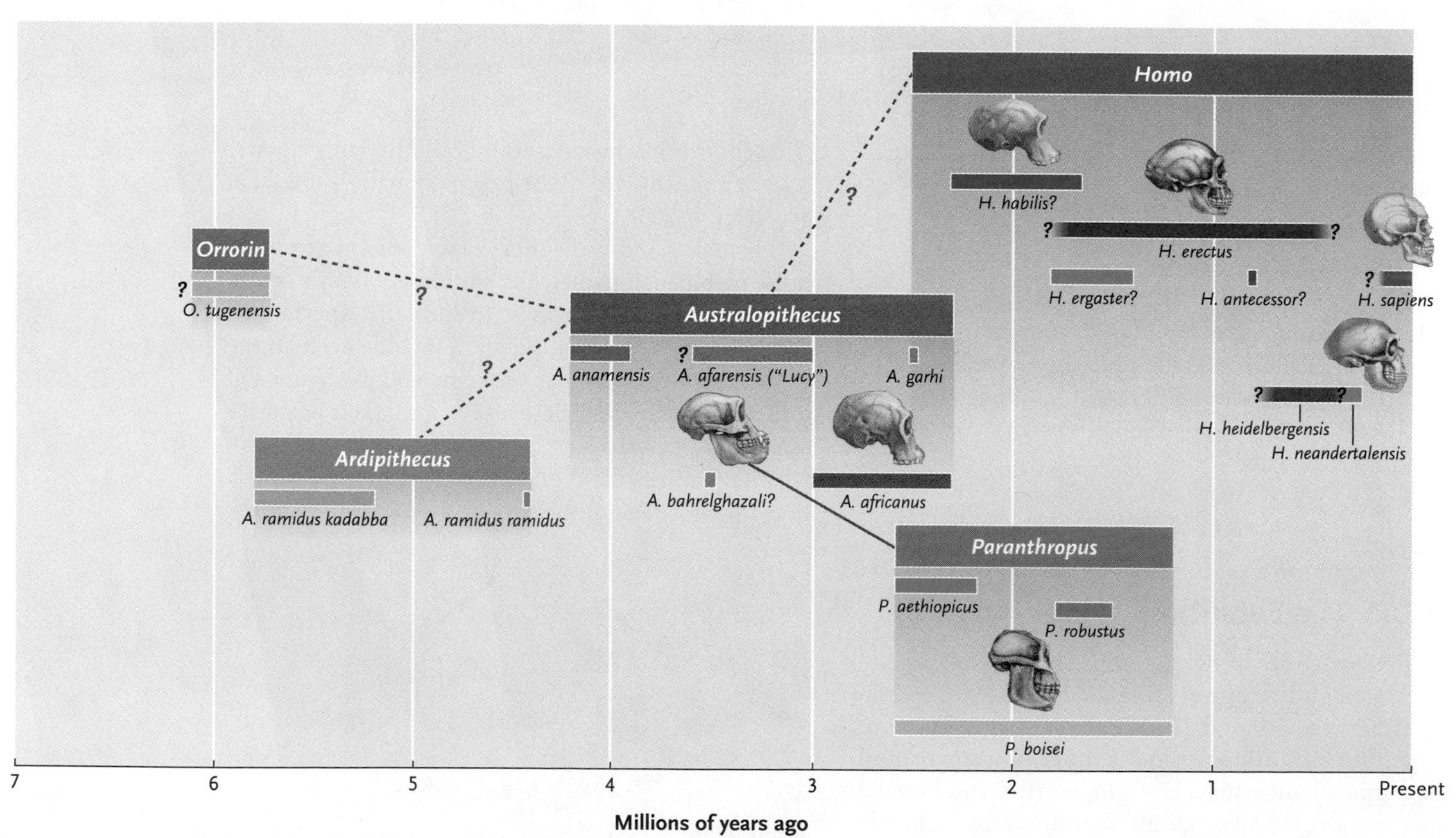

Figure 27.63
Hominid time line. Several species of hominids lived simultaneously at sites in eastern and southern Africa. The time line for each species reflects the ages of known fossils. Numerous question marks indicate uncertainty about classification and/or ages of fossils. Some skulls shown here are reconstructions from fragments.

Specimens of more than 60 individual *Australopithecus afarensis* have been found in northern Ethiopia, including about 40% of a female's skeleton, named "Lucy" by its discoverers (after the Beatles' song "Lucy in the Sky with Diamonds"; **Figure 27.64**). *A. afarensis* lived 3.5 to 3 million years ago, but it retained several ancestral characteristics. It had moderately large and pointed canine teeth and a relatively small brain. Males and females were 150 cm and 120 cm tall, respectively. Skeletal analyses suggest that Lucy was fully bipedal, a conclusion supported by fossilized footprints preserved in a layer of volcanic ash.

Other species of *Australopithecus* and *Paranthropus* lived in East Africa or South Africa between 3.7 and 1 million years ago. Adult males ranged from 40 to 50 kg in mass and from 130 to 150 cm in height; females were smaller. Most of these species had deep jaws and large molars. Several of them had a crest of bone along the midline of the skull, providing a large surface for the attachment of jaw muscles. These anatomical features suggest that they ate hard food, such as nuts, seeds, and other vegetable products. *Australopithecus africanus*, known only from South Africa, had small jaws and teeth, indicating that it probably had a softer diet. The phylogenetic relationships of the species classified as *Australopithecus* and *Paranthropus*, and their exact relationships to later hominids, are not yet fully understood.

a. "Lucy"

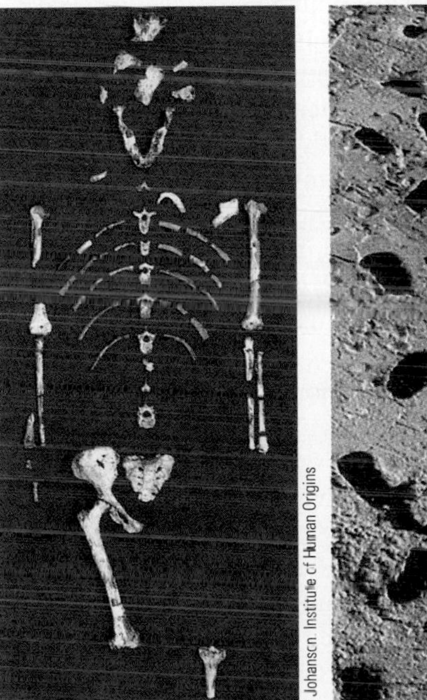

b. Australopithecine footprints

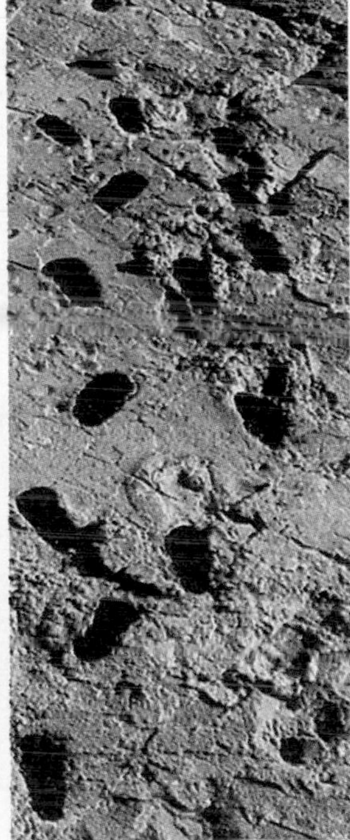

Figure 27.64
Australopithecines. "Lucy" is the most complete fossil of *Australopithecus afarensis* **(a).** Mary Leakey discovered footprints of australopithecines made in soft damp volcanic ash dating to about 3.7 million years ago. The **(b)** footprints indicate that these animals were fully bipedal.

Australopithecus was likely ancestral to humans, which are classified in the genus *Homo*.

Pliocene fossils of the earliest ancestors of humans are fragmentary and widely distributed in space and time. We can describe them as belonging to *Homo habilis* (meaning "handy man"). From 2.3 to 1.7 million years ago, *H. habilis* occupied the woodlands and savannas of eastern and southern Africa, sharing these habitats with various species of *Paranthropus*. The two genera are easy to distinguish because the brains of *H. habilis* were at least 20% larger, and they had larger incisors and smaller molars than their hominid cousins. They ate hard-shelled nuts and seeds, as well as soft fruits, tubers, leaves, and insects. They may also have hunted small prey or scavenged carcasses left by larger predators.

Researchers have found numerous tools dating to the time of *H. habilis* but are not sure which species made them. Many of the hominid species of that time probably cracked marrowbones with rocks or scraped flesh from bones with sharp stones. Paleoanthropologist Louis Leakey was the first to discover evidence of tool *making* at East Africa's Olduvai Gorge, which cuts through a great sequence of sedimentary rock layers. The oldest tools at this site are crudely chipped pebbles probably manufactured by *H. habilis*. However, humans are not the only animals to use tools (see Chapter 40).

Early in the Pleistocene, about 1.8 million years ago, a new species of humans, *Homo erectus* ("upright man"), appeared in East Africa, although several species may be involved. One nearly complete skeleton suggests that *H. erectus* was taller than its ancestors and had a much larger brain, a thicker skull, and protruding brow ridges.

H. erectus made fairly sophisticated tools, including the hand axe **(Figure 27.65b)** used to cut food

a. *Homo erectus*

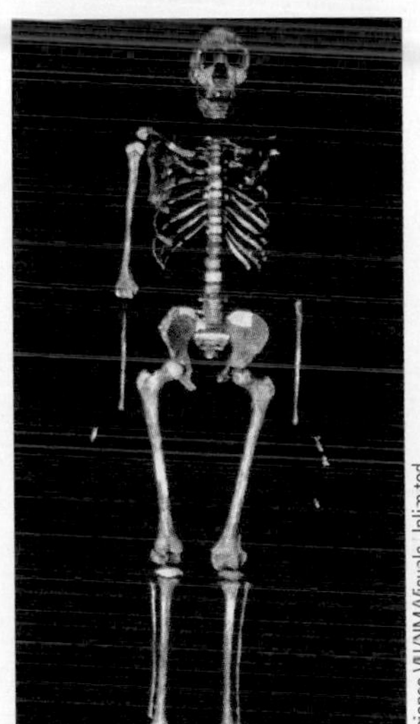

b. Hand axe

Figure 27.65
Homo erectus. A nearly complete skeleton from Kenya **(a).** Hand tools **(b)** are often found at sites used by *H. erectus*.

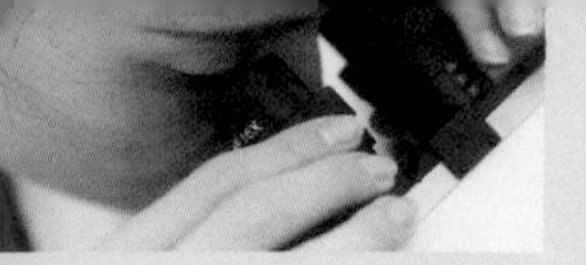

People Behind Biology
Norman John (Jack) Berrill (1903–1996)

Growing up on the edge of a city gave Jack Berrill ready access to the fauna and flora of the surrounding countryside, the woods, the streams, the ponds. As a first year premedical student at the University of Bristol, he was offered the chance to join a zoological expedition to the Indian Ocean, a life-changing experience that drew him into zoology. In 1929, he completed his Ph.D. (University College, London, England) and became an assistant professor of zoology at McGill University in Montreal, Quebec, where he remained until his retirement.

Jack Berrill is distinguished for his research on development, morphogenesis, and regeneration in the Tunicata (phylum Urochordata). He chose these animals for study because they were transparent, allowing him to see what was going on inside them with minimum disturbance. His contribution to our knowledge of tunicates was profound and continues to strongly influence the field.

In addition to his research, Jack was also an innovative teacher. He used 16-mm film (silent and in black and white) to illustrate some of his lectures. He provided commentary as he showed the film, stopping here and there, backing up, and then continuing. One can only imagine what he could have done with videos and PowerPoint.

But Jack's contributions did not stop there. He also wrote 10 books that popularized zoology, such as *The Living Tide* (1951), *Inherit the Earth* (1966), and *Animals in Action* (1972).

Jack Berrill influenced the lives of others through his research. His published findings opened new avenues of thought. He also influenced people through his teaching and nontechnical publications.

and other materials, to scrape meat from bones, and to dig for roots. *H. erectus* probably ate both plants and animals and may have hunted and scavenged animal prey. Archaeological data point to their use of fire to process food and to keep warm. Near Lake Turkana in Kenya, fossils identified as *Homo* and dating from 1.45 to 1.55 million years ago were described in 2007. These data suggest that *H. erectus* and *H. habilis* lived together in the same habitats for a considerable time, much as chimps and gorillas do today. Adult male *H. erectus* were much larger than adult females, suggesting a polygynous lifestyle, one male with several females (see Chapter 40).

About 1.5 million years ago, the pressure of growing populations apparently forced groups of *H. erectus* out of Africa. They dispersed northward from East Africa into both northwestern Africa and Eurasia. Some moved eastward through Asia as far as the island of Java. Recent discoveries in Spain indicate that *H. erectus* also occupied parts of Western Europe.

Judging from its geographic distribution, *H. erectus* was successful in many environments. It produced several descendant species, of which modern humans (*H. sapiens*, meaning "wise man") are the only survivors. Extinct descendants of *H. erectus*, archaic humans, first appeared at least 400 000 years ago. They generally had larger brains, rounder skulls, and smaller molars than *H. erectus*.

Neanderthals (*Homo neanderthalensis*), which lived in Europe and western Asia from 150 000 to 28 000 years ago, are the best-known archaic humans. Compared with modern humans, they had a heavier build, pronounced brow ridges, and slightly larger brains. Neanderthals were culturally and technologically sophisticated. They made complex tools, including wooden spears, stone axes, and flint scrapers and knives. At some sites, they built shelters of stones, branches, and animal hides, and they routinely used fire. They were successful hunters and probably ate nuts, berries, fishes, and bird eggs. Some groups buried their dead, and they may have had rudimentary speech.

Researchers once classified Neanderthals as a subspecies of *H. sapiens*, but most now believe that they were a separate species. In 1997, two teams of researchers independently analyzed short segments of mitochondrial DNA (mtDNA) extracted from the fossilized arm bone of a Neanderthal. Unlike nuclear DNA, which individuals inherit from both parents, only mothers pass mtDNA to offspring. It does not undergo genetic recombination (see Chapter 10), and it has a high mutation rate, making it useful for phylogenetic analyses. If mutation rates in mtDNA are fairly constant, this molecule can serve as a molecular clock (see Chapter 19). Comparing the Neanderthal sequence with mtDNA from 986 living humans revealed three times more differences between the Neanderthals and modern humans than between pairs of modern humans in their sample. These results suggest that Neanderthals and modern humans are different species that diverged from a common ancestor 690 000 to 550 000 years ago, well before modern humans appeared.

Modern humans (*H. sapiens*) differ from Neanderthals and other archaic humans in having a slighter build, less protruding brow ridges, and a more prominent chin. The earliest fossils of modern humans found in Africa and Asia are 150 000 years old; those from the Middle East are 100 000 years old. Fossils from about 20 000 years ago are known from

Western Europe, the most famous being those of the Cro-Magnon deposits in southern France. The widespread appearance of modern humans roughly coincided with the demise of Neanderthals in Western Europe and the Middle East 40 000 to 28 000 years ago. Although the two species apparently coexisted in some regions for thousands of years, we have little concrete evidence that they interacted, let alone interbred.

But when and where did modern humans first arise? Researchers use fossils and genetic data from contemporary human populations to address two competing hypotheses about this question.

The early descendants, archaic humans, left Africa and established populations in the Middle East, Asia, and Europe. Some time later, 200 000 to 100 000 years ago, *H. sapiens* arose in Africa. These modern humans also migrated into Europe and Asia and, through competition, eventually drove archaic humans to extinction. Thus, the African Emergence Hypothesis suggests that all modern humans are descended from a fairly recent African ancestor.

According to the Multiregional Hypothesis, populations of *H. erectus* and archaic humans had spread through much of Europe and Asia by 0.5 million years ago. Modern humans then evolved from archaic humans in many regions simultaneously. Although these geographically separated populations may have experienced some evolutionary differentiation (see Chapter 19), gene flow between them prevented reproductive isolation and maintained them as a single but variable species, *H. sapiens*.

Paleontological data do not clearly support either hypothesis, but in 2008, genetic data **(Figure 27.66)** generally support the African Emergence Hypothesis. Some scientists argue that human remains with a mixture of archaic and modern characteristics confirm the Multiregional Hypothesis. In late 1998, researchers in Portugal discovered a fossilized child that had been

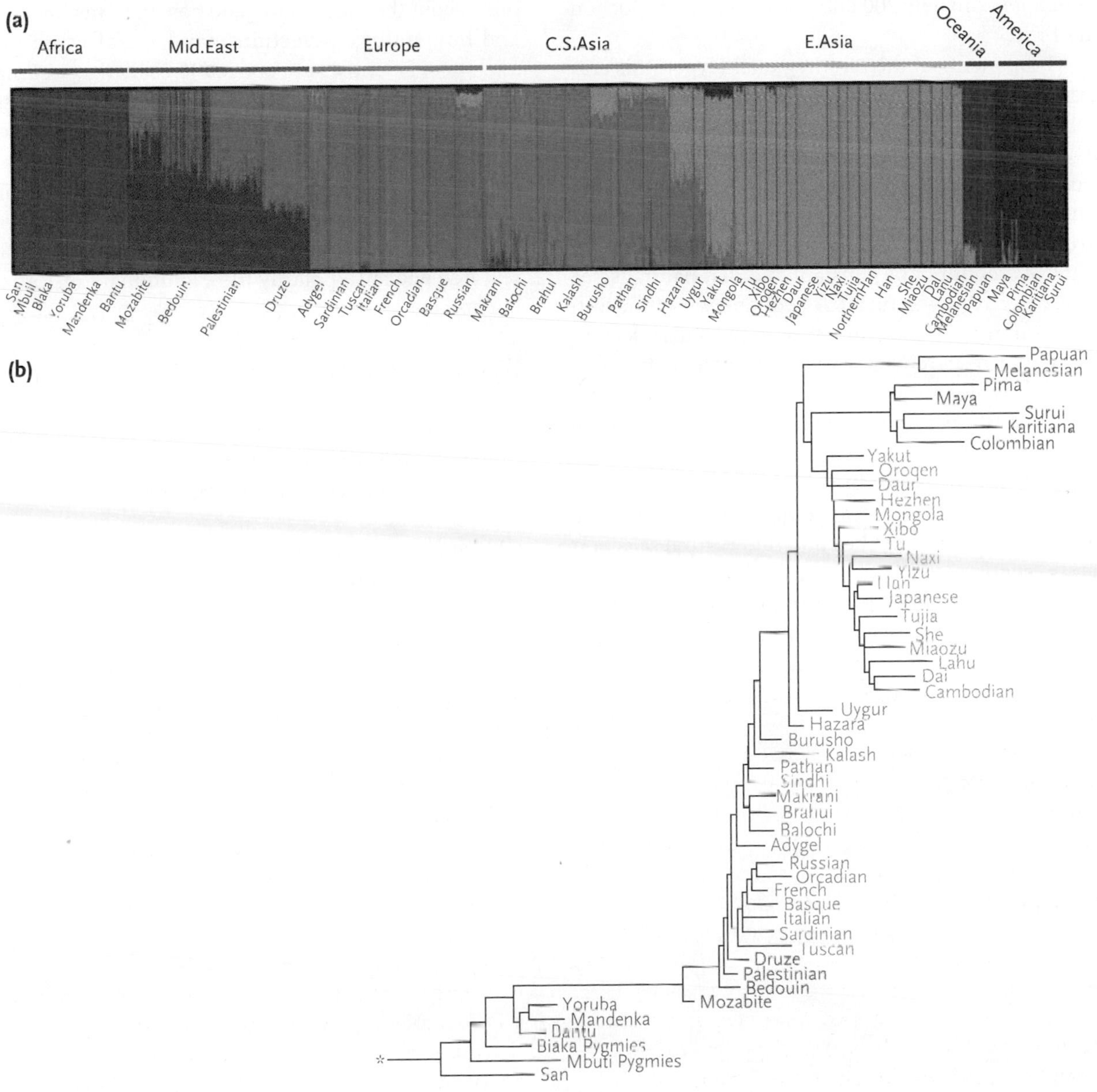

Figure 27.66
Out of Africa. Genetic data from 650 000 common single-nucleotide polymorphism loci from 928 humans were used to construct an individual ancestry and population dendogram. This maximum likelihood tree of 51 populations shows a single origin in sub-Saharan Africa and a subsequent radiation across Asia to the New World and Polynesia.

buried 24 000 years ago, when only modern humans were thought to have occupied Europe. This fossil shows a surprising mix of Neanderthal and modern human traits, possibly indicating that the two groups interbred. On the other hand, recent finds in the Middle East indicate that Neanderthals and modern humans coexisted without interbreeding for 50 000 years.

Scientists use DNA sequences from modern humans to evaluate the two hypotheses. In 1987, Rebecca Cann and colleagues published an analysis of mtDNA sequences from more than 100 ethnically diverse humans on four continents. They found that contemporary African populations contain the greatest variation in mtDNA. One explanation for this observation is that neutral mutations have been accumulating in African populations longer than in others, marking the African populations as the oldest on Earth. They also found that all human populations contain at least one mtDNA sequence of African origin, suggesting an African ancestry for all modern humans. Cann and her colleagues named the ancestral population, which lived approximately 200 000 years ago, the "mitochondrial Eve."

Proponents of the Multiregional Hypothesis criticized the statistical techniques used by Cann and her colleagues. Some also noted that if ancient populations in Africa were larger than those in other parts of the world, population size, rather than age, could account for high genetic variability (see Chapter 17). Moreover, recent research suggests that mutation rates in mtDNA might not be constant and that natural selection can influence mtDNA sequences, calling into question mtDNA's usefulness as a molecular clock.

Other researchers have examined genetic material that males inherit from their fathers. In 1995, L. Simon Whitfield and colleagues published a study of an 18 000 base-pair sequence from the Y chromosome, which does not undergo recombination with the X chromosome. Because the sequence contains no genes, it should not be subject to natural selection. Thus, sequence variations should result only from random mutations, which can serve as a molecular clock. The researchers discovered only three sequence mutations among the five subjects they examined. This was surprising because their sample included a European, a Melanesian, a native South American, and two Africans. By contrast, a chimpanzee exhibited 207 differences from the human version of the sequence. Using a sophisticated statistical analysis, the Whitfield team calculated that the common ancestor of these diverse humans, dubbed the "African Adam," lived between 37 000 and 49 000 years ago. The limited genetic diversity and relatively recent origin of a common ancestor clearly support the African Emergence Hypothesis. Follow-up studies on the Y chromosomes of thousands of men from Africa, Europe, Asia, Australia, and the Americas have confirmed that all modern humans are the descendants of a single migration out of Africa.

Some controversies about human evolution arise because researchers who use genetic data must make assumptions about the sizes and geographic ranges of ancient populations. They also must make assumptions about the amount of gene flow that was involved and how natural selection may have affected our ancestors. Scientists are obliged to challenge assumptions and conclusions arising from statistical analyses. Intellectual disputes are routine in science, and they challenge researchers to refine their hypotheses and to test them in new ways. Questions about the details of human origins are at the centre of one of the liveliest debates in evolutionary biology today; additional research will surely clarify the evolutionary history of our species.

Study Break

1. What key adaptations distinguish humans from apes? How did they arise?
2. What features distinguish *H. erectus* from its ancestors?
3. Describe Neanderthals and compare them with modern humans.

Unanswered Questions

Should birds be considered reptiles, or do they merit separation into a distinct class? (See also Chapter 19.)

How long ago did humans first arrive in the New World (North America, South America, Central America)? How do we know? Before 1000 A.D., was there one or were there several waves of human immigration into the New World?

Review

Go to CENGAGENOW™ at http://www.hed.nelson.com/ to access quizzing, animations, exercises, articles, and personalized homework help.

27.2 Phylum Echinodermata

- Echinodermata are slow-moving or sessile, bottom-dwelling animals. They are important herbivores and predators that occur from shallow coastal waters to the oceans' depths. Adult echinoderms develop from bilaterally symmetrical, free-swimming larvae. Developing larvae assume a secondary radial symmetry, often organized around five rays or "arms." The table below provides a comparison of echinoderms and humans:

System	Echinoderms	Humans
digestive	complete system	complete system
excretory	not present	complete system
respiratory	not present	complete system
circulatory	minimal system	closed, complete system
nervous system	no head or central	cephalized system

- Water enters the fluid-filled canals of the water vascular system through the madreporite (a sievelike plate) on the aboral surface. A tube connects the madreporite to the ring canal, which surrounds the esophagus. The ring canal branches into radial canals that extend into each arm and is connected to numerous mucus-covered tube feet. When ampullae, small muscular bulbs in each tube foot, contract, they force water into the tube foot, causing it to lengthen and attach to a substrate. The tube foot contracts, pulling the animal along and pushing water back into the ampulla; this causes the tube foot to release the substrate. Echinoderms reproduce either sexually or asexually. Sexual reproduction is usually achieved by releasing gametes into the water. Asexual reproduction involves clonal budding and may be stimulated by the odour of a predator.
- Asteroidea (sea stars) consist of a central disk surrounded by 5 to 20 radiating "arms." Small pincers at the base of pedicellariae (short spines) are used to remove debris that falls onto the animal's surface. The ossicles of their endoskeleton are not fused, permitting flexibility of the arms and disk. Most sea stars eat invertebrates and small fish.
- Ophiuroidea (brittle stars and basket stars) have a well-defined central disk and slender, elongated arms that are sometimes branched. They crawl swiftly across substrates by moving their arms in a coordinated fashion. They feed on small prey, suspended plankton, or detritus extracted from muddy deposits.
- Echinoidea (sea urchins and sand dollars) lack arms. Their ossicles are fused into tests that provide excellent protection but restrict flexibility. Echinoids use tube feet in locomotion. They graze on algae and other organisms that cling to marine surfaces.
- Holothuroidea (sea cucumbers) have a reduced endoskeleton consisting of widely separated microscopic plates. They have five rows of tube feet and a soft body elongated along the oral–aboral axis. Modified tube feet form a ring of tentacles around the mouth. Some species secrete a mucus net that traps plankton or other food particles. The net and tentacles are inserted into the mouth, where the food is ingested. Other species extract food from bottom sediments.
- Crinoidea (sea lilies and feather stars) have five to several hundred branched arms surrounding the disk containing the mouth. Branches of the arms are covered with mucus-coated tube feet that trap suspended microscopic organisms. Sessile sea lilies have a central disk attached to a flexible stalk that can reach a metre in length, whereas adult feather stars swim or crawl weakly.

27.3 Phylum Hemichordata

- Hemichordates (acorn worms) use a muscular, mucus-coated proboscis to construct burrows and trap food particles. Drawn in by beating cilia, water enters the pharynx and exits through the pharyngeal gill slits. As the water passes, suspended food is trapped and directed to the digestive system, while gases are exchanged across the partitions between gill slits.

27.4 Phylum Chordata

- A notochord, a dorsal hollow nerve cord, and gill slits distinguish chordates from all other deuterosomes. Gill slits are sets of paired openings in the pharynx. Water is drawn into the mouth, food is filtered out, and the water passes through the pharynx, where gas exchange takes place, and then out through the gill slits.
- Tunicates (sea squirts) belong to the subphylum Urochordata. They float in surface waters or attach to substrates in shallow waters. Many are sessile as adults and secrete a gelatinous or leathery "tunic" around their bodies. They squirt water through a siphon when disturbed. Some urochordates have larvae that resemble cephalochordates (or lancelets), and in a few species, these larvae are neotenous. Adult lancelets are mainly sedentary, lying partly buried in sand of shallow marine waters. They have well-developed body wall muscles and a prominent notochord. Adults have light receptors on the head and chemical sense organs on tentacles.

27.5 The Origin and Diversification of Vertebrates

- The internal skeleton of vertebrates provides structural support for muscles and protects the nervous system and other internal organs. The backbone surrounds and protects the dorsal nerve cord, and a bony cranium provides protection for the brain. The backbone acts as a place for muscle attachments, which allows quick movement.
- Homeotic (*Hox*) genes influence the three-dimensional shape of an animal and the locations of structures such as eyes, wings, and legs. *Hox* genes are arranged on chromosomes in a specific order to form the *Hox* gene complex. Each gene in the complex governs the development of particular structures. Species with simple anatomy have fewer *Hox* genes than more complex species, which have duplicated copies. These duplicate copies assumed new functions, directing the development of novel structures, such as the vertebral column and jaws.
- Vertebrates have four characteristic morphological innovations: cranium, vertebrae, bone, and neural crest cells.

27.6 Agnathans: Hagfishes and Lampreys, Conodonts, and Ostracoderms

- Agnatha are primitive vertebrates that use a muscular pharynx to suck water containing food particles into their mouths and gills to filter the food and perform gas exchange. Hagfishes and lampreys have a well-developed notochord but lack true vertebrae and paired fins. The hagfish skeleton is a cranium and a notochord. These marine scavengers feed on invertebrate prey and dead fish. They lack a larval stage. Lampreys have a more derived axial skeleton than hagfishes. Their notochord is surrounded by cartilage that partially covers the nerve cord, whereas hagfish have no specialized structures surrounding the nerve cord. Some species of lampreys are parasitic as adults, attaching to a host. Ammocoetes, the larval stage of lampreys, resemble cephalochordates and may develop for up to seven years before metamorphosing into adults.

27.7 Jawed Fishes: Jaws Expanded the Feeding Opportunities for Vertebrates

- Jaws meant that fishes could feed on larger items of food with higher energy content. Jaws also function to defend against predators, groom, transport young, and grasp, kill, and shred food items.
- Flexible fins, lightweight skeletons, streamlined bodies, and an absence of heavy body armour allow sharks to pursue prey rapidly. Sharks and their relatives have squalene, an oily substance contained within the liver. Squalene is lighter than water and increases the animals' buoyancy.
- The lateral line system of elasmobranchs and other fishes consists of a row of tiny sensors in canals along both sides of the body. This system allows detection of vibrations in water, which can be used when hunting.
- In many bony fishes, a gas-filled swim bladder serves as a hydrostatic organ to increase buoyancy. Bony fish also have small, smooth, lightweight scales and bodies that are covered with a protective coat of mucus that retards bacterial growth and smooths the flow of water past the body.

27.8 Early Tetrapods and Modern Amphibians

- Osteolepiforms (fleshy-finned fishes) and tetrapods had infoldings of their tooth surfaces. The shapes and positions of bones on the dorsum and side of their crania and in their appendages were similar. Osteolepiformes had strong fins enabling them to crawl on mud (making their move onto land) and possessed vertebral columns with crescent-shaped bones for support. Osteolepiformes had lungs allowing them to breathe atmospheric oxygen. They could excrete urea or uric acid rather than ammonium.
- The body wall of fish picks up sound vibrations and directly transfers them to sensory receptors. Sound waves are harder to detect in air. The development of a tympanum, or eardrum, allowed tetrapods to detect airborne vibrations and transfer them to the sensory cells of their inner ear.
- Amphibians have thin, scaleless skin, well supplied with blood vessels. Since some oxygen and carbon dioxide enter the body across a thin layer of water, most amphibians need moist skin, restricting them to aquatic or wet terrestrial habitats. Many amphibians need access to free-standing water to reproduce.

27.9 The Origin and Mesozoic Radiations of Amniotes

- Amniotes get their name from the amnion, a fluid-filled sac surrounding the embryo during development. Amniote eggs are resistant to desiccation because the developing embryos excrete uric acid that is stored in the allantois.
- Amniote eggs have four specialized membranes that protect the embryo and facilitate gas exchange and excretion. They also have a hard or leathery shell perforated by microscopic pores that mediates the exchange of air and water between the egg and its environment. Keratin and lipids are partly responsible for making the skin waterproof.

27.10 Sublcass Testudinata: Turtles and Tortoises

- There have been three major radiations of amniotes: anapsids, synapsids, and diapsids, distinguishable by the numbers of bony arches in the temporal region of the skull. The bony arches allow space for contraction (and expansion) of large and powerful jaw muscles. Anapsids lacked temporal arches, synapsids have one pair of temporal arches, and diapsids have two pairs of arches.
- Surviving anapsids are turtles and tortoises. A turtle's body is defined by a bony, boxlike shell, which includes a dorsal carapace and a ventral plastron. Its ribs are fused to the inside of the carapace, and the pectoral and pelvic girdles lie within the rib cage. Large keratinized scales cover the bony plates that form the shell.

27.11 Living Diapsids: Spenodontids, Squamates, and Crocodilians

- Diapsids evolved in two lines, lepidosaurs and archosaurs. Lepidosaurs include snakes and lizards and many extinct forms. Snakes and lizards use olfactory and vibrational cues to detect prey. Some even have thermal perception.
- Living archosaurs include crocodilians, animals with a four-chambered heart that is homologous to the heart in birds. Some crocodilians have muscles that originate on the pubis insert on the liver. When these muscles contract, the liver moves toward the tail, creating negative pressure in the chest cavity. This situation is analogous to the role of the diaphragm in mammals.

27.12 Aves: Birds

- Birds' ability to fly reflects a keeled sternum (breastbone), a furculum (wishbone), and uncinate processes on the ribs. These main adaptations, coupled with lightweight, strong bones and feathers, contributed to the success of birds. Flightless birds often lack a keeled sternum. Most birds have hollow limb bones with small supporting struts that criss-cross the internal cavities. Birds have fewer separate bony elements in the wings, skull, and vertebral column, so the skeleton is light and rigid. All modern birds have replaced dense and heavy teeth with a lightweight keratinized bill. Birds have much higher metabolic rates than comparably sized reptiles do, and they depend on energy-rich food. A complex and efficient respiratory system and a four-chambered heart enable them to consume and distribute oxygen efficiently. Other adaptations include modification of internal organs to reduce weight, elimination of a urinary bladder so that uric paste is eliminated with digestive wastes, and laying eggs as soon as they are shelled.
- Each feather has numerous barbs and barbules with tiny hooks and grooves that maintain the feathers' structure, even during vigorous activity. Flight feathers on the wings provide lift, whereas contour feathers streamline the surface of the body. Down feathers form an insulating cover close to the skin.
- The "top-down" theory suggests that ancestral birds lived in trees and glided down from those trees in pursuit of insect prey. The "bottom-up" theory proposes a cursorial ancestor that ran along in pursuit of prey and jumped up to catch it. The "ontogenic–transitional wing" (OTW) hypothesis is a third effort to explain the evolution of flight in birds. Its proponents suggest that flapping protowings gave the ancestors of birds greater mobility.

27.13 Mammalia: Monotremes, Marsupials, and Placentals

- Most living mammals are furry and endothermic (warm-blooded). Mammals usually bear live young and have a diaphragm, a left aortic arch leaving the heart, and two occipital condyles. Mammals also have a secondary palate and are heterodont (teeth specialized for different jobs) and diphyodont (two generations of teeth, milk or deciduous teeth and adult teeth). Heterodont teeth make mammals more efficient at mechanically dealing with their food (chewing), reducing the lagtime between consumption of food and availability of the food's energy.

- Monotremes lay leathery-shelled eggs. When newborns hatch, they lap up milk secreted by the mammary glands located on the mother's belly. Marsupials have short gestation periods of as few as 8 to 10 days. Young are born at an early stage of development and complete their development attached to a teat in the abdominal pouch (the marsupium) of their mother. Placental mammals complete embryonic development in the mother's uterus, nourished through a placenta until they reach a fairly advanced stage of development.

27.15 The Evolution of Humans

- Upright posture and bipedal locomotion are key adaptations distinguishing hominids from apes. Bipedalism may have arisen in an arboreal setting that allowed the ancestors of humans to move on flexible supports (branches). Bipedal locomotion freed the hands from locomotor functions, allowing them to become adapted for other activities, such as tool use.

- *Homo erectus* ("upright man") was taller than its ancestors and had a much larger brain, a thicker skull, and protruding brow ridges. *H. erectus* was able to make tools to cut food and other materials, to scrape meat from bones, and to dig for roots. They had a more complex diet, probably eating both plants and animals, and may have hunted and scavenged animal prey. They used fire to process food and keep themselves warm.

- Neanderthals had a heavier build, pronounced brow ridges, and slightly larger brains compared with modern humans. They were technologically sophisticated, making wooden spears, stone axes, and flint scrapers and knives. They built shelters and routinely used fire. They were successful hunters and used rudimentary speech. Modern humans differ from Neanderthals in having a slighter build, less protruding brow ridges, and a more prominent chin.
- The African Emergence Hypothesis states that between 1.5 and 0.5 million years ago, a population of *H. erectus* gave rise to several descendant species. These archaic humans left Africa and established populations in the Middle East, Asia, and Europe. Some time later, *H. sapiens* arose in Africa. These modern humans also migrated into Europe and Asia and eventually drove archaic humans to extinction. This hypothesis suggests that all modern humans are descended from a fairly recent African ancestor.
- The Multiregional Hypothesis proposes that populations of *H. erectus* and archaic humans had spread through much of Europe and Asia by 0.5 million years ago. Modern humans (*H. sapiens*) then evolved from archaic humans in many regions simultaneously. Although they were geographically separated, these populations may have experienced some evolutionary differentiation; gene flow between them prevented reproductive isolation and maintained them as a single species, *H. sapiens*.

Questions

Self-Test Questions

1. Which phylum includes animals with a water vascular system?
   a. Echinodermata
   b. Hemichordata
   c. Chordata
   d. Arthropoda
   e. Annelida
2. Which of the following is *not* a characteristic of all chordates?
   a. notochord
   b. segmental body wall and tail muscles
   c. segmented nervous system
   d. dorsal hollow nerve cord
   e. perforated pharynx
3. Which group of vertebrates has adaptations allowing reproduction on land?
   a. agnathans
   b. tetrapods
   c. gnathostomes
   d. amniotes
   e. ichthyosaurs
4. Which group of fishes has the most living species today?
   a. sarcopterygians
   b. actinopterygians
   c. chondrichthyans
   d. acanthodians
   e. ostracoderms
5. Modern amphibians
   a. closely resemble their Paleozoic ancestors.
   b. always occupy terrestrial habitats as adults.
   c. never occupy terrestrial habitats as adults.
   d. are generally larger than their Paleozoic ancestors.
   e. are generally smaller than their Paleozoic ancestors.
6. Which one of the following key adaptations allows amniotes to occupy terrestrial habitats?
   a. production of carbon dioxide as a metabolic waste product
   b. an unshelled egg protected by jellylike material
   c. a dry skin largely impermeable to water
   d. a lightweight skeleton with hollow bones
   e. feathers or fur providing insulation against cold weather
7. Which of the following characteristics are central to powered flight in birds?
   a. webbed feet, long legs, feathers
   b. efficient respiratory and excretory systems, flight muscles
   c. elongated forelimbs, keeled breast bone, flight muscles
   d. feathers, furculum, eyes
   e. short tail vertebrae, large nostrils, feathers.
8. Which of the following characteristics did *not* contribute to the evolutionary success of mammals?
   a. extended parental care of young
   b. an erect posture and flexible hip and shoulder joints
   c. specializations of the teeth and jaws
   d. enlarged brain
   e. high metabolic rate and homeothermy
9. The Hominoidea (hominids) is a monophyletic group that includes
   a. apes and monkeys.
   b. apes only.
   c. humans and human ancestors.
   d. apes and humans.
   e. monkeys, apes, and humans.
10. Which of the following hominids was the earliest?
    a. *Ardipithecus ramidus*
    b. *Australopithecus afarensis*
    c. *Homo habilis*
    d. *Homo erectus*
    e. *Homo neanderthalensis*

Questions for Discussion

1. Most sharks and rays are predatory, but the largest species feed on plankton. Construct a hypothesis to explain this observation. How would you test your hypothesis?
2. What selection pressures did tetrapods face when they first ventured onto land? What characteristics allowed them to meet these pressures?
3. Use binoculars to observe several species of birds in different environments, such as lakes and forests. How are their beaks and feet adapted to their habitats and food habits?
4. Imagine that you unearthed the complete fossilized remains of a mammal. How would you determine its diet?
5. Many myths about human evolution are embraced by popular culture. Using the information you have learned about human evolution, argue against each of the following myths:
   a. Humans evolved from chimpanzees.
   b. Evolution occurred in a steady linear progression from primitive primate to anatomically modern humans.
   c. All human characteristics, such as bipedal locomotion and an enlarged brain, evolved simultaneously and at the same rate.

The Chemical and Physical Foundations of Biology

Measurement and Scale

The SI System of Measurement

The International System of Units is the most widely used system of measurement in the world. Its abbreviation, *SI*, is from the French Système International d'Unités. It was adopted by the eleventh General Conference of Weights and Measures in 1960 and represents the latest modification of the metric system, which was first implemented by the French National Assembly in 1790.

The SI system uses seven base units, each of which measures or describes a different kind of physical quantity. Each unit is strictly defined, although the defintions have been modified (and made more accurate) over time. As an example, the metre was originally defined by the French Academy of Sciences as the length between two marks on a platinum–iridium bar, which was designed to represent 1/10 000 000 of the distance from the equator to the North Pole through Paris. This definition was changed in 1983 by the International Bureau of Weights and Measures as the distance travelled by light in absolute vacuum in 1/299 792 458 of a second.

The Seven Base Units of the SI System

Name	Symbol	Quantity
metre	m	length
kilogram	kg	mass
second	s	time
ampere	A	electric current
kelvin	K	temperature
mole	mol	amount of substance
candela	cd	luminous intensity

The SI system also uses a series of prefix names and prefix symbols to form the names and symbols of the decimal multiples of the base SI units. Note that the base unit for mass is the kilogram, not the gram. One kg = 10^3 g. This list has been extended several times: prefixes now range from yotta, at 10^{24} (one septillion), to yocto, at 10^{-24} (one septillionth).

Factor	Prefix	Symbol	Factor	Prefix	Symbol
10^{24}	yotta	Y	10^{-1}	deci	d
10^{21}	zetta	Z	10^{-2}	centi	c
10^{18}	exa	E	10^{-3}	milli	m
10^{15}	peta	P	10^{-6}	micro	μ
10^{12}	tera	T	10^{-9}	nano	n
10^{9}	giga	G	10^{-12}	pico	p
10^{6}	mega	M	10^{-15}	femto	f
10^{3}	kilo	k	10^{-18}	atto	a
10^{2}	hecto	h	10^{-21}	zepto	z
10^{1}	deca	da	10^{-24}	yocto	y

Derived SI Units

Several other units have been derived from combinations of the seven base units of measure. Three of the more common concern units of force (newton), pressure (pascal), and energy or heat (joule). The measurement of temperature in degrees Celsius is also considered a derived unit, even though one Celsius degree is the same size as one kelvin. However, 0°C = 273.16 K (note that no degree symbol is used when expressing temperature in kelvin).

Name	Symbol	Quantity	Expression
newton	N	force	$m \cdot kg \cdot s^{-2}$
pascal	Pa	pressure	$N \cdot m^{-2}$
joule	J	energy and work	$N \cdot m$

Non-SI Units in Common Usage

A number of units not derived from the base SI units are accepted for use with SI units.

Name	Symbol	Value in SI Units
minute	min	60 s
hour	h	3600 s
day	d	86 400 s
litre	L	1 dm^3 = 10^{-3} m^3
ångström	Å	10^{-10} m
calorie, a measure of food energy*	cal	4.184 J
unified atomic mass unit or Dalton**	u or Da	~1.66054 × 10^{-24} kg

*One food calorie = 1 Cal = 1000 cal

**Value determined experimentally to be one-twelfth of the mass of an unbound atom of carbon-12.

Why Everyone Should Use SI Units

In December 1998, NASA launched the Mars Climate Orbiter on a mission to study the Martian weather and climate. As it approached Mars, the spacecraft received instructions from flight control on Earth to fire thruster engines to enter into a proper orbit about 140 to 150 km above the Martian surface. However, as it approached the planet, a navigation error caused the spacecraft to descend into an orbit of only 57 km above the surface. The spacecraft was soon destroyed by the heat caused by atmospheric friction.

The review of the incident found that the root cause was a mix-up between the use of SI units and an older system of measure, imperial units (e.g., inches, feet, and pounds). More specifically, the software that was used to control the thruster engines of the spacecraft from the ground was written using the imperial unit of force, the pound-force, whereas onboard the spacecraft, information was interpreted in terms of newtons, the metric unit of force. Since 1 pound-force equals about 4.45 newtons, instructions from the ground were thus multiplied by 4.45.

The total cost of the mission was approximately $327 million.

Scale in Biology

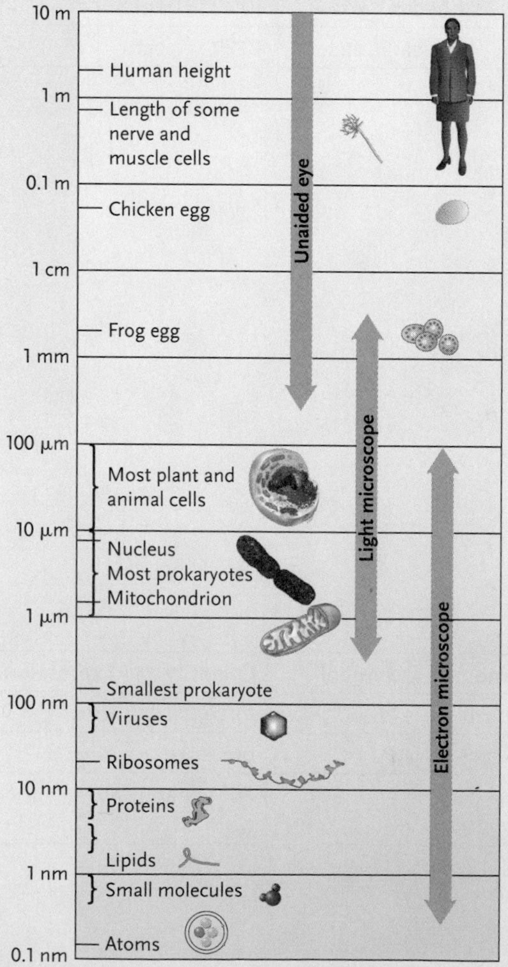

10 m
Human height
1 m
Length of some nerve and muscle cells
0.1 m
Chicken egg
1 cm
Frog egg
1 mm
100 μm
Most plant and animal cells
10 μm
Nucleus
Most prokaryotes
Mitochondrion
1 μm
Smallest prokaryote
100 nm
Viruses
Ribosomes
10 nm
Proteins
Lipids
1 nm
Small molecules
Atoms
0.1 nm
Unaided eye
Light microscope
Electron microscope

The Organization of Matter

Any substance in the universe that has mass and occupies space is defined as **matter.** The basic scientific concepts that explain how matter is organized in biological systems are no different from those for nonliving forms of matter. Living organisms are built from the same chemistry building blocks as nonliving systems and abide by the same laws of chemistry. Because of this, a basic understanding of these chemistry principles is important for our understanding of how biological systems operate.

Elements and Compounds

All matter in the universe—anything that occupies space and has mass—is composed of elements. An element is a pure substance that cannot be broken down into simpler substances by ordinary chemical or physical techniques. Ninety-two different elements occur naturally on Earth, and more than 15 artificial elements have been synthesized in the laboratory.

Living organisms are composed of about 25 elements, with only 4—carbon, hydrogen, oxygen, and nitrogen—accounting for more than 96% of the weight of living organisms. Seven other elements—calcium, phosphorus, potassium, sulphur, sodium, chlorine, and magnesium—contribute most of the remaining 4%. Nine additional elements occur in organisms in quantities so small (<0.01%) that they are known as trace elements. The proportions by mass of different elements differ markedly in seawater, the human body, a fruit, and Earth's crust.

Molecules whose component atoms are different (such as carbon dioxide) are called compounds. The chemical and physical properties of compounds are typically distinct from those of their atoms or elements. For example, we all know that water is a liquid at room temperature. We also know that water does not burn. However, the properties of the individual elements of water—hydrogen and oxygen—are quite different. Hydrogen and oxygen are gases at room temperature, and both are highly reactive.

Atoms combined chemically in fixed numbers and ratios form the molecules of living and nonliving matter. For example, the oxygen we breathe is a molecule formed from the chemical combination of two oxygen atoms; a molecule of the carbon dioxide that we exhale contains one carbon atom and two oxygen atoms. Because carbon dioxide is a molecule consisting of different elements, it is referred to as a compound.

Percentage Composition

Seawater		Human		Pumpkin		Earth's crust	
Oxygen	88.3	Oxygen	65.0	Oxygen	85.0	Oxygen	46.6
Hydrogen	11.0	Carbon	18.5	Hydrogen	10.7	Silicon	27.7
Chlorine	1.9	Hydrogen	9.5	Carbon	3.3	Aluminum	8.1
Sodium	1.1	Nitrogen	3.3	Potassium	0.34	Iron	5.0
Magnesium	0.1	Calcium	2.0	Nitrogen	0.16	Calcium	3.6
Sulphur	0.09	Phosphorus	1.1	Phosphorus	0.05	Sodium	2.8
Potassium	0.04	Potassium	0.35	Calcium	0.02	Potassium	2.6
Calcium	0.04	Sulphur	0.25	Magnesium	0.01	Magnesium	2.1
Carbon	0.003	Sodium	0.15	Iron	0.008	Other elements	1.5
Silicon	0.0029	Chlorine	0.15	Sodium	0.001		
Nitrogen	0.0015	Magnesium	0.05	Zinc	0.0002		
Strontium	0.0008	Iron	0.004	Copper	0.0001		
		Iodine	0.0004				

Steve Lissau/Rainbow

Jack Carey

Atomic Structure

Elements are composed of individual atoms—the smallest units that retain the chemical and physical properties of an element. Any given element has only one type of atom that is identified by a standard one- or two-letter symbol. The element carbon is identified by the single letter *C*, which stands for both the carbon atom and the element.

Each atom consists of an atomic nucleus, surrounded by one or more smaller, fast-moving particles called electrons. All atomic nuclei contain one or more positively charged particles called protons. The number of protons in the nucleus of each kind of atom is referred to as the atomic number. This number does not vary and thus specifically identifies the atom. The smallest atom, hydrogen, has a single proton in its nucleus, so its atomic number is 1. The heaviest naturally occurring atom, uranium, has 92 protons in its nucleus and therefore has an atomic number of 92. Similarly, carbon with six protons, nitrogen with seven protons, and oxygen with eight protons have atomic numbers of 6, 7, and 8, respectively.

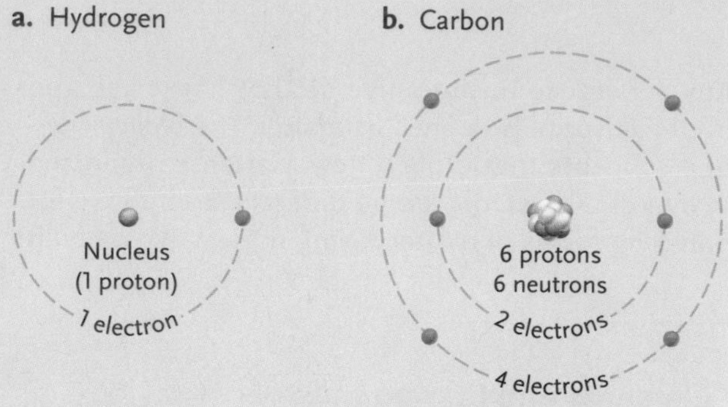

a. Hydrogen

Nucleus (1 proton)

1 electron

b. Carbon

6 protons
6 neutrons

2 electrons

4 electrons

Atomic Number and Mass Number of the Most Common Elements in Living Organisms

Element	Symbol	Atomic Number	Mass Number of the Most Common Form
Hydrogen	H	1	1
Carbon	C	6	12
Nitrogen	N	7	14
Oxygen	O	8	16
Sodium	Na	11	23
Magnesium	Mg	12	24
Phosphorus	P	15	31
Sulphfur	S	16	32
Chlorine	Cl	17	35
Potassium	K	19	39
Calcium	Ca	20	40
Iron	Fe	26	56
Iodine	I	53	127

With one exception, the nuclei of all atoms also contain uncharged particles called neutrons, which occur in variable numbers approximately equal to the number of protons. The single exception is the most common form of hydrogen, which has a nucleus that contains only a single proton.

A neutron and a proton have almost the same mass, about 1.66×10^{-24} grams (g). This mass is defined as a standard unit, the dalton. Atoms are assigned a mass number based on the total number of protons and neutrons in the atomic nucleus. Electrons are ignored in determinations of atomic mass because the mass of an electron is very small.

Isotopes

All atoms of a specific element have the same number of protons, but they may differ in the number of neutrons. These distinct forms of the atoms of an element that have the same atomic number but have different atomic masses are called isotopes.

The nuclei of some isotopes are unstable and break down, or *decay*, giving off particles of matter and energy that can be detected as radioactivity. The decay transforms the unstable, radioactive isotope—called a radioisotope—into an atom of another element. The decay continues at a steady, clocklike rate, with a constant proportion of the radioisotope breaking down at any instant. The rate of decay is not affected by chemical reactions or environmental conditions such as temperature or pressure. For example, the carbon isotope ^{14}C is unstable and undergoes radioactive decay in which one of its neutrons splits into a proton and an electron. The electron is ejected from the nucleus, but the proton is retained, giving a new total of seven protons and seven neutrons, which is characteristic of the most common form of nitrogen. Thus, the decay transforms the carbon atom into an atom of nitrogen.

Because unstable isotopes decay at a clocklike rate, they can be used to estimate the age of organic material, rocks, or fossils that contain them. These techniques have been vital in dating animal remains and tracing evolutionary lineages. Isotopes are also

continued on next page

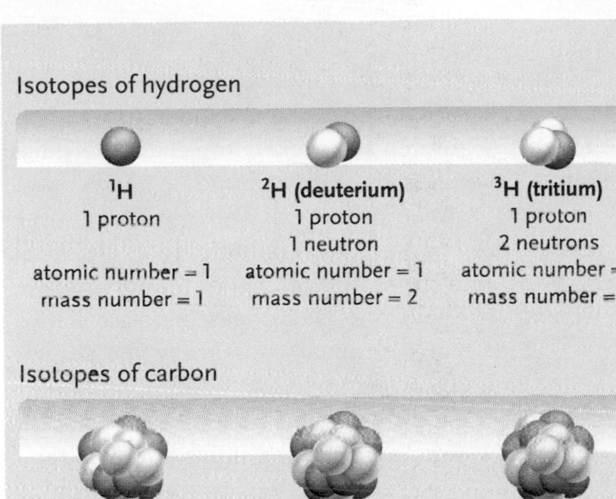

used in biological research as tracers to label molecules so that they can be tracked as they pass through biochemical reactions. Radioactive isotopes of carbon (^{14}C), phosphorus (^{32}P), and sulphur (^{35}S) can be traced easily by their radioactivity. A number of stable, nonradioactive isotopes, such as ^{15}N, can be detected by their mass differences and have also proved valuable as tracers in biological experiments.

Electrons and Electron Orbitals

In an atom, the number of electrons is equal to the number of protons in the nucleus. As they carry a negative charge that is exactly equal and opposite to the positive charge of the proton the total structure of an atom is electrically neutral. Electrons move around the atomic nucleus in a specific region called an orbital. An orbital is essentially the region of space where the electron "lives" most of the time. Although either one or two electrons may occupy an orbital, the most stable and balanced condition occurs when an orbital contains a pair of electrons. Orbitals are grouped into what are called energy levels or energy shells. These shells are numbered 1, 2, 3, and so on, to indicate their relative distance from the nucleus. The lowest energy level of an atom, the one nearest the nucleus, may be occupied by a maximum of two electrons in a single orbital. The second and third shells can hold a maximum of eight electrons each.

The first shell consists of a single spherical orbital, the 1*s* orbital. Hydrogen and helium, for example, consist of only a 1*s* orbital, containing one or two electrons, respectively. The second shell, if present, consists of the 2*s* orbital and three 2*p* orbitals. Collectively, the second shell holds a maximum of eight electrons. Neon is the element formed when both the first and the second shell contain a full complement of electrons. Neon is very stable, as explained in the next box.

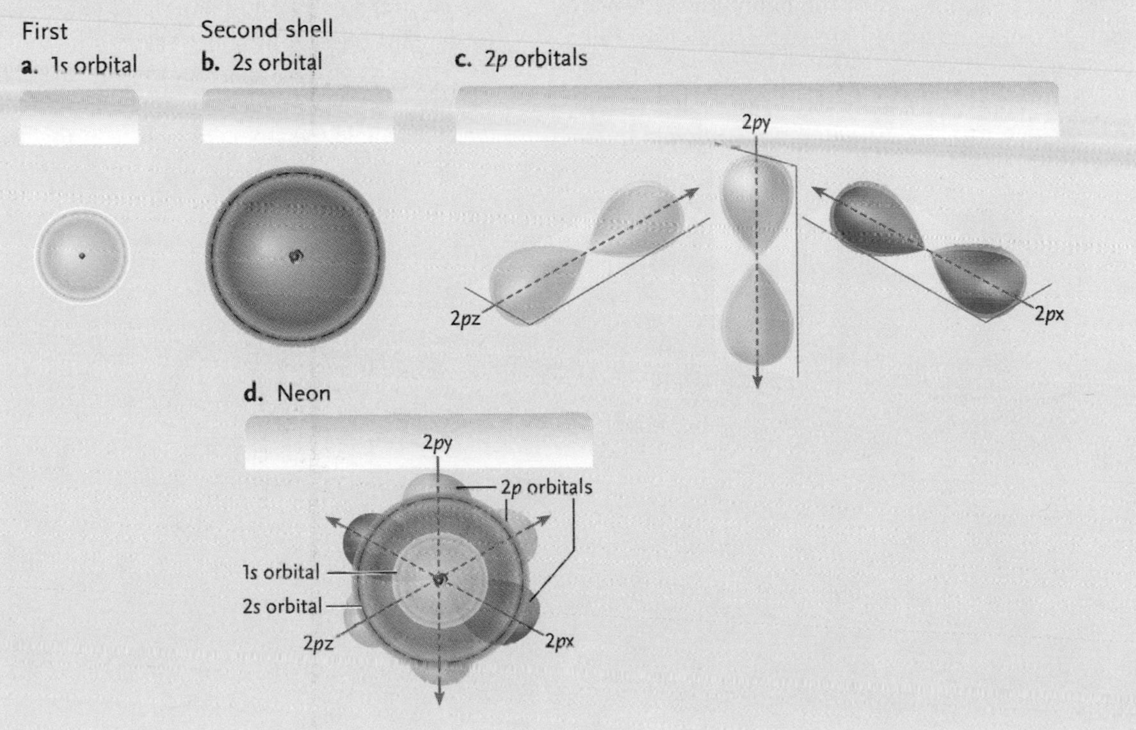

Valence Electrons

The electrons in an atom's outermost energy level are known as valence electrons. Atoms in which the outermost energy level is not completely filled with electrons tend to be chemically reactive; those with a completely filled outermost energy level are non-reactive, or inert. For example, hydrogen has a single, unpaired electron in its outermost and only energy level, and it is highly reactive; helium has two valence electrons filling its single orbital and is unreactive (stable), or inert. For atoms with two or more energy levels, only those with unfilled outer energy levels are reactive. Those with eight electrons completely filling the four orbitals of the outer energy levels, such as neon and argon, are stable and chemically unreactive.

Atomic number	Element	Electron shell			
	Element	I	II	III	IV
1	Hydrogen	○			
2	Helium	○○			
6	Carbon	○○	○○○○		
7	Nitrogen	○○	○○○○○		
8	Oxygen	○○	○○○○○○		
10	Neon	○○	○○○○○○○○		
11	Sodium	○○	○○○○○○○○	○	
12	Magnesium	○○	○○○○○○○○	○○	
15	Phosphorus	○○	○○○○○○○○	○○○○○	
16	Sulphur	○○	○○○○○○○○	○○○○○○	
17	Chlorine	○○	○○○○○○○○	○○○○○○○	
18	Argon	○○	○○○○○○○○	○○○○○○○○	
19	Potassium	○○	○○○○○○○○	○○○○○○○○	○
20	Calcium	○○	○○○○○○○○	○○○○○○○○	○○

Because an unfilled electron shell is less stable than a filled one, atoms with an incomplete outer shell have a strong tendency to interact with other atoms in a way that causes them to either gain or lose enough electrons to achieve a completed outermost shell. All elements commonly found in living organisms have unfilled outermost shells (yellow in the picture here) and can thus participate in chemical reactions with other atoms. By comparison, some elements that have only filled shells (blue are shown here) are chemically unreactive and are not found in living systems.

Atoms with outer energy levels that contain electrons near the stable numbers tend to gain or lose electrons to reach the stable configuration. For example, sodium has two electrons in its first energy level, eight in the second, and one in the third and outermost level. The outermost electron is readily lost to another atom, giving the sodium atom a stable second energy level (now the outermost level) with eight electrons. Chlorine, with seven electrons in its outermost energy level, tends to take up an electron from another atom to attain the stable number of eight electrons.

Atoms that differ from the stable configuration by more than one or two electrons tend to attain stability by *sharing* electrons in joint orbitals with other atoms rather than by gaining or losing electrons completely. Among the atoms that form biological molecules, electron sharing is most characteristic of carbon, which has four electrons in its outer energy level and thus falls at the midpoint between the tendency to gain or lose electrons. Oxygen, with six electrons in its outer level, and nitrogen, with five electrons in its outer level, also share electrons readily. Hydrogen may either share or lose its single electron. The relative tendency to gain, share, or lose valence electrons underlies the chemical bonds and forces that hold the atoms of molecules together.

Chemical Bonds

Atoms of the inert elements, such as helium, neon, or argon, occur naturally in uncombined forms, but atoms of reactive elements tend to combine into molecules by forming **chemical bonds**. Four types of chemical linkages are important in biological molecules: ionic bonds, covalent bonds, hydrogen bonds, and van der Waals forces. Because of their importance in hydrogen bonding, polar molecules are also discussed here.

Ionic Bonds

Ionic bonds form between atoms that gain or lose valence electrons completely. A sodium atom (Na) readily loses a single electron to achieve a stable outer energy level, and chlorine (Cl) readily gains an electron. After the transfer, the sodium atom, now with 11 protons and 10 electrons, carries a single positive charge. The chlorine atom, now with 17 protons and 18 electrons, carries a single negative charge. In this charged condition, the atoms are called ions: sodium with a positive charge is a cation, whereas chloride with a negative charge is the anion.

Ionic bonds are common among the forces that hold ions, atoms, and molecules together because these bonds have three key features:

- they exert an attractive force over greater distances than any other chemical bond
- their attractive force extends in all directions
- they vary in strength depending on the presence of other charged substances

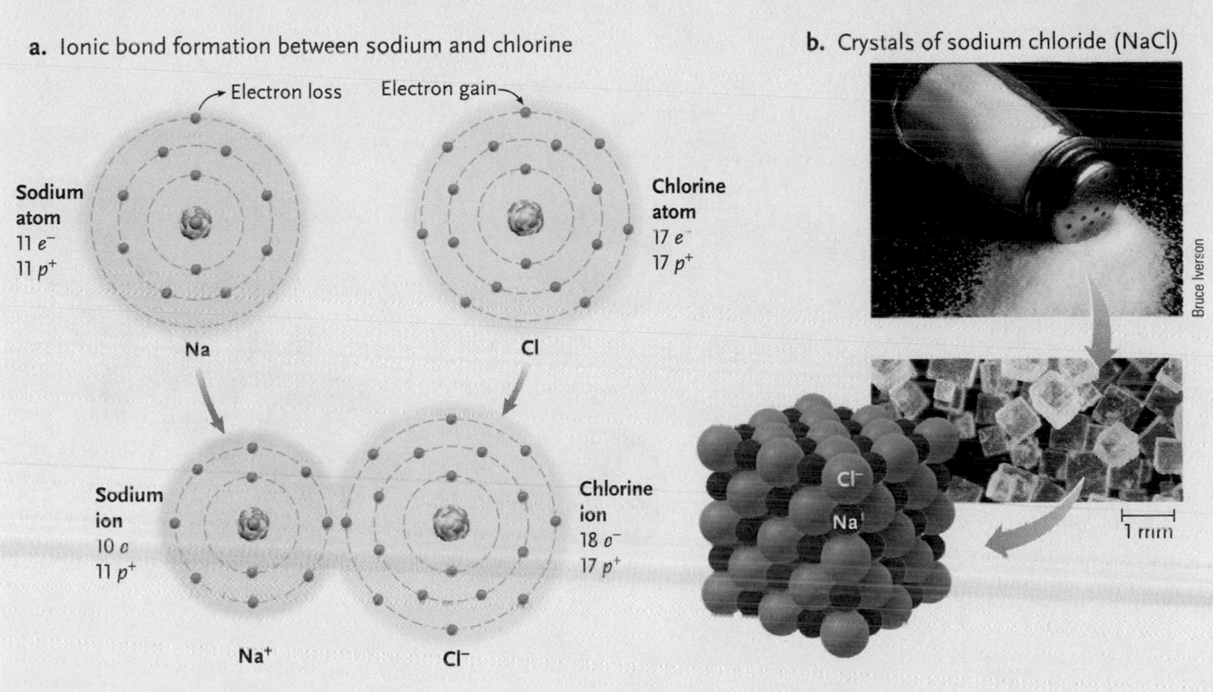

Covalent Bonds

Covalent bonds form when atoms share a pair of valence electrons rather than gaining or losing them. The formation of molecular hydrogen, H_2, by two hydrogen atoms is the simplest example of the sharing mechanism. If two hydrogen atoms collide, the single electron of each atom may join in a new, combined two-electron orbital that surrounds both nuclei. The two electrons fill the orbital; thus, the hydrogen atoms tend to remain linked stably together. The linkage formed by the shared orbital is a covalent bond.

In molecular diagrams, a covalent bond is represented by a pair of dots or a single line, designating the pair of shared electrons. For example, in H_2, the molecule is represented as H:H or H–H.

Unlike ionic bonds, which extend their attractive force in all directions, the shared orbitals that form covalent bonds extend between atoms at discrete angles and directions, giving covalently bound molecules distinct, three-dimensional forms. For biological molecules such as proteins, which are composed of amino acids linked together by covalent bonds, the three-dimensional form imparted by the bonds is critical to the molecule's overall function.

Carbon has four unpaired outer electrons and typically forms four covalent bonds to complete its outermost energy level. An example is methane, CH_4, the main component of natural gas. The four covalent bonds formed by the carbon atom are fixed at an angle of 109.5° from each other, forming a tetrahedron. The tetrahedral arrangement of the bonds allows carbon atoms to link extensively to each other in chains and rings in both branched and unbranched forms. Such structures form the backbones of an almost unlimited variety of molecules. Carbon can also form double bonds, in which two carbon atoms share two pairs of electrons, and triple bonds, in which two carbon atoms share three pairs of electrons.

Oxygen, hydrogen, nitrogen, and sulphur also have electrons that readily form covalent linkages, and they commonly combine with carbon in biological molecules. In these linkages, oxygen typically forms two covalent bonds; hydrogen, one; nitrogen, three; and sulphur, two.

a. Shared orbitals of methane (CH_4)

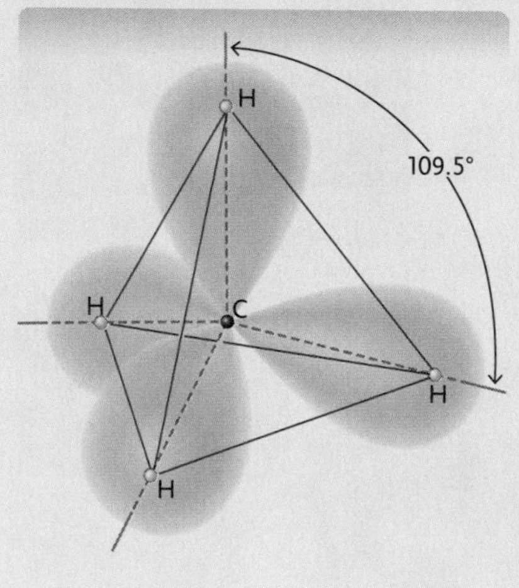

b. Space-filling model of methane

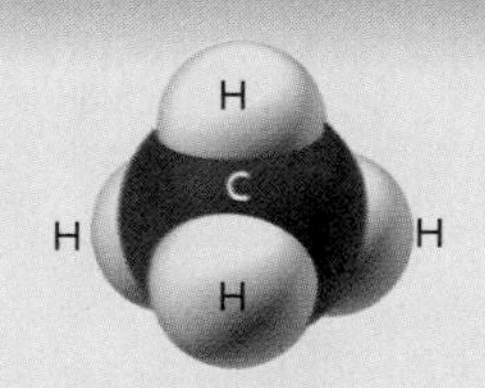

c. A carbon "building block" used to make molecular models

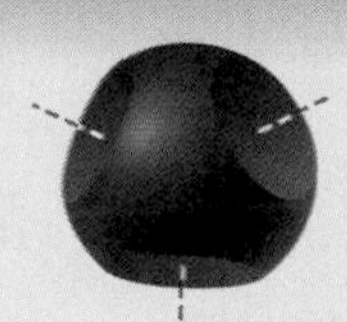

d. Cholesterol

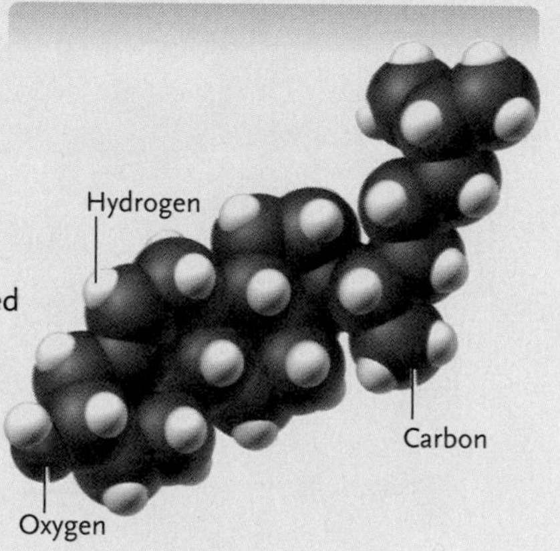

Polar Molecules

Although all covalent bonds involve the sharing of valence electrons, they differ widely in the degree of sharing. Electronegativity is the measure of an atom's attraction for the electrons it shares in a covalent bond with another atom. The more electronegative an atom is, the more strongly it attracts shared electrons. Among atoms, electronegativity increases as the number of protons in the nucleus increases and as the distance between the electrons and the nucleus increases. This unequal sharing of electrons between two atoms that differ in their electronegativity results in a polar covalent bond.

The atom that attracts the electron(s) more strongly carries a partial negative charge, which results in the other atom carrying a partial positive charge. The atoms carrying partial charges may give the whole molecule partially positive and negative ends; in other words, the molecule is *polar.*

continued on next page

For example, the oxygen atom in water forms polar covalent bonds with two hydrogen atoms. Because the oxygen nucleus with its eight protons attracts electrons much more strongly than the hydrogen nuclei do, the bonds are strongly polar. In addition, the water molecule is asymmetrical, with the oxygen atom located on one side and the hydrogen atoms on the other. This arrangement gives the entire molecule an unequal charge distribution, with the hydrogen end partially positive and the oxygen end partially negative, making water molecules strongly polar. Although less so than oxygen, sulphur and nitrogen are also electronegative, giving rise to polar bonds with hydrogen.

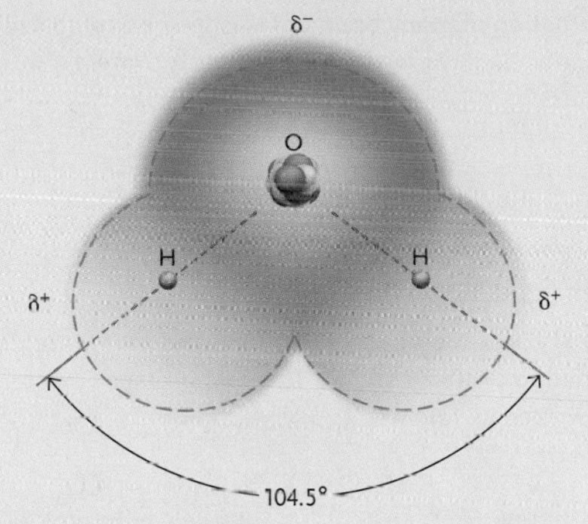

Polar molecules attract and align themselves with other polar molecules and with charged ions and molecules and tend to exclude nonpolar molecules. Polar molecules that associate readily with water because it is strongly polar are identified as hydrophilic (*hydro* = water; *philic* = preferring). Nonpolar substances that are excluded by water and other polar molecules (such as oils) are identified as hydrophobic (*phobic* = avoiding).

Hydrogen Bonding

When hydrogen atoms are made partially positive by sharing electrons unequally with oxygen, nitrogen, or sulphur, they may be attracted to nearby oxygen, nitrogen, or sulphur atoms made partially negative by unequal electron sharing in a different covalent bond. This attractive force is the hydrogen bond, illustrated by a dotted line in structural diagrams of molecules. Hydrogen bonds may form between atoms in the same or different molecules.

Individual hydrogen bonds are weak compared with ionic and covalent bonds. However, large biological molecules may offer many opportunities for hydrogen bonding, both within and between molecules. When numerous, hydrogen bonds are collectively strong and lend stability to the three-dimensional structure of molecules such as proteins. Hydrogen bonds between water molecules are responsible for many of the properties that make water uniquely important to life.

The weak attractive force of hydrogen bonds makes them much easier to break than covalent and ionic bonds, particularly when elevated temperature increases the movements of molecules. Hydrogen bonds begin to break extensively as temperatures rise above 45°C and become practically nonexistent at 100°C.

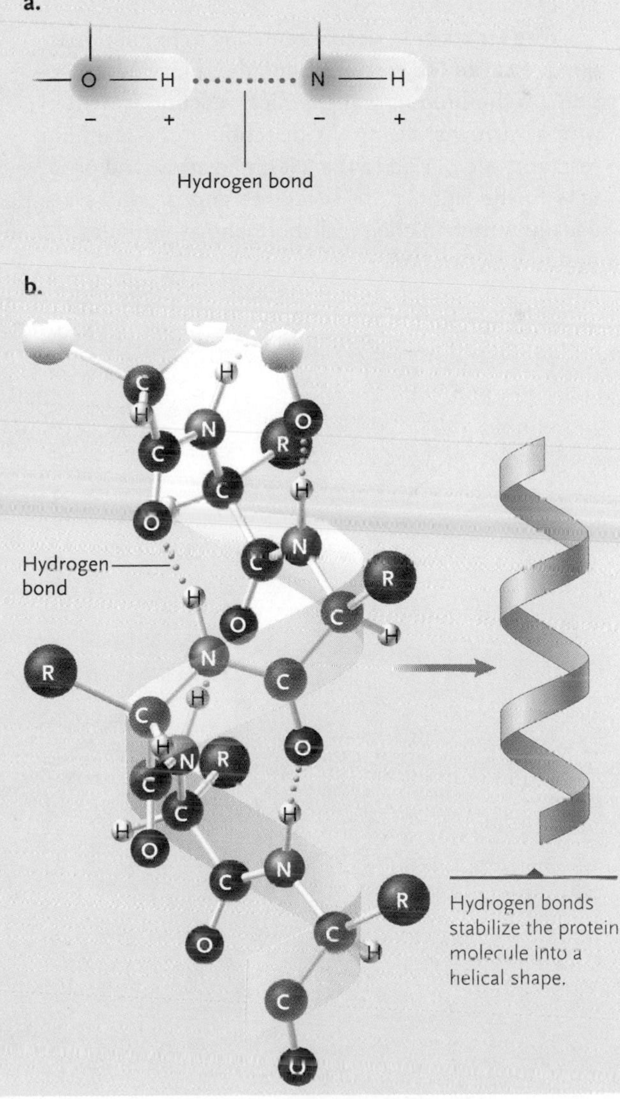

van der Waals Forces

van der Waals forces are even weaker than hydrogen bonds. These forces develop between nonpolar molecules or regions of molecules when, through their constant motion, electrons accumulate by chance in one part of a molecule or another. This process leads to zones of positive and negative charge, making the molecule polar. If they are oriented in the right way, the polar parts of the molecules are attracted electrically to one another and cause the molecules to stick together briefly. Although an individual bond formed with van der Waals forces is weak and transient, the formation of many bonds of this type can stabilize the shape of a large molecule, such as a protein.

Chemical Reactions

Chemical reactions occur when atoms or molecules interact to form new chemical bonds or break old ones. As a result of bond formation or breakage, atoms are added to or removed from molecules or the linkages of atoms in molecules are rearranged. When any of these alterations occur, molecules change from one type to another, usually with different chemical and physical properties. In biological systems, chemical reactions are accelerated by *enzymes*. Enzymes typically are proteins (see Chapter 4 for a more detailed discussion of enzymes).

The atoms or molecules entering a chemical reaction are called the reactants, and those leaving a reaction are the products. A chemical reaction is written with an arrow showing the direction of the reaction; reactants are placed to the left of the arrow and products to the right. Both reactants and products are usually written in chemical shorthand as formulas.

For example, the overall reaction of photosynthesis, in which carbon dioxide and water are combined to produce sugars and oxygen (see Chapter 9), is written as follows:

$$\underset{\text{carbon dioxide}}{6CO_2} + \underset{\text{water}}{6H_2O} \rightarrow \underset{\text{a sugar}}{C_6H_{12}O_6} + \underset{\text{molecular oxygen}}{6O_2}$$

The number in front of each formula indicates the number of molecules of that type among the reactants and products (the number 1 is not written). Notice that there are as many atoms of each element on the left of the arrow as there are on the right, even though the products are different from the reactants. This balance reflects the fact that in chemical reactions, atoms may be rearranged but are not created or destroyed. Chemical reactions written in balanced form are known as chemical equations.

Water

All living organisms contain water, and many kinds of organisms live directly in water. Even those that live in dry environments contain water in all their structures—different organisms range from 50% to more than 95% water by weight. The water inside organisms is crucial for life: it is required for many important biochemical reactions and plays major roles in maintaining the shape and organization of cells and tissues.

Hydrogen Bonds and the Properties of Water

The properties of water molecules that make them so important to life depend to a great extent on their polar structure and their ability to link to each other by hydrogen bonds (see PP3). Hydrogen bonds form readily between water molecules in both liquid water and ice. In liquid water, each water molecule establishes an average of 3.4 hydrogen bonds with its neighbours, forming an arrangement known as the water lattice. In liquid water, the hydrogen bonds that hold the lattice together constantly break and reform, allowing the water molecules to break loose from the lattice, slip past one another, and reform the lattice in new positions.

In ice, the water lattice is a rigid, crystalline structure in which each water molecule forms four hydrogen bonds with neighbouring molecules. The rigid ice lattice spaces the water molecules farther apart than the water lattice. Because of this greater spacing, water has the unusual property of being about 10% less dense when solid than when liquid. Imagine what Earth would be like if ice sank to the bottom, as most solids do.

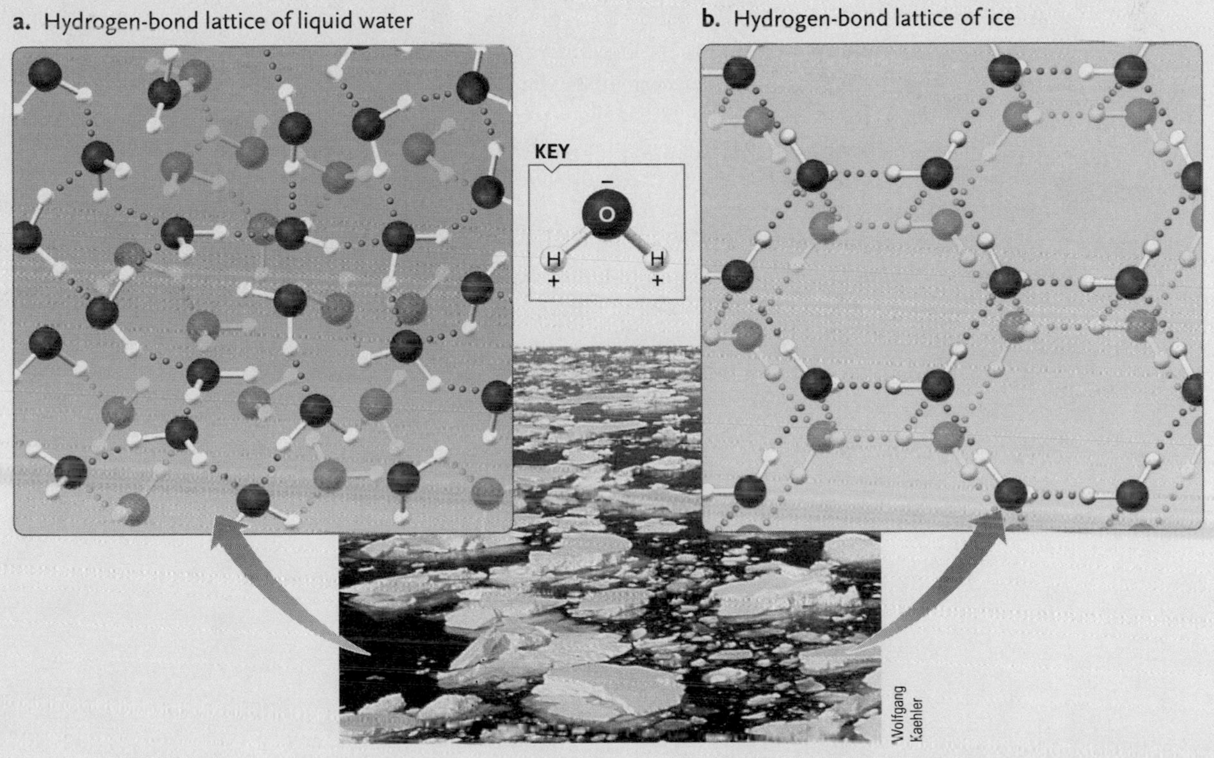

Specific Heat Capacity, Cohesion, and Surface Tension of Water

As a result of its stabilizing hydrogen-bond lattice, water has a relatively high specific heat capacity—that is, the amount of heat required to increase the temperature of a given quantity of water. As heat flows into water, much of it is absorbed in the breakage of hydrogen bonds. As a result, the temperature of water, reflected in the average motion of its molecules, increases relatively slowly as heat is added. As a result, relatively high temperatures and the addition of considerable heat are required to break enough hydrogen bonds to make water boil. The high boiling point maintains water as a liquid over the wide temperature range of 0° to 100°C. Compared to water, H_2S, which has a comparable molecular structure, is a gas at room temperature and has a melting point of −85°C and a boiling point of −60°C, a range of only 25 degrees. Without its hydrogen-bond lattice, water would boil at −81°C. If this were the case, most of the water on Earth would be in gaseous form and life as described in this book could not exist.

The hydrogen-bond lattice of water results in water molecules staying together, a phenomenon that is referred to as cohesion. For example, in land plants, cohesion holds water molecules in unbroken columns in the microscopic conducting tubes that extend from the roots to the highest leaves. As water evaporates from the leaves, water molecules in the columns, held together by cohesion, move upward through the tubes to replace the lost water.

Related to cohesion is surface tension, which is a measure of how difficult it is to stretch or break the surface of a liquid. The water molecules at surfaces facing air can form hydrogen bonds with water molecules beside and below them but not on the sides that face the air. This unbalanced bonding produces a force that places the surface water molecules under tension, making them more resistant to separation than the underlying water molecules. This force is strong enough to allow small insects such as water striders to walk on water.

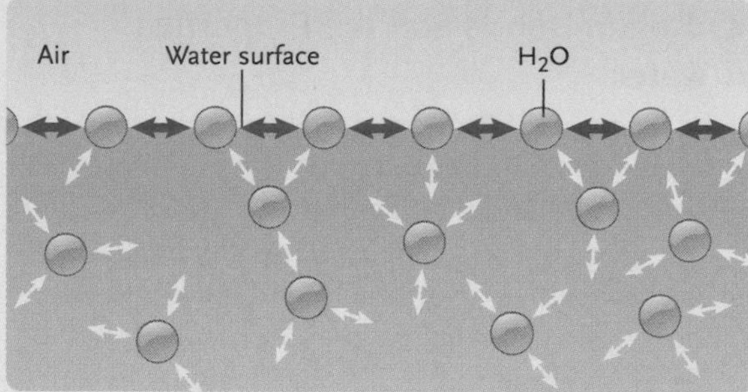

H. Eisenbeiss/Frank Lane Picture Agency

Aqueous Solutions

Because water molecules are small and strongly polar, they readily surround other polar and charged molecules and ions. The surface coat, called a hydration shell, reduces the attraction between the molecules or ions and promotes their separation and entry into a solution, where they are suspended individually, surrounded by water molecules. Once in solution, the hydration shell prevents the polar molecules or ions from reassociating. In such an aqueous solution, water is called the *solvent*, and the molecules of a substance dissolved in water are called the *solute*.

Sodium chloride (salt) dissolves in water because water molecules quickly form hydration layers around the Na^+ and Cl^+ ions in the salt crystals, reducing the attraction between the ions so much that they separate from the crystal and enter the surrounding water lattice as individual ions. In much the same way, hydration shells surround macromolecules such as nucleic acids and proteins, reducing their electrostatic interaction with other molecules.

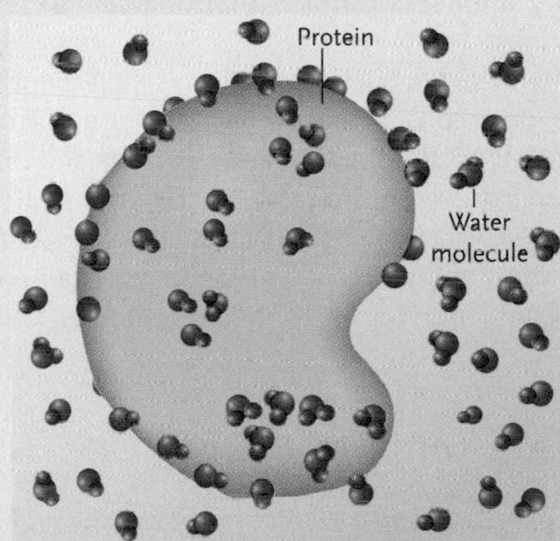

Determining Solute Concentration

In the cell, chemical reactions depend on solutes dissolved in aqueous solutions. To understand these reactions, you need to know the number of atoms and molecules involved. **Concentration** is the number of molecules or ions of a substance in a unit volume of space, such as a millilitre (mL) or litre (L). The number of molecules or ions in a unit volume cannot be counted directly, but it can be calculated indirectly by using the mass number of atoms as the starting point.

The mass number of an atom is equivalent to the number of protons and neutrons in its nucleus. From the mass number, and the fact that neutrons and protons weigh approximately the same (that is, 1.66×10^{-24} g), you can calculate the weight of an atom of any substance. For an atom of the most common form of carbon, with six protons and six neutrons in its nucleus, the total weight is

$$12 \times (1.66 \times 10^{-24}\ \text{g}) = 1.992 \times 10^{-23}\ \text{g}$$

For an oxygen atom, with eight protons and eight neutrons in its nucleus, the total weight is

$$16 \times (1.66 \times 10^{-24}\ \text{g}) = 2.656 \times 10^{-23}\ \text{g}$$

Dividing the total weight of a sample of an element by the weight of a single atom gives the number of atoms in the sample. Suppose you have a carbon sample that weighs 12 g—a weight in grams equal to the atom's mass number. (A weight in grams equal to the mass number is known as the atomic weight of an element.) Dividing 12 g by the weight of one carbon atom gives

$$\frac{12}{(1.992 \times 10^{23}\text{g})} = 6.02 \times 10^{23}\ \text{atoms}$$

If you divide the atomic weight of oxygen (16 g) by the weight of one oxygen atom, you get the same result:

$$\frac{16}{(2.656 \times 10^{23}\ \text{g})} = 6.02 \times 10^{23}\ \text{atoms}$$

In fact, dividing the atomic weight of any element by the weight of an atom of that element always produces the same number: 6.022×10^{23}. This number is called **Avogadro's number** after Amedeo Avogadro, the nineteenth-century Italian chemist who first discovered the relationship.

The same relationship holds for molecules. The **molecular weight** of any molecule is the weight in grams equal to the total mass number of its atoms. For NaCl, the total mass number is $23 + 35 = 58$ (a sodium atom has 11 protons and 12 neutrons, and a chlorine atom has 17 protons and 18 neutrons). The weight of an NaCl molecule is therefore

$$58 \times (1.66 \times 10^{-24}\ \text{g}) = 9.628 \times 10^{-23}\ \text{g}$$

Dividing a molecular weight of NaCl (58 g) by the weight of a single NaCl molecule gives

$$\frac{58}{(9.628 \times 10^{23}\text{g})} = 6.02 \times 10^{23}\ \text{molecules}$$

When concentrations are described, the atomic weight of an element or the molecular weight of a compound—the amount that contains 6.02×10^{23} atoms or molecules—is known as a **mole** (abbreviated **mol**). The number of moles of a substance dissolved in 1 L of solution is known as the **molarity** (abbreviated **M**) of the solution. This relationship is highly useful in chemistry and biology because we know that two solutions with the same volume and molarity but composed of different substances will contain the same number of molecules of the substances.

Water Ionization and pH

The most critical property of water that is unrelated to its hydrogen-bond lattice is its ability to separate or dissociate. This occurs when a hydrogen atom that is involved in a hydrogen bond between two water molecules moves from one molecule to the other. What actually leaves is a proton (H^+); the electron is left behind. This proton switch results in the formation of a hydroxide ion (OH^-) and a hydronium ion (H_3O^+). It is convention to simply use H^+ (the hydrogen ion) to denote the hydronium ion. The proportion of water molecules that dissociates to release hydrogen and hydroxide ions is small. However, because of the dissociation, water always contains some H^+ and OH^- ions.

In pure water, the concentrations of H^+ and OH^- ions are equal. However, adding other substances may alter the relative concentrations of H^+ and OH^-, making them unequal. Some substances, called acids, are proton donors that release hydrogen ions (and anions) when they are dissolved in water, effectively increasing the H^+ concentration. For example,

continued on next page

hydrochloric acid (HCl) dissociates into H^+ and Cl^- when dissolved in water:

$$HCl \rightarrow H^+ + Cl^-$$

Other substances, called bases, are proton acceptors that reduce the H^+ concentration of a solution. Most bases dissociate in water into hydroxide ions (OH^-) and cations. The hydroxide ion can act as a base by accepting a proton (H^+) to produce water. For example, sodium hydroxide (NaOH) separates into Na^+ and OH^- ions when dissolved in water:

$$NaOH \rightarrow Na^+ + OH^-$$

The excess OH^- combines with H^+ to produce water:

$$OH^- + H^+ \rightarrow H_2O$$

thereby reducing the H^+ concentration. Basic solutions are also called *alkaline* solutions.

Other bases do not dissociate to produce hydroxide ions directly. For example, ammonia (NH_3), a poisonous gas, acts as a base when dissolved in water, directly accepting a proton from water, producing an ammonium ion, and releasing a hydroxide ion:

$$NH_3 + H_2O \rightarrow NH_4{}^+ + OH^-$$

The concentration of H^+ ions compared with the concentration of OH^- ions in an aqueous solution determines the acidity of the solution. Scientists measure acidity using a numerical scale from 0 to 14, called the pH scale. Because the number of H^+ ions in solution increases exponentially as the acidity increases, the scale is based on logarithms of this number to make the values manageable:

$$pH = -\log_{10}[H^+]$$

In this formula, the brackets indicate concentration in moles per litre. The negative of the logarithm is used to give a positive number for the pH value. For example, in a water solution that is *neutral*—neither acidic nor basic—the concentration of *both* H^+ and OH^- ions is 1×10^{-7} M (0.000 000 1 M). The $\log_{10}$ of 1×10^{-7} is -7. The negative of the logarithm -7 is 7. Thus, a neutral water solution with an H^+ concentration of 1×10^{-7} M has a pH of 7. *Acidic* solutions have pH values less than 7, with pH 0 being the value for the highly acidic 1 M hydrochloric acid (HCl); *basic* solutions have pH values greater than 7, with pH 14 being the value for the highly basic 1 M sodium hydroxide (NaOH). Each whole number on the pH scale represents a value 10 times greater or less than the next number.

Acidity is important to cells because even small changes, on the order of 0.1 or even 0.01 pH unit, can drastically affect biological reactions. In large part, a small change in pH can cause structural changes in proteins that can damage or destroy the proteins' function. Consequently, all living organisms have elaborate systems that control their internal acidity by regulating H^+ concentration near the neutral value of pH 7.

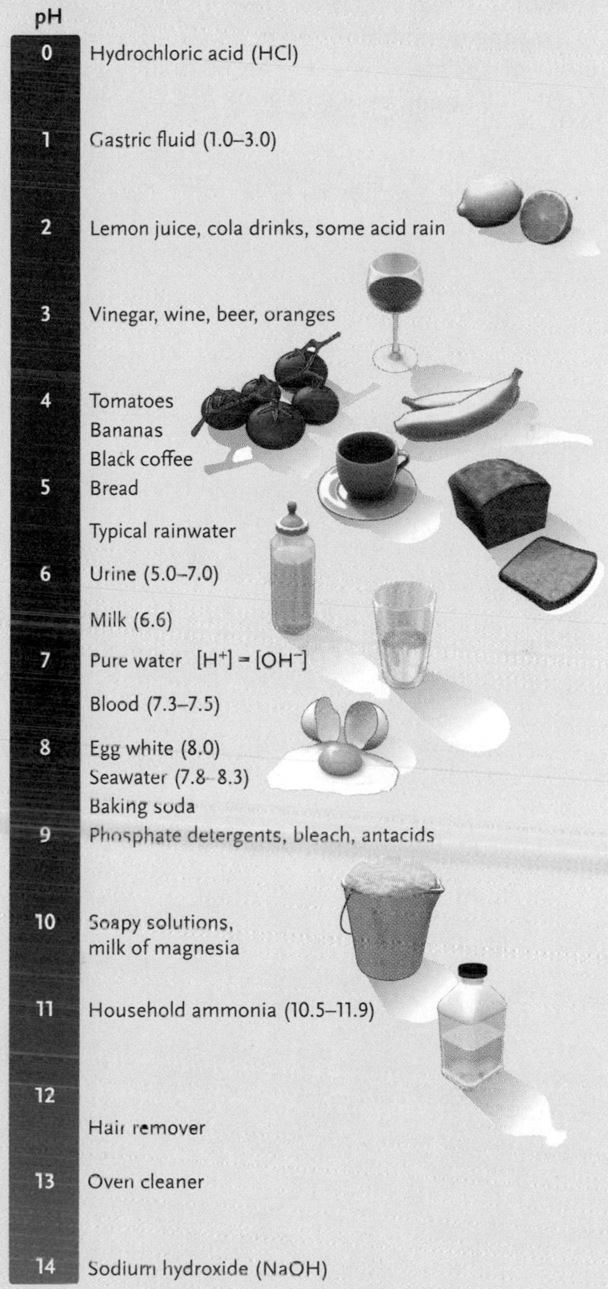

pH
0 Hydrochloric acid (HCl)
1 Gastric fluid (1.0–3.0)
2 Lemon juice, cola drinks, some acid rain
3 Vinegar, wine, beer, oranges
4 Tomatoes
Bananas
Black coffee
5 Bread
Typical rainwater
6 Urine (5.0–7.0)
Milk (6.6)
7 Pure water $[H^+] = [OH^-]$
Blood (7.3–7.5)
8 Egg white (8.0)
Seawater (7.8–8.3)
Baking soda
9 Phosphate detergents, bleach, antacids
10 Soapy solutions, milk of magnesia
11 Household ammonia (10.5–11.9)
12
Hair remover
13 Oven cleaner
14 Sodium hydroxide (NaOH)

Buffers Help Keep pH under Control

Living organisms control the internal pH of their cells with buffers, substances that compensate for pH changes by absorbing or releasing hydrogen ions. When hydrogen ions are released in excess by biological reactions, buffers combine with them and remove them from the solution; if the concentration of hydrogen ions decreases, buffers release H^+ to restore the balance. Most buffers are weak acids, weak bases, or combinations of these substances that dissociate reversibly in water solutions to release or absorb H^+ or OH^-. (Weak acids, such as acetic acid, or weak bases, such as ammonia, release relatively few H^+ or OH^- ions in an aqueous solution, whereas strong acids or bases dissociate extensively. HCl is a strong acid; NaOH is a strong base.)

The buffering mechanism that maintains blood pH near neutral values is a good example. In humans and many other animals, blood pH is buffered by a chemical system based on carbonic acid (H_2CO_3), a weak acid. In water solutions, carbonic acid dissociates readily into bicarbonate ions (HCO_3^-) and H^+:

$$H_2CO_3 \rightarrow HCO_3^- + H^+$$

The reaction is reversible. If hydrogen ions are present in excess, the reaction is pushed to the left—the excess H^+ ions combine with bicarbonate ions to form H_2CO_3. If the H^+ concentration declines below normal levels, the reaction is pushed to the right—H_2CO_3 dissociates into HCO_3^- and H^+, restoring the H^+ concentration. The back-and-forth adjustments of the buffer system help keep human blood close to its normal pH of 7.4.

Carbon Compounds

Carbon Bonding

Compounds that contain carbon form the structures of living organisms and take part in all biological reactions as well as serving as energy sources. Collectively, molecules based on carbon are known as organic molecules. All other substances, that is, those without carbon atoms in their structures, are inorganic molecules. A few of the smallest carbon-containing molecules that occur in the environment as minerals or atmospheric gases, such as $CaCO_3$ and CO_2, are also considered inorganic molecules.

Carbon's central role in life's molecules arises from its bonding properties: it can assemble into an astounding variety of chain and ring structures that form the backbones of all biological molecules. The reason for this is that carbon has four unpaired outer electrons that it readily shares to complete its outermost energy level, forming four covalent bonds. With different combinations of single, double, and even triple bonds, an almost limitless array of molecules is possible. Carbon atoms bond covalently to each other and to other atoms, chiefly hydrogen, oxygen, nitrogen, and sulphur, in molecular structures that range in size from a few to thousands or even millions of atoms. Molecules consisting of carbon linked only to hydrogen atoms are called hydrocarbons (*hydro-* refers to hydrogen, not water). The simplest hydrocarbon, CH_4 (methane), consists of a single carbon atom bonded to four hydrogen atoms. Removing one hydrogen from methane leaves a methyl group, which occurs in many biological molecules:

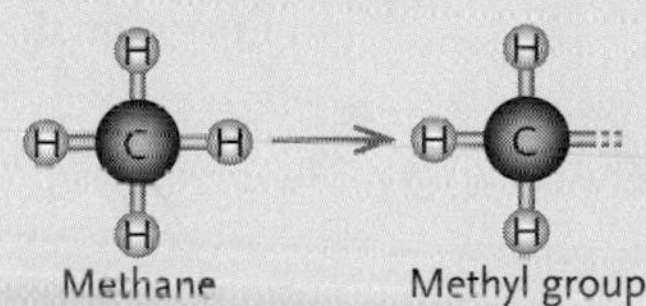

Now imagine bonding two methyl groups together. Removing a hydrogen atom from the resulting structure, ethane, produces an ethyl group:

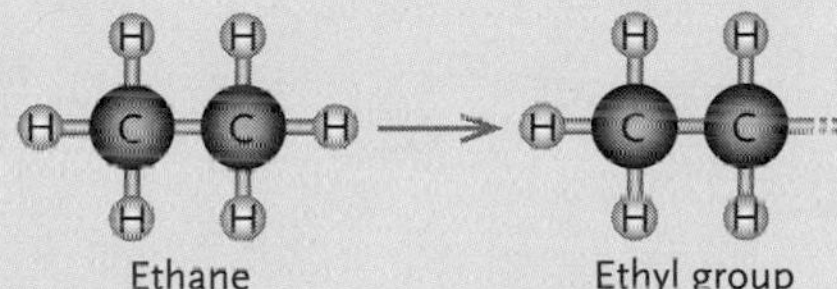

Repeating this process builds a linear hydrocarbon chain:

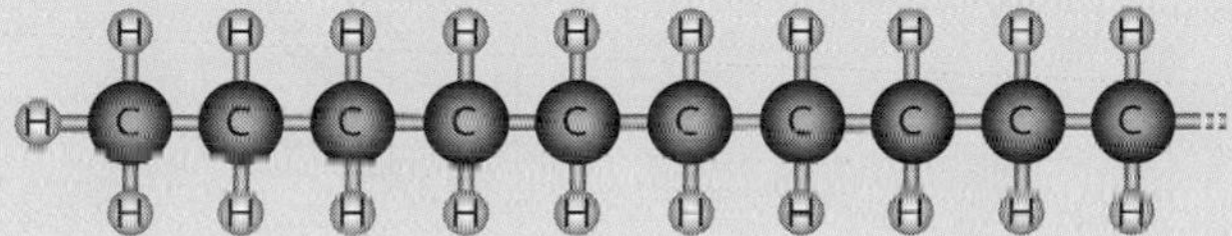

Branches can be added to produce a branched hydrocarbon chain:

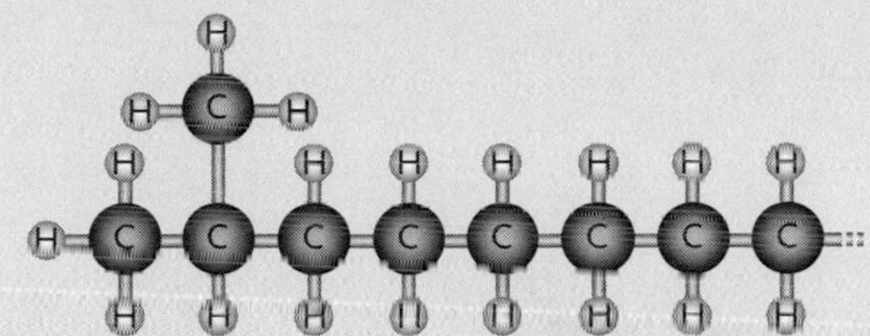

A chain can loop back on itself to form a ring. For example, cyclohexane, C_6H_{12}, has single covalent bonds between each pair of carbon atoms and two hydrogen atoms attached to each carbon atom:

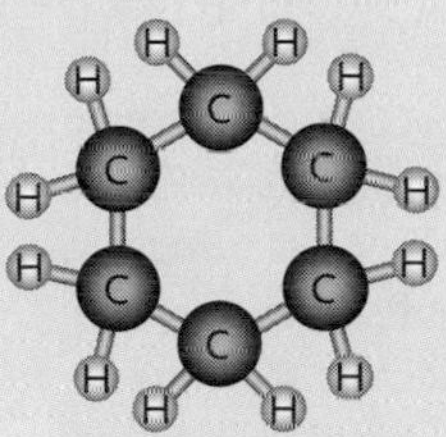

C_6H_{12}, cyclohexane

Hydrocarbons gain added complexity when neighbouring carbon atoms form double or triple bonds. Because each carbon atom can form a maximum of four bonds, the number of hydrogen atoms in a molecule decreases as the number of bonds between any two carbon atoms increases:

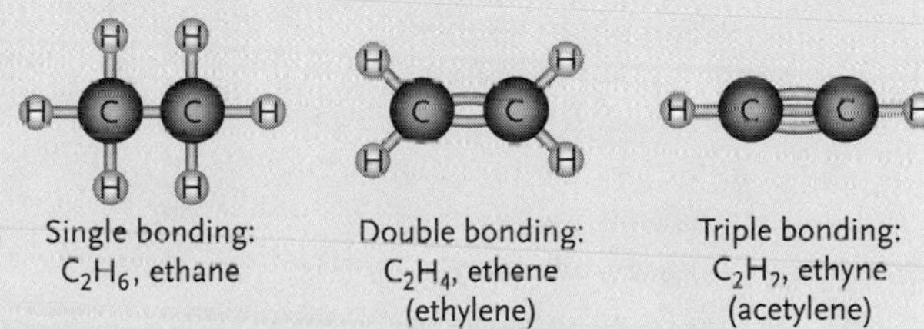

Double bonds between carbon atoms are also found in carbon rings:

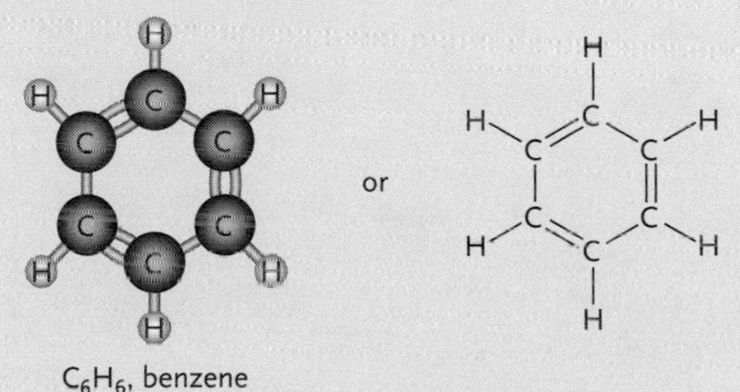

C_6H_6, benzene

We will also use this depiction of a carbon ring in figures:

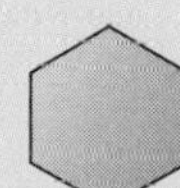

continued on next page

Many carbon rings can join together to produce larger molecules, as in the string of sugar molecules that makes up a polysaccharide chain:

There is almost no limit to the number of different hydrocarbon structures that carbon and hydrogen can form. However, the molecules of living systems typically contain other elements in addition to carbon and hydrogen. These other elements confer functional properties on organic molecules, producing the four major classes of organic molecules—*carbohydrates, lipids, proteins,* and *nucleic acids.*

Functional Groups

Carbohydrates, lipids, proteins, and nucleic acids are synthesized and degraded in living organisms through interactions between small, reactive groups of atoms attached to the organic molecules. The atoms in these reactive groups, called functional groups, occur in positions in which their covalent bonds are more readily broken or rearranged than the bonds in other parts of the molecules.

The functional groups that enter most frequently into biological reactions are the *hydroxyl, carbonyl, carboxyl, amino, phosphate,* and *sulfhydryl* groups. The unconnected covalent bonds written to the left of each structure link these functional groups to other atoms in biological molecules, usually carbon atoms. A double bond, such as that in the carbonyl group, indicates that two pairs of electrons are shared between the carbon and oxygen atoms.

Common Functional Groups of Organic Molecules

Functional Group	Major Classes of Molecules	Example
Hydroxyl —C—OH	Alcohols	Ethyl alcohol (in alcoholic beverages)
Carbonyl —C—C=O (with H)	Aldehydes	Acetaldehyde
—C—C=O (with C)	Ketones	Acetone (a solvent)
Carboxyl —C—COOH or —C—C(=O)OH	Organic acids	Acetic acid (in vinegar)
Amino $—C—NH_2$ or —C—N(H)H	Amino acids	Alanine (an amino acid)
Phosphate $—C—O—PO_3^{2-}$ or $—C—O—P(O^-)(=O)—O^-$	Nucleotides, nucleic acids, many other cellular molecules	Glyceraldehyde-3-phosphate (product of photosynthesis)
Sulfhydryl —C—O-	Many cellular molecules	Mercaptoethanol

Dehydration and Hydrolysis Reactions

In many of the reactions that involve functional groups, the components of a water molecule, —H and —OH, are removed from or added to the groups as they interact. When the components of a water molecule are *removed* during a reaction, usually as part of the assembly of a larger molecule from smaller subunits, the reaction is called a dehydration synthesis reaction or condensation reaction. For example, this type of reaction occurs when individual sugar molecules combine to form a starch molecule. In hydrolysis, the reverse reaction, the components of a water molecule are *added* to functional groups as molecules are broken into smaller subunits. For example, the breakdown of a protein molecule into individual amino acids occurs by hydrolysis.

a. Dehydration synthesis reactions

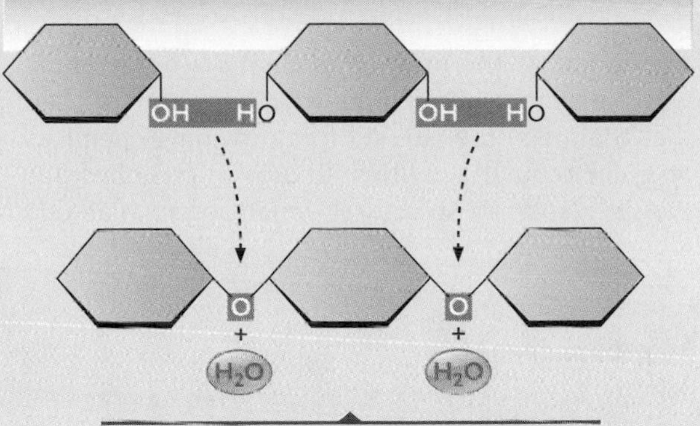

The components of a water molecule are removed as subunits join into a larger molecule.

b. Hydrolysis

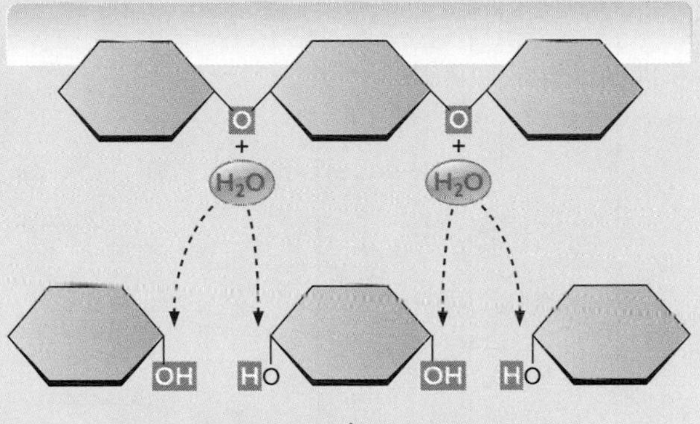

The components of a water molecule are added as molecules are split into smaller subunits.

Carbohydrates

Carbohydrates, the most abundant biological molecules, serve many functions. Together with fats, they act as the major fuel substances providing chemical energy for cellular activities. Chains of carbohydrate subunits also form structural molecules such as cellulose, one of the primary constituents of plant cell walls. Carbohydrates get their name because they contain carbon, hydrogen, and oxygen atoms, with the approximate ratio of the atoms being 1 carbon: 2 hydrogens:1 oxygen (CH_2O).

Monosaccharides

Carbohydrates occur either as monosaccharides or as chains of monosaccharide units linked together. Monosaccharides are soluble in water, and most have a distinctly sweet taste. Of the monosaccharides, those that contain three carbons (*trioses*), five carbons (*pentoses*), and six carbons (*hexoses*) are most common in living organisms. All monosaccharides can occur in the linear form, where each carbon atom in the chain except one has both an —H and an —OH group attached to it.

Monosaccharides with five or more carbons can fold back on themselves to assume a ring form. Folding into a ring occurs through a reaction between two functional groups in the same monosaccharide, as occurs in glucose. The ring form of most five- and six-carbon sugars is much more common in cells than the linear form.

When glucose forms into a ring, two alternative arrangements are possible (α-glucose and β-glucose) that differ in the arrangements of the —OH group bound to the carbon at position 1. These two different forms of glucose are called isomers, which are discussed below.

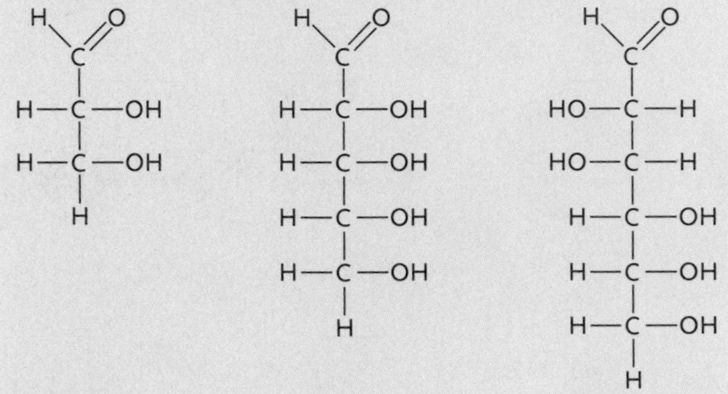

Glyceraldehyde (3 carbons; a triose)

Ribose (5 carbons; a pentose)

Mannose (6 carbons; a hexose)

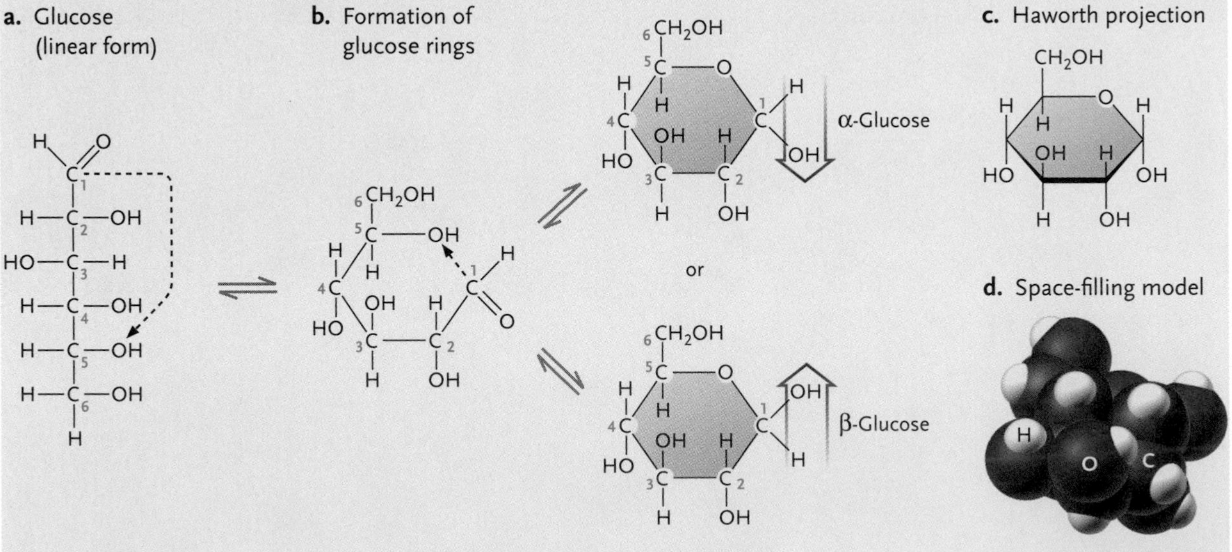

a. Glucose (linear form)

b. Formation of glucose rings

α-Glucose

or

β-Glucose

c. Haworth projection

d. Space-filling model

Isomers of the Monosaccharides

Typically, one or more of the carbon atoms in a monosaccharide links to four different atoms or chemical groups. Carbons linked in this way are called *asymmetrical* carbons; they have important effects on the structure of a monosaccharide because they can take either of two fixed positions with respect to other carbons in a carbon chain. For example, the middle carbon of the three-carbon sugar glyceraldehyde is asymmetrical because it shares electrons in covalent bonds with four different atoms or groups: —H, —OH, —CHO, and —CH_2OH. The —H and —OH groups can take either of two positions, with the —OH extending to either the left or the right of the carbon chain relative to the —CHO and —CH_2OH groups:

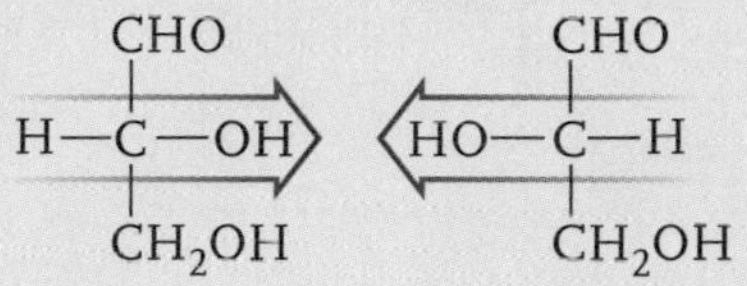

D-Glyceraldehyde L-Glyceraldehyde

Note that the two forms of glyceraldehyde have the same chemical formula, $C_3H_6O_3$. The difference between the two forms is similar to the difference between your two hands. Although both hands have four fingers and a thumb, they are not identical; rather, they are mirror images of each other. That is, when you hold your right hand in front of a mirror, the reflection looks like your left hand and vice versa.

Two or more molecules with the same chemical formula but different molecular structures are called isomers. Isomers that are mirror images of each other, like the two forms of glyceraldehyde, are called enantiomers, or optical isomers. One of the enantiomers—the one in which the hydroxyl group extends to the left in the view just shown—is called the l-form (*laevus* = left). The other enantiomer, in which the —OH extends to the right, is called the d-form (*dexter* = right). The difference between l- and d-enantiomers is critical to biological function. Typically, one of the two forms enters much more readily into cellular reactions; just as your left hand does not fit readily into a right-hand glove, enzymes (proteins that accelerate chemical reactions in living organisms) fit best to one of the two forms of an enantiomer. For example, most of the enzymes that catalyze the biochemical reactions of monosaccharides react more rapidly with the d-form, making this form much more common among cellular carbohydrates than l-forms. Many other kinds of biological molecules besides carbohydrates form enantiomers; an example is the amino acids.

In the ring form of many five- or six-carbon monosaccharides, including glucose, the carbon at the 1 position of the ring is asymmetrical because its four bonds link to different groups of atoms. This asymmetry allows monosaccharides such as glucose to exist as two different enantiomers. The glucose enantiomer with an —OH group pointing below the plane of the ring is known as *alpha-glucose,* or *α-glucose;* the enantiomer with an —OH group pointing above the plane of the ring is known as *beta-glucose,* or *β-glucose.* Other five- and six-carbon monosaccharide rings have similar α- and β-configurations.

The α- and β-rings of monosaccharides can give the polysaccharides assembled from them vastly different chemical properties. For example, starches, which are assembled from α-glucose units, are biologically reactive polysaccharides easily digested by animals; cellulose, which is assembled from β-glucose units, is relatively unreactive and, for most animals, completely indigestible.

Another form of isomerism is found in monosaccharides, as well as in other molecules. Two molecules with the same chemical formula but atoms that are arranged in different ways are called structural isomers. The sugars glucose and fructose are examples of structural isomers.

a. Glucose (an aldehyde)

b. Fructose (a ketone)

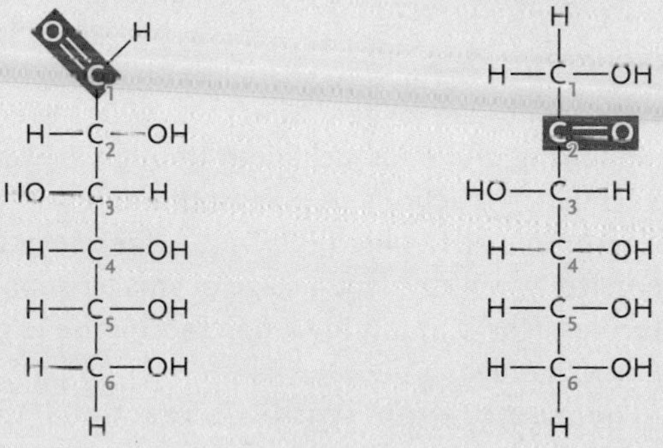

Disaccharides

Disaccharides typically are assembled from two monosaccharides linked together by a dehydration synthesis reaction. For example, the disaccharide maltose is formed by the linkage of two α-glucose molecules with oxygen as a bridge between the number 1 carbon of the first glucose unit and the 4 carbon of the second glucose unit. Bonds of this type, which commonly link monosaccharides into chains, are known as glycosidic bonds. A glycosidic bond between a 1 carbon and a 4 carbon is written in chemical shorthand as a 1→4 linkage. Linkages such as 1→2, 1→3, and 1→6 are also common in carbohydrate chains. The linkages are designated as α or β depending on the orientation of the —OH group at the 1 carbon that forms the bond. In maltose, the —OH group is in the α position. Therefore, the link between the two glucose subunits of maltose is written as an α(1→4) linkage. Maltose, sucrose, and lactose are common disaccharides.

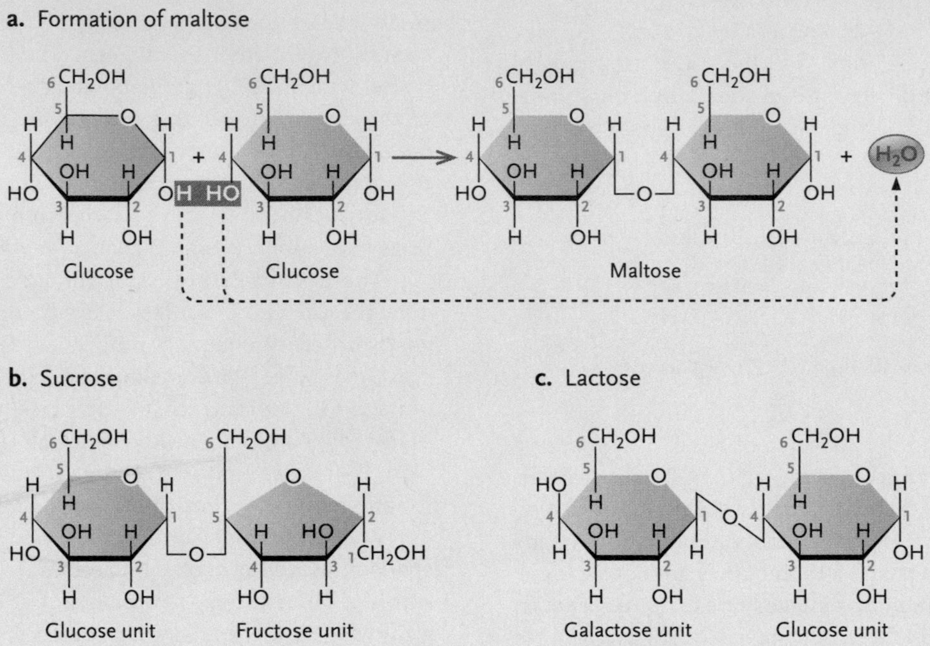

a. Formation of maltose

Glucose + Glucose → Maltose + H_2O

b. Sucrose

Glucose unit, Fructose unit

c. Lactose

Galactose unit, Glucose unit

Polysaccharides

Polysaccharides are longer chains formed by the end-to-end linking of monosaccharides through dehydration synthesis reactions. A polysaccharide is a type of macromolecule, which is a very large molecule assembled by the covalent linkage of smaller subunit molecules. The subunit for a polysaccharide is the monosaccharide.

The dehydration synthesis reactions that assemble polysaccharides from monosaccharides are examples of polymerization, in which identical or nearly identical subunits, called the monomers of the reaction, join like links in a chain to form a larger molecule called a polymer. Linkage of a relatively small number of nonidentical subunits can create highly diverse and varied biological molecules. Many kinds of polymers are found in cells, not just polysaccharides. DNA is a primary example of a highly diverse polymer assembled from various sequences of only four different types of monomers.

The most common polysaccharides—the plant starches, glycogen, and cellulose—are all assembled from hundreds or thousands of glucose units. Other polysaccharides are built up from a variety of different sugar units. Polysaccharides may be linear, unbranched molecules, or they may contain one or more branches in which side chains of sugar units are attached to a main chain.

continued on next page

a.

Amylose, formed from α-glucose units joined end to end in α(1→4) linkages. The coiled structures are induced by the bond angles in the α-linkages.

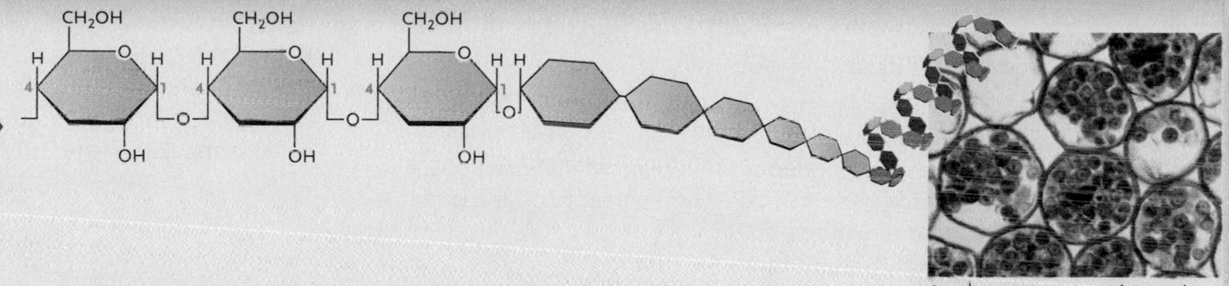

Amylose grains (purple) in plant root tissue (Ed Reschke/Peter Arnold, Inc.)

b.

Glycogen, formed from glucose units joined in chains by α(1→4) linkages; side branches are linked to the chains by α(1→6) linkages (boxed in blue).

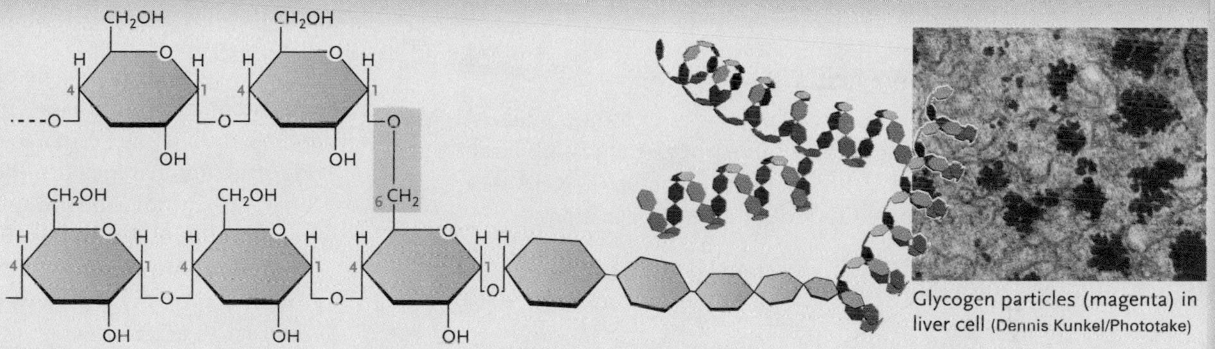

Glycogen particles (magenta) in liver cell (Dennis Kunkel/Phototake)

c.

Cellulose, formed from glucose units joined end to end by β(1→4) linkages. Hundreds to thousands of cellulose chains line up side by side, in an arrangement reinforced by hydrogen bonds between the chains, to form cellulose microfibrils in plant cells.

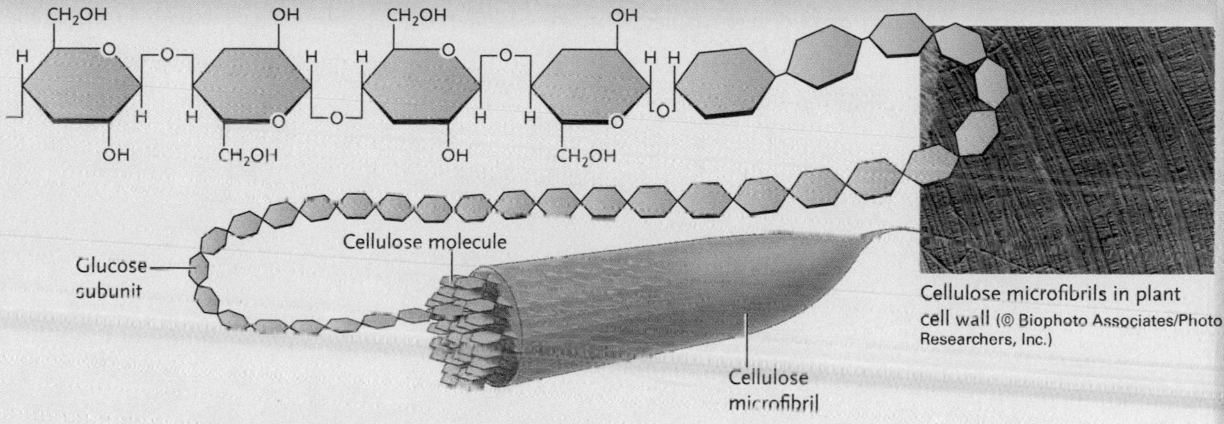

Cellulose molecule

Glucose subunit

Cellulose microfibril

Cellulose microfibrils in plant cell wall (© Biophoto Associates/Photo Researchers, Inc.)

d.

Chitin, formed from β-linkages joining glucose units modified by the addition of nitrogen-containing groups. The external body armor of the tick is reinforced by chitin fibres.

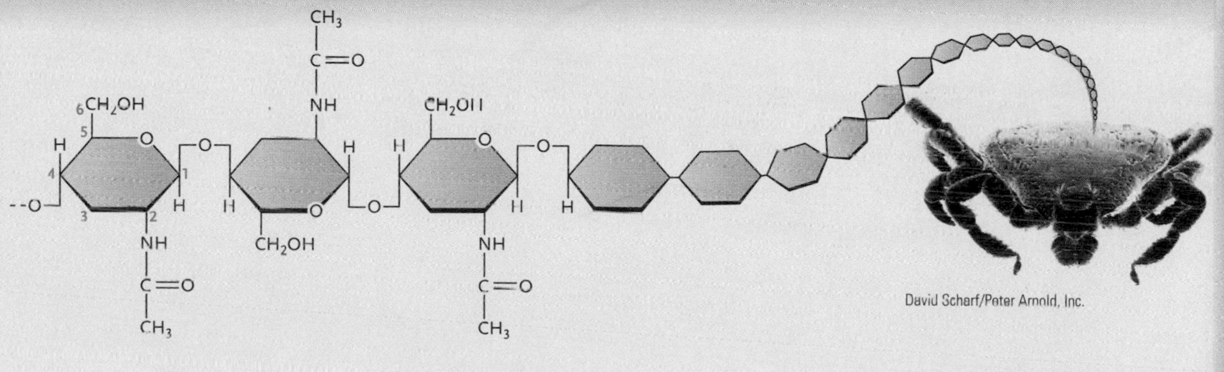

David Scharf/Peter Arnold, Inc.

Proteins

Proteins perform many vital functions in living organisms:

- Structural proteins provide much of the supporting framework of cells
- Enzymes accelerate the rate of cellular reactions.
- Motile proteins impart movement to cells and cellular structures.
- Transport proteins transport substances across biological membranes.
- Proteins serve as recognition and receptor molecules at cell surfaces.
- Proteins regulate the activity of other proteins and DNA.

Amino Acids

All proteins are polymers of amino acids. Amino acids share a similar structure with a central carbon atom attached to an amino group (—NH_2), a carboxyl group (—COOH), and a hydrogen atom:

$$\begin{array}{c} R \\ | \\ H_2N—C—COOH \\ | \\ H \end{array}$$

The remaining bond of the central carbon is linked to 1 of 19 different side groups represented by the *R*, ranging from a single hydrogen atom to complex carbon chains or rings. The one exception to this organization is the amino acid proline, which has a ring structure that includes the central carbon atom. Differences in the side groups give the amino acids their individual properties. Some side groups are polar and some are nonpolar; among the polar side groups, some carry a positive or negative charge and some act as acids or bases. Many of the side groups contain reactive functional groups, such as —NH_2, —OH, —COOH, or —SH, which may interact with atoms located elsewhere in the same protein or with molecules and ions outside the protein.

Nonpolar amino acids

Alanine
Ala
A

Valine
Val
V

Leucine
Leu
L

Isoleucine
Ile
I

Glycine
Gly
G

Cysteine
Cys
C

Phenylalanine
Phe
F

Tryptophan
Trp
W

Methionine
Met
M

Proline
Pro
P

Uncharged polar amino acids

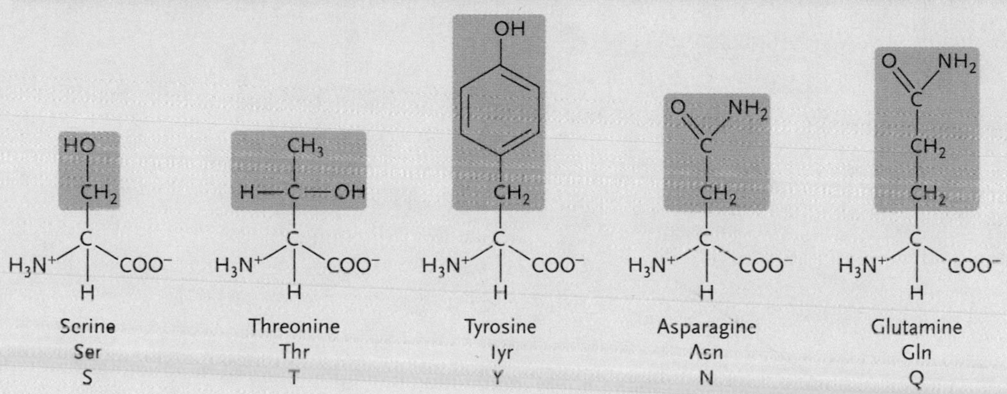

Negatively charged (acidic) polar amino acids

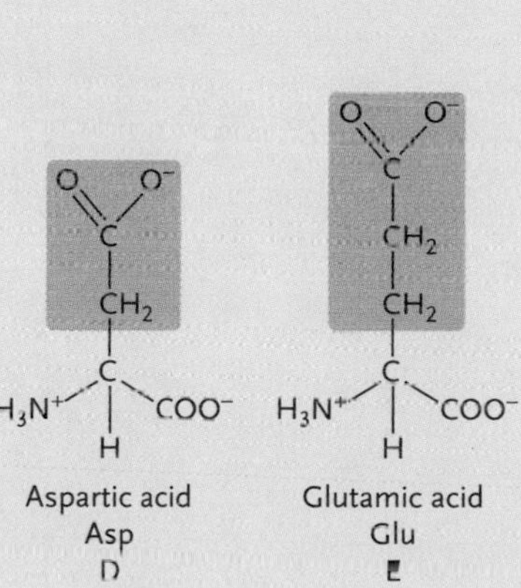

Positively charged (basic) polar amino acids

Lysine
Lys
K

Arginine
Arg
R

Histidine
His
H

Peptides

Covalent bonds link amino acids into chains of subunits that make proteins. The link, a peptide bond, is formed by a dehydration synthesis reaction between the —NH_2 group of one amino acid and the —COOH group of a second. An amino acid chain always has an —NH_2 group at one end, called the N-terminal end, and a —COOH group at the other end, called the C-terminal end. In cells, amino acids are added only to the —COOH end of the growing peptide strand.

The chain or polymer of amino acids formed by sequential peptide bonds is called a peptide. A *polypeptide* is usually defined as a peptide greater than 50 amino acids in length. A protein is one or more polypeptides that are folded into a precise three-dimensional shape. Only after this occurs is the polypeptide able to function.

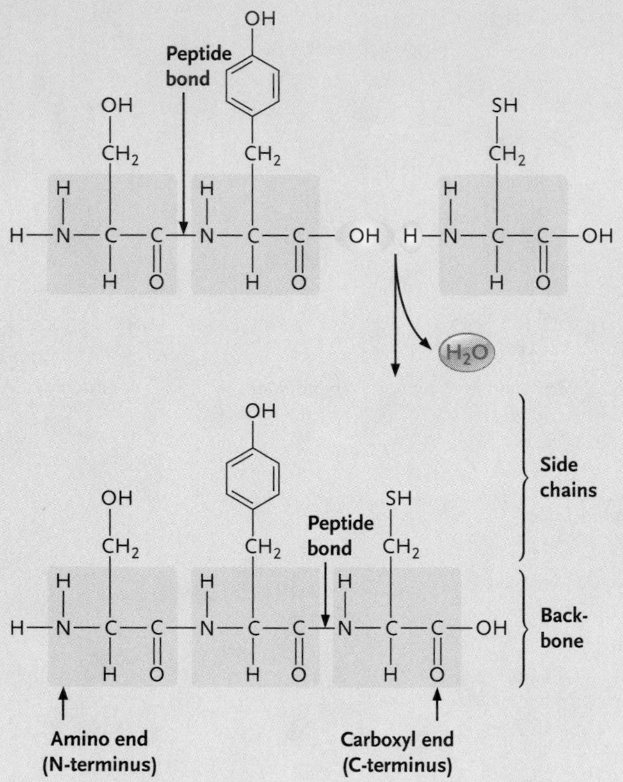

Protein Structure

Proteins potentially have four levels of structure, with each level imparting different characteristics and degrees of complexity to the molecule.

Primary Structure

The primary structure of a protein is the linear sequence of its amino acids. The types of amino acids and their order underlie all other higher levels of structure. Changing even a single amino acid of the primary structure alters the secondary, tertiary, and quaternary structures to at least some degree and, by so doing, can alter or even destroy the biological function of that protein.

H_3N^+—Phe|Val|Asn|Gln|His|Leu|Cys|Gly|Ala—COO^-

Secondary Structure

Most proteins have portions that repeatedly coil or fold into patterns that contribute to the overall shape of a protein. This secondary structure is the result of hydrogen bonding among molecules of the amino acid backbone. Specifically, hydrogen bonding occurs between the electronegative nitrogen and oxygen atoms and the hydrogen atoms. Two highly regular secondary structures are the alpha helix (right) and the beta pleated sheet (below). A beta sheet is formed by side-by-side alignment of two amino acid chains. The arrows point in the direction of the C-terminal end of the amino acid chain.

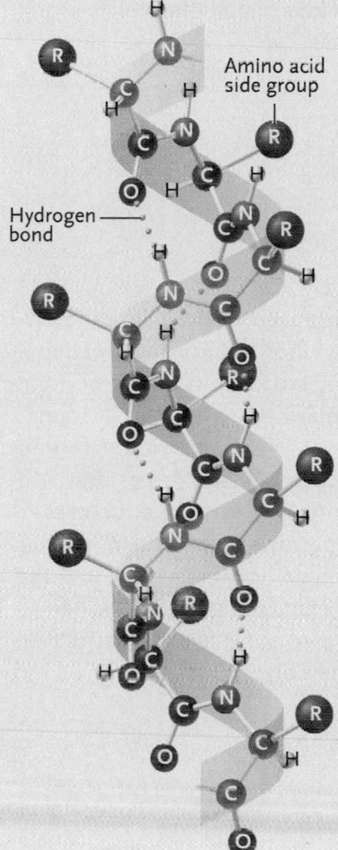

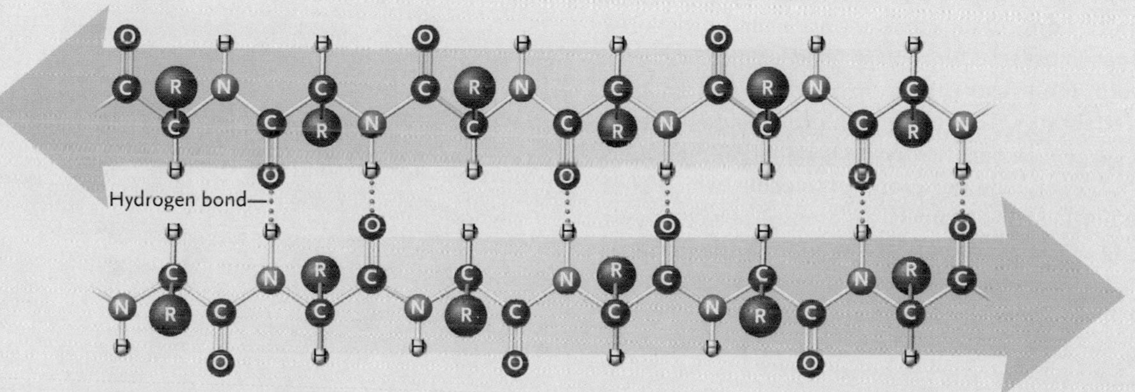

continued on next page

Tertiary Structure

Whereas the secondary structure of a protein is the result of interactions among molecules of the backbone, the overall shape of a protein is due to a range of bonding interactions among the amino acid R-groups. These include (1) ionic bonds, (2) hydrogen bonds, (3) hydrophobic interactions, and (4) disulphide bridges. The specific bonding arrangements between R groups give rise to a protein's distinctive three-dimensional shape, or *conformation*. This final conformation displays limited shape changes, a feature that is critical to the function of certain proteins, especially enzymes. Extreme conditions (temperature, pH, etc.) can unfold a protein from its conformation, causing denaturation, a loss of both the structure and the function of the protein.

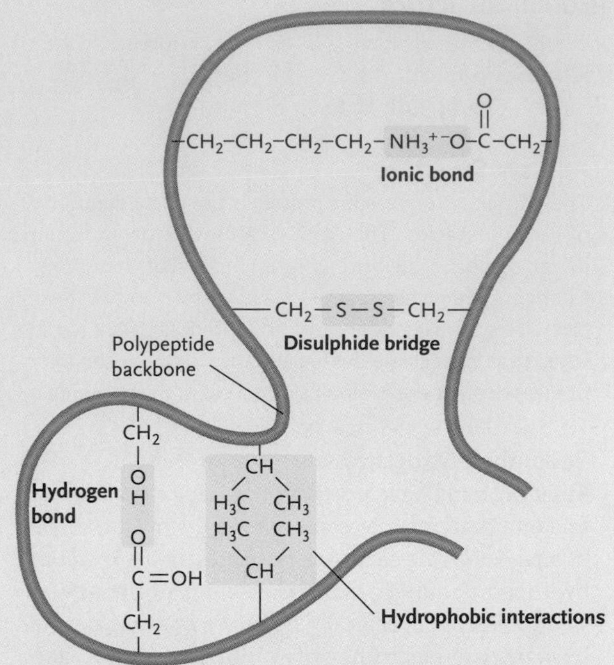

Quaternary Structure

Some proteins are composed of two or more polypeptides that come together to form the functional protein. This quaternary structure is a level of organization that exists in many proteins, such as hemoglobin, which comprises four individual folded polypeptides. The same bonds and forces that fold single amino acid chains into tertiary structures—including hydrogen bonds, polar and nonpolar attractions, and disulphide linkages—also hold the multiple polypeptide chains together. The hemoglobin molecule (left) displays quaternary structure as it is composed of four polypeptides.

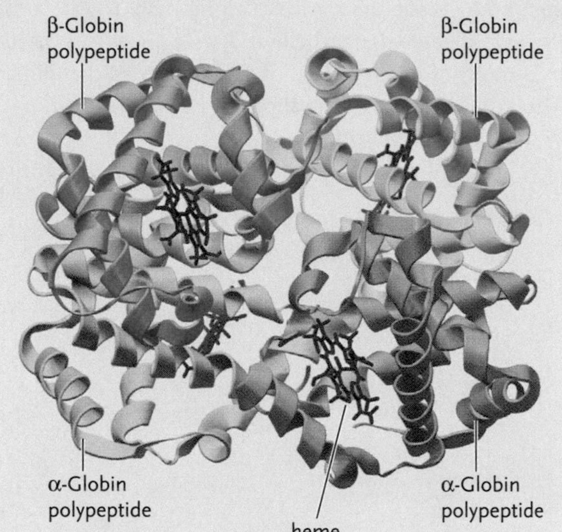

Prosthetic Groups

Besides properly folded peptides, many proteins require nonprotein components called prosthetic groups in order to function. A good example is hemoglobin, the major protein involved in O_2 transport in vertebrates. The four globin proteins do not bind the oxygen; rather, the oxygen is bound to molecules called *heme*, one per protein molecule, which bind specifically to the proteins. Chlorophyll is a prosthetic group of many proteins of the photosynthetic apparatus, and many enzymes require metal-containing prosthetic groups in order to function.

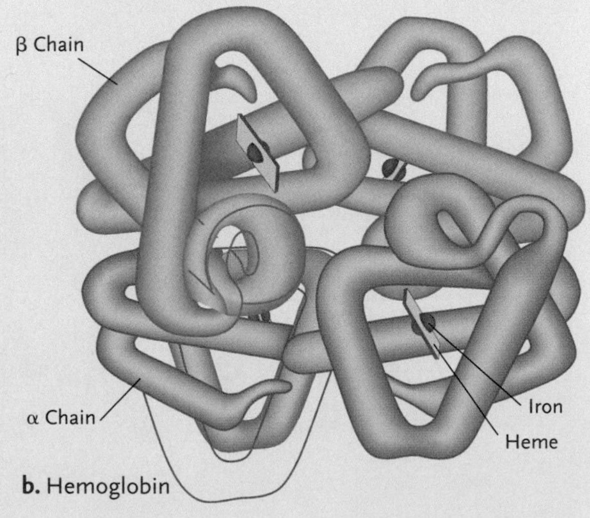

b. Hemoglobin

Nucleic Acids

Two types of nucleic acids exist: DNA and RNA. Deoxyribonucleic acid (DNA) stores the hereditary information responsible for inherited traits in all eukaryotes and prokaryotes and in many viruses. Ribonucleic acid (RNA) is the hereditary molecule of some viruses. Types of RNA are found in all organisms:

- Messenger RNA carries the instructions for assembling proteins from DNA to the ribosomes, the organelles that assemble proteins.
- Ribosomal RNA forms part of ribosomes.
- Transfer RNA brings amino acids to the ribosome for their assembly into proteins.

Nucleotides

All nucleic acids are polymers of nucleotides. A nucleotide consists of three parts linked together by covalent bonds: (1) a nitrogenous base formed from rings of carbon and nitrogen atoms; (2) a five-carbon, ring-shaped sugar; and (3) one to three phosphate groups.

In nucleotides, the nitrogenous bases link covalently to a five-carbon sugar, either **deoxyribose** or **ribose.** The carbons of the two sugars are numbered with a prime symbol—1′, 2′, 3′, 4′, and 5′. The prime symbols are added to distinguish the carbons in the sugars from those in the nitrogenous bases, which are written without primes. The two sugars differ only in the chemical group bound to the 2′ carbon: deoxyribose has an —H at this position, and ribose has an —OH group.

The two types of nitrogenous bases are pyrimidines, with one carbon–nitrogen ring, and purines, with two rings. Three pyrimidine bases—uracil (U), thymine (T), and cytosine (C)—and two purine bases—adenine (A) and guanine (G)—form parts of nucleic acids in cells.

All nucleic acids are polymers of nucleotides. A nucleotide consists of three parts linked together by covalent bonds:

a. Overall structural plan of a nucleotide

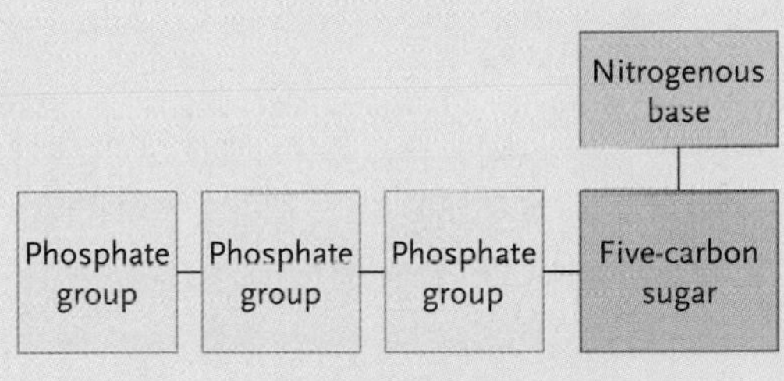

b. Chemical structures of nucleotides

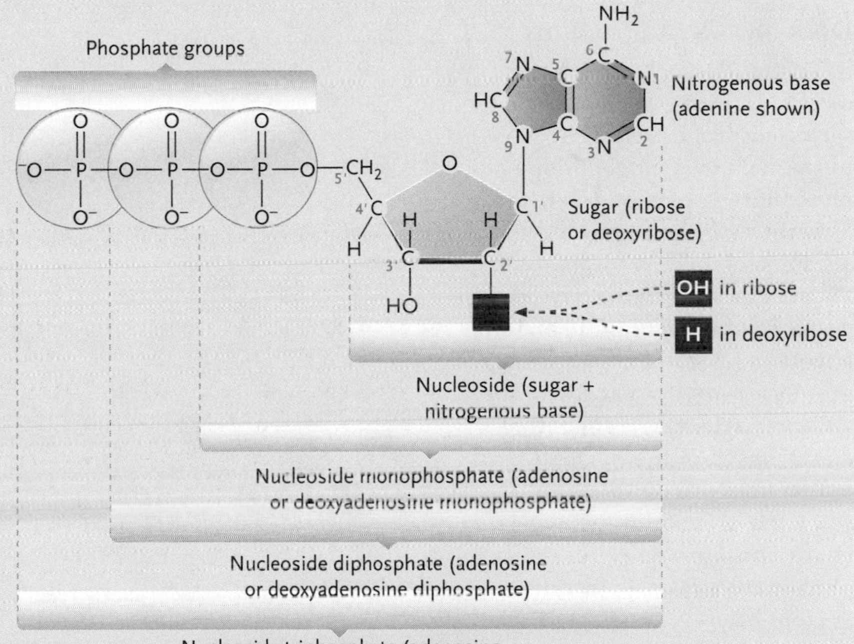

Other nucleotides:

Containing guanine:	Guanosine or deoxyguanosine monophosphate, diphosphate, or triphosphate
Containing cytosine:	Cytidine or deoxycytidine monophosphate, diphosphate, or triphosphate
Containing thymine:	Thymidine monophosphate, diphosphate, or triphosphate
Containing uracil:	Uridine monophosphate, diphosphate, or triphosphate

continued on next page

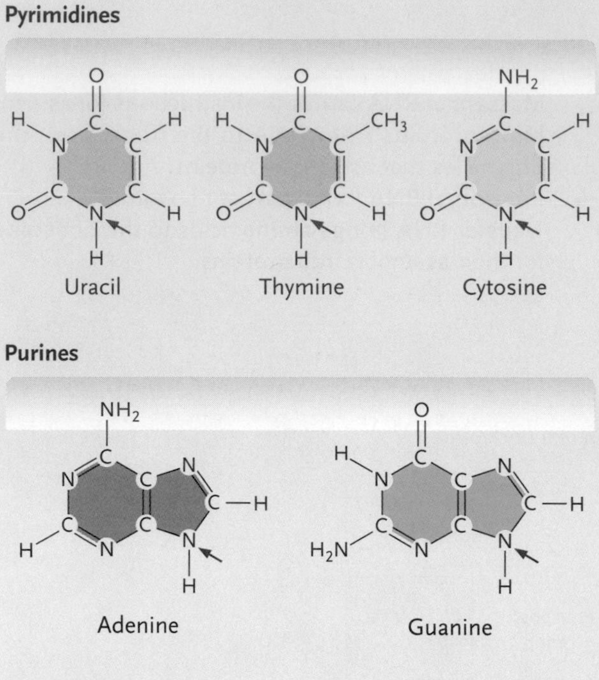

Pyrimidines

Purines

Nucleotides perform many functions in cells in addition to serving as the building blocks of nucleic acids. Two nucleotides in particular, adenosine triphosphate (ATP) and guanosine triphosphate (GTP), are the primary molecules that transport chemical energy from one reaction system to another; the same nucleotides function to regulate and adjust cellular activity.

DNA and RNA Structure

DNA and RNA consist of chains of nucleotides—*polynucleotide chains*—with one nucleotide linked to the next by a single bridging phosphate group between the 5′ carbon of one sugar and the 3′ carbon of the next sugar in line. This linkage is called a *phosphodiester bond.* This arrangement of alternating sugar and phosphate groups forms the backbone of a nucleic acid chain. The nitrogenous bases of the nucleotides project from this backbone.

Each nucleotide of a DNA chain contains deoxyribose, a phosphate group, and one of the four bases A, T, G, or C. Each nucleotide of an RNA chain contains ribose, a phosphate, and one of the four bases A, U, G, or C.

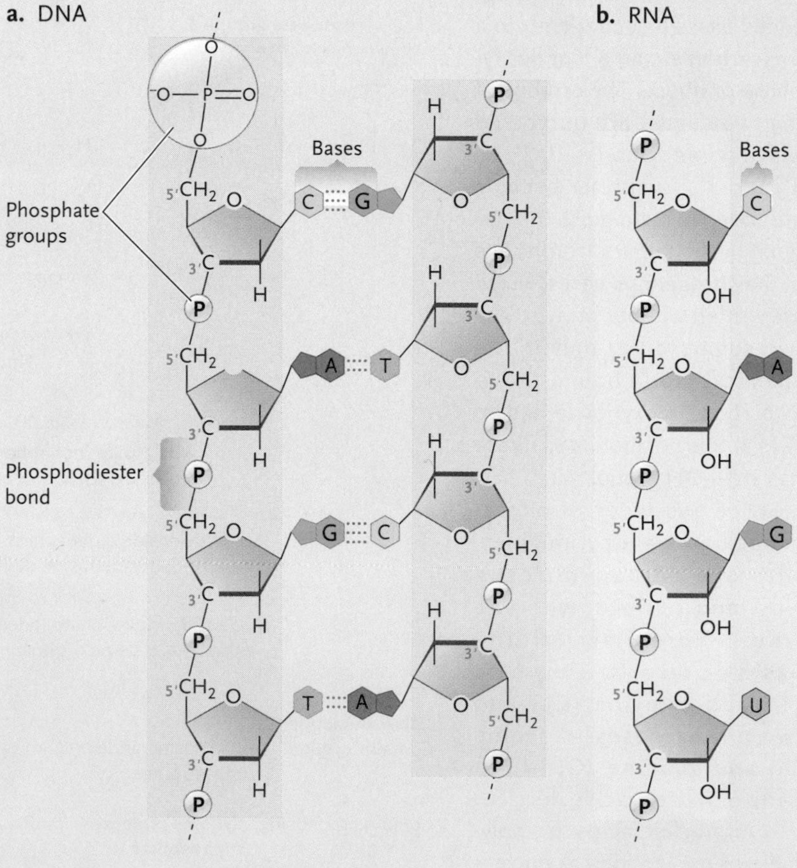

The DNA Double Helix

In cells, DNA takes the form of a double helix: two nucleotide chains wrapped around each other in a spiral that resembles a twisted ladder. The sides of the ladder are the sugar–phosphate backbones of the two chains, which twist around each other in a right-handed direction to form the double helix. The rungs of the ladder are the nitrogenous bases, which extend inward from the sugars toward the centre of the helix. Each rung consists of a pair of nitrogenous bases held in a flat plane roughly perpendicular to the long axis of the helix. The two nucleotide chains of a DNA double helix are held together primarily by hydrogen bonds between the base pairs. Slightly more than 10 base pairs are packed into each turn of the double helix. A DNA double-helix molecule is also referred to as double-stranded DNA.

The space separating the sugar–phosphate backbones of a DNA double helix is just wide enough to accommodate a base pair that consists of one purine and one pyrimidine. Purine–purine base pairs are too wide and pyrimidine–pyrimidine pairs are too narrow to fit this space exactly. More specifically, of the possible purine–pyrimidine pairs, only two combinations, adenine with thymine and guanine with cytosine, can form stable hydrogen bonds so that the base pair fits precisely within the double helix. An adenine–thymine (A-T) pair forms two stabilizing hydrogen bonds; a guanine–cytosine (G-C) pair forms three.

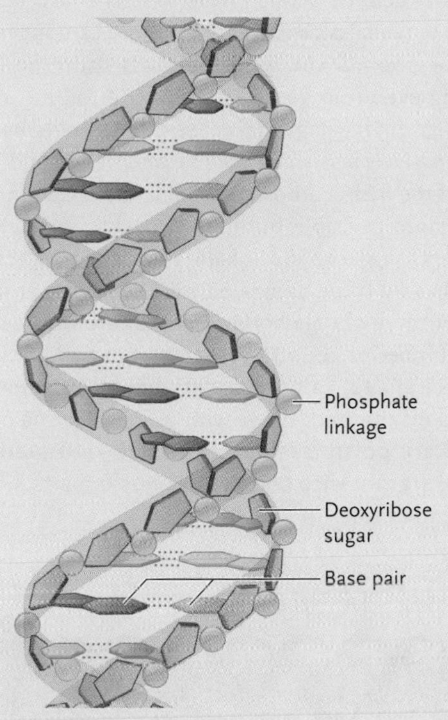

To deoxyribose

To deoxyribose

Adenine

Thymine

To deoxyribose

To deoxyribose

Guanine

Cytosine

Lipids

Lipids are a diverse group of water-insoluble, primarily nonpolar biological molecules composed mostly of hydrogen and carbon (hydrocarbons). The term lipid is a catch-all word for a range of nonpolar molecules. They are not large enough to be considered true macromolecules and, unlike nucleic acids and proteins, are not considered polymers of defined monomeric subunits. As a result of their nonpolar character, lipids typically dissolve much more readily in nonpolar solvents, such as acetone and chloroform, than in water. Their insolubility in water underlies their ability to form cell membranes. In addition, some lipids are stored and used in cells as an energy source. Other lipids serve as hormones that regulate cellular activities. Lipids in living organisms can be grouped into one of three categories—fats, phospholipids, and steroids.

Isoprenes and Fatty Acids

The structural backbone of all lipids is derived from one of two hydrocarbon molecules: isoprene or fatty acids. Isoprenes are five-carbon molecules that when linked together can form long hydrocarbon chains. Isoprenes are the structural unit in steroids and a number of phospholipids. A fatty acid consists of a single hydrocarbon chain with a carboxyl group (—COOH) linked at one end. The carboxyl group gives the fatty acid its acidic properties. The fatty acids in living organisms contain four or more carbons in their hydrocarbon chain, with the most common forms having even-numbered chains of 14 to 22 carbons. As their chain length increases, fatty acids become progressively less water soluble and more solid.

If the hydrocarbon chain of a fatty acid binds the maximum possible number of hydrogen atoms, so that only single bonds link the carbon atoms, the fatty acid is said to be saturated with hydrogen atoms. If one or more double bonds link the carbons, reducing the number of bound hydrogen atoms, the fatty acid is unsaturated. Fatty acids with one double bond are monounsaturated; those with more than one double bond are polyunsaturated. Unlike saturated fatty acids, the presence of double bonds imparts a "kink" in the molecule.

a. Isoprene

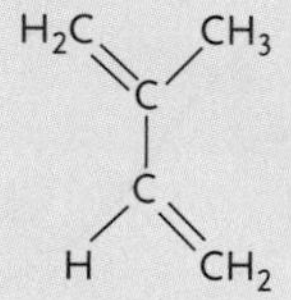

H_2C CH_3 C C H CH_2

b. Fatty acid

HO O C Carboxyl group

H_2C CH_2 H_2C CH_2 H_2C CH_2 H_2C CH_2 H_2C CH_2 H_2C CH_2 H_2C CH_2 H_2C CH_3 Hydrocarbon chain

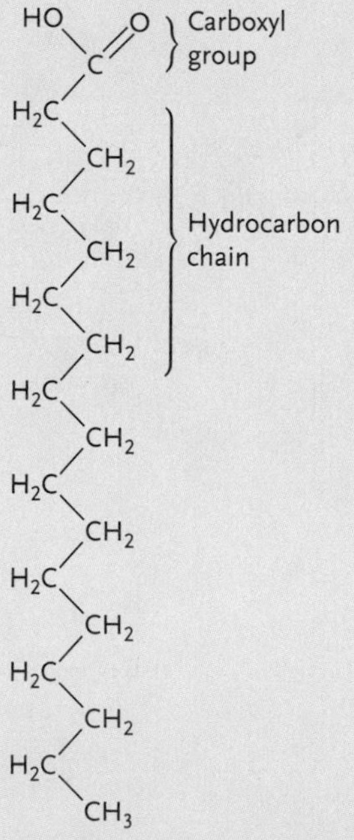

c. Stearic acid, $CH_3(CH_2)_{16}COOH$

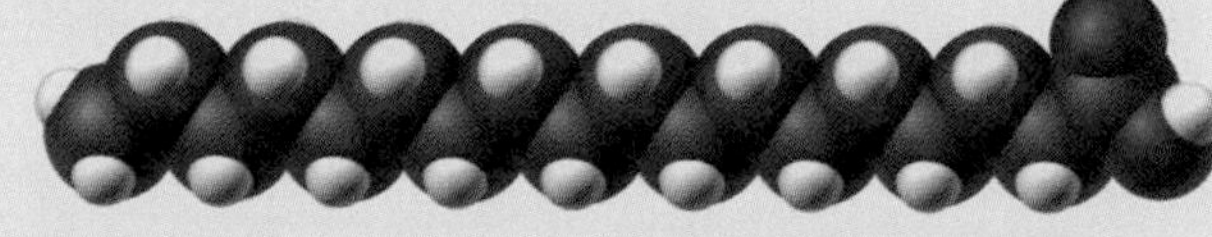

d. Oleic acid, $CH_3(CH_2)_7CH{=}CH(CH_2)_7COOH$

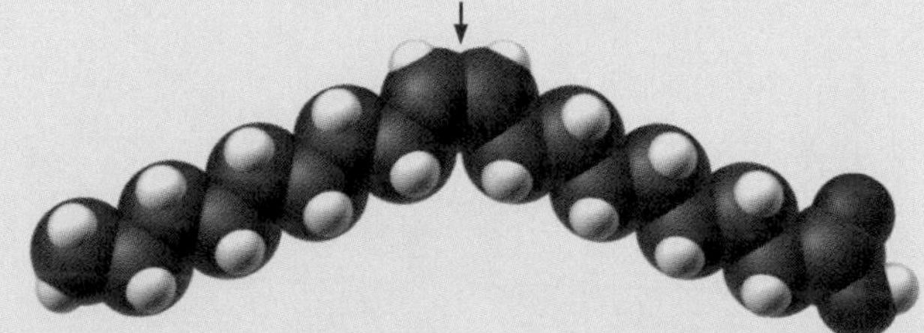

Fats

A fat consists of three fatty acid chains linked to a single molecule of glycerol. Because of this, fats are also often referred to as triacylglycerols or triglycerides. The three fatty acids linked to the glycerol may be different or the same. Different organisms usually have distinctive combinations of fatty acids in their triglycerides. As with individual fatty acids, triglycerides generally become less fluid as the length of their fatty acid chains increases; those with shorter chains remain liquid as oils at biological temperatures, and those with longer chains solidify.

Triglycerides are used widely as stored energy in animals. Gram for gram, they yield more than twice as much energy as carbohydrates. Therefore, fats are an excellent source of energy in the diet. Storing the equivalent amount of energy as carbohydrates rather than fats would add more than 100 pounds to the weight of an average man or woman. A layer of fatty tissue just under the skin also serves as an insulating blanket in humans, other mammals, and birds. Triglycerides secreted from special glands in waterfowl and other birds help make feathers water repellent.

a. Formation of a triglyceride

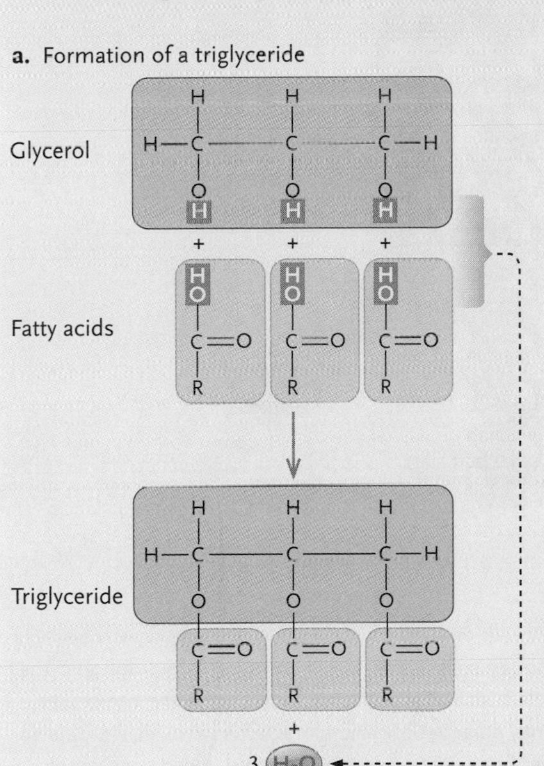

b. Glyceryl palmitate

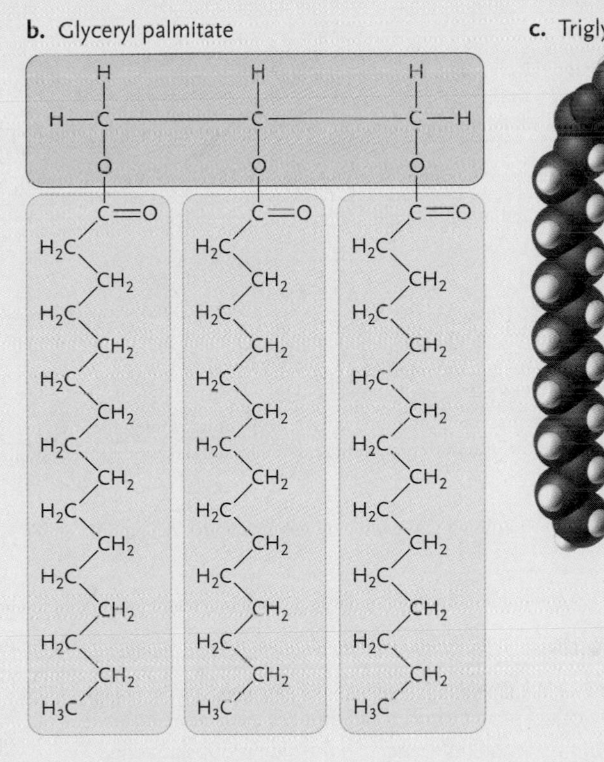

c. Triglyceride model

Phospholipids

Phosphate-containing lipids called phospholipids are the primary lipids of cell membranes. In the most common phospholipids, glycerol forms the backbone for the molecule as in triglycerides, but only two of its binding sites are linked to fatty acids. The third site is linked to a polar phosphate group, which also binds to another polar unit. Thus, a phospholipid contains two hydrophobic fatty acids at one end, attached to a hydrophilic polar group, often called the head group. Molecules that contain both hydrophobic and hydrophilic regions are called amphipathic molecules.

continued on next page

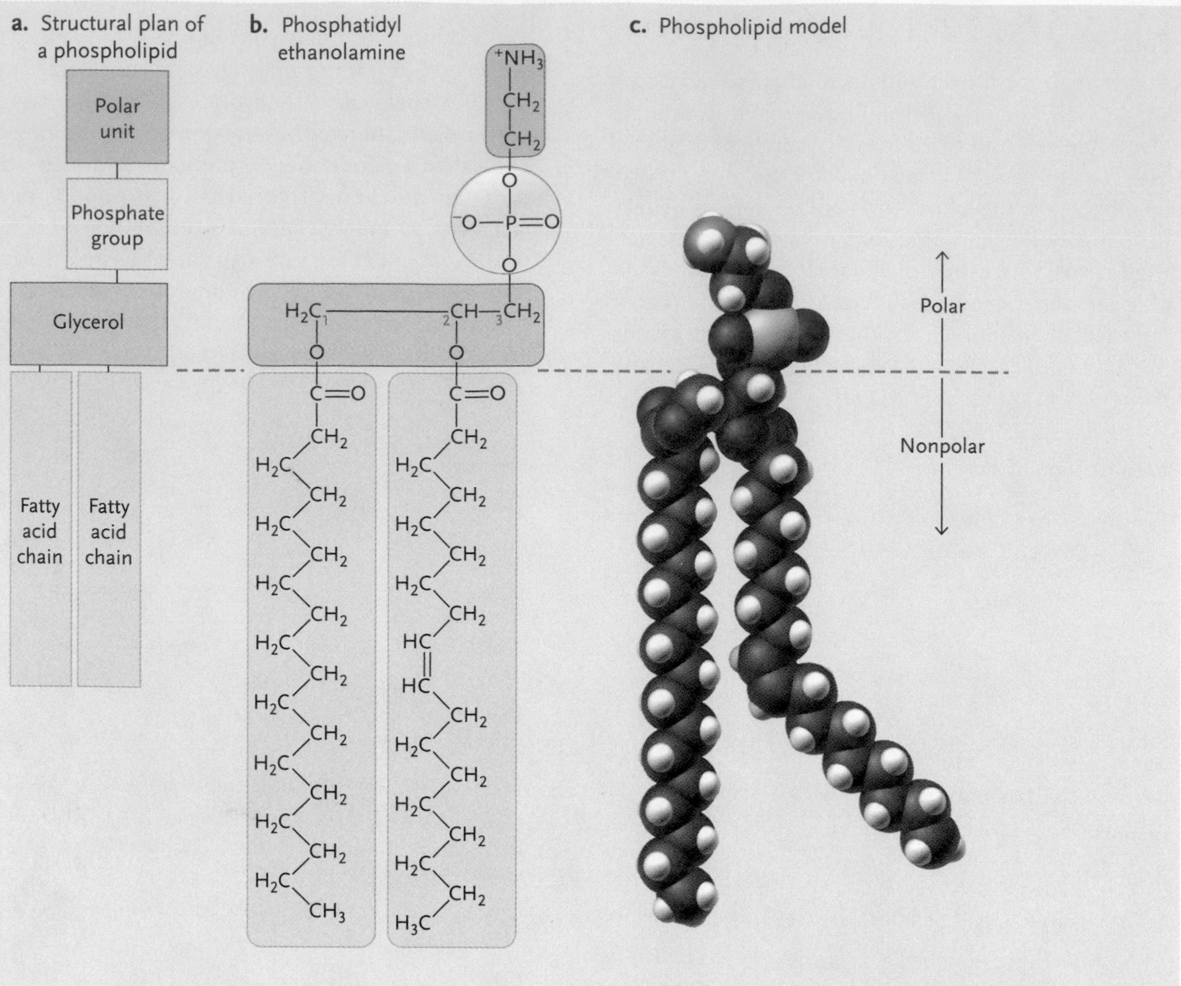

Steroids

Steroids are a group of lipids with structures based on a framework of four carbon rings that are derived from isoprene units. Small differences in the side groups attached to the rings distinguish one steroid from another. The most abundant steroids, the sterols, have a single polar —OH group linked to one end of the ring framework and a complex, nonpolar hydrocarbon chain at the other end.

Although sterols are almost completely hydrophobic, the single hydroxyl group gives one end of the molecules a slightly polar, hydrophilic character. As a result, sterols also have dual solubility properties and, like phospholipids, tend to assume positions that satisfy these properties.

Cholesterol is an important component of the plasma membrane surrounding animal cells; similar sterols, called phytosterols, occur in plant cell membranes.

a. Arrangement of carbon rings in a steroid

b. Cholesterol, a sterol

c. Cholesterol model

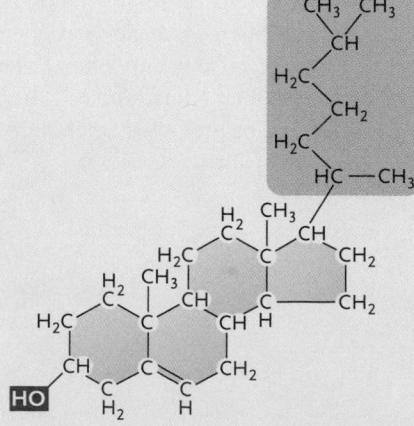

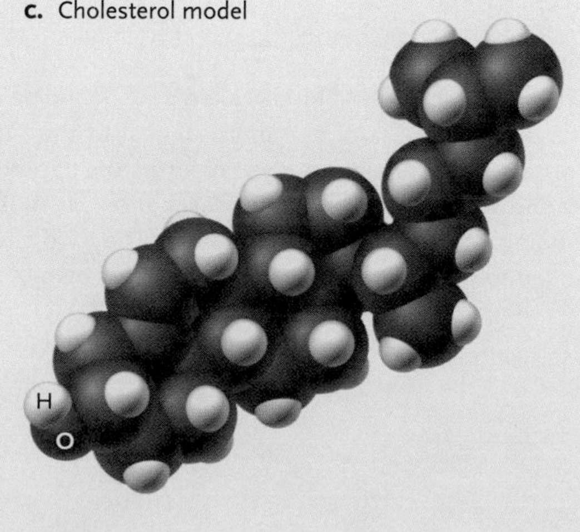

Model Research Organisms

Certain species or groups of organisms have become favourite subjects for laboratory and field studies because their characteristics make them relatively easy research subjects. In most cases, such **model organisms** became popular because they have rapid development, short life cycles, and small adult size. Thus, researchers can rear and house large numbers of them in the laboratory. Also, as fuller portraits of their genetics and other aspects of their biology emerge, their appeal as research subjects tends to grow because biologists have a better understanding of the biological context within which specific processes occur. Because the fundamental elements of biochemistry, development, and evolution are common to all organisms, research on these small and often simple model organisms provides insights into biological processes that operate in and among larger and more complex organisms.

As a cautionary note, you should also be aware that the very characteristics that make model organisms valuable for research may make them poor representatives of other organisms in that group. Thus, specific findings from *Drosophila* or *Caenorhabditis elegans* may not be generally applicable to other insects or nematodes, respectively. The use of model organisms only, to the exclusion of others, may obscure the richness of biological diversity.

Escherichia coli

We probably know more about *Escherichia coli* than any other organism. For example, microbiologists have deciphered the complete DNA sequence of the genome of a standard laboratory strain of *E. coli,* including the sequence of the approximately 4400 genes in its genome. The functions of about one-third of these genes are still unidentified; however, *E. coli* got its start in laboratory research because of the ease with which it can be grown in cultures. Because *E. coli* cells divide about every 20 minutes under optimal conditions, a clone of 1 billion cells can be grown in a matter of hours in only 10 mL of culture medium. The same amount of medium can accommodate as many as 10 billion cells before the growth rate begins to slow. *E. coli* strains can be grown in the laboratory with minimal equipment, requiring little more than culture vessels in an incubator held at 37°C.

The study of naturally occurring plasmids in *E. coli* and of enzymes that cut DNA at specific sequences eventually resulted in the development of recombinant DNA techniques—procedures to combine DNA from different sources. Today, ***E. coli*** is used extensively for creating such molecules and for amplifying (cloning) them once they are made. In essence, the biotechnology industry has its foundation in molecular genetics studies of *E. coli.* Large-scale *E. coli* cultures are widely used as "factories" for the production of desired proteins. For example, the human insulin hormone, required for treatment of certain forms of diabetes, can be produced by *E. coli* factories.

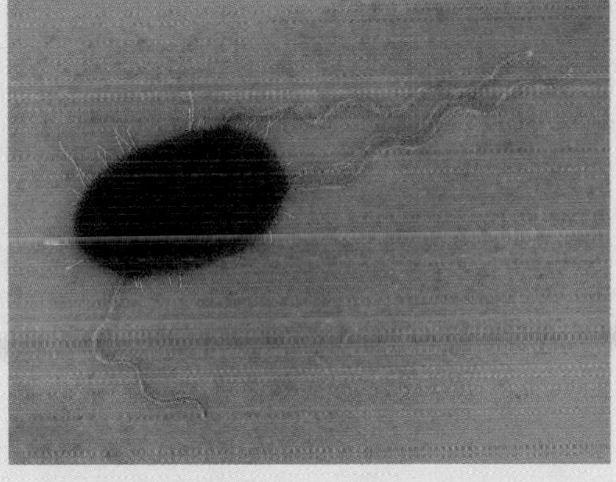

Dennis Kunkel Microscopy, Inc.

Saccharomyces cerevisiae

Commonly known as baker's yeast or brewer's yeast, *Saccharomyces cerevisiae* was probably the first microorganism to have been domesticated by humans—a beer-brewing vessel is basically a *Saccharomyces* culture. Favourite strains of baker's and brewer's yeasts have been kept in continuous cultures for centuries. The yeast has also been widely used in scientific research; its microscopic size and relatively short generation time make it easy and inexpensive to culture in large numbers in the laboratory.

The complete DNA sequence of *S. cerevisiae,* which includes more than 12 million base pairs that encode about 6000 genes, was the first eukaryotic genome to be determined. Plasmids, extrachromosomal segments of DNA, have been produced that are used to introduce genes into yeast cells. Using plasmids, researchers can experimentally alter any of the yeast genes to test their functions and can introduce genes or DNA samples from other organisms for testing or cloning. These genetic engineering studies have demonstrated that many mammalian genes can replace yeast genes when introduced into the fungi, confirming their close relationships, even though mammals and fungi are separated by millions of years of evolution. *S. cerevisiae* has been so important to genetic studies in eukaryotes that it is often called the eukaryotic *E. coli.* Research with another yeast, *Schizosaccharomyces pombe,* has been similarly productive, particularly in studies of genes that control the cell cycle.

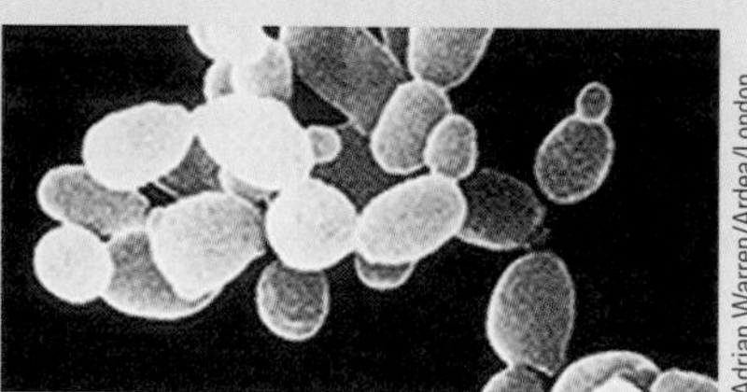

Adrian Warren/Ardea/London

Drosophila melanogaster

The unobtrusive little fruit fly that appears seemingly from nowhere when rotting fruit or a fermented beverage is around is one of the mainstays of genetic research. It was first described in 1830 by C. F. Fallén, who named it *Drosophila,* meaning "dew lover." The species identifier became *melanogaster,* which means "black belly." The great geneticist Thomas Hunt Morgan began to culture *D. melanogaster* in 1909 in the famous "Fly Room" at Columbia University. Many important discoveries in genetics were made in the Fly Room, including sex-linked genes and sex linkage and the first chromosome map. The subsequent development of methods to induce mutations in *Drosophila* led, through studies of the mutants produced, to many other discoveries that collectively established or confirmed essentially all the major principles and conclusions of eukaryotic genetics.

One reason for the success of *D. melanogaster* as a subject for genetics research is the ease of culturing it. It is grown usually at 25°C in small bottles stopped with a cotton or plastic foam wad and about one-third filled with a fermenting medium that contains water, cornmeal, agar, molasses, and yeast. The several hundred eggs laid by each adult female hatch rapidly and progress through larval and pupal stages to produce adult flies in about 10 days. These are ready to breed within 10 to 12 hours. Males and females can be identified easily with the unaided eye.

Many types of mutations produce morphological differences, such as changes in eye colour, wing shape, or the numbers and shapes of bristles, which can be seen with the unaided eye or under a low-power binocular microscope. The salivary gland cells of the fly larvae have giant chromosomes that are so large that differences can be observed directly with the light microscope. The availability of a wide range of mutants, comprehensive linkage maps of each of its chromosomes, and the ability to manipulate genes readily by molecular techniques made the fruit fly genome one of the first to be sequenced. The sequencing of *Drosophila*'s genome was completed in 2001; it has approximately 14 000 genes in its 165 million-base-pair genome. (A database of the *Drosophila* genome is available at http://flybase.bio.indiana.edu.) Importantly, the relationship between fruit fly and human genes is close, to the point that many human disease genes have counterparts in the fruit fly genome. This similarity enables the fly genes to be studied as models of human disease genes to understand better the functions of those genes and how alterations in them can lead to disease.

The analysis of fruit fly embryonic development has also contributed significantly to the understanding of development in humans. For example, experiments on mutants that affect fly development have provided insights into the genetic basis of many human birth defects. Before making a career as an environmentalist, Dr. David Suzuki studied temperature-sensitive neurological mutants at the University of British Columbia.

Herman Eisenbeiss/Photo Researchers, Inc.

Caenorhabditis elegans

Researchers studying the tiny, free-living nematode *C. elegans* have made many advances in molecular genetics, animal development, and neurobiology. It is so popular as a model research organism that most workers simply refer to it as "the worm." Several attributes make *C. elegans* a model research organism. The adult is about 1 mm long and thrives on cultures of *E. coli* or other bacteria; thus, thousands can be raised in a culture dish. It completes its life cycle from egg to reproductive adult within three days at room temperature. Furthermore, stock cultures can be kept alive indefinitely by freezing them in liquid nitrogen or in an ultra-cold freezer (−80°C). Researchers can therefore store new mutants for later research without having to clean, feed, and maintain active cultures. Best of all, the worm is anatomically simple; an adult contains just 959 cells (excluding the gonads). Having a fixed cell number is relatively uncommon among animals, and developmental biologists have made good use of this trait. The eggs, juveniles, and adults of the worm are completely transparent, and researchers can observe cell divisions and cell movements in living animals with straightforward microscopy techniques. There is no need to kill, fix, and stain specimens for study. And virtually every cell in the worm's body is accessible for manipulation by laser microsurgery, microinjection, and similar approaches.

The genome of *C. elegans*, which was sequenced in 1998, is also simple, consisting of 100 million base pairs organized into roughly 17 000 genes on 6 pairs of chromosomes. The genome, which is about the same size as 1 human chromosome, specifies the amino acid sequences of about 10 000 protein molecules—far fewer than are found in more complex animals.

The knowledge gained from research on *C. elegans* is highly relevant to studies of larger and more complex organisms, including vertebrates. Recent research demonstrates some striking similarities among nematodes, fruit flies, and mice in the genetic control of development; in some of the proteins that govern important events such as cell death; and in the molecular signals used for cell-to-cell communication. Using a relatively simple model such as *C. elegans*, researchers can answer research questions more quickly and more efficiently than they could if they studied larger and more complex animals.

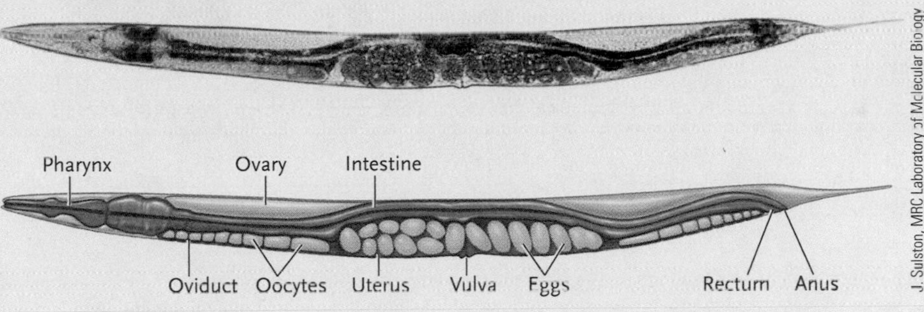

Arabidopsis thaliana

For plant geneticists, the little white-flowered thale cress, *Arabidopsis thaliana*, has attributes that make it a prime subject for genetic research. A tiny member of the mustard family, *Arabidopsis* is revealing answers to some of the biggest questions in plant development and physiology. Each plant grows only a few centimetres tall, so little laboratory space is required to house a large population. As long as *Arabidopsis* is provided with damp soil containing basic nutrients, it grows easily and rapidly in artificial light. Seeds grow to mature plants in just over a month and then flower and reproduce themselves in another three to four weeks. This permits investigators to perform desired genetic crosses and obtain large numbers of offspring with known, desired genotypes with relative ease.

The *Arabidopsis* genome was the first complete plant genome to be sequenced. Researchers have identified approximately 28 000 genes arranged on 5 pairs of chromosomes. The genome contains relatively little repetitive DNA, so it is fairly easy to isolate *Arabidopsis* genes, which can then be cloned using genetic engineering techniques. Cloned genes are inserted into bacterial plasmids, and the recombinant plasmids are transferred to the bacterial species *Agrobacterium tumefaciens*, which readily infects *Arabidopsis* cells. Amplified by the bacteria, the genes and their protein products can be sequenced or studied in other ways. Typically, researchers use chemical mutagens or recombinant bacteria to introduce changes in the *Arabidopsis* genome.

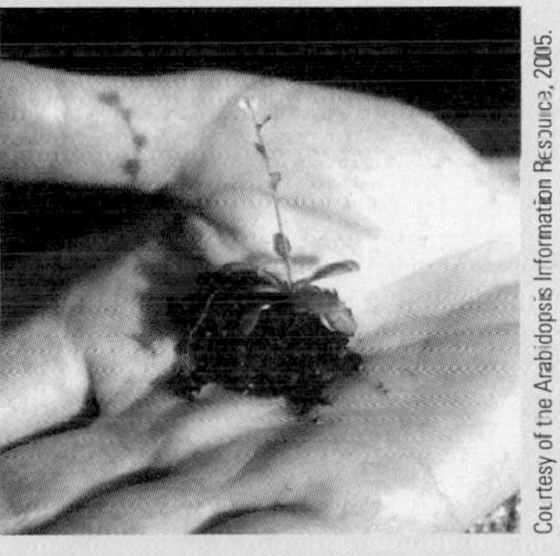

continued on next page

Arabidopsis mutants are also being used to probe fundamental questions such as how plant cells respond to gravity and the role of pigments called phytochromes in plant responses to light. An ambitious, multinational research effort called the 2010 Project aims to determine the functions of all *Arabidopsis* genes by 2010. In Canada, major projects are under way at the University of Toronto, the University of British Columbia, the National Research Council Plant Biotechnology Research Institute, and Agriculture Canada. The Arabidopsis Information Resource (TAIR) recently estimated the percentages of *A. thaliana* genes in different functional categories. The goal of Project 2010 is to create a comprehensive genetic portrait of a flowering plant—how each gene affects the functioning of not only individual cells but also the plant as a whole.

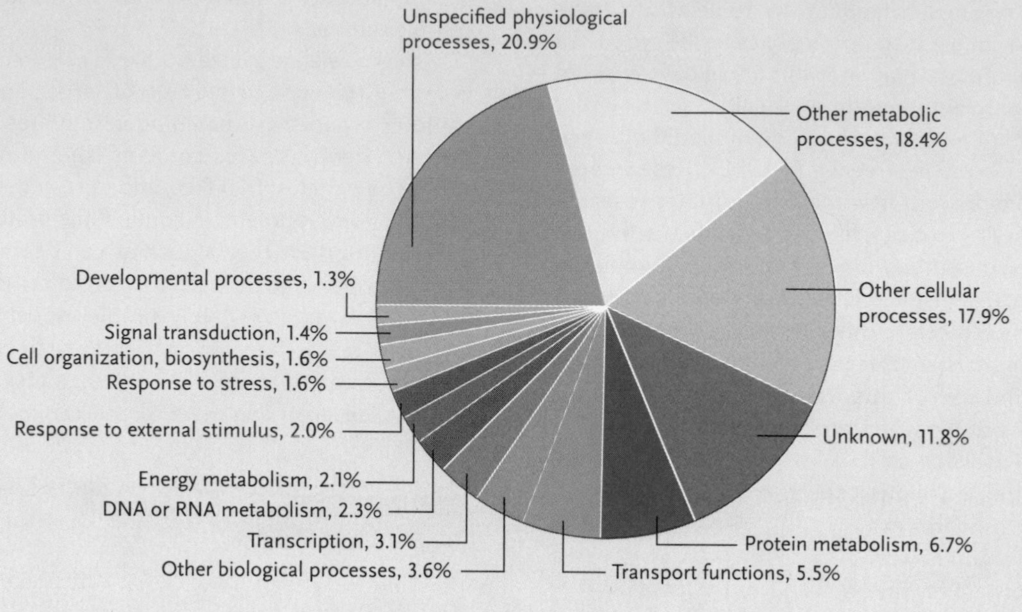

Danio rerio

The zebrafish (*Danio rerio*) is a small (3 cm) freshwater fish that gets its name from the black and white stripes running along its body. Native to India, it has spread around the world as a favourite aquarium fish. Beginning about 30 years ago, it began to be used in scientific laboratories as a model vertebrate organism for studying the roles of genes in development. Its use is now so widespread that it has been dubbed the "vertebrate fruit fly."

The zebrafish brings many advantages as a model research organism. It can be maintained easily in an ordinary aquarium on a simple diet. Although its generation time is relatively long (3 months for the zebrafish compared with 6 weeks for the mouse), a female zebrafish produces about 200 offspring at a time, compared with an average of 10 for the mouse. Embryonic development of the zebrafish takes place in eggs released to the outside by the female. The embryos develop rapidly, taking only three days from egg laying to hatching. Best of all, the eggs and embryos are transparent, providing an open window that allows researchers to observe developmental stages directly, with little or no disturbance to the embryo. Observational conditions are so favourable that the origin and fate of each cell can be traced from the fertilized egg to the hatchling. Individual nerve cells can be traced, for example, as they grow and make connections in the brain, spinal cord, and peripheral body regions. Removing or transplanting cells and tissues is also relatively easy. Biochemical and molecular studies can be carried out by techniques ranging from the simple addition of reactants to the water surrounding the embryos to injection of chemicals into individual cells.

The advantages of working with the zebrafish have spurred efforts to investigate its genetics, with particular interest in genes that regulate embryonic development. This work has already identified mutants of more than 2000 genes, including more than 400 genes that influence development. Most of the mechanisms controlled by the developmental genes resemble their counterparts in humans and other mammals. Developmental and physiological studies have revealed functions of some zebrafish genes that were previously unknown for their mammalian equivalents.

Mus musculus

The "wee, sleekit, cow'rin', tim'rous beastie," as the poet Robert Burns called the mouse (*Mus musculus*), has a much larger stature among scientists. The mouse and its cells have been used to great advantage as models for research on mammalian developmental genetics, immunology, and cancer. The availability of the mouse as a research tool enables scientists to carry out mammalian experiments that would not be practical or ethical with humans. Its small size makes the mouse relatively inexpensive and easy to maintain in the laboratory, and its short generation time, compared with most other mammals, allows genetic crosses to be carried out within a reasonable time span. Mice can be mated when they are 10 weeks old; in 18 to 22 days, the female gives birth to a litter of 5 to 10 offspring. A female may be rebred a little more than a day after giving birth.

Mice have a long and highly productive history as experimental animals. Gregor Mendel, the founder of genetics, is known to have kept mice as part of his studies. Toward the end of the nineteenth century, August Weissmann helped disprove an early evolutionary hypothesis, the inheritance of acquired characters, by cutting off the tails of mice for 22 successive generations and finding that it had no effect on tail length. The first example of a lethal allele was also found in mice, and pioneering experiments on the transplantation of tissues between individuals were conducted with mice. During the 1920s, Fred Griffith laid the groundwork for the research showing that DNA is the hereditary molecule in his work with pneumonia-causing bacteria in mice.

More recently, genetic experiments with mice have revealed more than 500 mutants that cause hereditary diseases, immunological defects, and cancer in mammals, including humans. The mouse has also been the mammal of choice for experiments that introduce and modify genes through genetic engineering. One of the most spectacular results of this research was the production of giant mice by introducing a human growth hormone gene into a line of dwarfed mice that were deficient for this hormone. Genetic engineering has also produced "knockout" mice, in which a gene of interest is completely nonfunctional. The effects of this lack of function often help investigators determine the role of the normal form of the gene. Some knockout mice are defective in genes homologous to human genes that cause serious diseases, such as cystic fibrosis, so researchers can study the disease in mice with the goal of developing cures or therapies.

The revelations in developmental genetics from studies with the mouse have been of great interest and importance in their own right. In 2002, the sequence of the mouse genome was reported. This sequence is enabling researchers to refine and expand their use of the mouse as a model organism for studies of mammalian biology and mammalian diseases. More and more, as we find that much of what applies to the mouse also applies to humans, the findings in mice have shed new light on human development and opened pathways to the possible cures of human genetic diseases.

Anolis Lizards of the Caribbean

The lizard genus *Anolis* has been a model system for studies in ecology and evolutionary biology since the 1960s, when Ernest E. Williams of Harvard University's Museum of Comparative Zoology first began studying it. With more than 400 known species—and new ones being described all the time—*Anolis* is one of the most diverse vertebrate genera known. Most anoles are less than 10 cm long, not including the tail, and many occur at high densities, making it easy to collect a lot of data in a relatively short time. Male anoles defend territories, and their displays make them conspicuous even in dense forests.

Anolis species are widely distributed in South America and Central America, but nearly 40% occupy Caribbean islands. The number of species on an island is generally proportional to the island's size. Cuba, the largest island, has more than 50 species, whereas small islands have just one or two. Studies by Williams and others suggest that the anoles on some large islands are the products of independent adaptive radiations. Eight of the 10 *Anolis* species now found on Puerto Rico probably evolved on that island from a common ancestor. Similarly, the seven *Anolis* species on Jamaica shared a common ancestor, which was different from the ancestor of the Puerto Rican species. The anole faunas on Cuba and Hispaniola are the products of several independent radiations on each island. Williams discovered that these independent radiations had produced similar-looking species on different islands. He developed the concept of the *ecomorph*, a group of species that have similar morphological, behavioural, and ecological characteristics even though they are not closely related within the genus. Williams named the ecomorphs after the vegetation that they commonly used. For example, grass anoles are small, slender species that usually perch on low, thin vegetation. Trunk-ground anoles have chunky bodies and large heads, and they perch low on tree trunks, frequently jumping to the ground to feed. Although the grass anoles or the trunk-ground anoles on different islands are similar in many ways, they are not closely related to each other. Their resemblances are the products of convergent evolution.

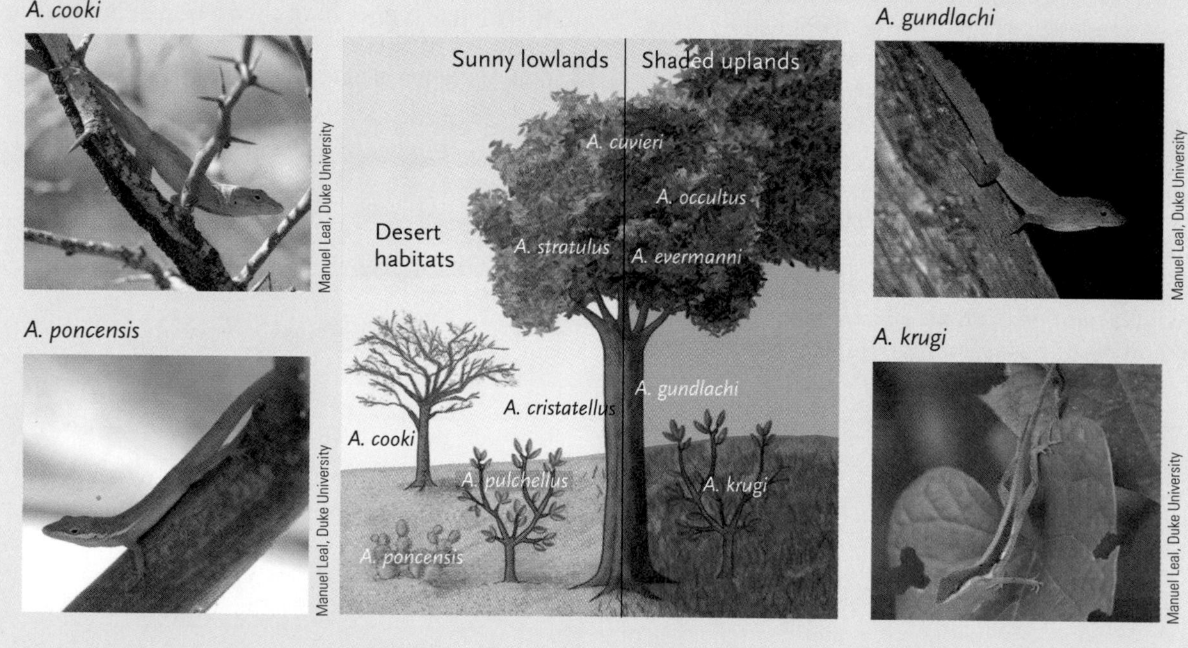

(a) Banyan tree (*Ficus* sp.), one type of "strangler fig."
(b) Close-up view of strangler fig roots on the trunk of a host plant.

Isabella M. Gioia

Adrian Jones, IAN Image Library (www.ian.umces.edu/imagelibrary/)

Study Plan

28 The Plant Body

Why It Matters

What is the largest plant in the world? The answer depends on how we define largest—is it the tallest? The one with the greatest mass? If we define largest as the plant with the biggest canopy (stem and branches), then the winner of the contest would be the banyan tree (see opening photograph). The banyan is one of several kinds of figs (*Ficus* species) that are known as strangler figs due to their aggressive growth habit. The seeds of strangler figs, dispersed by birds, are often deposited high up on the branches of other tree species in tropical rain forests. The seeds germinate in the bark of their host tree and send thin roots down the trunk of the host plant to the ground. Once the roots enter the ground, they grow and thicken quickly. Roots that cross over each other fuse together, trapping the host plant's trunk in a cage of roots that eventually fuse into a more or less solid mass. Meanwhile, the stem of the fig climbs upward, twining itself around the host's stem, and soon overtops the host, putting out many thick leaves that shade the host plant's leaves. The strangler fig can now outcompete the host plant for sunlight and for water and nutrients from the soil. The network of roots that surround the host's trunk prevent further lateral growth of the host, which eventually starves to death. The host trunk rots away, leaving a hollow cylinder of roots that form the main trunk of the fig tree. Some of these fig species continue to send down roots from their branches. When these aerial roots reach the ground, they become additional trunks to help support the canopy, which can become massive. In this way, a single fig tree and its numerous, interconnected trunks can spread out over a very large area. The largest banyan tree in the world has a canopy that is 420 m in diameter! This aggressive growth strategy is a definite advantage in rainforests, where competition for light is fierce as very little light penetrates beyond the upper canopy.

Even though strangler figs are unusual in that their seeds germinate in the bark of another plant rather than in the soil, fig seedlings develop into mature plants via the same processes as other plants. As you saw in Chapter 25, plants were able to successfully colonize diverse land habitats only as adaptations in form and function helped them solve problems posed by the terrestrial environment. These evolutionary adaptations included

- a *shoot system* that helps support leaves and other body parts in air,
- a *root system* that anchors the plant in soil and provides access to soil nutrients and water,
- tissues for internal transport of water and nutrients, and
- specializations for preventing water loss.

What structures make up the root and shoot systems of a plant? How do the different parts of a plant develop? How do some plants, such as these strangler figs, become woody? Starting in this chapter and continuing through the next three chapters, we investigate these questions and explore the structure and functioning of plants—their morphology, anatomy, and physiology.

A plant's *morphology* is its external form, such as the shape of its leaves, and its *anatomy* is the structure and arrangement of its internal parts. Plant *physiology* refers to the mechanisms by which the plant's body functions in its environment. Our focus in this chapter is the plant division called angiosperms, or flowering plants, which are the most successful plants on Earth in terms of distribution and sheer numbers of species.

28.1 Plant Structure and Growth: An Overview

In this chapter, we focus on the key characteristics of plant structure and growth and make several comparisons between land plants and terrestrial animals. We could compare plants with many other organisms since plants and animals are just two of the many kingdoms of life, but we tend to be most familiar with animals. It is obvious that plants are very different from animals, but why are they so different? We can think of plants and animals as representatives of two very different solutions to the challenges of life on land. If we generalize about "typical" plants and "typical" animals, we can get a clearer picture of these two different strategies. Animals are chemoheterotrophs: they obtain both energy and carbon from the food they eat. Their food sources tend to be fairly concentrated sources of nutrients. All terrestrial animals are motile (some aquatic animals are stationary) and can move from one place to another in search of food, water, or a mate. They can also flee from predators or move away from unfavourable conditions. Animal bodies, then, need to be fairly compact to facilitate moving around.

In contrast, plants are photosynthetic autotrophs—"self-feeders"—that need sunlight, carbon dioxide (available in air), and water (available in soil). In addition, plants require other nutrients that are usually available only in soil; these nutrients are usually patchily distributed in the soil and often available only at low concentrations. Thus, unlike animals, plants have to gather diffuse nutrients from both air and soil. How best to capture these diffuse nutrients? A large surface area is important, both above ground and below ground, so plant bodies are not compact but spreading and branched in form (the term for this form is *dendritic*, which literally means "treelike"). To visualize this dendritic growth, think about how the branches of an aspen or another poplar tree look in the spring before they have leafed out **(Figure 28.1)**. The root system of the tree is also dendritic, branching and spreading below ground. Thus, the evolutionary response to the challenges posed by life on land has resulted in a plant body consisting of two closely linked but quite different components—a photosynthetic *shoot system* extending upward into the air and a nonphotosynthetic *root system* extending downward into the soil **(Figure 28.2)**.

Figure 28.1
Dendritic growth shown by the above-ground portion of a tree.

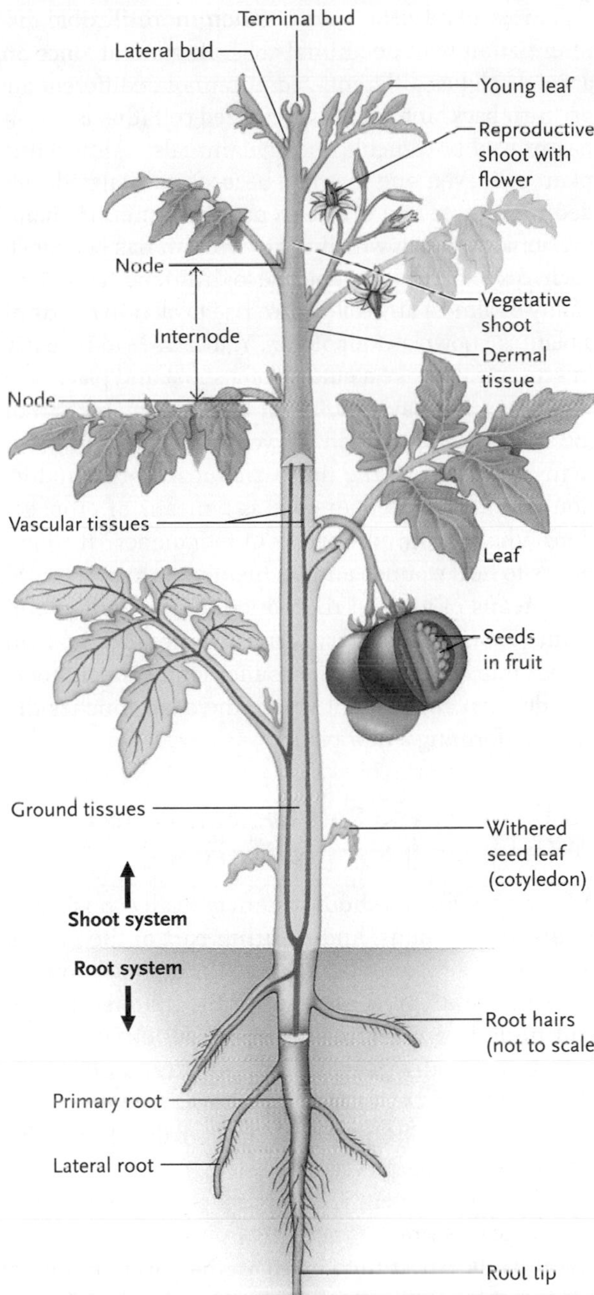

Figure 28.2
Body plan for the commercially grown tomato plant *Solanum lycopersicum*, a typical angiosperm. Vascular tissues (purple) conduct water, dissolved minerals, and organic substances. They thread through ground tissues, which make up most of the plant body. Dermal tissues (epidermis, in this case) cover the surfaces of the root and shoot systems.

Obviously, a plant cannot just pick up this extensive root system and move around in search of better conditions. Instead, plants are fixed in place (sessile), and they must therefore search for nutrients and water, find mates, and defend themselves from predators—everything that animals have to do—but while being fixed in place. As you read through this chapter, think about how plant morphology and growth relate to being sessile photoautotrophs.

28.1a Cells of All Plant Tissues Share Some General Features

Both root and shoot systems consist of various **organs**—body structures that contain two or more types of tissues and have a definite form and function. Plant organs include leaves, stems, and roots. A **tissue** is a group of cells and intercellular substances that function together in one or more specialized tasks.

Plant cells share some features with animal cells but differ in that they typically have a cell wall, a large vacuole, and, in many cells, chloroplasts. Chloroplasts function in photosynthesis and are discussed in more detail in Chapter 7. The vacuole may occupy most of the volume in a mature plant cell and plays an important role in cell elongation and maintenance of rigid tissues. Vacuoles may also act as storage compartments. In all plant tissues, the cells have a **primary cell wall** surrounding the plasma membrane and cell contents (cytoplasm and organelles) **(Figure 28.3a, p. 670).** These cell walls are the "skeleton" of a plant, serving as support, just as the skeleton for an animal does. A primary cell wall is made largely of microfibrils of **cellulose**, a polymer of glucose, embedded in a matrix of other polysaccharides. Cellulose is the most abundant polysaccharide on earth and is currently being investigated as a source of biofuel (see *Molecule Behind Biology*). The combination of cellulose fibrils and other polysaccharides gives the cell wall strength and flexibility. Primary cell walls also contain various proteins. Some of these are structural proteins that contribute to the wall's strength, whereas others are enzymes that catalyze the formation and modification of the cell wall. Don't think of the cell wall as a solid barrier, like a cement wall, but rather as a semipermeable "mesh" or filter, which allows some molecules (e.g., water) to pass through into the cell. As well, cytoplasmic connections between adjacent cells, called **plasmodesmata** (singular, plasmodesma), allow solutes such as amino acids and sugars to move from one cell to the next. The space between the primary cell walls of adjacent cells is filled with a polysaccharide layer called the middle lamella.

As a young plant grows, different types of cells deposit additional cellulose and other materials inside the primary wall, forming a strong **secondary cell wall (Figure 28.3b, p. 670).** Secondary walls often contain **lignin**, a complex water-insoluble polymer (see Chapter 24), which makes cell walls very strong, rigid, and impermeable to water. As we learned in Chapter 25, the evolution of large vascular plants became possible only after biochemical pathways producing lignin evolved, through modification of existing pathways, allowing a plant to produce lignified cells that both provided support and conducted water through the plant body. Lignin is also very resistant to decomposition, so its presence in cell walls makes the cell more resistant to attack by microbes (see Chapter 24). As you can see

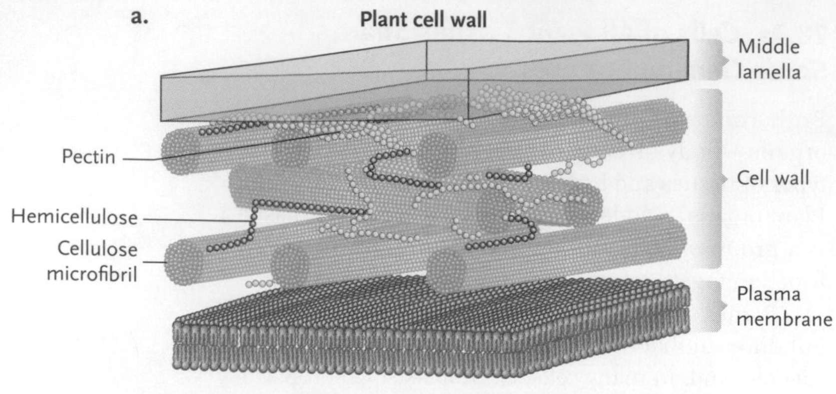

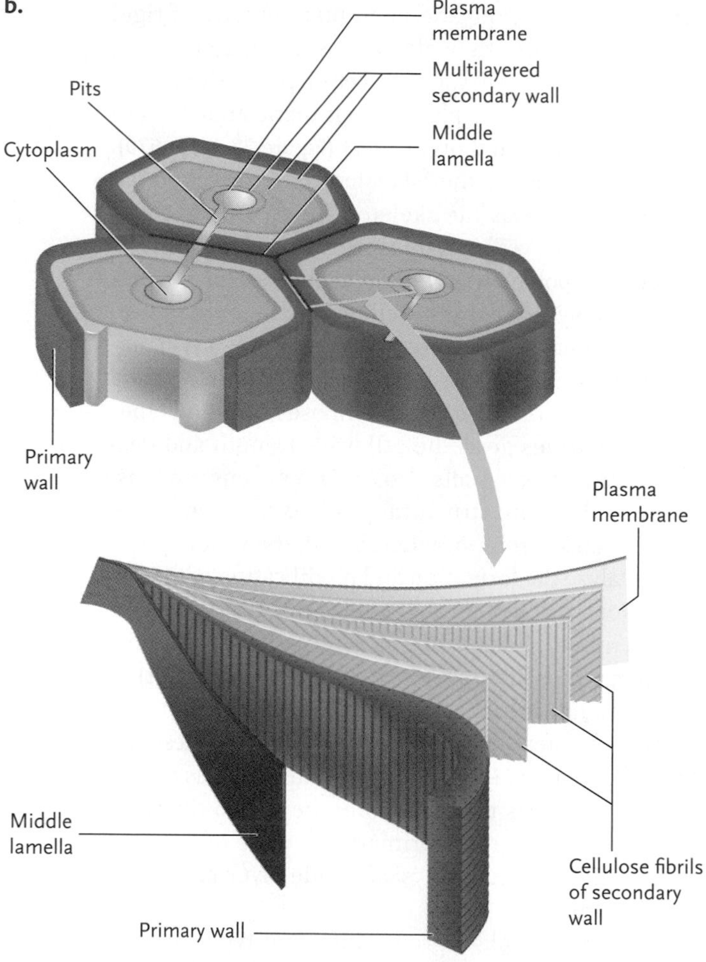

Figure 28.3
(a) Structure of a plant primary cell wall. **(b)** Structure of a plant cell wall. Upper figure shows cross-section of plant cells in which secondary wall layers have been deposited inside the primary wall. The lower figure is a close-up of the arrangement of primary and secondary layers.

from Figure 28.3b, some cells are very small relative to the amount of wall material that surrounds them.

As in animals, all of a plant's cells have the same genes in their nuclei. So how do specialized cells such as xylem arise in plants? As each cell matures and *differentiates* (becomes specialized for a particular function), specific genes are activated. For the most part, fully differentiated animal cells perform their functions while alive, but some types of plant cells die after differentiating, and their cytoplasm disappears. The walls that remain, however, serve key functions, particularly in xylem.

Most plant cells have a much more flexible differentiation than do animal cells. In general, once an animal cell has differentiated, it cannot dedifferentiate or "turn back" into an unspecialized cell (this is why it has proved so difficult to clone animals). Almost any plant cell, even one that has become specialized, can dedifferentiate and divide to produce an entire plant (obviously, cells in which the cytoplasm has been lost, such as xylem cells, are not able to dedifferentiate). This ability of almost any cell to give rise to all other parts of a plant is known as **totipotency.** You can see totipotency in action if you take a cutting of a shoot and place it in water: in a few days, roots will form on the bottom of the stem. Cloning of plants is very easy, something that many plants do all the time as a means of reproduction and many gardeners use as a means of propagation. What are the advantages of totipotency? It allows plants to heal wounds and, as mentioned above, is also one means of asexual reproduction; for example, in many plants (such as raspberries), if a branch or stem comes into contact with the soil for long enough, roots will develop at the point where the stem touches the ground, forming a new plant.

28.1b Shoot and Root Systems Perform Different but Integrated Functions

A flowering plant's **shoot system** typically consists of stems, leaves, buds, and—during part of the plant's life cycle—reproductive organs known as flowers (see Figure 28.2). A stem with its attached leaves and buds is a *vegetative* (nonreproductive) shoot; a bud eventually gives rise to an extension of the shoot or to a new, branching shoot. A *reproductive* shoot produces flowers, which later develop fruits containing seeds.

The shoot system is highly adapted for photosynthesis. Leaves greatly increase a plant's surface area and thus its exposure to light. Stems are frameworks for upright growth, which favourably positions leaves for light exposure and flowers for pollination. Some parts of the shoot system also store carbohydrates manufactured during photosynthesis. Many plants can change the orientation of their leaves to maximize light absorption or, in arid habitats, to prevent overheating.

The **root system** usually grows below ground. It anchors the plant and supports its upright parts. It also absorbs water and dissolved minerals from soil and stores carbohydrates. Adaptations in the structure and function of plant cells and tissues were an integral part of the evolution of shoots and roots, for example, the development of vascular tissues specialized to serve as internal pipelines that conduct water, minerals, and organic substances throughout the plant. The root hairs sketched in Figure 28.2 are surface cells specialized for absorbing water and nutrients from soil.

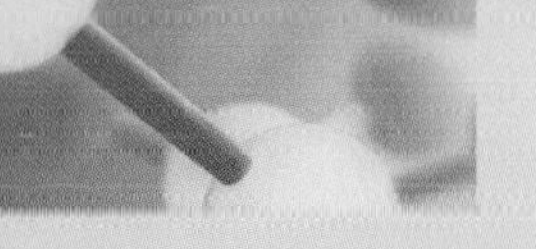

Molecule Behind Biology

Cellulose

Cellulose **(Figure 1)** is the most abundant organic compound on Earth, thanks to its presence in every cell wall of every plant. We have many uses for cellulose already: in paper, clothing, insulation, and a variety of industrial uses. But could we also use this abundant substance as a source of fuel? Driven by a desire for more "green" sources of energy and the high price of oil, people have been looking at various sources of biofuel—fuel from plants.

One such biofuel, ethanol, is currently produced primarily from corn. Corn kernels are mostly starch (and water), which is easily broken down into sugars that are then fermented to produce ethanol. Like starch, cellulose is also a polymer of glucose, so it, too, can be broken down to sugars that can be fermented. However, it is much more difficult to do this with cellulose. Why? The linkages between glucose monomers in cellulose are different from those in starch (see *The Chemical and Physical Foundations of Biology* pages). This seemingly minor difference makes a very big difference in not only the characteristics of the resulting polymers—cellulose is linear, whereas starch is coiled—but also in how difficult it is for decomposers to break the bonds between the monomers. Starch is readily decomposed by many organisms, including humans, but cellulose can be broken down only by a few organisms, mostly fungi and prokaryotes. Moreover, cellulose may be protected by lignin in some plant tissues, making the cellulose even harder to break down. Consequently, converting cellulose into liquid fuel is currently a very complex, difficult, and energy-consuming process.

But there are issues related to the use of corn for ethanol. World food prices rose 10% in 2006 partly because of rising biofuel demand; diverting corn from food to fuel use may be contributing to food shortages in some countries. There is also concern about the long-term effects on soil fertility of cultivating corn.

An advantage of converting cellulose to fuel is that all parts of the plants, not just the starch- and sugar-rich parts, could be converted to fuel. In Canada and the United States, a very promising source of cellulose for biofuel is switchgrass (*Panicum virgatum*), a native grass of the tall-grass prairies. It grows very quickly, is able to grow on marginal land that is unsuitable for crop production, and can withstand both drought and flooding. Switchgrass is perennial, so it would not need to be replanted every year. Although the problems related to converting cellulose from switchgrass to liquid fuel (ethanol) remain, we could avoid those problems if we focused on other forms of fuel. For example, in Canada, the biggest contributor to greenhouse gases is heating, not transportation. Researchers have found that switchgrass stems can be dried and compressed into fuel pellets that can be burned. Used in this way, switchgrass produced a whopping 540 times the amount of energy than was needed to grow, harvest, and process it. This yield is seven times more energy per hectare than corn yields. Switchgrass pellets could also be used to generate electricity.

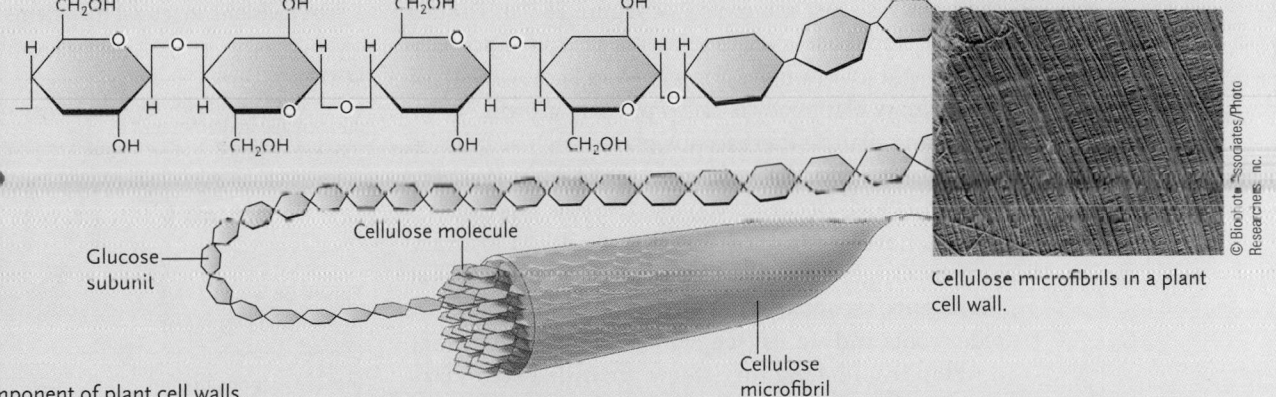

Cellulose, formed from glucose units joined end to end by β(1→4) linkages. Hundreds to thousands of cellulose chains line up side by side, in an arrangement reinforced by hydrogen bonds between the chains, to form cellulose microfibrils in plant cells.

CH₂OH, OH, H, O, Cellulose molecule, Glucose subunit, Cellulose microfibril, Cellulose microfibrils in a plant cell wall.

© Biophoto Associates/Photo Researchers, Inc.

Figure 1
Cellulose, the major component of plant cell walls.

28.1c Meristems Produce New Tissues Throughout a Plant's Life

Most animals grow to a certain size, and then their growth slows dramatically or stops. This pattern is called **determinate growth.** In contrast, plants can grow throughout their lives, a pattern called **indeterminate growth.** Individual plant parts exhibit determinate growth, such as leaves, flowers, and fruits, but every plant also has self-perpetuating embryonic tissue, called meristem (*merizein* = to divide), at the tips of shoots and roots. Under the influence of plant hormones, these **meristems** produce new tissues more or less continuously while the plant is alive.

Why do plants have indeterminate growth? A capacity for indeterminate growth gives plants a great deal of flexibility—or what biologists often call *plasticity*—in their possible responses to changes in environmental factors such as light, temperature, water, and nutrients. This plasticity has major adaptive benefits for an organism that cannot move about, as most animals can. For example, if external factors (such as a houseplant's owner) change the direction of incoming light for photosynthesis, stems can "shift gears" and grow in that direction. These and other plant movements, called tropisms, are a major topic of Chapter 31.

Remember, too, that nutrients are patchily distributed and diffuse in soil. Indeterminate growth allows a root system to extend and grow out of regions in which nutrients have been depleted and forage for patches with more nutrients; if plant root systems were determinate, plants would soon exhaust local nutrient supplies and be unable to forage for more.

As you know, animals grow mainly by mitosis, which increases the number of body cells. Plants, however, grow by two mechanisms—an increase in the number of cells by mitotic cell division in the meristems *and* an increase in the size of individual cells. In regions adjacent to the meristems in the tips of shoots and roots, the daughter cells rapidly increase in size—especially in length—for some time after they are produced. In contrast, when animal cells divide mitotically, the daughter cells are usually roughly the same size as the parent cell.

28.1d Meristems Are Responsible for Growth in Both Height and Girth

Some plants have only one kind of meristem, whereas others have two **(Figure 28.4)**. All plants have **apical meristems,** clusters of self-perpetuating tissue at the tips of their buds, stems, and roots (see Figure 28.4a). Tissues that develop from apical meristems are called **primary tissues** and make up the **primary plant body.** Growth of the primary plant body is called **primary growth.**

Some plants—herbaceous plants such as grasses and dandelions, for example—have only primary growth, which occurs at the tips of roots and shoots. Others have **secondary growth,** as well as primary growth. Originating at cylinders of tissue called **lateral meristems,** secondary growth increases the diameter of older roots and stems (see Figure 28.4b). Tissues that develop from lateral meristems are called **secondary tissues.** Woody plants, such as trees and shrubs, including the strangler fig discussed earlier, all have secondary tissues.

Primary and secondary growth can go on simultaneously in a single plant, with primary growth increasing the length of shoots and roots, whereas secondary growth adds girth to these organs. Each spring, for example, a poplar tree undergoes primary growth at each of its root and shoot tips, whereas secondary growth increases the diameter of its older, woody parts. Plant hormones govern these growth processes and other key events described in Chapter 31.

a. Plants increase in length by cell divisions in apical meristems and by elongation of the daughter cells.

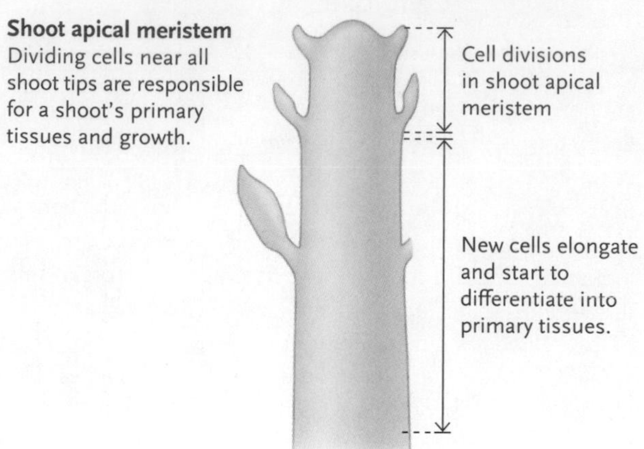
Shoot apical meristem
Dividing cells near all shoot tips are responsible for a shoot's primary tissues and growth.
Cell divisions in shoot apical meristem
New cells elongate and start to differentiate into primary tissues.
Root apical meristem
Dividing cells near all root tips are responsible for a root's primary tissues and growth.
New cells elongate and start to differentiate into primary tissues.
Cell divisions in root apical meristem

b. Some plants increase in girth by way of cell divisions in lateral meristems.

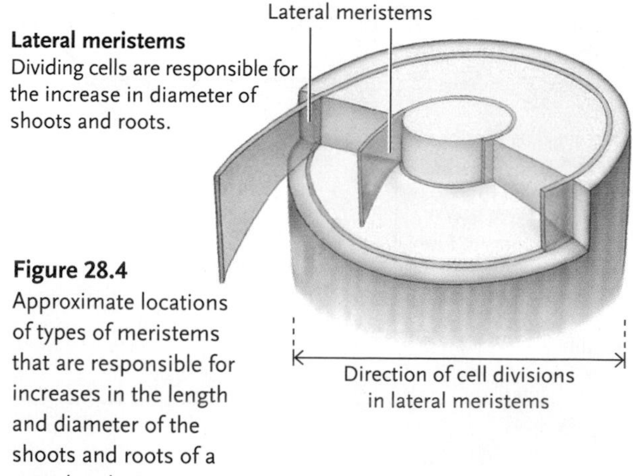
Lateral meristems
Lateral meristems
Dividing cells are responsible for the increase in diameter of shoots and roots.
Direction of cell divisions in lateral meristems

Figure 28.4
Approximate locations of types of meristems that are responsible for increases in the length and diameter of the shoots and roots of a vascular plant.

28.1e Monocots and Eudicots Are the Two General Structural Forms of Flowering Plants

Several broad categories of body architecture arose as flowering plants evolved, with the two major categories being the **monocot** and **eudicot** lineages. Grasses, lilies, cattails, corn, and rice are examples of monocots. Eudicots include nearly all familiar angiosperm trees and shrubs, as well as many nonwoody (herbaceous) plants. Examples are poplars, willows, oaks, cacti, roses, poppies, sunflowers, and garden beans and peas.

Monocots and eudicots get their names from the number of *cotyledons*—the seed leaves associated with plant embryos (see Chapter 25). Monocot seeds have one cotyledon and eudicot seeds have two. Although monocots and eudicots have similar types of tissues, their body structures differ in distinctive ways (**Table 28.1**). As we discuss the morphology of flowering plants, we refer frequently to these structural differences.

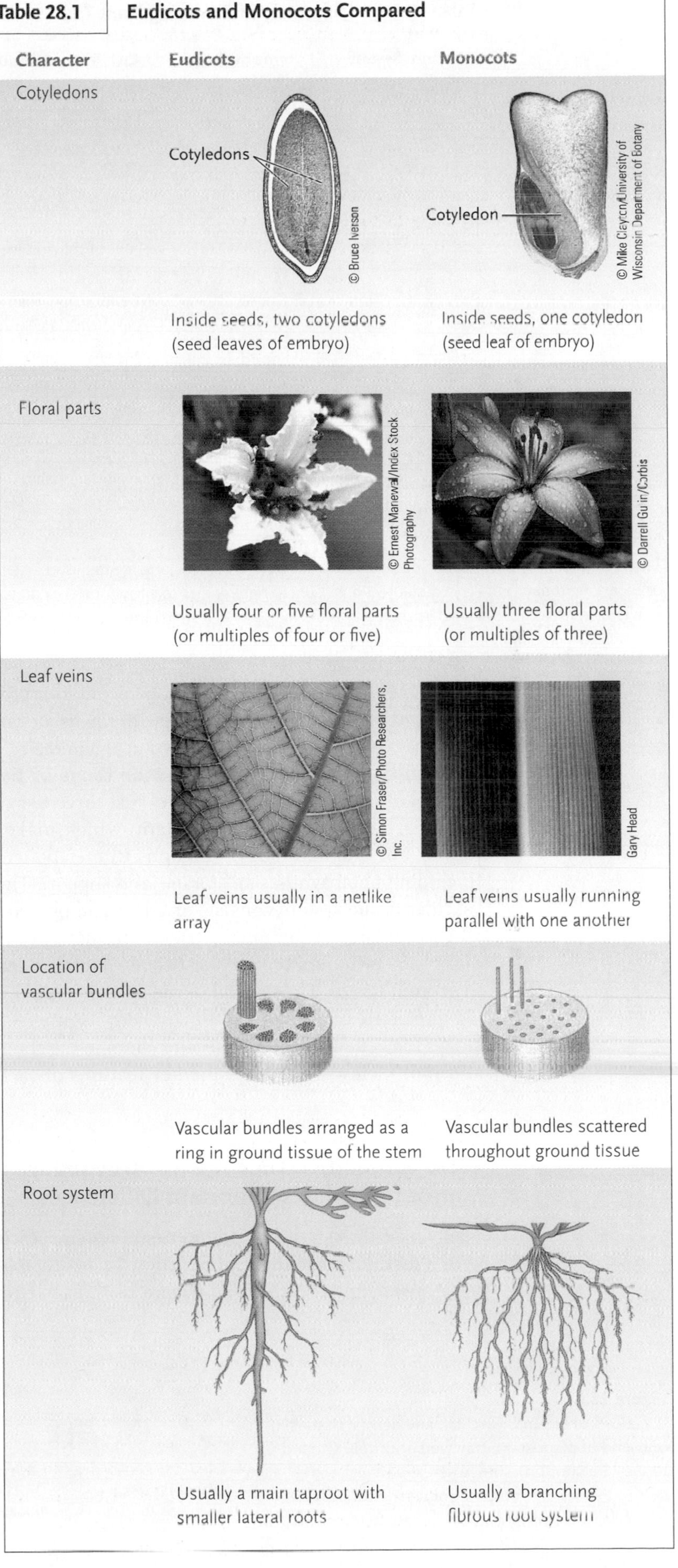

Table 28.1 Eudicots and Monocots Compared

Character	Eudicots	Monocots
Cotyledons	Inside seeds, two cotyledons (seed leaves of embryo)	Inside seeds, one cotyledon (seed leaf of embryo)
Floral parts	Usually four or five floral parts (or multiples of four or five)	Usually three floral parts (or multiples of three)
Leaf veins	Leaf veins usually in a netlike array	Leaf veins usually running parallel with one another
Location of vascular bundles	Vascular bundles arranged as a ring in ground tissue of the stem	Vascular bundles scattered throughout ground tissue
Root system	Usually a main taproot with smaller lateral roots	Usually a branching fibrous root system

28.1f Flowering Plants Can Be Grouped According to Type of Growth and Life Span

As you learned above, we can distinguish between flowering plants depending on whether they are herbaceous or woody plants and whether they are monocots or eudicots. We can also distinguish plants by life span. **Annuals** are herbaceous plants in which the life cycle is completed in one growing season. With minimal or no secondary growth, annuals typically have only apical meristems. Examples are tomatoes (a eudicot) and corn (a monocot). **Biennials** such as carrots complete their life cycle in two growing seasons, and limited secondary growth occurs in some species. In the first season, roots, stems, and leaves form; in its second year of growth, the plant flowers, forms seeds, and dies. In **perennials**, vegetative growth and reproduction continue year after year. Many perennials, such as trees, shrubs, and some vines, have secondary tissues, although others, such as irises and daffodils, do not.

Study Break

1. Compare the components and functions of a land plant's shoot and root systems.
2. Explain what meristem tissue is and name and describe the functions of the basic types of meristems.

28.2 The Three Plant Tissue Systems

As in animals, plant organs are composed of tissue systems. Each tissue system includes several types of tissue, and each tissue is made up of cells with specializations for different functions (**Table 28.2, p. 674**). *Simple* tissues have only one type of cell. Other tissues are *complex*, with organized arrays of two or

Table 28.2 Summary of Flowering Plant Tissues and Their Components

Tissue System	Name of Tissue	Cell Types in Tissue	Tissue Function
Ground tissue	Parenchyma	Parenchyma cells	Photosynthesis, respiration, storage, secretion
	Collenchyma	Collenchyma cells	Flexible strength for growing plant parts
	Sclerenchyma	Fibres or sclereids	Rigid support, deterring herbivores
Vascular tissue	Xylem	Conducting cells (tracheids, vessel members), parenchyma cells, sclerenchyma cells	Transport of water and dissolved minerals
	Phloem	Conducting cells (sieve tube members), parenchyma cells, sclerenchyma cells	Sugar transport
Dermal tissue	Epidermis	Undifferentiated cells, guard cells, other specialized cells	Control of gas exchange, water loss, protection
	Periderm	Cork, cork cambium, secondary cortex	Protection

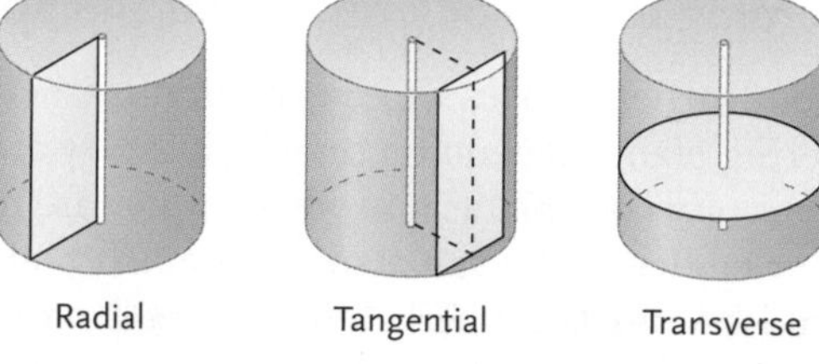

Figure 28.5
Terms that identify how tissue specimens are cut from a plant. Along the radius of a stem or root, longitudinal cuts give radial sections. Cuts at right angles to a root or stem radius give tangential sections. Cuts perpendicular to the long axis of a stem or root give transverse sections (cross sections).

more types of cells. **Figure 28.5** will help you interpret images of plant tissues, beginning with the tissues in a transverse section of a stem shown in **Figure 28.6.**

Unlike animals that have a wide range of tissues, plant organs are composed of just three tissue systems. The **ground tissue system**, which makes up most of the plant body, functions in metabolism (including photosynthesis), storage, and support. The **vascular tissue system** consists of xylem and phloem, which transport water and nutrients throughout the plant. The cylinders of vascular tissue are embedded in ground tissue. The **dermal tissue system** is a skin-like protective covering for the plant body. Figure 28.2 shows the general location of each system in the shoot and root. Below we discuss the key features of each tissue system.

28.2a Ground Tissues Are All Structurally Simple but Exhibit Important Differences

Plants have three types of ground tissue systems, each with a distinct structure and function—*parenchyma, collenchyma,* and *sclerenchyma* **(Figure 28.7).** Each type is structurally simple, being composed mainly of one kind of cell. In a very real sense, the cells in ground tissues are the "worker bees" of plants, carrying out photosynthesis, storing carbohydrates, providing mechanical support for the plant body, and performing other basic functions. Each kind of cell has a distinctive wall structure, and some have variations in the cytoplasmic contents as well.

Parenchyma: Soft Primary Tissues. Parenchyma (*para* = around; *chein* = fill in or pour) makes up the bulk of the primary growth of roots, stems, leaves, flowers, and fruits. Most parenchyma cells have only a thin primary wall and so are pliable and permeable to water. Often the cells are spherical or many-sided, although they also can be elongated like a sausage, as in Figure 28.7a. Parenchyma cells typically have air spaces between them, especially in leaves (see Section 28.3). Stems and leaves in aquatic plants often have very large air spaces between parenchyma cells, which facilitate the movement of oxygen to submerged parts of the plant and help the leaves float upward toward the light.

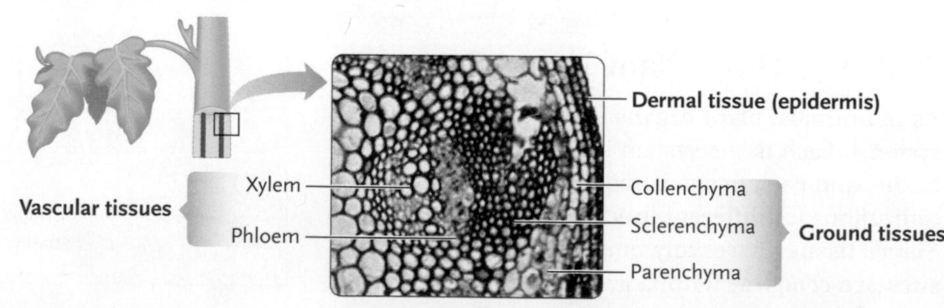

Figure 28.6
Locations of ground, vascular, and dermal tissues in one kind of plant stem, transverse section. Ground tissues are simple tissues, whereas vascular and dermal tissues are complex, containing various types of specialized cells (Micrograph:, Ed Reschke / Peter Arnold Inc.).

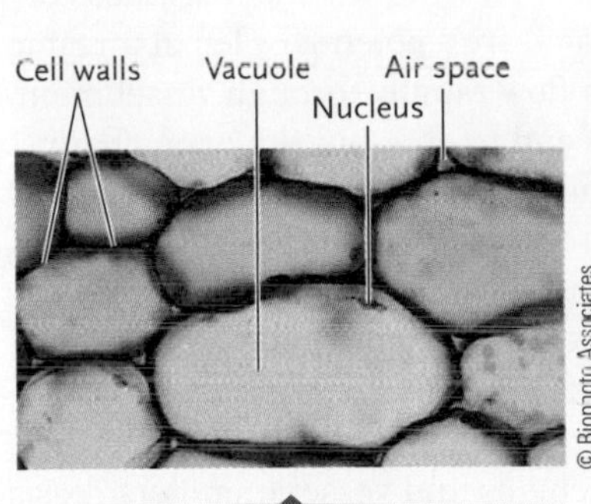

a. Parenchyma tissues consist of soft, living cells specialized for storage, other functions.

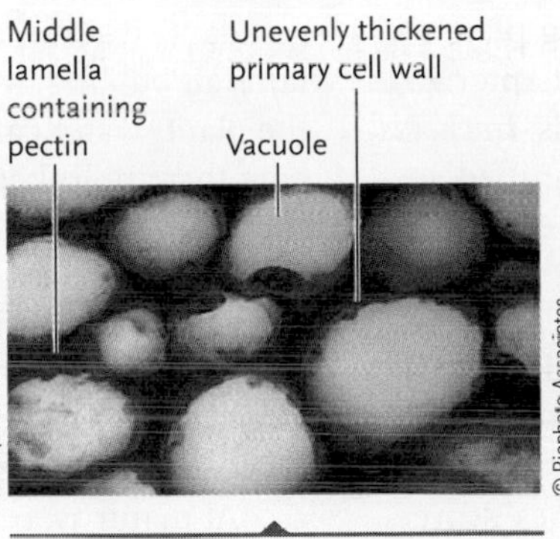

b. Collenchyma tissues provide flexible support.

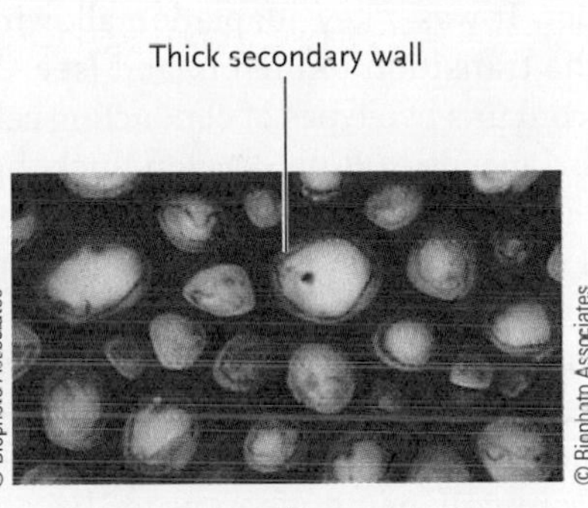

c. Sclerenchyma tissues provide rigid support and protection.

Figure 28.7
Examples of ground tissues from the stem of a sunflower plant (*Helianthus annuus*).

Parenchyma cells may be specialized for tasks as varied as storage, secretion, and photosynthesis. For example, the photosynthetic cells of leaves are parenchyma cells. In many plant species, modified parenchyma cells are specialized for short-distance transport of solutes. Such cells are common in tissues in which water and solutes must be rapidly moved from cell to cell. Parenchyma cells usually remain alive and metabolically active when mature.

Collenchyma: Flexible Support. The "strings" in celery are examples of the flexible ground tissue called **collenchyma** (*kolla* = glue; see Figure 28.7b), which helps strengthen plant parts that are still elongating. Collenchyma cells are typically elongated, and collectively, they often form strands under the dermal tissue of growing shoot regions and leaf stalks.

The primary walls of collenchyma cells are built of alternating layers of cellulose and pectin and are unevenly thickened. These walls can stretch as the cell enlarges, making them very suitable for support of young, growing organs. Mature collenchyma cells are alive and metabolically active, and they continue to synthesize primary wall layers as the plant grows.

Sclerenchyma: Rigid Support and Protection. Mature plant parts gain additional mechanical support and protection from **sclerenchyma** (*skleros* = hard), cells with thick, lignified secondary walls (see Figure 28.7c). Some regions of the cell wall lack secondary wall material, forming a *pit* where the cell wall is more porous than elsewhere. Water can flow from one sclerenchyma cell to another through these pits. After lignification occurs, sclerenchyma cells die because their cytoplasm can no longer exchange gases, nutrients, and other materials with the environment. The walls, however, continue to provide protection and support.

The two types of sclerenchyma cells—*sclereids* and *fibres*—differ in their shape and arrangement. **Sclereids** tend to be short and are often branched; they sometimes aggregate into protective sheets, forming the hard casings of a coconut shell or a peach pit, for example. Sclereids can also be scattered in tissue—cube-shaped sclereids dispersed in the flesh of a pear give it its gritty texture **(Figure 28.8a)**. **Fibres** are long, tapered cells **(Figure 28.8b)** that resist stretching but are more pliable than sclereids. Fibres often occur in bundles in stems and leaves, strengthening and supporting these tissues. We use plant fibres to manufacture rope, paper, and cloth. Linen, for example, is made of fibres extracted from the stems of flax plants (*Linum usitatissimum*).

28.2b Vascular Tissues Are Specialized for Conducting Fluids

Vascular tissue systems consist of complex tissues composed of specialized conducting cells, parenchyma cells, and fibres. *Xylem* and *phloem*, the two kinds of vascular tissues in flowering plants, are organized into cylinders of interconnected cells that extend throughout the plant.

Xylem: Transporting Water and Minerals. **Xylem** (*xylon* = wood) conducts water and dissolved minerals absorbed from the soil upward from a plant's roots to

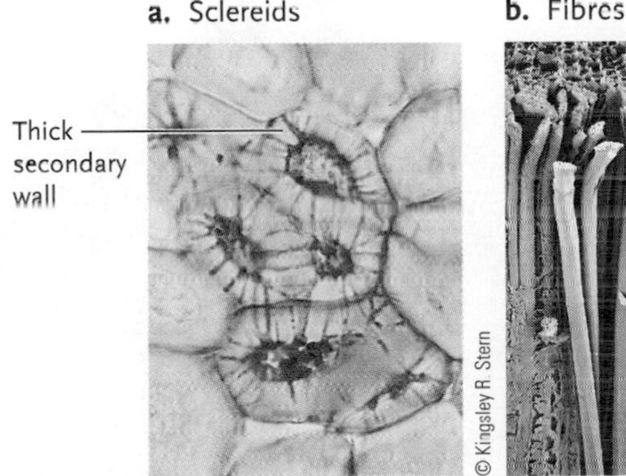

Figure 28.8
Examples of sclerenchyma cells. **(a)** From the flesh of a pear (*Pyrus*), one type of sclereid: stone cells, each with a thick, lignified wall. **(b)** Strong fibres from stems of a flax plant (*Linum*).

the shoot. It was a key adaptation allowing plants to make the transition to life on land (see Chapter 25). Xylem contains two types of conducting cells: *tracheids* and *vessel members*. Both develop thick, lignified secondary cell walls and die at maturity. The empty cell walls of abutting cells serve as pipelines for water and minerals.

Tracheids are elongated, with tapered, overlapping ends **(Figure 28.9a)**. In plants adapted to drier soil conditions, they have strong secondary walls that keep them from collapsing when water becomes scarce. As in sclerenchyma, water can move from cell to cell through pits. Usually, a pit in one cell is opposite a pit of an adjacent cell, so water seeps laterally from tracheid to tracheid.

Vessel members (or vessel elements) are shorter cells joined end to end in tubelike columns called vessels **(Figure 28.9b)**. **Vessels** are typically several centimetres long, and in some vines and trees, they may be many metres long. Like tracheids, vessel members have pits. However, they have another adaptation that greatly enhances water flow. As vessel members mature, enzymes break down portions of their end walls, producing perforations. Some vessel members have a single, large perforation, so that the end is completely open (see Figure 28.7b). Others have a cluster of small, round perforations, or ladderlike bars, extending across the open end. Water moves more efficiently through vessels than tracheids due to their greater diameter and perforated ends.

Fossil evidence shows that the forerunners of modern plant species relied solely on tracheids for water transport, and today ferns and most gymnosperms still have only tracheids. Nearly all angiosperms and a few gymnosperms and seedless vascular plants have *both* tracheids and vessel members, however, which confers an adaptive advantage. Flowing water sometimes contains air bubbles, which are a potentially lethal threat to the plant. Water can flow rapidly through vessel members that are linked end to end, but the open channel cannot prevent air bubbles from forming and possibly blocking the flow through the whole vessel. By contrast, even though water moves more slowly in tracheids, the pits are impermeable to air bubbles, and a bubble that forms in one tracheid stays there; water continues to move between other tracheids.

At maturity, tracheids and vessel members die as genetic cues cause their protoplasts to degenerate and lignin to be deposited in the cell walls.

Phloem: Transporting Sugars and Other Solutes. The vascular tissue **phloem** (*phloios* = tree bark) transports solutes, notably the sugars made in photosynthesis, throughout the plant body. The main conducting cells of phloem are **sieve tube members (Figure 28.10),** which are connected end to end, forming a **sieve tube.** As the name implies, their end walls, called sieve plates, are studded with pores. In flowering plants, the phloem is strengthened by fibres and sclereids.

Immature sieve tube members contain the usual plant organelles. Over time, however, the cell nucleus and internal membranes in plastids break down, mitochondria shrink, and the cytoplasm is reduced to a thin layer lining the interior surface of the cell wall. Even without a nucleus, the cell lives up to several years in most plants and much longer in some trees.

In many flowering plants, specialized parenchyma cells known as **companion cells** are connected to mature sieve tube members by plasmodesmata.

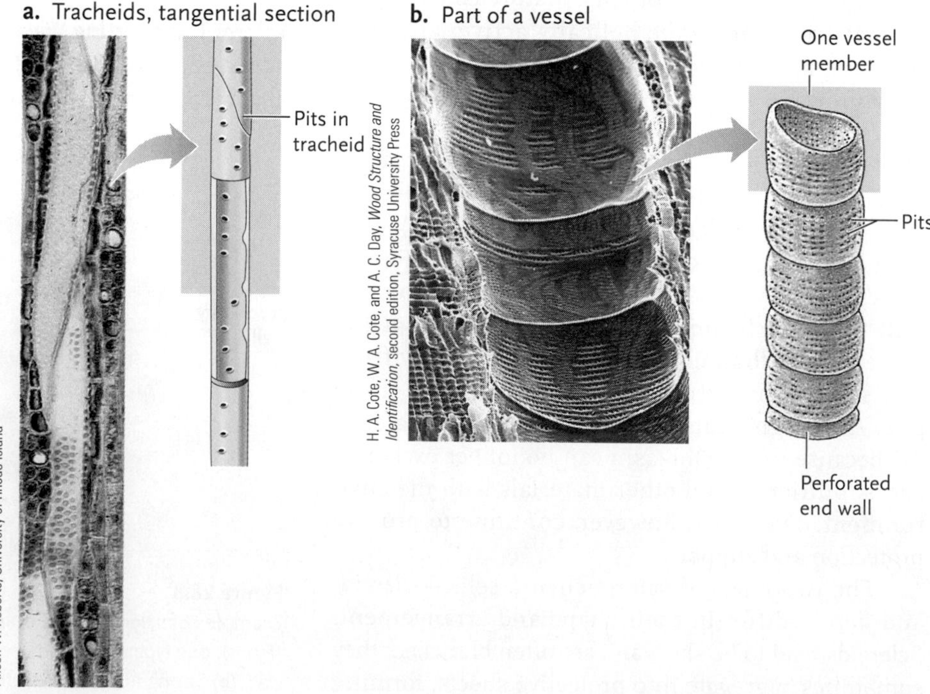

Figure 28.9
Representative tracheids and vessel members from woody stems, elements in xylem that conduct water and dissolved mineral salts through the body of a vascular plant. These images show **(a)** tracheids and **(b)** an electron micrograph of a vessel.

a. Sieve-tube members

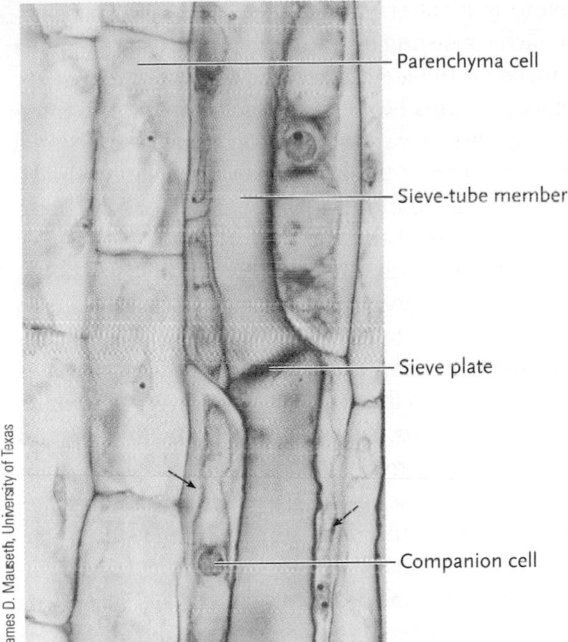

b. Sieve plate

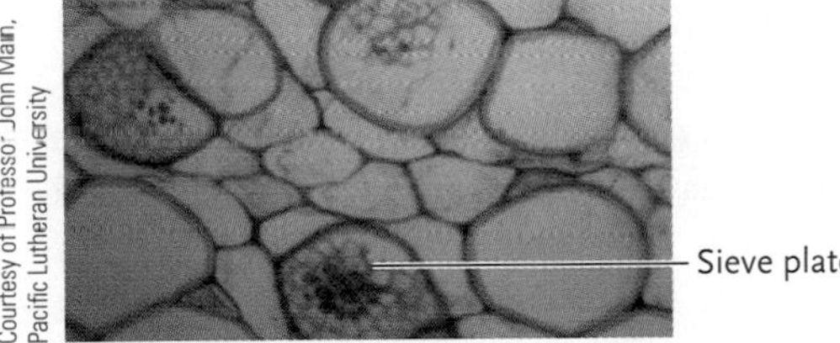

Figure 28.10
Structure of sieve tube members. (a) Micrograph showing sieve tube members in longitudinal section. The arrows point to companion cells. Long tubes of sieve tube members conduct sugars and other organic compounds. **(b)** Sieve plate in a cell in phloem, cross section.

Unlike sieve tube members, companion cells retain their nucleus when mature. They assist sieve tube members with both the uptake of sugars and the unloading of sugars in tissues engaged in food storage or growth. They may also help regulate the metabolism of mature sieve tube members. We return to the functions of xylem and phloem cells in Chapter 29.

28.2c The Dermal Tissue System Protects Plant Surfaces

A complex tissue called **epidermis** covers the primary plant body in a single continuous layer **(Figure 28.11a)** or sometimes in multiple layers of tightly packed cells. The external surface of epidermal cell walls is coated with waxes that are embedded in cutin, a network of chemically linked fats. Epidermal cells secrete this coating, or **cuticle**, which resists water loss and helps protect against attacks by microbes. A cuticle coats all plant parts except the very tips of the shoot and the most absorptive parts of roots; other root regions have an extremely thin cuticle.

Most epidermal cells are relatively unspecialized, but some are modified in ways that represent important adaptations for plants. Young stems, leaves, flower parts, and even some roots have pairs of crescent-shaped **guard cells (Figure 28.11b).** Unlike other cells of the epidermis, guard cells contain chloroplasts and so can carry out photosynthesis. The pore between a pair of guard cells is called a **stoma** (plural, stomata). Water vapour, carbon dioxide, and oxygen cross the epidermis through the stomata. Guard cells regulate opening and closing of stomata via mechanisms we consider in Chapter 29.

Other epidermal specializations are the single-celled or multicellular outgrowths collectively called **trichomes**, which give the stems or leaves of some plants a hairy appearance. Some trichomes exude sugars that attract insect pollinators. Leaf trichomes of *Urtica,* the stinging nettle, provide protection by injecting an irritating toxin into the skin of animals that brush against the plant or try to eat it. **Root hairs,** extensions of the outer wall of root epidermal cells **(Figure 28.11c),** are also trichomes. Root hairs absorb much of a plant's water and minerals from the soil.

The epidermal cells of flower petals (which are modified leaves) synthesize pigments that are partly responsible for a blossom's colours.

a. Leaf epidermis

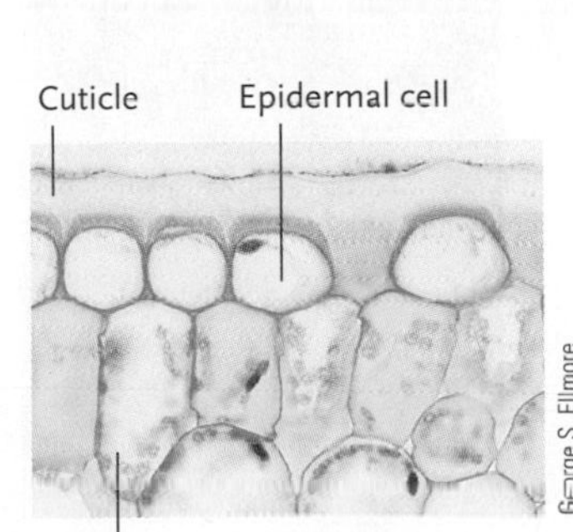

b. Leaf surface

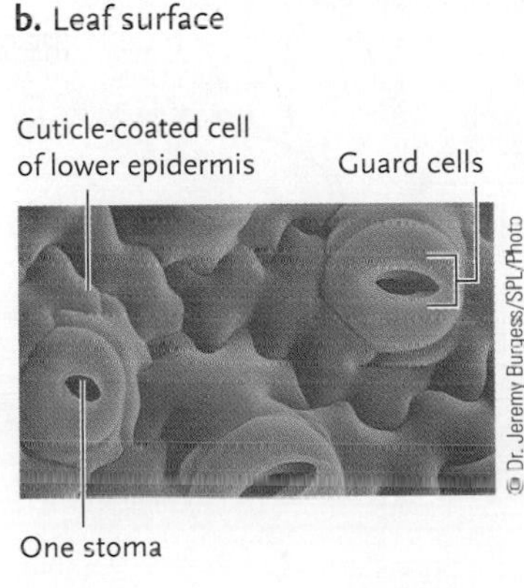

c. Root hairs

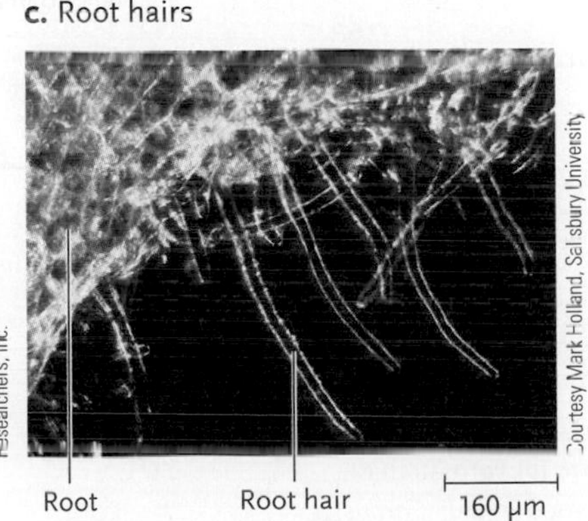

Figure 28.11
Structure and examples of epidermal tissue. (a) Cross section of leaf epidermis from a bush lily (*Clivia miniata*). **(b)** Scanning electron micrograph of a leaf surface, showing cuticle-covered epidermal cells and stomata. **(c)** Root hairs, an epidermal specialization.

Study Break

1. Describe the defining features, cellular components, and functions of the ground tissue system.
2. What are the functions of xylem and phloem?
3. What are the cellular components and functions of the dermal tissue system?

28.3 Primary Shoot Systems

A young flowering plant's shoot system consists of the main stem, leaves, and buds, as well as flowers and fruits. Chapter 30 looks more closely at flowers and fruits; here we focus on the growth and organization of stems, buds, and leaves of the primary shoot system.

28.3a Stems Are Adapted to Provide Support, Routes for Vascular Tissues, Storage, and New Growth

Stems are structurally adapted for four main functions:

- Stems provide mechanical support, generally along a vertical (upright) axis, for body parts involved in growth, photosynthesis, and reproduction. These parts include meristematic tissues, leaves, and flowers.
- Stems house the vascular tissues (xylem and phloem), which transport products of photosynthesis, water and dissolved minerals, hormones, and other substances throughout the plant.
- Stems are often modified to store water and food.
- Buds and specific stem regions contain meristematic tissue that gives rise to new cells of the shoot.

The Modular Organization of a Stem. A plant stem develops in a pattern that divides the stem into modules, each consisting of a *node* and an *internode*. A **node** is a place on the stem where one or more leaves are attached; the area between two nodes is thus an **internode**. New primary growth occurs in buds—a **terminal bud** at the apex of the main shoot, and **lateral buds,** which produce branches (lateral shoots) at the point where leaves meet the stem. Meristematic tissue in buds gives rise to leaves, flowers, or both **(Figure 28.12).**

In eudicots, most growth in a stem's length occurs directly below the apical meristem as internode cells divide and elongate. Internode cells nearest the apex are most active, so the most visible new growth occurs at the ends of stems. So why isn't the growth of grasses stopped when you mow your lawn or when cattle graze on them? In grasses and some other monocots, the upper cells of an internode stop dividing as the internode elongates, and cell divisions are limited to a meristematic region at the base of the internode. The stems of bamboo and other grasses elongate as the internodes are "pushed up" by the growth of such meristems. This adaptation allows grasses to grow back readily after grazing or mowing because the meristem is not removed.

Terminal buds release a hormone that inhibits the growth of nearby lateral buds, a phenomenon called **apical dominance.** Gardeners who want a bushier plant can stimulate lateral bud growth by periodically cutting off the terminal bud. The flow of hormone signals then dwindles to a level low enough that lateral buds begin to grow. In nature, apical dominance is an adaptation that directs the plant's resources into growing up toward the light.

Primary Growth and Structure of a Stem. Primary growth, the cell divisions and enlargement that produce the primary plant body, begins in the shoot and root apical meristems. The sequence of events is sim-

a. Location of nodes and buds

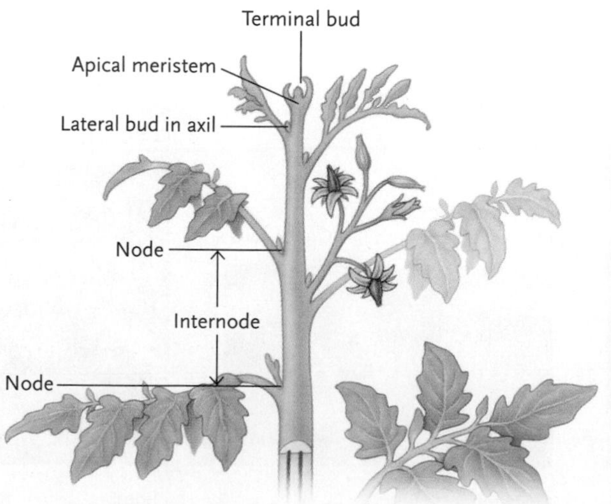

b. Leaves at a terminal bud

Figure 28.12
Modular structure of a stem. **(a)** The arrangement of nodes and buds on a plant stem. **(b)** Formation of leaves at a terminal bud of a dogwood (genus *Cornus*).

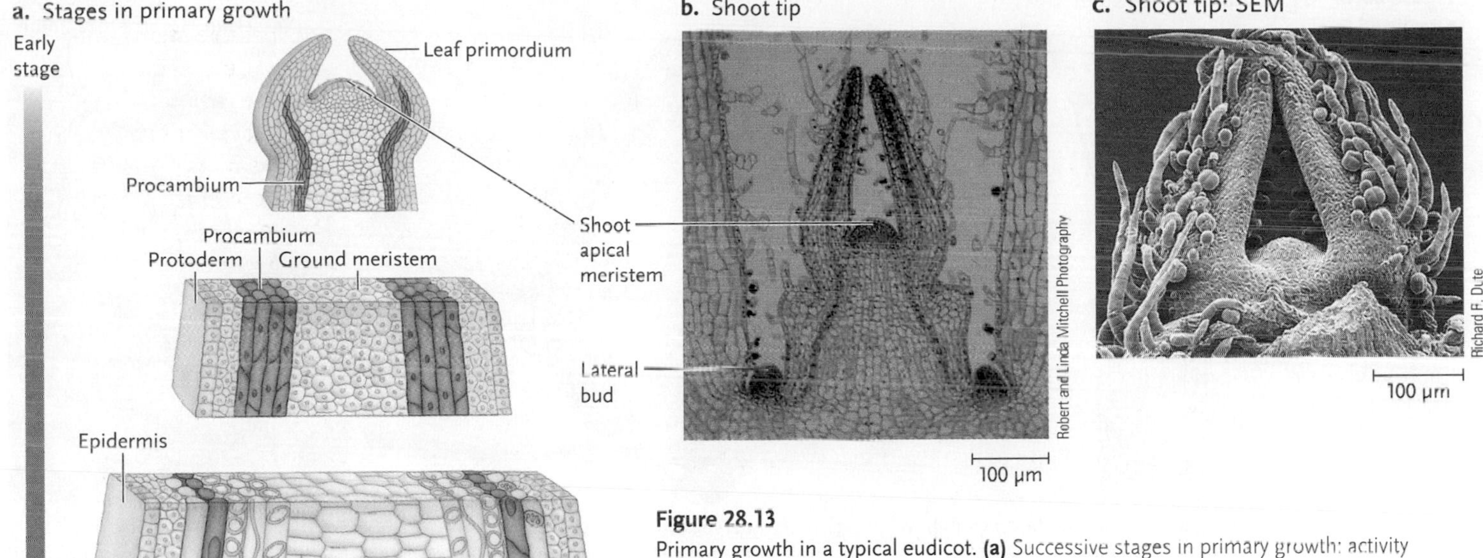

Figure 28.13
Primary growth in a typical eudicot. **(a)** Successive stages in primary growth: activity begins at the shoot apical meristem and continues at the primary meristems derived from it. Notice the progressive differentiation of most of the tissue regions. **(b)** Light micrograph of a *Solenostemon* shoot tip, cut longitudinally through its centre. **(c)** Scanning electron micrograph of its surface.

ilar in roots and shoots; it is shown for a eudicot shoot in **Figure 28.13.**

The shoot apical meristem is a dome-shaped mass of cells at the tip of shoots, surrounded by developing leaves. When a cell of this meristem divides, one of its daughter cells remains part of the meristem, whereas the other begins to differentiate to follow a particular developmental path.

The differentiating cells give rise to three **primary meristems:** *protoderm, procambium,* and *ground meristem* (see Figure 28.13a). These primary meristems are relatively unspecialized tissues with cells that differentiate, in turn, into specialized cells and tissues. In eudicots, the primary meristems are also responsible for elongation of the plant body.

Each primary meristem occupies a different position in the shoot tip, as shown in Figure 28.13a. Outermost is **protoderm,** a meristem that will produce the stem's epidermis. Inward from the protoderm is the **ground meristem,** which will give rise to ground tissue, most of it parenchyma. **Procambium,** which produces the primary vascular tissues, is sandwiched between ground meristem layers. Procambial cells are long and thin, and their spatial orientation foreshadows the future function of the tissues they produce. In most plants, inner procambial cells give rise to xylem and outer procambial cells to phloem. In plants with secondary growth, a thin region of procambium between the primary xylem and phloem remains undifferentiated. Later it will give rise to a lateral meristem.

The developing vascular tissues become organized into **vascular bundles,** cylinders of primary xylem and phloem that are wrapped in sclerenchyma. Eudicot stems have vascular bundles arranged in a circle that separates the ground tissue in the centre of the stem (the pith) from the ground tissue under the epidermis (the cortex) **(Figure 28.14a, p. 680).** Both cortex and pith consist mainly of parenchyma; in some plant species, the pith parenchyma stores starch reserves. Monocot stems also have vascular bundles, but these are scattered throughout the ground tissue, so distinct pith and cortical regions do not form **(Figure 28.14b).** In some monocots, including bamboo, the pith breaks down, leaving the stem with a hollow core. The hollow stems of certain hard-walled bamboo species are used to make bamboo flutes.

As leaves and buds develop along a stem, some vascular bundles in the stem branch off into these tissues. The arrangement of vascular bundles in a plant ultimately depends on the number of branch points to leaves and buds and on the number and distribution of leaves.

Stem Modifications. Evolution has produced a range of stem specializations, including structures modified for reproduction, food storage, or both **(Figure 28.15, p. 681).** An onion or a garlic head is a *bulb,* a modified shoot that consists of a bud with fleshy leaves. *Tubers* are stem regions enlarged by the presence of starch-storing parenchyma cells; examples of plants that form tubers are the potato and the cassava (the source of tapioca). The "eyes" of a potato are buds at nodes of the modified stem. Many grasses, such as quackgrass (*Elymus repens*), and some weeds are difficult to eradicate because they have *rhizomes*—long underground stems that can extend as much as 50 cm deep into the soil and rapidly produce new shoots when existing ones are pulled out. The pungent, starchy "root" of

Figure 28.14 Organization of cells and tissues inside the stem of a eudicot and a monocot. **(a)** Part of a stem from alfalfa (*Medicago*), **a eudicot.** In many species of eudicots and conifers, the vascular bundles develop in a more or less ringlike array in the ground tissue system, as shown here. **(b)** Part of a stem from corn (*Zea mays*), a monocot. In most monocots and some herbaceous eudicots, vascular bundles are scattered through the ground tissue, as shown here.

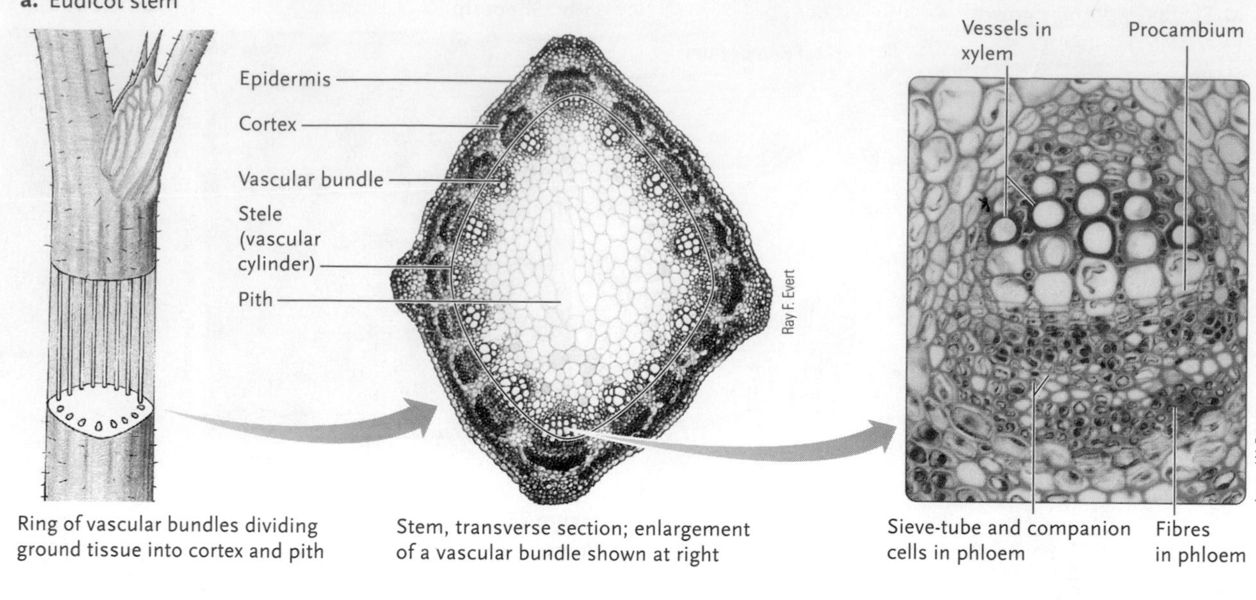

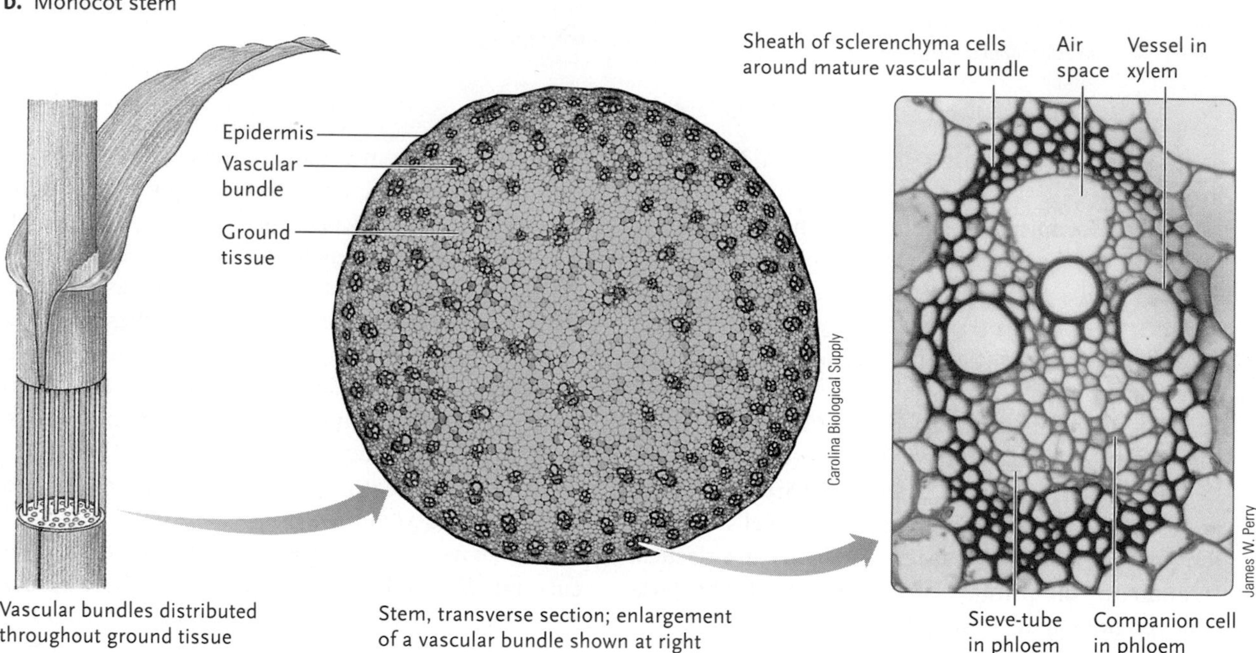

ginger is also a rhizome. Crocuses and some other ornamental plants develop elongated, fleshy underground stems called *corms,* another starch-storage adaptation. Tubers, rhizomes, and corms all have meristematic tissue at nodes from which new plants can be propagated—a vegetative (asexual) reproductive mode. Other plants, including strawberries (*Fragaria* spp.), reproduce vegetatively via slender stems called *stolons,* which grow along the soil surface. New plants arise at nodes along the stolon.

28.3b Leaves Carry Out Photosynthesis and Gas Exchange

Each spring, a mature maple tree heralds the new season by unfurling roughly 100 000 leaves. Some other tree species produce leaves by the millions. For these and most other plants, leaves are the main organs of photosynthesis and gas exchange (the movement of carbon dioxide and oxygen into and out of the leaf).

Leaf Morphology and Anatomy. In both eudicots and monocots, the leaf **blade** provides a large surface area for absorbing sunlight and carbon dioxide **(Figure 28.16).** Leaves of flowering plants are generally oriented on the stem axis so that they can capture the maximum amount of sunlight; the stems and leaves of some plants change position to follow the sun's movement during the day (this phenomenon is described in Chapter 31).

Many eudicot leaves, such as those of maples, have a broad, flat blade attached to the stem by a stalklike **petiole** (see Figure 28.16a); the celery stalks that we eat

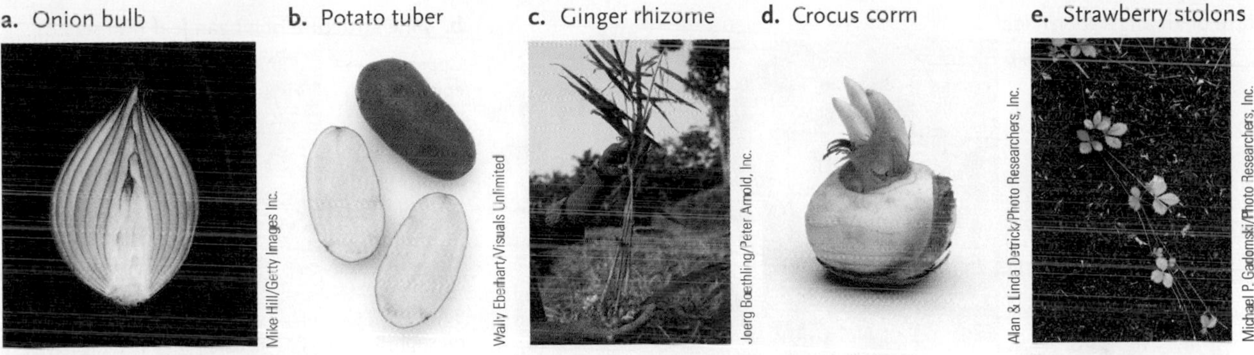

Figure 28.15
A selection of modified stems. **(a)** The fleshy bulbs of onions (*Allium cepa*) are modified shoots in which the plant stores starch. **(b)** A potato (*Solanum tuberosum*), a tuber. **(c)** Ginger "root," the pungent, starchy rhizome of the ginger plant (*Zingiber officinale*). **(d)** Crocus plants (genus *Crocus*) typically grow from a corm. **(e)** A strawberry plant (*Fragaria ananassa*) and stolon.

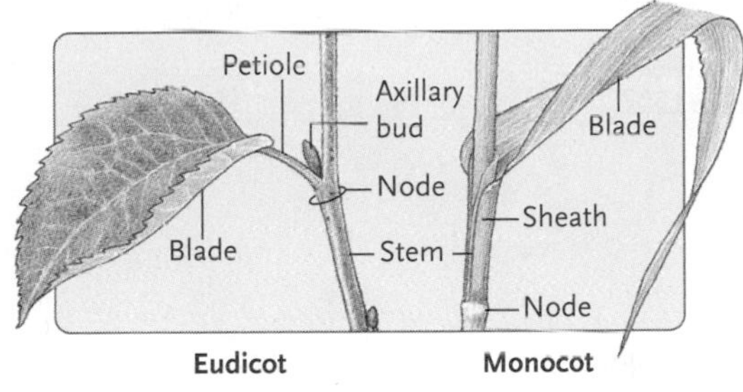

Figure 28.16
Leaf forms. Common forms of eudicot and monocot leaves.

are petioles. Petioles hold leaves away from the stem and help prevent individual leaves from shading one another. In many plant species, petioles allow leaves to move in the breeze—think about trembling aspen (*Populus tremuloides*) leaves rustling in a breeze—enhancing air circulation around leaves, thus replenishing the supply of carbon dioxide for photosynthesis. In most monocot leaves, such as those of grass or corn, the blade is longer and narrower and its base simply forms a sheath around the stem (see Figure 28.16b).

In plants of arid habitats, leaves may be reduced to spines to reduce water loss by evaporation **(Figure 28.17a)**; the stem takes over the task of photosynthesis. Leaves or parts of leaves may be modified into tendrils, such as those of the sweet pea (*Lathyrus odoratus*) **(Figure 28.17b)**, or other structures. Epidermal cells on the leaves of the saltbush *Atriplex spongiosa* form balloonlike structures **(Figure 28.17c)** that contain concentrated Na^+ and Cl taken up from the salty soil. Eventually, the salt-filled epidermal cells burst or fall off the leaf, releasing the salt to the outside. This adaptation helps control the salt concentration in the plant's tissues—another example of the link between structure, function, and the environment in which a plant lives.

Leaf Primary Growth and Internal Structure. As the shoot apical meristem divides, it produces a series of bumps on its sides, the **leaf primordia**, which give rise to leaves (see Figure 28.13a). As the plant grows and the internodes elongate, the leaves that form from leaf primordia become spaced at intervals along the length of the stem or its branches.

A leaf is typically composed of several layers **(Figure 28.18, p. 682)**. Uppermost is epidermis, with cuticle covering its outer surface. Just beneath the epidermis is **mesophyll** (*mesos* = middle; *phyllon* = leaf), ground tissue composed of loosely packed paren-

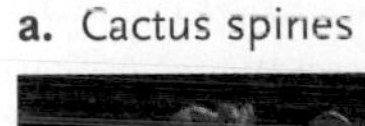

Figure 28.17
A few adaptations of leaves. **(a)** Spines on a barrel cactus (*Ferrocactus covillei*) thwart browsing herbivores and limit the surface area from which water is lost in the plant's arid environment. **(b)** The tendrils of a sweet pea (*Lathyrus odoratus*) help support the climbing plant's stem. **(c)** Salt bladders on the leaf of a saltbush plant (*Atriplex spongiosa*). The "bladders" are trichomes, specialized outgrowths of the leaf epidermis in which excess salt from the plant's tissue fluid accumulates. The salt-laden trichomes eventually burst or slough off.

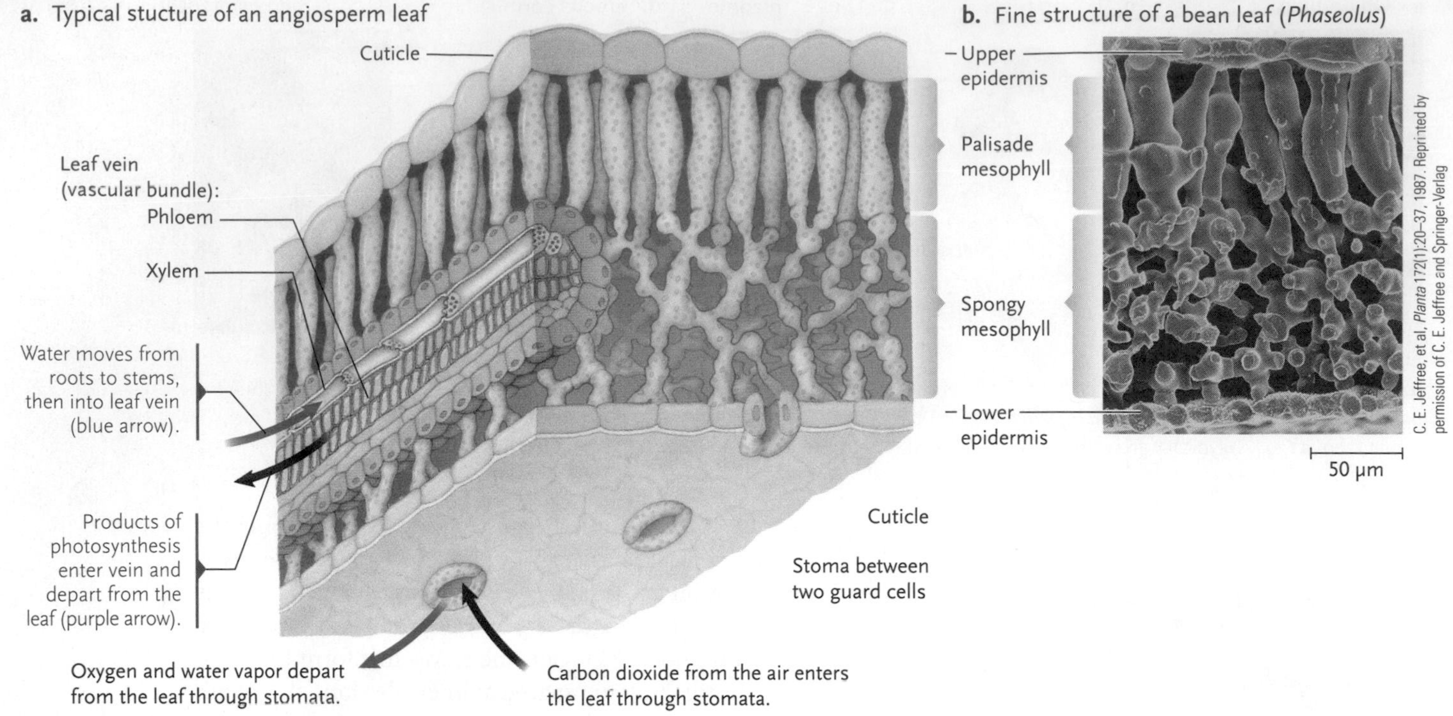

Figure 28.18
Internal structure of a leaf. (a) Diagram of a typical leaf structure for many kinds of flowering plants. **(b)** Scanning electron micrograph of tissue from the leaf of a kidney bean plant (*Phaseolus*), transverse section. Notice the compact organization of epidermal cells. See Figure 31.10 for a scanning electron micrograph of stomata.

chyma cells that contain chloroplasts. The leaves of many plants, especially eudicots, contain two layers of mesophyll. *Palisade mesophyll* cells contain more chloroplasts and are arranged in compact columns with smaller air spaces between them, typically toward the upper leaf surface. *Spongy mesophyll*, which tends to be located toward the underside of a leaf, consists of irregularly arranged cells with a conspicuous network of air spaces—between 15% and 50% of the leaf's volume—that give this layer a spongy appearance. What is the role of these air spaces? They enhance the uptake of carbon dioxide and release of oxygen during photosynthesis. Mesophyll also contains collenchyma and sclerenchyma cells, which support the photosynthetic cells.

Below the mesophyll is another cuticle-covered epidermal layer. Except in grasses and a few other plants, this layer contains most of the stomata through which water vapour exits the leaf and gas exchange occurs. For example, the upper surface of an apple leaf has no stomata, whereas a square centimeter of the lower surface has more than 20 000. A square centimeter of the upper epidermis of a tomato leaf has about 1200 stomata, whereas the same area of the lower epidermis has 13 000. Why are more stomata located on the underside of the leaf? This positioning protects stomata from direct exposure to sunlight, thus limiting water loss by evaporation through stomatal openings.

Vascular bundles form a lacy network of **veins** throughout the leaf. Eudicot leaves typically have a branching vein pattern; in monocot leaves, veins tend to run in parallel along the length of the leaf (see Table 28.1).

In temperate regions, most leaves are temporary structures. In deciduous species such as birches and maples, hormonal signals cause the leaves to drop from the stem as days shorten in autumn. Other temperate plants, such as most conifers, also drop their leaves (which are modified into needles in conifers), but they appear "evergreen" because the leaves may persist for several years and do not all drop at the same time.

Study Break

1. Describe the functions of stems and stem structures and list the basic steps in the primary growth of stems.
2. Explain the general function of leaves and how leaf anatomy supports this role in eudicots and monocots.
3. Describe the steps in the primary growth of a leaf and the structures that result from the process.

28.4 Root Systems

Plants cannot move around to find water and nutrients when they have depleted supplies in their immediate soil neighbourhood, so they must be able to forage for new supplies. Once found, the plant must absorb enough water and dissolved minerals to sustain growth and routine cellular maintenance. These tasks can require a tremendous root surface area, at least part of which is regularly replaced. In one study, rye plants (*Secale cereale*) that had been growing for only four months were measured. One plant's root system had a surface area of more than 700 m^2—about 130 times greater than the surface area of its shoot system!

In addition to taking up water and nutrients, roots store nutrients produced by photosynthesis, some of which is used by root cells and some transported later to cells of the shoot. As the root system penetrates downward and spreads out, it also anchors the aboveground parts.

28.4a Taproot and Fibrous Root Systems Are Specialized for Particular Functions

Most eudicots have a **taproot system**—a single main root, or taproot, that is adapted for storage, plus smaller branching roots called **lateral roots (Figure 28.19a).** As the main root grows downward, its diameter increases, and the lateral roots emerge along the length of its older, differentiated regions. The youngest lateral roots are near the root tip. Carrots and dandelions have a taproot system, as do pines and many other conifers. A pine's taproot system can penetrate 6 m or more into the soil.

Grasses and many other monocots develop a **fibrous root system** in which several main roots branch to form a dense mass of smaller roots **(Figure 28.19b).** Fibrous root systems are adapted to absorb water and nutrients from the upper layers of soil and tend to spread out laterally from the base of the stem. Fibrous roots are important ecologically because dense root networks help hold topsoil in place and prevent erosion. During the 1930s, overgrazing by livestock and intensive farming in the prairie provinces of Canada and the US Midwest destroyed hundreds of thousands of acres of native prairie grasses, contributing to soil erosion on a massive scale. Swirling clouds of soil particles prompted journalists to name the area the Dust Bowl and gave this decade the name "the Dirty Thirties."

In some plants, **adventitious roots** arise from the stem of the young plant. "Adventitious" refers to any structure arising at an unusual location, such as roots that grow from stems or leaves. Adventitious roots of Virginia creeper (*Parthenociccus quinquefolia*) and

a. Taproot system

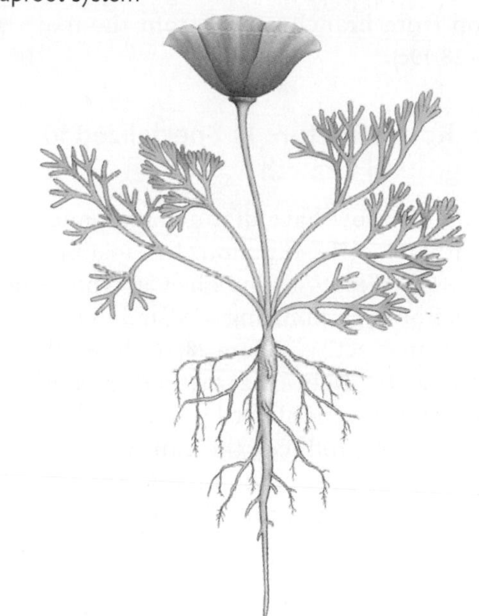

b. Fibrous root system

c. Adventitious roots

Figure 28.19
Types of roots.
(a) Taproot system of a California poppy (*Eschscholzia californica*). **(b)** Fibrous root system of a grass plant. **(c)** Example of adventitious roots, the numerous prop roots of red mangrove trees (*Rhizophora*).

some other climbing plants produce a gluelike substance that allows them to cling to vertical surfaces. The *prop roots* of a corn plant are adventitious roots that develop from the shoot node nearest the soil surface; they both support the plant and absorb water and nutrients. Mangroves and other trees that grow in marshy habitats often have huge prop roots, which develop from branches and from the main stem **(Figure 28.19c)**.

28.4b Root Structure Is Specialized for Underground Growth

Like shoots, roots have distinct anatomical parts, each with a specific function. In most plants, primary growth of roots begins when an embryonic root emerges from a germinating seed and its apical meristem becomes active. **Figure 28.20** shows the structure of a root tip. Notice that the root apical meristem terminates in a dome-shaped cell mass, the **root cap.** The meristem produces the cap, which, in turn, surrounds and protects the meristem as the root elongates through the soil. Certain cells in the cap respond to gravity, guiding the root tip downward. Cap cells also secrete a polysaccharide-rich substance that lubricates the tip and eases the growing root's passage through the soil. Outer root cap cells are continually abraded off and replaced by new cells at the cap's base.

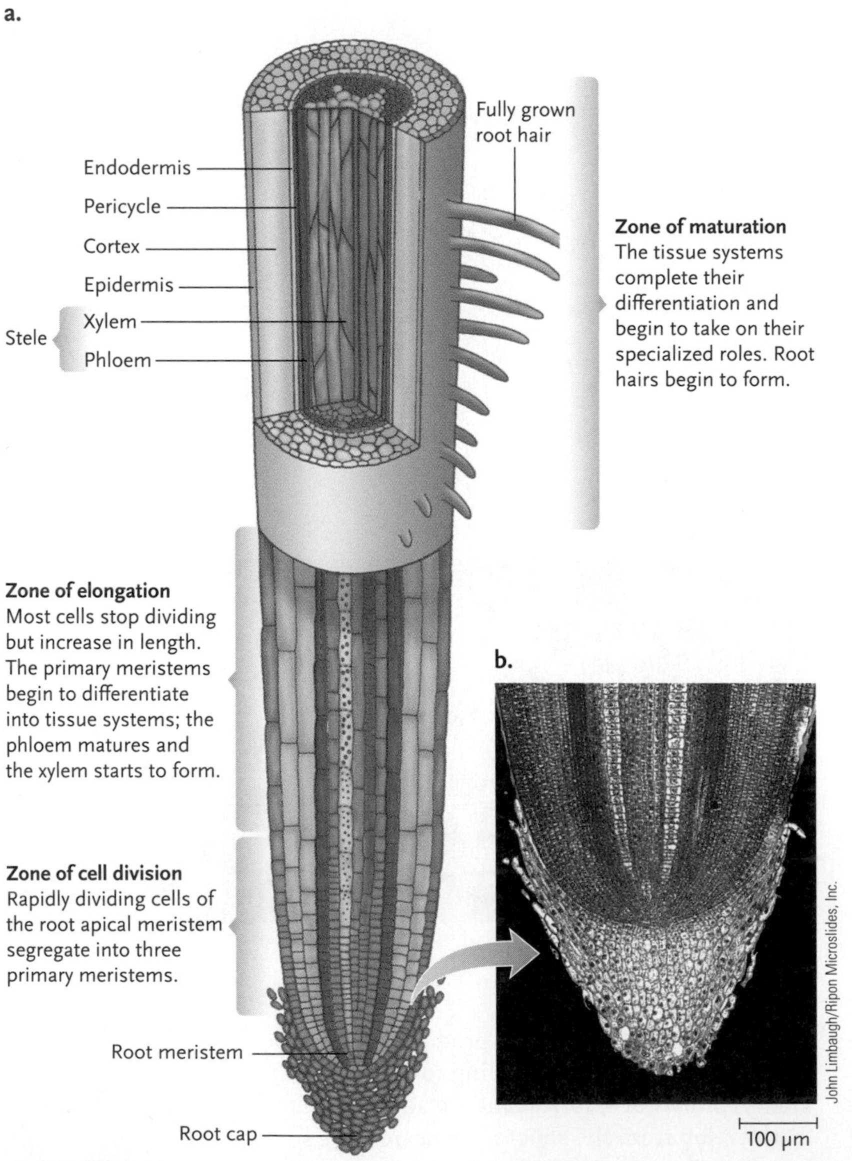

Zones of Primary Growth in Roots. Root primary growth takes place in successive stages, beginning at the root tip and progressing upward.

The root apical meristem and the actively dividing cells behind it form the **zone of cell division.** As in the stem, cells of the apical meristem divide to produce cells that remain as part of the meristem and other cells that differentiate into the three primary meristems. Cells in the centre of the root tip become the procambium, those just outside the procambium become ground meristem, and those on the periphery of the apical meristem become protoderm.

The zone of cell division merges into the **zone of elongation.** Most of the increase in a root's length comes from this region, where cells become longer as their vacuoles fill with water. This "hydraulic" elongation pushes the root cap and apical meristem through the soil by as much as several centimetres a day.

Above the zone of elongation, cells do not increase in length, but they may differentiate further and take on specialized roles in the **zone of maturation.** For example, epidermal cells in this zone give rise to root hairs, and the procambium, ground meristem, and protoderm complete their differentiation in this region.

Tissues of the Root System. Coupled with the primary growth of the shoot, primary root growth produces a unified system of vascular pipelines extending from root tip to shoot tip. The root procambium produces cells that mature into the root's xylem and phloem **(Figure 28.21)**. Ground meristem gives rise to the root's cortex, its ground tissue of starch-storing parenchyma cells that surround the stele. In eudicots, the stele runs through the centre of the root (see **Figure 28.21a**). In corn and some other monocots, the stele forms a ring that divides the ground tissue into cortex and pith (see **Figure 28.21b**).

The root cortex often contains air spaces that allow oxygen to reach all of the living root cells. In many flowering plants, the outer root cortex cells give rise to an **exodermis**, a thin band of cells that, among other functions, may limit water losses from roots and help regulate the absorption of ions. The innermost layer of the root cortex is the **endodermis**, a thin, selectively permeable barrier that helps control the movement of water and dissolved minerals into the stele. We look in more detail at the roles of exodermis and endodermis in Chapter 29.

a.
Fully grown root hair
Endodermis
Pericycle
Cortex
Epidermis
Stele
Xylem
Phloem
Zone of maturation
The tissue systems complete their differentiation and begin to take on their specialized roles. Root hairs begin to form.
Zone of elongation
Most cells stop dividing but increase in length. The primary meristems begin to differentiate into tissue systems; the phloem matures and the xylem starts to form.
Zone of cell division
Rapidly dividing cells of the root apical meristem segregate into three primary meristems.
Root meristem
Root cap
b.
100 μm
John Limbaugh/Ripon Microslides, Inc.

Figure 28.20
Tissues and zones of primary growth in a root tip. **(a)** Generalized root tip, longitudinal section. **(b)** Micrograph of a corn root tip, longitudinal section.

a. Eudicot root

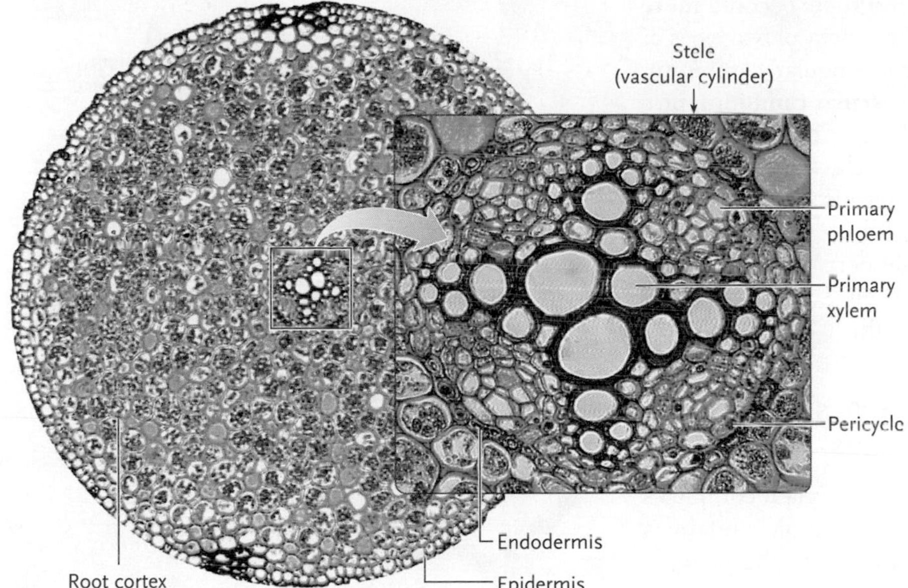

b. Monocot root

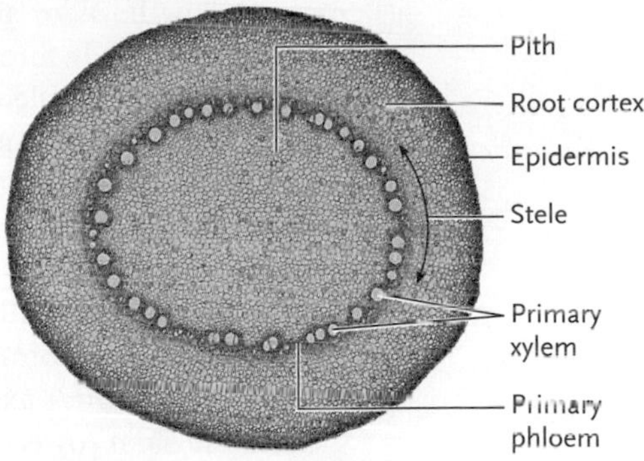

Figure 28.21
Stele structure in eudicot and monocot roots compared. **(a)** A young root of the buttercup *Ranunculus*, a eudicot. The close-up shows details of the stele.
(b) Root of a corn plant (*Zea mays*), a monocot. Notice how the stele divides the ground tissue into cortex and pith. Both roots are shown in transverse section.
(a: Chuck Brown; b: Carolina Biological Supply.)

Between the stele and the endodermis is the **pericycle**, consisting of one or more layers of parenchyma cells that have retained the ability to function as meristem. The pericycle produces lateral roots **(Figure 28.22)** in response to chemical growth regulators. These lateral roots grow out through the cortex and epidermis, producing enzymes that help break down the intervening cells. The distribution and frequency of lateral root formation partly control the overall shape of the root system and the extent of the soil area it can penetrate.

The outer surface of some cells in the developing root epidermis become elongated into root hairs (see Figure 28.20). Root hairs can be more than a centimeter long and can form in less than a day. Collectively, the thousands or millions of them on a plant's roots greatly increase the plant's absorptive surface. But it is not just the increased surface area provided by root hairs that increases nutrient uptake: each hair is a slender tube with thin walls made sticky on their surface by a coating of pectin. Soil particles tend to adhere to the walls, providing an intimate association between the hair and the surrounding earth, thus facilitating the uptake of water molecules and mineral ions from soil. When plants are transplanted, rough handling can tear off much of this fragile absorptive surface. Unable to take up enough water and minerals, the transplant may die before new root hairs can form.

Study Break

1. Compare the two general types of root systems.
2. Describe the zones of primary growth in roots.
3. Describe the various tissues that arise in a root system and their functions.

28.5 Secondary Growth

All plants undergo primary growth of the root and stem. In addition, some plants have secondary growth processes that add girth to roots and stems over two or

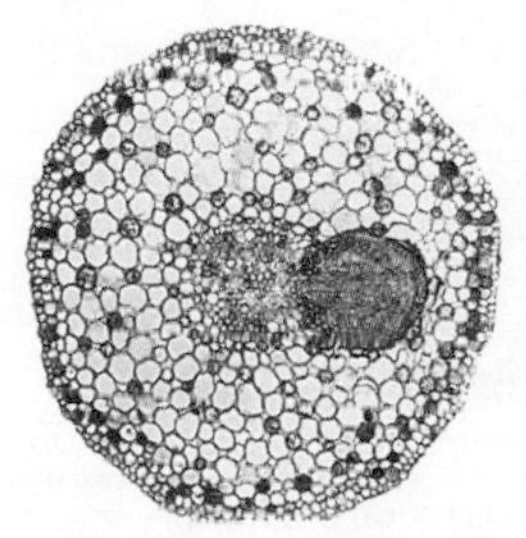
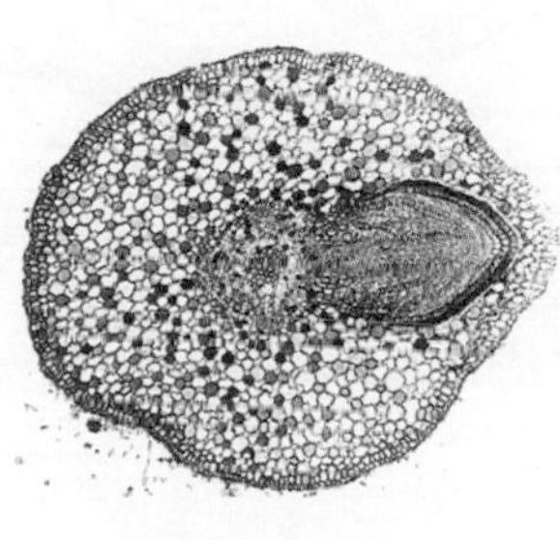
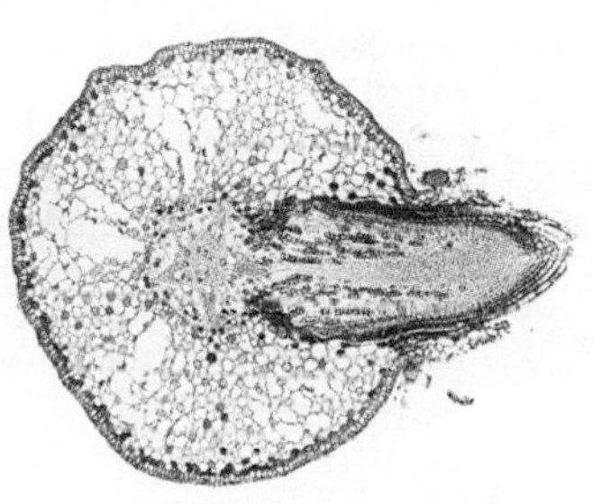

Figure 28.22
Micrographs showing the formation of a lateral root from the pericycle of a willow tree (*Salix*). These micrographs show transverse sections. (All images: © Omnikron/Photo Researches, Inc.)

more growing seasons. In plant species that have secondary growth, older stems and roots become more massive and woody through the activity of two types of lateral meristems called *cambia* (singular, cambium). One of these meristems, the **vascular cambium**, produces secondary xylem and phloem. The other, called the **cork cambium**, produces **cork**, a secondary tissue that replaces the original epidermis of the plant. In contrast to the cells of the apical meristerms, the cells of the lateral meristems divide perpendicular to the stem's longitudinal axis, so their descendants add girth to the stem instead of length.

28.5a Vascular Cambium Gives Rise to Secondary Growth in Stems

Recall that after the stem of a woody plant completes its primary growth, each vascular bundle contains a layer of undifferentiated cells between the primary xylem and the primary phloem. These cells, along with parenchyma cells between the bundles, eventually give rise to a continuous cylinder of vascular cambium that surrounds the xylem and pith of the stem **(Figure 28.23).** Secondary growth takes place as the cells of the vascular cambium divide. Division of the vascular cambium produces secondary xylem to the inside of the cambium and secondary phloem to the outside of the cambium.

With time, the mass of secondary xylem inside the ring of vascular cambium increases, forming the hard tissue known as **wood.** Outside the vascular cambium, secondary phloem cells are also added each year **(Figure 28.24).** (The primary phloem cells, which have thin walls, are destroyed as they are pushed outward by secondary growth.) As a stem increases in diameter, the growing mass of new tissue eventually causes the cortex, and the epidermis beyond it, to rupture. Such breaks in the outer protective "skin" of the plant are potentially harmful as they would allow easy entrance for pathogens. The cork cambium—produced early in the stem's secondary development by meristem cells in the cortex or epidermis—replaces the lost epidermis with cork cells. The walls of cork cells contain lignin and thick layers of **suberin**, a waxy substance that is very impermeable to water and gases. Cork cells are dead at maturity.

Bark encompasses all the tissues outside the vascular cambium; it thus includes the secondary phloem,

Vascular cambium
Stem surface
Primary xylem
Primary phloem
Tissues involved in primary growth
Vascular cambium
Secondary xylem
Secondary phloem
Tissues involved in secondary growth

Figure 28.23
Secondary and primary growth compared. In a woody plant, primary growth resumes each spring at the terminal and lateral buds. Secondary growth resumes at the vascular cambium inside the stem.

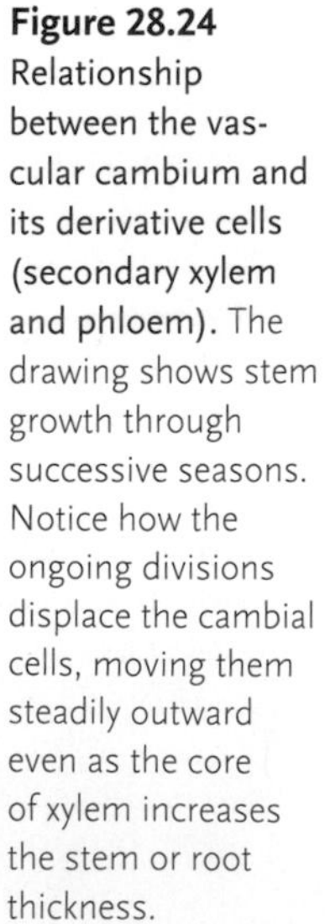

Figure 28.24
Relationship between the vascular cambium and its derivative cells (secondary xylem and phloem). The drawing shows stem growth through successive seasons. Notice how the ongoing divisions displace the cambial cells, moving them steadily outward even as the core of xylem increases the stem or root thickness.

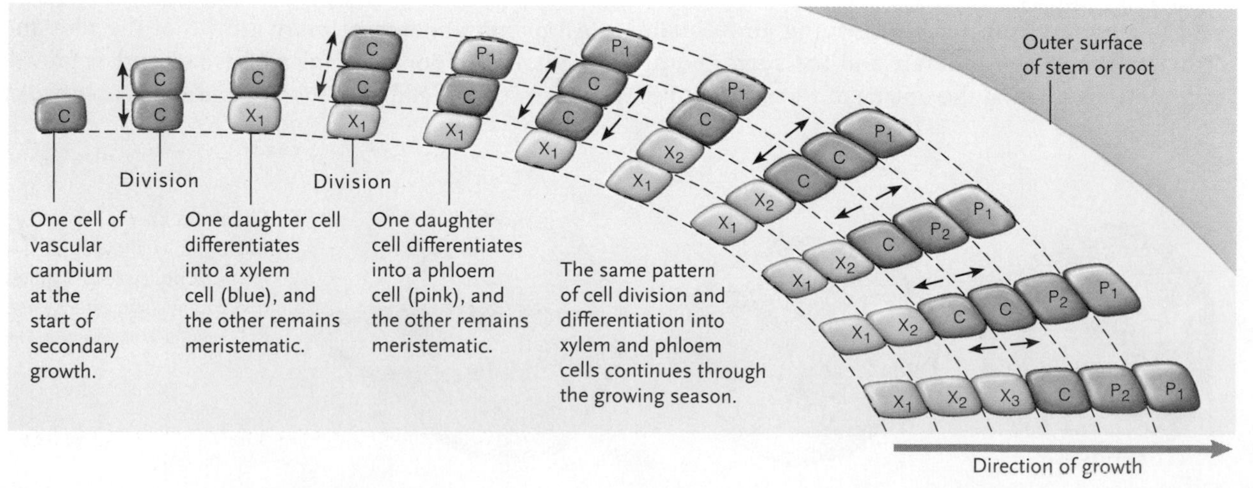

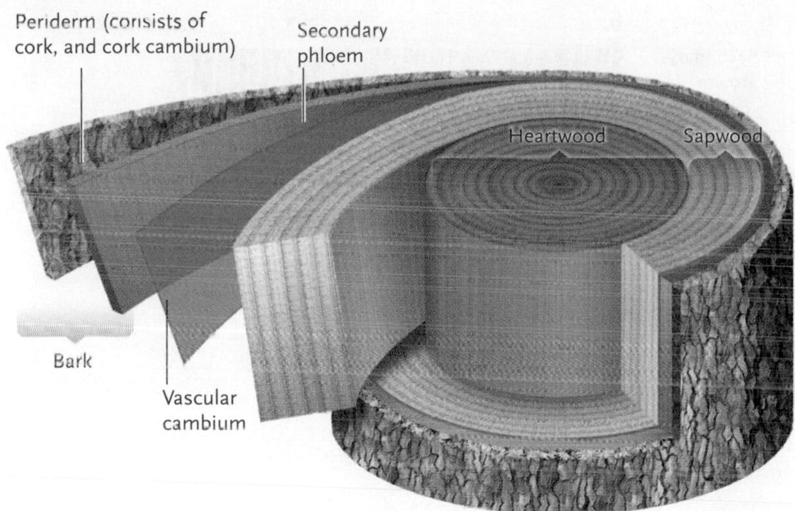

Figure 28.25
Structure of a woody stem showing extensive secondary growth. Heartwood, the mature tree's core, has no living cells. Sapwood, the cylindrical zone of xylem between the heartwood and vascular cambium, contains some living parenchyma cells among the nonliving vessels and tracheids. Everything outside the vascular cambium is bark. Everything inside it is wood.

the cork cambium, and the cork **(Figure 28.25)**. Girdling a tree by removing a strip of bark around the trunk is lethal because it destroys the secondary phloem layer, so nutrients from photosynthesis in leaves cannot reach the tree's roots. Cork for use in flooring and as bottle stoppers is harvested from the thick outer bark of the cork oak, *Quercus suber* **(Figure 28.26)**. Cork can be harvested from these trees once they are 25 years old and can be sustainably harvested every 9 to 12 years thereafter. Some trees can yield about 1 tonne of cork over the course of their lives!

How do the vascular cambium and other living tissues in a secondary stem obtain oxygen, given that the bark can be very thick on some trees? In some regions of the stem, the cork cambium divides very actively, forming spongy tissue with abundant air spaces (*lenticels*). Lenticels allow exchanges of oxygen and carbon dioxide between the living tissues and the outside air.

Figure 28.26
Cork oak (*Quercus suber*) that has recently had part of its bark harvested.

Daniel Mosquin

As a tree ages, changes also unfold in the appearance and function of the wood itself. In the centre of its older stems and roots is **heartwood**, dry tissue that no longer transports water and solutes and is a storage depot for some defensive compounds. In time, these substances—including resins, oils, gums, and tannins—clog and fill in the oldest xylem pipelines. Typically, they darken the heartwood, strengthen it, and make it more aromatic and resistant to decay. **Sapwood** is secondary growth located between heartwood and the vascular cambium. Compared with heartwood, it is wet and not as strong (see Figure 28.25).

In temperate climates, trees produce secondary xylem seasonally, with larger diameter cells produced in spring, when water is generally abundant, and smaller diameter cells in summer, when less water is available to be transported. The resulting "spring wood" and "summer wood" reflect light differently, and it is possible to identify them as alternating light and dark bands. The alternating bands represent annual growth layers known as "growth rings" **(Figure 28.27, p. 688)**. The age of a tree can be determined by counting the growth rings.

Growth rings also provide information on past climates: the wider spaced the rings, the more growth a tree was able to put on in one year, so the better the conditions (i.e., warmer and wetter). Dendroclimatologists use tree rings and other biological information to reconstruct past environments. This line of research is making significant contributions to our understanding of how the global climate has changed over time (see *People Behind Biology*).

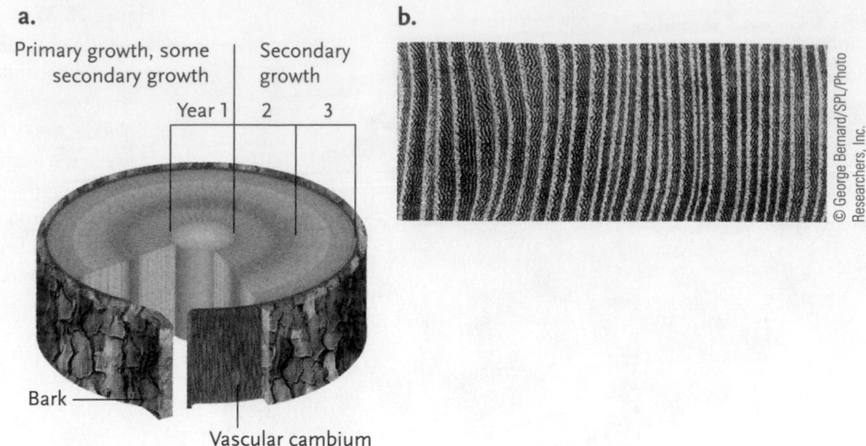

Figure 28.27
Secondary growth and tree ring formation. (a) Radial cut through a woody stem that has three annual rings, corresponding to secondary growth in years 2 through 4. **(b)** Tree rings in an elm (*Ulmas*). Each ring corresponds to one growing season. Differences in the widths of tree rings correspond to shifts in climate, including the availability of water.

28.5b Secondary Growth Can Also Occur in Roots

The roots of grasses, palms, and other monocots are almost always produced by primary growth alone, but in some plants, secondary growth also occurs in roots, although it is different from that in stems. In a root, the vascular cambium arises in part from a procambium layer between the xylem and phloem **(Figure 28.28,** step 1) and in part from the pericycle (step 2), eventually forming a complete cylinder (step 3). The vascular cambium functions in roots as it does in stems, producing secondary xylem to the inside and secondary phloem to the outside. As secondary xylem accumulates, older roots can become extremely thick and woody. Their ongoing secondary growth is powerful enough to break through concrete sidewalks and even dislodge the foundations of homes.

The pericycle also produces cork cambium in roots. In many woody eudicots and in all gym-

Figure 28.28
Secondary growth in the root of one type of woody plant.

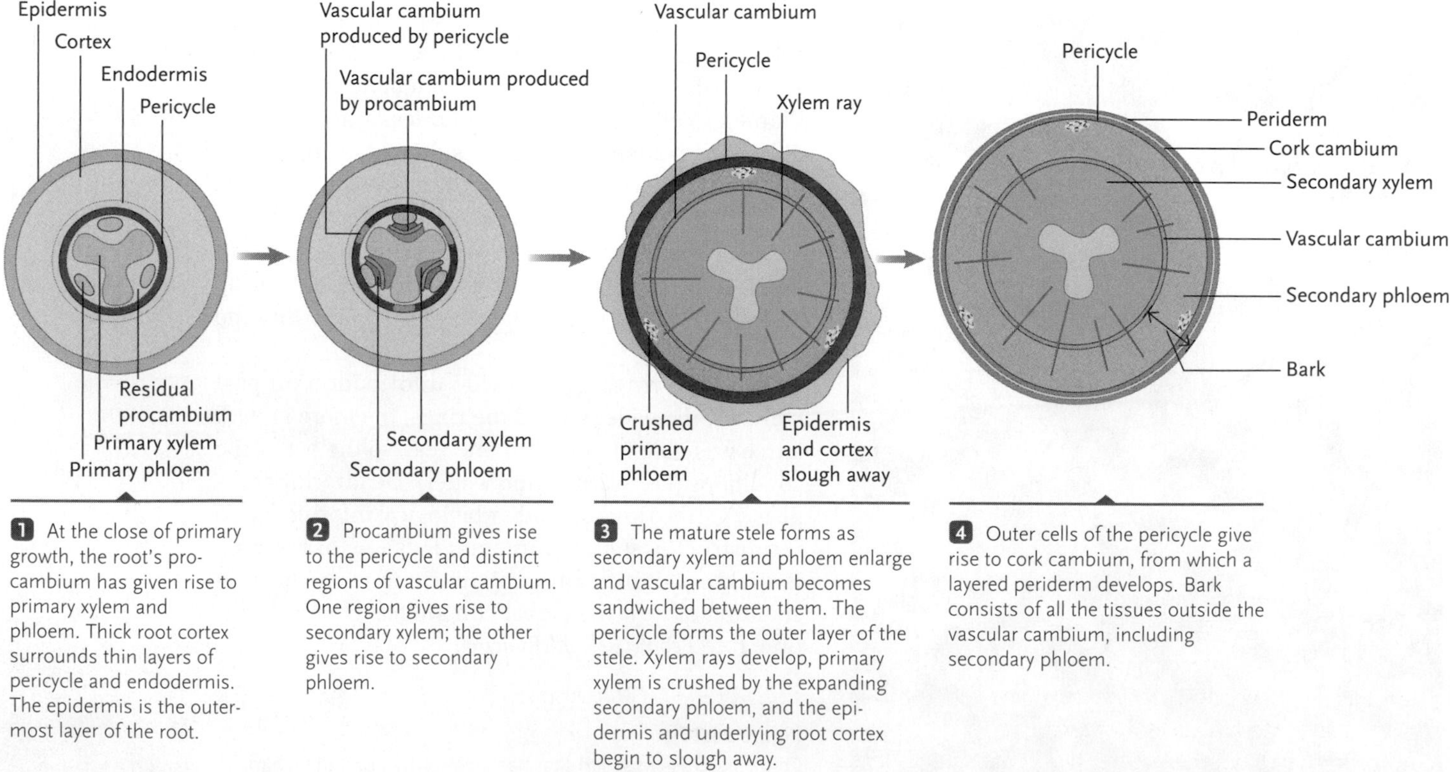

1 At the close of primary growth, the root's procambium has given rise to primary xylem and phloem. Thick root cortex surrounds thin layers of pericycle and endodermis. The epidermis is the outermost layer of the root.

2 Procambium gives rise to the pericycle and distinct regions of vascular cambium. One region gives rise to secondary xylem; the other gives rise to secondary phloem.

3 The mature stele forms as secondary xylem and phloem enlarge and vascular cambium becomes sandwiched between them. The pericycle forms the outer layer of the stele. Xylem rays develop, primary xylem is crushed by the expanding secondary phloem, and the epidermis and underlying root cortex begin to slough away.

4 Outer cells of the pericycle give rise to cork cambium, from which a layered periderm develops. Bark consists of all the tissues outside the vascular cambium, including secondary phloem.

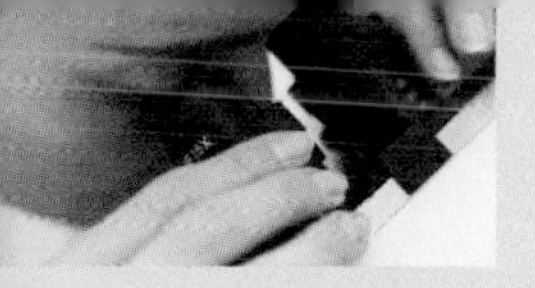

People Behind Biology

Doug Larson, University of Guelph

You might think that the biggest trees would also be the oldest, but this isn't necessarily the case. Some big trees are very old—the giant sequoias of California for example—but sometimes the oldest trees are slow-growing survivors of marginal habitats. In Canada, the oldest trees east of the Rocky Mountains are white cedars (*Thuja occidentalis*) growing in "vertical forests" on the cliffs of the Niagara Escarpment **(Figure 1).** The escarpment runs through southwestern Ontario from near Niagara Falls north to the Bruce Peninsula that juts out into Lake Huron.

These ancient trees were discovered in the 1980s by Doug Larson, a biologist at the University of Guelph, Ontario, and his graduate students. Larson was interested in how environmental gradients influence a plant community and had decided that the cliffs of the Niagara Escarpment would be an interesting gradient to study. As part of describing the forest community on the cliffs, Larson and his students sampled the trees to determine their age. This step sounds simple, but because the trees grow on steep cliffs, sampling them meant dangling over the edge of a cliff in harness and helmet using rock climbing skills. The trees were stunted, twisted, and very small, ranging from a few centimetres to a few metres in height and less than 25 cm in diameter. Thin cores were taken from living trees using a core borer. Rings are usually very obvious in both slices and cores (see Figure 28.27), but when Larson looked at the cores in the lab, he couldn't see any rings. Only after the cores were polished with sandpaper and checked under a microscope could the rings be counted. To the team's amazement, the tree was 350 years old! Larson did more extensive sampling of the cliff forests, in collaboration with Peter Kelly, a dendrochronologist (a biologist who uses tree-ring data to date past events), and found that these trees were indeed ancient, with some living specimens that were more than 1300 years old (they germinated in about 690 C.E.). Larson had discovered an ancient forest that had survived for centuries in one of the most heavily populated parts of Canada. Other ancient cliff forests—which are, literally, life on the edge—have since been discovered elsewhere in the world.

Cliff Ecology Research Group, Department of Integrative Biology, University of Guelph

Figure 1
White cedar (*Thuja occidentalis*) growing on a cliff of the Niagara Escarpment, Ontario.

nosperms, most of the root epidermis and cortex falls away, and the surface consists entirely of tissue produced by the cork cambium (see Figure 28.28, step 4).

28.5c Secondary Growth Is an Adaptive Response

Like all living organisms, plants compete for resources, and woody stems and roots confer some advantages. Plants with taller stems or wider canopies that defy the pull of gravity can intercept more of the light energy from the sun. With a greater energy supply for photosynthesis, they have the metabolic means to increase their root and shoot systems and thus are better able to acquire resources—and ultimately to reproduce successfully.

In every stage of a plant's growth cycle, growth maintains a balance between the shoot system and the root system. Leaves and other photosynthetic parts of the shoot must supply root cells with enough sugars to support their metabolism, and roots must provide the shoot structures with water and minerals. As long as a plant is growing, this balance is maintained, even as the complexity of the root and shoot systems increases. This happens in all plants, whether they live only a few months or—like some bristlecone pines—for 6000 years.

Life on the Edge

Not all plants shed their leaves at the end of the growing season; evergreen conifers retain their leaves for several years. The record holder for longest lived leaves is also a gymnosperm, and its leaves can be over 500 years old. This gymnosperm, *Welwitschia mirabilis,* is one of the weirdest plants in the world, and grows only in the Namib desert. The Namib Desert stretches along the Atlantic coast of southwestern Africa and receives an average of less than 10 mm of rain per year. In some years, there is no rain at all. Another source of moisture in the Namib Desert is the coastal fogs that form at night as the cold, moist ocean air meets the hot air rising off the desert. The fogs disperse in the early morning, leaving a crucial source of water for the few organisms that live in the desert. *Welwitschia* is one of the plants that can survive life in the Namib.

At first glance, *Welwitschia* doesn't really look like a plant **(Figure 1)** but rather like a pile of old leaves. The leaves really are the dominant feature of this plant. Like all seed plants, *Welwitschia* has roots, a stem, and leaves. Its woody stem is very short, growing only about 50 cm high. Its roots can extend to great depths in the sandy soil. The plant generally has only one pair of leaves, which are evergreen and shaped like broad, flat ribbons. Unlike other plants, *Welwitschia* never sheds these leaves, nor does it produce more leaves. The original leaves just continue to grow for the entire life of the plant—which is about 500 years, on average, with the oldest specimens being about 2000 years old. The leaves can be several metres long, although they sometimes split along their length, and the ends get tattered and torn by the wind. Wouldn't such large leaves be a disadvantage in a desert? Many desert plants have very reduced leaves—cacti, for example, have leaves reduced to spines. *Welwitschia's* large leaves are beneficial: they shade the soil around the stem of the plant, keeping that region of soil much cooler than the surrounding area, which can reach temperatures of up to 65°C. The leaves also absorb moisture from the nighttime fogs. This bizarre plant is a "living fossil," a survivor from the Jurassic period, when gymnosperms dominated the Earth.

Raymond G. Milewski

Figure 1
Welwitschia mirabilis growing in the Namib desert of Africa.

In this chapter, we've established the basic anatomy and morphology of the plant body, with an emphasis on angiosperms. In Chapter 31, we look at how plants control the patterns of growth and development described in this chapter. First, however, we need to consider how water and nutrients are transported in the plant body (see Chapter 29) and how angiosperm seedlings are formed (see Chapter 30).

Study Break

1. Explain the nature of secondary growth and where it typically occurs in plants.
2. Describe the components of vascular cambium and their roles in secondary growth in stems, including the development of tissues such as bark, cork, and wood.
3. Compare secondary growth in stems and in roots.

Unanswered Questions

Are plants developmental procrastinators?

It is well established that plants can survive physical insults and exposure to a wide range of environmental fluctuations. What biological resources of plants make them so resilient given their lifestyle constraints? What is the source of phenotypic plasticity that allows a plant's body form to change in response to changes in its habitats? Perhaps the answer lies in the ability of plants to put off making developmental decisions in response to environmental shifts.

Unlike most animal cells, plant cells are pluripotent, retaining their developmentally flexibility. Thus, they can behave as stem cells capable of proliferating and producing new structures and even new individuals. Furthermore, many types of plant cells will readily transdifferentiate and assume a new cellular identity even after reaching developmental maturity. In other words, few developmental decisions appear to be final, and many can be tailored to the environmental constraints imposed on the plant. Some plant species appear to have this flexibility even during more global developmental events, such as switching from vegetative growth to reproductive growth or flowering. Why is that the case? Recent findings suggest that by "leaving all options open," plants can quickly adapt to environmental changes and produce progeny, which is the ultimate biological goal for all living organisms.

Research has documented that shifts in environmental context activate genetic changes underlying plants' developmental and phenotypic plasticity. For example, at the whole-organism level, some plants, such as *Impatiens balsamina*, can switch between making leaves and making flowers if relative day length changes. In fact, these plants can make leaves that are partial flowers, or flowers that are partial leaves, if light conditions are alternated between short days and long days. Nicholas Battey at the University of Reading in England and his colleagues, who have investigated this phenomenon for many years, have demonstrated that a genetic basis exists for this ability to change body form in response to changing environmental cues. Furthermore, Battey's group suggests that among flowering plants, a genetic continuum exists from species that require constant reminders to initiate flowering to species that require only a single signal. For perennial plants such as trees, developmental reprogramming is essential because it allows them to orchestrate seasonally appropriate formation and growth of different organs from the same meristem. Currently, a major effort is under way to understand the genetic basis of developmental evolution, as well as how genetic variation may influence phenotypic plasticity. Since plasticity appears to be closely associated with environmental factors, one approach is to study the natural variants of a species from different geographic origins.

Plants respond to environmental variation both spatially and temporally. Perhaps a sort of biological global positioning system (GPS) exists that provides developmentally relevant information in time and space, which the plant translates into a variety of responses. In some species, the GPS may be on all the time, whereas in other species, it may operate only at certain times of the year, or it may function only once during the plant's lifetime. What might these genetic GPS devices be? How would we test this idea? Have candidate genes already been identified that might be components within the GPS? Is there a link between a plant's GPS and the genetic basis for its ability to procrastinate developmentally? In short, the answer to all of these questions appears to be "maybe," and in all likelihood, the full answer will be a complex one. Research conducted by Christopher Cullis at Case Western Reserve University shows that environmentally induced changes in the physical features of flax plants (*Linum usitatissimum*) are accompanied by changes in the entire genome of affected plants, and some of these genetic alterations are heritable. These findings are particularly striking because they demonstrate that in the short term, plants can respond to environmental fluctuations not only by altering their developmental output (body form and phenotype) but also by "reserving" their genomes. That the very blueprint of life, DNA, is also imbued with significant plasticity is particularly exciting and opens a new realm of inquiry into the mechanisms by which plants may respond to environmental challenges. In some biological contexts, being a procrastinator can be advantageous.

Marianne Hopkins is a postdoctoral fellow in the Biology Department at the University of Waterloo in Waterloo, Canada. Her expertise lies in plant genetics and plant molecular biology.

Susan Lolle is an associate professor of biology at the University of Waterloo in Waterloo, Canada. Her research interests include plant development, genetics, and genome biology. To learn more go to http://www.biology.uwaterloo.ca.

Review

Go to CENGAGENOW™ at http://hed.nelson.com/ to access quizzing, animations, exercises, articles, and personalized homework help.

28.1 Plant Structure and Growth: An Overview

- Differences between the structures and growth of plants and animals reflect their modes of nutrition.
- The plant body of an angiosperm consists of an above-ground shoot system with stems, leaves, and flowers and an underground root system.
- Meristems give rise to the plant body and are responsible for a plant's lifelong growth. Each meristem cell produces two daughter cells, one of which remains part of the meristem, whereas the other differentiates into a cell of one of the three primary tissues (protoderm, ground tissue, or procambium).
- Primary growth of roots and shoots originates at apical meristems at root and shoot tips. Some plants have lateral meristems that produce secondary growth and increase the diameter of stems and roots.
- The two major classes of flowering plants (angiosperms) are monocots and eudicots; angiosperms can also be differentiated based on pattern of growth (annuals versus perennials, woody versus herbaceous).

28.2 The Three Plant Tissue Systems

- All plant cells have primary cell walls composed primarily of cellulose. In some cells, secondary walls are laid down inside the primary walls. Maturing cells become specialized for specific functions, with some functions accomplished by the walls of dead cells.
- Plants have three tissue systems. Ground tissues make up most of the plant body, vascular tissues serve in transport, and dermal tissue forms a protective cover.
- Of the three types of ground tissues, parenchyma is active in photosynthesis, storage, and other tasks, whereas collenchyma and sclerenchyma provide mechanical support.
- Xylem and phloem are the plant vascular tissues. Xylem conducts water and dissolved minerals taken up from the soil and consists of conducting cells called tracheids and vessel members. Phloem, which conducts the products of photosynthesis from the leaves to the rest of the plant, contains living cells (sieve tube members) joined end-to-end in sieve tubes.
- The dermal tissue, epidermis, is coated with a waxy cuticle that restricts water loss. Water vapour and other gases enter and leave the plant through pores called stomata, which are flanked by specialized epidermal cells called guard cells. Epidermal specializations also include trichomes, such as root hairs.

28.3 Primary Shoot Systems

- The primary shoot system consists of the main stem, leaves, and buds, plus any attached flowers and fruits. Stems provide mechanical support, house vascular tissues, and may store food and fluid.
- Stems are organized into modular segments. Nodes are points where leaves and buds are attached, and internodes are the regions between nodes. The terminal bud at a shoot tip consists of shoot apical meristem. Lateral buds occur at intervals along the stem. Meristem tissue in buds gives rise to leaves, flowers, or both.
- Derivatives of the apical meristem produce three primary meristems: protoderm makes the stem's epidermis, procambium gives rise to primary xylem and phloem, and ground meristem gives rise to ground tissue.
- Vascular tissues are organized into vascular bundles, with phloem outside of the xylem in each bundle.
- Monocot and eudicot leaves have blades of different forms, all providing a large surface area for absorbing sunlight and carbon dioxide. Leaf modifications are adaptive responses to environmental selection pressures. Leaf characteristics such as shape or arrangement may change over the life cycle of a long-lived plant.

28.4 Root Systems

- Roots absorb water and dissolved minerals and conduct them to aerial plant parts; they anchor and sometimes support the plant and often store food. Root morphologies include taproot systems, fibrous root systems, and adventitious roots.
- During primary growth of a root, the primary meristem and actively dividing cells make up the zone of cell division, which merges into the zone of elongation. Past the zone of elongation, cells may differentiate and perform specialized roles in the zone of cell maturation.
- A root's vascular tissues (xylem and phloem) usually are arranged as a central stele. Parenchyma tissue around the stele forms the root cortex. The root endodermis also wraps around the stele. Inside it is the pericycle, containing parenchyma that can function as meristem. It gives rise to root primordia from which lateral roots emerge. Root hairs from the epidermis greatly increase the surface available for absorbing water and solutes.

28.5 Secondary Growth

- In plants with secondary growth, older stems and roots become more massive and woody via the activity of vascular cambium and cork cambium.
- Vascular cambium produces secondary phloem to the outside and secondary xylem to the inside of the stem.
- Cork cambium gives rise to cork, which replaces epidermis lost when stems increase in diameter.
- Bark consists of all tissues outside of the vascular cambium (secondary phloem, cork cambium, and cork).
- In root secondary growth, a thin layer of procambium cells between the xylem and phloem differentiates into vascular cambium. The pericycle produces root cork cambium.

Questions

Self-Test Questions

1. With respect to growth, plants differ from animals in that
   a. plant growth involves only an increase in the total number of the organism's cells.
   b. plant cells remain roughly the same size after cell division, whereas animal cells increase in size after they form.
   c. all plants form woody tissues during growth.
   d. plants have indeterminate growth; most animals have determinate growth.
   e. plants can grow only when young; animals grow for many years.
2. Identify the correct pairing of a plant tissue and its function.
   a. epidermis: rigid support
   b. xylem: sugar transport
   c. parenchyma: photosynthesis, respiration
   d. phloem: water and mineral transport
   e. periderm: control of gas exchange
3. Identify the correct pairing of a structure and its component(s).
   a. epidermis: companion cells
   b. phloem: sieve tube members
   c. sclerenchyma: lignin
   d. secondary cell wall: cuticle
   e. parenchyma: sclereids
4. Which of the following would be absent in a eudicot leaf?
   a. spongy mesophyll
   b. palisade mesophyll
   c. pericycle
   d. vascular bundles
   e. stoma
5. A student left a carrot in her refrigerator. Three weeks later, she noticed slender white fibres growing from its surface. They were not a fungus. Instead, they were
   a. lateral roots on a taproot.
   b. adventitious roots.
   c. root hairs on a fibrous root.
   d. root hairs on a lateral root.
   e. young prop roots.
6. Which of the following is *not* a structure that results from secondary plant growth?
   a. periderm
   b. a mature oak leaf
   c. cork
   d. pith
   e. heartwood
7. The greatest mitotic activity in a root takes place in the
   a. zone of maturation.
   b. zone of cell division.
   c. zone of elongation.
   d. root cap.
   e. endodermis.

Questions for Discussion

1. While camping in a national park, you notice a "Do Not Litter" sign nailed onto the trunk of a mature fir tree about 2 m off the ground. When you return five years later, will the sign be at the same height, or will the tree's growth have raised it higher? Explain your answer.
2. African violets and some other flowering plants are propagated commercially using leaf cuttings. A leaf detached from a parent plant is placed in a growth medium. In time, adventitious shoots and roots develop from the leaf blade, producing a new plant. Are all cells in the original leaf tissue equally likely to give rise to the new structures? If not, which one(s) are most likely to have done so? What property of the cells makes this propagation method possible?

Cross section of the stem of a geranium (*Pelargonium*) showing parenchyma (pink) wrapping around vessels that transport water and nutrients in plants. In this false colour SEM, large diameter vessels (xylem) that carry water and minerals appear whitish and bundles of smaller vessels (phloem), which transport sugars, appear pale green.

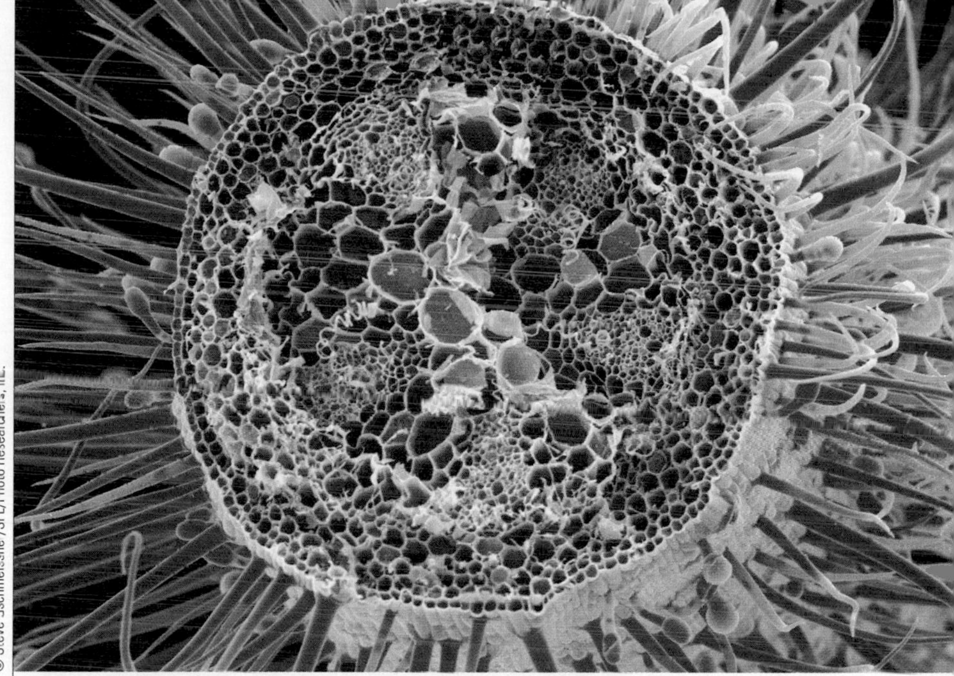

29 Transport in Plants

Study Plan

Why It Matters

The coast redwood, *Sequoia sempervirens* **(Figure 29.1, p. 696)**, takes life to extremes. Redwood trees can live for more than 2000 years, and they can grow taller than any other organism on Earth. The tallest known specimen, located in Redwood National Park in California, soars 115.5 m from the dank forest floor. Botanists who have studied these giants estimate that such massive plants consume thousands of litres of water each day to survive. And that water—with its cargo of dissolved nutrients—must be transported the great distances between roots and leaves.

At first, movement of fluids and solutes 100 m or more from a mature redwood's roots to its leafy crown may seem to challenge the laws of physics. Raising water that high above ground in a pipe requires a powerful mechanical pump at the base and substantial energy to counteract the pull of gravity. You also require a pump—your heart—to move fluid over a vertical distance of less than 3 m. Yet a redwood tree has no pump. As you'll learn in this chapter, the evolutionary adaptations that move water and solutes throughout the plant body can move large volumes over great distances by harnessing the cumulative effects of seemingly weak interactions such as cohesion

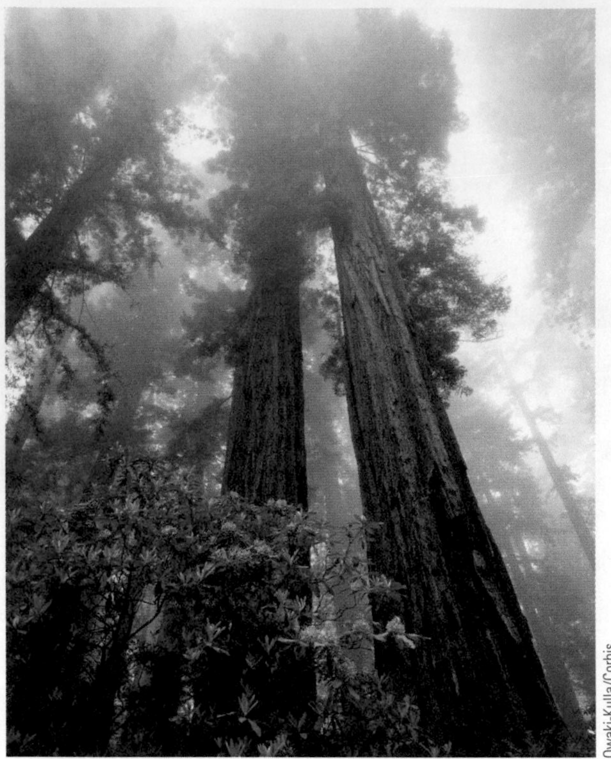

Figure 29.1
Redwoods (*Sequoia sempervirens*), such as this tree growing in coastal California, have reached recorded heights of over 100 m during life spans of more than 2000 years. Such extremely tall trees exemplify the ability of plants to move water and solutes from roots to shoots over amazingly long distances.

and evaporation. Overall, plant transport mechanisms solve a fundamental biological problem—the need to acquire materials from the environment and distribute them throughout the plant body.

Our discussion begins with a brief review of the principles of water and solute movement in plants, a topic introduced in Chapter 5. Then we examine how those principles apply to the movement of water and solutes into and through a plant's vascular pipelines.

29.1 Principles of Water and Solute Movement in Plants

In plants, as in all organisms, the movement of water and solutes begins at the level of individual cells and relies on mechanisms such as osmosis and the operation of transport proteins in the plasma membrane. Once water and nutrients enter a plant's specialized transport systems—the vascular tissues called xylem and phloem—other mechanisms carry them between various regions of the plant body in response to changing demands for those substances. Ultimately, these movements of materials result from the integrated activities of the individual cells, tissues, and organs of a single, smoothly functioning organism—the whole plant.

Plant transport mechanisms fall into two general categories—those for short-distance transport and those for long-distance transport. Short-distance transport mechanisms move substances into and between cells across membranes and to and from vascular tissues. For example, water, oxygen, and minerals enter roots by crossing the cell membranes of root hairs **(Figure 29.2a),** and nutrients such as carbohydrates from photosynthesis cross plasma membranes to nourish cells of the plant body. Similarly, water and other substances move short distances to and from a plant's xylem and phloem, which are arranged in vascular bundles **(Figure 29.2b).** Long-distance transport mechanisms move substances between roots and shoot parts **(Figure 29.2c).** Thus, water and dissolved minerals travel in the xylem from roots to other plant parts, and products of photosynthesis move in the phloem from the leaves and stems into roots and other structures. Carbon dioxide for photosynthesis enters photosynthetic tissues in the shoot.

We consider transport processes in the xylem and phloem later in this chapter. For the moment, our focus is on mechanisms that move water and solutes into and out of specific cells in roots, leaves, and stems. Keep in mind that the plant cell wall does not prevent solutes from moving into plant cells. Most solutes can cross the wall by way of the plasmodesmata that connect adjacent cells (see Chapter 28).

29.1a Both Passive and Active Mechanisms Move Substances into and out of Plant Cells

Recall from Chapter 5 that in all cells, there are two general mechanisms for transporting water and solutes across the plasma membrane into and between cells. In **passive transport,** substances move down a concentration gradient or, if the substance is an ion, down an electrochemical gradient. **Active transport** requires the cell to expend energy in moving substances *against* a gradient, usually by hydrolysis of ATP.

True to its name, simple diffusion is the simplest form of passive transport: oxygen, carbon dioxide, water, and some other small molecules can readily diffuse across cell plasma membranes, following a concentration gradient. By contrast, in all other types of membrane transport, ions and some larger molecules cross cell membranes assisted by carriers collectively called **transport proteins,** which are embedded in the membrane.

Passive transport of substances down an electrochemical gradient is called *facilitated diffusion* because the transport protein involved "facilitates" the process in some way. Transport proteins called *channel proteins* are configured to form a pore in the plasma membrane. Those called *carrier proteins* change shape in a way that releases the substance to the other side of the membrane.

In active transport, membrane transport proteins use energy to move substances against a concentration

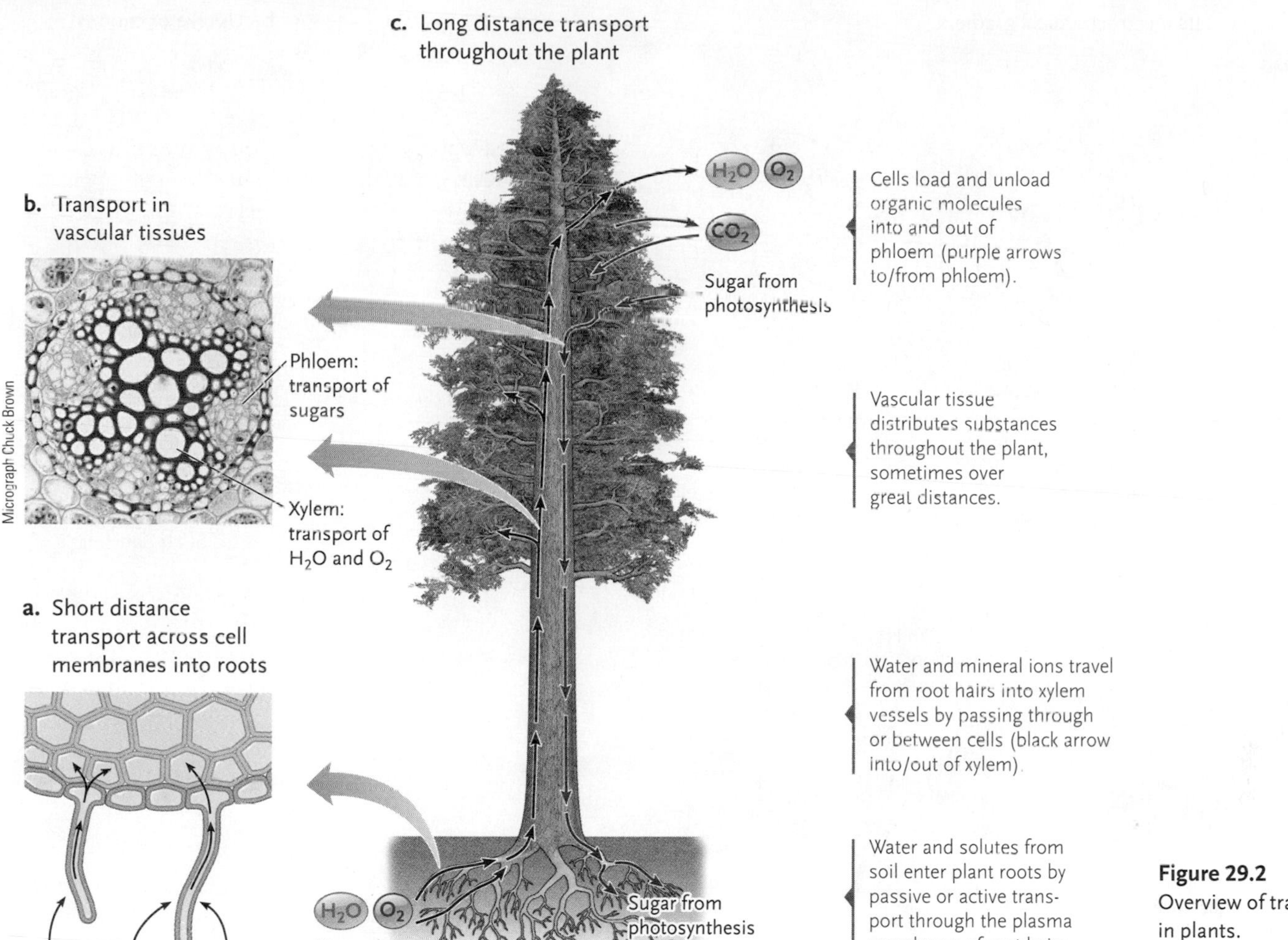
c. Long distance transport throughout the plant
b. Transport in vascular tissues
Micrograph Chuck Brown
Phloem: transport of sugars
Xylem: transport of H_2O and O_2
a. Short distance transport across cell membranes into roots
H_2O
O_2
Minerals
H_2O
O_2
Mineral ions
H_2O
O_2
CO_2
Sugar from photosynthesis
Sugar from photosynthesis
Cells load and unload organic molecules into and out of phloem (purple arrows to/from phloem).
Vascular tissue distributes substances throughout the plant, sometimes over great distances.
Water and mineral ions travel from root hairs into xylem vessels by passing through or between cells (black arrow into/out of xylem).
Water and solutes from soil enter plant roots by passive or active transport through the plasma membrane of root hairs.

Figure 29.2
Overview of transport routes in plants.

gradient or an electrochemical gradient. An electrochemical gradient exists across cell membranes when the concentrations of various ions differ between the inside and the outside of the cell. The differences in ion concentration result in a difference in electrical charge across the plasma membrane. In plant cells, the cytoplasm is slightly more negative than the fluid outside the cell. This charge difference is measured as an electrical voltage called the **membrane potential.** The word "potential" refers to the fact that the movement of ions across a membrane is a potential source of energy—that is, such ion movements can perform cellular work.

ATP provides the energy for active transport of substances into and out of plant cells. Hydrogen ions (protons), which tend to be more concentrated outside the cell than in the negatively charged cytoplasm, play a central role in the process. First, a proton pump pushes H^+ across the plasma membrane against its electrochemical gradient, from the inside to the outside of the cell **(Figure 29.3a, p. 698).** As protons accumulate outside the cell, the electrochemical gradient becomes steeper and significant potential energy is available. Crucial solutes such as cations (positively charged ions) often are more concentrated in the extracellular fluid. One result of the increased charge difference created by proton pumping is that cations move into the cell through their membrane channels **(Figure 29.3b, p. 698).** These cations include mineral ions that have essential roles in plant cell metabolism.

The H^+ gradient also powers *secondary active transport,* a process in which a concentration gradient of an ion is used as the energy source for active transport of another substance. The two secondary mechanisms—*symport* and *antiport*—actively transport ions, sugars, and amino acids into and out of plant cells against their concentration gradient. In **symport**, the potential energy released as H^+ follows its gradient into the cell is coupled to the simultaneous uptake of another ion or molecule **(Figure 29.3c, p. 698).** In this way, plant cells can take up metabolically important ions such as nitrate (NO_3^-) and potassium (K^+). Nearly all organic substances that enter plant cells move in by symport as well.

In **antiport**, the energy released as H^+ diffuses into the cell powers the active transport of a second molecule, such as Ca^{2+}, in the opposite direction, *out of* the cell **(Figure 29.3d, p. 698).** One of antiport's key functions is to remove excess Na^+, which readily moves into plant cells by facilitated diffusion through channel proteins. If the Na^+ were not eliminated, it would quickly build up to toxic levels.

a. H^+ pumped against its electrochemical gradient

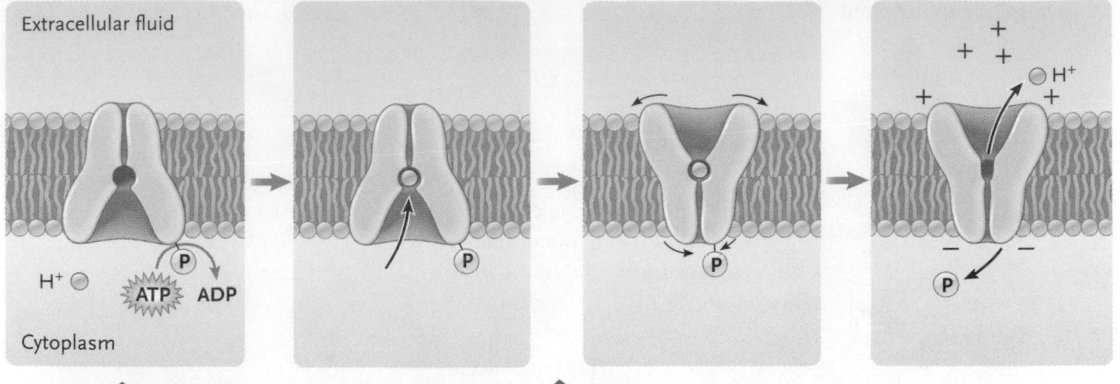

ATP energy pumps hydrogen ions (H^+) out of the cytoplasm, creating an H^+ gradient.

The concentration of H^+ becomes higher outside the membrane than inside. Inward diffusion of H^+ in response to the gradient becomes a source of energy for transporting other ions and neutral molecules such as sugar into the plant cell.

b. Uptake of cations

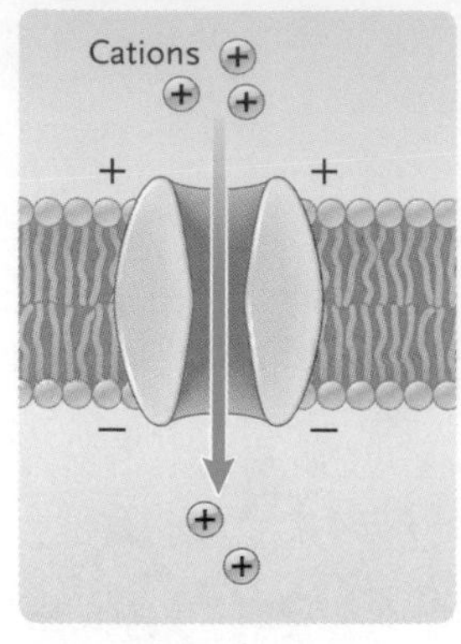

Some cations, such as NH_4^+, enter the cell through selective channel proteins, following the electrochemical gradient created by H^+ pumping.

c. Symport

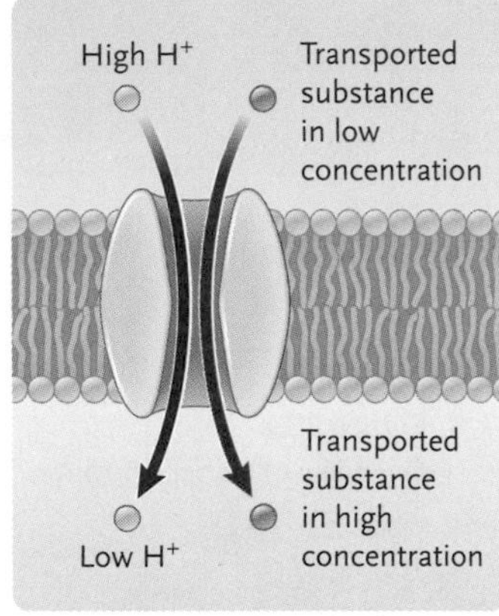

In symport, the inward diffusion of H^+ is coupled with the simultaneous active transport of another substance into the cell.

d. Antiport

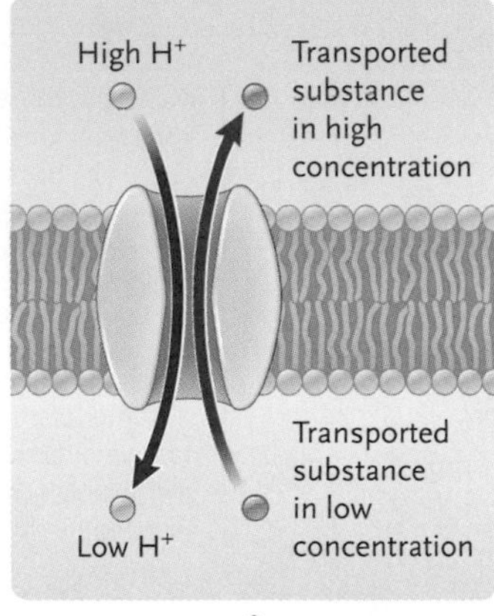

In antiport, H^+ moving into the cell powers the movement of another solute in the opposite direction.

Figure 29.3
Ion transport across the plasma membrane.

Both passive and active transport are selective transport mechanisms that transport specific substances. Two factors govern this specificity. One is the size of the interior channel, which allows only molecules in a particular size range to pass through. The other factor is the distribution of charges along the inside of the channel. A channel that permits cations such as Na^+ to pass through easily may completely bar anions, such as Cl^-, and vice versa.

Relatively speaking, only small amounts of mineral ions and other solutes move into and out of plant cells. As we see next, H_2O is another matter. Throughout a plant's life, large volumes of water enter and exit its cells and tissues by way of osmosis.

29.1b Osmosis Governs Water Movement in Plants

One of the most important aspects of plant physiology is how water moves into and through plant cells and tissues. Inside a plant's tubelike vascular tissues, large amounts of water or any other fluid travel by **bulk flow**—the group movement of molecules in response to a difference in pressure between two locations, like water in a closed plumbing system gushing from an open faucet. For example, the dilute solution of water and ions that flows in the xylem, called **xylem sap**, moves by bulk flow from roots to shoot parts. The solution is pulled upward through the plant body in a process that relies on the cohesion of water molecules, which we consider more fully later in this chapter. Individual cells, however, gain and lose water by **osmosis**, the passive movement of water across a selectively permeable membrane in response to solute concentration gradients, a pressure gradient, or both (see Chapter 5). The driving force for osmosis is energy stored in the water itself. This potential energy, called **water potential**, is symbolized by the Greek letter psi (ψ). By convention, pure water has a ψ value of zero. Two factors that strongly influence this value in living plants are the presence of solutes and physical pressure.

The effect of dissolved solutes on water's tendency to move across a membrane is called *solute potential,* symbolized by ψ_S. In practical terms, water potential is higher where there are more water molecules in a solution relative to the number of solute molecules. Likewise, the water potential is *lower* in a solution with relatively more solutes. The relationship between water potential and solute potential is vital to understanding transport phenomena in plants because water tends to move by osmosis from regions where water potential is higher to regions where it is lower. Solutes are usually more concentrated inside plant cells than in the fluid surrounding them. This means that the water potential is higher outside plant cells than inside them, so water tends to enter the cells by osmosis. This, in fact, is the mechanism that draws soil water into a plant's roots.

Recall from Chapter 5 that an animal cell placed in a hypotonic solution may swell to the point of bursting. In plants, this is prevented by the cell wall, which exerts a pressure that counters the further inward movement of water. This pressure, called turgor pressure, rises until it is high enough to prevent more water from entering a cell by osmosis. In effect, when osmotic water movement stops, turgor pressure has increased the water potential inside the cell until it equals the potential of the water outside the cell. The physical pressure required to halt osmotic water movement across a membrane is termed a solution's *pressure potential* and is symbolized as ψ_P.

By convention, plant physiologists measure water potential in units of pressure called **megapascals** (MPa). They use standard atmospheric pressure as a baseline, assigning it a value of zero. Accordingly, the water potential of pure water at standard atmospheric pressure is expressed as 0 MPa. This notation can be used to describe the changing effects under different conditions of solute potential and pressure potential **(Figure 29.4)**. Adding pressure increases the water pressure, whereas adding solutes reduces it (because the relative concentration of water is lower), and water will flow from a solution of higher MPa to a solution of lower MPa. With these principles in mind, consider now how they operate in living plant cells.

A large **central vacuole** occupies most of the volume of a mature plant cell. The central vacuole, which is surrounded by a vacuolar membrane or **tonoplast**, contains a dilute solution of sugars, proteins,

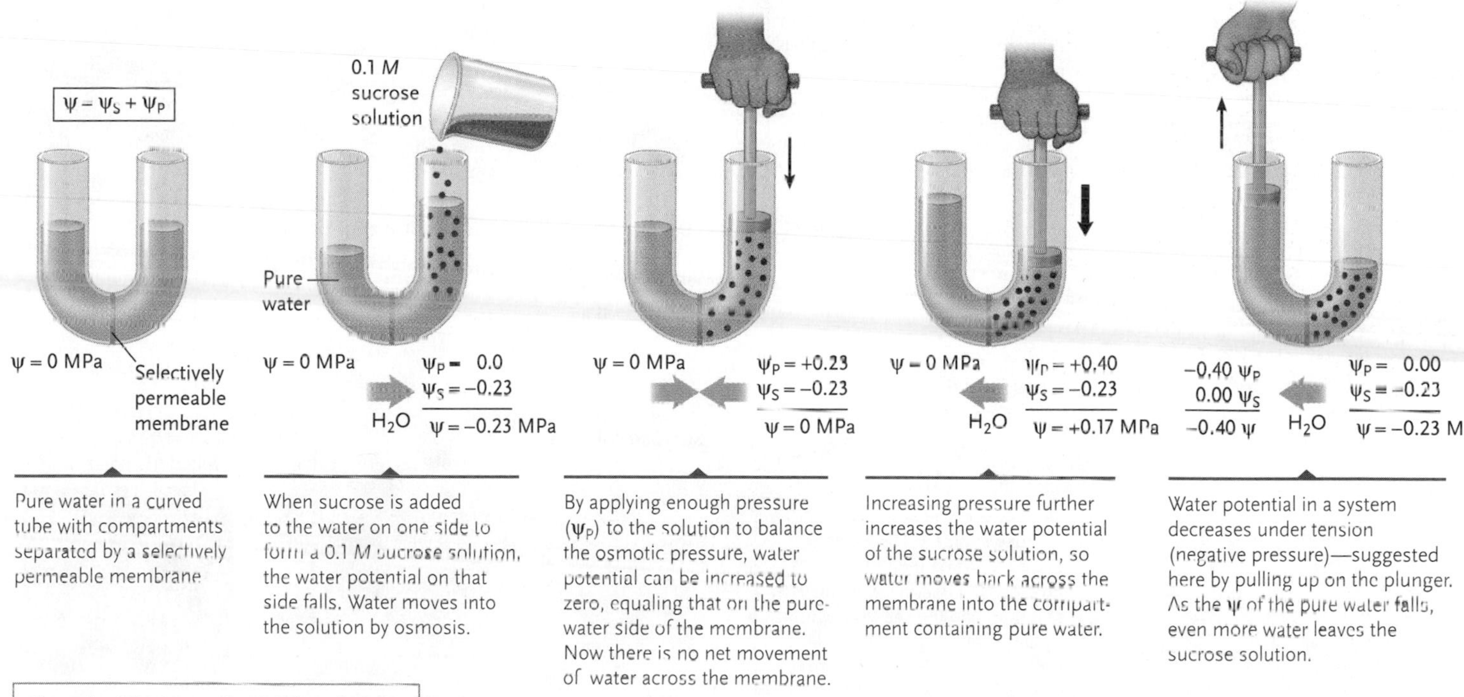

$\psi = \psi_S + \psi_P$
0.1 *M* sucrose solution
Pure water
ψ = 0 MPa
Selectively permeable membrane
ψ = 0 MPa
ψ_P = 0.0
ψ_S = −0.23
H_2O
ψ = −0.23 MPa
ψ = 0 MPa
ψ_P = +0.23
ψ_S = −0.23
ψ = 0 MPa
ψ = 0 MPa
ψ_P = +0.40
ψ_S = −0.23
H_2O
ψ = +0.17 MPa
−0.40 ψ_P
0.00 ψ_S
−0.40 ψ
H_2O
ψ_P = 0.00
ψ_S = −0.23
ψ = −0.23 M
Pure water in a curved tube with compartments separated by a selectively permeable membrane.
When sucrose is added to the water on one side to form a 0.1 *M* sucrose solution, the water potential on that side falls. Water moves into the solution by osmosis.
By applying enough pressure (ψ_P) to the solution to balance the osmotic pressure, water potential can be increased to zero, equaling that on the pure-water side of the membrane. Now there is no net movement of water across the membrane.
Increasing pressure further increases the water potential of the sucrose solution, so water moves back across the membrane into the compartment containing pure water.
Water potential in a system decreases under tension (negative pressure)—suggested here by pulling up on the plunger. As the ψ of the pure water falls, even more water leaves the sucrose solution.
Plant physiologists assign a value of 0 MPa to the water potential (ψ) of pure water in an open container under normal atmospheric pressure and temperature.

Figure 29.4
The relationship between osmosis and water potential. If the water potential is higher on one side of a selectively permeable membrane, water will cross the membrane to the area of lower water potential. This diagram shows pure water on one side of a selectively permeable membrane and a simple sucrose solution on the other side. In an organism, however, the selectively permeable membranes of cells are rarely, if ever, in contact with pure water.

other organic molecules, and salts. The cell cytoplasm is confined to a thin layer between the tonoplast and the plasma membrane. A major role of the central vacuole is to maintain turgor pressure in the cell. Many solutes that enter a plant cell are actively transported from the cytoplasm into the central vacuole through channels in the tonoplast. As the solutes accumulate, water follows by osmosis.

The plant cell's relatively small amount of cytoplasm must compensate fairly quickly for water gains or losses caused by changes in osmotic flow. If the medium around a plant cell becomes hypertonic (has a high solute concentration), for example, water flows rapidly out of the cell. Water from the central vacuole replaces it, entering the cytoplasm through water-conducting channel proteins called **aquaporins.**

The water mechanics we have been discussing have major implications for land plants. For instance, the drooping of leaves and stems called **wilting** occurs when environmental conditions cause a plant to lose more water than it gains. Conditions that lead to wilting include dry soil, in which case, the water potential in the soil falls below that in the plant. Then the turgor pressure inside the cells falls, and the protoplast shrinks away from the cell wall **(Figure 29.5a).** By contrast, as long as the ψ of soil is higher than that in root epidermal cells, water will follow the ψ gradient and enter root cells, making them turgid, or firm **(Figure 29.5b).** As we see in the next section, water and solutes entering roots may move through the plant body by several routes.

Study Break

1. Explain the role(s) of a gradient of protons in moving substances across a plant cell's plasma membrane.
2. How do symport and antiport differ? Give examples of key substances each mechanism transports.
3. What is "water potential," and why is it important with respect to plant cells?

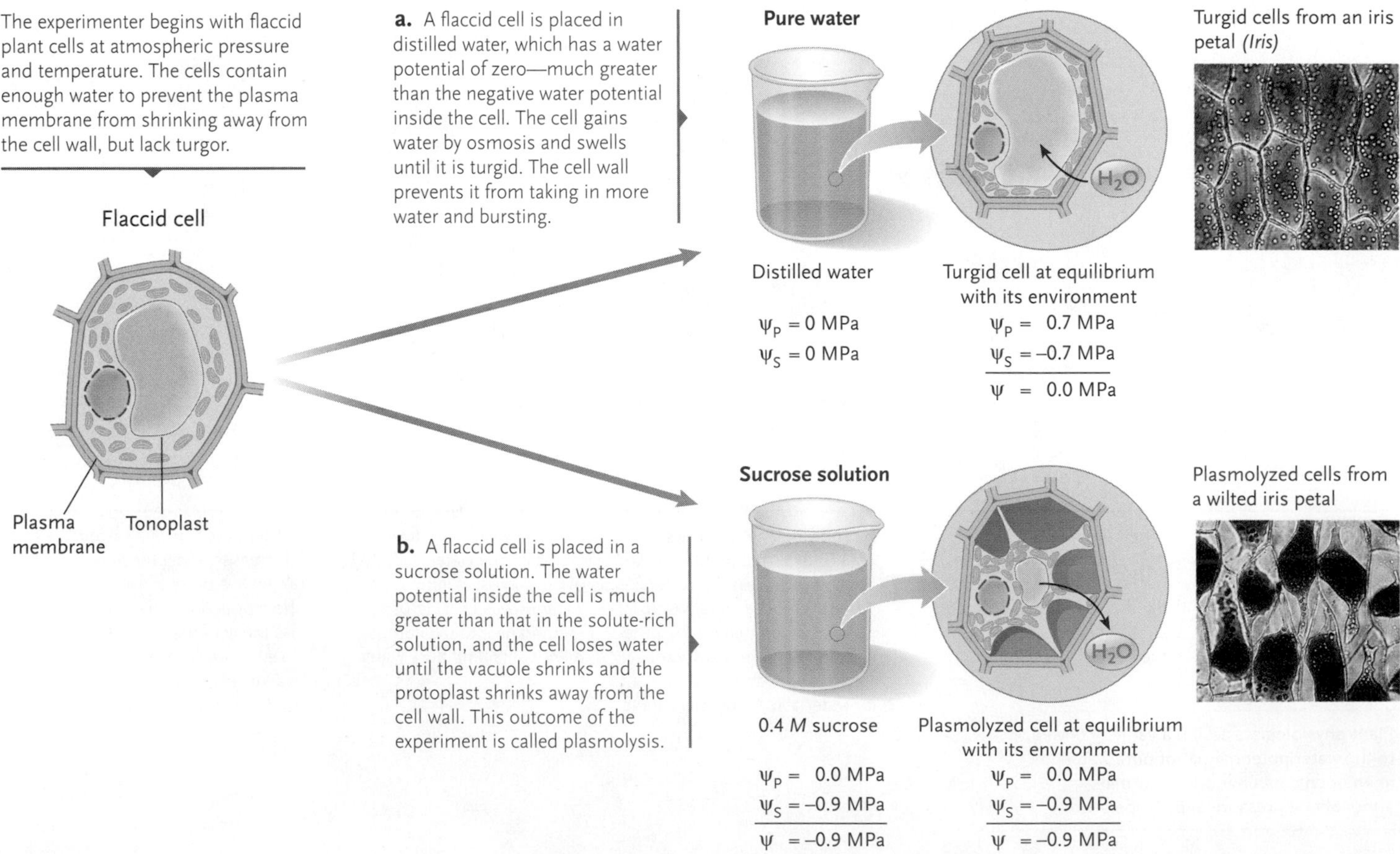

The experimenter begins with flaccid plant cells at atmospheric pressure and temperature. The cells contain enough water to prevent the plasma membrane from shrinking away from the cell wall, but lack turgor.
Flaccid cell
Plasma membrane
Tonoplast
a. A flaccid cell is placed in distilled water, which has a water potential of zero—much greater than the negative water potential inside the cell. The cell gains water by osmosis and swells until it is turgid. The cell wall prevents it from taking in more water and bursting.
Pure water
H_2O
Turgid cells from an iris petal (Iris)
Distilled water
ψ_P = 0 MPa
ψ_S = 0 MPa
Turgid cell at equilibrium with its environment
ψ_P = 0.7 MPa
ψ_S = –0.7 MPa
ψ = 0.0 MPa
b. A flaccid cell is placed in a sucrose solution. The water potential inside the cell is much greater than that in the solute-rich solution, and the cell loses water until the vacuole shrinks and the protoplast shrinks away from the cell wall. This outcome of the experiment is called plasmolysis.
Sucrose solution
H_2O
Plasmolyzed cells from a wilted iris petal
0.4 M sucrose
ψ_P = 0.0 MPa
ψ_S = –0.9 MPa
ψ = –0.9 MPa
Plasmolyzed cell at equilibrium with its environment
ψ_P = 0.0 MPa
ψ_S = –0.9 MPa
ψ = –0.9 MPa

Figure 29.5
An experiment to test the effects of different osmotic environments on plant cells. Notice that in both **(a)** and **(b)**, the final condition is the same: the water potential of the plant cell and its environment become equal. (Micrographs: © Claude Nuridsany and Marie Perennou/Science Photo Library/Photo Researchers, Inc.)

29.2 Transport in Roots

Soil around roots provides a plant's water and minerals, but roots don't simply "soak up" these essential substances. Instead, water and minerals that enter roots first travel laterally through the root cortex to the root xylem. Only then do they begin their journey upward to stems, leaves, and other tissues.

29.2a Water Travels to the Root Xylem by Three Pathways

Soil water always enters a root through the root epidermis. Once inside a root, however, water may take one of three routes into the root xylem, travelling either through living cells or in nonliving areas of the root **(Figure 29.6).** Nonliving regions of a plant such as the continuous network of adjoining cell walls and air spaces in root tissue are called the *apoplast.* Thus, water follows an **apoplastic pathway** when it moves through the apoplast of roots, a route that does not cross cell membranes. Botanists refer to a plant's living parts as the *symplast,* and water moving through roots in the **symplastic pathway** moves from cell to cell through the open channels of plasmodesmata. Water also can enter root cells across the cell plasma membranes, a **transmembrane pathway.** Water crosses the tonoplast of the central vacuole in this way as well.

When water enters a root, some diffuses into epidermal cells, entering the symplast. But a great deal of the water taken up by plant roots moves into the apoplast, moving along through cell walls and intercellular spaces. This apoplastic water (and any solutes dissolved in it) travels rapidly inward until it encounters the endodermis, the sheetlike single layer of cells that separates the root cortex from the stele. Cells in the root cortex generally have air spaces between them (which helps aerate the tissue), but endodermal cells are tightly packed **(Figure 29.7a , p. 702).** Each one also has a beltlike **Casparian strip** in its radial and transverse walls, positioned somewhat like a ribbon of packing tape around a rectangular package **(Figure 29.7c and d, p. 702).** The strip is impregnated with suberin, a waxy substance impermeable to water. Thus, the Casparian strip blocks the apoplastic pathway at the endodermis, preventing water and solutes in the apoplast from automatically passing on into the stele. Instead, if molecules are to move into the stele, they must detour across the plasma membranes of endodermal cells, entering the cells (and the symplast) where the wall is not blanketed by a Casparian strip (Figure 29.7d). From there, water and solutes can pass through plasmodesmata to cells in the outer layer of the stele (the pericycle) and then on into the xylem.

In the **apoplastic pathway** (red), water moves through nonliving regions—the continuous network of adjoining cell walls and tissue air spaces. However, when it reaches the endodermis, it passes through one layer of living cells.

In the **symplastic pathway** (green), water passes into and through living cells. After being taken up into root hairs water diffuses through the cytoplasm and passes from one living cell to the next through plasmodesmata.

In the **transmembrane pathway** (black), water that enters the cytoplasm moves between living cells by diffusing across cell membranes, including the plasma membrane and perhaps the tonoplast.

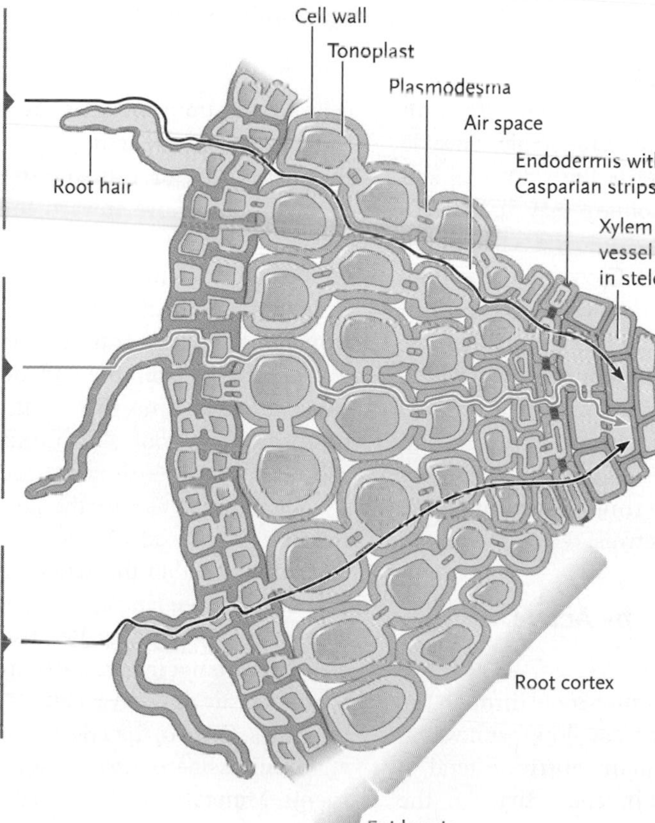

Figure 29.6
Pathways for the movement of water into roots. Ions also enter roots via these three pathways but must be actively transported into cells when they reach the Casparian strips of the endodermis. In this way, only certain solutes in soil water are allowed to enter the stele.

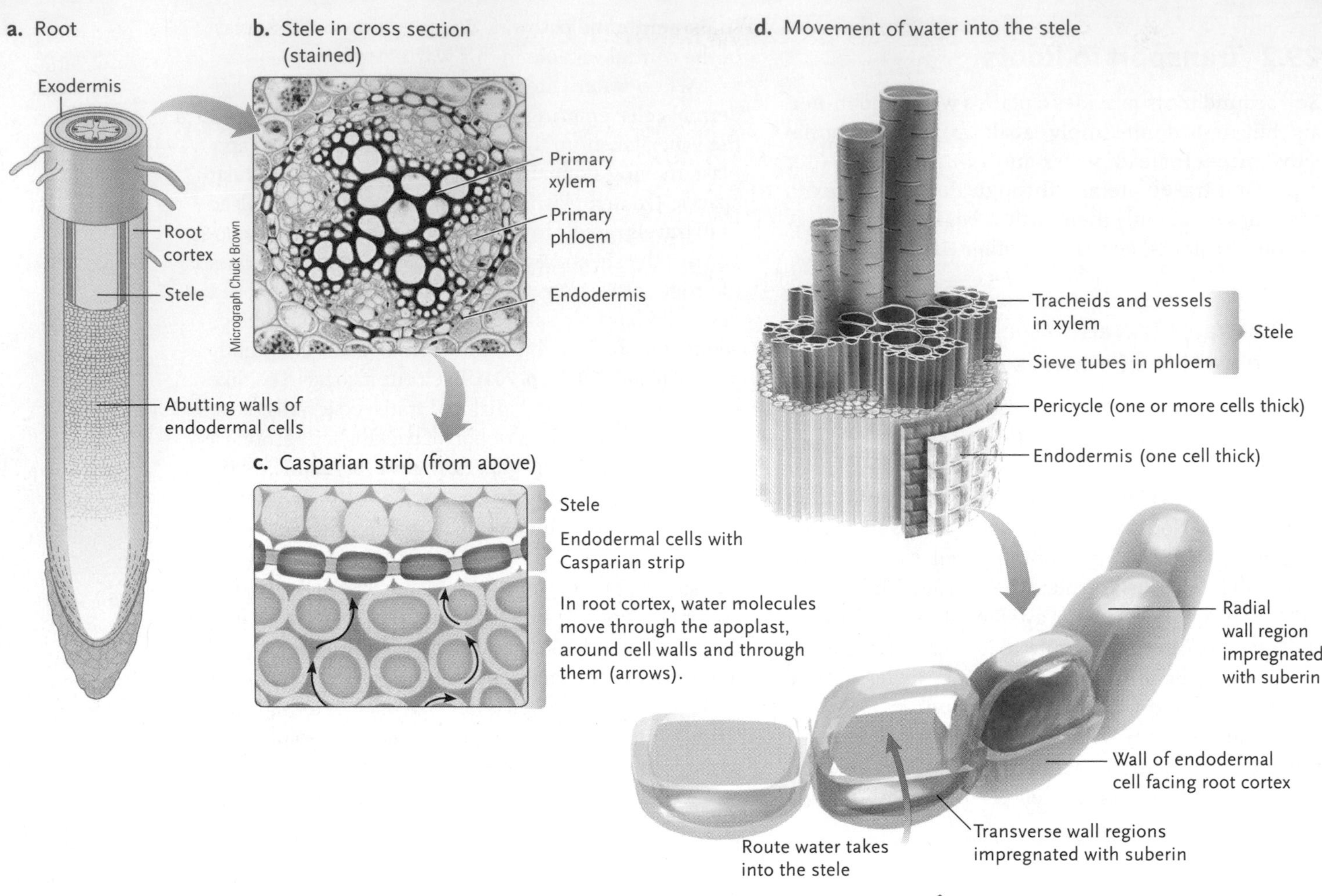

Figure 29.7
Location and function of Casparian strips in roots.

Although water molecules can easily cross an endodermal cell's plasma membrane, the semipermeable membrane allows only a subset of the solutes in soil water to cross. Undesirable solutes may be barred, whereas desirable ones may move into the cell by facilitated diffusion or active transport. Conversely, the endodermis prevents needed substances in the xylem from leaking out, back into the root cortex. In this way, the endodermis provides important control over which substances enter and leave a plant's vascular tissue. The roots of most flowering plants also have a second layer of cells with Casparian strips just inside the root epidermis. This layer, the exodermis (shown in Figure 29.7a), functions like the endodermis.

29.2b Roots Take Up Ions by Active Transport

Mineral ions in soil water also enter roots through the epidermis. Some enter the apoplast along with water, but most ions important for plant nutrition tend to be much more concentrated in roots than in the surrounding soil, so they cannot follow a concentration gradient into root epidermal cells. Instead, the epidermal cells actively transport ions inward—that is, ions enter the symplast immediately. They travel to the xylem via the symplastic or transmembrane pathways. Other ions can still move inward following the apoplastic pathway until they reach the Casparian strip of the endodermis. If they are to contribute to the plant's nutrition, however, they must be actively transported from the exodermis into cells of the root cortex and, as just described, from the endodermis into the stele. In short, mechanisms that control which solutes will be absorbed by root cells ultimately determine which solutes will be distributed through the plant.

Once an ion reaches the stele, it diffuses from cell to cell until it is "loaded" into the xylem. Experiments to determine whether the loading is passive (by diffusion) or active have been inconclusive, so the details of this final step are not entirely clear. Because the xylem's conducting elements are not living, water and ions in effect reenter the apoplastic pathway when they reach either tracheids or vessels. Once in the xylem, water can move laterally to and from tissues or travel upward in the conducting elements. Minerals are distributed to living cells and taken up by active transport. The following section examines how this "distribution of the wealth" takes place.

Molecule Behind Biology

Suberin

Suberin is a complex cell wall polymer. It is found in specific cell types, including root epidermis, root endodermis (including Casparian bands), bundle sheath cells, and the periderm (bark) of woody species and underground organs (e.g., tubers). Suberin is a unique macromolecule that contains two distinct polymeric domains: poly(phenolic) and poly(aliphatic). Each domain has a unique chemical composition and contributes different properties to the walls in the specialized cells in which it is found. That is, the poly(phenolic) domain provides a structural barrier, whereas the poly(aliphatic) domain provides a nearly perfect water barrier, preventing water loss and regulating solute transport. Combined, these two domains provide protection against pathogens. Suberin is also a component of the wound-healing process in plants, serving to isolate damaged cells from undamaged ones beneath while closing off the exposed tissue from the external environment.

The chemical compositions of both suberin domains have been well characterized for a number of plant species, and recent attention has turned to the specifics of their biosynthesis within the context of suberization: that is, the process through which cells become suberized. Recent work carried out in the laboratory of Mark Bernards at the University of Western Ontario has focused on identifying key metabolic steps, cloning the genes encoding the enzymes responsible for these steps, and functionally characterizing them. Two model systems for studying suberin biosynthesis have emerged: wound-healing potato (*Solanum tuberosum*) tubers and *Arabidopsis* (*Arabidopsis thaliana*). Of these, the potato tuber system offers the advantage of generating a large amount of synchronously suberizing cells after a single wounding event derived by cutting the tuber under sterile conditions. The cut tissue rapidly heals, forming a suberized layer that closely resembles native potato periderm. In addition to delineating the biochemical pathways leading to the monomeric components of suberin, the induction of wound suberin in potatoes also allows the study of how two disparate metabolic pathways (fatty acid biosynthesis/modification and phenolic biosynthesis) are coordinately regulated and ultimately converge to generate a complex macromolecular structure.

Study Break

1. Explain two key differences in how the apoplastic and symplastic pathways route substances laterally in roots.
2. How does an ion enter a root hair and then move to the xylem?

29.3 Transport of Water and Minerals in the Xylem

We return now to the question that opened this chapter: How does the solution of water and minerals called xylem sap move—100 m or more in the tallest trees—from roots to stems and then into leaves? Xylem sap is mostly water, and we know that it moves upward by bulk flow through the tracheids and vessels in xylem. Yet because mature xylem cells are dead, they cannot expend energy to move water into and through the plant shoot. Instead, the driving force for the upward movement of xylem sap from root to shoot is sunlight, which causes water to evaporate from leaves and other aerial parts of land plants. Experiments show that only a small fraction of the water in xylem sap is used in a plant's growth and metabolism. The rest evaporates into the air in a phenomenon called **transpiration.** As described next, transpiration drives the ascent of sap.

29.3a The Mechanical Properties of Water Have Key Roles in Its Transport

The Chemical and Physical Foundations of Biology pages review several biologically important mechanical properties of water. Two of them interest us here. First, water molecules are strongly *cohesive:* they tend to form hydrogen bonds with one another. Second, water molecules are *adhesive:* they form hydrogen bonds with molecules of other substances, including the carbohydrates in plant cell walls. Water's cohesive and adhesive forces jointly pull water molecules into exceedingly small spaces, such as crevices in cell walls or narrow tubes such as xylem vessels in roots, stems, and leaves. In 1914, plant physiologist Henry Dixon explained the ascent of sap in terms of the relationship between transpiration and water's mechanical properties. His model of xylem transport is now called the **cohesion–tension mechanism of water transport (Figure 29.8, p. 704).**

According to the cohesion–tension model, water transport begins as water evaporates from the walls of mesophyll cells inside leaves and into the intercellular spaces. This water vapour escapes by transpiration through open stomata, the minute passageways in the leaf surface. As water molecules exit the leaf, they are replaced by others from the mesophyll cell cytoplasm. The water loss gradually reduces the water potential in a transpiring cell below the water potential in the leaf xylem. Now, water from the xylem in the leaf veins

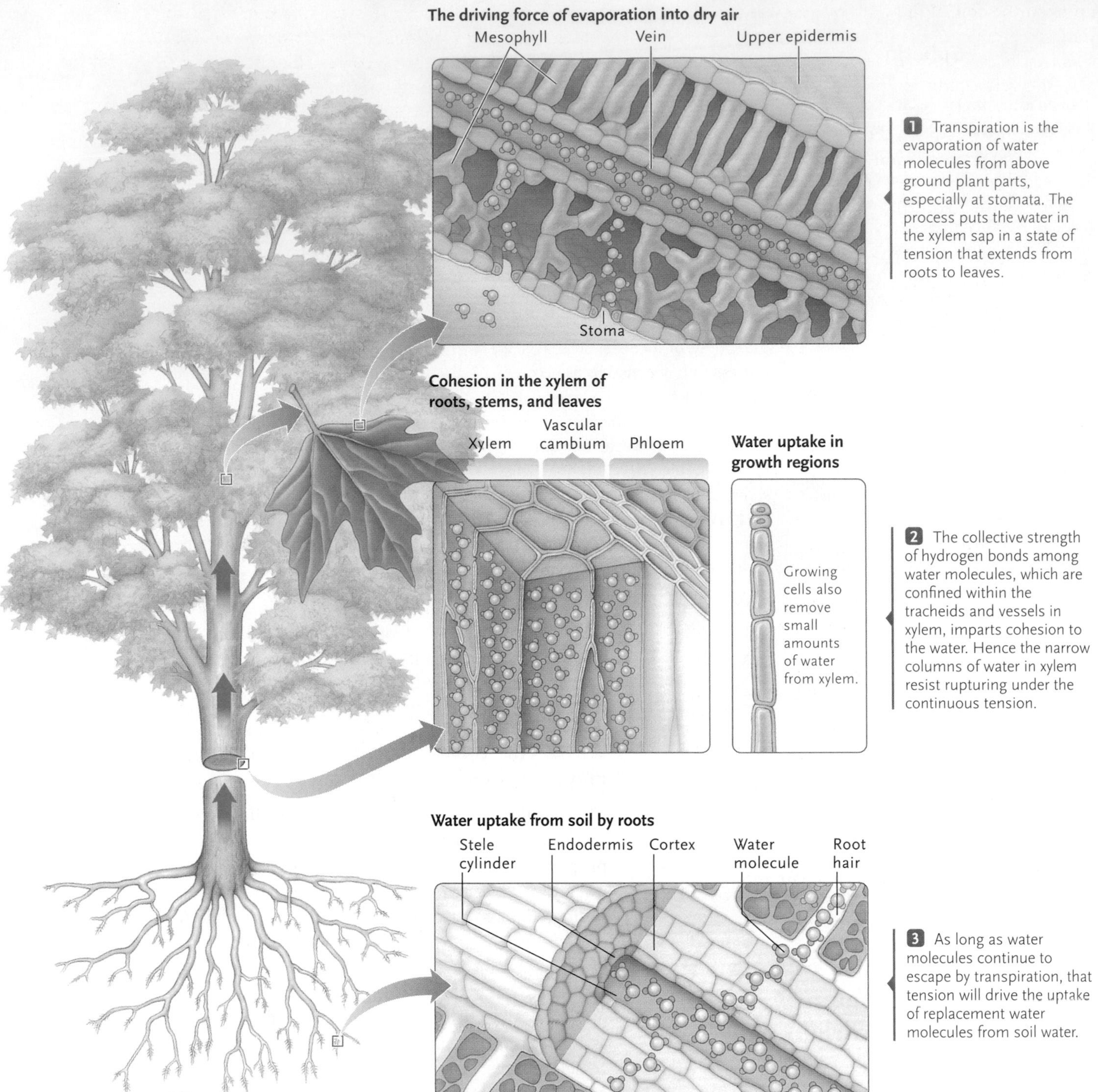

The driving force of evaporation into dry air
Mesophyll
Vein
Upper epidermis
Stoma
1 Transpiration is the evaporation of water molecules from above ground plant parts, especially at stomata. The process puts the water in the xylem sap in a state of tension that extends from roots to leaves.
Cohesion in the xylem of roots, stems, and leaves
Xylem
Vascular cambium
Phloem
Water uptake in growth regions
Growing cells also remove small amounts of water from xylem.
2 The collective strength of hydrogen bonds among water molecules, which are confined within the tracheids and vessels in xylem, imparts cohesion to the water. Hence the narrow columns of water in xylem resist rupturing under the continuous tension.
Water uptake from soil by roots
Stele cylinder
Endodermis
Cortex
Water molecule
Root hair
3 As long as water molecules continue to escape by transpiration, that tension will drive the uptake of replacement water molecules from soil water.

Figure 29.8

Cohesion–tension mechanism of water transport. Transpiration, the evaporation of water from shoot parts, creates tension on the water in xylem sap. This tension, which extends from root to leaf, pulls upward columns of water molecules that are hydrogen-bonded to one another.

follows the gradient into cells, replacing the water lost in transpiration.

In the xylem, water molecules are confined in narrow, tubular xylem cells. The water molecules form a long chain, like a string of weak magnets, held together by hydrogen bonds between individual molecules. When a water molecule moves out of a leaf vein into the mesophyll, its hydrogen bonds with the next molecule in line stretch but don't break. The stretching creates *tension*—a negative pressure gradient—in the column. Adhesion of the water column to xylem vessel walls adds to the tension. Under continuous tension from above, the entire column of water molecules in xylem is drawn upward, in a fashion somewhat analogous to the way water moves up through a drinking straw. Botanists refer to this root-to-shoot flow as the *transpiration stream*.

Transpiration continues regardless of whether evaporating water is replenished by water rapidly taken up from the soil. Wilting is visible evidence that the water-potential gradient between soil and a plant's shoot parts has shifted. Remember that as soil dries out, the remaining water molecules are held ever more tightly by the soil particles. In effect, the action of soil particles reduces the water potential in the soil surrounding plant roots, and as this happens, the roots take up water more slowly. However, because the water that evaporates from the plant's leaves is no longer being fully replaced, the leaves wilt as turgor pressure drops. Reducing the water potential in soil by adding solutes such as NaCl and other salts can have the same wilting effect. When the water potential in the soil finally equals that in leaf cells, a gradient no longer exists. Then movement of water from the soil into roots and up to the leaves comes to a halt.

29.3b Leaf Anatomy Contributes to Cohesion–Tension Forces

Leaf anatomy is key to the processes that move water upward in plants. To begin with, as much as two-thirds of a leaf's volume consists of air spaces—thus, there is a large internal surface area for evaporation. Leaves also may have thousands to millions of stomata, through which water vapour can escape. Both of these factors increase transpiration. Also, every square centimetre of a leaf contains thousands of tiny xylem veins, so most leaf cells lie within half a millimetre of a vein. This close proximity supplies water to cells and the spaces between them, from which the water can readily evaporate.

As water evaporates from a leaf, surface tension at the interface between the water film and the air in the leaf space translates into negative pressure that draws water from the leaf veins. This tension is multiplied many times over in all of the leaves and xylem veins of a plant. It increases further as the plant's metabolically active cells take up xylem sap.

29.3c In the Tallest Trees, the Cohesion–Tension Mechanism May Reach Its Physical Limit

A variety of experiments have tested the propositions of the cohesion–tension model, and thus far, the data strongly support it. For example, the model predicts that xylem sap will begin to move upward at the top of a tree early in the day when water begins to evaporate from leaves. Experiments with several different tree species have confirmed that this is the case. The experiments also showed that sap transport peaks at midday when evaporation is greatest and then tapers off in the evening as evaporative water loss slows.

Other experiments have probed the relationship between xylem transport and tree height. One team of researchers studied eight of the tallest living redwoods, including one that towers nearly 113 m above the forest floor. When the scientists measured the maximum tension exerted in the xylem sap in twigs at the tops of the trees, they discovered that it approached the known physical limit at which the bonds between water molecules in a column of water in a conifer's xylem will rupture. Based on this finding and other evidence, the team predicted that the maximum height for a healthy redwood tree is 122 to 130 m. Therefore, it is possible that the tallest redwoods alive today may grow taller still.

29.3d Root Pressure Contributes to Upward Water Movement in Some Plants

The cohesion–tension mechanism accounts for upward water movement in tall trees. In some nonwoody plant species, however—lawn grasses, for instance—a positive pressure can develop in roots and force xylem sap upward. This **root pressure** operates under conditions that reduce transpiration, such as high humidity or low light. In fact, the mechanism that produces root pressure often operates at night, when solar-powered transpiration slows or stops. Then active transport of ions into the stele sets up a water potential gradient across the endodermis. Because the Casparian strip of the endodermis tends to prevent ions from moving back into the root cortex, the water potential difference becomes quite large. It can move enough water and dissolved solutes into the xylem to produce a relatively high positive pressure. Although not sufficient to force water to the top of a very tall plant, in some smaller plant species, root pressure is strong enough to force water out of leaf openings, in a process called **guttation (Figure 29.9)**. Pushed up and out of vein endings by root pressure, tiny droplets of water that look like dew in the early morning emerge from modified stomata at the margins of leaves.

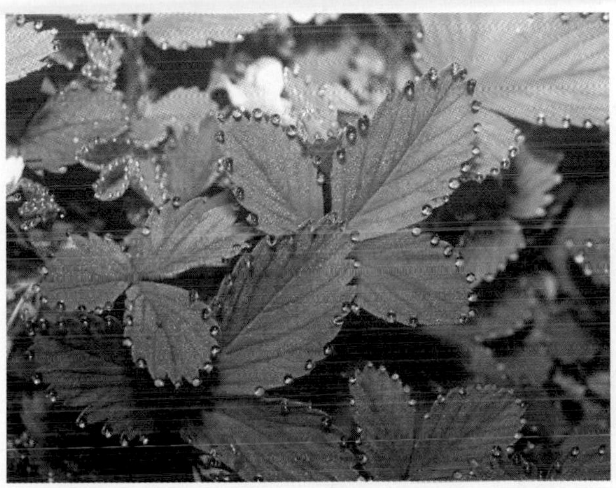

Dr. John D. Cunningham/Visuals Unlimited

Figure 29.9
Guttation, caused by root pressure. The drops of water appear at the endings of xylem veins along the leaf edges of a strawberry plant (*Fragaria*).

29.3e Stomata Regulate the Loss of Water by Transpiration

Three environmental conditions have major effects on the rate of transpiration: relative humidity, air temperature, and air movement. The most important is relative humidity, which is a measure of the amount of water vapour in air. The less water vapour in the air, the more evaporates from leaves (because the water potential is higher in the leaves than in the dry air). The air temperature at the leaf surface also speeds evaporation as it rises. Although evaporation does cool the leaf somewhat, the amount of water lost can double for each 10°C rise in air temperature. Air movement at the leaf surface carries water vapour away from the surface and so makes a steeper gradient. Together these factors explain why on extremely hot, dry, breezy days the leaves of certain plants must completely replace their water each hour.

Even when conditions are not so drastic, more than 90% of the water moving into a leaf can be lost through transpiration. Of the remaining water, about 2% is used in photosynthesis and other activities. These measurements emphasize the need for controls over transpiration for if water loss exceeds water uptake by roots, the resulting dehydration of plant tissues interferes with normal functioning, and the plant may wilt and die.

The cuticle-covered epidermis of leaves and stems reduces the rate of water loss from above-ground plant parts, but it also limits the rate at which CO_2 for photosynthesis can diffuse into the leaf. The functioning of stomata also affects a plant's water balance. When stomata are open, carbon dioxide can be absorbed, but unless the relative humidity of external air is 100%, water always moves out. However, plants have evolved adaptations that balance water loss with CO_2 uptake. This "transpiration–photosynthesis compromise" involves the regulation of transpiration and gas exchange by opening and closing stomata as environmental conditions change.

Opening and Closing of Stomata. Two guard cells flank each stomatal opening **(Figure 29.10).** Their elastic walls are reinforced by cellulose microfibrils that wrap around the walls like a series of belts. The inward-facing walls are thicker and less elastic than the outer walls.

The opening and closing of stomata are good examples of a symport mechanism (see Figure 29.3c). Stomata open when potassium ions (K^+) flow into the guard cells through ion channels. As a first step, an active transport pump in the plasma membrane begins pumping H^+ ions out of the guard cells. The H^+ pumped out of the cell can then follow its concentration gradient back into the cell. This inward flow of H^+ powers the active transport of K^+ into the guard cell. As a result, the K^+ concentration in turgid guard cells may be four to eight times higher than that in flaccid (limp) guard cells **(Figure 29.11).** Water follows inward by osmosis. As turgor pressure builds, the thick inner wall does not expand much, but the outer walls of each guard cell expand lengthwise, so the two cells bend away from each other and create a stoma ("mouth") between them. Stomata close when the H^+ active transport protein stops pumping. K^+ flows passively out of the guard cells, and water follows by osmosis. When the water content of the guard cells dwindles, turgor pressure drops. The guard cells collapse against each other, closing the stomata.

In most plants, stomata open at first light, stay open during daylight, and close at night. Experiments have shown that guard cells respond to a number of

a. Open stoma

Guard cell Guard cell

Stoma

b. Closed stoma

Chloroplast (guard cells are the only epidermal cells that have these organelles)

20 μm

Figure 29.10

Guard cells and stomatal action. (a) An open stoma. Water entered collapsed guard cells, which swelled under turgor pressure and moved apart, thus forming the stoma in the needlelike leaf of the rock needlebush (*Hakea gibbosa*). **(b)** A closed stoma. Water exited the swollen guard cells, which collapsed against each other and closed the stoma.

a. Open stomata, with potassium mostly in guard cells

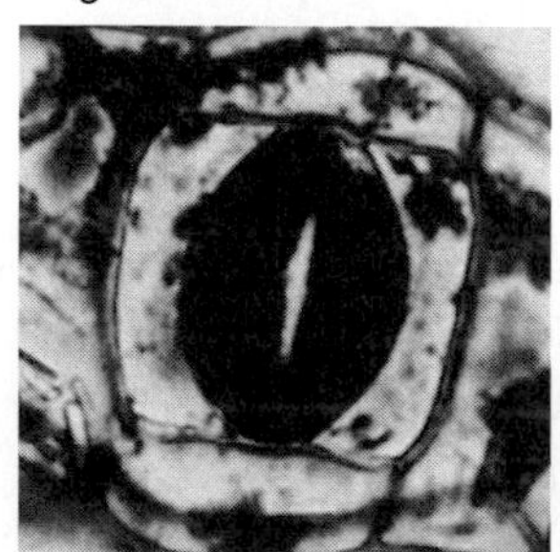

b. Closed stomata, with potassium mostly in epidermal cells

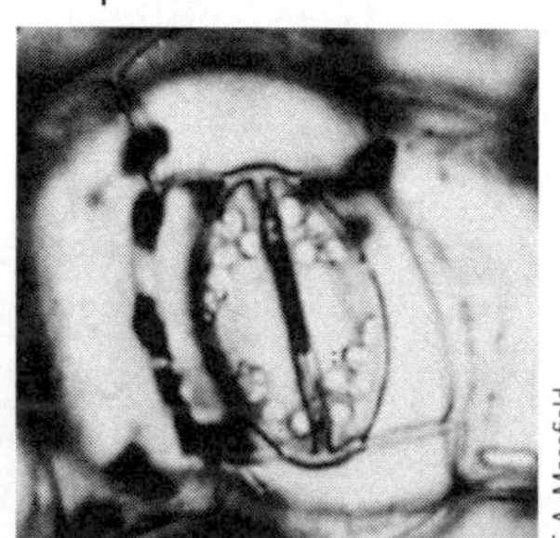

Figure 29.11

Evidence for potassium accumulation in stomatal guard cells undergoing expansion. Strips from the leaf epidermis of a dayflower (*Commelina communis*) were immersed in a solution containing a stain that binds preferentially with potassium ions. **(a)** In leaf samples with open stomata, most of the potassium was concentrated in the guard cells. **(b)** In leaf samples with closed stomata, little potassium was in guard cells; most was present in adjacent epidermal cells.

environmental and chemical signals, any of which can induce the ion flows that open and close stomata. These signals include light, CO_2 concentration in the air spaces inside leaves, and the amount of water available to the plant.

Light and CO_2 Concentration. Light induces stomata to open through stimulation of blue-light receptors, probably located in the plasma membrane of guard cells. When stimulated, the receptors start the chain of events leading to stomatal opening by triggering activity of the H^+ pumps. Also, as photosynthesis begins in response to light, CO_2 concentration drops in the leaf air spaces as chloroplasts use the gas in carbohydrate production. In some way, this drop in CO_2 concentration sets off the series of events increasing the flow of K^+ into guard cells and furthers stomatal opening. The effects of reduced CO_2 concentration have been tested by placing plants in the dark in air containing no CO_2. Even in the absence of light, as the CO_2 concentration falls in leaves, guard cells swell and the stomata open.

Normally, when the sun goes down, a plant's demand for CO_2 drops as photosynthesis comes to a halt. Yet aerobic respiration continues to produce CO_2, which accumulates in leaves. As CO_2 concentration rises, and the blue-light wavelengths that activated the H^+ pumps wane, K^+ is lost from the guard cells and they collapse, closing the stomata. Thus, at night, transpiration is reduced and water is conserved.

Water Stress. As long as water is readily available to a plant's roots, the stomata remain open during daylight. However, if water loss stresses a plant, the stomata close or open only slightly, regardless of light intensity or CO_2 concentration. Some simple but elegant experiments have shown that the stress-related closing of stomata depends on a hormone, abscisic acid (ABA), that is released by roots when water is unavailable. Test plants were suspended in containers so that only one-half of the root system received water. Even though the roots with access to water could absorb enough water to satisfy the needs of all the plants' leaves, the stomata still closed. Tissue analysis revealed that water-stressed roots rapidly synthesize ABA. Transported through the xylem, this hormone stimulates K^+ loss by guard cells, and water moves out of the cell by osmosis—so the stomata close **(Figure 29.12)**. Mesophyll cells also take up ABA from the xylem and release it, with the same effects on stomata, when their turgor pressure falls due to excessive water loss. ABA can also cause stomata to close when the hormone is added experimentally to leaves.

The Biological Clock. Besides responding to light, CO_2 concentration, and water stress, stomata apparently open and close on a regular daily schedule imposed by a biological clock. Even when plants are placed in continuous darkness, their stomata open and close (for a time) in a cycle that roughly matches the day/night cycle of Earth. Such *circadian rhythms* (*circa* = around; *dies* = day) are also common in animals, and several, including wake/sleep cycles in mammals, are known to be controlled by hormones.

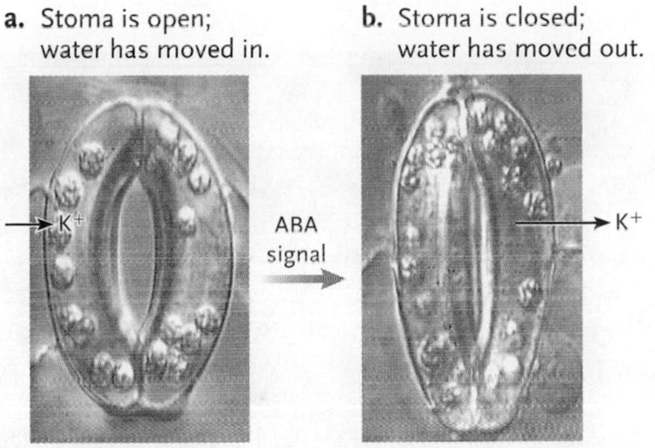

29.3f In Dry Climates, Plants Exhibit Various Adaptations for Conserving Water

Many plants have other evolutionary adaptations that conserve water, including modifications in structure or physiology **(Figure 29.13, p. 708)**. The stomata of oleanders, for example, lie at the bottom of pitlike invaginations that are lined by hairlike trichomes (see Figure 29.13b). Sunken stomata are less exposed to drying breezes, and trichomes help retain water vapour at the pore opening, so that water evaporates from the leaf much more slowly.

The leaves of *xerophytes*—plants adapted to hot, dry environments in which water stress can be severe—have a thickened cuticle that gives them a leathery feel and provides enhanced protection against evaporative water loss. An example is mesquite (*Prosopis*). In still other plants that inhabit arid landscapes, such as cacti, stems are thick, leaflike pads covered by sharp spines that actually are modified leaves (see Figure 29.13c). These structural alterations reduce the surface area for transpiration.

One intriguing variation on water-conservation mechanisms occurs in CAM plants, including cacti, orchids, and most succulents. As discussed in Chapter 7, **crassulacean acid metabolism** (CAM) is a biochemical variation of photosynthesis that was discovered in a member of the family Crassulaceae. CAM plants generally have fewer stomata than other types of plants, and their stomata follow a reversed

a. Stoma is open; water has moved in.

b. Stoma is closed; water has moved out.

K^+

ABA signal

K^+

Figure 29.12
Hormonal control of stomatal closing. **(a)** When a stoma is open, high solute concentrations in the cytoplasm of both guard cells have raised the turgor pressure, keeping the cells swollen open. **(b)** In a water-stressed plant, the hormone abscisic acid (ABA) binds to receptors on the guard cell plasma membrane. Binding activates a signal transduction pathway that lowers solute concentrations inside the cells, which lowers the turgor pressure—so the stoma closes.

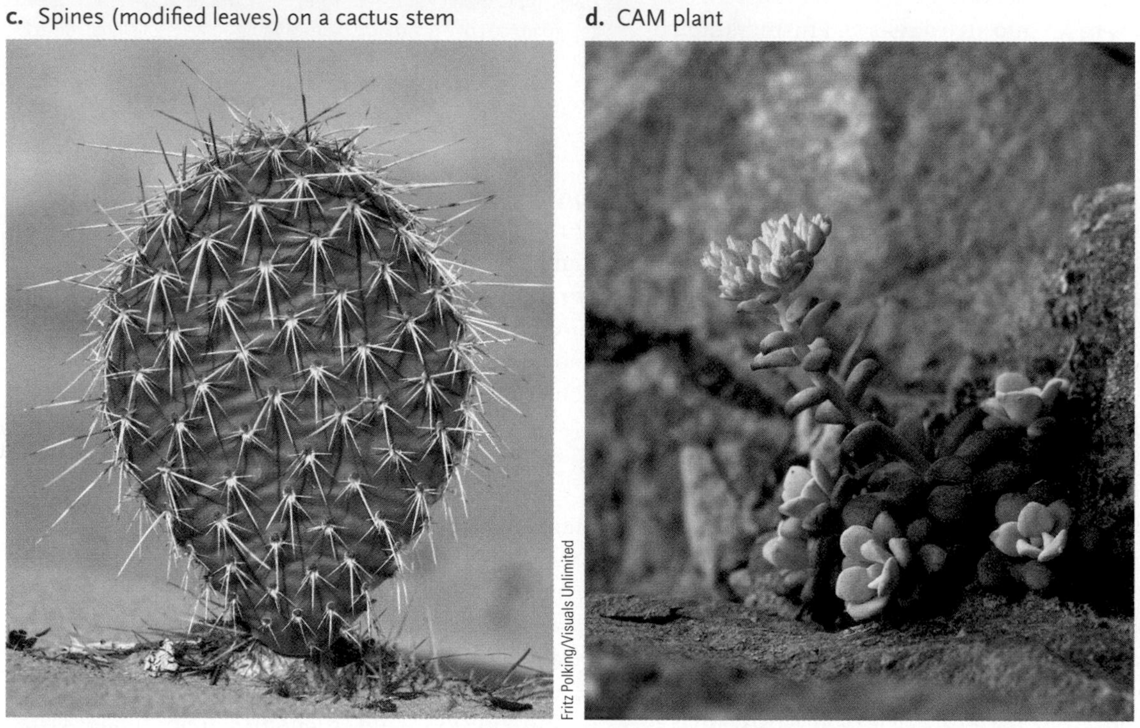

c. Spines (modified leaves) on a cactus stem
d. CAM plant
Fritz Polking/Visuals Unlimited
Fritz Polking/Visuals Unlimited

Figure 29.13
Some adaptations that enable plants to survive water stress. **(a)** Oleanders (*Nerium oleander*) are adapted to arid conditions. **(b)** As shown in the micrograph, oleander leaves have recessed stomata on their lower surface and a multilayer epidermis covered by a thick cuticle on the upper surface. **(c)** Like many other cacti, the leaves of the Graham dog cactus (*Opuntia grahamii*) are modified into spines that protrude from the underlying stem. Transpiration and photosynthesis occur in the green stems, such as the oval stem in this photograph. **(d)** *Sedum*, a CAM plant, in which the stomata open only at night.

schedule. They are closed during the day, when temperatures are higher and the relative humidity is lower, and open at night. At night, the plant temporarily fixes carbon dioxide by converting it to malate, an organic acid. In the daytime, the CO_2 is released from malate and diffuses into chloroplasts, so photosynthesis takes place even though a CAM plant's stomata are closed. This adaptation prevents heavy evaporative water losses during the heat of the day.

Study Break

1. Explain the key steps in the cohesion–tension mechanism of water transport in a plant.
2. How and when do stomata open and close? In what ways is their functioning important to a plant's ability to manage water loss?

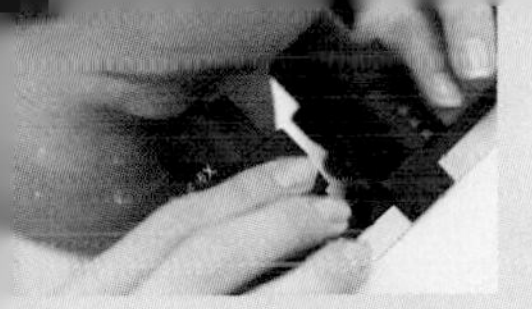

People Behind Biology
Julian Schroeder

As we have seen in this chapter, stomata opening is essential for CO_2 uptake into the plant, and yet, through the process of transpiration, it is also the cause of over 95% of the water lost by the plant. The control of stomatal aperture is governed by osmotic changes to the neighbouring guard cells, and this is influenced by a complex of integrated factors that include hormones, light conditions, and water status, as well as changes in temperature and CO_2. Being able to adjust stomatal aperture in the face of rapidly changing environmental conditions is critical to plant survival under diverse conditions.

The chain of events that links environmental conditions, for example, to alterations in guard cell function, is a major focus of the research carried out by the laboratory of Julian Schroeder in the Biology Department at San Diego State University in California. Much of the work of the Schroeder lab centres on using mutants of the model plant *Arabidopsis thaliana* that have altered guard cell function compared with wild-type plants. Using a range of sophisticated molecular, genetic, and cell biology approaches, including employing time-resolved Ca^{2+} imaging techniques, has allowed the Schroeder lab to identify and characterize novel signal transduction pathways controlling stomatal aperture. This work is aided by the considerable genomic and bioinformatics resources that are available for *Arabidopsis*, an organism that has had its nuclear genome completely sequenced.

The work of the Schroeder lab and others has led to the stomatal guard cells becoming a well characterized model system for characterizing early signal transduction mechanisms in plants, and for elucidating how individual signalling mechanisms can interact within a larger signalling network in a single cell. In a more applied way, his research may very well lead to the development of crop plants with increased tolerance to drought. Given the trend in the loss of freshwater resources, this may have a huge impact on the growth of plants in many parts of the world.

29.4 Transport of Organic Substances in the Phloem

A plant's phloem is another major long-distance transport system, and a superhighway at that: it carries huge amounts of carbohydrates; lesser but vital amounts of amino acids, fatty acids, and other organic compounds; and still other essential substances, such as hormones. And unlike the xylem's unidirectional upward flow, the phloem transports substances throughout the plant to wherever they are used or stored. Organic compounds and water in the sieve tubes of phloem are under pressure and driven by concentration gradients.

29.4a Organic Compounds Are Stored and Transported in Different Forms

Plants synthesize various kinds of organic compounds, including large amounts of carbohydrates that are stored mainly as starch. Yet regardless of where in a plant a particular compound is destined to be used or stored, starch, protein, and fat molecules cannot leave the cells in which they are formed because all are too large to cross cell membranes. They also may be too insoluble in water to be transported to other regions of the plant body. Consequently, in leaves and other plant parts, specific reactions convert organic compounds to transportable forms. For example, hydrolysis of starch liberates glucose units, which combine with fructose to form sucrose—the main form in which sugars are transported through the phloem of most plants. Proteins are broken down into amino acids, and lipids are converted into fatty acids. These forms are also better able to cross cell membranes by passive or active mechanisms.

29.4b Organic Solutes Move by Translocation

In plants, the long distance transport of substances is called **translocation.** Botanists most often use this term to refer to the distribution of sucrose and other organic compounds by phloem, and they understand the mechanism best in flowering plants. The phloem of flowering plants contains interconnecting sieve tubes formed by living sieve tube member cells (see Figure 28.10). Sieve tubes lie end to end within vascular bundles, and they extend through all parts of the plant. Water and organic compounds, collectively called **phloem sap**, flow rapidly through large pores on the sieve tubes' end walls—another example of a structural adaptation that suits a particular function.

29.4c Phloem Sap Moves from Source to Sink under Pressure

Over the decades, plant physiologists have proposed several mechanisms of translocation, but it was the tiny aphid, an insect that annoys gardeners, that helped demonstrate that organic compounds flow

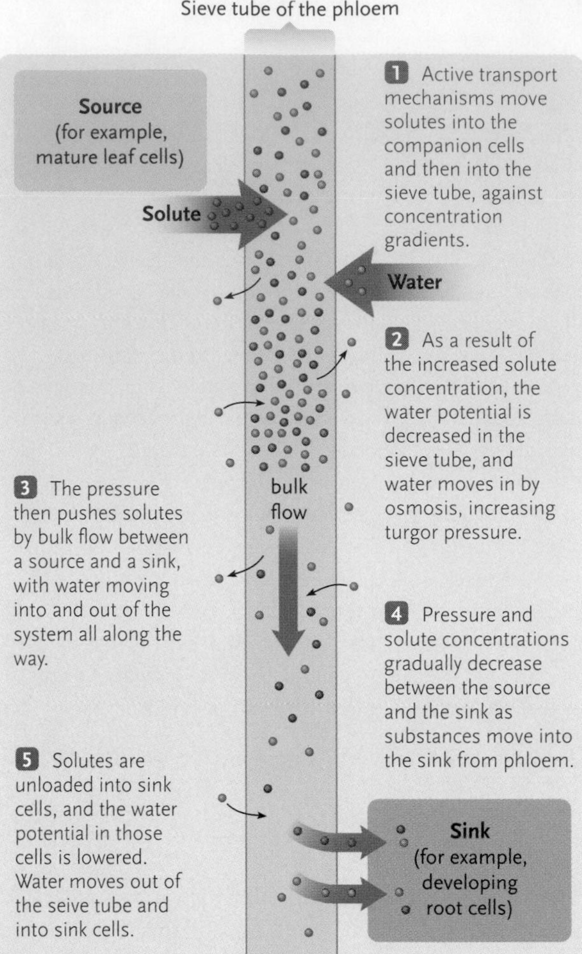

Sieve tube of the phloem
Source
(for example,
mature leaf cells)
Solute
1 Active transport mechanisms move solutes into the companion cells and then into the sieve tube, against concentration gradients.
Water
2 As a result of the increased solute concentration, the water potential is decreased in the sieve tube, and water moves in by osmosis, increasing turgor pressure.
3 The pressure then pushes solutes by bulk flow between a source and a sink, with water moving into and out of the system all along the way.
bulk
flow
4 Pressure and solute concentrations gradually decrease between the source and the sink as substances move into the sink from phloem.
5 Solutes are unloaded into sink cells, and the water potential in those cells is lowered. Water moves out of the seive tube and into sink cells.
Sink
(for example,
developing
root cells)

Figure 29.14
Summary of the pressure flow mechanism in the phloem of flowering plants. Organic solutes are loaded into sieve tubes at a source, such as a leaf, and move by bulk flow toward a sink, such as roots or rapidly growing stem parts.

under pressure in the phloem. An aphid attacks plant leaves and stems, forcing its needlelike stylet (a mouthpart) into sieve tubes to obtain the dissolved sugars and other nutrients inside. Numerous experiments with aphids have shown that in most plant species, sucrose is the main carbohydrate being translocated through the phloem. Studies also verify that the contents of sieve tubes are under high pressure, often five times as much as that of an automobile tire. When a live aphid feeds on phloem sap, this pressure forces the fluid through the aphid's gut and (minus nutrients absorbed) out its anus as "honeydew." If you park your car under a tree being attacked by aphids, it might get spattered with sticky honeydew droplets, thanks to the high fluid pressure in the tree's phloem.

A great deal of what botanists know about the transport of phloem sap has come from studies of sucrose transport in flowering plants. A fundamental discovery is that in flowering plants, sucrose-laden phloem sap flows from a starting location, called the *source,* to another site, called the *sink,* along gradients of decreasing solute concentration and pressure. A **source** is any region of the plant where organic substances are being loaded into the phloem's sieve tube system. A **sink** is any region where organic substances are being unloaded from the sieve tube system and used or stored. What causes sucrose and other solutes produced in leaf mesophyll to flow from a source to a sink? In flowering plants, the **pressure flow mechanism** builds up at the source end of a sieve tube system and pushes those solutes by bulk flow toward a sink, where they are removed. **Figure 29.14** summarizes this mechanism.

The site of photosynthesis in mature leaves is an example of a source. Another example is a tulip bulb. In spring, stored food is mobilized for transport upward to growing plant parts, but after the plants bloom, the bulb becomes a sink as sugars manufactured in the tulip plant's leaves are translocated into it for storage. Young leaves, roots, and developing fruits generally start out as sinks, only to become sources when the season changes or the plant enters a new developmental phase. In general, sinks receive organic compounds from sources closest to them. Hence, the lower leaves on a rose bush may supply sucrose to roots, whereas leaves farther up the shoot supply the shoot tip.

Most substances carried in phloem are loaded into sieve tube members by active transport **(Figure 29.15a).** Sucrose is our example here. In leaves, sucrose formed inside mesophyll cells is exported and eventually reaches the apoplast (adjoining cell walls and air spaces) next to a small phloem vein. Here, it is actively pumped into companion cells by symport (see Figure 29.3), in which H^+ ions move into the cell through the same carrier that takes up the sugar molecules. From the companion cells, most sucrose crosses into the living sieve tube members through plasmodesmata. Some sucrose also is loaded into sieve tube members by symport.

In some plants, companion cells become modified into **transfer cells** that facilitate the short-distance transport of organic solutes from the apoplast into the symplast. Transfer cells generally form when large amounts of solutes must be loaded or unloaded into the phloem, and they shunt substances through plasmodesmata to sieve tube members. As a transfer cell is forming, parts of the cell wall grow inward like pleats. This structural feature increases the surface area across which solutes can be taken up. The underlying plasma membrane, packed with transport proteins, then expands to cover the ingrowths. Transfer cells also enhance solute transport between living cells in the xylem, and they occur in glandlike tissues that secrete nectar. Botanists have discovered transfer cells in species from every taxonomic group in the plant kingdom, as well as in fungi and algae. In part because they arise from differentiated cells (instead

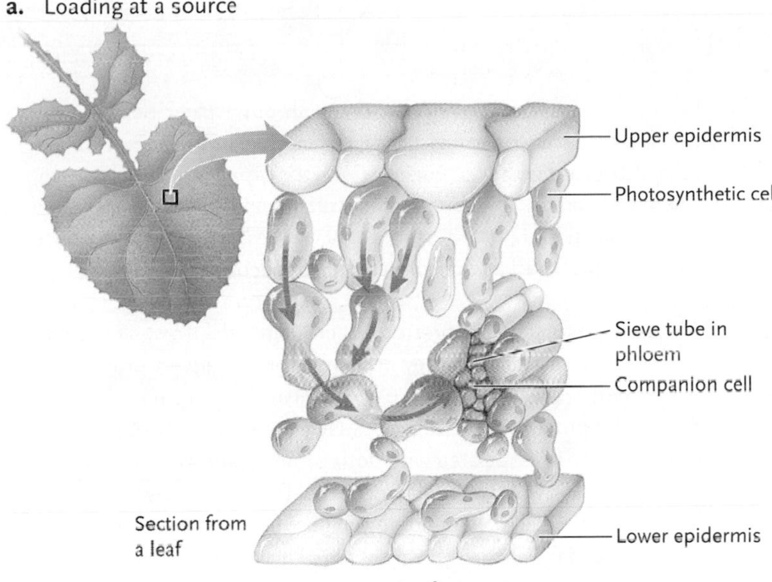

Photosynthetic cells in leaves are a common source of carbohydrates that must be distributed throughout a plant. Small, soluble forms of these compounds move from the cells into phloem (in a leaf vein).

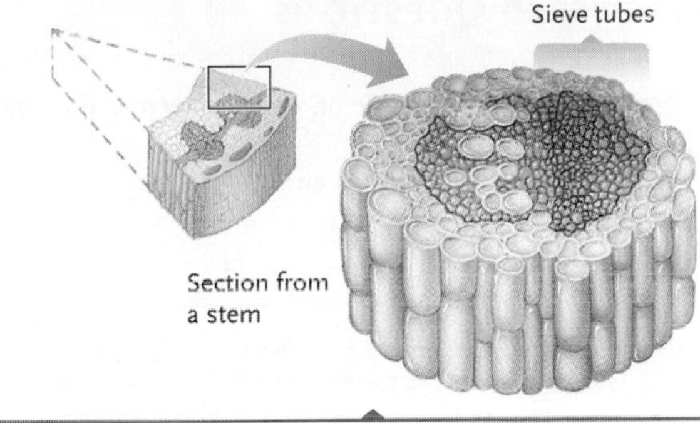

Fluid pressure is greatest inside sieve tubes at the source. It pushes the solute-rich fluid to a sink, which is any region where cells are growing or storing food. There, the pressure is lower because cells are withdrawing solutes from the tubes and water follows the solutes.

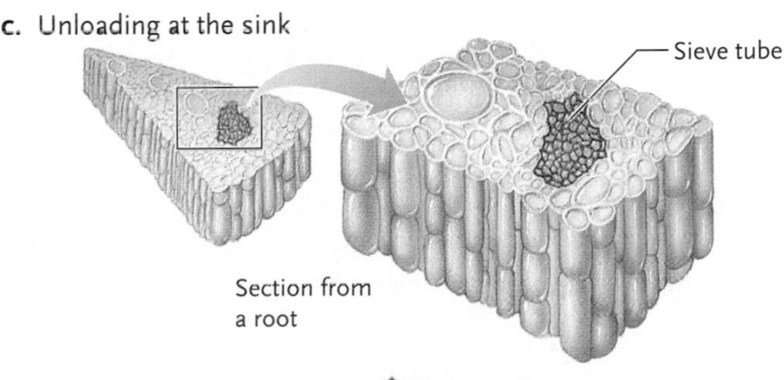

Solutes are unloaded from sieve tubes into cells at the sink; water follows. Translocation continues as long as solute concentration gradients and a pressure gradient exist between the source and the sink.

Figure 29.15
Translocation in the tissues of *Sonchus*, commonly called sow thistle. Research on *Sonchus* provided experimental evidence for the pressure flow mechanism.

of from meristem cells like other plant types of plant cells), researchers are working to define the molecular mechanisms that trigger their development.

When sucrose is loaded into sieve tubes, its concentration rises inside the tubes. Thus, the water potential falls, and water flows into the sieve tubes by osmosis. In fact, the phloem typically carries a great deal of water. As water enters sieve tubes, turgor pressure in the tubes increases, and the sucrose-rich fluid moves by bulk flow into the increasingly larger sieve tubes of larger veins. Eventually, the fluid is pushed out of the leaf into the stem and toward a sink **(Figure 29.15b)**. When sucrose is unloaded at the sink, water in the tube "follows solutes," moving by osmosis into the surrounding cells **(Figure 29.15c)**.

Sieve tubes are mostly passive conduits for translocation. The system works because companion cells supply most of the energy that loads sucrose and other solutes at the source, and because solutes are removed at their sinks. As sucrose enters a sink, for example, its concentration in sieve tubes decreases, with a corresponding decrease in pressure. Thus, for sucrose and other solutes transported in the phloem, there is always a gradient of concentration from source to sink—and a pressure gradient that keeps the solute moving along.

As noted previously, phloem sap moving through a plant carries a wide variety of substances, including hormones, amino acids, organic acids, and agricultural chemicals. The phloem also transports organic nitrogen compounds and mineral ions that are removed from dying leaves and stored for reuse in root tissue.

The transport functions of xylem and phloem are closely integrated with phenomena discussed later in this unit—reproduction and embryonic development and the hormone-based regulation of plant growth.

Study Break

1. Compare translocation and transpiration.
2. Using sucrose as your example, summarize how a substance moves from a source into sieve tubes and then is unloaded at a sink. What is this mechanism called, and why?

Unanswered Questions

What are plasmodesmata made of, and exactly how do they function?

Plasmodesmata, the cytoplasmic channels through plant cell walls, connect plant cells to each other. Yet two fundamental questions about plasmodesmata remain unanswered: Exactly how do plasmodesmata function, and what are their structural components?

As described in this chapter, botanists have long assumed that nutrients, water, and small molecules that serve as growth regulators move through plasmodesmata, which form part of the symplastic pathway in plant tissues. Recent studies have demonstrated that larger molecules, including viruses and important proteins involved in plant growth and development, also move from cell to cell through plasmodesmata. For example, Patricia Zambryski and K.M. Crawford at the University of California at Berkeley reported that proteins, including transcription factors, travel via plasmodesmata from the cell that produces the proteins to adjacent cells where the factors promote or inhibit the expression of particular genes.

Although the normal functions of plasmodesmata in plant growth and development still are not well understood, ongoing research by Zambryski and other plant scientists has begun to shed light on the workings of these vital channels. For instance, a variety of studies of the processes by which viruses spread through plant tissues have revealed that plasmodesmata are not simply static, open channels. Instead, they are dynamic structures with the capacity to close, reopen, widen, and narrow. This capacity for structural change is not triggered by viral infection: rather, it seems that viruses simply take over the plant's natural mechanism for moving molecules from one cell to another.

Plasmodesmata were first observed using electron microscopy several decades ago, and they appear to be lined with proteins as well as membranes. Multiple biochemical approaches have failed to identify the proteins, probably because of the difficulty of purifying proteins that are associated with both a membrane and the cell wall. Genetic screens to identify plasmodesmata proteins, as well as the genes that regulate the functioning of plasmodesmata, are currently under way and may finally reveal details of plasmodesmata structure. As our understanding of the architecture of plasmodesmata and how they function grows, so will insights into the mechanisms of plant development, how plants interact with viral pathogens, and other questions as well.

Beverly McMillan

Review

Go to CENGAGENOW™ at http://hed.nelson.com/ to access quizzing, animations, exercises, articles, and personalized homework help.

29.1 Principles of Water and Solute Movement in Plants

- Plants have mechanisms for moving water and solutes (1) into and out of cells, (2) laterally from cell to cell, and (3) long distance from the root to shoot or vice versa.
- Both passive and active mechanisms move substances into and out of plant cells. Solutes generally are transported by carriers (facilitated diffusion), either passively down a concentration or electrochemical gradient (in the case of ions), or actively against a gradient, which requires cellular energy. An H^+ gradient creates the membrane potential that drives the cross-membrane transport of many ions or molecules.
- Most organic substances enter plant cells by symport, in which the energy of the H^+ gradient is coupled with uptake of a different solute. Some substances cross the plant cell membrane by antiport, in which energy of the H^+ gradient powers movement of a second solute out of cells.
- Water crosses plant cell membranes by osmosis, which is driven by water potential (ψ). Water tends to move osmotically from regions where water potential is higher to regions where it is lower.
- Water potential reflects a balance between turgor pressure and solute potential. Water potential is measured in megapascals (MPa).
- Water and solutes also move into and out of the cell's central vacuole, transported from the cytoplasm across the tonoplast. Aquaporins across the tonoplast enhance water movement. Water in the central vacuole is vital for maintaining turgor pressure inside a plant cell.
- Bulk flow of fluid occurs when pressure at one point in a system changes with respect to another point in the system.

29.2 Transport in Roots

- Water and mineral ions entering roots travel laterally through the root cortex to the root xylem, following one or more of three major routes: the apoplastic pathway, the symplastic pathway, and the transmembrane pathway.
- In the apoplastic pathway, water diffuses into roots between the walls of root epidermal cells. By contrast, water and solutes absorbed by roots can enter either the symplastic or transmembrane pathway, both of which pass through cells.
- Casparian strips form a barrier that forces water and solutes in the apoplastic pathway to pass through cells in order to enter the stele. When an ion reaches the stele, it diffuses from cell to cell to reach the xylem. The roots of many flowering plants have a second layer of cells with Casparian strips (exodermis) just inside the root epidermis.

29.3 Transport of Water and Minerals in the Xylem

- In the conducting cells of xylem, tension generated by transpiration extends down from leaves to roots. By the cohesion–tension mechanism of water transport, water molecules are pulled upward by tension created as water exits a plant's leaves.
- In tall trees, negative pressure generated in the shoot drives bulk flow of xylem sap. In some plants, notably herbaceous species, positive pressure sometimes develops in roots and can force xylem sap upward.
- Transpiration and carbon dioxide uptake occur mostly through stomata. Environmental factors such as relative humidity, air temperature, and air movement at the leaf surface affect the transpiration rate.

- Most plants lose water and take up carbon dioxide during the day, when stomata are open. At night, when stomata close, plants conserve water and the inward movement of carbon dioxide falls.
- Stomata open in response to falling levels of carbon dioxide in leaves and also to incoming light wavelengths that activate photoreceptors in guard cells.
- Activation of photoreceptors triggers active transport of K^+ into guard cells. Simultaneous entry of anions, such as Cl^-, and synthesis of negatively charged organic acids increase the solute concentration, lowering the water potential so that water enters by osmosis. As turgor pressure builds, guard cells swell and draw apart, producing the stomatal opening.
- Guard cells close when light wavelengths used for photosynthesis wane. The stomata of water-stressed plants close regardless of light or CO_2 needs, possibly under the influence of the plant hormone ABA. The leaves of species native to arid environments typically have adaptations (such as an especially thick cuticle) that enhance the plant's ability to conserve water.

29.4 Transport of Organic Substances in the Phloem

- In flowering plants, phloem sap is translocated in sieve tube members. Differences in pressure between source and sink regions drive the flow. Sources include mature leaves; sinks include growing tissues and storage regions (such as the tubers of a potato).
- In leaves, the sugar sucrose is actively transported into companion cells adjacent to sieve tube members and then loaded into the sieve tubes through plasmodesmata.
- In some plants, transfer cells take up materials and pass them to sieve tube members. Transfer cells in xylem enhance the transport of solutes between tissues.
- As the sucrose concentration increases in the sieve tubes, water potential decreases. The resulting influx of water causes pressure to build up inside the sieve tubes, so the sucrose-laden fluid flows in bulk toward the sink, where sucrose and water are unloaded and distributed among surrounding cells and tissues.

Questions

Self-Test Questions

1. Antiport transport mechanisms
   a. move dissolved materials by osmosis.
   b. transport molecules in the opposite direction of H^+ transported by proton pumps.
   c. transport molecules in the same direction as H^+ is pumped.
   d. are not affected by the size of molecules to be transported.
   e. are not affected by the charge of molecules to be transported.
2. All of the following have roles in transporting materials between plant cells except
   a. the stele.
   b. symport.
   c. the cell membrane.
   d. stomata.
   e. transport proteins.
3. Turgor pressure is best expressed as the
   a. movement of water into a cell by osmosis.
   b. driving force for osmotic movement of water (ψ).
   c. group movement of large numbers of molecules due to a difference in pressure between two locations.
   d. equivalent of water potential.
   e. pressure exerted by fluid inside a plant cell against the cell wall.
4. Water potential is
   a. the driving force for the osmotic movement of water into plant cells.
   b. higher in a solution that has more solute molecules relative to water molecules.
   c. a measure of the physical pressure required to halt osmotic water movement across a membrane.
   d. a measure of the combined effects of a solution's pressure potential and its solute potential.
   e. the functional equivalent of turgor pressure.
5. To regulate the flow of water and minerals in the root, the
   a. Casparian strip of endodermal cells blocks the apoplastic pathway, forcing water and solutes to cross cell plasma membranes in order to pass into the stele.
   b. apoplastic pathway is expanded, allowing a greater variety of substances to move into the stele.
   c. symplastic pathway is modified in ways that make plasma membranes of root cortex cells more permeable to water and solutes.
   d. symplastic pathway shuts down entirely so that substances can move only through the apoplast.
   e. transmembrane pathway augments transport via the apoplast, shunting substances around cells.
6. An indoor gardener leaving for vacation completely wraps a potted plant with clear plastic. Temperature and light are left at low intensities. The effect of this strategy is to
   a. halt photosynthesis.
   b. reduce transpiration.
   c. cause guard cells to shrink and stomata to open.
   d. destroy cohesion of water molecules in the xylem.
   e. increase evaporation from leaf mesophyll cells.
7. Stomata open when
   a. water has moved out of the leaf by osmosis.
   b. K^+ flows out of guard cells.
   c. turgor pressure in the guard cells lessens.
   d. the H^+ active transport protein stops pumping.
   e. outward flow of H^+ sets up a concentration gradient that moves K^+ in via symport.
8. A factor that contributes to the movement of water up a plant stem is
   a. active transport of water into the root hairs.
   b. an increase in the water potential in the leaf's mesophyll layer.
   c. cohesion of water molecules in the stem and leaf xylem.
   d. evaporation of water molecules from the walls of cells in the root epidermis and cortex and in the stele.
   e. absorption of raindrops on a leaf's epidermis.
9. In translocation of sucrose-rich phloem sap,
   a. the sap flows toward a source as pressure builds up at a sink.
   b. crassulacean acid metabolism reduces the rate of photosynthesis.
   c. companion cells use energy to load solutes at a source and the solutes then follow their concentration gradients to sinks.

d. sucrose diffuses into companion cells while H^+ simultaneously leaves the cells by a different route.
e. companion cells pump sucrose into sieve tube members.

10. In Eastern Canada in early spring, miles of leafless maple trees have buckets hanging from "spigots" tapped into them to capture the fluid raw material for making maple syrup. This fluid flows into the buckets because
a. the tap drains phloem sap stored in the heartwood.
b. phloem sap is moving from its source in maple tree roots to its sink in the developing leaf buds.
c. phloem sap is moving from where it was synthesized to the closest sink.
d. bulk flow results as phloem sap is actively transported from smaller to larger veins.
e. phloem sap is diverted into the tap from transfer cells.

Questions for Discussion

1. Many popular houseplants are native to tropical rain forests. Among other characteristics, many nonwoody species have extraordinarily broad-bladed leaves, some so large that indigenous people use them as umbrellas. What environmental conditions might make a broad leaf adaptive in tropical regions, and why?
2. Insects such as aphids that prey on plants by feeding on phloem sap generally attack only young shoot parts. Other than the relative ease of piercing less mature tissues, suggest a reason why it may be more adaptive for these animals to focus their feeding effort on younger leaves and stems.
3. So-called systemic insecticides often are mixed with water and applied to the soil in which a plant grows. The chemicals are effective against sucking insects no matter which plant tissue the insects attack, but often don't work as well against chewing insects. Propose a reason for this difference.
4. Concerns about global warming and the greenhouse effect centre on rising levels of greenhouse gases, including atmospheric carbon dioxide. Plants use CO_2 for photosynthesis, and laboratory studies suggest that increased CO_2 levels could cause a rise in photosynthetic activity. However, as one environmentalist noted, "What plants do in environmental chambers may not happen in nature, where there are many other interacting variables." Strictly from the standpoint of physiological effects, what are some possible ramifications of a rapid doubling of atmospheric CO_2 on plants in temperate environments? In arid environments?

The reproductive structures of an ornamental poppy (*Papaver rhoeas*). Male reproductive structures, which produce pollen, surround the female reproductive structure, which produces eggs and is the site of fertilization and seed development (photographer's close-up).

30 Reproduction and Development in Flowering Plants

Study Plan

Why It Matters

What kinds of plants do we rely on most for our food? Think about the plants that you eat in a given day: most of what we eat comes from just one group of land plants, the angiosperms (flowering plants). Although we do eat the vegetative parts of these plants, we rely heavily on the seeds and fruits produced by these organisms. Worldwide, the top 10 crop plants are angiosperms; for example, consider the top three crop plants in the world: rice, maize, wheat **(Figure 30.1, p. 716).** Millions of people rely on the seeds and/or fruit either directly or on products made from these parts (e.g., flour). As in other flowering plants, seeds of rice, wheat, and corn result from sexual reproduction. Angiosperms have elaborate reproductive systems—housed in flowers—that produce and protect gametes and developing embryos. The flowers of many species also serve as invitations to animal pollinators.

Is there a downside to our reliance on angiosperm seeds and fruit? Whereas some angiosperms (including the top three crop plants mentioned above) are wind-pollinated, many others rely on animals to carry pollen from one plant to another to complete sexual reproduction. When populations of these pollinators are threatened or decline, the plants' survival is also put at risk.

Kashfia Rahman/StockXchng

b.

Ian Britton/FreeFoto.com

Photographer: David/www.3d-images.ws

Figure 30.1
The world's three most important crop plants (from a human perspective): **(a)** rice (*Oryza sativa*) plants in a rice paddy; **(b)** maize (*Zea mays*) plants; and **(c)** wheat (*Triticum aestivum*) plants.

This dire situation is now facing many angiosperms in North America that depend on honeybees for their pollination. About one-third of North American plants, including many important crop plants, rely on honeybees for pollination **(Figure 30.2).** In North America, honeybees pollinate more than $16 billion dollars worth of almonds, cucumbers, berries, apples, and canola. These honeybees are not native to North America but were introduced (along with many crop plants that they pollinate) about 400 years ago from Europe. These introduced bees displaced most native honeybees by the 1920s, and we now depend on these honeybees to pollinate many crops. In 2004, some beekeepers started to report "disappearing colonies": hives that were virtually abandoned, containing only a few larvae, sometimes a queen, and a lot of honey—but no adults. By 2006, the scale of these disappearances was large enough that they hit the news and were termed "colony collapse disorder" (CCD).

Figure 30.2
Honeybee covered with pollen.

NASA Earth Observatory

The cause of CCD is still a mystery; explanations put forward include various pathogens and pests, the effects of genetically modified plants, drought, and even interference from cellular phone towers (this last hypothesis is not supported by any evidence). Perhaps several of these factors are acting together to create a "perfect storm" that results in the collapse of honeybee populations. If CCD spreads, populations of both cultivated and native angiosperms that rely on honeybees to complete their life cycles could be at risk.

In this chapter, we first investigate how sexual reproduction occurs in flowering plants. We then compare sexual reproduction with asexual reproduction, which occurs in many angiosperms under certain circumstances to produce clones that are genetically identical to their parents. Whether formed by sexual or asexual reproduction, once a new individual begins to grow, finely regulated gene interactions guide the development of flowers and other plant parts. Using methods of molecular biology and a variety of model organisms, plant biologists are beginning to understand some of the mechanisms by which these developmental pathways unfold; we conclude the chapter by looking at some of these mechanisms.

30.1 Overview of Flowering Plant Reproduction

In plants, as in animals, sexual reproduction occurs when male and female haploid gametes unite to create a diploid zygote, which then embarks on a developmental course of mitotic cell divisions, cell enlargement, and cell differentiation. In flowering plants, subsequent steps result in distinctive haploid and diploid forms of an individual.

30.1a Diploid and Haploid Generations Arise in the Angiosperm Life Cycle

An angiosperm zygote develops into an embryo enclosed within a seed. In a seed, early versions of the basic plant tissue systems are already in place, so the embryo technically is already a **sporophyte**—a term that refers to the diploid, spore-producing body of a plant (see Chapter 25). When most people look at a flowering plant, such as a wild rose (*Rosa acicularis*), what they think of as "the plant" is the sporophyte **(Figure 30.3)**.

At some point during one or more seasons of an angiosperm sporophyte's growth and development, one or several of its vegetative shoots undergo changes in structure and function and become *floral shoots*—that is, reproductive shoots that will give rise to a flower or inflorescence (a group of flowers on the same floral shoot). Within the sexual organs of the flower, certain cells divide by meiosis. Unlike in animals, however, meiosis in plants does not yield gametes directly. Instead, meiosis gives rise to haploid **spores**, walled cells that develop by mitosis into multicellular haploid **gametophytes**. The gametophytes produce haploid gametes, again by mitosis. Male gametophytes produce sperm, and female gametophytes produce eggs. This division of a life cycle into a diploid, spore-producing generation and a haploid, gamete-producing one is called **alternation of generations** (a phenomenon described more fully in Chapter 25).

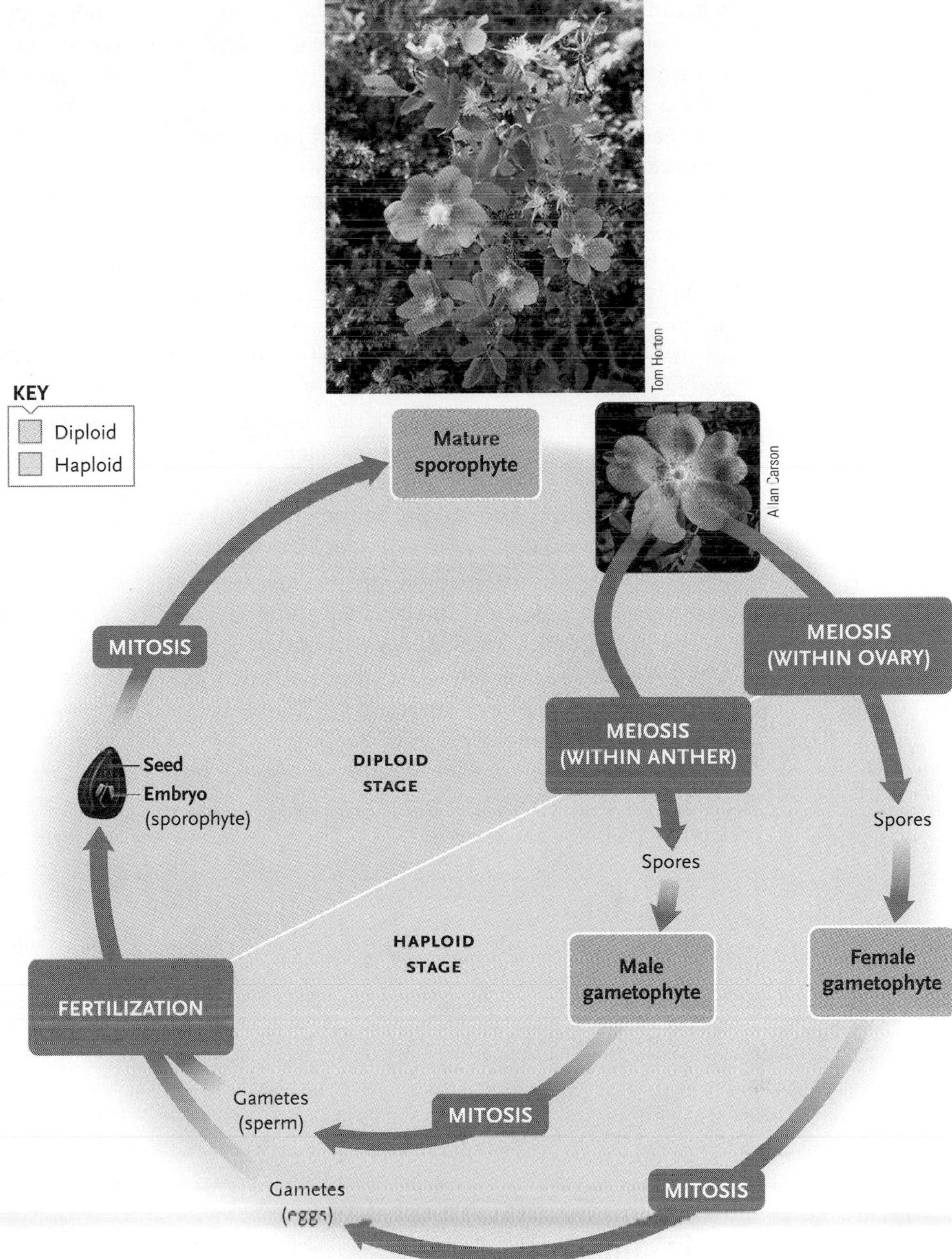

Figure 30.3
Overview of the flowering plant life cycle, using the wild rose (*Rosa acicularis*) as an example. This type of reproductive cycle, alternation of generations, has a haploid phase, in which multicellular but reduced gametophytes produce gametes, which fuse to form a zygote. This zygote develops into a multicellular embryo within a seed and then into a mature sporophyte. Meiotic divisions in the flower of the sporophyte produce spores, which give rise to new gametophytes.

In virtually all plants, the gametophyte and the sporophyte are strikingly different from one another in both function and structure. As we learned in Chapter 25, in mosses and other bryophytes, the gametophyte is usually larger than the sporophyte; the sporophyte grows out of the gametophyte and is nourished by it. In ferns, which are seedless vascular plants, the gametophyte is much smaller than the sporophyte and is free-living for much of its life span; in most fern species, the gametophyte nourishes itself by photosynthesis. In angiosperms and other seed plants, gametophytes are so reduced in size that they are retained *inside* the sporophyte for all or part of their lives. The female gametophyte of a flowering plant usually consists of only seven cells that are embedded in floral tissues, as you will read shortly. Male gametophytes are released into the environment as pollen grains that are so small that they are measured in micrometres. The pollen grain matures when it reaches floral tissue, producing a pollen tube that grows through floral tissue to the egg, carrying sperm with it. When the pollen tube reaches the egg, the sperm are released, resulting in fertilization and production of a new generation of seeds.

Sporophytes may also reproduce asexually. For instance, strawberry (*Fragaria* species) plants send out horizontal stolons, and new roots and shoots develop at each node along the stems. Short underground stems of onions and lilies put out buds that grow into new plants. In summer and fall, quackgrass (*Elymus repens*) produces new plants at nodes along its subterranean rhizomes. Asexual reproduction also can be induced artificially. Whole orchards of genetically identical fruit trees have been grown from the cuttings or buds of a single parent tree.

We turn now to our consideration of sexual reproduction in angiosperms, beginning with the crucial step in which flowers develop.

Study Break

1. What are the two "alternating generations" of plants?
2. How do these two life phases differ in structure and function?

30.2 The Formation of Flowers and Gametes

Flowering marks a developmental shift for an angiosperm. What triggers the formation of flowers? Biochemical signals—triggered in part by environmental cues such as day length and temperature—travel to the apical meristem of a shoot, as we will see in the next chapter, and set in motion changes in the activity of cells there. Instead of continuing vegetative growth, the shoot is modified into a floral shoot that will give rise to floral organs.

30.2a In Angiosperms, Flowers Contain the Organs for Sexual Reproduction

A flower develops from the end of the floral shoot, called the **receptacle.** Flowers consist of four concentric circles (*whorls*) of tissues, all of which are modified leaves; **Figure 30.4** shows a typical flower. The two outer whorls consist of nonfertile, vegetative tissues. The outermost whorl (whorl 1) is made up of leaflike **sepals.** Sepals are usually green and, early in the flower's development, enclose all the other parts, as in an unopened rose bud. The next whorl is made up of **petals,** the "showy" parts of flowers. Petals have distinctive colours, patterning, and shapes, which play important roles in attracting bees and other animal pollinators. Glands that produce nectar, a sugary liquid that attracts animal pollinators, are often located at the base of petals.

A flower's two inner whorls comprise the sexual organs. Inside the petals are the **stamens** (whorl 3), in which male gametophytes form. In almost all living flowering plant species, a stamen consists of a slender **filament** (stalk) capped by a bilobed **anther.** Each anther contains four **pollen sacs,** in which pollen develops.

The innermost whorl (whorl 4) consists of one or more **carpels,** in which female gametophytes form. The lower part of a carpel is the **ovary.** Inside it is one or more **ovules,** in which an egg develops and fertilization takes place. A seed is a mature ovule. In many flowers that have more than one carpel, the carpels fuse into a single, common ovary containing multiple ovules. Typically, the carpel's slender **style** widens at its upper end, terminating in the **stigma,** which serves as a landing platform for pollen. Fused carpels may share a single stigma and style, or each may retain separate ones. The name angiosperm ("seed vessel") refers to the carpel.

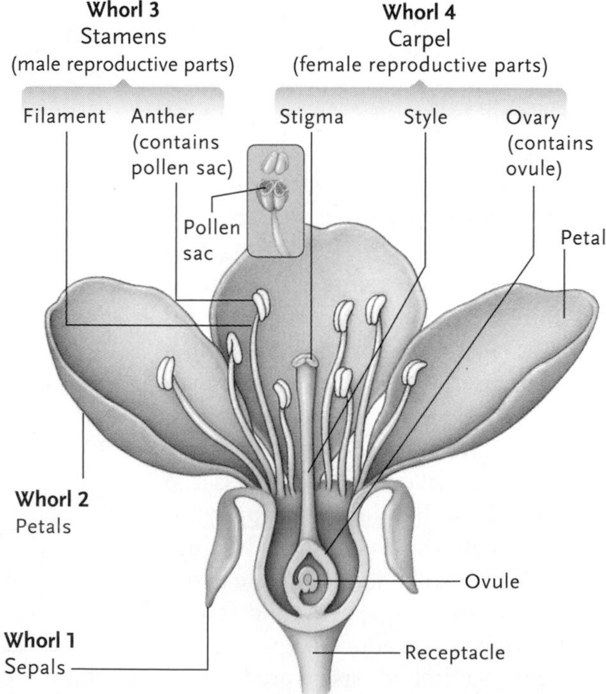

Figure 30.4
Structure of a wild rose (*Rosa acicularis*) flower, with the four whorls indicated. Like the flowers of many angiosperms, it has several stamens but also has numerous carpels. The anthers of the stamen produce haploid pollen. Stigmas of carpels receive pollen, and ovules inside the ovaries contain haploid eggs.

Not all plants have all four layers or whorls of tissue. Whereas many plants have flowers that have both male and female sexual organs, such as the flower shown in Figure 30.4, other plants' flowers have stamens or carpels, but not both. Some flowers lack the showy petals of the typical flower in Figure 30.4 or may have highly modified petals; these modifications often relate to attraction of specific pollinators (see *Molecule Behind Biology*). These **imperfect flowers** are further divided according to whether individual plants produce both sexual types of flowers or only one. In **monoecious** ("one house") species, such as corn (*Zea mays*), each plant has some "male" flowers with only stamens and some "female" flowers with only carpels. In **dioecious** ("two houses") species, such as willows (*Salix* species), a given plant produces flowers with only stamens or carpels **(Figure 30.5).** With this basic angiosperm reproductive anatomy in mind, we now turn to the processes that produce male and female gametes.

30.2b Pollen Grains Arise from Microspores in Anthers

Most of a flowering plant's reproductive life cycle, from production of sperm and eggs to production of a mature seed, takes place within its flowers. **Figure 30.6, p. 720** shows this cycle as it unfolds in a flower with both stamens and carpels. The spores that give rise to male gametophytes are produced in anthers (see Figure 30.6, left). The pollen sacs inside each anther hold diploid microsporocytes (also called *microspore mother cells*); each microsporocyte produces four small haploid **microspores** by meiosis. Inside the spore wall, each microspore divides again, this time by mitosis. The result is an immature, haploid male gametophyte—a **pollen grain.**

This male gametophyte consists of three cells—two sperm cells plus a third cell that will form a **pollen tube.** When pollen lands on a stigma, this tube grows

a.

Justin Voight/iStockPhoto

b.

Doug Waylett

Doug Waylett

Figure 30.5
Examples of monoecious and dioecious plants. (a) Corn (*Zea mays*) has separate male and female flowers on the same plant. **(b)** Willows (*Salix* species) have separate female (photo on the top) and male (photo on the bottom) plants.

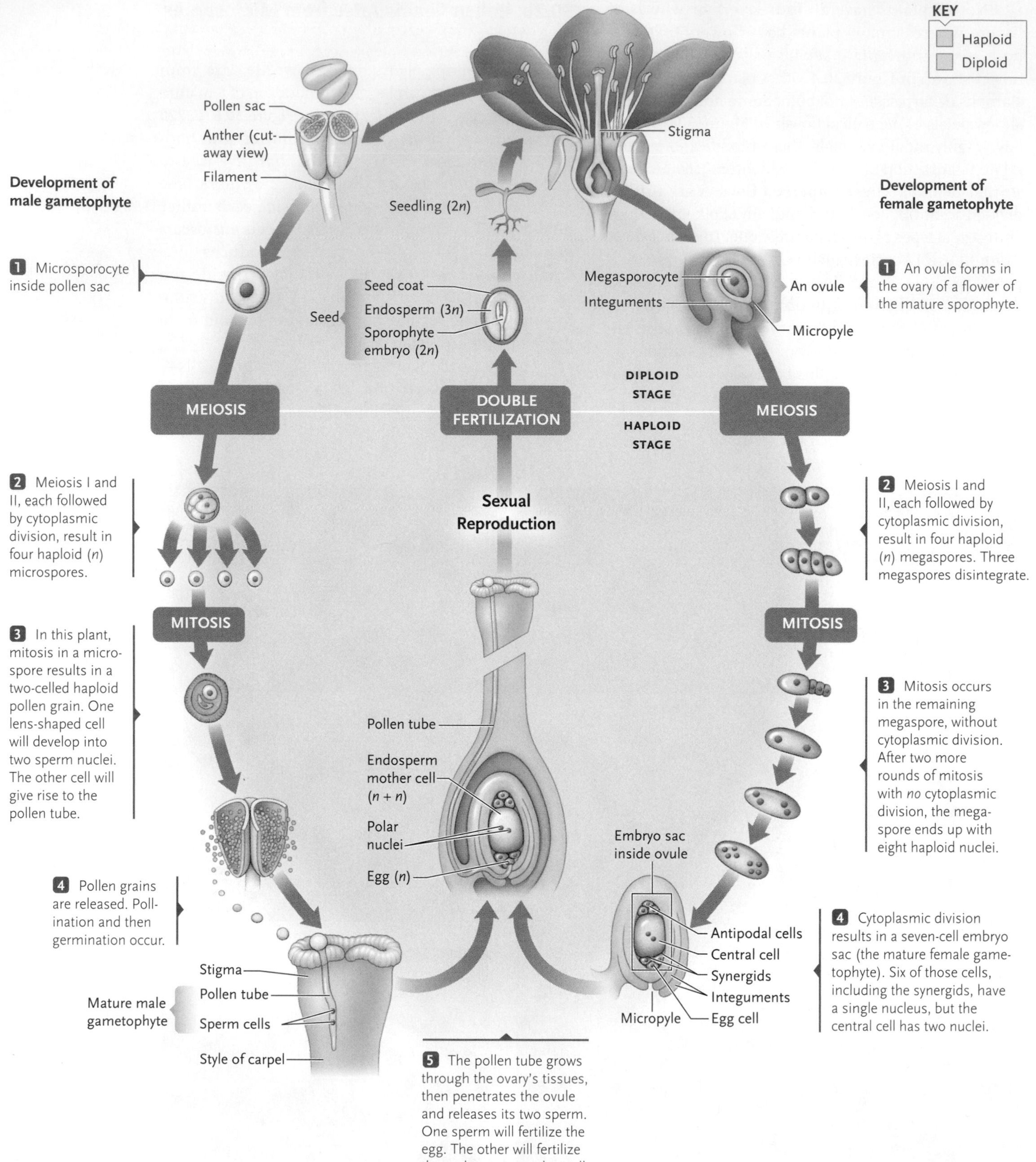

KEY
Haploid
Diploid
Pollen sac
Anther (cut-away view)
Filament
Stigma
Development of male gametophyte
Seedling (2n)
Development of female gametophyte
1 Microsporocyte inside pollen sac
Seed coat
Endosperm (3n)
Sporophyte embryo (2n)
Seed
Megasporocyte
Integuments
An ovule
Micropyle
1 An ovule forms in the ovary of a flower of the mature sporophyte.
DIPLOID STAGE
HAPLOID STAGE
MEIOSIS
DOUBLE FERTILIZATION
MEIOSIS
2 Meiosis I and II, each followed by cytoplasmic division, result in four haploid (n) microspores.
Sexual Reproduction
2 Meiosis I and II, each followed by cytoplasmic division, result in four haploid (n) megaspores. Three megaspores disintegrate.
MITOSIS
MITOSIS
3 In this plant, mitosis in a microspore results in a two-celled haploid pollen grain. One lens-shaped cell will develop into two sperm nuclei. The other cell will give rise to the pollen tube.
Pollen tube
Endosperm mother cell (n + n)
Polar nuclei
Egg (n)
3 Mitosis occurs in the remaining megaspore, without cytoplasmic division. After two more rounds of mitosis with no cytoplasmic division, the megaspore ends up with eight haploid nuclei.
Embryo sac inside ovule
4 Pollen grains are released. Pollination and then germination occur.
Antipodal cells
Central cell
Synergids
Integuments
Egg cell
Micropyle
4 Cytoplasmic division results in a seven-cell embryo sac (the mature female gametophyte). Six of those cells, including the synergids, have a single nucleus, but the central cell has two nuclei.
Stigma
Pollen tube
Sperm cells
Style of carpel
Mature male gametophyte
5 The pollen tube grows through the ovary's tissues, then penetrates the ovule and releases its two sperm. One sperm will fertilize the egg. The other will fertilize the endosperm mother cell.

Figure 30.6
Life cycle of the wild rose (*Rosa aciaularis*), a eudicot. Pollen grains develop in pollen sacs within the anthers. An embryo sac forms inside the ovules within an ovary, and an egg forms within the embryo sac. When the pollen grains are released and contact the stigma, double fertilization occurs. An embryo sporophyte and nutritive endosperm develop and become encased in a seed coat.

through the tissues of a carpel and carries the sperm cells to the ovary. A mature male gametophyte consists of the pollen tube and sperm cells—the male gametes.

The walls of pollen grains are tough enough to protect the male gametophyte during the somewhat precarious journey from anther to stigma. These walls are so distinctive that the family to which a plant belongs usually can be identified from pollen alone—based on the size and wall sculpturing of the grains, as well as the number of pores in the wall **(Figure 30.7)**. Because they withstand decay, pollen grains fossilize well and can provide revealing clues about the evolution of seed plants, as well as help biologists reconstruct ancient plant communities and determine how climates have changed over time.

30.2c Eggs and Other Cells of Female Gametophytes Arise from Megaspores in Ovaries

Meanwhile, in the ovary of a flower, one or more dome-shaped masses form on the inner wall. Each mass becomes an **ovule** (see Figure 30.6, right), which will develop into a seed after fertilization, if all goes well. Only one ovule forms in the carpel of some flowers, such as the cherry. Dozens, hundreds, or thousands may form in the carpels of other flowers, such as those of a bell pepper plant (*Capsicum annuum*). At one end, the ovule has a small opening, called the **micropyle.**

Inside the cell mass, a diploid megasporocyte (also called a *megaspore mother cell*) divides by meiosis, forming four haploid **megaspores.** In most plants, three of these megaspores disintegrate. The remaining megaspore enlarges and develops into the female gametophyte in a sequence of steps tracked in Figure 30.6.

First, three rounds of mitosis occur *without* cytoplasmic division; these divisions produce a single cell with eight nuclei arranged in two groups of four. Next, one nucleus in each group migrates to the centre of the cell; these two **polar nuclei** ("polar" because they migrate from opposite ends of the cell) may fuse or remain separate. The cytoplasm then divides, and a cell wall forms around the two polar nuclei, forming a single large *central cell*. A wall also forms around each of the other nuclei. Three of these walled nuclei form a cluster near the micropyle; one of them is an **egg cell** that may eventually be fertilized. The other two, called *synergids*, will have a role in pollination. The eventual result of all of these events is an **embryo sac** containing seven cells and eight nuclei. This embryo sac is the female gametophyte.

As the male and female gametophytes complete their maturation, the stage is set for fertilization and the development of a new individual.

Study Break

1. What is the biological role of flowers, and what fundamental physiological change must occur before an angiosperm can produce a flower?
2. Explain the steps leading to the formation of a mature male gametophyte, beginning with microsporocytes in a flower's anthers. Which structures are diploid and which are haploid?
3. Trace the development of a female gametophyte, beginning with the megasporocyte in an ovule of a flower's ovary. Which structures are diploid and which are haploid?

30.3 Pollination, Fertilization, and Germination

The process by which plants produce seeds—which have the potential to give rise to new individuals—begins with *pollination*, when pollen grains make contact with the stigma of a flower. Air or water currents, birds, bats, insects, or other agents make the transfer. (Chapter 25 discusses the complex relationship between some flowering plants and their animal pollinators; also see *Molecule Behind Biology* box for more on how flowers attract pollinators.) Plants that produce pollen are no longer dependent on water for fertilization, but pollen may bring pathogens with it to the female reproductive tissues. How do plants protect themselves from these pathogens? See *People Behind Biology*.

Pollination is the first in a series of events leading to *fertilization*, the fusion of an egg and sperm inside

a.

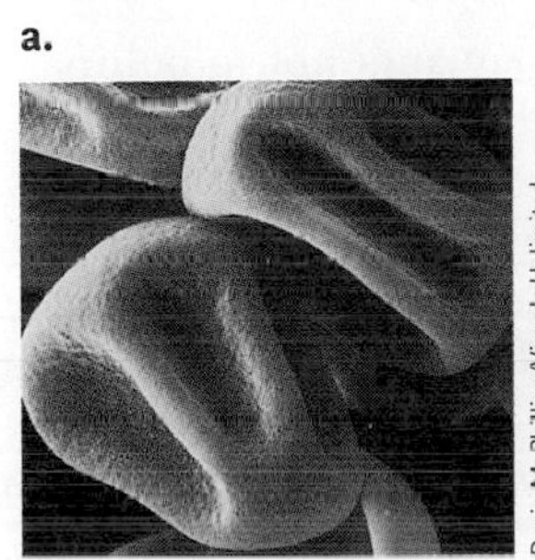

David M. Phillips/Visuals Unlimited

b.

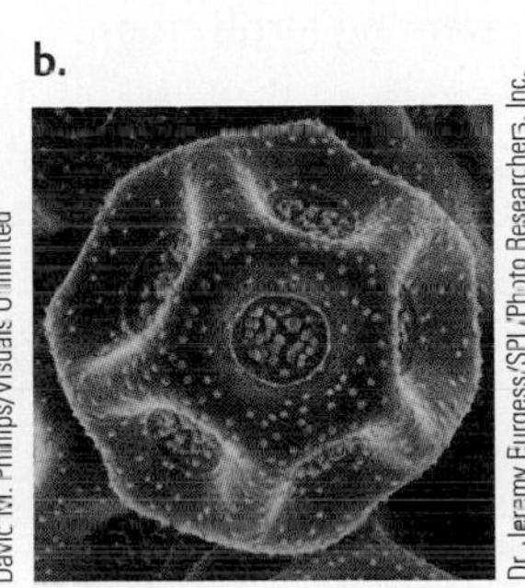

Dr. Jeremy Burgess/SPL/Photo Researchers, Inc.

c.

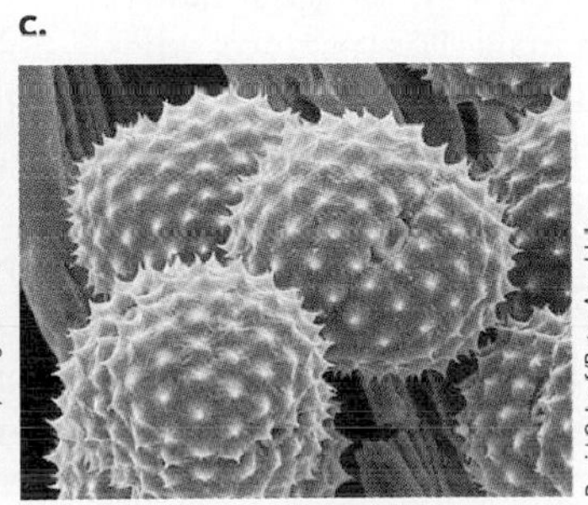

David Scharf/Peter Arnold, Inc.

Figure 30.7
Examples of pollen grain diversity. Scanning electron micrographs of pollen grains from **(a)** a grass, **(b)** chickweed (*Stellaria*), and **(c)** ragweed (*Ambrosia*) plants.

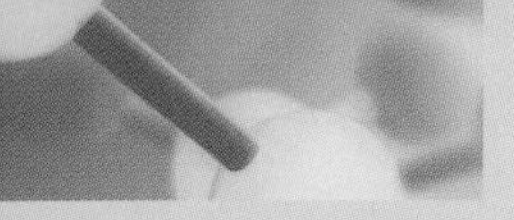

Molecule Behind Biology

Octenol

Not all flowers resemble the "typical" flower shown in Figure 30.4. Consider the flower shown in **Figure 1a:** this is *Dracula chestertonii*, an orchid. Orchid flowers are modifications of the typical flower shown below, and some are more extensively modified than others. As you can see, flowers of this species of *Dracula* are modified to resemble a mushroom—the pattern on the lower lip mimics the gills on the underside of a mushroom cap. And the mimicry doesn't end there: the flower produces a scent that smells very "mushroomy." The chemicals that create this mushroomy smell are octenols and related compounds **(Figure 1b)** that are also produced by fungi and give them their characteristic odour. Together, the scent and appearance of *Dracula* flowers attract female flies that normally lay their eggs in mushrooms. The flies are so convinced that the flower is really a mushroom that they deposit their eggs in the "mushroom cap" petal; in the process, they pick up pollen, which they will then carry to the next *Dracula* flower that tricks them in the same way. But isn't it harmful for the flower to attract insects that will lay eggs in it? Unfortunately for the fly, its larvae can't develop in the floral tissue, so it has not only been deceived into helping the flower, it also has wasted its eggs in the process.

a.

b.

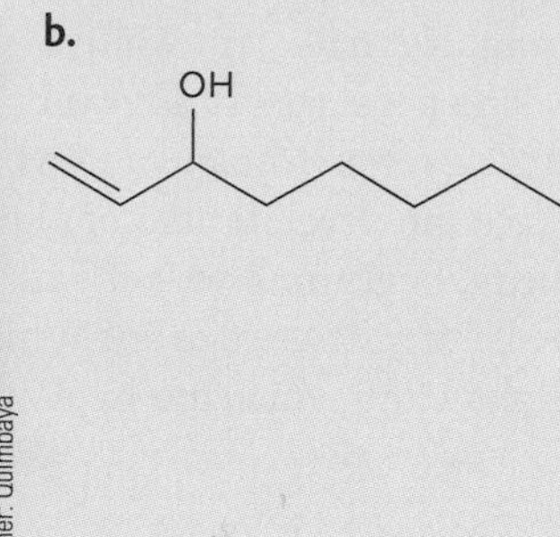

Figure 1
(a) *Draculax chestertonii* flower.
(b) Structure of octenol.

the flower's ovary. The resulting embryo and its ovule mature into a seed housing a young sporophyte, and when the seed *germinates,* or sprouts, the sporophyte begins to grow.

30.3a Pollination Requires Compatible Pollen and Female Tissues

Even after pollen reaches a stigma, in most cases, pollination and fertilization can take place only if the pollen and stigma are compatible. For example, if pollen from one species lands on a stigma from another, chemical incompatibilities usually prevent pollen tubes from developing.

Even when the sperm-bearing pollen and a stigma are from the same species, pollination may not lead to fertilization unless the pollen and stigma belong to genetically distinct individuals. For instance, when pollen from a given plant lands on that plant's own stigma, a pollen tube may begin to develop but stop before reaching the embryo sac. How is self-pollination detected and blocked? **Self-incompatibility** is a biochemical recognition and rejection process that prevents self-fertilization, and it apparently results from interactions between proteins encoded by *S* (self) genes.

Research has shown that *S* genes usually have multiple alleles—in some species, there may be hundreds—and a common type of incompatibility occurs when pollen and stigma carry an identical *S* allele. The result is a biochemical signal that prevents proper formation of the pollen tube **(Figure 30.8).** For example, studies on plants of the mustard family (*Brassicaceae,* which includes canola) have revealed that pollen contacting an incompatible stigma produces a protein that prevents the stigma from hydrating the relatively dry pollen grain, an essential step if the pollen tube is to grow. A wide range of self-incompatibility responses have been discovered, however. In some plants, when incompatible pollen contacts a stigma, a pollen tube grows normally, but a hormonal response soon causes the flower to drop off the plant, preventing fertilization.

Why is it desirable for plants not to pollinate themselves? Self-incompatibility prevents inbreeding and promotes genetic variation, which is the raw material for natural selection and adaptation. Even so, many flowering plants do self-pollinate, either partly or exclusively, because that mode, too, has benefits in some circumstances. (Mendel's peas are a classic example.) For instance, "selfing" may help preserve adaptive traits in a population. It also reduces or

People Behind Biology
Brett Poulis, University of Victoria

When pollen lands on the stigma of a flower (or on the female cone of a gymnosperm), it brings with it all sorts of unwelcome visitors: bacteria, viruses, and fungal spores are all present on the pollen. How can a plant allow pollen and pollen tubes to enter its tissue but still protect itself from these pathogens? Brett Poulis of the Centre for Forest Biology at the University of Victoria investigated this question in Douglas fir (*Pseudotsuga menziesii*), an important tree in Canada's forest industry, for his Ph.D. research. Conifers such as Douglas fir are all wind-pollinated; the contours of the female cones create air currents that draw the pollen toward the cones. Female cones also actively capture pollen by a variety of mechanisms, including sticky hairs and ovular secretions. These secretions, known as "pollination droplets," are released by the ovule; once a droplet has trapped pollen, the droplet is retracted into the ovule, carrying pollen with it **(Figure 1** shows a pollen droplet produced by a different gymnosperm, not Douglas fir). The pollen will then germinate to produce a pollen tube that carries sperm to the egg. Earlier studies showed that pollen droplets consisted of sugars and other simple water-soluble compounds. Poulis and his advisor, Patrick von Aderkas, used new techniques to probe the protein composition of the droplets—the presence of proteins in the droplets indicates that these secretions play a more important role than just capturing pollen—and found that the droplets contain antimicrobial proteins. Not only does Poulis's research answer the important biological question of how these plants prevent pathogens from attacking the egg and developing embryo, it may also have significant medical applications. The compounds identified in the secretions are effective against a wide range of pathogens, so perhaps they can be used as antibacterial and antifungal agents in humans. Since completing his Ph.D. research, Poulis, van Aderkas, and other colleagues have collaborated to start a biotechnology company that will develop medical products based on what they learned about conifer defence systems. For his work, Dr. Poulis was awarded a Networks of Centres of Excellence (NCE) Young Innovators Award in 2006.

(NCE are collaborations among universities, industry, not-for-profit organizations, and the federal government aimed at converting research findings into initiatives with economic and social benefits.).

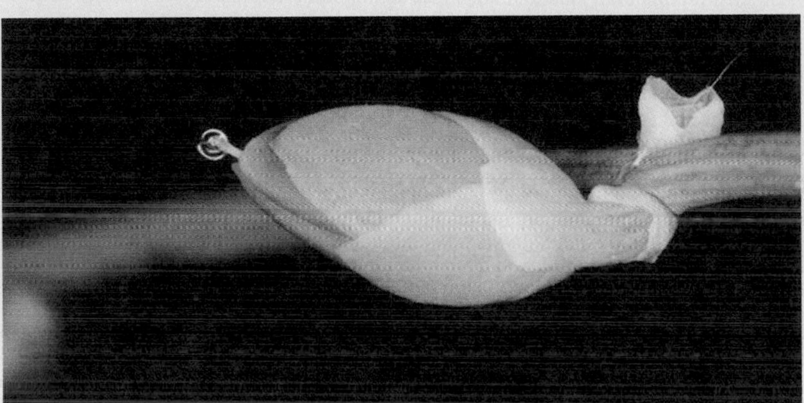

Figure 1
Pollination droplet produced by an ovule of a gymnosperm.

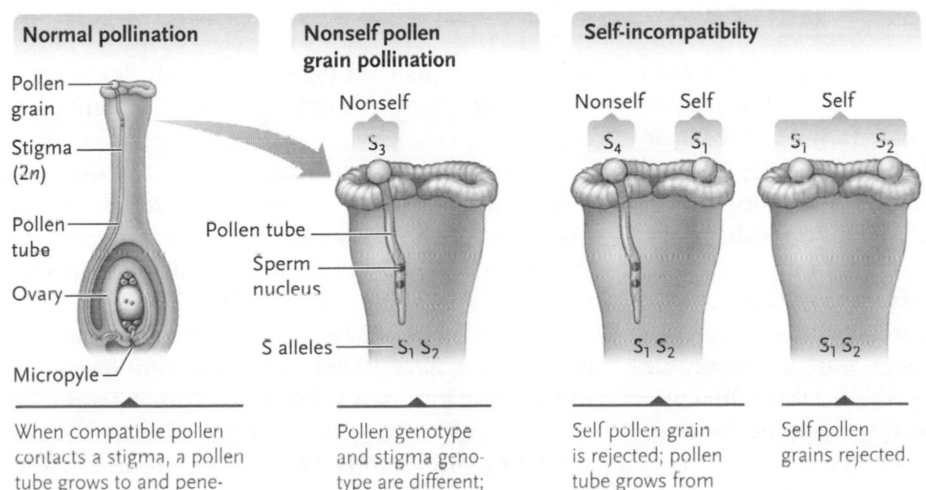

Figure 30.8
Self-incompatibility. When a pollen grain has an *S* allele that matches one in the stigma (which is diploid), the result is a biochemical response that prevents fertilization—in this illustration, by preventing the growth of a pollen tube.

eliminates a plant's reliance on wind, water, or animals for pollination and thus ensures that seeds will form when conditions for cross-pollination are unfavourable, as when pollinators or potential mates are scarce.

30.3b Double Fertilization Results in the Formation of Embryos and Endosperm

If a pollen grain lands on a compatible stigma, it absorbs moisture and germinates a pollen tube, which burrows through the stigma and style toward an ovule. We don't yet fully understand how the pollen tube finds an ovule, but it appears that chemical cues from the two synergid cells lying close to the egg cell help guide the pollen tube toward its destination (see *Unanswered Questions* at the end of this chapter). Before or during these events, the pollen grain's haploid sperm–producing cell divides by mitosis, forming two haploid sperm. When the pollen tube reaches the ovule, it enters through the micropyle, and an opening forms in its tip. By this time, one synergid has begun to die (an example of programmed cell death), and the two sperm are released into the disintegrating cell's cytoplasm. Experiments suggest that elements of the synergid's cytoskeleton guide the sperm onward, one to the egg cell and the other to the central cell.

Next a remarkable sequence of events occurs called **double fertilization**, which has been observed only in flowering plants and (in a somewhat different version) in the gnetophyte *Ephedra* (see Chapter 25). Typically, one sperm nucleus fuses with the egg to form a diploid ($2n$) zygote. The other sperm nucleus fuses with the central cell, forming a cell with a triploid ($3n$) nucleus. Tissues derived from that $3n$ cell are called **endosperm** ("inside the seed"). They nourish the embryo and, in monocots, the seedling, until its leaves form and photosynthesis has begun.

Embryo-nourishing endosperm forms only in flowering plants, and its evolution coincided with a reduction in the size of the female gametophyte. In other land plants, such as gymnosperms and ferns, the gametophyte itself contains enough stored food to nourish the embryonic sporophytes. Endosperm offers an advantage over female gametophyte tissue as a nutrient source for embryos because its development is tied to that of the embryo: if no embryo forms, the plant does not commit resources to endosperm. In gymnosperms, resources are committed to female gametophyte tissue even if no embryo forms. And if an angiosperm embryo is aborted, which can happen if environmental conditions become unfavourable for embryo development (e.g., in the case of drought), endosperm development also ceases, saving the plant energy and resources.

30.3c After Fertilization, Ovaries Develop into Fruits That Protect Seeds and Aid Seed Dispersal

Most angiosperm seeds are housed inside fruits, which provide protection and often aid seed dispersal. Contrary to popular assumption, the fruit does not provide any nutrients to the developing seeds. A **fruit** is a mature or ripened ovary. Usually, fruits begin to develop after ovules are fertilized. The fruit wall, called the **pericarp**, develops from the ovary wall and can have several layers. Hormones in pollen grains provide the initial stimulus that turns on the genetic machinery leading to fruit development; additional signals come from hormones produced by the developing seeds.

Fruits are extremely diverse, and biologists classify them into types based on combinations of structural features. A major defining feature is the nature of the pericarp, which may be fleshy (as in peaches) or dry (as in a hazelnut). A fruit also is classified according to the number of ovaries or flowers from which it develops. Simple fruits, such as peaches (*Prunus persica*) and tomatoes (*Solanum lycopersicum*), develop from a single ovary, and in many of them, at least one layer of the pericarp is fleshy and juicy **(Figure 30.9)**. Other simple fruits, including grains and nuts, have a thin, dry pericarp, which may be fused to the seed coat. The garden pea (*Pisum sativa*) is a simple fruit, the peas being the seeds and the surrounding pod the pericarp. Aggregate fruits are formed from several ovaries in a single flower. Examples are raspberries (*Rubus* species) and strawberries, which develop from clusters of ovaries. Strawberries also qualify as accessory fruits, in which floral parts in addition to the ovary become incorporated as the fruit develops. Anatomically, the fleshy part of a strawberry is an expanded receptacle (the end of the floral shoot) and the strawberry fruits are the tiny, dry nubbins (called *achenes*) you see embedded in the fleshy tissue of each berry. Multiple fruits develop from several ovaries in multiple flowers. For example, a pineapple (*Ananas* species) is a multiple fruit that develops from the enlarged ovaries of several flowers clustered together in an inflorescence. Figure 30.9 shows examples of some different types of fruits.

Fruits have two functions: they protect seeds, and they aid seed dispersal in specific environments. For example, the shell of a sunflower seed is a pericarp that protects the seeds within. A pea pod is a pericarp that in nature splits open to disperse the seeds (peas) inside. Maple fruits have winglike extensions for dispersal (see Figure 30.9e). When the fruit drops, the wings cause it to spin sideways and can carry it away on a breeze. This aerodynamic property propels maple seeds to new locations, where they will not have to

a. Peach (*Prunus*), a simple fruit

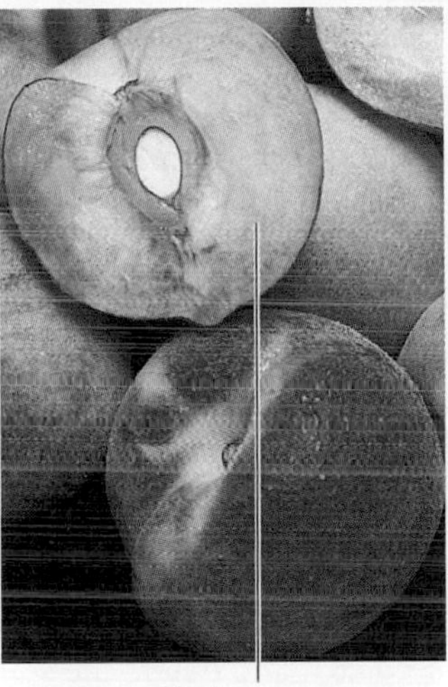

b. Raspberry (*Rubus*), an aggregate fruit

Siegel, R./Arco Images/Peter Arnold

c. Strawberry (*Fragaria*), an accessory fruit

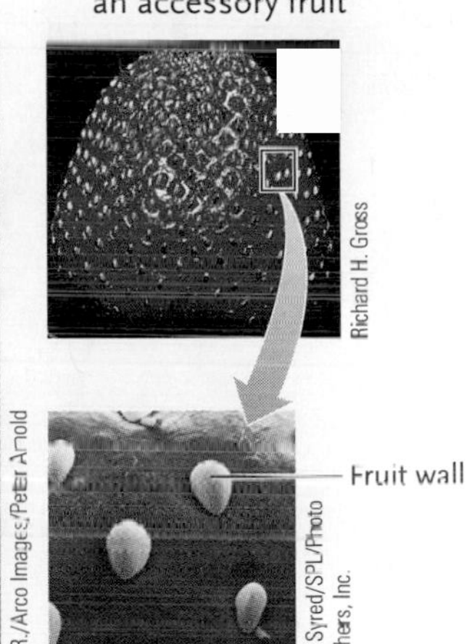

d. Pineapple (*Ananus comosus*), a multiple fruit

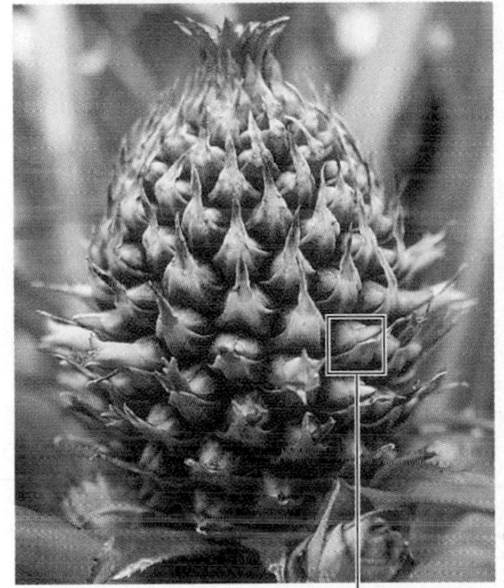

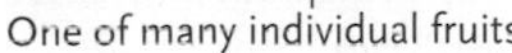

e. Maple (*Acer*) fruit

Figure 30.9
Fruits. **(a)** Peach (*Prunus persica*), a fleshy simple fruit. **(b)** Raspberry (*Rubus*), an aggregate fruit. **(c)** Strawberry (*Fragaria ananassa*), an accessory fruit that is also an aggregate fruit. **(d)** Pineapple (*Ananas comosus*), a multiple fruit. **(e)** Winged fruits of maple (*Acer*).

compete with the parent tree for water and minerals. Fruits also may have hooks, spines, hairs, or sticky surfaces, and they are ferried to new locations when they adhere to feathers, fur, or, sometimes, the socks of animals that brush against them. Fleshy fruits such as blueberries and cherries are nutritious food for many animals, and their seeds are adapted for surviving digestive enzymes in the animal gut. The seeds are distributed away from the parent plant in the animal's feces.

30.3d The Embryonic Sporophyte Develops Inside a Seed

When the zygote first forms, it starts to develop and elongate even before mitosis begins. Most of the organelles in the zygote, including the nucleus, become situated in the top half of the cell, whereas a vacuole takes up most of the lower half **(Figure 30.10, p. 726)**. The first round of mitosis divides the zygote into an upper *apical cell* and a lower *basal cell*. The apical cell then gives rise to the multicellular embryo, although most descendants of the basal cell form a simple row of cells, the **suspensor**, which transfers nutrients from the parent plant to the embryo (see Figure 30.10).

The first apical cell divisions produce a globe-shaped structure attached to the suspensor. As they continue to grow, eudicot embryos become heart-shaped (see Figure 30.10); each lobe of the "heart" is a developing **cotyledon** (seed leaf), which provides nutrients for growing tissues. By the time the ovule is mature—that is, a fully developed seed—it has become encased by a protective **seed coat**. Inside the seed, the sheltered embryo has a lengthwise axis with a root apical meristem at one end and a shoot apical meristem at the other.

Figure 30.10
Stages in the development of a eudicot embryo. Structures of eudicot seeds.

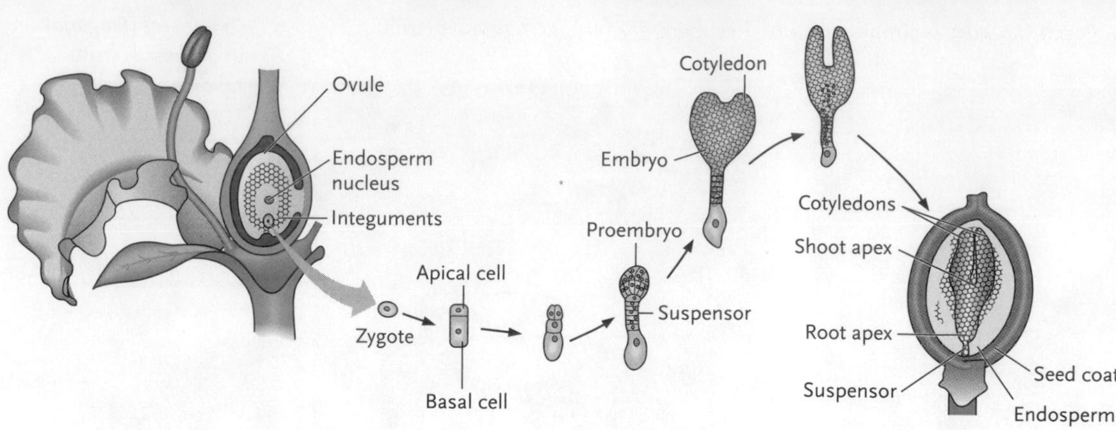

In some eudicots, such as castor bean, endosperm is maintained as a tissue outside of the embryo. In the seeds of these eudicots, the cotyledons form an interface between the rest of the embryo and the endosperm; they produce enzymes that digest the endosperm and transfer the liberated nutrients to the seedling. In other eudicot seeds, the cotyledons absorb much of the nutrient-storing endosperm and become plump and fleshy. For instance, mature seeds of a sunflower (*Helianthus annuus*) have no endosperm at all. Monocots have one large cotyledon that acts like pea seed cotyledons; that is, they are an interface between the endosperm and the embryo, transferring nutrients to the embryo.

Figure 30.11a and **Figure 30.11b** illustrate the structure of the seeds of two eudicots, the kidney bean (*Phaseolus vulgaris*) and the castor bean (*Ricinus communis*). The kidney bean has broad, fleshy cotyledons, whereas the castor bean has much thinner ones, but in other ways, the embryos are quite similar. The **radicle**, or embryonic root, is located near the micropyle, where the pollen tube entered the ovule prior to fertilization. The radicle attaches to the cotyledon at a region of cells called the **hypocotyl** ("below the cotyledons"). Beyond the hypocotyl is the **epicotyl** ("above the cotyledons"), which has the shoot apical meristem at its tip and which often bears a cluster of tiny foliage leaves, the **plumule.** At germination, when the root and shoot first elongate and emerge from the seed, the cotyledons are positioned at the first stem node with the epicotyl above them and the hypocotyl below them.

The embryos of monocots such as corn differ structurally from those of eudicots in several ways **(Figure 30.11c)**. In addition to having only one very large cotyledon, they also have protective tissues shield the root and shoot apical meristems of monocots. The shoot apical meristem and first leaves are covered by a **coleoptile**, a sheath of cells that protects them during upward growth through the soil. A similar covering, the **coleorhiza**, sheathes the radicle until it breaks out of the seed coat and enters the soil as the primary root. The actual embryo of a corn plant is buried deep within the corn "kernel," which technically is called a *grain*. Most of the moist interior of a fresh corn grain is endosperm; the single cotyledon forms a plump mass that absorbs nutrients from the endosperm.

30.3c Seed Germination Continues the Life Cycle

A mature seed is essentially dehydrated. Why is being dehydrated important? It allows the seed to stay in a state of "suspended animation." On average, only about 10% of a seed's weight is water—too little for cell expansion or metabolism. After a seed is dispersed and germinates, the embryo inside it becomes hydrated and resumes growth. Ideally, a seed germinates when external conditions favour the survival of the embryo and growth of the new sporophyte. This timing is important because once germination is under way, the embryo loses the protection of the seed coat and other structures that surround it. Overall, the amount of soil moisture and oxygen, the temperature, day length, and other environmental factors influence when germination takes place.

In some species, the life cycle may include a period of seed **dormancy** (*dormire* = to sleep), in which biological activity is suspended. Botanists have described a striking array of variations in the conditions required for dormant seeds to germinate. For instance, seeds may require minimum periods of daylight or darkness, repeated soaking, mechanical abrasion, or exposure to certain enzymes, the high heat of a fire, or a freeze–thaw cycle before they finally break dormancy. In some desert plants, hormones in the seed coat inhibit growth of a seedling until heavy rains flush the hormones away. This adaptation prevents seeds from germinating unless there is enough water in the soil to support

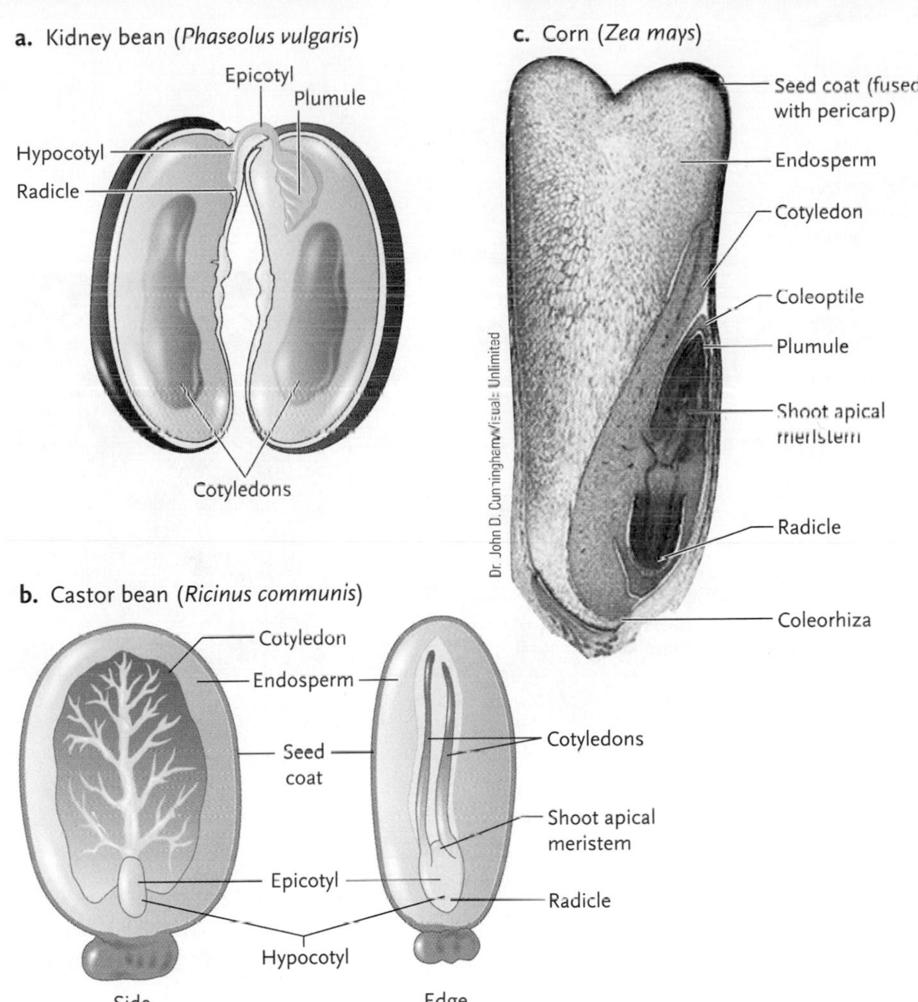

Figure 30.11
The structure of eudicot and monocot seeds. Eudicot seeds have two cotyledons, which store food absorbed from the endosperm, but the timing of this function varies in different species. **(a)** The cotyledons of a kidney bean (*Phaseolus vulgaris*) take up nutrients from endosperm while the seed develops, becoming plump and fleshy. **(b)** In the castor bean (*Ricinus communis*), the endosperm is thick and the cotyledons are thin until the seed germinates, when the cotyledons begin to take up endosperm nutrients. The drawing on the right gives a side view of the embryo. **(c)** A kernel of corn (*Zea mays*), a representative monocot seed, shown here in longitudinal section. Monocot seeds have a single cotyledon, which develops into a shield-shaped cotyledon that absorbs nutrients from endosperm.

the growth of the plant through the flowering and seed production stages before the soil dries once again. Many desert plants—and plants in harsh environments such as alpine tundra—cycle from germination to growth, flowering, and seed development in the space of a few weeks, and their offspring remain dormant as seeds until conditions once again favour germination and growth. Many seeds will not germinate until they have passed through the gut of an animal: their seed coats contain germination-inhibiting substances that are broken down by the acids and enzymes of an animal's digestive tract, allowing the seeds to germinate after they are deposited in the animal's feces.

The seeds of some species appear to remain viable for amazing lengths of time. Thousand-year-old lotus seeds (*Nelumbo lutea*) discovered in a dry lakebed have germinated trouble-free. The record for germination is held by a 2000-year-old date palm seed that germinated in 2005. To date, the seedling produced by this seed is thriving.

Germination begins with **imbibition**, in which water molecules move into the seed, attracted to hydrophilic groups of stored proteins. As water enters, the seed swells, the coat ruptures, and the radicle begins its downward growth into the soil. Within this general framework, however, there are many variations among plants.

Once the seed coat splits, water and oxygen move more easily into the seed. Metabolism switches into high gear as cells divide and elongate to produce the seedling. Stable enzymes that were synthesized before dormancy become active; other enzymes are produced as the genes encoding them begin to be expressed. Among other roles, the increased gene activity and enzyme production mobilize the seed's food reserves in cotyledons or endosperm. Nutrients released by the enzymes sustain the rapidly developing seedling until its root and shoot systems are established.

The events of seed germination have been studied extensively in cereal grains, which are monocots. As a hydrating seed imbibes water, the embryo produces *gibberellin,* a hormone that stimulates the production of enzymes. Some of these enzymes digest components of endosperm cell

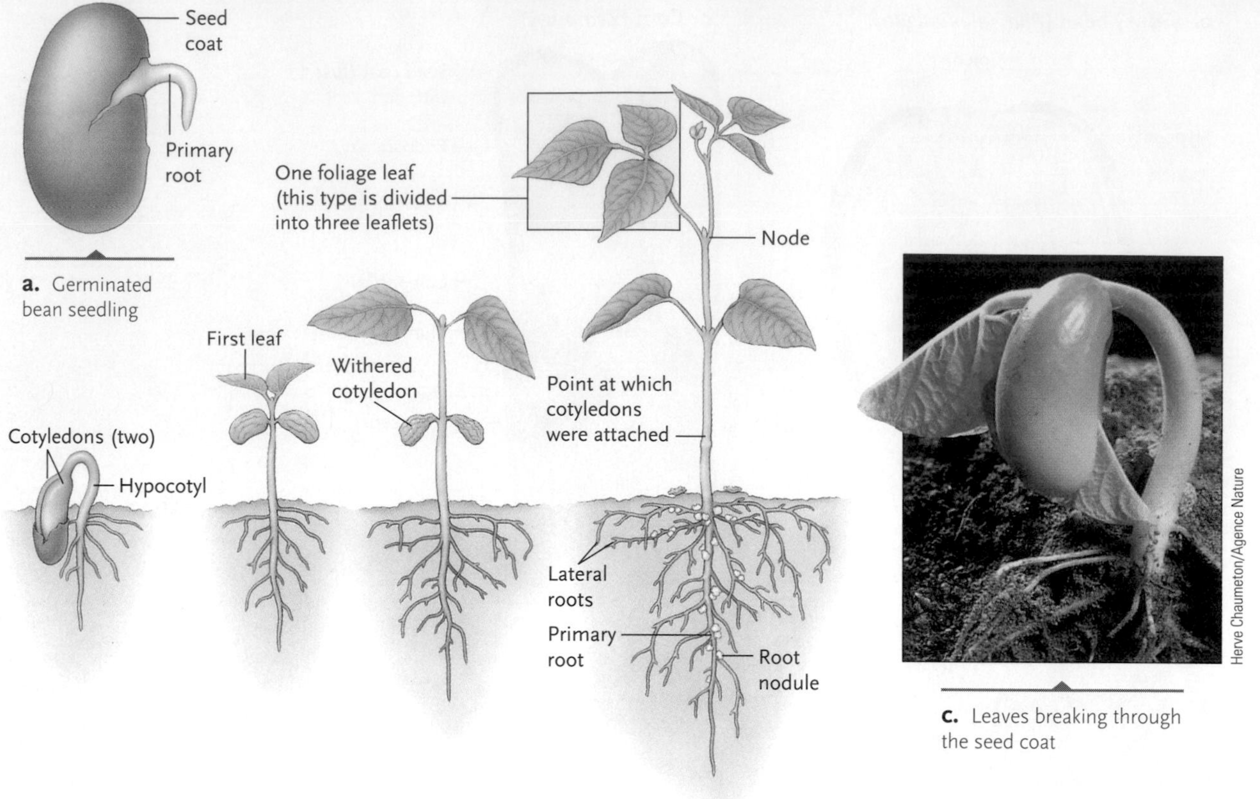

c. Leaves breaking through the seed coat

b. Food-storing cotyledons are lifted above the soil surface when cells of the hypocotyl elongate. The hypocotyl becomes hook-shaped and forces a channel through the soil as it grows. At the soil surface, the hook straightens in response to light. For several days, cells of the cotyledons carry out photosynthesis; then the cotyledons wither and drop off. Photosynthesis is taken over by the first leaves that develop along the stem and later by foliage leaves.

Figure 30.12
Stages in the development of a representative eudicot, the kidney bean (*Phaseolus vulgaris*).

walls; others digest proteins, nucleic acids, and starch of the endosperm, releasing nutrient molecules for use by cells of the young root and shoot. Although it is clear that nutrient reserves are also mobilized by metabolic activity in eudicots and in gymnosperms, the details of the process are not well understood.

Inside a germinating seed, embryonic root cells are generally the first to divide and elongate, producing a radicle. When the radicle emerges from the seed coat as the primary root, germination is complete. **Figure 30.12** and **Figure 30.13** depict the stages of early development in a kidney bean, a eudicot, and in corn, a monocot. As the young plant grows, its development continues to be influenced by interactions of hormones and environmental factors, as you will read in the next chapter.

Many plants produce large numbers of seeds because, in nature, only a tiny fraction of seeds survive, germinate, and eventually grow into another mature plant. Also, flowers, seeds, and fruits represent major investments of plant resources. Asexual reproduction, discussed next, is a more "economical" means by which many plants can propagate themselves.

Study Break

1. Explain the sequence of events in a flowering plant that begins with formation of a pollen tube and culminates with the formation of a diploid zygote and the $3n$ cell that will give rise to endosperm in a seed.
2. Early angiosperm embryos undergo a series of general changes as a seed matures. Summarize this sequence and then describe the structural differences that develop in the seeds of monocots and eudicots.

30.4 Asexual Reproduction of Flowering Plants

As noted in Chapter 28, nodes in the stolons of strawberries and the rhizomes of quackgrass each can give rise to new individuals. So can "suckers" that sprout from the roots of raspberry bushes and "eyes" in the tubers of potatoes. All of these examples involve asexual or **vegetative reproduction** from a

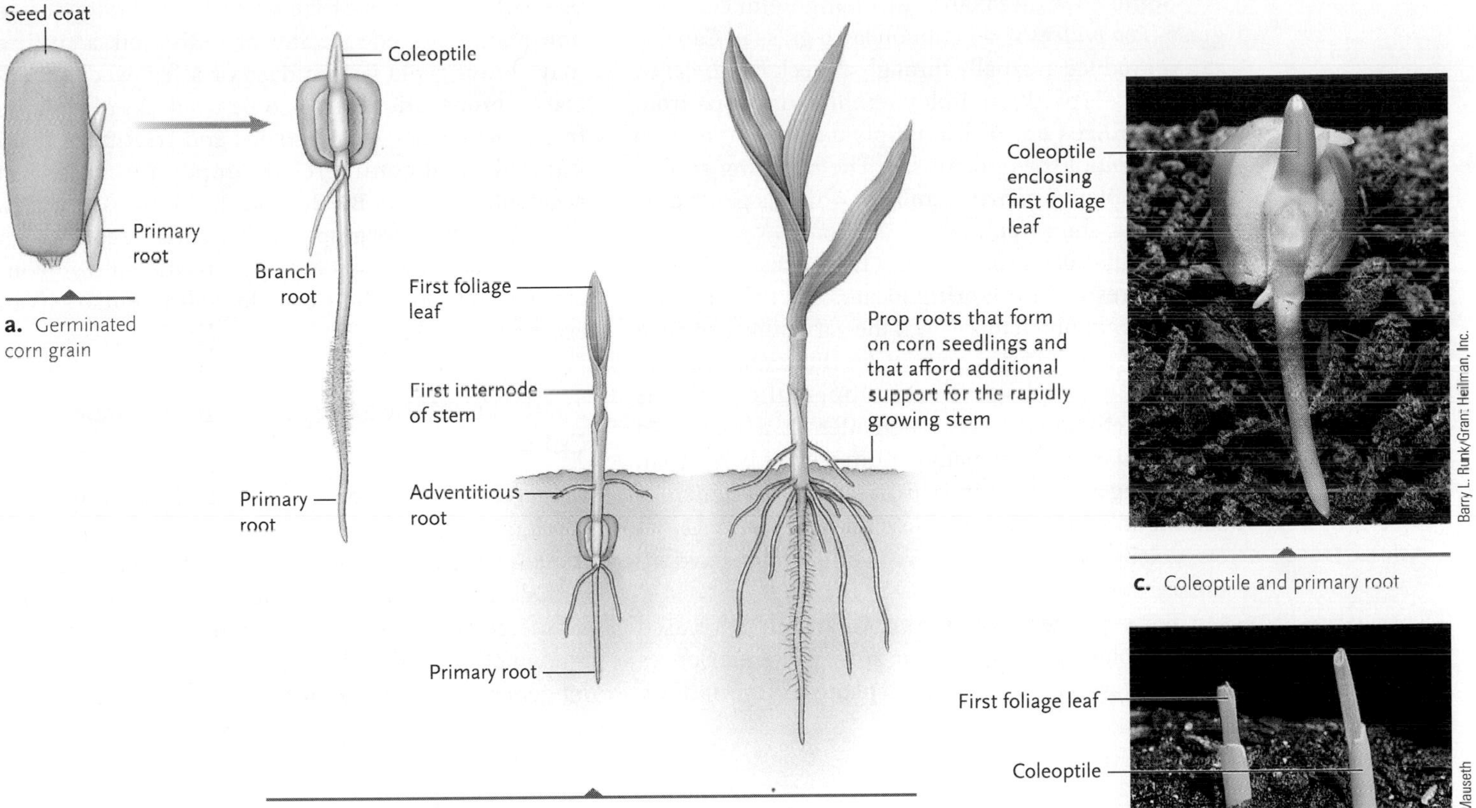

a. Germinated corn grain

b. The young leaves are enclosed in a coleoptile, which protects them during upward growth through the soil. Adventitious roots develop from the first node at the base of the coleoptile. When a corn grain is planted deep, the first internode elongates, separating the primary and adventitious roots. When a grain is planted close to the soil surface, light inhibits elongation of the first internode and the primary and adventitious roots look as if they originate in the same region of the stem.

c. Coleoptile and primary root

Barry L. Runk/Grant Heilman, Inc.

d. Coleoptile and first foliage leaf of two seedlings breaking through the soil surface

James Mauseth

Figure 30.13 Stages in the development of a representative monocot, the corn plant (*Zea mays*).

nonreproductive plant part, usually a bit of meristematic tissue in a bud on the root or stem. All of them produce offspring that are clones of the parent. Vegetative reproduction relies on an intriguing property of plants—namely, that many fully differentiated plant cells are **totipotent** ("all powerful"); that is, they have the genetic potential to develop into a whole, fully functional plant, as discussed in Chapter 28. Under appropriate conditions, a totipotent cell can *dedifferentiate:* it returns to an unspecialized embryonic state, and the genetic program that guides the development of a new individual is turned on.

Some animal stem cells are also totipotent (those in the first stage of embryo development); cells from later stages of animal development are *pluripotent* (cannot grow into a whole organism but can become many different kinds of cells) or *multipotent* (can only become some kinds of cells). In contrast, most plant cells are totipotent regardless of stage of development.

30.4a Vegetative Reproduction Is Common in Nature

Various plant species have developed different mechanisms for reproducing asexually. In the type of vegetative reproduction called **fragmentation,** cells in a piece of the parent plant dedifferentiate and then regenerate missing plant parts. Many gardeners have discovered to their frustration that a chunk of dandelion root left in the soil can rapidly grow into a new dandelion plant in this way.

When a leaf falls or is torn away from a jade plant (*Crassula* species), a new plant can develop from meristematic tissue in the detached leaf adjacent to the wound surface. In the "mother of thousands" plant, *Kalanchoe daigremontiana,* meristematic tissue in notches along the leaf margin gives rise to tiny plantlets **(Figure 30.14)** that eventually fall to the ground, where they can sprout roots and grow to maturity.

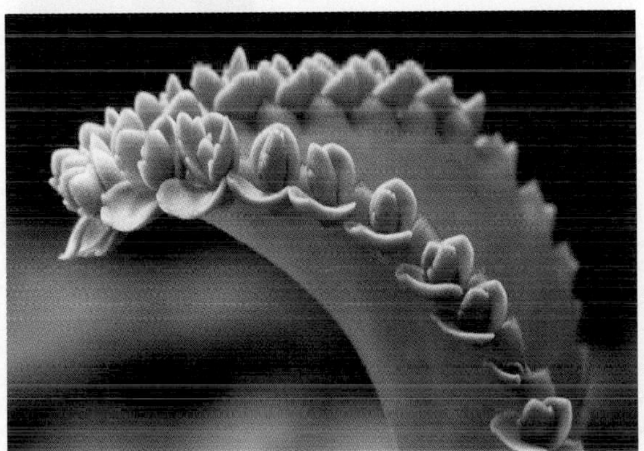

Ed Reschke/Peter Arnold

Figure 30.14 *Kalanchoe daigremontiana,* the **"mother of thousands" plant.** Each tiny plant growing from the leaf margin can become a new, independent adult plant.

Some flowering plants, including Kentucky bluegrass (*Poa pratensis*), a common lawn grass in Canada, can reproduce asexually through a mechanism called **apomixis.** Typically, a diploid embryo develops from an unfertilized egg or from diploid cells in the ovule tissue around the embryo sac. The resulting seed is said to contain a **somatic embryo,** which is genetically identical to the parent.

In native plant species, most types of asexual reproduction result in offspring located near the parent. These clonal populations lack the variability provided by sexual reproduction, variation that enhances the odds for survival when environmental conditions change. Yet asexual reproduction offers an advantage in some situations. It usually requires less energy than producing complex reproductive structures such as seeds and showy flowers to attract pollinators. Moreover, clones are likely to be well suited to the environment in which the parent grows.

For centuries, gardeners and farmers have used asexual plant propagation to grow particular crops and trees and some ornamental plants. They routinely use *cuttings,* pieces of stems or leaves, to generate new plants; placed in water or moist soil, a cutting may sprout roots within days or a few weeks. Vegetative propagation can also be used to grow plants from single cells. Rose bushes and fruit trees from nurseries and commercially important fruits and vegetables such as Bartlett pears, McIntosh apples, Thompson seedless grapes, and asparagus come from plants produced vegetatively in tissue culture conditions that cause their cells to dedifferentiate to an embryonic stage.

30.4b Vegetative Propagation in Tissue Culture

Researchers have taken advantage of the totipotency of plant cells to develop plant tissue culture techniques, which allow them to produce clones of plants with desirable traits or to generate entire plants from single cells that have been genetically modified, among other goals. Plant tissue culture is simple in its general outlines **(Figure 30.15).** Bits of tissue are

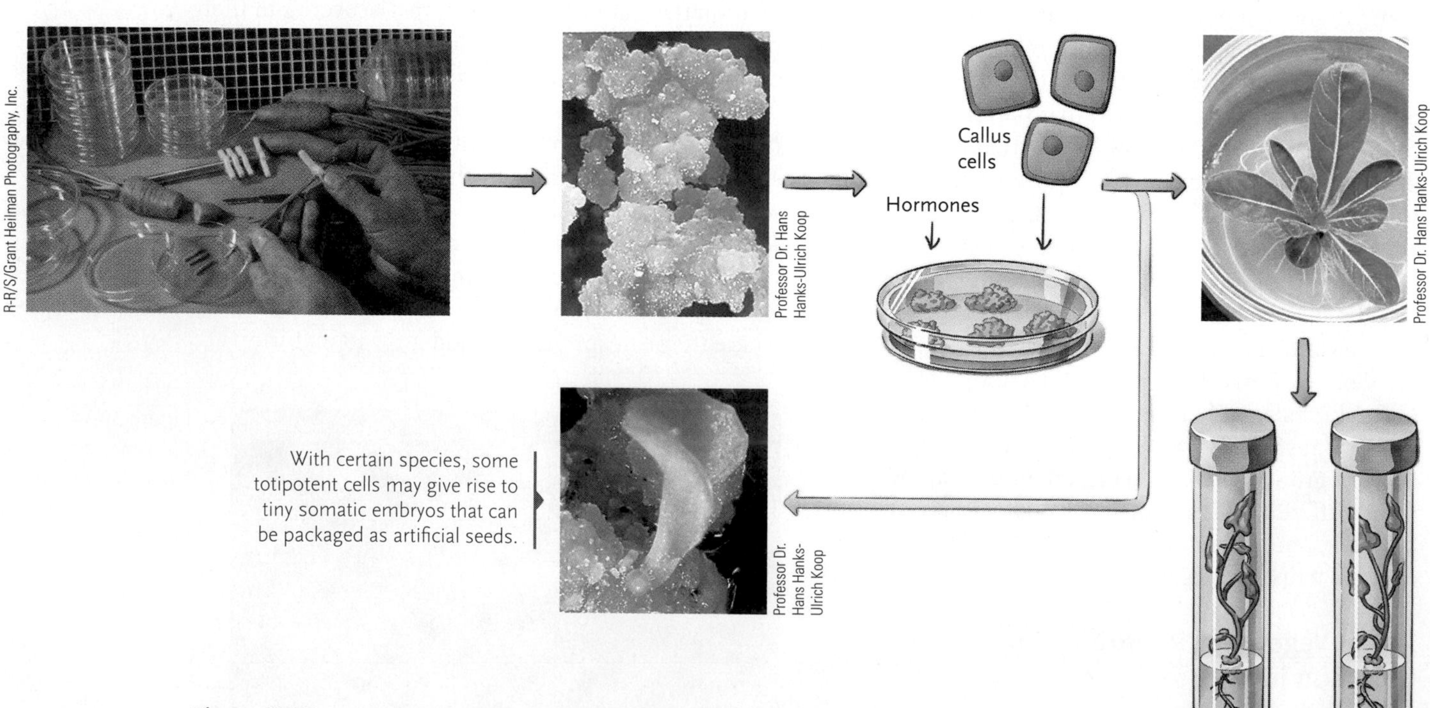

1. Typically, bits of somatic tissue are excised, often from root and shoot tips or meristems, because these parts tend to be free of viruses. The excised tissue is cultured in a nutrient medium, under strictly controlled environmental conditions.
2. Within a few days, cells in the excised tissue dedifferentiate and form an unorganized tissue mass called a callus.
3. Individual callus cells can be separated out and cultured in a medium containing growth hormones.
4. Totipotent cells eventually give rise to plantlets with roots and shoots.
R-R/S/Grant Heilman Photography, Inc.
Professor Dr. Hans Hanks-Ulrich Koop
Callus cells
Hormones
Professor Dr. Hans Hanks-Ulrich Koop
With certain species, some totipotent cells may give rise to tiny somatic embryos that can be packaged as artificial seeds.
Professor Dr. Hans Hanks-Ulrich Koop

Figure 30.15
Plant tissue culture protocol.

excised from a plant and grown in a nutrient medium. The procedure disrupts normal interactions between cells in the tissue, and the cells dedifferentiate and form an unorganized cell mass called a **callus.** When cultured with nutrients and growth hormones, some cells of the callus regain totipotency and develop into plantlets with roots and shoots.

Plant tissue culture is the foundation for a new field of research dealing with *somatic embryogenesis* in plants. Single cells derived from a callus generated from shoot meristem are placed in a medium containing nutrients and hormones that promote cell differentiation. With some species, totipotent cells in the sample eventually give rise to diploid somatic embryos that can be packaged with nutrients and hormones in artificial "seeds." Endowed with the same traits as their parent, crop plants grown from somatic embryos are genetically uniform.

Regardless of how it comes into being, a young sporophyte changes significantly as it begins the developmental journey toward maturity, when it will be capable of reproducing. Next we explore what researchers are learning about these developmental changes.

Study Break

1. Describe three modes of asexual reproduction that occur in flowering plants.
2. What is totipotency, and how do methods of tissue culture exploit this property of plant cells?

30.5 Early Development of Plant Form and Function

As we learned in Chapter 28, one difference between plants and animals is that plant organs, such as leaves and flowers, may arise from meristems throughout an individual's life, sometimes over a period of thousands of years. Accordingly, in plants, the biological role of embryonic development is not to generate the tissues and organs of the adult but to establish a basic body plan—the root–shoot axis and the radial, "outside-to-inside" organization of epidermal, ground, and vascular tissues (see Chapter 28)—and the precursors of the primary meristems. Although they may sound simple, these fundamentals and the stages beyond them all require an intricately orchestrated sequence of molecular events that plant scientists are defining through sophisticated experimentation.

One of the most fruitful experimental approaches has been the study of plants with natural or induced gene mutations that block or otherwise affect steps in development and thus lend insight into the developmental roles of the normal, wild-type versions of those abnormal genes. Although researchers work with various species to probe the genetic underpinnings of early plant development, the thale cress (*Arabidopsis thaliana*) has become an important model organism for plant genetic research.

The entire *Arabidopsis* genome has been sequenced, providing a powerful molecular "database" for determining how various genes contribute to shaping the plant body. Experimenters' ability to trace the expression of specific genes has shed considerable light on how the root–shoot axis is set and how the three basic plant tissue systems arise.

30.5a Within Hours, an Early Plant Embryo's Basic Body Plan Is Established

What determines which part of the embryo will be the root and which part the shoot? Studies done with *Arabidopsis* have revealed that the first, asymmetrical division of the zygote, in which the apical cell receives the majority of the zygote's cytoplasm, whereas the basal cell receives the zygote's large vacuole and less cytoplasm, results in the two daughter cells receiving very different mixes of mRNAs. This means that the apical and basal cells will produce very different proteins; of particular interest are the different *transcription factors* (proteins that regulate transcription) that will be produced in the two daughter cells. With different transcription factors triggering the expression of different genes in the apical and basal cells, distinct biochemical pathways unfold in the two cells, which set in motion steps leading to the differentiation of root and shoot systems.

As development proceeds, cells at different sites become specialized in prescribed ways as a particular set of genes is expressed in each type of cell—a process known as *differentiation*. Differentiated cells, in turn, are the foundation of specialized tissues and organs. We are starting to unravel how plants regulate differentiation but much of this topic is beyond the scope of this chapter.

In nature, genes that govern plant development switch on or off in response to changing environmental conditions. Their signals determine the course of a plant's vegetative growth throughout its life. In many perennials, new leaves begin to develop inside buds in autumn and then become dormant until the following spring, when external conditions favour further growth. Environmental cues stimulate the gene-guided production of hormones that travel through the plant in xylem and phloem, triggering renewed leaf growth and expansion. Leaves and other shoot parts also age, wither, and fall away from the plant as hormonal signals change. The far-reaching effects of plant hormones on growth and development are the subject of Chapter 31.

Unanswered Questions

What will happen to plant–pollinator relationships with climate change?

As you learned in this chapter and in Chapter 25, many plants and their pollinators have evolved together. This coevolution means that the life cycles of a plant must be in synchrony with that of its pollinator, so that both organisms will be at the right stage at the right time. For example, plants pollinated by honeybees need to have flowers producing pollen at the time that a honeybee colony has produced high numbers of mature workers. Lack of synchrony would mean either that there are no flowers ready for the bees and they would go hungry or that flowers do not get pollinated, potentially meaning that no seeds are produced. For many plant–pollinator partnerships, we don't yet know what the cues are or whether the two partners rely on the same cues. In many cases, the two likely use the same cue—such as air temperature—but in other cases, the two may use different cues. For example, the animal might use air temperature, whereas the plant would use snow melt, as the timing cue. So if climate change alters the timing for one partner, then synchrony might be lost. What will happen? Will the partnerships be disrupted? What effect will this have on the animal and plant populations? In the case of honeybees, there is evidence for such disruption: many of the plants they pollinate are flowering earlier, but the bees themselves are not developing earlier.

How does a pollen tube find the ovule?

This question has been investigated for over a century, and we still do not know exactly how a pollen tube is directed to an ovule—does the female gametophyte produce chemical signals that "lure" the pollen tube to an ovule? Or is there some mechanical guidance in the style; that is, do tissues of the style form "tracks" that direct the growth of the pollen tube? Evidence to support this latter hypothesis comes from research done with cut carpels that have had the ovary removed, leaving just the stigma and style. These studies reveal that pollen tubes will grow from the stigma down to the base of a style even if there is no female gametophyte. But biologists have investigated the other hypothesis: that the gametophyte produces directional signals that guide the pollen tube. Recent studies have indicated that the synergids (the cells on either side of the egg) appear to release an attractant, but it has not yet been identified. The two hypotheses aren't mutually exclusive; for example, chemical signals produced by the gametophyte might play a more important role later in pollen tube growth, once the tube gets closer to the ovule.

Review

Go to CENGAGENOW™ at http://hed.nelson.com/ to access quizzing, animations, exercises, articles, and personalized homework help.

30.1 Overview of Flowering Plant Reproduction

- In most flowering plant life cycles, a multicellular diploid stage, the sporophyte (spore-producing plant), alternates with a multicellular haploid stage, the gametophyte (gamete-producing plant). The sporophyte develops roots, stems, leaves, and, at some point, flowers. The separation of a life cycle into diploid and haploid stages is called alternation of generations.

30.2 The Formation of Flowers and Gametes

- A flower develops at the tip of a floral shoot. It can have up to four whorls supported by the receptacle. The outermost whorls consist of the sepals and petals, respectively. The third whorl consists of stamens, and carpels make up the innermost whorl.
- The anther of each stamen contains sacs where pollen grains develop. If compatible pollen lands on the stigma, the receptive surface of the carpel, it produces a pollen tube that grows down the style to the ovary, where ovules are formed. Eggs are produced by female gametophytes inside ovules.
- Flowers can contain both stamens and carpels, or they may contain only male or only female sex organs. Monoecious species have separate male and female flowers on the same plant; in dioecious species, the male and female flowers are on different plants.
- In pollen sacs, meiosis produces haploid microspores. Mitosis inside each microspore produces a pollen grain, an immature male gametophyte. One of its cells develops into two sperm cells, the male gametes of flowering plants. Another cell produces the pollen tube.
- In the ovule, four haploid megaspores form following meiosis. Usually all but one disintegrate. The remaining megaspore undergoes mitosis three times without cytokinesis, producing eight nuclei in a single large cell. Two of these, called polar nuclei, migrate to the centre of the cell. When cytokinesis occurs, cell walls form around the nuclei, with the two polar nuclei enclosed in a single wall. The result is the seven-celled embryo sac, one cell of which is the haploid egg. The cell with two polar nuclei will help give rise to endosperm.

30.3 Pollination, Fertilization, and Germination

- Upon pollination, the pollen grain resumes growth. A pollen tube develops from one cell, and mitosis of the male gametophyte's sperm-producing cell produces two sperm nuclei.
- In double fertilization, one sperm nucleus fuses with one egg nucleus to form a diploid ($2n$) zygote. The other sperm nucleus and the two polar nuclei of the remaining cell also fuse, forming a cell that will give rise to triploid ($3n$) endosperm in the seed.
- After the endosperm forms, the ovule expands, and the embryonic sporophyte develops. A mature ovule is a seed and is encased by a protective seed coat. Inside the seed, the embryo has a lengthwise axis with a root apical meristem at one end and a shoot apical meristem at the other.
- Eudicot embryos have two cotyledons. The embryonic shoot consists of an upper epicotyl and a lower hypocotyl; also present is an embryonic root, the radicle. The single cotyledon of a monocot absorbs nutrients from endosperm. The root and shoot apical meristems of a monocot embryo are protected by a coleoptile over the shoot tip and a coleorhiza over the radicle.
- A fruit is a matured or ripened ovary. Fruits protect seeds and disperse them by animals, wind, or water.

- Fruits are simple, aggregate, or multiple, depending on the number of flowers or ovaries from which they develop. Fruits also vary in the characteristics of their pericarp, which surrounds the seed.
- The seeds of most plants remain dormant until external conditions—moisture, oxygen, temperature, number of daylight hours, and other aspects—favour the survival of the embryo and the development of a new sporophyte.

30.4 Asexual Reproduction of Flowering Plants

- Many flowering plants also reproduce asexually, as when new plants arise by mitotic divisions at nodes or buds along modified stems of the parent plant. New plants also may arise by vegetative propagation, either natural or induced.
- Tissue culture methods for developing new plants from a parent plant's somatic (nonreproductive) cells include somatic embryogenesis.

30.5 Early Development of Plant Form and Function

- In plants that reproduce sexually, development starts at fertilization. In a sequence of gene-guided processes, a new embryo acquires its root–shoot axis, and cells in different regions begin to differentiate, becoming specialized for particular functions.

Questions

Self-Test Questions

1. An angiosperm life cycle includes
   a. meiosis within the male gametophyte to produce sperm.
   b. meiosis within the female gametophyte to produce eggs.
   c. meiosis within the ovary to produce megaspores.
   d. fertilization to produce microspores.
   e. fertilization to produce megaspores.
2. In a flower,
   a. the ovary contains the ovule.
   b. the stamens support the petals.
   c. the anther contains the megaspores.
   d. the carpel includes the sepals.
   e. the corolla includes the receptacle.
3. Double fertilization in a flower means that
   a. six sperm fertilize two groups of three eggs each.
   b. one sperm fertilizes the egg, and a second sperm fertilizes the polar nuclei.
   c. one microspore becomes a pollen grain; the other microspore becomes a sperm-producing cell.
   d. one sperm fertilizes the egg, and a second sperm fertilizes a synergid, forming endosperm.
   e. one sperm can fertilize two endosperm mother cells.
4. A seed is best described as a (an)
   a. epicotyl.
   b. endosperm.
   c. mature ovary.
   d. mature spore.
   e. mature ovule.
5. The primary root develops from the embryonic
   a. epicotyl.
   b. hypocotyl.
   c. coleoptile.
   d. radicle.
   e. plumule.

Questions for Discussion

1. A plant physiologist has succeeded in cloning a gene for pest resistance into petunia cells. How can she use tissue culture to propagate a large number of petunia plants with the gene?
2. Grocery stores separate displays of fruits and vegetables according to typical uses for these plant foods. For instance, bell peppers, cucumbers, tomatoes, and eggplants are in the vegetable section, whereas apples, pears, and peaches are displayed with other fruits. How does this practice relate to the biological definition of a fruit?
3. Before cherries, blueberries, and many other fruits ripen and the seeds inside them mature, their flesh is bitter or sour. Only later does it become palatable to animals that assist in seed dispersal. Develop a hypothesis of how this sequence improves the odds for the plant's reproductive success and then propose an experiment (or series of experiments) for testing the hypothesis.

Sunflower plants (*Helianthus*) with flower heads oriented toward the Sun's rays—an example of a plant response to the environment.

© Garry Black/Masterfile

Study Plan

31 Control of Plant Growth and Development

Why It Matters

It's a warm, sunny day in the summer, and in a field of corn (*Zea mays*), a caterpillar (*Mythimna separata*) **(Figure 31.1a, p. 736)** is munching away at the leaves of a corn plant. Unlike an animal being attacked by a predator, the corn plant cannot run away, nor can it just flap its leaves to dislodge the caterpillar. But just because the plant doesn't move doesn't mean that it is not defending itself. Unbeknownst to the caterpillar, the plant is busily synthesizing chemical responses to the attack; some of these chemicals are transported to other cells within the plant, but others are volatile compounds that, when released to the air, send signals to animals that prey on this species of caterpillar. These animals are parasitic wasps (*Cotesia marginiventris*) **(Figure 31.1b),** which soon descend on the unsuspecting caterpillar and lay eggs in its body, killing it **(Figure 31.1c).** Neighbouring plants can also detect volatile signals and ramp up synthesis of defensive compounds in their leaves, making them less attractive targets to other caterpillars. Inside the plant that sent the signals, other chemical messengers have passed from the wounded leaf to undamaged tissues, increasing their

Figure 31.1
Some plants recruit animals to assist in their defence. **(a)** Common armyworm caterpillar (*Mythimna separata*, larval stage) feeding on corn (*Zea mays*). **(b)** Parasitic wasp (*Cotesia* species) that lays eggs in bodies of armyworm caterpillars. **(c)** Larvae of a parasitic wasp emerging from the body of an armyworm caterpillar.

synthesis of defensive compounds. We don't yet understand all of the mechanisms by which these responses happen, but they are the subjects of intense research interest. Not only will studies of these responses help us understand how plants sense and respond to their environment, but we also might be able to use such a defence response to develop new pesticides that are toxic to the target pests but not to other organisms.

Defence responses such as those described above are one example of adaptations that promote the survival of plants as sessile organisms. These adaptations range from the triggers for seed germination to the development of a particular body form, the shift from a vegetative phase to a reproductive one, and the timed death of flowers, leaves, and other parts. Although many of the details remain elusive or disputed, ample evidence exists that an elaborate system of molecular signals regulates many of these phenomena. We know, for example, that plant hormones alter patterns of growth, cell metabolism, and morphogenesis in response to changing environmental rhythms, including seasonal changes in day length and temperature and the daily rhythms of light and dark. They also adjust those patterns in response to environmental conditions, such as the amount of sunlight or shade, moisture, soil nutrients, and other factors. Some hormones govern growth responses to directional stimuli, such as light, gravity, or the presence of nearby structures. Often hormonal effects involve changes in gene expression, although sometimes other mechanisms are at work.

We begin by surveying the different groups of plant hormones and other signalling molecules and then turn our attention to the remarkable diversity of responses to both internal and environmental signals.

31.1 Plant Hormones

The concept of hormones and their action was developed in the field of vertebrate animal physiology, but some aspects of animal hormones and how they work don't apply to plants. Animal hormones are chemicals that are produced by cells in one part of the body (often glands) and move via the circulatory systems to affect another part of the body. They are small molecules that are active at low concentrations to modify metabolism and development, and their various effects are integrated and coordinated by the central nervous system. There are a wide range of animal hormones (see Chapter 35). In contrast, plants lack a circulatory system comparable to the blood system of animals, so the long-distance action of hormones does not necessarily apply to plants; instead, plant hormones may have localized effects or effects on other parts of the plant (or both). Plant hormones can move via the vascular system, or just from cell to cell, or even via intercellular spaces. Plants also lack a central nervous system to integrate the action of various hormones. However, plants certainly do have molecules that regulate their growth and development and allow for communication between cells. There are fewer categories of plant hormones than animal hormones, and they do not all fit into the same classes as animal hormones; for example, ethylene, a plant hormone, is a gas.

In plants, a **hormone** (*horman* = to stimulate) is a signalling molecule that regulates or helps coordinate some aspect of the plant's growth, metabolism, or development. Plant hormones act in response to two general types of cues: (1) internal chemical conditions related to growth and development and (2) conditions in the external environment that affect plant growth, such as light or the availability of water. Some plant hormones are transported from the tissue that produces them to another plant part, whereas others exert their effects in the tissue where they are synthesized.

All plant hormones share certain characteristics. They are rather small organic molecules, and all are active in extremely low concentrations. Another shared feature is specificity: each one affects a given tissue in a particular way. Hormones that have effects outside the tissue where they are produced typically are transported to their target sites in vascular tissues, or they diffuse from one plant part to another. Within these general parameters, however, plant hormones vary greatly in their effects. Some stimulate one or more aspects of the plant's growth or development, whereas others have an inhibiting influence. Adding to the potential for confusion, a given hormone can have different effects in different tissues, and the effects also can differ depending on a target tissue's stage of development. And as researchers have increasingly discovered, many physiological responses result from the interaction of two or more hormones.

Biologists recognize at least seven major classes of plant hormones **(Table 31.1)**: auxins, gibberellins, cytokinins, ethylene, brassinosteroids, abscisic acid (ABA), and jasmonates. Recent discoveries have added other substances to the list of hormonelike signalling agents in plants. We now consider each major class of plant hormones and discuss some of the newly discovered signalling molecules as well.

31.1a Auxins Promote Growth

Auxins are synthesized primarily in the shoot apical meristem and young stems and leaves. Their main effects are to stimulate plant growth by promoting cell elongation in stems and coleoptiles and by governing growth responses to light and gravity. Our focus here is indoleacetic acid (IAA), the most important natural auxin **(Figure 31.2)**. Botanists often use the general term "auxin" to refer to IAA, a practice we follow in the following discussion.

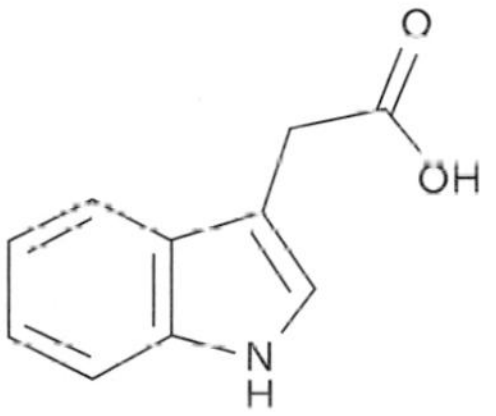

O
OH
N
H

Figure 31.2
Structure of indoleacetic acid (IAA).

Experiments Leading to the Discovery of Auxins. Auxins were the first plant hormones identified. The path to their discovery began in the late nineteenth century in

Table 31.1 **Major Plant Hormones and Signalling Chemicals**

Hormone/Signalling Compound	Where Synthesized	Tissues Affected	Effects
Auxins	Apical meristems, developing leaves and embryos	Growing tissues, buds, roots, leaves, fruits, vascular tissues	Promote growth and elongation of stems; promote formation of lateral roots and dormancy in lateral buds; promote fruit development; inhibit leaf abscission; orient plants with respect to light, gravity
Gibberellins	Root and shoot tips, young leaves, developing embryos	Stems, developing seeds	Promote cell divisions and growth and elongation of stems; promote seed germination
Cytokinins	Mainly in root tips	Shoot apical meristems, leaves, buds	Promote cell division; inhibit senescence of leaves; coordinate growth of roots and shoots (with auxin)
Ethylene	Shoot tips, roots, leaf nodes, flowers, fruits	Seeds, buds, seedlings, mature leaves, flowers, fruits	Regulates elongation and division of cells in seedling stems, roots; in mature plants, regulates senescence and abscission of leaves, flowers, and fruits
Brassinosteroids	Young seeds; shoots and leaves	Mainly shoot tips, developing embryos	Stimulate cell division and elongation, differentiation of vascular tissue
Abscisic acid	Leaves	Buds, seeds, stomata	Promotes responses to environmental stress, including inhibiting growth/promoting dormancy; stimulates stomata to close in water-stressed plants
Jasmonates	Roots, seeds, probably other tissues	Various tissues, including damaged ones	In defence responses, promote transcription of genes encoding protease inhibitors; possible role in plant responses to nutrient deficiencies
Oligosaccharins	Cell walls	Damaged tissues; possibly active in most plant cells	Promote synthesis of phytoalexins in injured plants; may also have a role in regulating growth
Systemin	Damaged tissues	Damaged tissues	To date, known only in tomato and closely related species; roles in defence, including triggering jasmonate-induced chemical defences
Salicylic acid	Damaged tissues	Many plant parts	Triggers synthesis of pathogenesis-related (PR) proteins, other general defences

People Behind Biology

Charles Darwin

When we think of Charles Darwin, we think of course of his theory of evolution by natural selection, which is the foundation of modern biology. But Darwin's contribution to biology is much more than just his work on evolution, key though it is: he was a very knowledgeable and creative naturalist, who carried out experiments on several other important biological questions. He published a detailed analysis of how earthworms improve the soil (The Formation of Vegetable Mould through the Action of Worms) and wrote books on several botanical topics, among them plants that eat animals (Insectivorous Plants), pollination and fertilization systems (Fertilisation in Orchids and The Effects of Self- and Cross-Fertilisation), and the tendency of plants to grow toward sunlight (The Power of Movement in Plants). Experiments on this last topic, carried out with his son Francis, are still cited today for their role in helping us understand how plants respond to light.

William Perlman/Star Ledger/Corbis

Darwin's study. Darwin undertook most of his life's work in this room at Down House. He hesitated to discard old papers and specimens, believing that he would find a use for them as soon as they were carried away in the trash.

the library of Charles Darwin's home in the English countryside (see *People Behind Biology*).

Among his many interests, Darwin was fascinated by plant tropisms—movements such as the bending of a houseplant toward light. This growth response, triggered by exposure to a directional light source, is an example of a phototropism.

Working with his son Francis, Darwin explored phototropisms by germinating the seeds of two species of grasses, oat (*Avena sativa*) and canary grass (*Phalaris canariensis*), in pots on the sill of a sunny window. Recall from Chapter 30 that the shoot apical meristem and plumule of grass seedlings are sheathed by a protective coleoptile—a structure that is extremely sensitive to light. Darwin did not know this detail, but he observed that as the emerging shoots grew, within a few days, they bent toward the light. He hypothesized that the tip of the shoot somehow detected light and communicated that information to the coleoptile. Darwin tested this idea in several ways **(Figure 31.3)** and concluded that when seedlings are illuminated from the side, "some influence is transmitted from the upper to the lower part, causing them to bend."

The Darwins' observations spawned decades of studies—a body of work that illustrates how scientific understanding typically advances step by step, as one set of experimental findings stimulates new research. First, scientists in Denmark and Poland showed that the bending of a shoot toward a light source was caused by something that could move through agar (a jellylike culture material derived from certain red algae) but not through a sheet of the mineral mica. This finding prompted experiments establishing that, indeed, the stimulus was a chemical produced in the shoot tip. Soon afterward, in 1926, experiments by the Dutch plant physiologist Frits Went confirmed that the growth-promoting chemical diffuses downward from the shoot tip to the stem below **(Figure 31.4)**. Using oat seeds, Went first sliced the tips from young shoots that had been grown under normal light conditions. He then placed the tips on agar blocks and left them there long enough for diffusible substances to move into the agar. Meanwhile, the decapitated stems stopped growing, but growth quickly resumed in seedlings that Went "capped" with the agar blocks (see Figure 31.4a). Clearly, a growth-promoting substance in the excised shoot tips had diffused into the agar and from there into the seedling stems. Went also attached an agar block to one side of a decapitated shoot tip; when the shoot began growing again, it bent away from the agar (see Figure 31.4b). Importantly, Went performed his experiments in total darkness, to avoid any "contamination" of his results by the possible effects of light.

Went did not determine the mechanism—differential elongation of cells on the shaded side of a shoot—by which the growth promoter controlled phototropism.

QUESTION: Why does a plant stem bend toward the light?

EXPERIMENT 1: The Darwins observed that the first shoot of an emerging grass seedling, which is sheathed by a coleoptile, bends toward sunlight shining through a window. They removed the shoot tip from a seedling and illuminated one side of the seedling.

RESULT: The seedling neither grew nor bent.

EXPERIMENT 2: The Darwins divided seedlings into two groups. They covered the shoot tips of one group with an opaque cap and the shoot tips of the other group with a translucent cap. All the seedlings were illuminated from the same side.

Figure 31.3
The Darwins' experiments on phototropism.

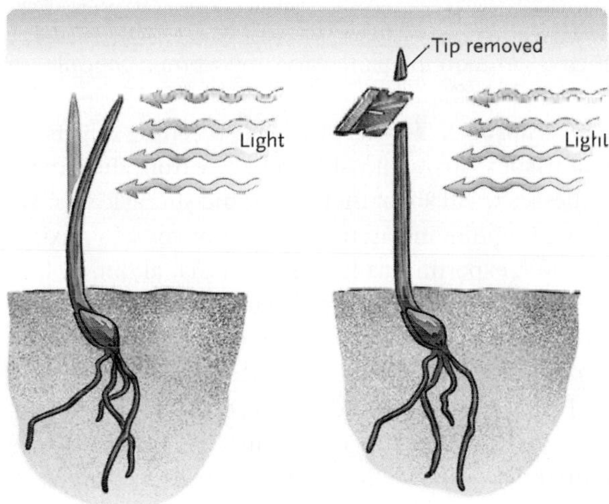

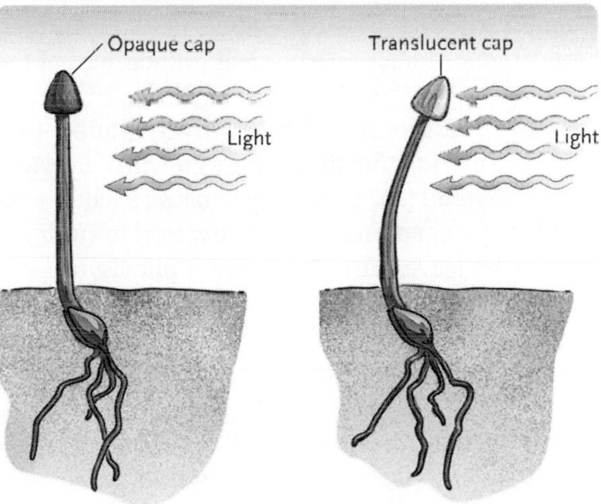

RESULT: The seedlings with opaque caps grew but did not bend. Those with translucent caps both grew and bent toward the light.

CONCLUSION: When seedlings are illuminated from one side, an unknown factor transmitted from a seedling's tip to the tissue below causes it to bend toward the light.

However, he did develop a test that correlated specific amounts of the substance, later named auxin (*auxein* = to increase), with particular growth effects. This careful groundwork culminated several years later when other researchers identified auxin as IAA.

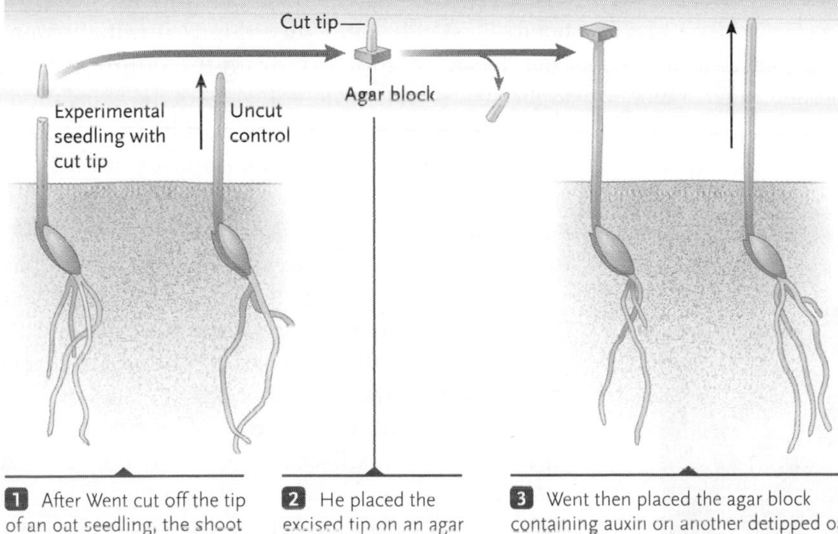

a. The procedure showing that IAA promotes elongation of cells below the shoot tip
Cut tip
Agar block
Experimental seedling with cut tip
Uncut control
1 After Went cut off the tip of an oat seedling, the shoot stopped elongating, whereas a control seedling with an intact tip continued to grow.
2 He placed the excised tip on an agar block for 1–4 hours. During that time, IAA diffused into the agar block from the cut tip.
3 Went then placed the agar block containing auxin on another detipped oat shoot, and the shoot resumed elongation, growing about as rapidly as that of a control seedling with an intact shoot tip.

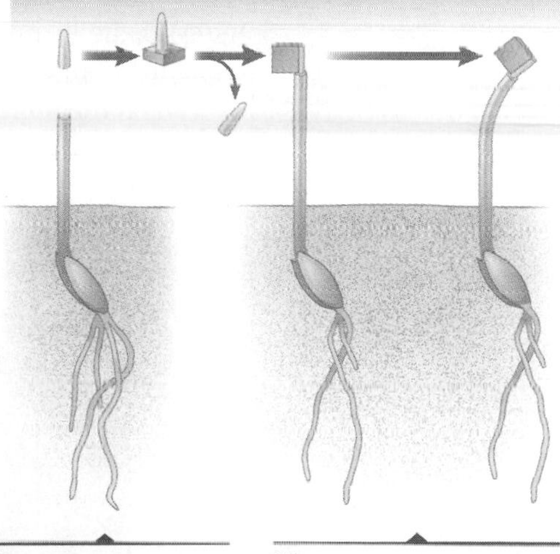

b. The procedure showing that cells in contact with IAA grow faster than those farther away
1 Went removed the tip of a seedling and placed it on an agar block.
2 He placed the agar block containing auxin on one side of the shoot tip. Auxin moved into the shoot tip on that side, causing it to bend away from the hormone.

Figure 31.4
Two experiments by Frits Went demonstrating the effect of IAA on an oat coleoptile. Went carried out the experiments in darkness to prevent the effects of light from skewing the results.

Effects of Auxins. As already noted, auxin stimulates aspects of plant growth and development. In fact, recent studies of plant development have revealed that auxin is one of the first chemical signals to help shape the plant body. When the zygote first divides, forming an embryo that consists of a basal cell and an apical cell, auxin exported by the basal cell to the apical cell helps guide the development of the various features of the embryonic shoot. As the embryo develops further, IAA is produced mainly by the leaf primordium of the young shoot (see Figure 28.14). While the developing shoot is underground, IAA is actively transported downward, stimulating the primary growth of the stem and root **(Figure 31.5).** Once an elongating shoot breaks through the soil surface, its tip is exposed to sunlight, and the first leaves unfurl and begin photosynthesis. Shortly thereafter, the leaf tip stops producing IAA, and that task is assumed first by cells at the leaf edges and then by cells at the base of the young leaf. Even so, as Section 31.3 discusses more fully, IAA continues to influence a plant's responses to light and plays a role in plant growth responses to gravity as well. IAA also stimulates cell division in the vascular cambium and promotes the formation of secondary xylem, as well as the formation of new root apical meristems, including lateral meristems. Not all of auxin's effects promote growth, however. IAA also maintains apical dominance, which inhibits growth of lateral meristems on shoots and restricts the formation of branches (see Section 31.3). Hence, auxin is a signal that the shoot apical meristem is present and active.

Commercial orchardists spray synthetic IAA on fruit trees because it promotes uniform flowering and helps set the fruit; it also helps prevent premature fruit drop. These effects mean that all the fruit may be picked at the same time, with considerable savings in labour costs.

Some synthetic auxins are used as herbicides, essentially stimulating a target plant to "grow itself to death." A **herbicide** is any compound that, at proper concentration, kills plants. Some herbicides are selective, killing one class of plants and not others. The most widely used herbicide in the world is the synthetic auxin 2,4-D (2,4-dichlorophenoxyacetic acid). This chemical is used extensively to prevent broadleaf weeds (which are eudicots) from growing in fields of cereal crops such as corn (which are monocots). By an unknown mechanism, 2,4-D causes an abnormal burst of growth in which eudicot stems elongate more than 10 times faster than normal—much faster than the plant can support metabolically.

Auxin Transport. To exert their far-reaching effects on plant tissues, auxins must travel away from their main synthesis sites in shoot meristems and young leaves. Yet xylem and phloem sap usually do not contain auxins. Moreover, experiments have shown that although IAA moves through plant tissues slowly—roughly 1 cm/hr—this rate is 10 times faster than could be explained by simple diffusion. How, then, is auxin transported?

Plant physiologists adapted the agar block method pioneered by Went to trace the direction and rate of auxin movements in different kinds of tissues. A research team led by Winslow Briggs at Stanford University determined that the shaded side of a shoot tip contains more IAA than the illuminated side. Hypothesizing that light causes IAA to move laterally from the illuminated to the shaded side of a shoot tip, the team then inserted a vertical barrier (a thin slice of mica) between the shaded and the illuminated sides of a shoot tip. IAA could not cross the barrier, and when the shoot tip was illuminated, it did not bend. In addition, the concentrations of IAA in the two sides of the shoot tip remained about the same. When the barrier was shortened so that the separated sides of the tip again touched, the concentration of IAA in the shaded portion increased significantly, and the tip *did* bend. The study confirmed that IAA initially moves laterally in the shoot tip, from the illuminated side to the shaded side, where it triggers the elongation of cells and curving of the tip toward light. Subsequent research showed that IAA then moves downward in a shoot by way of a top-to-bottom mechanism called **polar transport**. That is, IAA in a coleoptile or shoot tip travels from the apex of the tissue to its base, such as from the tip of a developing leaf to the stem. **Figure 31.6** outlines the experimental method that demonstrated polar transport. When IAA reaches roots, it moves toward the root tip.

Inside a stem, IAA appears to be transported via parenchyma cells adjacent to vascular bundles. IAA again moves by polar transport as it travels through and between cells: It enters at one end by diffusing passively through cell walls and exits at the opposite end by active transport across the plasma membrane. There is increasing evidence that auxin also may travel rapidly through plants in the phloem. As this work continues, researchers will undoubtedly gain a clearer

Figure 31.5
The effect of auxin treatment on a gardenia (*Gardenia*) cutting. Four weeks after an auxin was applied to the base of the cutting on the left, its stem and roots have elongated, but the number of leaves is unchanged. The plant cutting on the right was not treated.

Treated with auxin Untreated

Kingsley R. Stern

understanding of how plants distribute this crucial hormone to their growing parts.

Possible Mechanisms of IAA Action. Ever since auxin was discovered, researchers have actively sought to understand how IAA stimulates cell elongation. As a plant cell elongates, the cellulose meshwork of the cell wall is first loosened and then stretched by turgor pressure. Several hormones, and auxin especially, apparently increase the plasticity (irreversible stretching) of the cell wall. Two major hypotheses seek to explain this effect, and both may be correct.

Plant cell walls grow much faster in an acid environment—that is, when the pH is less than 7. The **acid-growth hypothesis** suggests that auxin causes cells to secrete acid (H^+) into the cell wall by stimulating the plasma membrane H^+ pumps to move hydrogen ions from the cell interior into the cell wall; the increased acidity activates proteins called *expansins*, which penetrate the cell wall and disrupt bonds between cellulose microfibrils in the wall **(Figure 31.7)**. In the laboratory, it is easy to measure an increase in the rate at which coleoptiles or stem tissues release acid when they are treated with IAA. Activation of the plasma membrane H^+ pump also produces a membrane potential that pulls K^+ and other cations into the cell; the resulting osmotic gradient draws water into the cell, increasing turgor pressure and helping to stretch the "loosened" cell walls.

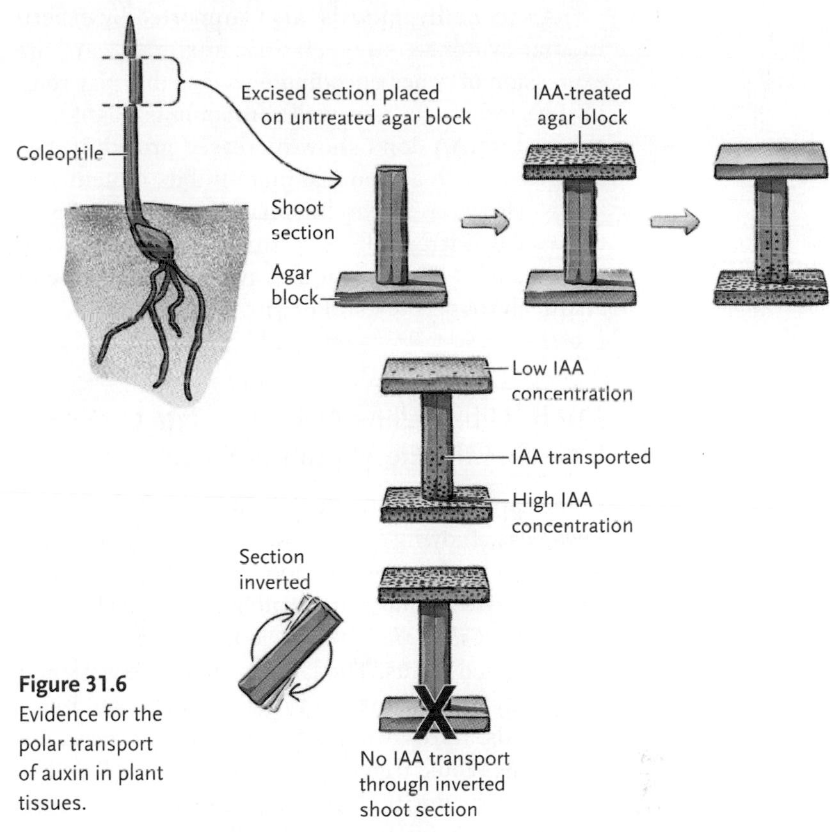

Figure 31.6
Evidence for the polar transport of auxin in plant tissues.

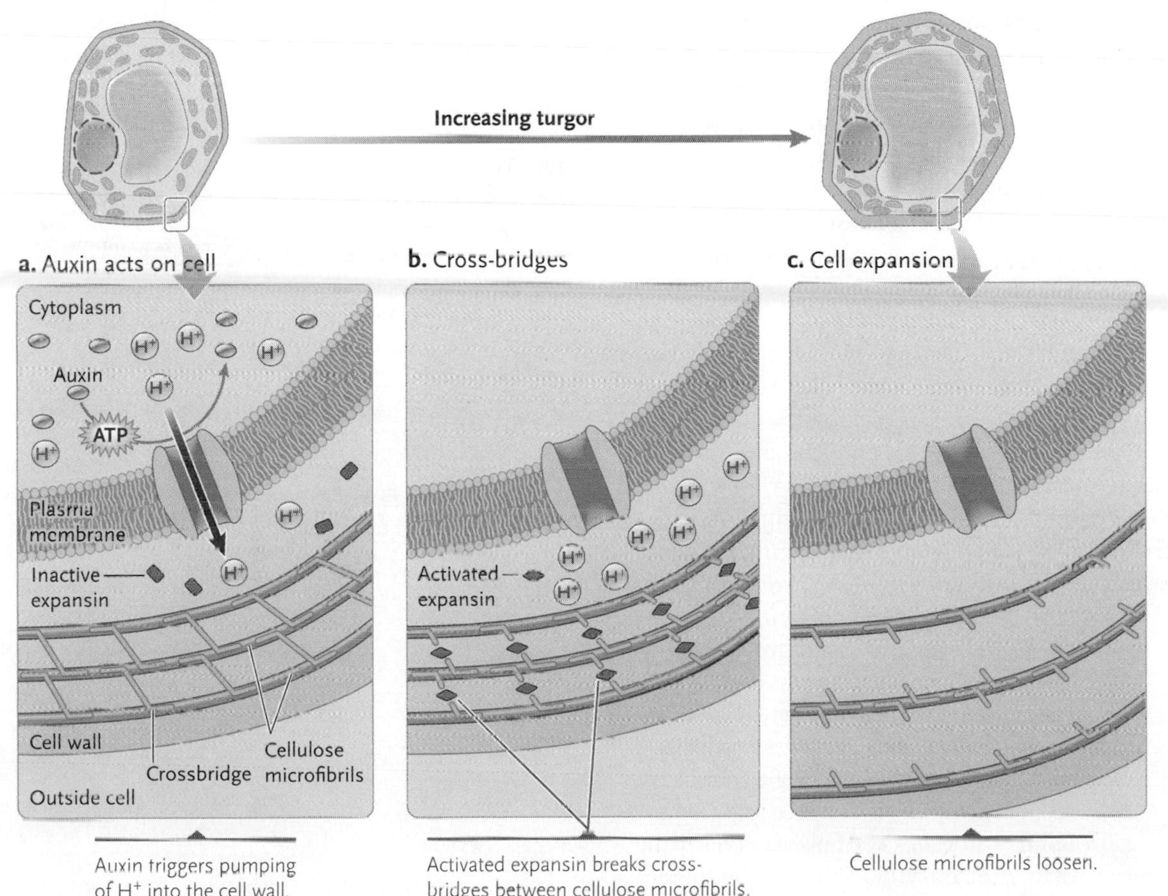

Figure 31.7
How auxin may regulate expansion of plant cells. According to the acid-growth hypothesis, plant cells secrete acid (H^+) when auxin stimulates the plasma membrane H^+ pumps to move hydrogen ions into the cell wall **(a)**; the increased acidity activates enzymes called *expansins*, which disrupt bonds between cellulose microfibrils in the wall **(b)**. As a result, the wall becomes extensible, and the cell can expand **(c)**.

A second hypothesis, also supported by experimental evidence, suggests that auxin triggers the expression of genes encoding enzymes that play roles in the synthesis of new wall components. Plant cells exposed to IAA don't show increased growth if they are treated with a chemical that inhibits protein synthesis. However, researchers have identified mRNAs that rapidly increase in concentration within 10 to 20 minutes after stem sections have been treated with auxin, although they still do not know exactly which proteins these mRNAs encode.

31.1b Gibberellins Also Stimulate Growth, Including the Elongation of Stems

In the early 1920s, a researcher in Japan, Eiichi Kurosawa, was studying a rice plant disease that the Japanese called *bakanae*—the "foolish seedling" disease. Stems of rice seedlings that had become infected with the fungus *Gibberella fujikuroi* elongated twice as much as uninfected plants. The lanky stems were weak and eventually toppled over before the plants could produce seeds. Kurosawa discovered that extracts of the fungus also could trigger the disease. Eventually, other investigators purified the fungus's disease-causing substance, naming it **gibberellin** (GA).

Gibberellins stimulate several aspects of plant growth. Perhaps most apparent to humans is their ability to promote the lengthening of plant stems by stimulating both cell division and cell elongation. Synthesized in shoot and root tips and young leaves, gibberellins, like auxin, modify the properties of plant cell walls in ways that promote expansion (although the gibberellin mechanism does not involve acidification of the cell wall). Perhaps both hormones affect expansins or are functionally linked in some other way yet to be discovered. Gibberellins have other known effects as well, such as helping to break the dormancy of seeds and buds. Scientists have isolated 100-plus compounds of the gibberellin family, although only a few are biologically active as hormones. The others are inactive forms or serve as precursors to active forms.

Gibberellins are active in eudicots and in a few monocots. In most plant species that have been analyzed, the main controller of stem elongation is the gibberellin called GA_1 **(Figure 31.8)**. Normally, GA_1 is synthesized in small amounts in young leaves and transported throughout the plant in the phloem. When GA_1 synthesis goes awry, the outcome is a dramatic change in the plant's stature. For example, experiments with a dwarf variety of peas (*Pisum sativum*) and some other species show that these plants and their taller relatives differ at a single gene locus. Normal plants make an enzyme required for gibberellin synthesis; dwarf plants of the same species lack the enzyme, and their internodes elongate very little.

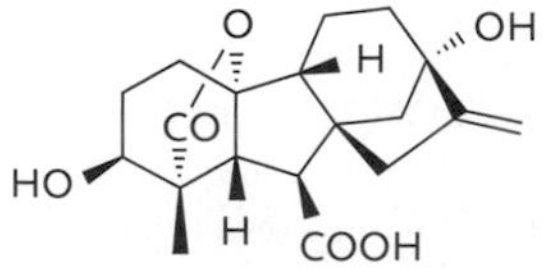

Figure 31.8
Structure of GA_1.

Another stark demonstration of the effect gibberellins can have on internode growth is **bolting**, growth of a floral stalk in plants that form vegetative rosettes, such as cabbages (*Brassica oleracea*) and iceberg lettuce (*Lactuca sativa*). In a rosette plant, stem internodes are so short that the leaves appear to arise from a single node. When these plants flower, however, the stem elongates rapidly, and flowers develop on the new stem parts. An experimenter can trigger exaggerated bolting by spraying a plant with gibberellin **(Figure 31.9)**. In nature, external cues such as increasing day length or warming after a cold snap stimulate gibberellin synthesis, and bolting occurs soon afterward. This observation supports the hypothesis that in rosette plants and possibly some others, gibberellins switch on internode lengthening when environmental conditions favour a shift from vegetative growth to reproductive growth.

Other experiments using gibberellins have turned up a striking number of additional roles for this hormone family. For example, one gibberellin helps stimulate buds and seeds to break dormancy and resume growth in the spring. Research on barley embryos showed that gibberellin provides signals during germination that lead to the enzymatic breakdown of endosperm, releasing nutrients that nourish the developing seedling (see Chapter 30). In monoecious species, which have flowers of both sexual types on the same plant, applications of gibberellin seem to encourage proportionately more "male" flowers to develop. Why would this be a benefit to the plant? The more "male" flowers present, the more pollen is

Sylvan H. Wittwer/Visuals Unlimited

Figure 31.9
A dramatic example of bolting in cabbage (*Brassica oleracea*), a plant commonly grown as a winter vegetable. The rosette form (left) reflects the plant's growth habit when days are short (and nights are long). Gibberellin was applied to the plants at the right, triggering the rapid stem elongation and subsequent flowering characteristic of bolting.

Figure 31.10
Effect of gibberellin on seedless grapes (*Vitis vinifera*). The grapes on the right developed on vines that were treated with a gibberellin.

available to pollinate "female" flowers, and, eventually, more fruits are produced. A gibberellin used by commercial grape growers promotes fruit set and lengthens the stems on which fruits develop, allowing space for individual grapes to grow larger. One result is fruit with greater consumer appeal **(Figure 31.10)**.

31.1c Cytokinins Enhance Growth and Retard Aging

Cytokinins play a major role in stimulating cell division (hence the name, which refers to cytokinesis). These hormones were first discovered during experiments designed to define the nutrient media required for plant tissue culture. Researchers found that in addition to a carbon source such as sucrose or glucose, minerals, and certain vitamins, cells in culture also required two other substances. One was auxin, which promoted the elongation of plant cells but did not stimulate the cells to divide. The other substance could be coconut milk, which is actually liquid endosperm, or it could be DNA that had been degraded into smaller molecules by boiling. When either was added to a culture medium along with an auxin, the cultured cells would begin dividing and grow normally.

We now know that the active ingredients in both boiled DNA and endosperm are cytokinins, which have a chemical structure similar to that of the nucleic acid base adenine. The most abundant natural cytokinin is zeatin, so called because it was first isolated from the endosperm of young corn seeds (*Zea mays*) **(Figure 31.11)**. In endosperm, zeatin probably promotes the burst of cell division that takes place as a fruit matures. As you might expect, cytokinins also are abundant in the rapidly dividing meristem tissues of root and shoot tips. Cytokinins occur not only in flowering plants but also in many conifers, mosses, and ferns. They are also synthesized by many soil-dwelling bacteria and fungi and may be crucial to the growth of mycorrhizas, which help nourish thousands of plant species (see Chapter 24). Conversely, *Agrobacterium* and other microbes that cause plant tumours carry genes that regulate the production of cytokinins.

Figure 31.11
Structure of zeatin.

Cytokinins are synthesized largely (although not only) in root tips and apparently are transported through the plant in xylem sap. Besides promoting cell division, they have a range of effects on plant metabolism and development, probably by regulating protein synthesis. For example, cytokinins promote the expansion of young leaves (as leaf cells expand), cause chloroplasts to mature, and retard leaf aging. Another cytokinin effect—coordinating the growth of roots and shoots, in concert with auxin—underscores the point that plant hormones often work together to evoke a particular response. Investigators culturing tobacco tissues found that the relative amounts of auxin and a cytokinin strongly influenced not only growth but also development **(Figure 31.12)**. When the concentrations of the two hormones were approximately equal, the growing tissue did not differentiate but instead

Figure 31.12
Effects of varying ratios of auxin and cytokinin on tobacco tissues (*Nicotiana tabacum*) grown in culture. The method starts with a block of stem pith, essentially a core of ground tissue removed from the centre of a stem. The callus growing on the pith is a disorganized mass of undifferentiated cells.

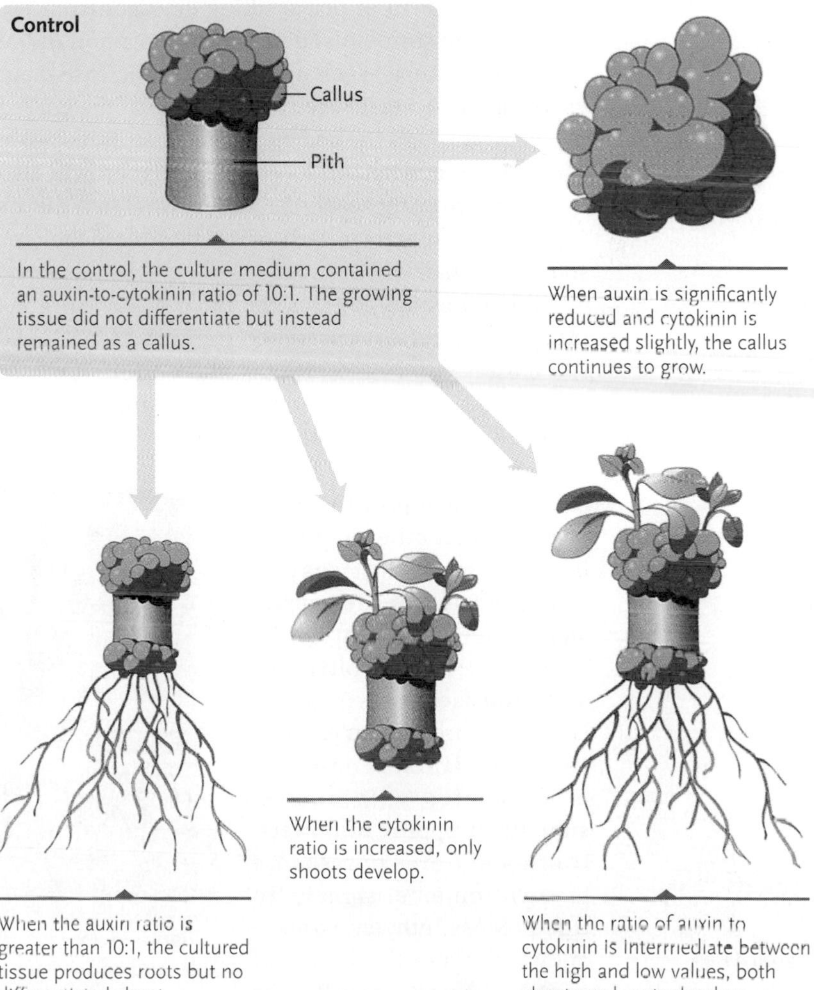

Control
Callus
Pith
In the control, the culture medium contained an auxin-to-cytokinin ratio of 10:1. The growing tissue did not differentiate but instead remained as a callus.
When auxin is significantly reduced and cytokinin is increased slightly, the callus continues to grow.
When the auxin ratio is greater than 10:1, the cultured tissue produces roots but no differentiated shoot.
When the cytokinin ratio is increased, only shoots develop.
When the ratio of auxin to cytokinin is intermediate between the high and low values, both shoots and roots develop.

remained as a loose mass of cells, or *callus*. When the relative auxin concentration was increased slightly, the callus produced roots. When the relative concentration of the cytokinin was increased, chloroplasts in the callus cells matured, the callus became green and more compact, and it produced shoots. In nature, the interaction of a cytokinin and auxin may produce the typical balanced growth of roots and shoots, with each region providing the other with key nutrients.

Natural cytokinins can prolong the life of stored vegetables. Similar synthetic compounds are already widely used to prolong the shelf life of lettuces and mushrooms and to keep cut flowers fresh.

31.1d Ethylene Regulates a Range of Responses, Including Senescence

Most parts of a plant can produce **ethylene**, which is present in fruits, flowers, seeds, leaves, and roots. In different species, it helps regulate a wide variety of plant physiological responses, including seed and bud dormancy, seedling growth, stem elongation, the ripening of fruit, and the eventual separation of fruits, leaves, and flowers from the plant body. Ethylene is an unusual hormone, in part because it is structurally simple **(Figure 31.13)** and in part because it is a gas at normal temperature and pressure.

Before a bean or pea seedling emerges from the soil, ethylene simultaneously slows elongation of the stem and stimulates cell divisions that increase stem girth **(Figure 31.14)**. These alterations push the curved hypocotyl through the soil and into the air (see Figure 31.14). Such ethylene-induced horizontal growth also can help a growing seedling "find its way" into the air if the seed happens to germinate under a pebble or some other barrier.

Ethylene also governs the biologically complex process of aging, or **senescence**, in plants. Senescence is a closely controlled process of deterioration that leads to the death of plant cells. In autumn, the leaves of deciduous trees senesce, often turning yellow or red as chlorophyll and proteins break down, so that other pigments become more noticeable. Ethylene triggers the expression of genes, leading to the synthesis of chlorophyllases and proteases, enzymes that launch the breakdown process. In many plants, senescence is associated with **abscission**, the dropping of flowers, fruits, and leaves in response to environmental signals. In this process, ethylene apparently stimulates the activity of enzymes that digest cell walls in an abscission zone—a localized region at the base of the petiole. The petiole detaches from the stem at that point **(Figure 31.15)**.

For some species, the funnelling of nutrients into reproductive parts may be a cue for senescence of leaves, stems, and roots. When the drain of nutrients is halted by removing each newly emerging flower or seed pod, a plant's leaves and stems stay green and vigorous much longer **(Figure 31.16)**. Gardeners routinely remove flower buds from many plants to maintain vegetative growth. Senescence requires other cues,

H H
C=C
H H

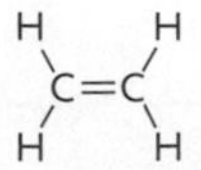

Figure 31.13
Structure of ethylene.

Kurt Stepnitz, Instructional Media Center, Michigan State University, East Lansing, MI 48824

Figure 31.14
Wild-type seedlings and one ethylene-insensitive mutant of *Arabidopsis thaliana* grown in an atmosphere containing ethylene. The wild-type seedlings show the reduced elongation characteristic for plants treated with ethylene. The ethylene-insensitive mutant elongated normally, just as wild-type seedlings would do in an atmosphere without ethylene.

N.R. Lersten

Figure 31.15
Abscission zone in a maple (*Acer*). This longitudinal section at the left is through the base of the petiole of a leaf.

Figure 31.16
Experimental results showing that the removal of seed pods from a soybean plant (*Glycine max*) delays its senescence.

however. For instance, when a cocklebur is induced to flower under winterlike conditions, its leaves turn yellow regardless of whether the nutrient-demanding young flowers are left on or pinched off. It is as if a "death signal" forms that leads to flowering and senescence when there are fewer hours of daylight (typical of winter days). This observation underscores the general theme that many plant responses to the environment involve the interaction of multiple molecular signals.

Fruit ripening is a special case of senescence. Although the precise mechanisms are not well understood, ripening begins when a fruit starts to synthesize ethylene. The ripening process may involve the conversion of starch or organic acids to sugars, the softening of cell walls, or the rupturing of the cell membrane and loss of cell fluid. The same kinds of events occur in wounded plant tissues, which also synthesize ethylene.

Ethylene from an outside source can stimulate senescence responses, including ripening, when it binds to specific protein receptors on plant cells. The ancient Chinese observed that they could induce picked fruit to ripen faster by burning incense; later, it was found that the incense smoke contains ethylene. Today, ethylene gas is widely used to ripen tomatoes, pineapples, bananas, honeydew melons, mangoes, papayas, and other fruit that has been picked and shipped while still green. Ripening fruit itself gives off ethylene, which is why placing a ripe banana in a closed sack of unripe peaches (or some other green fruit) often can cause the fruit to ripen. Oranges and other citrus fruits may be exposed to ethylene to brighten the colour of their rind. Conversely, limiting fruit exposure to ethylene can delay ripening. Apples will keep for months without rotting if they are exposed to a chemical that inhibits ethylene production or if they are stored in an environment that inhibits the hormone's effects—including low atmospheric pressure and a high concentration of CO_2, which may bind ethylene receptors.

31.1e Brassinosteroids Regulate Plant Growth Responses

The dozens of steroid hormones classed as **brassinosteroids (Figure 31.17)** all appear to be vital for normal growth in plants because they stimulate cell division and elongation in a wide range of plant cell types. Confirmed as plant hormones in the 1980s, brassinosteroids now are the subject of intense research on their sources and effects. Although brassinosteroids have been detected in a wide variety of plant tissues and organs, the highest concentrations are found in shoot tips and in developing seeds and embryos—all examples of young, actively developing parts. In laboratory studies, the hormone has different effects depending on the tissue where it is active. For example, it has been found to promote cell elongation, differentiation of vascular tissue, and elongation of a pollen tube after a flower is pollinated. By contrast, it inhibits the elongation of roots. First isolated from the pollen of a plant in the mustard family, *Brassica napus* (a type of canola), under natural conditions, brassinosteroids seem to regulate the expression of genes associated with a plant's growth responses to light.

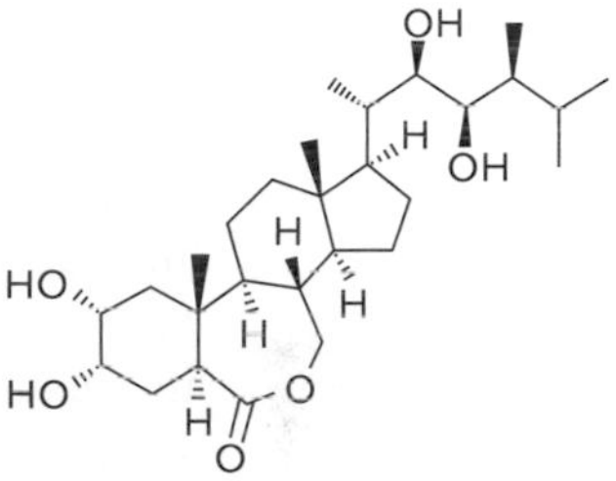

Figure 31.17
Structure of a brassinosteroid.

31.1f Abscisic Acid Suppresses Growth and Influences Responses to Environmental Stress

Plant scientists ascribe a variety of effects to the hormone **abscisic acid (ABA)**, many of which represent evolutionary adaptations to environmental challenges. Plants apparently synthesize ABA **(Figure 31.18)** from carotenoid pigments inside plastids in leaves and possibly other plant parts. In general, we can group its effects into changes in gene expression that result in long-term inhibition of growth and rapid, short-term physiological changes that are responses to immediate stresses, such as a lack of water, in a plant's surroundings. As its name suggests, at one time, ABA was thought to play a major role in abscission. As already

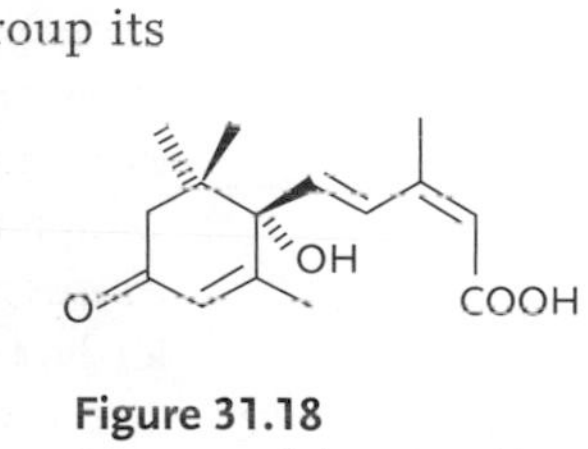

Figure 31.18
Structure of abscisic acid.

Figure 31.19
Bud scales, here on a perennial cornflower bud (*Centaurea montana*).

described, however, abscission is largely the domain of ethylene. So what are the functions of ABA?

Suppressing Growth in Buds and Seeds. Operating as a counterpoint to growth-stimulating hormones such as gibberellins, ABA inhibits growth in response to environmental cues, such as seasonal changes in temperature and light. This growth suppression can last for many months or even years. For example, one of ABA's major growth-inhibiting effects is apparent in perennial plants, in which the hormone promotes dormancy in leaf buds—an important adaptive advantage in places where winter cold can damage young leaves. If ABA is applied to a growing leaf bud, the bud's normal development stops, and instead, protective *bud scales*—modified, nonphotosynthetic leaves that are small, dry, and tough—form around the apical meristem and insulate it from the elements **(Figure 31.19)**. After the scales develop, most cell metabolic activity shuts down, and the leaf bud becomes dormant.

In some plants that produce fleshy fruits, such as apples and cherries, abscisic acid is associated with the dormancy of seeds as well. As the seed develops, ABA accumulates in the seed coat, and the embryo does not germinate even if it becomes hydrated. Before such a seed can germinate, it usually will require a long period of cool, wet conditions, which stimulate the breakdown of ABA. The buildup of ABA in developing seeds does more than simply inhibit development, however. As early development draws to a close, ABA stimulates the transcription of certain genes, and large amounts of their protein products are synthesized. These proteins are thought to store nitrogen and other nutrients that the embryo will use when it eventually does germinate. ABA and related growth inhibitors are often applied to plants slated to be shipped to plant nurseries. Dormant plants suffer less shipping damage, and the effects of the inhibitors can be reversed by applying a gibberellin.

Responses to Environmental Stress. ABA also triggers plant responses to various environmental stresses, including cold snaps, high soil salinity, and drought. A great deal of research has focused on how ABA influences plant responses to a lack of water. When a plant is water-stressed, ABA helps prevent excessive water loss by stimulating stomata to close. As described in Chapter 29, flowering plants depend heavily on the proper functioning of stomata. When a lack of water leads to wilting, mesophyll cells in wilted leaves rapidly synthesize and secrete ABA. The hormone diffuses to guard cells, where an ABA receptor binds it. Binding stimulates the release of K^+ and water from the guard cells, and within minutes, the stomata close.

31.1g Jasmonates and Oligosaccharins Regulate Growth and Have Roles in Defence

In recent years, studies of plant growth and development have helped define the roles—or revealed the existence—of several other hormonelike compounds in plants. Like the well-established plant hormones just described, these substances are organic molecules, and only tiny amounts are required to alter some aspect of a plant's functioning. Some have long been known to exist in plants, but the extent of their signalling roles has only recently become better understood. This group includes **jasmonates**, a family of about 20 compounds derived from fatty acids **(Figure 31.20)**. Experiments with *Arabidopsis* and other plants have revealed numerous genes that respond to jasmonate, including genes that help regulate root growth and seed germination. Jasmonate also appears to help plants "manage" stresses due to deficiencies of certain nutrients (such as K^+). The jasmonate family is best known, however, as part of the plant arsenal to limit damage by pathogens and predators, the topic of the following section.

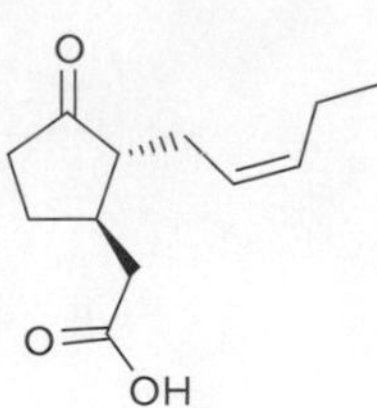

Figure 31.20
Structure of jasmonic acid.

Some other substances also are drawing keen interest from plant scientists, but because their signalling roles are still poorly understood, they are not widely accepted as confirmed plant hormones. A case in point involves the complex carbohydrates that are structural elements in the cell walls of plants and some fungi. Several years ago, researchers observed that in some plants, some of these oligosaccharides could serve as signalling molecules. Such compounds were named **oligosaccharins**, and one of their known roles is to defend the plant against pathogens. In addition, oligosaccharins have been proposed as growth regulators that adjust the growth and differentiation of plant cells, possibly by modulating the influences of growth-promoting hormones such as auxin. At this writing, researchers in many laboratories are pursuing a deeper understanding of this curious subset of plant signalling molecules.

Study Break

1. Which plant hormones promote growth, and which inhibit it?
2. Give examples of how some hormones have both promoting and inhibiting effects in different parts of the plant at different times of the life cycle.

31.2 Signal Responses at the Cellular Level

Auxin and the other hormones do not directly cause the plant responses outlined above instead, they alter a target cell's gene expression and elicit a cellular response, which leads to a change in growth or physiology. For decades, plant physiologists have looked avidly for clues about how those signals are converted into a chemical message that produces a change in cell metabolism or growth. Some of the basic mechanisms that have been discovered for animal cells also apply to plant cells (see Chapter 8).

31.2a Several Signal Response Pathways Operate in Plants

Hormones (and environmental stimuli, which we consider later in this chapter) alter the behaviour of target cells, which have receptors to which specific signal molecules can bind and elicit a cellular response. By means of a response pathway, a signal can induce changes in the cell's shape and internal structure or influence the transport of ions and other substances into and out of cells. Some signals cause cells to alter gene activation and the rate of protein synthesis; others set in motion events that modify existing cell proteins. Here, we briefly consider how signal molecules may operate in plants.

Certain hormones bind to receptors at the target cell's plasma membrane, on its endoplasmic reticulum (ER), or in the cytoplasm. For example, ethylene receptors are on the ER, and the auxin receptor is a protein in the cytoplasm. Research in several laboratories recently confirmed that auxin binds directly to this protein, setting in motion events that inhibit transcription. As a result, previously repressed genes are turned on. Thus, binding of a hormone triggers a complex pathway that leads to the cell response—the opening of ion channels, activation of transport proteins, or some other event.

Only some cells can respond to a particular signalling molecule because not all cells have the same types of receptors. For example, particular cells in ripening fruits and developing seeds have ethylene receptors, but few, if any, cells in stems do. Different signals also may have different effects on a single cell and may exert those effects by way of different response pathways. One type of signal might stimulate transcription, and another might inhibit it. In addition, as we've seen, some genes controlled by particular receptors encode proteins that regulate still *other* genes.

In plants, we know the most about pathways involving auxin, ethylene, salicylic acid, and blue light. **Figure 31.21** diagrams a general model for these response pathways in plant cells. As the figure shows, the response may lead to a change in the cell's structure, its metabolic activity, or both, either directly or by altering the expression of one or more genes.

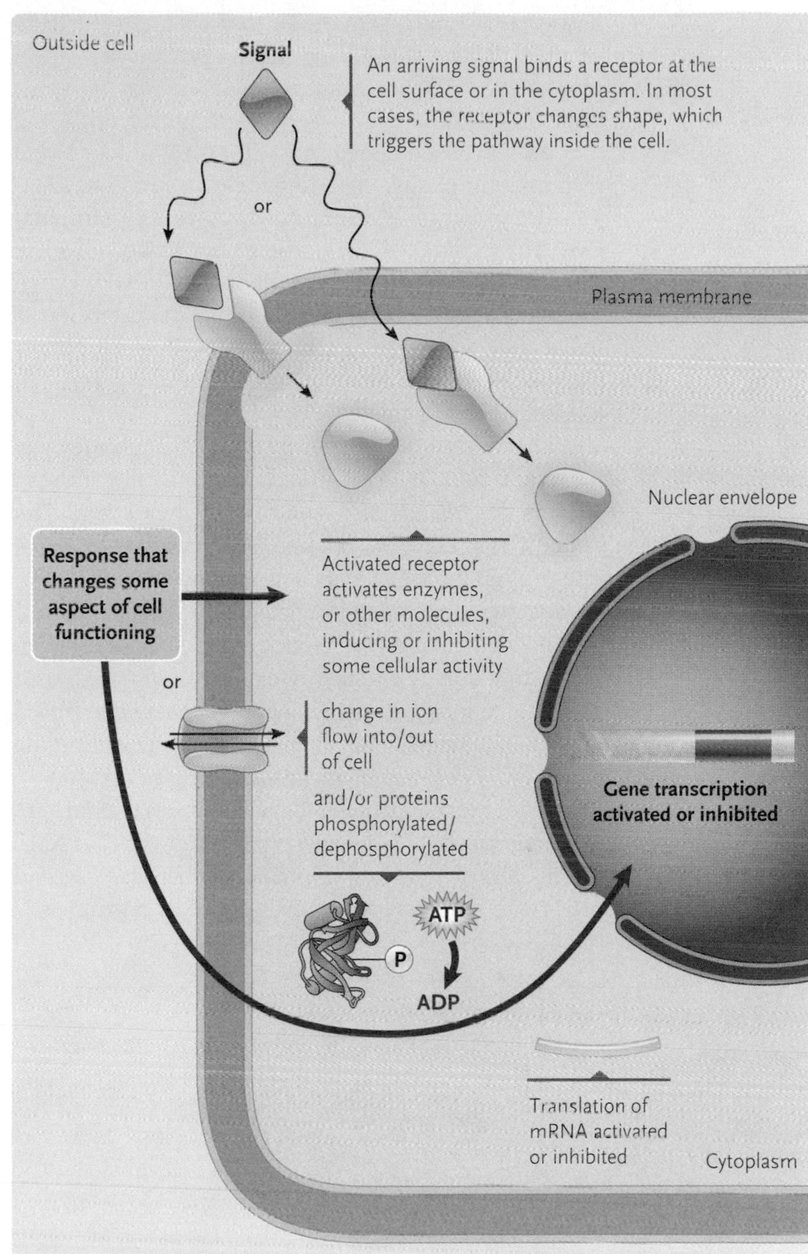

Figure 31.21
Signal response pathways in plant cells.

31.2b Second-Messenger Systems Enhance the Plant Cell's Response to a Hormone's Signal

We can think of plant hormones and other signalling molecules as external *first messengers* that deliver the initial physiological signal to a target cell. Often, as with salicylic acid, binding of the signal molecule triggers the synthesis of internal *second messengers* (see Chapter 8). These intermediary molecules diffuse rapidly through the cytoplasm and provide the main chemical signal that alters cell functioning.

Second messengers usually are synthesized in a sequence of chemical reactions that converts an external signal into internal cell activity. For many years, the details of plant second-messenger systems were sketchy and hotly debated. More recently, however, reaction sequences that occur in the cells of animals and some fungi have also been found in plants. The following example describes reactions that close plant stomata in response to a signal from ABA.

As discussed above, ABA helps regulate several responses in plants, including the maturation of seeds and the closing of stomata. ABA's role in stomatal closure—triggered by water stress or some other environmental cue—begins when the hormone activates a receptor in the plant cell plasma membrane. Experiments have shown that this binding ultimately stimulates the synthesis of second messengers, such as inositol triphosphate (IP_3).

The second messenger diffuses through the cytoplasm and binds with calcium channels in cell structures such as the ER, vacuole, and plasma membrane. The bound channels open, releasing calcium ions that activate protein kinase enzymes in the cytoplasm. In turn, the activated protein kinases activate their target proteins (by phosphorylating them). Each protein kinase can convert a large number of substrate molecules into activated enzymes, transport proteins, open ion channels, and so forth. Soon the number of molecules representing the final cellular response to the initial signal is enormous.

Recent experimental evidence indicates that, in similar fashion, auxin's hormonal signal is conveyed by cAMP (cyclic adenosine monophosphate), another major second messenger in the cells of animals and other organisms.

In addition to the basic pathways described here, other routes may exist that are unique to plant cells. Light is the driving force for photosynthesis, and it may not be far-fetched to suppose that plants have evolved other unique light-related biochemical pathways as well. For instance, exciting experiments are extending our knowledge of how plant cells respond to blue light, which, as we have discussed, triggers some photoperiod responses such as the opening and closing of stomata.

STUDY BREAK

1. Summarize the various ways that chemical signals reaching plant cells are converted to changes in cell functioning.
2. What basic task does a second messenger accomplish?

31.3 Plant Chemical Defences

Plants don't have immune systems like those that have evolved in animals (discussed in Chapter 44). Even so, over the millennia, plants have been constantly exposed to predation by herbivores, and this onslaught of pathogens has resulted in a striking array of chemical defences that ward off or reduce damage to plant tissues from infectious bacteria, fungi, worms, or plant-eating insects **(Table 31.2)**.

Table 31.2 Summary of Plant Chemical Defences

Type of Defence	Effects
General Defences	
Jasmonate (JA) responses to wounds/injury by pathogens; pathways often include other hormones, such as ethylene	Synthesis of defensive chemicals, such as protease inhibitors
Hypersensitive response to infectious pathogens (e.g., fungi, bacteria)	Physically isolates infection site by surrounding it with dead cells
PR (pathogenesis-related) proteins	Enzymes, other proteins that degrade cell walls of pathogens
Salicylic acid (SA)	Mobilized during other responses and independently; induces the synthesis of PR proteins, operates in systemic acquired resistance
Systemin (in tomato)	Triggers JA response
Secondary Metabolites	
Phytoalexins	Antibiotic
Oligosaccharins	Trigger synthesis of phytoalexins
Systemic acquired resistance (SAR)	Long-lasting protection against some pathogens; components include SA and PR proteins that accumulate in healthy tissues
Specific Defences	
Gene-for-gene recognition of chemical features of specific pathogens (by binding with receptors coded by R genes)	Triggers defensive response (e.g., hypersensitive response, PR proteins) against pathogens
Other	
Heat-shock responses (encoded by heat-shock genes)	Synthesis of chaperone proteins that reversibly bind other plant proteins and prevent denaturing due to heat stress
"Antifreeze" proteins	In some species, stabilize cell proteins under freezing conditions

You will discover in this section that as with the defensive strategies of animals, plant defences include both general responses to any type of attack and specific responses to particular threats. Some get under way almost as soon as an attack begins, whereas others help promote the plant's long-term survival. And more often than not, multiple chemicals interact as the response unfolds.

31.3a Jasmonates and Other Compounds Interact in a General Response to Wounds

When an insect begins feeding on a leaf or some other plant part, the plant may respond to the resulting wound by launching what in effect is a cascade of chemical responses. These complex signalling pathways often rely on interactions among jasmonates, ethylene, or some other plant hormone. As the pathway unfolds, it triggers expression of genes, leading to chemical and physical defences at the wound site. For example, in some plants, jasmonate induces a response leading to the synthesis of protease inhibitors, which disrupt an insect's capacity to digest proteins in the plant tissue. The protein deficiency, in turn, hampers the insect's growth and functioning.

A plant's capacity to recognize and respond to the physical damage of a wound apparently has been a strong selection pressure during plant evolution. When a plant is wounded experimentally, numerous defensive chemicals can be detected in its tissues in relatively short order. One of these, **salicylic acid**, or **SA** (a compound similar to aspirin, which is acetyl-salicylic acid), seems to have multiple roles in plant defences, including interacting with jasmonates in signalling cascades (see *Molecule Behind Biology*).

Researchers are regularly discovering new variations of hormone-induced wound responses in plants. For example, experiments have elucidated some of the steps in an unusual pathway that thus far is known only in tomato (*Solanum lycopersicum*) and a few other plant species. As diagrammed in **Figure 31.22**, the wounded plant rapidly synthesizes systemin, the first peptide hormone to be discovered in plants. (Various animal hormones are peptides, a topic covered in Chapter 35.) Systemin enters the phloem and is transported throughout the plant. Although various details of the signalling pathway have yet to be worked out, when receptive cells bind systemin, their plasma membranes release a lipid that is the chemical precursor of jasmonate. Next, jasmonate is synthesized, and it, in turn, sets in motion the expression of genes that encode protease inhibitors, which protect the plant against attack, even in parts remote from the original wound.

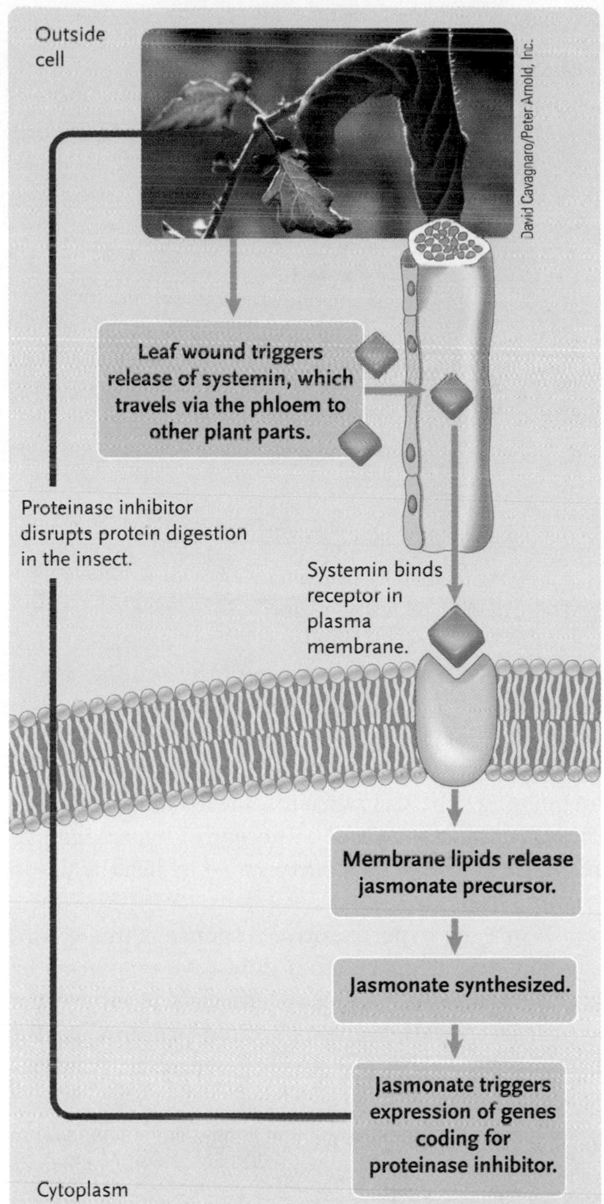

Figure 31.22
The system in response to wounding. When a plant is wounded, it responds by releasing the protein hormone systemin. Transported through the phloem to other plant parts, in receptive cells, systemin sets in motion a sequence of reactions that lead to the expression of genes encoding protease inhibitors—substances that can seriously disrupt an insect predator's capacity to digest protein.

31.3b The Hypersensitive Response and PR Proteins Are Other General Defences

Often a plant that becomes infected by pathogenic bacteria or fungi counters the attack by way of a **hypersensitive response**—a defence that physically cordons off an infection site by surrounding it with dead cells. Initially, cells near the site respond by producing a burst of highly reactive oxygen–containing compounds (such as hydrogen peroxide, H_2O_2) that can break down nucleic acids, inactivate enzymes, or have other toxic effects on cells. Enzymes in the cell's plasma membrane catalyze the burst of reactive oxygen compounds. It may begin the process of killing cells close to the attack site, and as the response advances, programmed cell death may also come into play. In short order, the "sacrificed" dead cells wall off the infected area from the rest of the plant. Thus denied

Molecule Behind Biology

Salicylic Acid

In plants, salicylic acid **(Figure 1)** functions in systemic acquired resistance, in which a damaged plant part signals to other parts, triggering defense responses in those tissues. We don't yet understand how this response works. Salicylic acid has also been the basis for one of the most widely consumed medicines, aspirin. As far back as 500 b.c., the Greek physician Hippocrates noted that chewing the bark of *Salix alba* (white willow) could relieve fevers and pain. The aboriginal people of North American boiled *Salix* bark as remedies for aches and fevers. In the 1820s, the active ingredient, salicin, was isolated from willow bark and also from leaves of meadowsweet (*Spirea ulmaria*). In the human body, salicin is broken down to salicylic acid, so that acid was soon synthesized commercially and sold as medicine. However, salicylic acid is very bitter tasting and causing stomach irritation (because it reduces the stomach wall secretions that protect the stomach lining from acid produced in digestion), so a modified version, acetyl salicylic acid (ASA) was developed that avoided these problems. This form of ASA was trademarked as "aspirin," with "a" standing for acetyl, and "spir" for *Spirea*, the source of the salicin used to make salicylic acid. **(Figure 2)** Why don't we just take salicin isolated from plants instead of going through the industrial process of making aspirin? It is safer to take a commercial product so that you know exactly how much of the active ingredient you are ingesting; the dosage of salicin in plant tissue is unpredictable, varying with conditions such as whether the plant has ramped up its production in response to attack by a predator.

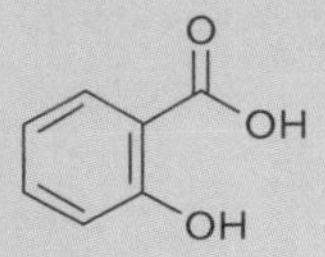

Figure 1.
Structure of salicylic acid.

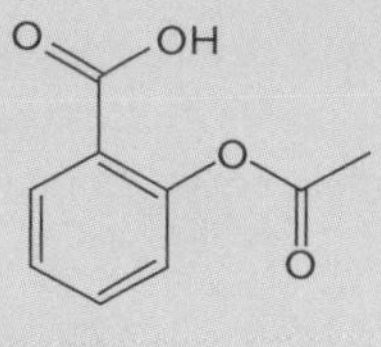

Figure 2.
Structure of aspirin.

an ongoing supply of nutrients, the invading pathogen dies. A common sign of a successful hypersensitive response is a dead spot surrounded by healthy tissue **(Figure 31.23).**

While the hypersensitive response is under way, salicylic acid triggers other defensive responses by an infected plant. One of its effects is to induce the synthesis of **pathogenesis-related proteins**, or **PR proteins**. Some PR proteins are hydrolytic enzymes that break down components of a pathogen's cell wall. Examples are chitinases that dismantle the chitin in the cell walls of fungi and so kill the cells. In some cases, plant cell receptors also detect the presence of fragments of the disintegrating wall and set in motion additional defence responses.

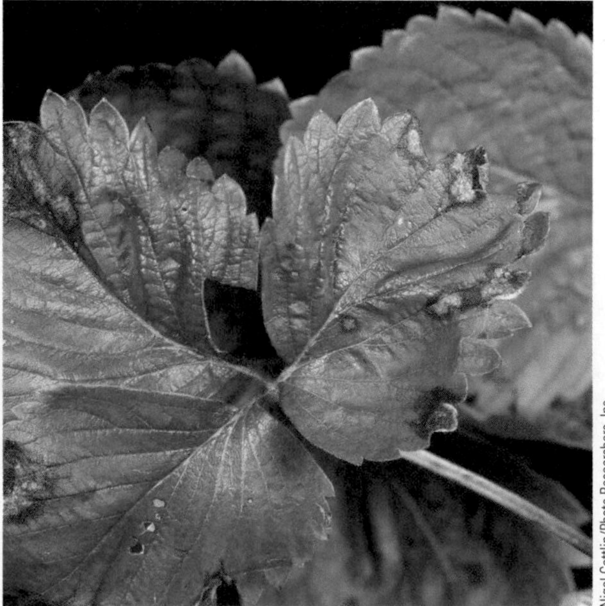

Nigel Cattlin/Photo Researchers, Inc.

Figure 31.23
Evidence of the hypersensitive response. The dead spots on these leaves of a strawberry plant (*Fragaria* species) are sites where a pathogen invaded, triggering the defensive destruction of the surrounding cells.

31.3c Secondary Metabolites Defend against Pathogens and Herbivores

Many plants counter bacteria and fungi by making **phytoalexins**, biochemicals of various types that function as antibiotics. When an infectious agent breaches a plant part, genes encoding phytoalexins begin to be transcribed in the affected tissue. For instance, when a fungus begins to invade plant tissues, the enzymes it secretes may trigger the release of oligosaccharins. In addition to their roles as growth regulators (described in Section 31.1), these substances also can promote the production of phytoalexins, which have toxic effects on a variety of fungi. Plant tissues may also synthesize phytoalexins in response to attacks by viruses.

Phytoalexins are among many *secondary metabolites* produced by plants. Such substances are termed "secondary" because they are not routinely synthesized in all plant cells as part of basic metabolism. A wide range of plant species deploy secondary metabolites as defences against feeding herbivores. Examples are alkaloids such as caffeine, cocaine, and the poison strychnine (in the seeds of the *nux vomica* tree, *Strychnos nux-vomica*), tannins such as those in oak acorns, and various terpenes. The terpene family includes insect-repelling substances in conifer resins and cotton and essential oils produced by sage and basil plants. Because these terpenes are volatile—they easily diffuse out of the plant and into the surrounding air—they also can provide indirect defence to a plant. Released from the wounds created by a munching insect, they attract other insects that prey on the herbivore. Chapter 46 looks in detail at the interactions between plants and herbivores.

31.3d Gene-for-Gene Recognition Allows Rapid Responses to Specific Threats

One of the most interesting questions with respect to plant defences is how plants first sense that an attack is under way. In some instances, plants apparently can detect an attack by a specific predator through a mechanism called **gene-for-gene recognition**. This term refers to a matchup between the products of the dominant alleles of two types of genes: a so-called ***R* gene** (for "resistance") in a plant and an ***Avr* gene** (for "avirulence") in a particular pathogen. Thousands of *R* genes have been identified in a wide range of plant species. Dominant R alleles confer enhanced resistance to plant pathogens, including bacteria, fungi, and nematode worms that attack roots.

The basic mechanism of gene-for-gene recognition is simple: The dominant R allele encodes a receptor in plasma membranes of a plant's cells, and the dominant pathogen Avr allele encodes a molecule that can bind the receptor. "Avirulence" implies "not virulent," and binding of the *Avr* gene product triggers an immediate defence response in the plant. Trigger molecules run the gamut from proteins to lipids to carbohydrates that have been secreted by the pathogen or released from its surface **(Figure 31.24)**. Experiments have demonstrated a rapid-fire sequence of early biochemical changes that follow binding of the Avr-encoded molecule; these include changes in ion concentrations inside and outside plant cells and the production of biologically active oxygen compounds that heralds the hypersensitive response. In fact, of the instances of gene-for-gene recognition plant scientists have observed thus far, most trigger the hypersensitive response and the ensuing synthesis of PR proteins, with their antibiotic effects.

Required precondition
A plant has a dominant R gene encoding a receptor that can bind the product of a specfic pathogen dominant *Avr* gene.

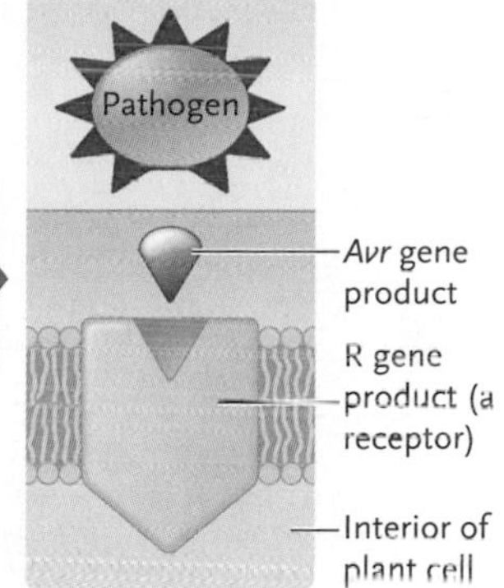

1 When the R-encoded receptor binds its matching *Avr* product, the binding triggers signalling pathways, leading to various defence responses in the plant.

2 Fluxes of ions and enzyme activity at the plasma membrane contribute to the hypersensitive response. Soon PR proteins, phytoalexins, and salicyic acid (SA) are synthesized. The PR proteins and phytoalexins combat pathogens directly. SA promotes systemic acquired resistance.

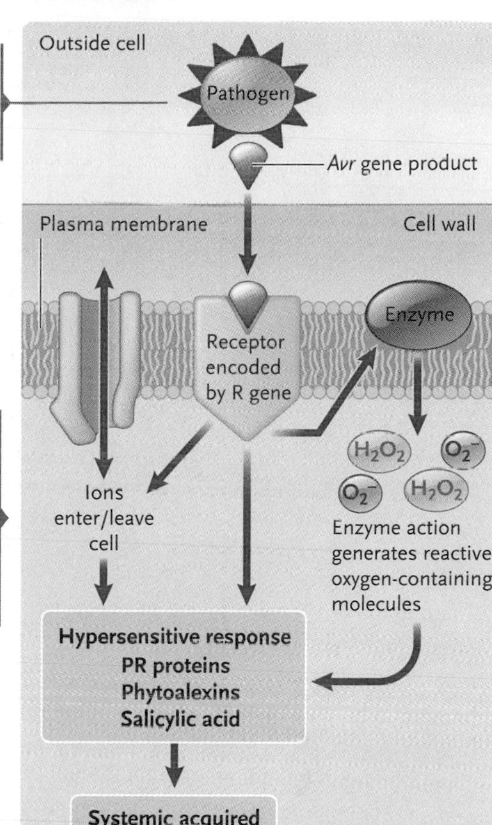

Figure 31.24
Model of how gene-for-gene resistance may operate. For resistance to develop, the plant must have a dominant *R* gene, and the pathogen must have a corresponding dominant *Avr* gene. The products of such "matching" genes can interact physically, rather like the lock-and-key mechanism of an enzyme and its substrate. Most *R* genes encode receptors at the plasma membranes of plant cells. As diagrammed in step 1, when one of these receptors binds an *Avr* gene's product, the initial result may be changes in the movements of specific ions into or out of the cell and the activation of membrane enzymes that catalyze the formation of highly reactive oxygen containing molecules. Such events help launch other signalling pathways that lead to a variety of defensive responses, including the hypersensitive response (step 2).

31.3e Systemic Acquired Resistance Can Provide Long-Term Protection

The defensive response to a microbial invasion may spread throughout a plant, so that the plant's healthy tissues become less vulnerable to infection. This phenomenon is called **systemic acquired resistance**, and experiments using *Arabidopsis* plants have shed light on how it comes about **(Figure 31.25, p. 752)**. In a key early step, SA builds up in the affected tissues. By some route, probably through the phloem, the SA passes from the infected organ to newly forming organs such as leaves, which begin to synthesize PR proteins—again, providing the plant with a "homegrown" antimicrobial arsenal. How does the SA exert this effect? It seems that when enough SA accumulates in a plant cell's cytoplasm, a regulatory protein called NPR-1 (for *n*on-expressor of *p*athogenesis-*r*elated genes) moves from the cytoplasm into the cell nucleus. There it interacts

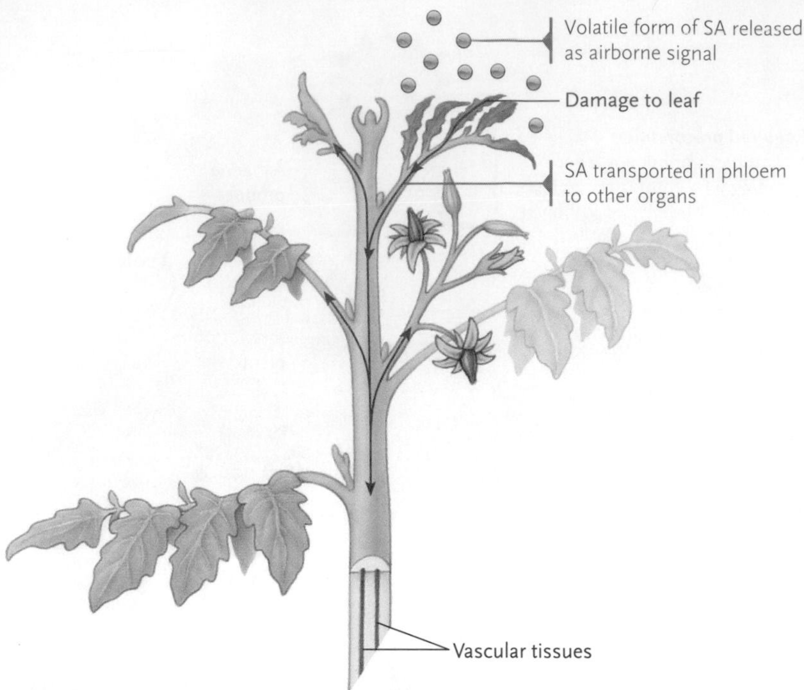

Figure 31.25
A proposed mechanism for systemic acquired resistance. When a plant successfully fends off a pathogen, the defensive chemical salicylic acid (SA) is transported in the phloem to other plant parts, where it may help protect against another attack by stimulating the synthesis of PR proteins. In addition, the plant synthesizes and releases a slightly different, more volatile form of SA. This chemical may serve as an airborne signal to other parts of the plant, as well as to neighbouring plants.

with factors that promote the transcription of genes encoding PR proteins.

In addition to synthesizing SA that will be transported internally in a plant's vascular system, the damaged leaf also synthesizes a chemically similar compound, methyl salicylate. This substance is volatile, and researchers speculate that it may serve as an airborne "harm" signal, promoting defence responses in the plant that synthesized it and possibly in nearby plants as well.

Study Break

1. Which plant chemical defences are general responses to attack, and which are specific to a particular pathogen?
2. Why is salicylic acid considered to be a general systemic response to damage?
3. How is the hypersensitive response integrated with other chemical defences?

31.4 Plant Responses to the Environment: Movements

Although a plant cannot move from place to place as external conditions change, plants can and do alter the orientation of their body parts in response to environmental stimuli. As noted earlier in the chapter, growth toward or away from a unidirectional stimulus, such as light or gravity, is called a tropism. Tropic movement involves permanent changes in the plant body because cells in particular areas or organs grow differentially in response to the stimulus. Plant physiologists do not fully understand how tropisms occur, but they are fascinating examples of the complex abilities of plants to adjust to their environment. This also touches on two other kinds of movements: developmental responses to physical contact and position changes that are not related to the location of the stimulus.

31.4a Phototropisms Are Responses to Light

As you learned in Chapter 1, light is a key environmental stimulus for many kinds of organisms. Phototropisms, which we have already discussed in the section on auxins, are growth responses to a directional light source. As the Darwins discovered, if light is more intense on one side of a stem, the stem may curve toward the light **(Figure 31.26a)**. Phototropic movements are extremely adaptive for photosynthesizing organisms because they help maximize the exposure of photosynthetic tissues to sunlight.

How do auxins influence phototropic movements? In a coleoptile that is illuminated from one side, IAA moves by polar transport into the cells on the shaded side **(Figure 31.26b–d)**. Phototropic bending occurs because cells on the shaded side elongate more rapidly than do cells on the illuminated side.

The main stimulus for phototropism is blue light. Experiments on corn coleoptiles have shown that a molecule called phototropin can absorb blue light, and it may play a role in stimulating the initial lateral transport of IAA to the dark side of a shoot tip. Studies with *Arabidopsis* suggest that there is more than one blue light receptor, however. One is a light-absorbing protein called **cryptochrome**, which is sensitive to blue light and may also be an important early step in the various light-based growth responses. As you will read later, cryptochrome appears to have a role in other plant responses to light as well.

31.4b Gravitropism Orients Plant Parts to the Pull of Gravity

Plants show growth responses to Earth's gravitational pull, a phenomenon called **gravitropism**. After a seed germinates, the primary root curves down, toward the "pull" (positive gravitropism), and the shoot curves up (negative gravitropism).

Several hypotheses seek to explain how plants respond to gravity. The most widely accepted hypothesis proposes that plants detect gravity much as animals do—that is, particles called **statoliths** in certain cells move in the direction gravity pulls them. In the

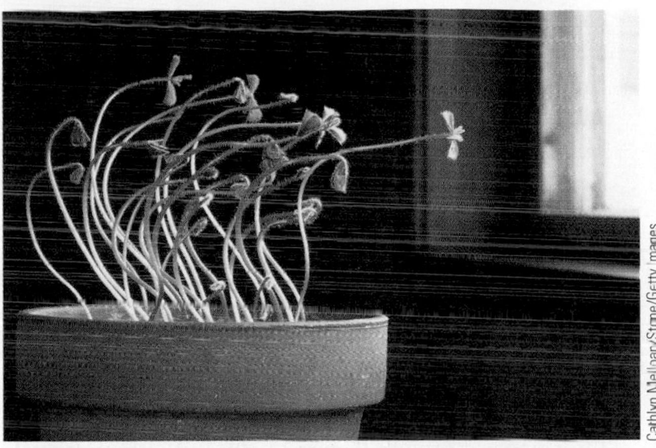

Cathlyn Melloan/Stone/Getty Images

a. Seedlings bend toward light.

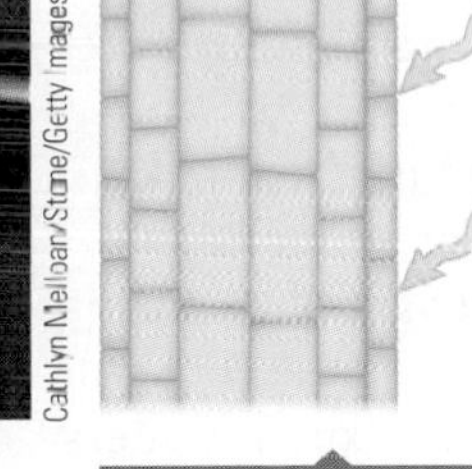

b. Rays from the sun strike one side of a shoot tip.

c. Auxin (red) diffuses down from the shoot tip to cells on its shaded side.

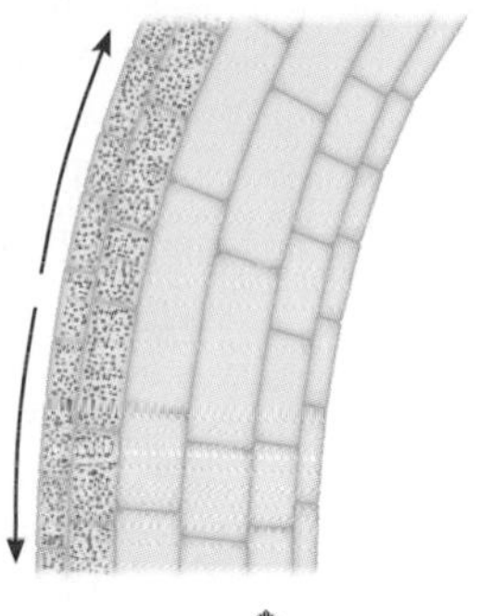

d. The auxin-stimulated cells elongate more quickly, causing the seedling to bend.

Figure 31.26
Phototropism in seedlings. (a) Tomato seedlings grown in darkness; their right side was illuminated for a few hours before they were photographed. **(b–d)** Hormone-mediated differences in the rates of cell elongation bring about the bending toward light.

semicircular canals of human ears, tiny calcium carbonate crystals serve as statoliths; in most plants, the statoliths are amyloplasts, modified plastids that contain starch grains. In eudicot angiosperm stems, amyloplasts often are present in one or two layers of cells just outside the vascular bundles. In monocots such as cereal grasses, amyloplasts are located in a region of tissue near the base of the leaf sheath. In roots, amyloplasts occur in the root cap. If the spatial orientation of a plant cell is shifted experimentally, its amyloplasts sink through the cytoplasm until they come to rest at the bottom of the cell **(Figure 31.27)**.

How do amyloplast movements translate into an altered growth response? The full explanation appears to be fairly complex, and there is evidence that somewhat different mechanisms operate in stems and roots. In stems, the sinking of amyloplasts may provide a mechanical stimulus that triggers a gene-guided redistribution of IAA. **Figure 31.28** shows what happens when a potted sunflower seedling is turned on its side in a dark room. Within 15 to 20 minutes, cell elongation decreases markedly on the upper side of the growing horizontal stem but increases on the lower side. With the adjusted growth pattern, the stem curves upward, even in the absence of light. Using different types of tests, researchers have been able to document the shifting of IAA from the top to the bottom side of the stem. The changing auxin gradient correlates with the altered pattern of cell elongation.

In roots, a high concentration of auxin has the opposite effect—it inhibits cell elongation. If a root is placed on its side, amyloplasts in the root cap accumulate near the side wall that now is the bottom side of the cap. In some way, this stimulates cell elongation in the opposite wall, and within a few hours, the root once again curves downward. In the root tips of many

a. Root oriented vertically

Statoliths

b. Root oriented horizontally

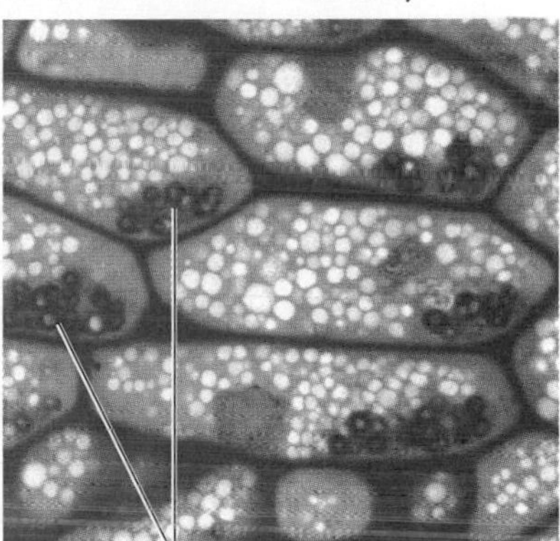

Statoliths

Figure 31.27
Evidence that supports the statolith hypothesis. When a corn root was laid on its side, amyloplasts—statoliths—in cells from the root cap settled to the bottom of the cells within 5 to 10 minutes. Statoliths may be part of a gravity-sensing mechanism that redistributes auxin through a root tip. Micrographs courtesy of Randy Moore, from "How Roots Respond to Gravity," M. L. Evans, R. Moore, and K. Hasenstein, Scientific American, December 1986.

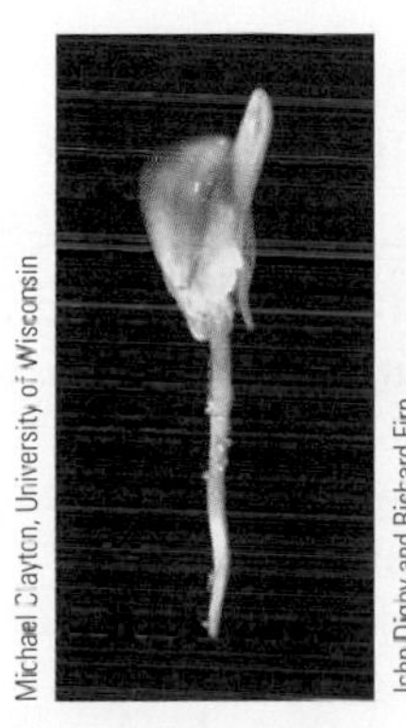

Michael Clayton, University of Wisconsin

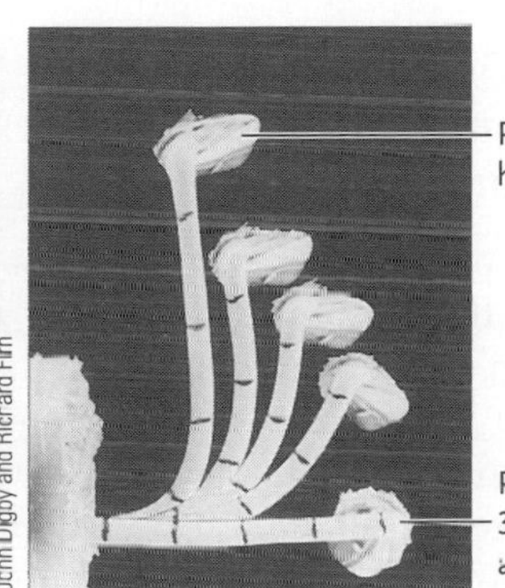

John Digby and Richard Firn

Figure 31.28
Gravitropism in a young shoot. A newly emerged sunflower seedling was grown in the dark for five days. Then it was turned on its side and marked at 0.5 cm intervals. Negative gravitropism turned the stem upright in 2 hours.

plants, however, especially eudicots, researchers have not been able to detect a shift in IAA concentration that correlates with the changing position of amyloplasts. One hypothesis is that IAA is redistributed over extremely short distances in root cells and therefore is difficult to measure. Root cells are much more sensitive to IAA than are cells in stem tissue, and even a tiny shift in IAA distribution could significantly affect their growth.

Along with IAA, calcium ions (Ca^{2+}) appear to play a major role in gravitropism. For example, if Ca^{2+} is added to an otherwise untreated agar block that is then placed on one side of a root cap, the root will bend toward the block. In this way, experimenters have been able to manipulate the direction of growth so that the elongating root forms a loop. Similarly, if an actively bending root is deprived of Ca^{2+}, the gravitropic response abruptly stops. By contrast, the negative gravitropic response of a shoot tip is inhibited when the tissue is exposed to excess calcium.

Just how Ca^{2+} interacts with IAA in gravitropic responses is unknown. One hypothesis posits that calcium plays a role. Calcium binds to a small protein called *calmodulin*, activating it in the process. Activated calmodulin, in turn, can activate a variety of key cell enzymes in many organisms, both plants and animals. One possibility is that calcium-activated calmodulin stimulates cell membrane pumps that enhance the flow of both IAA and calcium through a gravity-stimulated plant tissue.

Some of the most active research in plant biology focuses on the intricate mechanisms of gravitropism. For example, there is increasing evidence that in many plants, cells in different regions of stem tissue are more or less sensitive to IAA and that gravitropism is linked in some fundamental way to these differences in auxin sensitivity. In a few plants, including some cultivated varieties of corn and radish, the direction of the gravitropic response by a seedling's primary root is influenced by light. Clearly, there is much more to be learned.

31.4c Thigmotropism and Thigmomorphogenesis Are Responses to Physical Contact

Varieties of peas, grapes, and some other plants demonstrate **thigmotropism** (*thigma* = touch), which is growth in response to contact with a solid object. Thigmotropic plants typically have long, slender stems and cannot grow upright without physical support. They often have *tendrils*, modified stems or leaves that can rapidly curl around a fencepost or the sturdier stem of a neighbouring plant. If one side of a grapevine stem grows against a trellis, for example, specialized epidermal cells on that side of the stem tendril shorten, whereas cells on the other side of the tendril rapidly elongate. Within minutes, the tendril starts to curl around the trellis, forming tight coils that provide strong support for the vine stem. **Figure 31.29** shows thigmotropic twisting in the passionflower (*Passiflora*). Auxin and ethylene may be involved in thigmotropism, but most details of the mechanism remain elusive.

The rubbing and bending of plant stems caused by frequent strong winds, rainstorms, grazing animals, and even farm machinery can inhibit the overall growth of plants and can alter their growth patterns. In this phenomenon, called **thigmomorphogenesis**, a stem stops elongating and instead adds girth when it is regularly subjected to mechanical stress. Merely shaking some plants daily for a brief period will inhibit their upward growth **(Figure 31.30)**. But although such plants may be shorter, their thickened stems will be stronger. Thigmomorphogenesis helps explain why plants growing outdoors are often shorter, have somewhat thicker stems, and are not as easily blown over as plants of the same species grown indoors. Trees growing near the snowline of windswept mountains show an altered growth pattern that reflects this response to wind stress.

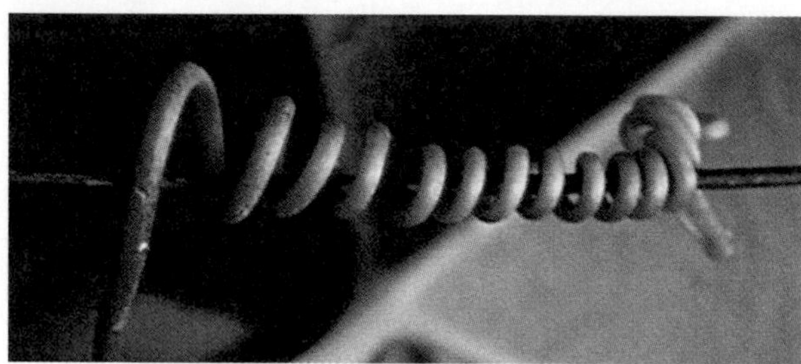

Figure 31.29
Thigmotropism in a passionflower (*Passiflora*) tendril, which is twisted around a support.

Figure 31.30
Effect of mechanical stress on tomato plants (*Lycopersicon esculentum*). **(a)** This plant was the control; it was grown in a greenhouse, protected from wind and rain. **(b)** Each day for 28 days, this plant was mechanically shaken for 30 seconds at 280 rpm. **(c)** This plant received the same shaking treatment, but twice a day for 28 days.

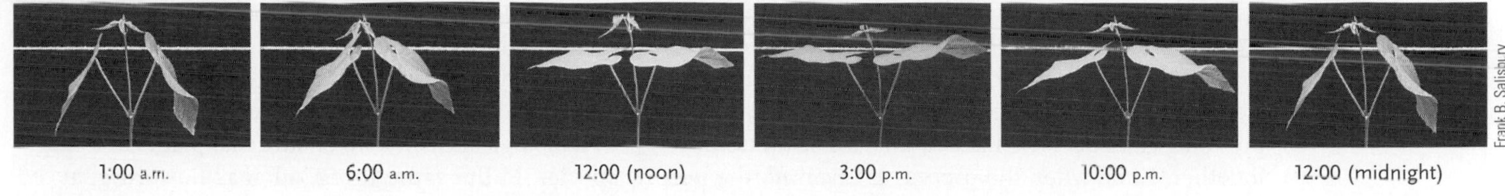

Figure 31.31
Nastic sleep movements in the leaves of a bean plant. Although this plant was kept in constant darkness for 23 hours, its sleep movements continued independently of sunrise (6 a.m.) and sunset (6 p.m.). Folding the leaves closer to the stem may prevent phytochrome from being activated by bright moonlight, which could interrupt the dark period necessary to trigger flowering. Or perhaps it helps slow heat loss from leaves otherwise exposed to the cold night air.

Research on the cellular mechanisms of thigmomorphogenesis has begun to yield tantalizing clues. In one study, investigators repeatedly sprayed *Arabidopsis* plants with water and imposed other mechanical stresses and then sampled tissues from the stressed plants. The samples contained as much as double the usual amount of mRNA for at least four genes, which had been activated by the stress. The mRNAs encoded calmodulin and several other proteins that may have roles in altering *Arabidopsis* growth responses. The test plants were also short, generally reaching only half the height of unstressed controls.

31.4d Nastic Movements Are Nondirectional

Tropisms are responses to directional stimuli, such as light striking one side of a shoot tip, but many plants also exhibit **nastic movements** (*nastos* = pressed close together)—reversible responses to nondirectional stimuli, such as mechanical pressure or humidity. We see nastic movements in leaves, leaflets, and even flowers. For instance, certain plants exhibit nastic sleep movements, holding their leaves (or flower petals) in roughly horizontal positions during the day but folding them closer to the stem at night **(Figure 31.31)**. Tulip flowers "go to sleep" in this way.

Many nastic movements are temporary and result from changes in cell turgor. For example, the daily opening and closing of stomata in response to changing light levels are nastic movements, as is the traplike closing of the lobed leaves of the Venus flytrap when an insect brushes against hairlike sensory structures on the leaves. The leaves of *Mimosa pudica*, the sensitive plant, also close in a nastic response to mechanical pressure. Each *Mimosa* leaf is divided into pairs of leaflets **(Figure 31.32a)**. Touching even one leaflet at the leaf tip triggers a chain reaction in which each pair of leaflets closes up within seconds **(Figure 31.32b)**.

In many turgor-driven nastic movements, water moves into and out of the cells in **pulvini** (*pulvinus* = cushion), thickened pads of tissue at the base of a leaf or petiole. Stomatal movements depend on changing concentrations of ions within guard cells, and pulvinar cells drive nastic leaf movements in *Mimosa* and numerous other plants by the same mechanism **(Figure 31.32c)**.

How is the original stimulus transferred from cells in one part of a leaf to cells elsewhere? The answer lies in the polarity of charge across cell plasma membranes (see Chapter 6). Touching a *Mimosa* leaflet triggers an **action potential**—a brief reversal in the polarity of the membrane charge. When an action potential occurs at the plasma membrane of a pulvinar

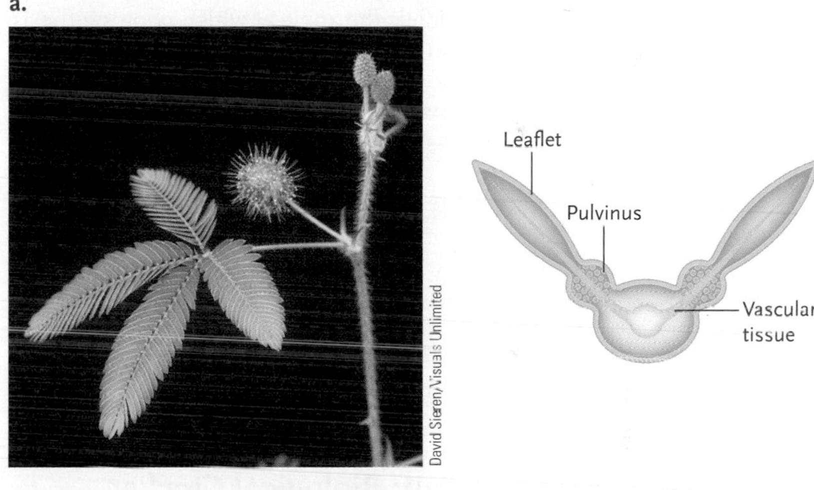

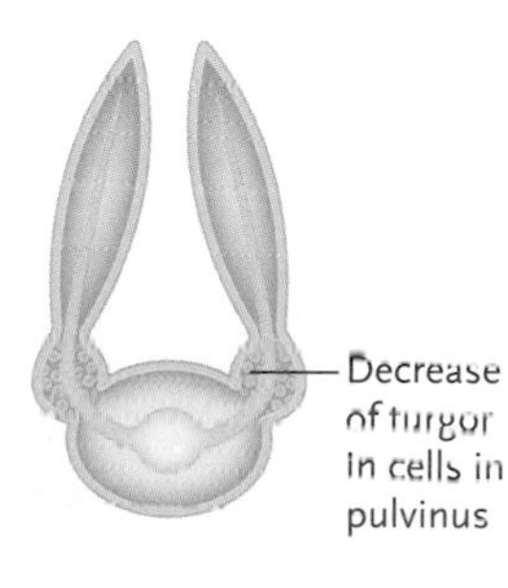

Figure 31.32
Nastic movements in the leaflets of *Mimosa pudica*, the sensitive plant. (a) In an undisturbed plant, the leaflets are open. If a leaflet near the leaf tip is touched, changes in turgor pressure in pulvini at the base cause the leaf to fold closed. **(b).** The diagrams show a cross-section of this folding movement. Other leaflets close in sequence as action potentials transmit the stimulus along the leaf.

cell, the change in polarity causes potassium ion (K^+) channels to open, and ions flow out of the cell, setting up an osmotic gradient that draws water out as well. As water leaves by osmosis, turgor pressure falls, pulvinar cells become flaccid, and the leaflets move together. Later, when the process is reversed, the pulvinar cells regain turgor, and the leaflets spread apart. Action potentials travel between parenchyma cells in the pulvini via plasmodesmata at the rate of about 2 cm/sec. Animal nerves conduct similar changes in membrane polarity along their plasma membranes (see Chapter 33). These changes in polarity, which are also called action potentials, occur much more rapidly—at velocities between 1 and 100 m/sec.

Stimuli other than touch also can trigger action potentials leading to nastic movements. Cotton, soybean, sunflower, and some other plants display *solar tracking*, nastic movements in which leaf blades are oriented toward the east in the morning and then steadily change their position during the day, following the sun across the sky. Such movements maximize the amount of time that leaf blades are perpendicular to the sun, which is the angle at which photosynthesis is most efficient.

Study Break

1. What is the direct stimulus for phototropisms? For gravitropism?
2. Explain how nastic movements differ from tropic movements.

31.5 Plant Responses to the Environment: Biological Clocks

Like all eukaryotic organisms, plants have internal time-measuring mechanisms called **biological clocks** that adapt the organism to recurring environmental changes. In plants, biological clocks help adjust both daily and seasonal activities.

31.5a Circadian Rhythms Are Based on 24-Hour Cycles

Some plant activities occur regularly in cycles of about 24 hours, even when environmental conditions remain constant. These are **circadian rhythms** (*circa* = around; *dies* = day). In Chapter 29, we noted that stomata open and close on a daily cycle, even where plants are kept in total darkness. Nastic sleep movements, described earlier, are another example of a circadian rhythm. Even when such a plant is kept in constant light or darkness for a few days, it folds its leaves into the "sleep" position at roughly 24-hour intervals. In some way, the plant measures time without sunrise (light) and sunset (darkness). Such experiments demonstrate that internal controls, rather than external cues, largely govern circadian rhythms.

Circadian rhythms and other activities regulated by a biological clock help ensure that plants of a single species do the same thing, such as flowering, at the same time. For instance, flowers of the aptly named four o'clock plant (*Mirabilis jalapa*) open predictably every 24 hours—in nature, in the late afternoon. Such coordination can be crucial for successful pollination. Although some circadian rhythms can proceed without direct stimulus from light, many biological clock mechanisms are influenced by the relative lengths of day and night.

31.5b Photoperiodism Involves Seasonal Changes in the Relative Length of Night and Day

Obviously, environmental conditions in a 24-hour period are not the same in summer as they are in winter. In North America, for instance, winter temperatures are cooler and winter day length is shorter. Experimenting with tobacco and soybean plants in the early 1900s, two American botanists, Wightman Garner and Henry Allard, elucidated a phenomenon they called **photoperiodism**, in which plants respond to changes in the relative lengths of light and dark periods in their environment during each 24-hour period. Through photoperiodism, the biological clocks of plants (and animals) make seasonal adjustments in their patterns of growth, development, and reproduction.

In plants, we now know that a blue-green pigment called **phytochrome** often serves as a switching mechanism in the photoperiodic response, signalling the plant to make seasonal changes. Plants synthesize phytochrome in an inactive form, P_r, which absorbs the light of red wavelengths. Sunlight contains relatively more red light than far-red light. During daylight hours, when red wavelengths dominate, P_r absorbs red light. Absorption of red light triggers the conversion of phytochrome to an active form designated P_{fr}, which absorbs the light of far-red wavelengths. At sunset, at night, or even in shade, where far-red wavelengths predominate, P_{fr} reverts to P_r **(Figure 31.33)**.

In nature, a high concentration of P_{fr} "tells" a plant that it is exposed to sunlight, an adaptation that is vital given that, over time, sunlight provides favourable conditions for leaf growth, photosynthesis, and flowering. The exact mechanism of this crucial transfer of environmental information is still not fully understood. Botanists suspect that P_{fr} controls the types of enzymes being produced in particular cells—and different enzymes are required for seed germination, stem elongation and branching, leaf expansion, and the formation of flowers, fruits, and seeds. When plants adapted to full sunlight are grown in darkness,

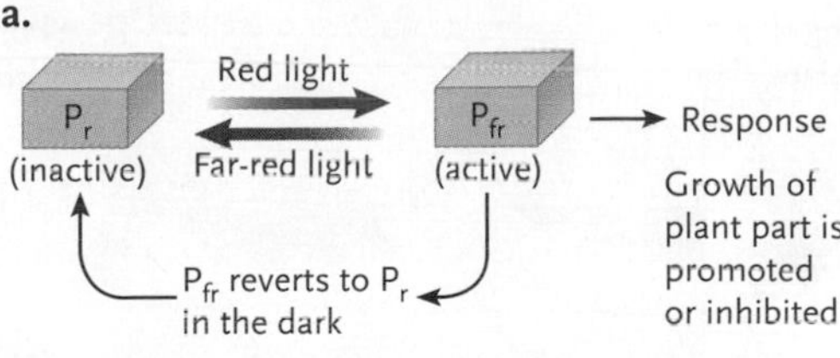

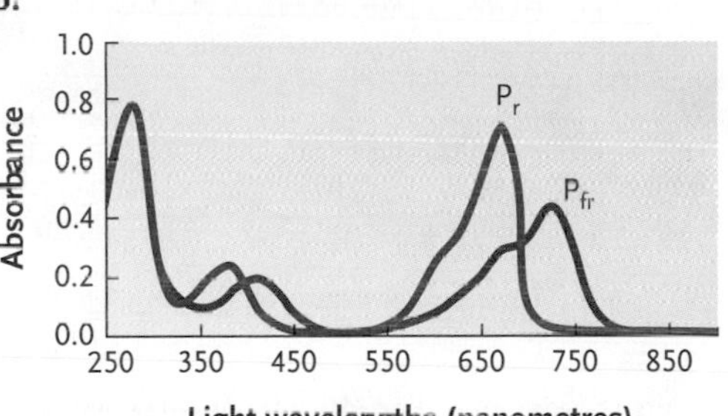

Figure 31.33
The phytochrome switching mechanism, which can promote or inhibit the growth of different plant parts. **(a)** Interconversion of phytochrome from the active form (P_{fr}) to the inactive form (P_r). **(b)** The absorption spectra associated with the interconversion of P_r and P_{fr}.

they put more resources into stem elongation and less into leaf expansion or stem branching **(Figure 31.34).**

Phytochrome also plays an important role in shade avoidance by plants. When seedlings germinate, they have a limited nutrient supply to support them until they can start to feed themselves by photosynthesis. They need to find a location with abundant light as soon as possible. Shade is rich in far-red light, which converts phytochrome to the P_r form, causing rapid elongation of the shoot, helping the seedling grow out of the shade and into sunlight.

Dwight Kuhn

Figure 31.34
Effects of the absence of light on young bean plants (*Phaseolus*). The two plants at the right, the control group, were grown in a greenhouse. The other two were grown in darkness for eight days. Note that the dark-grown plants are yellow; they could form carotenoid pigments but not chlorophyll in darkness. They have longer stems, smaller leaves, and smaller root systems than the controls.

Cryptochrome—which, recall, is sensitive to blue light and appears to influence light-related growth responses—also interacts with phytochromes in producing circadian responses. Researchers recently discovered that cryptochrome occurs not only in plants but also in animals such as fruit flies and mice (see *Molecule Behind Biology*). Does cryptochrome mediate a variety of light responses in animals as well as in plants? Recent research indicates that this may be the case. For example, cryptochromes are involved in bird navigation during migration. Migratory birds use a magnetic compass to orient themselves, and it appears that cryptochromes in the retinas of these birds allow the birds to "see" magnetic fields. Cryptochromes also play a role in photosensitive behaviour in animals that do not have eyes or other specialized light-sensing organs; for example, during the full moon in late spring, corals of the Great Barrier Reef undergo a mass spawning. Although biologists knew that changes in moonlight were one of the triggers for this mass spawning, they did not know how the corals were able to detect the light. Now a group of researchers from Australia and the United Kingdom have demonstrated that cryptochromes are present in these animals and that expression of one cryptochrome gene varies with the full moon.

31.5c Cycles of Light and Dark Often Influence Flowering

Photoperiodism is especially apparent in the flowering process. Like other plant responses, flowering is often keyed to changes in day length through the year and to the resulting changes in environmental conditions. Corn, soybeans, peas, and other annual plants begin flowering after only a few months of growth. Roses and other perennials typically flower every year or after several years of vegetative growth. Carrots, cabbages, and other biennials typically produce roots, stems, and leaves the first growing season; die back to soil level in autumn; and then grow a new flower-forming stem in the second season.

In the late 1930s, Karl Hamner and James Bonner grew cocklebur plants (*Xanthium strumarium*) in chambers in which the researchers could carefully control environmental conditions, including photoperiod. They made an unexpected discovery: flowering occurred only when the test plants were exposed to at least a single night of 8.5 hours of uninterrupted darkness. The length of the "day" in the growth chamber did not matter, but if light interrupted the dark period for even a minute or two, the plant would not flower at all. Subsequent research confirmed that for most angiosperms, the length of darkness, not light, controls flowering.

Kinds of Flowering Responses. The photoperiodic responses of flowering plants are so predictable that botanists have long used them to categorize plants

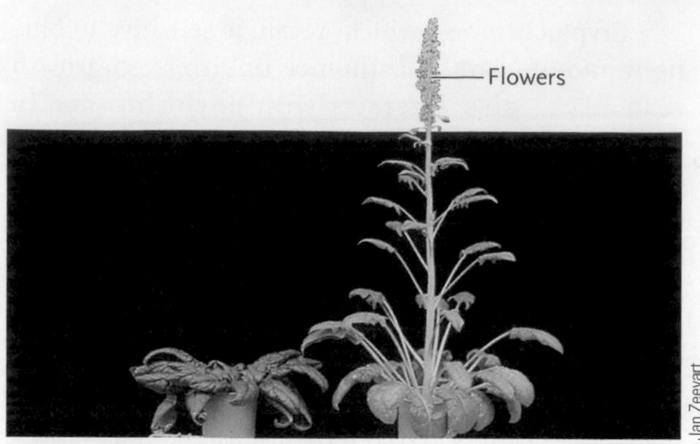

Figure 31.35
Effect of day length on spinach (*Spinacia oleracea*), a long-day plant.

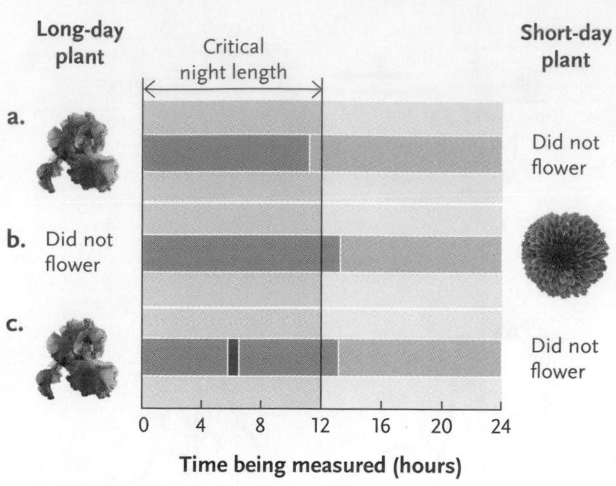

Figure 31.36
Experiments showing that short-day and long-day plants flower by measuring night length. Each horizontal bar signifies 24 hours. Blue bars represent night, and yellow bars represent day. **(a)** Long-day plants, such as bearded irises, flower when the night is shorter than a critical length, whereas **(b)** short-day plants, such as chrysanthemums, flower when the night is longer than a critical value. **(c)** When an intense red flash interrupts a long night, both kinds of plants respond as if it were a short night; the irises flowered, but the chrysanthemums did not.

(Figure 31.35). The categories, which refer to day length, reflect the fact that scientists recognized the phenomenon of photoperiodic flowering responses long before they understood that darkness, not light, was the cue. Long-day plants, such as irises, daffodils, and corn, usually flower in spring, when dark periods become shorter and day length becomes longer than some critical value—usually 9 to 16 hours. Short-day plants, including cockleburs, chrysanthemums, and potatoes, flower in late summer or early autumn, when dark periods become longer and day length becomes shorter than some critical value. Intermediate-day plants, such as sugarcane, flower only when day length falls between the values for long-day and short-day plants. Day-neutral plants, such as dandelions and roses, flower whenever they become mature enough to do so, without regard to photoperiod.

Experiments demonstrate what happens when plants are grown under the "wrong" photoperiod regimens. For instance, spinach, a long-day plant, flowers and produces seeds only if it is exposed to no more than 10 hours of darkness each day for 2 weeks (see Figure 31.27). **Figure 31.36** illustrates the results of an experiment to test the responses of short-day and long-day plants to night length. In this experiment, bearded iris plants (*Iris* species), which are long-day plants, and chrysanthemums, which are short-day plants, were exposed to a range of light conditions. In each case, when the researchers interrupted a critical dark period with a pulse of red light, the light reset the plants' clocks. The experiment showed clearly that short-day plants flower only when nights are longer than a critical value, and long-day plants flower only when nights are shorter than a critical value.

Chemical Signals for Flowering. When photoperiod conditions are right, what sort of chemical message stimulates a plant to develop flowers? In the 1930s, botanists began postulating the existence of "florigen," a hypothetical hormone that served as the flowering signal. In a somewhat frustrating scientific quest, researchers spent the rest of the twentieth century seeking this substance in vain. Recently, however, molecular studies using *Arabidopsis* plants have defined a sequence of steps that may collectively provide the internal stimulus for flowering. Here again, we see one of the recurring themes in plant development—major developmental changes guided by several interacting genes.

Figure 31.37 traces the steps of the proposed flowering signal. To begin with, a gene called *CONSTANS* is expressed in a plant's leaves in tune with the daily light/dark cycle, with expression peaking at dusk (step 1). The gene encodes a regulatory protein called CO (not to be confused with carbon monoxide). As days lengthen in spring, the concentration of CO rises in leaves, and as a result, a second gene is activated (step 2). The product of this gene, a protein called FT, travels in the phloem to shoot tips (step 3). Once there, the mRNA is translated into a second regulatory protein (step 4) that in some way interacts with yet a third regulatory protein that is synthesized only in shoot apical meristems (step 5). The encounter apparently sparks the development of a flower (step 6) by promoting the expression of floral organ identity genes in the meristem tissue (see Section 34.5).

Vernalization and Flowering. Flowering is more than a response to changing night length. Temperatures also change with the seasons in most parts of the world, and they, too, influence flowering. For instance, unless the buds of some biennials and perennials are exposed to low winter temperatures, flowers do not form on stems in spring. Low-temperature stimulation of flowering is called **vernalization** ("making springlike").

In 1915, the plant physiologist Gustav Gassner demonstrated that it was possible to influence the flowering

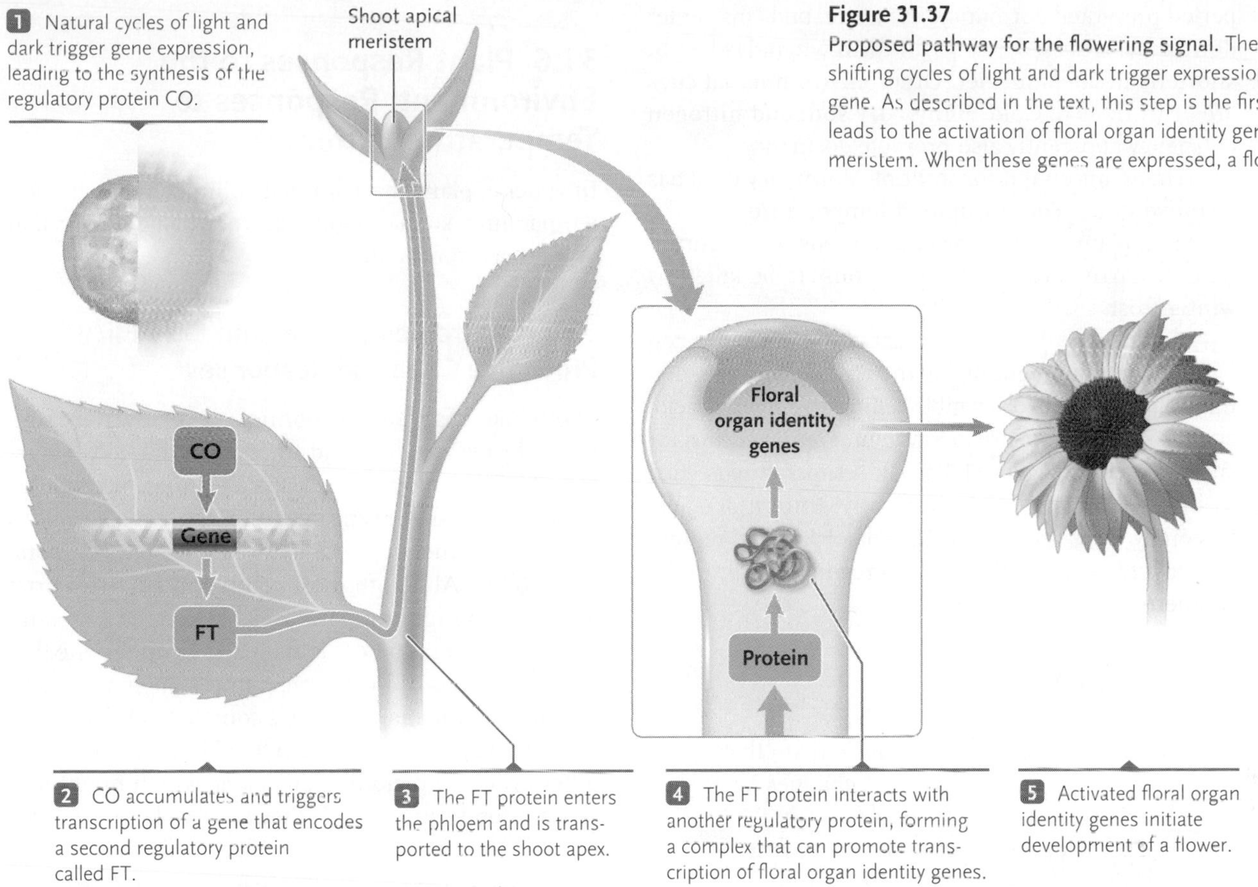

1 Natural cycles of light and dark trigger gene expression, leading to the synthesis of the regulatory protein CO.
Shoot apical meristem
CO
Gene
FT
Floral organ identity genes
Protein
2 CO accumulates and triggers transcription of a gene that encodes a second regulatory protein called FT.
3 The FT protein enters the phloem and is transported to the shoot apex.
4 The FT protein interacts with another regulatory protein, forming a complex that can promote transcription of floral organ identity genes.
5 Activated floral organ identity genes initiate development of a flower.

Figure 31.37
Proposed pathway for the flowering signal. The pathway starts as shifting cycles of light and dark trigger expression of the *CONSTANS* gene. As described in the text, this step is the first in a sequence that leads to the activation of floral organ identity genes in the shoot apical meristem. When these genes are expressed, a flower develops.

of cereal plants by controlling the temperature of seeds while they were germinating. In one case, he maintained germinating seeds of winter rye (*Secale cereale*) at just above freezing (1°C) before planting them. In nature, winter rye seeds planted in soil germinate during the winter, giving rise to a plant that flowers months later, in summer. Plants grown from Gassner's test seeds, however, flowered the same summer even when the seeds were planted in the late spring. Home gardeners can induce flowering of daffodils and tulips by putting the bulbs (technically, *corms*) in a freezer for several weeks before early spring planting. Commercial growers use vernalization to induce millions of plants, such as Easter lilies, to flower just in time for seasonal sales.

31.5d Dormancy Is an Adaptation to Seasonal Changes or Stress

As autumn approaches and days grow shorter, growth slows or stops in many plants even if temperatures are still moderate, the sky is bright, and water is plentiful. When a perennial or biennial plant stops growing under conditions that seem (to us) quite suitable for growth, it has entered a state of **dormancy**. Ordinarily, its buds will not resume growth until early spring.

Short days and long nights—conditions typical of winter—are strong cues for dormancy. In one experiment, in which a short period of red light interrupted the long dark period for Douglas firs, the plants responded as if the nights were shorter and the days were longer; they continued to grow taller **(Figure 31.38).** Conversion of P_r to P_{fr} by red light during the dark

Figure 31.38
Effect of the relative length of day and night on the growth of Douglas firs (*Pseudotsuga menziesii*). The young tree at the left was exposed to alternating periods of 12 hours of light followed by 12 hours of darkness for a year; its buds became dormant because day length was too short. The tree at the right was exposed to a cycle of 20 hours of light and 4 hours of darkness; its buds remained active, and growth continued. The middle plant was exposed each day to 12 hours of light and 11 hours of darkness, with a 1-hour light in the middle of the dark period. This light interruption of an otherwise long dark period also prevented buds from going dormant.

period prevented dormancy. In nature, buds may enter dormancy because less P_{fr} can form when day length shortens in late summer. Other environmental cues are at work also. Cold nights, dry soil, and nitrogen deficiency apparently also promote dormancy.

The requirement for multiple dormancy cues has adaptive value. For example, if temperature were the only cue, plants might flower and seeds might germinate in warm autumn weather—only to be killed by winter frost.

A dormancy-breaking process is at work between fall and spring. Depending on the species, breaking dormancy probably involves gibberellins and abscisic acid, and it requires exposure to low winter temperatures for specific periods **(Figure 31.39).** The temperature needed to break dormancy varies greatly among species. Generally, trees growing in Canada or Sweden require longer cold exposure than those growing in Italy or the southern United States.

Study Break

1. Summarize the switching mechanism that operates in plant responses to changes in photoperiod.
2. Give some examples of how relative lengths of dark and light can influence flowering.
3. Explain why dormancy is an adaptive response to a plant's environment.

Eric Welzel/Fox Hill Nursery, Freeport, Maine
Potted plant grown inside a greenhouse did not flower.
Branch exposed to cold outside air flowered.

Figure 31.39
Effect of cold temperature on dormant buds of a lilac (*Syringa vulgaris*). In this experiment, a branch of the plant was positioned so that it grew out of a hole in a greenhouse during winter; the rest of the plant was inside, at warm temperatures. Only the buds on the branch exposed to low outside temperatures resumed growth in spring. This experiment suggests that low-temperature effects are localized.

31.6 Plant Responses to the Environment: Responses to Temperature Extremes

In general, plants have limited ability to regulate their temperature, so their temperature usually mirrors that of their environment.

31.6a Extremes of Heat and Cold Elicit Protective Chemical Responses

Plants use evaporative cooling—loss of water from leaves by evaporation and transpiration—to regulate their leaf temperature. If water becomes limiting, as on a hot, dry day in the summer, a plant's stomates will close, reducing its ability to cool itself by evaporative cooling. Although most plants can survive a brief exposure to high temperatures, prolonged exposure to such temperatures is lethal, largely due to the detrimental effects of high temperatures on enzymes. As do other organisms, plant cells contain **heat-shock proteins (HSPs)**, a type of protein that binds and stabilizes other proteins, including enzymes, which might otherwise stop functioning if they were to become denatured by rising temperature. Plant cells may rapidly synthesize HSPs in response to a sudden temperature rise. For example, experiments with the cells and seedlings of soybean (*Glycine max*) showed that when the temperature rose 10° to 15°C, in less than 5 minutes, mRNA transcripts coding for as many as 50 different HSPs were present in the cells. When the temperature returns to a normal range, HSPs release bound proteins, which can then resume their usual functions. Further studies have revealed that HSPs help protect plant cells subjected to other environmental stresses as well, including drought, salinity, and cold.

Like extreme heat, freezing can also be lethal to plants. If ice crystals form in cells, they can literally tear the cell apart. In many cold-resistant species, dormancy is the long-term strategy for dealing with cold, but in the short term, such as an unseasonable cold snap, some species also undergo a rapid shift in gene expression that equips cold-stressed cells with so-called antifreeze proteins. Like HSPs, these molecules are thought to help maintain the structural integrity of other cell proteins.

Researchers are actively investigating mechanisms that regulate plant response to extreme temperatures as these offer promise for the development of new crop lines that can survive in harsh habitats.

Unanswered Questions

Do plants have a "backup" copy of their genome?

As described at the beginning of this chapter, land plants manifest adaptations that allow them to survive and reproduce in unfavourable or hostile conditions. Adaptations include changes in growth and development reflecting responses to environmental fluctuations that occur naturally during the normal life cycle of plants. Being physically anchored in one place has driven plant adaptation so that changes in the plant body can facilitate survival. It is also possible, however, that the sessile existence of land plants may have selected for unusual adaptive strategies. Might plants have devised a strategy to utilize previously unknown genetic resources and thereby expand their potential repertoire of adaptive responses? Recent findings demonstrating the existence of a previously unknown mechanism of genetic instability suggest that such a strategy may indeed have been in place during the evolution of land plants. These findings suggest that, at least in *Arabidopsis thaliana*, a "backup" copy of the genome exists that can be accessed under unfavourable conditions.

Why have a backup copy of the genome? Simply put, if the system crashes, it can be restored. By analogy, the genome could be considered the "operating system" stored on the "hard drive" of the organism. If that operating system becomes corrupted, for example, by a devastating power surge or a computer virus, a global systems failure might occur. However, if a backup copy were maintained at least in a subset of the population, then, under conditions that might lead to extinction, the backup copy could be used to "restore" the system and increase the chances of survival for that organism or population. In other words, the genome could adapt using the stored information.

An intriguing possibility is that such a backup genome might exist in the form of RNA. The fact that backup copies have not been found using conventional DNA-based detection methods or classical genetic approaches leaves open the exciting possibility that RNA might serve as the storage medium for this information. In a sense, having the information stored in an alternative chemical form (analogous to a different computer language or code) might also make it less susceptible to corruption. Furthermore, it may be that this backup genome is a remnant of an ancestral condition in which the genome was RNA based.

How would you go about testing these different possibilities? First, the findings would have to be independently verified and the existence of a "restoration" mechanism would have to be confirmed by other research groups working on *Arabidopsis* or other plant species. Second, the source and chemical nature of the backup information would need to be identified. Where is it, and is it RNA, DNA, protein, or a combination of these? The question of mechanism would also need to be addressed. How is the system restored, and when does it happen? The question of how global this phenomenon is would also need to be considered. Do all plant species maintain a backup copy, and do organisms outside the plant kingdom have a backup genome?

Susan Lolle is associate professor of biology at the University of Waterloo. Her research interests include plant development, genetics, and genome biology. To learn more, go to http://www.biology.uwaterloo.ca.

Review

Go to CENGAGENOW™ at http://hed.nelson.com/ to access quizzing, animations, exercises, articles, and personalized homework help.

31.1 Plant Hormones

- At least seven classes of hormones govern flowering plant development, including germination, growth, flowering, fruit set, and senescence.
- Auxins, mainly IAA, promote elongation of cells in the coleoptile and stem.
- Gibberellins promote stem elongation and help seeds and buds break dormancy.
- Cytokinins stimulate cell division, promote leaf expansion, and retard leaf aging.
- Ethylene promotes fruit ripening and abscission.
- Brassinosteroids stimulate cell division and elongation.
- Abscisic acid (ABA) promotes stomatal closure and may trigger seed and bud dormancy.
- Jasmonates regulate growth and have roles in defence.

31.2 Signal Responses at the Cellular Level

- Hormones and environmental stimuli alter the behaviour of target cells, which have receptors to which signal molecules can bind. By means of a response pathway that ultimately alters gene expression, a signal can induce changes in the cell's shape or internal structure or influence its metabolism or the transport of substances across the plasma membrane.
- Some plant hormones and growth factors may bind to receptors at the target cell's plasma membrane, changing the receptor's shape. This binding often triggers the release of internal second messengers that diffuse through the cytoplasm and provide the main chemical signal that alters gene expression.
- Second messengers usually act by way of a reaction sequence that amplifies the cell's response to a signal. An activated receptor, in turn, activates a series of proteins, including G proteins and enzymes that stimulate the synthesis of second messengers (such as IP_3) that bind ion channels on endoplasmic reticulum.
- Binding releases calcium ions, which enter the cytoplasm and activate protein kinases, enzymes that activate specific proteins that produce the cell response.

31.3 Plant Chemical Defences

- Plants have diverse chemical defences that limit damage from bacteria, fungi, worms, or plant-eating insects.
- The hypersensitive response isolates an infection site by surrounding it with dead cells. During the response, salicylic acid (SA) induces the synthesis of PR (pathogenesis-related) proteins.

- Oligosaccharins can trigger the synthesis of phytoalexins, secondary metabolites that function as antibiotics.
- Gene-for-gene recognition enables a plant to chemically recognize a pathogen and mount defences against it.
- Systemic acquired resistance provides long-term protection against some pathogens. Salicylic acid passes from the infected organ to newly forming organs such as leaves, which then synthesize PR proteins

31.4 Plant Responses to the Environment: Movements

- Plants adjust their growth patterns in response to environmental rhythms and unique environmental circumstances. These responses include tropisms.
- Phototropisms are growth responses to a directional light source. Blue light is the main stimulus for phototropism.
- Gravitropism is a growth response to Earth's gravitational pull. Stems exhibit negative gravitropism, growing upward, whereas roots show positive gravitropism.
- Some plants or plant parts demonstrate thigmotropism, growth in response to contact with a solid object.
- Mechanical stress can cause thigmomorphogenesis, which causes the stem to add girth.
- In nastic leaf movements, water enters or exits the cells of a pulvinus, a pad of tissue at the base of a leaf or petiole, in response to action potentials.

31.5 Plant Responses to the Environment: Biological Clocks

- Plants have biological clocks, internal time-measuring mechanisms with a biochemical basis. Environmental cues can "reset" the clocks, enabling plants to make seasonal adjustments in growth, development, and reproduction.
- In photoperiodism, plants respond to a change in the relative length of daylight and darkness in a 24-hour period. A switching mechanism involving the pigment phytochrome promotes or inhibits germination, growth, and flowering and fruiting.
- Phytochrome is converted to an active form (P_{fr}) during daylight, when red wavelengths dominate. It reverts to an inactive form (P_r) at sunset, at night, or in shade, when far-red wavelengths predominate. P_{fr} may control the types of metabolic pathways that operate under specific light conditions.
- Long-day plants flower in spring or summer, when day length is long relative to night. Short-day plants flower when day length is relatively short, and intermediate-day plants flower when day length falls between the values for long-day and short-day plants. Flowering of day-neutral plants is not regulated by light. In vernalization, a period of low temperature stimulates flowering.
- The direct trigger for flowering may begin in leaves, when the regulatory protein CO triggers the expression of the *FT* gene. The resulting mRNA transcripts move in phloem to apical meristems, where translation of the mRNAs yields a second regulatory protein, which, in turn, interacts with a third. This final interaction activates genes that encode the development of flower parts.
- Senescence is the sum of processes leading to the death of a plant or plant structure.
- Dormancy is a state in which a perennial or biennial stops growing even though conditions appear to be suitable for continued growth.

31.6 Plant Responses to the Environment: Responses to Temperature Extremes

- Heat-shock proteins can reversibly bind enzymes and other proteins in plant cells and prevent them from denaturing when the plant is under heat stress.
- Some plants can synthesize "antifreeze" proteins that stabilize cell proteins when cells are threatened with freezing.

Questions

Self-Test Questions

1. Which of the following plant hormones does *not* stimulate cell division?
   a. auxins
   b. cytokinins
   c. ethylene
   d. gibberellins
   e. abscisic acid
2. Which is the correct pairing of a plant hormone and its function?
   a. salicylic acid: triggers synthesis of general defence proteins
   b. brassinosteroids: promote responses to environmental stress
   c. cytokinins: stimulate stomata to close in water-stressed plants
   d. gibberellins: slow seed germination
   e. ethylene: promotes formation of lateral roots
3. Fruit bowls and hanging wire fruit baskets often have many holes or open spaces. The major advantage of these spaces is that they
   a. prevent gibberellins from causing bolting or the formation of rosettes on the fruit.
   b. allow the evaporation of ethylene and thus slow ripening of the fruit.
   c. allow oxygen in the air to stimulate the production of ethylene, which hastens the abscission of fruits.
   d. allow oxygen to stimulate brassinosteroids, which hasten the maturation of seeds in/on the fruits.
   e. allow carbon dioxide in the air to stimulate the production of cytokinins, which promotes mitosis in the fruit tissue and hastens ripening.
4. Which of the following is *not* an example of a plant chemical defence?
   a. ABA inhibits leaves from budding if conditions favour attacks by sap-sucking insects.
   b. Jasmonate activates plant genes encoding protease inhibitors that prevent insects from digesting plant proteins.
   c. Acting against fungal infections, the hypersensitive response allows plants to produce highly reactive oxygen compounds that kill selected tissue, thus forming a dead tissue barrier that walls off the infected area from healthy tissues.
   d. Chitinase, a PR hydrolytic protein produced by plants, breaks down chitin in the cell walls of fungi and thus halts the fungal infection.
   e. Attack by fungi or viruses triggers the release of oligosaccharins, which, in turn, stimulate the production of phytoalexins with antibiotic properties.

5. Which of the following statements about plant responses to the environment is true?
   a. The heat-shock response induces a sudden halt to cellular metabolism when an insect begins feeding on plant tissue.
   b. In gravitropism, amyloplasts sink to the bottom of cells in a plant stem, causing the redistribution of IAA.
   c. The curling of tendrils around a twig is an example of thigmotropism.
   d. Phototropism results when IAA moves first laterally and then downward in a shoot tip when one side of the tip is exposed to light.
   e. Nastic movements, such as the sudden closing of the leaves of a Venus flytrap, are examples of a plant's ability to respond to specific directional stimuli.
6. In nature, the poinsettia, a plant native to Mexico, blooms only in or around the month of December. This pattern suggests that
   a. the long daily period of darkness (short day) in December stimulates the flowering.
   b. vernalization stimulates the flowering.
   c. the plant is dormant for the rest of the year.
   d. phytochrome is not affecting the poinsettia flowering cycle.
   e. a circadian rhythm is in effect.
7. Which of the following steps is *not* part of the sequence that is thought to trigger flowering?
   a. Cycles of light and dark stimulate the expression of the *CONSTANS* gene in a plant's leaves.
   b. CO proteins accumulate in the leaves and trigger expression of a second regulatory gene.
   c. mRNA transcribed during expression of a second regulatory gene moves via the phloem to the shoot apical meristem.
   d. Interactions among several regulatory proteins promote the expression of floral organ identity genes in meristem tissue.
   e. CO proteins in the floral meristem interact with florigen, a so-called flowering hormone, which provides the final stimulus for expression of floral organ identity genes.
8. Damage from an infectious bacterium, fungus, or worm may trigger a plant defensive response when the pathogen or a substance it produces binds to
   a. a receptor encoded by the plant's *avirulence* (*Avr*) gene.
   b. an *R* gene in the plant cell nucleus.
   c. a receptor encoded by a dominant *R* gene.
   d. PR proteins embedded in the plant cell plasma membrane.
   e. salicylic acid molecules released from the besieged plant cell.

Questions for Discussion

1. You work for a plant nursery and are asked to design a special horticultural regimen for a particular flowering plant. The plant is native to northern Spain, and in the wild, it grows a few long, slender stems that produce flowers each July. Your boss wants the nursery plants to be shorter, with thicker stems and more branches, and she wants them to bloom in early-December in time for holiday sales. Outline your detailed plan for altering the plant's growth and reproductive characteristics to meet these specifications.
2. Synthetic auxins such as 2,4-D can be weed killers because they cause an abnormal growth burst that kills the plant within a few days. Suggest reasons why such rapid growth might be lethal to a plant.
3. In experiments, the shoots of mutant plants lacking differentiated endodermis in their root and shoot tissue don't respond normally to gravity, but the roots of such plants do respond normally. Explain this finding, based on your reading in this chapter.
4. In *A. thaliana* plants carrying a mutation called *pickle (pkl)*, the primary root meristem retains characteristics of embryonic tissue—it spontaneously regenerates new embryos that can grow into mature plants. However, when the mutant root tissue is exposed to a gibberellin (GA), this abnormal developmental condition is suppressed. Explain why this finding suggests that additional research is needed on the fundamental biological role of GA.

Magnetic resonance imaging (MRI) whole body scans of a man (left), a 9-year-old boy (middle), and a woman. Various organs can be seen in the scans: the whitish skeleton throughout the bodies, the brains within the skulls, lungs (dark) in the chests, lobes of the liver (green and brown ovals) in the abdomens, and bladders (dark ovals) in the lower abdomens.

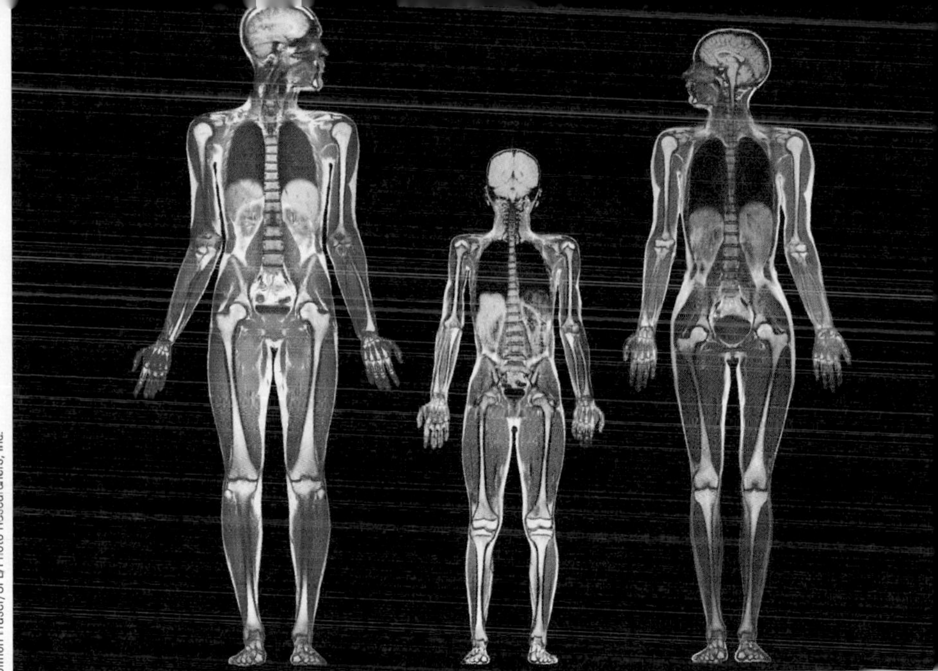

Simon Fraser/SFL/Photo Researchers, Inc.

32 Introduction to Animal Organization and Physiology

Study Plan

Why It Matters

After a cold night in Africa's Kalahari Desert, gray meerkats (*Suricata suricatta*), a type of mongoose, awaken in their burrows. Although, like all mammals, meerkats regulate their body temperature, their internal temperature falls during cold nights. If the sun is shining in the morning and warms their burrows, the meerkats emerge and stand on their hind legs facing east, warming their bodies in the rays of the sun **(Figure 32.1, p. 766)**. This sunning behaviour helps raise their body temperature.

Once the meerkats warm up, they fan out from their burrows looking for food, mainly insects and an occasional lizard. Their highly integrated body systems allow them to move about, sense the presence of prey, react with speed and precision to capture those prey, and consume them. Within their bodies, the food is broken down into glucose and other nutrient molecules, which are transported throughout the body to provide energy for living. At the same time, mechanisms are constantly at work to maintain the animals' internal environment at a level that keeps body cells functioning. The maintenance of the internal environment in a stable state is called **homeostasis** (*homeo* = the same; *stasis* = standing or stopping). The processes and activities

Figure 32.1 Meerkats lining up to warm themselves in sunlight.

responsible for homeostasis are called **homeostatic mechanisms.** These mechanisms compensate both for the external environmental changes that the meerkats encounter as they explore places with differences in temperature, humidity, and other physical conditions, as well as for changes in their own body systems.

All animals have body systems for acquiring and digesting nutrients to provide energy for life, growth, reproduction, and movement. Biologists are interested in the structures and functions of these systems. **Anatomy** is the study of the structures of organisms, and **physiology** is the study of their functions. An understanding of structure is essential to an understanding of physiology, and an understanding of normal physiology is essential to the diagnosis and treatment of many diseases, such as Parkinson disease.

In this chapter, we begin with the organization of individual cells into tissues, organs, and organ systems, the major body structures that carry out animal activities. Our discussion continues with the coordination of the processes and activities of organ systems that accomplish homeostasis. The other chapters in this unit discuss the individual organ systems that carry out major body functions such as digestion, movement, and reproduction. Although we emphasize vertebrates throughout the unit, with particular reference to human physiology, we also make comparisons with invertebrates, to keep the structural and functional diversity of the animal kingdom in perspective and to understand the evolution of the structures and processes involved.

32.1 Organization of the Animal Body

32.1a In Animals, Specialized Cells Are Organized into Tissues, Tissues into Organs, and Organs into Organ Systems

The individual cells of animals have the same requirements as cells of any kind. They must be surrounded by an aqueous solution that contains ions and molecules required by the cells, including complex organic molecules that can be used as energy sources. The concentrations of these molecules and ions must be balanced to keep cells from shrinking or swelling excessively due to osmotic water movement. Most animal cells also require oxygen to serve as the final acceptor for electrons removed in oxidative reactions. Animal cells must be able to release waste molecules and other by-products of their activities, such as carbon dioxide, to their environment. The physical conditions of the cellular environment, such as temperature, must also remain within tolerable limits.

The evolution of multicellularity (see Section 2.5) made it possible for organisms to create an *internal fluid environment* that supplies all the needs of individual cells, including nutrient supply, waste removal, and osmotic balance. This internal environment allows multicellular organisms to occupy diverse habitats, including dry terrestrial habitats that would be lethal to single cells. Multicellular organisms can also become relatively large because their individual cells remain small enough to exchange ions and molecules with the internal fluid. The fluid occupying the spaces between cells in multicellular animals is called **interstitial fluid** or **extracellular fluid.**

The evolution of multicellularity also allowed major life functions to be subdivided among specialized groups of cells, with each group concentrating on a single activity. In animals, some groups of cells became specialized for movement, others for food capture, digestion, internal circulation of nutrients, excretion of wastes, reproduction, and other functions. Specialization greatly increases the efficiency by which animals carry out these functions.

In most animals, these specialized groups of cells are organized into tissues, the tissues into organs, and the organs into organ systems **(Figure 32.2).** A **tissue** is a group of cells with the same structure and function, working together as a unit to carry out one or more activities. The tissue lining the inner surface of the intestine, for example, is specialized to absorb nutrients released by digestion of food in the intestinal cavity.

An **organ** integrates two or more different tissues into a structure that carries out a specific function. The eye, liver, and stomach are examples of organs. Thus, the stomach integrates several different tissues into an organ specialized for processing food.

An **organ system** coordinates the activities of two or more organs to carry out a major body function such as movement, digestion, or reproduction. The organ system carrying out digestion, for example, coordinates the activities of organs, including the mouth, stomach, pancreas, liver, and small and large intestines. Some organs contribute functions to more than one organ system. For instance, the pancreas forms part of the endocrine system as well as the digestive system.

Study Break

1. What are some advantages for an organism being multicellular?
2. What is the difference between a tissue, an organ, and an organ system?

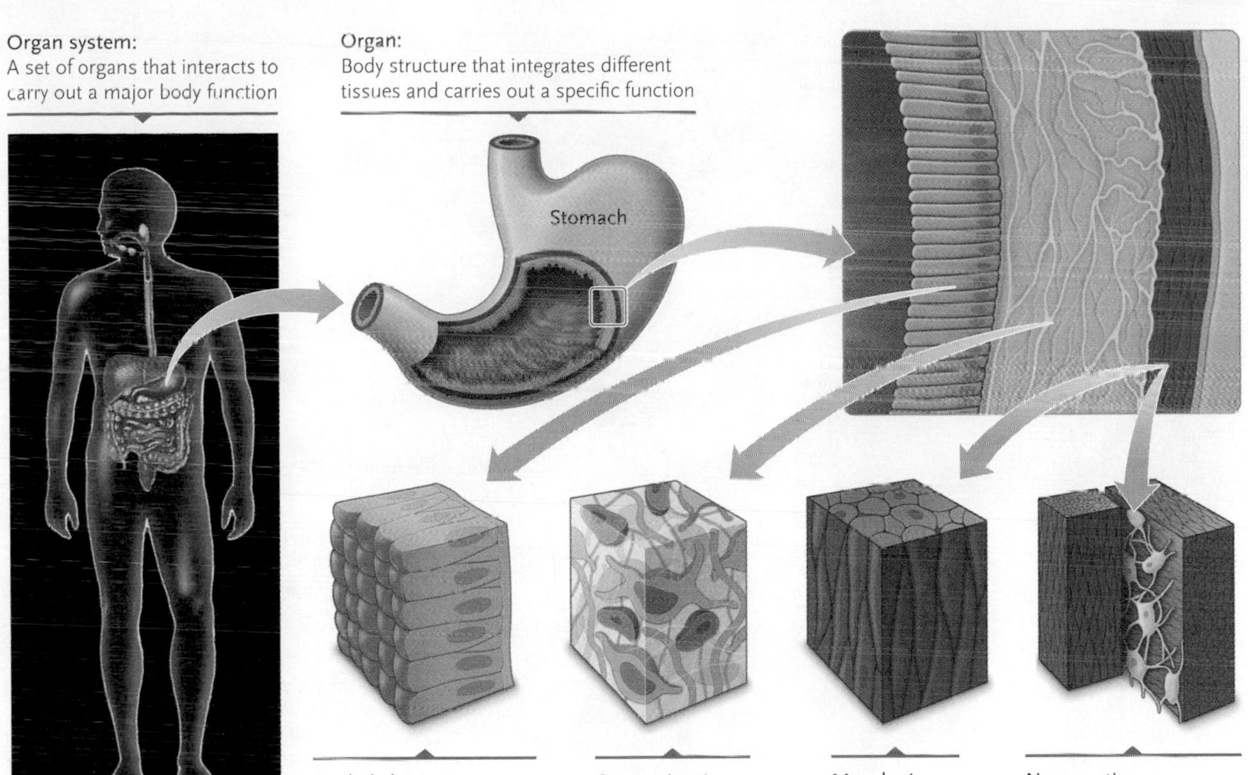

Figure 32.2 Organization of animal cells into tissues, organs, and organ systems.

32.2 Animal Tissues

Although the most complex animals may contain hundreds of distinct cell types, all can be classified into one of four basic tissue groups: *epithelial, connective, muscle,* and *nervous* (see Figure 32.2). Each tissue type is assembled from individual cells. The properties of those cells determine the structure and, therefore, the function of the tissue. More specifically, the structure and integrity of a tissue depend on the structure and organization of the cytoskeleton within the cell, the type and organization of the extracellular matrix surrounding the cell, and the junctions holding cells together. The **extracellular matrix** (ECM) is nonliving material secreted by cells consisting of a variety of proteins and glycoproteins. The ECM provides support and shape for tissues and organs. The cell walls of plants and the cuticle of arthropods are examples of specialized ECM.

Junctions of various kinds link cells into tissues (see **Figure 32.3, p. 768**). *Anchoring junctions* form buttonlike spots or belts that weld cells together. They are most abundant in tissues subject to stretching, such as skin and heart muscle. *Tight junctions* seal the spaces between cells, keeping molecules and even ions from leaking between cells. For example, tight junctions in the tissue lining the urinary bladder prevent waste molecules and ions from leaking out of the bladder into other body tissues. *Gap junctions* are open channels between cells in the same tissue, allowing ions and small molecules to flow freely from one to another. For example, gap junctions between muscle cells help muscle tissue to function as a unit.

Let us now consider the structural and functional features that distinguish the four types of tissues, with primary emphasis on the forms they take in vertebrates.

32.2a Epithelial Tissue Forms Protective, Secretory, and Absorptive Coverings and Linings of Body Structures

Epithelial tissue (*epi* = over; *thele* = covering) consists of sheetlike layers of cells that are usually joined tightly together, with little ECM material between them (**Figure 32.4, p. 769**). Also called *epithelia* (singular, *epithelium*), these tissues cover body surfaces and the surfaces of internal organs, as well as line cavities and ducts within the body. They protect body surfaces from invasion by bacteria and viruses and secrete or absorb substances. For example, the epithelium covering a fish's gill structures serves as a barrier to bacteria and viruses and exchanges oxygen, carbon dioxide, and ions with the aqueous environment. The epithelium of the external surface of arthropods secretes the tough cuticle that, in addition to acting as a barrier to the environment, functions

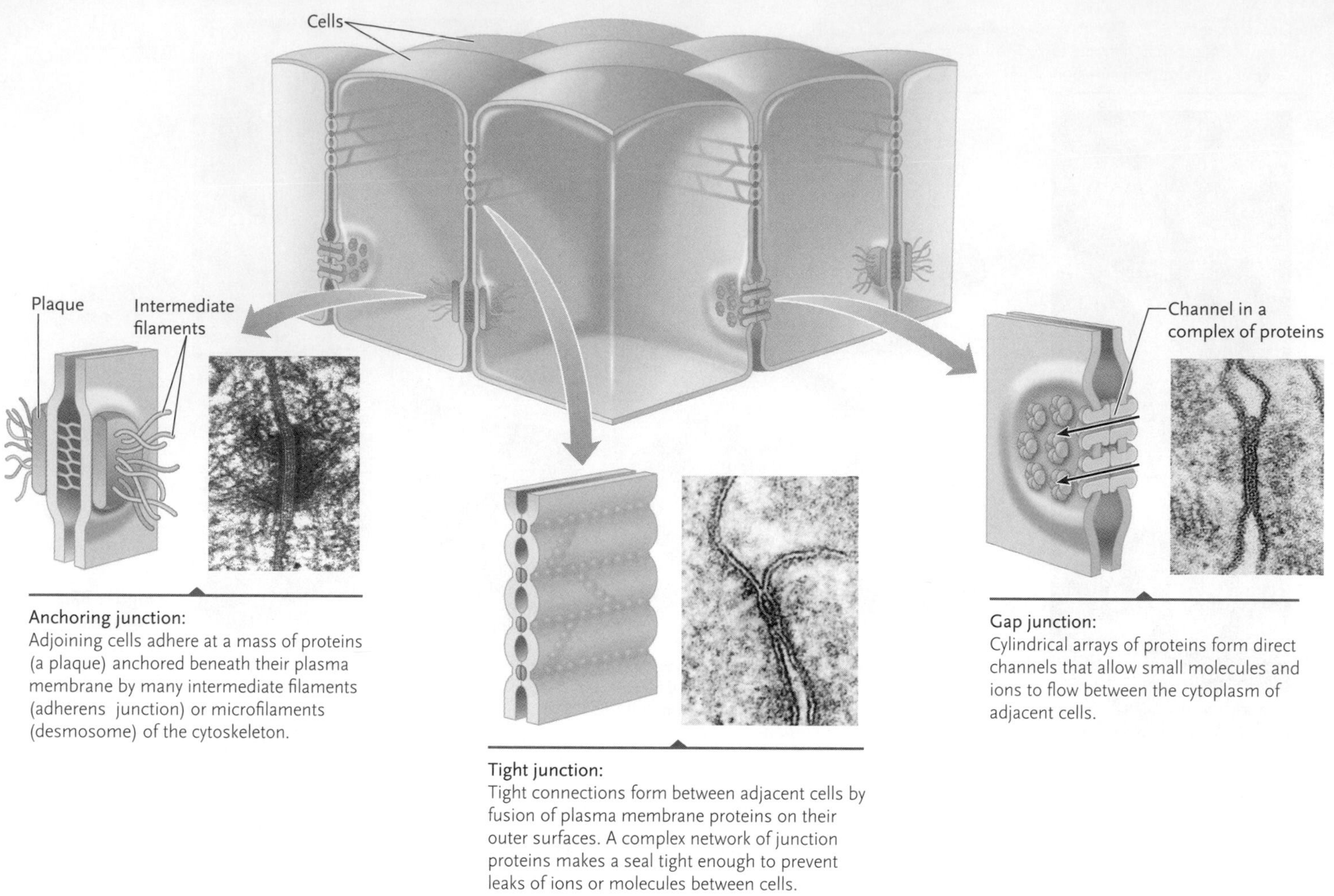

Cells
Plaque
Intermediate filaments
Channel in a complex of proteins
Anchoring junction:
Adjoining cells adhere at a mass of proteins (a plaque) anchored beneath their plasma membrane by many intermediate filaments (adherens junction) or microfilaments (desmosome) of the cytoskeleton.
Tight junction:
Tight connections form between adjacent cells by fusion of plasma membrane proteins on their outer surfaces. A complex network of junction proteins makes a seal tight enough to prevent leaks of ions or molecules between cells.
Gap junction:
Cylindrical arrays of proteins form direct channels that allow small molecules and ions to flow between the cytoplasm of adjacent cells.

Figure 32.3
Anchoring junctions, tight junctions, and gap junctions, which connect cells in animal tissues. Anchoring junctions reinforce the cell-to-cell connections made by cell adhesion molecules, tight junctions seal the spaces between cells, and gap junctions create direct channels of communication between animal cells.

as their skeleton. Nematodes also have a cuticle, but their skeleton is hydrostatic (see Chapter 26).

Some epithelia, such as those lining the capillaries of the circulatory system, act as filters, allowing ions and small molecules to leak from the blood into surrounding tissues while barring the passage of blood cells and large molecules such as proteins.

Because epithelia form coverings and linings, they have one free (or outer) surface, which may be exposed to water, air, or fluids within the body. In internal cavities and ducts, the free surface is often covered with *cilia,* which beat like oars to move fluids through the cavity or duct. The epithelium lining the oviducts in mammals, for example, is covered with cilia that generate fluid currents to move eggs from the ovaries to the uterus. In free-living flatworms, the ventral epithelium of the animal is frequently ciliated, allowing the worm to glide over surfaces. In some epithelia, including the lining of the small intestine, the free surface is crowded with *microvilli,* fingerlike extensions of the plasma membrane that increase the area available for secretion or absorption.

The inner surface of an epithelium adheres to a layer of glycoproteins secreted by the epithelial cells called the **basal lamina,** which is secreted by the epithelial cells. In many cases, such as the intestinal epithelium of vertebrates, there is a further layer of fibres secreted by underlying connective tissue, but this is lacking in most invertebrate epithelia. The entire assemblage is the **basement membrane.** The basal lamina is an example of an ECM.

Epithelial Cell Structure. Epithelia are classified as *simple*—formed by a single layer of cells—or *stratified*—formed by multiple cell layers (see **Figure 32.4a**). The shapes of cells within an epithelium may be *squamous* (mosaic, flattened, and spread out), *cuboidal* (shaped roughly like dice or cubes), or *columnar* (elongated, with the long axis perpendicular to the epithelial layer; see **Figure 32.4b**). For example, the outer epithelium of mammalian skin is stratified and contains columnar, cuboidal, and squamous cells; the epithelium lining blood vessels is

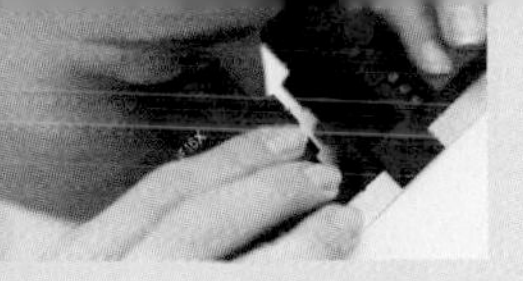

People Behind Biology
Samuel Weiss: Neural Stem Cells

Through much of the twentieth century, one of the dogmas of developmental biology held that the number of neurons in an adult brain was fixed. Once adulthood was reached, no new neurons appeared. Those neurons lost in the normal aging process or by trauma or disease could not be replaced.

In the early 1990s, Samuel Weiss at the University of Calgary, together with his graduate student, Brent Reynolds, was exploring how growth factors (see Chapter 8) might be used to protect the brain. When they applied the growth factors to mouse brain cells in culture, they discovered some cells that were capable of division and that could differentiate into both neurons and glial cells. They realized that they had found adult neural stem cells. The publication of their results in 1992 generated enormous excitement as scientists explored the possibility that brains damaged by trauma or disease might be stimulated to repair themselves.

This extraordinary discovery, as is so often the case, was accidental. But it required a receptive and agile mind to appreciate its significance and to explore what was previously considered to be impossible.

simple and squamous; and the intestinal epithelium is simple and columnar.

The cells of some epithelia, such as those forming the skin and the lining of the intestine, divide constantly to replace worn and dying cells. New cells are produced through division of stem cells in the basal (lowest) layer of the skin. *Stem cells* are undifferentiated (unspecialized) cells in the tissue that divide to produce more stem cells as well as cells that differentiate (that is, become specialized into one of the many cell types of the body). Stem cells are found in both adult organisms and embryos. Besides the skin, adult stem cells are found in tissues of the brain, bone marrow, blood vessels, skeletal muscle, and liver. Stem cells are an important aspect of development in many invertebrates. In some cases, these may be already programmed for a specific cell type as in the eye or wing disks of insect pupae, whereas in others, the stem cells may be totipotent, as in flatworms (Chapter 26).

a. Patterns by which cells are arranged in epithelia

Simple epithelium

Free surface

Epithelium

Stratified epithelium

b. The three common shapes of epithelial cells

Squamous epithelium

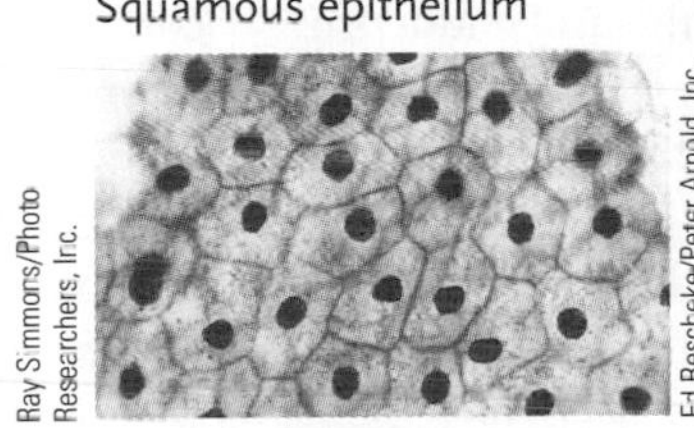

Cuboidal epithelium

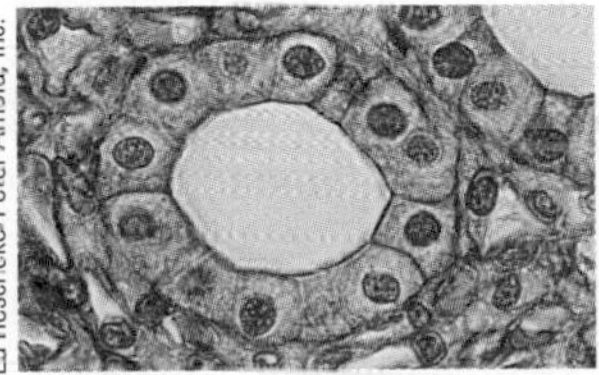

Columnar epithelium

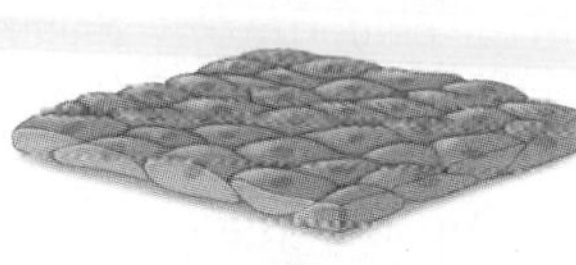

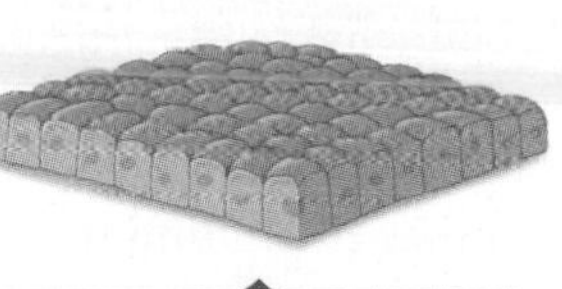

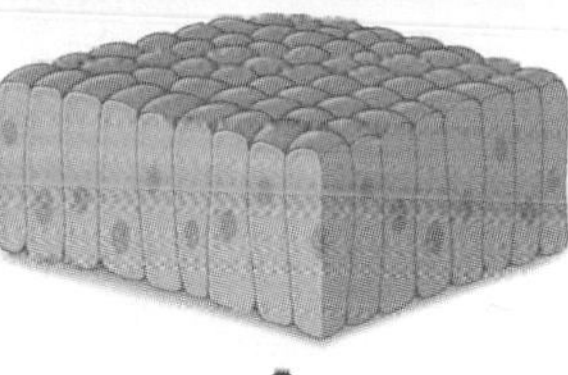

Description: Layer of flattened cells
Common locations: Walls of blood vessels; air sacs of lungs
Function: Diffusion

Description: Layer of cubelike cells; free surface may have microvilli
Common locations: Glands and tubular parts of nephrons in kidneys
Function: Secretion, absorption

Description: Layer of tall, slender cells; free surface may have microvilli
Common locations: Lining of gut and respiratory tract
Function: Secretion, absorption

Figure 32.4 Structure of epithelial tissues.

Glands Formed by Epithelia. Epithelia typically contain or give rise to cells that are specialized for secretion. Some of these secretory cells are scattered among nonsecretory cells within the epithelium. Others form structures called **glands**, which are derived from pockets of epithelium during embryonic development.

Some glands, called **exocrine glands** (*exo* = external; *crine* = secretion), remain connected to the epithelium by a duct, which empties their secretion at the epithelial surface. Exocrine secretions include mucus, saliva, digestive enzymes, sweat, earwax, oils, milk, and venom (**Figure 32.5a, p. 770** shows an exocrine gland in the skin of a poisonous tree frog). Other glands, called **endocrine** glands, may not be composed of epithelial cells. They have no ducts but secrete their products, hormones, into the interstitial fluid to be picked up by the blood for circulation to the organs

Figure 32.5
Exocrine and endocrine glands. The poison secreted by the blue poison frog (*Dendrobates azureus*) is one of the most lethal glandular secretions known.

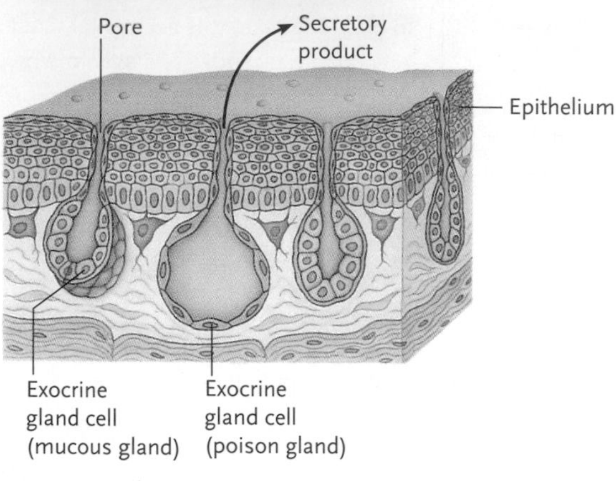

a. Examples of exocrine glands: The mucus- and poison-secreting glands in the skin of a blue poison frog

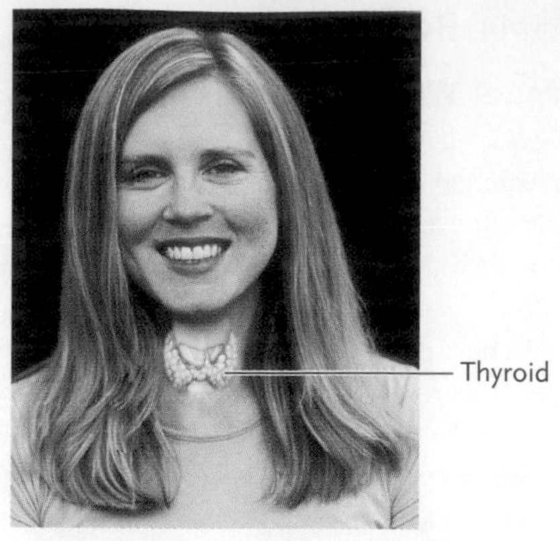

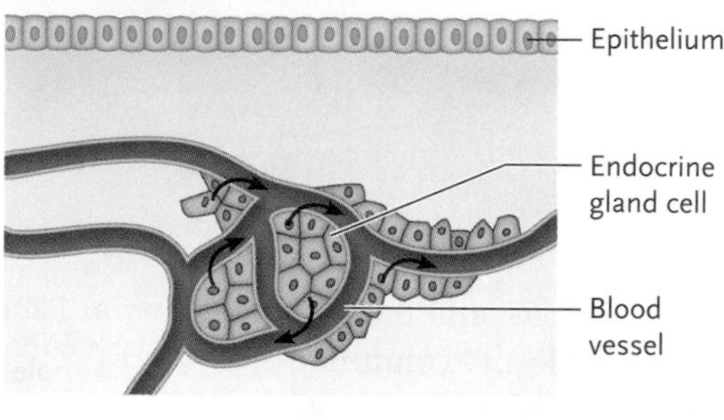

b. Example of an endocrine gland: The thyroid gland, which secretes hormones that regulate the rate of metabolism and other body functions

and tissues of the body **(Figure 32.5b)**. The endocrine glands are considered in detail in Chapter 35.

Some glands contain both exocrine and endocrine elements. The pancreas, for example, has an exocrine function of secreting pancreatic juice through a duct into the small intestine, where it plays an important role in food digestion (see Chapter 41), and different cells provide an endocrine function by secreting the hormones insulin and glucagon into the bloodstream to help regulate glucose levels in the blood (see Chapter 35).

Some epithelial cells, particularly in the epidermis of vertebrates, contain a network of fibres of keratin, a family of tough proteins. Keratin forms the scales of fish and reptiles (including the shells of turtles), the feathers of birds, and the hair, claws, hooves, horns, and fingernails of mammals.

32.2b Connective Tissue Supports Other Body Tissues

Most animal body structures contain one or more types of **connective tissue.** Connective tissues support other body tissues, transmit mechanical and other forces, and in some cases act as filters. They consist of cells that form networks or layers in and around body structures and that are separated by nonliving material, specifically the ECM secreted by the cells of the tissue. Many forms of connective tissue have more ECM material (both by weight and by volume) than cellular material.

The mechanical properties of a connective tissue depend on the type and quantity of its ECM. The consistency of the ECM ranges from fluid (as in blood and lymph), through soft and firm gels (as in tendons), to the hard and crystalline (as in bone). In most connective tissues, the ECM consists primarily of the fibrous glycoprotein **collagen** embedded in a network of proteoglycans—glycoproteins that are very rich in carbohydrates. Collagen is the most abundant protein in animals. More than 25 different forms have been described, and some form of collagen occurs in all Metazoa, including Porifera (sponges). The collagen molecule is thus an ancient one that has been modified during evolution. In bone, the glycoprotein network surrounding the collagen is impregnated with mineral deposits that produce a hard, yet still somewhat elastic, structure. Another class of glycoproteins, **fibronectin**, aids in the attachment of cells to the ECM and helps hold the cells in position.

In some connective tissues, another rubbery protein, **elastin**, adds elasticity to the ECM. It is able to return to its original shape after being stretched, bent, or compressed. Elastin fibres, for example, help the skin return to its original shape when pulled or stretched and give the lungs the elasticity required for their alternating inflation and deflation. Resilin is a protein related to elastin that occurs only in insects and some Crustacea. It is the most elastic material known and is the basis for the jumping of fleas and locusts (see *Molecule Behind Biology*).

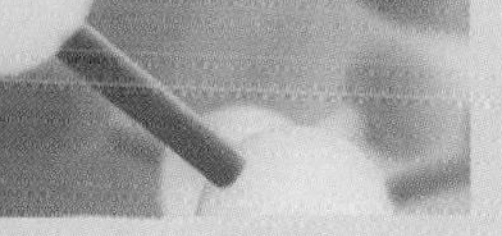

Molecule Behind Biology

Resilin: Insect Rubber

While Torkel Weis-Fogh, a young Danish comparative physiologist, was conducting his ground-breaking studies on insect flight in the Zoological Laboratory in Cambridge, England, in 1960, he discovered patches of highly elastic cuticle in the wing joints of locusts. Subsequently, the same elastic protein proved to be important to other insect movements. For example, it is involved in the movements of the membrane that produces the song of cicadas. Fleas are able to jump very large distances because muscle contractions store energy in pads of resilin in the hind legs **(Figure 1)**. The sudden release of this energy, in less than a millisecond, propels the jump with an instantaneous acceleration greater than that of the space shuttle.

Resilin belongs to the same family of proteins as elastin, an elastic protein in many animals, but it is restricted to insects and a few crustacea. Resilin's elastic properties have proved to be astonishing. It can be stretched to four times its length without breaking (elastin only manages two). It is 97% efficient, so that when energy stored in it by stretching is released, only 3% is released as heat. It survives huge numbers of cycles of stretch and relaxation. The membrane producing the song of cicadas vibrates several thousand times per second. Like other elastic proteins, resilin is composed of coiled protein molecules cross-linked to one another, and stretching involves uncoiling.

In 2005, a gene coding for *Drosophila* resilin was cloned in *E. coli* by a team led by Christopher Elvin of the Commonwealth Scientific and Industrial Research Organisation in Australia. That lab is now able to produce significant quantities of resilin. Ultimately, this insect rubber should find application, for example, as replacements for spinal disks in humans or as artificial blood vessels.

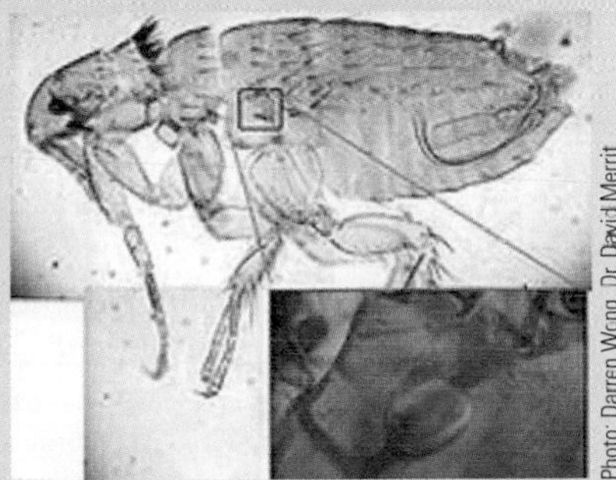

Figure 1 The pad of resilin (blue) in the coxa (part of the thigh) of the hind leg of a flea.

Vertebrates have six major types of connective tissue: *loose connective tissue, fibrous connective tissue, cartilage, bone, adipose tissue,* and *blood.* Each type has a characteristic function correlated with its structure **(Figure 32.6, p. 772).**

Loose Connective Tissue. **Loose connective tissue** consists of sparsely distributed cells surrounded by a more or less open network of collagen and other glycoprotein fibres (see Figure 32.6a). The cells, called **fibroblasts,** secrete most of the collagen and other proteins in this connective tissue.

In vertebrates, loose connective tissues support epithelia and form a corsetlike band around blood vessels, nerves, and some internal organs; they also reinforce deeper layers of the skin. Sheets of loose connective tissue, covered on both surfaces with epithelial cells, form the **mesenteries,** which hold the abdominal organs in place and provide lubricated, smooth surfaces that prevent chafing or abrasion between adjacent structures as the body moves. In insects, and perhaps some other invertebrates, the loose connective tissues suspending organs and providing support for epithelia are the products of specialized cells circulating in the blood.

Fibrous Connective Tissue. In **fibrous connective tissue,** fibroblasts are sparsely distributed among dense masses of collagen and elastin fibres that are lined up in highly ordered, parallel bundles (see Figure 32.5b). The parallel arrangement produces maximum tensile strength and elasticity. Examples include **tendons,** which attach muscles to bones, and **ligaments,** which connect bones to each other at a joint. The cornea of the eye is a transparent fibrous connective tissue formed from highly ordered collagen molecules.

In some invertebrates, fibrous connective tissue provides shape to the animal, as in many sponges (see Chapter 26) and echinoderms. In sea cucumbers (see Chapter 27), the rigidity of the connective tissue can be changed quickly by the animal, resulting in a loss or change of shape. This acts as an escape response.

Cartilage. **Cartilage** consists of sparsely distributed cells called **chondrocytes,** surrounded by networks of collagen fibres embedded in a tough but elastic matrix of the glycoprotein *chondroitin sulphate* (see Figure 32.6c). Elastin is also present in some forms of cartilage.

The elasticity of cartilage allows it to resist compression and stay resilient, like a piece of rubber. Bending your ear or pushing the tip of your nose, which are supported by cores of cartilage, gives a good idea of the flexible nature of this tissue. Cartilage also supports the larynx, trachea, and smaller air passages in the lungs. It forms the disks cushioning the vertebrae in the spinal column and the smooth, slippery capsules around the ends of bones in joints such as the hip and knee. Cartilage also serves as a precursor to bone during embryonic development;

Figure 32.6
The six major types of connective tissues in vertebrates.

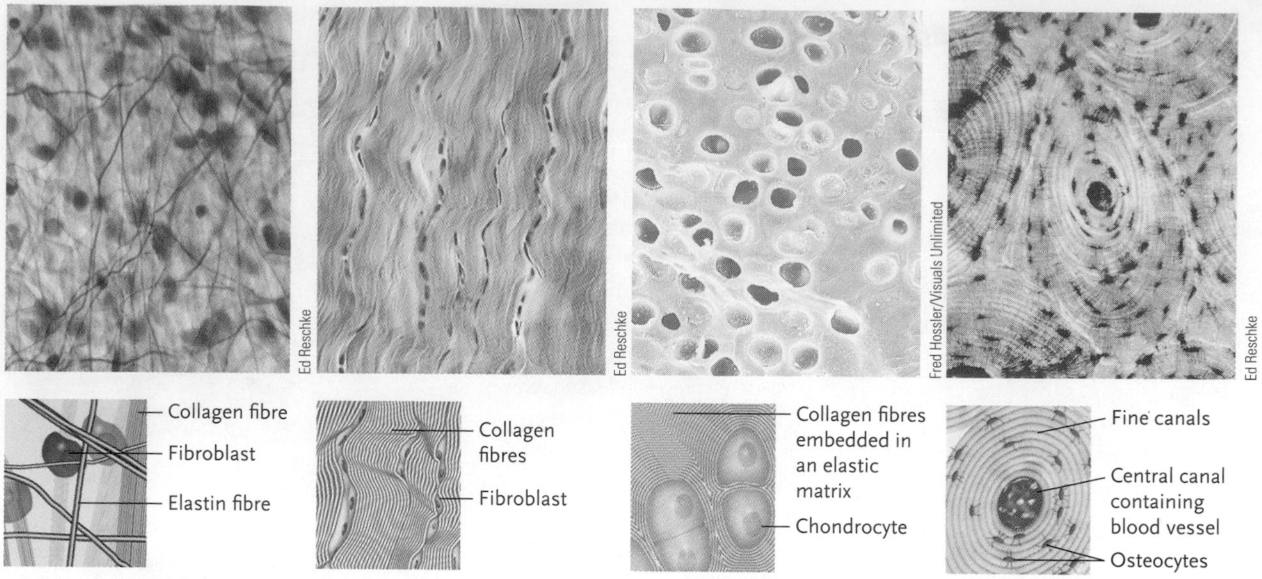

a. Loose connective tissue

Ed Reschke

Collagen fibre
Fibroblast
Elastin fibre

Description: Fibroblasts and other cells surrounded by collagen and elastin fibres forming a glycoprotein matrix

Common locations: Under the skin and most epithelia

Function: Support, elasticity, diffusion

b. Fibrous connective tissue

Ed Reschke

Collagen fibres
Fibroblast

Description: Long rows of fibroblasts surrounded by collagen and elastin fibres in parallel bundles with a dense extracellular matrix

Common locations: Tendons, ligaments

Function: Strength, elasticity

c. Cartilage

Fred Hossler/Visuals Unlimited

Collagen fibres embedded in an elastic matrix
Chondrocyte

Description: Chondrocytes embedded in a pliable, solid matrix of collagen and chondroitin sulphate

Common locations: Ends of long bones, nose, parts of airways, skeleton of vertebrate embryos

Function: Support, flexibility, low-friction surface for joint movement

d. Bone tissue

Ed Reschke

Fine canals
Central canal containing blood vessel
Osteocytes

Description: Osteocytes in a matrix of collagen and glycoproteins hardened with hydroxyapatite

Common locations: Bones of vertebrate skeleton

Function: Movement, support, protection

e. Adipose tissue

f. Blood

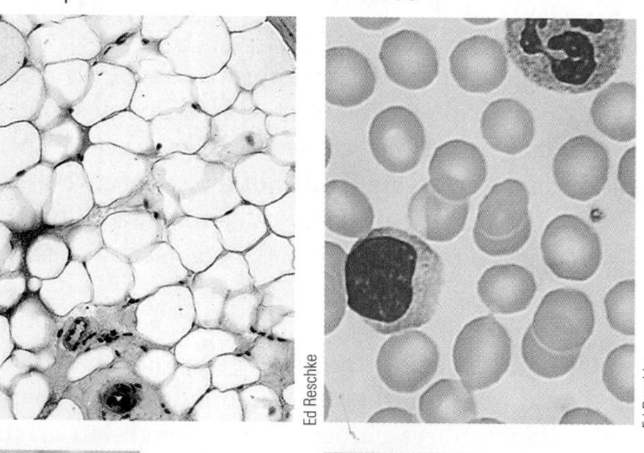

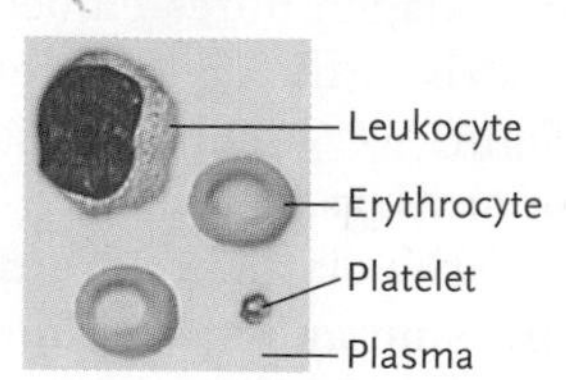

Description: Large, tightly packed adipocytes with little extracellular matrix

Common locations: Under skin; around heart, kidneys

Function: Energy reserves, insulation, padding

Description: Leukocytes, erythrocytes, and platelets suspended in a plasma matrix

Common locations: Circulatory system

Function: Transport of substances

in sharks and rays and their relatives, almost the entire skeleton remains as cartilage in adults.

Bone. The densest form of connective tissue, **bone**, forms the skeleton, which supports the body, protects softer body structures such as the brain, and contributes to body movements.

Mature bone consists primarily of cells called **osteocytes** (*osteon* = bone) embedded in an ECM containing collagen fibres and glycoproteins impregnated with *hydroxyapatite*, a calcium–phosphate mineral (see Figure 32.6d). The collagen fibres give bone tensile strength and elasticity; the hydroxyapatite resists compression and allows bones to support body weight. Cells called **osteoblasts** (*blast* = bud or sprout) produce the collagen and mineral of bone—as much as 85% of the weight of bone is mineral deposits. Osteocytes, in fact, are osteoblasts that have become trapped and surrounded by the bone materials they themselves produce. **Osteoclasts** (*clast* = break) remove the minerals and recycle them through the bloodstream. Bone is not a stable tissue; it is reshaped continuously by the bone-building osteoblasts and the bone-degrading osteoclasts.

Although bones appear superficially to be solid, they are actually porous structures consisting of a system of microscopic spaces and canals. The structural unit of bone is the **osteon.** It consists of a minute central canal surrounded by osteocytes embedded in concentric layers of mineral matter (see Figure 32.6d). A blood vessel and extensions of nerve cells run through the central canal, which is connected to the spaces containing cells by very fine, radiating canals filled with interstitial fluid. The blood vessels supply nutrients to the cells with which the bone is built, and the nerve cells connect the bone and its cells to the body's nervous system.

Adipose Tissue. The connective tissue called **adipose tissue** mostly contains large, densely clustered cells called *adipocytes* that are specialized for fat storage (see Figure 32.6e). It has little ECM. Adipose tissue also cushions the body and, in mammals, forms an especially important insulating layer under the skin.

The animal body stores limited amounts of carbohydrates, primarily in muscle and liver cells. Excess carbohydrates are converted into the fats stored in adipocytes. The storage of chemical energy as fats offers animals a weight advantage. For example, the average human would weigh about 45 kg (100 pounds) more if the same amount of chemical energy were stored as carbohydrates instead of fats. Adipose tissue is richly supplied with blood vessels, which move fats or their components to and from adipose cells.

In invertebrates, fat or glycogen storage may occur in a variety of tissues. Insects have a fat body, an organ that functions both for storage and as an important structure for metabolism, much like the vertebrate liver. In nematodes and flatworms, the muscle cells take on this function.

Blood. Blood is considered to be a connective tissue because the fluid portion is essentially a fluid form of ECM. Blood functions as the principal transport vehicle to carry nutrients, oxygen (in most animals), and hormones to the tissues and to remove metabolic wastes for transport to the organs specialized for waste removal. It is also frequently involved in defence against disease (Chapter 44) and may be important in wound healing.

Vertebrates have two basic types of cells suspended in a straw-coloured fluid, the plasma (see Figure 32.6f). Erythrocytes (erythros = red), or red blood cells, contain haemoglobin, a protein to which O_2 binds; these are specialized for O_2 transport. Several types of leukocytes (leukos = white) protect the body against foreign elements such as viruses and bacteria. These are considered in Chapter 37. Vertebrate blood also contains platelets (often called thrombocytes), which are membrane-bound fragments of specialized leukocytes. They play an essential role in the formation of blood clots to heal wounds.

In invertebrates, the functions of vertebrate blood are carried out in several different ways. Some, such as annelids and cephalopods, have blood enclosed in blood vessels; others, such as the arthropods and many molluscs, have a more open system. Haemoglobin or other oxygen-carrying pigments may be present either within special cells, as in some annelids, or as part of the plasma. Blood cells in insects are known to take part in wound healing and protection against foreign bodies.

32.2c Muscle Tissue Produces the Force for Body Movements

Muscle tissue consists of cells that have the ability to contract (shorten). The contractions, which depend on the interaction of two proteins—*actin* and *myosin*—move body limbs and other structures, pump the blood, and produce a squeezing pressure in organs such as the intestine and uterus. Three types of muscle tissue, *skeletal, cardiac,* and *smooth,* produce body movements in vertebrates **(Figure 32.7, p. 774).**

Skeletal Muscle. Skeletal muscle is so called because most muscles of this type are attached by tendons to the skeleton. Skeletal muscle cells are also called **muscle fibres** because each is an elongated cylinder (see Figure 32.7a). These cells contain many nuclei and are packed with actin and myosin molecules arranged in highly ordered, parallel units that give the tissue a banded or striated appearance when viewed under a microscope. Muscle fibres packed side by side into parallel bundles surrounded by sheaths of connective tissue form many body muscles, such as the biceps.

Skeletal muscle contracts in response to signals carried by the nervous system. The contractions of skeletal muscles, which are characteristically rapid and powerful, move body parts and maintain posture. The contractions also release heat as a by-product of cellular metabolism. This heat helps mammals, birds, and some other vertebrates maintain their body temperatures when environmental temperatures fall. (Skeletal muscle is discussed further in Chapter 36.)

Cardiac Muscle. Cardiac muscle is the contractile tissue of the heart (see Figure 32.7b). Cardiac muscle has a striated appearance because it contains actin and myosin molecules arranged like those in skeletal muscle. However, cardiac muscle cells are short and branched, with each cell connecting to several neighbouring cells; the joining point between two such cells is called an *intercalated disk.* Cardiac muscle cells thus form an interlinked network, which is stabilized by anchoring junctions and gap junctions. This network makes heart muscle contract in all directions, producing a squeezing or pumping action rather than the lengthwise, unidirectional contraction characteristic of skeletal muscle.

Figure 32.7
Structure of skeletal, cardiac, and smooth muscle.

a. Skeletal muscle

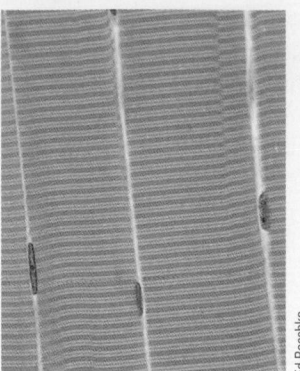

Width of one muscle cell (muscle fibre)

Cell nucleus

Description: Bundles of long, cylindrical, striated, contractile cells called muscle fibres

Typical location: Attached to bones of skeleton

Function: Locomotion, movement of body parts

b. Cardiac muscle

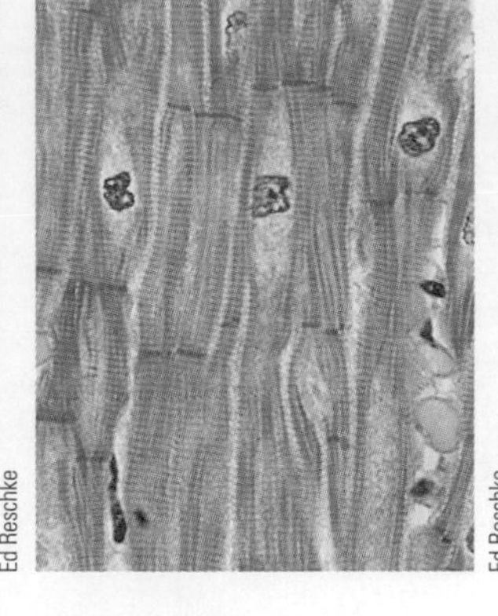

Cell nucleus

Intercalated disk

Description: Cylindrical, striated cells that have specialized end junctions

Location: Wall of heart

Function: Pumping of blood within circulatory system

c. Smooth muscle

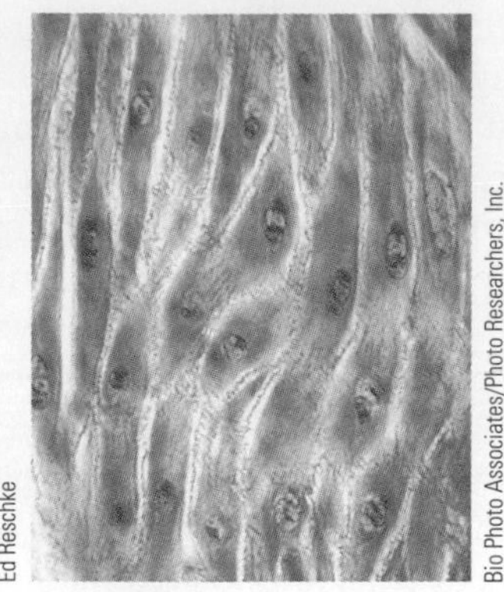

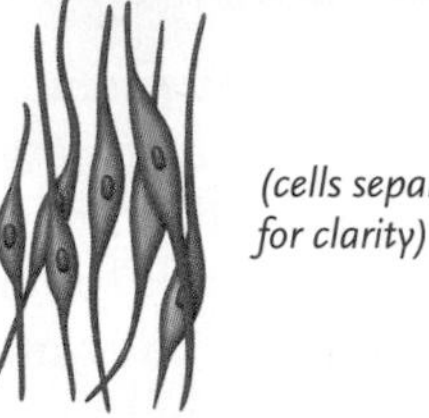

Description: Contractile cells with tapered ends

Typical location: Wall of internal organs, such as stomach

Function: Movement of internal organs

Smooth Muscle. **Smooth muscle** is found in the walls of tubes and cavities in the body, including blood vessels, the stomach and intestine, the bladder, and the uterus. Smooth muscle cells are relatively small and spindle-shaped (pointed at both ends), and their actin and myosin molecules are arranged in a loose network rather than in bundles (see Figure 32.7c). This loose network makes the cells appear smooth rather than striated when viewed under a microscope. Smooth muscle cells are connected by gap junctions and enclosed in a mesh of connective tissue. The gap junctions transmit ions that make smooth muscles contract as a unit, typically producing a squeezing motion. Although smooth muscle contracts more slowly than skeletal and cardiac muscles do, its contractions can be maintained at steady levels for a much longer time. These contractions move and mix the stomach and intestinal contents, constrict blood vessels, and push the infant out of the uterus during childbirth.

Invertebrate Muscle. In general, most invertebrates have striated muscles throughout, even muscles involved with structures such as the intestine or reproductive ducts. There are, however, some differences in the way that these muscles are organized. In nematodes, the muscle cell includes both a contractile area and a large expansion of the cell containing the nucleus, which acts as a glycogen store **(Figure 32.8)**. The cell does not receive nerves but makes a connection with the nervous system by an extension of the muscle to the nerve cords. The muscles of cestodes and possibly all flatworms have a similar form, but they are unstriated. In insects, the striated muscles that control the movements of some of the viscera, such as the ovaries and parts of the digestive system, are frequently branched and interconnected to form a lattice.

32.2d Nervous Tissue Receives, Integrates, and Transmits Information

Nervous tissue contains cells called **neurons** (also called *nerve cells*) that serve as lines of communication and control between body parts. Billions of neurons are packed into the human brain; others extend throughout the body. Nervous tissue also contains **glial cells** (*glia* = glue), which physically support and provide nutrients to neurons, provide electrical insulation between them, and scavenge cellular debris and foreign matter. Some neurons are specialized to form endocrine glands, as in the pituitary of vertebrates and the corpus cardiacum of insects (see Chapter 35).

A neuron consists of a *cell body,* which houses the nucleus and organelles, and two types of cell extensions, dendrites and axons **(Figure 32.9)**. *Dendrites* receive chemical signals from other neurons or from body cells of other types and convert them into an electrical signal that is transmitted to the cell body of the receiving neuron. Dendrites are usually highly

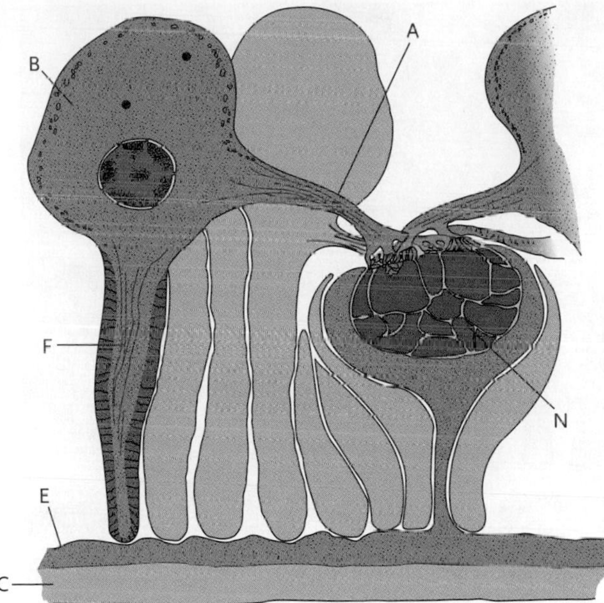

Figure 32.8
Muscle cell in *Ascaris lumbricoides.* The foot, F, of the muscle contains the contractile elements; the body, B, has the nucleus and is packed with glycogen; the arm, A, is an extension that makes contact with the nerve cord, N. The muscle cell is attached by fine fibres to the epidermis, E, beneath the cuticle, C.

branched. *Axons* conduct electrical signals away from the cell body to the axon terminals, or endings. At their terminals, axons convert the electrical signal to a chemical signal that stimulates a response in nearby muscle cells, gland cells, or other neurons. Axons are usually unbranched except at their terminals. Depending on the type of neuron and its location in the body, its axon may extend from a few micrometres or millimetres to more than a metre. (Neurons and their organization in body structures are discussed further in Chapter 33.)

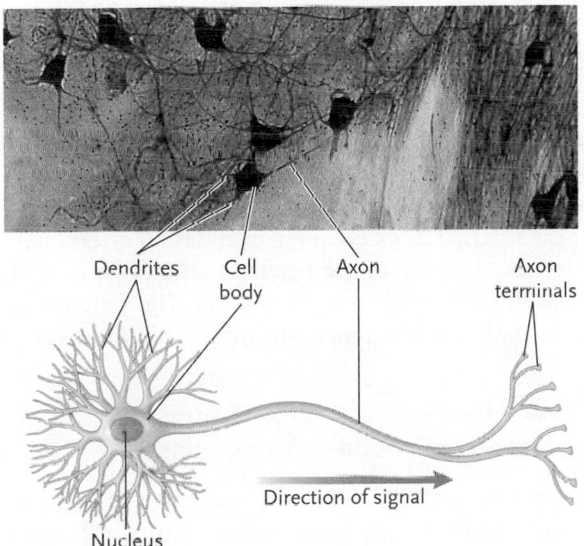

All four major tissue types—epithelial, connective, muscle, and nervous—combine to form the organs and organ systems of animals. The next section depicts the major organs and organ systems of vertebrates and outlines their main tasks.

Study Break

1. Distinguish between exocrine and endocrine glands. What is the tissue type of each of these glands?
2. What are the six major types of connective tissue in vertebrates?

32.3 Coordination of Tissues in Organs and Organ Systems

32.3a Organs and Organ Systems Function Together to Enable an Animal to Survive

In the tissues, organs, and organ systems of an animal, each cell engages in the basic metabolic activities that ensure its own survival and performs one or more functions of the system to which it belongs. All vertebrates have 11 major organ systems, which are summarized in **Figure 32.10, p. 776–777.** Most invertebrates have the same systems but do not have a separate system of lymphatic ducts.

The functions of all these organ systems are coordinated and integrated to accomplish collectively a series of tasks that are vital to all animals, whether a flatworm, a salmon, a meerkat, or a human. These functions include

1. acquiring nutrients and other required substances, such as oxygen, coordinating their processing, distributing them throughout the body, and disposing of wastes.
2. synthesizing the protein, carbohydrate, lipid, and nucleic acid molecules required for body structure and function.
3. sensing and responding to changes in the environment, such as temperature, pH, and ion concentrations.
4. protecting the body against injury or attack from other animals and from viruses, bacteria, and other disease-causing agents.
5. reproducing and, in many instances, nourishing and protecting offspring through their early growth and development.

Figure 32.9
Neurons and their structure. The micrograph shows a network of motor neurons, which relay signals from the brain or spinal cord to muscles and glands. (Micrograph: Lennart Nilsson from Behold Man, © 1974 Albert Bonniers Forlag and Little, Brown and Company, Boston.)

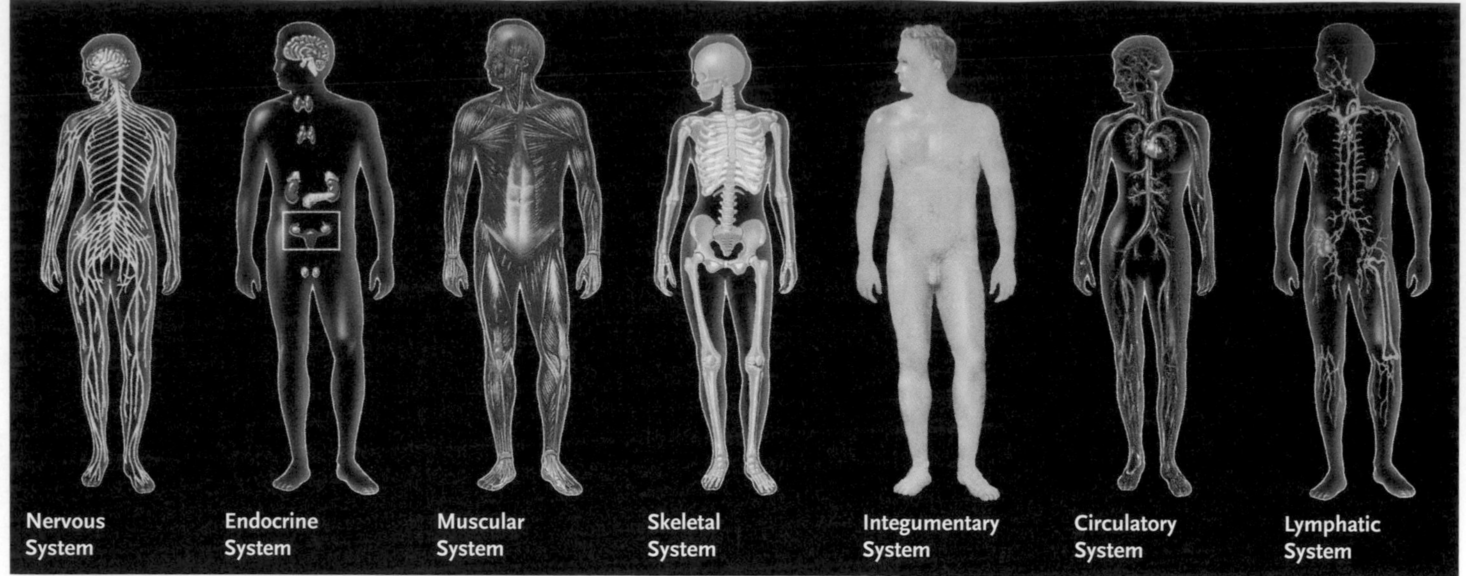

Nervous System

Main organs:
Brain, spinal cord, peripheral nerves, sensory organs

Main functions:
Principal regulatory system; monitors changes in internal and external environments and formulates compensatory responses; coordinates body activities. Nervous systems are present in all metazoans except sponges.

Endocrine System

Main organs:
Pituitary, thyroid, adrenal, pancreas, and other hormone-secreting glands

Main functions:
Regulates and coordinates body activities through secretion of hormones. Endocrine systems are also present in most metazoans.

Muscular System

Main organs:
Skeletal, cardiac, and smooth muscle

Main functions:
Moves body parts; helps run bodily functions; generates heat. Specialized muscle cells do not appear in evolution until triploblastic animals.

Skeletal System

Main organs:
Bones, tendons, ligaments, cartilage

Main functions:
Supports and protects body parts; provides leverage for body movements. An internal skeleton composed of bone and/or cartilage occurs only in the vertebrates. Similar functions in invertebrates are carried out by an external skeleton or by internal hydrostatic pressure.

Integumentary System

Main organs:
Skin, sweat glands, hair, nails

Main functions:
Covers external body surfaces and protects against injury and infection; helps regulate water content and body temperature. All Metazoa except sponges have an integument of some sort.

Circulatory System

Main organs:
Heart, blood vessels, blood

Main functions:
Distributes water, nutrients, oxygen, hormones, and other substances throughout body and carries away carbon dioxide and other metabolic wastes; helps stabilize internal temperature and pH. Specialized circulatory systems occur in all vertebrates and in the annelids, molluscs, and arthropods.

Lymphatic System

Main organs:
Lymph nodes, lymph ducts, spleen, thymus

Main functions:
Returns excess fluid to the blood; defends body against invading viruses, bacteria, fungi, and other pathogens as part of immune system. Invertebrates do not have a specialized lymphatic system.

Together these tasks maintain homeostasis, preserving the internal environment required for survival of the body. Homeostasis is the topic of the next section.

Study Break

1. What are the major functions of each of the 11 organ systems?
2. What are the major organ systems in a duck? in a shark? in an insect? in an earthworm?

32.4 Homeostasis

Homeostasis is the process by which animals maintain their internal environment in a steady state (constant level) or between narrow limits. Homeostasis depends on a number of the body's organ systems, with the nervous system and endocrine system being the most important. For example, blood pH is controlled by both the nervous and endocrine systems, blood glucose by the endocrine system, internal temperature by the nervous and endocrine systems, and oxygen and carbon dioxide concentrations by the nervous system.

Although the *stasis* part of homeostasis might suggest a static, unchanging process, homeostasis is actually a dynamic process, in which internal adjustments are made continuously to compensate for changes in the internal or external environment. For example, internal adjustments are needed to maintain homeostasis during exercise or hibernation. The factors controlled by homeostatic mechanisms all require energy.

32.4a Homeostasis Is Accomplished by Negative Feedback Mechanisms

The primary mechanism of homeostasis is **negative feedback**, in which a stimulus resulting from a

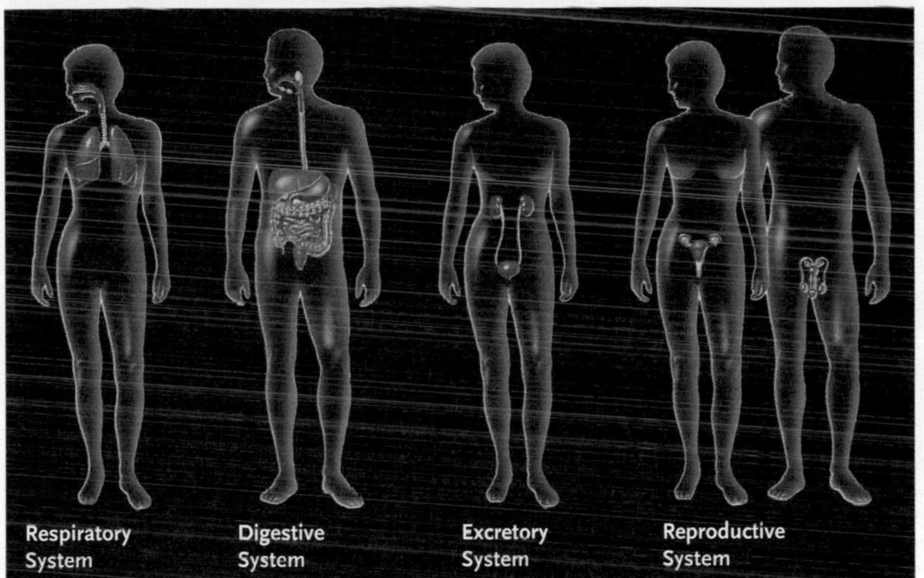

Respiratory System	Digestive System	Excretory System	Reproductive System
Main organs: Lungs, diaphragm, trachea, and other airways	Main organs: Pharynx, esophagus, stomach, intestines, liver, pancreas, rectum, anus	Main organs: Kidneys, bladder, ureter, urethra	Main organs: *Female*: ovaries, oviducts, uterus, vagina, mammary glands *Male*: testes, sperm ducts, accessory glands, penis
Main functions: Exchanges gases with the environment, including uptake of oxygen and release of carbon dioxide. Fish have a respiratory system that involves gills. Some form of specialized respiratory system occurs in most invertebrates.	Main functions: Converts ingested matter into molecules and ions that can be absorbed into body; eliminates undigested matter; helps regulate water content. Most metazoans, with the exception of some parasitic forms, have a digestive system.	Main functions: Removes and eliminates excess water, ions, and metabolic wastes from body; helps regulate internal osmotic balance and pH. All animals perform these functions. All vertebrates have kidneys, and most invertebrates have specialized excretory organs and systems.	Main functions: Maintains the sexual characteristics and passes on genes to the next generation. Most triploblastic animals have specialized reproductive organs and systems.

Figure 32.10
Organ systems of the human body. The immune system, which is primarily a cellular system, is not shown. The functions performed by these organ systems are also performed by all other animals, although different organs and systems may be involved.

change in the external or internal environment triggers a response that compensates for the environmental change **(Figure 32.11)**. Homeostatic mechanisms typically include three elements: a sensor, an integrator, and an effector. The **sensor** consists of tissues or organs that detect a change in external or internal factors such as pH, temperature, or the concentration of a molecule such as glucose. The **integrator** is a control centre that compares the detected environmental change with a **set point**, the level at which the condition controlled by the pathway is to be maintained. The **effector** is a system, activated by the integrator, that returns the condition to the set point if it has strayed away. In most animals, the integrator is part of the central nervous system or endocrine system, whereas effectors may include parts of any body tissue or organ.

The Thermostat as a Negative Feedback Mechanism. The concept of negative feedback may be most familiar in systems designed by human engineers. The thermostat maintaining temperature at a chosen level in a house provides an example. A sensor within the thermostat measures the temperature. If the room temperature changes more than a degree or so from the set point—the temperature that you set in the thermostat—an integrator circuit in the thermostat activates an effector that returns the room temperature

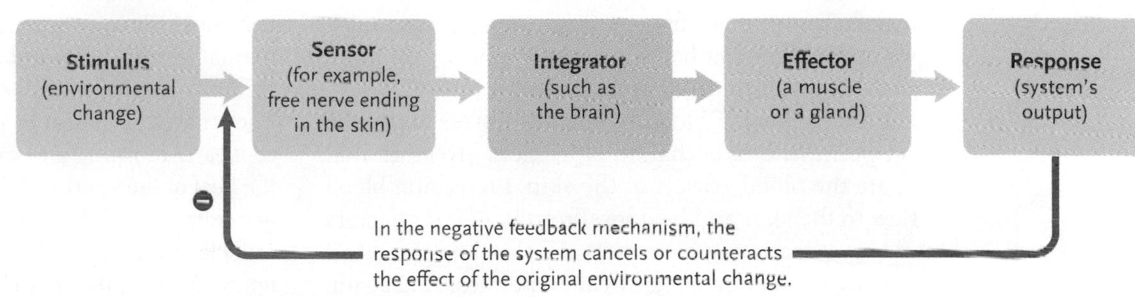

Figure 32.11
Components of a negative feedback mechanism maintaining homeostasis. The integrator coordinates a response by comparing the level of an environmental condition with a set point that indicates where the level should be.

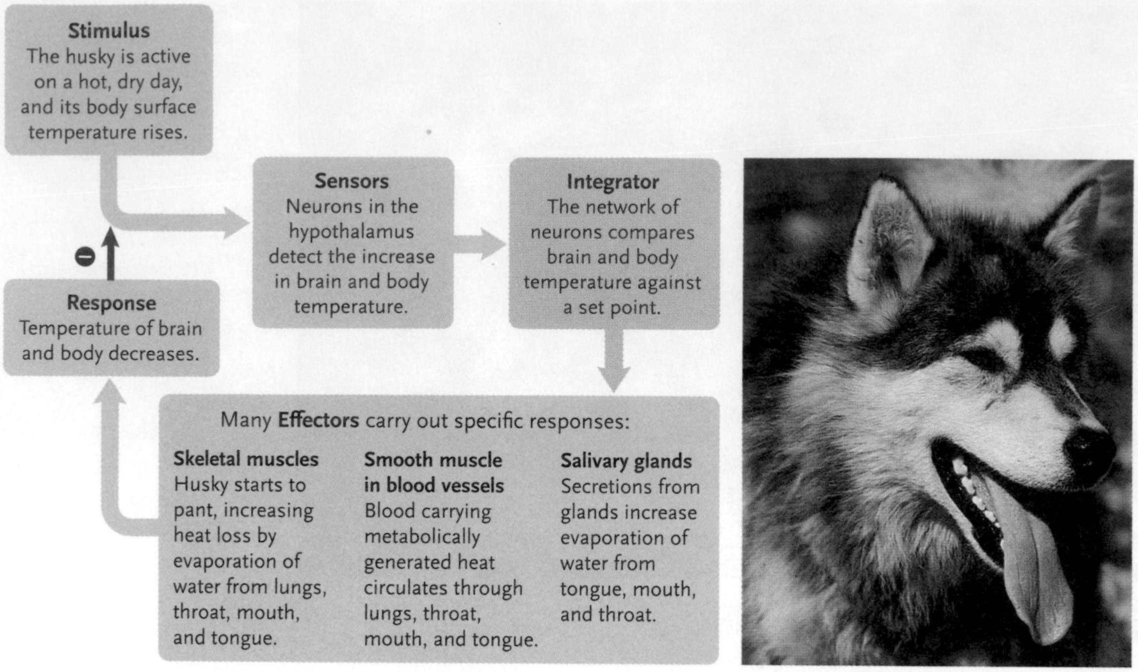

Stimulus
The husky is active on a hot, dry day, and its body surface temperature rises.

Sensors
Neurons in the hypothalamus detect the increase in brain and body temperature.

Integrator
The network of neurons compares brain and body temperature against a set point.

Many **Effectors** carry out specific responses:

Skeletal muscles
Husky starts to pant, increasing heat loss by evaporation of water from lungs, throat, mouth, and tongue.

Smooth muscle in blood vessels
Blood carrying metabolically generated heat circulates through lungs, throat, mouth, and tongue.

Salivary glands
Secretions from glands increase evaporation of water from tongue, mouth, and throat.

Response
Temperature of brain and body decreases.

Fred Bruemmer

Figure 32.12
Homeostatic mechanisms maintaining the body temperature of a husky when environmental temperatures are high.

to the set point. If the temperature has fallen below the set point, the effector is the furnace, which adds heat to the house until the temperature rises to the set point. If the temperature has risen above the set point, the effector is the air conditioner, which removes heat from the room until the temperature falls to the set point.

Negative Feedback Mechanisms in Animals. Mammals and birds also have a homeostatic mechanism that maintains body temperature within a relatively narrow range around a set point. The integrator (thermostat) for this mechanism is located in a brain centre called the *hypothalamus*. A group of neurons in the hypothalamus detects changes in the temperature of the brain and the rest of the body and compares it with a set point. For humans, the set point has a relatively narrow range centred at about 37°C.

One or more effectors are activated in humans if the temperature varies beyond the limits of the set point. If the temperature falls below the lower limit, the hypothalamus activates effectors that constrict the blood vessels in the skin. The reduction in blood flow means that less heat is conducted from the blood through the skin to the environment; in short, heat loss from the skin is reduced. Other effectors may induce shivering, a physical mechanism to generate body heat. Also, integrating neurons in the brain, stimulated by signals from the hypothalamus, make us consciously sense a chill, which we may counteract behaviourally by putting on more clothes or moving to a warmer area.

Conversely, if blood temperature rises above the set point, the hypothalamus triggers effectors that dilate the blood vessels in the skin, increasing blood flow to the skin and heat loss from it. Other effectors induce sweating, which cools the skin and the blood flowing through it as the sweat evaporates. And again, through integrating neurons in the brain, we may consciously sense being overheated, which we may counteract by shedding clothes, moving to a cooler location, or taking a dip in a pool.

Sometimes the temperature set point changes, and the negative feedback mechanisms then operate to maintain body temperature at the new set point. For example, if you become infected by certain viruses and bacteria, the temperature set point increases to a higher level, producing a fever to help overcome the infection. Once the infection is combated, the set point is readjusted down again to its normal level.

All other mammals have similar homeostatic mechanisms that maintain or adjust body temperature. Dogs and birds pant to release heat from their bodies **(Figure 32.12)** and shiver to increase internal heat production. Many terrestrial vertebrates enter or splash water over their bodies to cool off. Also, recall from the beginning of the chapter how meerkats use behavioural mechanisms to regulate their body temperature.

Whereas mammals and birds regulate their internal body temperature within a narrow range around a set point, certain other vertebrates regulate over a broader range. These vertebrates use other negative feedback mechanisms for their temperature regulation. Snakes and lizards, for example, respond behaviourally to compensate for variations in environmental temperatures and use other, less precise negative feedback mechanisms for their temperature regulation. They may absorb heat by basking on sunny rocks in the cool early morning and move to cooler, shaded spots in the heat of the afternoon. Some fishes, such as the tuna, generate enough heat by contraction of the swimming muscles to maintain body temperature well above the temperature of the surrounding water.

Many insects employ similar mechanisms to raise their body temperature. Some caterpillars group together, increasing their body temperatures by a degree or two and shortening the time of development by as much as three days. Flight requires energy, and the flight muscles operate best at higher temperatures. Some insects bask in the sun to warm the muscles. Many, such as dragonflies, bumblebees, butterflies, and moths, contract the flight muscles rapidly in a process similar to shivering in order to warm them. This is particularly important in moths that fly at night, when the environmental temperature is lower. Honeybees form masses in the winter and maintain the temperature by contracting the wing muscles.

Once insects are in flight, however, the energy production is so high that they must dissipate the heat produced. In bees, the most important method is evaporative cooling by regurgitation of some of the intestinal contents onto the mouthparts, a process equivalent to panting in vertebrates.

32.4b Animals Also Have Positive Feedback Mechanisms That Do Not Result in Homeostasis

Under certain circumstances, animals respond to a change in internal or external environmental condition by a **positive feedback** mechanism that intensifies or adds to the change. Such mechanisms, with some exceptions, do not result in homeostasis. They operate when the animal is responding to life-threatening conditions (an attack, for instance) or as part of reproductive processes.

The birth process in mammals is a prime example. During human childbirth, initial contractions of the uterus push the head of the fetus against the cervix, the opening of the uterus into the vagina. The pushing causes the cervix to stretch. Sensors that detect the stretching signal the hypothalamus to release a hormone, oxytocin, from the pituitary gland. Oxytocin increases the uterine contractions, intensifying the squeezing pressure on the fetus and further stretching the cervix. The stretching results in more oxytocin release and stronger uterine contractions, repeating the positive feedback circuit and increasing the squeezing pressure until the fetus is pushed entirely out of the uterus.

Because positive feedback mechanisms such as the one triggering childbirth do not result in homeostasis, they occur less commonly than negative feedback in animals. They also operate as part of larger, more inclusive negative feedback mechanisms that ultimately shut off the positive feedback pathway and return conditions to normal limits.

We learned in this chapter about the various tissues and organ systems of the body and provided an example of the involvement of organ systems in homeostasis. Next, we begin a series of chapters describing the organ systems in detail, starting with the nervous system.

Study Break

What is the difference between a positive and a negative feedback loop?

Unanswered Questions

What Determines the Fate of Stem Cells?

The discovery in the early 1960s by Ernest McCullough and James Till of the Ontario Cancer Institute in Toronto that bone marrow contained cells that can be grown outside the body and that have the potential to differentiate into a number of different cell types stimulated a frenzy of research, much of it directed toward the possible use of such cells, **stem cells,** in medicine. It is known that there are two basic types of stem cells. **Embryonic stem cells** are from the early embryo, before the cells have begun to differentiate into the cell layers and tissues. These can be grown in culture indefinitely and have the potential to develop into any adult cell type. They're referred to as totipotent. **Adult stem cells** can also be grown in culture and are morphologically undifferentiated, but their potential for further differentiation is normally limited to the tissue in which they are found: for example, nerve stem cells can differentiate only into the cell types normally found in the nervous system. In some cases, adult stem cells can be induced in culture to form a variety of cell types: these are referred to as pluripotent. Embryonic stem cells have the greatest potential in medicine, but there are ethical debates about establishing cultures of them from humans since the cultures require the destruction of an embryo, albeit at a very early stage. A good deal of research is focused on how adult stem cells might be deprogrammed so that they have the potential to make other types of tissues.

But there are other, more fundamental, biological questions. What are the signals that set embryonic stem cells on different developmental paths leading to different adult stem cell types? In some cases, scientists have found conditions that can reverse this process, but an understanding of the natural factors that lead to differentiation is fundamental to an understanding of development. What are the conditions in a particular tissue that activate the existing stem cells in that tissue to divide and differentiate into the functional cells? Given the potential importance of stem cells in the treatment of disease, there has been an understandable concentration on the mouse as a model system. But stem cells are important in a wide variety of animals. In the trematode flatworms, for example (see Chapter 26), stem cells are reserved at each larval stage, and these stem cells give rise to the next larval stage, which may be morphologically very different. Are systems such as this, far removed from mammals, able to provide useful clues?

Review

Go to CENGAGENOW™ at http://hed.nelson.com/ to access quizzing, animations, exercises, articles, and personalized homework help.

32.1 Organization of the Animal Body

- Multicellularity permits organisms to maintain an internal environment, allowing them to exploit a greater variety of environments; allows organisms to become larger; and allows for differentiation of cells specialized to perform specific functions.
- In most animals, cells are specialized and organized into tissues, tissues into organs, and organs into organ systems. A tissue is a group of cells with the same structure and function, working as a unit to carry out one or more activities. An organ is an assembly of tissues integrated into a structure that carries out a specific function. An organ system is a group of organs that carry out related steps in a major physiological process.

32.2 Animal Tissues

- Animal tissues are classified as epithelial, connective, muscle, or nervous. The properties of the cells of these tissues determine the structures and functions of the tissues.
- Various kinds of junctions link cells in a tissue. Anchoring junctions "weld" cells together. Tight junctions seal the cells into a leak-proof layer. Gap junctions form direct avenues of communication between the cytoplasm of adjacent cells in the same tissue.
- Epithelial tissue consists of sheetlike layers of cells that cover body surfaces and the surfaces of internal organs, and line cavities and ducts within the body.
- Exocrine glands are secretory structures derived from epithelia. Exocrine glands are connected by a duct that empties on the epithelial surface. Endocrine glands are ductless. Not all endocrine glands are derived from epithelium.
- Connective tissue consists of cell networks or layers and a prominent extracellular matrix (ECM) that separates the cells. It supports other body tissues and transmits mechanical and other forces.
- Loose connective tissue consists of sparsely distributed fibroblasts surrounded by an open network of collagen and other glycoproteins. It supports epithelia and organs of the body and forms a covering around blood vessels, nerves, and some internal organs.
- Fibrous connective tissue contains sparsely distributed fibroblasts in a matrix of densely packed, parallel bundles of collagen and elastin fibres. It forms high tensile-strength structures such as tendons and ligaments.
- Cartilage consists of sparsely distributed chondrocytes surrounded by a network of collagen fibres embedded in a tough but highly elastic matrix of branched glycoproteins. Cartilage provides support, flexibility, and a low-friction surface for joint movement.
- In bone, osteocytes are embedded in a collagen matrix hardened by mineral deposits. Osteoblasts secrete collagen and minerals for the ECM; osteoclasts remove the minerals and recycle them into the bloodstream.
- Adipose tissue consists of cells specialized for fat storage. It also cushions the body and provides an insulating layer under the skin.
- Blood in most animals consists of a fluid matrix, the plasma, in which cells may be suspended. In vertebrates, the erythrocytes carry oxygen to body cells and the leukocytes produce antibodies and initiate the immune response against disease-causing agents.
- Muscle tissue contains cells that have the ability to contract forcibly. Skeletal muscle, containing long cells called muscle fibres, moves body parts and maintains posture.
- Cardiac muscle, which contains short contractile cells with a branched structure, forms the heart.
- Smooth muscle consists of spindle-shaped contractile cells that form layers surrounding body cavities and ducts.
- Nervous tissue contains neurons and glial cells. Neurons communicate information between body parts in the form of electrical and chemical signals. Glial cells support the neurons or provide electrical insulation between them.

32.3 Coordination of Tissues in Organs and Organ Systems

- Organs and organ systems are coordinated to carry out vital tasks, including maintenance of internal body conditions; nutrient acquisition, processing, and distribution; waste disposal; molecular synthesis; environmental sensing and response; protection against injury and disease; and reproduction.
- In all vertebrates, the major organ systems that accomplish these tasks are the nervous, endocrine, muscular, skeletal, integumentary, circulatory, lymphatic, immune, respiratory, digestive, excretory, and reproductive systems. Many invertebrates also have these organ systems, with the exception of a lymphatic system.

32.4 Homeostasis

- Homeostasis is the process by which animals maintain their internal environment at conditions their cells can tolerate. It is a dynamic state, in which internal adjustments are made continuously to compensate for environmental changes.
- Homeostasis is accomplished by negative feedback mechanisms that include a sensor, which detects a change in an external or internal condition; an integrator, which compares the detected change with a set point; and an effector, which returns the condition to the set point if it has varied.
- Animals also have positive feedback mechanisms, in which a change in an internal or external condition triggers a response that intensifies the change, and typically does not result in homeostasis.

Questions

Self-Test Questions

1. Which tissue is a constant source of adult stem cells in a mammal?
   a. bone marrow
   b. pancreas
   c. basal lamina
   d. heart muscle
   e. kidneys
2. The bones of an elderly woman break more easily than those of a younger person. You would surmise that with aging, the cell type that diminishes in activity is the
   a. osteocyte.
   b. osteoblast.
   c. osteoclast.
   d. chondrocyte.
   e. fibroblast.
3. Which of the following is *not* a homeostatic response?
   a. In a contest, a student eats an entire chocolate cake in 10 minutes. Due to hormonal secretions, his blood glucose level does not change dramatically.
   b. The basketball players are dripping sweat at half time.
   c. The pupils in the eyes constrict when looking at a light.
   d. Slower breathing in sleep changes carbon dioxide and oxygen blood levels, which affect blood pH.
   e. The brain is damaged when a fever rises above 40.5°C.
4. A decrease in body temperature causes the pituitary to release a hormone that stimulates the release of thyroxine from the thyroid gland. Thyroxine increases metabolism, generating heat. As the body temperature increases, the release of the pituitary hormone decreases and less thyroxine is released. This is an example of:
   a. osmolarity.
   b. environmental sensing.
   c. integration.
   d. positive feedback.
   e. negative feedback.
5. The system that coordinates other organ systems is the
   a. skeletal system.
   b. reproductive system.
   c. muscular system.
   d. nervous system.
   e. integumentary system.

Questions for Discussion

1. Astronauts lose bone mass during space travel. Why do you think this happens? To test your hypothesis, can you devise an experiment that does not involve space travel?
2. There are at least 25 known collagens. What information would you need to have and how would you use that information to propose a hypothesis that explains the way that evolution has acted to produce so many versions of the same molecule?
3. Positive feedback mechanisms are rare in animals compared with negative feedback mechanisms. Why do you think this is so?

Section through the cerebellum, a part of the brain that integrates signals coming from particular regions of the body (confocal light micrograph). Neurons, the cells that send and receive signals, are red; glial cells, which provide structural and functional support for neurons, are yellow; and nuclei are purple.

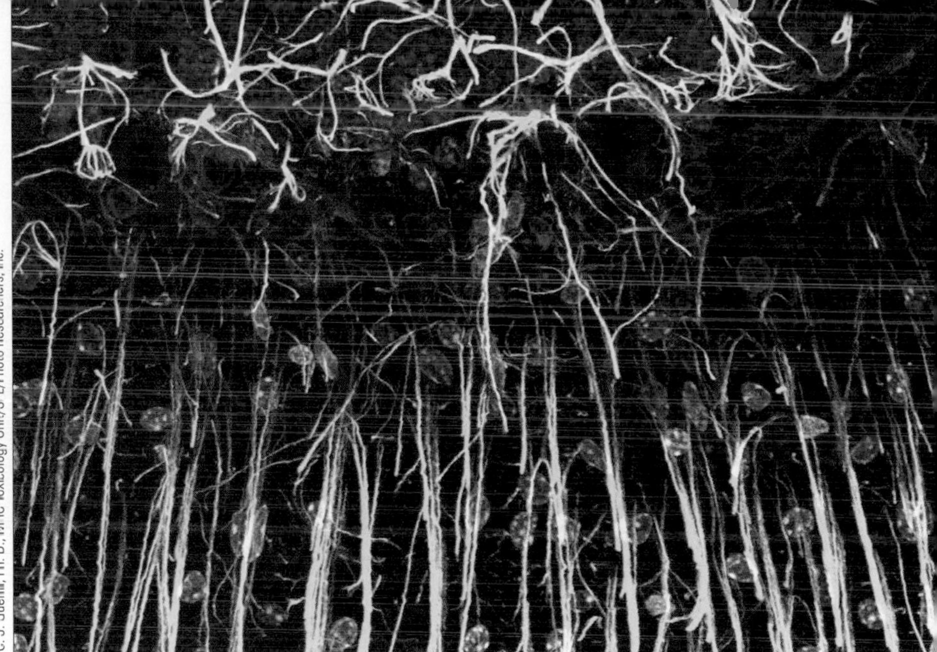

Study Plan

Continued on next page

33 Information Flow: Nerves, Ganglia, and Brains

Why It Matters

On a warm evening in early summer, the twilight in a garden in Montreal is punctuated by brief bursts of light from the abdomen of a flying male of the beetle *Photuris versicolor*, the "lightning bug." The flashes of light have a specific duration and come at specific intervals, constituting a code unique to that species. These visible mating calls are answered by a female perched on the vegetation below **(Figure 33.1, p. 784)**, who emits flashes with the same code. The male orients himself toward the female and flies toward her. This photonic conversation continues until the male lands on the vegetation and mates with the female, who then ceases flashing. A day or two later, the mated female has begun to make eggs and again responds to flashes from males flying overhead. But now she responds to and mimics codes of flashing from males of other species of firefly. A male, lured to her by her mimicry of the flashing code for his species, lands and expects to mate but becomes prey and provides nutrition, enabling her to enhance egg production.

This "femme fatale" behaviour is a marvel of communication both within and between the beetle species. The brain of the male sends the appropriate rhythmic nervous signals to the

Continued from previous page

Figure 33.1
Photinus species female with abdomen flashing.

light-producing organ in his abdomen, whereas his lower nervous system controls the beating of his wings. The female's eyes detect the light flashes, and her nervous system processes the information, causing her brain to send the appropriate signals to her own light-producing organ so that she responds with the appropriate code. The male detects her signal, and his nervous system alters signals to the muscles controlling the wings so that he can fly toward the female. Mating is a complex behaviour involving coordinated movements not only of the genital apparatus but also of the other appendages. This act of mating turns off the flashing response of the female and signals the endocrine system of the female to release the hormones involved in egg production. A chemical transferred by the male in his semen acts on the brain of the female so that it no longer responds to the code for her species and causes her to mimic the codes of other species. The detection and flow of information from the environment and between the individuals, and the instantaneous analysis and processing of that information to produce specific behaviour, are astounding, even in relatively simple animals. Much of this information flow is mediated by the nervous system, but the endocrine system may also be involved in information flow.

In this chapter, we first examine the properties of the cells that make up the nervous system responsible for the reception, transmission, and analysis of the information. These functions result from the activities of only two major cell types: *neurons* and *glial cells*. In most animals, these cells are organized into complex networks called *nervous systems*, and we describe how these networks are organized into *ganglia* and brains.

33.1 Neurons and Their Organization in Nervous Systems: An Overview

An animal is constantly receiving stimuli from both internal and external sources. **Neural signalling**—communication by neurons—is the process by which an animal responds appropriately to a stimulus. In most animals, the four components of neural signalling are *reception, transmission, integration,* and *response.* **Reception**, the detection of a stimulus, is performed by **neurons**, the cellular components of nervous systems, and by specialized sensory receptors such as those in the eye and skin. **Transmission** is the sending of a message along a neuron and then to another neuron or to a muscle or gland. **Integration** is the sorting and interpretation of neural messages and determination of the appropriate response(s). **Response** is the "output" or action resulting from the integration of neural messages. For a *P. versicolor* male flying at dusk, for example, sensors in the eye (see Chapter 34) detect flashes of light, and this information is transmitted to the brain, where it is integrated with internal information about the positions of its wings, gravity, and other factors related to its orientation. This integration results in outputs along nerves controlling the flight apparatus to turn the male toward the source of the flashing.

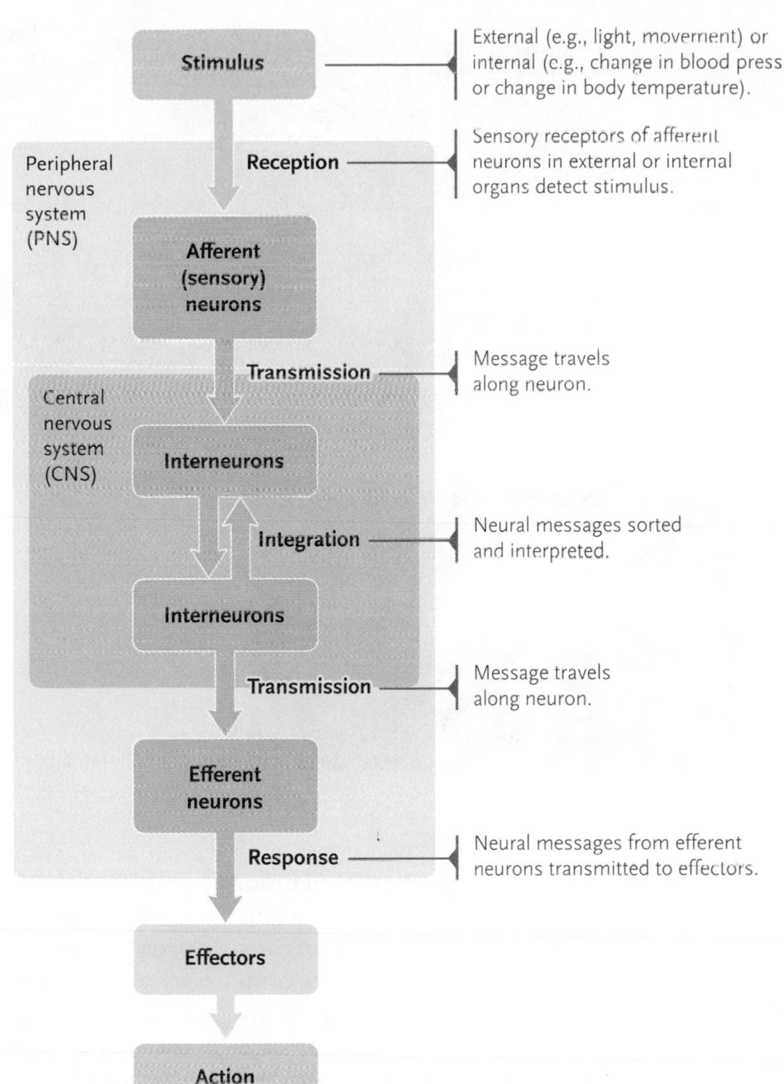

Figure 33.2
Neural signalling: information-processing steps in the nervous system

33.1a Neurons Are Cells Specialized for the Reception and Transmission of Informational Signals

Neural signalling involves three functional classes of neurons **(Figure 33.2)**. **Afferent neurons** (also called **sensory neurons**) transmit stimuli collected by sensory receptors on those neurons to **interneurons**, which integrate the information to formulate an appropriate response. In humans and some other primates, 99% of neurons are interneurons. **Efferent neurons** carry the signals indicating a response away from the interneuron networks to the **effectors**, the muscles and glands. Efferent neurons that carry signals to skeletal muscle are called **motor neurons**. The information-processing steps in the nervous system can be summarized as (1) reception by sensory receptors on afferent neurons; (2) transmission of messages by afferent neurons to interneurons; (3) integration of neural messages in interneurons; and (4) response by transmission of neural messages by efferent neurons to effectors where action appropriate to the stimulus occurs.

Neurons vary widely in shape and size. All have an enlarged cell body and two types of extensions or processes, dendrites and axons **(Figure 33.3, p. 786)**. The **cell body**, which contains the nucleus and the majority of cell organelles, synthesizes most of the proteins, carbohydrates, and lipids of the neuron. Dendrites and axons conduct electrical signals that are produced by ions flowing down concentration gradients through channels in the plasma membrane of the neuron. **Dendrites** receive the signals and transmit them toward the cell body. They are generally highly branched, forming a treelike outgrowth at one end of the neuron (*dendros* = tree). **Axons** (*axon* = axis) conduct signals away from the cell body to another neuron or an effector. Neurons typically have a single axon that arises from a junction with the cell body called an **axon hillock**. The axon has branches at its tip that end as small, buttonlike swellings called **axon terminals**. The more terminals contacting a neuron, the greater its capacity to integrate incoming information.

Connections between the axon terminals of one neuron and the dendrites or cell body of a second neuron form the basic elements of a **neuronal circuit**. A typical neuronal circuit contains an afferent neuron,

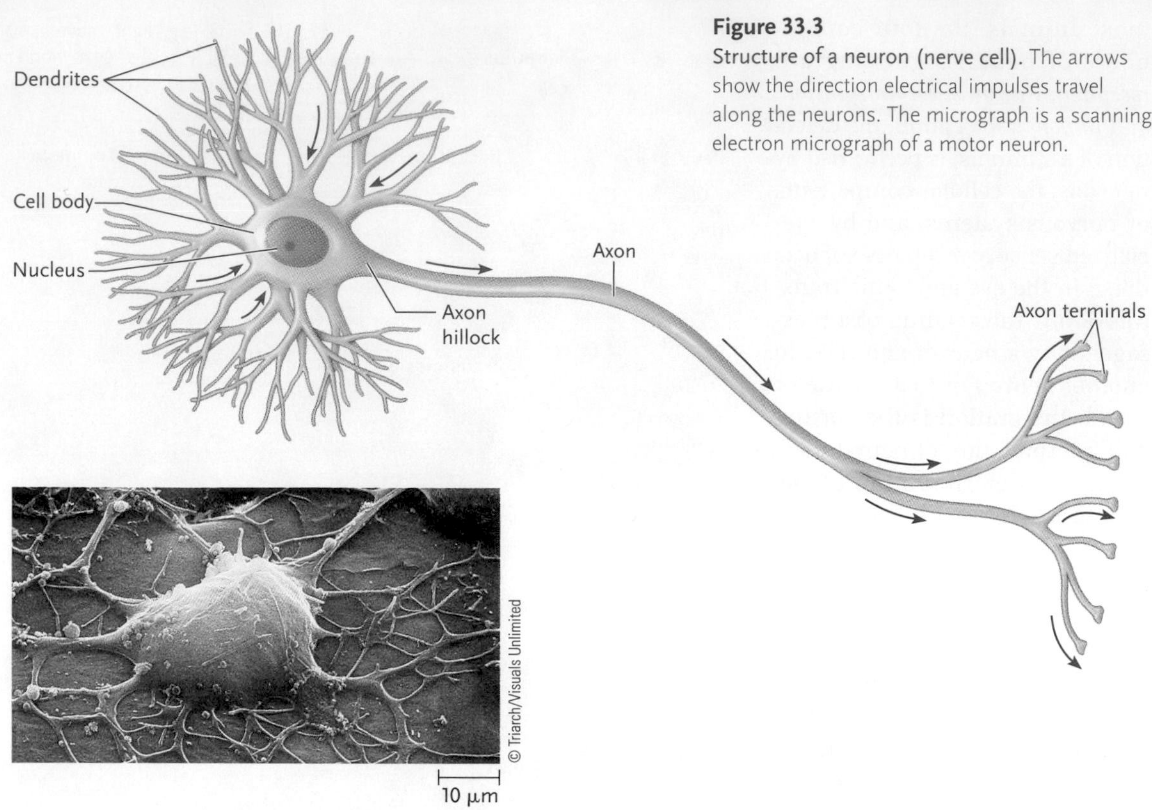

Figure 33.3
Structure of a neuron (nerve cell). The arrows show the direction electrical impulses travel along the neurons. The micrograph is a scanning electron micrograph of a motor neuron.

one or more interneurons, and an efferent neuron. Interneurons may receive input from several axons and may, in turn, connect to other interneurons and several efferent neurons. In this way, circuits combine into networks that interconnect the parts of the nervous system. In vertebrates, the afferent (sensory) neurons and efferent neurons collectively form the *peripheral nervous system* (*PNS*). The interneurons form the brain and spinal cord, called the *central nervous system* (*CNS*). As depicted in Figure 33.2, afferent (carrying toward) information is ultimately transmitted to the CNS, where efferent (carrying away) information is initiated. The nervous systems of most invertebrates are also divided into central and peripheral divisions.

33.1b Neurons Are Supported Structurally and Functionally by Glial Cells

Glial cells are non-neuronal cells that provide nutrition and support to neurons. One type, called **astrocytes** because they are star-shaped **(Figure 33.4),** were formerly thought to play only a supporting role in the CNS by maintaining ion concentrations in the interstitial fluid surrounding the neurons. More recently, however, scientists have realized that in vertebrates and some invertebrates, astrocytes communicate with neurons and may influence their activity.

Figure 33.4
An astrocyte from a rat brain.

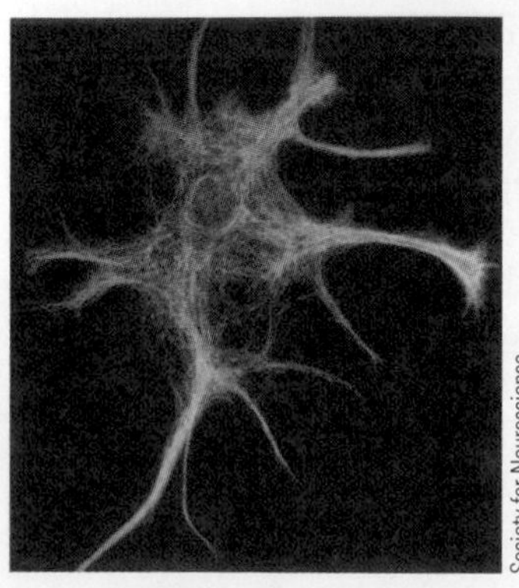

Two other types of glial cells, **oligodendrocytes** in the CNS and **Schwann cells** in the PNS, form tightly wrapped layers of plasma membrane, called myelin sheaths, around axons **(Figure 33.5).** These myelin sheaths act as electrical insulators due to the membrane's high lipid content. The gaps between Schwann cells, called **nodes of Ranvier**, expose the axon membrane directly to extracellular fluids. This arrangement of insulated stretches of the axon punctuated by gaps speeds the rate at which electrical impulses move along the axons they protect.

Unlike most neurons, glial cells retain the capacity to divide throughout the life of the animal. This capacity allows glial tissues to replace damaged or dead cells but also makes them the source of almost all brain tumours, which are produced when regulation of glial cell division is lost.

33.1c Neurons Communicate via Synapses

A **synapse** (*synapsis* = juncture) is a site where a neuron makes a communicating connection with either another neuron or an effector such as a muscle fibre or gland. On one side of the synapse is the axon terminal of a **presynaptic cell**, the neuron that transmits the signal. On the other side is the dendrite or cell body of a **postsynaptic cell**, the neuron or the surface of an effector that receives the signal. Communication across a synapse may occur by the direct flow of an electrical signal or by means of a **neurotransmitter**, a chemical released by an axon terminal at a synapse.

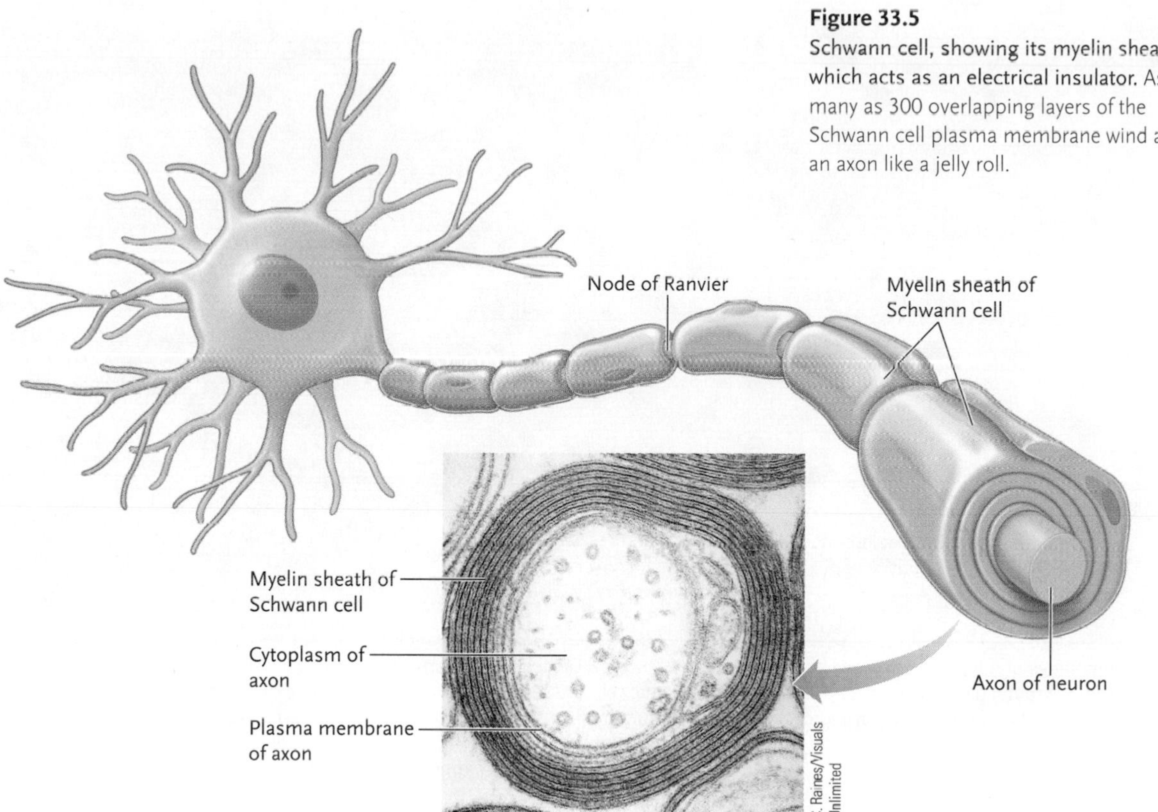

Figure 33.5
Schwann cell, showing its myelin sheath, which acts as an electrical insulator. As many as 300 overlapping layers of the Schwann cell plasma membrane wind around an axon like a jelly roll.

In **electrical synapses**, the plasma membranes of the presynaptic and postsynaptic cells are in direct contact (**Figure 33.6a, p. 788**). When an electrical impulse arrives at the axon terminal, gap junctions (see Chapter 32) allow ions to flow directly between the two cells, leading to unbroken transmission of the electrical signal. Electrical synapses are useful for two types of functions.

- They allow for very rapid transmission. They were first discovered in the nervous system of crayfish, where they are involved in the rapid movements for escape from predators.
- They allow for synchronous activity in a group of neurons. For example, the neurons controlling the secretion of hormones from the hypothalamus of mammals are connected by electrical synapses, thus ensuring a coordinated burst of secretion of some hormones.

The vast majority of vertebrate neurons communicate by means of neurotransmitters (**Figure 33.6b, p. 788**). In these **chemical synapses**, the plasma membranes of the presynaptic and postsynaptic cells are separated by a narrow gap, about 25 nm wide, called the **synaptic cleft**. When an electrical impulse arrives at an axon terminal, it causes the release of a neurotransmitter into the synaptic cleft. The neurotransmitter diffuses across the synaptic cleft and binds to a receptor in the plasma membrane of the postsynaptic cell. If enough neurotransmitter molecules bind to these receptors, the postsynaptic cell generates a new electrical impulse that travels along its axon to reach a synapse with the next neuron or effector in the circuit. A chemical synapse is more than a simple on–off switch because many factors can influence the generation of a new electrical impulse in the postsynaptic cell, including neurotransmitters that inhibit that cell rather than stimulate it. The balance of stimulatory and inhibitory effects in chemical synapses contributes to the integration of incoming information in a receiving neuron.

Study Break

1. Distinguish between the functions and locations of afferent neurons, efferent neurons, and interneurons.
2. What are the differences between an electrical synapse and a chemical synapse?

33.2 Signal Conduction by Neurons

All animal cells have a **membrane potential**, a separation of positive and negative charges across the plasma membrane. Outside the cell is positive, and inside the cell is negative. This charge separation in part produces voltage, an electrical potential difference, across the plasma membrane.

a. Electrical synapse

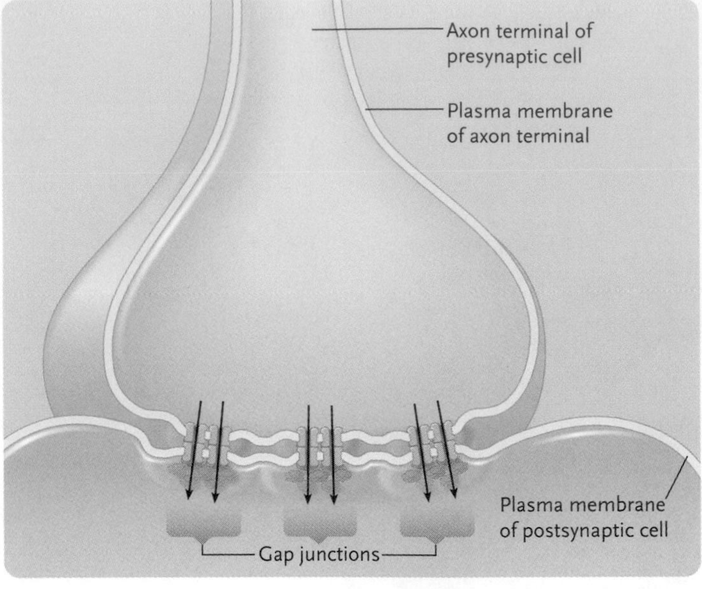

In an electrical synapse, the plasma membranes of the presynaptic and post-synaptic cells make direct contact. Ions flow through gap junctions that connect the two membranes, allowing impulses to pass directly to the postsynaptic cell.

b. Chemical synapse

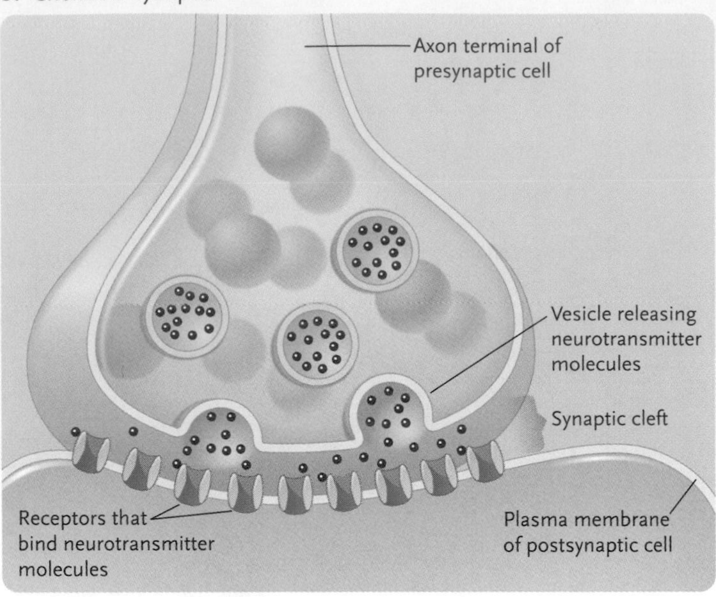

In a chemical synapse, the plasma membranes of the presynaptic and post-synaptic cells are separated by a narrow synaptic cleft. Neurotransmitter molecules diffuse across the cleft and bind to receptors in the plasma membrane of the postsynaptic cell. The binding opens channels to ion flow that may generate an impulse in the postsynaptic cell.

Figure 33.6
The two types of synapses by which neurons communicate with other neurons or effectors.

The membrane potential is caused by the uneven distribution of Na^+ and K^+ inside and outside the cell. As you learned in Chapter 5, plasma membranes are *selectively* permeable in that they allow some ions but not others to move across the membrane through protein channels embedded in the phospholipid bilayer. Plasma membrane–embedded Na^+/K^+ active transport pumps use energy from ATP hydrolysis to pump simultaneously three Na^+ out of the cell for every two K^+ pumped in, generating a higher Na^+ concentration outside the cell than inside, and a higher K^+ concentration inside the cell than outside. This explains the positive charge outside the cell. The inside of the cell is negatively charged because the cell also contains many anions (negatively charged molecules), such as proteins, amino acids, and nucleic acids.

For most cells, the membrane potential remains unchanged. However, neurons and muscle cells use the membrane potential in a specialized way. In response to electrical, chemical, mechanical, and certain other types of stimuli, their membrane potential changes rapidly and transiently. Cells with this property are said to be *excitable*. Excitability, produced by a sudden flow of ions across the plasma membrane, is the basis for nerve impulse generation.

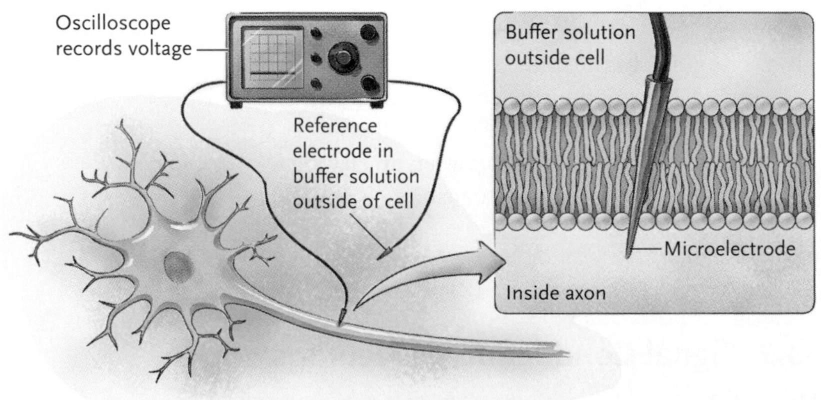

Figure 33.7
Membrane potential is measured by inserting a very fine electrode through the cell membrane of the axon. This electrode and another in the fluid bathing the neuron are connected to an oscilloscope, which measures the potential difference (volts) between the two electrodes and which can track the very rapid changes during an action potential.

33.2a Resting Potential Is the Unchanging Membrane Potential of an Unstimulated Neuron

The membrane of a neuron that is not conducting an impulse exhibits a steady negative membrane potential called the **resting potential** because the neuron is at rest. The resting potential has been measured at about −70 mV in isolated neurons **(Figure 33.7)**. A neuron exhibiting a resting potential is said to be *polarized.*

The distribution of ions inside and outside of an axon that produces the resting potential is shown in **Figure 33.8.** As described earlier, the Na^+/K^+ pump creates the imbalance of Na^+ and K^+ inside and outside the cell: the concentration of positively charged anions within the cell results in the inside being negatively charged and the outside being positively charged. As we will see in the following discussion of the changes in a neuron that occur when it is stimulated, the

Figure 33.8
The distribution of ions inside and outside an axon that produces the resting potential, −70 mV. The distribution of ions that do not directly affect the resting potential, such as Cl^-, is not shown. The voltage-gated ion channels open and close when the membrane potential changes.

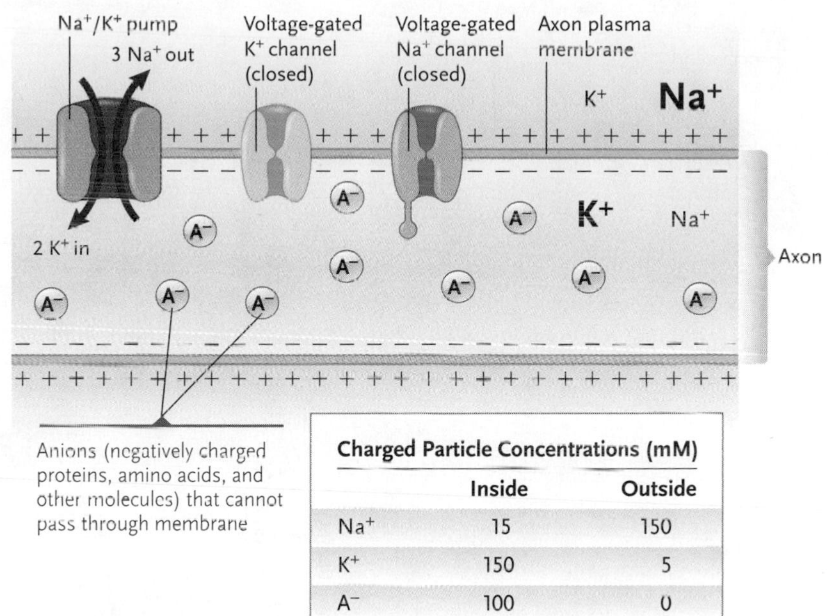

Charged Particle Concentrations (mM)

	Inside	Outside
Na^+	15	150
K^+	150	5
A^-	100	0

voltage-gated ion channels for Na^+ and K^+ open and close when the membrane potential changes.

33.2b The Membrane Potential Changes from Negative to Positive during an Action Potential

When a neuron conducts an electrical impulse, there is an abrupt and transient change in membrane potential; this is called the **action potential**. An action potential begins as a stimulus that causes positive charges from outside the neuron to flow inward, making the cytoplasmic side of the membrane less negative **(Figure 33.9)**.

As the membrane potential becomes less negative, the membrane (which was polarized at rest) becomes **depolarized**. Depolarization proceeds relatively slowly until it reaches a level known as the **threshold potential**, about −50 to −55 mV in isolated neurons. Once the threshold is reached, the action potential fires, which causes the membrane potential to suddenly increase. In less than 1 ms (millisecond, one-thousandth of a second), it rises so high that the inside of the plasma membrane becomes positive because of an influx of positive ions across the cell membrane, momentarily reaching a value of +30 mV or more. The potential then falls, in many cases dropping to about −80 mV before rising again to the resting potential. When the potential is below the resting value, the membrane is said to be **hyperpolarized**. The entire change, from initiation of the action potential to the return to the resting potential, takes less than 5 ms in the fastest neurons. Action potentials take the same basic form in neurons of all types, with differences in the values of the resting potential and the peak of the action potential and in the time required to return to the resting potential.

All stimuli cause depolarization of a neuron, but an action potential is produced only if the stimulus is strong enough to cause the depolarization to reach the threshold. This is referred to as the **all-or-nothing principle**; once triggered, the changes in membrane potential take place independently of the strength of the stimulus.

Beginning at the peak of an action potential, the membrane enters a **refractory period** of a few milliseconds, during which the threshold required for generation of an action potential is much higher than normal. The refractory period lasts until the membrane has stabilized at the resting potential. As we will see, the refractory period keeps impulses travelling in a one-way direction in neurons.

33.2c The Action Potential Is Produced by Ion Movements through the Plasma Membrane

The action potential is produced by movements of Na^+ and K^+ through the plasma membrane that are controlled by specific **voltage-gated ion channels**, membrane-embedded proteins that open and close as the membrane potential changes (see Figure 33.8).

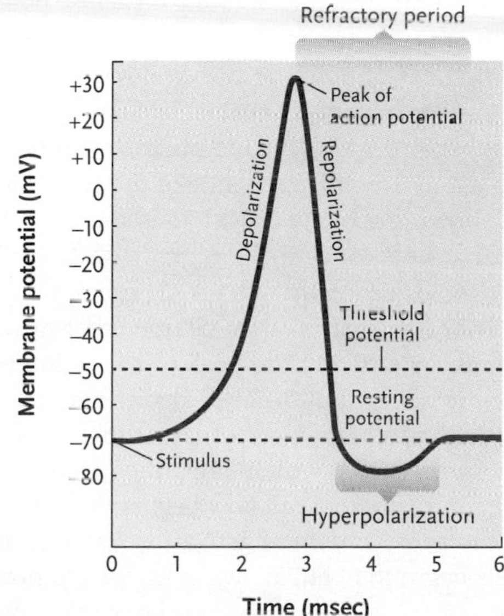

Figure 33.9
Changes in membrane potential during an action potential.

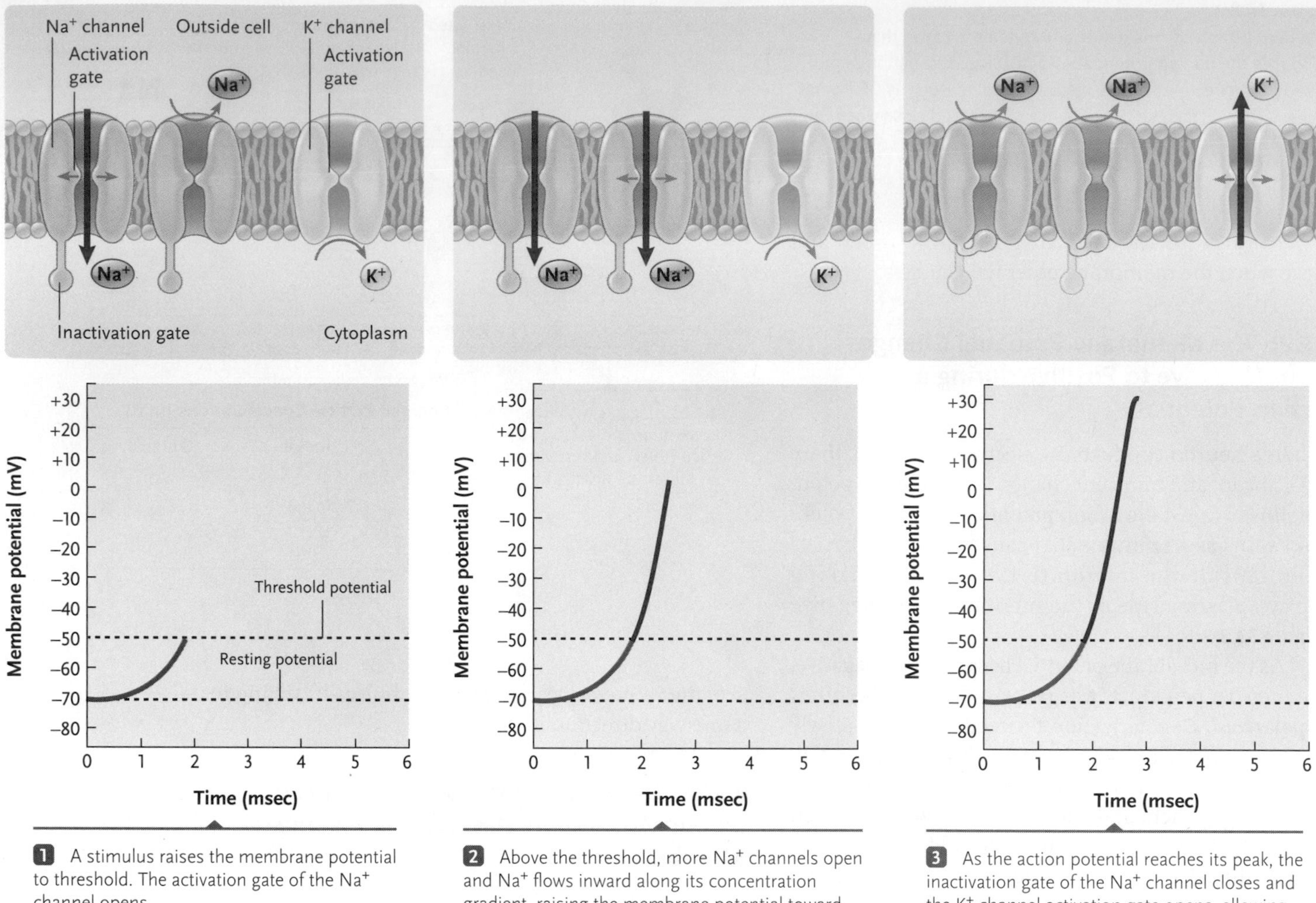

1 A stimulus raises the membrane potential to threshold. The activation gate of the Na^+ channel opens.

2 Above the threshold, more Na^+ channels open and Na^+ flows inward along its concentration gradient, raising the membrane potential toward the peak of the action potential.

3 As the action potential reaches its peak, the inactivation gate of the Na^+ channel closes and the K^+ channel activation gate opens, allowing K^+ ions to flow outward.

Figure 33.10
Changes in voltage-gated Na^+ and K^+ channels that produce the action potential.

Voltage-gated Na^+ channels have two gates, an *activation gate* and an *inactivation gate*, whereas voltage-gated K^+ channels have one gate, an *activation gate*.

Figure 33.10 shows how the two voltage-gated ion channels operate when generating an action potential. When the membrane is at the resting potential, the activation gates of both the Na^+ and K^+ channels are closed. A depolarizing stimulus, such as neurotransmitter substance, raises the membrane potential to the threshold and the activation gate of the Na^+ channels opens, allowing a burst of Na^+ ions to flow into the axon along their concentration gradient. Once above the threshold, more Na^+ channels open, causing a rapid inward flow of positive charges that raises the membrane potential to the peak of the action potential. As the action potential peaks, the inactivation gate of the Na^+ channel closes (resembling putting a stopper in the sink), which stops the inward flow of Na^+. The refractory period now begins.

At the same time, the activation gates of the K^+ channels begin to open, allowing K^+ ions to flow rapidly outward in response to their concentration gradient. The K^+ ions contribute to the refractory period and compensate for the inward movement of Na^+ ions, returning the membrane to the resting potential. As the resting potential is reestablished, the activation gates of K^+ channels close, as do those of Na^+ channels, and the inactivation gates of Na^+ channels open. These events end the refractory period and ready the membrane for another action potential.

In some neurons, closure of the gated K^+ channels lags, and K^+ continues to flow outward for a brief time after the membrane returns to the resting potential. This excess outward flow causes the hyperpolarization shown in Figure 33.9 and Figure 33.10 (step 6), in which the membrane potential dips briefly below the resting potential.

At the end of an action potential, the membrane potential has returned to its resting state, but the ion distribution has been changed slightly. That is, some Na^+ has entered the cell, and some K^+ has left the cell. Actually, relatively few of the total number of Na^+ and K^+ ions change locations during an action potential. Hence, additional action potentials can occur without the need to completely correct the altered ion distribution. In the long term, the Na^+/K^+ active transport pumps restore the Na^+ and K^+ to their original locations.

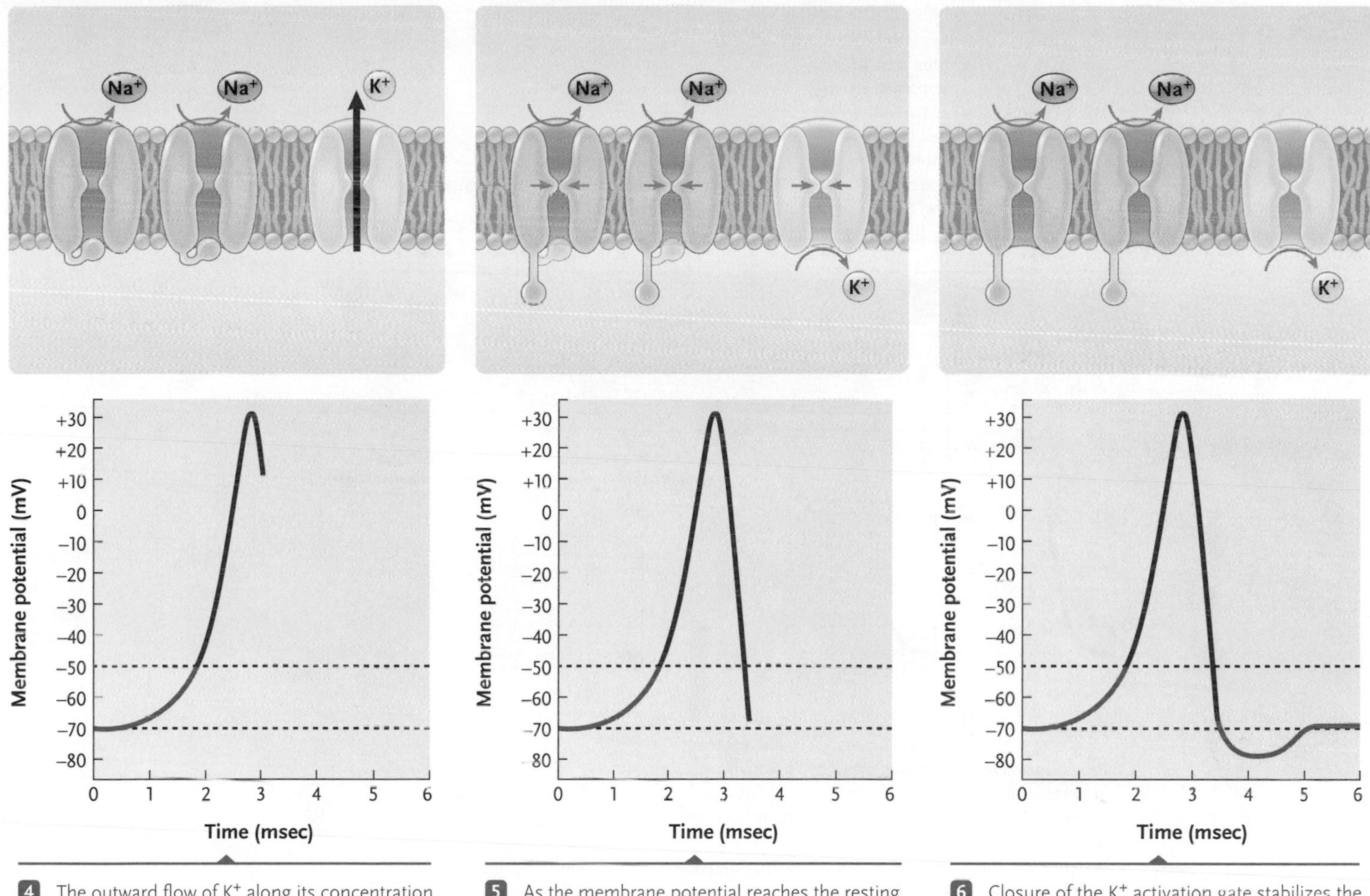

4 The outward flow of K^+ along its concentration gradient causes the membrane potential to begin to fall.

5 As the membrane potential reaches the resting value, the activation gate of the Na^+ channel closes and the inactivation gate opens. The K^+ activation gate also closes.

6 Closure of the K^+ activation gate stabilizes the membrane potential at the resting value.

33.2d Nerve Impulses Move by Propagation of Action Potentials

Once an action potential is initiated at the dendrite end of the neuron, it passes along the surface of a nerve or muscle cell as an automatic wave of depolarization. It travels away from the stimulation point without requiring further triggering events **(Figure 33.11, p. 792)**. This is called **propagation** of the action potential. In a segment of an axon generating an action potential, the outside of the membrane becomes temporarily negative and the inside positive. Because opposites attract, as the region outside becomes negative, local current flow occurs between the area undergoing an action potential and the adjacent downstream inactive area, both inside and outside the membrane (see arrows, Figure 33.11). This current flow makes nearby regions of the axon membrane less positive on the outside and more positive on the inside; in other words, the membrane of these adjacent regions depolarizes.

The depolarization is large enough to push the membrane potential past the threshold, opening the voltage-gated Na^+ and K^+ channels and starting an action potential in the downstream adjacent region. In this way, each segment of the axon stimulates the next segment to fire, and the action potential moves rapidly along the axon as a nerve impulse.

The refractory period keeps an action potential from reversing direction at any point along an axon; only the region in front of the action potential can fire. The refractory period results from the properties of the voltage-gated ion channels. That is, once they are opened to their activated state, the upstream voltage-gated ion channels need time to reset to their original positions before they can open again. Therefore, only downstream voltage-gated ion channels are able to open, ensuring the one way movement of the action potential along the axon toward the axon terminals. By the time the refractory period ends in a membrane segment that has just fired an action potential, the action potential has moved too far away to cause a second action potential to develop in the same segment.

The magnitude of an action potential stays the same as it travels along an axon, even where the axon branches at its tips. Thus, the propagation of an action potential resembles a burning fuse, which burns with the same intensity along its length and along

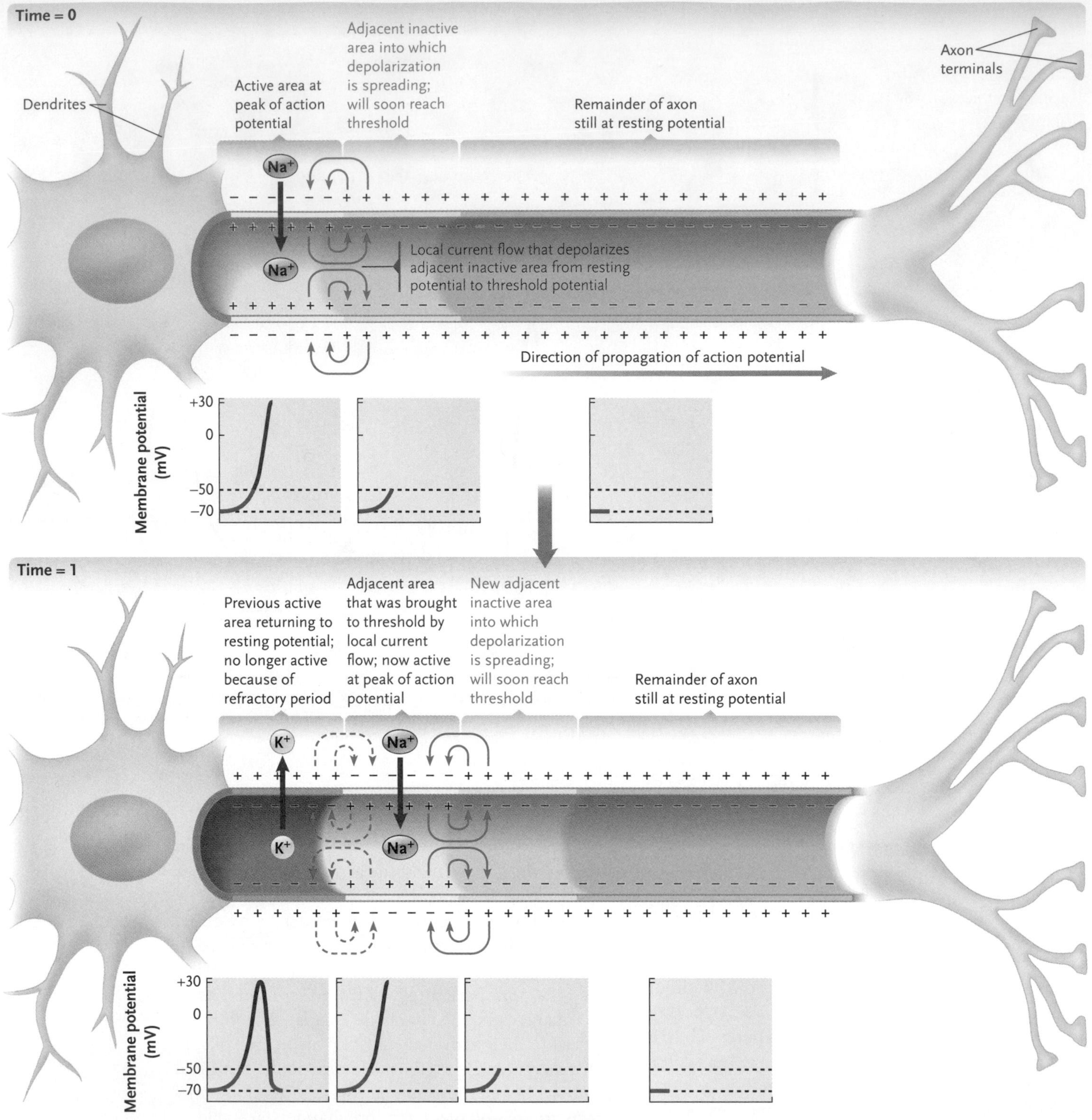

Figure 33.11
Propagation of an action potential along an unmyelinated axon by ion flows between a firing segment and an adjacent unfired region of the axon. Each firing segment induces the next to fire, causing the action potential to move along the axon.

any branches, once it is lit at one end. Unlike a fuse, however, an axon can fire another action potential of the same intensity within a few milliseconds after an action potential passes through.

The all-or-nothing principle of action potential generation means that the intensity of a stimulus is reflected in the *frequency* of action potentials rather than the size of the action potential. The greater the stimulus, the more action potentials per second, up to a limit depending on the axon type. For most neuron types, the limit lies between 10 and 100 action potentials per second.

33.2e Saltatory Conduction Increases Propagation Rate in Small-Diameter Axons

In the propagation pattern shown in Figure 33.11, an action potential spreads along every patch of the membrane along the length of the axon. The rate of conduction increases with the diameter of the axon. Some specialized axons with very large diameters occur in invertebrates such as lobsters, earthworms, and squids, as well as a few marine fishes. Giant axons typically carry signals that produce an escape or withdrawal response, such as the sudden flexing of the tail (abdomen) in lobsters that propels the animal backward. The largest known axons, 1.7 mm in diameter, occur in fanworms (Phylum Annelida, Class Polychaeta; see Figure 26.30a). The signals they carry contract a muscle that retracts the fanworm's body into a protective tube when the animal is threatened. The giant axons of the squid were used in the early experiments that led to the current conceptual model of the axon.

Although large-diameter axons can conduct impulses as rapidly as 25 m/s (over twice the speed of the world record 100-m race), they take up a great deal of space. In the jawed vertebrates, **saltatory conduction** (*saltere* = to leap) allows action potentials to "hop" rapidly along axons instead of burning smoothly like a fuse.

Saltatory conduction depends on the gaps in the insulating myelin sheath that surrounds many axons. These gaps, known as nodes of Ranvier, expose the axon membrane to extracellular fluids. Voltage-gated Na^+ and K^+ channels crowded into the nodes allow action potentials to develop at these positions **(Figure 33.12).** The inward movement of Na^+ ions produces depolarization, but the excess positive ions are unable to leave the axon through the membrane regions covered by the myelin sheath. Instead, they diffuse rapidly to the next node, where they cause depolarization, inducing an action potential at that node. As this mechanism repeats, the action potential jumps rapidly along the axon from

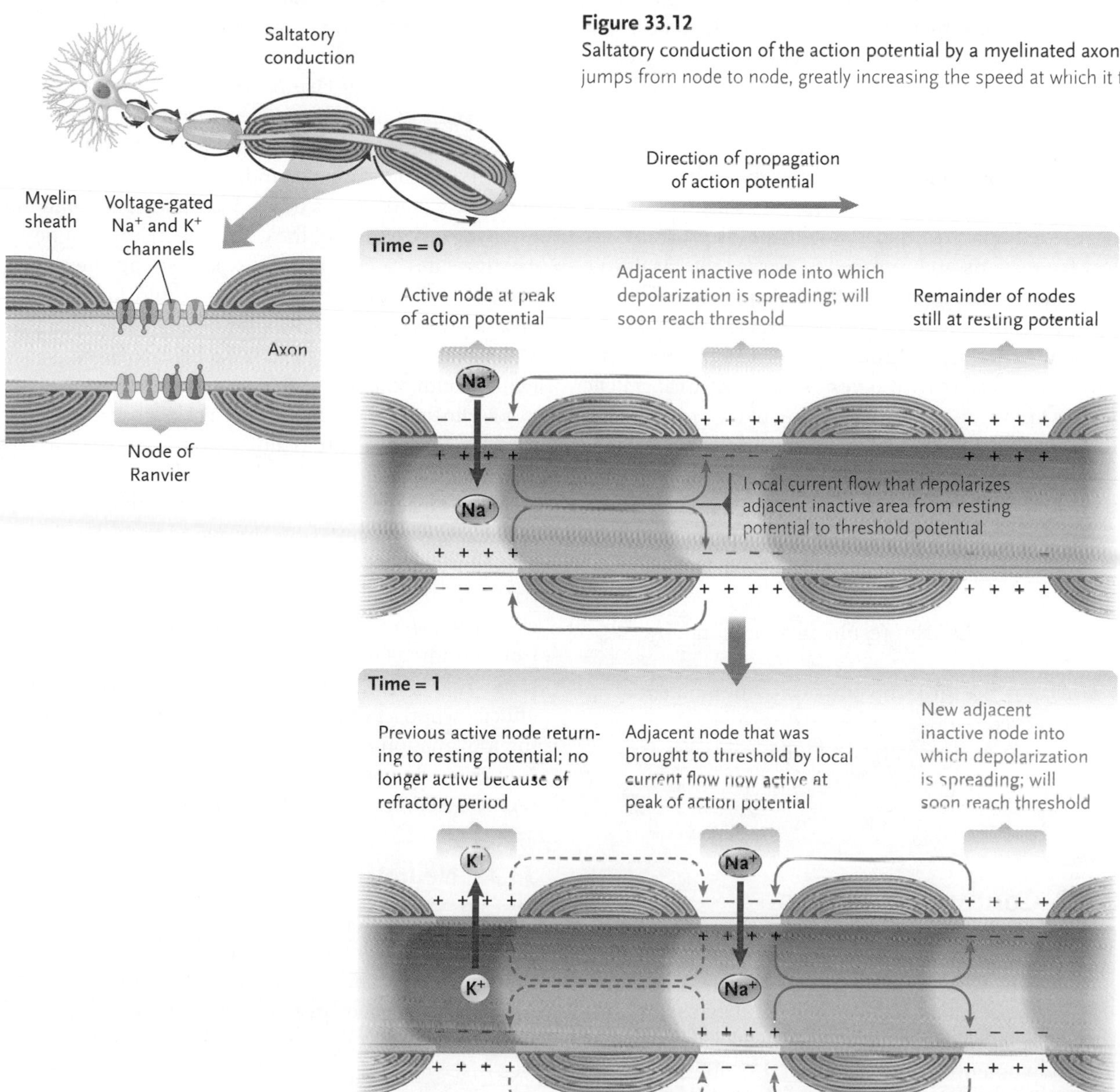

Figure 33.12
Saltatory conduction of the action potential by a myelinated axon. The action potential jumps from node to node, greatly increasing the speed at which it travels along the axon.

node to node. Saltatory conduction proceeds at rates up to 130 m/s, whereas an unmyelinated axon of the same diameter conducts action potentials at about 1 m/s.

Saltatory conduction allows thousands to millions of fast-transmitting axons to be packed into a relatively small diameter. For example, in humans, the 3-mm diameter optic nerve leading from the eye to the brain is packed with more than a million axons. If those axons were unmyelinated, each would have to be about 100 times thicker to conduct impulses at the same velocity, producing an optic nerve about 300 mm in diameter.

Among invertebrates, Schwann cells also form concentric coatings around many nerves, but the layers are not so compact, leaving some cytoplasm in the Schwann cells and some intercellular space between the layers. Nevertheless, fully myelinated fibres occur in oligochaete annelids and some crustaceans, complete with gaps to permit saltatory transmission. The occurrence of myelin in some protostome invertebrates and its absence from the lower vertebrates suggests that this important mechanism has evolved more than once, presenting another example of convergent evolution. The embryonic origin of Schwann cells is different in vertebrates and invertebrates, confirming the independent evolution of myelination in vertebrates and invertebrates.

The disease *multiple sclerosis* (*sclero* = hard) underscores the importance of myelin sheaths to the operation of the vertebrate nervous system. In this disease, myelin is attacked by the immune system and is progressively lost from axons and replaced by hardened scar tissue. The changes block or slow the transmission of action potentials, producing numbness, muscular weakness, faulty coordination of movements, and paralysis that worsens as the disease progresses. Although clear genetic factors are involved, the environment also plays a role: the incidence of the disease increases with the distance from the equator. The incidence in Canada, 2.4 people per 1000 population, is one of the highest in the world.

Study Break

1. What mechanism results in a membrane potential?
2. How is the directionality of an action potential achieved?
3. How is the intensity of action potential signals measured?

33.3 Conduction across Chemical Synapses

Action potentials are transmitted directly across electrical synapses, but they cannot jump across the synaptic cleft in a chemical synapse. Instead, the arrival of an action potential causes neurotransmitter molecules synthesized in the cell body of the neuron to be released by the plasma membrane of the axon terminal, called the **presynaptic membrane (Figure 33.13).** The neurotransmitter diffuses across the cleft and alters ion conduction by activating *ligand-gated ion channels* in the **postsynaptic membrane**, the plasma membrane of the postsynaptic cell. **Ligand-gated ion channels** are channels that open or close when a specific chemical, the ligand, binds to the channel.

Neurotransmitters work in one of two ways. **Direct neurotransmitters** bind directly to a ligand-gated ion channel in the postsynaptic membrane, which opens or closes the channel gate and alters the flow of a specific ion or ions in the postsynaptic cell. The time between arrival of an action potential at an axon terminal and alteration of the membrane potential in the postsynaptic cell may be as little as 0.2 ms.

Indirect neurotransmitters work more slowly (on the order of hundreds of milliseconds). They act as *first messengers*, binding to G protein–coupled receptors (see Chapter 8) in the postsynaptic membrane, which activates the receptors and triggers the generation of a *second messenger* such as cyclic AMP or other processes. The cascade of second-messenger reactions opens or closes ion-conducting channels in the postsynaptic membrane. Indirect neurotransmitters typically have effects that may last for minutes or hours. Some substances can act as either direct or indirect neurotransmitters, depending on the types of receptors they bind to in the receiving cell. Not all of the chemicals released at nerve terminals directly stimulate the postsynaptic neuron to fire. Some may inhibit the neuron from firing, whereas others may enhance the action of other transmitters. Actions that modify the effects of other transmitters may not be confined to the single synaptic cleft but may act to coordinate groups of neurons. These transmitters are sometimes called neuromodulators.

The time required for the release, diffusion, and binding of neurotransmitters across chemical synapses delays transmission compared with the almost instantaneous transmission of impulses across electrical synapses. However, communication through chemical synapses allows neurons to receive inputs from hundreds to thousands of axon terminals at the same time. Some neurotransmitters have stimulatory effects, whereas others have inhibitory effects. All of the information received at a postsynaptic membrane is integrated to produce a response that consists of the receptor neuron firing with a particular frequency.

33.3a Neurotransmitters Are Released by Exocytosis

Neurotransmitters are stored in secretory vesicles, called synaptic vesicles, in the cytoplasm of an axon terminal. The arrival of an action potential at the terminal releases the neurotransmitters by *exocytosis*: the vesicles fuse with the presynaptic membrane and release the neurotransmitter molecules into the synaptic cleft.

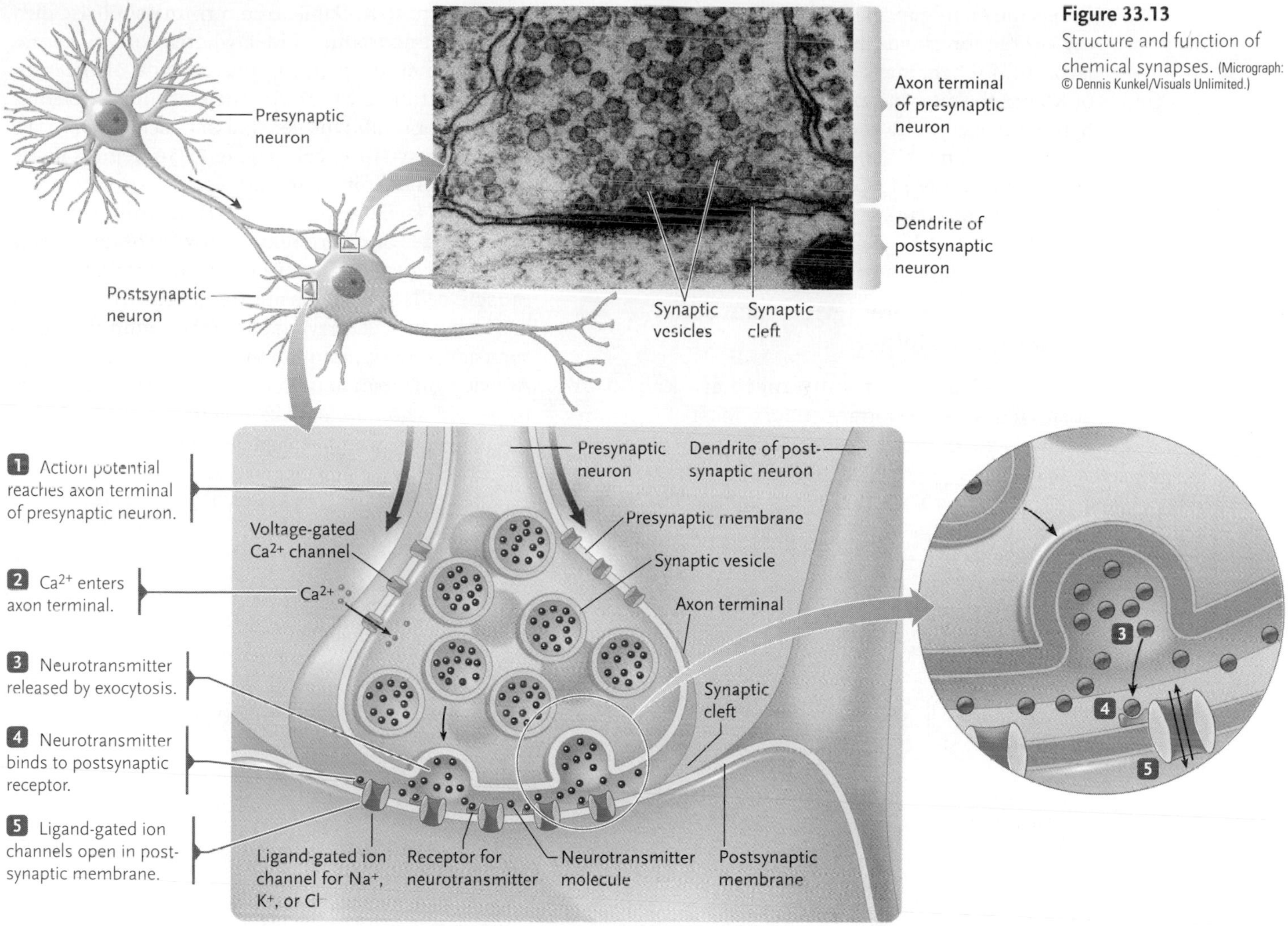

Figure 33.13
Structure and function of chemical synapses. (Micrograph: © Dennis Kunkel/Visuals Unlimited.)

The release of synaptic vesicles depends on voltage-gated Ca^{2+} channels in the plasma membrane of an axon terminal (see Figure 33.13). Ca^{2+} ions are constantly pumped out of all animal cells by an active transport protein in the plasma membrane, keeping their concentration higher outside than inside. As an action potential arrives, the change in membrane potential opens the Ca^{2+} channel gates in the axon terminal, allowing Ca^{2+} to flow back into the cytoplasm. The rise in Ca^{2+} concentration triggers a protein in the membrane of the synaptic vesicle that allows the vesicle to fuse with the plasma membrane, releasing neurotransmitter molecules into the synaptic cleft.

Each action potential arriving at a synapse typically causes approximately the same number of synaptic vesicles to release their neurotransmitter molecules. For example, arrival of an action potential at one type of synapse causes about 300 synaptic vesicles to release a neurotransmitter called acetylcholine. Each vesicle contains about 10 000 molecules of the neurotransmitter, giving a total of some 3 million acetylcholine molecules released into the synaptic cleft by each arriving action potential.

When a stimulus is no longer present, action potentials are no longer generated. When action potentials stop arriving at the axon terminal, the voltage-gated Ca^{2+} channels in the axon terminal close, and the Ca^{2+} in the axon cytoplasm is quickly pumped to the outside. The drop in cytoplasmic Ca^{2+} stops vesicles from fusing with the presynaptic membrane, and no further neurotransmitter molecules are released. Any free neurotransmitter molecules remaining in the cleft are either broken down by enzymes in the cleft or reuptake occurs, meaning that they are pumped back into the axon terminals or into glial cells by active transport. Transmission of impulses across the synaptic cleft ceases within milliseconds after action potentials stop arriving at the axon terminal.

33.3b Most Neurotransmitters Alter Flow through Na^+ or K^+ Channels

Most neurotransmitters work by opening or closing membrane-embedded ligand-gated ion channels that conduct Na^+ or K^+ across the postsynaptic membrane, although some regulate chloride ions (Cl^-). The resulting ion flow may stimulate or inhibit the generation of action potentials by the postsynaptic cell. If Na^+ channels are opened, the inward Na^+ flow brings the membrane potential of the postsynaptic cell toward the threshold (the membrane becomes depolarized). If K^+ channels are opened, the outward flow of K^+ has the opposite effect (the membrane becomes hyperpolarized). The combined effects of the various stimulatory and inhibitory neurotransmitters at all the chemical synapses of a postsynaptic neuron or muscle cell determine whether the postsynaptic cell triggers an action potential.

33.3c Many Different Molecules Act as Neurotransmitters

Nearly 100 different substances are known or suspected to be neurotransmitters. Most of them are relatively small molecules that diffuse rapidly across the synaptic cleft. Some axon terminals release only one type of neurotransmitter, whereas others release several types. Depending on the type of receptor to which it binds, the same neurotransmitter may stimulate or inhibit the generation of action potentials in the postsynaptic cell. **Figure 33.14** depicts some examples of neurotransmitters.

Acetylcholine acts as a neurotransmitter in both invertebrates and vertebrates. In vertebrates, it acts as a direct neurotransmitter between neurons and muscle cells and as an indirect neurotransmitter between neurons carrying out higher brain functions such as memory, attention, perception, and learning. Acetylcholine-releasing neurons in the brain degenerate in people who develop Alzheimer disease, in which memory, speech, and perceptual abilities decline.

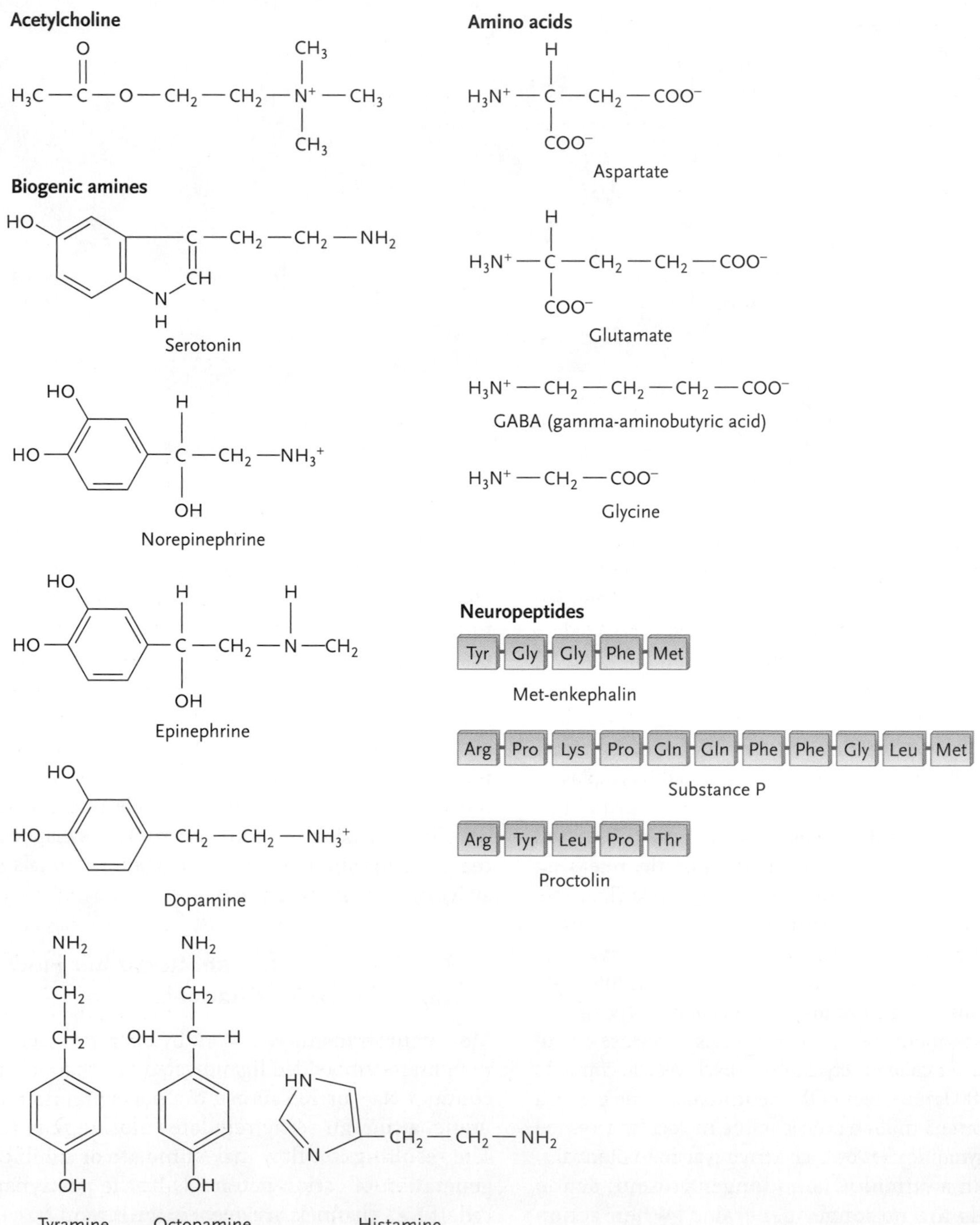

Figure 33.14 Chemical structures of the major neurotransmitter types.

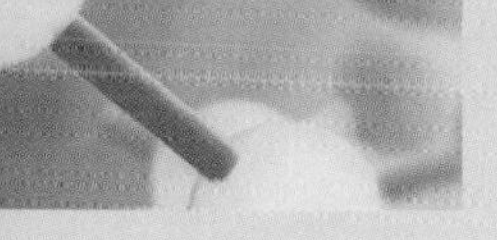

Molecule Behind Biology

Botulinum Toxin: From Poison to Therapy

Botulinum toxin is the product of the bacterium *Clostridium botulinum*, a common organism that thrives in anaerobic environments, such as preserved foods. The toxin is a protein that is destroyed by heat, but if it is ingested, it is extraordinarily toxic 1 000 000 times more toxic than strychnine. The protein can exist as up to seven serotypes, A to G. The protein is produced as a 150 kDa (1000 Daltons) molecule that is cleaved into a 100 kDa toxin and a 50 kDa protease. The heavy chain toxin acts at acetylcholine-mediated synapses (nerve–muscle junctions in vertebrates) by promoting the entry of the light chain protease into the neuron at the synapse, where the enzyme attacks one of the molecules essential for the release of acetycholine. The effect is long lasting: up to several months. Recovery from the effect has been hypothesized to involve the sprouting of new axon terminals.

These properties have been used since 1989 to treat a number of disorders that involve muscle spasms, such as strabismus ("crossed eyes"), by injecting minute quantities of the A serotype directly into the muscles. Ophthalmologists using the toxin in this way noted that "frown lines" around the eyes disappeared as a side effect, and the Botox cosmetic industry was born.

Acetylcholine is the target of many natural and artificial poisons. Curare, a plant extract used as an arrow poison by some indigenous peoples of South America, blocks muscle contraction and produces paralysis by competing directly with acetylcholine for binding sites in synapses that control muscle cells. Atropine, an ingredient in the drops an eye doctor uses to dilate your pupils, is also a plant extract; it relaxes the iris muscles by blocking their acetylcholine receptors. Nicotine also binds to acetylcholine receptors but acts as a stimulant by turning the receptors on rather than off.

Several amino acids operate as direct neurotransmitters in the CNS of vertebrates and in the nerve–muscle synapses of insects and crustaceans. *Glutamate* and *aspartate* stimulate action potentials in postsynaptic cells. They are directly involved in brain functions such as memory and learning, as well as some other functions. *Gamma-aminobutyric acid (GABA)*, a derivative of glutamate, acts as an inhibitor by opening Cl^- channels in postsynaptic membranes. *Glycine* is also an inhibitor.

Other substances can block the operation of these neurotransmitters. For example, tetanus toxin, released by the bacterium *Clostridium tetani*, blocks GABA release in synapses that control muscle contraction. The body muscles contract so forcibly that the body arches painfully and the teeth become tightly clenched, giving the condition its common name of lockjaw. Once the effects extend to respiratory muscles, the victim quickly dies. The disease is entirely preventable, thanks to vaccination with inactivated tetanus toxin.

Biogenic amines are derived from amino acids. Norepinephrine, epinephrine, dopamine, tyramine, and octopamine are all derived from tyrosine. Serotonin is derived from tryptophan, and histamine is derived from histidine. Serotonin, histamine, and dopamine function in both vertebrates and invertebrates. Epinephrine and norepinephrine are characteristic of vertebrates, whereas octopamine and tyramine function in invertebrates.

These amines function primarily in the CNS, and in humans they have been associated with a diversity of brain activities such as consciousness, memory, mood, blood pressure, and sleep. For example, cocaine binds to the transporters for active reuptake of neurotransmitters such as norepinephrine, dopamine, and serotonin from the synaptic cleft. As a result, the concentrations of these neurotransmitters increase in the synapses, leading to amplification of their natural effects. That is, the affected neurons produce the symptoms characteristic of cocaine use: high energy from norepinephrine, euphoria from dopamine, and feelings of confidence from serotonin. Parkinson disease, in which there is progressive loss of muscle control, results from degeneration of dopamine-releasing neurons in regions of the brain coordinating movement.

Neuropeptides are short chains of two or more amino acids that act as indirect neurotransmitters in the central and peripheral nervous systems of both vertebrates and invertebrates. More than 50 neuropeptides are now known for vertebrates and as many as 2000 for invertebrates. Neuropeptides that act as neurotransmitters are also released into the general body circulation as peptide hormones. An example is the peptide proctolin, which occurs only in invertebrates.

Neuropeptides called *endorphins* ("endogenous morphines") are released during periods of pleasurable experience, such as eating or sexual intercourse, or physical stress, such as childbirth or extended physical exercise. These neurotransmitters have the opiate-like property of reducing pain and inducing euphoria, well known to exercise buffs as a pleasant by-product of their physical efforts. Most endorphins act on the PNS and effectors such as muscles, but *enkephalins*, a subclass of the endorphins, bind to particular receptors in the CNS. Morphine, a potent drug extracted from the opium poppy, blocks the sensation of pain and produces a sensation of well-being by binding to the same enkephalin receptors in the brain.

Another neuropeptide associated with pain response is *substance P*, which is released by special neurons in the spinal cord. Its effect is to increase messages associated with intense, persistent, or severe pain. If you put your hand on a hot barbecue grill, you snatch your hand away immediately by reflex action, but you don't feel the "ouch" of the pain until a little later. Why do events occur in this order? The reflex action is driven by rapid nerve impulse conduction along myelinated neurons. The neurons that release substance P are not myelinated, however, so their signal is conducted more slowly, and the feeling of pain is delayed. The action of endorphins is antagonistic to substance P, reducing the perception of pain.

In mammals and other animals, some neurons synthesize and release dissolved carbon monoxide (CO) and nitric oxide (NO), both gases, as neurotransmitters. For example, in the brain, CO regulates the release of hormones from the hypothalamus. NO contributes to many nervous system functions, such as learning, sensory responses, and muscle movements. By relaxing smooth muscles in the walls of blood vessels, NO causes the vessels to dilate, increasing the flow of blood. For example, when a male mammal is sexually aroused, neurons release NO into the erectile tissues in the penis. The relaxation of the muscles increases blood flow into the tissues, causing them to fill with blood and produce an erection. The drug sildenafil (Viagra) aids erection by inhibiting an enzyme that normally reduces NO concentration in the penis.

Study Break

1. Which of the following molecules is not a neurotransmitter: acetylcholine, substance P, octopamine, norepinephrine, or nicotine?
2. Describe how a direct neurotransmitter in a presynaptic neuron controls action potentials in a postsynaptic neuron.

33.4 Integration of Incoming Signals by Neurons

Most neurons receive a multitude of stimulatory and inhibitory signals carried by both direct and indirect neurotransmitters. These signals are integrated by the postsynaptic neuron into a response that reflects their combined effects. The integration depends primarily on the patterns, number, types, and activity of the synapses that the postsynaptic neuron makes with presynaptic neurons. Inputs from other sources, such as indirect neurotransmitters and other signal molecules, can modify the integration. The response of the postsynaptic neuron is elucidated by the frequency of action potentials it generates.

33.4a Integration at Chemical Synapses Occurs by Summation

As mentioned earlier, depending on the type of receptor to which it binds, a neurotransmitter may stimulate or inhibit the generation of action potentials in the postsynaptic neuron. If a neurotransmitter opens a ligand-gated Na^+ channel, Na^+ enters the cell, causing a depolarization. This change in membrane potential pushes the neuron closer to threshold; that is, it is excitatory and is called an **excitatory postsynaptic potential**, or **EPSP**. On the other hand, if a neurotransmitter opens a ligand-gated ion channel that allows Cl^- to flow into the cell and K^+ to flow out, hyperpolarization occurs. This change in membrane potential pushes the neuron farther from threshold; that is, it is inhibitory and is called an **inhibitory postsynaptic potential**, or **IPSP**. In contrast to the all-or-nothing operation of an action potential, EPSPs and IPSPs are **graded potentials**, in which the membrane moves up or down in potential without necessarily triggering an action potential. There are no refractory periods for EPSPs and IPSPs.

A neuron typically has hundreds to thousands of chemical synapses formed by axon terminals of presynaptic neurons contacting its dendrites and cell body **(Figure 33.15)**. The events that occur at each synapse produce either an EPSP or an IPSP in that postsynaptic neuron. But how is an action potential produced if a single EPSP is not sufficient to push the postsynaptic neuron to threshold? The answer involves the summation of all the inputs received through all the

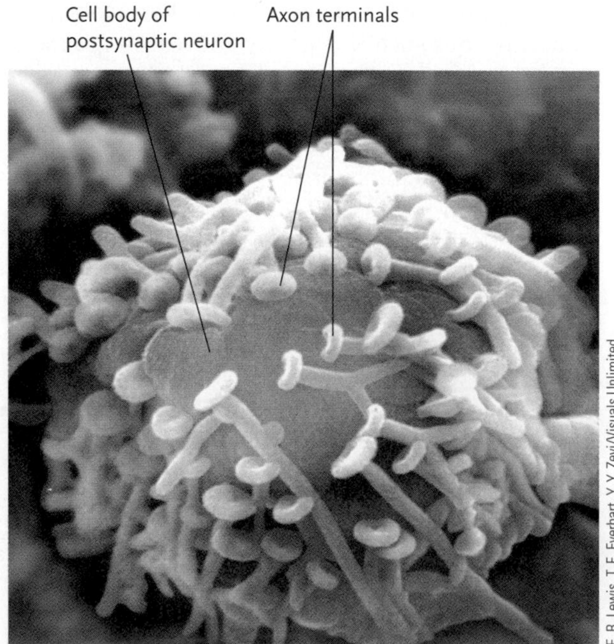

Figure 33.15
The multiple chemical synapses relaying signals to a neuron. The drying process used to prepare the neuron for electron microscopy has toppled the axon terminals and pulled them away from the neuron's surface.

chemical synapses formed by presynaptic neurons. At any given time, some or many of the presynaptic neurons may be firing, producing EPSPs and/or IPSPs in the postsynaptic neuron. The sum of all the EPSPs and IPSPs at a given time determines the total potential in the postsynaptic neuron and, therefore, how that neuron responds. **Figure 33.16** shows, in a greatly simplified way, the effects of EPSPs and IPSPs on membrane potential and how the summation of inputs brings a postsynaptic neuron to threshold.

The postsynaptic neuron in Figure 33.16 has three neurons, N1 to N3, forming synapses with it. Suppose that the axon of N1 releases a neurotransmitter that produces an EPSP in the postsynaptic cell (see Figure 33.16a). The membrane depolarizes, but not enough to reach threshold. If N1 input causes a new EPSP after the first EPSP has died down, it will be of the same magnitude as the first EPSP, so no progression toward threshold happens because no summation has occurred. If, instead, N1 input causes a new EPSP before the first EPSP has died down, the second EPSP will sum with the first, leading to a greater depolarization (see Figure 33.16b). This summation of several EPSPs produced by successive firing of a single presynaptic neuron over a short period of time is called **temporal summation.** If the total depolarization achieved in this way reaches threshold, an action potential will be produced in the postsynaptic neuron.

The postsynaptic cell may also be brought to threshold by **spatial summation**, the summation of EPSPs produced by the firing of different presynaptic neurons, such as N1 and N2 (see Figure 33.16c). Lastly, EPSPs and IPSPs can cancel each other out. In the example shown in Figure 33.16d, firing of N1 alone produces an EPSP, firing of N3 alone produces an IPSP, whereas the simultaneous firing of N1 and N3 produces no change in the membrane potential.

The summation point for EPSPs and IPSPs is the axon hillock of the postsynaptic neuron. The greatest density of voltage-gated Na^+ channels occurs in that region, resulting in the lowest threshold potential in the neuron.

33.4b The Patterns of Synaptic Connections Contribute to Integration

The total number of connections made by a neuron may be very large. Some single interneurons in the human brain, for example, form as many as 100 000 synapses with other neurons. The synapses are not absolutely fixed; they can change through modification, addition, or removal of synaptic connections, or even entire neurons, as animals mature and experience changes in their environments. The combined activities of all the neurons in an animal provide the flow of information on which the integrated functioning of increasingly complex organisms depends. In the remainder of this chapter, we explore the ways that neurons are organized into nervous systems in the various major groups of animals.

STUDY BREAK

Differentiate between spatial and temporal summation.

33.5 Integration in Protostomes: Networks, Nerves, Ganglia, and Brains

In Chapter 26, we learned about some key innovations in animal evolution. Two of these, the appearance of bilateral symmetry and the independent evolution of

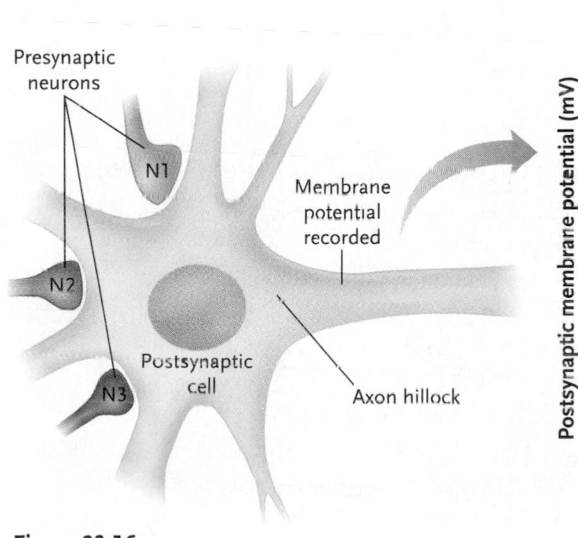

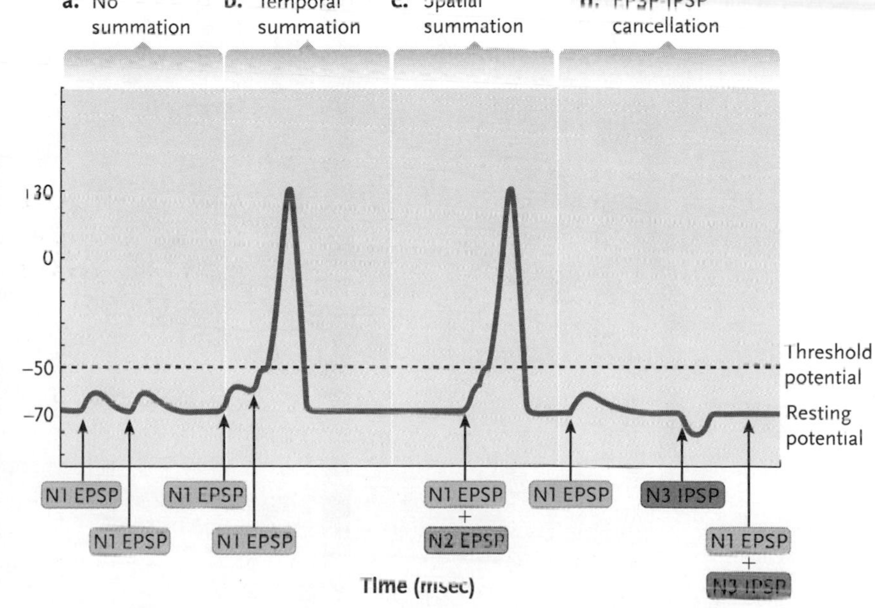

Figure 33.16
Summation of EPSPs and IPSPs by a postsynaptic neuron.

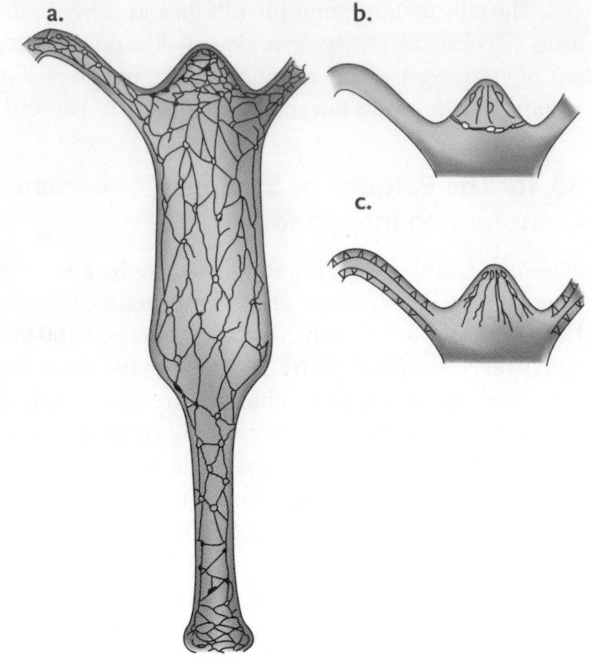

Figure 33.17
The nervous system of *Hydra*. **(a)** The entire nerve net. **(b)** The nerve ring around the hypostome. **(c)** The distribution of sensory neurons.

segmentation in two phyla of the protostomes, were accompanied by evolutionary changes in the organization of the nervous systems. In radially symmetrical protostomes such as the cnidarian *Hydra*, a network of neurons extends over the entire organism just beneath the epithelium **(Figure 33.17).** The neurons are more numerous toward the oral end, and several neurons form a nerve ring around the hypostome. Some of the neurons are sensory. Neurons do not have dendrites and axons. Instead, there are synapses wherever the neurons cross ("en passant" synapses). Moreover, both neurons involved in a synapse may produce transmitters and have receptors for transmitters. This simple system permits the coordination of tentacles for feeding.

In medusoid cnidarians (jellyfish), some of which have coordinated swimming movements, the network is very extensive, forming a very fine meshwork of neurons in the entire animal. This network is connected to two nerve rings that circle the medusa **(Figure 33.18).** Sense organs that detect light and gravity (see Chapter 34) are grouped together and have clusters of nerve cell bodies associated with them. These clusters of neurons ("pace makers") are responsible for generating the rhythmic action potentials that lead to the coordinated muscle contractions involved in swimming.

Even in these simple animals with radial symmetry, neurons are grouped into nerves, sensory structures are localized, and neurons are concentrated around the mouth. Neurons are imposing some degree of localized coordination or control.

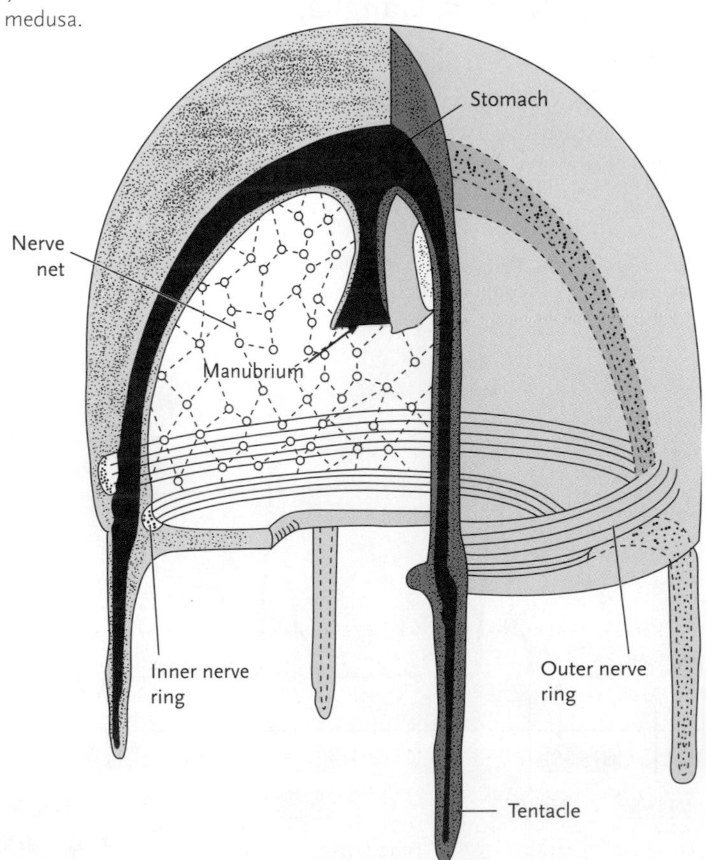

Figure 33.18
Nervous system in a cnidarian medusa.

33.5a Ganglia Enhance Integration in Invertebrates

Groups of nerve cell bodies with localized interconnections are called **ganglia** (singular, ganglion; **Figure 33.19).** In protostomes, the cell bodies of a ganglion

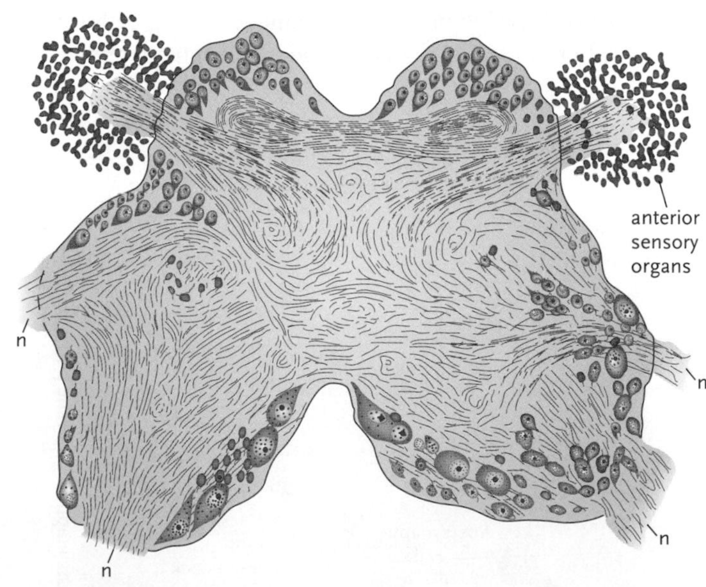

Figure 33.19
A section of a typical invertebrate cerebral ganglion. The cell bodies (blue) are located on the periphery, with a mass of axons and dendrites forming the neuropile in the centre. Nerves (n) bring sensory information into the ganglion and carry motor information outward.

are located on its periphery, with the interconnections located in a tangled mass of axons and dendrites, the **neuropile**, in the centre. This anatomical localization of interconnections allows rapid integration of sensory information and more complex reactions to that information. Bilaterally symmetrical animals, which have an anterior and a posterior end, have a concentration of ganglia at the anterior end, forming a "brain" or cerebral ganglion. Many of the sense organs are also found at the anterior end.

The appearance of bilateral symmetry is accompanied by structures that ensure coordination between the right and left halves of the animal. In the most primitive bilateria, the flatworms **(Figure 33.20)**, the cerebral ganglion is frequently bilobed, with the two halves joined by a commissure. Flatworms always have a pair of prominent ventral nerves, and some have less prominent paired lateral and dorsal nerves leading to the cerebral ganglion. These are connected at intervals by transverse commissures. The cerebral ganglion, or brain, and its associated nerve cords represent the CNS. A nerve net connected to the nerve cords forms a complex PNS. This general pattern of anterior ganglia and nerve cords connected by commissures can be seen in many other invertebrates, although only the flatworms have a nerve net. In most of the protostomes, the anterior ganglia forming the brain surround the anterior digestive system. In cephalopod molluscs, cephalization is the most pronounced of any of the invertebrates. In the octopus **(Figure 33.21)**, for example, several ganglia surrounding the anterior digestive system fuse to form a brain with distinct motor and sensory areas and a series of paired nerves connect to sense organs and muscles. Octopuses are capable of rapid movement to hunt prey and have the capacity to learn complex behaviours.

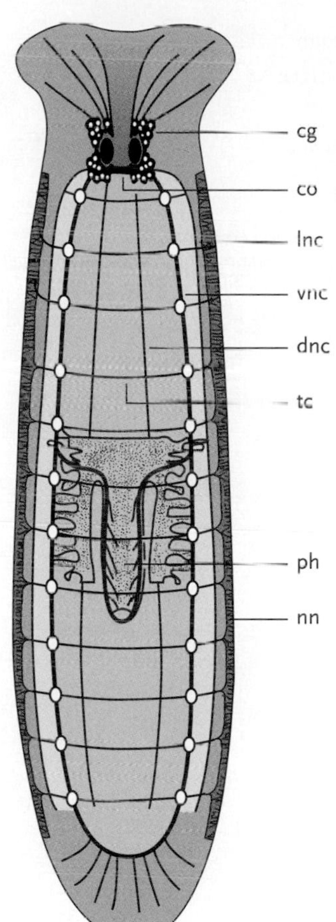

Figure 33.20
Nervous system in a free-living platyhelminth. The cerebral ganglion (cg) has two lobes connected by a commissure (co). It receives nerves from sense organs in the head and gives rise to three pairs of nerve cords: prominent ventral cords (vnc) and the less prominent lateral (lnc) and dorsal (dnc) cords, all linked to a nerve net (nn) and connected at intervals by transverse commissures (tc). The pharynx (ph) has prominent innervation.

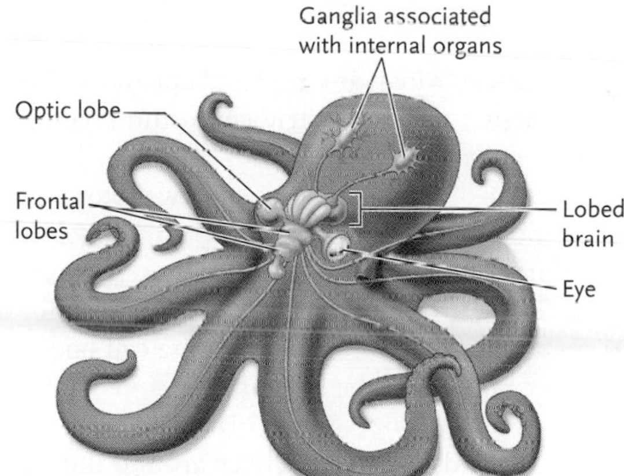

Figure 33.21
The nervous system of an octopus.

33.5b Segmentation Includes the Nervous System

We saw in Chapter 26 that segmental development has occurred twice in the evolution of the protostomes, and the effects on the nervous system have been very similar. In both the annelids and the arthropods, each segment has a separate pair of ganglia, joined by a short commissure. In insects **(Figure 33.22, p. 802)**, for example, the ganglia of each segment are connected to those anterior and posterior to it by paired connectives, forming a chain of ganglia. Each ganglion gives rise to nerves that serve the segment and its appendages. Although there is some independence, the actions of one ganglion may be coordinated with those of adjacent ganglia and with the CNS through the paired intersegmental connectives. For example, a leg of a cockroach can make a stepping motion when the intersegmental connectives are cut, but walking requires an intact nervous system.

33.5c Brains in Segmental Animals Are Fused Segmental Ganglia

As cephalization proceeds during evolution, recognizable heads appear. Appendages have been modified to form sense organs or for feeding, and the paired ganglia associated with those structures are fused. In the insect head (see Figure 33.22), embryologists have recognized six ganglia. The protocerebrum is largely concerned with vision (the eyes are an extension of the brain); the deutocerebrum processes information

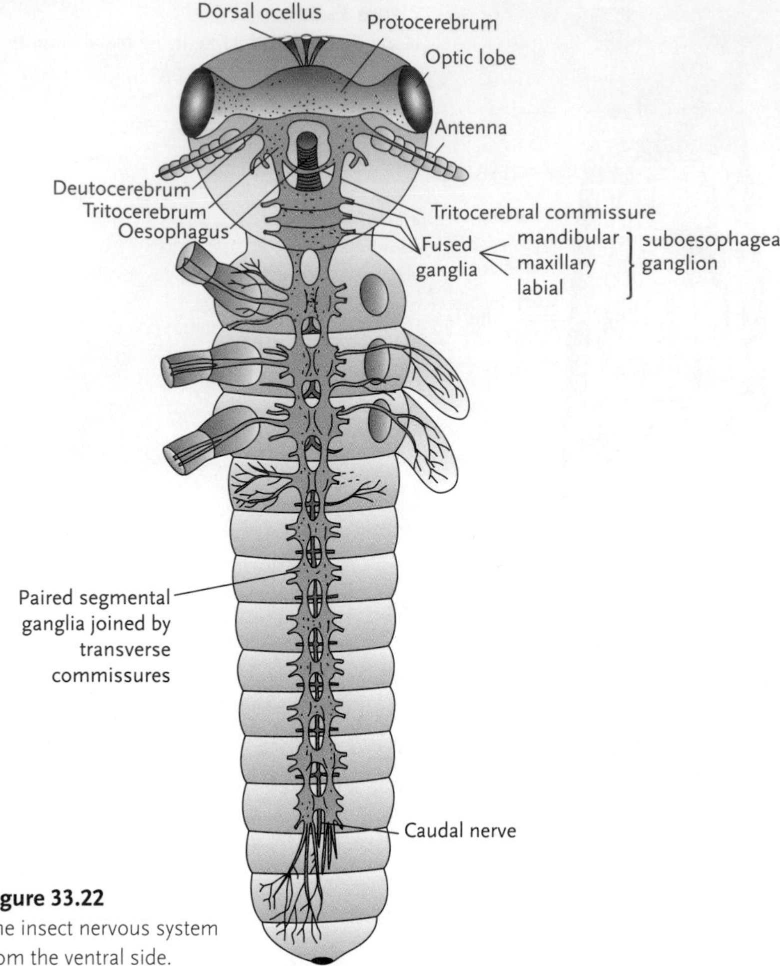

Figure 33.22
The insect nervous system from the ventral side.

from the antennae, which are modified appendages of the second segment; and the tritocerebrum receives nerves from the labrum and anterior intestine. These three ganglia constitute the brain. Very few motor neurons are associated with the brain; most are involved with the information from the anterior sense organs or are associative neurons involved in processing information. As in all protostome ganglia, the cell bodies are at the periphery and the neuropile lies inside the ganglia.

The brain sends two connectives around the gut to connect with the suboesophageal ganglion. This is made up of three fused ganglia, one for each of the modified appendages that form the mouthparts. Thus, the insect head represents six primitive segments, three anterior to the mouth and three posterior. Similar analyses can be performed for other arthropods.

Study Break

1. Distinguish among nerve nets, nerves, and nerve cords.
2. What are segmental ganglia?

33.6 Vertebrates Have the Most Complex Nervous Systems

Vertebrates are thought to have evolved from the larval form of a primitive chordate, such as an ascidian (see Chapter 27). The ancestor probably resembled the lancelet *Branchiostoma*. The lancelet has a segmental organization, but the segmentation does not include the body surface. During development, blocks of mesodermal tissue arise that develop as segmental blocks of muscle, the myotomes. These develop before the nervous system and nerves grow out from the developing nerve cord to innervate them. Thus, the nervous system is not segmental in the same sense as arthropods or annelids. As in all chordates, the nerve cord is dorsal and contains a central cavity. This is a reflection of the different ways in which the nervous systems develop. In protostomes, differentiating nerve cells group together to form ganglia in the ventral part of the animal. In chordates, by contrast, the nervous system is formed dorsally as the hollow **neural tube**, the anterior end of which develops into the brain and the rest into the **spinal cord** (see Chapter 39). In the lancelet, the anterior end of the nerve cord is larger than the rest of it. Detailed anatomical studies by Thurston Lacalli at the University of Saskatchewan, supported by emerging molecular data, have identified three regions of the lancelet "brain" that are probably homologous with the forebrain, midbrain, and hindbrain regions of the vertebrate brain.

In vertebrates, the CNS consists of the brain and spinal cord, and the PNS consists of all the nerves that connect the brain and spinal cord to the rest of the body. The brain and nerve cord of vertebrates are hollow, fluid-filled structures located dorsally. The central cavity of the neural tube becomes the fluid-filled **ventricles** of the brain and the narrow **central canal** through the spinal cord.

Although the lancelet nervous system is simple and shows only minimal cephalization, all vertebrate nervous systems are highly cephalized, with major concentrations of neurons in a brain located in the head. During evolution, the complexity of the general structure of the brain has increased, and differences appear in the brains of the major groups.

The organization of the brain is exceedingly complex. One way to understand its evolution is to examine its embryological development from the embryonic neural tube. A generalized vertebrate brain approximately midway through its embryonic development **(Figure 33.23a)** shows the principal regions shared by all vertebrate brains. Early in embryonic development, the anterior part of the neural tube enlarges into three distinct regions. The **forebrain** was originally associated with olfaction or the sense of smell, the **midbrain** was primarily associated with vision, and the **hindbrain** was mainly associated with balance. Later, the embryonic hindbrain subdivided into the *metencephalon* (*met* = behind; *encephalon* = brain) and the *myelencephalon* (*myelo* = spinal cord), the midbrain developed into the *mesencephalon* (*mes* = middle), and the forebrain subdivided into the *telencephalon* (*tel* = distant) and the *diencephalon* (*di* = across).

Later still, the metencephalon, associated with the developing ear (when present) and balance organs, gave rise to the *cerebellum*, a major traffic centre that integrates sensory signals from the eyes, ears, and muscle spindles. The myelencephalon gave rise to the *medulla oblongata* (commonly shortened to medulla) that controls many vital involuntary tasks, such as respiration and blood circulation. The mesencephalon, or midbrain, received fibres from the optic nerves and from the ear and acts as a relay centre passing information forward for processing. The diencephalon is associated with the eyes, and the optic nerve is an outgrowth of it. The telencephalon, embryologically associated with olfaction, gave rise to the olfactory bulb and the cerebrum, the major processing centre of the brain. These events and the functions of the areas are summarized in **Figure 33.23b.**

The general pattern of brain development underwent major modification in the evolution of

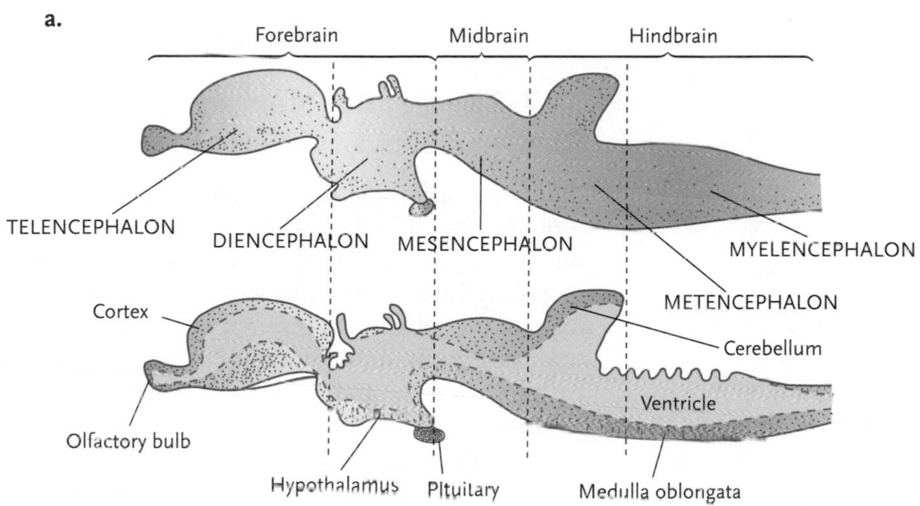

Figure 33.23
(a) Diagram of a vertebrate brain midway in development. Upper, lateral view; lower, vertical section. At this stage, only a few of the adult structures are easily identified. During later development in birds and mammals, the elongate form of the brain becomes folded so that the very prominent forebrain lies above the other regions. During development to the adult, the size of the ventricle is reduced. **(b)** The regions of the brain of a bird or mammal during development and their functions in the adult.

b.

Regions in early embryo	Regions in mid-development	Neural tube	Regions in adult	Functions in adult
Forebrain	Telencephalon		Telencephalon (cerebrum)	Higher functions, such as thought, action, and communication
	Diencephalon		Thalamus	Coordinates sensory input and relays it to cerebellum
			Hypothalamus	Centre for homeostatic control of internal environment
Midbrain	Mesencephalon		Midbrain	Coordinates involuntary reactions and relays signals to telencephalon
Hindbrain	Metencephalon		Cerebellum	Integrates signals for muscle movement
			Pons	Centre for information flow between cerebellum and telencephalon
	Myelencephalon		Medulla oblongata	Controls many involuntary tasks

various groups of animals (**Figure 33.24**). In sharks, the cerebrum is relatively small, but the olfactory bulbs are prominent, testifying to the importance of olfaction in these very successful predators. Frogs are hunters that rely on vision, so the optic lobes of the mesencephalon are prominent, whereas the olfactory bulbs are less so. Birds also rely on vision for feeding and navigation, and their optic lobes reflect that.

One of the major trends in the evolution of the brain, however, is the increasing prominence of the cerebrum. Beginning with reptiles, it increased in size relative to the rest of the brain. In mammals, convolutions or folds appeared, increasing the amount of brain material in a particular volume. As well, the total mass of the brain relative to the size of the animal increased, permitting animals to undertake more complex tasks. The mass of bird and mammal brains is about 15 times greater than that of other taxa when corrected for the size of the animal. With their advanced locomotor and navigational skills, birds and mammals also exhibit an increase in the cerebellum, a major coordinating centre for automatic activities. Because we know most about the functioning of the human brain, the following sections examine the structure and function of the human nervous system, beginning with the CNS.

Study Break

1. From what part of the embryonic brain does the cerebellum come? What does it control?
2. How does the frog brain differ from that of sharks?

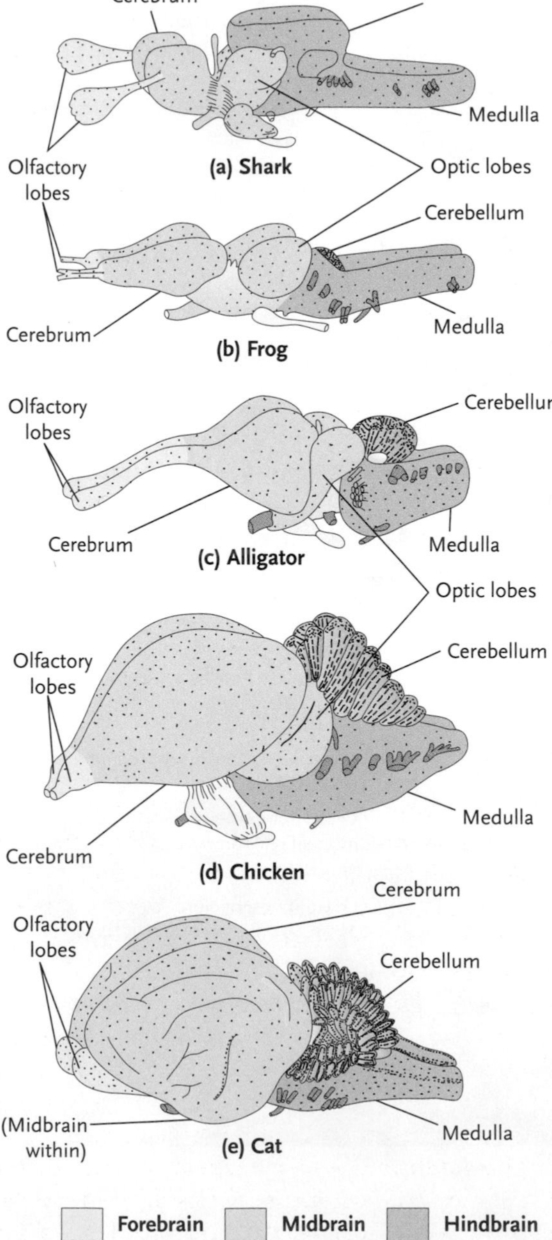

Figure 33.24
A comparison of brain structures in five different groups of vertebrates, illustrating the evolutionary trends described in the text.

33.7 The Central Nervous System (CNS) and Its Functions

The brain and spinal cord are surrounded and protected by three layers of connective tissue, the **meninges** (*meninga* = membrane), and by the **cerebrospinal fluid**, which circulates through the central canal of the spinal cord, through the ventricles of the brain, and between two of the meninges. The fluid cushions the brain and spinal cord from jarring movements and impacts, nourishes the CNS, and protects it from toxic substances.

The CNS manages body activities by integrating incoming sensory information from the PNS into compensating responses. Our examination of the vertebrate CNS begins with the spinal cord and then considers the brain and its functions.

33.7a The Spinal Cord Relays Signals between the PNS and the Brain and Controls Reflexes

The spinal cord, which extends dorsally from the base of the brain, carries impulses between the brain and the PNS and contains the interneuron circuits that control motor reflexes. In cross section, the spinal cord has a butterfly-shaped core of **grey matter**, consisting of nerve cell bodies and dendrites. This is surrounded by **white matter**, consisting of axons, many of them surrounded by myelin sheaths (**Figure 33.25**, left side). Note that this arrangement is the reverse of that in invertebrate ganglia, where cell bodies are at the periphery (see Figure 33.19). Pairs of spinal nerves connect with the spinal cord at spaces between the vertebrae.

The afferent (incoming) axons entering the spinal cord make synapses with interneurons in the grey

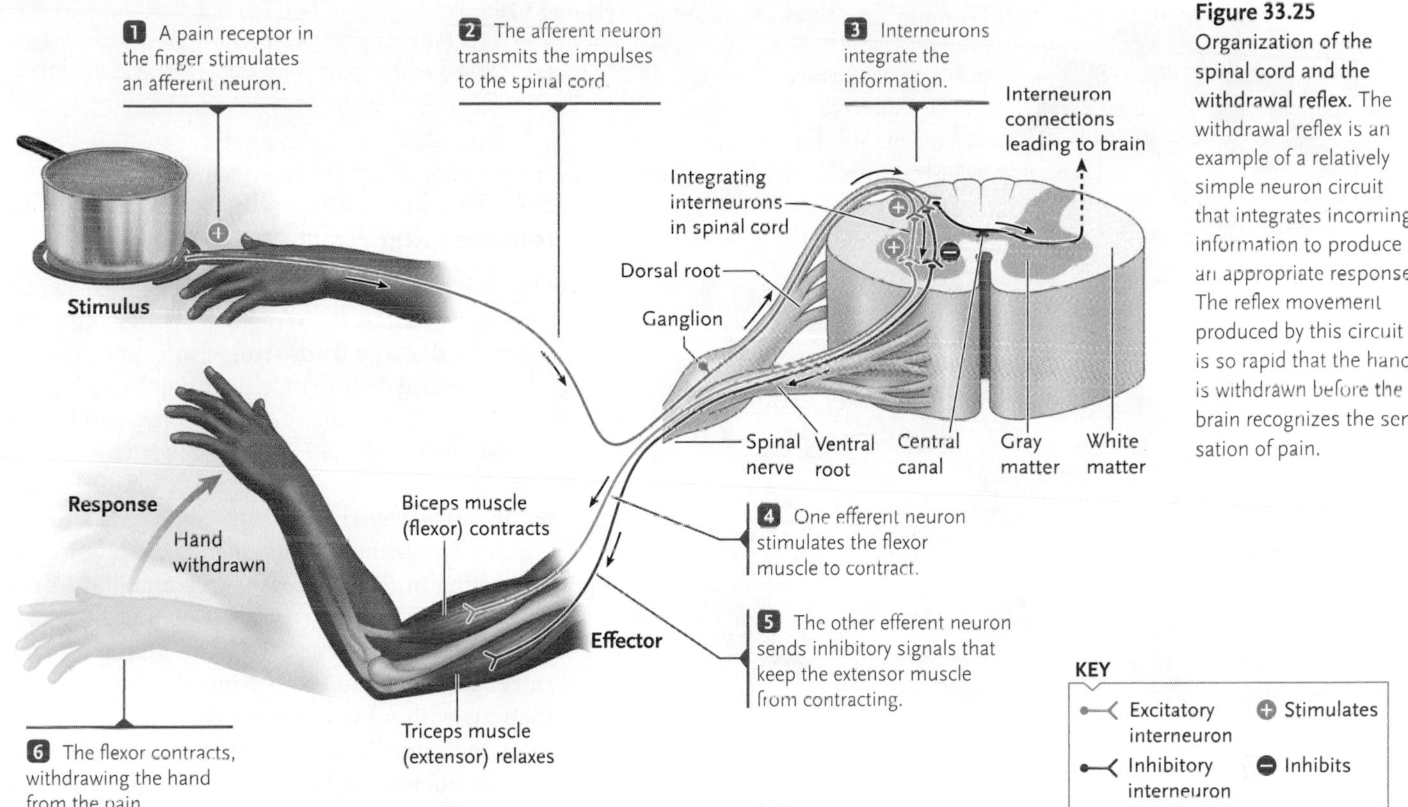
1 A pain receptor in the finger stimulates an afferent neuron.
2 The afferent neuron transmits the impulses to the spinal cord.
3 Interneurons integrate the information.
Interneuron connections leading to brain
Integrating interneurons in spinal cord
Dorsal root
Ganglion
Stimulus
Spinal nerve
Ventral root
Central canal
Gray matter
White matter
Response
Hand withdrawn
Biceps muscle (flexor) contracts
4 One efferent neuron stimulates the flexor muscle to contract.
Effector
5 The other efferent neuron sends inhibitory signals that keep the extensor muscle from contracting.
Triceps muscle (extensor) relaxes
6 The flexor contracts, withdrawing the hand from the pain.
KEY
Excitatory interneuron
Inhibitory interneuron
Stimulates
Inhibits

Figure 33.25
Organization of the spinal cord and the withdrawal reflex. The withdrawal reflex is an example of a relatively simple neuron circuit that integrates incoming information to produce an appropriate response. The reflex movement produced by this circuit is so rapid that the hand is withdrawn before the brain recognizes the sensation of pain.

matter, which send axons upward through the white matter of the spinal cord to the brain. Conversely, axons from interneurons of the brain pass downward through the white matter of the cord and make synapses with the dendrites and cell bodies of efferent neurons in the grey matter of the cord. The axons of these efferent (outgoing) neurons exit the spinal cord through the spinal nerves.

The grey matter of the spinal cord also contains interneurons of the pathways involved in reflexes, programmed movements that take place without conscious effort, such as the sudden withdrawal of a hand from a hot surface (shown in Figure 33.25). When your hand touches the hot surface, the heat stimulates an afferent neuron, which makes connections with at least two interneurons in the spinal cord. One of these interneurons stimulates an efferent neuron, causing the *flexor* muscle of the arm to contract. This bends the arm and withdraws the hand almost instantly from the hot surface. The other interneuron synapses with an efferent neuron connected to an *extensor* muscle, relaxing it so that the flexor can move more quickly. Interneurons connected to the reflex circuits also send signals to the brain, making you aware of the stimulus causing the reflex. You know from experience that when a reflex movement withdraws your hand from a hot surface or other damaging stimulus, you feel the pain shortly *after* the hand is withdrawn. This is the extra time required for impulses to travel from the neurons of the reflex to the brain.

33.7b The Brain Integrates Sensory Information and Formulates Compensating Responses

The brain is the major centre that receives, integrates, stores, and retrieves information. Its interneuron networks generate responses that provide the basis for our voluntary movements, consciousness, behaviour, emotions, learning, reasoning, language, and memory, among many other complex activities.

Major Brain Structures. We have noted that the three major divisions of the embryonic brain give rise to the structures of the adult brain. Like the spinal cord, each brain structure contains both grey matter and white matter and is surrounded by meninges and circulating cerebrospinal fluid **(Figure 33.26, p. 806)**.

The hindbrain of vertebrates develops into the *medulla oblongata* (the *medulla*) and the *cerebellum* (see Figure 33.23). In higher mammals, a mass of fibres connecting the cerebellum to higher centres in the brain is so prominent that it is identified as the *pons* (bridge). The medulla and pons, along with the midbrain, form a stalklike structure known as the **brain stem**, which connects the forebrain with the spinal cord. All but 2 of the 12 pairs of cranial nerves (see Section 33.8) also originate from the brain stem.

The forebrain, which makes up most of the mass of the brain in humans, forms the *telencephalon* (*cerebrum*). Its surface layer, the **cerebral cortex**, is a thin

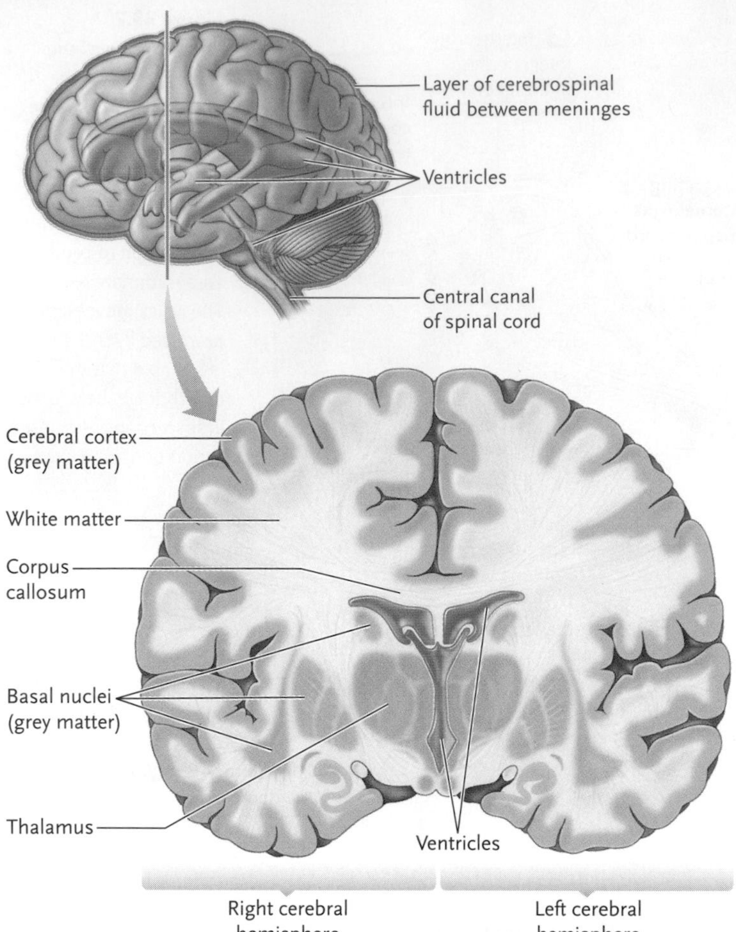

Figure 33.26
The human brain, illustrating the distribution of grey matter, and the locations of the four ventricles (in blue) with their connection to the central canal of the spinal cord.

layer of grey matter in which numerous unmyelinated neurons are found. The telencephalon, which is divided into right and left *cerebral hemispheres,* is corrugated by fissures and folds that increase the surface area of the cerebral cortex (see Figure 33.26). This structure reflects two of the evolutionary tendencies in the brain of mammals: the corrugation of the hemispheres and the development of a layer of grey matter on the periphery.

The Blood–Brain Barrier. Unlike the epithelial cells that form capillary walls elsewhere in the body, which allow small molecules and ions to pass freely from the blood to surrounding fluids, those forming capillaries in the brain are sealed together by tight junctions (Chapter 32). The tight junctions set up a **blood–brain barrier** that prevents most substances dissolved in the blood from entering the cerebrospinal fluid, protecting the brain and spinal cord from viruses, bacteria, and toxic substances that may circulate in the blood. A few types of molecules and ions, such as oxygen, carbon dioxide, alcohol, and anaesthetics, can move directly across the lipid bilayer of the epithelial cell membranes by diffusion. A few other substances are moved across the plasma membrane by highly selective transport proteins. The most significant of these transported molecules is glucose, the important source of metabolic energy for the cells of the brain.

33.7c The Brain Stem Regulates Many Vital Housekeeping Functions of the Body

Physicians and scientists have learned much about the functions of various brain regions by studying patients with brain damage from stroke, infection, tumours, and mechanical disturbance. Techniques such as *functional magnetic resonance imaging* (*fMRI*) and *positron emission tomography* (*PET*) allow researchers to identify the normal functions of specific brain regions in noninvasive ways. The instruments record a subject's brain activity during various mental and physical tasks by detecting minute increases in blood flow or metabolic activity in specific regions **(Figure 33.27).**

From such analyses, we know that grey-matter centres in the brain stem control many vital body functions without conscious involvement or control by the cerebrum. Among these functions are the heart and respiration rates, blood pressure, constriction and dilation of blood vessels, coughing, and reflex activities of the digestive system, such as vomiting.

33.7d The Cerebellum Integrates Sensory Inputs to Coordinate Body Movements

Although the cerebellum is connected to the pons, it is separate in structure and function from the brain stem. Through its extensive connections with other parts of the brain, the **cerebellum** receives sensory input originating from receptors in muscles and joints, from balance receptors in the inner ear, and from the receptors of touch, vision, and hearing. These signals

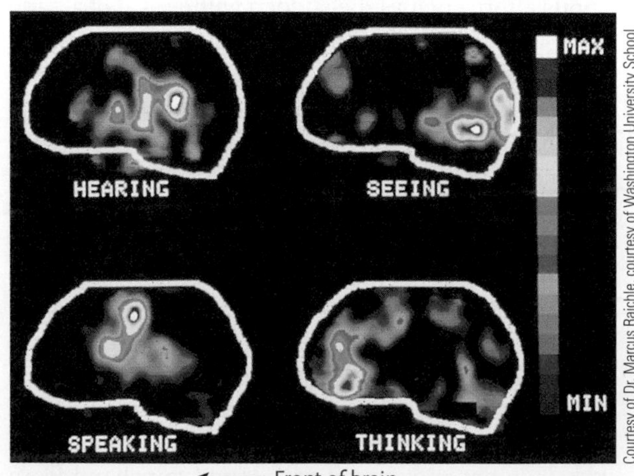

Figure 33.27
PET scans showing regions of the brain active when a person performs specific mental tasks. The colours show the relative activity of the sections, with white being the most active.

convey information about how the body trunk and limbs are positioned, the degree to which different muscles are contracted or relaxed, and the direction in which the body or limbs are moving. The cerebellum integrates these sensory signals and compares them with signals from the cerebrum that control voluntary body movements. Outputs from the cerebellum to the cerebrum, brain stem, and spinal cord modify and fine-tune the movements to keep the body in balance and directed toward targeted positions in space. The cerebellum is particularly important in birds, and, like the mammalian cerebellum, it has a folded structure, increasing its relative size.

33.7e Basal Nuclei, Thalamus, and Hypothalamus Grey-Matter Centres Control a Variety of Functions

Grey-matter centres derived from the embryonic telencephalon include the thalamus, hypothalamus, basal nuclei, and limbic system **(Figure 33.28).** They contribute to the control and integration of voluntary movements, body temperature, glandular secretions, osmotic balance of the blood and extracellular fluids, wakefulness, and the emotions, among other functions. Some of the grey-matter centres route information to and from the cerebral cortex and between the forebrain, brain stem, and cerebellum.

The **thalamus** (see Figure 33.28) forms a major switchboard that receives sensory information and relays it to the appropriate regions of the cerebral cortex. It also plays a role in alerting the cerebral cortex to full wakefulness or in inducing drowsiness or sleep.

The **hypothalamus** is a relatively small conical area that occurs in all vertebrates. It contains centres that regulate basic homeostatic functions of the body. Some centres set and maintain body temperature by triggering reactions such as shivering or sweating. Others constantly monitor the osmotic balance of the blood by testing its composition of ions and other substances. If departures from normal levels are detected, the hypothalamus triggers responses such as thirst or changes in urine output that restore the osmotic and fluid balance. The hypothalamus is an important part of the endocrine system (see Chapter 35). It produces some of the hormones released by the pituitary and governs the release of other pituitary hormones.

The centres of the hypothalamus that detect blood composition and temperature are directly exposed to the bloodstream: they are the only parts of the brain *not* protected by the blood–brain barrier. Parts of the hypothalamus also coordinate responses triggered by the autonomic system (see Section 33.8), making it an important link in such activities as control of the heartbeat, contraction of smooth muscle cells in the digestive system, and glandular secretion. Some regions of the hypothalamus establish a biological clock that sets up daily metabolic rhythms, such as the regular changes in body temperature that occur on a daily cycle.

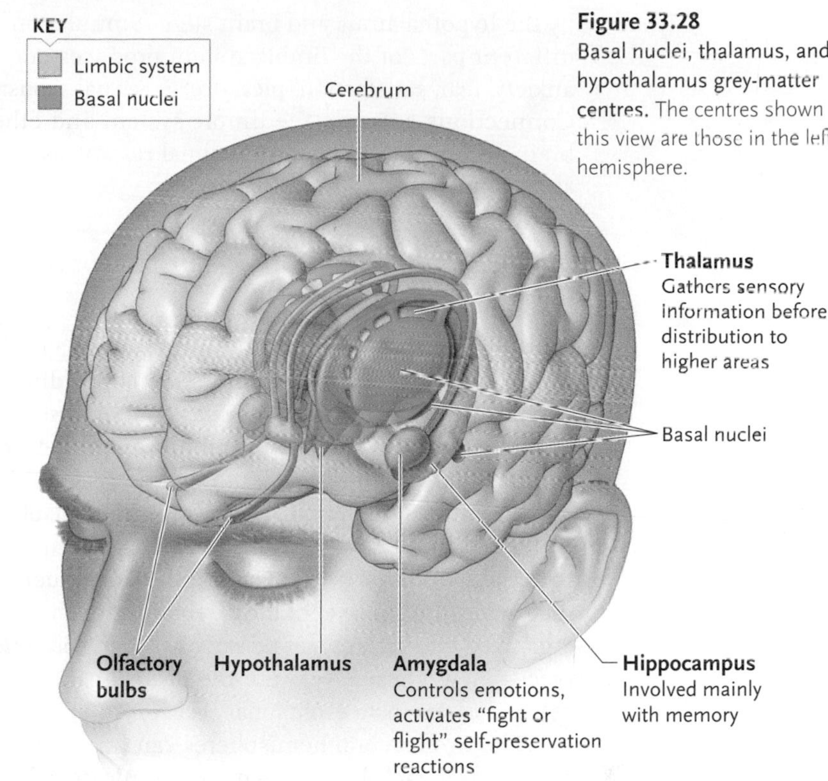

Figure 33.28
Basal nuclei, thalamus, and hypothalamus grey-matter centres. The centres shown in this view are those in the left hemisphere.

The **basal nuclei** are grey-matter centres that surround the thalamus on both sides of the brain (see Figure 33.28). They moderate voluntary movements directed by motor centres in the cerebrum and can be recognized in all amniotes. Damage to the basal nuclei can affect the planning and fine-tuning of movements, leading to stiff, rigid motions of the limbs and unwanted or misdirected motor activity, such as tremors of the hands and inability to start or stop intended movements at the intended place and time. Parkinson disease, in which affected individuals exhibit all of these symptoms, results from degeneration of centres in and near the basal nuclei.

Parts of the thalamus, hypothalamus, and basal nuclei, along with other nearby grey-matter centres—the amygdala, hippocampus, and olfactory bulbs—form a functional network called the **limbic system** (*limbus* = belt), sometimes called our "emotional brain" (see Figure 33.28). The **amygdala** works as a switchboard, routing information about experiences that have an emotional component through the limbic system. The **hippocampus** is involved in sending information to the frontal lobes, and the **olfactory bulbs** relay inputs from odour receptors to both the cerebral cortex and the limbic system. The olfactory connection to the limbic system may explain why certain odours can evoke particular, sometimes startlingly powerful, emotional responses.

The limbic system controls emotional behaviour and influences the basic body functions regulated by the hypothalamus and brain stem. Stimulation of different parts of the limbic system produces anger, anxiety, fear, satisfaction, pleasure, or sexual arousal. Connections between the limbic system and other brain regions bring about emotional responses such as smiling, blushing, or laughing.

33.7f The Cerebral Cortex Carries Out All Higher Brain Functions

Over the course of evolution, the surface area of the cerebral cortex increased by continuously folding in on itself, thereby expanding the structure into sophisticated information encoding and processing centres. Primates have cerebral cortices with the largest number of convolutions. In humans, each cerebral hemisphere is divided by surface folds into *frontal*, *parietal*, *temporal*, and *occipital* lobes **(Figure 33.29)**. Uniquely in mammals, the top layer of the cerebral hemispheres is organized into six layers of neurons called the *neocortex* (*neo* = new; these layers are the newest part of the cerebral cortex in an evolutionary sense).

The two cerebral hemispheres can function separately, and each has its own communication lines internally and with the rest of the CNS and the body. The left cerebral hemisphere responds primarily to sensory signals from, and controls movements in, the right side of the body. The right hemisphere has the same relationships to the left side of the body. This opposite connection and control reflect the fact that the nerves carrying afferent and efferent signals cross from left to right within the spinal cord or brain stem. Thick axon bundles, forming a structure called the **corpus callosum**, connect the two cerebral hemispheres and coordinate their functions.

Sensory Regions of the Cerebral Cortex. Areas that receive and integrate sensory information are distributed over the cerebral cortex. In each hemisphere, the primary somatosensory area, which registers information on touch, pain, temperature, and pressure, runs in a band across the parietal lobes of the brain (see Figure 33.29). Experimental stimulation of this band in one hemisphere causes prickling or tingling sensations in specific parts on the opposite side of the body, beginning with the toes at the top of each hemisphere and running through the legs, trunk, arms, and hands, to the head (**Figure 33.30** and *People Behind Biology*).

Other sensory regions of the cerebral cortex have been identified with hearing, vision, smell, and taste (see Figure 33.30). Regions of the temporal lobes on both sides of the brain receive auditory inputs from the ears, whereas inputs from the eyes are processed in the primary visual cortex in both occipital lobes. Olfactory input from the nose is processed in the olfactory lobes, located on the ventral side of the temporal lobes. Regions in the parietal lobes receive inputs from taste receptors on the tongue and other locations in the mouth.

Motor Regions of the Cerebral Cortex. The **primary motor area** of the cerebral cortex runs in a band just in front of the primary somatosensory area (see Figure 33.29). Experimental stimulation of points along this

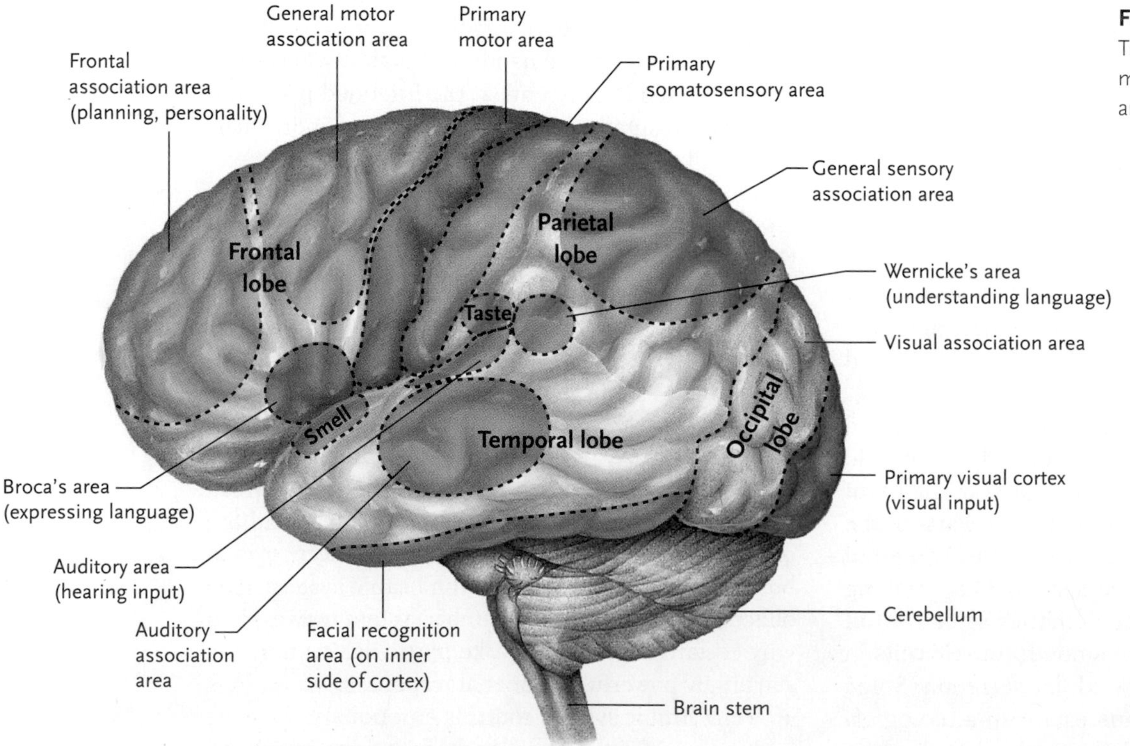

Figure 33.29
The lobes of the cerebrum, showing major regions and association areas of the cerebral cortex.

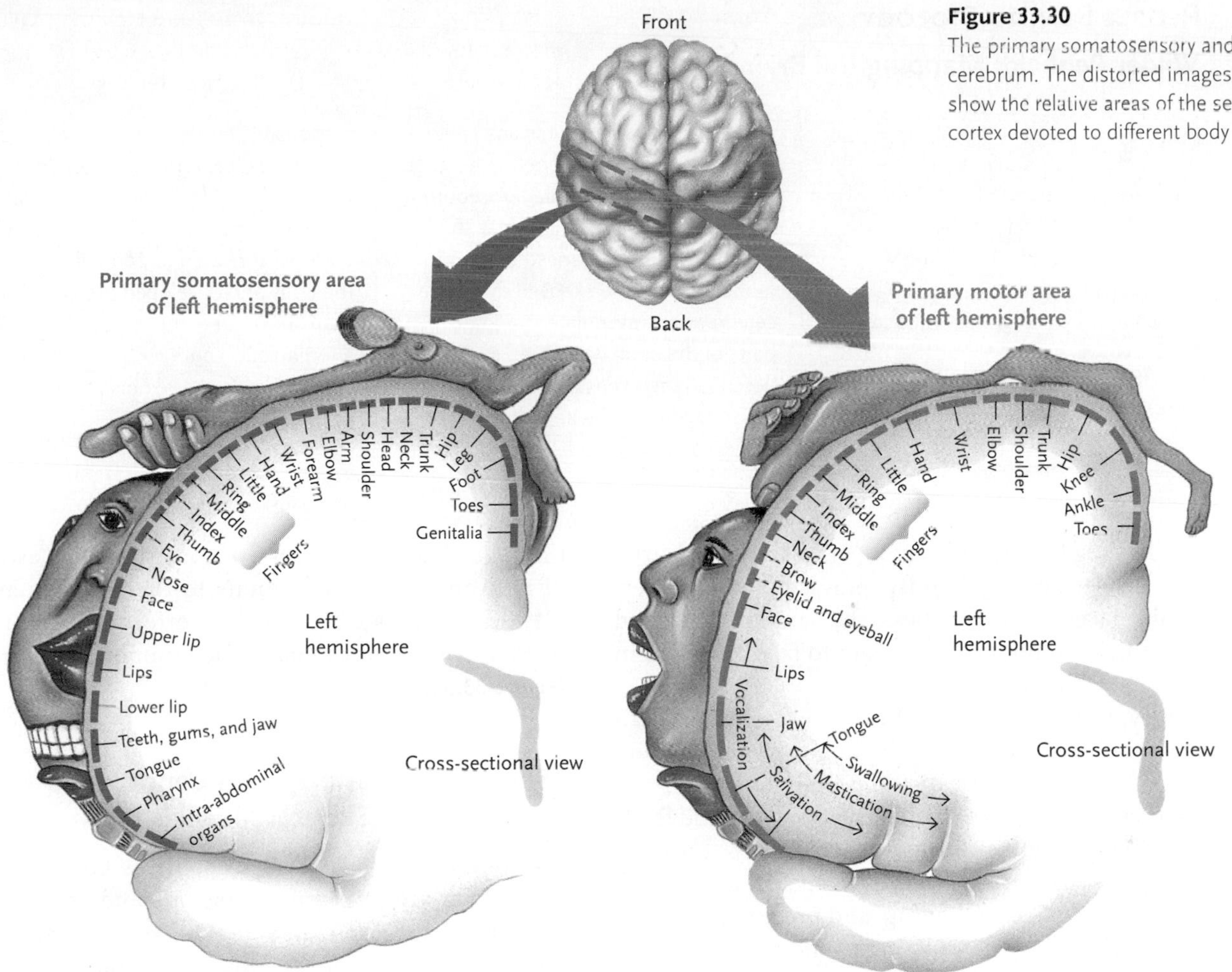

Figure 33.30
The primary somatosensory and motor areas of the cerebrum. The distorted images of the human body show the relative areas of the sensory and motor cortex devoted to different body regions.

band in one hemisphere causes movement of specific body parts on the opposite side of the body, corresponding generally to the parts registering in the primary somatosensory area at the same level (see Figure 33.30). Other areas that integrate and refine motor control are located nearby.

In both the primary somatosensory and motor areas, some body parts, such as the lips and fingers, are represented by large regions, and others, such as the arms and legs, are represented by relatively small regions. As shown in Figure 33.30, the relative sizes produce a distorted image of the human body that is quite different from the actual body proportions. The differences are reflected in the precision of touch and movement in structures such as the lips, tongue, and fingers.

Association Areas. The sensory and motor areas of the cerebral cortex are surrounded by **association areas** (see Figure 33.29) that integrate information from the sensory areas, formulate responses, and pass them on to the primary motor area. Two of the most important association areas are *Wernicke's area* and *Broca's area*, which function in spoken and written language. They are usually present on only one side of the brain, in the left hemisphere in 97% of the human population. Comprehension of spoken and written language depends on Wernicke's area, which coordinates inputs from the visual, auditory, and general sensory association areas. Interneuron connections lead from Wernicke's area to Broca's area, which puts together the motor program for coordination of the lips, tongue, jaws, and other structures producing the sounds of speech and passes the program to the primary motor area. The brain-scan images in Figure 33.27 dramatically illustrate how these brain regions participate as a person performs different linguistic tasks.

33.7g Some Higher Functions Are Distributed in Both Cerebral Hemispheres; Others Are Concentrated in One Hemisphere

Most of the other higher functions of the human brain, such as abstract thought and reasoning; spatial recognition; mathematical, musical, and artistic ability; and the associations forming the basis of personality, involve the coordinated participation of many regions of the cerebral cortex. Some of these regions are equally distributed in both cerebral hemispheres, and some are more concentrated in one hemisphere.

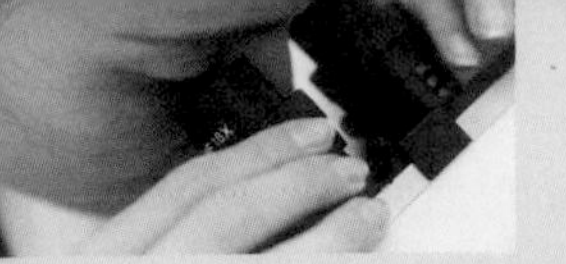

People Behind Biology

Wilder Penfield: Mapping the Brain

Born in the United States at the end of the nineteenth century, Wilder Penfield graduated in literature from Princeton and won a Rhodes Scholarship to Oxford. He graduated as an M.D. from Johns Hopkins and worked in neurosurgery at Columbia. Attracted to McGill University in Montreal in 1928, he realized his dream by establishing the Montreal Neurological Institute, where scientists and clinicians could work together. It was here that he established the "Montreal Procedure" for the treatment of epilepsy. With patients under local anesthesia and fully conscious, he exposed the entire cerebrum and stimulated various parts of the brain while the patients described their sensations. In this way, he could identify the area of the brain responsible for the epileptic seizures and, if feasible, remove or destroy it. In the course of this work, he was able to identify those areas of the cerebral cortex that related to particular parts of the body and developed the well-known map shown in Figure 33.30. This was a remarkably courageous procedure at the time and required his patients to trust him absolutely.

Among the functions more or less equally distributed between the two hemispheres is the ability to recognize faces. Consciousness, the sense of time, and recognizing emotions also seem to be distributed in both hemispheres.

Typically, some brain functions are more localized in one of the two hemispheres, a phenomenon called lateralization. Studies of people with split hemispheres and surveys of brain activity by PET and fMRI have confirmed that, for the vast majority of people, the left hemisphere specializes in spoken and written language, abstract reasoning, and precise mathematical calculations. The right hemisphere specializes in nonverbal conceptualizing, intuitive thinking, musical and artistic abilities, and spatial recognition functions, such as fitting pieces into a puzzle. The right hemisphere also handles mathematical estimates and approximations that can be made by visual or spatial representations of numbers. Thus, the left hemisphere in most people is verbal and mathematical, and the right hemisphere is intuitive, spatial, artistic, and musical.

Study Break

1. What part of the brain is responsible for maintaining homeostasis? Where is it located? What is unique about this part of the brain?
2. Distinguish the functions of the cerebellum from those of the cortex.

33.8 The Peripheral Nervous System (PNS)

The PNS can be divided into two main systems. The afferent system of the PNS includes all the neurons that transmit sensory information from receptors to the CNS. The efferent system consists of the axons of neurons that carry signals to the muscles and glands acting as effectors. The efferent system is further divided into somatic and autonomic systems **(Figure 33.31)**.

33.8a The Somatic System Controls the Contraction of Skeletal Muscles

The **somatic nervous system** controls body movements that are primarily conscious and voluntary. In mammals, 31 pairs of **spinal nerves** carry signals between the spinal cord and the body trunk and limbs. These spinal nerves, emanating from between each of the vertebrae, reflect the segmental organization of the vertebrate body. Each spinal nerve is made up of a dorsal root and a ventral root (see Figure 33.25) that emerge from the nerve cord to form the nerve. In lower vertebrates, such as sharks, the ventral root contains motor axons for the somatic muscles (those associated with movement), and the dorsal root contains the afferent axons from the sense organs and the efferent axons to the visceral muscles. The cell bodies for the sensory nerves are located outside the spinal cord within the dorsal root, forming the dorsal root ganglion. In mammals, the visceral motor axons have become included in the ventral root. Its neurons, called motor neurons, carry efferent signals from the CNS to the skeletal muscles, exiting from the nerve cord in the ventral root. The dendrites and cell bodies of motor neurons are located in the spinal cord; their axons extend from the spinal cord to the skeletal muscle cells they control. As a result, the somatic portions of the spinal nerves consist only of axons.

Although the somatic system is primarily under conscious, voluntary control, some contractions of skeletal muscles are unconscious and involuntary. These include reflexes, shivering, and the constant muscle contractions that maintain body posture and balance.

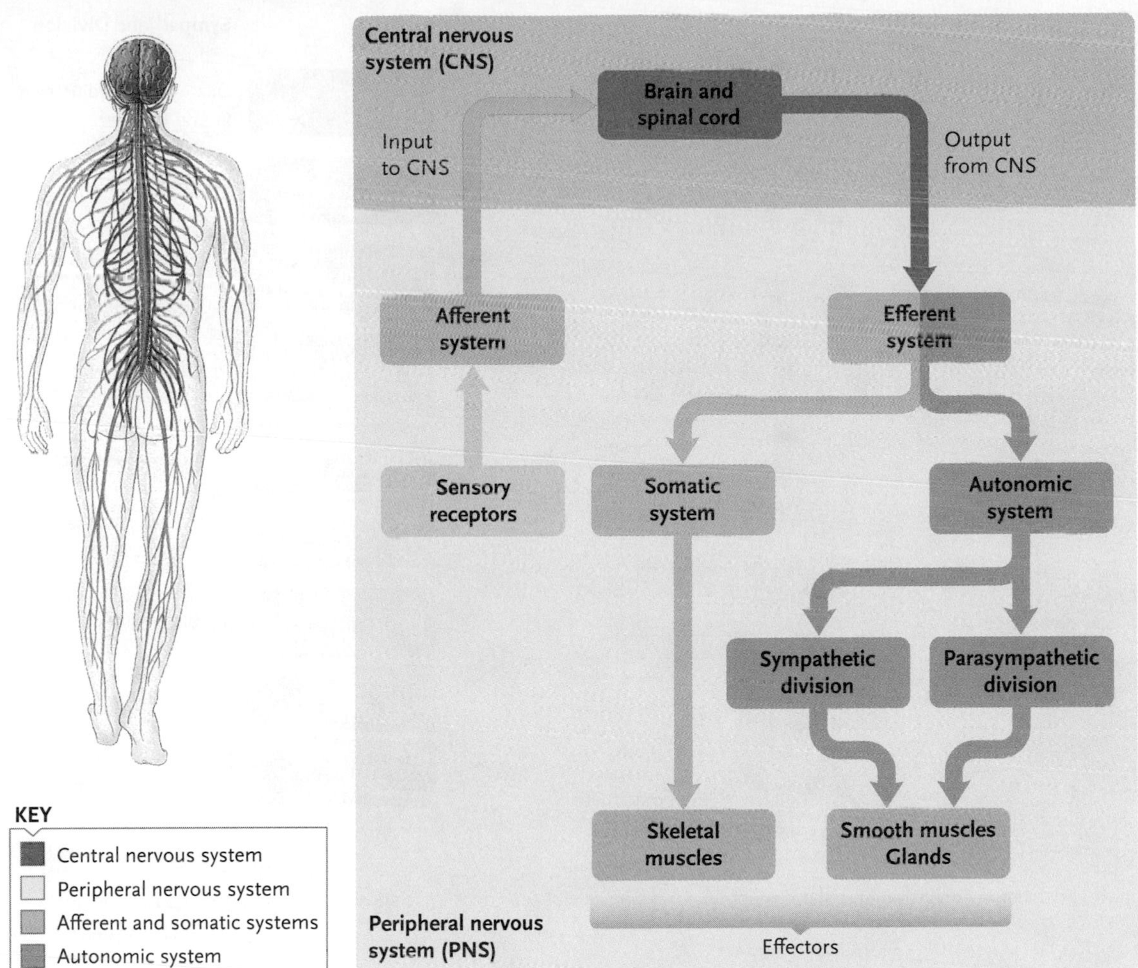

Figure 33.31
The central nervous system (CNS) and peripheral nervous system (PNS) and their subsystems.

33.8b The Autonomic System Is Divided into Sympathetic and Parasympathetic Pathways

The **autonomic nervous system** controls largely involuntary processes such as digestion, secretion by sweat glands, circulation of the blood, many functions of the reproductive and excretory systems, and contraction of smooth muscles in all parts of the body. It is organized into *sympathetic* and *parasympathetic* divisions, which are always active and have opposing effects on the organs that they affect, thereby enabling precise control (**Figure 33.32, p. 812**). For example, in the circulatory system, sympathetic neurons stimulate the force and rate of the heartbeat, and parasympathetic neurons inhibit these activities. In the digestive system, sympathetic neurons inhibit the smooth muscle contractions that move materials through the small intestine, whereas parasympathetic neurons stimulate the same activities. These opposing effects precisely control involuntary body functions.

The pathways of the autonomic nervous system include two neurons. The first neuron has its dendrites and cell body in the CNS, and its axon extends to a ganglion outside the CNS. There it synapses with the dendrites and cell body of the second neuron in the pathway. The axon of the second neuron extends from the ganglion to the effector carrying out the response.

The sympathetic division is associated primarily with the nerves of the thorax and abdomen, and the ganglia of the sympathetic division occur as a chain of segmental ganglia just ventral to the vertebral column.

The parasympathetic division has ganglia located within the brain, and the axons exit as cranial nerves or as the posterior or sacral parasympathetic nerves. The **cranial nerves** connect the brain directly to the head, neck, and body trunk. These are thought to represent the dorsal or ventral roots of the segmental nerves associated with the head and reflect the segmental origin of the head. The sacral parasympathetic nerves innervate the lower digestive tract and the external genitalia. The sacral nerves have additional ganglia in their target tissues.

The sympathetic division predominates in situations involving stress, danger, excitement, or strenuous

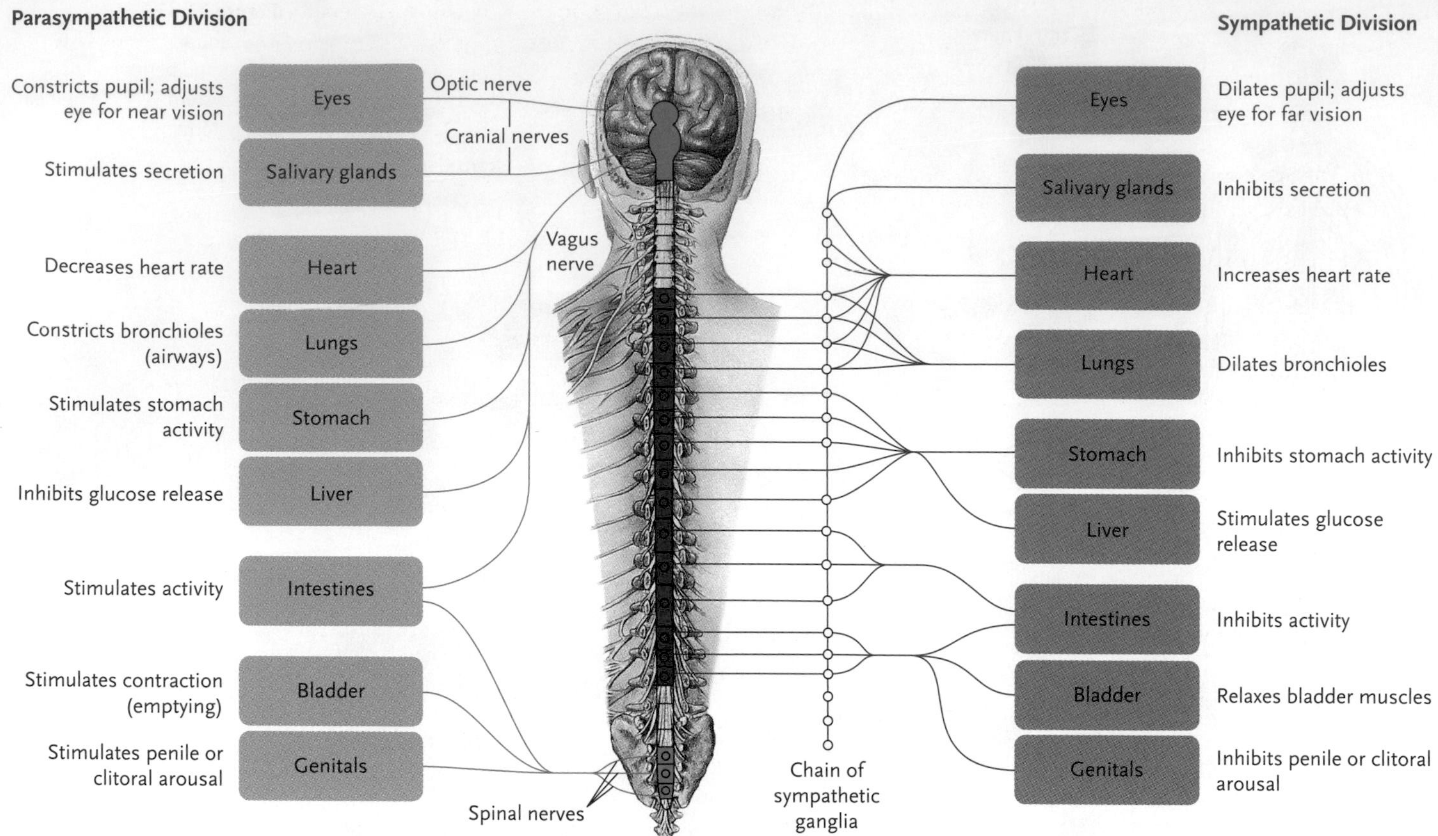

Figure 33.32
Effects of sympathetic and parasympathetic divisions on organ and gland function. Only one side of each division is shown; both are duplicated on the left and right sides of the body.

physical activity. Signals from the sympathetic division increase the force and rate of the heartbeat, raise the blood pressure by constricting selected blood vessels, dilate air passages in the lungs, induce sweating, and open the pupils wide. Activities that are less important in an emergency, such as digestion, are suppressed by the sympathetic system. The parasympathetic division, in contrast, predominates during quiet, low-stress situations, such as relaxation. Under its influence, the effects of the sympathetic division, such as rapid heartbeat and elevated blood pressure, are reduced, and "housekeeping" (maintenance) activities such as digestion predominate.

Study Break

1. What two systems comprise the peripheral nervous system, and what do they generally control?
2. When an impala (*Aepyceros melampus*, a deer-like ungulate from Africa) attempts to evade an attacking pack of African wild dogs (*Lycaon pictus*), what division of its autonomic nervous system would dominate? What effects might result?

33.9 Memory, Learning, and Consciousness

We set memory, learning, and consciousness apart from the other CNS functions because they appear to involve coordination of structures from the brain stem to the cerebral cortex. **Memory** is the storage and retrieval of a thought or a sensory or motor experience. **Learning** involves a change in the response to a stimulus, based on information or experiences stored in memory. **Consciousness** is not easily defined. In a narrow sense, it involves awareness, a state of alertness to our surroundings. But there is a broader and deeper meaning that involves awareness of ourselves, our identity, and an understanding of the significance and likely consequences of events that we experience. In this section, we deal with sleep as a decrease in awareness.

33.9a Memory Takes Two Forms, Short Term and Long Term

Psychology research and our everyday experience indicate that humans have at least two types of memory. **Short-term memory** stores information for seconds, minutes, or at most an hour or so.

Long-term memory stores information from days to years or even for life. Short-term memory, but not long-term memory, is usually erased if a person experiences a disruption such as a sudden fright, a blow, a surprise, or an electrical shock. For example, a person knocked unconscious by an accident typically cannot recall the accident itself or the events just before it, but long-standing memories are not usually disturbed.

To explain these differences, investigators propose that short-term memories depend on transient changes in neurons that can be erased relatively easily, such as changes in the membrane potential of interneurons caused by EPSPs and IPSPs (excitatory and inhibitory postsynaptic potentials) and the action of indirect neurotransmitters that lead to reversible changes in ion transport. By contrast, storage of long-term memory is considered to involve more or less permanent molecular, biochemical, or structural changes in interneurons, which establish signal pathways that cannot be switched off easily.

All memories probably register initially in short-term form. They are then either erased and lost or committed to long-term form. The intensity or vividness of an experience, the attention focused on an event, emotional involvement, or the degree of repetition may all contribute to the conversion from short-term to long-term memory.

The storage pathway typically starts with an input at the somatosensory cortex that then flows to the amygdala, which relays information to the limbic system, and to the hippocampus, which sends information to the frontal lobes, a major site of long-term memory storage. People with injuries to the hippocampus cannot remember information for more than a few minutes; long-term memory is limited to information stored before the injury occurred. Squirrels hoard food for the winter in a number of caches and can locate these by remembering the location from landmarks rather than by tracking a smell. Each autumn, the hippocampus of a squirrel increases in size by about 15%.

How are neurons and neuron pathways permanently altered to create long-term memory? One change that has been much studied is **long-term potentiation**: a long-lasting increase in the strength of synaptic connections in activated neural pathways following brief periods of repeated stimulation. The synapses become increasingly sensitive over time, so that a constant level of presynaptic stimulation is converted into a larger postsynaptic output that can last hours, weeks, months, or years. Other changes consistently noted as part of long-term memory include more or less permanent alterations in the number and the area of synaptic connections between neurons, in the number and branches of dendrites, and in gene transcription and protein synthesis in interneurons. Experiments on both vertebrates and invertebrates demonstrate that long-term memory depends on protein synthesis. For example, goldfish were trained to avoid an electrical shock by swimming to one end of an aquarium when a light was turned on. The fish could remember the training for about a month under normal conditions, but if they were exposed to a protein synthesis inhibitor while being trained, they forgot the training within a day.

33.9b Learning Involves Combining Past and Present Experiences to Modify Responses

As with memory, most animals appear to be capable of learning to some degree. Learning involves three sequential mechanisms: (1) storing memories, (2) scanning memories when a stimulus is encountered, and (3) modifying the response to the stimulus in accordance with the information stored as memory.

One of the simplest forms of memory is an increased responsiveness to mild stimuli after experiencing a strong stimulus, often called sensitization. The process was nicely illustrated by Eric Kandel of Columbia University and his associates in experiments with a shell-less marine snail, the Pacific sea hare, *Aplysia californica*. The first time the researchers administered a single sharp tap to the siphon (which admits water to the gills), the slug retracted its gills by a reflex movement. However, at the next touch, whether hard or gentle, the siphon retracted much more quickly and vigorously. Sensitization in *Aplysia* has been shown to involve changes in synapses, which become more reactive when more serotonin is released by action potentials. The cephalopod molluscs, such as the octopus, are capable of much more complex learning: they can distinguish and remember shapes and textures using only their tentacles.

33.9c Sleep Involves Different States of Awareness

Most animals that have been investigated, including some invertebrates, experience a daily rhythm of activity and inactivity. The inactive period, sleep, is essential to normal functioning. Sleep deprivation leads to disruption of a number of functions, including memory and learning, and, if prolonged, can be fatal. During sleep, there is some degree of awareness since external stimuli such as sound or internal stimuli such as a full bladder can interrupt sleep.

In humans and other mammals, sleep is accompanied by changes in the electrical activity of the cerebrum as detected by electrodes applied to the scalp during an *electroencephalogram*. The waking state is characterized by rapid, irregular *beta waves* **(Figure 33.33, p. 814).** As the eyes close and you become fully relaxed, these give way to slower, more regular *alpha waves*. As you become more drowsy, these are replaced by slower *theta waves*.

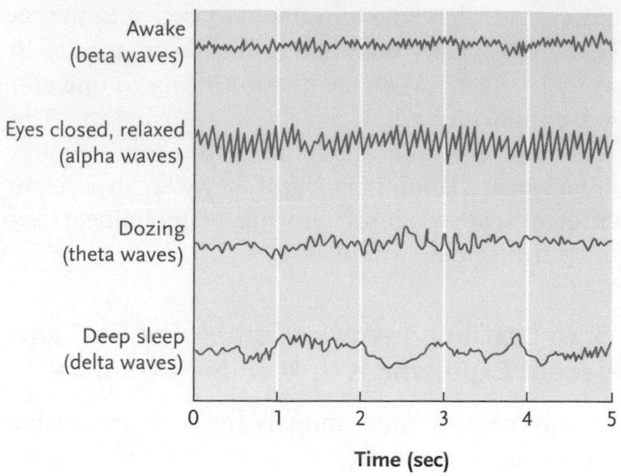

Figure 33.33
Brain waves characteristic of various states of consciousness.

Full sleep is characterized by even slower *delta waves*. The heart rate falls, and the muscles are relaxed.

During full sleep, the brain returns at intervals to periods of beta waves, during which the heart rate increases, the muscles may twitch, and the eyes move rapidly behind the closed lids, giving these periods the name **rapid eye movement**, or **REM, sleep**. This brief period of about 10 to 15 minutes occurs every 90 minutes or so in healthy adults.

This pattern of alternating periods of greater or lesser cerebral activity is also characteristic of bird sleep, although birds may sleep on one side of the brain while the other remains fully alert as protection against predators. Reptiles, with their less developed cerebrum, experience alternating patterns of activity in the amygdala.

Although we know that sleep is essential, we do not understand the physiological basis for these effects. The fruit fly *Drosophila melanogaster* exhibits cycles of sleep. At night, it feeds and then seeks out an isolated place and becomes inactive for about eight hours. Interrupting the sleep interferes with memory and learning in the flies. Many labs are now using the flies as models to identify genes involved in the sleep process.

Study Break

In the sleep cycle, what are beta waves, and where do they originate? How do they differ from delta waves?

Unanswered Questions

Although great progress is being made in understanding many brain functions, it is in the area of "consciousness" that our understanding is very limited. If we restrict our definition of that word to alertness and awareness, then we have been able to describe some of the physiological characteristics of that state, if only by describing what happens when we are "unconscious" or asleep. But humans have an awareness of self and identity that is presumably a function of the brain. In some individuals, two or more "selfs" have been known to exist, or a new "self" suddenly appears to replace the original. The description of this broader consciousness, the self-awareness and its relationship to brain activity, is one of the major challenges of neuroscience.

Much of neuroscience is focused on humans. But we are a product of evolution, and we do not understand the evolution of many of the functions that define humans. Our ability to learn and to pass the learning on to offspring is not unique—killer whales teach their young to hunt, and birds learn songs from their parents. Understanding how these functions arose requires novel approaches. Scientists are beginning to look at very simple models to understand memory, a prerequisite for learning. For example, the nematode *Caenorhabditis elegans* has been demonstrated to learn: offered a choice between pathogenic and nonpathogenic bacteria, they will at first not discriminate but will do so after experience. The simplicity of its nervous system and the extensive structural and genetic information available led Cathy Rankin at the University of British Columbia to explore the molecular basis of learning in *C. elegans*. She finds that learning can be associated with the level of expression of specific genes, depending on the response being studied.

Review

Go to CENGAGENOW™ at http://hed.nelson.com/ to access quizzing, animations, exercises, articles, and personalized homework help.

33.1 Neurons and Their Organization in Nervous Systems: An Overview

- The nervous system of an animal (1) receives information about conditions in the internal and external environment, (2) transmits the message along neurons, (3) integrates the information to formulate an appropriate response, and (4) sends out signals to effector organs.
- Neurons are cells specialized for the reception and transmission of signals. They have dendrites, which receive information and conduct signals toward the cell body, and axons, which conduct signals away from the cell body to another neuron or an effector.
- Afferent neurons conduct information from sensory receptors to interneurons, which integrate the information into a response. The response signals are passed to efferent neurons, which activate the effectors carrying out the response.

- Glial cells provide structural and functional support to neurons. They help maintain the balance of ions surrounding neurons and form insulating layers around the axons.
- Neurons make connections by two types of synapses, electrical and chemical. In an electrical synapse, impulses pass directly from the sending to the receiving cell. In a chemical synapse, neurotransmitter molecules released by the presynaptic neuron diffuse across a narrow synaptic cleft and bind to receptors in the plasma membrane of the postsynaptic cell. Binding of the neurotransmitters may generate an electrical impulse in the postsynaptic cell.

33.2 Signal Conduction by Neurons

- The membrane potential of a cell depends on the unequal distribution of positive and negative charges on either side of the membrane, which establishes a potential difference, the resting potential, across the membrane.
- The resting potential results from an active transport pump that sets up concentration gradients of Na^+ ions (higher outside) and K^+ ions (higher inside) and negatively charged proteins and other molecules inside the cell that cannot pass through the membrane.
- An action potential is generated when a stimulus pushes the resting potential to the threshold value at which voltage-gated Na^+ channels open in the plasma membrane. The inward flow of Na^+ changes membrane potential abruptly from a negative to a positive peak, which opens the voltage-gated K^+ channels. The potential falls to the resting value again as the gated K^+ channels allow this ion to flow out.
- Action potentials move along an axon as the ion flows generated in one location on the axon depolarize the potential in the adjacent location.
- Action potentials are prevented from reversing direction by a brief refractory period, during which a sector of membrane that has just generated an action potential cannot be stimulated to produce another for a few milliseconds and the action potential has moved too far away for its electrical disturbances to cause the preceding sector to depolarize again.
- In myelinated axons, ions can flow across the plasma membrane only at the nodes of Ranvier, where the insulating myelin sheath is interrupted.
- The intensity of a stimulus is reflected in the frequency of action potentials.

33.3 Conduction across Chemical Synapses

- Neurotransmitters released into the synaptic cleft bind to receptors in the plasma membrane of the postsynaptic cell, altering the flow of ions across the plasma membrane of the postsynaptic cell and pushing its membrane potential toward or away from the threshold potential.
- A direct neurotransmitter binds to a receptor associated with a ligand-gated ion channel in the postsynaptic membrane; the binding opens or closes the channel.
- An indirect neurotransmitter works as a first messenger, binding to a receptor in the postsynaptic membrane and triggering generation of a second messenger, which leads to the opening or closing of a gated channel.
- Neurotransmitters are released from synaptic vesicles into the synaptic cleft by exocytosis, which is triggered by entry of Ca^{2+} ions into the cytoplasm of the axon terminal through voltage-gated Ca^{2+} channels opened by the arrival of an action potential.
- Neurotransmitter release stops when action potentials cease arriving at the axon terminal. Neurotransmitters remaining in the synaptic cleft are broken down by enzymes or taken up by the axon terminal or glial cells.
- Types of neurotransmitters include acetylcholine, amino acids, biogenic amines, neuropeptides, and gases such as NO and CO.

33.4 Integration of Incoming Signals by Neurons

- Integration of incoming information by a neuron determines the frequency at which the receiving neuron sends out action potentials.
- Neurons carry out integration by summing excitatory postsynaptic potentials (EPSPs) and inhibitory postsynaptic potentials (IPSPs). The summation may occur over time (temporal) or from different neurons at the same time (spatial). This summation pushes the membrane potential of the receiving cell toward or away from the threshold for an action potential.

33.5 Integration in Protostomes: Networks, Ganglia, and Brains

- Identifiable nerves first appear in radially symmetrical animals as nerve nets composed of single neurons that are more concentrated around the mouth and that may have localized groupings of cell bodies that control particular functions.
- The development of bilateral symmetry resulted in the concentration of parts of the nerve net into several longitudinal nerve cords composed of several axons, with paired ventral cords becoming increasingly dominant.
- Ganglia, local concentrations of nerve cell bodies permitting enhanced coordination of sensory and motor functions, first appeared in the flatworms, with the anterior ganglia prominent and acting as a brain. Protostome ganglia have the cell bodies at the periphery and the neuropile of axons and dendrites in the interior.
- Molluscs have well-developed nervous systems with paired ventral nerve cords and a brain consisting of several fused ganglia that permits advanced behaviour in the cephalopods.
- In segmented protostomes, each segment has a pair of ganglia connected by a lateral commissure and connected to adjacent ganglia by paired ventral nerve cords. Segmental ganglia control the functions of the segment and its appendages and are subject to control from the brain.
- The brain in segmental animals consists of the fused ganglia of the segments that make up the head.

33.6 Vertebrates Have the Most Complex Nervous Systems

- The protovertebrate nervous system, represented by the lancelet, is a hollow dorsal tube with nerves leading to each segmental block of muscle. The anterior end of the tube is larger, and three regions equivalent to the forebrain, midbrain, and hindbrain of the vertebrate embryonic brain can be recognized.
- In the development of the vertebrate brain, the hindbrain subdivides into the myelencephalon, which becomes the medulla oblongata, or brain stem, responsible for many involuntary functions, and the metencephalon associated with hearing and balance. The cerebellum, a major processing center for balance and navigation, is an outgrowth of the metencephalon. The midbrain, or mesencephalon, coordinates hearing and vision. The forebrain subdivides into the diencephalon, which gives rise to the optic nerves, and the telencephalon, which is responsible for olfaction and gives rise to the cerebrum, the major processing centre of the brain.

- During evolution, some parts of the brain are more prominent, reflecting the lifestyle of the animal. Sharks have large olfactory centres, whereas frogs have larger optic centres.
- The evolution of the brain also involves an increase in its mass relative to the body weight of the animal and, in particular, an increase in the mass of the cerebrum relative to the rest of the brain. Birds and mammals exhibit an increased prominence of the cerebellum.
- In vertebrates, the CNS consists of a large brain located in the head and a hollow spinal cord, and the PNS consists of all the nerves and ganglia connecting the CNS to the rest of the body.

33.7 The Central Nervous System (CNS) and Its Functions

- The CNS consists of the brain and spinal cord. The spinal cord carries signals between the brain and the PNS. Its neuron circuits also control reflex muscular movements and some autonomic reflexes.
- The adult derivatives of the hindbrain—the pons, medulla oblongata, and cerebellum—together with the relatively reduced midbrain, form the brain stem, which connects the telencephalon with the spinal cord.
- The telencephalon (cerebrum) is divided into right and left cerebral hemispheres, which are connected by a thick band of nerve fibres, the corpus callosum. The cerebral cortex, the surface of the cerebrum, is formed by grey matter. Other collections of grey matter, such as the thalamus, hypothalamus, and basal nuclei, lie at deeper layers of the telencephalon.
- Cerebrospinal fluid provides nutrients to and cushions the CNS. A blood–brain barrier set up by tight junctions between the cells of the capillary walls in the CNS allows only selected substances to enter the cerebrospinal fluid.
- Grey-matter centres in the pons and medulla control involuntary functions such as heart rate, blood pressure, respiration rate, and digestion. Centres in the midbrain coordinate responses to visual and auditory sensory inputs.
- The cerebellum integrates sensory inputs on the positions of muscles and joints, along with visual and auditory information, to coordinate body movements.
- Certain grey-matter centres of the telencephalon control a number of functions. The thalamus receives, filters, and relays sensory and motor information to and from regions of the cerebral cortex. The hypothalamus, the only part of the brain not protected by the blood–brain barrier, regulates basic homeostatic functions of the body and contributes to the endocrine control of body functions. The basal nuclei affect the planning and fine-tuning of body movements.
- The limbic system includes parts of the thalamus, hypothalamus, and basal nuclei, as well as the amygdala and hippocampus. It controls emotional behaviour and influences the basic body functions controlled by the hypothalamus and brain stem.
- The primary somatosensory areas of the cerebral cortex register incoming information on touch, pain, temperature, and pressure from all parts of the body. The temporal lobes receive input from the ears, the primary visual cortex from the eyes, the olfactory lobes from the nose, and the parietal lobes from taste receptors in the mouth. In general, the right cerebral hemisphere receives sensory information from the left side of the body, and vice versa.
- The primary motor areas of the cerebrum control voluntary movements of skeletal muscles in the body.
- The association areas integrate sensory information and formulate responses that are passed on to the primary motor areas. Importantly, Wernicke's area integrates visual, auditory, and other sensory information into the comprehension of language, whereas Broca's area coordinates movements of the lips, tongue, jaws, and other structures to produce the sounds of speech.
- Some functions, such as long-term memory and consciousness, are equally distributed between the two cerebral hemispheres. In contrast, the left hemisphere in most people specializes in spoken and written language, abstract reasoning, and precise mathematical calculations. The right hemisphere specializes in nonverbal conceptualizing, mathematical estimation, intuitive thinking, spatial recognition, and artistic and musical abilities.

33.8 The Peripheral Nervous System (PNS)

- Afferent neurons in the PNS conduct signals to the CNS, and signals from the CNS go via efferent neurons to the muscles and glands that carry out responses.
- The somatic system of the PNS controls the skeletal muscles that produce voluntary body movements, as well as involuntary muscle contractions that maintain balance, posture, and muscle tone.
- The autonomic system of the PNS controls involuntary functions such as heart rate and blood pressure, glandular secretion, and smooth muscle contraction.
- The autonomic system is organized into sympathetic and parasympathetic divisions that balance and fine-tune involuntary body functions. The sympathetic system predominates in situations involving stress, danger, or strenuous activities, whereas the parasympathetic system predominates during quiet, low-stress situations.

33.9 Memory, Learning, and Consciousness

- Memory is the storage and retrieval of a sensory or motor experience, or a thought. Short-term memory involves temporary storage of information, probably resulting from changes in the membrane potential of interneurons, whereas long-term memory is essentially permanent, involving molecular, biochemical, or structural changes in interneurons.
- Learning involves modification of a response through comparisons made with information or experiences that are stored in memory.
- Consciousness is the awareness of ourselves, our identity, and our surroundings. It varies through states from full alertness to sleep.
- Sleep is characterized by alternations in patterns of electrical activity in the cerebrum between slow, relatively regular delta waves, characteristic of deep sleep, and brief periods of rapid, irregular beta waves signalling REM sleep.

Questions

Self-Test Questions

1. Nerve signals travel in the following manner:
   a. A dendrite of a sensory neuron receives the signal; its cell body transmits the signal to a motor neuron's axon, and the signal is sent to the target.
   b. An axon of a motor neuron receives the signal; its cell body transmits the signal to a sensory neuron's dendrite, and the signal is sent to the target.
   c. Efferent neurons conduct nerve impulses toward the cell body of sensory neurons, which send them on to interneurons and, ultimately, to afferent motor neurons.
   d. A dendrite of a sensory neuron receives a signal; the cell's axon transmits the signal to an interneuron; the signal is then transmitted to dendrites of a motor neuron and sent via its axon to the target.
   e. The axons of oligodendrocytes transmit nerve impulses to the dendrites of astrocytes.
2. An example of a synapse could be the site where
   a. neurotransmitters released by an axon travel across a gap and are picked up by receptors on a muscle cell.
   b. an electrical impulse arrives at the end of a dendrite, causing ions to flow onto axons of presynaptic neurons.
   c. postsynaptic neurons transmit a signal across a cleft to a presynaptic neuron.
   d. the axons of a presynaptic neuron directly contact the dendrites of a postsynaptic neuron.
   e. an on–off switch stimulates an electrical impulse in a presynaptic cell to stimulate, not inhibit, other presynaptic cells.
3. Ganglia first became enlarged and fused into a lobed brain in the evolution of
   a. vertebrates.
   b. annelids.
   c. flatworms.
   d. cephalopods.
   e. mammals.
4. The metencephalon is the origin of the
   a. spinal cord.
   b. cerebellum.
   c. mesencephalon.
   d. medulla oblongata.
   e. cerebrum.
5. Persons who have had damage to the right side of the cerebellum
   a. will have difficulty reading.
   b. will be unable to distinguish colours.
   c. will have difficulty with balance.
   d. will be unable to speak.
   e. will be unable to hear.

Questions for Discussion

1. The mechanism for the propagation of the action potential along an axon was worked out using the giant axons of squids. How confident should we be that this model applies to vertebrates? Is there an evolutionary link between the nerves of vertebrates and those of molluscs, or did the mechanism arise twice?
2. Brain function in many animals changes with age, and not all of these changes are degenerative. How would you explore the hypothesis that changes in gene expression were involved, and what would be a useful model animal?
3. How did evolution of chemical synapses make higher brain function possible?

Male eastern red bat, *Lasiurus borealis*. This tree-roosting bat flies south for the winter, returning every summer to the same hunting grounds across much of North America.

M. E. Fenton

34 Sensory Systems

Study Guide

Why It Matters

Echolocation, also known as biosonar, allows some bats and other animals to operate in the dark and in situations where lighting is unpredictable. Many (but not all) bats, toothed whales, some birds, and some insectivores (insect-eating mammals) echolocate. Echolocation may have been a key development allowing the ancestors of bats to move into the niche of a nocturnal aerial insectivore perhaps about 60 million years ago. To echolocate, an animal produces a pulse of sound and listens for echoes of it. The differences between what the animal says and what it hears are the data used in echolocation.

A male pink moth (*Scoliopteryx libatrix*) flies silently through the night sky in search of a receptive female. Suddenly, it hears the faint echolocation calls of a hunting eastern red bat (as in the chapter opening photograph). The moth has a pair of ears, one on each side of its thorax. Vibrations of the moth's tympanic membranes (eardrums) generate stimuli in its auditory nerves. By comparing the left and right stimuli from the bat's calls, the moth can turn its back to the bat and fly away from it. Most of the time, moths never appear on the bat's echolocation screen. Had the bat been closer, its strong calls

Figure 34.1
A painted lichen moth, *Hypoprepia fucosa.* This colourful moth uses acoustic signals to warn would-be bat predators of its bad taste. It uses bright colours to provide the same warning to insectivorous birds.

would have alerted the moth to the immediate danger and it would have dived for the ground.

The red bat flies on, oblivious to the insect it never detected. But picking up an echo from another insect, a painted lichen moth **(Figure 34.1)**, the bat turns and closes with its target. As it attacks, the bat adjusts its echolocation calls to ensure that its outgoing pulses do not deafen it to faint returning echoes. The bat increases the rate at which it produces echolocation calls, shortening each call and the intervals between them **(Figure 34.2)**. Just as the bat is about to make contact, the moth produces a sequence of clicks. The bat aborts its attack and the moth flies on, holding a steady course.

Caterpillars of painted lichen moths feed on lichens, sequestering toxic chemicals that remain in the adult moth. The moth's clicks warn the bat that it tastes bad. Experienced red bats get the message and abort their attacks. Inexperienced red bats (or those fooled by an experimenter into attacking a painted lichen moth) finish the attack and grab the moth but quickly spit it out.

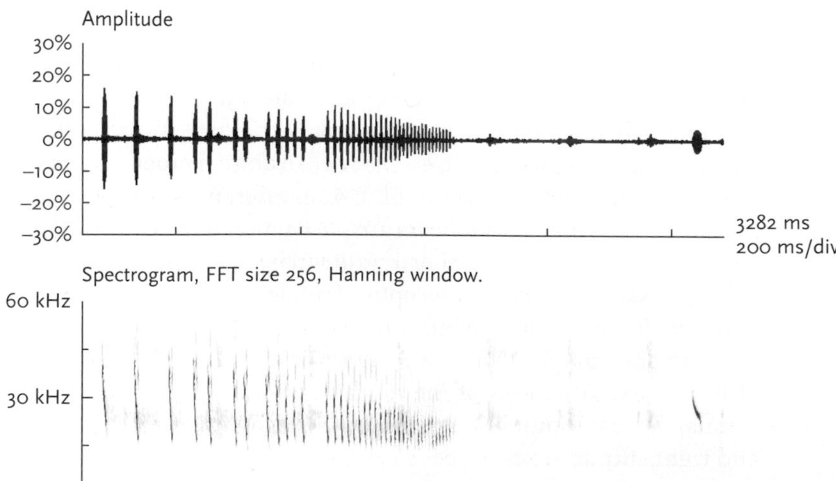

Figure 34.2
Echolocation call sequence of a red bat attacking a flying prey.

Many bats use echolocation to detect insect prey. Some insects have chemical defences and use sounds to warn bats of their bad taste. Painted lichen moths deal with two threats, using the clicking sounds for the bats and bright colours to warn birds that they taste bad.

The purpose of this chapter is to review information about sensory systems and describe how information from within and from without is acquired and used by animals.

34.1 Overview of Sensory Receptors and Pathways

Sensory systems begin with **sensory receptors (transducers)** that detect sensory information, convert it to neural activity, and pass the information along neurons to the central nervous system (CNS). Sensory receptors are formed by the dendrites of afferent neurons or by specialized receptor cells **(Figure 34.3)**. Receptors collect information about the internal and external environments of organisms. In organisms with a developed head region (cephalized), many receptors for external stimuli are located there so that the organism can collect information about where it is going. Receptors associated with eyes, ears, skin, and other surface organs detect stimuli from the external environment. Sensory receptors associated with internal organs detect stimuli arising in the body interior.

Sensory transduction occurs when stimuli cause changes in membrane potentials in the sensory receptors. Usually, this is achieved by changes in rates at which channels conduct positive ions (Na^+, K^+, or Ca^{2+}) across the plasma membrane. Stimuli may be in the form of light, heat, sound waves, mechanical stress, or chemicals. The change in membrane potential may generate one or more action potentials that travel along the axon of an afferent neuron to reach interneuron networks of the CNS. These interneurons integrate the action potentials, and the brain formulates a compensating response, that is, a response appropriate for the stimulus (see Chapter 33). In animals with complex nervous systems, interneuron networks may produce an awareness of a stimulus in the form of a conscious sensation or perception.

34.1a Basic Types of Receptors: What an Animal Needs to Know

Many sensory receptors are positioned individually in body tissues. Others are part of complex sensory organs, such as the eyes or ears, specialized for reception of physical or chemical stimuli. Receptors, particularly for external information, usually occur in pairs,

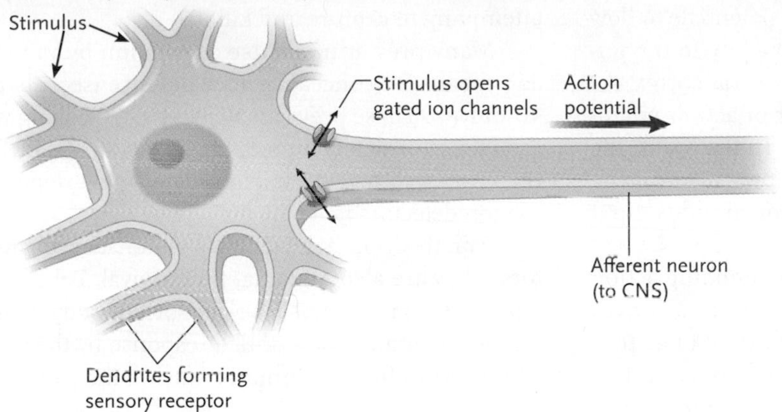
a. Sensory receptor formed by dendrites of an afferent neuron
Stimulus
Stimulus opens gated ion channels
Action potential
Afferent neuron (to CNS)
Dendrites forming sensory receptor
In sensory receptors formed by the dendrites of afferent neurons, a stimulus causes a change in membrane potential that generates action potentials in the axon of the neuron. Temperature and pain receptors are among the receptors of this type.

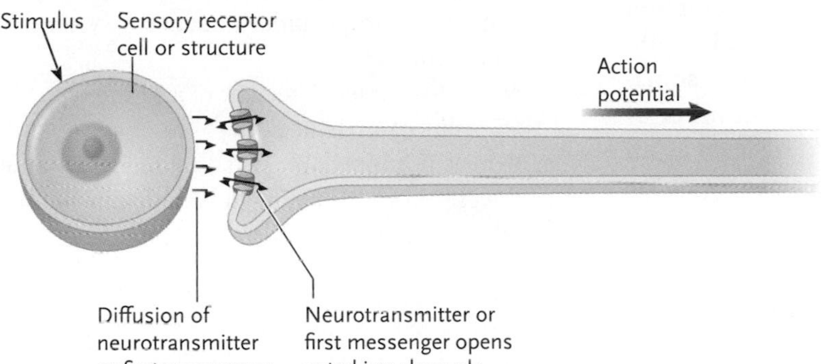
b. Sensory receptor formed by a cell that synapses with an afferent neuron
Stimulus
Sensory receptor cell or structure
Action potential
Diffusion of neurotransmitter or first messenger
Neurotransmitter or first messenger opens gated ion channels
In sensory receptors consisting of separate cells, a stimulus causes a change in membrane potential that releases a neurotransmitter from the cell. The neurotransmitter triggers an action potential in the axon of a nearby afferent neuron. Mechanoreceptors, photoreceptors, and chemoreceptors are examples of receptors of this type.

Figure 34.3 Sensory receptors, formed **(a)** by the dendrites of an afferent neuron or **(b)** by a separate cell or structure that communicates with an afferent neuron via a neurotransmitter.

providing the opportunity for the animal to localize the stimulus. Eyes, ears, and antennae are examples of paired sensory organs. There are exceptions. *Opabinia* species from the Burgess Shales (see Chapter 26) had five eyes, and some species of preying mantis have only one ear. Some spiders have rows of simple eyes.

Sensory receptors are classified into five major types, based on the type of stimulus that each detects:

- **Mechanoreceptors** detect mechanical energy, such as changes in pressure, body position, or acceleration. The auditory receptors in the ears are examples of mechanoreceptors.
- **Photoreceptors** detect the energy of light. In vertebrates, photoreceptors are mostly located in the retina of the eye.
- **Chemoreceptors** detect specific molecules or chemical conditions such as acidity. Taste buds on the tongue are examples of chemoreceptors.
- **Thermoreceptors** detect the flow of heat energy. Receptors of this type are located in the skin, where they detect changes in the temperature of the body surface.
- **Nociceptors** detect tissue damage or noxious chemicals; their activity registers as pain. Pain receptors are located in the skin and in some internal organs.

Some animals also have receptors that detect electrical or magnetic fields. Traditionally, humans are said to have five senses: vision, hearing, taste, smell, and touch. In reality, we can detect almost twice as many kinds of environmental stimuli as suggested by these labels. The traditional list should also include external heat, internal temperature, gravity, acceleration, the positions of muscles and joints, body balance, internal pH, and the internal concentrations of substances such as oxygen, carbon dioxide, salts, and glucose.

34.1b Afferent Links to the Central Nervous System (CNS)

Sensory pathways begin at a sensory receptor and proceed by afferent neurons to the CNS. Each type of receptor conveys information to a specific part of the CNS. Action potentials arising in the retina of the eye travel along the optic nerves to the visual cortex, where they are interpreted by the brain as differences in pattern, colour, and intensity of light. A blow to the eye is a stimulus that is interpreted in the visual cortex as differences in the colour and intensity of light detected by the eyes. Therefore, you "see stars" after receiving the blow even though the stimulus was mechanical.

The frequency of action potentials that the stimulus generates in the afferent neuron (number per unit time) can indicate the intensity and extent of the stimulus. Stronger stimuli cause more action potentials than weaker ones (see Chapter 33). A light touch to the hand, for example, causes action potentials to flow at low frequencies along the axons leading to the primary somatosensory area of the cerebral cortex. As the pressure increases, the number of action potentials per second rises in proportion. In the brain, the increase is interpreted as greater pressure on the hand. In the sensory cortex, maximum stimulus input is interpreted as pain.

The numbers of afferent neurons sending action potentials in response to a stimulus can also convey information about the intensity and extent of a stimulus. The more sensory receptors that are activated, the more axons carry information to the brain. A light touch activates a relatively small number of receptors in a small area near the surface of the finger. But as the pressure increases, the resulting indentation of the finger's surface increases in area and depth, activating more receptors. In the appropriate somatosensory area of the brain, the larger number of axons carrying action potentials is interpreted as an increase in pressure spread over a greater area of the finger.

34.1c Minimizing Sensory Overload: Reducing Background Noise

In many sensory systems, the effect of a stimulus is reduced if it continues at a constant level. This reduction is called **sensory adaptation** (do not confuse this with adaptation used in the context of evolution). Some receptors adapt quickly and broadly; other receptors adapt only slightly. In bed, you are initially aware of the touch and pressure of the covers on your skin. Within a few minutes, the sensations lessen or are lost, even though your position remains the same. The loss reflects adaptation of mechanoreceptors in your skin. If you move so that the stimulus changes, the mechanoreceptors again become active. In contrast, receptors detecting painful stimuli show little or no adaptation.

In some sensory receptors, biochemical changes in the receptor cell contribute to adaptation. When you move from a dark movie theatre into the bright sunshine, the photoreceptors of the eye adapt to the sudden bright light partly through breakdown of some of the pigments that absorb light.

Sensory adaptation is crucial to survival. Adaptation of photoreceptors in our eyes keeps us from being blinded indefinitely as we pass from the dark into bright sunlight. Sensory adaptation also increases the sensitivity of receptor systems to *changes* in environmental stimuli. These can be more important to survival than keeping track of constant environmental factors. Consider a cat sitting motionless, its attention focused on a stationary mouse. As long as the mouse stays still (environmental stimuli are constant), the cat also does not move. But if the mouse moves (change in environmental stimuli), the cat responds rapidly, attempting to capture and kill it.

Many prey animals use adaptation by predators as a means for concealment or defence (see Chapters 40 and 46). These prey instinctively stop moving when they sense or detect a predator. Freezing often allows them to avoid detection by predators that depend on motion detectors to locate prey.

Pain detectors are examples of nonadapting receptors. They are also essential for survival. Pain signals a potential danger to some part of the body, and the signals are maintained until a response by the animal compensates for the stimulus causing the pain.

Study Break

1. What is the importance of sensory systems for an organism?
2. Name five sensory receptors and the type of stimulus each detects.
3. Why is it important that some receptors allow the effect of a stimulus to be reduced, whereas other receptors do not?

34.2 Mechanoreceptors and the Tactile and Spatial Senses

Mechanoreceptors detect mechanical stimuli such as touch and pressure. In this situation, mechanical forces of the stimulus distort proteins in the plasma membrane of receptors, altering the flow of ions through the membrane. Ion flows change the membrane potential of the receptors and generate action potentials in afferent neurons leading from the receptors to the CNS. Sensory information from these receptors informs the brain of the body's contact with objects in the environment, providing information on the movement, position, and balance of body parts and underlying the sense of hearing. The distinction between sound (vibrations in air) and seismic waves (vibrations in the substrate) may not always be clear (see *Good Vibrations*). The five basic types of mechanoreceptors are described below.

34.2a Touch and Pressure

In vertebrates, mechanoreceptors that detect touch and pressure are embedded in the skin and other surface tissues, in skeletal muscles, in the walls of blood vessels, and in internal organs. In humans, touch receptors in the skin are concentrated in greatest numbers in the fingertips, lips, and tip of the tongue, giving these regions the greatest sensitivity to mechanical stimuli. In other areas, such as the skin of the back, arms, and legs, the receptors are more widely spaced.

Good Vibrations

Seismic signals—vibrations in the ground—are used by a variety of animals for different purposes. Nocturnal scorpions (*Paruroctonus mesaensis*) use vibrations in sand to detect prey under the surface, as do some golden moles (Chrysochloridae family). Meanwhile, frogs, snakes, and various mammals use seismic vibrations as part of their communication repertoires.

The scorpion uses sense organs at the end of each of its six walking legs, a basitarsal compound slit sensillum and tarsal sensory hairs **(Figure 1).** Both receptors are stimulated by vibrations in sand: the tarsal hairs to compressional waves and the basitarsal compound slit sensillum to surface (Raleigh) waves. The tarsal hairs provide information about nearby (<15 cm) sources of vibration and the slit sensilla to more distant ones. Both receptors are sensitive to a very small amplitude of <10 Å (angstroms) mechanical stimuli, and receptor pairs on six legs give the scorpion information about the direction of the sources of detected vibrations.

Male white-lipped frogs (*Leptodactylus albilabris*) vocalize from within clumps of grass or from shallow depressions or burrows in the mud in their native Puerto Rico. These frogs are ground-dwelling, and males produce two distinct types of vocal signals: chirps that advertise the species' identity and chuckles that are aggressive signals to conspecifics. Males typically call with only the anterior half of their body above ground, and as the vocal sac expands explosively during the chirp call, it strikes the ground with enough force to generate a surface wave. The chirp and the associated surface waves indicate the position of calling males.

Vibration detectors in frogs **(Figure 2)** appear to be located in the sacculus of

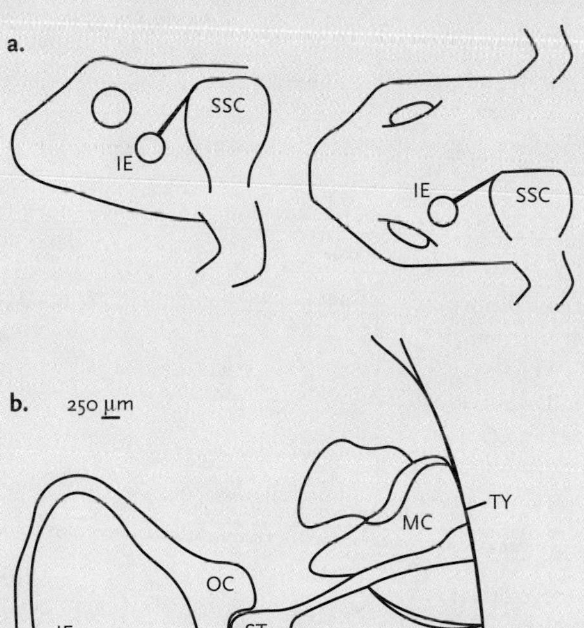

Figure 2
Ranid frogs typically have this orientation of the opercularis muscle (OM), the m. opercularis connecting the suprascapular cartilage (SSC) of the pectoral girdle to the operculum in the middle ear. IE – inner ear; MC – middle ear; OC – otic capsule; OP – operculum; ST – stapes; TY – typanum.

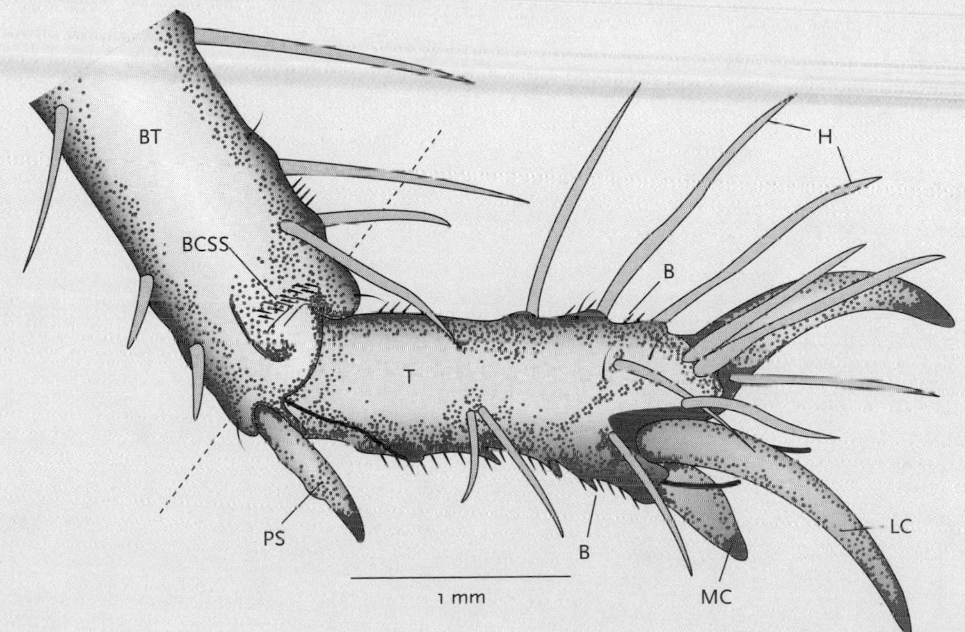

Figure 1
Right fourth leg of *Paruroctonus mesaensis*, showing tarsal hairs (H) and basitarsal compound slit sensillum (BCSS). B – bristle hairs; BT – basitarsus; LC and MC – lateral and medial claws; PS – pedal spur; T – tarsus.

the inner ear. This otolithic organ contains a membranous sac containing a slurry of dense calcium carbonate crystals. Vibrations are conducted to the sacculus by a chain of connections that includes the opercularis muscle that connects the pectoral girdle with the operculum, which is a movable cartilaginous element in the oval window of the otic capsule.

Golden moles (family Chrysochloridae) are fossorial insectivorous mammals from southern Africa. They make and live in burrows, rarely venturing onto the surface. Species within this group show striking variation in the structure of the malleus, one of the three mammalian auditory ossicles **(Figure 3; Table 1).** The auditory ossicles of *Amblysomus hottentotus* are generally like those of other mammals, including humans. However, other species of golden moles show considerable enlargement of the malleus culminating in *Chrysospala trevelyani*, in which it is pea shaped and about twice as large as it is in a normal mammal. The differences suggest that some species of golden moles are specialized for detecting low-frequency ground vibrations (Rayleigh waves), using the combination of the horizontal orientation of the malleus and its expanded size. The extended anterior process of the malleus also increases the overall size of the bone. Specialized golden moles, such as *C. stuhlmanni*, appear to use their sensitivity to surface waves to detect prey. Moles with these specializations may have much less acute hearing than less specialized species.

Do humans use seismic information? Why do people stamp their feet (see Chapter 40, *People Behind Biology*) in frustration and/or anger?

There are times when using vibrations can make you less conspicuous to predators. Although katydids are notorious for producing acoustic signals, usually males trying to attract females, the cost of sound production can be predation. Many species of insect-eating bats listen for the courtship sounds of male katydids (see Figure 34.14) and use these signals to detect and home in on prey. Males of at least 13 species of katydids from the New World tropics use short songs supplemented by complex, species-specific vibrations (tremulations) to advertise themselves to females while avoiding marauding bats. The same general situation applies to frogs that are vulnerable to bat predation.

Table 1

Species	$M \bullet d \bullet IL^{-1}$, mg	dB re human
Amblysomus hottentotus	0.52	−28.91
Amblysomus gunningi	2.38	−15.70
Amblysomus julianae	0.60	−27.67
Eremitalpa granti	65.28	13.06
Chrysochloris asiatica	63.76	12.86
Chrysochloris stuhlmanni	49.78	10.71
Chrysospalax trevelyani	1145.35	37.95
Chrysospalax villosus	1545.90	40.55
Homo sapiens	14.51	0.00

Figure 3
The auditory ossicles (middle ear bones) of three species of golden moles, *Amblysomus hottentotus* **(a)**, *Chrysochloris stuhlmanni* **(b)**, and *Chrysospalax trevelyani* **(c)**. The scale bar is 5 mm with respect to *A. hottentotus* and *C. stuhlmanni* and 10 mm for *C. trevelyani*.

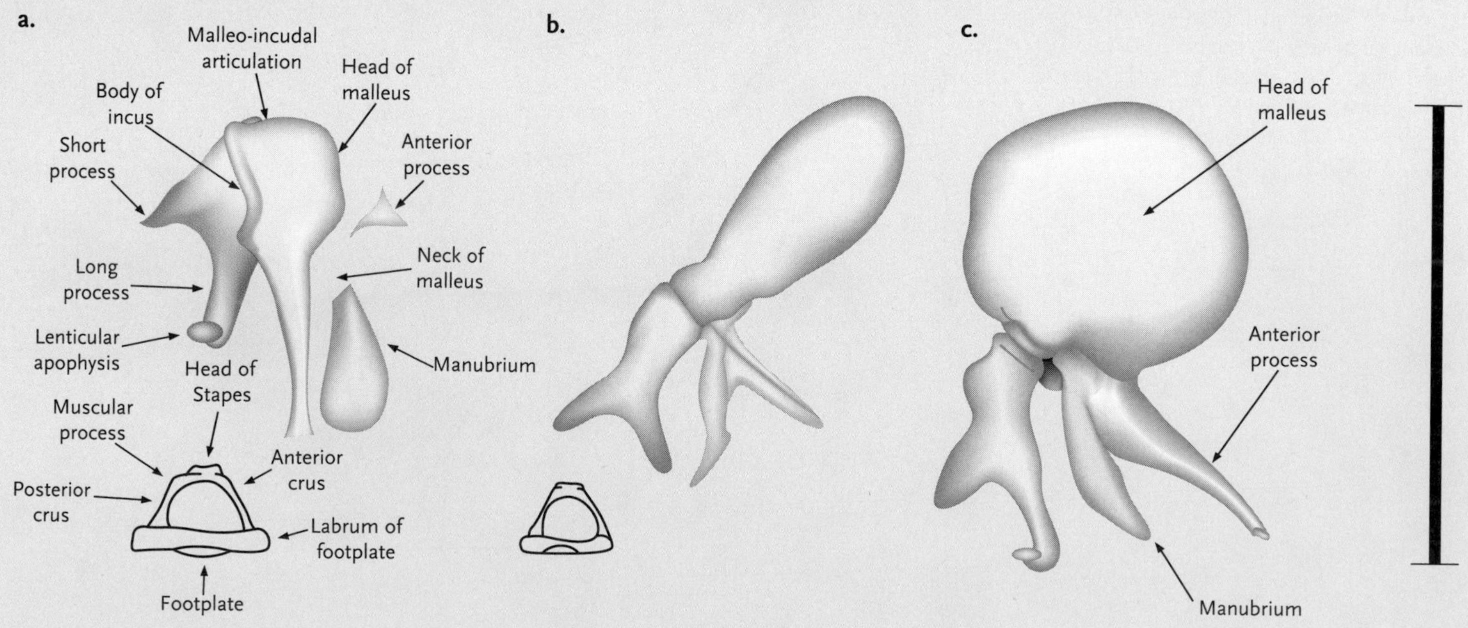

Forked Tongues

The forked tongues of serpents (see Figure 34.32) are deeply embedded in the world's religious iconography, often as a representation of deceit and malevolence. Aristotle thought that the forked tongue could double taste sensations. Hodierna proposed that the forked tongue allowed snakes to pick dirt out of both nostrils simultaneously.

Snake tongues are involved in chemoreception and serve as the delivery mechanism for paired sensors in Jacobson's organs (vomeronasal organs) on the roofs of snakes' mouths. Jacobson's organs connect with the oral cavity through two small openings in the palate (vomeronasal fenestrae).

However, forked tongues are not restricted to snakes, and lepidosaurian reptiles (see Chapter 27) show considerable variation in tongue structure **(Figure 1).** Forked tongues allow snakes (or lizards) to follow the pheromone trails of prey and conspecifics. The forked tongue specifically allows animals to use tropotaxis, which means simultaneously sampling chemical stimuli at two points. In some snakes, varanid lizards, and teiid lizards, the distance between the tongue tips exceeds the width of the head. Forked tongues have evolved at least twice and perhaps as many as four times in lepidosaurian reptiles **(Figure 2).**

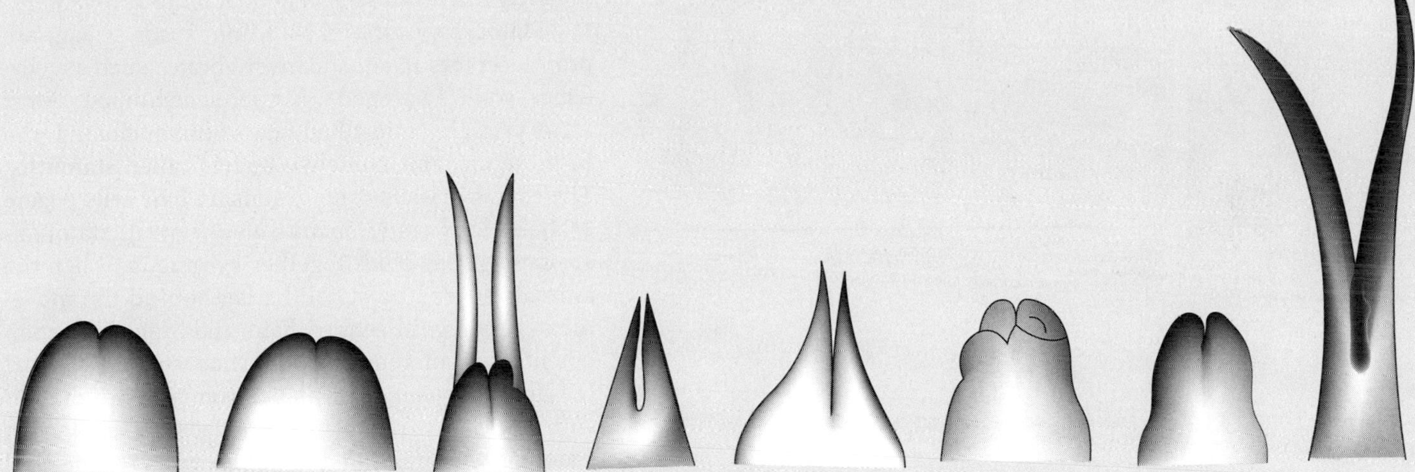

Figure 1
Tongue tips vary in squamate reptiles, from simple notches to deep forks. Shown here, from left to right, are the tongues of *Sceloporus* (Iguania), *Coleonyx* (Gekkonidae), *Cnemidophorus* (Teiidae), *Lacerta* (Lacertidae), *Bipes* (Amphisbaenia), *Scincella* (Scincidae), *Abronia* (Anguidae), and *Varanus* (Varanidae). Most snake tongues look like the *Varanus*.

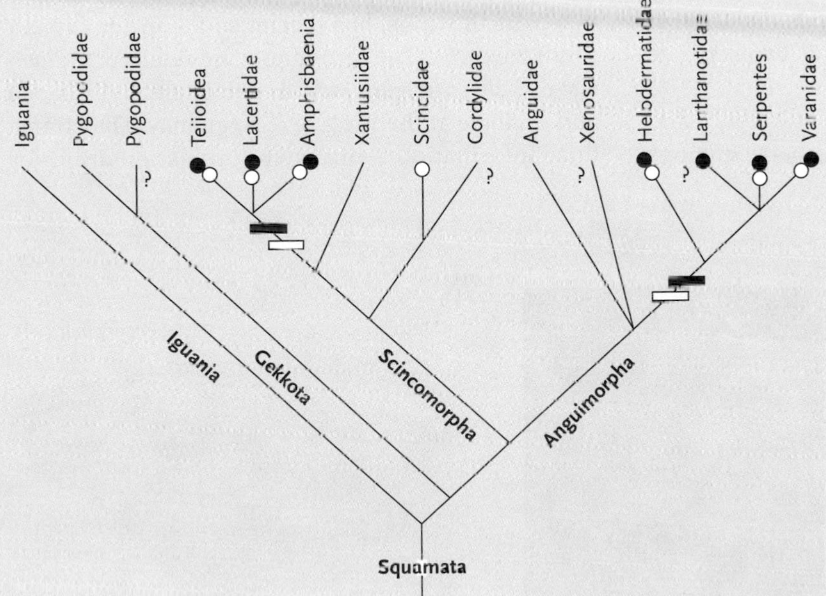

Figure 2
A cladistic phylogeny of Squamata.
The black circles identify taxa with forked tongues.

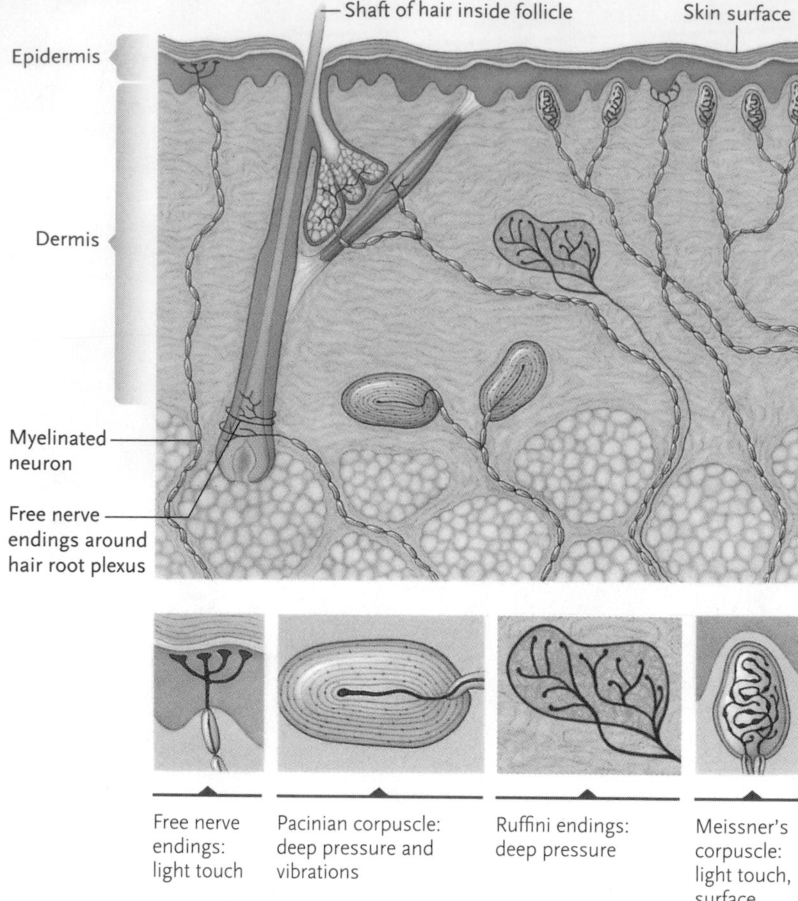

Figure 34.4
In human skin, four types of mechanoreceptors detect tactile stimulation.

You can compare the spacing of receptors by pressing two toothpicks lightly against a fingertip and then against the skin of your arm or leg. On your fingertip, two toothpicks separated by ~1 mm can be discerned as two separate points. On your arm or leg, the two toothpicks must be nearly 50 mm (almost 2 inches) apart to be distinguished as two separate points.

Human skin contains several types of touch and pressure receptors **(Figure 34.4)**. Free nerve endings are dendrites of afferent neurons with no specialized structures surrounding them. In Pacinian corpuscles, structures surrounding the nerve endings contribute to reception of stimuli. Free nerve endings wrapped around hair follicles respond when the hair is bent, making you instantly aware of a spider exploring your arm or leg as it brushes against the hairs.

34.2b Proprioceptors: What's Happening Inside

Proprioceptors are mechanoreceptors (*proprius* = one's own) that detect stimuli that are used by the CNS to maintain body balance and equilibrium and to monitor changes in the position of the head and limbs. The activity of proprioceptors allows you to touch the tip of your nose with your eyes closed or to precisely reach and scratch an itch on your back.

Statocysts (*statos* = standing; *kystis* = bag) are proprioceptors in aquatic invertebrates such as jellyfishes, some gastropods, and some arthropods. Most statocysts are fluid-filled chambers enclosing one or more movable stonelike bodies called **statoliths**. The chamber walls contain **sensory hair cells (Figure 34.5)**. In lobsters (*Homarus americanus*), statoliths are sand grains stuck together by mucus. When the animal moves, the statoliths lag behind the movement, bending the sensory hairs and triggering action potentials in afferent neurons. Thus, statocysts signal the brain about the body's position and orientation with respect to gravity. If you replace the sand grain statoliths with iron filings, you can use a magnet and emulate the lobster's response to the pull of gravity. In plants, statoliths control the direction of growth (see Chapter 31).

Information about self-motion is particularly important for flying animals and must be quickly (almost instantaneously) available. Typical insects have two pairs of wings, but species in the order Diptera (flies) have one. The second pair are reduced and persist as *halteres* **(Figure 34.6)**. Halteres are club-shaped and oscillate at the wing beat frequency. They transduce information about pitch (oscillation around a

Figure 34.5
A statocyst, in invertebrates an organ of equilibrium, in this case located at the base of the antenna of a lobster. The statoliths inside are usually formed from fused grains of sand, as they are in the lobster, from calcium carbonate.

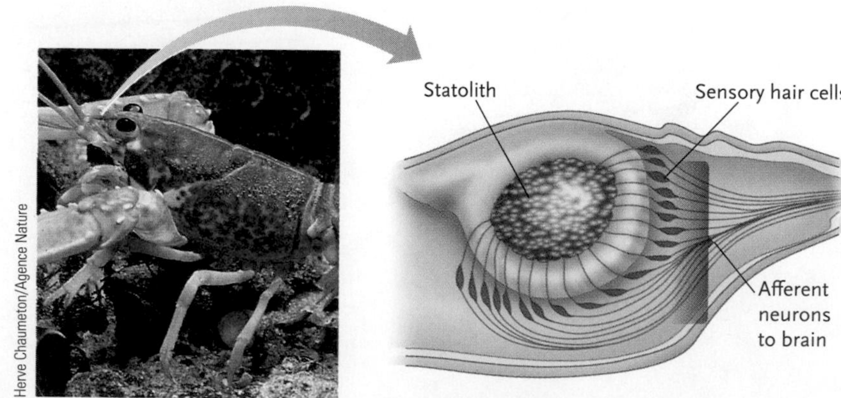

horizontal axis perpendicular to the direction of movement), roll (sway on the axis parallel to the direction of movement), and yaw (oscillation about a vertical axis) movements to the CNS. Coriolis (gyroscopic) forces cause the halteres to deviate in their plane of motion. Hawk moths, with two pairs of wings, use mechanosensors on their antennae to mediate flight control. Mechanical input to Johnston's organs **(Figure 34.7)** at the base of the antennae is essential for flight stability in moths. In bats, small hairs on the ventral surfaces of the wings are important for complex flight manoeuvres. Birds also must have mechanoreceptors associated with wings and flight, and, presumably, pterosaurs did as well.

Fishes and some aquatic amphibians use mechanoreceptors along the lateral line system to detect vibrations and currents in the water **(Figure 34.8, p. 828)**. Fishes have *neuromasts*, mechanoreceptors that provide information about the fish's orientation with respect to gravity, as well as its swimming velocity. In some fishes, neuromasts are exposed on the body surface; in others, they are recessed in water-filled canals with porelike openings to the outside **(Figure 34.9, p. 828;** see also Figure 34.8). Sensory hairs are clustered at the base of each dome-shaped neuromast hair cell. One surface of the hair cell is covered with **stereocilia**, microvilli or cell processes reinforced by bundles of microfilaments. Stereocilia extend into a gelatinous structure, the **cupula** (*cupule* = little cup), which moves with pressure changes in the surrounding water. Movement of the cupula bends the stereocilia, causing depolarization of the hair cell's plasma membrane and release of neurotransmitter molecules that generate action potentials in associated afferent neurons.

Vibrations detected by the lateral line enable fishes to avoid obstacles, orient in a current, and monitor the presence of other moving objects in the water. The system is also responsible for the ability of schools of fish to move in unison, turning and diving in what appears to be a perfectly synchronized aquatic ballet. In actuality, the movement of each fish creates a pressure wave in the water that is detected by the lateral line systems of other fishes in the school. Schooling fishes can still swim in unison even if blinded, but if the nerves leading from the lateral line system to the brain are severed, the ability to school is lost.

Some fish neuromasts provide additional information. Blind cavefishes, such as *Typhlichthys subterraneus*

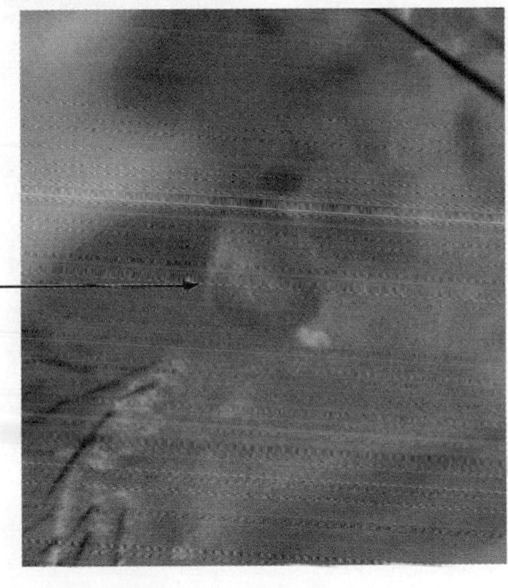

Figure 34.6
Halteres, vestigial hind wings of flies (enlarged image on the right at the end of the arrow), transduce information about pitch, roll, and yaw during flight. The fly shown here is a *Drosophila*.

a.

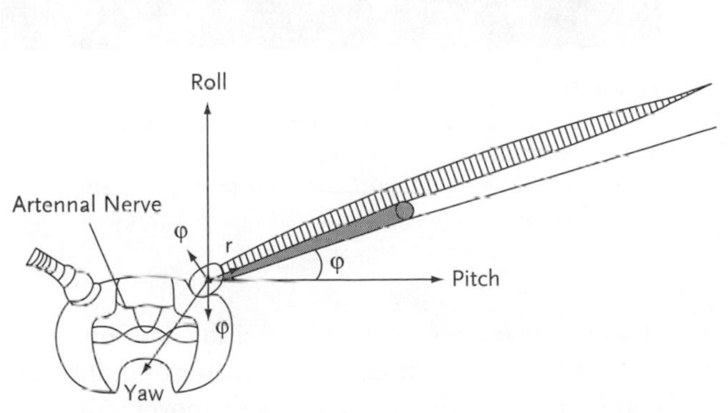

b.

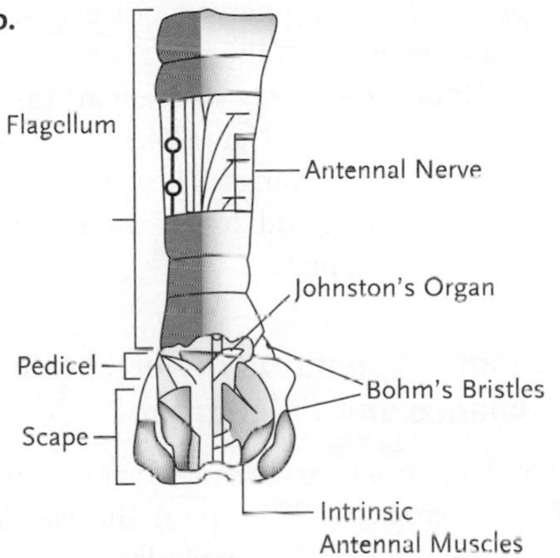

Figure 34.7
(a) Free flight kinetics of a hawk moth. Along the radial, elevation, and azimuthal directions, Φ, r, and q are unit vectors. Pitch, yaw, and roll are presented as a Cartesian coordinate system. **(b)** The head and brain of a hawk moth, including the anatomy of the antenna with the Johnston's organ.

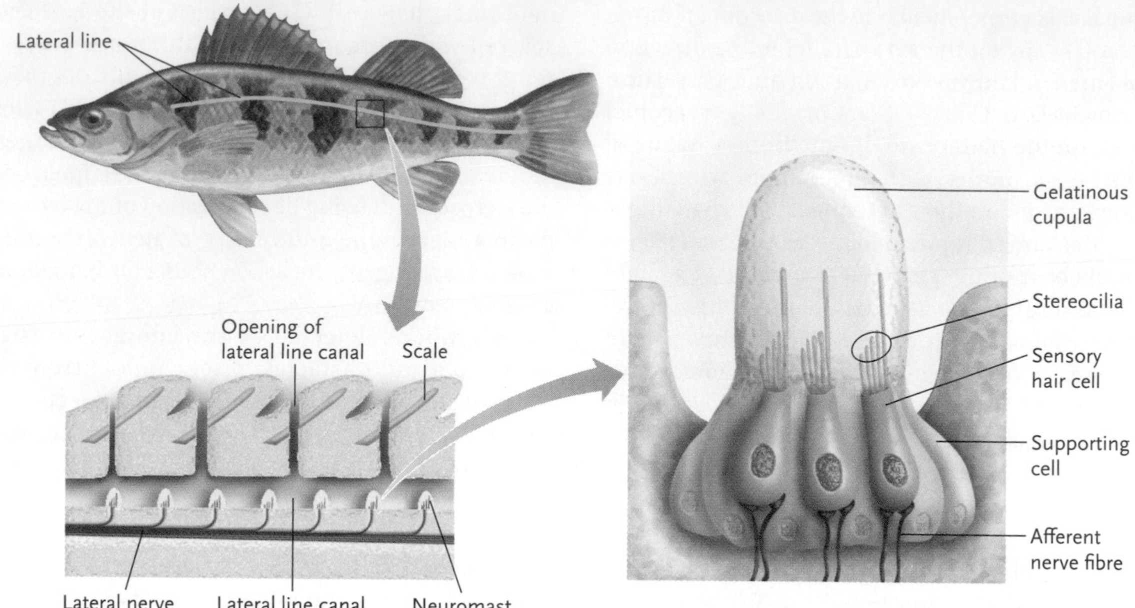

Figure 34.8
The lateral line system of fishes. Neuromasts are the sensory receptors in the lateral line system. Neuromasts have a gelatinous cupula that is pushed and pulled by vibrations and currents transmitted through the lateral line canal. As the cupula moves, the stereocilia of the sensory hair cells are bent, generating action potentials in afferent neurons that lead to the brain.

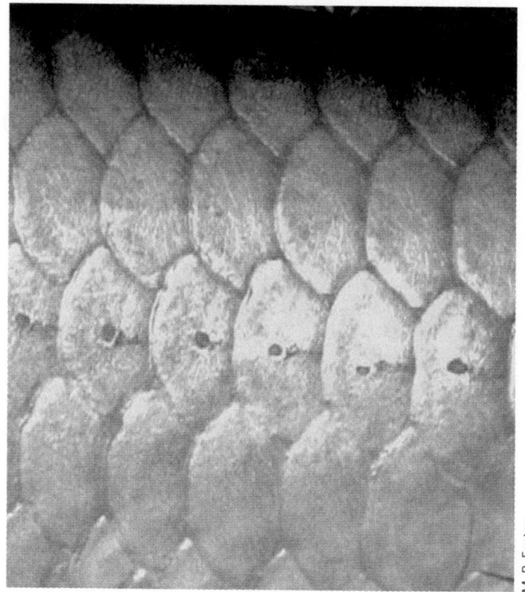

Figure 34.9
Pores along the lateral line of an arrowhana (*Scleropages* species).

Figure 34.10
Cavefish. Whereas *Typlichthys subterraneus* uses specialized neuromast cells to detect the vibrations of swimming prey, *Astyanyx jordani* does not. **(a)** *T. subterraneus* lives in energy-poor caves, whereas **(b)** *A. jordani* lives in energy-rich caves where bat droppings are the basal energy source.

(Figure 34.10a), that live in energy-poor ecosystems use neuromast cells to detect the vibrations of swimming prey. The more commonly seen aquarium blind cavefishes (*Astyanax jordani*; **Figure 34.10b**) live in an energy-rich soup of bat droppings. They appear to find food by random searching and do not use neuromast cells to detect swimming prey.

34.2c Vestibular Apparatus of Vertebrates: Sense of Balance and Orientation

The inner ear of most terrestrial vertebrates has two specialized sensory structures, the *vestibular apparatus* and the *cochlea*. The **vestibular apparatus** is responsible for perceiving the position and motion of the head and is essential for maintaining equilibrium and for coordinating head and body movements. The cochlea is used in hearing (see Section 34.3).

The vestibular apparatus (**Figure 34.11**) consists of three **semicircular canals** and two chambers, the **utricle** and the **saccule**, filled with a fluid called *endolymph*. The semicircular canals are positioned at angles corresponding to the three planes of space. They detect rotational (spinning) motions. Each canal has an *ampulla*, a swelling at its base that is topped with sensory hair cells embedded in a cupula similar to that found in lateral line systems. Cupulas protrude into the endolymph of the canals. When the body or head rotates horizontally, vertically, or diagonally, endolymph in the semicircular canal corresponding to that direction lags behind, pulling the cupula with it. Displacement of the cupula bends the sensory hair cells and generates action potentials in afferent neurons that make synapses with the hair cells.

When the body is spinning at a constant rate and direction, fluid in the semicircular canal soon catches up with the movement, so the cupula is no longer displaced and the action potentials stop. When the spinning stops, the fluid in the canals continues to move for a time in the original direction, displacing the cupula and producing a new burst of signals to the brain.

The utricle and saccule provide information about the position of the head with respect to gravity (up versus down), as well as changes in the rate of linear movement of the body. The utricle and saccule are oriented approximately 30° to each other, and each contains sensory hair cells with stereocilia. The hair cells are covered with a gelatinous *otolithic membrane* (which is similar to a cupula) in which **otoliths**, small crystals of calcium carbonate (*oto* = ear; *lithos* = stone), are embedded (see Figure 34.4); the function of otoliths is analogous to that of statoliths of invertebrates.

When a tetrapod is standing in its normal posture, the sensory hairs in the utricle are oriented vertically and those in the saccule are oriented horizontally. When the head is tilted in any other direction or when there is a change in the linear motion of the body, the otolithic membrane of the utricle moves and bends the sensory hairs. Depending on the direction of movement, the hair cells release more or less neurotransmitter, and the brain integrates the signals it receives and generates a perception of the movement. In humans, the saccule responds to the tilting of the head away from the horizontal (such as in diving) and to a change in movement up and down (such as

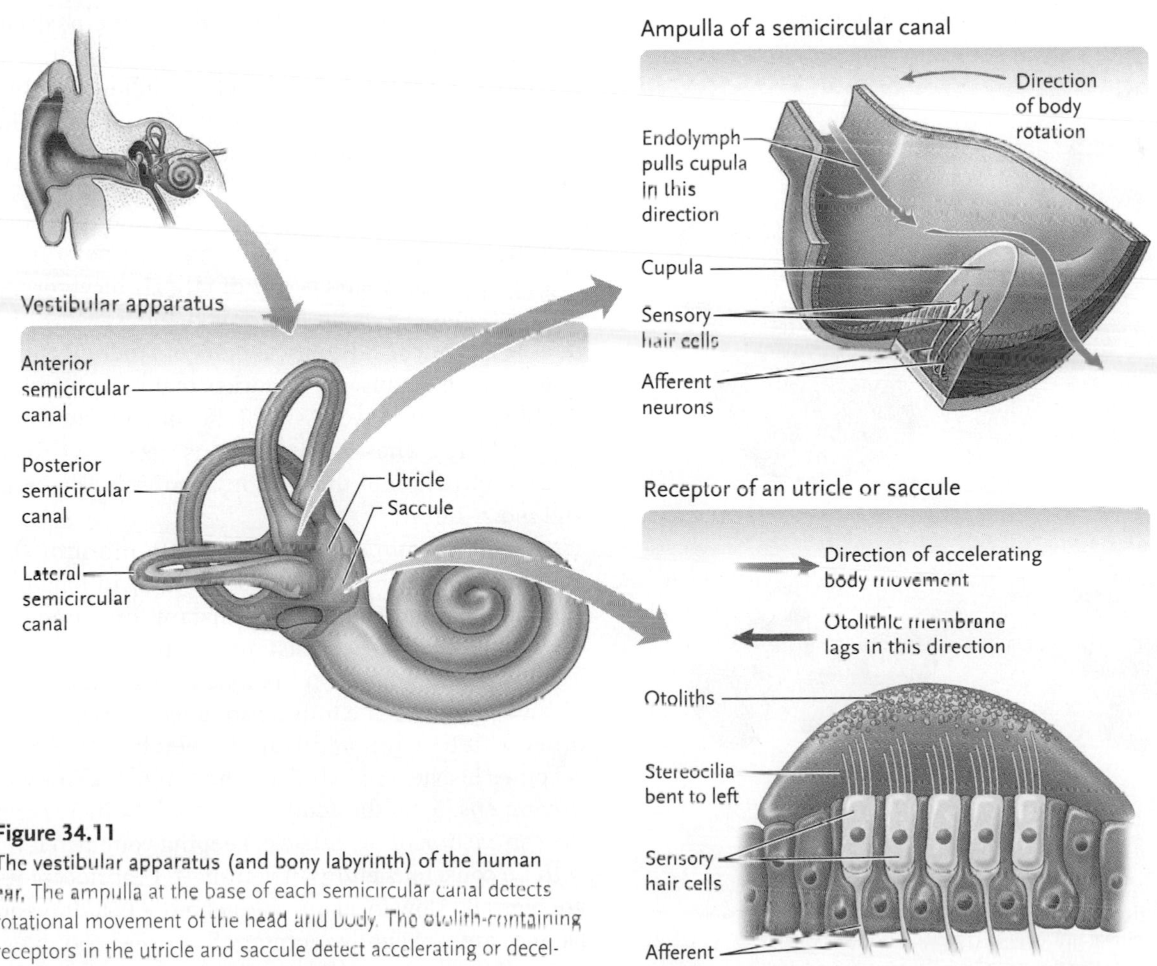

Figure 34.11
The vestibular apparatus (and bony labyrinth) of the human ear. The ampulla at the base of each semicircular canal detects rotational movement of the head and body. The otolith-containing receptors in the utricle and saccule detect accelerating or decelerating movements and the position of the head relative to gravity.

jumping up to dunk a basketball). The utricle and saccule adapt quickly to the body's motion, decreasing their response when there is no change in the rate and direction of movement.

Senses of up and down vary among animals, suggesting differences in how data from the utricle and saccule are interpreted. When it comes to posture and the definition of "dorsal," as bipeds, humans are aberrant compared with most other animals. The "normal" posture of upside-down catfish (*Synodontis nigriventris*), many bats (Chiroptera), and sloths (genera *Choloepus* and *Bradypus*) also differs from what is "normal" in other animals.

The bony labyrinths of mammals vary considerably **(Figure 34.12),** reflecting lifestyle. Agile, arboreal mammals have semicircular canals with large radii. The large radii make the vestibular system extremely sensitive to changes in body position. Such sensitivity is not compatible with the lifestyles of cetacaeans because they frequently make fast body rotations. Cetaceans typically have semicircular canals with small radii (see Figure 34.12).

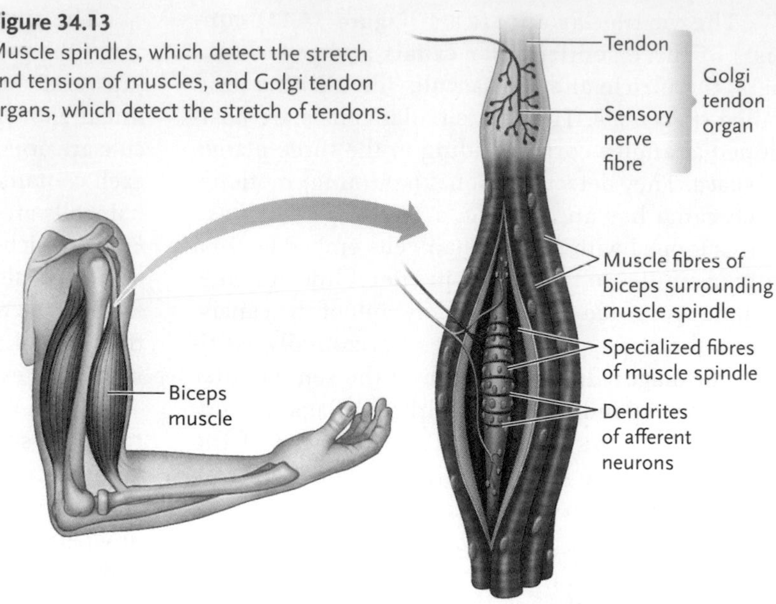

Figure 34.13
Muscle spindles, which detect the stretch and tension of muscles, and Golgi tendon organs, which detect the stretch of tendons.

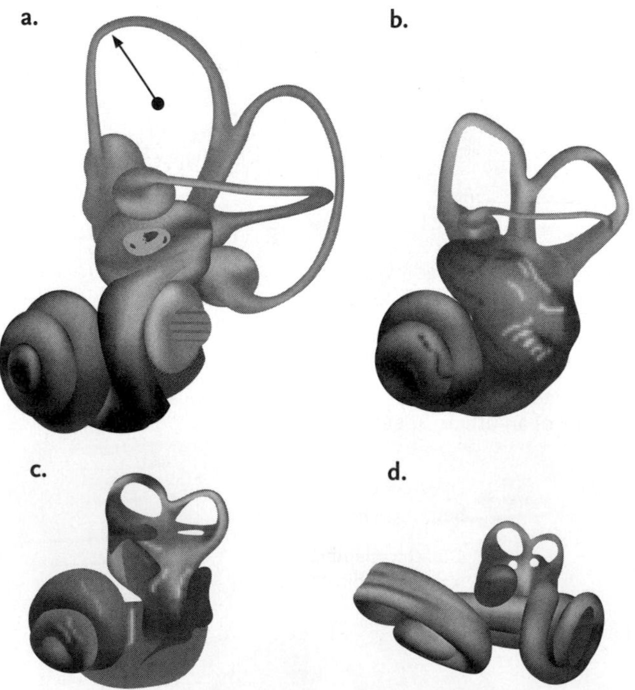

Figure 34.12
Bony labyrinths of four species of mammals. Lateral left view of the labyrinth organs of *Galago moholi* **(a)**, *Ichthyolestes pinfoldi* **(b)**, *Indocetus ramani* **(c)**, and *Tursiops truncatus* **(d)**. *I. pinfoldi* and *I. ramani* are fossil cetaceans (whales), *T. truncatus* is an extant species of dolphin, and *G. moholi* is an arboreal primate.

34.2d Stretch Receptors in Vertebrates: Keeping Track of Tension on Muscles

Stretch receptors are proprioceptors in the muscles and tendons of vertebrates that detect the position and movement, for example, of the limbs. Stretch receptors in muscles are **muscle spindles**, bundles of small, specialized muscle cells wrapped with the dendrites of afferent neurons and enclosed in connective tissue **(Figure 34.13).** When the muscle stretches, the spindle stretches too, stimulating the dendrites and triggering the production of action potentials. The strength of the response of stretch receptors to stimulation depends on how much and how fast the muscle is stretched. Proprioceptors of tendons, called **Golgi tendon organs**, are dendrites that branch within the fibrous connective tissue of the tendon (shown in Figure 34.13). These nerve endings measure stretch and compression of the tendon as muscles contract and move limbs.

Proprioceptors allow the CNS to monitor the body's position and help keep the body in balance. They allow muscles to apply constant force under a constant load and to adjust almost instantly as the load changes. When you hold a cup while someone fills it with coffee, the muscle spindles in your biceps muscle detect the additional stretch as the cup becomes heavier. Signals from the spindles allow you to compensate for the additional weight by increasing the contraction of the muscle, keeping your arm level with no conscious effort on your part. Proprioceptors are typically slow to adapt, so the body's position and balance are constantly monitored.

Study Break

1. If two fruit flies landed on you, one on your face and the other on your leg, which one would you be most likely to detect by touch receptors? Why?
2. What is the purpose of the vestibular apparatus in the inner ear of most vertebrates?
3. On what does the strength of the response of stretch receptors depend?

34.3 Mechanoreceptors and Hearing

34.3a Sound

Sounds are vibrations that travel as waves produced by the alternating compression and decompression of air or water. Although sound waves travel through air at about 340 $m.s^{-1}$ at sea level, individual air molecules transmitting the waves move back and forth over only a short distance as the wave passes. Water is denser than air, so sounds move approximately three times faster under water.

We can measure several features of a sound. The **energy** in a sound is measured as intensity, expressed in decibels (dB) sound pressure level (SPL) at a specific distance from the sound source. Some echolocating eastern red bats produce signals of 130 dB SPL @ 10 cm. Compare this with the shriek of a typical smoke detector, 108 dB SPL @ 10 cm. Remember that decibels are a logarithmic scale.

The duration of a sound signal is the time it lasts, measured in seconds (s) or milliseconds (ms). The time between signals is also measured in seconds or milliseconds. Loudness refers to the way an animal perceives sound. To the eastern red bat, its echolocation calls are loud, but they are not to humans, who do not hear them because they are too high in pitch (frequency). The pitch of a sound is the perceived frequency that reflects the wavelength (λ) of the sound measured in Hertz (cycles per second). More cycles per second means higher pitch (1000 Hz versus 50 000 Hz). Humans are said to hear sounds between 40 Hz and 20 000 Hz (20 kHz), so we cannot hear the eastern red bat's echolocation calls, which have most of their energy around 35 kHz. Therefore, they are ultrasonic, above the range of human hearing. Infrasounds, frequencies below the range of human hearing (40 Hz), are used by African elephants to communicate.

34.3b Hearing in Invertebrates: Mechanoreceptors and Ears

Most invertebrates detect sound and other vibrations through mechanoreceptors in their skin or on other surface structures. An earthworm, for example, quickly retracts into its burrow at the smallest vibration of the surrounding earth, even though it has no specialized structures serving as ears. Cephalopods (squid and octopus) have a system of mechanoreceptors on their head and tentacles, similar to the lateral line of fishes. These mechanoreceptors detect vibrations in the surrounding water. In many insets and other arthropods, hairs or bristles are sensory receptors because they vibrate in response to sound waves, often at particular frequencies.

Insects such as grasshoppers and crickets have ears, complex auditory organs on each side of the abdomen or on the first pair of walking legs, whereas in moths, these "ears" have been found on the head (mouthpart), thorax, and abdomen **(Figure 34.14).** These "ears" consist of a thinned region of the insect's exoskeleton forming a **tympanum** (*tympanum* = drum) over a hollow chamber. Sounds reaching the tympanum cause it to vibrate. Mechanoreceptors connected to the tympanum translate vibrations into nerve impulses. Some insect ears respond to sounds only at certain frequencies, such as to the pitch of a cricket's song.

34.3c Hearing in Vertebrates: Auditory Systems

The auditory structures of terrestrial vertebrates transduce vibrations in air (sound) to sensory hair cells that respond by triggering action potentials. The auditory system of humans is typical for mammals **(Figure 34.15, p. 832).** The *pinna* (**outer ear**; *pinna* = wing or leaf) concentrates and focuses sound waves. Some

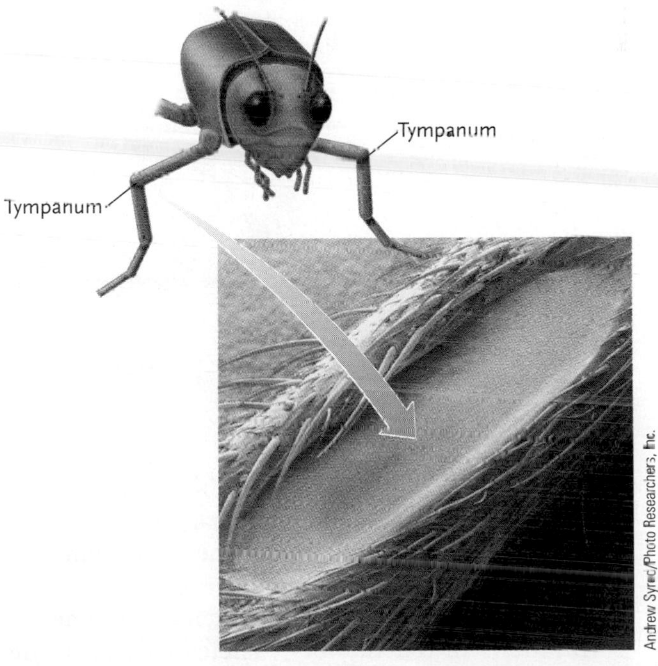

Figure 34.14
The tympanum or eardrum of a cricket, located on the front walking legs.

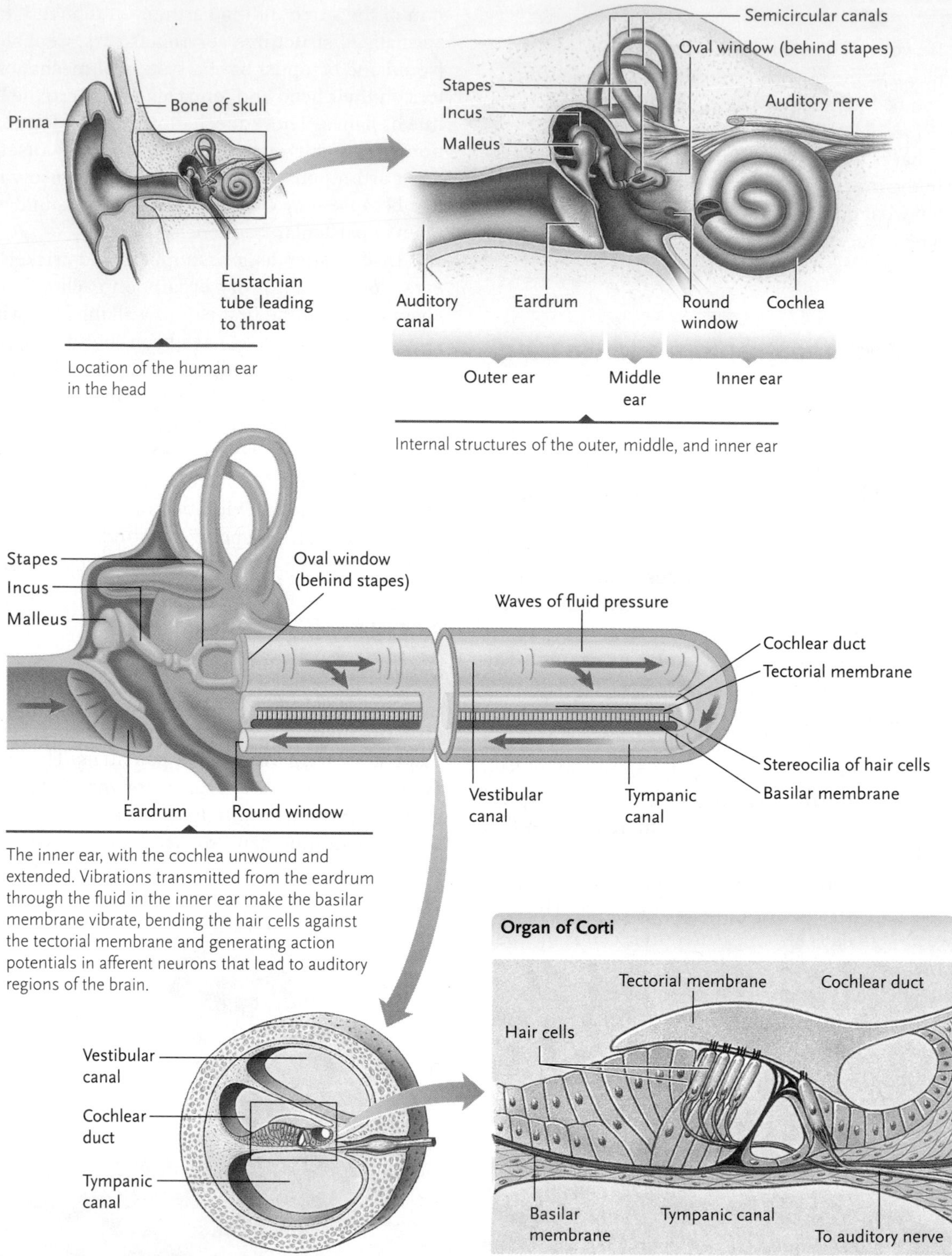

Figure 34.15
Structures of the human ear.

animals have pinnae; others lack them **(Figure 34.16).** Sound waves enter the auditory canal and strike a thin sheet of tissue (tympanic membrane or eardrum) and start it vibrating.

Vibrations in the tympanic membrane generate vibrations in the auditory ossicles located in the middle ear, which is an air-filled cavity. Mammals have three auditory ossicles, the **malleus** (hammer), **incus** (anvil), and **stapes** (stirrup). The manubrium of the malleus sits immediately behind the eardrum, and the eardrum's vibrations are conducted from the malleus to the incus and the stapes. The stapes abuts the inner ear at the **oval window**, a thin, elastic membrane where vibrations in bone are converted to vibrations in the fluid in the vestibular canal. Between the eardrum and the oval window, sounds are amplified at least 20 times.

The **inner ear** contains several fluid-filled compartments, the vestibular apparatus (see Section 34.2) and the **cochlea**, a spiral tube (*kochlias* = snail). In

a.

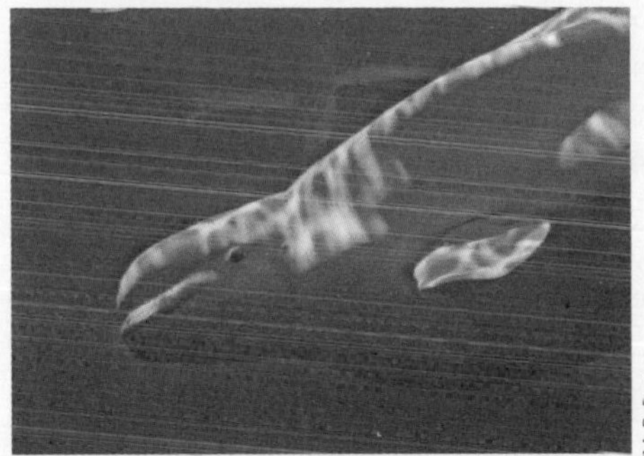

b.

c.

d.

Figure 34.16
Pinnae (external ears) are lacking in mammals such as **(a)** the beluga (*Delphinapterus leucas*), **(b)** birds (*Struthio camelus*), and **(c)** reptiles (*Varunus komodoensis*), but large and conspicuous in **(d)** a bat (*Otonycteris hemprichii*).

humans, the cochlea twists through about 2.5 turns (if flattened, it would be about 3.5 cm long in an adult). The spiralling of the cochlea appears to make it more sensitive to lower frequency sounds. Thin membranes divide the cochlea into three longitudinal chambers, the *vestibular canal* at the top, the *cochlear duct* in the middle, and the *tympanic canal* at the bottom (see Figure 34.16). The vestibular canal and the tympanic canal join at the outer tip of the cochlea, so the fluid they contain is continuous. The **organ of Corti** lies within the cochlear duct. It contains sensory hair cells that detect vibrations transmitted to the inner ear (see Figure 34.16). Vibrations of the oval window pass through the fluid in the vestibular canal, make the turn at the end, and travel back through the fluid in the tympanic canal. At the end of the tympanic canal, they are transmitted to the **round window**, a thin membrane that faces the middle ear.

Vibrations in the fluid of the inner ear cause vibrations in the **basilar membrane**. The basilar membrane forms part of the floor of the cochlear duct and anchors the sensory hair cells in the organ of Corti. The stereocilia of these cells are embedded in the *tectorial membrane* extending the length of the cochlear canal. Vibrations of the basilar membrane cause the hair cells to bend, stimulating them to release a neurotransmitter that triggers action potentials in afferent neurons leading from the inner ear.

The basilar membrane is narrowest near the oval window and gradually widens toward the outer end of the cochlear duct. High-frequency vibrations produced by high-pitched sounds vibrate the basilar membrane most strongly near its narrow end, whereas vibrations of lower frequency vibrate the membrane nearer the outer end. Thus, each frequency of sound waves causes hair cells in a different segment of the basilar membrane to initiate action potentials. More than 15 000 hair cells are distributed in small groups along the basilar membrane. Each group of hairs is connected by synapses to afferent neurons, the axons of which are bundled together in the *auditory nerve*, a cranial nerve leading to the thalamus. From there, the signals are routed to specific regions in the auditory centre of the temporal lobe.

The **eustachian tube**, a duct leading from the air-filled middle ear to the throat (see Figure 34.15), protects the eardrum from damage caused by changes in environmental atmospheric pressure. As we swallow or yawn, the tube opens, allowing air to flow into or out of the middle ear, equalizing pressure on both sides of the eardrum. When swelling or congestion prevents the tube from admitting air, we complain of having stopped-up ears because we sense a pressure difference between the outer and middle ear caused by the eardrum bulging inward or outward; this interferes with the transmission of sounds.

Study Break

1. How do most invertebrates detect sound? Give an example.
2. Explain in detail how a human hears.
3. Why are the echolocation calls of many bats inaudible to humans despite their high intensity?

34.4 Photoreceptors and Vision

Photoreceptors detect light at particular wavelengths, converting the stimuli to action potentials that move the information to visual centres in the CNS or the central ganglion, where the signals are integrated into a perception of light. Eyes are the organs that detect light (see Chapter 1). In their simplest forms, eyes distinguish only light from dark. The most complex eyes form images (have a lens), allowing the animal to distinguish shapes and to focus an accurate image of viewed objects on a layer of photoreceptors. Signals originating at the photoreceptors are integrated in the brain into an accurate, point-by-point perception of the viewed object. Image-forming eyes **(Figure 34.17)** have evolved in at least some species in five phyla: Cnidaria, Mollusca, Arthropoda, Onycophora, and Chordata. However, 99% of species with image-forming eyes belong to the phyla Arthropoda and Chordata. Pigments in some image-forming eyes allow animals to see in colour.

Annelids such as earthworms lack eyes but have photoreceptors in their skin. Input from the photoreceptors allows them to sense and respond to light. Earthworms respond negatively to light, as you can easily discover by shining a flashlight on an earthworm outside its burrow at night. The photoreceptors of nonchordates are depolarized when they absorb light and generate action potentials or increase their release of neurotransmitter molecules when stimulated.

34.4a Ocelli: Eyes that Detect Light

The **ocellus** (plural *ocelli*; also called an *eyespot* or *eyecup*) is the "simplest" eye, lacking a lens and not leading to image formation. Ocelli may each consist of <100 photoreceptor cells lining a cup or pit. Planarians (Platyhelminthes) are usually negatively phototropic. Their photoreceptor cells are located in two cuplike depressions below the epidermis. The photoreceptor cells are connected to the dendrites of afferent neurons, the axons of which are bundled into nerves that travel from the ocelli to the cerebral ganglion (see Figure 1.14). Each ocellus is covered on one side by a layer of pigment cells that blocks most light rays arriving from the opposite side of the animal. Therefore, a planarian can identify which side is brightest, orient its body to equalize the stimuli, and then move away from the light source. Similar ocelli are found in a variety of animals, including a number of insects, other arthropods, and molluscs. There is evidence that a collection of ocelli can constitute an image-forming system, blurring the distinction between image-forming and non-image-forming eyes.

34.4b Image-Forming Eyes Get the Picture

There are two main types of image-forming eyes: compound eyes with multiple lenses and single-lens eyes. Compound eyes occur in arthropods (crustaceans, trilobites, insects). Each compound eye can contain hundreds to thousands of faceted visual units called **ommatidia** (*omma* = eye) fitted closely together **(Figure 34.18;** see also Figure 1.15). In insects, light entering an ommatidium is focused by a transparent **cornea** and a *crystalline cone* (just below the cornea) onto a bundle of photoreceptor cells. Microvilli in these cells interdigitate like the fingers of clasped hands, forming a central axis that contains **rhodopsin**, a photopigment also found in the rods of vertebrate eyes. Absorption of light by rhodopsin causes action potentials to be generated in afferent neurons connected to the base of the ommatidium. Each ommatidium samples a small part of the visual field. From these signals, the brain receives a mosaic image of the world. Because even the slightest motion is detected simultaneously by many ommatidia, compound eyes are sensitive movement detectors. Anyone who has tried to swat a fly knows this from personal experience.

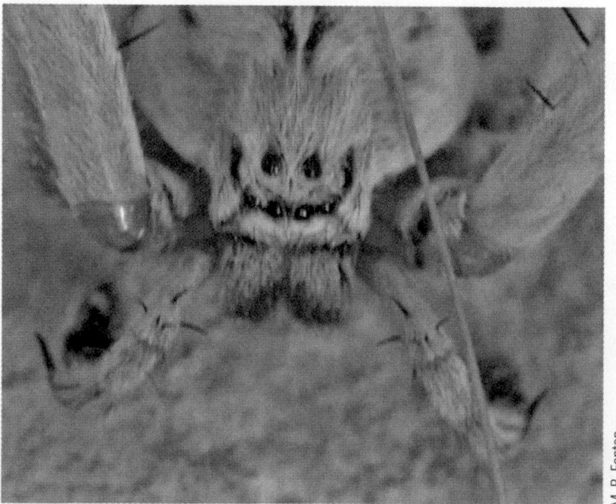

M. B. Fenton

Figure 34.17
This spider has a wonderful array of eyes.

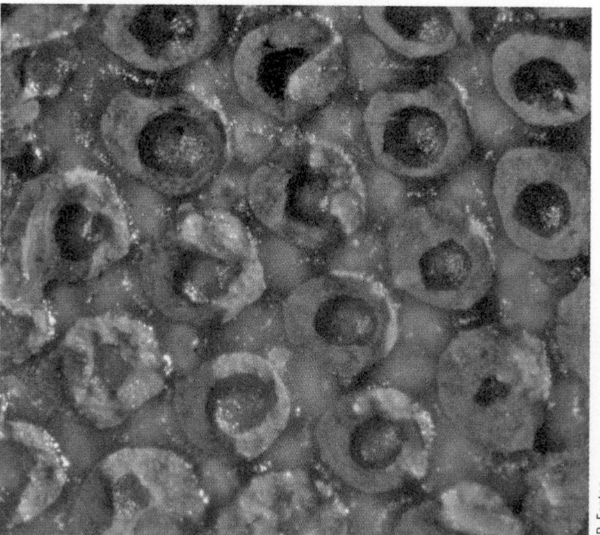

M. B. Fenton

Figure 34.18
The compound eye of a trilobite, *Phacops iowensis*, consists of many ommatidia. Each of the 16 complete circles shown here is an ommatidium, each with a cornea that directs light into the crystalline cone. The cone focuses light on the photoreceptor cells. A light-blocking pigment layer at the sides of the ommatidium prevents light from scattering laterally in the compound eye.

Single-lens eyes of cephalopods (see Figure 1.16) and vertebrates **(Figure 34.19)** operate like a camera, but the eyes differ in developmental details and operation. They also differ in the molecular structure of the rhodopsin in the photoreceptors **(Figure 34.20)**.

In both cephalopod and vertebrate eyes, light enters through the transparent cornea and passes through the pupil and then the lens, which focuses the image and projects it onto the retina, a layer of photoreceptors at the back of the eye. The iris is behind the cornea and surrounds the **pupil**. Muscles in the iris adjust the size of the pupil to vary the amount of light entering the eye. When the light is bright, circular muscles in the iris contract, shrinking the size of the pupil and reducing the amount of light that enters the eye. In dim light, radial muscles contract, enlarging the pupil and increasing the amount of light that enters the eye. Muscles move the lens forward and back with respect to the retina to focus the image. This process is called accommodation.

In most terrestrial vertebrates, accommodation is achieved through changes in the shape of the lens. The soft, flexible lens is held in place by the ciliary body, fine ligaments that anchor it to a surrounding layer of connective tissue and muscle. When the ciliary muscle is relaxed, the lens is put under tension and flattened, focusing light from distant objects onto the retina. When the ciliary muscles contract, tension on the lens is reduced, and the lens becomes more spherical in shape and focuses light from nearby objects onto the retina **(Figure 34.21, p. 836)**.

In vertebrates and cephalopods, axons of afferent neurons originating in the retina converge to form the optic nerve leading from the eye to the brain. In cephalopods, the neural network lies under the retina, so light rays do not have to pass through the neurons to reach the photoreceptors. Some vertebrate eyes have the opposite arrangement, with retinal cells below the neural networks and blood vessels. This and other differences in structure and function indicate that mollusc and vertebrate eyes evolved independently.

In vertebrate eyes, the **aqueous humour** is a clear fluid that fills the space between the cornea and lens. This fluid carries nutrients to the lens and cornea, which do not contain any blood vessels. The main chamber of the eye, located between the lens and the retina, is filled with the jellylike **vitreous humour** (*vitrum* = glass). The outer wall of the eye contains a tough layer of connective tissue (the *sclera*). Inside the sclera is a darkly pigmented layer (the *choroid*) that prevents light from entering except through the pupil. It also contains the blood vessels that nourish the retina.

Rods and cones are two types of photoreceptors that occur in the retina along with layers of neurons that perform an initial integration of visual

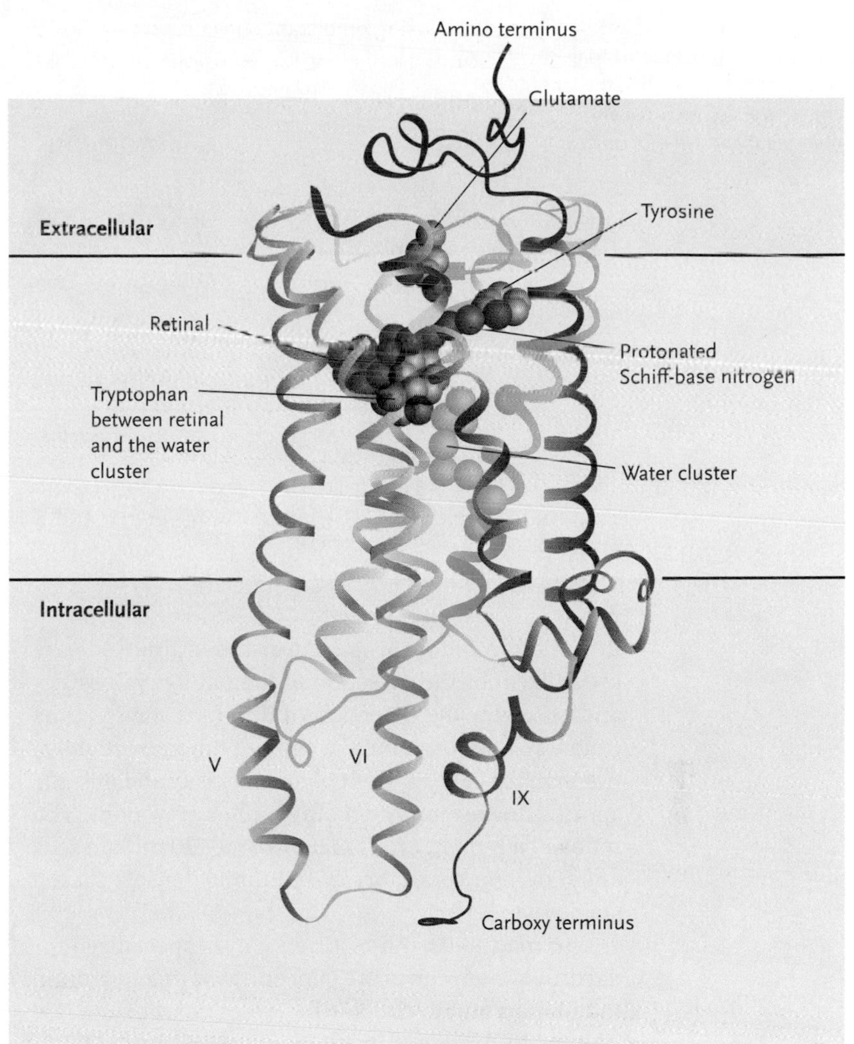

Figure 34.19
The rhodopsin of squid eyes is quite different from that of vertebrates. Like vertebrate rhodopsin, squid rhodopsin is a G protein–coupled receptor with seven transmembrane domains (helices that cross membranes). Helices V and VI protrude deeply into the cytoplasm of the photoreceptor cell. Retinol (red) is a light-sensitive chromatophore. The rhodopsin data demonstrate another difference between the eyes of squid and the eyes of vertebrates.

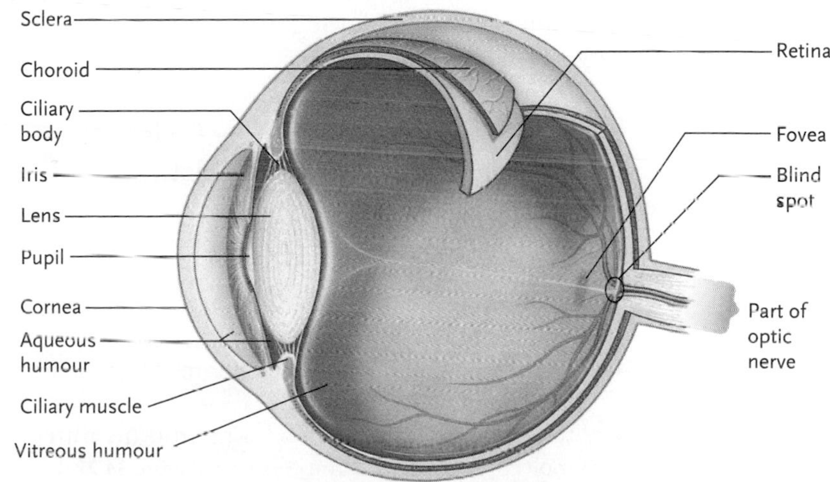

Figure 34.20
Structures of the human eye.

Figure 34.21
Accommodation in terrestrial vertebrates occurs when the lens changes shape to focus on distant **(a)** and near **(b)** objects.

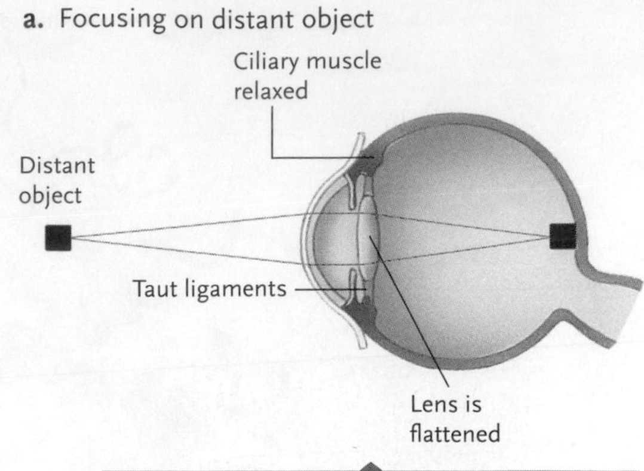

When the eye focuses on a distant object, the ciliary muscles relax, allowing the ligaments that support the lens to tighten. The tightened ligaments flatten the lens, bringing the distant object into focus on the retina.

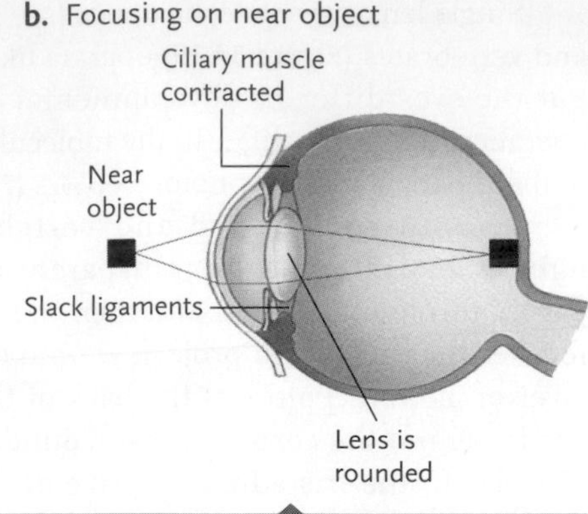

When the eye focuses on a near object, the ciliary muscles contract, loosening the ligaments and allowing the lens to become rounder. The rounded lens focuses a near object on the retina.

information before it is sent to the brain. Rods are specialized for the detection of light at low intensities and cones for the detection of different wavelengths (colours). The rods of mammals are much more sensitive than the cones to light of low intensity and in some species can respond to a single photon of light. The retina of a human eye contains about 120 million rods and 6 million cones, organized into a densely packed single layer.

In mammals and birds with eyes specialized for daytime vision, cones are concentrated in and around the fovea, a small, circular region of the retina that is <1 mm in diameter in humans (see Figure 34.19). Some birds have two foveas. Rods are spread over the remainder of the retina. The retinas of mammals and birds with eyes specialized for night vision contain mostly rods and no clearly defined fovea. In many nocturnal animals, the tapetum lucidum, a layer of tissue behind the retina, reflects light back through the retina. The tapetum lucidum accounts for conspicuous eyeshine in many nocturnal vertebrates. Some fishes and many reptiles have cones generally distributed throughout their retinas and very few rods.

34.4c Sensory Transduction by Rods and Cones: Converting Signals to Electrical Impulses

A photoreceptor cell has three parts:

- an outer segment consisting of stacked, flattened, membranous disks,
- an inner segment where the cell's metabolic activities occur, and
- the synaptic terminal where neurotransmitter molecules are stored and released **(Figure 34.22a).**

The photoreceptors of different animals contain different forms of *retinal*, a lipidlike pigment synthesized from vitamin A as their light-absorbing pigment. Retinal is bonded covalently with an opsin protein to produce rhodopsin, by far the most common photopigment in the animal kingdom. Photopigments are embedded in the membranous disks of the photoreceptors' outer segments **(Figure 34.22b).** Rhodopsin is the retinal–opsin photopigment in rods.

In the dark, the retinal segment of unstimulated rhodopsin is *cis*-retinal, an inactive form (see Figure 34.22b), and rods steadily release the neurotransmitter glutamate. When rhodopsin absorbs a photon of light, retinal converts to *trans*-retinal, the active form, and the rods *decrease* the amount of glutamate they release.

Rhodopsin is a membrane-embedded G protein–coupled receptor. Recall (see Chapter 8) that an extracellular signal received by a G protein–coupled receptor activates the receptor, triggering a signal transduction pathway within the cell and generating a cellular response. Here, activated rhodopsin triggers a signal transduction pathway that leads to the closure of Na^+ channels in the plasma membrane **(Figure 34.23, p. 838).** Closure of the channels hyperpolarizes the photoreceptor's membrane, decreasing neurotransmitter release. The response is graded because as light absorption by photopigment molecules increases, the amount of neurotransmitter released is reduced proportionately. If light absorption decreases, neurotransmitter release by the photoreceptor increases proportionately. Transduction in rods works in the opposite way from most sensory receptors in which a stimulus increases neurotransmitter release.

34.4d Visual Processing in the Retina: Events at the Back of the Eye

In the vertebrate retina, the two types of photoreceptors are linked to a network of neurons that carry out initial integration and processing of visual information.

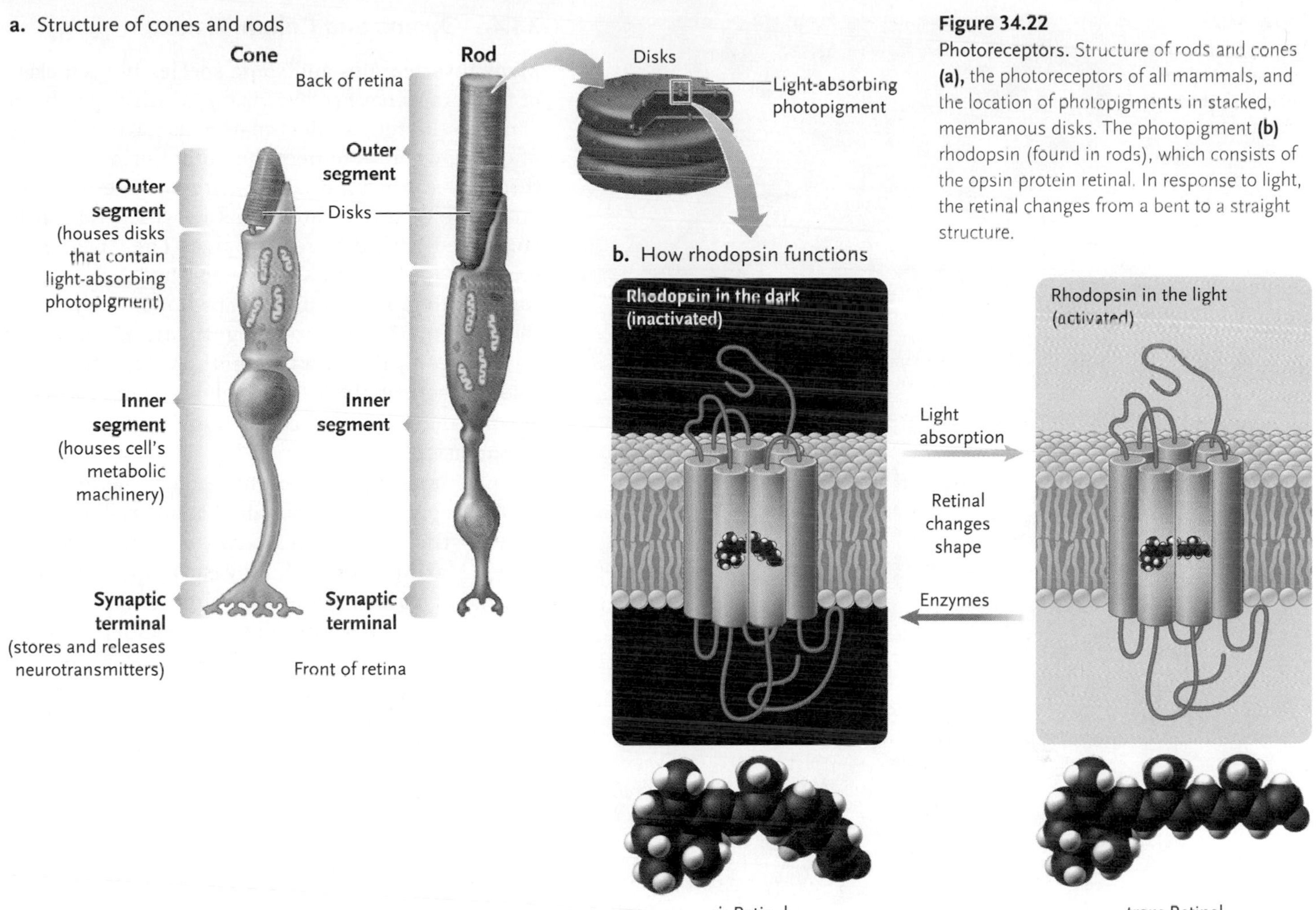

Figure 34.22
Photoreceptors. Structure of rods and cones **(a),** the photoreceptors of all mammals, and the location of photopigments in stacked, membranous disks. The photopigment **(b)** rhodopsin (found in rods), which consists of the opsin protein retinal. In response to light, the retinal changes from a bent to a straight structure.

The retina of mammals has four types of neurons **(Figure 34.24, p. 838).** There is a layer of bipolar cells just in front of the rods and cones. These neurons synapse with rods or cones at one end and with ganglion cells, a layer of neurons, at the other end. The axons of ganglion cells extend over the retina and collect at the back of the eyeball to form the optic nerve, which transmits action potentials to the brain. The point where the optic nerve exits the eye lacks photoreceptors. This *blind spot* can be several millimetres in diameter in humans. Horizontal cells connect photoreceptor cells, whereas amacrine cells connect bipolar and ganglion cells.

In the dark, the steady release of glutamate from rods and cones depolarizes some postsynaptic bipolar cells and hyperpolarizes others. In the light, the decrease in neurotransmitter release from rods and cones results in hyperpolarization of polarized bipolar cells. Changes in membrane potential in response to light are transmitted to the brain for processing.

Signals from the rods and cones may move vertically or laterally in the retina. Signals move vertically from the photoreceptors to bipolar cells and then to ganglion cells. Whereas the human retina has over 120 million photoreceptors, it has only about 1 million ganglion cells. This disparity is explained by the fact that each ganglion cell receives signals from a clearly defined set of photoreceptors constituting the *receptive field* for that cell. Therefore, stimulating numerous photoreceptors in a ganglion cell's receptive field results in only a single message to the brain from that cell. Receptive fields are typically circular and are of different sizes. Smaller receptive fields result in sharper images because they send more precise information to the brain about the location in the retina where the light was received.

Lateral movement of signals from a rod or cone proceeds to a horizontal cell and continues to bipolar cells with which the horizontal cell makes inhibitory connections. To understand this, consider a spot of light falling on the retina. Photoreceptors detect the light and send a signal to bipolar cells and horizontal cells. Horizontal cells inhibit more distant bipolar cells that are outside the spot of light, causing the light spot to appear lighter and its surrounding dark area to appear darker. This type of visual processing is called **lateral inhibition** and serves both to sharpen the edges of objects and enhance contrast in an image.

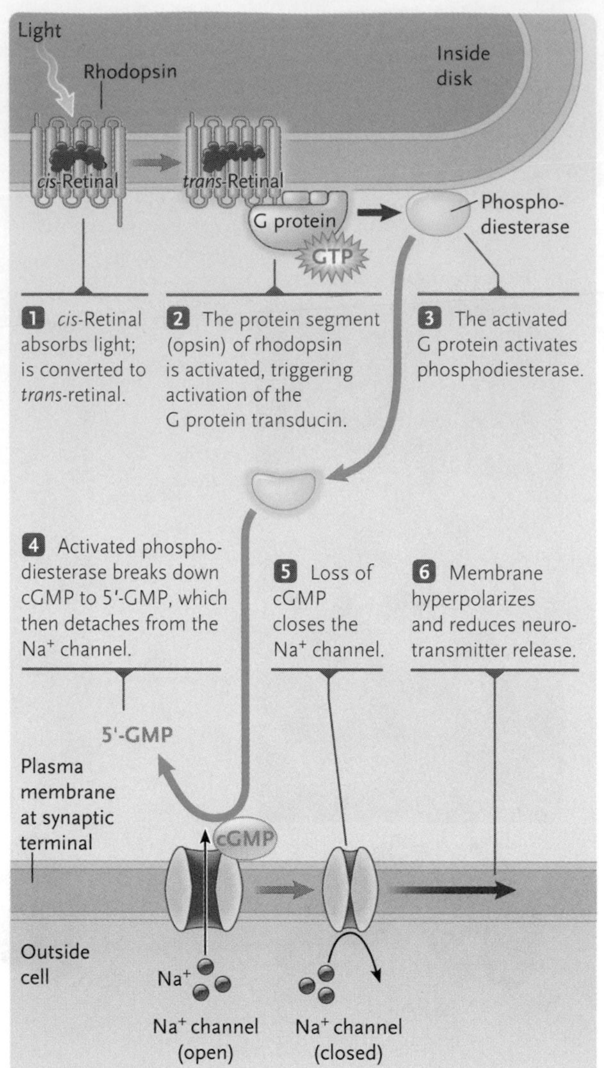

Figure 34.23
The signal transduction pathway that closes Na^+ channels in photoreceptor plasma membranes when rhodopsin absorbs light.

34.4e Opsins and Colour Vision

Many invertebrates and some species in each class of vertebrates have colour vision, which depends on cones in the retina. Most mammals have two types of cones, whereas humans and other primates have three types. Each human or primate cone cell contains one of three photopsins in which retinal is combined with different opsins. The three photopsins absorb light over different, but overlapping, wavelength ranges, with peak absorptions at 445 nm (blue light), 534 nm (green light), and 570 nm (red light). The farther a wavelength is from the peak colour absorbed, the less strongly the cone responds. Having more types of cones translates into better colour vision.

Overlapping wavelength ranges for the three photoreceptors means that light at any visible wavelength stimulates at least two of three types of cones. Maximal absorption by each type of cone at a different wavelength leads to differential stimulation of different types of cones. These differences are relayed to the visual centres of the brain, where they are integrated into the perception of a colour corresponding to the particular wavelength absorbed. Light stimulating all three receptor types equally is seen as white.

Colourblindness results from inherited defects in opsin proteins of one or more of the three types of cones. For example, people with a mutation preventing cones from making a functional form of red-absorbing opsin see orange, yellow, and red as the same grey or greenish colour.

Figure 34.24
Microscopic structure of the retina showing the network of neurons (bipolar cells, horizontal cells, amacrine cells, and ganglion cells) that carry out the initial integration of visual information.

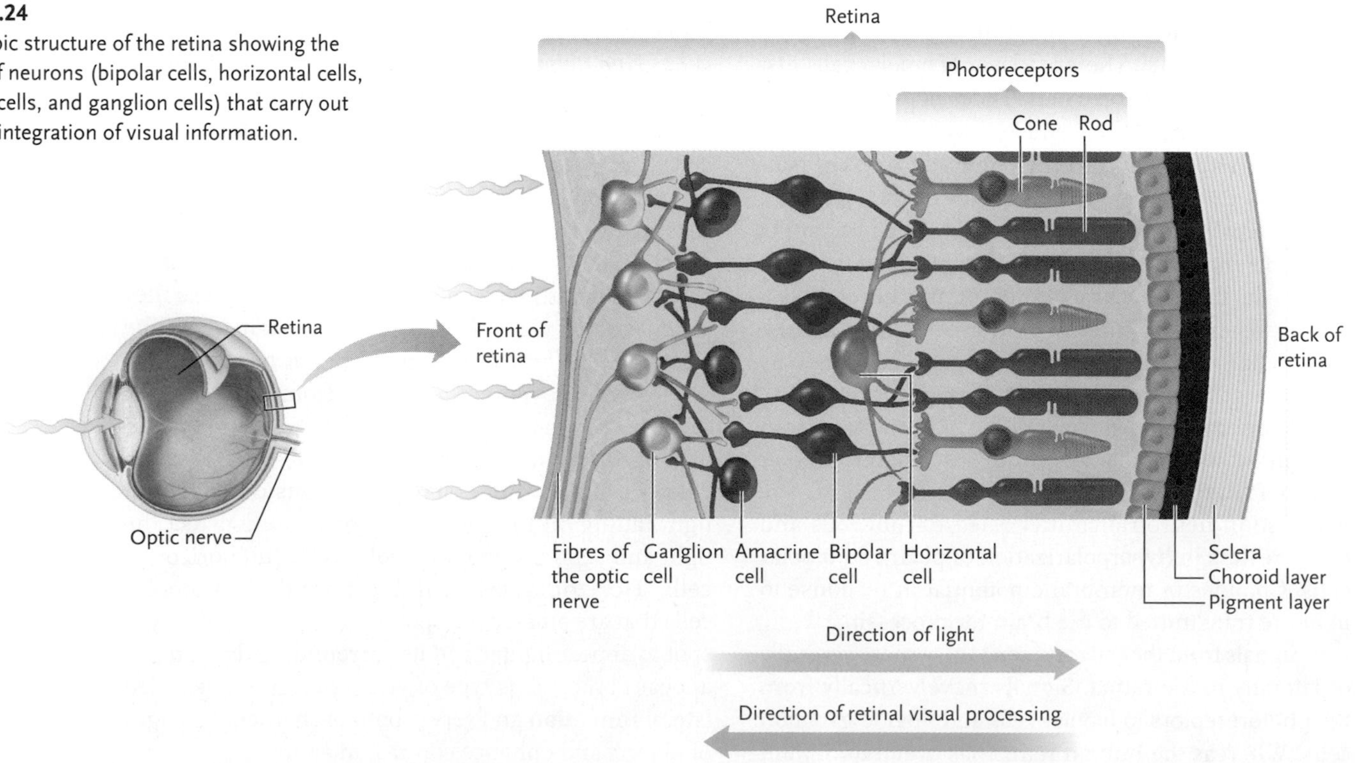

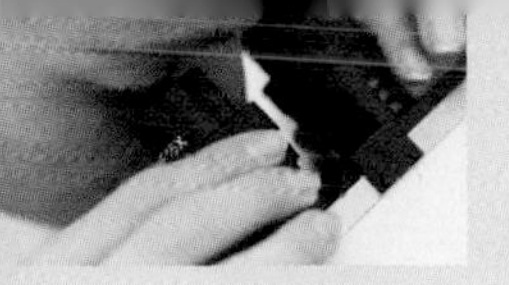

People Behind Biology

Lazzaro Spallanzani and Donald R. Griffin

In 1794, the Italian scientist Lazzaro Spallananzi finished one stage of studying the nocturnal orientation behaviour of bats and owls. His experiments had progressively denied his study animals—barn owls (*Tyto alba*) and pipistrelle bats (*Pipistrellus pipistrellus*)—access to sensory information. Although the owls depended on vision to detect and avoid obstacles, the bats did not. Only when Spallanzani blocked one of the bats' ears did they become disoriented. Spallanzani concluded that "bats could see with their ears." In 1794, this suggestion was considered to be preposterous, and some scientists of note mocked him, asking if bats could see with their ears, could they hear with their eyes? But Spallanzani's data supported his conclusion, and his data had been collected by experimentation.

Fast-forward to the 1930s. Donald R. Griffin, then an undergraduate at Harvard University, knew of what had become known as "Spallanzani's bat problem." Using little brown bats (*Myotis lucifugus*), Griffin repeated many of Spallanzani's experiments. Unlike Spallanzani, Griffin had the use of a "sonic detector," a microphone sensitive to the high-frequency acoustic signals (beyond the range of human hearing, or ultrasonic) of the bats. He and his colleague Robert Galambos determined that bats flying in the dark produced pulses of high-frequency sound. They coined the term "echolocation" to describe how bats used echoes of the sounds they produced to detect objects in their path.

By 1960, Griffin and his colleagues had demonstrated that little brown bats could use echolocation to detect insects as small as fruit flies (*Drosophila*) and mosquitoes. Both Lazzaro Spallanzani and Donald Griffin opened our eyes to animals' use of biosonar or echolocation. Each of them used the tools available at the time to design and conduct experiments whose results led to the conclusion that bats could "see with their ears."

The apparatus available to Spallanzani in 1794 was quite different from that available to Griffin in 1937. Griffin solved "Spallanzani's bat problem" because he could eavesdrop on sounds beyond the range of human hearing. But neither Spallanzani nor Griffin worked alone, and each benefitted from interactions with colleagues, Jurine for Spallanzani and Galambos and Pearce for Griffin.

Spallanzani is also known for other contributions, particularly relating to the question of spontaneous generation. In 1780, he demonstrated fertilization of frogs' eggs with semen collected from a male frog. In 1783, he used other experiments to disprove spontaneous generation of microscopic organisms.

Griffin, too, is well known for contributions across a wide range of topics. One central theme is the orientation behaviour of animals, a logical jump from echolocation. Another was the question of animal awareness—are animals more than "boxes of reflexes"?—a topic that remains controversial.

It is no wonder that curious and innovative scientists such as Spallanzani and Griffin led the way to the discovery of echolocation.

34.4f Visual Cortex: Images in the Brain

Just behind the eyes, the optic nerves converge before entering the base of the brain. A portion of each optic nerve crosses over to the opposite side, forming the **optic chiasm** (*chiasma* = crossing place). Most axons enter the **lateral geniculate nuclei** in the thalamus, where they synapse with interneurons leading to the visual cortex **(Figure 34.25, p. 840)**.

Because of the optic chiasm, the left half of the image seen by both eyes is transmitted to the visual cortex in the right cerebral hemisphere, and the right half of the image is transmitted to the left cerebral hemisphere. The right hemisphere thus sees objects to the left of the centre of vision, and the left hemisphere sees objects to the right of the centre of vision. Communication between the right and left hemispheres integrates this information into a perception of the entire visual field seen by the two eyes.

If you look at a nearby object with one eye and then the other, you will notice that the point of view is slightly different. Integration of the visual field by the brain creates a single picture with a sense of distance and depth. The greater the difference between the images seen by the two eyes, the closer the object appears to the viewer.

When both eyes are used together, the animal has a wider field of view (in humans 180° versus 150°). Binocular vision also enhances the ability to see faint objects (binocular summation). Perhaps most importantly, binocular vision allows stereopsis because of the overlap in the angles of view between two eyes. Stereopsis allows the animal to make fine depth discriminations from parallax, the apparent difference in position of an object viewed from the different position of the eyes. In some cases, stereopsis involves neurons with binocular receptive fields. Humans have excellent stereopsis, but so do many other primates, as well as some birds and fishes.

Archerfish **(Figure 34.26, p. 840)** live in fresh water and knock flying or resting insects onto the water's surface with spit droplets. The fish then catches and eats the insects. During the spitting attacks, the fish's

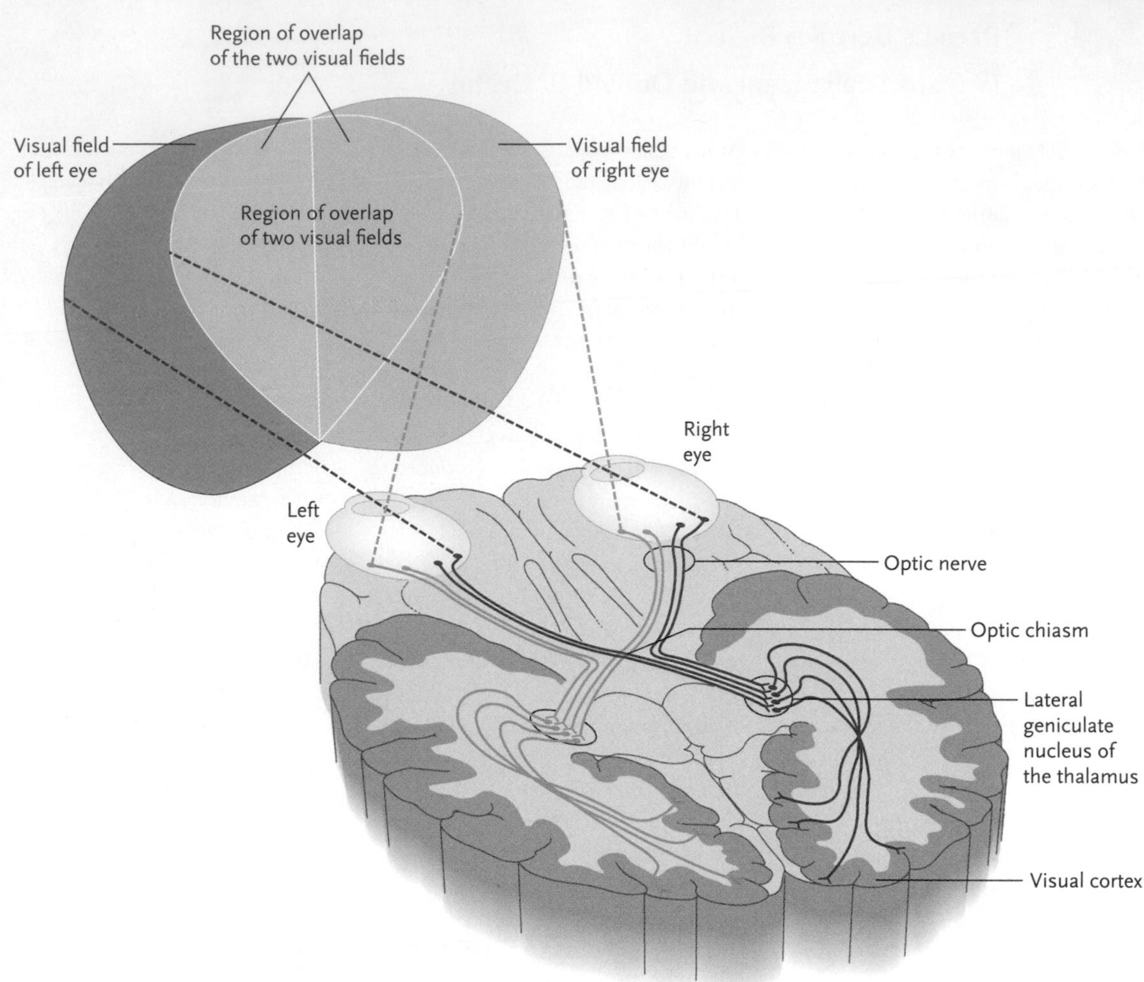

Figure 34.25
Neural pathways for vision. Because half of the axons carried by the optic nerves cross over in the optic chiasma, the left half of the field seen by both eyes (blue segment) is transmitted to the visual cortex in the right cerebral hemisphere. The right half of the field seen by both eyes (red segment) is transmitted to the visual cortex in the left cerebral hemisphere. As a result, the right hemisphere of the brain sees objects to the left of the centre of vision, and the left hemisphere sees objects to the right of the centre of vision.

Figure 34.26
An archerfish, *Toxotes chatareus*.

eyes are below the surface of the water, posing a potentially serious problem because of refraction, the deflection of rays of light at the air–water interface. Some evidence suggests that archerfish spit from directly under the prey, but further observations showed that this is not always true. Archerfish correctly set their spitting angle to compensate for the refraction they experience at different positions. They also correct for curvature of the water droplet's trajectory. Other fish also spit at aerial prey, and some birds hunt fish from above the water's surface; both deal with the problems of refraction from a different standpoint.

The two optic nerves together contain more than a million axons, more than all other afferent neurons of the body put together. Almost one-third of the grey matter of the cerebral cortex is devoted to visual information. These numbers give some idea of the complexity of the information integrated into the visual image formed by the brain.

Study Break

1. What is the "simplest" eye? Why is it an eye, and how does it differ from image-forming eyes?
2. What causes colourblindness?
3. Why are compound eyes so adept at detecting motion?
4. What is accommodation?

34.5 Chemoreceptors

Chemoreceptors provide information about taste (gustation) and smell (olfaction), as well as measures of intrinsic levels of molecules such as oxygen, carbon dioxide, and hydrogen ions. All chemoreceptors probably work through membrane receptor proteins that are stimulated when they bind with specific molecules in the environment and generate action potentials in afferent nerves leading to the CNS.

34.5a Invertebrate Animals: A Rich World of Odours

In many invertebrates, the same receptors serve for sensing smell and taste. These receptors may be concentrated around the mouth or distributed over the body surface. The cnidarian *Hydra* has chemoreceptors around its mouth that respond to glutathione, a chemical released from prey organisms ensnared in the cnidarian's tentacles. Stimulation of chemoreceptors by glutathione causes the tentacles to retract, resulting in ingestion of the prey. In contrast, earthworms have taste and smell receptors distributed over the entire body surface.

Some terrestrial invertebrates have clearly differentiated receptors for taste and smell. In insects, taste receptors occur inside hollow sensory bristles called *sensilla* (singular, *sensillum*), usually located on the antennae, mouthparts, or feet **(Figure 34.27)**. Pores in the sensilla admit molecules from potential food to the chemoreceptors, which are specialized to detect sugars, salts, amino acids, or other chemicals. Many female insects have chemoreceptors on their ovipositors, allowing them to lay their eggs on food appropriate for the larvae when they hatch.

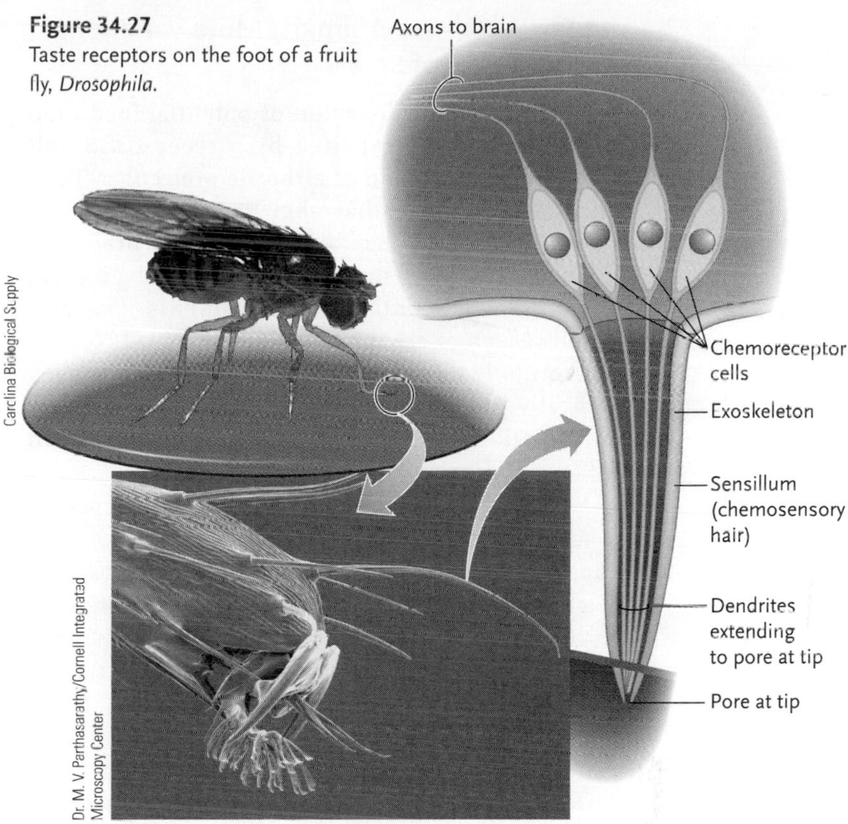

Figure 34.27
Taste receptors on the foot of a fruit fly, *Drosophila*.

Pheromones are chemicals used in communication by both animals and plants (see Chapter 40). Insects are excellent examples of animals that make extensive use of pheromones. Female insects use pheromones to attract males, or vice versa. Olfactory receptors in the bristles on the antennae of male silkworm moths (*Bombyx mori*) **(Figure 34.28)** bind a pheromone released by female conspecifics. If an antenna from a silkworm moth is connected to electrodes at its base and tip, action potentials from olfactory receptors can be detected at pheromone concentrations as low as one attractant molecule per 10^{17} air molecules! The male moth responds by flying rapidly when as few as 40 of the 20 000 receptor cells on an antenna have been stimulated by pheromone molecules. Ants, bees, and wasps may use odour to recognize conspecifics, to identify members of the same hive or nest, or to alert nestmates to danger.

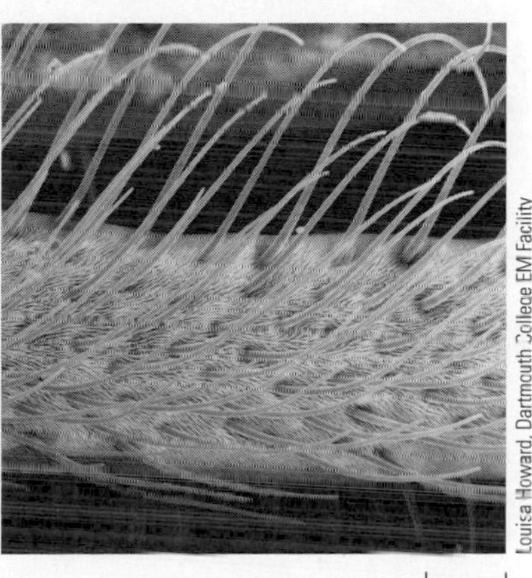

Figure 34.28
The brushlike antennae of a male silkworm moth. Fine sensory bristles containing olfactory receptor cells cover the filaments of the antennae.

34.5b Vertebrate Animals: More Variations on the Sense of Smell

Taste involves the detection of potential food molecules in objects touched by a receptor. Smell involves the detection of airborne molecules. Taste and smell receptors have hairlike extensions that contain proteins that bind environmental molecules. Hairs of taste receptors are derived from microvilli and contain microfilaments. Hairs of smell receptors are derived from cilia and contain microtubules. Information from taste receptors is typically processed in the parietal lobes, whereas information from smell receptors is processed in olfactory bulbs and temporal lobes.

Taste receptors of most vertebrates form part of a structure called a taste bud, a small, pear-shaped capsule with a pore at the top opening to the exterior **(Figure 34.29)**. Sensory hairs of taste receptors pass through the pore of a taste bud and project to the exterior. The opposite end of the receptor cells synapses with dendrites of an afferent neuron.

Taste receptors of terrestrial vertebrates are concentrated in the mouth. Humans have about 10 000 taste buds, each 30 to 40 μm in diameter, scattered over the tongue, roof of the mouth, and throat. Those on the tongue are embedded in outgrowths called *papillae* (*papula* = pimple), which give the surface of the tongue its rough or furry texture. Taste receptors on the human tongue respond to five basic tastes: sweet, sour, salty, bitter, and umami (savoury). Some receptors for umami respond to the amino acid glutamate (familiar as monosodium glutamate or MSG). Some taste receptors are stimulated on inhalation (orthonasal) and others on exhalation (retronasal) **(Figure 34.30; Table 34.1)**.

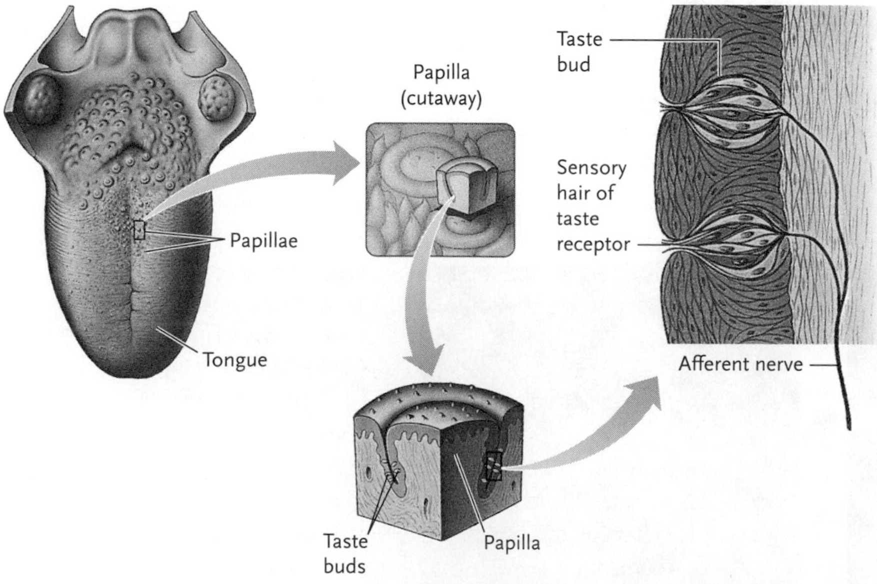

Signals from taste receptors are relayed to the thalamus. From there, some signals lead to gustatory centres in the cerebral cortex, which integrate them into the perception of taste. Others lead to the brain stem and limbic system, which link tastes to involuntary visceral and emotional responses. Through brain stem and limbic connections, a pleasant taste may lead to salivation, secretion of digestive juices, sensations of pleasure, and sexual arousal, whereas an unpleasant taste may produce revulsion, nausea, and vomiting.

Receptors that detect odours are located in the nasal cavities in terrestrial vertebrates. Bloodhounds have more than 200 million olfactory receptors in patches of olfactory epithelium in the upper nasal passages; humans have about 5 million olfactory receptors. On one end, each olfactory receptor cell has 10 to 20 sensory hairs projecting into a layer of mucus covering the olfactory area in the nose. To be detected, airborne molecules must dissolve in the watery mucus solution. At the other end, the olfactory receptor cells make synapses with interneurons in the olfactory bulbs. Olfactory receptors are the only receptor cells that make direct connections with brain interneurons rather than via afferent neurons.

From the olfactory bulbs, nerves conduct signals to the olfactory centres of the cerebral cortex, where they are integrated into the perception of tantalizing or unpleasant odours from a rose to a rotten egg. Most odour perceptions arise from combinations of different olfactory receptors. About 1000 different human genes give rise to an equivalent number of olfactory receptor types, each specific for a different class of chemicals. Recent experiments demonstrate that rats smell in stereo, accurately localizing odours in one or two sniffs. They could do so only with bilateral sampling. Some neurons in the olfactory bulb neurons respond differently to stimuli from the left than from the right. Furthermore, some receptors in the olfactory cortex of mammals fire only upon stimulation by combinations of odourants, perhaps explaining why mixes of odours are perceived as novel by humans.

As in taste, other connections from the olfactory bulbs lead to the limbic system and brain stem, where the signals elicit emotional and visceral responses similar to those caused by pleasant and unpleasant tastes. Olfaction contributes to the sense of taste because vapourized molecules from foods are conducted from the throat to the olfactory receptors in the nasal cavities. Olfactory input is the reason why anything that dulls

Figure 34.29
Taste receptors in the human tongue. The receptors occur in microscopic taste buds that line the sides of the furry papillae.

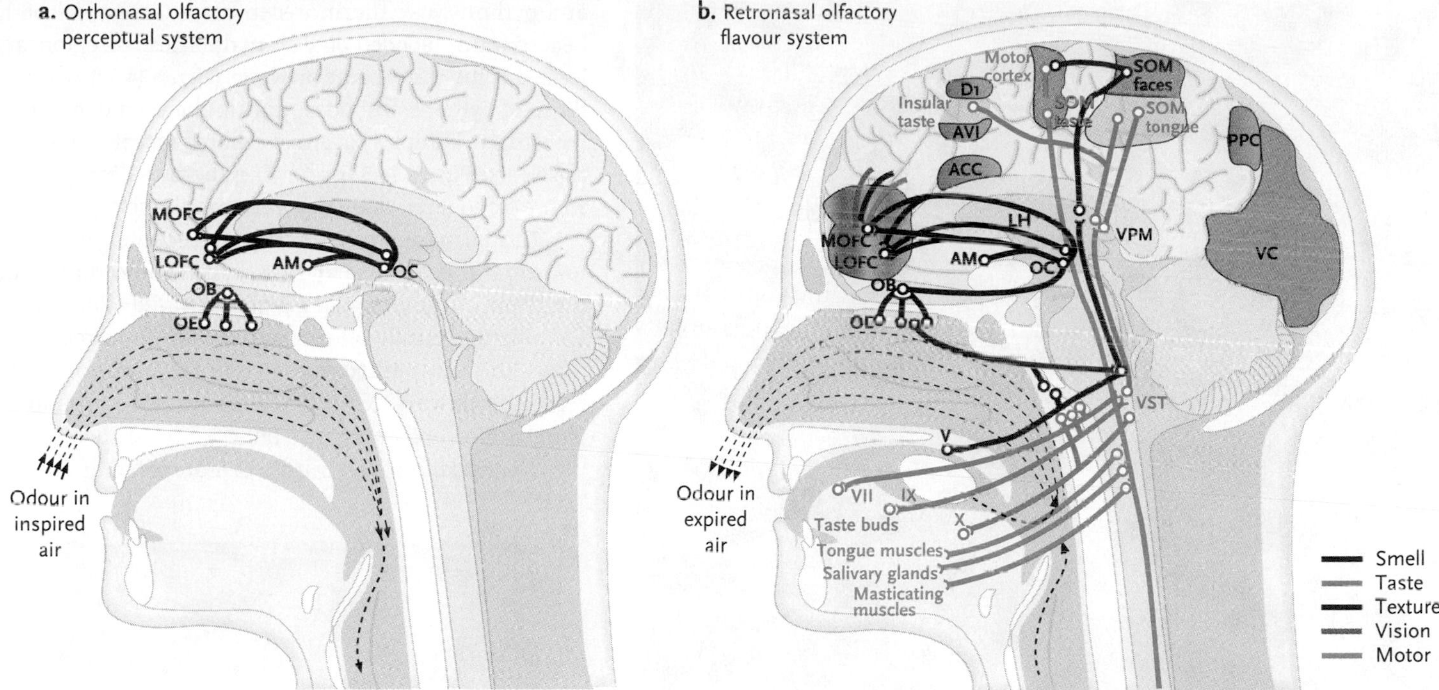

Figure 34.30
The dual olfactory system (see Table 34.1) means that some smells are perceived during inhalation and activate some parts of the brain **(a)**, whereas others are perceived during exhalation, activating other parts of the brain **(b)**. ACC – accumbens; AM – amygdala; AVI – anterior ventral insular cortex; D1 – dorsal insular cortex; LH – lateral cortex; MOFC – medial orbitofrontal cortex; NST – nucleus of the solitary tract; OB – olfactory bulb; OC – olfactory cortex; OE – olfactory epithelium; PPC – posterior parietal cortex; SOM – somatosensory cotex; V, VII, IX, and X – cranial nerves; VC – primary visual cortex; VPM – ventral posteriomedial thalamic nucleus.

Table 34.1 The Dual Olfactory System

Operations	Orthonasal olfaction	Retronasal olfaction
Stimulation route	Through the external nares	From the back of the mouth through the nasopharynx
Stimuli	Floral scents Perfumes Smoke Food aromas Prey/predator smells Social odors Pheromones MHC molecules	Food volatiles
Processed by	Olfactory pathway influences by the visual pathway	Olfactory pathway combined with pathways for taste, touch, sound, and active sensing by proprioception form a "flavour system"

Note the interesting contrast, that orthonasal olfactory perception involves a wide range of types of odors processed through only the olfactory pathway, in comparison with retronasal olfactory perception which involves only food volatiles but processed in combination with many brain pathways.

your sense of smell, such as a head cold or holding your nose, diminishes the apparent flavour of food.

34.5c Communication: Odours as Signals

Like other animals, many mammals communicate with odours, as anyone who has walked a dog knows. Individuals of the same family or colony are identified by their odour; odours are also used to attract mates and to mark territories and trails. In mammals, odourants are detected by ~1000 different odourant receptors. In the olfactory epithelium of mice, trace amine-associated receptors (TAARs) recognize volatile amines found in urine. TAARs were described in 2006, and the genes encoding them are known in humans and fishes, as well as in mice. Humans use the fragrances of perfumes and colognes as artificial sex attractants. The presence of TAARs in humans implies that we make more use of pheromones than previously suspected.

Although olfaction is obviously important to terrestrial animals, it has commonly been believed that, at least in mammals, the olfactory epithelium does not detect odourants in water. Star-nosed moles (*Condylura cristata*) and water shrews (*Sorex palustris*) exhale bubbles while diving. They reinhale the bubbles and, in this way, gain access to airborne olfactory cues **(Figure 34.31, p. 844)**.

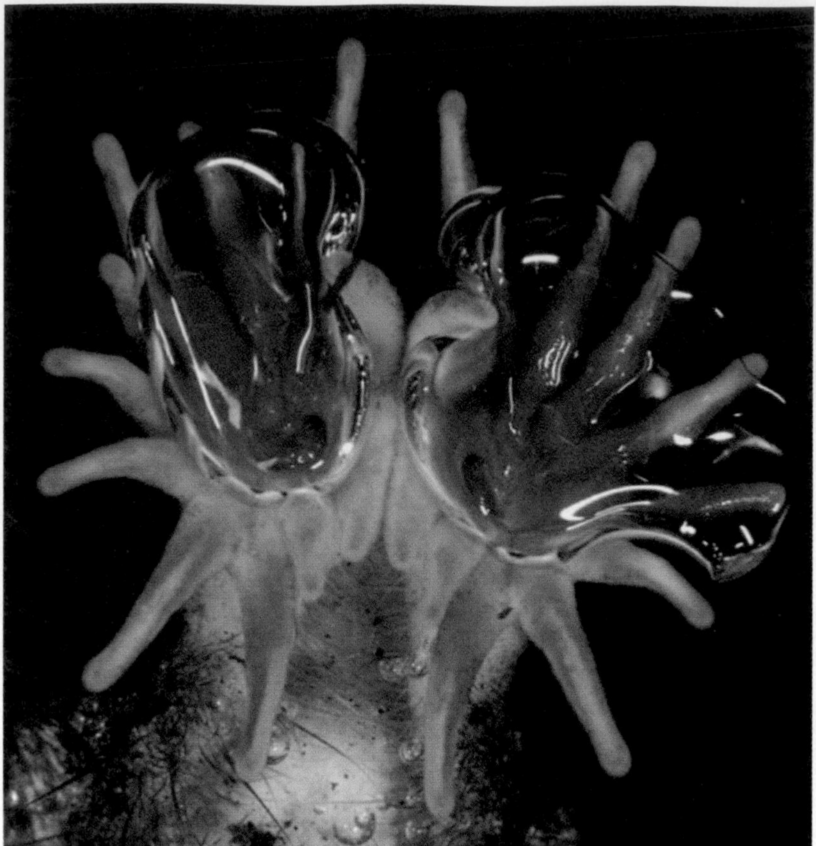

Reprinted by permission from Macmillan Publishers Ltd: Nature, Kenneth C. Catania, "OlfactionUnderwater 'sniffing' by semi-aquatic mammals", Vol. 444, pp. 1024-1025, copyright (2006).

Figure 34.31
Star-nosed moles (*Condylura cristata*) have papillae around their noses. Shown here, the papillae capture bubbles of air, allowing the submerged mole to smell airborne odours.

Study Break

1. What is the difference between taste and smell? What are the similarities?
2. What are the five basic tastes to which human receptors respond?
3. To where are taste signals relayed after the thalamus?

34.6 Thermoreceptors and Nociceptors

Thermoreceptors detect changes in the surrounding temperature. Nociceptors respond to stimuli that may potentially damage the surrounding tissues. Both types of receptors consist of free nerve endings formed by the dendrites of afferent neurons, with no specialized receptor structures surrounding them.

34.6a Thermoreception: Heat Detection

Most animals have thermoreceptors. Invertebrates such as mosquitoes and ticks use thermoreceptors to locate warm-blooded prey. Some snakes, including rattlesnakes and pythons, use thermoreceptors to detect the body heat of warm-blooded prey animals. These receptors are located in the pits of some pit vipers **(Figure 34.32),** whereas those of pythons and boas may not have an opening to the surface. Vampire bats have infrared receptors on their noseleafs **(Figure 34.33),** allowing them to detect places where blood (their food) flows close to the skin.

In mammals, distinct thermoreceptors respond to heat and cold. Researchers have shown that three members of the *transient receptor potential* (TRP)-gated Ca^{2+} channel family act as heat receptors. One responds when the temperature reaches 33°C and another responds above 43°C, at which point, heat starts to be painful. Both receptors are believed to be involved in thermoregulation. The third receptor responds at 52°C

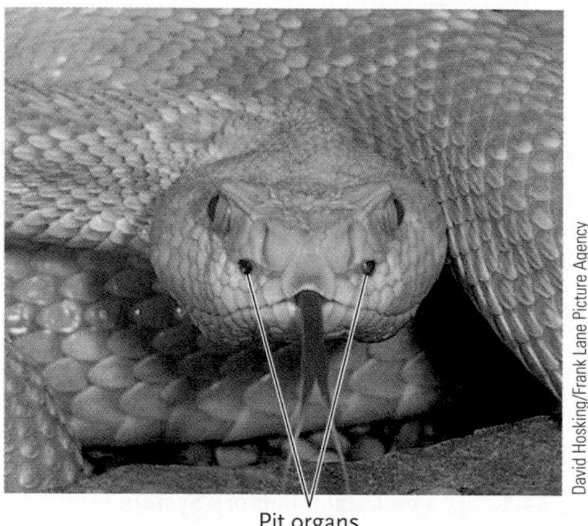

David Hosking/Frank Lane Picture Agency

Figure 34.32
The pit organs of an albino western diamondback rattlesnake (*Crotalus atrox*) are located in depressions on both sides of the head below the eyes. These thermoreceptors detect infrared radiation emitted by warm-blooded prey such as mice and kangaroo rats.

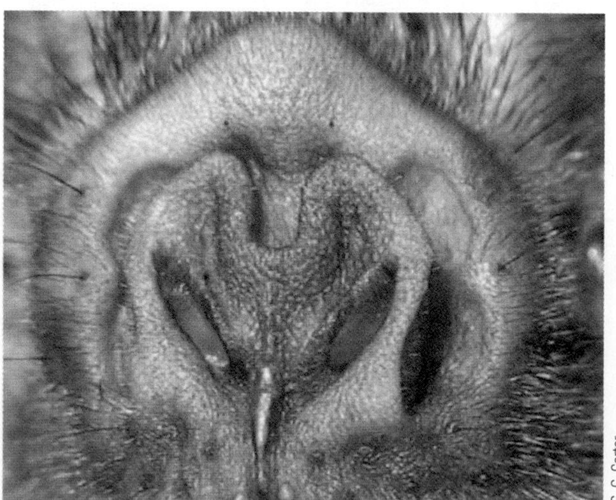

G. G. Carter

Figure 34.33
The noseleaf on the face of a vampire bat (*Desmodus rotundus*) houses an infrared detector, allowing the bat to find places where blood flows close to the skin. The bat then uses razor-sharp teeth to remove a divot of skin and antibleeding chemicals in its saliva to allow it to get a blood meal.

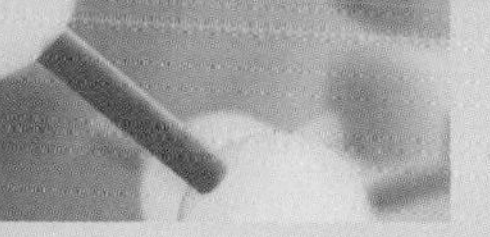

Molecule Behind Biology
Capsaicin

Biting into a jalapeño pepper (a variety of *Capsicum annuum*) can produce a burning pain in your mouth strong enough to bring tears to your eyes. This painfully hot sensation is due primarily to *capsaicin* **(Figure 1)**, a chemical that probably evolved in pepper plants as a defence against foraging animals. The defence is obviously ineffective for the humans who relish peppers and other foods containing capsaicin (such as hot sauce).

David Julius and his coworkers revealed the molecular basis for detection of capsaicin by nociceptors. They designed their experiments to test the hypothesis that the responding nociceptors have a cell surface receptor that binds capsaicin. Binding the chemical opens a membrane channel in the receptor that admits calcium ions and initiates action potentials interpreted as pain.

The Julius team isolated the total complement of messenger RNAs from nociceptors that respond to capsaicin and made complementary DNA (cDNA) clones of the mRNAs. The cDNAs contained thousands of different sequences that encode proteins made in the nociceptors. The team transferred the cDNAs individually into embryonic kidney cells (which do not normally respond to capsaicin), and the transformed cells were screened with capsaicin to identify which took in calcium ions. These would be the cells that had received a cDNA encoding a capsaicin receptor. Messenger RNA transcribed from the identified cDNA clone was injected into both frog oocytes and cultured mammalian cells. Both oocytes and cultured cells responded to capsaicin by admitting calcium ions, confirming that the researchers had found the capsaicin receptor cDNA.

Among the effects noted when the receptor was introduced into oocytes was a response to heat. Increasing the temperature of the solution surrounding the oocytes from 22°C to about 48°C produced a strong calcium inflow. In short, capsaicin and heat produce the same response in cells containing the receptor. Therefore, the feeling that your mouth is on fire when you eat a hot pepper probably results from the fact that, as far as your nociceptors and CNS are concerned, it *is* on fire.

Chili peppers were domesticated in different parts of the New World (from Chile to the Caribbean) by 6000 years b.p., and their use in cooking has spread throughout the world (see Chapter 49).

Figure 1
A capsaicin molecule.

and above, in this case producing a pain response rather than being involved in thermoregulation.

Two cold receptors are known in mammals. One responds between 8 and 28°C and is thought to be involved in thermoregulation. The second responds to temperatures below 8°C and appears to be associated with pain rather than thermoregulation. The molecular mechanisms controlling the opening and closing of heat and cold receptor chemical channels are not currently known.

Some neurons in the hypothalamus of mammals function as thermoreceptors, sensing changes in brain temperature and receiving afferent thermal information. They are highly sensitive to shifts from the normal body temperature and trigger involuntary responses such as sweating, panting, or shivering, which restore normal body temperature.

34.6b Nociceptors: Pain

Signals from nociceptors in mammals and possibly other vertebrates detect damaging stimuli that are interpreted by the brain as pain. Pain is a protective mechanism. In humans, pain prompts us to do something immediately to remove or decrease the damaging stimulus. Often pain elicits a reflex response, such as withdrawing the hand from a hot stove, that proceeds before we are consciously aware of the sensation.

Mechanical damage, such as a cut, pin prick, or blow to the body, and temperature extremes can cause pain. Some nociceptors are specific for a particular type of damaging stimulus, whereas others respond to more than one kind. Axons that transmit pain are part of the somatic system of the PNS (see Chapter 33). They synapse with interneurons in the grey matter of the spinal cord and activate neural pathways to the CNS by releasing the neurotransmitters glutamate or substance P (see Chapter 33). Glutamate-releasing axons produce sharp, prickling sensations that can be localized to a specific body part, such as the pain of stepping on a tack. Substance P–releasing axons produce dull, burning, or aching sensations that are not easily localized, such as the pain of tissue damage when you stub your toe.

As part of their protective function, pain receptors adapt very little, if at all. Some pain receptors gradually intensify the rate at which they send out action potentials if the stimulus continues at a constant level. The

Magnetic Sense in Sea Turtles

To determine if loggerhead sea turtles (*Caretta caretta*) use a magnetoreceptor system for orientation, Kenneth Lohmann and colleagues tested the responses of hatchling turtles to magnetic fields. They placed each turtle hatchling they tested in a harness and tethered it to a swivelling, electronic system in the centre of a circular pool of water **(Figure 1a).** The pool was surrounded by a large coil system, allowing the researchers to reverse the direction of the magnetic field **(Figure 1b).** The direction the turtle swam was recorded by the tracking system and relayed to a computer.

The turtles swam under two experimental conditions: half of them in Earth's magnetic field and the other half in a reversed magnetic field. Turtle hatchlings tested in Earth's magnetic field swam, on average, in an east-to-northeast direction, mimicking the direction they follow normally when migrating at sea. The hatchlings tested in the reversed magnetic field swam, on average, in a direction 180° opposite that of the hatchlings swimming in Earth's magnetic field.

The results indicate that loggerhead sea turtle hatchlings have the ability to detect Earth's magnetic field and use it to help them orient their migration. Their direction of migration, east to northeast, matches the inclination of Earth's magnetic field in the Atlantic Ocean where they migrate (see **Figure 1c**).

Figure 1
(a) Harnessed hatchling loggerhead sea turtles **(b)** were tested in a circular pool in which the magnetic field could be altered. **(c)** Hatchlings swimming in the normal magnetic field of Earth swam in the directions they would travel at sea on migration.

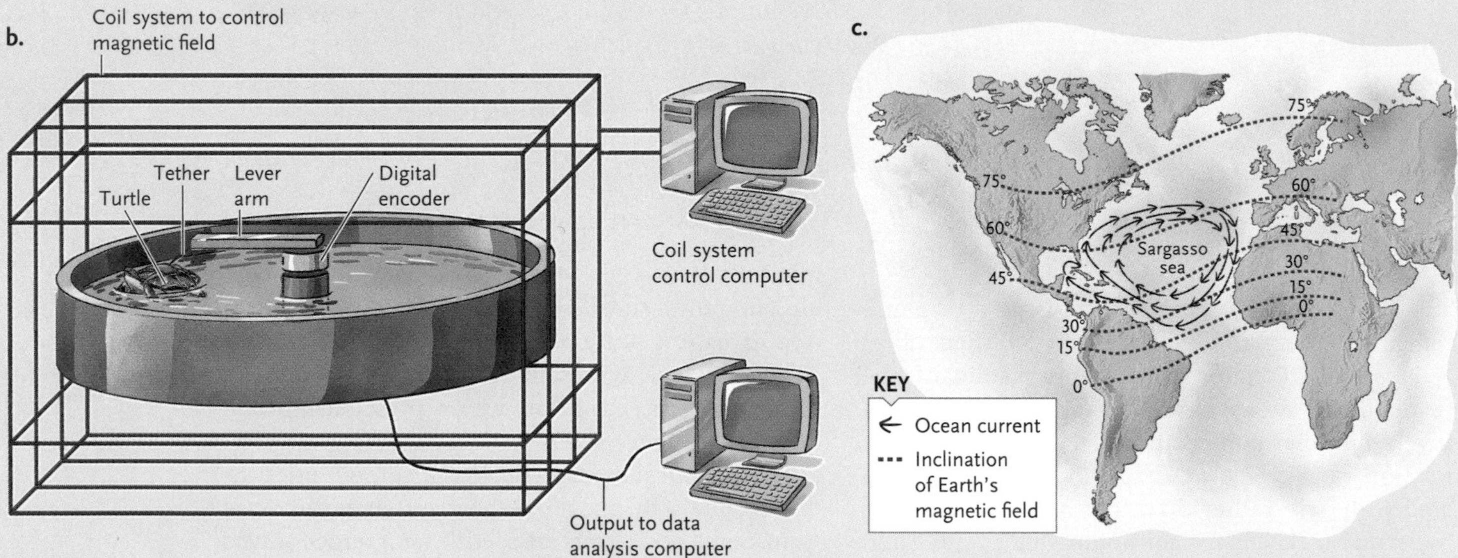

CNS also has a pain-suppressing system. In response to stimuli, such as exercise, hypnosis, and stress, the brain releases *endorphins,* natural painkillers that bind to membrane receptors on substance P neurons, reducing the amount of neurotransmitter released.

Nociceptors contribute to the taste of some spicy foods, particularly those containing capsaicin, the active ingredient in hot peppers. Researchers who study pain use *capsaicin* to identify nociceptors. To some, the burning sensation from capsaicin is addictive because in its presence, nociceptors in the mouth, nose, and throat immediately transmit pain messages to the brain. The brain responds by releasing endorphins that act as a painkiller and create temporary euphoria (see *Molecule Behind Biology*).

Study Break

1. What do thermoceptors and nociceptors have in common?
2. What are the three heat thermoceptors found in humans?
3. Why do pain receptors not adapt?

34.7 Electroreceptors and Magnetoreceptors

Some animals gain information about their environment by sensing electrical or magnetic fields. In so doing, they directly sense stimuli that humans can detect only with scientific instruments.

34.7a Electroreception

Electroreception is an ancient trait in vertebrates. Although it was lost in ancestral bony fish, it persists today in many sharks and has reappeared in some bony fishes and some amphibians. Mammals such as the star-nosed mole and duck-billed platypus detect electric fields with specialized **electroreceptors**.

Electroreceptors depolarize in an electric field, and the plasma membrane of an electroreceptor cell generates action potentials. The electrical stimuli detected by the receptors are used in different ways. Electrical information can be used to locate prey, to negotiate a way around obstacles in muddy water, or, by some fishes, in communication. Some electroreception systems are passive, detecting electric fields in the environment, not the animal's own electric currents. Passive systems are used mainly to find prey. Sharks and rays use electroreceptors to locate prey buried under sand by detecting electrical currents generated by the prey's heartbeat or by the muscle contractions moving water over the gills.

34.7b Electric Fishes

Fishes in the orders Mormyriformes (elephant fish from Africa) and Gymnotiformes (knifefish from South America; **Figure 34.34a**) emit and receive low-voltage electrical signals, using them to locate prey (electrolocation) and in intraspecific communication. Electric fishes have two kinds of electroreceptors, ampullary and tuberous. Ampullary receptors respond to low-frequency alternating current (AC) fields usually associated with other fishes, vegetation, or electrical stimuli from other electric fishes. Tuberous electroreceptors detect electric organ discharge. Electrical signals are generated by electric organs that are specialized muscle cells.

Some electric fishes can produce discharges of several hundred volts (e.g., *Electrophorus electricus*, the electric eel, **Figure 34.34b**, and *Malapturus electricus*, the electric catfish) that stun or kill prey. The voltage discharged by an electric eel is high enough to stun, but not kill, a human.

34.7b Magnetoreception

Just as the development of a magnetic compass was a pivotal point in humans' ability to navigate, some animals use magnetic compasses in long-distance navigation. Magnetoreceptors allow animals to detect and use Earth's magnetic field as a source of directional information. The list includes butterflies, beluga whales, sea turtles (see *Magnetic Sense in Sea Turtles*), homing pigeons, and foraging honeybees (*Apis mellifera*).

a.

b.

M. B. Fenton

Figure 34.34 Two electric fishes from South America. *Eigenmannia eigenmannia* **(a)** is a weakly electric fish that uses electrolocation, whereas *Electrophorus electricus* **(b)**, the electric eel, stuns prey with an electric discharge.

The pattern of Earth's magnetic field differs from region to region yet remains almost constant over time, largely unaffected by changing weather or day and night. Animals with magnetic receptors can reliably monitor their location. Although little is known about the receptors that detect magnetic fields, they may depend on the fact that moving a conductor, such as an electroreceptor cell, through a magnetic field generates an electric current. Some magnetoreceptors may depend on the effect of Earth's magnetic field on the mineral *magnetite*, which is found in the bones or teeth of many vertebrates, including humans, and in insects, such as the abdomen of the honeybee and the heads and abdomens of certain ants.

Animals such as homing pigeons (*Columbia livia*), famous for their ability to find their way back to their nests even when released far from home, navigate by detecting their position with reference to both Earth's magnetic field and the Sun. Magnetite is located in the beaks of these birds, which is where magnetoreception likely occurs. Big brown bats (*Eptesicus fuscus*) also have a magnetic sense that influences their navigational abilities.

Study Break

1. How do animals use electrical information?
2. What are the two types of electroreceptors in electric fishes?
3. Why would a magnetic navigational system be favourable?

Unanswered Questions

Do humans have a magnetic sense? What is the evidence for a magnetic sense? What is the basis for a magnetic sense—what is the transducer?

Review

Go to CENGAGENOW™ at http://hed.nelson.com/ to access quizzing, animations, exercises, articles, and personalized homework help.

34.1 Overview of Sensory Receptors and Pathways

- Receptors in the sensory system collect information (i.e., stimuli) from internal and external sensors (transducers) and convert (transduce) the information into neural activity. Dendrites of an afferent neuron pick up the stimuli. The axon of the afferent neuron conveys the stimulus to the CNS, providing the organisms with sensory data used to influence behaviour and homeostasis.
- Mechanoreceptors detect mechanical energy (pressure); photoreceptors detect the energy of light; chemoreceptors detect specific molecules or chemical conditions; thermoreceptors detect the flow of heat energy; and nociceptors detect tissue damage or noxious chemicals.
- Some receptors allow the effect of a stimulus to be reduced over time. Otherwise, the receptor could become overloaded and not function properly. Receptors also need a period of rest.

34.2 Mechanoreceptors and the Tactile and Spatial Senses

- You would more likely detect a fruit fly walking on your face than on your leg because touch receptors are more concentrated on a human's face than on a human's leg.
- The vestibular apparatus and cochlea are specialized sensory structures. The vestibular apparatus is responsible for maintaining equilibrium and coordinating head and body movements. The cochlea is used in hearing.
- The strength of the responses of stretch receptors depends on how much and how fast the muscle is stretched.

34.3 Mechanoreceptors and Hearing

- Most invertebrates detect sound through mechanoreceptors in their skin or other surface structures. An example are ears in the common cricket. Crickets detect sound using tympana (ears) on each side of the abdomen or on the first pair of walking legs. The ears are areas of thin exoskeleton (tympanum, singular; tympana, plural).
- Sound waves cause vibrations of the tympanum, which are converted into nerve impulses that travel along the auditory nerve to the CNS.
- Vertebrates use ears to hear sounds. Some vertebrates have pinnae (outer ears) that collect sounds (vibrations) and channel them down the auditory canal to the tympanum (eardrum). There, vibrations in air are converted (transduced) into vibrations of the membrane comprising the tympanum. These vibrations are amplified by vibrations of the malleus, incus, and stapes (auditory ossicles) and conveyed to the oval window, where they are converted to vibrations in the fluid of the coiled cochlea. Vibrations in the fluid inside the cochlea cause vibrations of the basilar membrane, which are detected by cilia and converted to nerve impulses. The nerve impulses move down the auditory nerve to the brain, where they are processed and interpreted.
- The echolocation calls of bats range from about 8 kHz to over 200 kHz. Many are inaudible to humans because they are ultrasonic, above the range of human hearing (20 000 Hz = 20 kHz). Infrasounds (<40 Hz), used by elephants and whales, are below the range of human hearing.

34.4 Photoreceptors and Vision

- The ocellus, the "simplest" eye, lacks a lens and therefore is not image forming. Ocelli (plural) are light receptors that often allow animals to detect differences in the brightness of light. Image-forming eyes (compound eyes and single-lens eyes) are photoreceptors too, but they have lenses that allow light to be focused on the retina, the layer with photosensitive cells.
- Colourblindness is a result of inherited defects in opsin proteins of one or more of the three types of cones. Genes controlling colour vision are located on the X chromosome. Therefore, human males have only one set of genes controlling colour vision, whereas females have two sets. Colourblindness is relatively common in men and relatively rare in women.
- Compound eyes are composed of ommatidia, many individual visual units. Each ommatidium samples a small part of the visual field, and many ommatidia provide the animal with an image that is a mosaic of many individual views. Motion is detected by many ommatidia at once, giving compound eyes special sensitivity to motion.
- Accommodation is the movement of the lens to focus the image on the retina. In cephalopods, muscles move the lens forward and back. In terrestrial vertebrates, muscles change the shape of the lens.
- Rods and cones, the photoreceptor cells in the retina, consist of an outer segment of stacked, flattened membranous disks with photopigments, an inner segment for cellular metabolic activities, and the synaptic terminal for storage and release of neurotransmitter.

34.5 Chemoreceptors

- Taste is the detection of potential food molecules *touched* by a receptor, whereas smell is the detection of *airborne* particles and molecules. Information from taste receptors is processed in the parietal lobes. Information from smell is processed in the olfactory bulb and temporal lobes. Both taste and smell receptors have hairlike extensions that bind molecules.

- The five basic tastes are sweet, sour, bitter, salty, and umami (savoury). Some lead to the gustatory centres of the cerebral cortex, whereas others are linked to the brain stem and limbic system, producing visceral and emotional responses, including physiological responses such as salivation and secretion of gastric juices. The same responses may occur in response to smells.

34.6 Thermoreceptors and Nociception

- Thermoreceptors and nociceptors consist of free nerve endings formed by the dendrites of afferent neurons. No specialized receptor structures surround them. All are members of the *transient receptor potential* (TRP)-gated Ca^{2+} channel family. One responds to temperatures above 33°C, one to temperatures above 43°C, and the third to temperatures above 53°C. The first two are involved in thermoregulation, whereas the last elicits a strong pain response.
- The pain response (nociception) is a protective mechanism. These receptors do not adapt; otherwise, organisms would not withdraw from a prolonged painful stimulus, increasing the level of damage associated with the pain.

34.7 Electroreceptors and Magnetoreceptors

- Electric field information can be used to detect prey, for example, a shark's passive system. Some fishes generate electric signals to detect obstacles and prey and to communicate.
- The two types of electroreceptors are ampullary receptors and tuberous receptors. Ampullary receptors respond to low-frequency alternating current (AC) fields usually associated with other fishes, vegetation, or electrical stimuli from other electric fishes. Tuberous electroreceptors detect electric organ discharge.
- The pattern of the magnetic field of Earth varies from region to region. Animals with a magnetic compass can detect the magnetic field and use the information in navigation (as people use compasses). Earth's magnetic field remains constant over time and so is reliable from year to year. Many animals have magnetic receptors. Other animals use Sun compasses.

Questions

Self-Test Questions

1. Some preying mantises have
   a. two ears.
   b. two eyes.
   c. two antennae.
   d. one ear.
   e. one eye.
2. Sensory adaptation involves
   a. the loss of eyes in cave-dwelling fish.
   b. the development of ears in insects preyed upon by bats.
   c. a reduction in the effect of stimuli.
   d. the development of an acute sense of smell.
   e. all of the above.
3. Which of the following are examples of proprioceptors?
   a. eyes
   b. statocysts
   c. ears
   d. halteres
   e. b and d
4. The vestibular system of vertebrates involves the
   a. retina.
   b. Golgi apparatus.
   c. utricle.
   d. semicircular canals.
   e. c and d.
5. The malleus, incus, and stapes occur in
   a. birds.
   b. mammals.
   c. bony fish.
   d. amphibians.
   e. insects.
6. Golden rice provides ____________, which is vital to the development of vision.
   a. vitamin E
   b. rhodopsin
   c. vitamin A
   d. fatty acids
   e. chlorophyll
7. Accommodation occurs in the eyes of cephalopods when
   a. the shape of the lens is changed.
   b. the retina moves toward the lens.
   c. the retina moves away from the lens.
   d. the lens moves toward or away from the retina.
   e. light is focused on the fovea.
8. Chemoreceptors in *Hydra* are concentrated
   a. in the tentacles.
   b. around the mouth.
   c. in the base.
   d. in the gasteron.
   e. in/around all of the above.
9. Thermoreceptors are widespread in
   a. earthworms.
   b. vampire bats.
   c. pit vipers.
   d. birds.
   e. animals.
10. Nociceptors are sensitive to
    a. pheromones.
    b. pain.
    c. touch.
    d. light.
    e. vibration.

Questions For Discussion

1. What is an eye? What are the key elements in the definition? Can robots have eyes?
2. Which are better at evoking memories in humans: visual or olfactory stimuli? What is the evidence supporting either point of view? Why would one kind of stimulus be more effective than the other?
3. Find examples of redundancy in the sensory systems of animals. What are the advantages of redundant systems? What are the disadvantages?

The larva, pupa, and adult moth of the tobacco hornworm, *Manduca sexta*, a model insect that has been used in exploring the hormonal control of metamorphosis.

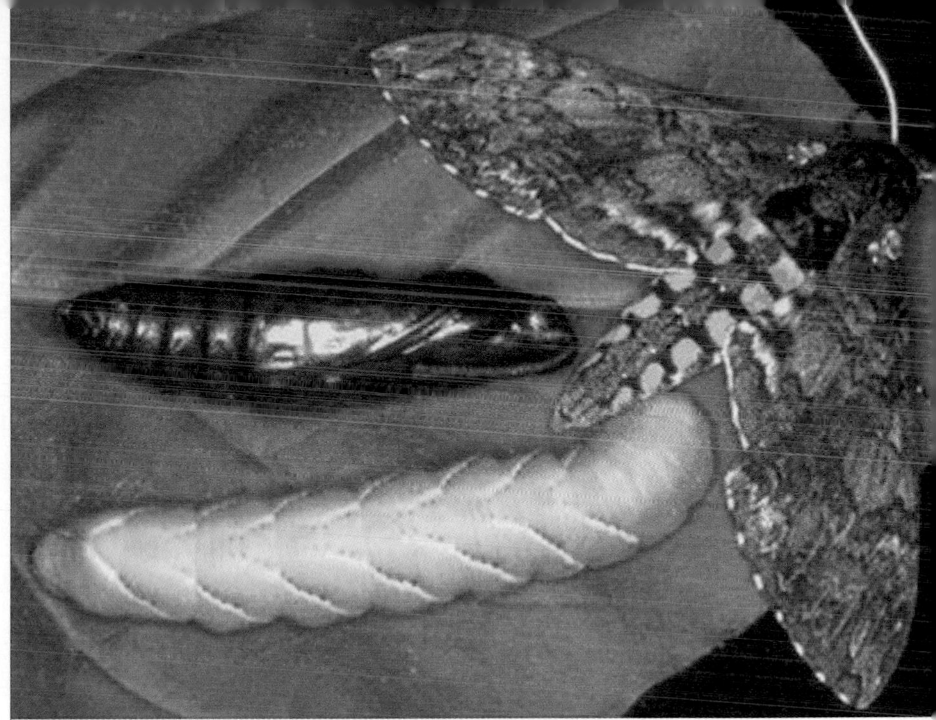

Study Plan

35 The Endocrine System

Why It Matters

The larva of the tobacco hornworm, *Manduca sexta*, having reached its critical weight, stops feeding, drops to the ground, and burrows into the soil where it moults into the pupal stage. Within the pupa, nearly all of the old larval tissues are destroyed and replaced by the tissues of the moth, which have been waiting in embryonic form for the signal to develop. When the moth is formed, it wriggles, still enclosed in the pupal cuticle, to the surface of the soil. It begins the behaviour leading to rupture of the pupal cuticle and its emergence as the adult moth as a soft animal with still rumpled wings. Once emergence is complete, it inflates its body and expands its wings. Only then does the cuticle harden. Moths are nocturnal, and the female, feeding on the nectar of several species of flowers, completes the development of its eggs begun in the pupal stage and releases the pheromone that will attract males. After mating, the female takes flight and searches for a suitable host plant in the family Solanaceae, where she lays the 100 or so eggs that she carries.

This carefully timed sequence of developmental and behavioural events is orchestrated by several hormones released in response to internal and external environmental cues. This marvel of communication between the environment and the cells, tissues, and organs of animals involving interactions between the nervous system and endocrine structures is a feature of everyday life in even the simplest of organisms. It is impossible to understand the functioning of any animals in the absence of knowledge of the endocrine system. For more complex animals such as insects and mammals, a galaxy of hormones regulates development, reproduction, and behaviours and helps maintain a stable internal environment.

Hormones are secreted by cells of the **endocrine system** (*endo* = within; *krinein* = separate), so called because it forms a distinct control system within the body. The endocrine system, like the nervous system, regulates and coordinates distant organs. The two systems are structurally, chemically, and functionally related, but they control different types of activities. The nervous system (Chapter 33), through high-speed electrical signals, enables an organism to interact rapidly with the external environment, whereas the endocrine system controls activities that involve slower, longer-acting responses.

The nervous system directs highly specific localized targets: it is a "private" mode of communication. The endocrine system is more "public," often affecting several tissues or organs. Ultimately, the nervous system controls the endocrine system. The mechanisms and functions of the endocrine system are the subjects of this chapter.

35.1 Hormones and Their Secretion

Cells signal other cells using neurotransmitters (see Chapter 33), hormones, and local regulators. Our focus in this chapter is hormones, but we also deal briefly with local regulators, molecules that act locally rather than over long distances.

35.1a The Endocrine System Includes Four Major Types of Cell Signalling

Four types of cell signalling occur in the endocrine system. In *classical endocrine signalling,* hormones are secreted into the blood or extracellular fluid by the cells of ductless secretory organs called **endocrine glands (Figure 35.1a).** In contrast, *exocrine glands,* such as the sweat and salivary glands, release their secretions into ducts that lead outside the body or into the cavities of the digestive tract (see Chapter 32). Hormones are circulated throughout the body in the blood or other body fluids, and, as a result, most body cells are constantly exposed to a wide variety of hormones. Only the *target cells* of a hormone, those with *receptor proteins* (Chapter 8) recognizing and binding that hormone, respond to it. Hormones are cleared from the body at a steady rate by enzymatic breakdown in their target cells or blood or organs such as the liver or kidneys, and the breakdown products are excreted.

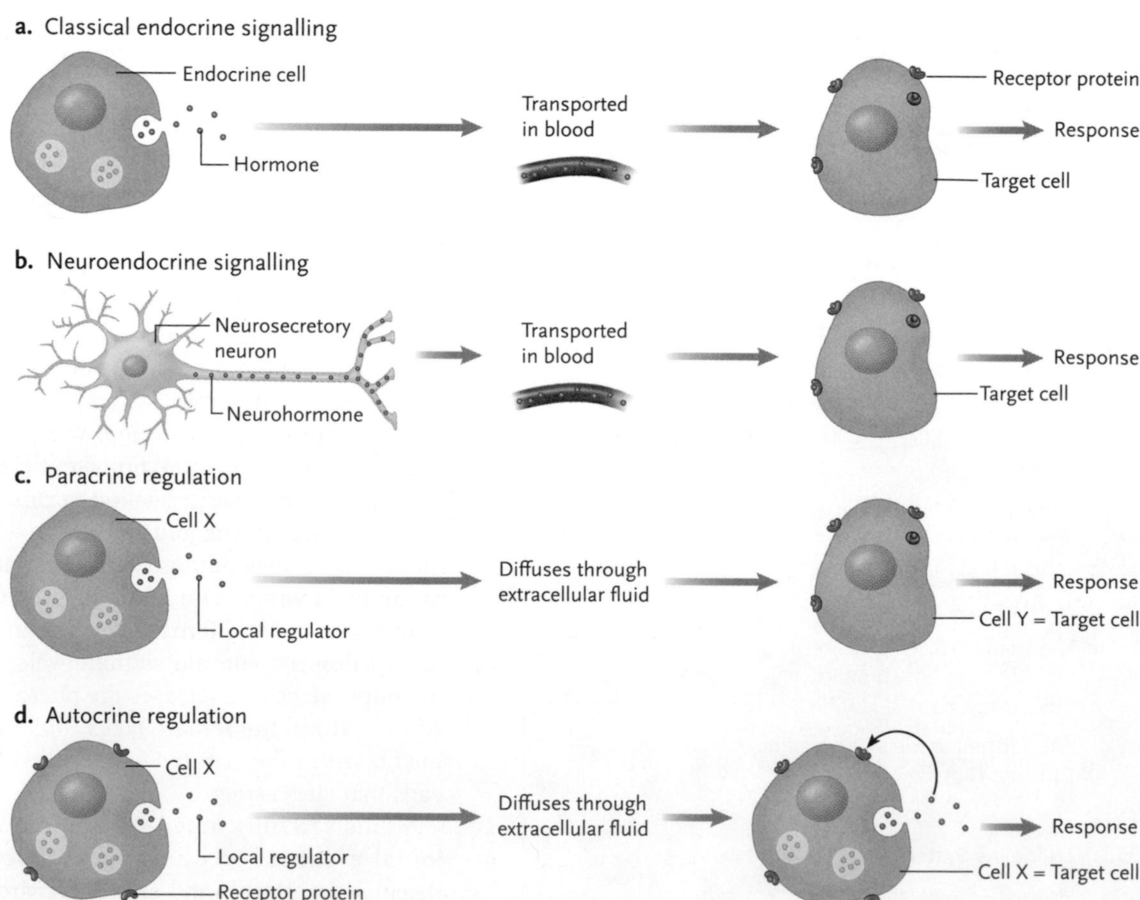

Figure 35.1
The four major types of cell signalling in the endocrine system.

In *neuroendocrine signalling,* specialized **neurosecretory neurons** respond to and conduct electrical signals, but rather than synapsing with target cells, they release a neurohormone into the circulation when appropriately stimulated **(Figure 35.1b).** The hormone is produced in the cell body and packaged in membrane-bound vesicles that are transported along the axon to the release sites. The neurohormone is usually distributed in blood or other body fluids and elicits a response in target cells that have receptors for the neurohormone. The peptide vasopressin secreted by the pituitary gland acts on the kidney, reducing the water excreted in the urine, and on muscles of blood vessels, increasing blood pressure. It is also released directly into the brain to cause a myriad of social effects, such as pair bonding in some mammals.

Two other sorts of chemical communication between cells are not normally thought of as part of the hormonal signalling system. In *paracrine regulation,* a cell releases a signalling molecule that diffuses through the extracellular fluid and acts on nearby cells. Regulation is *local* **(Figure 35.1 c)** rather than at a distance. In *autocrine regulation,* the local regulator acts on the same cells that release it **(Figure 35.1d).** Many of the growth factors that regulate cell division and differentiation act in both a paracrine and an autocrine fashion.

35.1b Hormones and Local Regulators Can Be Grouped into Four Classes Based on Their Chemical Structures

More than 60 hormones and local regulators have been identified in humans. Many human hormones are either identical or very similar in structure and function to those in other animals, but other vertebrates, as well as invertebrates, may have hormones not found in humans. Most of these chemicals can be grouped into four molecular classes: amine, peptide, steroid, and fatty acid-derived molecules.

Amine hormones are involved in classical endocrine signalling and neuroendocrine signalling. Most amine hormones are based on tyrosine. With one major exception, they are hydrophilic molecules, which diffuse readily into the blood and extracellular fluids. On reaching a target cell, they bind to receptors at the cell surface. The amines include epinephrine–norepinephrine and, in protostomes, octopamine, already familiar as neurotransmitters released by some neurons (see Chapter 33). The exception is the thyroid hormones secreted by the thyroid gland. These hormones, based on a pair of tyrosines, enter the cell by receptor-mediated endocytosis. Inside the cell, one form of the hormone binds to nuclear receptors in the same way as described for steroids below. Thyroid hormones also act via membrane receptors not only on the surface of the cells but also on mitochondrial membranes.

Peptide hormones consist of amino acid chains, ranging in length from as few as 3 amino acids to more than 200. Some have carbohydrate groups attached. They are involved in classical endocrine signalling and neuroendocrine signalling. Mostly hydrophilic hormones, peptide hormones are released into the blood or extracellular fluid by exocytosis when cytoplasmic vesicles containing the hormones fuse with the plasma membrane. One large group of peptide hormones, the **growth factors**, regulates the division and differentiation of many cell types in the body. Many growth factors act in both a paracrine and an autocrine manner, as well as in classical endocrine signalling.

Steroid hormones are involved in classical endocrine signalling. All are hydrophobic molecules derived from cholesterol and are sparingly soluble in water. They combine with hydrophilic carrier proteins to form water-soluble complexes that diffuse easily in blood or other fluids. On contacting a cell, the hormone is released from its carrier protein, passes through the plasma membrane of the target cell (a process that is sometimes mediated by receptors), and binds to internal receptors in the nucleus or cytoplasm. Steroid hormones include aldosterone, cortisol, the vertebrate sex hormones, and ecdysone, the hormone that governs the formation of new cuticles in ecdyzoan protostomes. Steroid hormones may vary little in structure but produce very different effects. Testosterone and estradiol, two major sex hormones responsible for the development of mammalian male and female characteristics, respectively, differ only in the presence or absence of a methyl group. Steroids can also act via membrane receptors, controlling cellular events such as apoptosis and cell proliferation and more complex events such as behaviour.

Fatty acids represent a very specialized category of hormones. In arthropods and possibly annelids, hormones derived from farnesoic acid include the juvenile hormones that govern metamorphosis and reproduction in arthropods (see Chapter 26, *Molecule Behind Biology*). Prostaglandins and their relatives are important local regulators derived from arachidonic acid. They are involved in paracrine and autocrine regulation in all animals. First discovered in semen, they enhance the transport of sperm through the female reproductive tract by increasing the contractions of muscle cells in both vertebrates and insects. In at least some insects, prostaglandins act as endocrines: they are synthesized in the sperm storage organs of mated females and initiate egg laying by acting on the oviducts and possibly the nervous system.

35.1c Many Hormones Are Regulated by Feedback Pathways

The secretion of many hormones is regulated by feedback pathways, some of which operate partially or completely independently of neuronal controls. Most

Figure 35.2
A negative feedback loop regulating secretion of the thyroid hormones. As the concentration of thyroid hormones in the blood increases, the hormones inhibit an earlier step in the pathway (indicated by the negative sign).

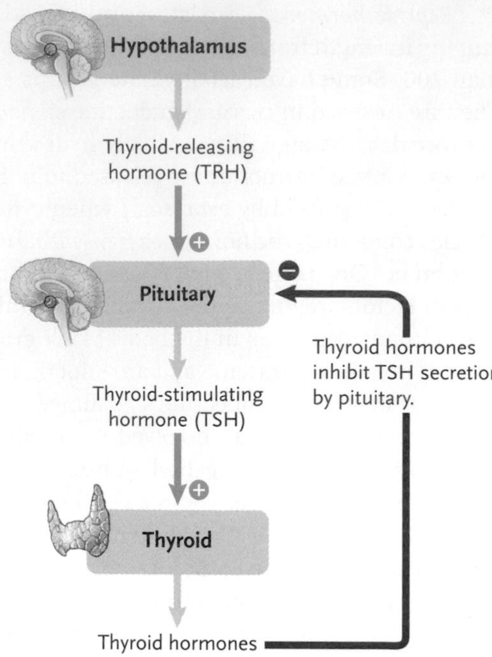

pathways are controlled by negative feedback in which a product of the pathway inhibits an earlier step in the pathway. In vertebrates, secretion by the thyroid gland is regulated by a negative feedback loop **(Figure 35.2)**. Neurosecretory neurons in the hypothalamus secrete thyroid-releasing hormone (TRH) into a vein connecting the hypothalamus to the pituitary gland. In response, the pituitary releases thyroid-stimulating hormone (TSH) into the blood, which stimulates the thyroid gland to release thyroid hormones. As the thyroid hormone concentration in the blood increases, it begins to inhibit TRH secretion by the hypothalamus. In turn, TSH and secretion of the thyroid hormones are reduced.

35.1d Body Processes Are Regulated by Coordinated Hormone Secretion

Although we mostly discuss individual hormones in the remainder of the chapter, body processes are affected by more than one hormone. The blood concentrations of glucose, fatty acids, and ions such as Ca^{2+}, K^+, and Na^+ are regulated by the coordinated activities of several hormones secreted by different glands. Similarly, body processes such as oxidative metabolism, digestion, growth, sexual development, and reactions to stress are all controlled by multiple hormones.

In many of these systems, negative feedback loops adjust the levels of secretion of hormones that act in antagonistic (opposing) ways, creating a balance in their effects that maintains body homeostasis (see Chapter 43). Consider the regulation of fuel molecules such as glucose, fatty acids, and amino acids in the blood. We usually eat three meals a day and fast to some extent between meals. During these periods of eating and fasting, five hormone systems act in a coordinated fashion to keep the fuel levels in balance: (1) gastrin and ghrelin secreted by the stomach and secretin from the intestine; (2) insulin and glucagon, secreted by the pancreas; (3) growth hormone, secreted by the anterior pituitary; (4) epinephrine–norepinephrine, released by the sympathetic nervous system and the adrenal medulla; and (5) glucocorticoid hormones, released by the adrenal cortex.

The entire system of hormones regulating fuel metabolism resembles the fail-safe mechanisms designed by engineers, in which redundancy, overlapping controls, feedback loops, and multiple safety valves ensure that vital functions are maintained at appropriate levels in the face of changing and even extreme circumstances.

Study Break

1. What are the functions of the endocrine and nervous systems? How are they the same, and how do they differ?
2. What are the four major types of cell signalling that occur in the endocrine system? How do they work?

35.2 Mechanisms of Hormone Action

Hormones control cell functions by binding to receptor molecules in their target cells. Small quantities of hormones can typically produce profound effects in cells and body functions due to **amplification**. In amplification, an activated receptor activates many proteins, which then activate an even larger number of proteins for the next step in the cellular pathway and so on in each subsequent step (see Chapter 8).

35.2a The Secreted Hormone May Not Be the Active Form

Many hormones are secreted in an inactive or less active form (a "prohormone") and converted by target cells or enzymes in the blood or other tissues to the active form. The best known example is thyroxine, discussed below. Many other hormones are subject to similar processes. **Ecdysone**, a steroid governing the formation of new cuticle in insects, is converted to the much more active functional hormone, 20-OH ecdysone, by the addition in the target cells of a single hydroxyl group. Peptide hormones are commonly synthesized as prohormones that undergo posttranslational conversion to the active forms in the source cell. In some cases, however, further conversion occurs once the hormone has been secreted. Angiotensin is a hormone that governs blood pressure in humans. It is secreted by the liver as angiotensinogen. An inactive form of angiotensin is cleaved from angiotensinogen by an enzyme. This inactive form is converted to the active hormone by angiotensin-converting enzyme (ACE). ACE inhibitors are often prescribed for control of high blood pressure.

35.2b Hormones May Bind to Surface Receptors, Usually Activating Protein Kinases Inside Cells

Hormones that bind to receptor molecules in the plasma membrane produce their responses through signal transduction pathways. In brief, when a surface receptor binds a hormone, it transmits a signal through the plasma membrane. Within the cell, the signal is transduced, changed into a form that causes the cellular response **(Figure 35.3a).** Typically, the reactions of signal transduction pathways involve protein kinases, enzymes that add phosphate groups to proteins. Adding a phosphate group to a protein may activate or inhibit it, depending on the protein and the reaction. The particular response produced by a hormone depends on the kinds of protein kinases activated in the cell and the types of target proteins they phosphorylate (Chapter 8). The signal transduction pathway may not stop at the cytoplasm: many growth factors and some peptide hormones ultimately affect events in the nucleus. Although action via membrane receptors is characteristic of and most extensively studied in peptide and amine hormones, many steroid and fatty acid hormones also exert some of their actions in this way.

The peptide hormone glucagon illustrates the mechanisms triggered by surface receptors. When glucagon binds to surface receptors on liver cells, it triggers a series of steps leading to the phosphorylation and activation of the enzyme governing the breakdown of glycogen stored in those cells into glucose.

35.2c Hydrophobic Hormones Bind to Receptors Inside Cells, Activating or Inhibiting Genetic Regulatory Proteins

After passing through the plasma membrane, the hydrophobic steroid and thyroid hormones bind to internal receptors in the nucleus or cytoplasm **(Figure 35.3b).** Binding of the hormone activates the receptor, which then binds to a control sequence of specific genes. Depending on the gene, binding the control sequence either activates or inhibits its transcription, leading to changes in protein synthesis that accomplish the cellular response. The characteristics of the response depend on the specific genes controlled by the activated receptors and on the presence of other proteins that modify the activity of the receptor.

Figure 35.3
The reaction pathways activated by hormones that bind to receptor proteins in plasma membrane **(a)** or inside cells **(b).** In both mechanisms, the signal—the binding of the hormone to its receptor—is transduced to produce the cellular response.

a. Hormone binding to receptor in the plasma membrane

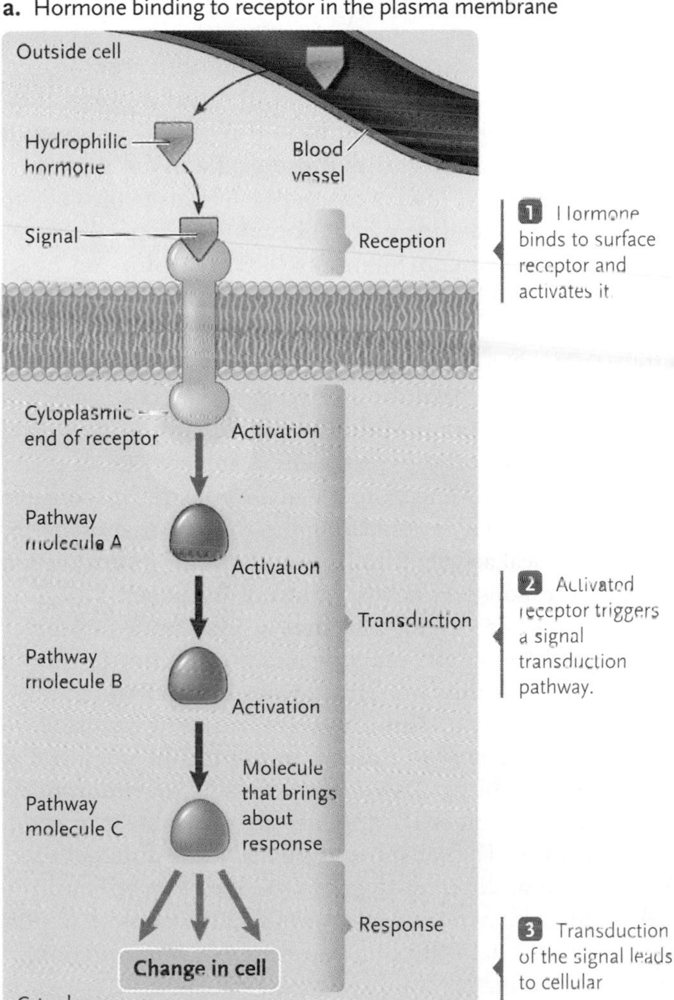

b. Hormone binding to receptor inside the cell

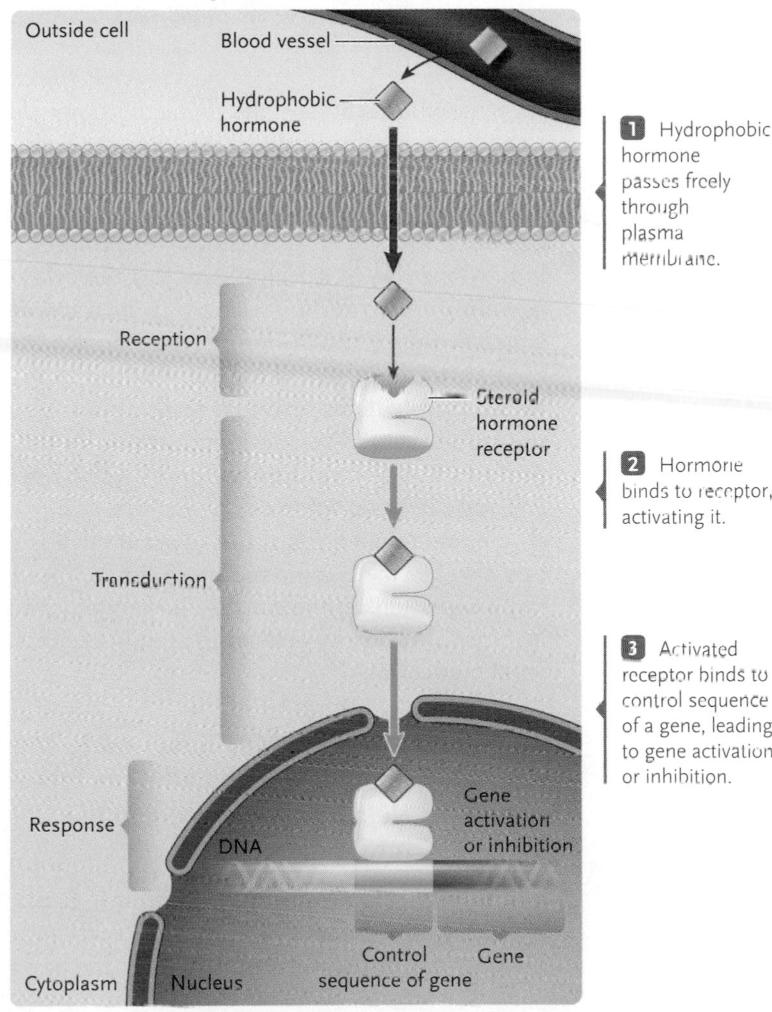

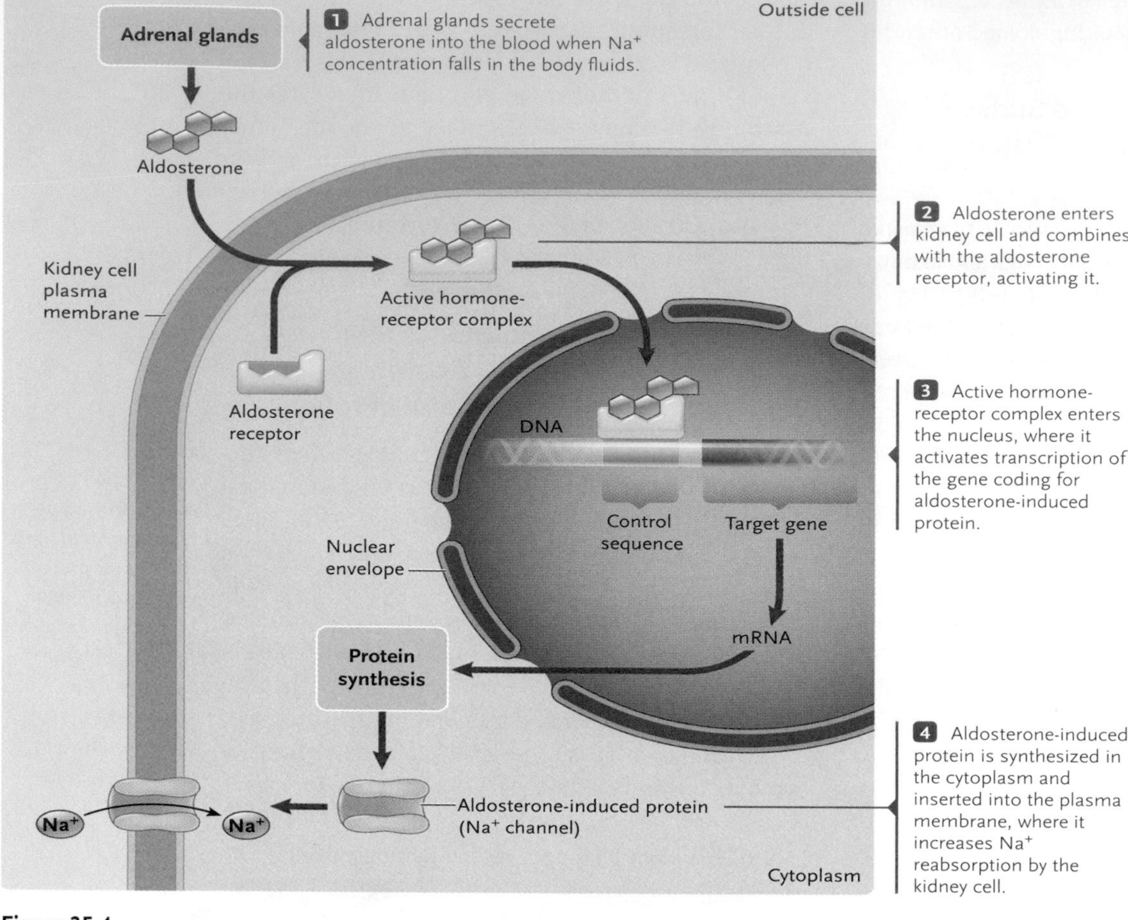

Adrenal glands
1 Adrenal glands secrete aldosterone into the blood when Na+ concentration falls in the body fluids.
Outside cell
Aldosterone
Kidney cell plasma membrane
Active hormone-receptor complex
2 Aldosterone enters kidney cell and combines with the aldosterone receptor, activating it.
Aldosterone receptor
DNA
3 Active hormone-receptor complex enters the nucleus, where it activates transcription of the gene coding for aldosterone-induced protein.
Control sequence
Target gene
Nuclear envelope
mRNA
Protein synthesis
4 Aldosterone-induced protein is synthesized in the cytoplasm and inserted into the plasma membrane, where it increases Na+ reabsorption by the kidney cell.
Na+
Na+
Aldosterone-induced protein (Na+ channel)
Cytoplasm

Figure 35.4
The action of aldosterone in the increasing Na^+ reabsorption in the kidneys when concentration of the ion falls in the blood.

One of the actions of the steroid hormone aldosterone illustrates the mechanisms triggered by internal receptors **(Figure 35.4).** If blood pressure falls below optimal levels, aldosterone is secreted by the adrenal glands. The hormone affects only cells (mostly in the kidney but also in sweat glands and the colon) that contain the aldosterone receptor in their cytoplasm. When activated by aldosterone, the receptor binds to the control sequence of a gene, leading to the synthesis of proteins that increase reabsorption of Na^+ by the kidney cells. The resulting increase in Na^+ concentration in body fluids increases water retention and, with it, blood volume and pressure.

Many steroid hormones that act at nuclear receptors also use membrane receptors, sometimes in the same cell. Aldosterone can also have rapid effects on Na^+ reabsorption by activating membrane receptors on kidney cells.

35.2d Target Cells May Respond to More than One Hormone, and Different Target Cells May Respond Differently to the Same Hormone

A single target cell may have receptors for several hormones and respond differently to each hormone. Vertebrate liver cells have receptors for the pancreatic hormones insulin and glucagon. Insulin increases glucose uptake and conversion to glycogen, which decreases blood glucose levels, whereas glucagon stimulates the breakdown of glycogen into glucose, which increases blood glucose levels.

Conversely, particular hormones interact with different types of receptors in or on a range of target cells. Different responses are then triggered in each target cell type because the receptors trigger different transduction pathways. For example, the amine hormone epinephrine prepares the body for handling stress (including dangerous situations) and physical activity. In mammals, epinephrine can bind to three different plasma membrane–embedded receptors: α, β_1, and β_2 receptors. When epinephrine binds to α receptors on smooth muscle cells, such as those of the blood vessels, it triggers a response pathway that causes the cells to constrict, cutting off circulation to peripheral organs. When epinephrine binds to β_1 receptors on heart muscle cells, the contraction rate of the cells increases, which, in turn, enhances blood supply. When epinephrine binds to β_2 receptors on liver cells, it stimulates the breakdown of glycogen to glucose, which is released from the cell. The overall effect of these and a number of other responses to epinephrine secretion is to supply energy to the major muscles responsible for locomotion, preparing the animal for stress or for physical activity. Similar tissue-specific diversification of responses is known for many hormones.

Moreover, the response to a hormone may differ in different animals. For example, melatonin, an amine derived from tryptophan, is important in regulating daily and annual cycles in most animals. However, it also plays a role in regulating the salt gland of marine birds. Thyroxine promotes metamorphosis in amphibians but inhibits metamorphosis in cyclostomes. The same hormone may have different functions at different stages in the life of an animal. The juvenile hormone of insects acts to maintain insects in a larval state but also controls reproduction in the adult.

In summary, the mechanisms by which hormones work have four major features. First, only the cells that contain surface or internal receptors for the hormones respond to them. Second, once bound by their receptors, hormones may produce a response that involves stimulation or inhibition of cellular processes through the specific types of internal molecules triggered by the hormone action. Third, because of the amplification that occurs in both the surface and internal receptor mechanisms, hormones are effective in very small concentrations. Fourth, the response to a hormone differs among target organs and among animals.

In the next two sections, we discuss the major endocrine cells and glands of vertebrates. The locations of these cells and glands in the human body and their functions are summarized in **Figure 35.5** and **Table 35.1, pp. 858–859.** In addition to these major endocrine organs, important hormones are also secreted by organs that have other primary functions, including the kidney, heart, liver, and intestine.

In particular, the digestive system is the source of several peptide hormones, many of which are also produced elsewhere. It is the only known source for peptides such as gastrin, secretin, and ghrelin, which coordinate the digestive secretions of the gut and its associated glands and send signals associated with hunger to the brain. The gut is increasingly recognized as an important endocrine organ in many animals. Among vertebrates, it is a more important source for circulating levels of melatonin than the pineal body with which that hormone is traditionally associated. In insects, several peptide hormones, such as proctolin, produced by neuroendocrine cells in the central nervous system (CNS) are also produced by cells in the intestine.

Study Break

What are the four major features of a hormone mechanism?

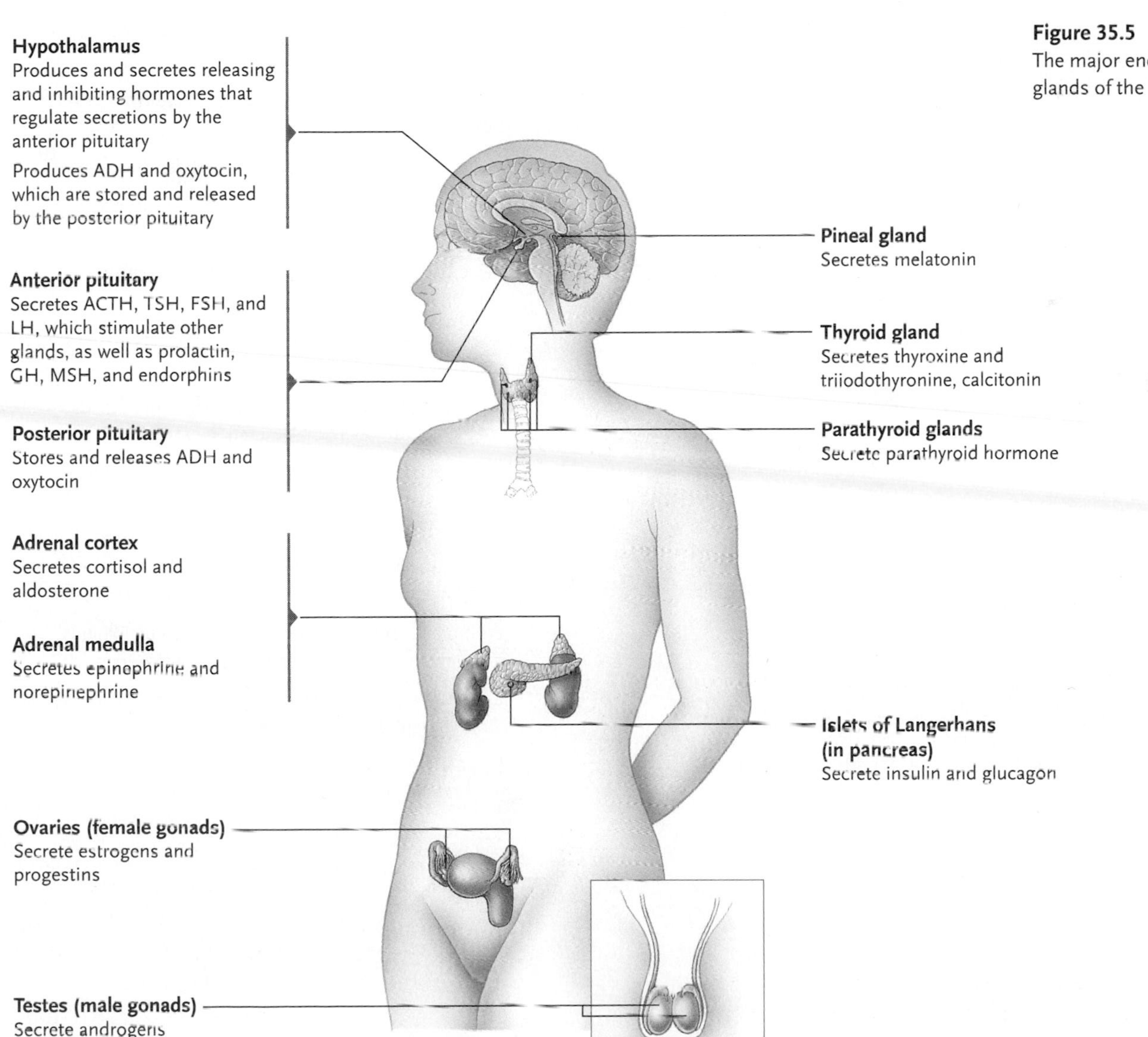
Hypothalamus
Produces and secretes releasing and inhibiting hormones that regulate secretions by the anterior pituitary
Produces ADH and oxytocin, which are stored and released by the posterior pituitary
Anterior pituitary
Secretes ACTH, TSH, FSH, and LH, which stimulate other glands, as well as prolactin, GH, MSH, and endorphins
Posterior pituitary
Stores and releases ADH and oxytocin
Adrenal cortex
Secretes cortisol and aldosterone
Adrenal medulla
Secretes epinephrine and norepinephrine
Ovaries (female gonads)
Secrete estrogens and progestins
Testes (male gonads)
Secrete androgens
Pineal gland
Secretes melatonin
Thyroid gland
Secretes thyroxine and triiodothyronine, calcitonin
Parathyroid glands
Secrete parathyroid hormone
Islets of Langerhans (in pancreas)
Secrete insulin and glucagon

Figure 35.5
The major endocrine cells and glands of the human body.

Table 35.1 The Major Human Endocrine Glands and Hormones

Secretory Tissue or Gland	Hormones	Molecular Class	Target Tissue	Principal Actions
Hypothalamus	Releasing and inhibiting hormones	Peptide	Anterior pituitary	Regulate secretion of anterior pituitary hormones
Anterior pituitary	Thyroid-stimulating hormone (TSH)	Peptide	Thyroid gland	Stimulates secretion of thyroid hormones and growth of thyroid gland
	Adrenocorticotropic hormone (ACTH)	Peptide	Adrenal cortex	Stimulates secretion of glucocorticoids by adrenal cortex
	Follicle-stimulating hormone (FSH)	Peptide	Ovaries in females, testes in males	Stimulates egg growth and development and secretion of sex hormones in females; stimulates sperm production in males
	Luteinizing hormone (LH)	Peptide	Ovaries in females, testes in males	Regulates ovulation in females and secretion of sex hormones in males
	Prolactin (PRL)	Peptide	Mammary glands	Stimulates breast development and milk secretion
	Growth hormone (GH)	Peptide	Bone, soft tissue	Stimulates growth of bones and soft tissues; helps control metabolism of glucose and other fuel molecules
	Melanocyte-stimulating hormone (MSH)	Peptide	Melanocytes in skin of some vertebrates	Promotes darkening of the skin
	Endorphins	Peptide	Pain pathways of PNS	Inhibit perception of pain
Posterior pituitary	Antidiuretic hormone (ADH)	Peptide	Kidneys	Raises blood volume and pressure by increasing water reabsorption in kidneys
	Oxytocin	Peptide	Uterus, mammary glands	Promotes uterine contractions; stimulates milk ejection from breasts
Thyroid gland	Calcitonin	Peptide	Bone	Lowers calcium concentration in blood
	Thyroxine and triiodothyronine	Amine	Most cells	Increase metabolic rate; essential for normal body growth
Parathyroid glands	Parathyroid hormone (PTH)	Peptide	Bone, kidneys, intestine	Raises calcium concentration in blood; stimulates vitamin D activation
Adrenal medulla	Epinephrine and norepinephrine	Amine	Sympathetic receptor sites throughout body	Reinforce sympathetic nervous system; contribute to responses to stress
Adrenal cortex	Aldosterone (mineralocorticoid)	Steroid	Kidney tubules	Helps control body's salt–water balance by increasing Na^+ reabsorption and K^+ excretion in kidneys
	Cortisol (glucocorticoid)	Steroid	Most body cells, particularly muscle, liver, and adipose cells	Increases blood glucose by promoting breakdown of proteins and fats
Testes	Androgens, such as testosterone*	Steroid	Various tissues	Control male reproductive system development and maintenance; most androgens are made by the testes
	Oxytocin	Peptide	Uterus	Promotes uterine contractions when seminal fluid is ejaculated into vagina during sexual intercourse
Ovaries	Estrogens, such as estradiol**	Steroid	Breast, uterus, other tissues	Stimulate maturation of sex organs at puberty and development of secondary sexual characteristics
	Progestins, such as progesterone**	Steroid	Uterus	Prepare and maintain uterus for implantation of fertilized egg and the growth and development of embryo

*Small amounts secreted by ovaries and adrenal cortex.
**Small amounts secreted by testes.

Table 35.1	The Major Human Endocrine Glands and Hormones (Continued)			
Secretory Tissue or Gland	**Hormones**	**Molecular Class**	**Target Tissue**	**Principal Actions**
Pancreas (islets of Langerhans)	Glucagon (alpha cells)	Peptide	Liver cells	Raises glucose concentration in blood; promotes release of glucose from glycogen stores and production from noncarbohydrates
	Insulin (beta cells)	Peptide	Most cells	Lowers glucose concentration in blood; promotes storage of glucose, fatty acids, and amino acids
Pineal gland	Melatonin	Amine	Brain, anterior pituitary, reproductive organs, immune system, possibly others	Helps synchronize body's biological clock with day length; may inhibit gonadotropins and initiation of puberty
Many cell types	Growth factors	Peptide	Most cells	Regulate cell division and differentiation
	Prostaglandins	Fatty acid	Various tissues	Have many diverse roles

35.3 The Hypothalamus and Pituitary

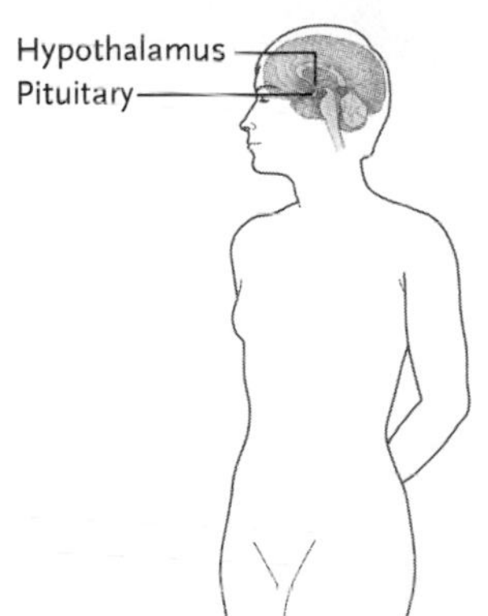

Hormones of vertebrates work in coordination with the nervous system. The action of several hormones is closely coordinated by the hypothalamus–pituitary complex.

The hypothalamus is a region of the brain located in the floor of the cerebrum (see Chapter 33). The **pituitary gland**, consisting mostly of two fused lobes, is suspended just below it by a slender stalk of tissue that contains both neurons and blood vessels **(Figure 35.6, p. 860)**. The **posterior pituitary** contains axons and endings of neurosecretory neurons that originate in the hypothalamus. The **anterior pituitary** contains non-neuronal endocrine cells that form a distinct gland. The two lobes are separate in structure and embryonic origins.

35.3a Under Regulatory Control by the Hypothalamus, the Anterior Pituitary Secretes Eight Hormones

The secretions of the anterior pituitary are under the control of peptide neurohormones called **releasing hormones (RHs)** and **inhibiting hormones (IHs)**, produced by the hypothalamus. These neurohormones are carried in the blood to the anterior pituitary in a *portal vein*, a special vein that connects the capillaries of the two glands. The portal vein provides a critical link between the brain and the endocrine system, ensuring that most of the blood reaching the anterior pituitary first passes through the hypothalamus.

RHs and IHs are **tropic hormones** (*tropic* means "stimulating," not to be confused with *trophic*, which means "nourishing") that regulate hormone secretion by another endocrine gland, in this case, the anterior pituitary. The hormones of the anterior pituitary, in turn, control many other endocrine glands of the body and some body processes directly.

Secretion of hypothalamic RHs is controlled by neurons containing receptors that monitor the blood to detect changes in body chemistry and temperature. For example, when body temperature drops, TRH is secreted. Input to the hypothalamus also comes through numerous connections from control centres elsewhere in the brain, including the brain stem and the limbic system. Negative feedback pathways regulate secretion of the releasing hormones, such as the pathway regulating TRH secretion.

Under the control of the hypothalamus, the anterior pituitary secretes six major hormones into the bloodstream (see Figure 35.6): prolactin, growth hormone, thyroid-stimulating hormone, adrenocorticotropic hormone, follicle-stimulating hormone, and luteinizing hormone. **Prolactin (PRL)**, a *nontropic hormone* (a hormone that does not regulate hormone secretion by another endocrine gland), influences reproductive activities and parental care in vertebrates. In mammals, PRL stimulates development of the secretory cells of mammary glands during late pregnancy and milk synthesis after birth. Stimulation of the mammary glands and the nipples, as occurs during suckling, leads to PRL release. PRL occurs in nonmammalian vertebrates, where it has a variety of functions. In fish, for example, it is among the hormones controlling water balance. In all vertebrates, it has a role in promoting both maternal and paternal behaviour.

Growth hormone (GH) stimulates cell division, protein synthesis, and bone growth in children and adolescents, thereby causing body growth. GH also stimulates protein synthesis and cell division in adults. For these actions, GH acts as a tropic hormone by binding to target tissues, mostly liver cells, causing

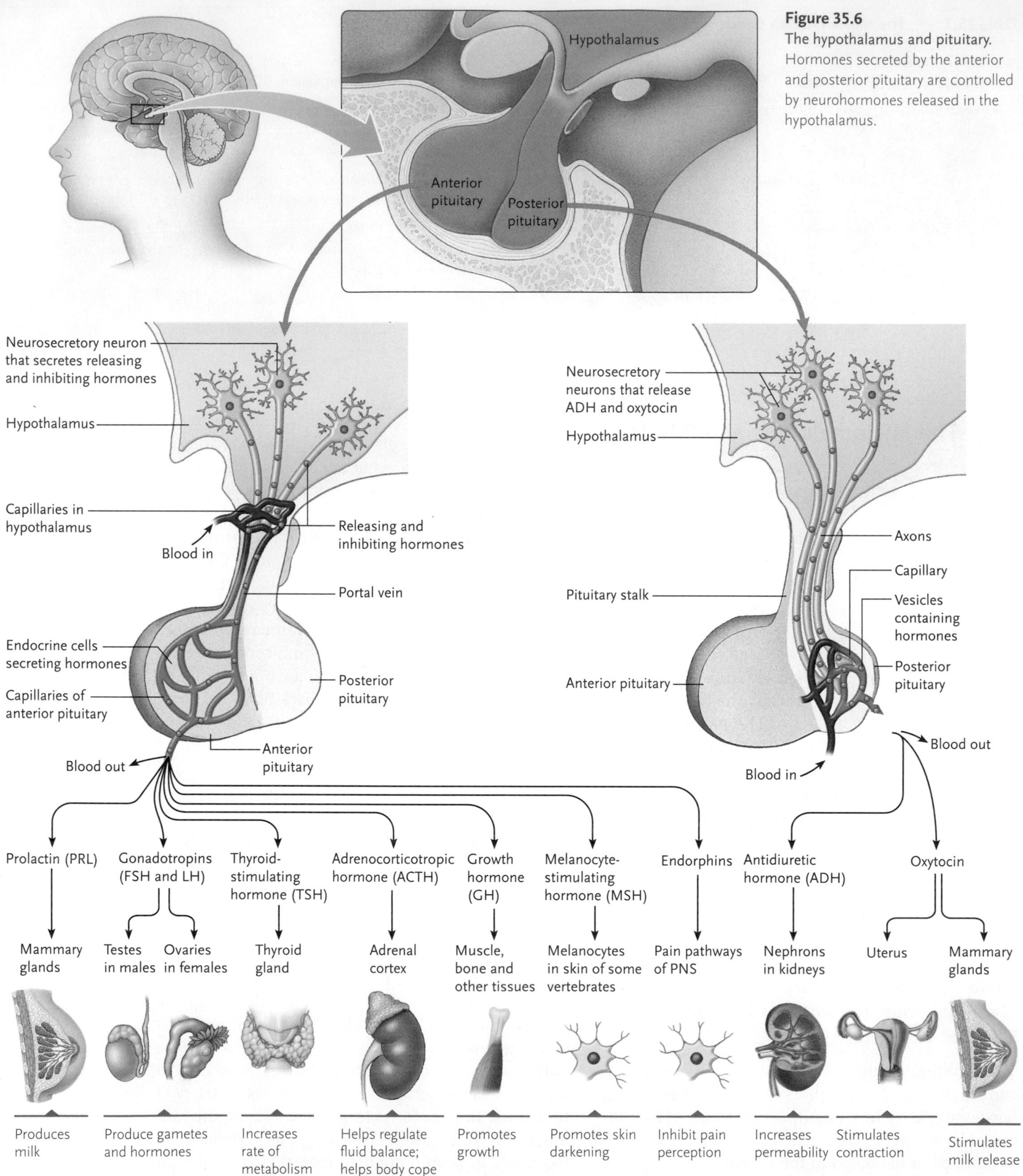

Figure 35.6
The hypothalamus and pituitary. Hormones secreted by the anterior and posterior pituitary are controlled by neurohormones released in the hypothalamus.

them to release **insulinlike growth factor (IGF)**, a peptide that directly stimulates growth processes. GH also acts as a nontropic hormone to control a number of major metabolic processes in mammals of all ages, including the conversion of glycogen to glucose and fats to fatty acids as a means of regulating their levels in the blood. GH also stimulates body cells to take up fatty acids and amino acids and limits the rate at

Figure 35.7
The results of overproduction and underproduction of growth hormone by the anterior pituitary. The man on the left is of normal height. The man in the centre is a pituitary giant, whose pituitary produced excess GH during childhood and adolescence. The man on the right is a pituitary dwarf, whose pituitary produced too little GH.

which muscle cells take up glucose. These actions help maintain the availability of glucose and fatty acids to tissues and organs between feedings; this is particularly important for the brain. In humans, deficiencies in GH secretion during childhood produce *pituitary dwarfs*, who remain small in stature **(Figure 35.7)**. Overproduction of GH during childhood or adolescence, often due to a tumour of the anterior pituitary, produces *pituitary giants*, who may grow to above two metres in height.

Many of the other hormones secreted by the anterior pituitary are tropic hormones that control endocrine glands elsewhere in the body. **Thyroid-stimulating hormone (TSH)** stimulates the thyroid gland to grow in size and secrete thyroid hormones. **Adrenocorticotropic hormone (ACTH)** triggers hormone secretion by cells in the adrenal cortex. **Follicle-stimulating hormone (FSH)** affects egg development in females and sperm production in males. It also has a tropic effect by stimulating the secretion of sex hormones in female mammals. **Luteinizing hormone (LH)** regulates part of the menstrual cycle in human females and the secretion of sex hormones in males. FSH and LH are grouped together as **gonadotropins** because they regulate the activity of the gonads (ovaries and testes). The roles of the gonadotropins and sex hormones in the reproductive cycle are described in Chapter 38.

Melanocyte-stimulating hormone (MSH) and **endorphins** are nontropic hormones secreted by the anterior pituitary. MSH is named because of its effect in some vertebrates on melanocytes, skin cells that contain the black pigment melanin. An increase in secretion of MSH produces a marked darkening of the skin of fishes, amphibians, and reptiles. The darkening is produced by a dispersal of melanin in melanocytes so that it covers a greater area. In humans, an increase in MSH secretion also causes skin darkening, although the effect is by no means as obvious as in the other vertebrates mentioned. MSH secretion increases in pregnant women. Combined with the effects of increased estrogens, MSH results in increased skin pigmentation. The effects are reversed after the birth of the child.

Endorphins, nontropic peptide hormones produced by the hypothalamus and pituitary, are also released by the intermediate lobe of the pituitary. In the peripheral nervous system (PNS), endorphins act as neurotransmitters in pathways that control pain, thereby inhibiting the perception of pain. Hence, endorphins are often called "natural painkillers."

35.3b The Posterior Pituitary Secretes Two Hormones into the Body Circulation

The neurosecretory neurons in the posterior pituitary secrete two nontropic peptide hormones, antidiuretic hormone and oxytocin, directly into the body circulation (see Figure 35.6).

Antidiuretic hormone (**ADH**, also known as vasopressin) stimulates kidney cells to absorb more water from urine, thereby increasing the volume of the blood. The hormone is released when sensory receptor cells of the hypothalamus detect an increase in the blood's Na^+ concentration during periods of dehydration or after a salty meal. Ethyl alcohol and caffeine inhibit ADH secretion, explaining in part why alcoholic drinks and coffee increase the volume of urine excreted. Nicotine and emotional stress, in contrast, stimulate ADH secretion and water retention. After severe stress is relieved, the return to normal ADH secretion often makes a trip to the bathroom among our most pressing needs. The hypothalamus also releases a flood of ADH when an injury results in heavy blood loss or some other event triggers a severe drop in blood pressure. ADH helps maintain blood pressure by reducing water loss and by causing small blood vessels in some tissues to constrict.

Hormones with structure and action similar to those of ADH are also secreted in fishes, amphibians, reptiles, and birds. In amphibians, these ADH-like hormones increase the amount of water entering the body through the skin and from the urinary bladder.

Oxytocin stimulates the ejection of milk from the mammary glands of a nursing mother. Stimulation of the nipples in suckling sends neuronal signals to the hypothalamus and leads to the release of oxytocin from the posterior pituitary. The released oxytocin stimulates more oxytocin secretion by a positive feedback mechanism. Oxytocin causes the smooth muscle cells surrounding the mammary glands to contract, forcibly expelling the milk through the nipples. The entire cycle, from the onset of suckling to milk ejection, takes less than a minute in mammals. Oxytocin also plays a key role in childbirth (see Chapter 38).

In males, oxytocin is secreted into the seminal fluid by the testes. When the seminal fluid is ejaculated into the vagina during sexual intercourse, the hormone stimulates contractions of the uterus that aid movement of sperm through the female reproductive tract.

Study Break

1. Distinguish between tropic and nontropic hormones.
2. Distinguish between the anterior and the posterior pituitary. How is the release of hormones from each of these controlled?
3. Name and state the function of the eight hormones released by the anterior pituitary.

35.4 Other Major Endocrine Glands of Vertebrates

In addition to the hypothalamus and pituitary, the body has seven major endocrine glands or tissues, many of them regulated by the hypothalamus–pituitary connection. Included are the thyroid gland, parathyroid glands, adrenal medulla, adrenal cortex, gonads, pancreas, and pineal gland (shown in Figure 35.5 and summarized in Table 35.1).

35.4a The Thyroid Hormones Stimulate Metabolism, Development, and Maturation

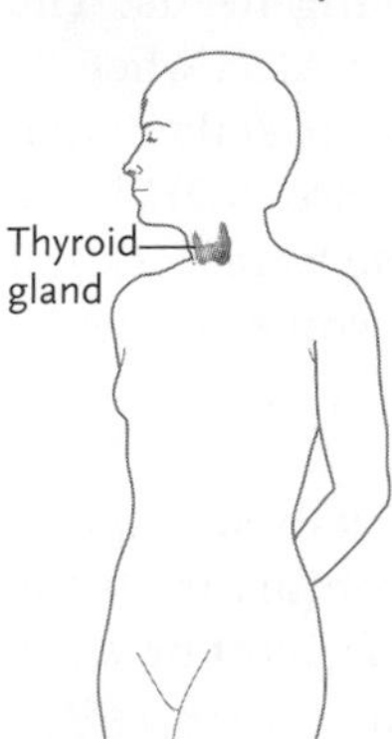

The **thyroid gland** is located in the front of the throat in humans and is shaped like a bowtie. It secretes the same hormones in all vertebrates. The thyroid hormones have an extraordinarily wide range of effects. The primary thyroid hormone, **thyroxine,** is known as T_4 because it contains four iodine atoms. The thyroid also secretes smaller amounts of a closely related hormone, **triiodothyronine** or T_3, which contains three iodine atoms. A supply of iodine in the diet is necessary for production of these hormones. Normally, their concentrations are kept at finely balanced levels in the blood by negative feedback loops such as the loop described in Figure 35.2. Most of the circulating hormone is bound to a transport protein, thyroglobulin, and only the free hormone is available to enter cells.

Thyroid hormones act both in the nucleus and via membrane receptors. Both T_4 and T_3 enter cells, probably via specific uptake receptors. Once inside, the T_4 is deiodinated, forming T_3 and in some cases T_2 (contains two iodine atoms). T_3 is the form that combines with nuclear receptors. Binding of T_3 to receptors alters gene expression, which brings about many of the hormone's effects. In addition, T_2 can act directly on mitochondria. T_3 also acts on receptors on the cell membrane of some cells. It can increase the Ca^{2+}ATPase activity of red blood cells.

Thyroid hormones are vital to growth, development, maturation, and metabolism in all vertebrates. They interact with GH for their effects on growth and development. Thyroid hormones also increase the sensitivity of many body cells to the effects of epinephrine and norepinephrine, hormones released by the adrenal medulla as part of the "fight-or-flight response" (discussed further below).

In amphibians, rising concentrations of thyroid hormones trigger **metamorphosis,** or a change in body form from tadpole to adult **(Figure 35.8).** Teleost fish

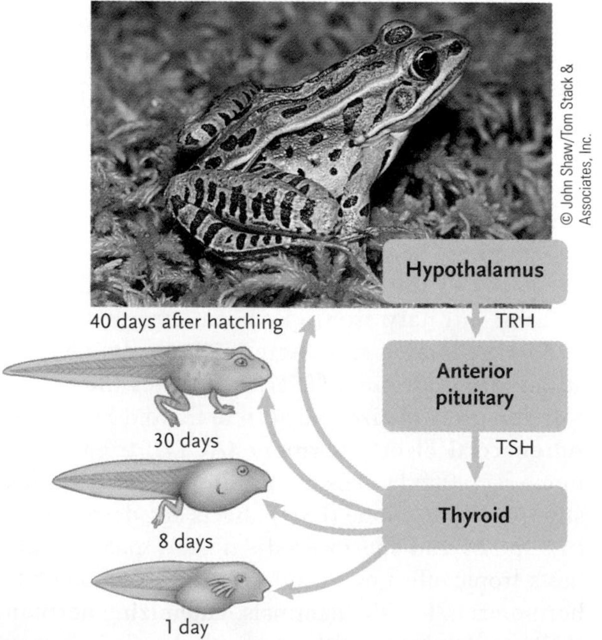

Figure 35.8
Metamorphosis of a tadpole into an adult frog, under the control of thyroid hormones. As part of the metamorphosis, changes in the gene activity lead to a change from an aquatic to a terrestrial habitat. TRH – thyroid-releasing hormone; TSH – thyroid-stimulating hormone.

undergo a form of metamorphosis during their early development, and the transformation from a hatchling "larval" form to a juvenile form is also triggered by rising T_4 concentrations. Curiously, however, the opposite is true in the agnathan lamprey. Their metamorphosis is triggered by decreasing concentrations of T_4. Thyroid hormones also contribute to seasonal moulting, leading to changes in the plumage of birds and coat colour in mammals.

The thyroid also has specialized cells that secrete **calcitonin**, a peptide originally discovered in fish by Harold Copp working at the University of British Columbia. The hormone lowers the level of Ca^{2+} in the blood by inhibiting the ongoing dissolution of calcium from bone. Calcitonin secretion is stimulated when Ca^{2+} levels in blood rise above the normal range and inhibited when Ca^{2+} levels fall below the normal range. Although the specialized cells of the thyroid are the principal source, calcitonin is also synthesized in the lung and intestine. In nonmammalian vertebrates, a separate gland, the ultimobrachial gland, produces calcitonin.

35.4b The Parathyroid Glands Regulate Ca^{2+} Level in the Blood

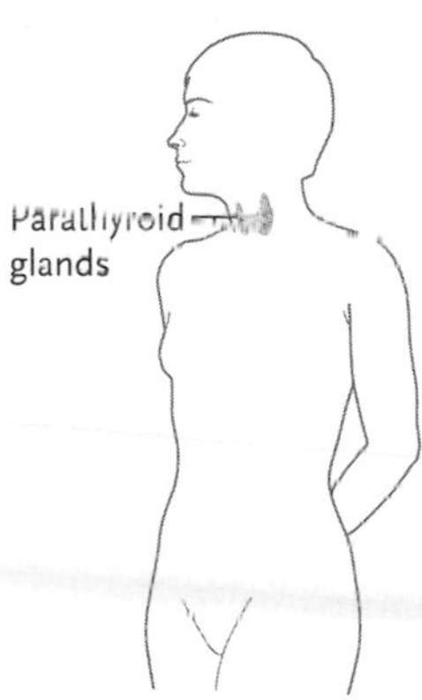

The **parathyroid glands** occur only in tetrapod vertebrates (amphibians, reptiles, birds, and mammals). Each is a spherical structure about the size of a pea. Mammals have four parathyroids located on the posterior surface of the thyroid gland, two on each side. The single hormone they produce, a nontropic hormone called **parathyroid hormone (PTH)**, is secreted in response to a fall in blood Ca^{2+} levels. PTH stimulates bone cells to dissolve the mineral matter of bone tissues, releasing both calcium and phosphate ions into the blood. The released Ca^{2+} is available for enzyme activation, conduction of nerve signals across synapses, muscle contraction, blood clotting, and other uses. How blood Ca^{2+} levels control PTH and calcitonin secretion is shown in **Figure 35.9.**

Stimulus: rising blood Ca^{2+} level
Thyroid gland
Calcitonin
Reduces Ca^{2+} uptake in kidneys
Stimulates Ca^{2+} deposition in bones
Blood Ca^{2+} declines to set point
Homeostasis
Blood Ca^{2+} rises to set point
Increases Ca^{2+} uptake in intestines
Stimulates Ca^{2+} release from bone
Stimulates Ca^{2+} uptake in kidneys
PTH
Parathyroid glands
Stimulus: falling blood Ca^{2+} level

Figure 35.9
Negative feedback control of PTH and calcitonin secretion by blood Ca^{2+} levels.

PTH also stimulates enzymes in the kidneys that convert **vitamin D**, a steroidlike molecule, into its fully active form in the body. The activated vitamin D increases the absorption of Ca^{2+} and phosphates from ingested food by promoting the synthesis of a calcium-binding protein in the intestine. It also increases the release of Ca^{2+} from bone in response to PTH.

PTH underproduction causes Ca^{2+} concentration to fall steadily in the blood, disturbing nerve and muscle function—the muscles twitch and contract uncontrollably, and convulsions and cramps occur. Without treatment, the condition is usually fatal because the severe muscular contractions interfere with breathing. Overproduction of PTH results in the loss of so much calcium from the bones that they become thin and fragile. At the same time, the elevated Ca^{2+} concentration in the blood causes calcium deposits to form in soft tissues, especially in the lungs, arteries, and kidneys (where the deposits form kidney stones).

Although fish do not have a parathyroid gland, they produce PTH, and PTH receptors are known to be present in fish, but the origin of the hormone and its precise function remain uncertain.

35.4c The Adrenal Medulla Releases Two "Fight-or-Flight" Hormones

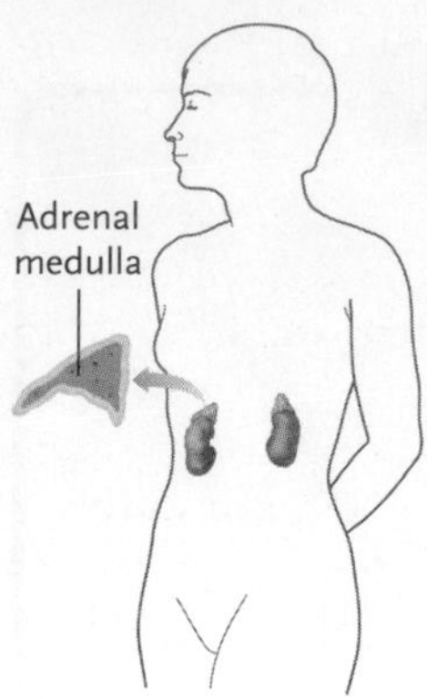

The adrenal glands (*ad* = next to; *renes* = kidneys) of mammals have two distinct regions. The central region, the **adrenal medulla**, contains highly modified neurosecretory neurons that have lost their axons and dendrites. The tissue surrounding it, the **adrenal cortex**, contains non-neural endocrine cells. The two regions secrete hormones with entirely different functions. Nonmammalian vertebrates have glands equivalent to the adrenal medulla and adrenal cortex of mammals, but the two parts are separate entities. Most of the hormones produced by these glands have essentially the same functions in all vertebrates. The only major exception is aldosterone, which is secreted by the adrenal cortex or its equivalent only in tetrapod vertebrates.

In most species, the adrenal medulla secretes two nontropic amine hormones, **epinephrine** and **norepinephrine**, which are **catecholamines**, chemicals derived from tyrosine that can act as hormones or neurotransmitters. They bind to receptors in the plasma membranes of their target cells. Norepinephrine is also released as a neurotransmitter by neurons of the sympathetic nervous system.

Epinephrine and norepinephrine reinforce the action of the sympathetic nervous system and are secreted when the body encounters stresses such as emotional excitement, danger (fight-or-flight situations), anger, fear, infections, injury, and even midterm and final exams. Epinephrine in particular prepares the body for handling stress or physical activity. The heart rate increases. Glycogen and fats break down, releasing glucose and fatty acids into the blood as fuel molecules. In the heart, skeletal muscles, and lungs, the blood vessels dilate to increase blood flow. Elsewhere in the body, the blood vessels constrict, raising blood pressure, reducing blood flow to the intestine and kidneys, and inhibiting smooth muscle contractions, which reduces water loss and slows down the digestive system. Airways in the lungs also dilate, helping to increase the flow of air.

The effects of norepinephrine on heart rate, blood pressure, and blood flow to the heart muscle are similar to those of epinephrine. However, in contrast to epinephrine, norepinephrine causes blood vessels in skeletal muscles to constrict. This contrary effect is largely cancelled out because epinephrine is secreted in much greater quantities.

35.4d The Adrenal Cortex Secretes Two Groups of Steroid Hormones

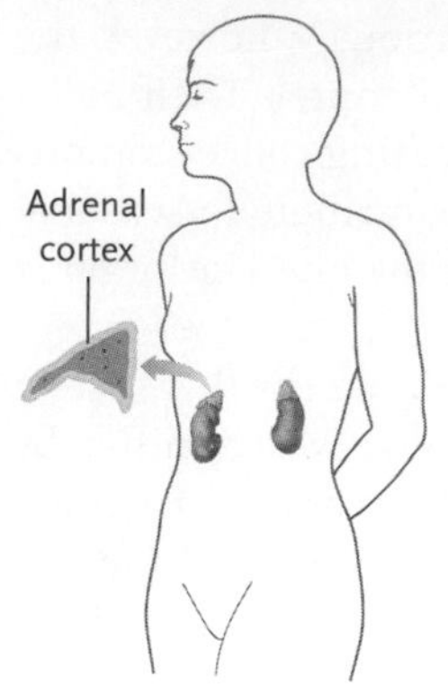

The adrenal cortex of mammals secretes two major classes of steroid hormones: **glucocorticoids** help maintain the blood concentration of glucose and other fuel molecules, and **mineralocorticoids** regulate the levels of Na^+ and K^+ ions in the blood and extracellular fluid.

The Glucocorticoids. The glucocorticoids help maintain glucose levels in the blood by three major mechanisms: (1) stimulating the synthesis of glucose from noncarbohydrate sources such as fats and proteins, (2) reducing glucose uptake by body cells except those in the CNS, and (3) promoting the breakdown of fats and proteins, which releases fatty acids and amino acids into the blood as alternative fuels when glucose supplies are low. The favouring of glucose uptake in the CNS keeps the brain well supplied with glucose between meals and during periods of extended fasting. **Cortisol** is the major glucocorticoid secreted by the adrenal cortex.

Secretion of glucocorticoids is ultimately under control of the hypothalamus **(Figure 35.10)**. Low glucose concentrations in the blood, or elevated levels of epinephrine secreted by the adrenal medulla in response to stress, are detected in the hypothalamus, leading to secretion of the tropic hormone ACTH by the anterior pituitary. ACTH promotes the secretion of glucocorticoids by the adrenal cortex.

Glucocorticoids also have anti-inflammatory properties; consequently, they are used to treat conditions such as arthritis or dermatitis. They also suppress the immune system and are used in the treatment of autoimmune diseases such as rheumatoid arthritis.

The Mineralocorticoids. In tetrapods, the mineralocorticoids, primarily **aldosterone**, increase the amount of Na^+ reabsorbed from the urine in the kidneys and absorbed from foods in the intestine. They also reduce the amount of Na^+ secreted by salivary and sweat glands and increase the rate of K^+ excretion by the kidneys. The net effect is to keep Na^+ and K^+ balanced at the levels required for normal cellular functions, including those of the nervous system. Relatedly, secretion of aldosterone is tightly linked to blood volume and indirectly to blood pressure. The adrenal cortex also secretes small amounts of androgens, steroid sex hormones responsible for maintenance of male characteristics, which are synthesized primarily by the gonads.

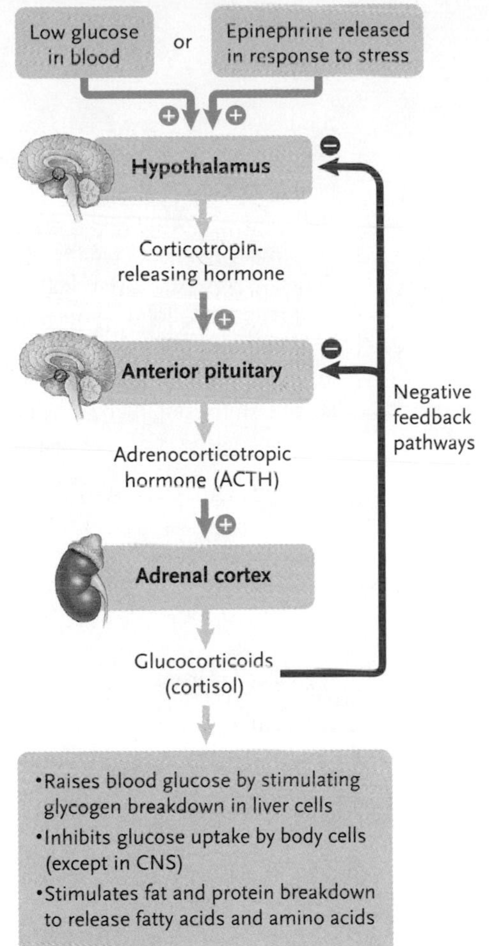

Figure 35.10
Pathways linking secretion of glucocorticoids to low blood sugar and epinephrine secretion in response to stress.

35.4e The Gonadal Sex Hormones Regulate the Development of Reproductive Systems, Sexual Characteristics, and Mating Behaviour

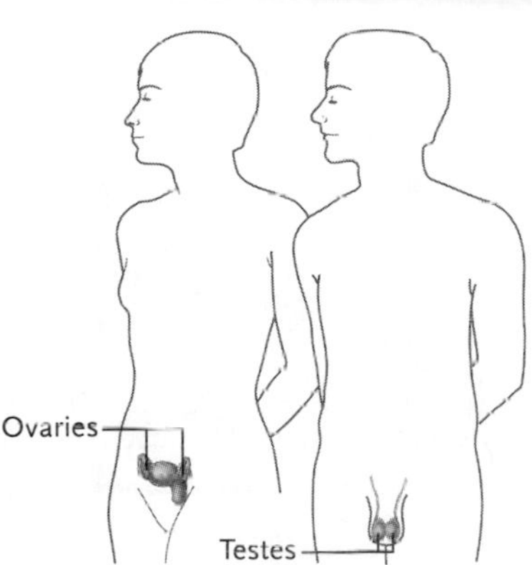

The **gonads**, the testes and ovaries, are the primary source of sex hormones in vertebrates. The steroid hormones they produce, the **androgens**, **estrogens**, and **progestins**, have similar functions in regulating the development of male and female reproductive systems, sexual characteristics, and mating behaviour. Both males and females produce all three types of hormones, but in different proportions. Androgen production is predominant in males, whereas estrogen and progestin production is predominant in females. An outline of the actions of these hormones is presented here, and a more complete picture is given in Chapter 38.

The **testes** (singular, testis) of male vertebrates secrete androgens, steroid hormones that stimulate and control the development and maintenance of male reproductive systems. The principal androgen is testosterone, the male sex hormone. In young adult males, a jump in **testosterone** levels stimulates puberty and the development of secondary sexual characteristics, including the growth of facial and body hair, muscle development, changes in vocal cord morphology, and development of normal sex drive. The synthesis and secretion of testosterone by cells in the testes are controlled by the release of LH from the anterior pituitary, which, in turn, is controlled by **gonadotropin-releasing hormone (GnRH)**, a tropic hormone secreted by the hypothalamus.

Androgens are natural types of **anabolic steroids**, hormones that stimulate muscle development. Natural and synthetic anabolic steroids have been in the news over the years because of their use by body builders and other athletes from sports in which muscular strength is important.

The **ovaries** (singular, ovary) of females produce estrogens, steroid hormones that stimulate and control the development and maintenance of female reproductive systems. The principal estrogen is **estradiol**, which stimulates maturation of sex organs at puberty and the development of secondary sexual characteristics. Ovaries also produce progestins, principally **progesterone**, the steroid hormone that prepares and maintains the uterus for implantation of a fertilized egg and the subsequent growth and development of an embryo. The synthesis and secretion of progesterone by cells in the ovaries are controlled by the release of FSH from the anterior pituitary, which, in turn, is controlled by the same GnRH as in males.

35.4f The Pancreatic Islets of Langerhans Hormones Regulate Glucose Metabolism

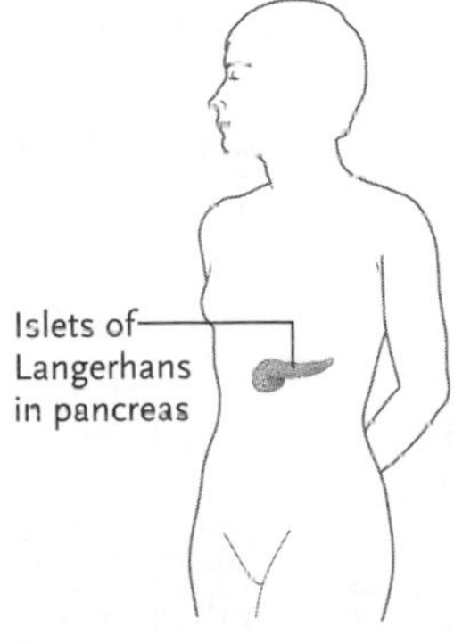

Most of the **pancreas**, a relatively large gland located just behind the stomach, forms an exocrine gland that secretes digestive enzymes into the small intestine (see Chapter 41). About 2% of the cells in the pancreas are endocrine cells that form the **islets of Langerhans.** Found in all vertebrates, the islets secrete the peptide hormones insulin and glucagon into the bloodstream.

Molecule Behind Biology

Insulin: More Than Diabetes

Insulin was discovered in 1922 by J.R. Banting and his colleagues, McLeod, Best, and Collip, working at the University of Toronto. Banting and McLeod were awarded the Nobel Prize in 1923. (They were disturbed that their colleagues had not been recognized and shared the prize with them.) In 1955, Frederick Sanger of Cambridge University worked out insulin's complete amino acid sequence (the first protein to be fully sequenced) and was awarded a Nobel Prize in 1958 for this work.

Insulin is a very large peptide of 51 amino acids. Molecular studies show that the insulin gene is present in all vertebrates but is absent from invertebrates. Insulin is a member of a family of genes. Two other members of that family encode two structurally related peptides, IGF I and II. Although they are similar in structure to insulin, they have different but structurally related receptors, and their cellular action is different. They act as growth factors, regulating cell and tissue growth. IGFs are widely distributed in animals, protists, bacteria, and fungi. In molluscs, insects, and nematodes, these insulinlike peptides (ILPs) are neurohormones, expressed in neurosecretory cells in the brain. Surgical removal of these cells and their reimplantation demonstrate that they control growth, like the IGFs in vertebrates. The impact of these studies on the origin and evolution of the insulin gene is not yet clear.

Insulin and glucagon regulate the metabolism of fuel substances in the body. **Insulin** (see *Molecule Behind Biology*) is secreted by *beta cells* in the islets. It acts mainly on nonworking skeletal muscles, liver cells, and adipose tissue (fat). Brain cells do not require insulin for glucose uptake. Insulin lowers blood glucose, fatty acid, and amino acid levels and promotes their storage. The actions of insulin include stimulation of glucose transport into cells, glycogen synthesis from glucose, uptake of fatty acids by adipose tissue cells, fat synthesis from fatty acids, and protein synthesis from amino acids. Insulin inhibits glycogen degradation to glucose, fat degradation to fatty acids, and protein degradation to amino acids.

Glucagon, secreted by *alpha cells* in the islets, has effects opposite to those of insulin: it stimulates glycogen, fat, and protein degradation. Glucagon also uses amino acids and other noncarbohydrates as the input for glucose synthesis; this aspect of glucagon function operates during fasting. Negative feedback mechanisms keyed to the concentration of glucose in the blood control secretion of both insulin and glucagon to maintain glucose homeostasis **(Figure 35.11)**.

Diabetes mellitus, a disease that afflicts more than 2 million people in Canada, results from problems with insulin production or action. The three classic diabetes symptoms are frequent urination, increased thirst (and consequently increased fluid intake), and increased appetite. Frequent urination occurs because the ability of body cells to take up glucose is impaired in diabetics, leading to abnormally high glucose concentration in the blood. Excretion of the excess glucose in the urine requires water to carry it, which causes increased fluid loss and frequent trips to the bathroom. The need to replace the excreted water causes increased thirst. Increased appetite comes about because cells have low glucose levels as a result of the insulin defect; therefore, proteins and

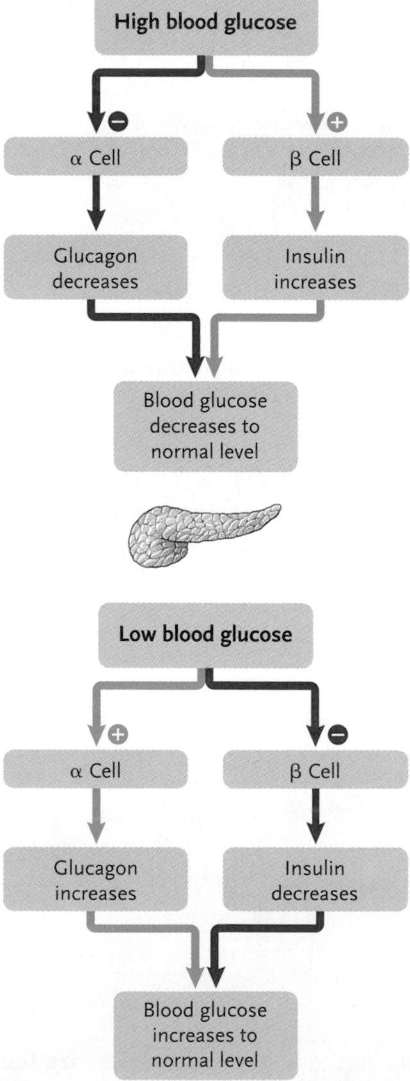

Figure 35.11
The action of insulin and glucagon in maintaining the concentration of blood glucose at an optimal level.

People Behind Biology

William Rowan: Photobiology Pioneer

In the 1920s, it was generally accepted that birds migrated south from Canada in response to falling temperatures. William Rowan of the University of Alberta had a different view. Recognizing that temperature is an unreliable indicator of seasons, he hypothesized that day length was important. In addition, he recognized that migration was simply part of the annual breeding cycle: birds migrating south were known to have inactive reproductive organs, which became active when they returned in the spring. Rowan conducted two very simple but crucial experiments. In the first, he exposed juncos (*Junco hyemalis*) to artificially lengthened daily light in the autumn; their gonads became active. In the second, he used 500 crows. These were caged in the autumn, and half were exposed to increasing day length, and the others to natural day length. He dyed their tails yellow and released them, alerting surrounding homesteaders to be on the lookout for crows with yellow tails. Those exposed to increased day length headed north, whereas those experiencing normal day length headed south. The association of day length with migration and gonadal development implicated the endocrine system, and these deceptively simple experiments set in motion the entire field of photobiology. Rowan is recognized as among the most influential biologists in the field.

fats are broken down as energy sources. Food intake is necessary to offset the negative energy balance, or weight loss will occur. Two of these classic symptoms gave the disease its name: diabetes is derived from a Greek word meaning "siphon," referring to the frequent urination, and mellitus, a Latin word meaning "sweetened with honey," refers to the sweet taste of a diabetic's urine. (Before modern blood or urine tests were developed, physicians tasted a patient's urine to detect the disease.)

35.4g The Pineal Gland Regulates Some Biological Rhythms

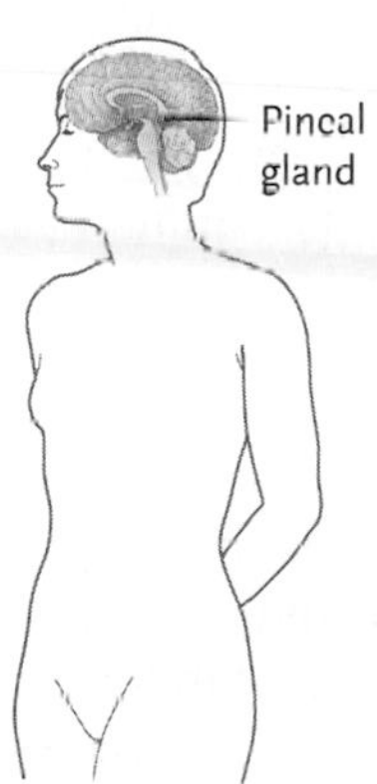

The **pineal gland** is found at different locations in the brains of vertebrates. In mammals, it is near the centre of the brain, whereas in birds and reptiles, it is on the surface of the brain just under the skull and is directly sensitive to light. The pineal gland regulates some biological rhythms.

The earliest vertebrates had a third, light-sensitive eye at the top of the head, and *Sphenodon* and some lizards have an eyelike structure in this location. In most vertebrates, the third eye became modified into a pineal gland, which in many groups retains some degree of photosensitivity. In mammals, it is too deeply buried in the brain to be affected directly by light; nonetheless, specialized photoreceptors in the eyes make connections to the pineal gland.

The pineal gland secretes the amine hormone **melatonin,** derived from tryptophan, which helps maintain daily biorhythms. Secretion of melatonin is regulated by an inhibitory pathway. Light hitting the eyes generates signals that inhibit melatonin secretion; consequently, the hormone is secreted most actively during periods of darkness. Melatonin targets a part of the hypothalamus called the *suprachiasmatic nucleus,* which is the primary structure coordinating body activity to a daily cycle. The nightly release of melatonin may help synchronize the biological clock with daily cycles of light and darkness. The physical and mental discomfort associated with jet lag may reflect the time required for melatonin secretion to reset a traveller's daily biological clock to match the period of daylight in a new time zone.

Melatonin occurs throughout the animal kingdom, as well as in many plants and fungi. In invertebrates, it is known to be important in the control of diurnal (daily) rhythms.

Study Break

1. What are the hormones controlling Ca^{2+} levels in the blood of vertebrates?
2. Distinguish between the adrenal medulla and the adrenal cortex.
3. How are levels of glucose in the blood maintained?

35.5 Endocrine Systems in Invertebrates

Some invertebrates have fewer hormones, regulating a narrower range of body processes and responses, than vertebrates. However, in even the simplest animals, such as the cnidarian *Hydra,* hormones produced by neurosecretory neurons control the reproduction, growth, and development of some body features. In

Life on the Edge
Stress

The notion of "stress" may be familiar to all as a vague concept. It was originated by Hans Selye, working with rats at the University of Montreal, as the "General Adaptation Syndrome," in which what he called "nocuous agents" ranging from physical damage to psychological events led to the activation of the fight-or-flight response. This was characterized at the time as the activation of the hypothalamus–pituitary pathway leading to the release of a number of hormones, particularly those from the adrenal glands, which led to increased heart rate, blood pressure, cessation of growth, and, in severe cases, tissue damage and, ultimately, death.

Although we are accustomed to thinking of stress as a human or mammalian phenomenon, it has emerged as a response in a wide range of animals. Any unaccustomed sensory input (whether from external or internal events) leads to release of many hormones, and if the input continues, this can result in pathology or death. Stress, with the release of the corticosteroid hormones, is well studied in most vertebrates. Even in cockroaches, forced activity or forced inactivity will cause the release of many neurohormones, and the insect will die.

annelids, arthropods, and molluscs, endocrine cells and glands produce hormones that regulate development, reproduction, water balance, heart rate, sugar levels, and behaviour.

The known vertebrate hormones, particularly the peptides, also occur in a wide range of organisms. Thus, insulinlike hormones can be found in most invertebrates and receptors are known from insects and nematodes. The protist *Tetrahymena* binds and exhibits responses to insulin and T_4. Whereas some hormones, such as the peptide proctolin and the insect juvenile hormones, do not occur in vertebrates, many of the growing number of peptide hormones identified in invertebrates have structural homologues in the vertebrates, although their functions may be different. Some peptides controlling diuresis in insects are structural homologues of vertebrate corticotropin-releasing factor. Other diuretic peptides in insects are related to calcitonin. The larva of the tapeworm *Spirometra mansonoides* has developed the capacity to secrete vertebrate growth hormone so that its host rat grows larger.

The endocrinology of the more complex invertebrates, formerly thought to be relatively simple, is emerging as very complex: about 200 bioactive peptides have thus far been described in insects, which are probably more closely governed by hormones than any other animals. The development of the eggs and the egg-laying behaviour of insects are controlled by more than a dozen hormones.

35.5a Hormones Regulate Development in Insects

Among the best known invertebrate hormonal systems is the one governing growth and development in insects **(Figure 35.12)**. As insects grow, they undergo a series of moults during which a new cuticle is laid down beneath the old cuticle and the old cuticle is shed (see Chapter 26). The signal to the epidermal cells to begin the process is provided by a steroid hormone, ecdysone, from the prothoracic glands. The prothoracic glands are stimulated to secrete ecdysone by a tropic peptide, prothoracicotropic hormone (PTTH), produced in neuroendocrine cells in the brain and released from the corpus cardiacum. The corpus cardiacum secretes several other hormones and contains both the nerve endings of neurons in the brain and neuroendocrine cells that lack axons and dendrites.

The corpus allatum is an endocrine gland that secretes **juvenile hormone**, a fatty acid derivative (see Chapter 26, *Molecule Behind Biology*). Juvenile hormone controls metamorphosis: when it is present, the insect remains larval. In its absence, the next moult is metamorphic, producing a pupa and then an adult in those insects with a pupal stage or proceeding directly to the adult in those lacking a pupal stage. In the adult of most insects, the corpus allatum becomes active once more, secreting juvenile hormone and stimulating a number of reproductive processes, especially egg development. The secretion of juvenile hormone by the corpus allatum is controlled by both inhibitory and stimulatory tropic peptides from the brain.

The intricate process of shedding the old cuticle involves complex behaviours that are controlled by the interaction of up to five neurohormones, and the hardening of the new cuticle requires a sixth.

Hormones that control moulting have also been detected in crustaceans, including lobsters, crabs, and crayfish. During the period between moults, **moult-inhibiting hormone (MIH)**, a peptide neurohormone secreted by cells in the eyestalks (extensions of the

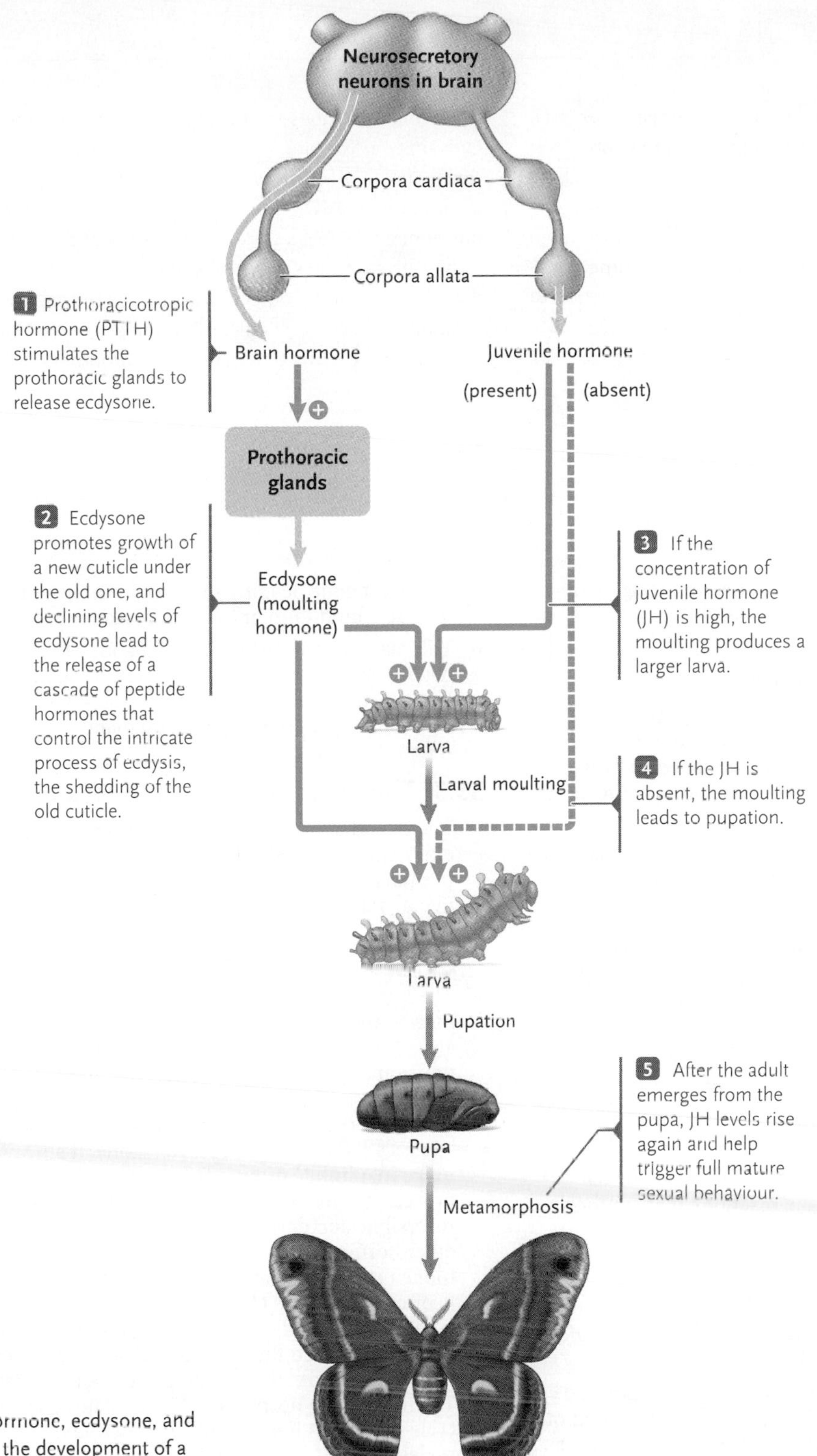

Neurosecretory neurons in brain
Corpora cardiaca
Corpora allata
1 Prothoracicotropic hormone (PTTH) stimulates the prothoracic glands to release ecdysone.
Brain hormone
Juvenile hormone
(present)
(absent)
Prothoracic glands
2 Ecdysone promotes growth of a new cuticle under the old one, and declining levels of ecdysone lead to the release of a cascade of peptide hormones that control the intricate process of ecdysis, the shedding of the old cuticle.
Ecdysone (moulting hormone)
3 If the concentration of juvenile hormone (JH) is high, the moulting produces a larger larva.
Larva
Larval moulting
4 If the JH is absent, the moulting leads to pupation.
Larva
Pupation
5 After the adult emerges from the pupa, JH levels rise again and help trigger full mature sexual behaviour.
Pupa
Metamorphosis
Adult

Figure 35.12
The roles of brain hormone, ecdysone, and juvenile hormone in the development of a silkworm moth.

brain leading to the eyes), inhibits ecdysone secretion. The first step in the moulting process is the inhibition of MIH secretion. Ecdysone secretion increases, and the processes leading to the replacement of the exoskeleton are initiated. As in insects, metamorphosis and reproduction are governed by a hormone different from but structurally related to JH.

Study Break

1. What are the known functions of insect juvenile hormone?
2. How are the pituitary and the corpus cardiacum similar? How do they differ?

Unanswered Questions

The realization that many of the hormones that govern function in vertebrates also occur in protostomes raises the question of the origin of these molecules and their evolution. Some researchers believe that the steroid and fatty acid hormones may have originated as signals in the environment and that animals have simply captured them as internal signals. The sensitivity of protists to some vertebrate hormones supports this view. But this raises the question of the origin and evolution of the receptors for these molecules. It is not immediately obvious, for example, that the sensitivity of protists to thyroid hormones is of evolutionary importance. Research at York University in Toronto suggests that the membrane receptors for thyroxine, present in both vertebrates and insects, may have originated as receptors for CO_2. The origin and evolution of the galaxy of peptide hormones remain a puzzle. Insulinlike peptide (ILP) receptors appear to be active on the surface of some protists. ILPs are present in protists, but their function is not yet clear: are they a means of communication between individuals? Does this suggest that hormones used preexisting receptors that detected environmental signals?

Review

Go to CENGAGENOW™ at http://hed.nelson.com/ to access quizzing, animations, exercises, articles, and personalized homework help.

35.1 Hormones and Their Secretion

- Hormones are molecules secreted by cells of the endocrine system that control the activities of cells elsewhere in the body. The cells that respond to a hormone are its target cells. This contrasts with the nervous system, which controls specific target cells in close proximity to its endings.
- The endocrine system includes four major types of cell signalling: classical endocrine signalling, in which endocrine glands secrete hormones; neuroendocrine signalling, in which neurosecretory neurons release neurohormones into the circulation; paracrine regulation, in which cells release local regulators that diffuse through the extracellular fluid to regulate nearby cells; and autocrine regulation, in which cells release local regulators that regulate the same cells that produced it.
- Most hormones and local regulators fall into one of four molecular classes: amines, peptides, steroids, and fatty acids.
- Neurosecretory neurons secrete hormones under direct control of the central nervous system.
- Many hormones are controlled by negative feedback mechanisms in which a hormone inhibits the reactions that synthesize or release it when its concentration rises in the body.

35.2 Mechanisms of Hormone Action

- Many hormones undergo modification after release that renders them more active
- Only cells that have receptors for the hormone can respond to the hormone. Cells may respond by stimulation or inhibition of a process. Because of amplification involved in receptor mechanisms, hormones are present in body fluids at low concentrations. The response to a hormone may differ among cells and tissues.
- Hormones may bind to receptor proteins in the plasma membrane. When a receptor binds a hormone, its cytoplasmic end is activated, triggering a series of cytoplasmic reactions that may include the activation of protein kinases.
- Hydrophobic hormones bind to receptors in the cytoplasm or nucleus, activating them so that they can bind to the control sequences of specific genes in the cell nucleus. Binding to the control sequence either stimulates or inhibits transcription of the target gene, leading to changes in protein synthesis. They may also bind to membrane receptors.
- The major endocrine cells and glands of vertebrates are the hypothalamus, pituitary gland, thyroid gland, parathyroid gland, adrenal medulla, adrenal cortex, testes, ovaries, islets of Langerhans of the pancreas, and pineal gland.

35.3 The Hypothalamus and Pituitary

- The hypothalamus and pituitary together regulate many other endocrine cells and glands in the body. The posterior pituitary contains the terminals of neurosecretory cells in the hypothalamus.
- The anterior pituitary contains endocrine cells derived from nonnervous tissue.
- The hypothalamus produces tropic hormones (releasing hormones and inhibiting hormones) that control the secretion of eight hormones by the anterior pituitary. Prolactin (PRL), a nontropic hormone, regulates mammary gland development and milk secretion in mammals. As a nontropic hormone, growth hormone (GH) stimulates body growth in children and adolescents, and as a tropic hormone, it stimulates liver cells to make insulinlike growth factor (IGF), which stimulates growth processes. Melanocyte-stimulating hormone (MSH) controls reversible skin darkening. Endorphins can reduce pain. The four other hormones are tropic hormones: thyroid-stimulating hormone (TSH) stimulates secretion by the thyroid gland; adrenocorticotropic hormone (ACTH) regulates hormone secretion by the adrenal cortex; follicle-stimulating hormone (FSH) controls egg development and the secretion of sex hormones by the ovaries in female mammals and the production of sperm cells in males; and luteinizing hormone (LH) regulates part of the menstrual cycle in human females and the secretion of sex hormones in males.
- Antidiuretic hormone (ADH) and oxytocin are secreted by the posterior pituitary. ADH regulates body water balance. In female mammals, oxytocin stimulates the contraction of smooth muscle in the uterus as part of childbirth and triggers milk release from the mammary glands during suckling of the young.
- The intermediate lobe of the pituitary produces the nontropic hormones MSH and endorphins. MSH secretion in some vertebrates produces a darkening of the skin. Endorphins are neurotransmitters that affect pain pathways in the peripheral nervous system, inhibiting the perception of pain.

35.4 Other Major Endocrine Glands of Vertebrates

- The thyroid gland secretes the thyroid hormones and, in mammals, calcitonin. In mammals, the thyroid hormones stimulate the oxidation of carbohydrates and lipids and coordinate with growth hormone to stimulate body growth and development. Calcitonin lowers the Ca^{2+} level in the blood by inhibiting the release of Ca^{2+} from bone. In many vertebrates, thyroid hormones control metamorphosis.
- The parathyroid gland secretes parathyroid hormone (PTH), which stimulates bone cells to release Ca^{2+} into the blood. PTH also stimulates the activation of vitamin D, which promotes Ca^{2+} absorption into the blood from the small intestine.
- The adrenal medulla secretes epinephrine and noreprinephrine, which reinforce the sympathetic nervous system in responding to stress. The adrenal cortex secretes glucocorticoids and mineralocorticoids. Glucocorticoids help maintain glucose at normal levels in the blood; mineralocorticoids regulate Na^+ balance and extracellular fluid volume. The adrenal cortex also secretes small amounts of androgens.
- The gonadal sex hormones, androgens, estrogen, and progestins, regulate the development of reproductive systems, sexual characteristics, and mating behaviour. Both sexes secrete all three, but males primarily produce androgens (secreted by the testes), and females primarily produce estrogens and progestins (secreted by the ovaries).
- The islets of Langerhans of the pancreas secrete insulin and glucagon. Insulin lowers the concentration of glucose in the blood by stimulating glucose uptake by cells, glycogen synthesis from glucose, uptake of fatty acids by adipose tissue cells, fat synthesis from fatty acids, and protein synthesis from amino acids; it inhibits the conversion of noncarbohydrate molecules into glucose. Glucagon raises blood glucose by stimulating glycogen, fat, and protein degradation. The balance of insulin and glucagon regulates the concentration of fuel substances in the blood.
- The pineal gland secretes melatonin, which interacts with the hypothalamus to set the body's daily rhythms.

35.5 Endocrine Systems in Invertebrates

- Even the simplest protostomes use hormones to coordinate growth and reproduction.
- Many of the hormones that occur in vertebrates also occur in invertebrates, although their function may be different.
- Three major hormones, prothoracicotropic hormone (PTTH) from the brain, ecdysone from prothoracic glands, and juvenile hormone (JH) from the corpus allatum, control moulting and metamorphosis in insects. PTTH is a tropic hormone that stimulates the secretion of ecdysone, which initiates and maintains the secretion of the new cuticle. If JH is present, metamorphosis is suppressed, and in its absence, metamorphosis proceeds. The activity of the corpus allatum is governed by stimulatory and inhibitory tropic hormones from the brain. The shedding of the old cuticle and the hardening of the new cuticle are governed by a cascade of neuropeptides.
- JH controls reproduction in the adult insect.
- Similar hormones that control moulting and reproduction are also present in crustaceans, but the secretion of ecdysone is under the control of an inhibitory neurohormone.

Questions

Self-Test Questions

1. When the concentration of thyroid hormone in the blood increases, it
   a. inhibits TRH secretion by the hypothalamus.
   b. stimulates a secretion by the hypothalamus.
   c. stimulates the pituitary to secrete TRH.
   d. stimulates the pituitary to secrete TSH.
   e. activates a positive feedback loop.
2. Blood levels of calcium are regulated directly by
   a. insulin synthesized by the alpha cells of the pancreas.
   b. PTH made by the pituitary.
   c. vitamin D activated in the liver.
   d. prolactin synthesized by the intermediate lobe of the pituitary.
   e. calcitonin secreted by specialized thyroid cells.
3. Proctolin
   a. is secreted by the intestine of mammals.
   b. is a steroid acting on nematodes.
   c. acts on smooth muscle in invertebrates.
   d. is a peptide secreted by insects.
   e. governs egg development in invertebrates.
4. Which of the following functions in mammals is not controlled by a hormone from the anterior pituitary?
   a. growth of muscle
   b. milk production
   c. metabolic rate
   d. contraction of uterine muscles
   e. egg production
5. When blood glucose rises in healthy humans,
   a. the alpha cells of the pancreas increase glucagon secretion.
   b. the beta cells of the pancreas increase insulin production.
   c. the pituitary secretes a tropic hormone controlling the pancreas.
   d. glucagon uses amino acids as an energy source.
   e. target cells decrease their insulin receptors.

Questions for Discussion

1. The occurrence in many invertebrates of peptide hormones that closely resemble those in vertebrates is striking. What are the possible explanations for this in evolutionary terms? What research would you do to help you choose among the possibilities?
2. Stress is commonly regarded as a diseaselike condition that can lead to death. Stresslike phenomena are widely spread in other taxa. If it is pathological, why has evolution not eliminated it? What are the advantages that have led to its retention?
3. A physician sees a patient who complains of a lack of energy and intolerance to cold. What are the possible hormonal causes of these symptoms?

Movement in a long-tailed field mouse (*Apodemus sylvaticus*). Movement of animals occurs as a result of contractions and relaxations of skeletal muscles. When stimulated by the nervous system, actin filaments in the muscles slide over myosin filaments to cause muscle contractions.

G. Delcho/Peter Arnold Inc.

36 Muscles, Skeletons, and Body Movements

Study Plan

Why It Matters

A Mexican leaf frog (*Pachymedusa dacnicolor*) sits motionless, its prominent eyes staring into space **(Figure 36.1, p. 874)**. But when the frog detects an approaching cricket, it lunges forward at just the right moment, thrusts out its sticky tongue, and captures the prey. This sequence of events, from the beginning of the movement until the frog's mouth closes, sealing the cricket's fate, requires only 260 milliseconds (ms)—about one quarter of a second. How does the frog move so swiftly, and so surely?

As its prey draws near, the muscles that extend the frog's hindlegs contract and propel the frog forward on its forelimbs toward the cricket. Within 50 ms after the jump begins, the muscles of the lower jaw contract, opening the mouth. Then a muscle on the upper surface of the tongue contracts, which raises the tongue and flips it out of the mouth. As the tongue shoots forward, muscle contractions along the ventral side of the trunk arch the body and direct the head downward toward the prey. Within 80 ms after the lunge begins, the tip of the frog's tongue contacts the cricket. Completion of the lunge folds the tongue—and the cricket—into the frog's mouth, aided by contraction of a muscle on the bottom of the tongue. After the mouth

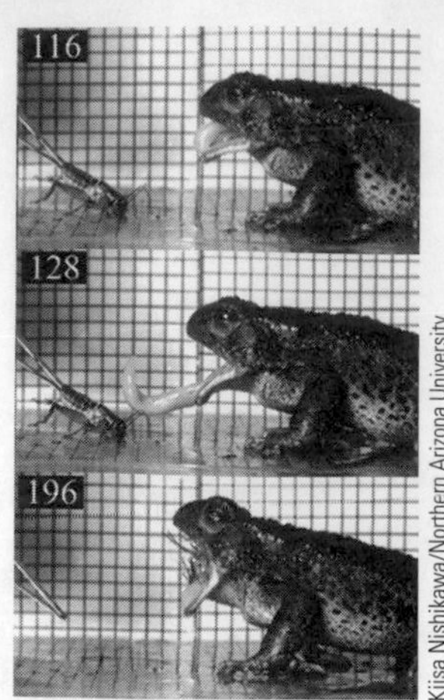

Figure 36.1
A Mexican leaf frog (*Pachymedusa dacnicolor*) capturing a grasshopper.

closes, further muscle contractions pull the legs forward and fold them under the body.

We know this because Kiisa Nishikawa, Lucie Gray, and James O'Reilly of Northern Arizona University recorded the frog's movements using a high-speed video camera linked to a millisecond timer, with a grid in the background that allowed precise measurement of the distances body parts travelled during the capture. Nishikawa's research group uses the camera's record to study movement in frogs in particular, and animals in general.

In Chapter 32, you learned that there are three types of muscle tissue in vertebrates: skeletal, cardiac, and smooth. Skeletal muscle is so named because most muscles of this type are attached by tendons to the skeleton of vertebrates. Cardiac muscle is the contractile muscle of the heart, and smooth muscle is found in the walls of tubes and cavities of the body, including blood vessels and the intestines. In this chapter, we describe the structure and function of skeletal muscles, the skeletal systems found in invertebrates and vertebrates, and how muscles bring about movement.

36.1 Vertebrate Skeletal Muscle: Structure and Function

Vertebrate **skeletal muscles** connect to the bones of the skeleton. The cells forming skeletal muscles are typically long and cylindrical and contain many nuclei (see Chapter 32). Skeletal muscle is controlled by the somatic nervous system (see Chapter 33).

Most skeletal muscles in humans and other vertebrates are attached at both ends across a joint to bones of the skeleton. (Some, such as those that move the lips, are attached to other muscles or connective tissues under skin.) Depending on its points of attachment, contraction of a single skeletal muscle may extend or bend body parts or may rotate one body part with respect to another. The human body has more than 600 skeletal muscles, ranging in size from the small muscles that move the eyeballs to the large muscles that move the legs.

Skeletal muscles are attached to bones by cords of connective tissue called *tendons* (see Chapter 32). Tendons vary in length from a few millimetres to some, such as those that connect the muscles of the forearm to the bones of the fingers, that are 20 to 30 cm long.

36.1a The Striated Appearance of Skeletal Muscle Fibres Results from a Highly Organized Internal Structure

A skeletal muscle consists of bundles of elongated, cylindrical cells called **muscle fibres**, which are 10 to 100 μm in diameter and run the entire length of the muscle **(Figure 36.2)**. Muscle fibres contain many nuclei, reflecting their development by fusion of smaller cells. Some very small muscles, such as some of the muscles of the face, contain only a few hundred muscle fibres; others, such as the larger leg muscles, contain hundreds of thousands. In both cases, the muscle fibres are held in parallel bundles by sheaths of connective tissue that surround them in the muscle and merge with the tendons that connect muscles to bones or other structures. Muscle fibres are richly supplied with nutrients and oxygen by an extensive network of blood vessels that penetrates the muscle tissue.

Muscle fibres are packed with **myofibrils**, cylindrical contractile elements about 1 μm in diameter that run lengthwise inside the cells. Each myofibril consists of a regular arrangement of **thick filaments** (13–18 nm in diameter) and **thin filaments** (5–8 nm in diameter) (see Figure 36.2). The thick and thin filaments alternate with one another in a stacked set.

The thick filaments are parallel bundles of myosin molecules; each myosin molecule consists of two protein subunits that together form a *head* connected to a long double helix forming a *tail*. The head is bent toward the adjacent thin filament to form a *crossbridge*. In vertebrates, each thick filament contains some 200 to 300 myosin molecules and forms as many crossbridges. The thin filaments consist mostly of two linear chains of actin molecules twisted into a double helix, which creates a groove running the length of the molecule. Bound to the actin are *tropomyosin* and *troponin* proteins. Tropomyosin molecules are elongated fibrous proteins that are organized end-to-end next to the groove of the actin double helix. Troponin is a three-subunit globular protein that binds to tropomyosin at intervals along the thin filaments.

The arrangement of thick and thin filaments forms a pattern of alternating dark bands and light bands, giving skeletal muscle a striated appearance under the microscope (see Figure 36.2). The dark bands, called *A bands,* consist of stacked thick filaments along with the parts of thin filaments that overlap both ends. The lighter-appearing middle region of an A band, which contains only thick filaments, is the *H zone.* In the centre of the H zone is a disk of proteins called the *M line,* which holds the stack of thick filaments together. The light bands, called *I bands,* consist of the parts of the thin filaments not in the A band. In the centre of each I band is a thin *Z line,* a disk to which the thin filaments are anchored. The region between two adjacent Z lines is a **sarcomere** (*sarco* = flesh; *meros* = segment); sarcomeres are the basic units of contraction in a myofibril.

At each junction of an A band and an I band, the plasma membrane folds into the muscle fibre to form a **T (transverse) tubule (Figure 36.3, p. 876)**. Encircling the sarcomeres is the **sarcoplasmic reticulum**, a complex system of vesicles modified from the smooth endoplasmic reticulum. Segments of the sarcoplasmic retic-

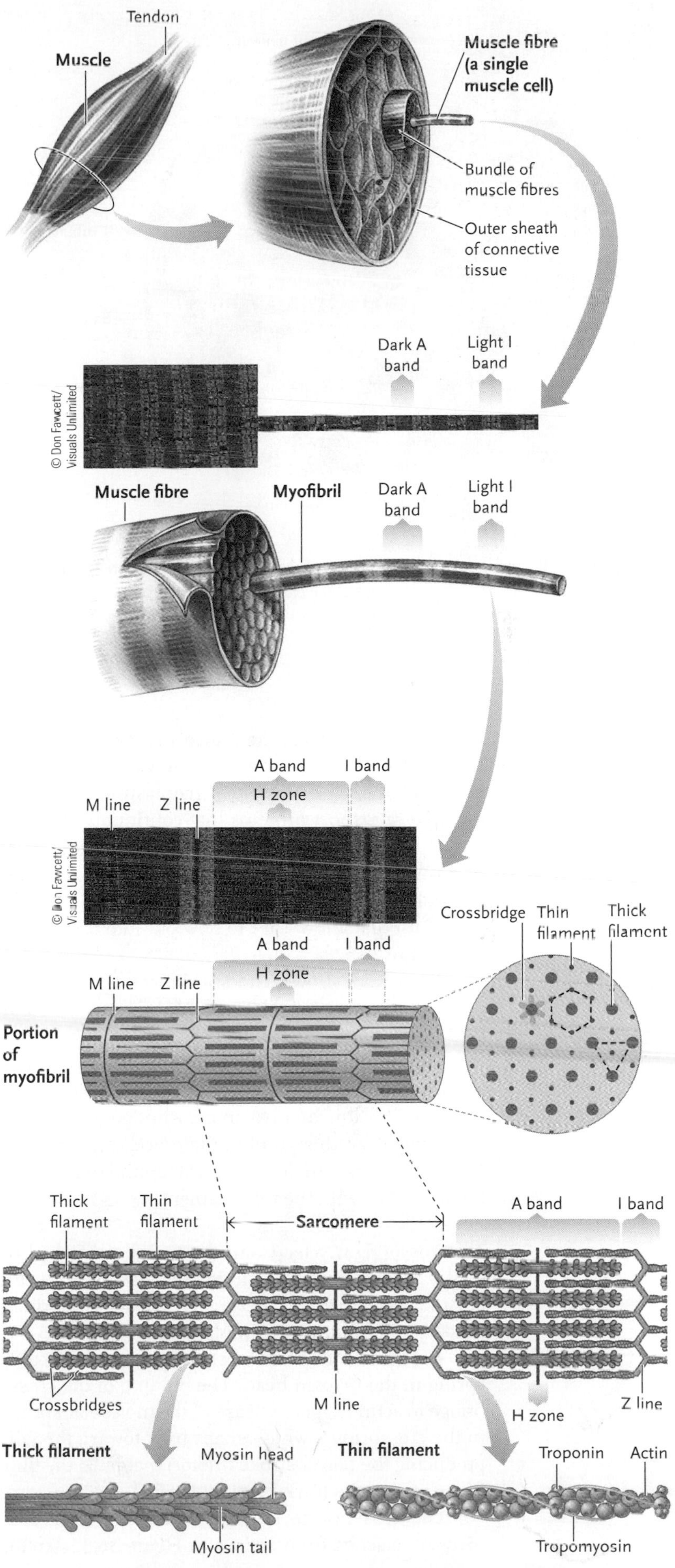

Figure 36.2
Skeletal muscle structure. Muscles are composed of bundles of cells called muscle fibres; within each muscle fibre are longitudinal bundles of myofibrils. The unit of contraction within a myofibril, the sarcomere, consists of overlapping myosin thick filaments and actin thin filaments. The myosin molecules in the thick filaments each consist of two subunits organized into a head and a double-helical tail. The actin subunits in the thin filaments form twisted, double helices, with tropomyosin molecules arranged head to tail in the groove of the helix and troponin bound to the tropomyosin at intervals along the thin filaments.

ulum are wrapped around each A band and I band and are separated from the T tubules in those regions by small gaps.

An axon of an efferent neuron leads to each muscle fibre. The axon terminal makes a single, broad synapse with a muscle fibre called a **neuromuscular junction** (see Figure 36.3). The neuromuscular junction, T tubules, and sarcoplasmic reticulum are key components in the pathway for stimulating skeletal muscle contraction by neural signals—which starts with action potentials travelling down the efferent neuron—as is described next.

36.1b During Muscle Contraction, Thin Filaments on Each Side of a Sarcomere Slide over Thick Filaments

The precise control of body motions depends on an equally precise control of muscle contraction by a signalling pathway that carries information from nerves to muscle fibres. An action potential arriving at the neuromuscular junction leads to an increase in the concentration of Ca^{2+} in the cytosol of the muscle fibre. The increase in Ca^{2+} triggers a process in which the thin filaments on each side of a sarcomere slide over the thick filaments toward the centre of the A band, which brings the Z lines closer together, shortening the sarcomeres and contracting the muscle **(Figure 36.4, p. 876)**. This *sliding filament mechanism* of muscle contraction depends on dynamic interactions between actin and myosin proteins in the two filament types. That is, the myosin crossbridges make and break contact with actin and pull the thin filaments over the thick filaments—the action is similar to rowing, or a ratcheting process. A model for muscle contraction is shown in **Figure 36.5, p. 877.**

Conduction of an Action Potential into a Muscle Fibre. Like neurons, skeletal muscle fibres are *excitable,* meaning that the electrical potential of their plasma membrane can change in response to a stimulus. When an action potential arrives at the neuromuscular junction, the axon terminal releases a neurotransmitter, *acetylcholine,* which triggers an action potential in the muscle fibre (see Figure 36.5, step 1). The action potential travels in all directions over the muscle fibre's surface membrane and penetrates into the interior of the fibre through the T tubules.

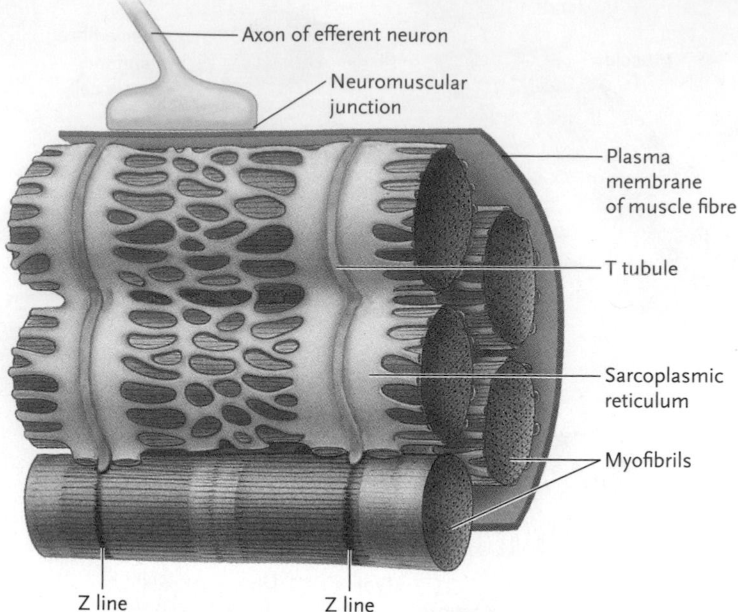

Figure 36.3
Components in the pathway for the stimulation of skeletal muscle contraction by neural signals. T (transverse) tubules are infoldings of the plasma membrane into the muscle fibre originating at each A band–I band junction in a sarcomere. The sarcoplasmic reticulum encircles the sarcomeres and segments of it end in close proximity to the T tubules.

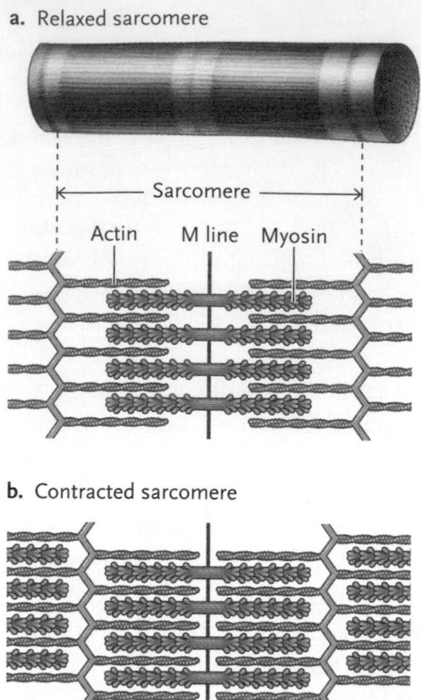

Figure 36.4
Shortening of sarcomeres by the sliding filament mechanism, in which the thin filaments are pulled over the thick filaments.

Release of Calcium into the Cytosol of the Muscle Fibre. In the absence of a stimulus, the Ca^{2+} concentration is kept high inside the sarcoplasmic reticulum by active transport proteins that continuously pump Ca^{2+} out of the cytosol and into the sarcoplasmic reticulum. When an action potential reaches the end of a T tubule, it opens ion channels in the sarcoplasmic reticulum that allow Ca^{2+} to flow out into the cytosol (see Figure 36.5, step 2).

When Ca^{2+} flows into the cytosol, the troponin molecules of the thin filament bind the calcium and undergo a conformational change that causes the tropomyosin fibres to slip into the grooves of the actin double helix. The slippage uncovers the actin's binding sites for the myosin crossbridge (see Figure 36.5, step 3). At this point in the process, the myosin crossbridge has a molecule of ATP bound to it, and is not in contact with the thin filament.

The Crossbridge Cycle. Using the energy of ATP hydrolysis, the myosin crossbridge bends away from the tail and binds to a newly exposed myosin crossbridge binding site on an actin molecule (see Figure 36.5, step 4). In effect, this bending compresses a molecular spring in the myosin head. The binding of the crossbridge to actin triggers release of the molecular spring in the crossbridge, which snaps back toward the tail, producing the power stroke (motor) that pulls the thin filament over the thick filament (step 5).

The crossbridge now binds another ATP and myosin detaches from actin (see Figure 36.5, step 6). The cycle repeats again, starting with ATP hydrolysis (step 4). Contraction ceases when action potentials stop: Ca^{2+} is pumped back into the sarcoplasmic reticulum, and its effect on troponin is reversed, leading to tropomyosin again blocking myosin crossbridge binding sites on actin. Contraction ceases, and the actin thin filaments slide back over the myosin thick filaments to their original relaxed positions (step 7). Crossbridge cycles based on actin and myosin power movements in all living organisms, from cytoplasmic streaming in plant cells and amoebae to muscle contractions in animals.

Although the force produced by a single myosin crossbridge is comparatively small, it is multiplied by the hundreds of crossbridges acting in a single thick filament and by the billions of thin filaments sliding in a contracting sarcomere. The force, multiplied further by the many sarcomeres and myofibrils in a muscle fibre, is transmitted to the plasma membrane of a muscle fibre by the attachment of myofibrils to elements of the cytoskeleton. From the plasma membrane, it is transmitted to bones and other body parts by the connective tissue sheaths surrounding the muscle fibres and by the tendons.

From Contraction to Relaxation. As long as action potentials continue to arrive at the neuromuscular junction, Ca^{2+} is released in response, and ATP is available, the crossbridge cycle continues to run, shortening the sarcomeres and contracting the muscle fibre.

When action potentials stop, excitation of the T tubules ceases, and the Ca^{2+} release channels in

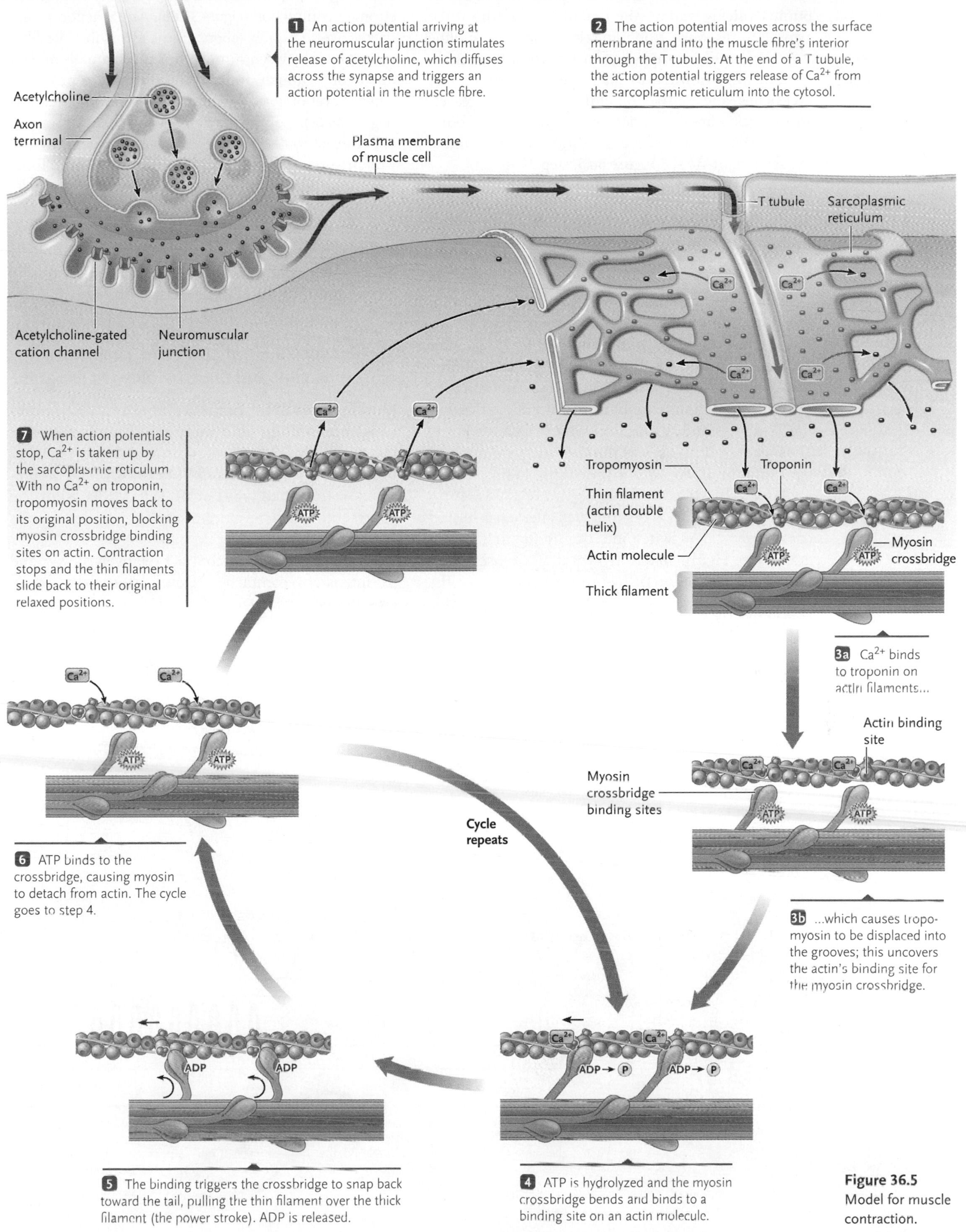

1 An action potential arriving at the neuromuscular junction stimulates release of acetylcholine, which diffuses across the synapse and triggers an action potential in the muscle fibre.
2 The action potential moves across the surface membrane and into the muscle fibre's interior through the T tubules. At the end of a T tubule, the action potential triggers release of Ca^{2+} from the sarcoplasmic reticulum into the cytosol.
Acetylcholine
Axon terminal
Plasma membrane of muscle cell
T tubule
Sarcoplasmic reticulum
Acetylcholine-gated cation channel
Neuromuscular junction
Ca^{2+}
7 When action potentials stop, Ca^{2+} is taken up by the sarcoplasmic reticulum With no Ca^{2+} on troponin, tropomyosin moves back to its original position, blocking myosin crossbridge binding sites on actin. Contraction stops and the thin filaments slide back to their original relaxed positions.
ATP
Tropomyosin
Troponin
Thin filament (actin double helix)
Actin molecule
Myosin crossbridge
Thick filament
3a Ca^{2+} binds to troponin on actin filaments...
Actin binding site
Myosin crossbridge binding sites
3b ...which causes tropomyosin to be displaced into the grooves; this uncovers the actin's binding site for the myosin crossbridge.
Cycle repeats
6 ATP binds to the crossbridge, causing myosin to detach from actin. The cycle goes to step 4.
ADP
ADP → P
5 The binding triggers the crossbridge to snap back toward the tail, pulling the thin filament over the thick filament (the power stroke). ADP is released.
4 ATP is hydrolyzed and the myosin crossbridge bends and binds to a binding site on an actin molecule.

Figure 36.5
Model for muscle contraction.

the sarcoplasmic reticulum close. The active transport pumps quickly remove the remaining Ca^{2+} from the cytosol. In response, troponin releases its Ca^{2+} and the tropomyosin fibres are pulled back to cover the myosin binding sites in the thin filaments. The crossbridge cycle stops, and contraction of the muscle fibre ceases. In a muscle fibre that is not contracting, ATP is bound to the myosin head and the crossbridge is not bound to the actin filament (see Figure 36.5, step 7).

36.1c The Response of a Muscle Fibre to Action Potentials Ranges from Twitches to Tetanus

A single action potential arriving at a neuromuscular junction usually causes a single, weak contraction of a muscle fibre called a **muscle twitch (Figure 36.6a).** After a muscle twitch begins, the tension of the muscle fibre increases in magnitude for about 30 to 40 ms and then peaks as the action potential runs its course through the T tubules and the Ca^{2+} channels begin to close. Tension then decreases as the Ca^{2+} ions are pumped back into the sarcoplasmic reticulum, falling to zero in about 50 ms after the peak.

If a muscle fibre is restimulated after it has relaxed completely, a new twitch identical to the first is generated (see Figure 36.6a). However, if a muscle fibre is restimulated before it has relaxed completely, the second twitch is added to the first, producing what is called *twitch summation,* which is basically a summed, stronger contraction **(Figure 36.6b).** And if action potentials arrive so rapidly (about 25 ms apart) that the fibre cannot relax between stimuli, the Ca^{2+} channels remain open continuously and twitch summation produces a peak level of continuous contraction called **tetanus (Figure 36.6c).** Contractile activity will then decrease if either the stimuli cease or the muscle fatigues.

Tetanus is an essential part of muscle fibre function. If we lift a moderately heavy weight, for example, many of the muscle fibres in our arms enter tetanus and remain in that state until the weight is released. Even body movements that require relatively little effort, such as standing still but in balance, involve tetanic contractions of some muscle fibres.

36.1d Muscle Fibres Differ in Their Rate of Contraction and Susceptibility to Fatigue

Muscle fibres differ in their rate of contraction and resistance to fatigue and thus can be classified as slow, fast aerobic, and fast anaerobic muscle fibres. Their properties are summarized in **Table 36.1.** The proportions of the three types of muscle fibres tailor the contractile characteristics of each muscle to suit its function within the body.

Slow muscle fibres contract relatively slowly, and the intensity of contraction is low because their myosin crossbridges hydrolyze ATP relatively slowly. They can

Figure 36.6
The relationship of the tension produced in a muscle fibre to the frequency of action potentials.

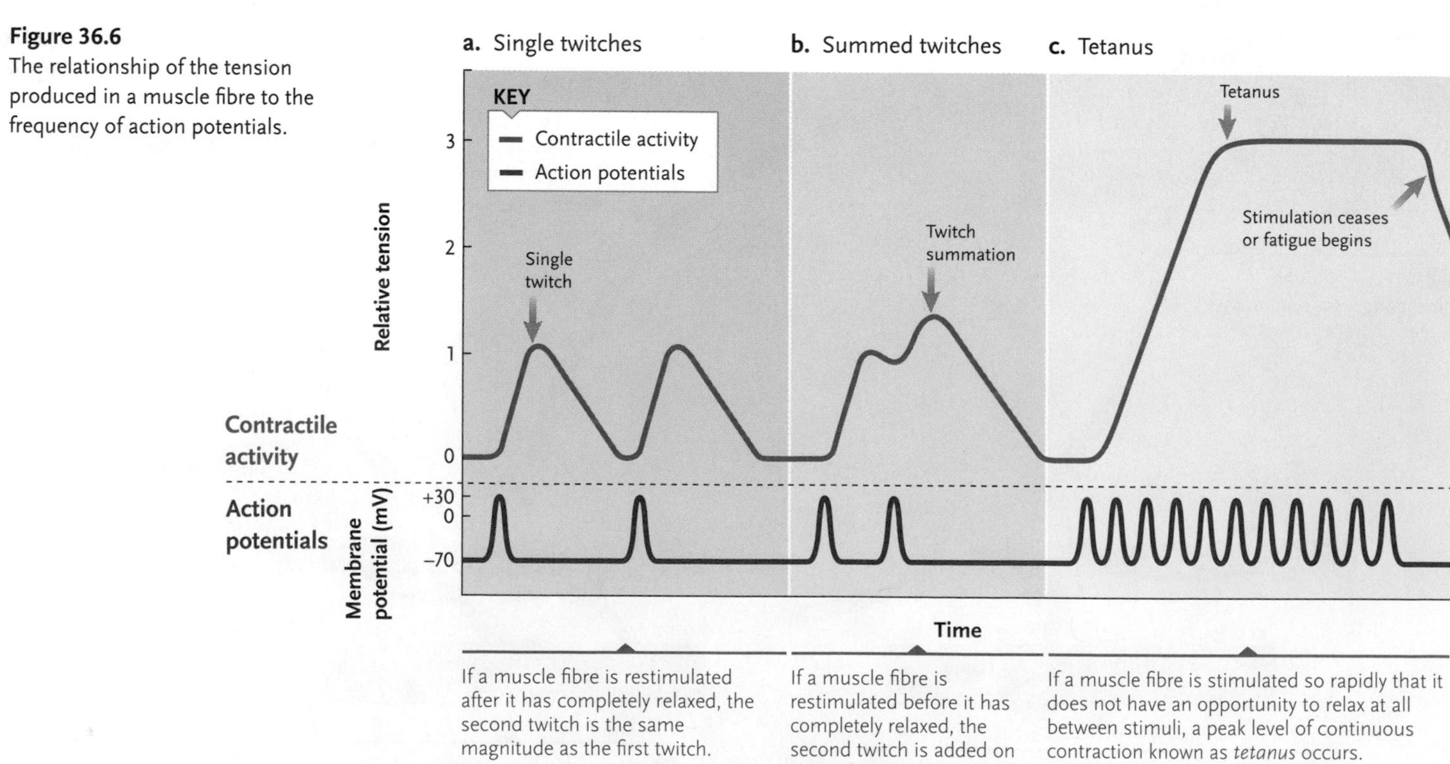

remain contracted for relatively long periods without fatiguing. Slow muscle fibres typically contain many mitochondria and make most of their ATP by oxidative phosphorylation (aerobic respiration). They have a low capacity to make ATP by anaerobic glycolysis. They also contain high concentrations of the oxygen-storing protein **myoglobin,** which greatly enhances their oxygen supplies. Myoglobin is closely related to haemoglobin, the oxygen-carrying protein of red blood cells. Myoglobin gives slow muscle fibres, such as those in the legs of ground birds such as quail, chickens, and ostriches, a deep red colour. In sharks and bony fishes, strips of slow muscles concentrated in a band on either side of the body are used for slow, continuous swimming and maintaining body position.

Fast muscle fibres contract relatively quickly and powerfully because their myosin crossbridges hydrolyze ATP faster than those of slow muscle fibres. Fast aerobic fibres have abundant mitochondria, a rich blood supply, and a high concentration of myoglobin, which makes them red in colour. They have a high capacity for making ATP by oxidative phosphorylation, and an intermediate capacity for making ATP by anaerobic glycolysis. They fatigue more quickly than slow fibres, but not as quickly as fast anaerobic fibres. Fast aerobic muscle fibres are abundant in the flight muscles of migrating birds such as ducks and geese.

Fast anaerobic fibres typically contain high concentrations of glycogen, relatively few mitochondria, and a more limited blood supply than fast aerobic fibres. They generate ATP mostly by anaerobic respiration (glycolysis) and have a low capacity to produce ATP by oxidative respiration. Fast anaerobic fibres produce especially rapid and powerful contractions but are more susceptible to fatigue. Because their myoglobin supply is limited and they contain few mitochondria, they are pale in colour. Some ground birds have flight muscles consisting almost entirely of fast anaerobic muscle fibres. These muscles can produce a short burst of intensive contractions allowing the bird to escape a predator, but they cannot produce sustained flight. Most muscles of lampreys, sharks, fishes, amphibians, and reptiles also contain fast anaerobic muscle fibres, allowing the animals to move quickly to capture prey and avoid danger.

The muscles of most animals are mixed and contain different proportions of slow and fast muscle fibres, depending on their functions. Muscles specialized for prolonged, slow contractions, such as the postural muscles of the back, have a high proportion of slow fibres and are a deep red colour. The muscles of the forearm that move the fingers have a higher proportion of fast fibres and are a paler red than the back muscles. These muscles can contract rapidly and powerfully, but they fatigue much more rapidly than the back muscles.

Table 36.1 Characteristics of Slow and Fast Muscle Fibres in Skeletal Muscle

	Fibre Type		
Property	**Slow**	**Fast Aerobic**	**Fast Anaerobic**
Contraction speed	Slow	Fast	Fast
Contraction intensity	Low	Intermediate	High
Fatigue resistance	High	Intermediate	Low
Myosin–ATPase activity	Low	High	High
Oxidative phosphorylation capacity	High	High	Low
Enzymes for anaerobic glycolysis	Low	Intermediate	High
Mitochondria	Many	Many	Few
Myoglobin content	High	High	Low
Fibre colour	Red	Red	White
Glycogen content	Low	Intermediate	High

36.1e Skeletal Muscle Control Is Divided among Motor Units

The control of muscle contraction extends beyond the simple ability to turn the crossbridge cycle on and off. We can adjust a handshake from a gentle squeeze to a strong grasp or exactly balance a feather or dumbbell in the hand. How are entire muscles controlled in this way? The answer lies in activation of the muscle fibres in blocks called **motor units.**

The muscle fibres in each motor unit are controlled by branches of the axon of a single efferent neuron **(Figure 36.7, p. 880).** As a result, all of those fibres contract each time the neuron fires an action potential. All of the muscle fibres in a motor unit are of the same type— either slow, fast aerobic, or fast anaerobic. When a motor unit contracts, its force is distributed throughout the entire muscle because the fibres are dispersed throughout the muscle rather than being concentrated in one segment.

For a delicate movement, only a few efferent neurons carry action potentials to a muscle, and only a few motor units contract. For more powerful movements, more efferent neurons carry action potentials, and more motor units contract.

Muscles that can be precisely and delicately controlled, such as those moving the fingers in humans, have many motor units in a small area, with only a few muscle fibres—about 10 or so—in each unit. Muscles that produce grosser body movements, such as those moving the legs, have fewer motor units in the same volume of muscle but thousands of muscle fibres in each unit. In the calf muscle that raises the heel, for example, most motor units contain nearly 2000 muscle fibres. Other skeletal muscles fall between these extremes, with an average of about 200 muscle fibres per motor unit.

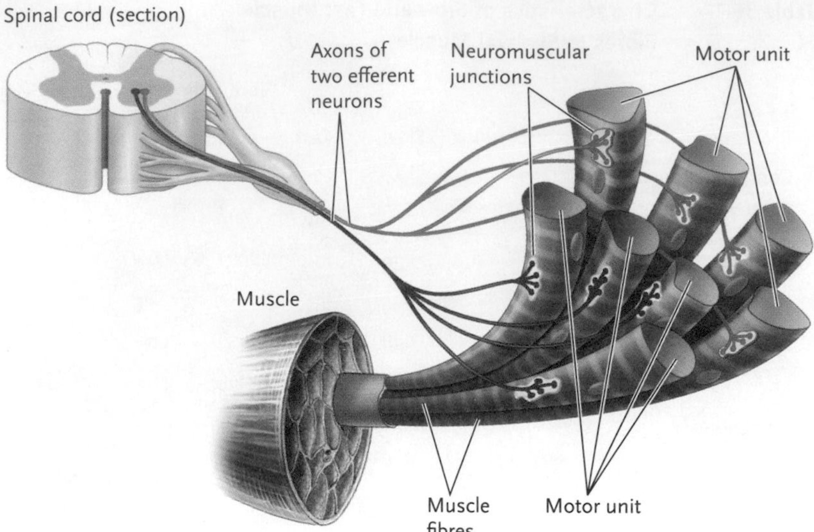

Figure 36.7
Motor units in vertebrate skeletal muscles. Each motor unit consists of groups of muscle fibres activated by branches of a single efferent (motor) neuron.

36.1f Invertebrates Move Using a Variety of Striated Muscles

Invertebrates also have muscle cells in which actin-based thin filaments and myosin-based thick filaments produce movements by the same sliding mechanism as in vertebrates. In Cnidaria and flatworms, the muscles are not striated, but in most other invertebrates (annelids, molluscs, echinoderms, nematodes, and arthropods), the actin and myosin fibrils are arranged in sarcomeres, forming striated muscle. In general, striated muscle is the dominant muscle type for these invertebrates and functions not only in locomotion but also in movements of the viscera, like the gut and heart. In some invertebrates, muscle cells lacking striations may occur. In the muscles that close the shells of clams and other bivalves (see Chapter 26), smooth muscle cells are present among the striated muscle cells.

In invertebrates, an entire muscle is typically controlled by one or a few motor neurons. Nevertheless, invertebrate muscles are capable of finely graded contractions because individual neurons make large numbers of synapses with the muscle cells. In arthropods, the muscles may receive up to three types of innervation: fast, slow, and inhibitory. All muscles receive fast innervation in which release of a neuromuscular transmitter produces a twitch. Some also receive slow innervation, in which a graded response results from increased action potentials. As action potentials arrive more frequently, more Ca^{2+} is released into the cells, and they contract more strongly. In addition, there may be inhibitory nerves that prevent the release of Ca^{2+}. The excitatory transmitter for both fast and slow nerves is glutamate, and the inhibitory transmitter is GABA (see Chapter 33).

The muscles responsible for the movement of the wings in insects are highly specialized striated muscles, called fibrillar muscles. They possess a large number of gigantic mitochondria, in some cases about the size of a vertebrate red blood cell, so that the energetic demands of flight can be met. The frequency of wing beat of many flies, bees, and wasps is very high, up to 600 beats per second in mosquitoes. How is this achieved without tetanus being induced? The flight muscles occur in antagonistic pairs **(Figure 36.8).** When one muscle of the pair contracts, the other is stretched back to its "relaxed" length. Nerve impulses arrive only about three times per second, and this keeps the muscles activated. The frequency with which they contract is determined by the elastic properties of the whole system.

Study Break

1. Compare thick and thin muscle filaments.
2. What is the role of the sarcoplasmic reticulum in muscle contraction?
3. What are the three types of muscle fibres, and how do they differ?

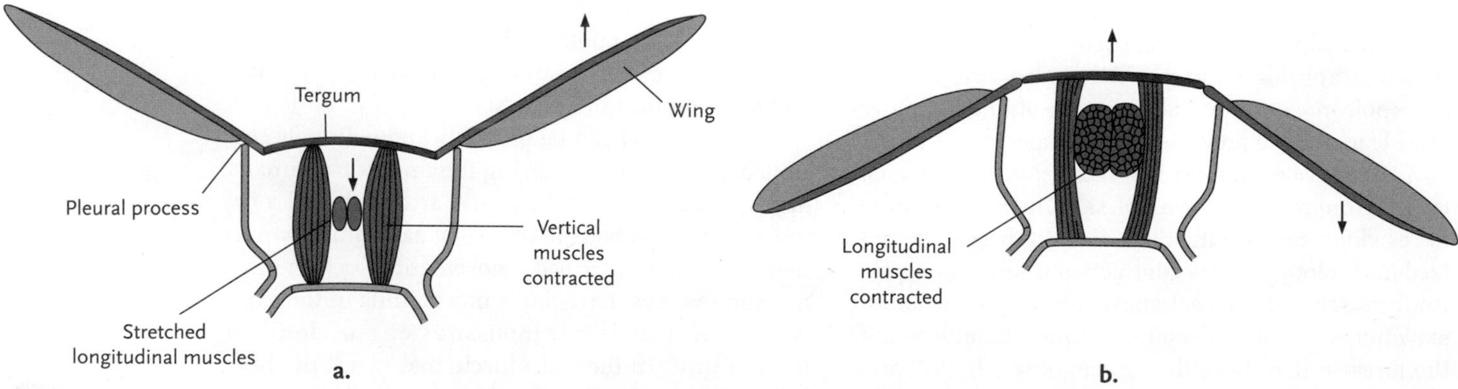

Figure 36.8
The muscles in a flying insect. When the vertical flight muscles contract, they pull on the cuticle forming the top of the segment, elevating the wings. The segment is constructed so that this action also elongates the cuticle of the thorax from front to rear (at right angles to the plane of the page), extending the longitudinal muscles. This stimulates the activated longitudinal muscles to contract, pushing up the tergum, elevating the wings, and elongating the vertical muscles. Because the cuticle is elastic, the whole system vibrates, producing very rapid wing beats.

36.2 Skeletal Systems

Animal skeletal systems provide physical support for the body and protection for the soft tissues. They also act as a framework against which muscles work to move parts of the body or the entire organism. Three main types of skeletons are found in both invertebrates and vertebrates: hydrostatic skeletons, exoskeletons, and endoskeletons.

36.2a A Hydrostatic Skeleton Consists of Muscles and Fluid

A **hydrostatic skeleton** (*hydro* = water; *statikos* = causing to stand) is a structure consisting of muscles and fluid that, by themselves, provide support for the animal or part of the animal; no rigid support, such as a bone, is involved. A hydrostatic skeleton consists of a body compartment or compartments filled with water or body fluids, which are incompressible liquids. When the muscular walls of the compartment contract, they pressurize the contained fluid. If muscles in one part of the compartment are contracted while muscles in another part are relaxed, the pressurized fluid will move to the relaxed part of the compartment, distending it. In short, the contractions and relaxations of the muscles surrounding the compartments change the shape of the animal.

Hydrostatic skeletons are the primary support systems of cnidarians, flatworms, roundworms, and annelids. In all of these animals, compartments containing fluids under pressure make the body semirigid and provide a mechanical support on which muscles act. For example, sea anemones have a hydrostatic skeleton consisting of several fluid-filled body cavities. The body wall contains longitudinal and circular muscles that work against that skeleton. Between meals, longitudinal muscles are contracted (shortened), whereas the circular ones are relaxed, and the animal looks short and squat **(Figure 36.9a).** It lengthens into its upright feeding position by contracting the circular muscles and relaxing the longitudinal ones **(Figure 36.9b).** In flatworms, roundworms, and annelids, striated muscles in the body wall act on the hydrostatic skeleton to produce creeping, burrowing, or swimming movements. Among these animals, annelids have the most highly developed musculoskeletal systems, with an outer layer of circular muscles surrounding the body, and an inner layer of longitudinal muscles **(Figure 36.10).** Contractions of the circular muscles reduce the diameter of the body and increase the length; contractions of the longitudinal muscles shorten the body and increase its diameter. Because the coelom and musculature are divided into segments, expansion and contraction can be localized to individual segments. Annelids move along a surface or burrow by means of alternating waves of contraction of the two muscle layers that pass along the body, working against the fluid-filled body compartments of the hydrostatic skeleton.

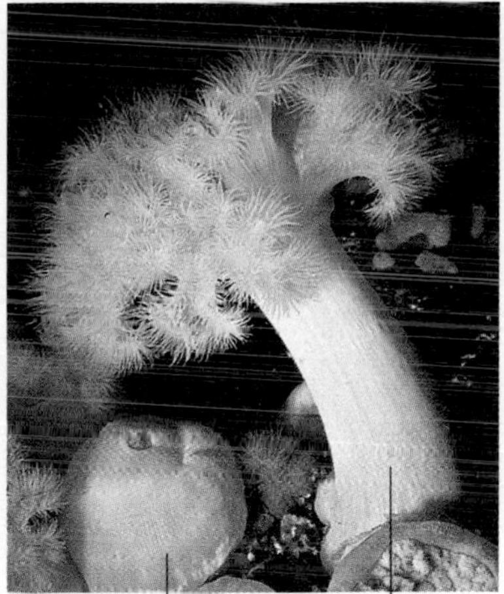

Figure 36.9
Sea anemones in (a) the resting and (b) the feeding position. In **(a),** longitudinal muscles in the body wall are contracted, and circular muscles are relaxed. In **(b),** the longitudinal muscles are relaxed, and the circular muscles are contracted. Both sets of muscles work against a hydrostatic skeleton.

Some structures of echinoderms are supported by hydrostatic skeletons. The tube feet of sea stars and sea urchins, for example, have muscular walls enclosing the fluid of the water vascular system (see Chapter 27).

In vertebrates, the erectile tissue of the penis is a fluid-filled hydrostatic skeletal structure, although many mammals other than humans also possess a penis bone, the *os penis* or baculum (Figure 36.12d).

Hydrostatic movement may not involve a fluid but may simply depend on the incompressibility of muscles themselves. Although the muscles in the structure may contract, the total body of muscles remains at a constant volume. Our tongues and lips are capable of a range of movements, but no skeletal element supports the movement. The elephant's trunk can lift a large log

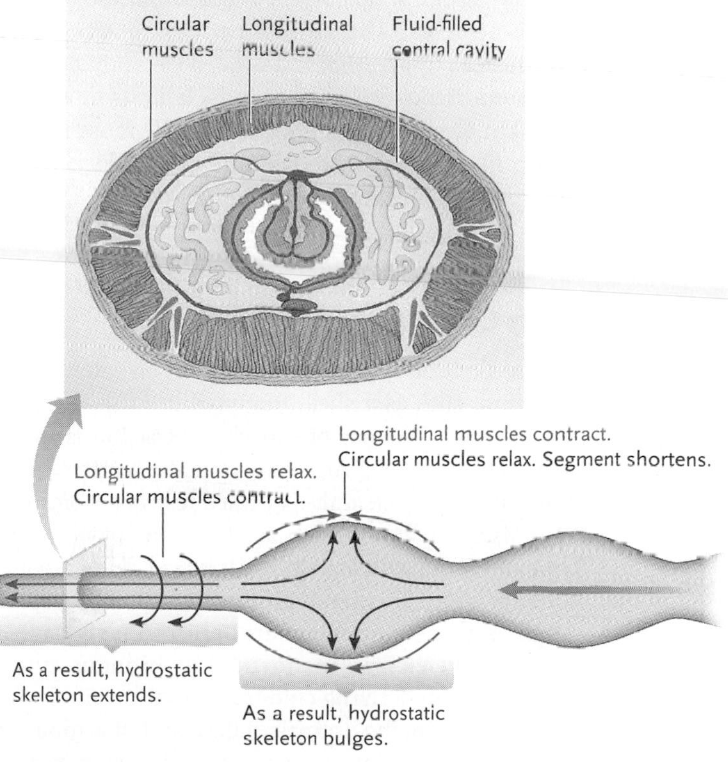

Figure 36.10
Movement of an earthworm, showing how muscles in the body wall act on its hydrostatic skeleton. Contraction of the circular muscles reduces body diameter and increases body length, whereas contraction of the longitudinal muscles decreases body length and increases body diameter.

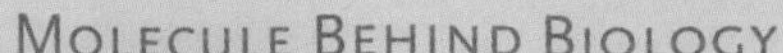

MOLECULE BEHIND BIOLOGY

Chitin: An Abundant and Useful Polysaccharide

Chitin is a polymer composed of many repeating units of *N*-acetylglucosamine **(Figure 1).** It is a strong, insoluble material that is the principal component of the cuticle of arthropods, where it is crosslinked to proteins. When arthropods moult, the proteins are resorbed, and the cast cuticle is made up almost entirely of chitin. Given the dominance of arthropods in the Earth's biomass, it is thus not surprising that, after cellulose, chitin is the most abundant polymer on Earth, with an annual production of about 10 billion tonnes. Chitin also occurs in molluscs, the eggshells of nematodes, and the cell walls of fungi and algae. Chitin is degraded by bacteria, particularly members of the genus *Vibrio*. Because chitin does not occur in vertebrates, chitin synthesis is a target of some successful insecticides.

Chitin and its closely related compound chitosan, produced by heating chitin in a strongly alkaline solution, are widely used in a variety of fields. Chitosan was found to have healing properties and has been used for medical sutures and as a support for growing skin over severe wounds. The compounds are also said to confer protection against disease in plants, and seeds treated with chitosan have gained some acceptance. Chitin stimulates the growth of soil bacteria that secrete material toxic to nematodes that attack plants: compounds for this purpose are under development. Because the compounds have a strong positive charge, they have the potential to bind negatively charged compounds. Chitosans have been used in water purification plants for many years. More recently, chitosans, because of their ability to bind fats, have been promoted by the natural health products industry as a means to prevent fat absorption, leading to weight loss, but these claims are not supported by good scientific evidence.

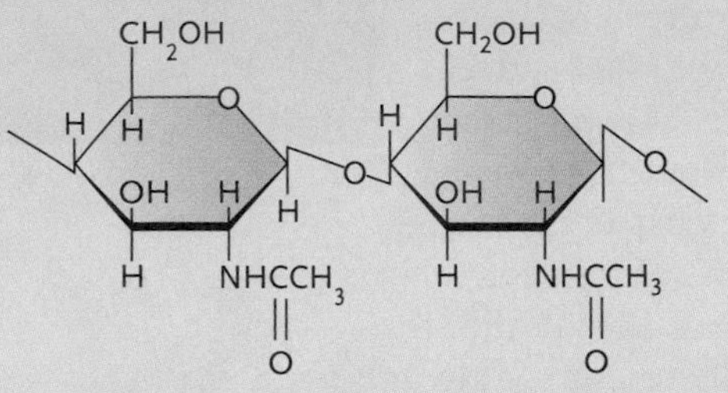

N-acetyl-D-glucosamine

Figure 1
Chitin is a polymer made up of many repeating units of *N*-acetyl-D-glucosamine.

but can also pick up objects of a few millimetres. How is this achieved? The trunk is basically an extension of the nose and upper lip. It has no skeleton but consists of an enormous number of muscle units attached to the skin or to one another. The muscle mass remains at a constant volume, and contractions of local muscle groups result in movement.

36.2b An Exoskeleton Is a Rigid External Body Covering

An **exoskeleton** (*exo* = outside) is a rigid external body covering, such as a shell, that provides support. In an exoskeleton, the force of muscle contraction is applied against that covering. An exoskeleton also protects delicate internal tissues such as the brain and respiratory organs.

Many molluscs, such as clams and oysters, have an exoskeleton consisting of a hard calcium carbonate shell secreted by glands in the mantle. Arthropods, such as insects, spiders, and crustaceans, have an external skeleton in the form of a chitinous cuticle, secreted by underlying epidermis, that covers the outside surfaces of the animals. Like a suit of armour, the arthropod exoskeleton has movable joints, flexed and extended by muscles. Most muscles attach directly to the cuticle by extensions of the myofibrils and extend from the inside surface of one section of the cuticle to the inside surface of another section. Since the sections are separated by flexible cuticle, contraction results in movement about the joint **(Figure 36.11).** The exoskeleton protects against dehydration, serves as armour against predators, and provides the levers against which muscles work. In many flying insects, elastic flexing of the exoskeleton contributes to the movements of the wings.

In vertebrates, the shell of a turtle or tortoise is an exoskeletal structure.

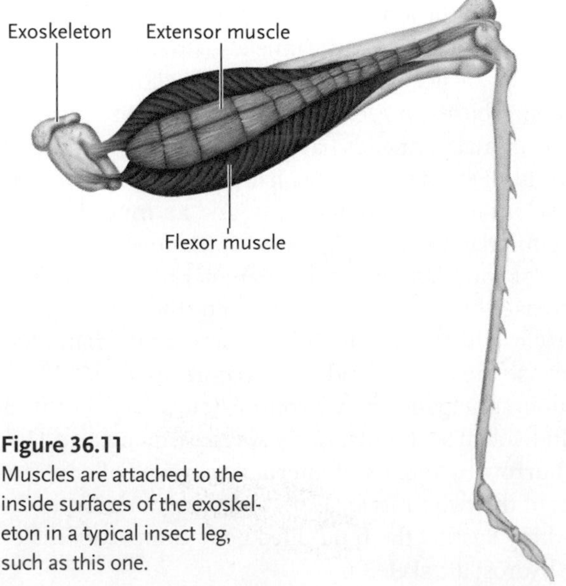

Figure 36.11
Muscles are attached to the inside surfaces of the exoskeleton in a typical insect leg, such as this one.

36.2c An Endoskeleton Consists of Supportive Internal Body Structures Such as Bones

An **endoskeleton** (*endon* = within) consists of internal body structures, such as bones, that provide support. In an endoskeleton, the force of contraction is applied against those structures. Like exoskeletons, endoskeletons also protect delicate internal tissues such as the brain and respiratory organs.

In cephalopod molluscs, the shell has been reduced and internalized. In most squids, it is a long, flat plate of chitin (see *Molecule Behind Biology*), the "pen," that provides support for the mantle. In cuttlefish, it is present as a material such as the shell of snails, but it is divided into air-filled chambers. It may provide some support, but its principal function is to provide buoyancy. The animal has the ability to vary the content of air in the "cuttlebone," providing control of buoyancy. *Nautilus* (see Chapter 26), the only living cephalopod with an external shell, has similar chambers in its shell. Squids also have an internal case of cartilage that surrounds and protects the brain; other segments of cartilage (not chemically identical to vertebrate cartilage) support the gills and siphon in squids and octopuses.

Echinoderms have an endoskeleton consisting of *ossicles* (*ossiculum* = little bone), formed from calcium carbonate crystals. The shells of sand dollars and sea urchins are the endoskeletons of these animals.

The endoskeleton is the primary skeletal system of vertebrates. An adult human, for example, has an endoskeleton consisting of 206 bones arranged in two structural groups **(Figure 36.12, p. 884)**. The **axial skeleton**, which includes the skull, vertebral column, sternum, and rib cage, forms the central part of the structure (shaded in red in Figure 36.12). The **appendicular skeleton** (shaded in green) includes the shoulder, hip, leg, and arm bones. The human skeleton is, of course, highly specialized, reflecting our large brain and our upright movement, using only our hindfeet. Three other mammalian skeletons are included in Figure 36.12, illustrating how skeletons are adapted for particular lifestyles.

36.2d Bones of the Vertebrate Endoskeleton Are Organs with Several Functions

The vertebrate endoskeleton supports and maintains the overall shape of the body and protects internal organs. In addition, the bones are a storehouse for calcium and phosphate ions, releasing them as required to maintain optimal levels of these ions in body fluids. Bones are also sites where new blood cells form.

Bones are complex organs built up from multiple tissues, including bone tissue with cells of several kinds, blood vessels, nerves, and, in some, stores of adipose tissue. Bone tissue is distributed between dense, compact bone regions, which have essentially no spaces other than the microscopic canals of the osteons (see Chapter 32), and spongy bone regions, which may open into larger spaces (see Figure 36.12). Compact bone tissue generally forms the outer surfaces of bones and spongy bone tissue the interior. The interior of some flat bones, such as the hip bones and the ribs, are filled with *red marrow,* a tissue that is the primary source of new red blood cells in mammals and birds. The shaft of long bones such as the femur is opened by a large central canal filled with adipose tissue called *yellow marrow,* which is a source of some white blood cells.

Throughout the life of a vertebrate, calcium and phosphate ions are constantly deposited and withdrawn from bones. Hormonal controls maintain the concentration of Ca^{2+} ions at optimal levels in the blood and extracellular fluids (see Chapter 35), ensuring that calcium is available for proper functioning of the nervous system, muscular system, and other physiological processes.

STUDY BREAK

What is a hydrostatic skeleton? How is it different from an exoskeleton or endoskeleton?

36.3 Vertebrate Movement: The Interactions between Muscles and Bones

The skeletal system acts as a framework against which muscles work to move parts of the body or the entire organism. In this section, the muscle–bone interactions that are responsible for the movement of vertebrates are described.

36.3a Joints of the Vertebrate Endoskeleton Allow Bones to Move and Rotate

The bones of the vertebrate skeleton are connected by joints, many of them movable. The most movable joints, including those of the shoulders, elbows, wrists, fingers, knees, ankles, and toes, are *synovial joints,* consisting of the ends of two bones enclosed by a fluid-filled capsule of connective tissue **(Figure 36.13a, p. 885)**. Within the joint, the ends of the bones are covered by a smooth layer of cartilage and lubricated by synovial fluid, which makes the bones slide easily as the joint moves. Synovial joints are held together by straps of connective tissue called *ligaments,* which extend across the joints outside the capsule **(Figure 36.13b)**. The ligaments restrict the motion of the joint and help prevent it from buckling or twisting under heavy loads.

Figure 36.12
Mammalian skeletons. **(a)** Major bones in the human. Inset shows the structure of the femur (thigh)bone, with the location of red and yellow marrow. Internal spaces lighten the bone's density. At the joints a cartilage layer forms a smooth slippery cushion between bones. Compare the general features of this skeleton with those shown in **(b), (c),** and **(d).** Note general and specific resemblances among the skeletons of the four mammals. **(b)** The new world monkey (family Cebidae) lives in trees. **(c)** The gliding lemur (family Cynocephalidae) also is arboreal, but a glider. **(d)** The raccoon (family Procyonidae) is terrestrial. Note the differences in skull shape, limb lengths and feet. The raccoon is a male reflected by the conspicuous baculum or penis bone (see also Fig. 38.14).

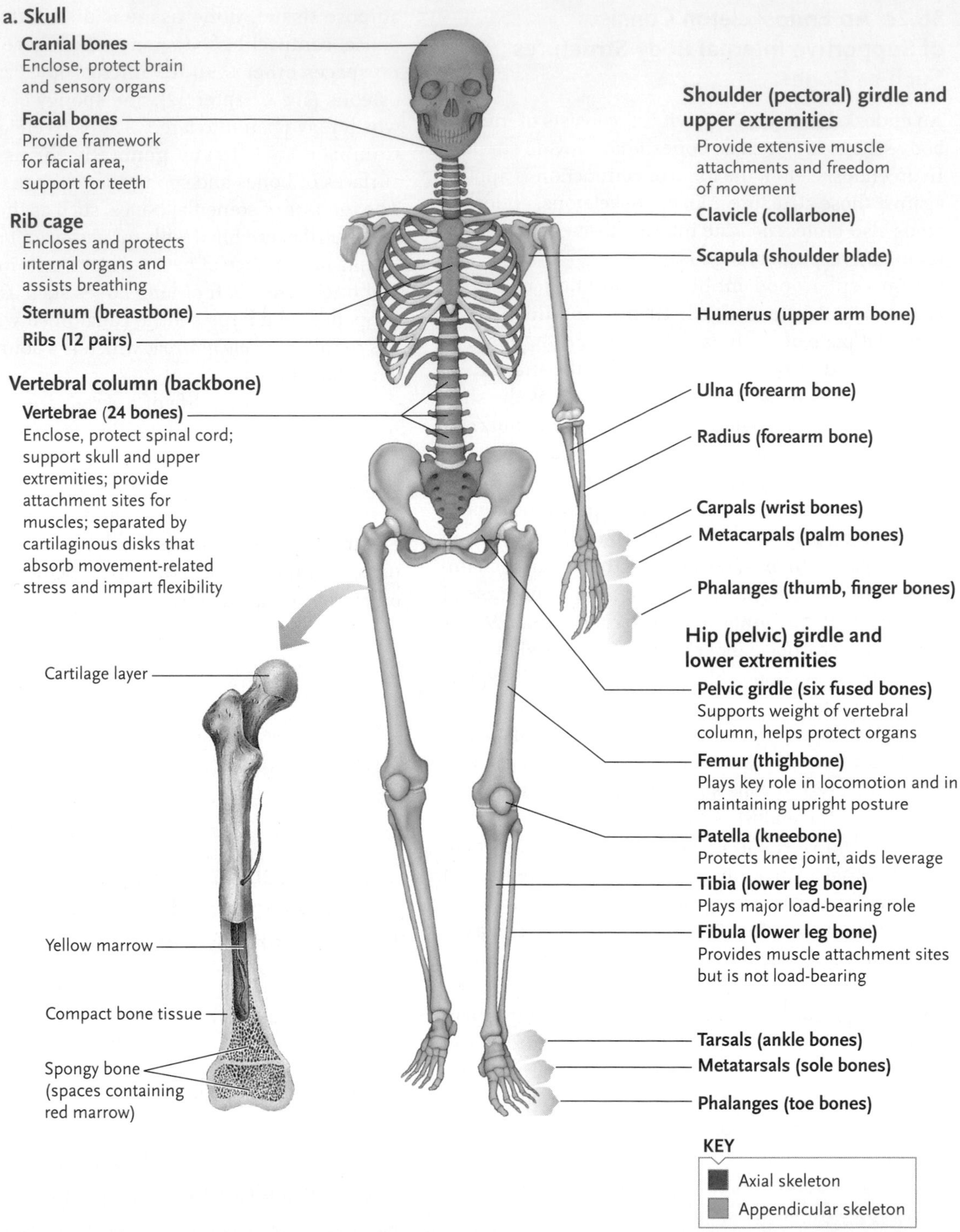

a. Skull

Cranial bones
Enclose, protect brain and sensory organs

Facial bones
Provide framework for facial area, support for teeth

Rib cage
Encloses and protects internal organs and assists breathing

Sternum (breastbone)

Ribs (12 pairs)

Vertebral column (backbone)

Vertebrae (24 bones)
Enclose, protect spinal cord; support skull and upper extremities; provide attachment sites for muscles; separated by cartilaginous disks that absorb movement-related stress and impart flexibility

Cartilage layer

Yellow marrow

Compact bone tissue

Spongy bone (spaces containing red marrow)

Shoulder (pectoral) girdle and upper extremities
Provide extensive muscle attachments and freedom of movement

Clavicle (collarbone)

Scapula (shoulder blade)

Humerus (upper arm bone)

Ulna (forearm bone)

Radius (forearm bone)

Carpals (wrist bones)

Metacarpals (palm bones)

Phalanges (thumb, finger bones)

Hip (pelvic) girdle and lower extremities

Pelvic girdle (six fused bones)
Supports weight of vertebral column, helps protect organs

Femur (thighbone)
Plays key role in locomotion and in maintaining upright posture

Patella (kneebone)
Protects knee joint, aids leverage

Tibia (lower leg bone)
Plays major load-bearing role

Fibula (lower leg bone)
Provides muscle attachment sites but is not load-bearing

Tarsals (ankle bones)

Metatarsals (sole bones)

Phalanges (toe bones)

KEY
Axial skeleton
Appendicular skeleton

b.

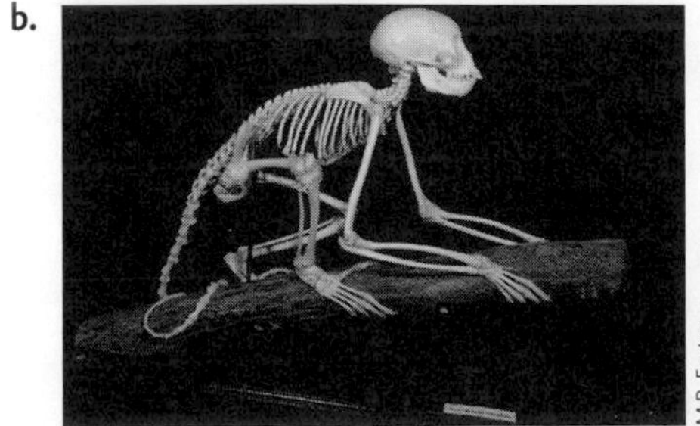

M.B. Fenton

c.

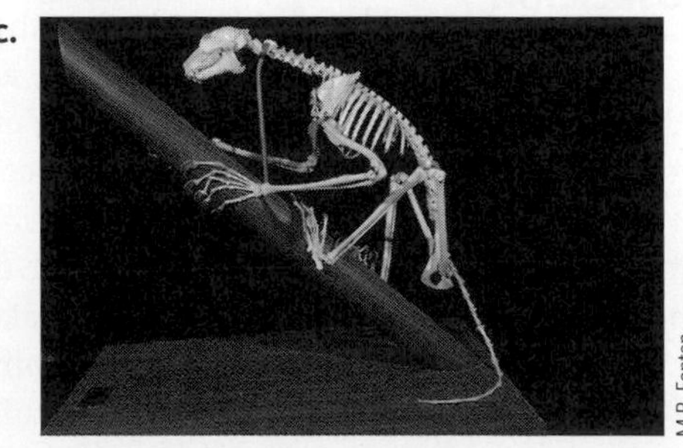

M.B. Fenton

d.

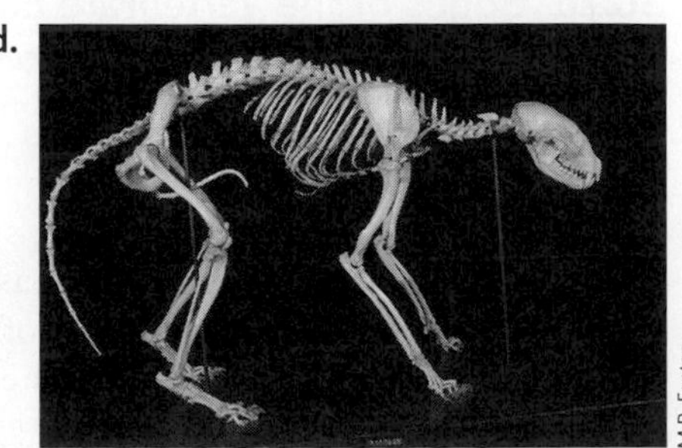

M.B. Fenton

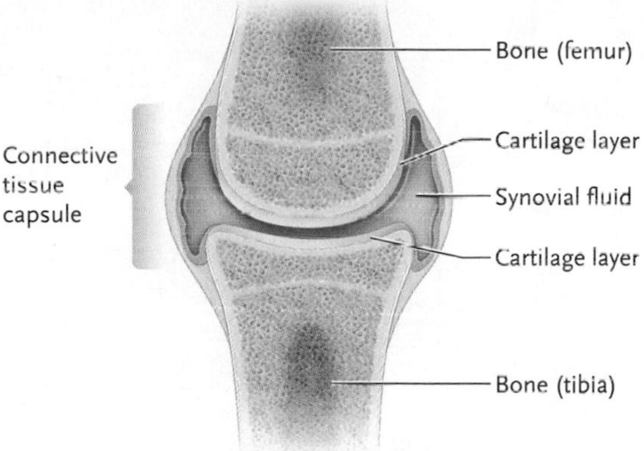

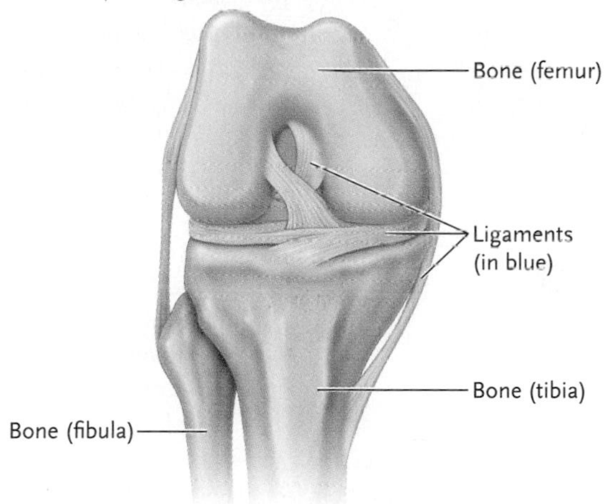

Figure 36.13
A synovial joint. **(a)** Cross section of a typical synovial joint. **(b)** Ligaments reinforcing the knee joint.

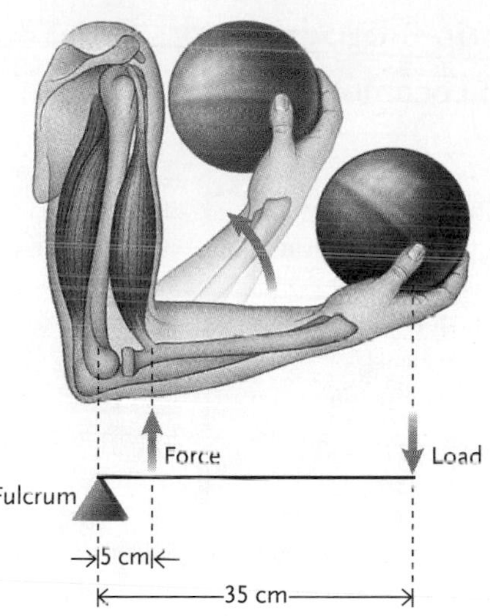

Figure 36.14
A body lever: The lever formed by the bones of the forearm. The fulcrum (the hinge or joint) is at one end of the lever, the load is placed on the opposite end, and the force is exerted at a point on the lever between the fulcrum and the load.

In other, less movable joints, called *cartilaginous joints,* the ends of bones are covered with layers of cartilage but have no fluid-filled capsule surrounding them. Fibrous connective tissue covers and connects the bones of these joints, which occur between the vertebrae and some rib bones.

In still other joints, called *fibrous joints,* stiff fibres of connective tissue join the bones and allow little or no movement. Fibrous joints occur between the bones of the skull and hold the teeth in their sockets.

The bones connected by movable joints work like levers. A lever is a rigid structure that can move around a pivot point known as a *fulcrum.* Levers differ with respect to where the fulcrum is located along the lever and where the force is applied. The most common type of lever system in the body—exemplified by the elbow joint—has the fulcrum at one end, the load at the opposite end, and the force applied at a point between the ends **(Figure 36.14).** For this lever, the force applied must be much greater than the load, but it increases the distance the load moves compared with the distance over which the force is applied. This allows small muscle movements to produce large body movements, as well as allows movements such as running or throwing to be carried out at high speed.

At a joint, a muscle that causes movement in the joint when it contracts is called an **agonist.** In many cases, other muscles that assist the action of an agonist are involved in the movement of a joint. For instance, deltoid and pectoral muscles assist the biceps brachii muscle in lifting a weight.

Most of the bones of vertebrate skeletons are moved by muscles arranged in **antagonistic pairs:** *extensor muscles* extend the joint, meaning increasing the angle between the two bones, whereas *flexor muscles* do the opposite. (Antagonistic muscles are also used in invertebrates for movement of body parts—for example, the limbs of insects and arthropods.) In humans, one such pair is formed by the biceps brachii muscle at the front of the upper arm and the triceps brachii muscle at the back of the upper arm **(Figure 36.15).** When the biceps muscle contracts, the bone of the lower arm is bent (flexed) around the elbow joint, and the triceps muscle is passively stretched (see **Figure 36.15a**); when the triceps muscle contracts, the lower

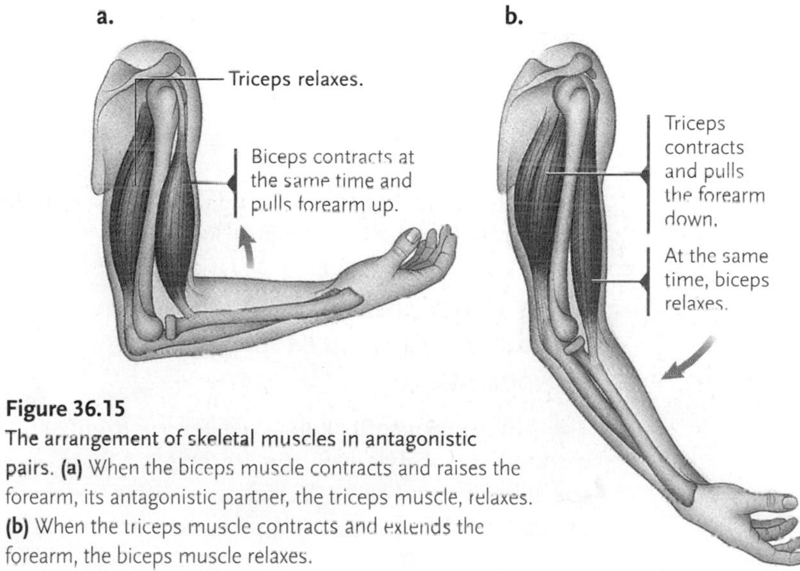

a.
Triceps relaxes.
Biceps contracts at the same time and pulls forearm up.
b.
Triceps contracts and pulls the forearm down.
At the same time, biceps relaxes.

Figure 36.15
The arrangement of skeletal muscles in antagonistic pairs. **(a)** When the biceps muscle contracts and raises the forearm, its antagonistic partner, the triceps muscle, relaxes. **(b)** When the triceps muscle contracts and extends the forearm, the biceps muscle relaxes.

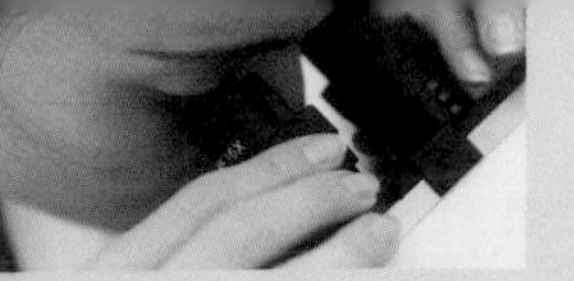

People Behind Biology

Keir Pearson: Locomotion Step by Step

The act of walking is both unconscious and deceptively simple when viewed from a human perspective, involving two legs. But in insects, in which walking on six legs usually involves two legs on one side and one leg on the other being lifted, while the remaining legs form a triangular support, and in nonhuman mammals, in which the order of movement of the legs may differ for various speeds of locomotion, the real complexity of walking becomes more obvious.

Keir G. Pearson of the University of Alberta became interested in this challenging problem while he was a Rhodes Scholar at Oxford University, where he demonstrated the complexity of the patterns of nervous activity controlling a single muscle. He has continued that interest for more than 40 years, progressing to an analysis of walking in insects and vertebrates (usually cats). The techniques he has used are challenging, involving the recording of electrical activity in the leg muscles and the ganglia controlling those muscles. They have revealed that walking in insects is driven by a pattern of rhythmic activity, the central pattern generator (CPG) in the neurons of the ganglia associated with the limbs, influenced by information flowing from proprioceptors (see Chapter 34) in the limbs and by environmental information processed through the brain. These results have influenced the construction of walking robots and physiotherapy for humans with spinal cord damage.

Pearson recently turned his attention to the way in which visual information influences walking. A simple and revealing experiment involved cats **(Figure 1).** A cat approaching a small barrier steps over the barrier, first with the forelegs and then with the hindlegs. To a less inquiring mind, that might seem simple enough. But a scientist such as Pearson notes that when the hindlegs step over the barrier, the barrier is no longer in the visual field. The CPG in some sense remembers the position of the barrier. Pearson then asked the question: What if there is a delay after the forefeet step over? By offering food, he was able to interrupt the cat before its hindlegs had stepped over the barrier. It turns out that the hindlegs remember the position of the barrier for at least 10 minutes, even if the barrier is removed after the front feet have stepped over it. This is far longer than the memory of the image in the eye. These clear and simple results demonstrate the way in which information processed unconsciously through the brain influences "automatic" events.

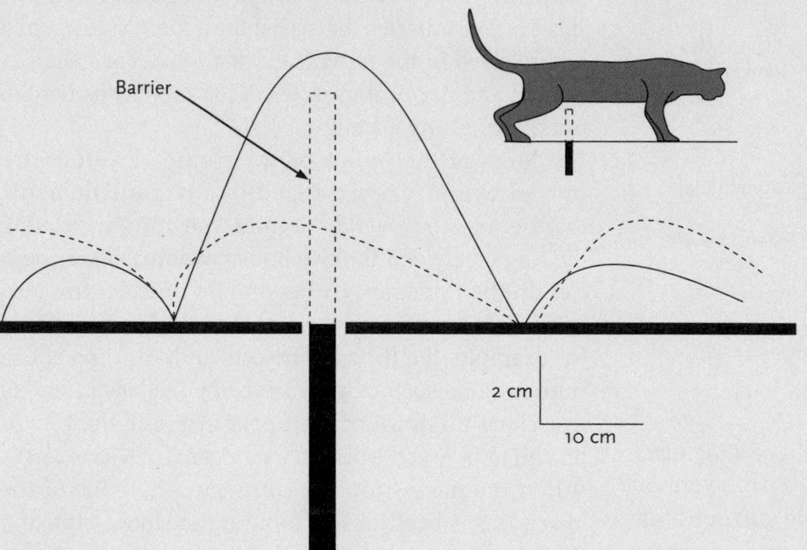

Figure 1
Experiment demonstrating the memory of CPG in the cat. The cat stepped over the barrier with the front feet but was then delayed by offering it food. The barrier, which it could no longer see, was removed. The solid line indicates the path taken by the hindfoot when walking resumed up to 10 minutes later. The dotted line indicates the path taken by the hindfoot when the cat does not encounter a barrier.

arm is straightened (extended), and the biceps muscle is passively stretched (see Figure 36.15b).

36.3b Vertebrates Have Muscle–Bone Interactions Optimized for Specific Movements

The human musculoskeletal system is highly specialized, scarcely revealing its origins from less specialized vertebrates. Vertebrates differ widely in the patterns by which muscles connect to bones and in the length and mechanical advantage of the levers produced by these connections. The segmental muscles of fish, attached to the vertebrae, many ribs, and the skin, are efficient in propelling fish through the water with side-to-side movements. The appearance of limbs and the movement onto land rendered that form of locomotion less useful, although it is often combined with leg movement in some amphibians and reptiles. Crocodiles use a side-to-side movement in the water but can move rapidly on land using their legs. The dinosaurs include bipedal species, able to

a.

Jupiter Images

b.

Petr Kratochvil/Publ c Domain Pictures

Figure 36.16
(a) A sea turtle. Note that the forelegs are winglike paddles that enhance swimming. The turtle has limited mobility on land. **(b)** A penguin swimming, using modified forelimbs (wings). Note the resemblance in shape to the paddlelike forelegs of the sea turtle. Locomotion on land depends entirely on the hindlegs.

walk on their hind legs. Other reptiles have lost their legs. Snakes use a wavelike motion to propel themselves on the surface of the ground. Sea turtles have paddlelike forelimbs that they use in swimming, very much like those of penguins, an example of parallel evolution **(Figure 36.16)**. Those mammals that have returned to the sea, such as whales, propel themselves by an up-and-down movement of their huge tail. This up-and- down movement is also used by elite human swimmers during some races.

The development of flight, represented by birds and, among the mammals, bats, is accompanied by some common modifications. In both groups, but particularly in birds, the sternum is greatly enlarged to provide attachment for the powerful pectoral muscles. The bones of the forelimb are greatly modified. In bats, the bones of the hand are extended to provide a framework for the sheets of skin that form the wing. In birds, the bones of the hand are fused and support the feathers that make up the wing. The bones generally contain many cavities or spaces, making the body lighter. Penguins are birds that exploit the marine environment. They do not fly, but they use their reduced wings to "fly" through the water.

Burrowing mammals have short, very stout forelimbs with muscles arranged so that contraction provides relatively little movement but great force.

Study Break

1. Distinguish synovial joints, cartilaginous joints, and fibrous joints.
2. What are antagonistic muscle pairs?

Unanswered Questions

Is there a genetic predisposition to elite performance?

It is generally accepted that elite performance in some sports is often associated with a general body shape. Sprinters tend to be tall and thin, with long legs. Weight lifters are shorter, and their arms and legs are shorter. These body shapes are the result of the expression of many genes during development. But individual genes have also been associated with performance in specific sports. The *ACTN3* gene is one of a family of genes that code for actin-binding proteins (α-actinins) that are important in attaching the actin (thin filaments) to the Z line. *ACTN3*, producing α-actinin 3, is expressed only in fast muscle fibres, whereas an isoform, *ACTN2*, is expressed in both fast and slow fibres. Moreover, there is a mutant form of *ACTN3* that results in loss of the protein. This appears not to affect health and occurs in about 20% of the population.

In 2003, a group of Australian scientists associated *ACTN3* with power athletes, for whom fast twitch muscles are important (sprinters, weight lifters), whereas endurance athletes (long-distance runners) were more likely to have the mutant form of the *ACTN3* gene, leading to a greater proportion of slow fibres. *ACTN3* has been identified in the media as a "speed gene." It is crucial, however, to recognize that the Australian research simply identified a correlation between the gene and a particular type of athletic activity. The research has not identified a causal relationship: there is no direct evidence that the presence or absence of the functional form of *ACTN3* will result in superior performance in any specific activity. The question remains open, and the issue raises many ethical concerns.

Review

Go to CENGAGENOW™ at http://hed.nelson.com/ to access quizzing, animations, exercises, articles, and personalized homework help.

36.1 Vertebrate Skeletal Muscle: Structure and Function

- Skeletal muscles move the joints of the body. They are formed from long, cylindrical cells called muscle fibres, which are packed with myofibrils, contractile elements consisting of myosin thick filaments and actin thin filaments. The two types of filaments are arranged in an overlapping pattern of contractile units called sarcomeres.
- Infoldings of the plasma membrane of the muscle fibre form T tubules. The sarcomeres are encircled by the sarcoplasmic reticulum, a system of vesicles with segments separated from T tubules by small gaps.
- In the sliding filament mechanism of muscle contraction, the simultaneous sliding of thin filaments on each side of sarcomeres over the thick filaments shortens the sarcomeres and the muscle fibres, producing the force that contracts the muscle.
- The sliding motion of thin and thick filaments is produced in response to an action potential arriving at the neuromuscular junction. The action potential causes the release of acetylcholine, which triggers an action potential in the muscle fibre that spreads over its plasma membrane and stimulates the sarcoplasmic reticulum to release Ca^{2+} into the cytosol. The Ca^{2+} combines with troponin, inducing a conformational change that moves tropomyosin away from the myosin-binding sites on thin filaments. Exposure of the sites allows myosin crossbridges to bind and initiate the crossbridge cycle in which the myosin heads of thick filaments attach to a thin filament, pull, and release in cyclic reactions powered by ATP hydrolysis.
- When action potentials stop, Ca^{2+} is pumped back into the sarcoplasmic reticulum, leading to Ca^{2+} release from troponin, which allows tropomyosin to cover the myosin-binding sites in the thin filaments, thereby stopping the crossbridge cycle.
- A single action potential arriving at a neuromuscular junction causes a muscle twitch. Restimulation of a muscle fibre before it has relaxed completely causes a second twitch, which is added to the first, causing a summed, stronger contraction. Rapid arrival of action potentials causes the twitches to sum to a peak level of contraction called tetanus. Normally, muscles contract in a tetanic mode.
- Vertebrate muscle fibres occur in three types. Slow muscle fibres contract relatively slowly, but do not fatigue rapidly. Fast aerobic fibres contract relatively quickly and powerfully and fatigue more quickly than slow fibres. Fast anaerobic fibres can contract more rapidly and powerfully than fast aerobic fibres, but fatigue more rapidly. The fibres differ in their number of mitochondria and capacity to produce ATP.
- Skeletal muscles are divided into motor units, consisting of a group of muscle fibres activated by branches of a single motor neuron. The total force produced by a skeletal muscle is determined by the number of motor units that are activated.
- Most invertebrate muscles contain thin and thick filaments arranged in sarcomeres, and contract by the same sliding filament mechanism that operates in vertebrates. In arthropods, fast twitches and slower, graded contractions result from differences in innervation. Insect flight muscle is specialized to contract at high frequency.

36.2 Skeletal Systems

- A hydrostatic skeleton is a structure consisting of a muscle-surrounded compartment or compartments filled with fluid under pressure. Contraction and relaxation of the muscles changes the shape of the animal.
- In an exoskeleton, a rigid external covering provides support for the body. The force of muscle contraction is applied against the covering. An exoskeleton can also protect delicate internal tissues.
- In an endoskeleton, the body is supported by rigid structures within the body, such as bones. The force of muscle contraction is applied against those structures. Endoskeletons also protect delicate internal tissues. In vertebrates, the endoskeleton is the primary skeletal system. The vertebrate axial skeleton consists of the skull, vertebral column, sternum, and rib cage, whereas the appendicular skeleton includes the shoulder bones, the forelimbs, the hip bones, and the hindlimbs.
- Bone tissue is distributed between compact bone, with no spaces except the microscopic canals of the osteons, and spongy bone tissue, which has spaces filled by red or yellow marrow.
- Calcium and phosphate ions are constantly exchanged between the blood and bone tissues. The turnover keeps the Ca^{2+} concentration balanced at optimal levels in body fluids.

36.3 Vertebrate Movement: The Interactions between Muscles and Bones

- The bones of a skeleton are connected by joints. A synovial joint, the most movable type, consists of a fluid-filled capsule surrounding the ends of the bones forming the joint. A cartilaginous joint, which is less movable, has smooth layers of cartilage between the bones, with no surrounding capsule. The bones of a fibrous joint are joined by connective tissue fibres that allow little or no movement.
- The bones moved by skeletal muscles act as levers, with a joint at one end forming the fulcrum of the lever, the load at the opposite end, and the force applied by attachment of a muscle at a point between the ends.
- At a joint, an agonist muscle, perhaps assisted by other muscles, causes movement. Most skeletal muscles are arranged in antagonistic pairs, in which the members of a pair pull a bone in opposite directions. When one member of the pair contracts, the other member relaxes and is stretched.
- Vertebrates have a variety of patterns in which muscles connect to bones, giving different properties to the levers produced. Those properties are specialized for the activities of the animal.

Questions

Self-Test Questions

1. Vertebrate skeletal muscle
   a. is attached to bone by means of ligaments.
   b. may bend but not extend body parts.
   c. may rotate one body part with respect to another.
   d. is found in the walls of blood vessels and intestines.
   e. is usually attached at each end to the same bone.
2. In a resting muscle fibre,
   a. sarcomeres are regions between two H zones.
   b. disks of M line proteins called the A band separate the thick filaments.
   c. I bands are composed of the same thick filaments seen in the A bands.
   d. Z lines are adjacent to H zones, which attach thick filaments.
   e. dark A bands contain overlapping thick and thin filaments with a central thin H zone composed only of thick filaments.
3. The sliding filament contractile mechanism
   a. causes thick and thin filaments to slide toward the centre of the A band, bringing the Z lines closer together.
   b. is inhibited by the influx of Ca^{2+} into the muscle fibre cytosol.
   c. lengthens the sarcomere to separate the I regions.
   d. depends on the isolation of actin and myosin until a contraction is completed.
   e. uses myosin crossbridges to stimulate delivery of Ca^{2+} to the muscle fibre.
4. Which of the following is *not* an example of a hydrostatic skeletal structure?
   a. the tube feet of sea urchins
   b. the body wall of annelids
   c. the body wall of a grasshopper
   d. the body wall of cnidarians
   e. the penis of mammals
5. Endoskeletons
   a. protect internal organs and provide structures against which the force of muscle contraction can work.
   b. differ from exoskeletons in that endoskeletons do not support the external body.
   c. cannot be found in molluscs and echinoderms.
   d. are composed of appendicular structures that form the skull.
   e. compose the arms and legs, which are part of the axial skeleton.

Questions for Discussion

1. A coach must train young athletes for the 100 m sprint. They need muscles specialized for speed and strength rather than for endurance. What kinds of muscle characteristics would the training regimen aim to develop? How would it be altered to train marathoners?
2. Astronauts in zero gravity tend to lose bone mass, particularly in the hip, the long bones of the legs, and the vertebrae. Instruments that measure bone loss cannot be taken on space missions. Can you think of experimental procedures that might be used on earth to explore the phenomenon?
3. If you were a leading researcher in a pharmaceutical company interested in controlling bone loss, what cells and processes would you target?

Illustrations from William Harvey's book, published in 1658, in which he demonstrated for the first time that the blood circulates. In one of the experiments, he used a tourniquet to reveal the veins and their valves. Part of the intellectual excitement of the Renaissance period, Harvey was the first experimental biologist.

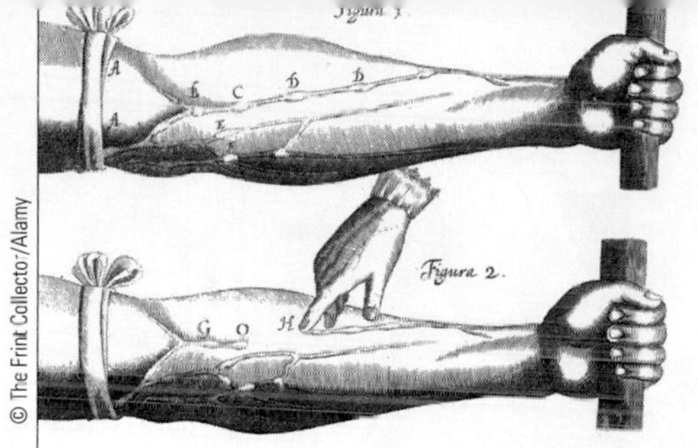

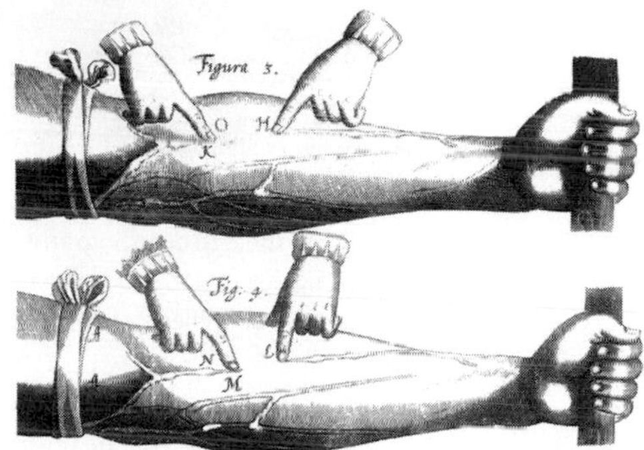

37 The Circulatory System

Study Plan

Why It Matters

Jimmie the bulldog stood on the stage of a demonstration laboratory at a meeting of the Royal Society in London in 1909, with one front paw and one rear paw in laboratory jars containing salt water **(Figure 37.1, p. 892)**. Wires leading from the jars were connected to a galvanometer, a device that can detect electrical currents.

Jimmie's master, Dr. Augustus Waller, a physician at St. Mary's Hospital, was relating his experiments in the emerging field of *electrophysiology*. Among other discoveries, Waller found that his apparatus detected the electrical currents produced each time the dog's heart beat.

Waller had originally experimented on himself. He already knew that the heart produces an electrical current as it beats; other scientists had discovered this by attaching electrodes directly to the heart of experimental animals. Looking for a painless alternative to that procedure, Waller reasoned that because the human body can conduct electricity, his arms and legs might conduct the currents generated by the heart if they were connected to a galvanometer. Accordingly, Waller set up two metal pans containing salt water and connected wires from the pans to a galvanometer. He put his bare left foot in one pan and

a. Jimmie the bulldog

From A. D. Waller, Physiology, The Servant of Medicine, Hitchcock Lectures, University of London Press, 1910

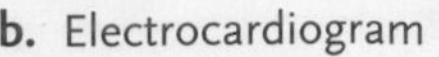

b. Electrocardiogram

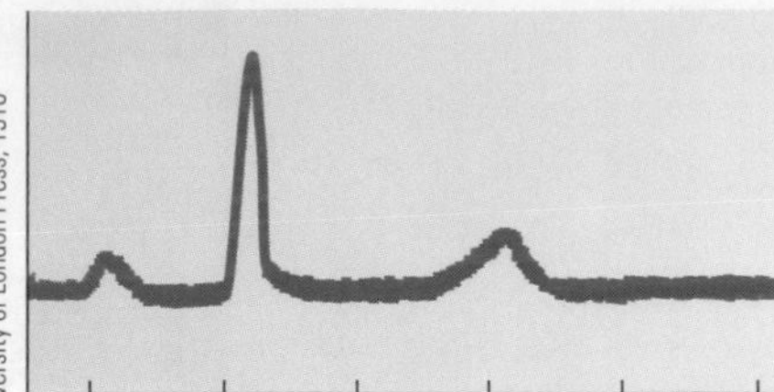

Figure 37.1
The first electrocardiograms. (a) Jimmie the bulldog standing in laboratory jars containing salt water, with wires leading to a galvanometer that recorded the electrical currents produced by his heartbeat. **(b)** One of Waller's early electrocardiograms.

his right hand in the other. The technique worked; the indicator on the galvanometer jumped each time his heart beat. And it worked with Jimmie, too.

Waller also invented a method for recording the changes in current, which became the first electrocardiogram (ECG). He constructed a galvanometer by placing a column of mercury in a fine glass tube, with a conducting salt solution layered above the mercury. Changes in the current passing through the tube caused corresponding changes in the surface tension of the mercury, which produced movements that could be detected by reflecting a beam of light from the mercury surface. By placing a moving photographic plate behind the mercury tube, Waller could record the movements of the reflected light on the plate (Figure 37.1b shows one of his records). These were the first ECGs.

The beating of Jimmie's heart, recorded as an electrical trace by Augustus Waller, is part of the actions of the **circulatory system**, an organ system consisting of a fluid, a pump (the heart), and vessels for moving important molecules, and often cells, from one tissue to another. Examples of transported molecules are oxygen (O_2), nutrients, hormones, and wastes.

We study these systems in this chapter with emphasis on the circulatory system of humans and other mammals. We also discuss the **lymphatic system**, an accessory system of vessels and organs that helps balance the fluid content of the blood and surrounding tissues and participates in the body's defences against invading disease organisms.

37.1 Animal Circulatory Systems: An Introduction

Protostomes with simple body plans, including sponges, cnidarians, flatworms, and nematodes, function with no specialized circulatory system. Nearly all of these animals are aquatic or, like parasitic flatworms, live surrounded by the body fluids or intestinal contents of a host animal. Their bodies are structured as thin sheets of cells that lie close to the fluids of the surrounding environment. The products of digestion diffuse among the cells via the interstitial fluids, and O_2 and CO_2 are exchanged with the medium through the surface of the animal. Nematodes have a fluid-filled body cavity but no special mechanism for circulating that fluid.

37.1a Animal Circulatory Systems Share Basic Elements

In larger and more complex animals, most cells lie in cell layers too deep within the body to exchange substances directly with the environment via diffusion. Instead, the animals have a circulatory system, composed of tissues and organs, that conducts O_2, CO_2, nutrients, and the products of metabolism among the cells and tissues. The circulatory system may connect with specialized regions of the animal where substances are exchanged with the external environment. For example, oxygen is absorbed from the environment in the gills or lungs of many animals and is carried by the blood to all parts of the body; CO_2 released from body cells is carried by the blood to the lungs or gills, where it is released to the environment. Soluble wastes are conducted from body cells to the kidneys or other excretory organs, which remove wastes from the circulation and excrete them into the environment.

Animal circulatory systems carrying out these roles share certain basic features:

- A specialized fluid medium, usually containing at least some cells. This medium carries nutrients from the digestive system, the products of metabolism, and soluble wastes. With the conspicuous exception of the insects, it also transports O_2 and CO_2.
- In most groups, the fluid is contained in tubular vessels that distribute it to the various organs. Most arthropods and molluscs have an open system that lacks vessels.

a. Open circulatory system: no distinction between haemolymph and interstitial fluid

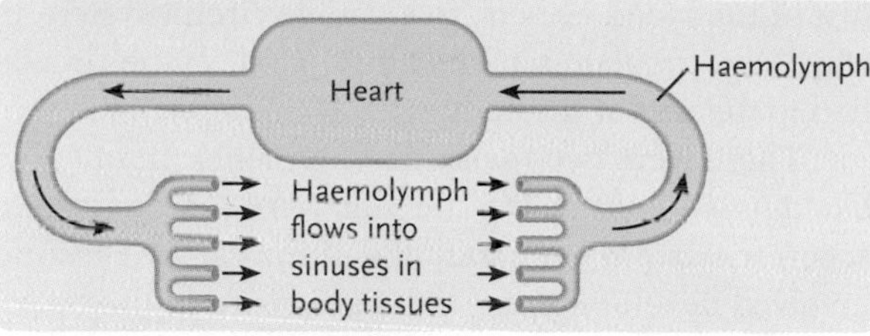

b. Closed circulatory system: blood separated from interstitial fluid

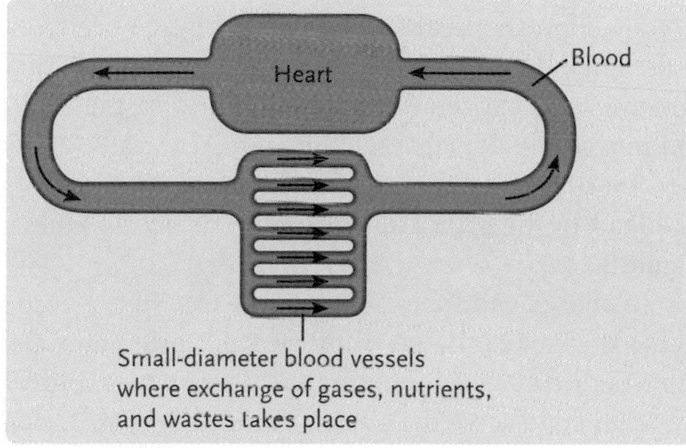

Figure 37.2
(a) Open circulatory system: haemolymph bathes the organs and body tissues. **(b)** Closed circulatory system: blood confined in tubes that lie among the cells of all tissues.

- A muscular heart that pumps the fluid through the circulatory system. Words associated with the heart often include *cardio,* from *kardia,* Greek for heart.

Animal circulatory systems take one of two forms, either *open* or *closed* **(Figure 37.2)**. In an **open circulatory system,** vessels leaving the heart release fluid, usually termed **haemolymph,** directly into body spaces or into sinuses surrounding organs. Thus, the organs and tissues are directly bathed in the haemolymph. The haemolymph reenters the heart through valves in the heart wall that close each time the heart pumps, thereby maintaining a unidirectional flow. In a **closed circulatory system,** the blood is confined to blood vessels and is distinct from the interstitial fluid. Substances are exchanged between the blood and the interstitial fluid and then between the interstitial fluid and cells.

37.1b Most Invertebrates Have Open Circulatory Systems

Among the protostomes, arthropods and most molluscs have open circulatory systems with one or more muscular hearts **(Figure 37.3a).** The blood is not conveyed directly to the cells by tubes but bathes the body tissues. In an open system, most of the fluid pressure generated by the heart dissipates when the blood is released into body spaces. Although the pressure remains low, the rate at which the blood circulates can be increased by an increase in the rate of beating of the heart(s). In highly active invertebrates, such as flying insects, the heart rate may rise to three or

a.

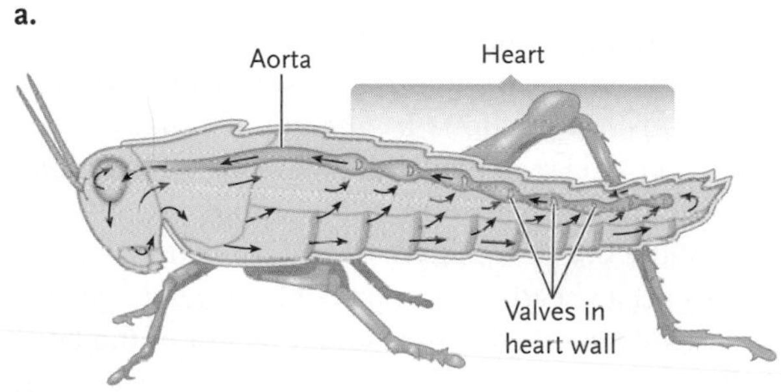

b.

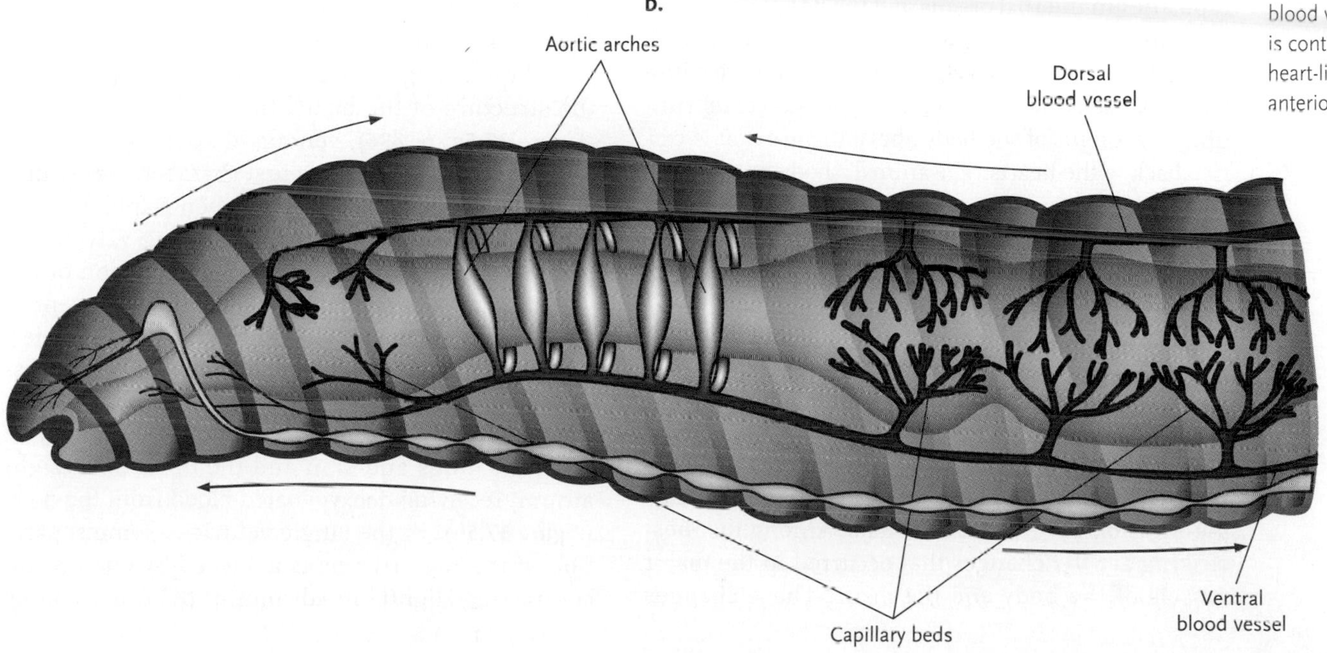

Figure 37.3
(a) Open circulatory system of a grasshopper. **(b)** Closed circulation in an earthworm. Aortic arches help to pump the blood into the ventral vessel that conveys blood to capillaries. The blood returns to the hearts from the capillary beds via the dorsal blood vessel, which is contractile and heart-like at the anterior end.

more times the resting rate, increasing the circulation of the hemolymph among the tissues. In addition, most insects have accessory hearts associated with the wings and each leg, which experience the same increases in rate during periods of high metabolic activity. In insects and molluscs, heart rate is controlled in some cases by nerves but largely by a variety of amine and peptide hormones (see Chapter 35).

37.1c Some Invertebrates and All Vertebrates Have Closed Circulatory Systems

Annelids, cephalopod molluscs such as squids and octopuses, most deuterostome invertebrates, and all vertebrates have closed circulatory systems. In these systems, vessels called **arteries** conduct blood away from the heart at relatively high pressure. From the arteries, the blood enters highly branched networks of microscopic, thin-walled vessels called **capillaries** that are well adapted for diffusion of substances. Nutrients and wastes are exchanged between the blood and body tissues as the blood moves through the capillaries. The blood then flows at relatively low pressure from the capillaries to larger vessels, the **veins,** which carry the blood back to the heart. Typically, the blood is maintained at a higher pressure and moves more rapidly through the body in closed systems than in open systems.

In many animals, closed systems allow precise control of the distribution and rate of blood flow to different body regions by means of muscles that contract or relax to adjust the diameter of the blood vessels. In an earthworm, for example, the anterior part of the dorsal blood vessel and five pairs of aortic arches act as hearts to pump the blood into large ventral blood vessels that extend the length of the body below the gut (Figure 37.3b). In the body segments, lateral branches of the ventral blood vessels lead to capillaries in internal organs and the body wall, where exchange of substances with interstitial fluids takes place. The blood is collected from the capillaries into lateral vessels that lead to a large dorsal vessel running the length of the body above the gut and is carried back to the hearts. The animal's body movements and contractions of the dorsal blood vessel help keep the blood flowing, and one-way valves in the hearts and dorsal blood vessel keep the flow from reversing.

37.1d Vertebrate Circulatory Systems Have Evolved from Single to Double Blood Circuits

A comparison of the different vertebrate groups reveals several evolutionary trends that accompanied the invasion of terrestrial habitats. Among the most striking are the changes that occurred in the major vessels of the body and the heart. These changes converted the single-circuit system of sharks and bony fish, in which the gills are in the same circuit as the rest of the blood vessels, to a double-circuit system in which the circulation to the lungs parallels the circulation to the rest of the body.

There were two major developments. In one, the blood vessels supplying the gills were reorganized to accommodate the appearance of lungs. The second involved developments in the structure of the heart. In the hypothetical chordate ancestor (see Chapter 27), there were six pairs of gills, each supplied by a branch of a single ventral artery, the ventral aorta, that led directly from the heart. After gas exchange occurred in the gills, the blood was collected in two vessels that conveyed the oxygenated blood forward to the brain and in a single dorsal vessel, the dorsal aorta, to carry the blood back to the rest of the body. The vessels that lead to the gills are referred to as aortic arches **(Figure 37.4a).**

In sharks and their relatives, the first of the aortic arches that appear in the embryos of all vertebrates disappears during development, and only arches II to VI are retained to serve the gills in the adult **(Figure 37.4b).** In lungfish **(Figure 37.4c),** the reduction in gill function that accompanies the appearance of lungs is associated with two changes. Arches III and IV no longer run through gills, and, more significantly, arch VI supplies both a gill and the lungs. In a terrestrial amphibian such as a salamander **(Figure 37.4d),** arch III loses its connection with the other arterial arches to become the carotid arteries. As a result, there is a separate blood supply to the brain directly from the heart. In most reptiles **(Figure 37.4e),** arch V appears only in the embryo, and the connection between arch VI and the dorsal aorta disappears. Arch VI is exclusively devoted to supplying the lungs as the pulmonary artery. In birds **(Figure 37.4f)** and mammals, arch IV becomes a single rather than a paired vessel, leading to a single dorsal aorta. In birds, the right arch survives, whereas mammals retain the left arch.

These changes are accompanied by changes in the structure of the heart. In a shark or bony fish **(Figure 37.5a, p. 896),** venous, deoxygenated blood from the tissues enters the first chamber, the atrium. The atrium contracts, forcing open flaplike valves leading into the ventricle and closing valves that prevent backflow into the veins. Contraction of the ventricle propels the blood forward into the ventral aorta leading to the aortic arches, the gill capillaries, and the dorsal aorta, which carries blood to the tissues. In amphibians, the atrium is divided, with one side (left atrium) receiving oxygenated blood from the lungs and skin and the other side (right atrium) receiving deoxygenated blood from the body **(Figure 37.5b).** In the single ventricle, some separation of the two streams is achieved by one atrium contracting slightly in advance of the other and by

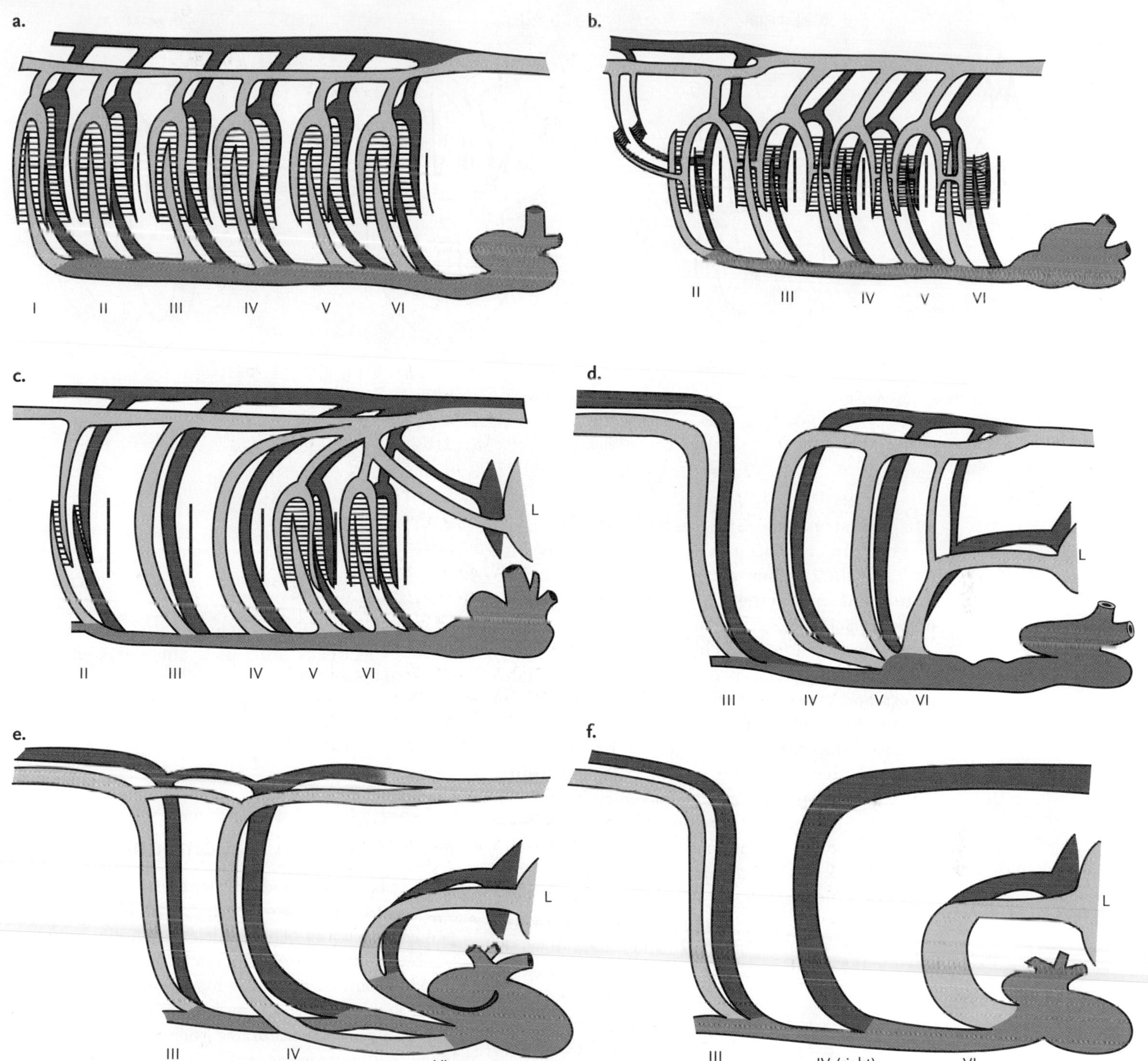

Figure 37.4

Evolution of the aortic arches in vertebrates. The darkest shading indicates the vessels of the right side, the lightest the vessels of the left side, and intermediate shading indicates the single ventral aorta. **(a)** The six arches in a hypothetical ancestor or in embryos. **(b)** In a shark, arch I has disappeared in the adult. **(c)** In lungfish, the lungs and one pair of gills are served from arch VI and the gills are reduced in number. **(d)** In a terrestrial amphibian, the lungs (L) are served by arch VI, which also retains its connection to the general circulation. The supply to the brain via arch III is separate from the general circulation. **(e)** In modern reptiles (snakes and lizards), although arches III and IV are still connected dorsally, arch VI serves only the lungs. **(f)** In birds, the supply to the brain is separated as the carotid arteries. Arch IV is present on the right side only and becomes the dorsal aorta. In mammals, the left side of arch IV remains as the dorsal aorta and the right side disappears.

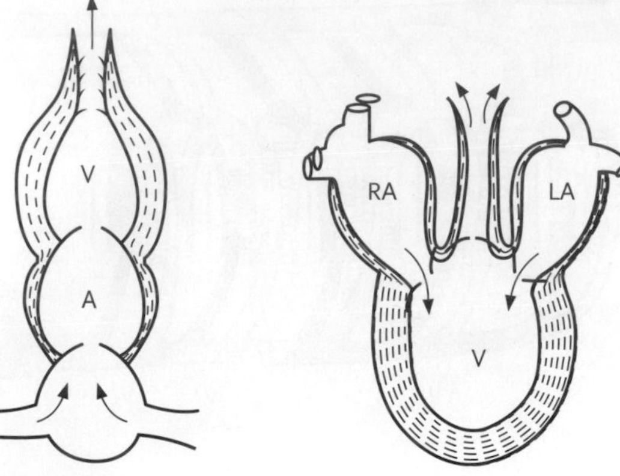

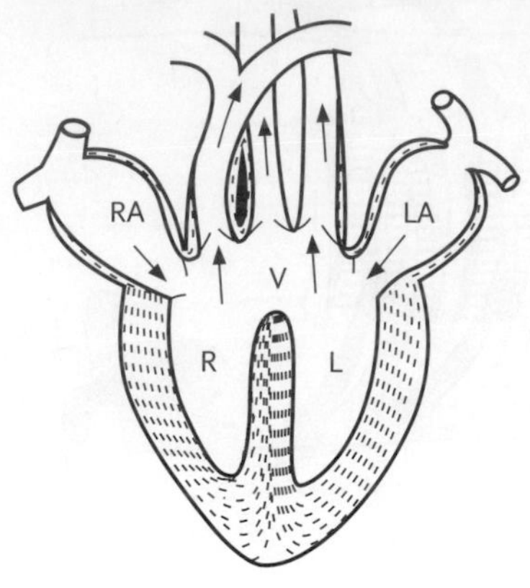

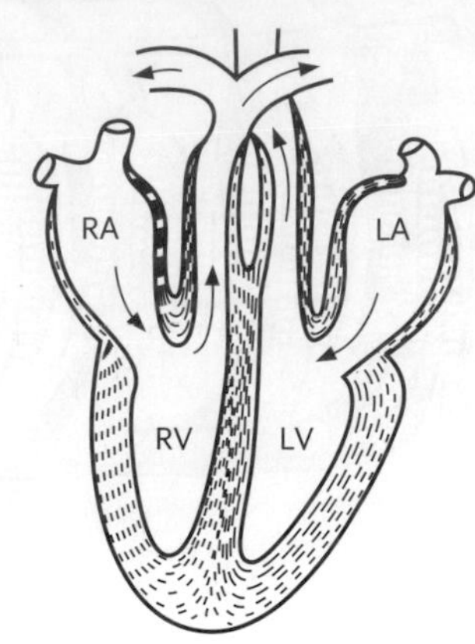

Figure 37.5
Major steps in the evolution of the heart leading to separate circulation for the lungs. **(a)** The two-chambered heart in a shark or a bony fish, **(b)** two atria in an amphibian, **(c)** partial division of the ventricle in modern reptiles, and **(d)** complete separation into two ventricles in crocodilians, birds, and mammals.

a flaplike structure in the vessel leaving the heart that can direct blood into arch VI alternately with the remaining arches. In modern reptiles, such as lizards and snakes, the ventricle is partially divided **(Figure 37.5c).**

Full separation of the blood supply to the lungs occurs in mammals, birds, and crocodilians (alligators and crocodiles share ancestry with birds) by complete division of the ventricle **(Figure 37.5d).** There are thus two separate circuits: one delivering oxygenated blood from the lungs into the left atrium, which then propels it into the left ventricle. The contraction of the left ventricle sends blood to the body circulation via the carotid arteries to the head (remnants of arch III) and the dorsal aorta (derived from arch IV), which supplies the remainder of the body. Deoxygenated blood from the body and head enters the right atrium and, via the right ventricle, is propelled to the lungs in the pulmonary artery (arch VI). This separation of the body and lung circulation is illustrated in a flow diagram in **Figure 37.6.**

Lung capillaries
PULMONARY CIRCUIT
Right atrium
Left atrium
Right ventricle
Left ventricle
SYSTEMIC CIRCUIT
Capillary networks in other body tissues
■ Oxygenated blood
■ Deoxygenated blood

Figure 37.6
The separation of circulation to the lungs (pulmonary circulation) and to the body (systemic circulation) in mammals.

These gradual changes in the heart and aortic arches illustrate two principles:

- the segmental nature of the vertebrate body plan
- although evolution happens by changes in existing structures, changes in one set of structures (the aortic arches) are correlated with changes in other structures (the heart).

Study Break

1. Distinguish between open and closed circulatory systems.
2. Which of the following have closed circulatory systems: snails, arthropods, annelids, squids, vertebrates?
3. Which vertebrates have a separate pulmonary circulation?

37.2 Blood and Its Components

In both vertebrates and invertebrates, blood is a complex connective tissue that may contain blood cells suspended in a liquid matrix called the *plasma*. Although the blood of all vertebrates contains blood cells, the blood of some invertebrates may consist exclusively of plasma with few or no suspended cells, as in the Nematoda. In other invertebrates, such as the arthropods, blood cells or haemocytes of various recognizable types may occur in large numbers (up to 275 000 per μL in crickets) that can vary with activity and developmental stage. Whereas some haemocytes circulate with the haemolymph, others may attach temporarily to various tissues. These haemocyctes can be mobilized rapidly and enter the circulation, for example, to take part in wound healing or in defence against disease and parasites. In addition to transporting nutrients, dissolved gases, and metabolic wastes, blood helps stabilize the internal pH and salt composition of body fluids and serves as a highway for cells of the immune system and the antibodies produced by some of these cells.

In vertebrates, blood also helps regulate body temperature by transferring heat between warmer and cooler body regions and between the body and the external environment (see Chapter 43). The total blood volume of an average-sized adult human is about 4 to 5 L and makes up about 8% of body mass. The *plasma*, a clear, straw-coloured fluid, is about 55% of the volume of blood in human males and 58% in human females. Suspended in the plasma are three main types of blood cells, *erythrocytes, leukocytes,* and *platelets,* which account for the remainder of the blood volume. The typical components of human blood are shown in **Figure 37.7.**

37.2a Plasma Is an Aqueous Solution of Proteins, Ions, Nutrient Molecules, and Gases

Plasma is so complex that its complete composition is unknown for any animal. Its known components in humans are given in Figure 37.7. The plasma proteins of vertebrates fall into three classes: the *albumins,* the *globulins,* and *fibrinogen.* The **albumins,** the most abundant proteins of the plasma, are important for osmotic balance and pH buffering. They also transport a wide variety of substances through the circulatory system, including hormones, therapeutic drugs, and metabolic wastes. The **globulins** transport lipids (including cholesterol) and fat-soluble vitamins; a specialized subgroup of globulins, the *immunoglobulins,* includes antibodies and other molecules that contribute to the immune response. Some globulins are also enzymes. **Fibrinogen** plays a central role in the mechanism clotting the blood.

The ions of the plasma include Na^+, K^+, Ca^{2+}, Cl^-, and HCO_3^- (bicarbonate) ions. The Na^+ and Cl^- ions are the most abundant ions. Some of the ions, particularly the bicarbonate ion, help maintain arterial blood at its characteristic pH, which in humans is slightly on the basic side at pH 7.4 (see Chapter 43).

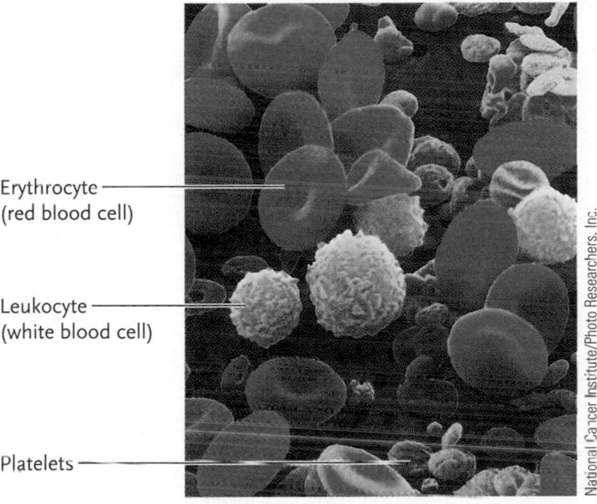

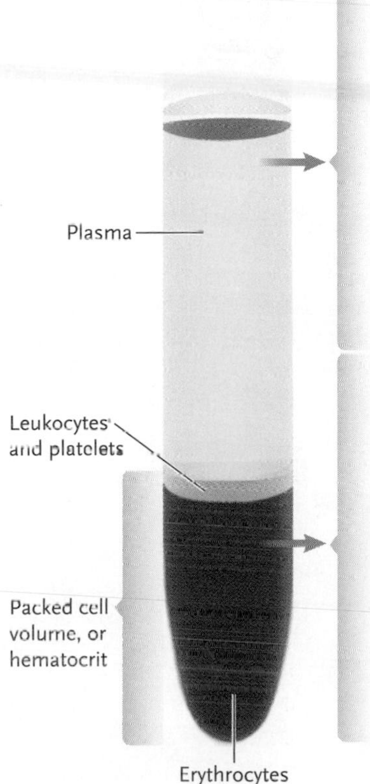

Plasma Portion (55%–58% of total volume):		
Components	**Relative Amounts**	**Functions**
1. Water	91%–92% of plasma volume	Solvent
2. Plasma proteins (albumin, globulins, fibrinogen, etc.)	7%–8%	Defence, clotting, lipid transport, roles in extracellular fluid volume, etc.
3. Ions, sugars, lipids, amino acids, hormones, vitamins, dissolved gases, urea and uric acid (metabolic wastes)	1%–2%	Roles in extracellular fluid volume, pH, eliminating waste products, etc.
Cellular Portion (45%–42% of total volume):		
1. Erythrocytes (red blood cells)	4 800 000–5 400 000 per microliter	Oxygen, carbon dioxide transport
2. Leukocytes (white blood cells)		
Neutrophils	3 000–6 750	Phagocytosis during inflammation
Lymphocytes	1 000–2 700	Immune response
Monocytes/macrophages	150–720	Phagocytosis in all defence responses
Eosinophils	100–360	Defence against parasitic worms
Basophils	25–90	Secrete substances for inflammatory response and for fat removal from blood
3. Platelets	250 000–300 000	Roles in clotting

Figure 37.7
Typical components of human blood. The colourized scanning electron micrograph shows the three major cellular components. The sketch of the test tube shows what happens when you centrifuge a blood sample. The blood separates into three layers: a thick layer of straw-colored plasma on top, a thin layer containing leukocytes and platelets, and a thick layer of erythrocytes. The table shows the relative amounts and functions of the various components of blood.

37.2b Erythrocytes Are the Oxygen Carriers of Vertebrate Blood

Erythrocytes, or red blood cells, carry O_2 from the lungs to body tissues. Each microlitre of human blood normally contains about 5 million erythrocytes, which are small, flattened, and disklike. They measure about 7 μm in diameter and 2 μm in thickness. Microtubules of the cytoskeleton (see Chapter 2) are arranged beneath the surface of the cell so that they are *biconcave*—thinner in the middle than at the edges (see Figure 37.7). The proteins of the cytoskeleton that determine their shape also give them the flexibility to squeeze through narrow capillaries.

Like all blood cells, erythrocytes arise from stem cells in the red bone marrow. As they mature, mammalian erythrocytes lose their nucleus, cytoplasmic organelles, and ribosomes, limiting their metabolic capabilities and life span. The remaining cytoplasm contains enzymes, which carry out glycolysis, and large quantities of *haemoglobin*, the O_2-carrying protein of the blood. The erythrocytes of nearly all other vertebrates retain a nucleus.

Haemoglobin, the molecule that gives erythrocytes, and thus blood, its red colour, consists of four polypeptides, each linked to a nonprotein *haem* group (see *Molecule Behind Biology*) that contains an iron atom in its centre. The iron atom binds O_2 molecules as the blood circulates through the lungs and releases the O_2 as the blood flows through other body tissues.

Some 2 to 3 *million* erythrocytes are produced in the average human each second. The life span of an erythrocyte in the circulatory system is about

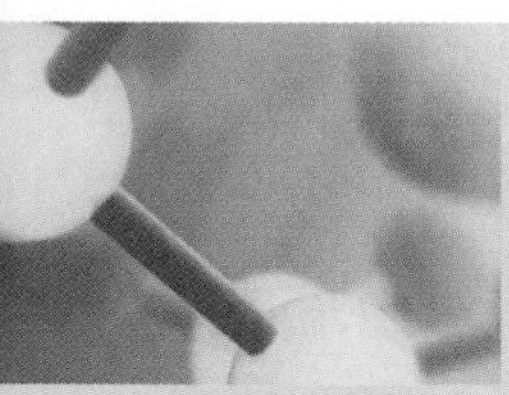

MOLECULE BEHIND BIOLOGY

Haem: Ubiquitous Oxygen Carrier

Haem is a member of a family of complex polycyclic chemicals called porphyrins **(Figure 1).** Among the properties of porphyrins is their ability to bind metals. In haem, the metal bound is iron. The complex attracts O_2, which binds to the iron. As a constituent of three proteins, haem is an important carrier of O_2 in biological systems. Because these three protein molecules are coloured, they are often referred to as oxygen-carrying pigments.

Haemoglobin is a protein that includes four haem molecules. In the lungs, the higher concentration of O_2 loads the haemoglobin in the erythrocytes with O_2, and in the tissues, the low concentration leads to unloading. The process of unloading the O_2 is assisted by higher concentrations of CO_2 in the tissues.

Myoglobin, a protein that contains one molecule of haem, occurs in muscle. The oxygen that is bound to myoglobin serves as a reservoir that can be called on during periods of high metabolic demand resulting from increased muscle activity.

Cytochrome oxidase, the terminal enzyme in the complex that transfers electrons to molecular O_2 (see Chapter 5), also contains a haem molecule.

Other oxygen-carrying pigments, such as haemocyanin, which occurs in molluscs and some arthropods, and haemerythrin, found in a variety of invertebrates, also function as O_2 carriers. They do not, however, contain haem as the functional group.

Figure 1
The haem molecule.

120 days. At the end of their useful life, erythrocytes are engulfed and destroyed by *macrophages* (*macro* = big; *phagein* = to eat), a type of large leukocyte, in the spleen, liver, and bone marrow.

A negative feedback mechanism keyed to the blood's O_2 content stabilizes the number of erythrocytes in blood. If the O_2 content drops below the normal level, the kidneys synthesize **erythropoietin**, a peptide hormone that stimulates stem cells in bone marrow to increase erythrocyte production. Erythropoietin is also secreted after blood loss and when mammals move to higher altitudes. As new red blood cells enter the bloodstream, the O_2-carrying capacity of the blood rises. If the O_2 content of the blood rises above normal levels, erythropoietin production falls and red blood cell production drops. Erythropoietin has been used in "blood doping" by some athletes to improve their performance.

37.2c Leukocytes Provide the Body's Front Line of Defence against Disease

Leukocytes eliminate dead and dying cells from the body, remove cellular debris, and provide the body's first line of defence against invading organisms. They are called white cells because they are colourless, in contrast to the red blood cells. Because leukocytes retain their nuclei, cytoplasmic organelles, and ribosomes, they are fully functional cells.

Like red blood cells, leukocytes arise from the division of stem cells in red bone marrow. As they mature, they are released into the bloodstream, from which they enter body tissues in large numbers. Some types of leukocytes are capable of continued division in the blood and body tissues. The specific types of leukocytes and their functions in the immune reaction are discussed in Chapter 44.

37.2d Platelets Induce Blood Clots that Seal Breaks in the Circulatory System

Blood **platelets** are oval or rounded cell fragments, 2 to 4 μm in diameter, each enclosed in its own plasma membrane. They are produced in red bone marrow by the division of stem cells. Platelets contain enzymes and other factors that take part in blood clotting. When blood vessels are damaged, collagen fibres in the extracellular matrix are exposed to the leaking blood. Platelets in the blood stick to the collagen fibres and release signalling molecules that induce additional platelets to stick to them. The process continues, forming a plug that helps seal off the damaged site. As the plug forms, the platelets release other factors that convert the soluble plasma protein, fibrinogen, into long, insoluble threads of **fibrin**. Crosslinks between the fibrin threads form a meshlike network that traps blood cells and platelets and further seals the damaged area **(Figure 37.8)**. The entire mass is a blood clot.

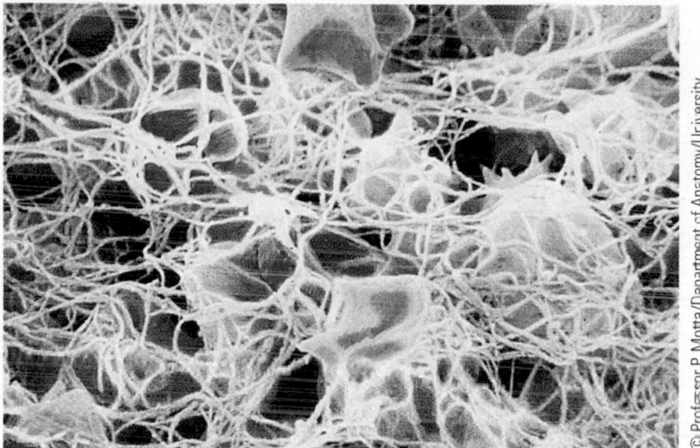

Figure 37.8
Red blood cells caught in a meshlike network of fibrin threads during formation of a blood clot.

Study Break

What are the functions of the three main cellular components of vertebrate blood?

37.3 The Heart

The vertebrate heart is composed of cardiac muscle cells (see Chapter 36). In mammals, we have seen that the heart is a four-chambered pump, with two atria (singular, atrium) at the anterior of the heart and two ventricles at the posterior **(Figure 37.9)**. The atria pump blood into the ventricles, and then powerful contractions of the ventricles push the blood at relatively high pressure into arteries leaving the heart. This arterial pressure is responsible for the blood circulation. Valves between the atria and the ventricles, and between the

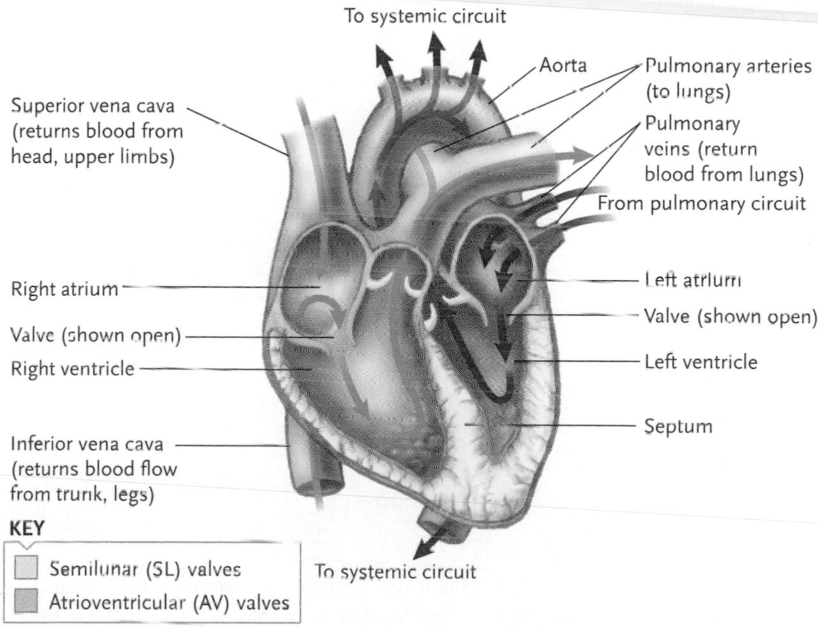

Figure 37.9
Cutaway view of the human heart showing its internal organization.

ventricles and the arteries leaving the heart, keep the blood from flowing backward.

The mammalian heart pumps the blood through two completely separate circuits of blood vessels: the systemic circuit and the pulmonary circuit **(Figure 37.10)**. The right atrium (toward the right side of the body) receives blood returning from the entire body, except for the lungs. The *superior vena cava* conveys blood from the head and forelimbs, and the *inferior vena cava* conveys blood from the abdominal organs and hindlimbs. (Most mammals do not have an upright posture, so superior and inferior are anterior and posterior, respectively.) This blood is depleted of O_2 and has a high CO_2 content. The right atrium pumps the blood into the right ventricle, which contracts to push the blood into the *pulmonary arteries* (derived from arch VI) leading to the lungs. In the capillaries of the lungs, the blood releases CO_2 and picks up O_2. The oxygenated blood completes this pulmonary circuit by returning in *pulmonary veins* to the heart.

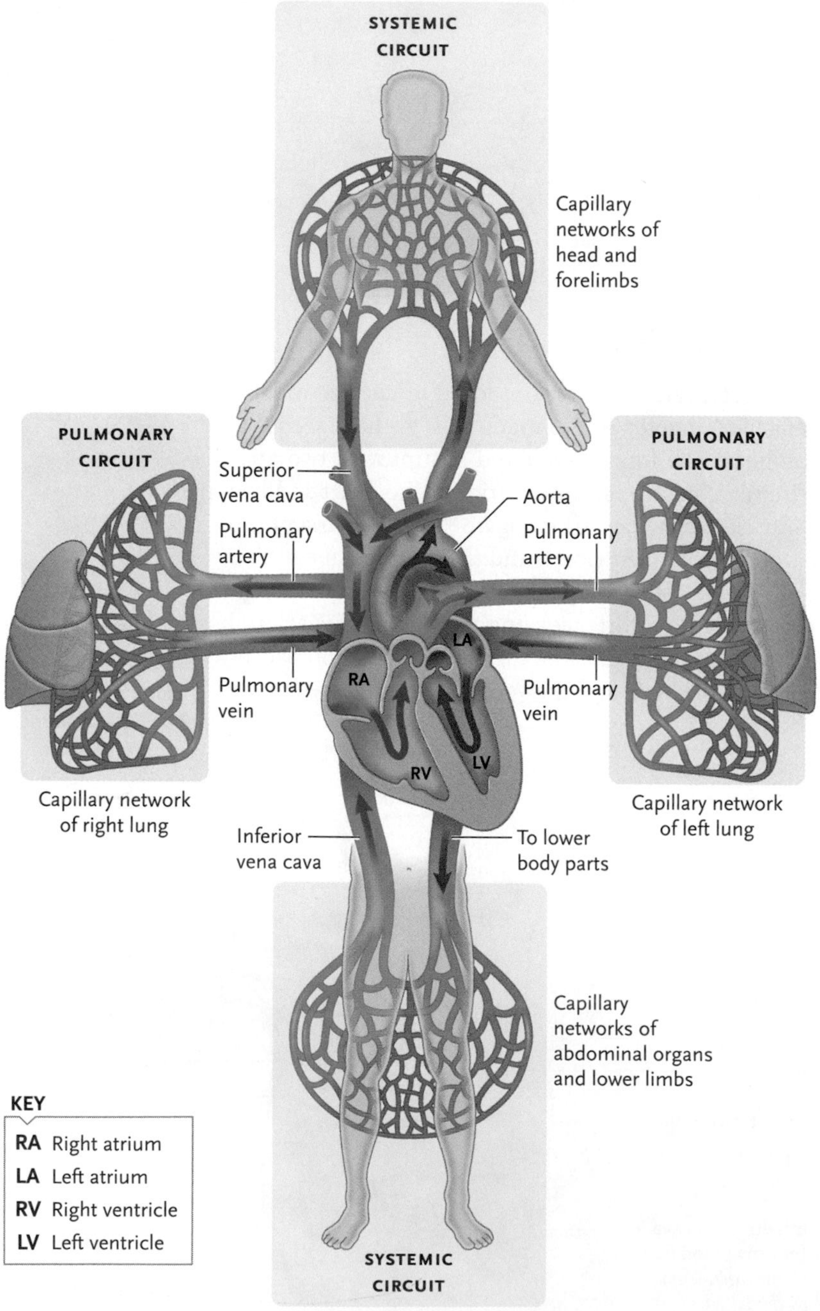

Blood returning from the pulmonary circuit enters the left atrium, which pumps it into the left ventricle. This ventricle, the most thick-walled and powerful chamber, contracts to send the oxygenated blood into a large artery, the **aorta** (the dorsal aorta, derived from arch IV), which branches into arteries leading to all body regions except the lungs.

The arteries divide into smaller and smaller arteries and then into capillary networks, in which the blood releases O_2 and picks up CO_2. The O_2-depleted blood collects in veins, which complete the systemic circuit. The blood from the veins enters the right atrium. The amount of blood pumped by the two halves of the heart is normally balanced so that neither side pumps more than the other.

The heart also has its own circulation, called the *coronary circulation*. Two small *coronary arteries* branch off the aorta and then branch extensively over the heart, leading to dense capillary beds that serve the cardiac muscle cells. The blood from the capillary networks collects into veins that empty into the right atrium. If a coronary artery becomes blocked, the muscle cells it supplies can die and the person can suffer a heart attack (see *People Behind Biology*).

37.3a The Heartbeat Is Produced by a Cycle of Contraction and Relaxation of the Atria and Ventricles

Average heart rates vary among mammals (and among vertebrates generally), depending on body size and the overall level of metabolic activity. A human heart beats 72 times each minute, on average, with each beat lasting about 0.8 second. The heart rate of a trained endurance athlete is typically much lower. The heart of a flying bat may beat 1200 times a minute, whereas that of an elephant beats only 30 times a minute. **Systole** is the period of contraction and emptying of the heart, and **diastole** is the period of relaxation and filling of the heart between contractions. The systole–diastole sequence of the heart is called the **cardiac cycle (Figure 37.11)**. The following discussion goes through one cardiac cycle.

Starting when both atria and ventricles are relaxed in diastole, the atria begin to fill with blood (step 1 in Figure 37.11). At this point, the **atrioventricular valves (AV valves)** between each atrium and ventricle and the **semilunar valves (SL valves)** between the ventricles and the aorta and pulmonary arteries are closed. As the atria fill, the pressure pushes open the AV valves and begins to fill the relaxed ventricles (step 2). When the ventricles are about 80% full, the atria contract

KEY
RA Right atrium
LA Left atrium
RV Right ventricle
LV Left ventricle

Figure 37.10
The pulmonary and systemic circuits of humans. The right half of the heart pumps blood into the pulmonary circuit, and the left half of the heart pumps blood into the systemic circuit.

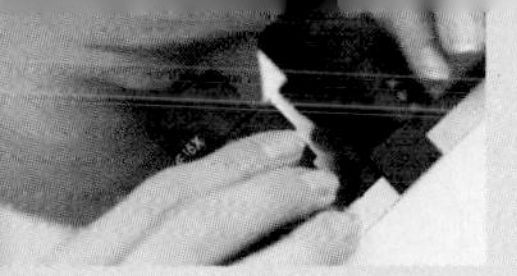

PEOPLE BEHIND BIOLOGY

Lorrie Kirshenbaum: Controlling the Death of Heart Cells

Cardiac muscle cells do not divide after birth; the growth of the heart is the result of an increase in the size of the muscle cells. When the cells are damaged in a heart attack, they cannot repair themselves, nor can they be replaced.

Lorrie Kirshenbaum, Canada Research Chair in Molecular Cardiology at the University of Manitoba, explores the molecular events controlling the growth and death of cardiac muscle. *BNIP3* is one of a family of genes that can initiate cell death. It is particularly associated with a lack of oxygen. His lab has been active in describing the pathways leading to activation of the *BNIP3* gene and the intracellular pathways that the protein product of the gene uses to kill the cells. Dr. Kirshenbaum is also exploring how this information might be used to prevent the activation of the gene or its effects and thus prevent the death of cells when deprived of oxygen. Conversely, could the gene be activated to kill cancer cells in other tissues?

A different approach involves exploring ways to replace damaged heart cells. Cardiac muscle cells, which do not divide, have the normal cell division pathway blocked. Dr Kirshenbaum's lab is using growth factors, delivered as genes in viruses, to activate the cell division pathway. However, it turns out that adult myocytes that have the cell division pathway turned on enter a pathway leading to death. To get around this difficulty, he also delivers growth factors that block the self-destructive pathway together with the growth factors that stimulate cell division. This is a promising alternative to using stem cells to replace damaged heart cells.

KEY
Aortic pressure (mm Hg)
Ventricular pressure (mm Hg)
Atrial pressure (mm Hg)
Oxygen-poor blood (deoxygenated blood)
Oxygen-rich blood (oxygenated blood)

Systolic blood pressure
Diastolic blood pressure
Pressure (mm Hg)
0 20 40 60 80 100 120

SL valves
Left atrium
AV valves
Right atrium
Right ventricle
Left ventricle

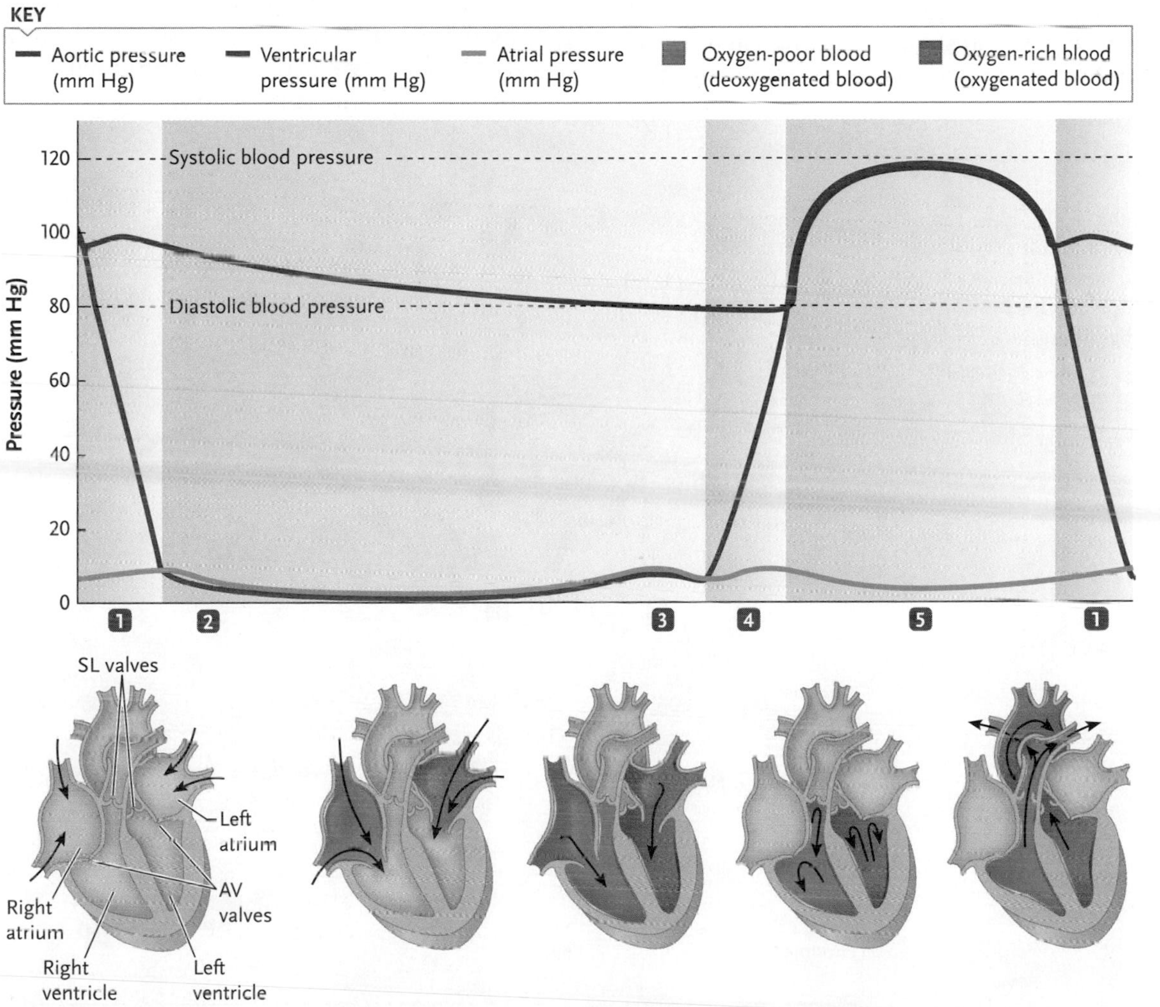

1 Heart is fully relaxed; atria begin to fill with blood; AV and SL valves are closed.

2 Blood fills atria and pushes AV valves open; ventricles begin to fill.

3 Atria contract, filling ventricles completely.

4 Ventricles begin to contract, forcing AV valves closed; SL valves remain closed.

5 Ventricles contract fully, forcing SL valves open and ejecting blood into arteries.

Figure 37.11
The cardiac cycle.

and completely fill the ventricles with blood (step 3). Although there are no valves where the veins open into the atria, the atrial contraction compresses the openings, sealing them so that little backflow occurs into the veins.

As the ventricular muscles begin to contract, rising pressure in the ventricular chambers forces the AV valves shut (step 4). As they continue to contract, the pressure in the ventricular chambers rises above that in the arteries leading away from the heart, forcing open the SL valves. Blood now rushes from the ventricles into the aorta and the pulmonary arteries (step 5).

Completion of the contraction squeezes about two-thirds of the blood in the ventricles into the arteries. Now the ventricles relax, lowering pressure in ventricular chambers below that in arteries. This reversal of the pressure gradient reverses the direction of blood flow in the regions of the SL valves, causing them to close. For about half a second, both atria and ventricles remain in diastole and blood flows into the atria and ventricles. Then the blood-filled atria contract, and the cycle repeats.

In an adult human at rest, each ventricle pumps roughly 5 L of blood per minute, an amount roughly equivalent to the entire volume of blood in the body. At maximum rate and strength, the human heart pumps about five times the resting amount, or more than 25 L/min.

37.3b The Cardiac Cycle Is Initiated within the Heart

Contraction of cardiac muscle cells is triggered by action potentials that spread across the muscle cell membranes. Crustaceans, such as crabs and lobsters, have **neurogenic hearts**, that is, hearts that beat under the control of signals from the nervous system. Each contraction is initiated by signals from a cardiac ganglion located in the heart, and the heart will continue to beat and respond to some environmental signals in isolation from the central nervous system, as long as the ganglion is intact. Other animals, including all insects and all vertebrates, have **myogenic hearts** that maintain their contraction rhythm with no requirement for signals from the nervous system. Isolated cardiac myocytes contract rhythmically when grown in a suitable medium. Both neurogenic and myogenic hearts can also be influenced by signals from the central nervous system and by hormones.

The rate and timing of the contraction of individual cardiac muscle cells in a mammalian myogenic heart are coordinated by a region of the heart called the **sinoatrial node (SA node).** The SA node consists of **pacemaker cells**, which are specialized cardiac muscle cells in the upper wall of the right atrium **(Figure 37.12,** step 1). Ion channels in these cells open in a cyclic,

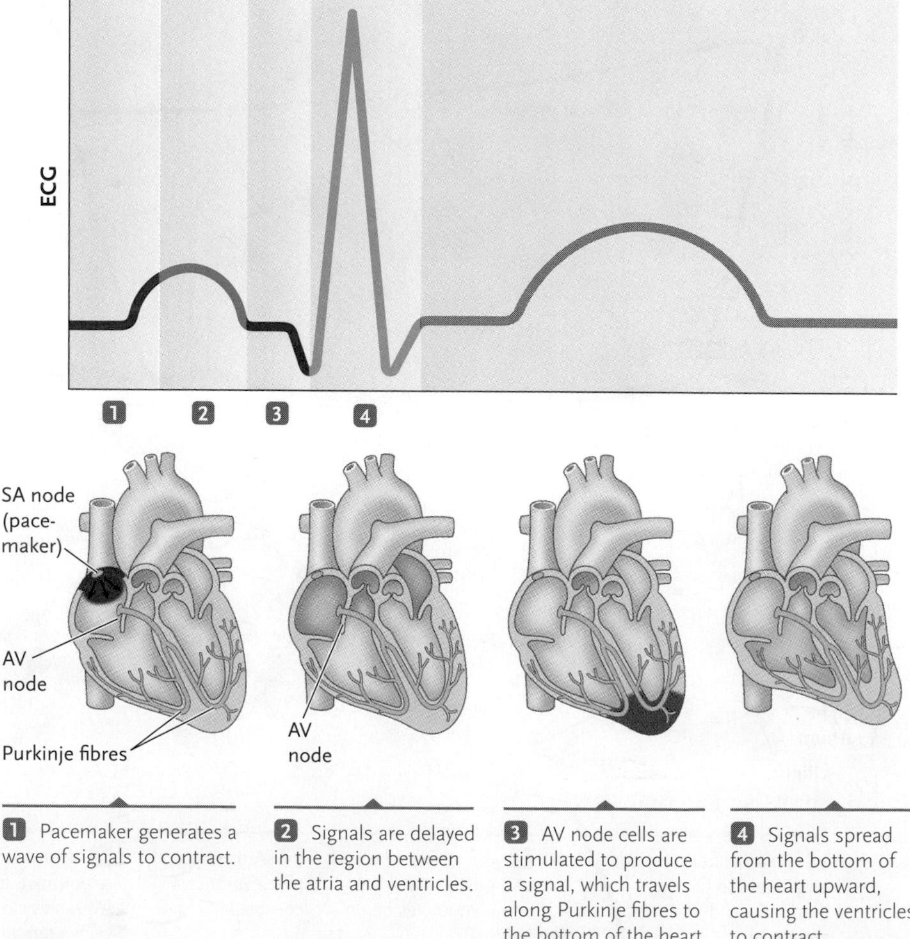

ECG
1
2
3
4
SA node (pace-maker)
AV node
Purkinje fibres
AV node
1 Pacemaker generates a wave of signals to contract.
2 Signals are delayed in the region between the atria and ventricles.
3 AV node cells are stimulated to produce a signal, which travels along Purkinje fibres to the bottom of the heart.
4 Signals spread from the bottom of the heart upward, causing the ventricles to contract.

Figure 37.12
The electrical control of the cardiac cycle. The bottom part of the figure shows how a signal originating at the SA node leads to ventricular contraction. The top part of the figure shows the electrical activity for each of the stages as seen in an ECG. The colours in the hearts show the location of the signal at each step and correspond to the colours in the ECG.

self-sustaining pattern that alternately depolarizes and repolarizes their plasma membranes. The regularly timed depolarizations initiate waves of contraction that travel over the heart, causing the atria to contract.

A layer of connective tissue separates the atria from the ventricles, acting as a layer of electrical insulation between the top and the bottom of the heart. The insulating layer keeps a contraction signal from the SA node from spreading directly from the atria to the ventricles (step 2). Instead, the atrial wave of contraction excites cells of the **atrioventricular node (AV node)**, located in the heart wall between the right atrium and right ventricle, just above the insulating layer of connective tissue. The signal produced travels from the AV node to the bottom of the heart via *Purkinje fibres* (step 3). These fibres follow a path downward, through the insulating layer, to the bottom of the heart, where they branch through the walls of the ventricles. The signal carried by the Purkinje fibres induces a wave of contraction that begins at the bottom of the heart and proceeds upward, squeezing the blood from the ventricles into the aorta and pulmonary arteries (step 4). The transmission of a signal from the AV node to the ventricles takes about 0.1 second; this delay gives the atria time to finish their contraction before the ventricles contract.

As Augustus Waller found in experiments with Jimmie the bulldog, the electrical signals passing through the heart can be detected by attaching electrodes to different points on the surface of the body. The signals change in a regular pattern corresponding to the electrical signals that trigger the cardiac cycle, producing what is known as an **electrocardiogram** (ECG; also EKG, from German, *Elektrocardiogramm*). The highlighted region of the ECG above each stage of the cardiac cycle in Figure 37.12 indicates the electrical activity measured in those stages.

37.3c Arterial Blood Pressure Cycles between a High Systolic and a Low Diastolic Pressure

The pressure exerted by a fluid in a confined space is called *hydrostatic pressure*. That is, fluid in a container exerts some pressure on the wall of the container. Blood vessels are essentially tubular containers that are part of a closed system filled with fluid. Hence, the blood in vessels exerts hydrostatic pressure against the walls of the vessels. *Blood pressure* is the measurement of that hydrostatic pressure on the walls of the arteries as the heart pumps blood through the body. Blood pressure is determined by the force and amount of blood pumped by the heart and the size and flexibility of the arteries. In any animal, blood pressure changes in response to activity, temperature, body position, behaviour, time of day, and diet.

As the ventricles contract, a surge of high-pressure blood moves outward through the arteries leading from the heart. This peak of high pressure, called the *systolic blood pressure*, can be felt as a *pulse* by pressing a finger against an artery that lies near the skin, such as the arteries of the neck or the artery that runs along the inside of the wrist. Between ventricular contractions, the arterial blood pressure reaches a low point called the *diastolic blood pressure*. In healthy humans at rest, the systolic pressure, measured in the large artery in the forearm, is equivalent to between 90 and 120 mm of mercury and the diastolic to between 60 and 80 mm. These pressures are illustrated in Figure 37.11.

The blood pressure in the systemic and pulmonary circuits is highest in the arteries leaving the heart and drops as the blood passes from the arteries into the capillaries. By the time the blood returns to the heart, its pressure has dropped to 2 to 5 mm Hg, with no differentiation between systolic and diastolic pressures. The reduction in pressure occurs because the blood encounters resistance as it moves through the vessels, primarily due to the friction created when blood cells and plasma proteins move over each other and over vessel walls.

Study Break

1. Distinguish between systolic and diastolic blood pressure.
2. What is the function of the sinoatrial node?

37.4 Blood Vessels of the Circulatory System

Both systemic and pulmonary circuits consist of a continuum of different blood vessel types that begin and end at the heart (**Figure 37.13**). From the heart, large arteries carry blood and branch into progressively

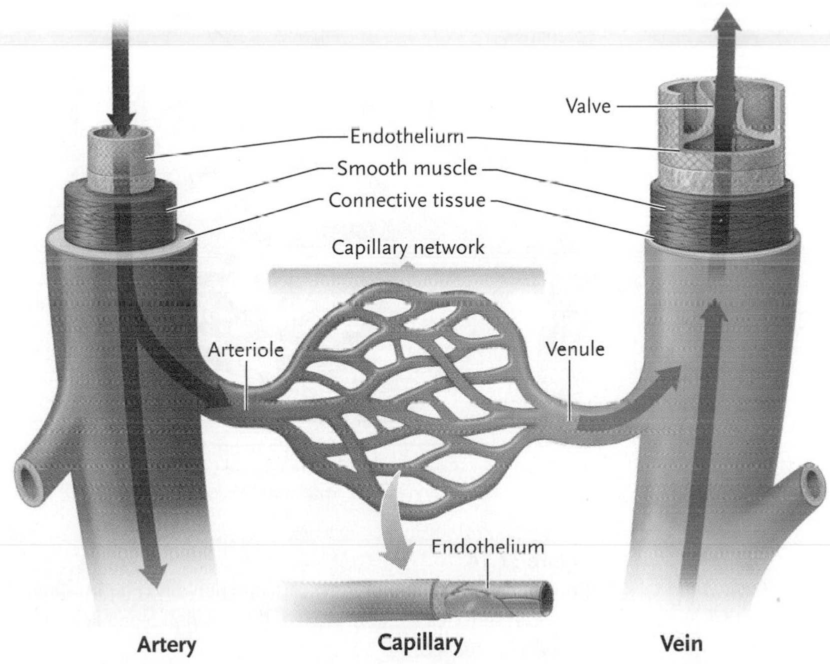

Figure 37.13
The structure of arteries, capillaries, and veins and their relationship in blood circuits.

smaller arteries, delivering blood to the various parts of the body. When a small artery reaches the organ it supplies, it branches into yet smaller vessels, the **arterioles.** Within the organ, arterioles branch into capillaries, the smallest vessels of the circulatory system. Capillaries form a network in the organ, where they exchange substances between the blood and the surrounding interstitial fluid. Capillaries rejoin to form small **venules,** which merge into the small veins that leave the organ. The small veins progressively join to form larger veins that eventually become the large veins that enter the heart.

37.4a Arteries Transport Blood Rapidly to the Tissues and Serve as a Pressure Reservoir

Arteries have relatively large diameters and therefore provide little resistance to blood flow. They are structurally adapted to the relatively high pressure of the blood passing through them. The walls of arteries consist of three major tissue layers (see Figure 37.13):

- an outer layer of connective tissue containing collagen fibres mixed with fibres of the protein elastin, giving the vessel recoil ability,
- a relatively thick middle layer of vascular smooth muscle cells also mixed with elastin fibres, and
- an inner layer of flattened cells only one cell in thickness, forming an endothelium.

In addition to being conduits for blood travelling to the tissues, arteries also act as a pressure reservoir for blood movement when the heart is relaxing. When contraction of the ventricles pumps blood into arteries, a greater volume of blood enters the arteries than leaves them to flow into the smaller vessels downstream because of the higher resistance to blood flow in those smaller vessels. Arteries accommodate the excess volume of blood because of their elastic walls, which allow the arteries to expand in diameter. When the heart relaxes and blood is no longer being pumped into the arteries, the arterial walls recoil passively back to their original state. The recoil pushes the excess blood from the arteries into the smaller downstream vessels. As a result, blood flow to tissues is continuous during systole and diastole.

37.4b Capillaries Are the Sites of Exchange between the Blood and Interstitial Fluid

Capillaries thread through nearly every tissue in the body and are arranged in networks bringing them within 0.01 mm of most body cells. In humans, they are estimated to have a surface area of about 2600 km^2 for the exchange of gases, nutrients, and wastes with the interstitial fluid. Capillary walls consist of a single layer of endothelial cells, resting on a thin basement membrane (see Chapter 32).

Control of Blood Flow through Capillaries. Blood flow through capillary networks is controlled by contraction of smooth muscle in arterioles **(Figure 37.14).** In addition to the normal layer of smooth muscle, some arterioles may have circular rings of smooth muscle at the entrance to a capillary, called *precapillary sphincter muscles.* When the arteriole and sphincter smooth muscles are relaxed, blood flows readily through the arterioles and capillary networks. In the most contracted state, the blood flow is limited through the arterioles and capillary networks. Variation in the contraction of the arteriole and sphincter smooth muscles adjusts the rate of flow through the capillary networks

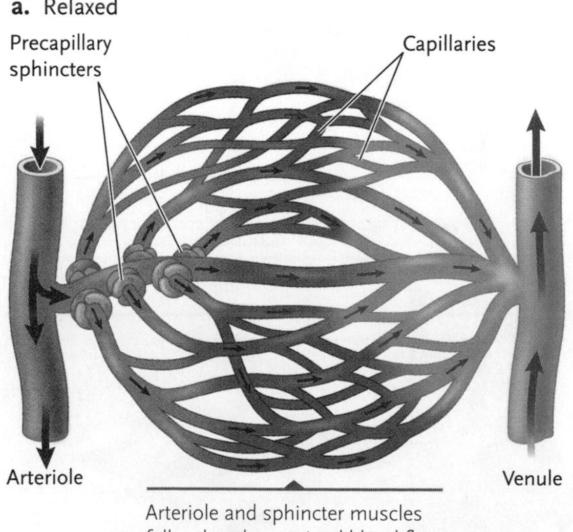

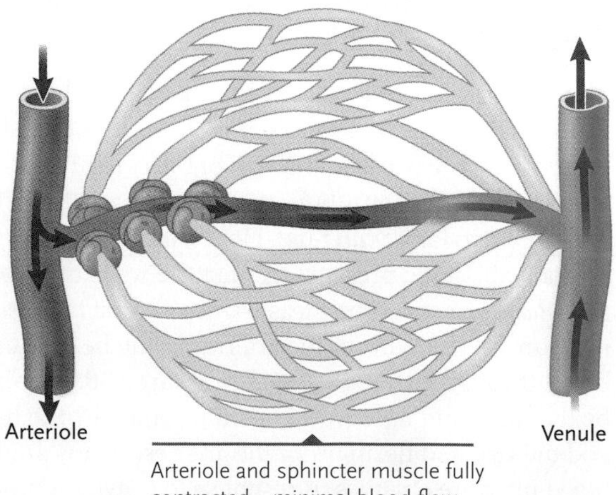

Figure 37.14
Control of blood flow through capillary networks. (a) Maximal blood flow when arteriole and sphincter muscles are fully relaxed. **(b)** Minimal blood flow when the arteriole and sphincter muscles are fully contracted.

for particular organs. For example, the flow of blood through the capillary networks of the intestines is increased after a meal.

The Velocity of Blood Flow through Capillaries. Although their total surface area is astoundingly large, the diameter of individual capillaries is so small that red blood cells must squeeze through most of them in single file **(Figure 37.15)**. As a result, each capillary presents a high resistance to blood flow. In addition, there are so many billions of capillaries in the networks that their combined diameter is about 1300 times greater than the cross-sectional area of the aorta. As a result of the resistance and the vastly increased diameter of the combined tubes, blood slows considerably as it moves through capillaries, maximizing opportunities for exchange between the blood and the interstitial fluids. As they leave the tissues, capillaries rejoin to form venules and veins. Veins have a total cross-sectional area that is smaller than the total cross-sectional area of capillaries, so the velocity of flow increases as blood returns to the heart.

The Exchange of Substances across Capillary Walls. In most body tissues, narrow spaces between the capillary endothelial cells allow water, ions, and small molecules such as glucose to pass freely between blood and interstitial fluid. Erythrocytes, platelets, and most plasma proteins are too large to pass between the cells and are retained inside capillaries, except for molecules that are transported through epithelial cells by specific carriers. Leukocytes, however, can squeeze actively between the cells and pass from the blood to the interstitial fluid.

There are exceptions to these general properties. In the brain, endothelial cells are tightly sealed together, preventing all molecules and ions from passing between them. The tight seals set up the *blood–brain barrier* (Chapter 33). This limits the exchange between capillaries and brain tissues to molecules and ions that are specifically transported through the capillary endothelial cells. At the other extreme are capillaries in the liver, in which the spaces between endothelial cells are wide enough to admit most plasma proteins (most plasma proteins are synthesized in the liver), and in the small intestines, where wide spaces between capillary endothelial cells allow many nutrient molecules to pass into the bloodstream. In bone marrow and other sites of erythrocyte production, spaces are large enough to admit red blood cells.

37.4c Venules and Veins Serve as Blood Reservoirs in Addition to Conduits to the Heart

The walls of venules and veins are thinner than those of arteries and contain little elastin. Many veins have flaps of connective tissue that extend inward from their walls. These flaps form one-way valves that keep blood flowing toward the heart (see Figure 37.13).

Rather than stretching and contracting elastically, like arteries, the relatively thin walls of venules and veins can expand and contract over a relatively wide range, allowing them to act as blood reservoirs as well as conduits. At times, venules and veins may contain from 60 to 80% of the total blood volume of the body. The stored volume is adjusted by skeletal muscle contraction and the valves, in response to metabolic conditions and signals carried by hormones and neurotransmitters.

Although blood pressure in the venous system is relatively low, several mechanisms assist the movement of blood back to the heart. The contraction of skeletal muscles compresses nearby veins, increasing their internal pressure **(Figure 37.16)**. The one-way valves in the veins, especially numerous in the larger veins of the limbs, keep the blood from flowing backward when the muscles relax. Respiratory movements also force blood from the abdomen toward the chest cavity.

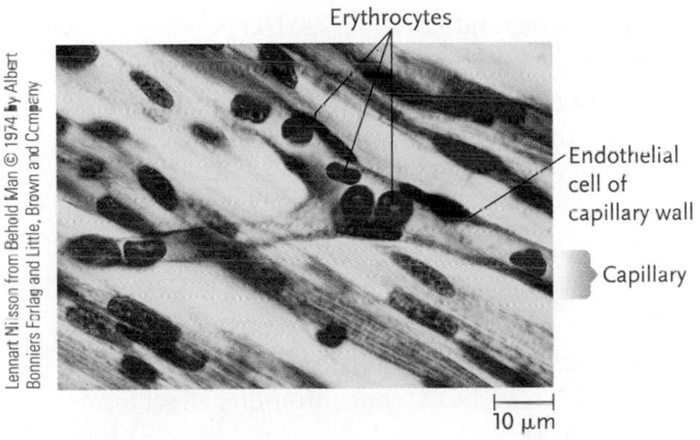

Figure 37.16
How skeletal muscle contraction and the valves inside veins help move blood toward the heart.

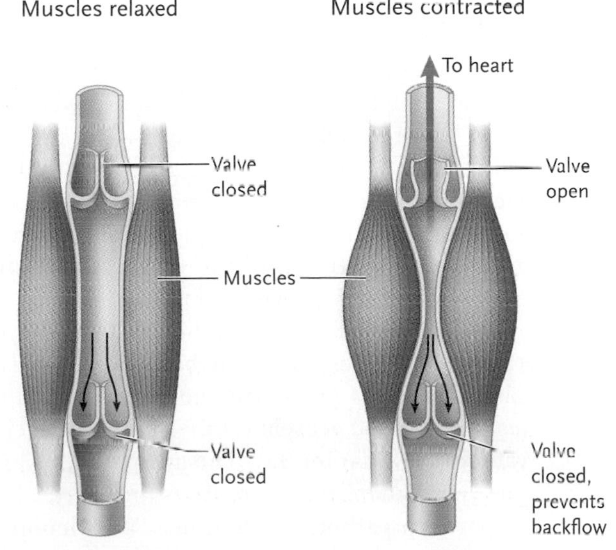

Erythrocytes
Endothelial cell of capillary wall
Capillary
10 μm

Figure 37.15
Erythrocytes moving through a capillary that is just wide enough to admit the cells in single file.

Study Break

1. What are the three major tissue layers in arteries?
2. What is the role of skeletal muscles in circulation?

37.5 Maintaining Blood Flow and Pressure

Arterial blood pressure is the principal force moving blood to the tissues. Blood pressure must be regulated carefully so that the brain and other tissues receive adequate blood flow, but not so high that the heart is overburdened, risking damage to blood vessels. The three main regulators of blood pressure are

- *cardiac output* (the pressure and amount of blood pumped by the left and right ventricles),
- the degree of constriction of the blood vessels (primarily the arterioles), and
- the total blood volume.

The autonomic nervous system and the endocrine system interact to coordinate the mechanisms controlling these factors. The system effectively counteracts the effects of constantly changing internal and external conditions, such as movement from rest to physical activity or ending a period of fasting by eating a large meal. In humans, for example, moderate physical activity results in an increase in blood flow to the heart itself by 360%, to the muscles of the skin by 370% (increases loss of heat), and to the skeletal muscles by 1060%. Flow is decreased to the digestive tract and liver by 60%, to the kidneys by 40%, and to the bone and most other tissues by 30%. Only the blood flow to the brain remains unchanged. These changes are the result of cardiac output together with adjustments to the muscles in the arterioles supplying the various organs.

37.5a Cardiac Output Is Controlled by Regulating the Rate and Strength of the Heartbeat

Regulation of the strength and rate of the heartbeat starts at stretch receptors called *baroreceptors* (a type of mechanoreceptor; see Chapter 34), located in the walls of blood vessels. The baroreceptors in the cardiac muscle, aorta, and carotid arteries (which supply blood to the brain) are the most crucial. By detecting the amount of stretch of the vessel walls, baroreceptors constantly provide information about blood pressure, sending signals to the medulla within the brain stem. In response, the brain stem sends signals to the heart (primarily the SA node) and muscles of the blood vessels via the autonomic nervous system (see Chapter 33). The sympathetic system, using norepinephrine, stimulates the heart, whereas the parasympathetic system uses acetylcholine to slow the rate. These signals adjust the rate and force of the heartbeat: the heart beats more slowly and contracts less forcefully when arterial pressure is above normal levels, and it beats more rapidly and contracts more forcefully when arterial pressure is below normal levels.

The O_2 content of the blood, detected by chemoreceptors in the aorta and carotid arteries, also influences cardiac output. If O_2 concentration falls below normal levels, the brain stem integrates this information with the baroreceptor signals and issues signals that increase the rate and force of the heartbeat. Too much O_2 in the blood has the opposite effect, reducing cardiac output.

37.5b Hormones Regulate Both Cardiac Output and Arteriole Diameter

Hormones secreted by several glands contribute to the regulation of blood pressure and flow. For example, as part of the stress response, the adrenal medulla reinforces the action of the sympathetic nervous system by secreting epinephrine and norepinephrine into the bloodstream (see Chapter 35). Epinephrine in particular raises blood pressure by increasing the strength and rate of the heartbeat and stimulating vasoconstriction (decrease in diameter) of arterioles in some parts of the body, including the skin, gut, and kidneys. At the same time, by inducing vasodilation (increase in diameter) of arterioles that deliver blood to the heart, skeletal muscles, and lungs, epinephrine increases blood flow to these structures.

37.5c Local Controls Also Regulate Arteriole Diameter

Several automated mechanisms also operate locally to increase the flow of blood to body regions engaged in increased metabolic activity. Repeated contraction of the muscles of your legs during an extended uphill bike ride produces local low O_2 and high CO_2 concentrations because of the increased oxidation of glucose and other fuels. This increases vasodilation of the arterioles and hence the blood supply serving the muscles. At least part of the vasodilation is caused by nitric oxide (NO) produced by arterial endothelial cells. NO is broken down quickly after its release, ensuring that its effects are local.

Life on the Edge discusses aquatic animals and their specialized circulatory systems that allow deep and prolonged dives.

Study Break

1. What are the three factors by which blood pressure and flow are controlled?
2. How do O_2 and CO_2 concentrations affect local blood flow?
3. What are baroreceptors, and how do they affect circulation?

Life on the Edge

Taking a Dive

Reptiles, birds, and mammals evolved as land animals, but many species (e.g., snakes, turtles, penguins, loons, otters, seals, and whales) have taken up life in freshwater or marine environments and feed under water. This may involve prolonged dives, sometimes to considerable depths and for extended times. One of the physiological responses to diving is a slowing of the heart rate, which comes into play as soon as the face or equivalent of the animal is wet. This "diving reflex" is a characteristic of all birds and mammals, including humans, but it is more prominent among those animals that dive for their food. Many of these species do not dive to great depths and remain submerged for a relatively brief period that still exceeds the abilities of land dwellers.

Whales dive to very great depths and may remain submerged for more than an hour. The champion divers are sperm whales, *Physeter macrocephalus* **(Figure 1).** These gigantic animals (up to 18 m in length and weighing up to 40 t [t – tonne, or 1000 kg]) feed on schools of deep water squid and other animals that live near the bottom of the ocean. The whales can dive to depths of 2000 m (typically less than 1000 m) and remain submerged for as long as 90 minutes. Of course, air-breathing animals swimming to and at such depths encounter several problems. There is the enormous pressure: for each 10 m of depth, the pressure increases by about 1 atmosphere, so these animals are experiencing pressure changes of up to 200 atmospheres! They require a great deal of muscular effort to swim to such depths. The supply of oxygen to the muscles, the brain, and the other tissues needs to be maintained throughout the dive. How does a whale "hold its breath" for more than an hour while swimming actively?

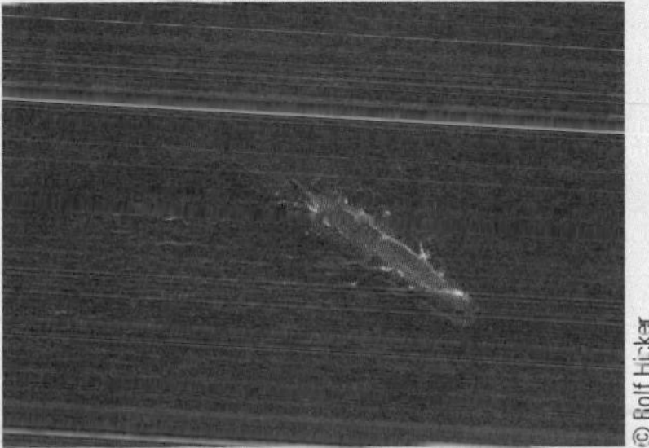

© Rolf Hicker

Figure 1
A sperm whale resting between dives.

The diving reflex is particularly well developed in marine mammals. It involves a slowing of the heart rate by about 90% and a redirection of blood flow, by adjustment of arteriole muscles, away from skin and digestive organs and toward the heart, brain, and skeletal muscles. The reduction in blood flow to the skin in particular permits the temperature of that organ to drop and reduces its metabolic rate.

Sperm whales have gigantic heads (macrocephalus means large head), which accommodate large quantities of an oil, ambergris, that may help maintain neutral buoyancy, reducing the muscular effort required for swimming. As a whale descends and the pressure increases, the specially adapted rib cage collapses; the lungs, which are not large in whales, shrink; and the air contained in them is compressed. Thus, whales do not "hold their breath": the oxygen that they require is stored in the blood and muscles. Whales, particularly sperm whales, have more erythrocytes per unit of blood than other animals, and these erythrocytes are larger. Moreover, whale muscles contain far more myoglobin (see *Molecule Behind Biology*) than terrestrial mammals. Thus, they are able to store oxygen in the blood and muscles. More than 40% of the oxygen taken in at the surface is stored in muscle, whereas a human diver is able to store only about 13% in muscle.

When the whale returns to the surface, the air in the lungs expands and circulation returns to the surface condition. CO_2 accumulated during the dive is exhaled during the familiar "blow," and the animal breathes on the surface for about 10 minutes before diving again to feed.

37.6 The Lymphatic System

Under normal conditions, a little more fluid from the blood plasma in the capillaries enters the interstitial fluid than is reabsorbed into the plasma. The **lymphatic system** is an extensive network of vessels that collect excess interstitial fluid and return it to the venous blood **(Figure 37.17, p. 908)**. Interstitial fluid picked up by the lymphatic system is called **lymph**. This system also collects fats that have been absorbed from the small intestine and delivers them to the blood circulation. The lymphatic system is also a key component of the immune system (see Chapter 44).

37.6a Vessels of the Lymphatic System Extend throughout Most of the Body

Vessels of the lymphatic system collect lymph and transport it to *lymph ducts* that empty into the veins of the circulatory system. *Lymph capillaries,* the smallest vessels of the system, are distributed throughout the body, intermixed intimately with the capillaries of the circulatory system. Although they are several times larger in diameter than the blood capillaries, the walls of lymph capillaries also consist of a single layer of endothelial cells resting on a basement membrane. Interstitial fluid becomes lymph when it enters the lymph capillaries at sites in their walls where the endothelial cells overlap, forming a flap that is forced

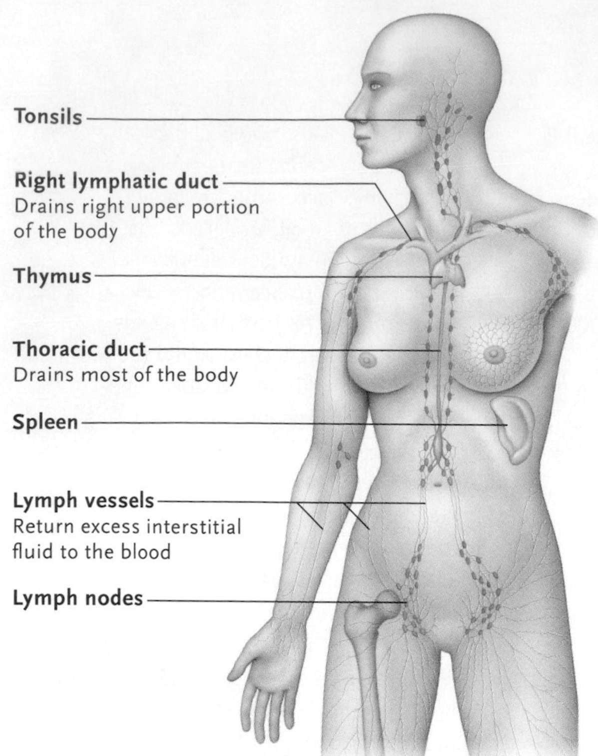

Figure 37.17
The human lymphatic system. Patches of lymphoid tissue in the small intestine and in the appendix are also part of the lymphatic system.

open by the higher pressure of the interstitial fluid. The openings are wide enough to admit all components of the interstitial fluid, including bacteria, damaged cells, cellular debris, and lymphocytes.

Lymph capillaries merge into *lymph vessels,* which contain one-way valves that prevent the lymph from flowing backward. Lymph vessels lead to the thoracic duct and the right lymphatic duct (see Figure 37.17), which empty the lymph into a vein beneath the clavicles (collarbones).

Breathing movements and movements of skeletal muscles adjacent to lymph vessels help move lymph through the vessels, just as they help move the blood through veins. Over a day, the human lymphatic system returns about 3 to 4 L of fluid to the bloodstream. In fishes, amphibians, and reptiles, the lymphatic vessels have lymphatic hearts, regions of the ducts equipped with striated muscle that propels the lymph through the vessels.

37.6b Lymphoid Tissues and Organs Act as Filters and Participate in the Immune Response

Tissues and organs of the lymphatic system include the *lymph nodes,* the *spleen,* the *thymus,* and the *tonsils.* They play primary roles in filtering viruses, bacteria, damaged cells, and cellular debris from the lymph and bloodstream and in defending the body against infection and cancer. Lymphoid tissue also occurs in other regions of the body, particularly the digestive tract, where patches of lymph cells can be found beneath the epithelium of the intestine, in the colon, and in the appendix.

Lymph nodes are small, bean-shaped organs spaced along the lymph vessels and clustered along the sides of the neck, in the armpits and groin, and in the centre of the abdomen and chest cavity (see Figure 37.17). Spaces in nodes contain macrophages, a type of leukocyte that engulfs and destroys cellular debris and infecting bacteria and viruses in the lymph. The lymph nodes also contain other leukocytes that produce antibodies that aid in the destruction of invading pathogens (see Chapter 44).

Study Break

1. What are the three functions of the lymphatic system?
2. What are the main organs of the lymphatic system?

Unanswered Questions

Can gene therapy be used to treat genetic diseases? Haemophilia is a disease in which normal blood clotting is inhibited because the sufferer lacks one of the proteins important in the pathway leading to the formation of clots. It is a sex-linked genetic disease associated with the X chromosome (see Chapter 12). Therapies in the past have included regular transfusions of normal blood concentrates, but that process carries with it the risk of transmitting viruses, including hepatitis and AIDS. People with haemophilia lack either factor VIII or factor IX of the blood-clotting proteins. The cloning of the genes for these two proteins has made recombinant proteins available for injection, but these are expensive. An ideal solution would have the haemophiliac produce his own clotting factors as the result of some form of genetic technology.

Dr. David Lillicrap at Queen's University is leading two approaches. The first involves the delivery of the gene to the haemophiliac's cells using a vector virus. The virus is stripped of most of its genes, the clotting factor genes are added, and the virus is injected. The results from mice have been promising. In the second approach, Dr. Lillicrap leads a team in the Stem Cell Network, a large international group of researchers with headquarters at the University of Ottawa. They will insert the gene for factor VIII into stem cells from haemophiliac dogs. The cells will then be cultured to greatly increase the numbers before returning them to the dog.

Review

Go to CENGAGENOW™ at http://hed.nelson.com/ to access quizzing, animations, exercises, articles, and personalized homework help.

37.1 Animal Circulatory Systems: An Introduction

- Those invertebrates with a simple internal structure (sponges, cnidarians, flatworms, and nematodes) have no specialized circulatory systems.
- Animals with circulatory systems have a muscular heart that pumps a specialized fluid, such as blood, from one body region to another through tubular vessels. The blood carries O_2 and nutrients to body tissues and carries away CO_2 and wastes.
- Animal circulatory systems are either open or closed. In an open system, the heart pumps haemolymph into vessels that empty into body spaces. The haemolymph collects in other vessels to be returned to the heart. In a closed system, the blood is confined in blood vessels throughout the body and does not mix directly with the interstitial fluid. Closed systems circulate the blood at higher pressures and allow more rapid distribution of O_2 and nutrients and clearance of CO_2 and wastes.
- In the protostome invertebrates, open circulatory systems occur in arthropods and most molluscs, whereas closed circulatory systems occur in annelids and in cephalopod molluscs (squids and octopuses).
- In vertebrates, the circulatory system has evolved from a heart with a single series of chambers, pumping blood through a single circuit to the gills and then on to the brain and other organs, to a double heart in birds and mammals that pumps blood through separate pulmonary and systemic circuits.
- The changes in the structure of the heart are accompanied by alterations in the six segmental aortic arches that originally served the gills of the chordate ancestor.

37.2 Blood and Its Components

- Mammalian blood is a fluid connective tissue consisting of erythrocytes, leukocytes, and platelets suspended in a fluid matrix, the plasma.
- Plasma contains water, ions, dissolved gases such as O_2 and CO_2, glucose, amino acids, lipids, vitamins, hormones, and plasma proteins. The plasma proteins include albumins, which transport substances through the blood or act as enzymes; globulins, which transport lipids and include antibodies; and fibrinogen, which takes part in the clotting reaction.
- Erythrocytes contain haemoglobin, which transports O_2 between the lungs and all body regions. Erythrocytes also transport some CO_2 from interstitial fluid to the lungs and contribute to the reactions maintaining blood pH. They are formed by division of stem cells in the red bone marrow.
- Leukocytes engulf cellular debris and dead and diseased cells, and they defend the body against infecting pathogens. Leukocytes are produced by division of stem cells in the red bone marrow and by division of existing leukocytes.
- Platelets are functional cell fragments that trigger clotting reactions at sites of damage to the circulatory system.

37.3 The Heart

- The mammalian heart is a four-chambered pump. Two atria at the anterior of the heart pump the blood into two ventricles at the posterior of the heart, which pump blood into two separate pulmonary and systemic circuits of blood vessels.
- In both circuits, the blood leaves the heart in large arteries, which branch into smaller arteries, the arterioles. The arterioles deliver the blood to capillary networks, where substances are exchanged between the blood and the interstitial fluid. Blood is collected from the capillaries in small veins, the venules, which join into larger veins that return the blood to the heart.
- Contraction of the ventricles pushes blood into the arteries at a peak pressure, the systolic pressure. Between contractions, the blood pressure in the arteries falls to a minimum pressure, the diastolic pressure. The systole–diastole sequence is the cardiac cycle.
- Contraction of the atria and ventricles is initiated by signals from the sinoatrial (SA) node (pacemaker) of the heart. The signals move over the atria and then activate cells in the atrioventricular (AV) node. From there, the signals move along Purkinje fibres to trigger contraction of the ventricles starting at the bottom of the heart and moving upward.

37.4 Blood Vessels of the Circulatory System

- The walls of arteries consist of an inner endothelial layer, a middle layer of smooth muscle, and an outer layer of elastic fibres. By expanding during systole and rebounding during diastole, the elastic arteries ensure that blood flow is continuous.
- Capillary walls consist of a single layer of endothelial cells and their basement membrane. Blood flow through capillaries is controlled by contraction and relaxation of the smooth muscles of arterioles and precapillary sphincters.
- In the capillary networks, the rate of blood flow is considerably slower than in arteries and veins. This maximizes the time for exchange of substances between blood and tissues. Two major mechanisms drive the exchange of substances: diffusion along concentration gradients and bulk flow.
- Venules and veins have thinner walls than arteries, allowing the vessels to expand and contract over a wide range. As a result, they act both as blood reservoirs and conduits.
- The return of blood to the heart is aided by pressure exerted on the veins when surrounding skeletal muscles contract and by respiratory movements, which force blood from the abdomen toward the chest cavity. One-way valves in the veins prevent the blood from flowing backward.

37.5 Maintaining Blood Flow and Pressure

- Blood pressure and flow are regulated by controlling cardiac output, the degree of constriction of blood vessels (primarily arterioles), and the total blood volume. The autonomic nervous system and the endocrine system interact to coordinate these mechanisms.
- Regulation of cardiac output starts with baroreceptors, which detect blood pressure changes in the large arteries and veins and send signals to the medulla of the brain stem. In response, the brain stem sends signals via the autonomic nervous system that alter the rate and force of the heartbeat.
- Hormones secreted by several glands contribute to the regulation of blood pressure and flow. Epinephrine increases blood pressure by increasing the strength and rate of the heartbeat and stimulating vasoconstriction of arterioles in some areas of the body.
- Local controls respond primarily to O_2 and CO_2 concentrations in tissues. Low O_2 and high CO_2 concentration cause dilation of arteriole walls, increasing the arteriole diameter and blood flow. High O_2 and low CO_2 concentrations have the opposite effects. Nitric oxide released by arterial endothelial cells acts locally to increase arteriole diameter and blood flow.

37.6 The Lymphatic System

- The lymphatic system is an extensive network of vessels that collect excess interstitial fluid, which becomes lymph, and return it to the venous blood. The system also collects fats absorbed from the small intestine and delivers them to the blood circulation, and it is a key component of the immune system.
- The tissues and organs of the lymphatic system include the lymph nodes, the spleen, the thymus, and the tonsils. They remove viruses, bacteria, damaged cells, and cellular debris from the lymph and bloodstream and defend the body against infection and cancer.

Questions

Self-Test Questions

1. Which circulatory system best describes the animal?
   a. Squids and octopuses have open circulatory systems with ventricles that pump blood away from the heart.
   b. Fishes have a single-chambered heart with an atrium that pumps blood through gills for oxygen exchange.
   c. Amphibians have the most oxygenated blood in the pulmocutaneous (leading to and from the lungs and skin) circuit and the most deoxygenated blood in the systemic circuit.
   d. Amphibians and reptiles use a two-chambered heart to separate oxygenated and deoxygenated blood.
   e. Birds and mammals pump blood to separate pulmonary and systemic systems from two separate ventricles in a four-chambered heart.
2. A characteristic of blood circulation through or to the mammalian heart is that
   a. the superior vena cava conveys blood to the head.
   b. the inferior vena cava conveys blood to the right atrium.
   c. the pulmonary arteries convey blood from the lungs to the left atrium.
   d. the pulmonary veins convey blood into the left ventricle.
   e. the aorta branches into two coronary arteries that convey blood from heart muscle.
3. Which of the following is correct? (Any number of answers from a–e may be correct.)
   a. Carotid arteries supply the brain with oxygenated blood.
   b. Vertebrate hearts are neurogenic.
   c. Red blood cells in vertebrates contain no nuclei.
   d. The mammalian aorta is derived from aortic arch VI on the left side.
   e. Erythropoietin is secreted by red blood cells.
4. Characteristics of veins and venules are
   a. thick walls.
   b. large muscle mass in walls.
   c. a large quantity of elastin in the walls.
   d. low blood volume compared with arteries.
   e. one-way valves to prevent backflow of blood.
5. To increase cardiac output,
   a. the adrenal medulla and sympathetic nervous system secrete epinephrine and norepinephrine.
   b. baroreceptors in the brain signal the sympathetic nerves.
   c. the brain stem signals the baroreceptors, causing the heart to beat faster.
   d. the autonomic nervous system responds to low oxygen detected by chemoreceptors and decreases the force of the heartbeat.
   e. chemoreceptors, stimulated by excessive blood oxygen, increase the rate of the heartbeat.

Questions for Discussion

1. *Aplastic anaemia* develops when certain drugs or radiation destroy red bone marrow, including the stem cells that give rise to erythrocytes, leukocytes, and platelets. Predict some symptoms a person with aplastic anaemia would be likely to develop. Include at least one symptom related to each type of blood cell.
2. Haemoglobin occurs in the blood of many animals, but in many invertebrates, it occurs free in the plasma. What advantages can you think of that might have led to its incorporation in erythrocytes during evolution of vertebrates? The nonvertebrate chordates do not have haemoglobin in their blood, but they do have cells in their blood that have a role in defence, suggesting that erythrocytes may have originated from such cells. What evidence could be used to examine this hypothesis?
3. In some people, the pressure of the blood pooling in the legs leads to a condition called *varicose veins,* in which the veins stand out like swollen, purple knots. Explain why this might happen and why veins closer to the leg surface are more susceptible to the condition than those in deeper leg tissues.

Acropora millepora.

38 Animal Reproduction

Study Plan

Why It Matters

Over a few nights each year along the Great Barrier Reef off the east coast of Australia, many species of reef-building corals synchronously spawn, releasing eggs and sperm into the water. Timing is important for the corals because they rely on external fertilization. Male and female gametes must be released at the same time to maximize the chances of fertilization.

The circadian clocks of the corals control the reproductive event, which is synchronized to the lunar cycle. The massed spawning occurs over several nights after the full moon. Spawning is triggered by changes in lunar irradiance intensity. *Acropora millepora* (as seen in the opening photograph) is one coral involved in the mass reproductive event, providing a spectacular example of photosensitive responses.

A. millepora and other corals are sensitive to blue light (see Chapter 1) that entrains the circadian clocks of insects and mammals. The light sensors, called cryptochromes (CRYs), are DNA photolyaselike receptor proteins (see *Molecule Behind Biology*). Until 2007, cryptochromes had been reported only in higher animals (vertebrates and insects), and related but different proteins have now been found in plants and eubacteria. In *A. millepora,* the gene *cry2* showed increased

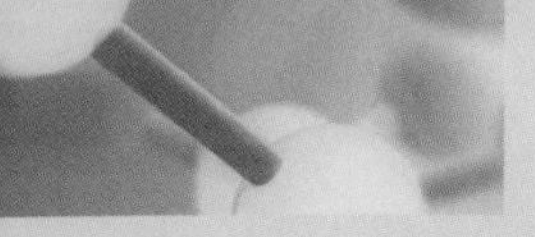

Molecule Behind Biology

Cryptochromes

In 1881, Charles Darwin reported that the growth of plants toward the sun (heliotropism) could be eliminated by filtering blue wavelengths (380 to 500 nm) from the light reaching the plant. Cryptochromes **(Figure 1)** is the name given to the photoreceptors sensitive to blue light—blue, ultraviolet-A receptors. The prefix "crypto-" was used because the identity of the pigments was unknown for some time.

We now know that many organisms respond to blue light and that the absorption spectrum of flavins is similar to the action spectrum of blue light. Repair of DNA is mediated by photolyases, which are flavoproteins. Cryptochromes also regulate the circadian clocks in animals and plants. The operation of cryptochromes depends on both the *cry1* and *cry2* genes for normal expression of circadian behavioural rhythms in organisms ranging from corals to *Arabidopsis* (a small plant related to mustard) and from *Drosophila* to mammals.

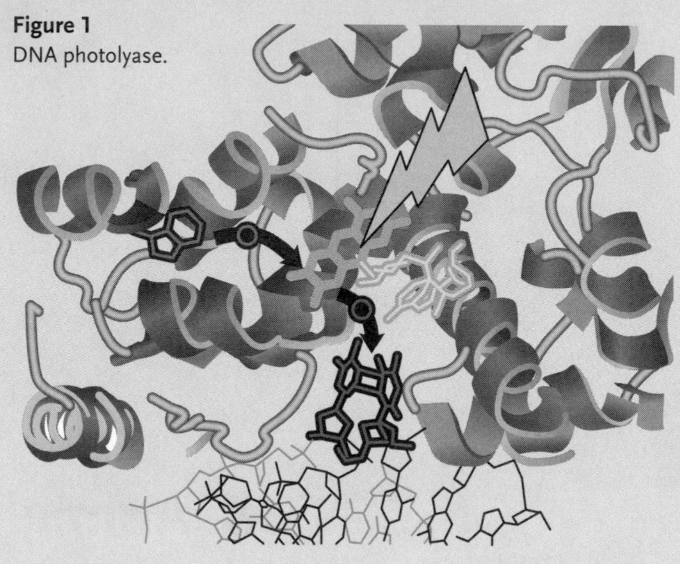

Figure 1
DNA photolyase.

expression on full moon versus new moon nights. These findings suggest that cryptochromes underlie synchronization of mass spawning events in many other invertebrates.

Many species of corals release eggs and sperm at the same time, but chemicals in the egg coatings and in the sperm acrosomes interact to ensure fertilization of eggs only by sperm of the same species.

38.1 The Drive to Reproduce

Organisms have a strong drive to reproduce, and most will go to considerable lengths to ensure that their genes are represented in future generations. The behaviour of some parasitic worms provides a telling example.

Acanthocephalan worms (*Moniliformis dubius;* **Figure 38.1**) are dioecious parasites that live in the alimentary systems of vertebrates. When laboratory rats are experimentally infected with juvenile acanthocephalan worms, the worms occupy different parts of a rat's gastrointestinal tract. Females live in the carbohydrate-rich anterior region just posterior to the stomach, whereas males migrate anteriorly. Females reach sexual maturity more or less synchronously in a 20-cm long portion of intestine. In the experimental system, males had access to many females, and each individual inseminated, on average, eight females.

Acanthocephalan worms are long-lived and presumably have many opportunities to mate. The density of these worms can be quite high, perhaps forcing males to compete for access to females. The male testes empty into the vas deferens and then into the *cirrus,* which terminates in a bursa or eversible cup. When copulating, a male wraps his everted bursa around the posterior end of the female so that the bursa can enter the female's gonopore (vagina). After mating, a male uses cement from glands in front of his testes to seal closed

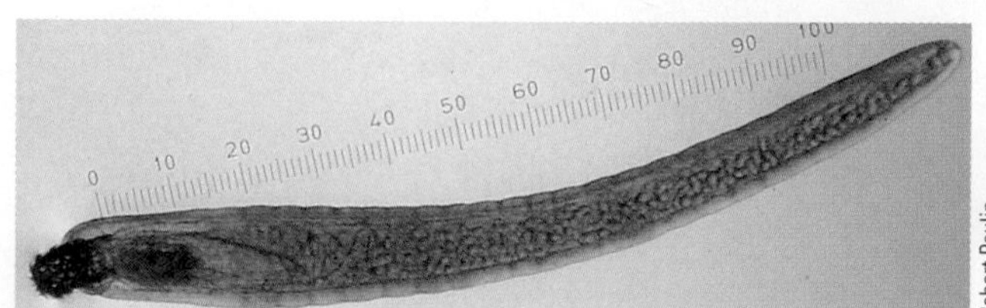

Robert Poulin

Figure 38.1
An acanthocephalan worm, *Moniliformis dubius.*

(or cap) the female's gonopore. This behaviour protects the male's investment in the female, perhaps ensuring that his sperm fertilizes her eggs and effectively outcompetes other males. Presumably, the plug is lost when the female releases her eggs. This is an example of the role that accessory glands (in this case cement glands) can play in reproduction.

Male acanthocephalan worms take other steps to outcompete other males for access to females. In addition to attempting to copulate with females, male *M. dubius* attempt to mate with other males, this time using the cement gland secretions to render the other males' genitalia inoperable.

Some variations in the mating and reproductive behaviour and biology of animals are best understood in the context of individuals protecting their investments in mate selection and production of young.

Study Break

How do acanthocephalan worms protect their investment in mate choice? Why?

38.2 Asexual and Sexual Reproduction

Reproduction is the means of passing on an individual's genes to a new generation, making it the most vital function of living organisms. In **asexual reproduction**, a single individual gives rise to offspring with no genetic input from another individual. In **sexual reproduction**, male and female parents produce zygotes (fertilized eggs) through the union of egg and sperm.

38.2a Asexual Reproduction: Reproduction without Recombination

Many aquatic invertebrates and some terrestrial annelids and insects reproduce asexually. This mode of reproduction is much less common among vertebrates. In asexual reproduction, from one to many cells of a parent's body develop directly into a new individual. Cells involved in asexual reproduction in animals are usually produced by mitosis, less commonly by meiosis. When cells involved in asexual reproduction are produced by mitosis, the resulting offspring are genetically identical to one another and to the parent (clonal reproduction).

Genetic uniformity of offspring can be advantageous in stable, uniform environments. In these cases, successful individuals with the "best" combinations of genes perpetuate the most competitive genotypes through asexual reproduction. Individuals do not have to expend energy to produce gametes or find a mate. Asexual reproduction is also advantageous to individuals living in sparsely settled populations or to sessile animals.

In animals, asexual reproduction involving mitosis occurs by three basic mechanisms: *fission, budding,* and *fragmentation*. In **fission**, the parent splits into two or more offspring of approximately equal size. Some species of planarians (Platyhelminthes) reproduce asexually by fission, dividing transversely or longitudinally. In **budding**, a new individual grows and develops while attached to the parent. Sponges, tunicates, and some cnidarians reproduce asexually by budding, and offspring may break free from the parent or remain attached to form a *colony*. In the cnidarian *Hydra*, an offspring buds and grows from one side of the parent's body and then detaches to become a separate individual **(Figure 38.2)**. Often in corals, buds remain attached when their growth is complete, forming colonies of thousands of interconnected individuals. In **fragmentation**, pieces separate from a parent's body and develop (*regenerate*) into new individuals. Many species of cnidarians, flatworms, annelids, and some echinoderms can reproduce by fragmentation.

Some animals produce offspring by **parthenogenesis** (*parthenos* = virgin; *genesis* = birth), which is the growth and development of an unfertilized egg. Offspring produced by parthenogenesis may be haploid or diploid, depending on the species. When the eggs involved in parthenogenesis are produced by meiosis, the offspring are not genetically identical to the parent or to each other.

Parthenogenesis occurs in some invertebrates, including certain aphids, water fleas, bees, and crustaceans. In bees, haploid drones (males) are produced parthenogenetically from unfertilized eggs produced by reproductive females (queens). New queens and sterile workers develop from fertilized eggs. Parthenogenesis also occurs in some vertebrates (e.g., certain fishes, salamanders, amphibians, lizards, and

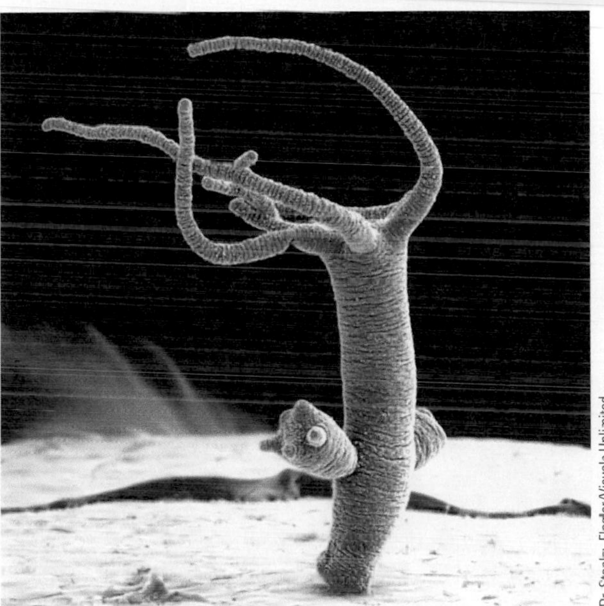

Figure 38.2
Asexual reproduction by budding in *Hydra* species.

Dr. Stanley Flegler/Visuals Unlimited

turkeys). In these animals, an egg, produced by meiosis, typically doubles its chromosomes to produce a diploid cell that begins development. In species in which females have two identical sex chromosomes, the offspring are female, whereas in single-sex species, in which males have two identical sex chromosomes, the offspring are males. All whip-tail lizard (*Cnemidophorus* spp.; **Figure 38.3**) species consist of females produced by parthenogenesis. These females still go through the motions of mating with each other.

In 2008, Eugene A. Gladyshev and two colleagues reported that bdelloid rotifers (see Chapter 26) contain many genes that apparently originated in other organisms (bacteria, fungi, and plants). Horizontal gene transfer—the capture and functional assimilation of exogenous genes—may be important in the evolution of bdelloid rotifers and be a factor allowing them to circumvent overt recombination during reproduction.

38.2b Sexual Reproduction: Add Recombination

Animals reproduce sexually through the union of **sperm** (motile gamete) and **eggs** (nonmotile gametes), both produced by **meiosis.** The overriding advantage of sexual reproduction is the generation of genetic diversity among offspring. Genetic diversity increases the chances that at least some offspring will be better adapted to local conditions and be more likely to survive and reproduce. Genetic recombination and independent assortment of chromosomes are two mechanisms of meiosis that give rise to genetic diversity in eggs and sperm (see Chapter 9). Genetic recombination mixes the alleles of parents into new combinations within chromosomes. Independent assortment randomly combines maternal and paternal chromosomes in the gamete nuclei. Additional variability is generated at fertilization when eggs and sperm from genetically different individuals fuse together at random to initiate the development of new individuals. Adding to the effects of genetic recombination and independent assortment, random mutations in DNA are the ultimate source of variability for both sexual and asexual reproduction.

Sexual reproduction can be a disadvantage because of the costs in energy and raw materials associated with producing gametes and finding mates. Finding mates can expose animals to predation and may conflict with the need to find food and shelter and caring for existing offspring.

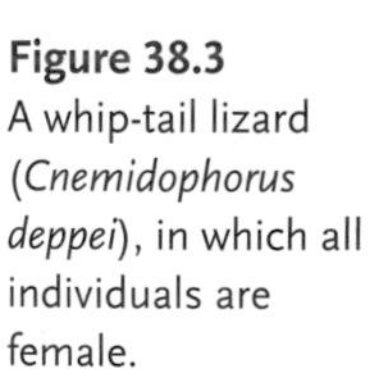

Figure 38.3
A whip-tail lizard (*Cnemidophorus deppei*), in which all individuals are female.

STUDY BREAK

What are the advantages of sexual reproduction over asexual reproduction?

38.3 Cellular Mechanisms of Sexual Reproduction

The cellular mechanisms of sexual reproduction include **gametogenesis**, the formation of male and female gametes, and **fertilization**, the union of gametes that initiate development of a new individual. Mating is the pairing of a male and a female for sexual reproduction.

38.3a Gametogenesis: Production of Gametes

Gametes in most animals are formed from **germ cells**, cell lines set aside early in embryonic development that remain distinct from **somatic cells** of the body. During development, germ cells collect in gonads, specialized gamete-producing organs: **testes** (singular, testis) in males and **ovaries** in females. Mitotic division of germ cells produces **spermatogonia** (singular, spermatogonium) in males and **oogonia** (singular, oogonium) in females. These cells then undergo meiosis to produce gametes **(Figure 38.4).** In some animals, germ cells give rise to families of cells that assist gamete development.

Meiosis reduces the number of chromosomes from diploid to haploid. Somatic cells have two copies of each chromosome; gametes have one. Fertilization, the fusion of a haploid sperm and a haploid egg, restores the diploid condition and produces a **zygote** or fertilized egg, the first cell of a new individual.

At the beginning of meiosis, developing gametes start as **spermatocytes** or **oocytes** and by the end are *spermatids* or *ootids*. When meiosis is complete, haploid cells develop into mature sperm cells (**spermatozoa**; singular, spermatozoon = sperm) or eggs (**ova**; singular, ovum). Spermatogenesis is the process of producing sperm; oogenesis is the process of producing eggs. Sperm are specialized to move toward, contact, and penetrate eggs. Sperm must be numerous, so each spermatid produces four sperm. Mobility means small size, a flagellum (**Figure 38.5**, **p. 916**) for propulsion, and mitochondria for energy. Sperm have nuclei that carry the male's chromosomal contributions to the zygote. The *acrosome* allows sperm to enter the egg.

Although sperm are usually smaller than eggs, they show considerable range in size, for example, from

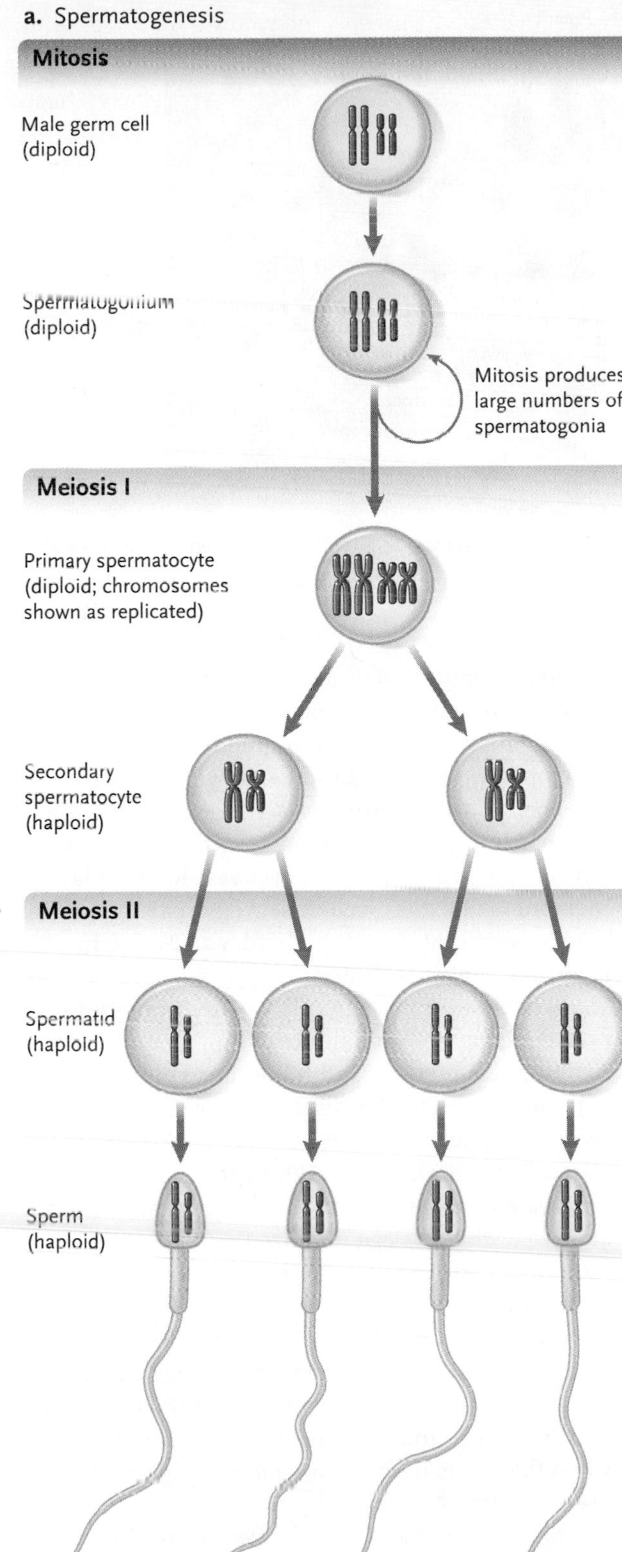

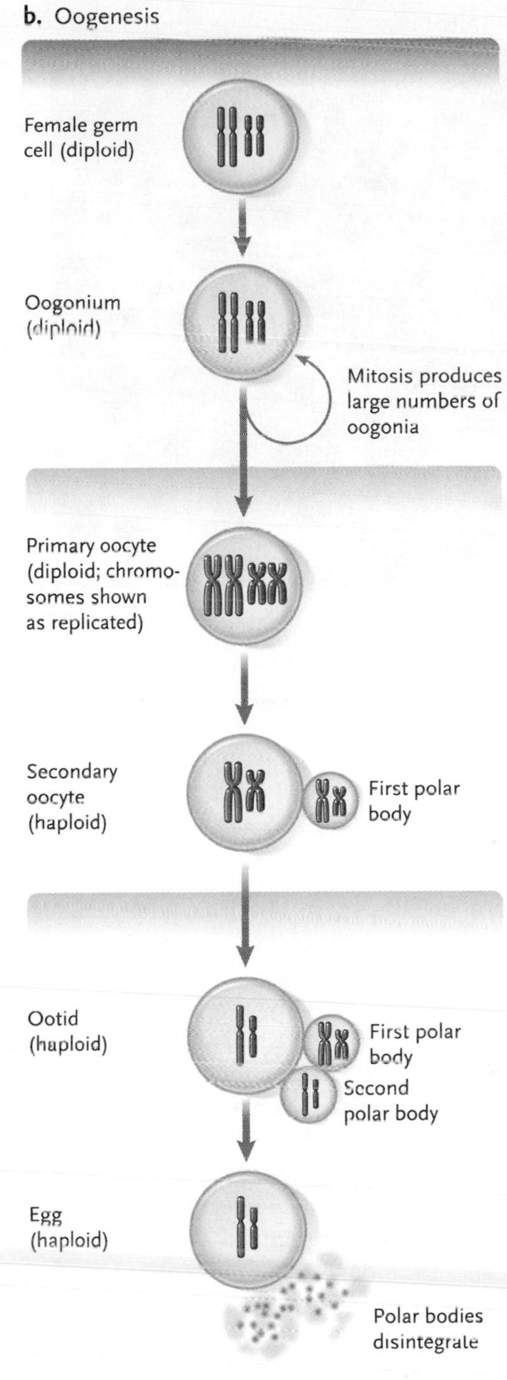

Figure 38.4
The mitotic and meiotic divisions that produce eggs and sperm from germ cells. **(a)** Spermatogenesis. **(b)** Oogenesis. The first polar body may or may not divide, depending on the species, so that either two or three polar bodies may be present at the end of meiosis. Two are shown in this diagram

4.5 to 16.5 μm long among *Drosophila* species. The size of individual sperm influences the speed at which they swim (longer sperm move more quickly than shorter sperm). But producing longer sperm may reduce total sperm production and limit a male's reproductive success because sperm must be numerous to maximize the chances of fertilization. In mammals, variations in sperm size, volume of ejaculate, and sperm density often reflect mating behaviour (see Chapter 40).

Spermatogenesis produces haploid cells specialized to deliver their nuclei to conspecific eggs. Two meiotic divisions produce four haploid spermatids (see Figure 38.4a) that each develop into a mature sperm (see Figure 38.5). During sperm maturation, most of the cytoplasm is lost. Mitochondria are in the cytoplasm around the base of the flagellum. These mitochondria produce ATP, the energy source for beating of the flagellum. At the opposite end of the sperm, the acrosome is a specialized secretory vesicle forming a cap over the nucleus. The acrosome contains enzymes and other

Figure 38.5
Spermatozoa.
(a) Photomicrograph of human sperm and **(b)** the structure of a sperm.

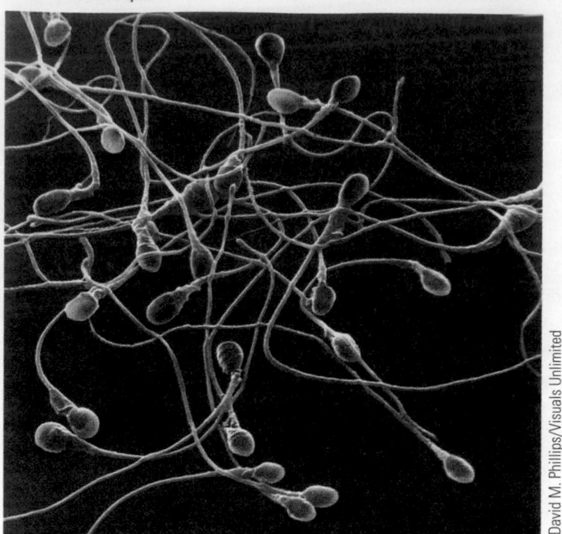

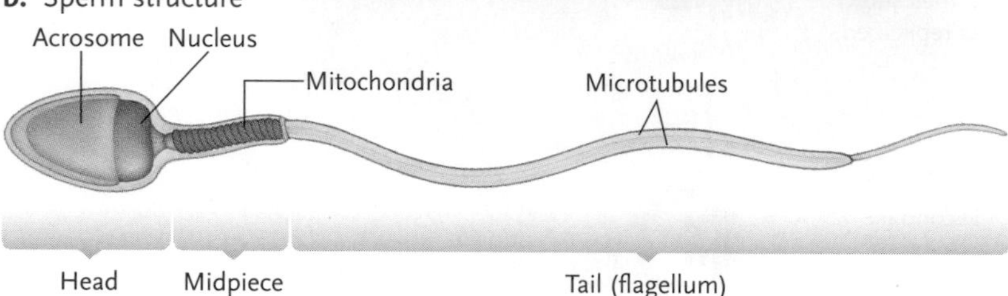

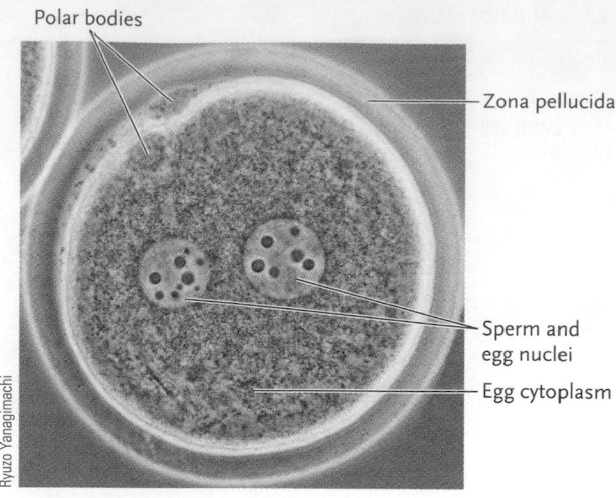

Figure 38.6
A mature hamster egg that has been fertilized. The sperm and egg nuclei are about to fuse together.

proteins that help the sperm attach to and penetrate the surface coatings of an egg of the same species.

Oogenesis produces eggs. Only one of the cell products of meiosis develops into a functional egg, with that cell retaining almost all of the cytoplasm of the parent. The other products form polar bodies (see Figure 38.4b). Unequal cytoplasmic divisions concentrate nutrients and other molecules required for development in the egg. In most species, polar bodies eventually disintegrate and do not contribute to fertilization or embryonic development.

Meiosis in the oogonia of most animals can be very protracted, taking as long as from embryonic development until fertilization of the next generation's zygote. Within a few weeks after a female mammal is born, her oocytes stop developing at the end of the first meiotic prophase. Oocytes remain in the ovary in this stage until the female is sexually mature. Then one to several oocytes advance to metaphase of the second meiotic division and are released from the ovary. The timing of egg release varies among mammals according to species and season. As in other animals, mammalian eggs complete meiosis at fertilization to produce the fully mature egg **(Figure 38.6)**. In humans, some oocytes may remain in prophase of the first meiotic division for 50 years.

The egg typically has specialized features, including stored nutrients required for at least the early stages of embryonic development, as well as one or more kinds of coatings that protect the egg from mechanical injury and infection. In some species, egg coats protect the embryo immediately after fertilization and prevent penetration by more than one sperm.

Egg coats are surface layers added during oocyte development or fertilization. The **vitelline coat** (the **zona pellucida** in mammals; see Figure 38.6) is a gel-like matrix of proteins, glycoproteins, and/or polysaccharides lying immediately outside the plasma membrane of the egg cell. Insect eggs have additional outer protein coats forming a hard, water-impermeable layer that prevents desiccation. In amphibians and some echinoderms, egg jelly forms the outer coat protecting the egg from desiccation.

In birds, reptiles, and monotremes (see Chapter 27), egg white, a thick solution of proteins, surrounds the vitelline coat. Outside the white is the *shell* of the egg, which is flexible and leathery in reptiles and mineralized and brittle in birds. Both egg white and shell are added while the egg (fertilized or not) moves along the **oviduct**, the tube connecting the ovary to the outside of the body.

In the mammalian ovary, the egg is surrounded by **follicle cells** during its development. Follicle cells grow from ovarian tissue and nourish the developing egg. They also make up part of the zona pellucida while the egg is in the ovary and remain as a protective layer after it is released.

Mature eggs can be the largest cells in an animal (see Figure 27.44). Mammalian eggs are microscopic, with few stored nutrients, because the embryo develops inside the mother and is supplied with nutrients by her body. The eggs of birds are huge because they contain all of the nutrients required for complete embryonic development. The bird egg includes the "yolk," which contains the nutrients for the developing egg, the ovum or egg cell, and the white. Regardless of size, cytoplasm makes up most of the volume of an animal egg and the nucleus of the egg is usually microscopic or nearly so.

38.3b Fertilization: Union of Egg and Sperm

Eggs and sperm are delivered from the ovaries and testes to the site of fertilization by oviducts (females) and sperm ducts (males). In many species, external accessory sex organs participate in the delivery of gametes. The basic design of vertebrate and invertebrate reproductive systems **(Figure 38.7)** is similar. Nonmotile eggs move through oviducts on currents generated by the beating of cilia that line the oviducts or by contractions of the oviducts or the body wall.

Fertilization may be external (outside the body of either parent) in a watery medium or internal in a watery fluid inside a female's body. **External fertilization** occurs in most aquatic invertebrates, bony fishes, and amphibians. Sperm and eggs are shed into the surrounding water. Sperm swim until they collide with an egg of the same species. The process is helped by synchronization of the release of eggs and sperm and by the enormous numbers of gametes released (see *Why It Matters*). In animals such as sea urchins and amphibians, sperm are attracted to eggs by diffusible attractant molecules released by the egg.

Most amphibians, even terrestrial species such as toads, mate in an aquatic environment. Frogs typically mate by a reflex response called *amplexus,* in which the male clasps the female tightly around the body with his forelimbs **(Figure 38.8, p. 918)**. Amplexus stimulates the female to shed a mass of eggs into the water through the *cloaca*. The cloaca is the cavity into which intestinal, urinary, and genital tracts empty in reptiles, birds, amphibians, and many fishes. As the eggs are released, they are fertilized by sperm released by the male.

Internal fertilization is widespread in animals, and is not restricted to mammals. Internal fertilization occurs in invertebrates such as annelids, some arthropods, and some molluscs and in vertebrates from fishes and salamanders to reptiles, birds, and mammals. In internal fertilization, sperm are released by the male close to or inside the entrance to the female's reproductive tract. Sperm swim through fluids in the reproductive tract until one reaches and fertilizes an egg. In some species, molecules released by the egg attract the sperm. Internal fertilization involves copulation, which occurs when a male's accessory sex organ (e.g., a penis) is inserted into a female's accessory sex organ (e.g., a vagina). Internal fertilization makes terrestrial life possible because the female's body provides the aquatic medium required for fertilization without the danger of gametes drying when exposed to the air. Effecting internal fertilization means close contact between individuals.

Male sharks and rays use a pair of modified pelvic fins as accessory sex organs that channel sperm directly into the female's cloaca. Male reptiles, birds, and mammals also use accessory sex organs to place sperm directly inside the reproductive tract of females, where fertilization takes place. In reptiles and birds, sperm fertilize eggs as they are released from the ovary and

a. *Drosophila* (fruit fly)

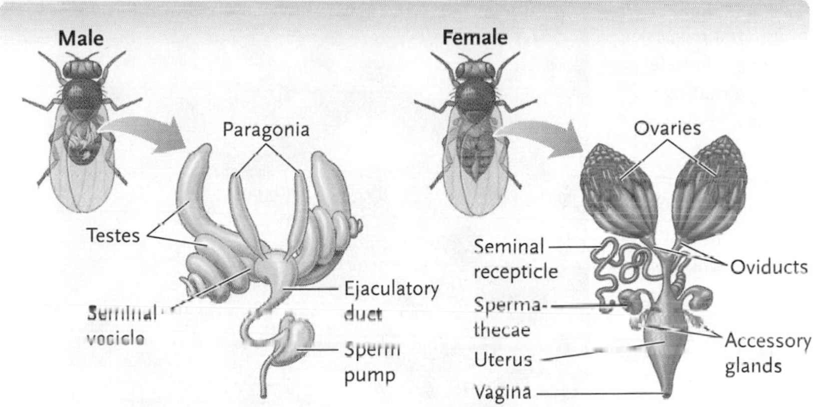

b. Amphibian (frog)

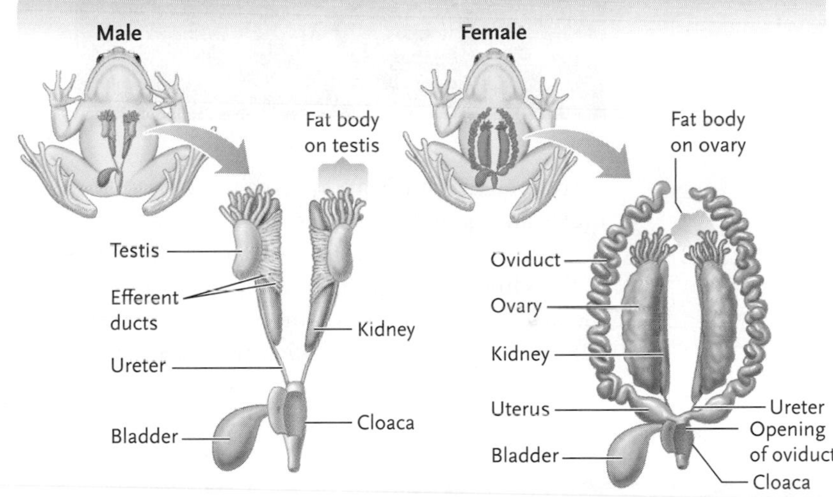

c. Mammal (cat)

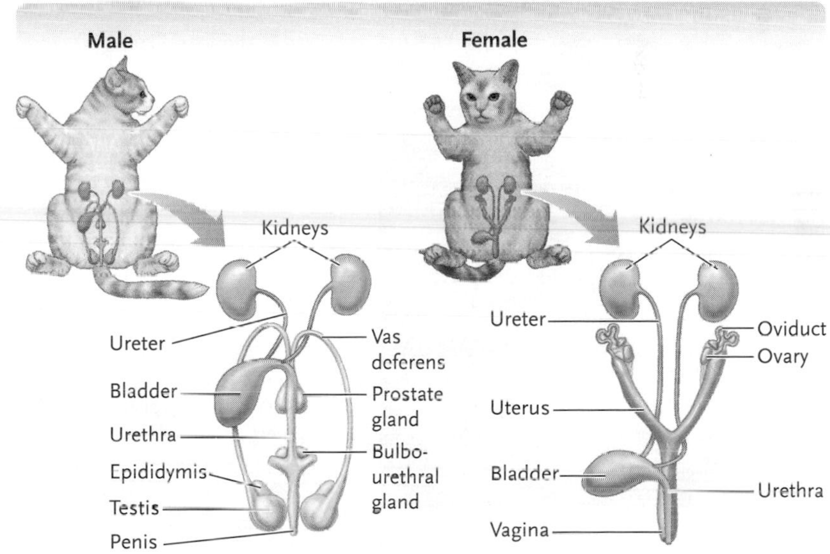

Figure 38.7
Some reproductive systems. **(a)** An insect, *Drosophila* (fruit fly). **(b)** An amphibian, a frog. **(c)** A mammal, a cat. Female systems are shown in blue and male systems in yellow.

travel through the oviducts, before the shell is added. In mammals, the penis delivers sperm into the female's vagina, which is a specialized structure for

Hans Pfl etschinger

Figure 38.8
A male leopard frog (*Rana pipiens*) clasping a female during a mating embrace known as **amplexus.** The tight squeeze by the male frog stimulates the female to release her eggs, which can be seen streaming from her body, embedded in a mass of egg jelly. Sperm released by the male fertilize the eggs as they pass from the female.

reproduction. Fertilization takes place when a sperm meets an egg in the oviducts.

Once a sperm touches the outer surface of an egg of the same species **(Figure 38.9a),** receptor proteins in the sperm plasma membrane bind the sperm to the vitelline coat or zona pellucida (**Figure 38.9b,** step 4). In most animals, only a conspecific sperm is recognized and binds to the egg surface. Species recognition between sperm and eggs is particularly important in animals using external fertilization because water surrounding the egg may contain sperm from many different species. This aspect is less important in species using internal fertilization where structural adaptations and behavioural patterns usually limit sperm transfer from males to females of the same species (see *Variations in Internal Fertilization*).

After initial attachment of sperm to egg, the events of fertilization proceed in rapid succession (see Figure 38.9b). The acrosome of the sperm releases its contents, including enzymes that dissolve a path through the egg coats. The sperm, with its tail still beating, follows the path until its plasma membrane touches and fuses with the egg's plasma membrane (step 5). Fusion introduces the sperm nucleus into the egg cytoplasm and activates the egg to complete meiosis and begin development.

38.3c Polyspermy: Keeping Sperm Out of the Fertilized Egg

Protection against polyspermy (more than one sperm fertilizing an egg) is widespread in the animal kingdom. Two mechanisms help prevent polyspermy: a

a. Sperm adhering to egg

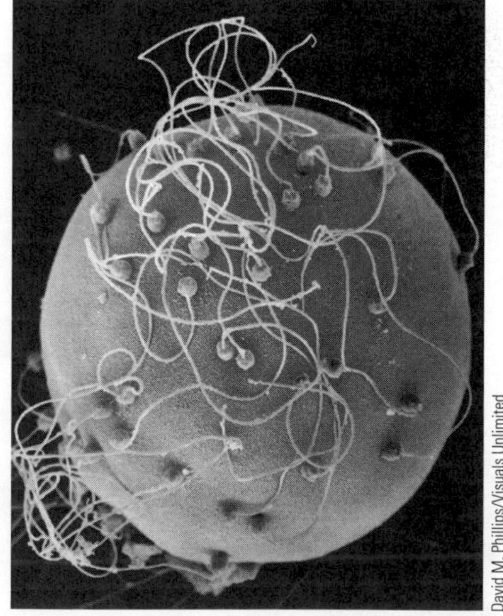

David M. Phillips/Visuals Unlimited

b. Steps in fertilization

1 A sperm contacts the jelly layer of the egg.

2 The acrosomal reaction begins.

3 Acrosomal enzymes dissolve a path through the jelly layer.

4 Proteins in its plasma membrane bind the sperm to the vitelline coat.

5 The sperm lyses a hole in the vitelline coat. The sperm and egg plasma membranes fuse.

6 Membrane depolarization produces the fast block to polyspermy.

7 The sperm nucleus and centriole enter the egg. The sperm nucleus then fuses wtih the egg nucleus.

8 Cortical granules discharge their contents, producing the slow block to polyspermy.

Sperm
Nucleus
Centriole
Actin
Acrosome
Jelly layer
Acrosomal process
Vitelline coat
Plasma membrane
Cortical granule
Egg

Figure 38.9
Fertilization. **(a)** Sperm adhering to the surface coat of a sea urchin egg. Of the many sperm that may initially adhere to the outer surface of the egg, usually only one accomplishes fertilization. **(b)** Steps of fertilization in a sea urchin.

Variations in Internal Fertilization

Internal fertilization benefits animals in several ways. The placement of sperm in the female's reproductive system maximizes the chances of fertilization. Specializations of the male and female genitalia increase the precision with which sperm is delivered, whereas a combination of behavioural and structural (often referred to as "lock-and-key") arrangements minimizes the chances of mistaken identity (cross-species matings). Internal fertilization can give both males and females more control over which sperm fertilize which eggs.

Invertebrate animals such as bedbugs, insects in the family Cimicidae, have well-developed genitalia but practise "traumatic insemination." This involves the male bedbug (e.g., *Cimex lectularius*) piercing the female's abdominal wall with his external genitalia and delivering sperm directly into her coelom (body cavity). The male always pierces the female's body at the spermalege, consisting of an ectospermalege and a mesospermalege, where the sperm are deposited **(Figure 1).**

Females are wounded during traumatic insemination, and the spermalege appears to be an anatomical counterstrategy to minimize the damage associated with this form of mating. "Last male precedence," the fact that the sperm of the last male to mate fertilizes the eggs, appears to be the main benefit of this approach to mating. The spermalege also reduces the chances of infection by pathogens transferred in the mating process.

a.

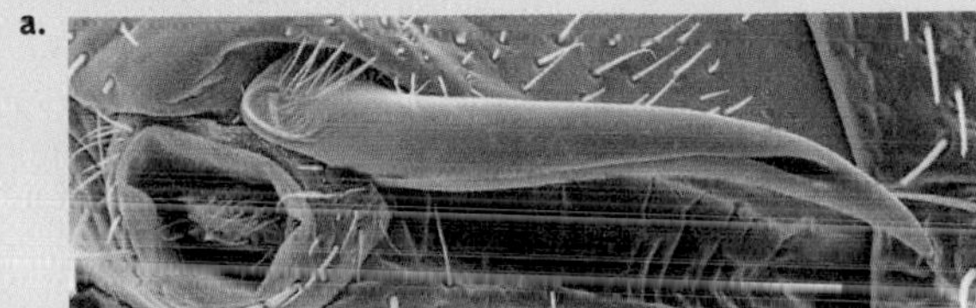

b.

c.

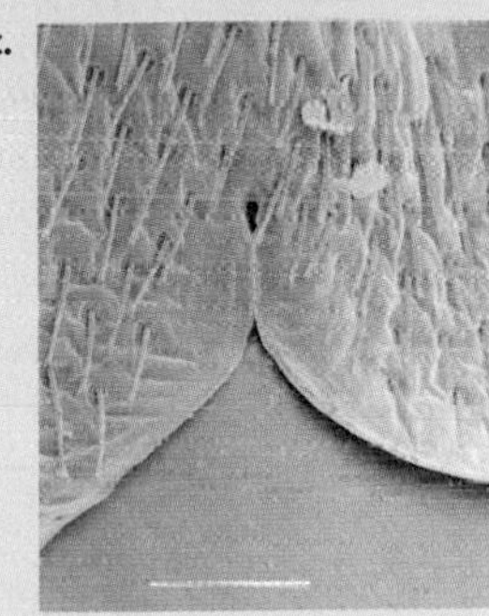

Figure 1

(a) The intromittant organ (penis) of *Cimex lectularius* (scale bar 0.1 μm) is shown with **(b)** a ventral view of the whole animals and **(c)** the ectospermalege, an incurving in one of the female's sternites that guides the male's intromittant organ (scale bar 1.5 μm).

fast block that works within seconds of fertilization and a **slow block** that works in minutes. In invertebrate species such as the sea urchin, fusion of egg and sperm opens ion channels in the egg's plasma membrane, spreading a wave of electrical depolarization over the egg surface (much like a nerve impulse travelling along a neuron). Depolarization alters the egg plasma membrane so that it cannot fuse with any additional sperm, eliminating the possibility that more than one set of paternal chromosomes enters the egg. This fast block occurs within a few seconds of fertilization.

The fast block depends on a change in the egg's membrane potential from negative to positive. It is not established when the membrane potential of a sea urchin egg is experimentally kept at a negative value. In this case, additional sperm fuse with the plasma membrane. Fertilization was entirely blocked if the membrane was kept positive before sperm contact.

In vertebrates, the wave of membrane depolarization following sperm–egg fusion is not as pronounced as it is in sea urchins and does not prevent additional sperm from fusing with the egg. However, additional sperm nuclei that enter the egg cytoplasm usually break down and disappear, so only the first sperm nucleus to enter fuses with the egg nucleus.

In both invertebrates and vertebrates, fusion of egg and sperm also triggers the release of stored calcium (Ca^{2+}) ions from the endoplasmic reticulum into the cytosol. Ca^{2+} ions activate control proteins and enzymes that initiate intense metabolic activity in the fertilized egg, including a rapid increase in cellular oxidations and synthesis of proteins and other molecules.

Ca^{2+} ions also cause cortical granules to fuse with the egg's plasma membrane and release their contents to the outside (see Figure 38.9b, step 8). Enzymes released from cortical granules alter the egg coats within minutes of fertilization, so no further sperm can attach to or penetrate the egg. This process is the slow block to polyspermy.

The importance of Ca^{2+} to cortical granule release has been demonstrated experimentally. Granules are released in unfertilized eggs if Ca^{2+} is added experimentally to the cytoplasm. Conversely, if chemicals that bind Ca^{2+} are added to the cytoplasm of unfertilized eggs, the concentration of Ca^{2+} cannot rise and cortical granule release does not occur after fertilization.

After the sperm nucleus enters the egg cytoplasm, microtubules move the sperm and egg nuclei together in the egg cytoplasm until they fuse. The chromosomes of egg and sperm nuclei then assemble together and enter mitosis. The subsequent, highly programmed events of embryonic development convert the fertilized egg into an individual capable of independent existence.

The paternal chromosomes, the microtubule organizing centre, and one or two centrioles (see Chapter 9) are the only components of sperm to survive in the egg. Therefore, almost all cytoplasmic structures of the embryo and of the new individual are maternal in origin.

On the Road to Vivipary

Although mammals could be considered the archetypical viviparous animals, not all living mammals are viviparous. Furthermore, living therian mammals (marsupials and placentals) do not all have the same kind of placenta. We have no data about whether early mammals such as *Castorocauda* (see Figures 19.8 and 19.9) were viviparous. At least 50 gene loci regulate the development of the placenta in "placental" mammals such as mice and rats. Included are gene families that produce protein hormones and hemoglobin. Some of these genes and gene families are adapted to fetal development.

Guppies, familiar aquarium fish, (see Ch. 45 *Life Histories of Guppies*)and other related fish in the genus *Poeciliopsis* exhibit a range of reproductive patterns. Some species are oviparous. Females in other species retain eggs in their bodies after fertilization and give birth to live young with no further provisioning, whereas the females of still other species develop a "follicular pseudoplacenta" that functions much like the placenta of a mouse (or a human). The level of maternal investment (matrotrophic index) ranges from none to extensive **(Figure 1).** A phylogeny of *Poeciliopsis* and other species **(Figure 2)** shows repeated evolution of placentalike structures in these fish.

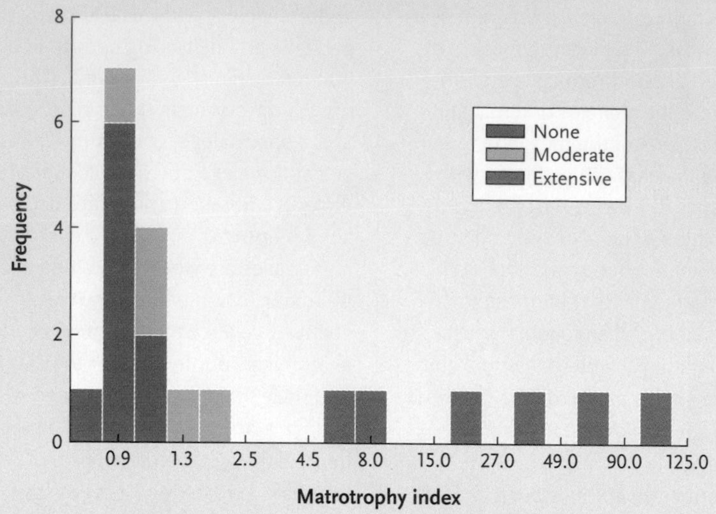

Figure 1
A matrotrophy index (MI) results when values are assigned to the levels of investment that females make in their young. Matrotrophy indices range from low (ovipary) to high (some ovovivipary and vivipary), and there are intermediate conditions. There is a range of MI indices for species in the genus *Poeciliopsis,* illustrating the range of conditions. Low MI values are the most common (highest frequency values), but there are significant differences among species. In this figure, species with the same colour do not differ significantly in MI values.

Vivipary also appears in different evolutionary lines of elasmobranchs (sharks, rays, and holocephalians; see Chapter 27). The young of various rays and tiger sharks (*Galaeocerdo cuvier*) develop inside the mother and are nourished by her, but there is no evidence of a placenta. Species such as grey nurse sharks (*Ginglymostoma cirratum*), mako sharks (*Isurus oxyrinchus*), porbeagle sharks (*Lamna nasus*), and thresher sharks (*Alopias* species) are oophagous. This means that while pregnant, the females of these species of sharks continue to produce large numbers of small eggs that are consumed by the developing embryos. At least one species of fossil holocephalan chondrichthyian fish (*Delphyodontos dacriformes*) appears to have been oophagous. The evidence comes from the well-developed slashing and piercing teeth of this lower Carboniferous fossil **(Figure 3).**

By retaining developing young in their bodies, adults (usually females) better protect them from predators, provide an appropriate environment for development, and, in many cases, ensure an adequate food supply. As a recurring theme in animals, viviparity is of little value in determining phylogeny (evolutionary relationships). We explore this subject in more detail when we consider development in Chapter 39.

The centrioles of the new individual are normally of paternal origin.

38.3d Patterns of Development: Moving from Zygote to Complete Organism

Ovipary, vivipary, and ovovivipary are three patterns of embryonic support. **Oviparous** animals lay eggs, whereas viviparous and ovoviviparous animals bear live young. The eggs of oviparous animals contain all of the nutrients necessary for development of the embryo outside the mother's body. In **viviparous** animals, the mother's body provides nutrients and oxygen to and removes wastes from the developing embryo. In **ovoviviparous** animals, eggs with yolk are retained in the mother's body, but embryonic development and growth are supported by the yolk (see *On the Road to Vivipary*).

Viviparous animals (*vivi* = alive) retain the embryo within the mother's body and nourish it during at least early embryo development. All living mammals except monotremes are viviparous. Vivipary occurs in other vertebrate groups except crocodilians, turtles, and birds. An exceptionally well-preserved Devonian fossil placoderm (*Materpiscis attenboroughi*) reveals that vivipary is an ancient trait in vertebrates. This fossilized female was connected by an umbilical cord to one embryo in

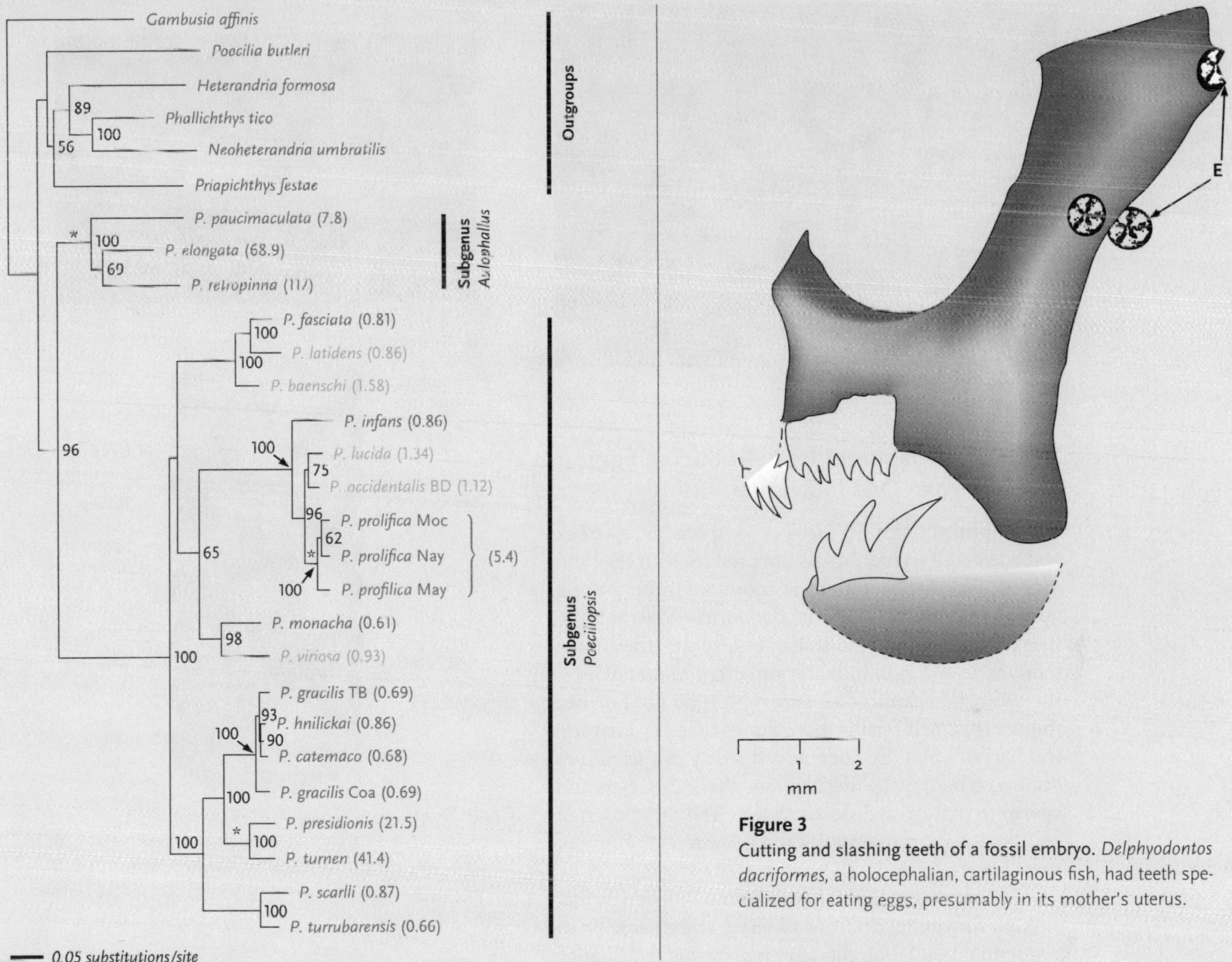

Figure 3
Cutting and slashing teeth of a fossil embryo. *Delphyodontos dacriformes*, a holocephalian, cartilaginous fish, had teeth specialized for eating eggs, presumably in its mother's uterus.

Figure 2
Matrotrophy index values are shown for species in a phylogeny (phylogram) that illustrates proposed evolutionary relationships among species in the genus *Poeciliopsis* and other species. This phylogeny demonstrates that different evolutionary lineages of guppylike fish have independently achieved different levels of association between mothers and their developing young. The colour codes as per MI indices in Figure 1 in *Variations in Internal Fertilization*.

her uterus. Another fossilized female placoderm from the same deposit contains three embryos.

In viviparous animals, embryonic development takes place in the **uterus** (womb), a specialized, saclike organ. There are two basic groups of viviparous mammals. In placental mammals (Eutheria), a specialized temporary structure called the placenta facilitates the transfer of nutrients from the mother's blood to the embryo and of wastes in the opposite direction. The young are born with fully developed limbs. In marsupials (Metatheria), the young are born at an earlier stage before their hindlimbs have developed. Metatherians have a placenta, but it is derived from a different tissue than that of eutherians. The metatherian placenta provides nutrients to the embryo from an attached membranous sac containing yolk, but only for the early stages of its development. In marsupials such as kangaroos, koalas, wombats, and opossums, the tiny newborn crawls from the opening of the birth canal to its mother's pouch (marsupium), where it attaches to a nipple and completes its development **(Figure 38.10, p. 922).**

Ovovivipary (adjective, **ovoviviparous**) is common in some fishes, lizards, and amphibians; many snakes; and many invertebrates. No uterus or placenta is involved. When development is complete, the eggs hatch inside the mother and the young are released to the exterior.

Figure 38.10 Developing offspring of a marsupial mammal, an opossum (*Didelphis virginiana*), attached to a nipple in the marsupium (pouch) of its mother.

a.

b. Sex organs

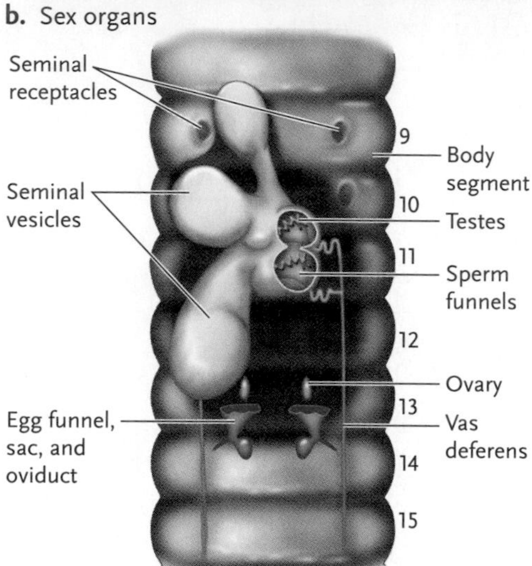

Figure 38.11
Simultaneous hermarphroditism in the earthworm. **(a)** Copulation by a mating pair of earthworms, in which each individual releases sperm that fertilizes the eggs in its partner. **(b)** The sex organs in the earthworm.

38.3e Hermaphroditism: Producing Eggs and Sperm in One Individual

Hermaphroditic (from *Hermes* + *Aphrodite,* a Greek god and goddess) individuals can produce both eggs and sperm. **Hermaphroditism** is more common among sponges (Porifera), cnidaria, flatworms (Platyhelminthes), earthworms, land snails, and some other invertebrates than it is in humans and other mammals.

Most hermaphroditic individuals do not fertilize themselves. Self-fertilization is prevented by anatomical barriers that preclude introduction of sperm into their own body or by mechanisms that cause eggs and sperm to mature at different times. The prevention of self-fertilization maintains the genetic variability of sexual reproduction.

Simultaneous hermaphrodites are individuals that develop functional ovaries and testes at the same time. Sequential hermaphrodites are individuals that change from one sex to the other. Earthworms, as shown in **Figure 38.11,** are a good example of simultaneous hermaphroditism. The only known vertebrate simultaneous hermaphrodites are hamlets (genus *Hypoplectrus*), a group of predatory sea basses **(Figure 38.12).** Sequential hermaphroditism occurs in many invertebrates (for example, some crustaceans) and some ectothermic vertebrates. Well-known examples include the genus *Amphiprion,* in which, in some species, the initial sex is male (as in clownfish), whereas in others, it is female. In still other species, individuals start as males, turn into females, and then turn back into males.

Study Break

1. When does meiosis occur in animal life cycles? How does this compare with the situation in plants?
2. Why do the eggs of animals differ so much in size? What are the implications for development?
3. What are the benefits of internal fertilization?

Figure 38.12
Hypoplectrus gummigutta, a predatory sea bass that is a simultaneous hermaphrodite.

38.4 Sexual Reproduction in Humans

Reproductively, humans are typical eutherian (placental) mammals. Males and females each have a pair of gonads (testes or ovaries). As in other vertebrates, gonads serve a dual function, producing gametes and secreting hormones responsible for sexual development and mating behaviour (see Chapters 35, 39, and 40).

38.4a Females: Produce Eggs, Get Pregnant, Lactate

Human females have a pair of ovaries suspended in the abdominal cavity. An oviduct leads from each ovary to the uterus, which is hollow with walls that contain smooth muscle. The uterus is lined by the endometrium, formed by layers of connective tissue with embedded glands and richly supplied with blood vessels. If an egg is fertilized and begins development, it must implant in the endometrium to continue developing. The lower end of the uterus, the cervix, opens into a muscular canal, the vagina, which leads to the exterior. Sperm enter the female reproductive tract via the vagina, and at birth, the baby passes from the uterus to the vagina to the outside.

The **vulva**, external female sex organs (genitalia), surround the opening of the vagina **(Figure 38.13).** Two folds of tissue, the **labia minora**, run from front to rear on either side of the opening. Labia minora are partially covered by labia majora, a pair of fleshy, fat-padded folds that also run from front to rear on either side of the vagina. At the anterior end of the vulva, the labia minora join to partly cover the **clitoris**, a bulblike erectile organ with the same embryonic origins as the penis. Two **greater vestibular glands** open near the entrance to the vagina and secrete a mucus-rich fluid that lubricates the vulva. The urethra that conducts urine from the bladder to the outside opens between the clitoris and the vaginal opening. Most nerve endings associated with erotic sensations are concentrated in the clitoris and the labia minora and around the opening of the vagina. When a human female is born, a thin flap of tissue, the **hymen**, partially covers the opening of the vagina. This membrane, if it has not already been ruptured by physical exercise or other disturbances, is broken during the first sexual intercourse.

At birth, each ovary contains about 1 million oocytes whose development is arrested at the end of the first meiotic prophase. Although 200 000 to 380 000 oocytes survive until a female reaches sexual maturity, only about 380 are actually ovulated, released as immature eggs into the abdominal cavity and pulled into the nearby oviduct by the current produced by the beating of the cilia that line the oviduct. The cilia propel the egg along the oviduct and into the uterus. Fertilization usually occurs in the oviduct.

In most vertebrates, **ovulation**, the release of the egg from the ovary, usually occurs during a well-defined mating season, the time of year when males and females are *fertile*—physiologically and behaviourally ready to reproduce. The timing of mating seasons is usually under the general control of day length (photoperiod), with some adjustment for local weather. This pattern ensures that the young are born at a time of year when food is plentiful. Humans, however, do not show any evidence of a mating season. Mating and fertilization can occur at any time of the year. Furthermore, ovulation appears to be cryptic in humans, meaning that women do not know when they are ovulating, nor do their partners.

Reproduction in human females is under neuroendocrine control, involving complex interactions between the hypothalamus, pituitary, ovaries, and uterus. The *ovarian cycle* occurs from puberty to menopause and involves the events in the ovaries leading to the release of a mature egg approximately every 28 days. The ovarian cycle is coordinated with the **uterine cycle** or **menstrual cycle** (*menses* = month), events in

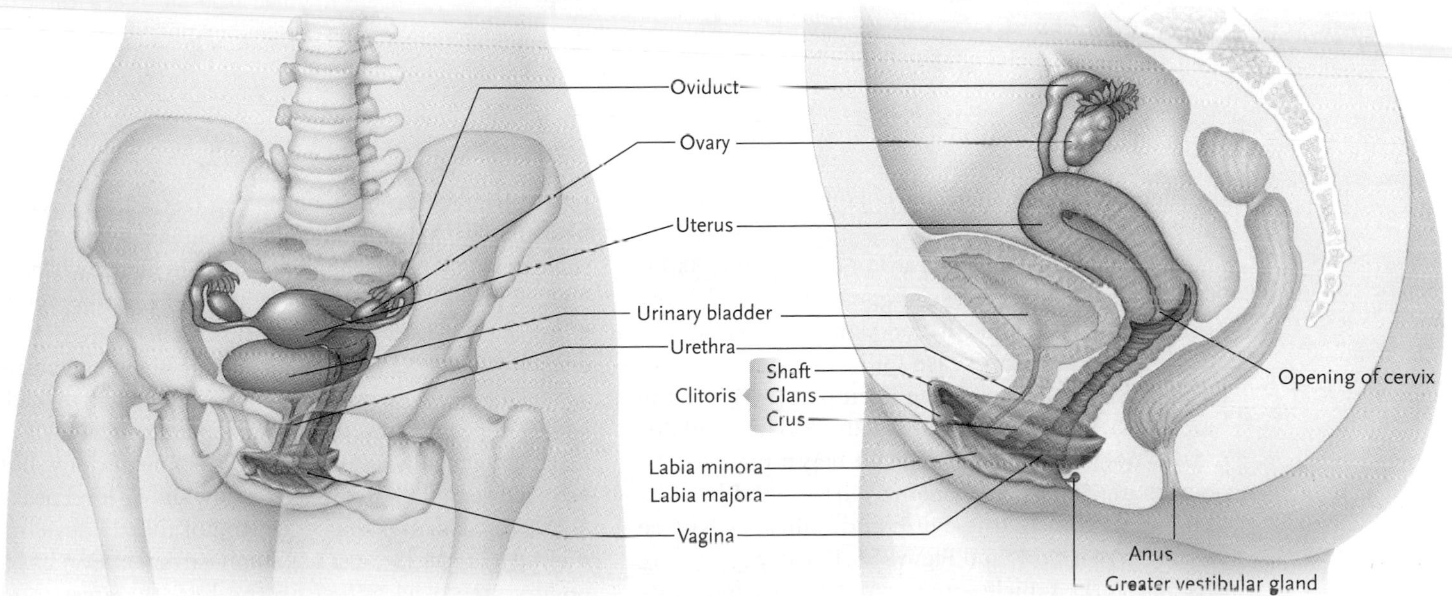

Figure 38.13
The reproductive organs of a human female.

Delaying Reproduction

Many animals have a distinct reproductive season. Its timing is often triggered by changes in photoperiod that herald the changing seasons of the year or by lunar events (e.g., *Acoropora millepora*). Other animals are more opportunistic. Sea turtles and seals are two examples of animals that separate the acts of mating from the timing of egg laying or birth. Both sea turtles and seals must go ashore to lay eggs or give birth to their young, but for the rest of the year, the animals lead largely pelagic lives. In sea turtles **(Figure 1)**, males gather off the beaches where females come to lay their eggs and mate with females en route to the beach. But males and females also mate during chance meetings in the open ocean. Females can store sperm for up to five years so that they can be ready to lay eggs and fertilize them (from their supply of stored sperm) at any time.

Figure 1
A pair of green turtles (*Chelonia mydas*) mate in the waters of Tortuguero in Costa Rica.

Many species of seals also disassociate the act of mating from, in their case, birth (also known as parturition). Males defend territories on beaches where females haul out to give birth. Females undergo a postpartum estrus, so they are ready to mate (fertile) immediately after giving birth. The seals mate, the egg is fertilized, and the zygote is formed, but implantation is delayed for several months, and the young are born a year later. The time between mating and birth is considerably longer than the gestation period (the time needed for growth and development of the fetus). This approach to reproduction maximizes the chances of males and females finding mates.

Bats in the families Rhinolophidae and Vespertilionidae separate the acts of copulation and ovulation. The gestation periods in these species are about 60 days. In temperate regions, species in both families mate in late summer and early autumn **(Figure 2)**. Females store the sperm **(Figure 3)** in their uteri and then enter hibernation. Ovulation and fertilization occur when females leave hibernation in the spring, and the young are born when spring is well advanced.

Fertilization followed by delays in development or implantation can allow males and females more control over mate choice through interactions among sperm or between sperm and the females' reproductive tract.

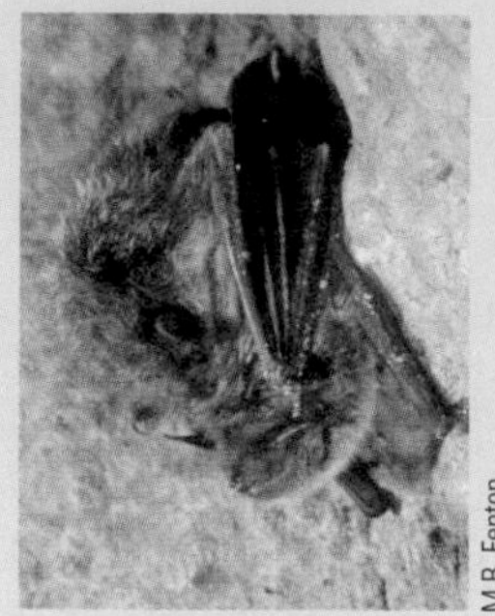

Figure 2
A pair of little brown bats, *Myotis lucifugus*, mate in an abandoned mine in southern Ontario. The male is on the female's back.

Delays achieved by sperm storage and postponement of ovulation raise possibilities of competition between sperm or other mechanisms for selecting the sperm that fertilizes the egg.

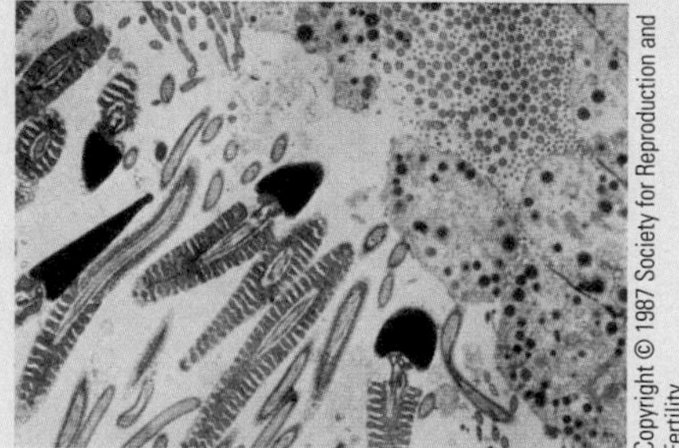

Figure 3
Sperm stored in the uterus of a female *M. lucifugus*.

the uterus that prepare it to implant the egg if fertilization occurs.

The beginning of the ovarian cycle **(Figure 38.14)** is stimulated by the release of gonadotropin-releasing hormone (GnRH) by the hypothalamus. GnRH stimulates the pituitary to release follicle-stimulating hormone (FSH) and luteinizing hormone (LH) into the bloodstream **(Figure 38.15a, p. 926)**. FSH stimulates 6 to 20 oocytes in the ovaries to begin meiosis. As oocytes develop, they become surrounded by cells that form a follicle (the ovum and follicle cells) (see Figure 38.14, step 1, and Figure 38.15a, day 2). During this phase, the follicle grows and develops and, at its largest size, becomes filled with fluid and may be 12 to 15 mm in diameter. Usually, only one follicle develops to maturity with release of the egg (secondary ooctye) by ovulation. Multiple births can result if two or more follicles develop and their eggs ovulate in one cycle.

As the follicle enlarges, FSH and LH interact to stimulate estrogen (female sex hormone, primarily estradiol) secretion by follicular cells. Initially, estrogens are secreted in low amounts and have a negative feedback effect on the pituitary, inhibiting secretion of FSH. As a result, FSH secretion declines briefly. But estrogen secretion increases steadily, and its level peaks about 12 days after the beginning of follicle development (**Figure 38.15c**, day 12). High estrogen level has a positive feedback effect on the hypothalamus and pituitary, increasing secretion of GnRH and stimulating the pituitary to release a burst of FSH and LH.

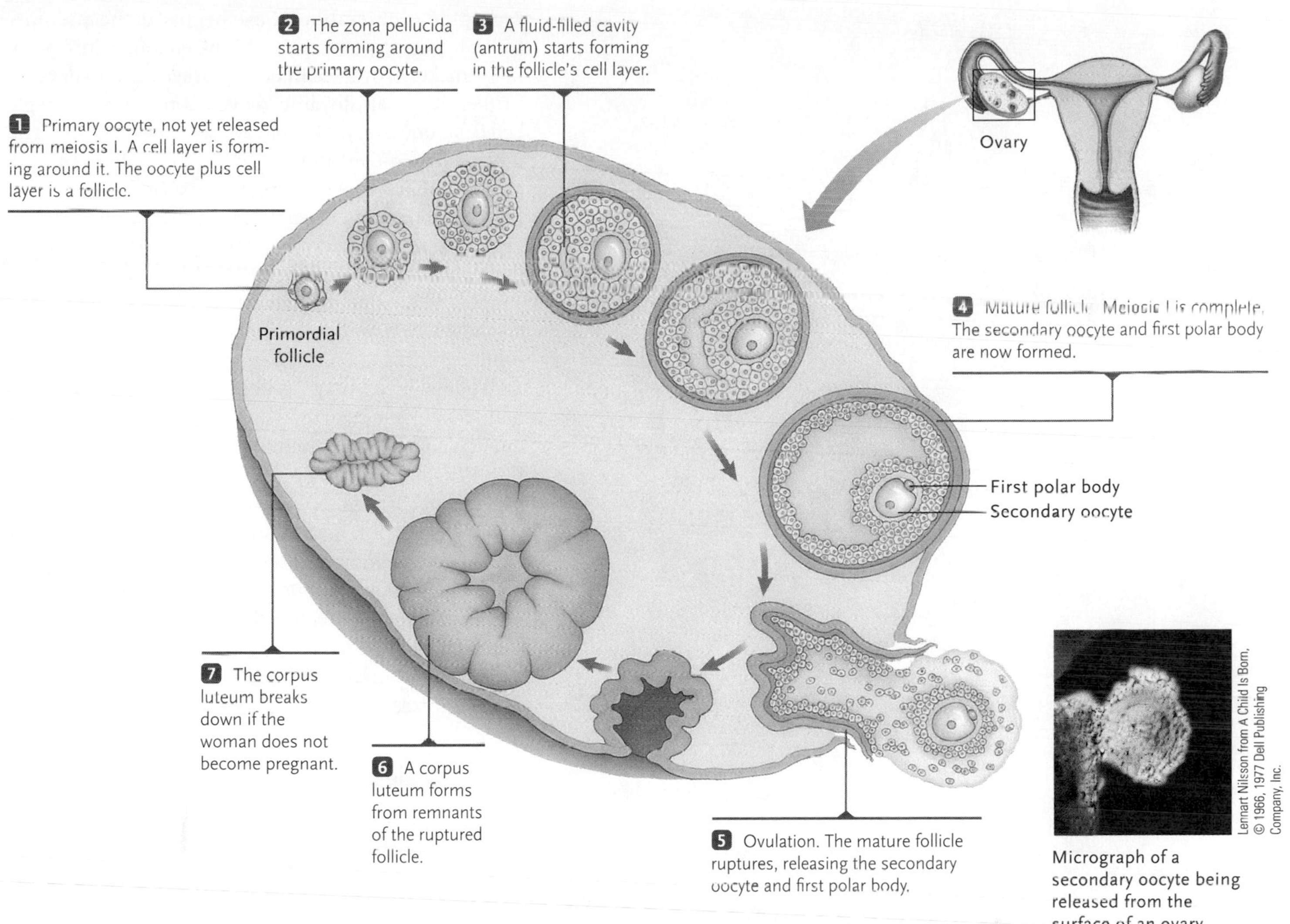

1 Primary oocyte, not yet released from meiosis I. A cell layer is forming around it. The oocyte plus cell layer is a follicle.
2 The zona pellucida starts forming around the primary oocyte.
3 A fluid-filled cavity (antrum) starts forming in the follicle's cell layer.
Ovary
Primordial follicle
4 Mature follicle. Meiosis I is complete. The secondary oocyte and first polar body are now formed.
First polar body
Secondary oocyte
7 The corpus luteum breaks down if the woman does not become pregnant.
6 A corpus luteum forms from remnants of the ruptured follicle.
5 Ovulation. The mature follicle ruptures, releasing the secondary oocyte and first polar body.
Lennart Nilsson from A Child Is Born, © 1966, 1977 Dell Publishing Company, Inc.
Micrograph of a secondary oocyte being released from the surface of an ovary

Figure 38.14
The growth of a follicle, ovulation, and the formation of the corpus luteum in a human ovary.

Increased estrogen levels convert the mucus secreted by the uterus to a thin and watery consistency, making it easier for sperm to swim through the uterus.

Ovulation occurs after the burst in LH secretion stimulates the follicle cells to release enzymes that digest away the wall of the follicle, causing it to rupture and release the egg (see Figure 38.14, step 5). LH also causes the follicle cells remaining at the surface of the ovary to grow into the corpus luteum, an enlarged, yellowish structure (*corpus* = body; *luteum* = yellow), initiating the luteal phase. The corpus luteum (see Figure 38.14, step 6) acts as an endocrine gland that secretes estrogens, as well as large quantities of progesterone, a second female sex hormone, and inhibin, another hormone. Progesterone stimulates growth of the uterine lining and inhibits contractions of the uterus. Progesterone and inhibin have a negative feedback effect on the hypothalamus and pituitary. Progesterone inhibits secretion of GnRH and, in turn, secretion of FSH and LH by the pituitary. Inhibin specifically inhibits FSH secretion. The fall in FSH and LH levels diminishes the signal for follicular growth, and no new follicles begin to grow in the ovary.

If fertilization does not occur, the corpus luteum gradually shrinks, perhaps because of the low levels of LH. About 10 days after ovulation, the shrinkage has inhibited secretion of estrogen, progesterone, and inhibin. In the absence of progesterone, *menstruation* begins. As progesterone and inhibin levels decrease, FSH and LH secretion is no longer inhibited, and a new monthly cycle begins.

The uterine (menstrual) cycle includes the changes in the uterus over one ovarian cycle. The hormones that control the ovarian cycle also control the menstrual cycle **(Figure 38.15d)**, physiologically connecting the two processes. Day 0 of the monthly cycle is the beginning of follicular development in the ovary **(Figure 38.15b)**, and in the uterus, menstrual flow begins.

Menstrual flow results from the breakdown of the endometrium, which releases blood and tissue breakdown products from the uterus to the outside through the vagina. When the flow ceases (at day 4 to 5 of the

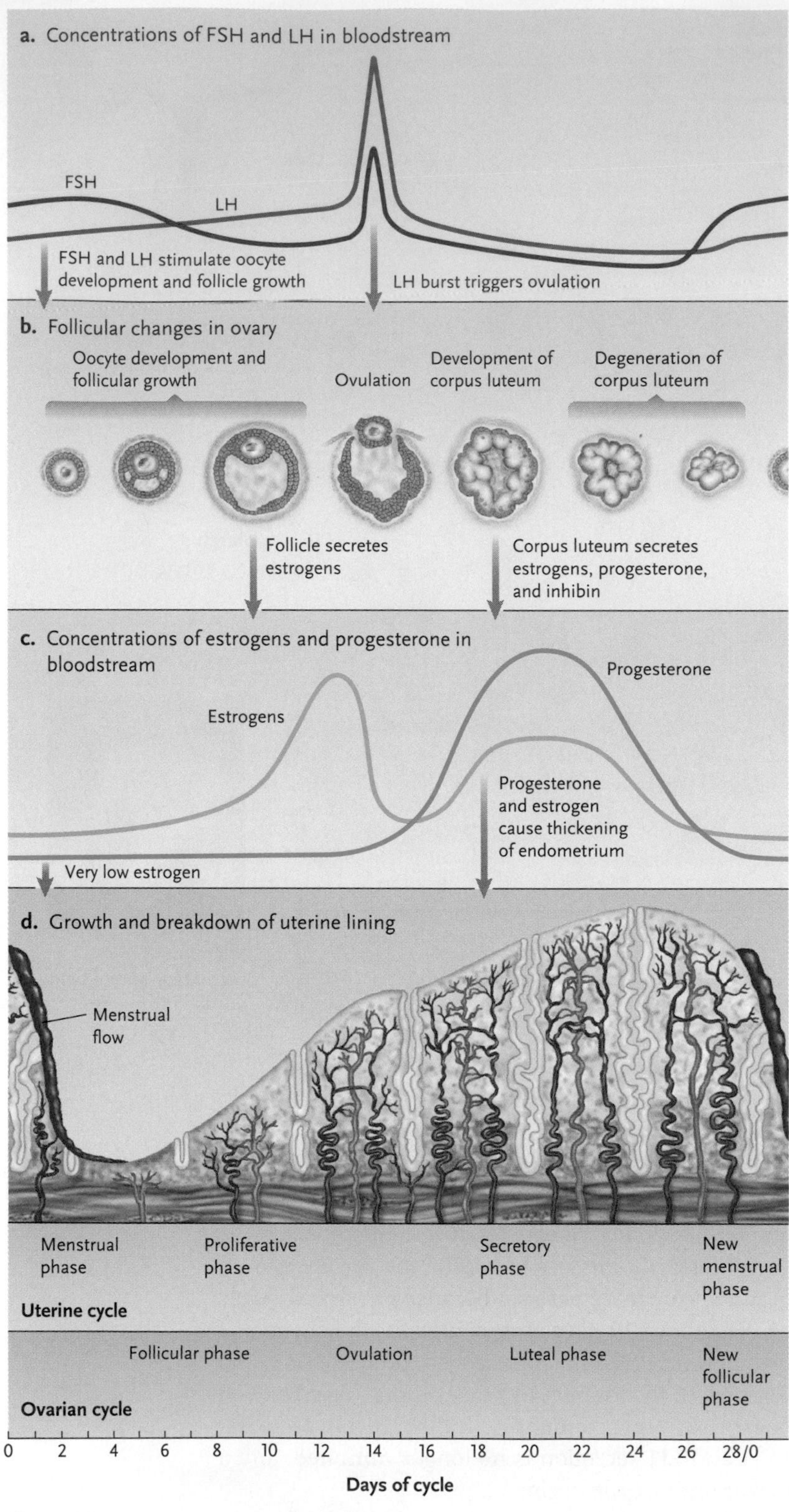

Figure 38.15

The ovarian and uterine (menstrual) cycles of a human female. The days of the monthly cycle are given in the scale at the bottom of the diagram. **(a)** The changing concentrations of FSH and LH in the bloodstream, triggered by GnRH secretion by the hypothalamus. **(b)** The cycle of follicle development, ovulation, and formation of the corpus luteum in the ovary. **(c)** The concentrations of estrogens and progesterone in the bloodstream. **(d)** The growth and breakdown of the uterine lining.

cycle), the proliferation phase begins as the endometrium begins to grow again. As the endometrium gradually thickens, oocytes in both ovaries begin to develop further, eventually leading to ovulation (usually a single egg from one ovary) at about 14 days into the cycle. The uterine lining continues to grow for another 14 days after ovulation. This is the secretory phase. At that time, if fertilization has not taken place, the absence of progesterone results in contraction of the arteries supplying blood to the uterine lining, shutting down the blood supply and causing the lining to disintegrate. The menstrual flow begins. Contractions of the uterus, no longer inhibited by progesterone, help expel the debris. Prostaglandins released by the degenerating endometrium add to uterine contractions, making them severe enough to be felt as the pain of "cramps" and sometimes producing other effects, such as nausea, vomiting, and headaches.

Menstruation occurs only in human females and our closest primate relatives, gorillas and chimpanzees. In other mammals, the uterine lining is completely reabsorbed if a fertilized egg does not implant during the period of reproductive activity. The uterine cycle in those mammals is called the *estrous* cycle, and females are said to be *in estrus* when fertile.

38.4b Males: Produce and Deliver Sperm

Organs that produce and deliver sperm comprise the male reproductive system **(Figure 38.16).** Human males have a pair of testes (singular, testis), suspended in a baglike **scrotum.** Keeping the testes at cooler temperatures than the body core provides an optimal environment for sperm development. Some land mammals such as elephants and monotremes with relatively low body temperatures have internal (cryptic) testes carried within the body. Marine mammals such as whales and dolphins also have internal testes despite relatively high body temperatures. In these animals, countercurrent exchange between cool blood flowing from the tail flukes is delivered to the testes, cooling them enough to allow the production of fertile sperm. In many mammals (e.g., grey squirrels, *Sciurus carolinensis*), the testes descend into the scrotum only during the mating season. Otherwise, they are cryptic, kept in the body captivity, where temperatures are too warm to produce fertile sperm.

In human males, each testicle is packed with about 125 metres of seminiferous tubules, in which sperm proceed through all stages of spermatogenesis **(Figure 38.17, p. 928).** The entire process, from spermatogonium to sperm, takes 9 to 10 weeks, and the testes produce about 130 million fertile sperm each day.

Sertoli cells are supportive cells, completely surrounding the developing spermatocytes in the seminiferous tubules. Sertoli cells supply nutrients to the spermatocytes and seal them off from the body's blood

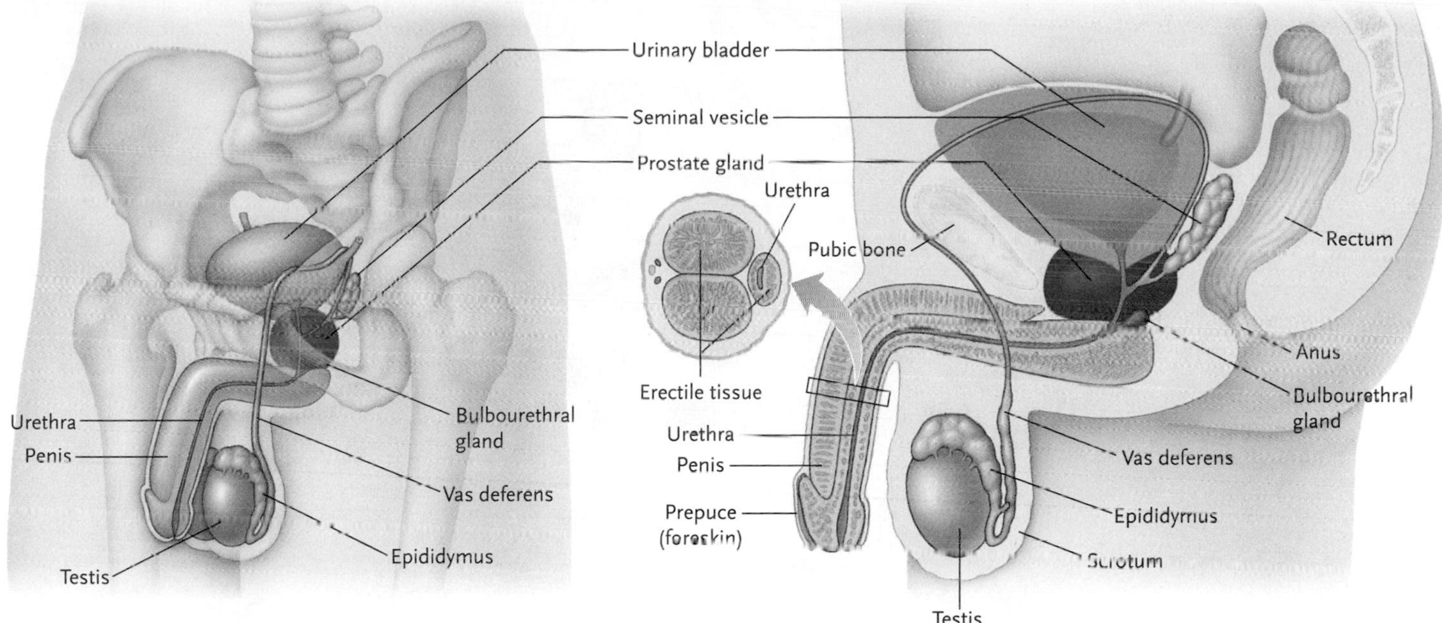

Figure 38.16
The reproductive organs of a human male.

supply. Leydig cells, located in the tissue surrounding the developing spermatocytes, produce the male sex hormones (**androgens**), particularly **testosterone.**

Mature sperm flow from seminiferous tubules into the **epididymis,** a coiled storage tubule attached to the surface of each testis. Rhythmic muscular contractions of the epididymis move sperm into a thick-walled, muscular tube, the **vas deferens** (plural, vasa deferentia), which extends through the abdominal cavity. Just below the bladder, the vasa deferentia join the urethra. During ejaculation, muscular contractions force the sperm into the urethra and out of the penis. At this time, the sperm are activated and become motile when they come in contact with alkaline secretions added to the ejaculated fluid by accessory glands.

About 150 to 350 million sperm are released in a single ejaculation. Semen, the ejaculate, is a mixture of sperm and the secretions of several accessory glands. In humans, about two-thirds of the volume is produced by a pair of **seminal vesicles** that secrete seminal fluid, a thick, viscous liquid, into the vasa deferentia near the point where they join with the urethra. Seminal fluid contains prostaglandins that, when ejaculated into the female, trigger contractions of the female reproductive tract that help move the sperm into and through the uterus.

The **prostate gland**, which surrounds the region where the vasa deferentia empty into the urethra, adds a thin, milky fluid to the semen. The alkaline prostate secretion makes up about one-third of the volume of semen, raising its pH (and that of the vagina) to about pH 6, the level of acidity best tolerated by sperm. This pH level also fosters sperm motility. As part of the prostate secretion, a fast-acting enzyme converts the semen to a thick gel at ejaculation. The thickened consistency helps keep the semen from draining from the vagina when the penis is withdrawn. A second, slower-acting enzyme in the prostate secretion gradually breaks down the semen clot and releases the sperm to swim freely in the female reproductive tract.

Finally, a pair of **bulbourethral glands** secretes a clear, mucus-rich fluid into the urethra before and during ejaculation. This fluid lubricates the tip of the penis and neutralizes the acidity of any residual urine in the urethra. In total, the secretions of the accessory glands make up more than 95% of the volume of semen; less than 5% is sperm.

Most of the interior of the penis is filled with three cylinders of spongelike tissue (corpora cavernosa) that become filled with blood and cause erection during sexual arousal. Although the human penis depends solely on engorgement of spongy tissue for erection, the males of many mammals, including bats, rodents, carnivores, and most other primates, have a baculum or penis bone **(Figure 38.18, p. 928)** that helps maintain the penis in an erect state. The presence of bacula in a species usually coincides with the presence of a baubellum (clitoris bone) in females.

The penis ends in the **glans**, a soft, caplike structure. Most nerve endings producing erotic sensations are crowded into the glans and the region of the penile shaft just behind the glans. The prepuce or foreskin is a loose fold of skin that covers the glans (see Figure 38.16). In many human cultures, the foreskin is removed for hygienic, religious, or other ritualistic reasons by **circumcision** ("around cut"). In 2007, the World Health Organization stated that male circumcision is an important strategy to

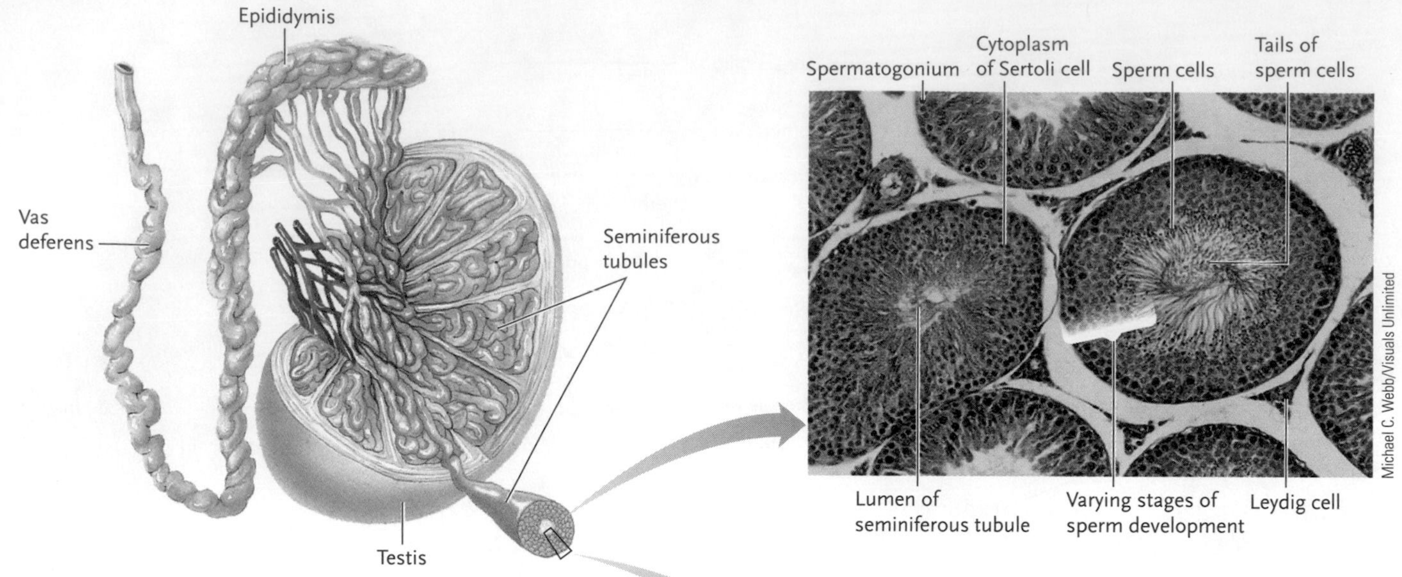

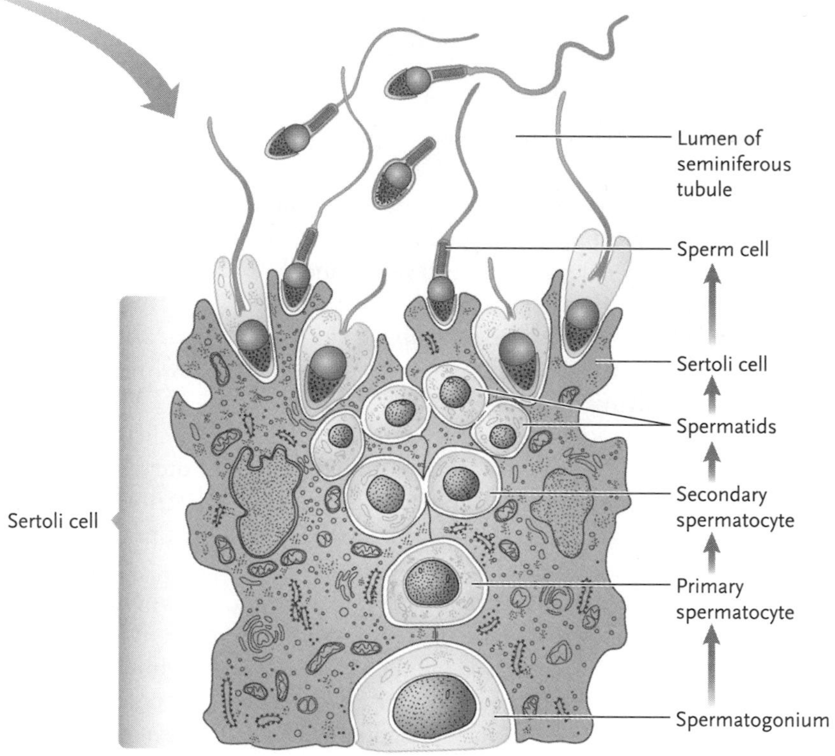

Figure 38.17
The structure of seminiferous tubules and the stages of spermatogenesis. Spermatogonia are located nearest the outer wall and mature sperm cells nearest the tubule lumen. Sertoli cells completely surround the developing spermatocytes and protect them from attack by the immune system.

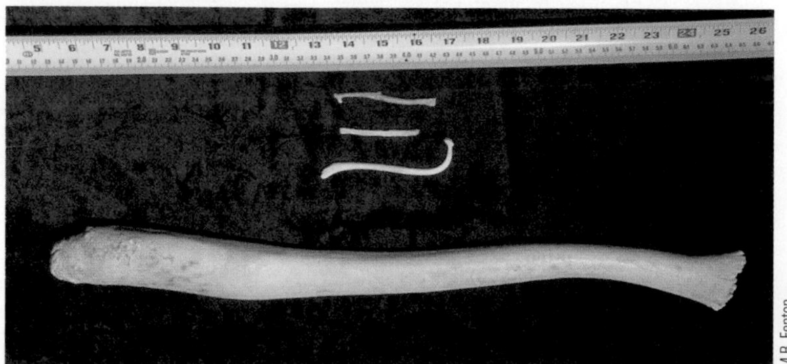

Figure 38.18
The bacula of a wolverine (*Gulo luscus*), a red fox (*Vulpes fulva*), a raccoon (*Procyon lotor*), and a walrus (*Odobenus rosmarus*) (top to bottom).

prevent heterosexually acquired HIV infection in males. Female circumcision, the removal of the labia minora and the clitoris, is often called female genital mutilation or FGM.

Many of the hormones regulating the menstrual cycle, including GnRH, FSH, LH, and inhibin, also regulate male reproductive functions. Testosterone, secreted by the Leydig cells in the testes, also plays a key role **(Figure 38.19).** In sexually mature males, the hypothalamus secretes GnRH in brief pulses every 1 to 2 hours. GnRH stimulates the pituitary to secrete LH and FSH. LH stimulates the Leydig cells to secrete testosterone, which stimulates sperm production and controls the

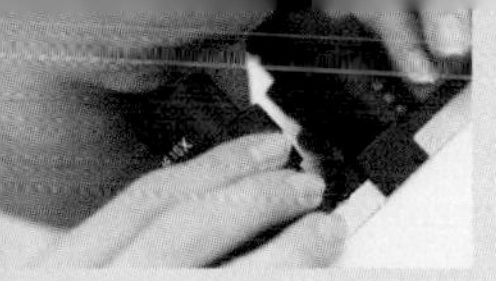

People Behind Biology

John P. Wiebe

What happens to hormones after they are produced? John P. Wiebe, professor emeritus in the Department of Biology at the University of Western Ontario in London, and his graduate students study two steroid hormones derived from progesterone. Specifically, 5α-pregnane-3,20 dione (5αP) and 3α-hydroxy-4-pregen-20-one (3αP) are metabolites of progesterone. 5αP is cancer promoting, stimulating cells to proliferate (tumour growth) and detach (metastasis). 3αP is cancer inhibiting because it suppresses cell proliferation and metastasis.

Wiebe and his colleagues have demonstrated that tumorigenic cells produce higher levels of 5αP and lower levels of 3αP. When cells become tumorigenic, there are strong increases in the mRNA expression of the enzyme that catalyzes conversion of progesterone to 5αP, specifically 5α-reductase. This increase is paralleled by a decrease in 3α-hydroxysteroidoxidoreductase that catalyzes conversion to 3αP.

It is clear that this work has potential in the control and treatment of breast cancer. It also alerts us to the impact of exposure to hormones, whether in the food we eat or in the water we drink (see Box 45.4).

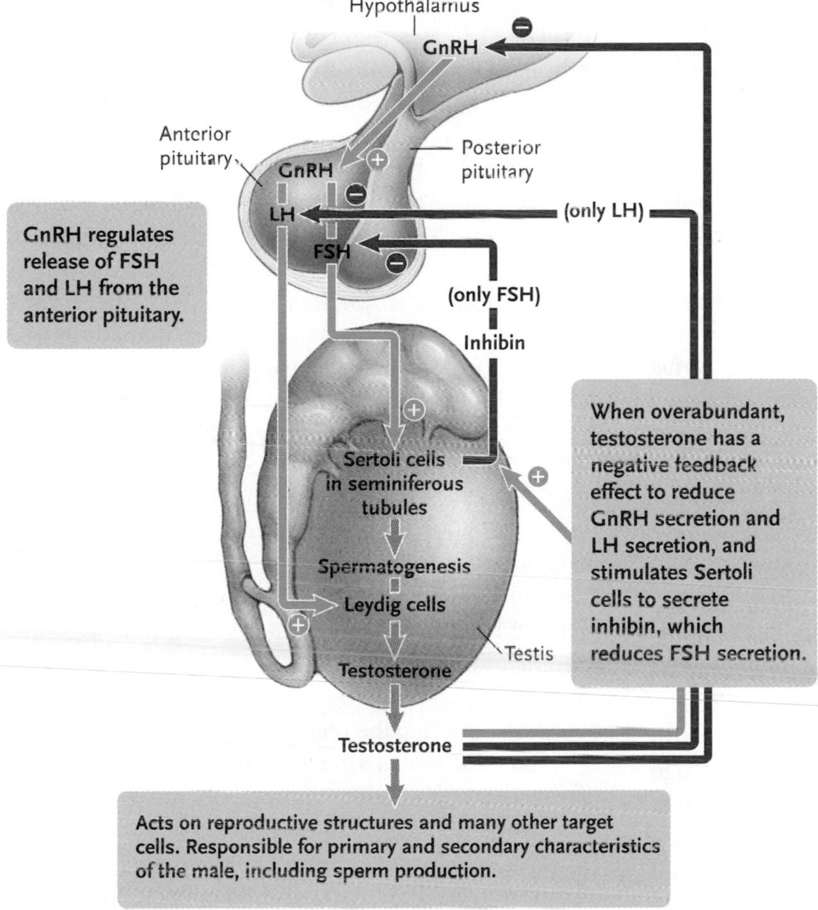

Figure 38.19
Hormonal regulation of reproduction in the male and the negative feedback systems controlling hormone levels.

growth and function of male reproductive structures. FSH stimulates Sertoli cells to secrete a protein and other molecules required for spermatogenesis.

Concentrations of male reproductive hormones are maintained by negative feedback mechanisms. If the concentration of testosterone falls in the bloodstream, the hypothalamus responds by increasing GnRH secretion. If testosterone levels rise too high, the overabundance inhibits LH secretion. An overabundance of testosterone also stimulates Sertoli cells to secrete inhibin, which inhibits FSH secretion by the pituitary. As a result, testosterone secretion by the Leydig cells drops off, returning the concentration to optimal levels in the bloodstream.

When the male is sexually aroused, sphincter muscles controlling the flow of blood to the spongy erectile tissue of the penis relax, allowing the tissue to become engorged with blood (the penis is a hydrostatic skeleton structure; see Chapter 37). As the spongy tissue swells, it maintains the pressure by compressing and almost shutting off the veins draining blood from the penis. The engorgement produces an erection in which the penis lengthens, stiffens, and enlarges. During continued sexual arousal, lubricating fluid secreted by the bulbourethral glands may be released from the tip of the penis.

Female sexual arousal results in enlargement and erection of the clitoris, in a process analogous to erection of the penis. The labia minora become engorged with blood and swell in size, and lubricating fluid is secreted onto the surfaces of the vulva by the vestibular glands. In addition to these changes, the nipples become erect by contraction of smooth muscle cells, and the breasts swell in size due to engorgement with blood.

Insertion of the penis into the vagina and the thrusting movements of copulation lead to the reflex actions of ejaculation, including spasmodic contractions of muscles surrounding the vasa deferentia, accessory glands, and urethra. During ejaculation, the sphincter muscles controlling the exit from the bladder close tightly, preventing urine from mixing with the ejaculate. Ejaculation is usually accompanied by *orgasm,* a sensation of intense physical pleasure that is the peak (climax) of excitement for sexual intercourse, followed by feelings of relaxation and gratification.

The motions of copulation stretch the vagina and stimulate the clitoris, sometimes inducing orgasm in females. Vaginal stretching also stimulates the hypothalamus to secrete oxytocin, which induces contractions of the uterus. The contractions keep the sperm in suspension and aid their movement through the reproductive tract. Uterine contractions are also induced by the prostaglandins in the semen.

Sperm reach the site of fertilization in the oviducts within 30 minutes of being ejaculated. Of the millions of sperm released in a single ejaculation, only a few hundred actually reach the oviducts. After orgasm, the penis, clitoris, and labia minora gradually return to their unstimulated size. Females can experience additional orgasms within minutes or even seconds of a first orgasm, but most males enter a *refractory period* lasting 15 minutes or longer before they can regain an erection and have another orgasm.

38.4c Fertilization of Human Eggs: Producing Zygotes

A human egg can be fertilized only during its passage through the third of the oviduct nearest the ovary. If the egg is not fertilized during the 12 to 24 hours that it is in this location, it disintegrates and dies. Sperm do not swim randomly for a chance encounter with the egg. Rather, they first swim up the cervical canal to reach the oviduct and then are propelled up the oviduct by contractions of the oviduct's smooth muscles. There is evidence that eggs release chemical attractant molecules that the sperm recognize, causing them to swim directly toward the egg.

Sperm must first penetrate the layer of follicle cells surrounding the egg, aided by enzymes in the sperm plasma membrane **(Figure 38.20).** Then the sperm adhere to receptor molecules on the surface of the zona pellucida. This contact triggers the **acrosome reaction,** in which enzymes contained in the acrosome are released from the sperm onto the zona pellucida, where they digest a path to the plasma membrane of the egg. As soon as the first sperm cell reaches the egg, sperm and egg plasma membranes fuse, and the sperm cell is engulfed by the cytoplasm of the egg. Although only one sperm fertilizes the egg, the combined release of acrosomal enzymes from many sperm greatly increases the chance that a complete channel will be opened through the zona pellucida. This is in part why a low sperm count is often a source of male infertility. Low sperm counts can be caused by infection, heat, frequent intercourse, smoking, and excess alcohol consumption.

Membrane fusion activates the egg. The sperm that enters the egg releases nitric oxide that stimulates the release of stored Ca^{2+} in the egg. Ca^{2+} triggers cortical granule release to the outside of the egg. Enzymes from the cortical granules crosslink molecules in the zona pellucida, hardening it and sealing the channels opened by acrosomal enzymes. The enzymes also destroy receptors that bind sperm to the surface of the zona pellucida. As a result, no further sperm can bind to the zona pellucida or reach the plasma membrane of the egg. The Ca^{2+} also triggers the completion of meiosis of the egg. The sperm and egg nuclei then fuse, and the cell is now considered the zygote. Mitotic divisions of the zygote soon initiate embryonic development.

The first cell divisions of embryonic development take place while the fertilized egg is still in the oviduct. About seven days after ovulation, the embryo passes from the oviduct and implants in the uterine lining. During and after implantation, cells associated with the embryo secrete **human chorionic gonadotropin (hCG),** a hormone that keeps the corpus luteum in the ovary from breaking down. Excess hCG is excreted in the urine; its presence in urine or blood provides the basis of pregnancy tests.

Continued activity of the corpus luteum keeps estrogen and progesterone secretion at high levels, which maintain the uterine lining and prevent menstruation. The high progesterone level also thickens the mucus secreted by the uterus, forming a plug that seals the opening of the cervix from the vagina. The plug keeps bacteria, viruses, and sperm cells from further copulations from entering the uterus.

About 10 weeks after implantation, the placenta takes over the secretion of progesterone, hCG secretion drops off, and the corpus luteum regresses. However, the corpus luteum continues to secrete the hormone *relaxin,* which inhibits contraction of the uterus until near the time of birth.

Study Break

1. How does the reproductive pattern of human females differ from that of other mammals? (See also Chapters 27, 46, and 49.)
2. Which hormones are good predictors of ovulation?
3. What role does follicle-stimulating hormone play?

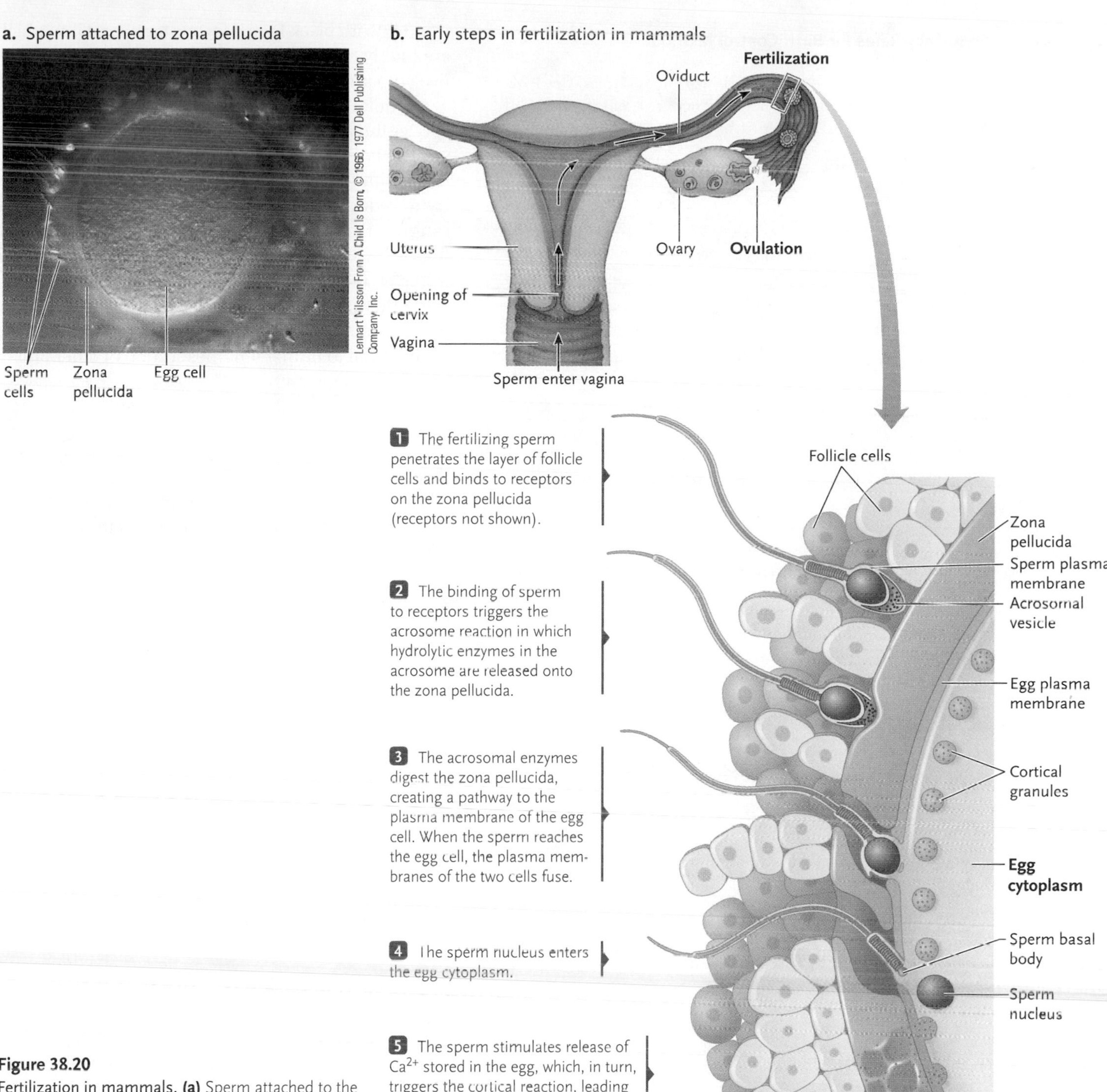

a. Sperm attached to zona pellucida
Sperm cells
Zona pellucida
Egg cell
Lennart Nilsson From A Child Is Born, © 1966, 1977 Dell Publishing Company Inc.
b. Early steps in fertilization in mammals
Fertilization
Oviduct
Uterus
Ovary
Ovulation
Opening of cervix
Vagina
Sperm enter vagina
1 The fertilizing sperm penetrates the layer of follicle cells and binds to receptors on the zona pellucida (receptors not shown).
2 The binding of sperm to receptors triggers the acrosome reaction in which hydrolytic enzymes in the acrosome are released onto the zona pellucida.
3 The acrosomal enzymes digest the zona pellucida, creating a pathway to the plasma membrane of the egg cell. When the sperm reaches the egg cell, the plasma membranes of the two cells fuse.
4 The sperm nucleus enters the egg cytoplasm.
5 The sperm stimulates release of Ca^{2+} stored in the egg, which, in turn, triggers the cortical reaction, leading to the slow block in polyspermy.
Follicle cells
Zona pellucida
Sperm plasma membrane
Acrosomal vesicle
Egg plasma membrane
Cortical granules
Egg cytoplasm
Sperm basal body
Sperm nucleus

Figure 38.20
Fertilization in mammals. **(a)** Sperm attached to the zona pellucida of a human egg cell. **(b)** Early steps in the fertilization process.

38.5 Controlling Reproduction

Knowledge about the details of reproduction can allow us to control fertility. In some cases, this means increasing the chances of reproducing, whereas in other cases, it means minimizing them. In human society, pregnancy can be a blessing or a disaster, depending on the situation. Statistics describing the effectiveness of different means of limiting human reproductive output **(Table 38.1, p. 932)** illustrate our progress in the area of family planning. Knowledge about the timing of ovulation, for example (see Figure 38.16), can provide the means to maximize or minimize the chances of pregnancy.

Biologists working to conserve biodiversity often attempt to control reproduction. When a species is on the brink of extinction, the goal is to maximize reproductive output. Techniques can range from the use of foster parents to raise young to using reproductive technologies such as in vitro fertilization and implantation of embryos. For example, biologists

Table 38.1 Pregnancy Rates for Birth Control Methods

Method	Lowest Expected Rate of Pregnancy[a]	Typical-Use Rate of Pregnancy[b]
Rhythm method	1%–9%	25%
Withdrawal	4%	19%
Condom (male)	3%	14%
Condom (female)	5%	21%
Diaphragm and spermicidal jelly	6%	20%
Vasectomy (male sterilization)	0.1%	0.15%
Tubal ligation (female sterilization)	0.5%	0.5%
Contraceptive pill (combination estrogen–progestin)	0.1%	5%
Contraceptive pill (progestin only)	0.5%	5%
Implant (progestin)	0.09%	0.09%
Intrauterine device (IUD) (copper T)	0.6%	0.8%

[a]Rate of pregnancy when the birth control method was used correctly every time.
[b]Rate of pregnancy when the method was used typically, meaning that it may not have been always used correctly every time.
Source: U.S. Food and Drug Administration, http://www.fda.gov/fdac/features/1997/conceptbl.html. Data reported in 1997 for effectiveness of methods in a 1-year period.

working with black-footed ferrets (see Box 45.2), which are highly endangered, strive to maximize reproductive output to increase the population.

Similarly, when an increasing population of one species threatens to overwhelm other species or an ecosystem, the goal is to prevent reproduction. Biologists faced with growing populations of African elephants try to reduce reproductive output using techniques ranging from the application of contraceptives to females (see Box 45.4) to "culling" (killing) individuals in the population. Culling usually targets females because they produce young (see Chapter 45). The same principles of controlling reproductive output have been central to humans' domestication of other organisms (see Chapter 49).

Study Break

1. How can biologists control reproduction? Why is access to control of reproduction important?
2. What are the advantages and disadvantages of different approaches to contraception for mammals?

Unanswered Questions

What factors could have led to the evolution of sexual reproduction? Does the evidence suggest that sexual reproduction evolved once, or did it evolve several times? What are the advantages of sexual versus asexual reproduction?

Review

Go to CENGAGENOW™ at http://hed.nelson.com/ to access quizzing, animations, exercises, articles, and personalized homework help.

38.1 The Drive to Reproduce

- After mating, a male acanthocephalan worm (*Moniliformis dubius*) uses a cement gland to seal the vagina of the female, preventing her from mating with other males. This protects his investment. To reduce competition from other males, a male *M. dubius* may "rape" other males and use the product of his cement gland to prevent the other male from mating.

38.2 Asexual and Sexual Reproduction

- One important advantage of sexual reproduction over asexual reproduction is the generation of genetic diversity in offspring. Genetic recombination and independent assortment of chromosomes during meiosis give rise to diversity and reduce vulnerability to deleterious effects carried on recessive alleles.
- Meiosis in animals occurs during the production of gametes, although the actual timing of meiosis varies between males and females and among species. In plants and fungi, meiosis is not always used to produce gametes.

38.3 Cellular Mechanisms of Sexual Reproduction

- The amount of yolk in eggs varies enormously, influencing egg size and the time of incubation and development. Development in eggs with large amounts of yolk often involves a small embryonic disk floating on top of the yolk (e.g., bird) as opposed to development around the yolk (e.g., frog).
- Internal fertilization can reduce the amounts of sperm necessary to achieve fertilization. Internal fertilization also can increase the certainty of mate choice where only the sperm of a male that mated come in contact with the egg(s) of a female.
- Polyspermy, more than one sperm entering an egg, is prevented in two ways. The fast block depends on a change in the egg's membrane potential from negative to positive, whereas the slow block involves Ca^{2+} ions that cause cortical granules to fuse with the egg's plasma membrane and release their enzyme contents to the outside.
- Viviparous animals give birth to live young. Before birth, the mother provides the developing embryos with food and oxygen and removes its metabolic wastes. Usually, but not always, this occurs in the body of the female. Ovoviviparous animals may also give birth to live young, but here the eggs develop and grow

inside the mother using yolk as the source of energy. Oviparous animals lay eggs that develop outside the mother's body.

- Most mammals show a well-defined mating season, the time when copulation, fertilization, and development take place. The onset of the mating season is often triggered by changes in photoperiod (day length). Mammalian females typically display behavioural and physiological signs of fertility (estrus). Humans, on the other hand, do not have a mating season, and both sexes are receptive to mating at any time.
- Follicle-stimulating hormone (FSH) is released by the pituitary in response to gonadotropin-releasing hormone. FSH stimulates the development of oocytes in the ovaries. Developing oocytes are surrounded by cells that form a follicle. A peak in the level of luteinizing hormone is a clear indicator of ovulation (the release of the secondary oocyte).
- Cryptic testes (e.g., elephants and whales) are housed inside the body. In many mammals, testes are housed in a scrotum outside the body because sperm develop best at temperatures below the core temperature of a mammal. A baculum is a penis bone, a feature of many mammals but not humans. The baubellum (clitoris bone) is the equivalent in females.

38.4 Sexual Reproduction in Humans

- Alkaline prostate secretions raise the pH of semen and the vagina to about pH 6, activating sperm motility. When enzymes contained within the acrosome of a sperm are released into the zona pellucida, they digest a path to the plasma membrane of the egg. This process is initiated by contact between and then adherence of the sperm to receptor molecules on the surface of the zona pellucida.

38.5 Controlling Reproduction

- Controlling (promoting or reducing) reproductive output is important for our species in social and political contexts. It is also important in conservation.

Questions

Self-Test Questions

1. Asexual reproduction can involve
   a. fission.
   b. budding.
   c. copulation.
   d. parthenogenesis.
   e. All of the above are correct.
2. Germ cells give rise to
   a. eggs.
   b. somatic cells.
   c. sperm.
   d. muscles.
   e. Only a and c are correct.
3. Internal fertilization is rarely seen in
   a. platyhelminthes.
   b. bedbugs.
   c. mammals.
   d. frogs.
   e. bony fishes.
4. In slow blocks, more than one sperm is prevented from fertilizing an egg by changes in
   a. Ca^{2+} ions.
   b. Cl^- ions.
   c. Na^+ ions.
   d. K^+ ions.
   e. cortical granules.
5. Ovulation in women is signalled by a rise in
   a. luteinizing hormone.
   b. follicle-stimulating hormone.
   c. estrogen.
   d. testosterone.
   e. relaxin.
6. In mammals, cryptic testes are typical of
   a. humans.
   b. elephants.
   c. dogs.
   d. bulls.
   e. hermaphrodites.
7. The reproductive cycle of some bats and turtles involves
   a. delayed fertilization.
   b. delayed implantation.
   c. delayed development.
   d. postpartum estrus.
   e. All of the above are correct.
8. Cryptochromes are sensitive to
   a. red light.
   b. white light.
   c. blue light.
   d. green light.
   e. All of the above are correct.
9. Amplexus is the term used to describe mating behaviour in
   a. birds.
   b. frogs and toads.
   c. salmon.
   d. mammals.
   e. sharks.

Questions for Discussion

1. How do plants exploit animals to effect pollination and dispersal of seeds? Are there examples of animals exploiting plants to achieve reproduction?
2. How does variation in the pattern of fertilization (internal versus external) differ among the animal phyla? Do these variations indicate different ancestral conditions? How do these patterns differ between plants and animals?
3. What methods do zoos and botanical gardens use to control reproduction of captive organisms? Is this appropriate?
4. What steps could conservation biologists take to increase reproductive output of rare and endangered species?

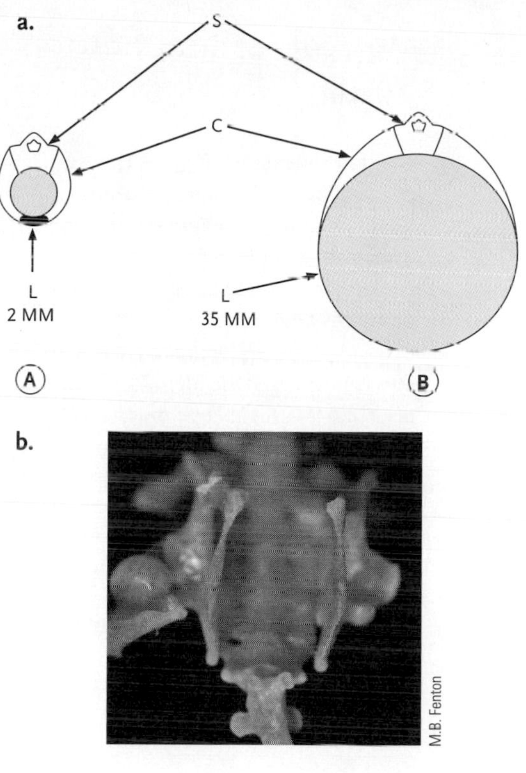

(a) A diagrammatic view of the bony birth canal of (A) a nonpregnant Brazilian free-tailed bat (*Tadarida brasiliensis*) and (B) a female in the process of giving birth. The sacrum (S), coxal bone (C), and interpubic ligament (L) are shown. **(b)** The ventral view of the pelvis of another nonpregnant free-tailed bat. There is no connection between the pubic bones, making it possible for the animal to achieve the expansion of the birth canal required during birth.

39 Animal Development

Study Plan

Why It Matters

The size of the mother and of the young can be a challenging aspect of the process of giving birth (parturition). Bats are an extreme example when it comes to offspring size. Typically, a female bat bears a pup that is 25 to 30% of her normal body mass—the equivalent of a 60-kg woman bearing a 15-to 20-kg baby. The birth canal of placental mammals (such as bats and people) passes between the two halves of the pelvic girdle. Not surprisingly, the pelvis of adult female placental mammals differs from that of males.

The magnitude of the challenge of parturition to a female Brazilian free-tailed bat is shown above. In a nonpregnant female, the bony birth canal is 2 mm in diameter, but it expands to 35 mm in diameter during birth. In these bats, birth takes about 90 seconds.

The elasticity of the interpubic ligament is the key to the birth process in female mammals that give birth to large young. This ligament has an abundance of elastic fibres, which intermingle with collagen fibres at the ligament's core. The situation in bats appears to be the same as in other mammals: elastic fibres stretch, whereas collagen fibres slide in relation to each other. The hormone relaxin plays a fundamental role in this process, promoting the stretchability

MOLECULE BEHIND BIOLOGY

Relaxin

The hormone relaxin **(Figure 1)** is a polypeptide produced by the ovaries during pregnancy. In humans, relaxin occurs at higher levels earlier in pregnancy than closer to parturition. Relaxin promotes angiogenesis, the growth of new blood vessels, and influences the interface between the uterus and the placenta. Relaxin inhibits muscular contractions of the uterus that could terminate pregnancy and stimulates the growth of glands that produce milk in breast tissue.

Near parturition, relaxin causes relaxation of the pubic ligaments and softens and enlarges the cervical opening.

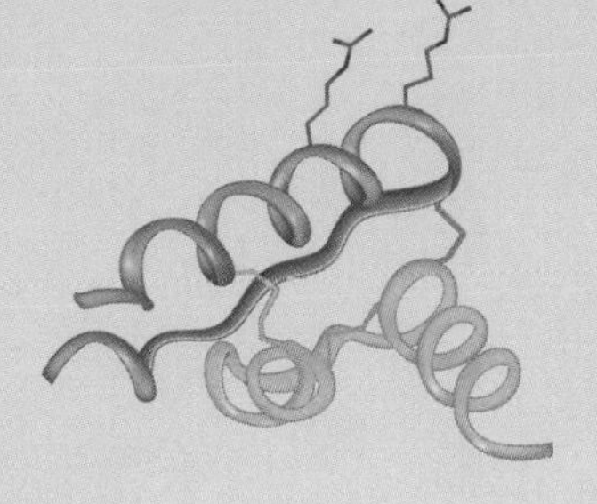

Figure 1
Relaxin.

of interpubic ligaments at the time of parturition (see *Molecule Behind Biology*).

39.1 Housing and Fuelling Developing Young

Some animal parents invest significant energy in housing and feeding their developing young. This is one aspect of the genetically selfish drive to ensure that their genes are represented in future generations.

39.1a Housing: Providing a Place in Which the Embryo Can Develop

There is a recurring tendency across phyla for parents to put eggs and developing young in situations that minimize their exposure to predators and parasites while maximizing favourable conditions for growth and development. Many species of birds use nests to house their eggs and unfledged young. Parents of other species, such as some species of scorpions (see Figure 3.22a), frogs, and insects, carry their young with them, often on their backs. This allows the parent (parents) to avoid or actively deter would-be predators.

An escalation in parental investment is moving eggs and young inside the parent's body (vivipary and ovovivipary; see Chapter 38). This approach to parental care has several different stages (see Chapter 38, *On the Road to Vivipary*). Although we associate vivipary with mammals, many species of fish are mouth-breeders, keeping eggs and, for a time, developing young in their mouths. Other fish, such as sea horses and pipefish (family Syngnathidae, order Gasterosteiformes; **Figure 39.1**), keep eggs and developing young in specialized incubation areas, called brood pouches, located on the tail or trunk of the male. "Pregnancy" in male sea horses represents an increase in parental investment. It also allows males to be confident about the paternity of the young they raise.

Some amphibians also show high levels of parental care. In Australia, female frogs, *Rheobatrachus silus,* use their stomachs as brood pouches. While the young are developing, they secrete prostaglandin E_2, which inhibits the secretion of gastric acid in the stomach and saves the developing young from being digested. On Mount Nimba in west Africa, female toads *Nectophrynoides occidentalis* harbour developing young in their uterus, where the young feed on uterine secretions in the absence of a placenta. The gestation period for these toads is nine months, and newborns are 7 to 8 mm long and weigh 30 to 60 mg. Retention of developing embryos in the oviducts has evolved independently in each of the three living groups of Amphibia: Anura, Urodela, and Gymnophiona (see Chapter 27).

39.1b Feeding: Aiding and Abetting Developing Young

Almost everyone has seen pictures of parent birds feeding their young (see Figures 40.2 and 40.4). In many species, both males and females deliver food to the nestlings. Some fruit-eating adult birds feed insects to their young

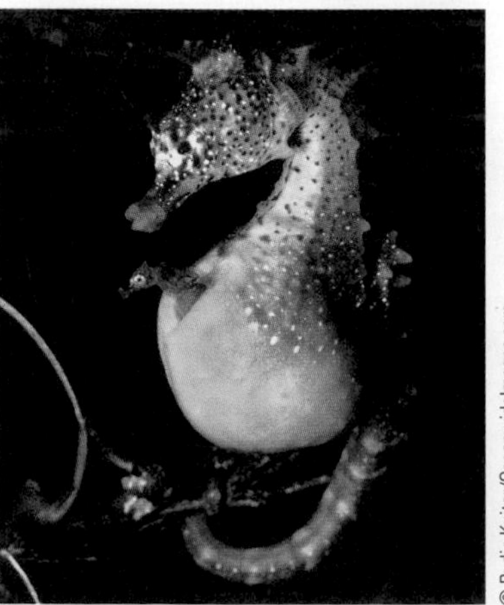

Figure 39.1
A male sea horse gives birth.

Joseph G. Kunkel

Figure 39.2
Diploptera punctata, a cockroach that produces live young. Starting from the left, an adult female and male, egg, last stage fetus, larval instars.

because a higher protein diet promotes rapid growth of the young. Producing high-quality food is the next level of parental investment, and "milk" is a prime example.

The term "milk" is usually applied to secretions of the mammary glands of mammals, and it is the quintessentially mammalian food. However, other animals also make "milk." Female cockroaches **(Figure 39.2)** house developing embryos in a brood sac and give birth to them as first-instar (first stage) larvae. The brood sac is an infolding of a ventral intersegmental membrane, and its epithelium produces the milk, a blend of water-soluble proteins encoded by a multigene family.

Both male and female discus fish **(Figure 39.3)** feed their hatchling young (known as "fry") skin secretions, the first and only food eaten by the fry. This fish "milk" appears as a slight mucus coating on the adults' bodies, particularly above the lateral lines. Skin feeding also occurs in a caecilian (an amphibian). The skin in brooding females **(Figures 39.4 and 39.5)** is transformed

M.B. Fenton

Figure 39.3
Symphysodon discus, a fish that produces "'milk'" to feed its young.

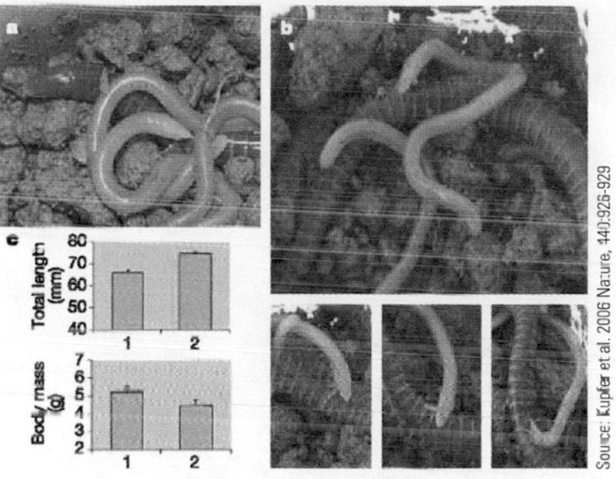

Source: Kupfer et al. 2006 Nature, 440:926-929

Figure 39.4
A female caecilian (*Boulengerula taitanus*) feeding her young skin secretions.

to provide a rich supply of nutrients, and the young have specialized teeth for peeling and eating the outer layer of their mother's skin **(Figure 39.6, p. 938)**. In some other caecilians, young develop in the uterus and feed on the lining of the oviduct. "Milk" also has been reported in birds, where the crop milk of pigeons (*Columba livia domestica*) is fed to young (known as squabs) from hatching to about age 19 days. In some cases, pigeon lactation continues to day 28. Pigeon crop milk is composed mainly of proteins and lipids and is highly nutritious. Obviously, female mammals have not cornered the "milk market." There are records of male mammals lactating, the most notable being *Dyacopterus spaediucus*, a fruit bat from Indonesia. Some male *D. spaediucus* produce milk, although not as much as females, but the behavioural significance of male lactation in this species remains unknown.

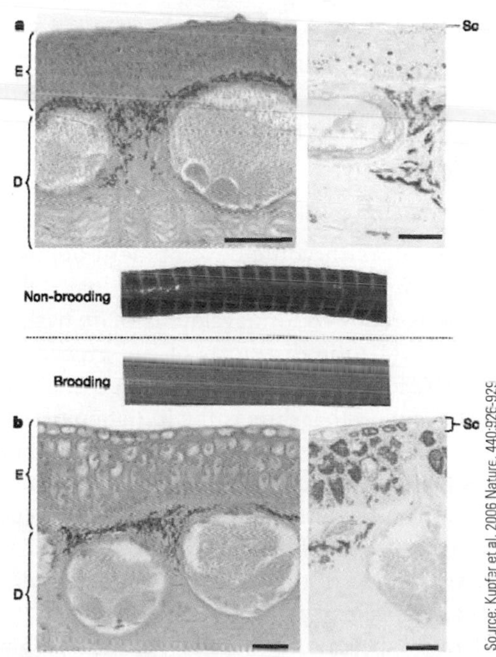

Source: Kupfer et al. 2006 Nature, 440:926-929

Figure 39.5
Details of the skin of **(a)** a nonbrooding and **(b)** a brooding female caecilian.

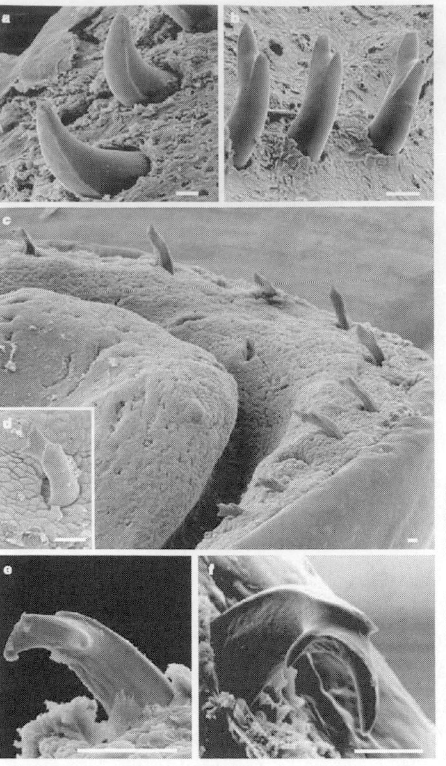

Figure 39.6
Scanning electron micrographs of the specialized teeth of young caecilians.

Study Break

1. What is relaxin? What role does it play?
2. Where can embryos develop in a parent?
3. What is milk? What animals produce it?

39.2 Mechanisms of Embryonic Development

When a sperm fertilizes an egg, a zygote is produced. At this point, embryonic development begins, ultimately producing a free-living individual. All of the instructions required for development are packed into the zygote. Mitotic divisions of the zygote are the beginning of developmental activity (see Chapter 9).

Information that directs the initiation of development is stored in two locations in the zygote. The nucleus houses the DNA derived from egg and sperm nuclei. This DNA directs development as individual genes are activated or turned off in a regulated and ordered manner. The balance of the information is stored in the zygote's cytoplasm.

Because sperm contribute essentially no cytoplasm to the zygote, its cytoplasm is maternal in origin. The mRNA and proteins stored in the egg cytoplasm are known as *cytoplasmic determinants,* which direct the first stages of animal development before genes become active. Depending on the animal group, control of early development by cytoplasmic determinants may be limited to the first few divisions of the zygote (e.g., in mammals), or it may last until the actual tissues of the embryo are formed (e.g., in most invertebrates).

The zygote's cytoplasm also contains ribosomes and other cytoplasmic components required for protein synthesis and early divisions of embryonic cells. Zygote cytoplasm contains the tubulin molecules required to form spindles for early cell divisions, as well as mitochondria and nutrients stored in granules in the yolk and in lipid droplets. In many animals, zygotes contain pigments that colour the egg or regions of it.

Yolk contains nutrients. In the eggs of typical insects, reptiles, and birds, large amounts of yolk supply all of the nutrients for development of the embryo. In contrast, the eggs of placental mammals contain very little yolk, which is used only to support the earliest stages of development.

Depending on the species, yolk may be concentrated at one end or in the centre or distributed evenly throughout the egg. Yolk distribution influences the rate and location of cell division during early embryonic development. Typically, cell division proceeds more slowly in the region of the egg containing the yolk. In the large, yolky eggs of birds and reptiles, cell division takes place only in a small, yolk-free patch at the egg's surface.

Unequal distribution of yolk and other components in the egg is termed **polarity.** In most species, the egg's nucleus is located toward one end, called the **animal pole.** The animal pole typically gives rise to surface structures and the anterior end of the embryo. The opposite end of the egg, the **vegetal pole,** typically gives rise to internal structures such as the gut, along with the posterior end of the embryo. When yolk is unequally distributed in the egg cytoplasm, it is usually concentrated in the vegetal half of the egg. Egg polarity plays a role in setting the three body axes of bilaterally symmetrical animals, namely the anterior–posterior axis, the dorsal–ventral (back-front) axis, and the left–right axis **(Figure 39.7).**

39.2a Cleavage and Gastrulation: Zygote to Multicellular Embryo

Soon after fertilization, the zygote begins a series of mitotic cleavage divisions in which cycles of DNA replication and division occur without the production of new cytoplasm. Thus, the cytoplasm of the zygote is partitioned into successively smaller cells without increasing the size or mass of the embryo **(Figure 39.8).** In the frog *Xenopus laevis,* 12 cleavage divisions produce an embryo of about 4000 cells that collectively occupy about the same volume and mass as the original zygote.

Cleavage is the first of three major developmental stages that, with modifications, are common to the early development of most animals. **Gastrulation,** the

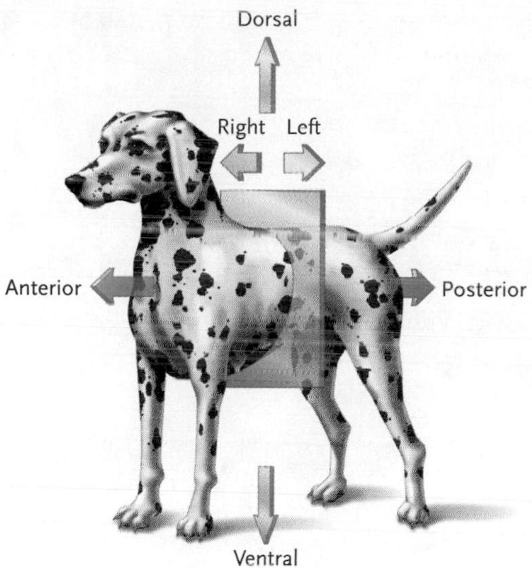

Figure 39.7
Body axes: anterior–posterior, dorsal–ventral, and left–right.

stage following cleavage, produces an embryo with three distinct primary tissue layers. **Organogenesis** follows gastrulation and gives rise to development of major organ systems. At the end of organogenesis, the embryo has the body organization characteristic of its species. Cell division, cell movements, and cell rearrangements occur during gastrulation and in organogenesis. **Figure 39.9, p. 940,** shows these stages as part of the life cycle of a frog.

In frogs, cleavage divisions form two different structures in succession. The **morula** (*morula* = mulberry) is a solid ball or layer of cells. As cleavage divisions continue, the ball or layer hollows out to form the **blastula** (*blast* = bud or offshoot; *ula* = small), the second structure in which cells, now called **blastomeres** (*mere* = part or division), enclose a fluid-filled cavity, the **blastocoel** (*coel* = hollow).

After cleavage is complete, cells of the blastula migrate and divide to produce the **gastrula** (*gaster* = gut or belly). Gastrulation, a morphogenetic process, dramatically rearranges the cells of the blastula into the three primary cell layers of the embryo: **ectoderm,** the outer layer (*ecto* = outside; *derm* = skin); **endoderm,** the inner layer (*endo* = inside); and **mesoderm** (*meso* = middle), the middle layer between ectoderm and endoderm. Gastrulation establishes the body pattern. Each tissue and organ of the adult animal originates from one of the three primary cell layers of the gastrula **(Table 39.1, p. 940).** Cell movements also contribute to the formation of the **archenteron** (*arch* = beginning; *enteron* = intestine or gut), a new cavity within the embryo that is lined with endoderm.

As the blastula develops into the gastrula, embryonic cells begin to differentiate, becoming recognizably different in biochemistry, structure, and function. The developmental potential of each cell becomes more limited than that of the zygote from which it originated. Although a fertilized egg could develop into a complete embryo, a mesoderm cell may develop into muscle or bone but does not normally develop into outside skin or brain. Scientists once thought that this restriction of developmental potential resulted because cells lost all of their genes except those required for the structure and function of the cell type they would become. However, differentiating cells each contain the complete genome of the organism, but each type of cell has a different program of gene expression.

Although development in all animals is accomplished by mechanisms under genetic control, the mechanisms are influenced to some extent by environmental factors such as temperature. The six mechanisms are as follows:

- Mitotic cell divisions
- Cell movements
- **Selective cell adhesions,** in which cells make and break specific connections to other cells or to the extracellular matrix (ECM)
- **Induction,** in which one group of cells (inducing cells) causes or influences another nearby group of cells (responding cells) to follow a particular developmental pathway. The key to induction is that only certain cells can respond to the signal from the inducing cells. Induction typically involves signal transduction events (see Chapter 35). Some induction events are triggered by direct cell–cell contact involving interaction between a membrane-embedded protein on the inducing cell and a receptor protein on the responding cell's surface. Others are triggered by

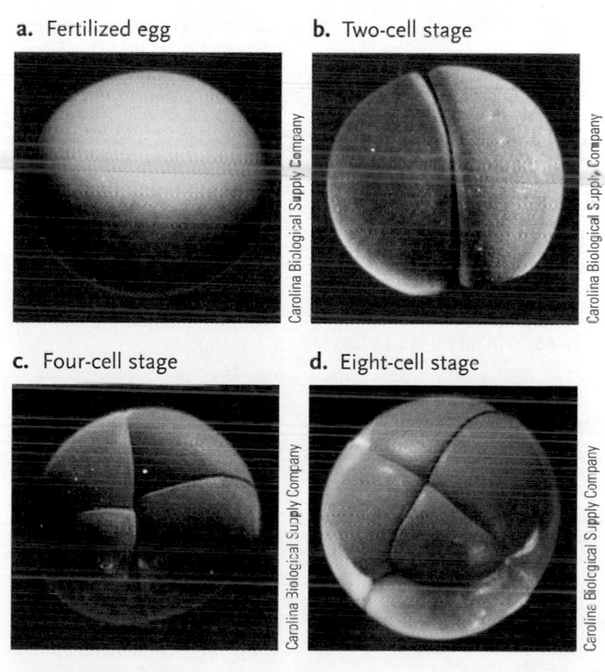

Figure 39.8
The first three cleavage divisions of a frog embryo, which convert the fertilized egg into the eight-cell stage. Note that the cleavage divisions cut the volume of the fertilized egg into successively smaller cells.

Figure 39.9
Stages of animal development shown in a frog.

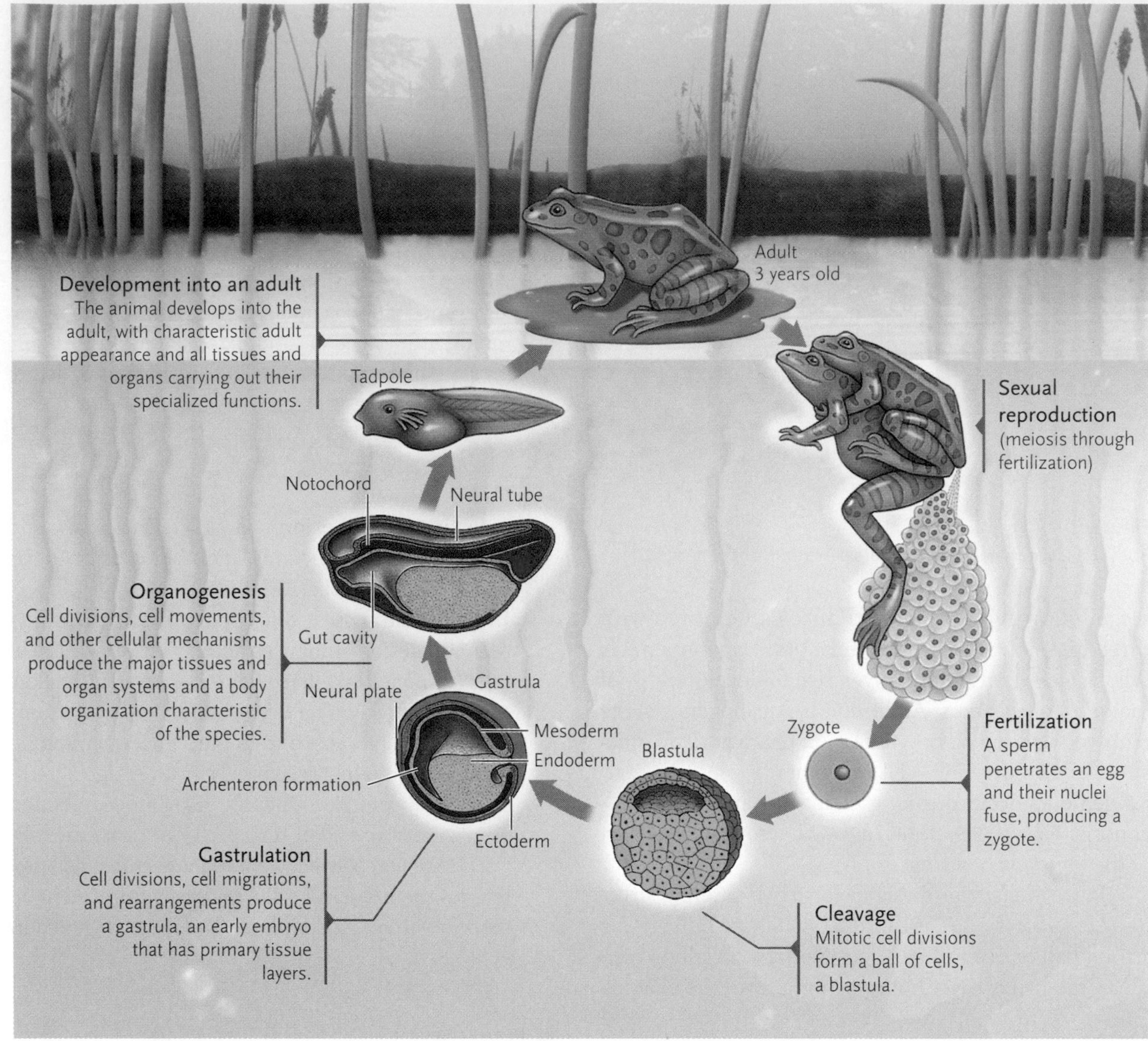

Adult
3 years old
Development into an adult
The animal develops into the adult, with characteristic adult appearance and all tissues and organs carrying out their specialized functions.
Tadpole
Sexual reproduction (meiosis through fertilization)
Notochord
Neural tube
Organogenesis
Cell divisions, cell movements, and other cellular mechanisms produce the major tissues and organ systems and a body organization characteristic of the species.
Gut cavity
Neural plate
Gastrula
Mesoderm
Endoderm
Archenteron formation
Ectoderm
Blastula
Zygote
Fertilization
A sperm penetrates an egg and their nuclei fuse, producing a zygote.
Gastrulation
Cell divisions, cell migrations, and rearrangements produce a gastrula, an early embryo that has primary tissue layers.
Cleavage
Mitotic cell divisions form a ball of cells, a blastula.

a signal molecule released by the inducing cell that interacts with a receptor on the responding cell (e.g., paracrine regulation; see Chapter 35).

Table 39.1 **Origins of Adult Tissues and Organs in the Three Primary Tissue Layers**

Primary Tissue Layer	Adult Tissues and Organs
Ectoderm	Skin and its elaborations, including hair, feathers, scales, and nails; nervous system, including brain, spinal cord, and peripheral nerves; lens, retina, and cornea of eye; lining of mouth and anus; sweat glands, mammary glands, adrenal medulla, and tooth enamel
Mesoderm	Muscles; most of skeletal system, including bones and cartilage; circulatory system, including heart, blood vessels, and blood cells; internal reproductive organs; kidneys and outer walls of digestive tract
Endoderm	Lining of digestive tract, liver, pancreas, lining of respiratory tract, thyroid gland, lining of urethra, and urinary bladder

- **Determination** sets the developmental fate of a cell. Before determination, a cell has the potential to become any cell type of the adult. Afterward, the cell is committed to becoming a particular cell type. Typically, determination results from induction, although in some cases, it results from the asymmetric segregation of cellular determinants.
- **Differentiation** follows determination and involves the establishment of a cell-specific developmental program in the cells. Differentiation results in cell types with clearly defined structures and functions. These features are derived from specific patterns of gene expression in cells.

Study Break

1. What is yolk? What role does it play?
2. What mechanisms are involved in animal development from the zygote?

39.3 Major Patterns of Cleavage and Gastrulation

39.3a Sea Urchin

Cleavage divisions proceed at approximately the same rate in all regions of a sea urchin embryo (**Figure 39.10**, step 1), reflecting uniform distribution of yolk in the egg. These divisions continue until a blastula containing about a thousand cells is formed (step 2).

Gastrulation begins at the vegetal pole of the blastula. Through induction, some cells in the middle of the vegetal pole become elongated and cylindrical, causing the region to flatten and thicken. Then some cells (primary mesenchyme: *mesen* = middle; *chyme* = juice) break loose and migrate into the blastocoel (step 3), making and breaking adhesions until eventually they attach along the ventral sides of the blastocoel. These cells form the future mesoderm (see Figure 39.10, step 7), which give rise to skeletal elements of the embryo. Next, the flattened vegetal pole of the blastula invaginates, pushing gradually into the interior (steps 4 and 5). The cells that invaginate will become endoderm cells. The inward movement, much like pushing in the side of a hollow rubber ball, generates the archenteron, a new cavity that opens through the blastopore.

As the archenteron forms, extensions of cells of the invaginated layer stretch across the blastocoel and contact the inside of the ectoderm (step 6). These extensions make tight adhesions and then contract, pulling the invaginated cell layer inward with them, eliminating most of the blastocoel.

Now the embryo has two complete cell layers. The outer layer—the original blastula surface—forms embryonic ectoderm. Cells of the second, inner layer are derived from the archenteron and become endoderm. Mesodermal cells, which begin to form a third layer, are derived from the primary mesenchyme cells and from *secondary mesenchyme* cells that migrated into the space between the ectoderm and endoderm (step 7). After the formation of the three primary cell layers, cells begin to differentiate based on synthesis of different proteins in each layer.

As ectoderm, mesoderm, and endoderm layers develop, the embryo lengthens into an ellipsoidal shape, with the blastopore marking the posterior end of the embryo. From here on, further cell divisions, combined with cell movements, selective cell adhesions, induction, and differentiation, lead to differentiation of organ systems. In sea urchins and other deuterostomes, the blastopore forms the anus, and the mouth will form at the opposite, anterior end of the gut.

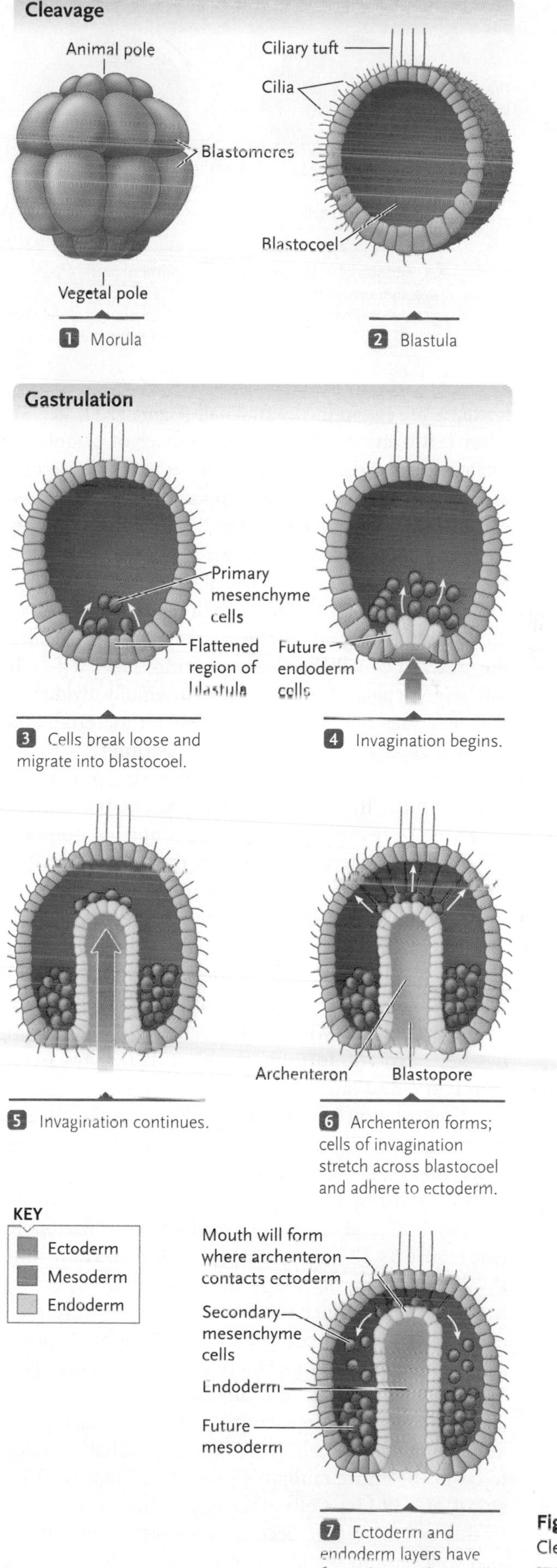

Figure 39.10
Cleavage and gastrulation in the sea urchin.

39.3b Amphibians

In the eggs of amphibians such as frogs, yolk is concentrated in the vegetal half, giving it a pale colour. The animal half is darkly coloured because of a layer of pigment granules just below the surface. A sperm normally

Figure 39.11
Rotation of the pigment layer and development of the grey crescent after fertilization in a frog egg. The grey crescent marks the site where gastrulation of the embryo will begin.

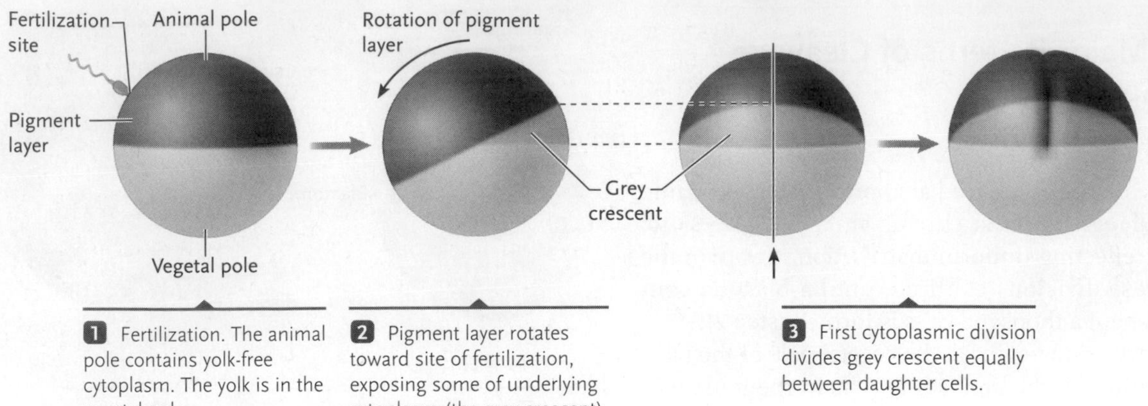

Fertilization site
Animal pole
Pigment layer
Vegetal pole
Rotation of pigment layer
Grey crescent
1 Fertilization. The animal pole contains yolk-free cytoplasm. The yolk is in the vegetal pole.
2 Pigment layer rotates toward site of fertilization, exposing some of underlying cytoplasm (the grey crescent).
3 First cytoplasmic division divides grey crescent equally between daughter cells.

fertilizes the egg in the animal half (**Figure 39.11,** step 1). After fertilization, the pigmented layer of cytoplasm rotates toward the site of sperm entry, exposing a crescent-shaped region of underlying cytoplasm at the side opposite the point of sperm entry (step 2). This region, the **grey crescent**, establishes the dorsal–ventral axis of the embryo and marks the future dorsal side of the animal.

Normally, the first cleavage division runs perpendicular to the long axis of the grey crescent and divides the crescent equally between resulting cells (step 3). If the first two blastomeres are experimentally divided so that one does not receive grey crescent material, and the two cells are separated, the blastomere without grey crescent material divides but ends up in a disordered mass that stops developing. The blastomere receiving grey crescent produces a normal embryo. Cytoplasmic material localized in the grey crescent is essential to normal development in frog embryos.

As cleavage of the frog embryo continues, cell divisions proceed more rapidly in the animal half, producing smaller and more numerous cells there than in the yolky vegetal half. By the time cleavage has produced an embryo with 15 000 cells, the animal half has hollowed out, forming the blastula (**Figures 39.12,** step 1, and **39.13a**).

Gastrulation begins when cells from the animal pole begin to migrate across the embryo surface to reach the region derived from the grey crescent. This site is marked by a crescent-shaped depression rotated clockwise 90° and called the **dorsal lip of the blastopore** (see Figure 39.12, step 2, and **Figure 39.13b**). These cells invaginate, changing shape and pushing inward from the surface to produce the depression. The depression eventually forms a complete circle (the blastopore) after further inward movement of additional cells (see Figure 39.12, step 3, and **Figure 39.13c**).

By involution, cells migrate into the blastopore, and the pigmented cell layer of the animal half expands to cover the entire embryo surface (see Figures 39.12, step 4, and 39.13c). Cells of the vegetal half are enclosed by this cell migration, becoming visible on the outside as a yolk plug in the blastopore. The blastopore gives rise to the anus.

Continuing involution moves cells into the interior and upward (see Figure 39.12, steps 3 and 4), forming two layers that line the inside top half of the embryo. Dorsal mesoderm (shown in red) is the uppermost of these induced layers. Beneath it is the endoderm

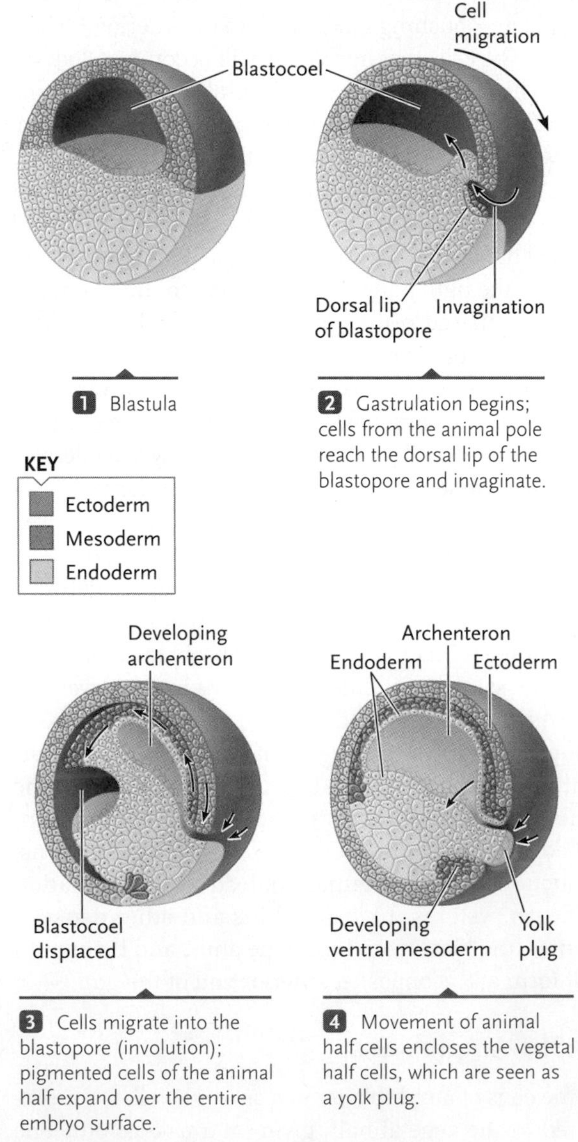

Blastocoel
Cell migration
Dorsal lip of blastopore
Invagination
1 Blastula
2 Gastrulation begins; cells from the animal pole reach the dorsal lip of the blastopore and invaginate.
KEY
Ectoderm
Mesoderm
Endoderm
Developing archenteron
Blastocoel displaced
Archenteron
Endoderm
Ectoderm
Developing ventral mesoderm
Yolk plug
3 Cells migrate into the blastopore (involution); pigmented cells of the animal half expand over the entire embryo surface.
4 Movement of animal half cells encloses the vegetal half cells, which are seen as a yolk plug.

Figure 39.12
Gastrulation in a frog embryo. Yolk cells are shown in paler yellow.

a. Blastula

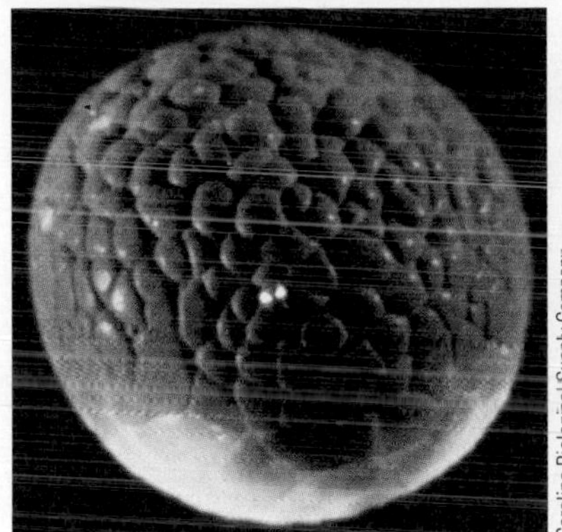

b. Early gastrulation

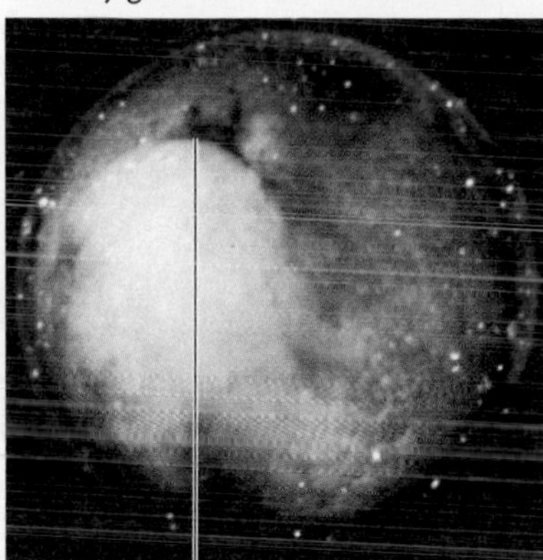

c. Late gastrulation

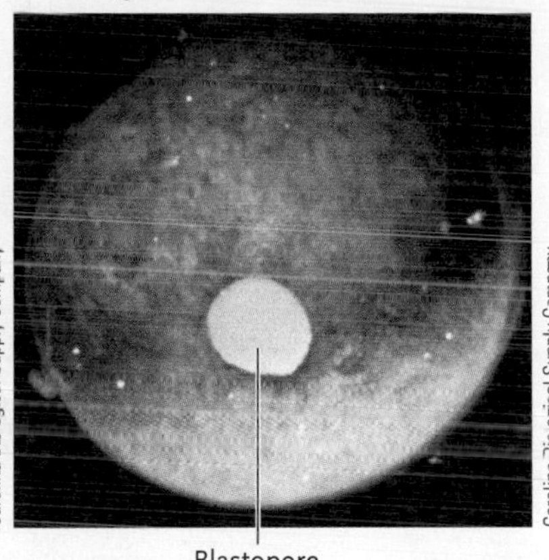

Figure 39.13 Photomicrographs of a frog embryo. **(a)** Blastula. **(b)** Early gastrulation and the formation of the dorsal lip of the blastopore. **(c)** Late gastrulation, showing the completed blastopore, closed by the yolk plug.

(shown in yellow), containing cells originating from both the outer surface of the embryo and the yolky interior. Ectoderm (shown in blue) forms from pigmented cells remaining at the surface of the embryo. Induction of the ventral mesoderm begins near the vegetal pole.

As mesoderm and endoderm form, the depression created by inward cell movements gradually deepens and extends inward as the archenteron (see Figure 39.12, steps 3 and 4), displacing the blastocoel. Cells of the three primary cell layers continue to increase in number by further migrations and divisions as development proceeds.

The major induction centre during frog gastrulation is the dorsal lip of the blastopore. If cells are removed from the dorsal lip and transplanted elsewhere in the egg, they form a second blastopore (and a second embryo).

39.3c Birds

Gastrulation in amniotes (see Chapter 27) such as birds and reptiles is modified by the distribution of the yolk, which occupies almost the entire volume of the egg. A thin layer of cytoplasm at the egg's surface gives rise to primary tissues of the embryo. Although mammalian eggs have relatively little yolk, gastrulation in them follows a similar pattern.

Early cleavage divisions in birds produce the **blastodisk**, a thin layer of cells at the yolk's surface (**Figure 39.14, p. 944,** step 1). The complete blastodisk is a layer with about 20 000 cells. Cells of the blastodisk then separate into two layers, the **epiblast** (top layer) and the **hypoblast** (bottom layer). The blastocoel is the flattened cavity between them (step 2).

Gastrulation begins as cells in the epiblast stream toward the midline of the blastodisk, thickening it in this region. The thickened layer (or **primitive streak**) is first evident in the posterior end of the embryo and extends toward the anterior end as more cells of the epiblast move into it (step 3). A thickening at the anterior end of the primitive streak (the *primitive knot*) is the functional equivalent of the amphibian dorsal lip of the blastopore. The primitive streak initially marks the future posterior end of the embryo, and by the time it has elongated fully, it has established the left and right sides of the embryo. The streak forms on what will become the dorsal side of the embryo, with the ventral side below.

As the primitive streak forms, its midline sinks, forming the **primitive groove**, a conduit for migrating cells to move into the blastocoel. Epiblasts are the first cells to migrate through the primitive groove (see Figure 39.14, step 4) and produce the endoderm. Mesoderm is formed from cells migrating laterally between the epiblast and endoderm. Epiblast cells remaining at the surface of the blastodisk form ectoderm (step 4).

In the chick embryo, all primary tissue layers arise from the epiblast. Only a few of the hypoblast cells—near the posterior end of the embryo—contribute directly to the embryo. These form *germ cells* that later migrate to developing gonads, founding cell lines leading to eggs and sperm (see Chapter 9).

Initially, ectoderm, mesoderm, and endoderm are located in three more or less horizontal layers in the chick embryo. During gastrulation, the endoderm pushes upward along its midline and its left and right sides fold downward, forming a tube that is oriented parallel to the primitive streak (see Figure 39.14, step 5). The archenteron is the central cavity of the tube, the primitive gut. Mesoderm separates into two layers, forming the coelom, a fluid-filled body cavity lined with mesoderm. These movements complete the formation of the gastrula.

39.3d Extraembryonic Membranes: Amnion, Chorion, Allantois

Each primary tissue layer of a bird embryo extends outside the embryo to form **extraembryonic membranes (Figure 39.15, p. 944)** that conduct nutrients from yolk to embryo, exchange gases with the environment outside the egg, or store metabolic wastes removed from the embryo. The **yolk sac** is an extension of mesoderm and endoderm enclosing the yolk.

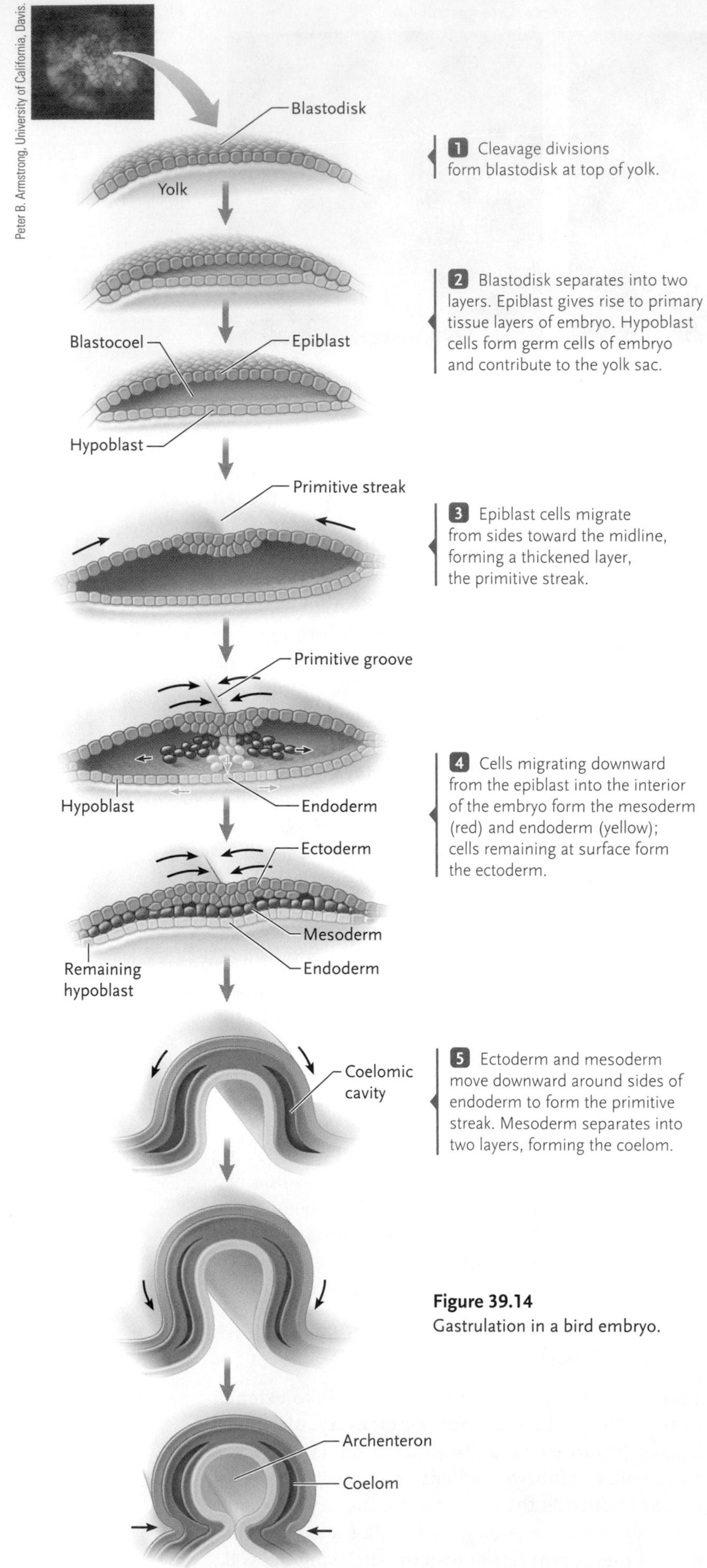

Peter B. Armstrong, University of California, Davis.
Blastodisk
Yolk
1 Cleavage divisions form blastodisk at top of yolk.
Blastocoel
Epiblast
Hypoblast
2 Blastodisk separates into two layers. Epiblast gives rise to primary tissue layers of embryo. Hypoblast cells form germ cells of embryo and contribute to the yolk sac.
Primitive streak
3 Epiblast cells migrate from sides toward the midline, forming a thickened layer, the primitive streak.
Primitive groove
Hypoblast
Endoderm
Ectoderm
Mesoderm
Endoderm
Remaining hypoblast
4 Cells migrating downward from the epiblast into the interior of the embryo form the mesoderm (red) and endoderm (yellow); cells remaining at surface form the ectoderm.
Coelomic cavity
5 Ectoderm and mesoderm move downward around sides of endoderm to form the primitive streak. Mesoderm separates into two layers, forming the coelom.
Archenteron
Coelom

Figure 39.14
Gastrulation in a bird embryo.

Embryo
Amnion
Amniotic cavity
Allantois
Chorion
Shell
Albumin
Yolk
Yolk sac
Allantois

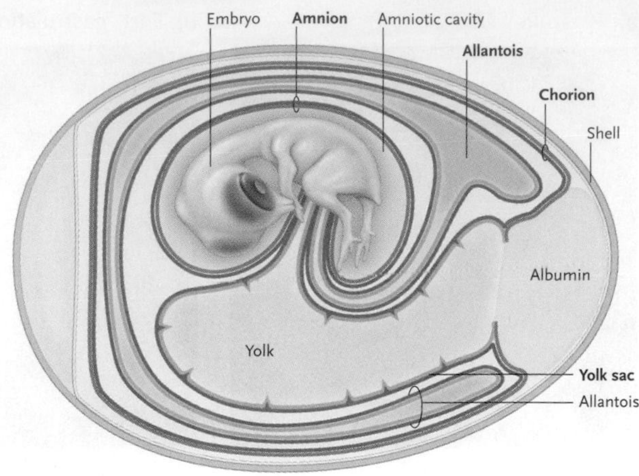

Figure 39.15
The four extraembryonic membranes in a bird embryo (in bold).

Although the yolk sac remains connected to the gut of the embryo by a stalk, yolk does not directly enter the embryo by this route. Rather, it is absorbed by blood in vessels in the membrane, which then transport the nutrients to the embryo.

The **chorion**, produced from ectoderm and mesoderm, completely surrounds the embryo and yolk sac and lines the inside of the shell. The chorion exchanges oxygen and carbon dioxide with the environment through the egg's shell. The **amnion** closes over the embryo to form the *amniotic cavity*. Cells of the amnion secrete *amniotic fluid* into the cavity, which bathes the embryo and provides an aquatic environment in which it can develop. Reptilian and mammalian embryos are also surrounded by an amnion and amniotic fluid. Providing the embryo with an aquatic environment is presumed to have been a key factor in the evolution of fully terrestrial vertebrates, the **Amniota**.

The **allantoic membrane** forms from mesoderm and endoderm that has bulged outward from the gut. It encloses the allantois, a sac that closely lines the chorion and fills much of the space between chorion and yolk sac. The **allantois** stores nitrogenous wastes (primarily uric acid) removed from the embryo. The part of the allantoic membrane lining the chorion forms a rich bed of capillaries connected to the embryo by arteries and veins. This circulatory system delivers carbon dioxide to the chorion and picks up the oxygen that is absorbed through the shell and chorion. At hatching, part of the allantoic membrane becomes the lining of the bladder.

Study Break

1. What are the main developmental differences between protostomes and deuterostomes?
2. What are important differences between typical patterns of development in birds and in mammals?
3. What are the features of an amniote egg? What is its evolutionary significance?

39.4 Organogenesis: Gastrulation to Adult Body Structures

Following gastrulation, organogenesis gives rise to the body organization characteristic of the species. Organogenesis involves the same mechanisms used in gastrulation, namely cell division, cell movements, selective cell adhesion, induction, and differentiation. Organogenesis also involves an additional mechanism, **apoptosis**, in which certain cells are programmed to die (see Chapter 9). To illustrate how cellular mechanisms of development interact in organogenesis, we follow the formation of major organ systems in the bird embryo. Then we describe the generation of one organ, the eye, which follows a pathway typical of eye development in all vertebrates.

39.4a Ectoderm and the Nervous System: Neural Tube and Neural Crest Cells

In vertebrates, organogenesis begins with **neurulation**, which is the development of nervous tissue from ectoderm. As a preliminary to neurulation, cells of the mesoderm form the notochord, a solid rod of tissue extending the length of the embryo under the dorsal ectoderm. Notochord cells carry out a major induction, causing the overlying ectoderm to form the neural plate, a thickened and flattened longitudinal band of cells (**Figure 39.16**, steps 1 and 2). The neural plate does not form if the notochord is removed.

Once induced, the neural plate sinks downward along its midline (steps 2 and 3), creating a deep longitudinal groove and ridges (neural crests) that rise along the sides of the neural plate. The neural tube forms when the neural crests move together and close over the centre of the groove along the length of the developing embryo (steps 4 and 5). The neural tube then pinches off from the overlying ectoderm, which closes over the tube (step 6). The central nervous system, including the brain and spinal cord, develops directly from the neural tube.

During formation of the neural tube, **neural crest** cells (see Figure 39.16) migrate into the mesoderm and follow specific routes to reach distant points in the developing embryo, where they contribute to the formation of a variety of organ systems. Some cells develop into cranial nerves in the head, whereas others contribute to the bones of the inner ear and skull, cartilage of facial structures, and teeth. Still others form ganglia of the autonomic nervous system, peripheral nerves leading from the spinal cord to body structures, and nerves of the developing gut. Neural crest cells also move to the skin, where they form pigment cells, and to the adrenal glands, where they form the medulla of the kidney. The migration of neural crest cells contributes to development in all vertebrates (see *People Behind Biology*).

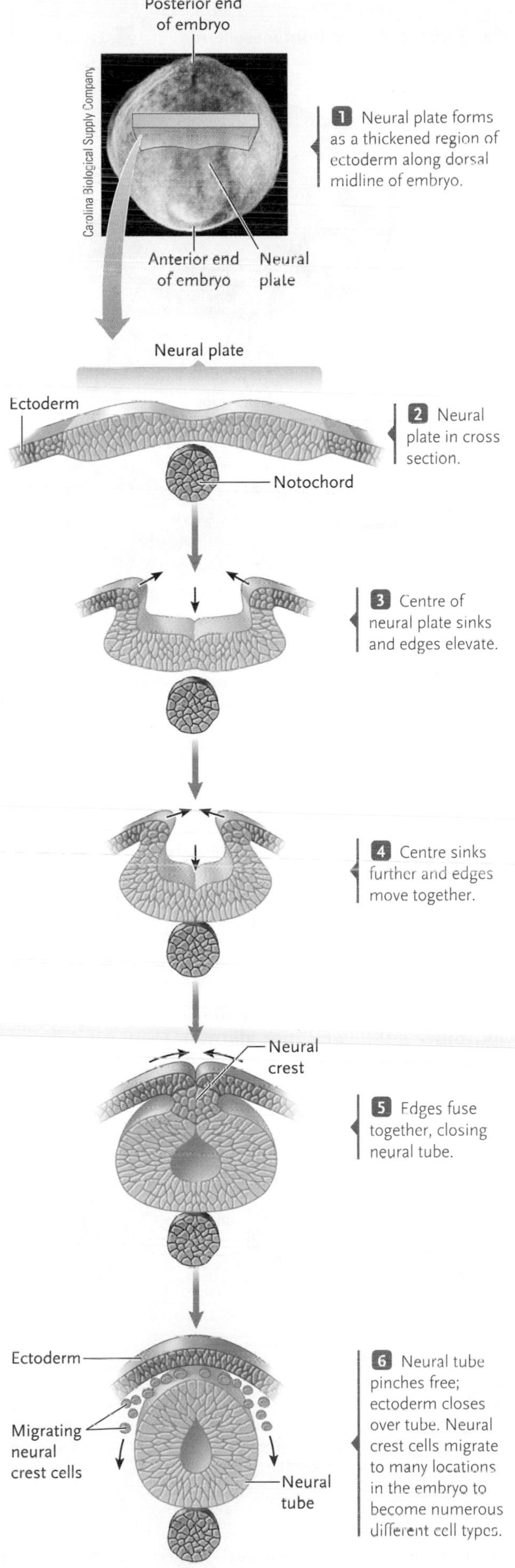

Posterior end of embryo
Carolina Biological Supply Company
1 Neural plate forms as a thickened region of ectoderm along dorsal midline of embryo.
Anterior end of embryo
Neural plate
Neural plate
Ectoderm
2 Neural plate in cross section.
Notochord
3 Centre of neural plate sinks and edges elevate.
4 Centre sinks further and edges move together.
Neural crest
5 Edges fuse together, closing neural tube.
Ectoderm
Migrating neural crest cells
Neural tube
6 Neural tube pinches free; ectoderm closes over tube. Neural crest cells migrate to many locations in the embryo to become numerous different cell types.

Figure 39.16 **Development of the neural tube and neural crest cells in vertebrates.** Photo is of an amphibian embryo; drawings show steps in a bird embryo.

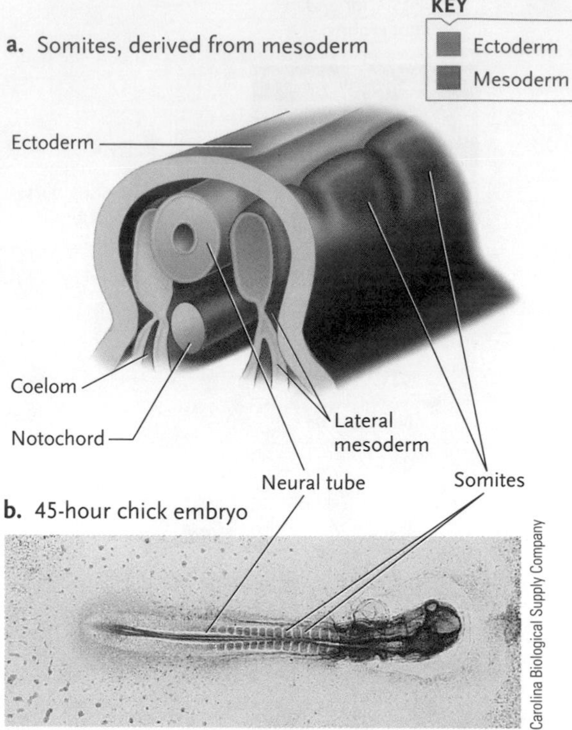

Figure 39.17
Later development of the mesoderm. (a) Somites develop into segmented structures such as the vertebrae, the ribs, and the musculature between the ribs. The lateral mesoderm gives rise to other structures, such as the heart and blood vessels and the linings of internal body cavities. **(b)** The somites in a 45-hour chick embryo.

Other structures differentiate in the embryo while the neural tube is forming. On each side of the notochord, mesoderm separates into somites, blocks of cells spaced one after the other **(Figure 39.17)**. Somites give rise to the vertebral column, ribs, repeating sets of muscles associated with the ribs and vertebral column, and limb muscles. Mesoderm outside the somites extends around the primitive gut (lateral mesoderm in Figure 39.17) and splits into two layers, one covering the surface of the gut and the other lining the body wall. The space between the layers is the adult coelom.

39.4b Development of the Eye: Interactions between Cells

Eyes develop by the same basic five-step pathway in all vertebrates **(Figure 39.18)**. The brain forms at the anterior end of the neural tube from a cluster of hollow vesicles that swell outward from the neural tube (see Figure 39.18, step 1). Each of the two optic vesicle develops into an eye. Figure 39.18 depicts the development of a frog eye; the development of the rest of the brain is not shown.

The optic vesicles grow outward until they contact the overlying ectoderm, inducing a series of developmental responses in both tissues. The optic cup, a double-walled structure, forms when the outer surface of the optic vesicle thickens and flattens at the region of contact and then pushes inward. The optic cup ultimately becomes the retina. The lens forms from the lens placode, a disklike swelling that arises when the optic cup induces thickening of overlying ectoderm (step 2). The centre of the lens placode sinks inward toward the optic cup, and its edges eventually fuse together, forming the lens vesicle, a ball of cells (step 3).

The developing lens cells begin to synthesize crystallin, a fibrous protein that collects into clear, glassy deposits. Lens cells finally lose their nuclei and form the elastic, crystal-clear lens.

As the lens develops, it contacts the overlying ectoderm that has closed over it. In response, the ectoderm cells form the cornea by losing their pigment granules and becoming clear. Eventually, the developing cornea joins with the edges of the optic cup to complete the primary structure of the eye (step 4). Other cells contribute to accessory structures of the eye. Mesoderm and neural crest cells contribute to reinforcing tissues

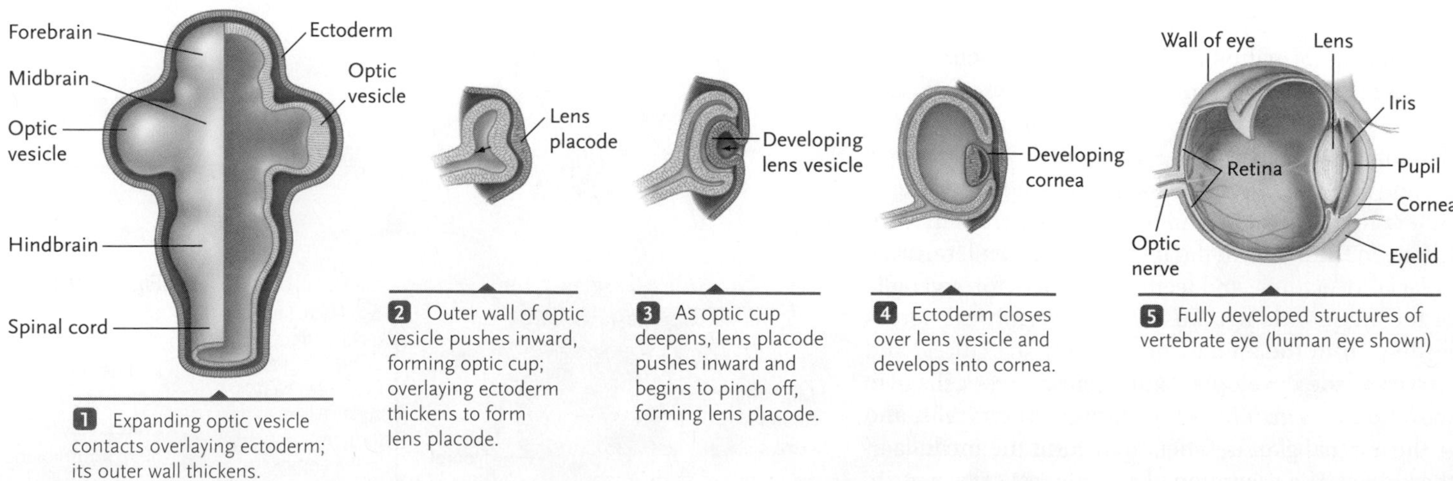

Forebrain
Midbrain
Optic vesicle
Hindbrain
Spinal cord
Ectoderm
Optic vesicle
1 Expanding optic vesicle contacts overlaying ectoderm; its outer wall thickens.
Lens placode
2 Outer wall of optic vesicle pushes inward, forming optic cup; overlaying ectoderm thickens to form lens placode.
Developing lens vesicle
3 As optic cup deepens, lens placode pushes inward and begins to pinch off, forming lens placode.
Developing cornea
4 Ectoderm closes over lens vesicle and develops into cornea.
Wall of eye
Lens
Iris
Retina
Pupil
Cornea
Eyelid
Optic nerve
5 Fully developed structures of vertebrate eye (human eye shown)

Figure 39.18
Stages in the development of the vertebrate eye from the optic vesicle of the brain and the overlying ectoderm.

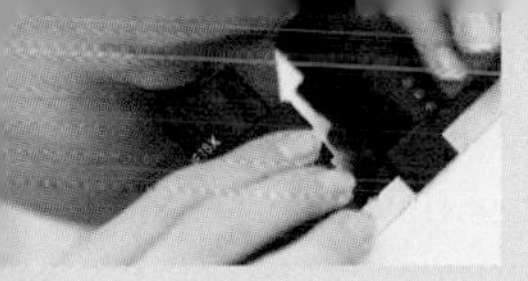

People Behind Biology

Brian K. Hall

Brian K. Hall, a professor of biology at Dalhousie University in Halifax, Nova Scotia, and his students study developmental patterns in the embryos of fishes, frogs, and chicks, in particular the development of the skeleton. Considerable work has focused on the embryonic origins of the cells that form the cartilages of the head and shows that skeletal elements in vertebrates often originate in the developing nervous system, specifically in neural crest cells. The research produces insight into the evolution of structures by showing how they are derived and from where (see Chapter 20).

Honours thesis students working with Professor Hall have studied a range of topics, from looking at asymmetry between the left and right limbs of mice to the impact of thyroxine on metamorphosis in a South African frog (*Hymenochirus*). Other research on this frog has explored its capacity to regenerate hindlimbs and the patterns of migration of neural crest cells and pigment cells. This work makes Professor Hall one of the founding fathers of evolutionary developmental biology, or "evo-devo," which is really an extension of traditional developmental biology.

His work on development has led Professor Hall to consider how biologists use words to describe what they see in the natural world. For example, how does one distinguish "rudimentary" and "vestigial" features in animals? It is well known that snakes evolved from limbed ancestors and that whales evolved from ancestors that had teeth. Studies on the development of snakes clearly show that they have rudimentary limbs, partly formed or incomplete transformations of developing features. Vestiges, evolutionary remnants of ancestral features, also occur in animals. The tooth buds (fetal teeth) of baleen whales are examples of vestigial features, as are the rudimentary clavicles that appear in the developing embryos of toothed whales. Once again, the problem of imposing specific terms and definitions on a natural continuum can make the study of biology unnecessarily complex.

Professor Hall's detailed studies of development make it easier to understand the patterns that emerge, which also means appreciating the shortcomings of the labels we use.

in the wall of the eye and the muscles that move the eye. Figure 39.18, step 5, shows a fully developed vertebrate eye.

Initial induction by optic vesicles is necessary for development of the eye. If an optic vesicle is removed before lens formation, ectoderm fails to develop into the lens placode and vesicle. Moreover, placing a removed optic vesicle under the ectoderm in other regions of the head causes a lens to form in the new location. If ectoderm over an optic vesicle is removed and ectoderm from elsewhere in the embryo is grafted in its place, a normal lens develops in the grafted ectoderm. This occurs even though in its former location it would not differentiate into lens tissue.

Eye development also demonstrates differentiation. Ectoderm cells induced to form the lens synthesize crystallin. In other locations, ectoderm cells synthesize mainly keratin, a different protein. Keratin is a component of surface structures such as skin, hair, feathers, scales, and horns. In response to induction by the optic vesicle, genes of ectoderm cells coding for crystallin are activated, but genes coding for keratin are not.

39.4c Apoptosis: Programmed Cell Death

Induction and differentiation build complex, specialized organs from three fundamental tissue types. Apoptosis (see Chapter 9), programmed cell death, complements these processes by removing tissues needed during development but not present in the fully formed organ. Apoptosis plays an important role in the development of both invertebrates and vertebrates. The best example of apoptosis in frog development occurs during metamorphosis, when the tadpole changes into an adult frog. The tadpole's tail becomes progressively smaller and finally disappears because its cells disintegrate and their components are absorbed and recycled by other cells. Cells eliminated by apoptosis, like those of a tadpole's tail, are parts of structures required at one stage of development but not later.

Study Break

1. What processes and embryonic layers are involved in the development of the eye?
2. How does the neural tube develop?

39.5 Embryonic Development of Humans and Other Mammals

The embryonic development of humans is representative of placental mammals. In the uterus, the embryo is nourished by the placenta, which supplies oxygen and nutrients to the embryo and carries carbon dioxide and nitrogenous wastes away from it.

Pregnancy or gestation, the period of mammalian in utero development, varies among species. Larger mammals bearing larger young tend to have longer gestation periods. From fertilization to birth, pregnancy

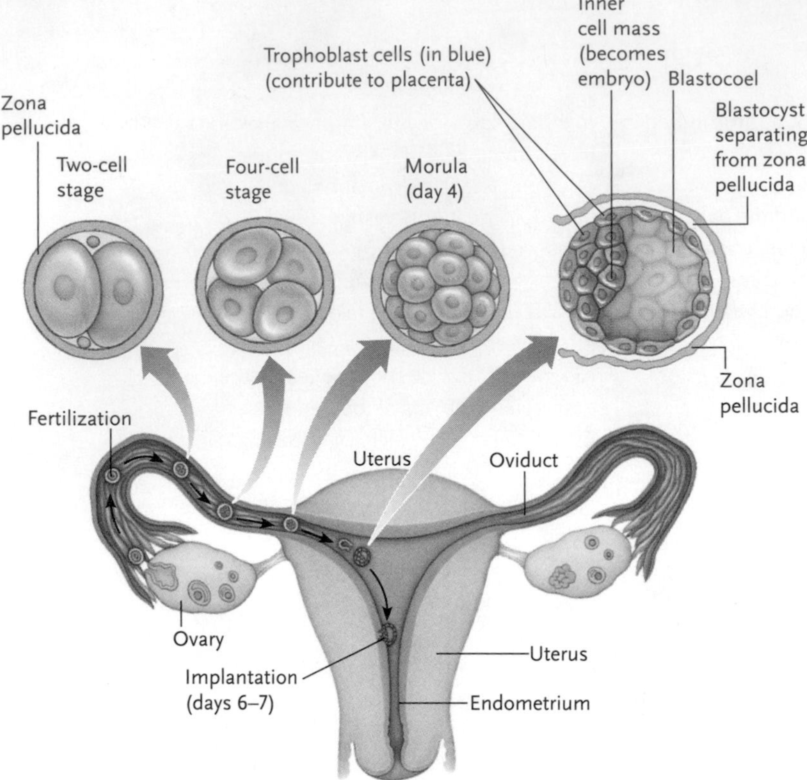

Figure 39.19
Early stages in the development of the human embryo.

lasts about 600 days in elephants, about 365 days in blue whales, and 21 days in hamsters.

In humans, gestation takes an average of 266 days, about 38 weeks. Because the date of fertilization can be difficult to establish, human gestation is usually calculated from the beginning of the menstrual cycle in which fertilization took place. The nine-month period is divided into three **trimesters**, each three months long.

Major developmental events in human gestation—cleavage, gastrulation, and organogenesis—take place during the first trimester. By week 4, the embryo's heart is beating, and by the end of week 8, the major organs and organ systems have formed. From this point until birth, the developing human is called a **fetus**. Only 5 cm long by the end of the first trimester, the fetus grows during the second and third trimesters to an average length of 50 cm and an average mass of 3.5 kg.

Cleavage occurs during the passage of the developing embryo down the fallopian tube and while it is still enclosed in the zona pellucida, the original coat of the egg **(Figure 39.19)**.

By day 4, the morula, a ball of 16 to 32 cells, has been produced. By the time the endometrium (uterine lining) is ready for implantation (about seven days after ovulation), the morula has reached the uterus and, through further cell divisions and differentiation, has become a blastocyst. The **blastocyst** is a single-cell-layered hollow ball of about 120 cells with a fluid-filled cavity, the *blastocoel*, which has a dense mass of cells localized on one side. This **inner cell mass** will become the embryo itself, whereas the outer single layer of cells of the blastocyst, the **trophoblast**, will become tissues that support development of the embryo in the uterus.

When ready to implant, the blastocyst breaks out of the zona pellucida and sticks to the endometrium on its inner cell mass side **(Figure 39.20a)**. Implantation begins when the trophoblast cells that overlie the inner cell mass secrete proteases that digest pathways between endometrial cells. Dividing trophoblast cells fill in the digested spaces, appearing as fingerlike projections into the endometrium. These cells continue to digest nutrient-rich endometrial cells, producing a hole in the endometrium for the blastocyst and releasing nutrients for the developing embryo after it has consumed the small amount of yolk contained in egg cytoplasm. While the blastocyst burrows into the endometrium, the inner cell mass separates into the *embryonic disk*, which consists of two distinct cell layers (see Figure 39.20a). The epiblast, the layer farther from the blastocoel, gives rise to the embryo proper. The hypoblast, the layer nearer the blastocoel, generates part of the extraembryonic membranes. When implantation is complete, the blastocyst has completely burrowed into the endometrium and is covered by a layer of endometrial cells **(Figure 39.20b)**.

Gastrulation proceeds as in birds (see Figure 39.14), with the formation of a primitive streak in the epiblast. Soon after the inner cell mass separates into epiblast and hypoblast, a layer of cells separates from the epiblast along its top margin (see Figure 39.20b). The amniotic cavity is the fluid-filled space created by the separation. The layer of cells forming its roof becomes the amnion, which expands until it completely surrounds the embryo, suspending it in amniotic fluid.

Also as in birds, the hypoblast develops into the yolk sac. In mammals, the mesoderm of the yolk sac gives rise to the blood vessels in the embryonic portion of the placenta. The allantois stores nitrogenous wastes in birds, but it is a small, vestigial sac in human embryos because most nitrogenous wastes are transferred across the placenta to the mother via blood vessels in the placenta and the umbilical cord.

While the amnion is expanding around the embryo, blood-filled spaces form in maternal tissue, and trophoblast cells grow rapidly around both the embryo and amnion to form the chorion **(Figure 39. 20c)**, the membrane that forms most of the embryonic portion of the placenta. Next, a connecting stalk forms between the embryonic disk and the chorion, which begins to grow into the endometrium as fingerlike extensions called **chorionic villi** (singular, villus) **(Figure 39.20d)**. Chorionic villi increase the surface area of the chorion. The placenta forms in the area where these villi grow into the endometrium. As the chorion develops, mesodermal cells of the yolk sac grow into it and form a rich network of blood vessels, the embryonic circulation of the placenta. At the same time, the expanding chorion stimulates the blood vessels of the endometrium to

Figure 39.20
Implantation of a human blastocyst in the endometrium of the uterus and the establishment of the placenta.

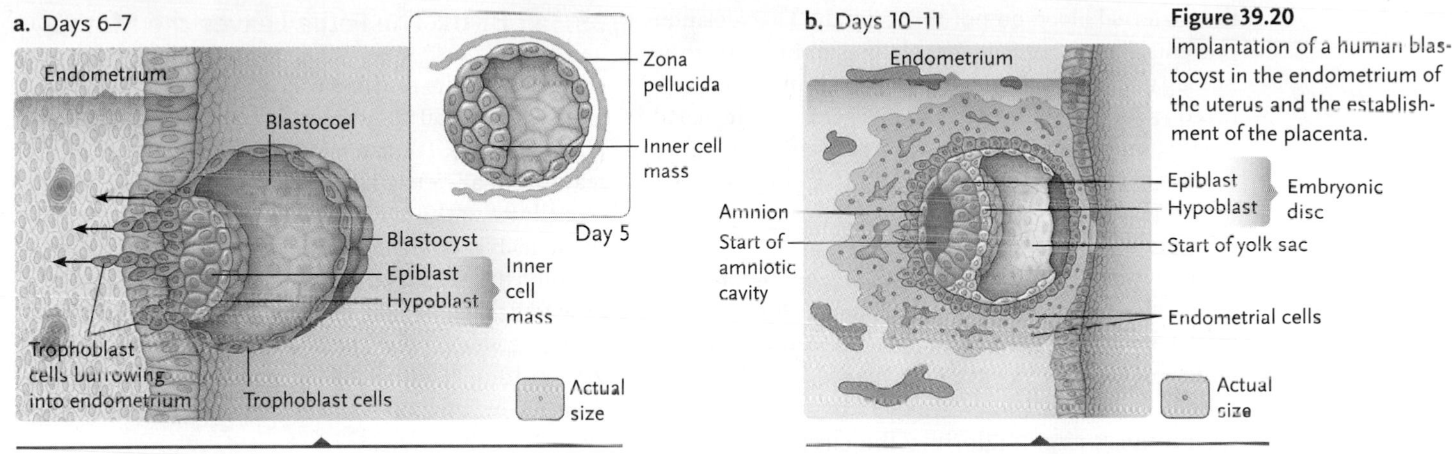

Surface cells of the blastocyst attach to the endometrium and start to burrow into it. Implantation is under way.

A layer of epiblast cells separates, producing the amniotic cavity. The cells above the cavity become the amnion, which eventually surrounds the embryo. The hypoblast begins to form around the yolk sac.

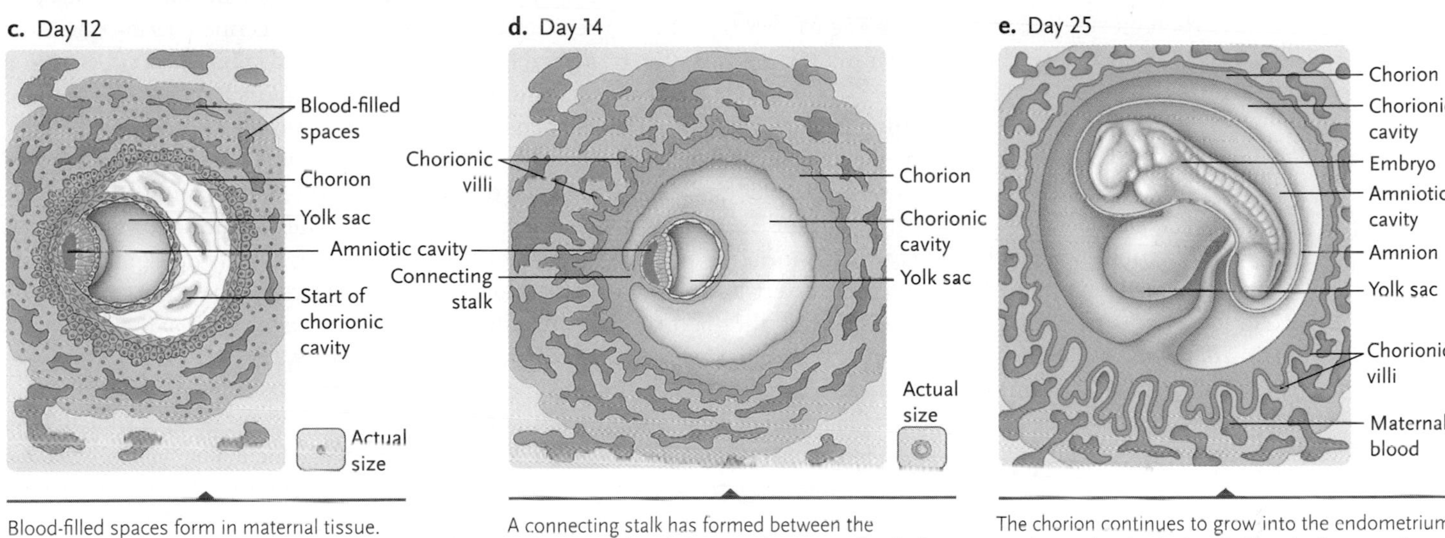

Blood-filled spaces form in maternal tissue. The chorion forms, derived from trophoblast cells, and encloses the chorionic cavity.

A connecting stalk has formed between the embryonic disk and chorion. Chorionic villi, which will be features of a placenta, start to form.

The chorion continues to grow into the endometrium, producing the chorionic villi. The chorion growth stimulates blood vessels of the endometrium to grow into the maternal circulation of the placenta.

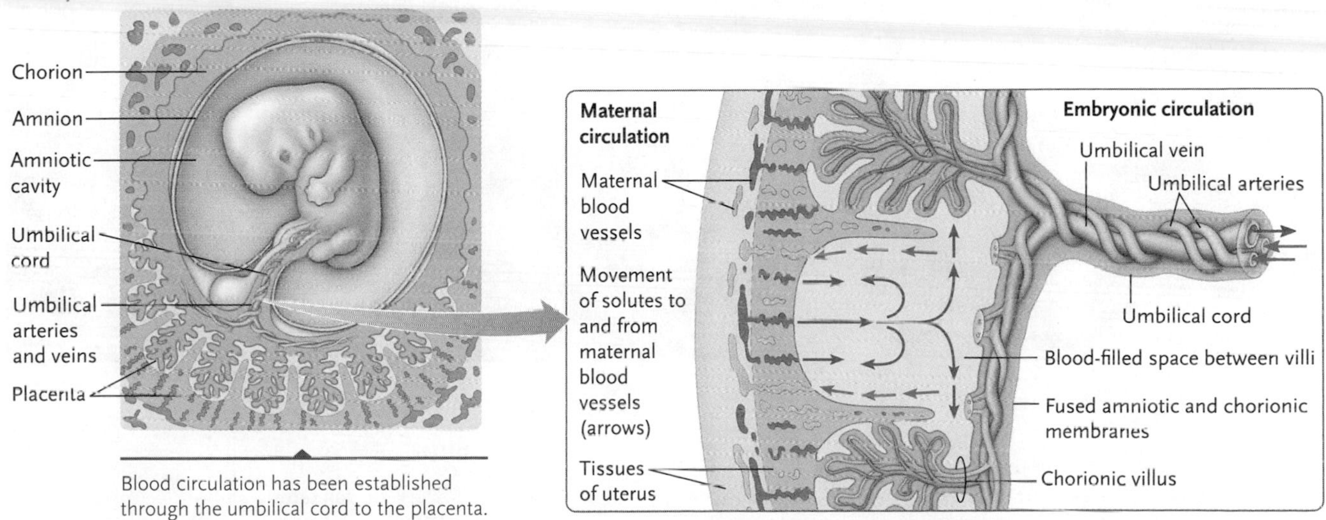

Blood circulation has been established through the umbilical cord to the placenta.

grow into the maternal circulation of the placenta **(Figure 39.20e)**.

Within the placenta of humans, apes, monkeys, and rodents, the maternal circulation opens into spaces where maternal blood directly bathes capillaries coming to the placenta from the embryo **(Figure 39.20f)**. (Other mammals have different types of placentae.) Embryonic circulation remains closed so that the embryonic blood and the maternal blood do not mix directly. This isolation prevents the mother from developing an immune reaction against cells of the embryo, which may be recognized as foreign. Eventually, the placenta and its blood circulation grow to cover about a quarter of the inner surface of the enlarged uterus and reach the size of a dinner plate.

When the amnion forms (see Figure 39.20e), the embryo remains connected to the developing placenta through the **umbilicus**, a cord of tissue. Blood vessels in the umbilical cord conduct blood between the embryo and the placenta (see Figure 39.20f, inset). Within the placenta, nutrients and oxygen pass from the mother's circulation into the circulation of the embryo. Besides nutrients and oxygen, many other substances taken in by the mother, such as alcohol, caffeine, drugs, pesticide residues, and toxins in smog and cigarette smoke, can pass from mother to embryo. Carbon dioxide and nitrogenous wastes pass from the embryo to the mother and are disposed of by the mother's lungs and kidneys.

Cells from the embryonic portion of the placenta or from the amniotic fluid are derived from the embryo. To test for the presence of genetic diseases such as cystic fibrosis or Down syndrome, these cells can be obtained by chorionic villus sampling or by amniocentesis (*centesis* = puncture, referring to the use of a needle, which is pushed through the abdominal wall to obtain fluid from the amniotic cavity). Chorionic villus sampling can be carried out as early as the eighth week of pregnancy, compared with 14 weeks for amniocentesis.

39.5a Birth: The Fetus Leaves the Mother

By the end of its fourth week, a human embryo is 3 to 5 mm long, 250 to 500 times the size of the zygote **(Figure 39.21a)**. It has a tail and gill arches, embryonic features of all vertebrates (see Chapter 27). Gill arches contribute to the formation of the face, neck, mouth, nasal cavities, larynx, and pharynx. After five to six weeks, most of the tail has disappeared, and the embryo begins to be a recognizable human form **(Figure 39.21b)**. At eight weeks, the embryo, now a fetus, is about 2.5 cm long **(Figure 39.21c)**. Its organ systems have formed, and its limbs, with fingers or toes at their ends, have developed.

After about 38 weeks, fetal growth comes to a close, the cervix of the uterus softens, and the fetus typically turns so that its head is downward, pressed against the cervix. At this time, a steep rise in levels of estrogen secreted by the placenta cause uterine cells to express the gene for the receptor of the hormone *oxytocin* (secreted by the pituitary gland). Receptors become inserted into the plasma membranes of uterine cells. Oxytocin binds to its receptors, triggering contractions of smooth muscle cells of the uterine wall, beginning the rhythmic contractions of labour. These contractions mark the beginning of the three steps culminating in birth or **parturition** (*parturire* = to be in labour).

Contractions push the fetus against the cervix and stretch its walls (**Figure 39.22**, step 1). In response, stretch receptors in the walls send nerve signals to the hypothalamus, which responds by stimulating the pituitary to secrete more oxytocin. Oxytocin stimulates

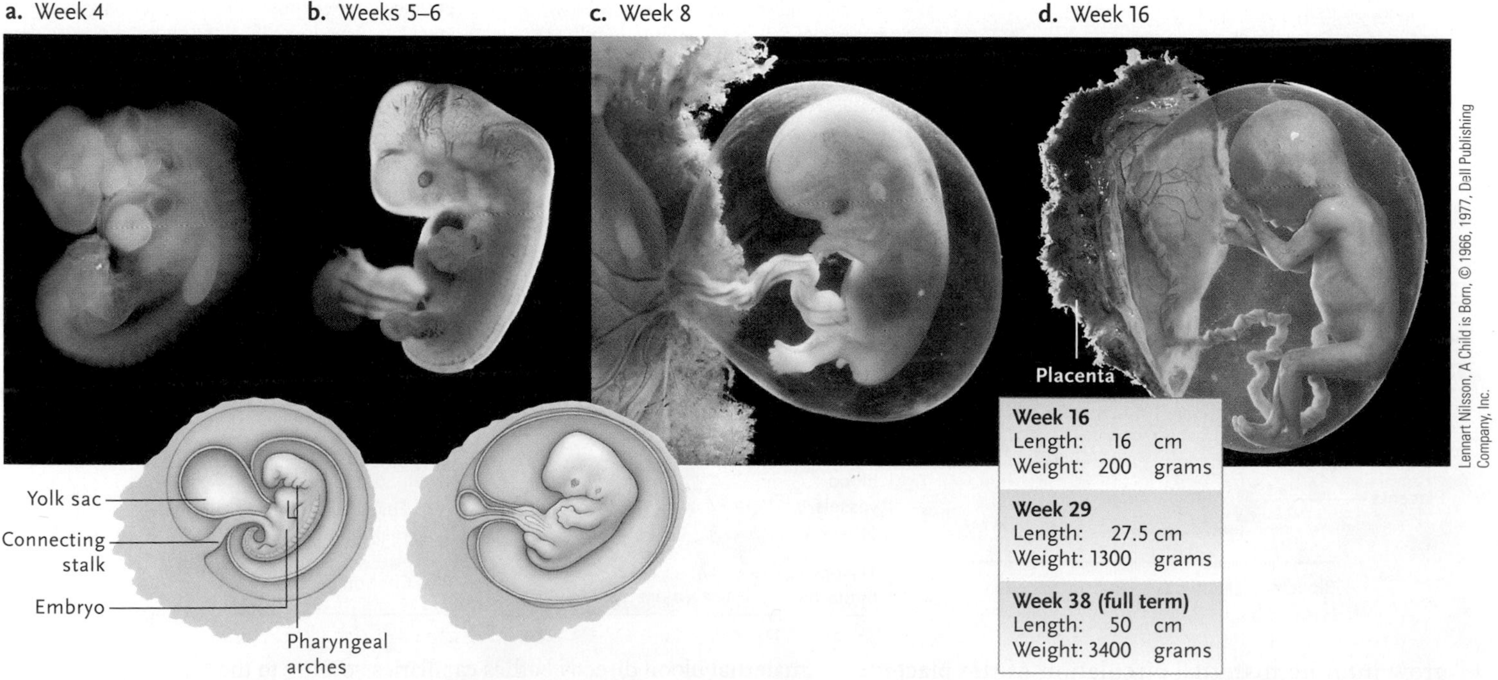

Figure 39.21
The human embryo at various stages of development, beginning at week 4. The chorion has been moved aside to reveal the embryo in the amnion at week 8 and week 16. By week 16, movements begin as nerves make functional connections with the forming muscles.

Figure 39.22
Birth of the fetus. Hormonal events of birth are at the top, and physical events are at the bottom.

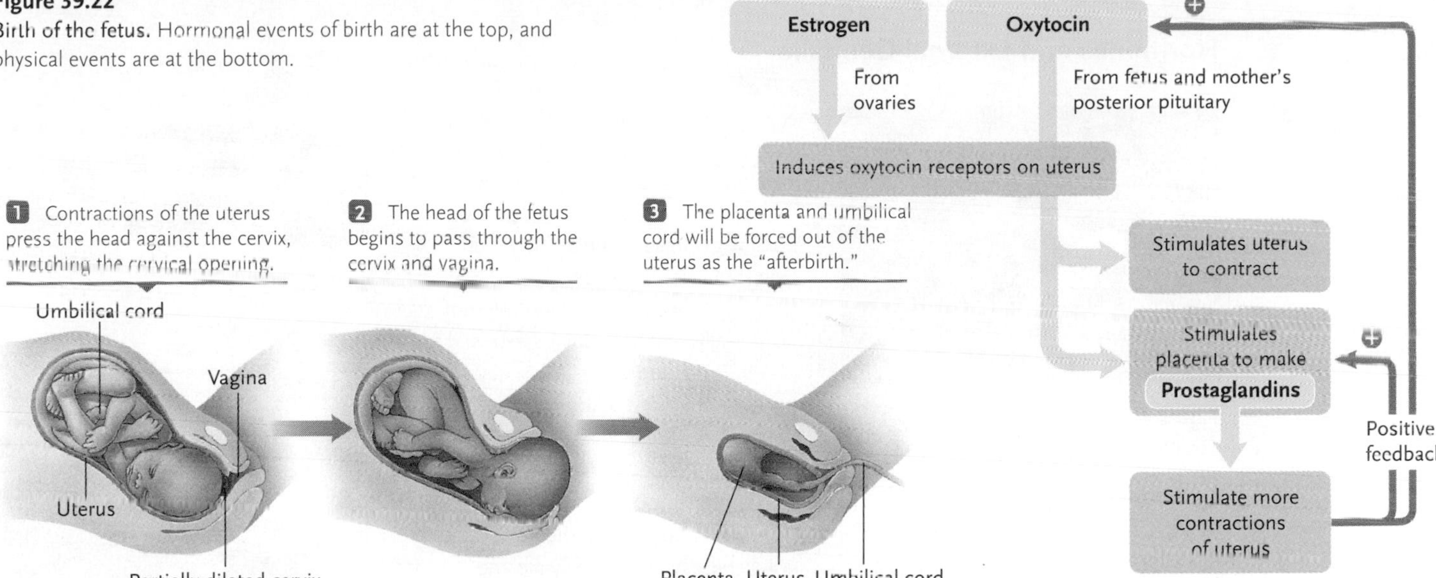

Estrogen
Oxytocin
From ovaries
From fetus and mother's posterior pituitary
Induces oxytocin receptors on uterus
Stimulates uterus to contract
Stimulates placenta to make
Prostaglandins
Stimulate more contractions of uterus
Positive feedback
1 Contractions of the uterus press the head against the cervix, stretching the cervical opening.
2 The head of the fetus begins to pass through the cervix and vagina.
3 The placenta and umbilical cord will be forced out of the uterus as the "afterbirth."
Umbilical cord
Vagina
Uterus
Partially dilated cervix
Placenta
Uterus
Umbilical cord

more forceful contractions of the uterus, pressing the fetus more strongly against the cervix and further stretching its walls. The positive feedback cycle continues, steadily increasing the strength of the uterine contractions.

As the contractions force the head of the fetus through the cervix (step 2), the amniotic membrane bursts, releasing the amniotic fluid. Usually after 12 to 15 hours from the onset of uterine contractions, the head passes entirely through the cervix. Once the head is through, the rest of the body follows quickly and the entire fetus is forced out through the vagina, still connected to the placenta by the umbilical cord (step 3).

After the baby takes its first breath, the umbilical cord is cut and tied off by the birth attendant. Uterine contractions continue expelling the placenta and any remnants of the umbilical cord and embryonic membranes as the afterbirth, usually within 15 to 60 minutes after the infant's birth. The short length of umbilical cord still attached to the infant dries and shrivels within a few days. Eventually, it separates entirely and leaves a scar, the umbilicus or navel, to mark its former site of attachment during embryonic development. Immediately after birth, some mammals (e.g., *Gazella* species) can stand and are soon able to run. The newborns of these precocial species contrast with those of altricial species, which are immobile and helpless for some considerable time after birth. The same terms, precocial and altricial, also apply to other animals.

39.5b Milk: Food for the Young

Before birth, estrogen and progesterone secreted by the placenta stimulate the growth of the mammary glands in the mother's breasts. But high levels of these hormones prevent mammary glands from responding to *prolactin*, the hormone secreted by the pituitary that stimulates the glands to produce milk. After birth and the release of the placenta, levels of estrogen and progesterone in the mother's bloodstream fall steeply, and the breasts begin to produce milk (stimulated by prolactin) and secrete it (stimulated by oxytocin).

Continued milk secretion depends on whether the infant suckles. Stimulation of the nipples sends nerve impulses to the hypothalamus, which responds by signalling the pituitary to release a burst of prolactin and oxytocin. Hormonal stimulation of milk production and secretion continues as long as the infant is breast-fed.

39.5c Gonadal Development: The Gender of the Fetus

Gonads and their ducts begin to develop in the fetus during week 4 of gestation. Until week 7, male and female embryos have the same set of internal structures derived from mesoderm, including a pair of gonads **(Figure 39.23a, p. 953)**. Each gonad is associated with two primitive ducts, the **Wolffian duct** and the **Müllerian duct**, that lead to a cloaca. These internal structures are *bipotential* because they can develop into either male or female sexual organs.

The presence or absence of a Y chromosome determines whether the internal structures develop into male or female sexual organs. In a fetus with XY combination of sex chromosomes, *SRY* (the sex-determining region of the Y), a single gene on the Y chromosome, becomes active in week 7. The protein encoded by *SRY* induces a molecular switch that causes primitive gonads to develop into testes. Fetal testes secrete two hormones, testosterone and the *anti-Müllerian hormone* (*AMH*). Testosterone stimulates development of Wolffian ducts into a male reproductive tract, including the epididymis, vas deferens, and seminal vesicles **(Figure 39.23b)**.

Hormones and External Genitalia

M.B. Fenton

Figure 1
Crocuta crocuta, a spotted hyena.

Many Africans believe that spotted hyenas (*Crocuta crocuta,* **Figure 1**) are hermaphroditic because the females have external genitalia resembling those of the males. Specifically, the clitoris is peniform, and there is a pseudoscrotum **(Figure 2).** The combined effect means that anyone looking at a spotted hyena easily confuses males and females. Confusion turns to puzzlement when the apparent male is obviously lactating, nursing young. Spotted hyenas are not hermaphroditic. Males mate with females, and fertilized eggs develop into fetuses that are born as in other placental mammals.

How do females come to look like males? In mammals, the neutral condition for genitalia is the arrangement typical of females. The derived condition is what we associate with males. Genetically, female embryos exposed to testosterone during gestation develop malelike genitalia. Blood samples obtained from pregnant female spotted hyenas had relatively high levels of circulating testosterone, 5α-dihydrotestosterone, and androstenedione, albeit not as high as in males. Male and female fetuses experience the same levels of maternal androgens; therefore, females have malelike genitalia.

What selective advantage would female spotted hyenas gain from looking like males? Spotted hyenas are social animals that live in clans. As adults, females are larger and more aggressive than males. During greeting ceremonies, when members of a clan meet after a separation, individuals sniff one another's genitals. During these encounters, males erect their penises and females their peniform clitorises. Females appear to dominate spotted hyena societies even though their levels of testosterone and 5α-dihydrotestosterone are lower than in adult males. This does not support the proposal that females are more aggressive because of levels of circulating male hormones. Spotted hyena cubs are precocial and aggressive to the point of siblicide, perhaps reflecting hormone levels at birth. Masculinization of female genitalia could be a side effect of selection for aggressive neonates.

Masculinization of female genitalia occurs in some other members of the order Carnivora, for example, the fossa (*Cryptoprocta ferox*) from Madagascar **(Figure 3).** Transient masculinization of young female (but not adult female) fossas could allow them to avoid sexual harassment by adult males and to escape from aggression by adult females.

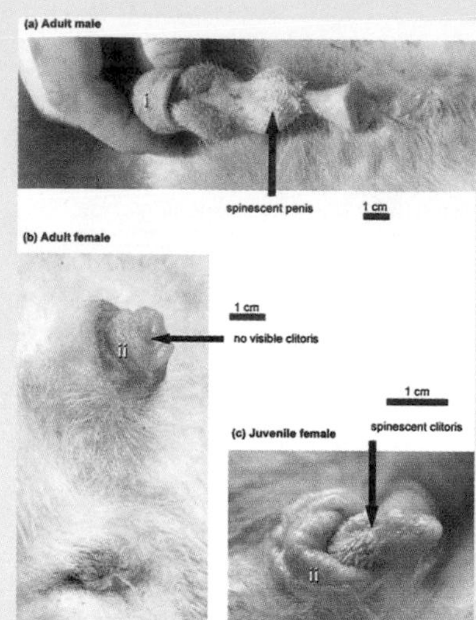

Figure 3
In their external genitalia, specifically their clitorises, (c) subadult female fossas (*Cryptoprocta ferox*) resemble (a) males, whereas (b) adult females do not.

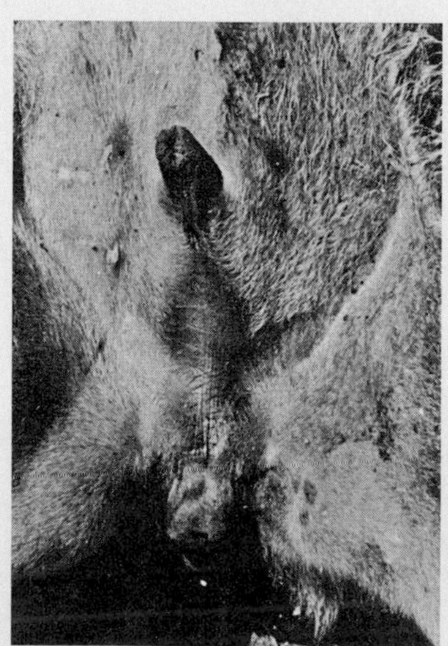

Figure 2
In spotted hyenas (*C. crocuta*), the external genitalia of a nulliparous female (left) resembles that of a male (right). Note the peniform clitoris and pseudoscrotum on the female.

AMH causes the Müllerian ducts to degenerate and disappear. Testosterone also stimulates development of male genitalia.

In a fetus with XX chromosomes, no *SRY* protein is produced. The primitive gonads, under the influence of estrogens and progesterone secreted by the placenta, develop into ovaries. Müllerian ducts develop into oviducts, the uterus, and part of the vagina, and the Wolffian ducts degenerate and disappear **(Figure 39.23c).** Female sex hormones also stimulate the development

Figure 39.23 Development of the internal sexual organs of males and females from common bipotential origins.

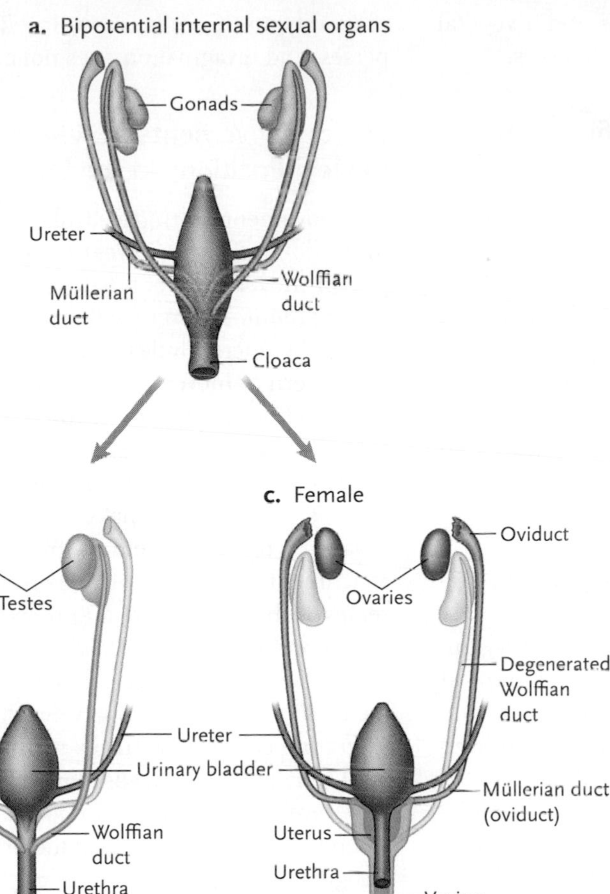

of the external female genitalia (see *Hormones and External Genitalia*).

39.5d Further Development

Once fetal development is over, the newborn animal follows a prescribed course of further growth and development leading to the mature adult. In humans, internal and external sexual organs mature and secondary sexual characteristics appear at puberty (see Figure 20.18). Similar changes occur in most mammals.

There are many examples among different animal groups of developmental changes that take place after hatching or birth. In some cases, offspring hatch in forms distinctly different in structure from the adult. Examples among invertebrates include insects such as *Drosophila* and butterflies, in which eggs hatch to produce larvae that undergo metamorphosis into adults. Some frogs hatch as tadpoles, which undergo metamorphosis to produce adults.

Study Break

1. Define the terms blastocyst, chorionic villi, and parturition.
2. What is a placenta? Name some animals with placentae.
3. What is *SRY*? What role does it play?

39.6 Cellular Basis of Development

Orientation and *rate* of mitotic cell division have special significance in the development of the shape, size, and location of organ systems of the embryo. Regulation of the orientation and rate occurs at all stages of development.

"Orientation of cell division" refers to the angles at which daughter cells are added to older cells as development proceeds. Orientation is determined by the location of the furrow separating the cytoplasm after mitotic division of the nucleus (see Chapter 9). The furrow forms in alignment with the spindle midpoint so that when the spindle is centrally positioned in the cell, the furrow leads to symmetrical division of the cell. When the spindle is displaced to one end of the cell, the furrow leads to asymmetrical division into a smaller cell and a larger cell. Little is known about how spindle positioning is regulated.

The rate of cell division primarily reflects the time spent in the G_1 period of interphase (see Chapter 9). Once DNA replication begins, the rest of the cell cycle takes the same time in all cells of a species. As an embryo develops and cells differentiate, the time spent in interphase increases and varies in different cell types. Therefore, different cell types proliferate at various rates as they differentiate, giving rise to tissues and organs with different cell numbers. When fully differentiated, some cells remain fixed in interphase and stop replicating DNA or dividing. Nerve cells in the mammalian brain and spinal cord stop dividing once the nervous system is fully formed. Ultimately, the rate of cell division is under genetic control.

Frog egg cleavage provides examples of how both changes in orientation and rate of mitotic division affect development. The first two cleavages start at the animal pole and extend to the vegetal pole, producing four equal blastomeres (see Figure 39.8). The third cleavage occurs equatorially, but because of yolk in the vegetal region of the embryo, this cleavage furrow forms toward the animal pole. This cleavage produces an eight-cell embryo with four small blastomeres near the animal pole and four large blastomeres in the vegetal region. Blastomeres in the animal region of the embryo proceed to divide rapidly, whereas blastomeres in the vegetal region divide more slowly because division is inhibited by yolk. The resulting morula consists of an animal region with many small cells and a vegetal region with relatively few but larger blastomeres.

39.6a Microtubules and Microfilaments: Movements of Cells

Embryonic cells undergo changes in shape that generate movements, such as the infolding of surface layers to produce endoderm or mesoderm. Entire cells also move during embryonic growth, both singly and in groups. Movements are also produced by changes in rates of growth or by breakdowns of microtubules and microfilaments. Changes in both cell shape and cell movement play important roles in cleavage, gastrulation, and organogenesis.

39.6b Change in Cell Shape: Adjusting to New Roles

Changes in cell shape typically result from reorganization of the cytoskeleton. During development of the neural plate in frogs, the ectoderm flattens and thickens and cells in the ectoderm layer change from cubelike to columnar in shape **(Figure 39.24a)**.

Sinking of the neural plate downward along its midline reflects changes in cell shape from columnar to wedgelike **(Figure 39.24b)**. As one end of each cell narrows, the entire cell layer invaginates (is forced inward). How does this occur? Each wedge-shaped cell contains a group of microfilaments arranged in a circle at the top. Microfilaments slide over each other, tightening the ring like a drawstring and narrowing the top of the cell. If an experimenter adds cytochalasin, a chemical that interferes with microfilament assembly, to the cells, the microfilament circle disperses, and invagination does not occur.

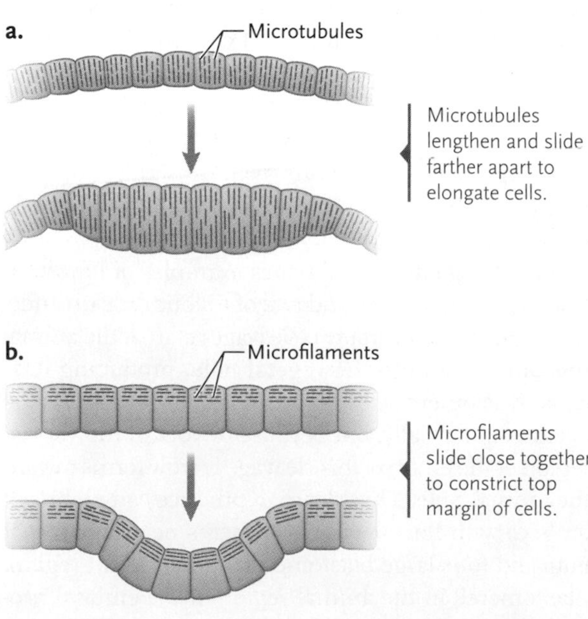

a.
Microtubules
Microtubules lengthen and slide farther apart to elongate cells.
b.
Microfilaments
Microfilaments slide close together to constrict top margin of cells.

Figure 39.24
The roles of **(a)** microtubules and **(b)** microfilaments in the changes in cell shape that produce developmental movements.

39.6c Movements of Whole Cells to New Positions in the Embryo

Cell movements during gastrulation and long-distance migrations of neural crest cells are striking examples of movements of whole cells during embryonic development. These movements involve coordinated activity by microtubules and microfilaments. The typical pattern of movement is a repeating cycle of extension, anchoring, and contracting. First, a cell attaches to the substrate (**Figure 39.25,** step 1), and then it moves forward by elongating from the point of attachment (step 2). The cell then makes a new attachment at the advancing tip (step 3) and contracts until the rearmost attachment breaks (step 4). The front attachment now serves as the base for another movement.

How do the cells know where to go? Typically, cells migrate over the surfaces of stationary cells in one of the embryo's layers. In many developmental systems, migrating cells follow tracks formed by molecules of the ECM, secreted by cells along the route over which they travel. Fibronectin, an important track molecule, is a fibrous, elongated protein of the ECM. Migrating cells recognize and adhere to fibronectin, and in response, internal changes in cells trigger their movement in a direction based on alignment of fibronectin molecules.

Some migrating cells follow concentration gradients rather than molecular tracks. Gradients are created by diffusion of molecules (often proteins) released by cells in one part of an embryo. Cells with receptors for the diffusing molecule follow the gradient toward or away from the source.

Selective cell adhesion—the ability of an embryonic cell to make and break specific connections to other cells—is closely related to cell movement. As development proceeds, many cells break initial adhesions, move, and form new adhesions in different locations. Final cell adhesions hold the embryo in its correct shape and form. Junctions of various kinds, including tight, anchoring, and gap junctions, reinforce final adhesions. Selective cell adhesions were first demonstrated in a classic experiment by Johannes Holtfreter and P.L. Townes (see *Making Cell Connections*).

Many cell surface proteins are responsible for selective cell adhesions, including **cell adhesion molecules** (CAMs) and **cadherins** (*calcium-dependent adhesion molecules*). Cadherins require calcium ions to set up adhesions—hence their name. As cells develop, different types of CAMs or cadherins appear or disappear from their surfaces as they make and break cell adhesions. The changes reflect alterations in gene activity, often in response to molecular signals arriving from other cells. During early development in the chick, cells of the ectoderm are held together by E- and N-cadherins. As the neural plate appears, cells destined to form the neural

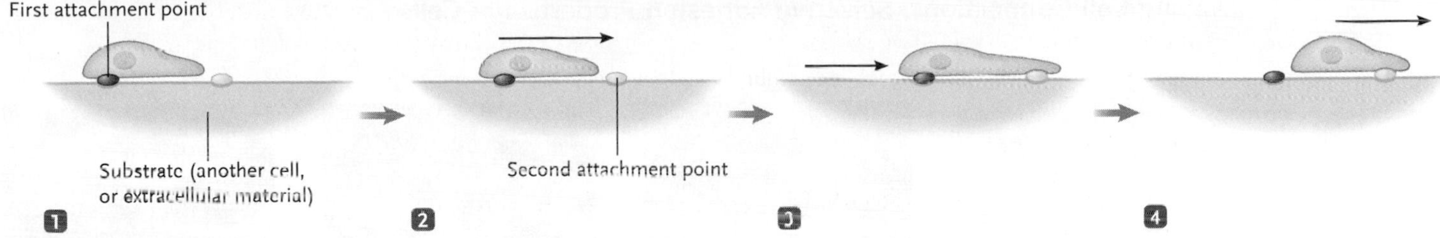

Figure 39.25
The cycle of attachment, stretching, and contraction by which a cell moves over other cells or extracellular materials in embryos.

tube lose their cadherins, and N-CAMs appear on their surfaces. As these surface molecules appear, the neural tube cells break loose from the ectoderm and adhere to each other to form the neural tube. If N-cadherin is added experimentally to ectoderm cells, the neural tube stays anchored and never separates.

39.6d Induction: Interactions between Cells

Induction is the process in which a group of inducing cells causes or influences a nearby group of responding cells to follow a particular developmental pathway. Induction is the major process responsible for *determination*, in which the developmental fate of a cell is set. Induction occurs through the combination of signal molecules with surface receptors on the responding cells. The signal molecules may be located on the surface of the inducing cells or released by inducing cells. The surface receptors are activated by binding the signal molecules. In the activated form, signal molecules trigger internal response pathways that produce the developmental changes (see Chapter 15). Often responses include changes in gene activity.

In the 1920s, Hans Spemann and Hilde Mangold conducted the first experiments identifying induction in embryos. They found that if the dorsal lip of a newt embryo was removed and grafted into a different position of another embryo, cells moving inward from the dorsal lip induced a neural plate, a neural tube, and eventually an entire embryo at the new location (see *Spemann and Mangold's Experiment Demonstrating Induction in Embryos*). They proposed that the dorsal lip is an *organizer*, acting on other cells to alter the course of development. This action is now known as *induction*. Spemann received the Nobel Prize in 1935 for his research. (Mangold had died in a tragic accident in 1924 when her kitchen gasoline heater exploded, the year their research paper was published. She would likely have also received the Nobel Prize, but it is never awarded posthumously.)

Spemann and Mangold's findings touched off a search for inducing molecules that must pass from inducing cells to responding cells. In 1992, researchers constructed a DNA library from *Xenopus* gastrulas. By isolating and cloning cellular DNA in gene sized pieces, they made mRNA transcripts of cloned genes and injected them into early *Xenopus* embryos in which the inducing ability of mesoderm had been destroyed by exposure to ultraviolet light. Some injected mRNAs, translated into proteins in the embryos, were able to induce formation of a neural plate and tube, leading to a normal embryo. More than 10 proteins that act as inducing molecules have been identified in the *Xenopus* system.

Differentiation produces specialized cells without the loss of genes. By this process, cells that have committed to a particular developmental fate by the determination process (see Section 39.2) develop into specialized cell types with distinct structures and functions. As part of differentiation, cells concentrate on the production of molecules characteristic of the specific types. For example, 80 to 90% of the total protein synthesized by lens cells is crystallin.

Research into differentiation confirmed that as cells specialize, they retain all of the genes of the original egg cell. Except in rare instances, differentiation does not occur through selective gene loss. Robert Briggs and Thomas King, and later John B. Gurdon, used ultraviolet light to destroy the nucleus of a fertilized frog egg. A micropipette was then used to transfer a nucleus from a fully differentiated tissue, intestinal epithelium, to the enucleated egg. Some eggs receiving transplanted nuclei subsequently developed into normal tadpoles and adult frogs. This outcome is possible only if the differentiated intestinal cells retained the full complement of genes. This conclusion was extended to mammals in 1997 when Ian Wilmut and his colleagues successfully cloned a sheep (named Dolly) starting with an adult cell nucleus.

From the early days of studying development, embryologists focused on describing not only how embryos form and develop but also exactly how adult tissues and organs are produced from embryonic cells. An important goal of embryology was to trace cell lineages from embryo to adult. For most organisms, it is not possible to trace lineages at the individual cell level, primarily because of the complexity of the developmental process and the opacity of embryos. Experimenters developed *fate mapping*, mapping adult or larval structures onto the region of the embryo from which each structure developed. Fate mapping is done by following the development of living embryos under the microscope, either using species in which the embryo is transparent or by marking cells so they can be followed. Cells may be marked with vital dyes

Making Cell Connections: Selective Adhesion Properties of Cells

1. Holtfreter and Townes separated ectoderm, mesoderm, and endoderm tissue from amphibian embryos soon after the neural tube had formed. They used embryos from amphibian species that had cells of different colours and sizes, so they could follow under the microscope where each cell type ended up. (The colours shown here are for illustrative purposes only.)

2. The researchers placed the tissues individually in alkaline solutions, which caused the tissues to break down into single cells.

3. Holtfreter and Townes then combined suspensions of single cells in various ways. Shown here are ectoderm + mesoderm and ectoderm + mesoderm + endoderm. When the pH was returned to neutrality, the cells formed aggregates. Through a microscope, the researchers followed what happened to the aggregates on agar-filled petri dishes.

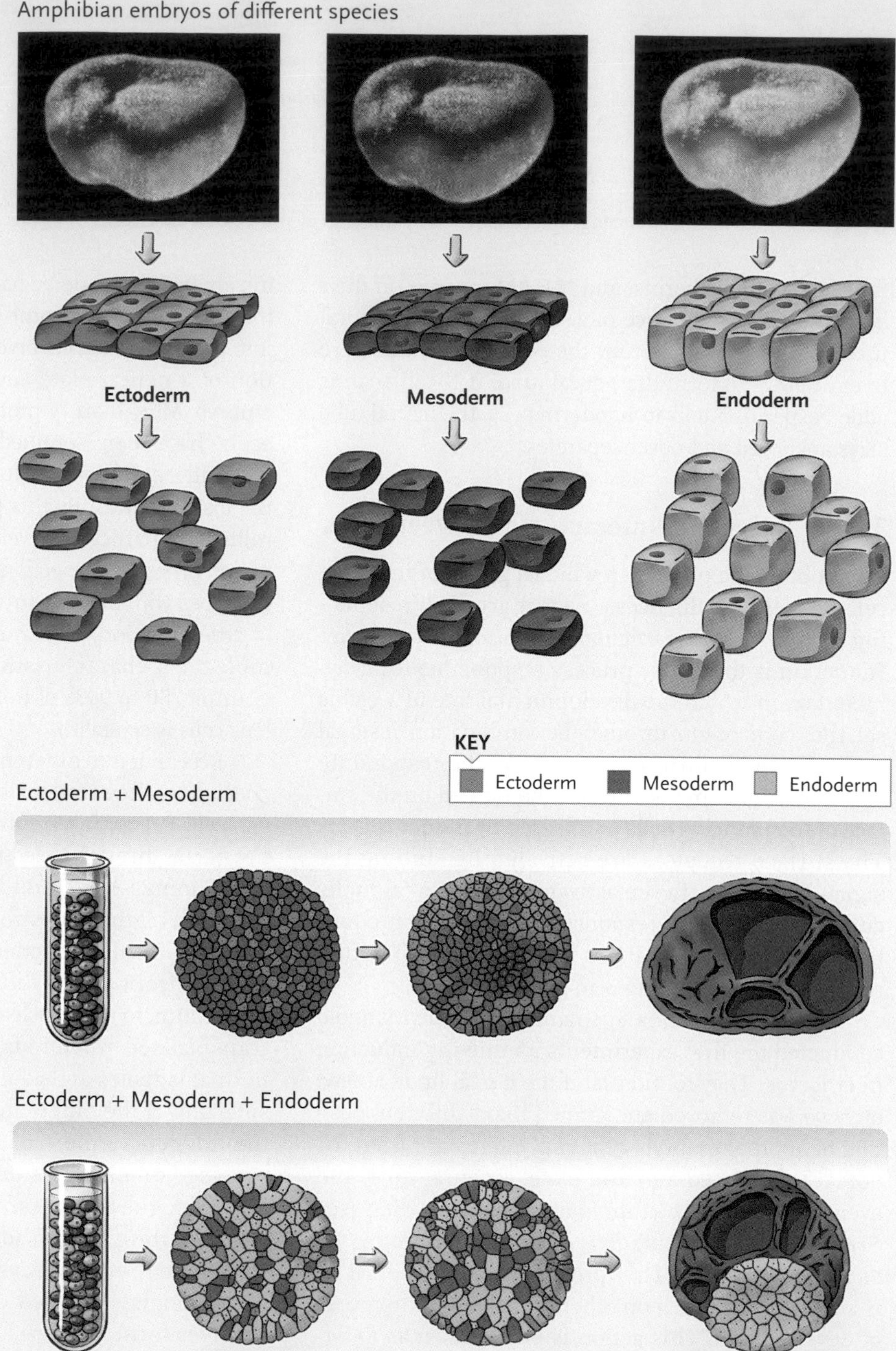

RESULTS: In time, the reaggregated cells sorted themselves with respect to cell type; that is, instead of the cell types remaining mixed, each cell type became separated spatially. That is, in the ectoderm + mesoderm mixture, the ectoderm moved to the periphery of the aggregate, surrounding mesoderm cells in the centre. In no case did the two cell types remain randomly mixed. The ectoderm + mesoderm + endoderm aggregate showed further that cell sorting in the aggregates generated cell positions reflecting the positions of the cell types in the embryo. That is, the endoderm cells separated from the ectoderm and mesoderm cells and became surrounded by them. In the end, the ectoderm cells were located on the periphery, the endoderm cells were internal, and the mesoderm cells were between the other two cell types.

CONCLUSION: Holtfreter interpreted the results to mean that cells have selective affinity for each other; that is, cells have selective adhesion properties. Specifically, he proposed that ectoderm cells have positive affinity for mesoderm cells but negative affinity for endoderm cells, whereas mesoderm cells have positive affinity for both ectoderm cells and endoderm cells. In modern terms, these properties result from cell surface molecules that give cells specific adhesion properties.

(that do not kill cells), fluorescent dyes, or radioactive labels. Fate maps have been produced for *Xenopus*, the chick, and *Drosophila*.

In most cases, a fate map is not detailed enough to show how particular cells in the embryo gave rise to cells of the adult. The exception is the fate map of the

Spemann and Mangold's Experiment Demonstrating Induction in Embryos

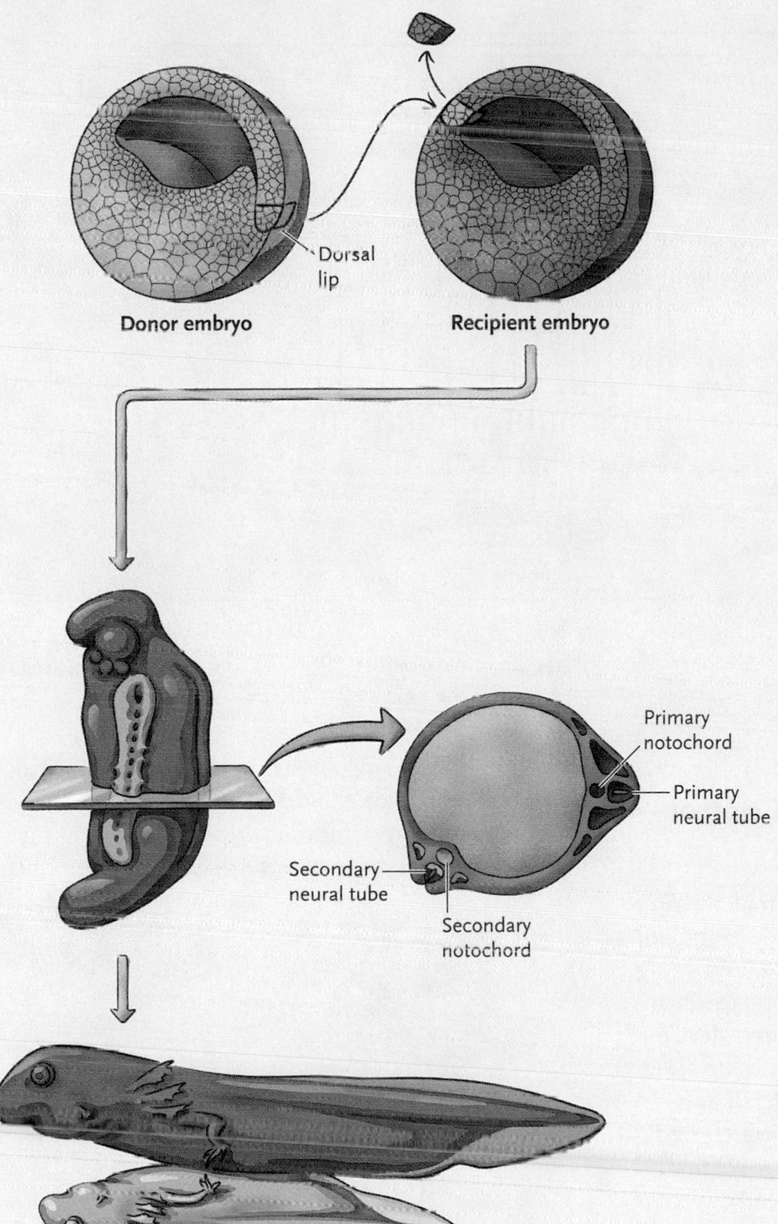

QUESTION: Does induction occur in embryonic development?

EXPERIMENT: Hans Spemann and Hilde Mangold performed transplantation experiments with newt embryos, the results of which demonstrated that specific induction of development occurs in the embryos. The researchers removed the dorsal lip of the blastopore from one newt embryo and grafted it onto a different position—the ventral side—of another embryo. The two embryos were from different newt species that differed in pigmentation, allowing them to follow the fate of the tissue easily. The embryo with the transplant was allowed to develop.

CONCLUSION: The grafted dorsal lip of the blastopore induced a second gastrulation and subsequent development in the ventral region of the recipient embryo. The result demonstrated the ability of particular cells to induce the development of other cells.

nematode *Caenorhabditis elegans*, an organism with a fixed, reproducible developmental pattern. *C. elegans* has a transparent body, and scientists have mapped the fate (traced the **cell lineage**) of every cell as the zygote divides and the resulting embryo differentiates into a 959-cell adult hermaphrodite or 1031-cell adult male **(Figure 39.26, p. 958).** All somatic cells of the adult can be traced from five somatic *founder cells* produced during early development. Knowing the cell lineages of *C. elegans* has been a valuable tool for research into the genetic and molecular control of development because mutants affecting development can be easily visualized.

Study Break

1. What role do microtubules and microfilaments play in development?
2. What happens during induction? Where does it occur?
3. How has work with *Caenorhabditis elegans* advanced our knowledge of developmental biology? What about *Xenopus*?

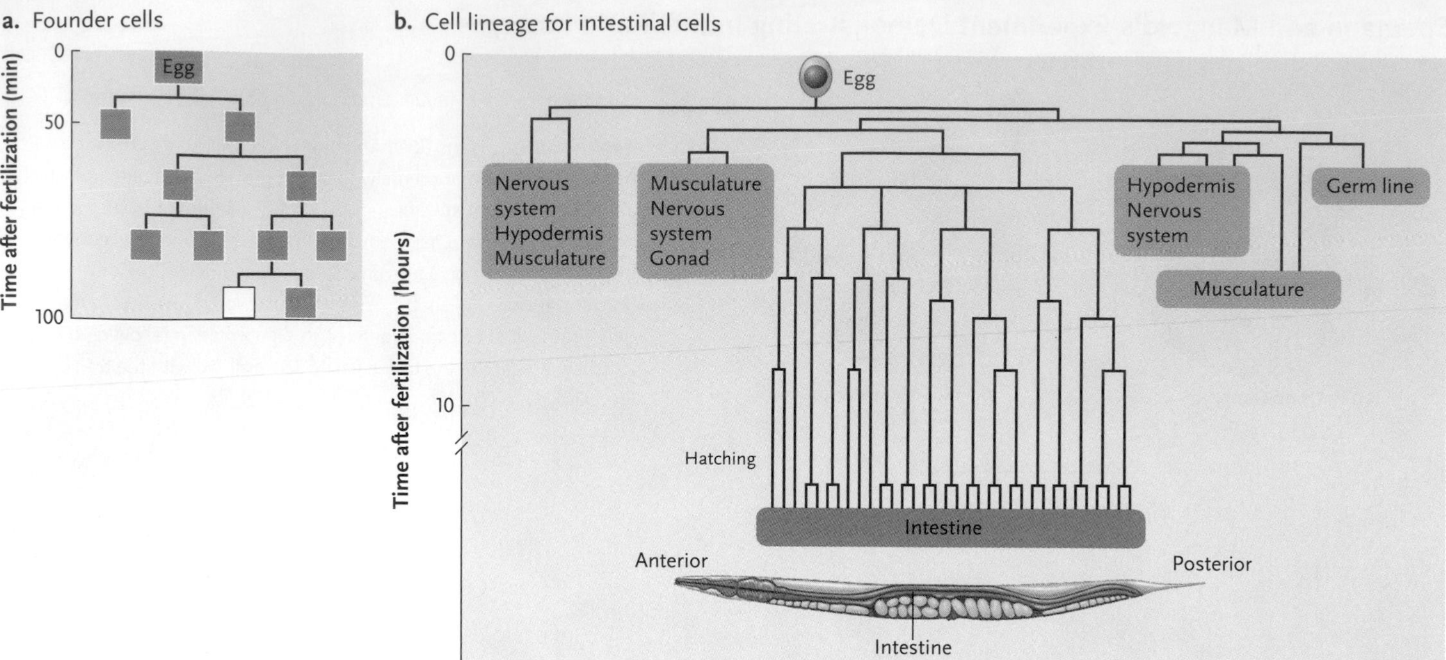

Figure 39.26
Cell lineages of *C. elegans.* **(a)** The founder cells (blue) produced in early cell divisions from which all adult somatic cells are produced. The white cell gives rise to germ-line cells. (b) The cell lineage for cells that form the intestine. The detailed lineages for the other parts of the adult are not shown.

39.7 Genetic and Molecular Control of Development

Developmental biologists are interested in identifying and characterizing the genes involved in development and defining how gene products regulate and bring about elaborate events. One productive research approach has been to isolate mutants that affect developmental processes and then identify the genes involved, clone these genes, and analyze them in detail to build models for molecular functions of gene products in development. Model organisms used for these studies include the fruit fly (*Drosophila melanogaster*) and *C. elegans* among invertebrates, and the zebrafish (*Danio rerio*) and the house mouse (*Mus musculus*) among vertebrates.

39.7a Genetic Control of Development

Gene expression regulates changes that occur through determination and differentiation. One well-studied example of the genetic control of these processes is the production of skeletal muscle cells from somites in mammals **(Figure 39.27).** Somites are blocks of mesoderm cells that form along both sides of the notochord (see Figure 39.17). Under genetic control, some cells of each somite differentiate into skeletal muscle cells. First, paracrine signalling from nearby cells induces somite cells to express the master regulatory gene, *myoD*. The product of *myoD* is the transcription factor MyoD. By turning on specific muscle-determining genes, the action of MyoD brings about determination of those cells, converting them to undifferentiated muscle cells, called **myoblasts.** Among genes that MyoD regulates are *myogenin* and *MEF* genes. Both are regulatory genes, expressing transcription factors in myoblasts that turn on yet another set of genes. The products

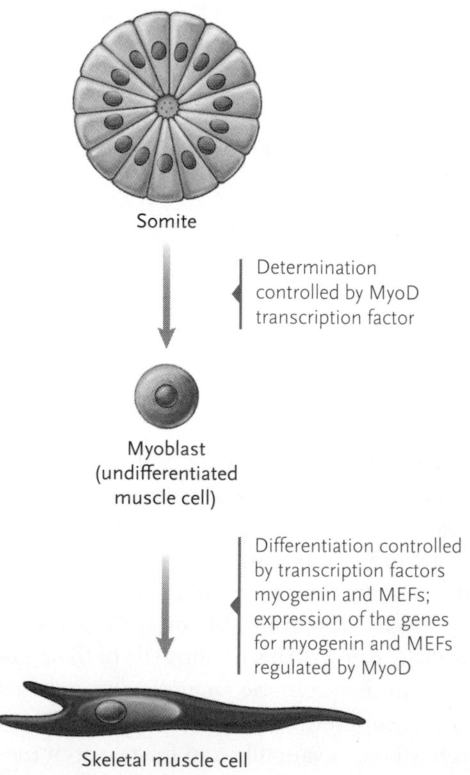

Figure 39.27
The genetic control of determination and differentiation involved in mammalian skeletal muscle cell formation.

of those genes, including myosin (a major protein involved in muscle contraction), promote differentiation of myoblasts into specific types of muscle cells, such as skeletal muscle cells or cardiac muscle cells.

Molecular mechanisms involved in determination and differentiation usually depend on regulatory genes that encode regulatory proteins that control the expression of other genes. Regulatory genes act as master regulators, and in most cases, the expression of the regulatory genes is controlled by induction.

39.7b Gene Control of Pattern Formation: Developing a Body

As part of the signals guiding differentiation, cells receive positional information that tells them where they are in the embryo. Positional information is vital to **pattern formation**, the arrangement of organs and body structures in their proper three-dimensional relationships. Positional information is laid down primarily as concentration gradients of regulatory molecules produced by genetic control. In most cases, gradients of several different regulatory molecules interact to tell a cell, or a cell nucleus, where it is in the embryo. Genetic control of pattern formation is well documented in *Drosophila melanogaster*. Developmental principles discovered in *D. melanogaster* also apply to many other animal species, including humans.

39.7c Embryogenesis in *Drosophila*: Fruit Fly Model

Production of an adult fruit fly from a fertilized egg occurs in a sequence of genetically controlled development events. Following fertilization, division of the nucleus begins by mitosis. This produces a multinucleate blastoderm because the cytoplasm does not divide in the early embryo (cytokinesis does not occur) **(Figure 39.28).** At the tenth nuclear division, the nuclei migrate to the periphery of the embryo, where, three divisions later, the 6000 or so nuclei are organized into separate cells. At this stage, the embryo is a *cellular blastoderm*, corresponding to the late blastula stage in the animals discussed above. Ten hours after fertilization, the cellular blastoderm develops into a segmented embryo (an embryo with distinct segments). About 24 hours after fertilization, the egg hatches into a larva that will undergo three moults before becoming a pupa. The adult fly emerges after metamorphosis 10 to 12 days after fertilization. The colours in Figure 39.28 illustrate how segments of the embryo can be mapped to the segments of the adult fly.

The study of developmental mutants has provided important information about *Drosophila* development. Three researchers performed key, pioneering research with developmental mutants: Edward B. Lewis, Christiane Nüsslein-Volhard, and Eric Wieschaus. The three shared a Nobel Prize in 1995 "for their discoveries about the genetic control of early embryonic development."

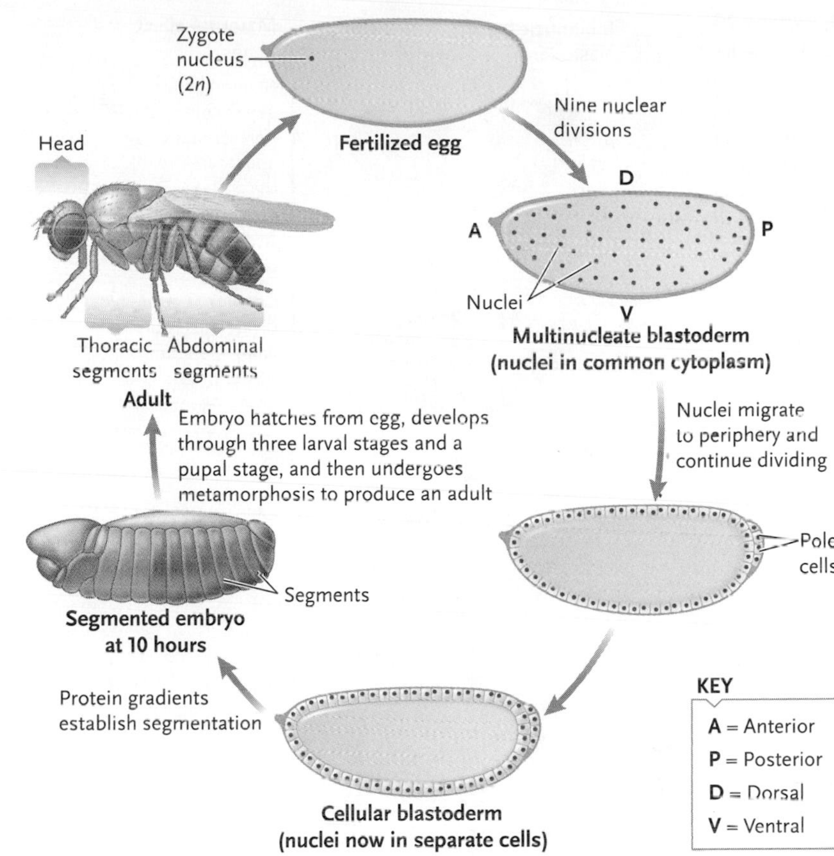

Figure 39.28
Embryogenesis in *Drosophila* and the relationship between segments of the embryo and segments of the adult.

Nüsslein-Volhard and Wieschaus studied early embryogenesis. They searched for *every* gene required for early pattern formation in the embryo by looking for recessive, *embryonic lethal* mutations. When homozygous, these mutations result in embryo death during development. By determining the stage at which the embryo died and how development was disrupted, they gained insights into the role of the particular genes in embryogenesis.

Lewis studied mutants that changed the fates of cells in particular embryonic regions, producing structures in the adult that normally were produced by other regions. His work was the foundation of research identifying master regulatory genes that control the development of body regions in a wide range of organisms.

39.7d Maternal-Effect Genes and Segmentation Genes: Segmenting the Body

A number of genes control the establishment of the embryo's body plan. These genes regulate the expression of other genes. Two classes, *maternal-effect genes* and *segmentation genes*, work sequentially **(Figure 39.29, p. 960).** Many **maternal-effect genes** are expressed by the mother during oogenesis. These genes control egg polarity and thus embryo polarity. Some of these genes

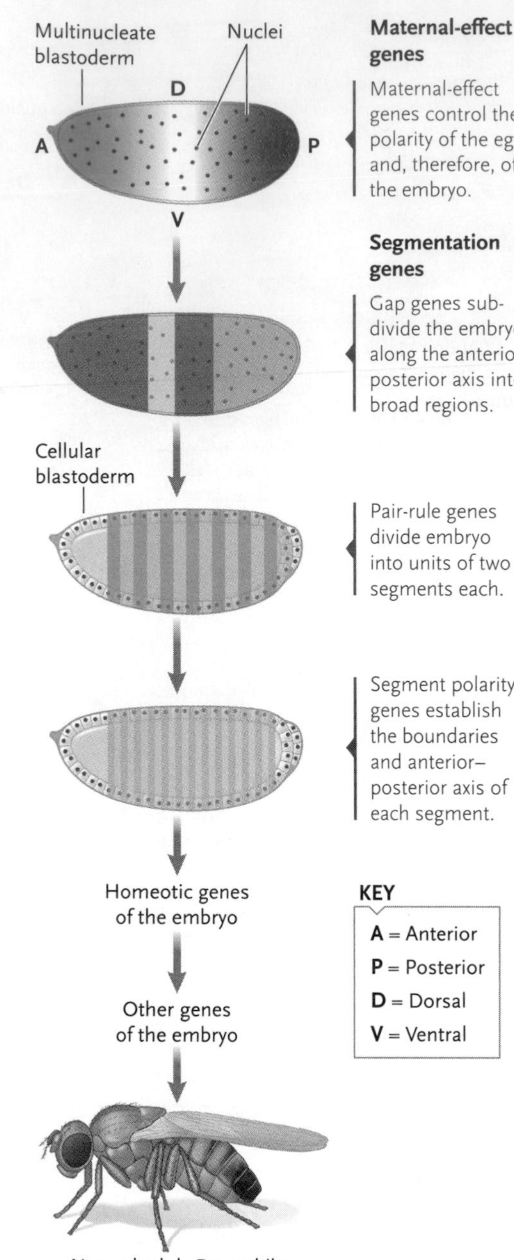

Figure 39.29
Maternal-effect genes and segmentation genes and their role in *Drosophila* embryogenesis.

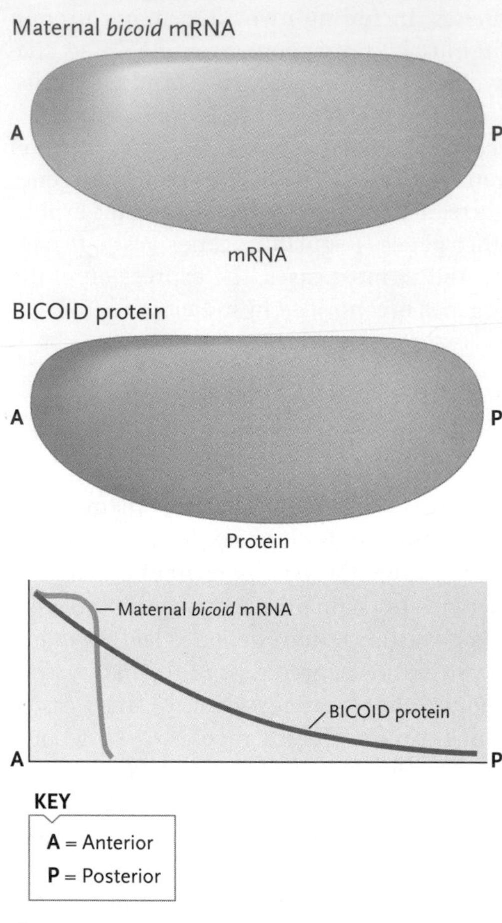

Figure 39.30
Gradients of *bicoid* mRNA and BICOID protein in the *Drosophila* egg.

control formation of embryonic anterior structures, whereas others control formation of posterior structures. Still others control formation of the terminal end.

The *bicoid* gene is the key maternal-effect gene responsible for development of the head and thorax. This gene is transcribed in the mother during oogenesis, and the resulting mRNAs are deposited in the egg, localizing near the anterior pole **(Figure 39.30).** After fertilization, translation of mRNAs produces BICOID protein, which diffuses through the zygote to form a gradient with highest concentration at the anterior end and fading to none at the posterior end. BICOID is a transcription factor that activates some genes and represses others along the anterior–posterior axis of the embryo. Embryos with mutations in the *bicoid* gene lack thoracic structures but have posterior structures at each end. In normal embryos, the *bicoid* gene is a master regulator gene controlling the expression of genes for the development of anterior structures (head and thorax).

The activities of products of other maternal-effect genes in gradients in the embryo are also involved in axis formation. The *nanos* gene is the key maternal-effect gene for the posterior structures. When the *nanos* gene is mutated, embryos lack abdominal segments.

Once the axis of the embryo is set, expression of at least 24 **segmentation genes** progressively subdivides the embryo into regions, determining the segments of the embryo and the adult (see Figure 39.29). Gradients of BICOID and other proteins encoded by maternal-effect genes regulate expression of the embryo's segmentation genes differentially. So each segmentation gene is expressed at a particular time and in a particular location during embryogenesis.

Three sets of segmentation genes are regulated in a cascade of gene activations. Gap genes such as *hunchback* and *tailless* are the first to be expressed. These genes are activated based on their positions in the maternally directed anterior–posterior axis of the zygote by reacting to the concentrations of BICOID and other proteins. Products of gap genes control subdivision of the embryo into several broad regions along the anterior–posterior axis. Mutations in gap genes

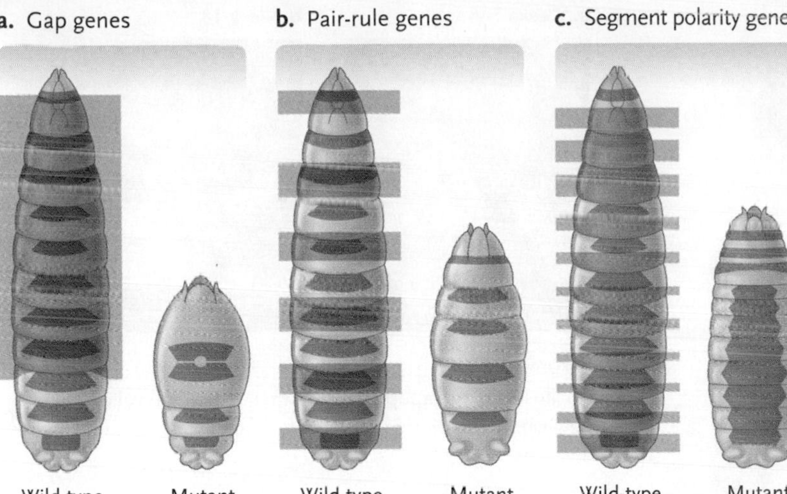

Figure 39.31
Examples of mutations in the different types of segmentation genes of *Drosophila*. Orange highlights indicate wild-type segments that are mutated. **(a)** Gap gene mutants lack one or more segments. **(b)** Pair-rule gene mutants are missing every other segment. **(c)** Segment polarity genes have segments with one part missing and the other part duplicated as a mirror image.

result in the loss of one or more body segments in the embryo **(Figure 39.31a)**.

Products of gap genes are transcription factors that activate **pair-rule genes**, such as *even-skipped* and *fushi tarazu*. The products of pair-rule genes divide the embryo into units of two segments each. Mutations in pair-rule genes lead to the deletion of every other segment of the embryo **(Figure 39.31b)**.

Expression of segment polarity genes, *engrailed* and *gooseberry*, is regulated by products of pair-rule genes. The actions of the products of segment polarity genes set boundaries and the anterior–posterior axis of each segment in the embryo. Mutations in segment polarity genes produce segments in which one part is missing and the other part is duplicated as a mirror image **(Figure 39.31c)**. The products of segment polarity genes are transcription factors and other molecules that regulate other genes involved in laying down the pattern of the embryo.

39.7c Homeotic Genes: Structure and Determining Outcomes

Once the segmentation pattern has been set, **homeotic** (structure-determining) **genes** of the embryo specify what each segment will become after metamorphosis. In normal flies, homeotic genes are master regulatory genes controlling development of structures such as eyes, antennae, legs, and wings on particular segments **(Figure 39.32)**. Mutations of these genes allowed researchers to discover the role of homeotic genes. In the *Antennapedia* mutant fly, legs develop instead of antennae (see Figure 39.32).

How do homeotic genes regulate development? Homeotic genes encode transcription factors that regulate expression of genes responsible for the development of adult structures. Each homeotic gene has a common region called a homeobox that is key to its function. A homeobox corresponds to an amino acid section of the encoded transcription factor called the **homeodomain**. The homeodomain of each protein binds to a region in the promoters of the genes whose transcription it regulates.

Eight homeobox (*Hox*) genes in *Drosophila* are organized along a chromosome in the same order as they are expressed along the anterior–posterior body axis **(Figure 39.33, p. 962)**. The discovery of *Hox* genes in *Drosophila* led to a search for equivalent genes in other organisms. *Hox* genes are present in all major animal phyla, where they control the development of segments or regions of the body and are arranged in order in the genome. Homeobox sequences in *Hox* genes are highly conserved, indicating common function in the wide range of animals in which they occur. Homeobox sequences of mammals are the same as or similar to those of the fruit fly (see Figure 39.33). Homeotic genes also are found in plants, where they affect flower development. Homeobox genes have been identified and analyzed in *Arabidopsis* (see Chapter 31).

Normal

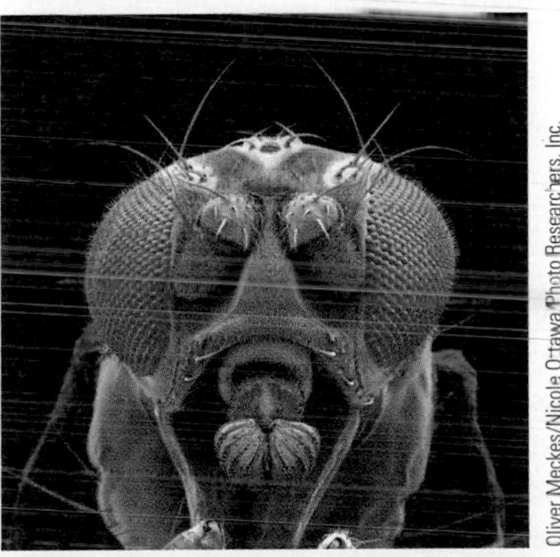

Oliver Meckes/Nicole Ottawa/Photo Researchers, Inc.

Antennapedia mutant

UCSF Computer Graphics Laboratory, National Institutes, NCRR Grant 01081

Figure 39.32
Antennapedia, a homeotic mutant of *Drosophila*, in which legs develop in place of antennae.

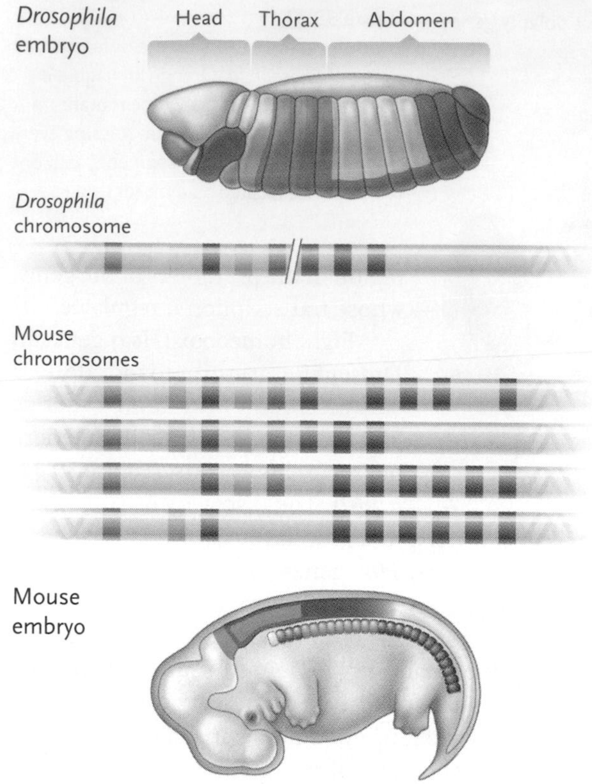

Figure 39.33
The *Hox* genes of the fruit fly and the corresponding regions of the embryo they affect. The mouse has four sets of *Hox* genes on four different chromosomes. Their relationship to the fruit fly genes is shown by the colours.

a. Weeks 5–6

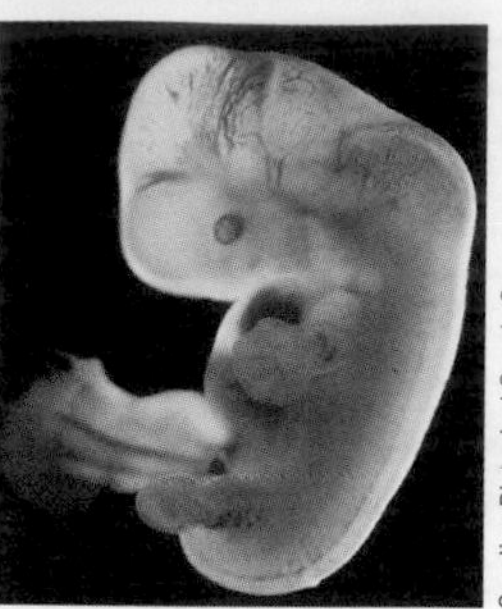

b. Week 18

Lennart Nilsson from A Child Is Born, © 1966, 1977 Dell Publishing Company, Inc.

Figure 39.34
An illustration of apoptosis in humans: the removal of tissue between developing fingers and toes to produce the free fingers and toes.

39.7f Cell-Death Genes: Apoptosis

Apoptosis plays a role in the breakdown of a tadpole's tail and in many other patterns of development in vertebrates and invertebrates. In humans, developing fingers and toes are initially connected by tissue, forming paddle-shaped structures. Later in development, cells of this tissue die by apoptosis, resulting in separated fingers and toes **(Figure 39.34)**. Like many other mammals, kittens and puppies are born with their eyes sealed shut by an unbroken layer of skin. Just after birth, cells die in a thin line across the middle of each eyelid, freeing the eyelids and allowing them to open. During pupation from caterpillar to butterfly, many tissues of the larva break down by apoptosis to be replaced by newly formed adult tissues.

Apoptosis results from gene activation in response to molecular signals from receptors on the surfaces of marked cells. In effect, the signals are death notices, delivered at a specific time during embryonic development. In the nematode *C. elegans*, division of the zygote produces 1090 cells. Of these, exactly 131 die at prescribed times to produce a total of 959 cells in the adult hermaphrodite.

In *C. elegans*, a "death signal" molecule that binds to a receptor in the plasma membrane of the target cell results in apoptosis. When the receptor is activated, it leads to activation of proteins that kill the cell. The killing proteins remain inactive in the absence of the death signal.

In the absence of a death signal, the membrane receptor is inactive **(Figure 39.35a)**. This allows CED-9, a protein associated with the outer mitochondrial membrane (encoded by the *ced-9* *c*ell-*d*eath gene), to inhibit CED-4 (encoded by the *ced-4* gene) and CED-3 (encoded by the *ced-3* gene). These two proteins are needed to turn on the cell-death program. Cells with the *ced-9* gene expressed and its product CED-9 active normally survive in the adult nematode. When a death signal binds to and activates a receptor, the resulting events are typical of signal transduction pathways (see Figure 39.37). Now the activated receptor leads to inactivation of CED-9. In the absence of CED-9, CED-4 is activated, which, in turn, activates CED-3. Activated CED-3 triggers a cascade of reactions, including activation of proteases and nucleases that degrade cell structures and chromosomes.

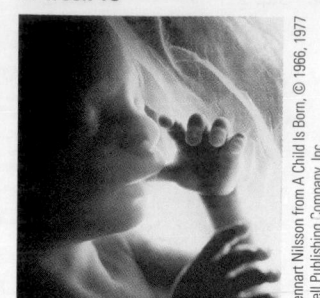

Studies of mutants have helped us understand the role of cell-death genes in *C. elegans*. In mutants lacking normal *ced-3* or *ced-4* genes, the 131 marked cells fail to die, producing a disorganized embryo. In the nervous system, the 103 cells that normally die by apoptosis live to form extra neurons in mutants. These extra neurons are inserted at random in the embryo, leading to a disorganized, nonfunctional nervous system.

Genes related to *ced-3* and *ced-4* occur in all animals tested for their presence. In humans and other mammals, the *caspase-9* gene is equivalent to *ced-3*. The *caspase-9* gene, which encodes a protease that degrades cell structures, is activated in cells that form the webbing between the fingers and toes in a human embryo, causing it to break down. The equivalent of *ced-4* is the *Apaf* gene (for *a*poptotic *p*rotease-*a*ctivating *f*actor). Mammalian cells are saved from death by the *Bcl* family of genes, which are the equivalent of *ced-9* in *C. elegans*. The genes are so closely related that they retain their effects if they are exchanged between *C. elegans* and human cells.

Study Break

1. Give two examples of genetic control of development.
2. What are maternal-effect genes?
3. What are homeotic genes, and what do they do?

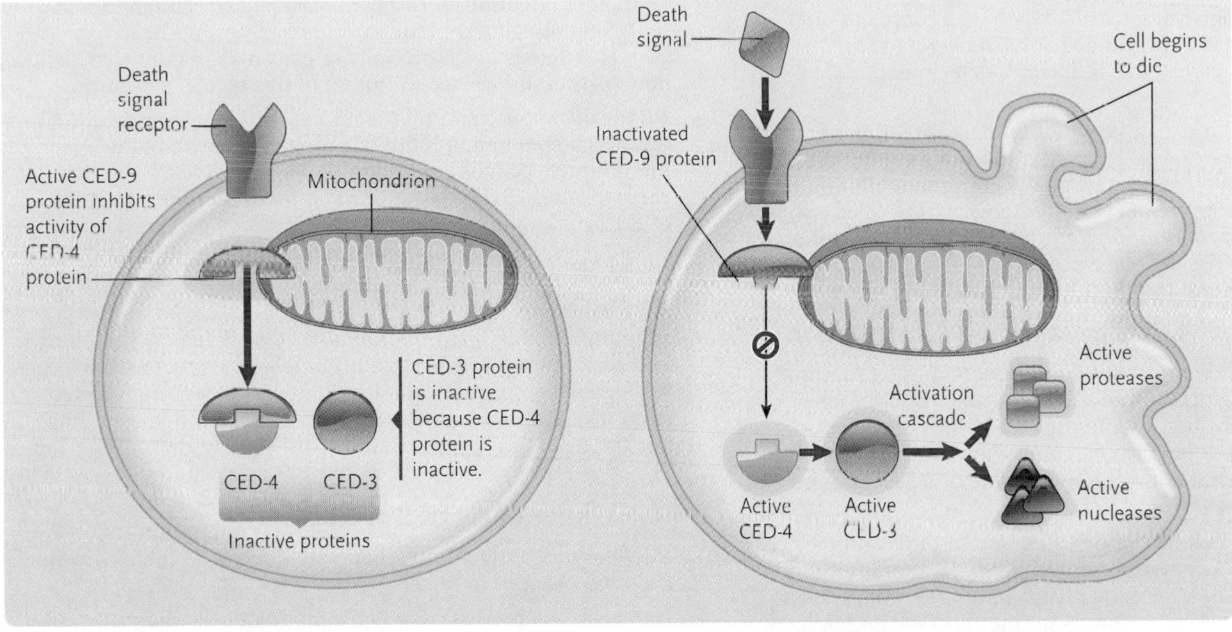
a. No death signal
b. Death signal
Death signal receptor
Active CED-9 protein inhibits activity of CED-4 protein
Mitochondrion
CED-3 protein is inactive because CED-4 protein is inactive.
CED-4
CED-3
Inactive proteins
Death signal
Cell begins to die
Inactivated CED-9 protein
Activation cascade
Active proteases
Active nucleases
Active CED-4
Active CED-3
Apoptosis is inhibited as long as CED-9 protein is active; cell remains alive.
When a death signal binds to the death signal receptor, it activates the receptor, which leads to inactivation of CED-9 protein. As a result, CED-4 protein is no longer inhibited and becomes active, activating CED-3 protein. Active CED-3 triggers a cascade of activations producing active proteases and nucleases, which cause the changes seen in apoptotic cells and eventually to cell death.

Figure 39.35
The molecular basis of apoptosis in C. *elegans*. **(a)** In the absence of a death signal, no apoptosis occurs. **(b)** In the presence of a death signal, activation of CED-4 and CED-3 proteins triggers a pathway that leads to the cell's death.

UNANSWERED QUESTION

How can the use of stem cells in the development of human medical procedures be informed by changes in development from zygote to gastrula?

Review

Go to CENGAGENOW™ at http://hed.nelson.com/ to access quizzing, animations, exercises, articles, and personalized homework help.

39.1 Housing and Fuelling Developing Young

- In mammals, relaxin is a polypeptide hormone produced by the ovaries during pregnancy. Relaxin inhibits muscular contractions of the uterus and promotes the growth of glands that produce milk. As the time for parturition approaches, relaxin causes relaxation of the pubic ligaments and softens and enlarges the opening to the cervix.
- Vivaparous animal embryos often develop in the uterus (or a uteruslike structure in the reproductive tract). Ovoviviparous animal embryos may develop in the oviduct, the stomach (at least one species of frog), the mouth (several species of fish), or a brood pouch (other fish, such as sea horses). Ovoviviparous animals lay eggs, and the embryos develop outside the body.
- Strictly defined, milk is produced by female mammals to feed their young. Milklike substances (milk analogues) are produced by many other animals: the "crop milk" of pigeons, secretions of the skin in some fish and caecilians, or the uterine milk of a variety of animals, from some cockroaches to elasmobranchs.
- Yolk is food housed within the egg and used to support the growth and development of the embryo. The eggs of birds, insects, reptiles, and many other animals have large deposits of yolk that support the complete development of the young. Other animals have varying amounts of yolk corresponding to shorter periods of in-egg development.

39.2 Mechanisms of Embryonic Development

- The process of progressing from a zygote to a complete organism involves mitotic cell divisions, movements of cells, selective cell adhesions, induction, determination, and differentiation.
- The zygote divides by cleavage, without increasing the overall size or mass of the embryo. It forms a morula, or sphere of blastomeres (cells), which forms the blastula, a single-cell-layered hollow ball of cells enclosing the blastocoel, a fluid-filled cavity. The blastula invaginates to form the gastrula, a hollow ball of cells with an opening, the blastopore.

39.3 Major Patterns of Cleavage and Gastrulation

- Protostomes show determinant development in the progression from egg to animal. From the first divisions, blastomeres develop into specific tissues and organs. Deuterostomes show indeterminant development. Blastomeres produced by the first several divisions remain totipotent, capable of developing into a complete organism.
- Differences in the patterns of development of birds and typical mammals are functions of ovipary (egg-laying) versus vivipary (bearing live young). Mammalian eggs have little yolk, and the developing embryo depends on its mother for food and oxygen, as well as the collection and removal of wastes. The eggs of birds have large amounts of yolk, and the complete development of the embryo takes place independent of the mother's body. Bird embryo development begins with the formation of the blastodisk, a layer of cells on the surface of the yolk.

39.4 Organogenesis: Gastrulation to Adult Body Structures

- In the amniote egg, the amnion (an extraembryonic membrane) encloses the developing embryo in a pool of amniotic fluid. The chorion, another extraembryonic membrane, is produced from ectoderm and mesoderm and lines the inside of the egg shell. It is the site of oxygen exchange for the developing embryo. The allantois is enclosed by the allantoic membrane, which forms from mesoderm and endoderm. The allantois is the storage site for metabolic end products such as uric acid. The amniote egg allows development outside of water and was a fundamental breakthrough in the evolution of fully terrestrial vertebrates.
- In vertebrates, the eye forms when two sides of the anterior end of the neural tube (optic vesicles) swell outward until they contact the ectoderm. The optic cup, a double-walled structure, forms when the outer surface of the optic vesicle thickens and flattens at the region of contact and then pushes inward. The optic cup becomes the retina. The lens forms from the lens placode, a swelling arising when the optic cup induces thickening of the overlying ectoderm. Developing lens cells synthesize crystallin, a fibrous protein that collects into glassy deposits. Lens cells lose their nuclei and form the lens.

39.5 Embryonic Development of Humans and Other Mammals

- The chorion of the mammalian embryo forms chorionic villi, fingerlike extensions into the endometrium that increase the surface area of the chorion where the placenta will form.
- The placenta is the interface between the developing embryo and its mother. There are a variety of placental structures in mammals, and placentalike structures (analogues) occur in fishes and insects. There is a rich diversity of placentae in guppylike fishes, demonstrating repeated evolution of this type of structure.
- *SRY* is the sex-determining region of the Y chromosome. *SRY* encodes a protein that induces a molecular switch causing the primitive gonads to develop into testes. Fetuses with XX chromosomes do not produce *SRY*, and under the influence of estrogens and progesterone, the primitive gonads develop into ovaries. High levels of circulating testosterone in a pregnant female cause masculinization of the genitalia in some mammals.
- In many animals, a larval stage is intermediate between embryo and adult. Larval stages occur in some species that produce eggs with small amounts of yolk. Larvae are often strikingly different from the adults and may be the feeding and/or dispersal stage of the species.

39.6 Cellular Basis of Development

- Microtubules and microfilaments produce movements of whole cells and changes in cell shape
- Induction is a process by which a group of cells causes or influences changes in a nearby group of cells, leading them to follow a particular pathway. Induction works through interactions between signal molecules from inducing cells and surface receptors on responding cells. When signal molecules bind to surface receptors, the responding cells are activated or inactivated.

39.7 Genetic and Molecular Control of Development

- Work with the nematode worm *Caenorhabditis elegans* has allowed biologists to follow development patterns and trace the fate of every cell produced from the zygote. *C. elegans* is transparent, making it even more appropriate for this kind of work.
- Skeletal muscles in mammals develop from somites, blocks of mesoderm along either side of the notochord. Paracrine signalling by nearby cells induces somite cells to express *myoD*, which turns on specific muscle-determining genes, converting them to myoblasts, undifferentiated muscle cells.
- Maternal-effect genes expressed by the mother during oogenesis control egg polarity and thus embryo polarity. The *bicoid* gene is a key maternal-effect gene responsible for the development of the head and thorax. Segmentation genes subdivide the embryo into regions, determining the segmentation in the body plan.
- Homeotic genes determine structure. In *Drosophila*, they are master regulatory genes controlling the development of body parts such as eyes, antennae, legs, and wings. In each homeotic gene is a common region called a homeobox. Homeobox-containing genes are called *Hox* genes.
- Apoptosis is programmed cell death, a process central to the development of some parts of the body. The process results from gene activation in response to molecular signals from receptors on the surfaces of marked cells.

Questions

Self-Test Questions

1. Vivipary occurs in
   a. class Osteichthyes.
   b. class Amphibia.
   c. class Mammalia.
   d. class Chondrihthyes.
   e. All of the above are correct.
2. Gastrulation occurs in
   a. all chordates.
   b. only in amniotes.
   c. only in echinoderms.
   d. only in amphibians.
   e. all metazoa.
3. Large amounts of yolk occur in the eggs of all
   a. bony fish.
   b. amphibians.
   c. birds.
   d. mammals.
   e. none of the above.
4. In vertebrates, the blastopore becomes
   a. the mouth.
   b. the nostrils.
   c. the anus.
   d. gill slits.
   e. the auditory meatus.
5. Apoptosis occurs in the development of
   a. mammals.
   b. birds.
   c. reptiles.
   d. bony fish.
   e. all of the above.
6. *Pax*-6 genes control the development of eyes in
   a. chordates.
   b. arthropods.
   c. mammals.
   d. cnidarians.
   e. all of the above.
7. Milk produced by mammary glands is a characteristic of
   a. discus fish.
   b. pigeons.
   c. caecilians.
   d. mammals.
   e. birds.
8. Induction results from interactions between cells and occurs in the development of
   a. eggs.
   b. tissues.
   c. embryos.
   d. nervous systems.
   e. b, c, and d.
9. Segmentation of developing embryos is controlled by
   a. *Pax*-6 genes.
   b. gap genes.
   c. pair-rule genes.
   d. homeotic genes.
   e. b and c.
10. Relaxin is important in the process of birth in
    a. sea horses.
    b. sharks.
    c. mammals.
    d. birds.
    e. cockroaches.

Questions for Discussion

1. How can apoptosis be used in the treatment of cancer?
2. How does the process of development differ between fraternal and identical twins? In humans, what is the incidence of fraternal twins with two fathers? How does this compare with other species of mammals?
3. How does the pattern of development of compound eyes differ from that of the eyes of vertebrates and molluscs?
4. What is the role of ectoderm in the development of the nervous system?

A little brown bat (*Myotis lucifugus*) flies through an abandoned mine. Mouth open, the animal produces echolocation calls that, in this setting, allow it to orient through the underground space.

M.B. Fenton

Study Plan

40 Animal Behaviour

Why It Matters

When it comes to food, many animals quickly learn to take advantage of new opportunities and show great versatility in behaviour from hunting to planning. Here are four examples.

During the Vietnam War (1959–1975), tigers (*Panthera tigris*) learned to associate the sound of gunfire with an opportunity to eat. The tigers' behaviour meant that some wounded soldiers waiting for treatment received a different kind of attention than what they expected. During the Second World War, wolves (*Canis lupis*) showed the same behaviour in some areas of Poland. A food reward is a strong reinforcer of behaviour.

In the 1970s, Kim McCleneghan and Jack Ames were studying sea otters (*Enhydra lutris*) in California waters. These otters dive and collect food (sea urchins, *Pisaster brevispinnis*, and clams, *Saxidomus nuttallii*) from the bottom and bring their catch to the surface to eat it. The observers were surprised to see some otters resurfacing with empty beverage cans. These otters would lie on their backs in the ocean swells, take a can, bite it open, and, in some cases, remove and eat something before discarding the can. Some cans appeared to be empty and were discarded after opening. The biologists collected their own beverage cans and discovered that many harboured young octopods (*Octopus* species). Populations of these cephalopods are limited by the number of shelters available. Young octopods were exploiting new opportunities for shelter, and the sea otters, in turn, were taking advantage of the molluscs' behaviour.

Meanwhile, in savannah woodlands in Senegal (West Africa), Jill Pruetz and Paco Bertolani observed chimpanzees (*Pan troglodytes*) hunting bushbabies (*Galago senegalensis*). The fact that the chimps were not vegetarians was no surprise because they had been reported using grass stalks to fish for termites and working in gangs to hunt young baboons (*Papio ursinus*). The discovery that savannah chimps in Senegal used "spears" to impale bushbabies hidden in tree hollows extended the repertoire of chimps. Pruetz and Bertolani watched chimps modifying branches they had broken off by biting to sharpen them prior to using them against bushbabies. The chimps that Pruetz and Bertolani studied appeared to plan their hunts in advance.

Other experiments have revealed how Western Scrub Jays (*Aphelocoma californica*) cache food in preparation for the next day's breakfast. Proving that animals plan ahead means that the experiments have to demonstrate that the animal executes a novel action or combination of actions and anticipates an emotional state different from the one at the time of planning. These two conditions rule out behaviours associated with migration and hibernation or those associated with meeting an immediate need for food.

In foraging behaviour, animals exhibit an array of opportunism and adaptation that we often believe is the exclusive domain of *Homo sapiens*. The purpose of this chapter is to introduce you to the topic of animal behaviour.

40.1 Genes, Environment, and Behaviour

Learning, as demonstrated by the foraging animals introduced above, illustrates how some behaviour patterns are acquired rather than inherited. But animal behaviourists had long debated whether animals are born with the ability to perform most behaviours completely or whether experience is necessary to shape their actions. Today, the emerging picture is that no behaviour is determined entirely by genetics or entirely by environmental factors. Rather, behaviours develop through complex gene–environment interactions.

Why do adult male White-crowned Sparrows sing a song that no other species sings **(Figure 40.1)**? They could have an innate (inborn) ability to produce their particular song, an ability so reliable that young males sing the "right" song the first time they try. According to this hypothesis, their distinctive song would be an **instinctive behaviour**, one genetically or developmentally "programmed" that appears in complete and functional form the first time it is used. An alternative hypothesis is that they acquire the song as a result of certain experiences, such as hearing the songs of adult male White-crowned Sparrows that live nearby. If so, this species' distinctive song might be an example of a **learned behaviour**, one that depends on having a particular kind of experience during development.

How can we determine which of these two hypotheses is correct? If the White-crowned Sparrow's song is instinctive, isolated male nestlings that have never heard other members of their species should be able to sing their species' song when they mature. If the learning hypothesis is correct, young birds deprived

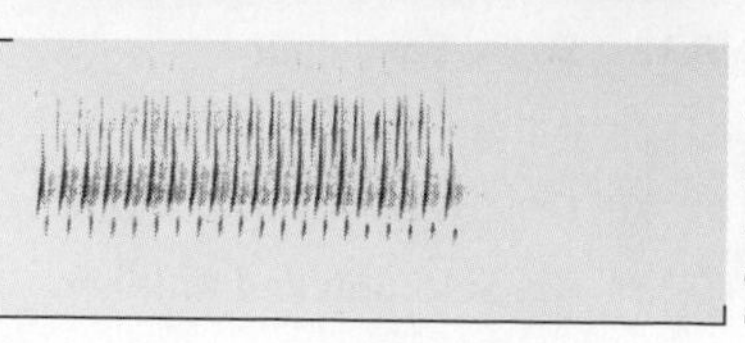

Figure 40.1 Songbirds and their songs. Sound spectrograms (visual representations of sound graphed as frequency versus time) illustrate differences in the songs of the White-crowned Sparrow (*Zonotricha leucophrys*), Song Sparrow (*Melospiza melodia*), and Swamp Sparrow (*Melospiza georgiana*).

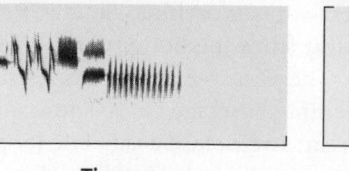

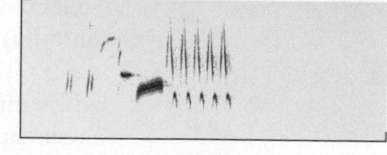

of certain essential experiences should not sing "properly" when they become adults.

Peter Marler tested these two hypotheses. He took newly hatched White-crowned Sparrows from nests in the wild and reared them individually in soundproof cages in his laboratory. Some of the chicks heard recordings of a male White-crowned Sparrow's song when they were 10 to 50 days of age, whereas others did not. Juvenile males in both groups first started to vocalize at about 150 days of age. For many days, the birds produced whistles and twitters that only vaguely resembled the songs of adults. Gradually, the young males that had listened to tapes of their species' song began to sing better and better approximations of that song. At about 200 days of age, these males were right on target, producing a song that was nearly indistinguishable from the one they had heard months before. Males that had not heard recordings of White-crowned Sparrow songs never sang anything close to the songs typical of wild males.

These results show that learning is essential for a young male White-crowned Sparrow to acquire the full song of its species. Although birds isolated as nestlings sang instinctively, they needed the acoustical experience of listening to their species' song early in life if they were to reproduce it months later. These data allow us to reject the hypothesis that White-crowned Sparrows hatch from their eggs with the ability to produce the "right" song. Their species-specific song, and perhaps the songs of many other songbirds, have both instinctive and learned components.

Early researchers generally classified behaviours as either instinctive or learned, but we now know that most behaviours include both instinctive and learned components. Nevertheless, some behaviours have a stronger instinctive component than others and vice versa.

a. Herring Gulls *(Larus argentatus)*

b.

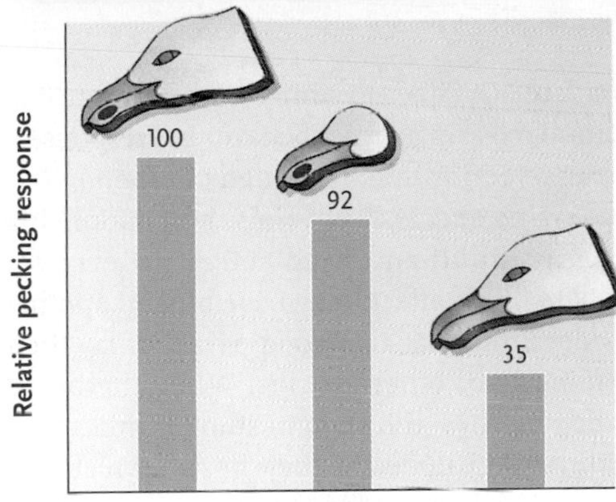

Figure 40.2
(a) A Herring Gull (*Larus argentatus*) chick begs its parent for food. **(b)** Nestling Herring Gulls also begged when presented with various models of an adult gull. In the experiment, nestlings pecked at a model with a red spot on the lower jaw almost as often as they did to a real gull. A model lacking the jaw spot elicited much fewer begging pecks from the nestling.

Study Break

1. How can the study of bird song lend itself to understanding the influence of genes on behaviour?
2. How is behaviour learned?

40.2 Instinct

Instinctive behaviours presumably can be performed without the benefit of previous experience. They can be grouped into functional categories, such as feeding, defence, mating, and parental care. We assume that they have a strong genetic basis and that natural selection has preserved them as adaptive behaviours.

Many instinctive behaviours are highly stereotyped. When an animal is triggered by a specific cue, it performs the same response over and over in almost exactly the same way. These **fixed action patterns** are triggered by **sign stimuli**. Very young Herring Gull chicks use a begging response **(Figure 40.2),** a fixed action pattern, to secure food from their parents. Begging chicks peck at the red spot on the parent's bill, and the tactile stimulus serves as a sign stimulus inducing the adult to regurgitate food from its crop. Baby gulls eat the chunks of fish, clams, or other food that have been regurgitated for them. We know that the spot on the parent's bill releases the begging response of the young gull because the same response is triggered by an artificial bill that looks only vaguely like an adult bill, provided that it has a dark contrasting spot near the tip (see Figure 40.2). Simple cues can activate fixed action patterns.

Human infants often respond innately to the facial expressions of adults **(Figure 40.3, p. 970).** Researchers can trigger smiling in even very young babies simply by moving a mask toward the infant, as long as the mask has two simple, diagrammatic eyes. Clearly, the infant, like a nestling Herring Gull, is not reacting to every

Evan Cerasoli

Figure 40.3
Instructive responses in humans. The smiling face of an adult is a sign stimulus that triggers smiling in very young infants.

feature of a face but rather to simple cues that function as sign stimuli releasing a fixed behavioural response.

Natural selection has moulded the behaviour of some parasitic species to exploit the relationship between sign stimuli and fixed action patterns for their own benefit. In effect, they have broken another species' code. Birds that are brood parasites lay their eggs in the nests of other species. When the brood parasite's egg hatches, the alien nestling mimics sign stimuli ordinarily exhibited by their hosts' own chicks. The parasitic chick begs for food by opening its mouth, bobbing its head, and calling more vigorously than the host's chicks. These exaggerated behaviours elicit feeding by the foster parents, and the young brood parasite often receives more food than the hosts' own young **(Figure 40.4)**.

Although instinctive behaviours are often performed completely the first time an animal responds to a stimulus, they can be modified by an individual's experiences. The fixed action patterns of a young Herring Gull change over time. Although the youngster initially begs by pecking at almost anything remotely similar to an adult gull's bill, it eventually learns to recognize the distinctive visual and vocal features associated with its parents. The chick uses this information to become increasingly selective about which stimuli elicit its begging behaviour. During their early performances, instinctive behaviours can be modified in response to particular experiences.

Behavioural differences between individuals may reflect genetic differences because performance of instinctive behaviours does not depend on previous experience. Stevan Arnold studied innate responses of captive newborn garter snakes to olfactory stimuli provided by potential food items they had never before encountered. Arnold measured the snakes' responses to cotton swabs that had been dipped in a smelly extract of banana slug, a shell-less mollusc. Young snakes born to a mother captured in coastal California, where adult garter snakes regularly eat banana slugs, almost always began tongue-flicking at slug-scented cotton swabs **(Figure 40.5)**. Newborn snakes whose parents came from central California, where banana slugs do not occur, rarely tongue-flicked at the swabs. Although the coastal and inland snakes belong to the same species, their instinctive responses to banana slug chemicals differed markedly.

© Stephen Dalton/Photo Researchers, Inc.

Figure 40.4
This European Cuckoo Hedge Sparrow (*Cuculus canorus*) is a brood parasite that stimulates food delivery by its foster parent, a Hedge Sparrow (*Prunella modularis*). The cuckoo elicits food delivery by displaying exaggerated versions of the sign stimuli used by the host offspring. The exaggerated stimuli are "releasers" initiating the appropriate behaviour from a parent with food.

a. Banana slug

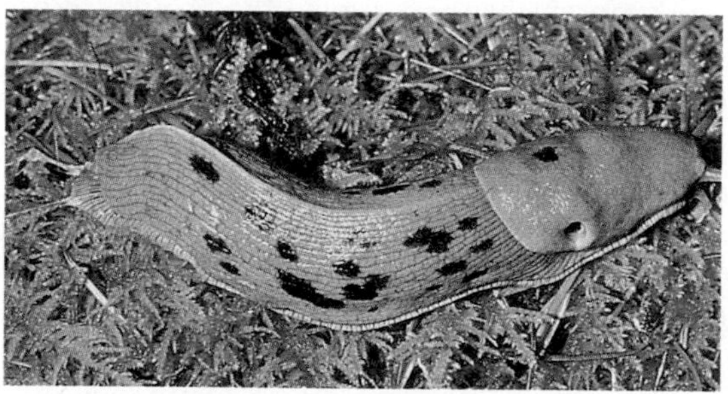

Eugene Kozloff

b. Adult coastal garter snake eating a banana slug

Stevan Arnold

c. Newborn coastal garter snake "smelling" slug extra

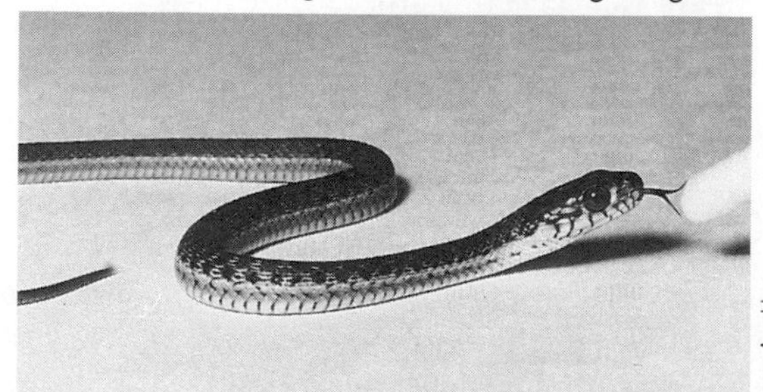

Stevan Arnold

Figure 40.5
Genetic control of food preference. (a) Banana slugs (*Ariolimax columbianus*) are a preferred food of **(b)** an adult garter snake (*Thamnophis elegans*) from coastal California. **(c)** A newborn snake from a coastal population of garter snakes flicks its tongue at a cotton swab drenched with tissue fluids from a banana slug.

Knockouts: Genes and Behaviour

Almost all eukaryotic organisms share a series of developmental interactions called the *wingless/Wnt* pathway. The name comes from the original discovery of the pathway in the fruit fly *Drosophila melanogaster,* in which mutant genes of the pathway cause alterations in the wings and other segmental structures. Recently, three genes closely related to *dishevelled,* one of the genes of the *Drosophila wingless/ Wnt* pathway, were isolated from and identified in mice. No functions have yet been identified for the proteins encoded in the three mouse *dishevelled* genes, but they are highly active in both embryos and adults. Their function must be important, but what could it be?

Nardos Lijam and his coworkers sought an answer to this question by developing a line of mice that totally lacked one of the *dishevelled* genes, *Dvl1,* in genetic shorthand. First, they constructed an artificial copy of the *Dvl1* gene with the central section scrambled so that no functional proteins could be made from its encoded directions. Next, they introduced the artificial gene into embryonic mouse cells. Cells that successfully incorporated the gene were injected into very early mouse embryos. Some mice grown from these embryos were heterozygotes, with one normal copy of the *Dvl1* gene and one nonfunctional copy. Interbreeding of the heterozygotes produced some individuals that carried two copies of the altered *Dvl1* gene and no normal copies. Individuals lacking the normal gene are called "knockout" mice for the missing gene.

Surprisingly, knockout mice grew to maturity with no apparent morphological defects in any tissue examined, including the brain. Their motor skills, sensitivity to pain, cognition, and memory all appeared to be normal. However, their social behaviour was different. In cages with normal mice, the knockouts failed to take part in the common activities of mouse social groups: social grooming, tail pulling, mounting, and sniffing. Although normal mice build nests and sleep in huddled groups, knockouts tended to sleep alone, without constructing full nests from cage materials. Mice heterozygous for the *Dvl1* gene (those with one normal and one altered copy of the gene) behaved normally in all of these social activities.

The knockout mice also jumped around wildly in response to an abrupt, startling sound, whereas the response of normal mice was less extreme. A neural circuit of the brain inhibits the startle response of normal mice, so the reaction of knockout mice suggested that this inhibitory circuit was probably altered. Humans with schizophrenia, obsessive–compulsive disorders, Huntington disease, and some other brain dysfunctions also show an intensified startle reflex similar to that of the ***Dvl1*** knockout mice.

The researchers' analysis revealed that the *Dvl1* gene modifies developmental pathways affecting complex social behaviour in mice and probably in other mammals. It is one of the first genes identified that affects mammalian behaviour. The similarity in startle reflex intensity between the knockout mice and humans with neurological or psychiatric disorders suggests that mutations in the *Dvl* genes and the *wingless* developmental pathway may underlie some human mental illnesses. If so, further studies of the *Dvl* genes may give us clues to the molecular basis of these diseases and a possible means to their cure.

Arnold then tested whether newborn snakes would eat bite-sized chunks of slug. After a brief flick of the tongue, 85% of newborn snakes from a coastal population routinely struck at the piece of slug and swallowed it even though they had no previous experience with this food. Even when no other food was available, only 17% of newborn snakes from the inland population consistently tongue-flicked at or ate pieces of slug. Arnold hypothesized that coastal and inland garter snakes have different alleles at one or more gene loci controlling their odour-detection mechanisms and leading to differences in their behaviour. Arnold crossbred coastal and inland snakes. If genetic differences contribute to the food preferences of snakes from the two populations, hybrid offspring receiving genetic information from each parent should behave in an intermediate fashion. The results of the experiment confirmed the prediction. When presented with bite-sized chunks of slug, 29% of the newborn snakes of mixed parentage ate them every time.

Many other experiments have confirmed that genetic differences between individuals can translate into behavioural differences between them (see *Knockouts: Genes and Behaviour*). Bear in mind, however, that single genes do not control complex behaviour patterns directly. Rather, the alleles determine the kinds of enzymes that cells can produce, influencing biochemical pathways involved in the development of an animal's nervous system. The resulting neurological differences can translate into a behavioural difference between individuals that have certain alleles and those that do not.

Study Break

1. What are the differences between instinctive and learned behaviours?
2. What are fixed action patterns and sign stimuli?
3. How did experiments with garter snakes demonstrate the influence of genetics on behaviour?

40.3 Learning

Unlike instinctive behaviours, learned behaviours are not performed completely the first time an animal responds to a specific stimulus. They change in response to environmental stimuli that an individual experiences as it develops. Behavioural scientists generally define learning as a process in which experiences change an animal's behavioural responses. Different types of learning occur under different environmental circumstances.

Imprinting occurs when animals learn the identity of a caretaker or the key features of a suitable mate during a **critical period**, a stage of development early in life. Newly hatched geese imprint on their mother's appearance and identity, staying near her for months. When they reach sexual maturity, young geese try to mate with other geese exhibiting the visual and behavioural stimuli on which they had imprinted as youngsters. When Konrad Lorenz, a founder of ethology (the study of animal behaviour), tended a group of newly hatched Greylag Geese, they imprinted on him rather than on an adult of their own species **(Figure 40.6)**. Male geese not only followed Lorenz, but at sexual maturity, they also courted humans.

Other forms of learning can occur throughout an animal's lifetime. Ivan Pavlov, a Russian physiologist, demonstrated classical conditioning in experiments with dogs. Like many other animals, dogs developed a mental association between two phenomena that are usually unrelated. Dogs typically salivate when they eat. Food is an *unconditioned stimulus* because the dogs instinctively respond to it and do not need to learn to salivate when presented with food. Pavlov rang a bell just before offering food to dogs. After about 30 trials in which dogs received food immediately after the bell rang, the dogs associated the bell with feeding time and drooled profusely whenever it rang, even when no food was forthcoming. The bell had become a *conditioned stimulus*, one that elicited a particular learned response. In classical conditioning, an animal learns to respond to a conditioned stimulus (e.g., the bell) when it precedes an unconditioned stimulus (e.g., food) that normally triggers the response (e.g., salivation). If your pet cat becomes exceptionally friendly whenever it hears the sound of a can opener, its behaviour is the result of classical conditioning.

Operant conditioning, trial-and-error learning, is another form of associative learning. Here animals learn to link a voluntary activity, an *operant*, with its favourable consequences, a *reinforcement*. A laboratory rat will explore a new cage randomly. If the cage is equipped with a bar that releases food when it is pressed, the rat eventually leans on the bar by accident (the operant) and immediately receives a morsel of food (the reinforcement). After a few such experiences, a hungry rat learns to press the bar in its cage more frequently, provided that the bar-pressing behaviour is followed by access to food. Laboratory rats also have learned to press bars to turn off disturbing stimuli, such as bright lights.

Insight learning occurs when an animal can abruptly learn to solve problems without apparent trial-and-error attempts at the solution. Captive chimpanzees solved a novel problem: how to get bananas hung far out of reach. The chimps studied the situation and then stacked several boxes, stood on them, and used a stick to knock the fruit to the floor.

Habituation occurs when animals lose their responsiveness to frequent stimuli not quickly followed by the usual reinforcement. Habituation can save the animal the time and energy of responding to stimuli that are no longer important. Sea hares (*Aplysia* species) are shell-less molluscs that typically retract their gills when touched on the side. Gill retraction helps protect sea hares from approaching predators. But a sea hare stops retracting its gills when it is touched repeatedly over a short period of time with no harmful consequences.

Cross-fostering experiments with song birds, Blue Tits (*Cyanistes caeruleus*), and Great Tits (*Parus major*) revealed that early learning is essential to the realization of ecological niches. In this work, Tore Slagsvold and Karen Wiebe transferred fertilized eggs from the nests of Great Tits to those of Blue Tits and vice versa. Compared with their genetic parents, the fostered young shifted their feeding niches, and the shift was lifelong. The changes in foraging behaviour were greater for fostered Great Tits, the species with more specialized foraging behaviour.

© Nina Leen/Time and Life Pictures/Getty Images

Figure 40.6
Imprinting. Having imprinted on him shortly after hatching, young Greylag Geese (*Anser anser*) frequently joined Karl Lorenz for a swim.

Study Break

1. How do the examples of feeding behaviour (see also *Why It Matters*) inform us about learning?
2. What are the differences between instinctive and learned behaviours? Give examples of each.

40.4 Neurophysiology and Behaviour

Research in neuroscience has shown that all behavioural responses, whether mostly instinctive or mostly learned, depend on an elaborate physiological foundation provided by the biochemistry and structure of the nerve cells. Nerve cells that regulate an innate response and make it possible for an animal to learn something are products of a complex developmental process. Here genetic information and environmental contributions are intertwined. Although the anatomical and physiological basis for some behaviours is present at birth, an individual's experiences alter the cells of its nervous system in ways that produce particular patterns of behaviour.

Marler's experiments helped explain the physiological underpinnings of singing behaviour in male White-crowned Sparrows. If acoustical experience shapes singing, a sparrow chick's brain must be able to acquire and store information present in the songs of other males. Then, months later, when the young male starts to sing, its nervous system must have special features enabling the bird to match its vocal output to the stored memory of the song that it heard earlier. Eventually, when it achieves a good match, the sparrow's brain must "lock" on the now complete song and continue to produce it when the bird sings.

Additional experiments demonstrated that when young birds did not hear a taped song during their critical period (10–50 days of age), they never produced the full song of their species, even if they heard it later in life. In addition, young birds that heard recordings of *other* bird species' songs during the critical period never generated replicas of those songs as they matured. These and other findings suggested that certain nerve cells in the young male's brain are influenced only by appropriate stimuli, in this case, acoustical signals from individuals of its own species, and only during the critical period. Neuroscientists have identified nuclei (singular, *nucleus*), clusters of nerve cells that make song learning and song production possible.

Every behavioural trait appears to have its own neural basis. Another songbird, a male Zebra Finch **(Figure 40.7)**, can discriminate between the songs of strangers and those of established neighbours. These finches live in territories, plots of land defended by individual males or breeding pairs. Defence of the territory ensures that the residents have exclusive access to food and other necessary resources.

Zebra Finches' ability to discriminate between the songs of neighbours and those of strangers involves a nucleus in the forebrain. Cells in this nucleus fire frequently the first time the Zebra Finch hears the song of a new conspecific. As the song is played again and again, the cells of this nucleus cease to respond, indicating that the bird has become habituated to a now familiar song. The same bird still reacts to the songs of strangers. Neurophysiological networks that make this selective learning possible enable male Zebra Finches to behave differently toward familiar neighbours that they largely ignore and unfamiliar singers they attack and drive away.

Figure 40.7
Zebra Finches (*Taeniopygia guttata*) are native to Indonesia. They have played an important role in studies of the physiological basis of song learning. The male has the striped throat.

Molecular and cellular techniques have been used to identify the role of genes in learning. When a bird is exposed to relevant acoustical stimuli, such as songs of potential rivals, certain genes are "turned on" within neurons in the song-controlling nuclei of the bird's brain. When a Zebra Finch hears the elements of its species' song, a gene called *zenk* becomes active in the brain, producing an enzyme that changes the structure and function of neurons. The ZENK enzyme programs nerve cells of the bird's brain to "anticipate" key acoustical events of potential biological importance. When they occur, these events trigger additional changes in the bird's brain, affecting its actions. In this way, a territory owner learns to ignore (= habituates to) a singing neighbour with which it shares an established territorial boundary. The same bird retains the ability to detect and respond to new intruding conspecifics because they are a real threat to its continued control of its territory.

Study Break

1. What role does the ZENK enzyme play?
2. How do nerve connections influence behaviour?

40.5 Hormones and Behaviour

Hormones are chemical signals that can trigger the performance of specific behaviours. Hormones often work by regulating the development of neurons and neural networks or by stimulating cells within endocrine organs to release chemical signals.

How did the neurons in an adult Zebra Finch acquire the remarkable capacity to change in response to specific stimuli? In Zebra Finches, only males produce courtship songs. Very early in its life, certain cells in the brain of a male songbird produce estrogen, which affects target neurons in the higher vocal centre, an area of the developing brain. Estrogen leads to a complex series of biochemical changes resulting in the production of more nerve cells in the parts of the brain that regulate singing. Brains of developing females do not produce estrogen. In the absence of estrogen, the number of neurons in the higher vocal centre of females *declines* over time **(Figure 40.8).** If young female Zebra Finches are given estrogen, they produce more nerve cells in the higher vocal centre and are capable of singing. Specific stimuli, such as the songs of familiar or unfamiliar males, can alter the genetic activity of the nerve cells that control the behaviour of adult birds.

Just as estrogen influences the development of singing ability in Zebra Finches, other hormones mediate the development of the nervous system in other species. A change in the concentration of a certain hormone can be the physiological trigger that induces important changes in an animal's behaviour as it matures.

As they age, worker honeybees perform different tasks. Bees less than 15 days old after emerging from the pupa tend to care for larvae and maintain the hive. Bees older than 15 days often make foraging excursions from the hive to collect food, nectar and pollen **(Figure 40.9).** These behavioural changes are induced by rising concentrations of juvenile hormone (see Chapter 35) released by a gland near the bee's brain. Despite its name, circulating levels of juvenile hormone actually increase as a honeybee ages.

Juvenile hormone may exert its effect on bee behaviour by stimulating genes in certain brain cells to produce proteins that affect nervous system function. Octopamine, for example, stimulates neural transmissions and reinforces memories. Octopamine is concentrated in the antennal lobes, parts of the bee's brain that contribute to the analysis of chemical scents in the external environment. Octopamine is found at higher concentrations in older, foraging bees that have higher levels of juvenile hormone. When extra juvenile hormone is experimentally administered to bees, their production of octopamine increases. Increased octopamine levels in the antennal lobes may help a foraging bee home in on the odours of flowers from which it can collect nectar and pollen.

The honeybee example illustrates how genes and hormones interact in the development of behaviour. Genes code for the production of hormones that become part of the intracellular environment of assorted target cells. Hormones then directly or indirectly change genetic activity and enzymatic biochemistry in their

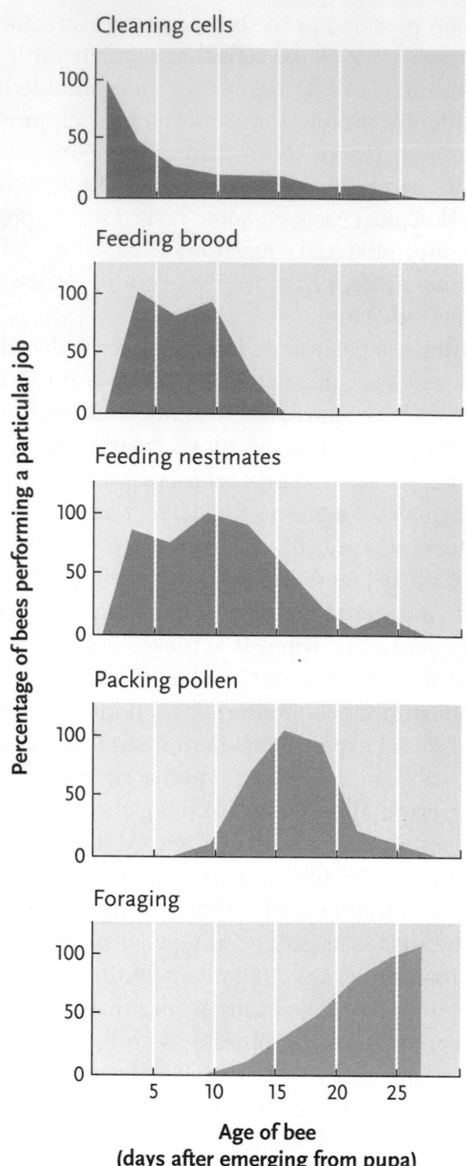

Figure 40.9
Age and task specialization in honeybee (*Apis mellifera*) workers. Newly emerged bees typically clean cells and feed the brood, whereas older workers leave the hive to forage for food.

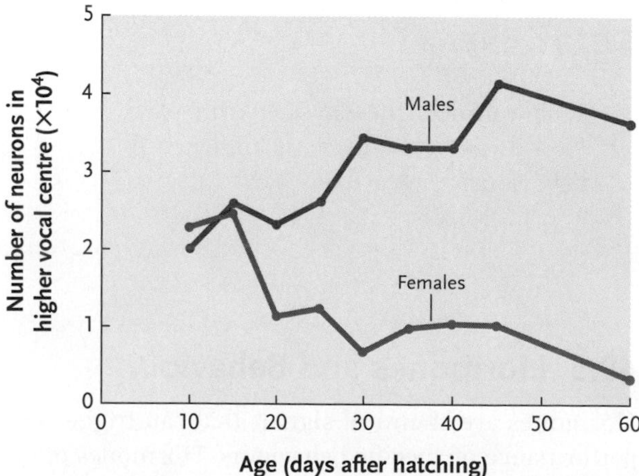

Figure 40.8
Hormonally induced changes in brain structure. The brains of young male Zebra Finches secrete estrogen, which stimulates production of additional neurons in the higher vocal centre. Lacking estrogen, young female Zebra Finches have fewer neurons in this region of the brain.

targets. When the target cells are neurons, changes in biochemistry translate into changes in the animal's behaviour.

The African cichlid fish illustrates how hormones regulate reproductive behaviour. Some adult males maintain nesting territories on the bottom of Lake Tanganyika in East Africa **(Figure 40.10).** Territory holders are relatively brightly coloured and exhibit elaborate behavioural displays to attract egg-laden females. These males defend their real estate aggressively against neighbouring territory holders and against incursions by males without territories of their own. Nonterritorial males (called "drifters") are much less colourful and aggressive and do not control a patch of suitable nesting habitat. They make no effort to court females.

Differences in levels of GnRH (gonadotropin-releasing hormone; see Chapter 38) cause behavioural differences between the two types of males. In the hypothalamus of the brain of territorial males, large, biochemically active cells produce GnRH. The same cells in the brains of drifters are small and inactive. GnRH stimulates the testes to produce testosterone and sperm. When circulating sex hormones are carried to the brain of the fish, they modulate the activity of nerve cells that regulate sexual and aggressive behaviour. In the absence of GnRH, male fish do not court females or attack other males.

What causes the differences in the neuronal and hormonal physiology of the two types of male fish? Russell Fernald and his students manipulated the territorial status of males. Some territorial males were changed into nonterritorial males and vice versa, whereas the territorial status of other males was left unchanged as a control **(Figure 40.11).** Four weeks after the changes, Fernald and his students compared experimental and control fish. They considered colouration and behaviour, as well as the size of the GnRH-producing cells in the brains. Territorial males that had been changed to nonterritorial males quickly lost their bright colours and stopped being combative. Moreover, their GnRH-producing cells were smaller than those of the territory-holding controls. Conversely, males that gained a territory in the experiment quickly developed bright colours and displayed aggressive behaviours toward other males. GnRH-producing cells in their brains were larger than those of fish that had maintained their status as non-territory-holding controls.

This example shows how what is happening inside a fish affects its environmental situation—its success or failure at gaining and holding a territory. Fish can detect and store information about their aggressive interactions. Neurons that process this information transmit their input to the hypothalamus, where it affects the size of cells producing GnRH, in turn dictating the hormonal state of the male. A decrease in GnRH production can turn a feisty territorial male into a subdued drifter. Drifters bide their time and build energy reserves for a future attempt at defeating a weaker male and taking over his territory. If successful in regaining territorial status, the male's GnRH levels will increase again. The once peaceful male reverts to vigorous sexual and aggressive behaviour.

Note the general similarity of these processes to those described for the White-crowned Sparrow's song learning. The fish's brain has cells that can change their biochemistry, structure, and function in response

African cichlid fish (*Haplochromis burtoni*)

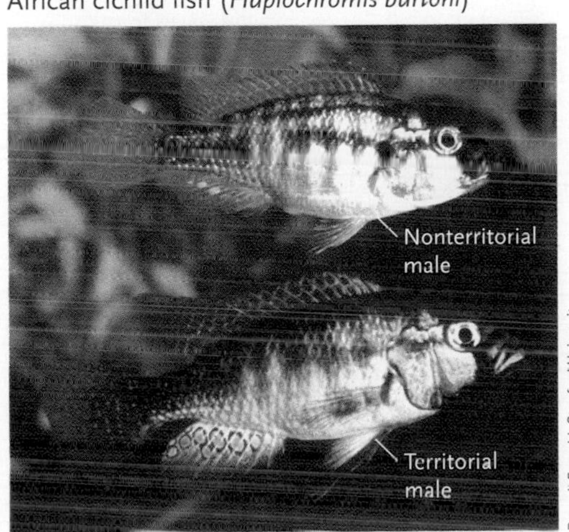

Figure 40.10
A comparison of a territorial and a nonterritorial male *Haplochromis burtoni*.

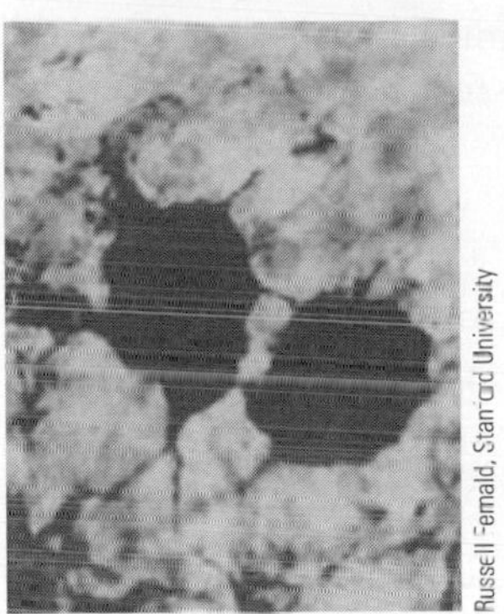

Territorial control

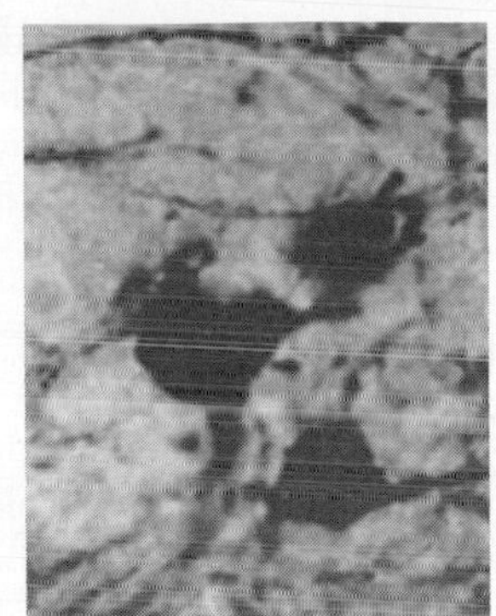
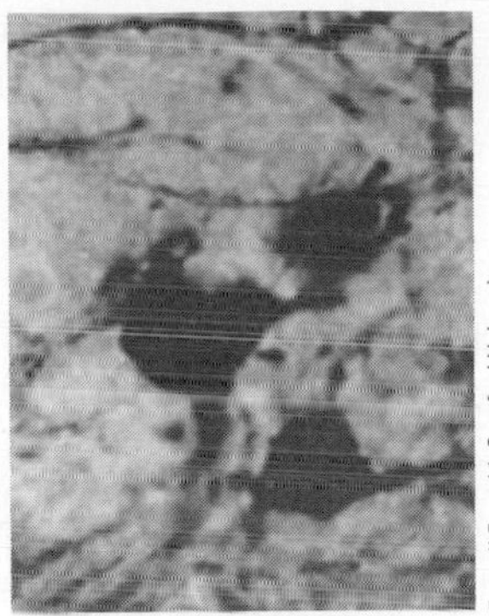

Territorial to nonterritorial experimentals

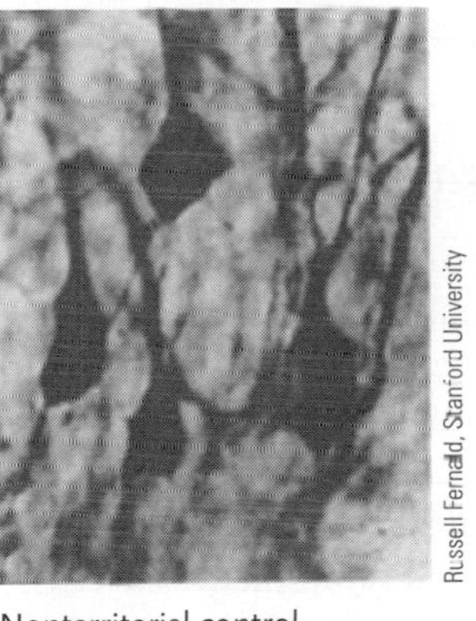

Nonterritorial control

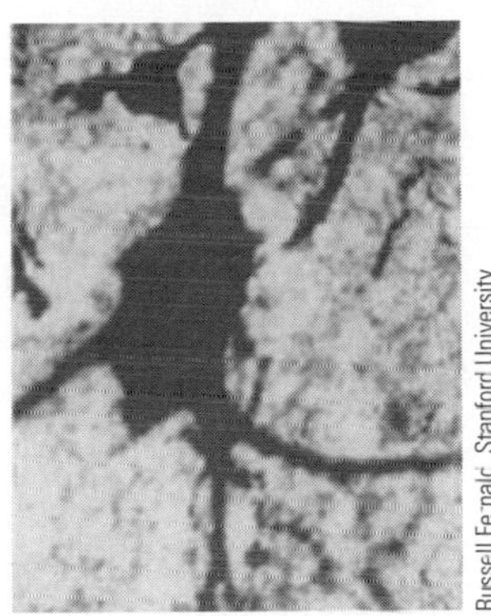

Nonterritorial to territorial experimentals

Figure 40.11
Gonadotropin-releasing hormone (GnRH) cells in male *Haplochromis burtoni*.

to well-defined social stimuli. These physiological changes make it possible for the fish to modify its behaviour depending on its social circumstances.

Study Break

1. How has research on White-crowned Sparrows and Zebra Finches advanced our knowledge of the impact of neurobiology on behaviour?
2. How does juvenile hormone affect the behaviour of adult bees?
3. How does gonadotropin-releasing hormone affect the behaviour of fish?

40.6 Neural Anatomy and Behaviour

Some specific behaviours are produced by anatomical structures in an animal's nervous system. The nervous systems of many animal species allow them to respond rapidly to key stimuli. Often sensory systems are structured to acquire a disproportionately large amount of information about the stimuli that are most important to survival and reproductive success.

Important information acquired by the senses can be relayed directly to motor neurons, for example, providing prey animals with behaviour that can save them from a predator's attack. Insects such as crickets that fly mainly at night avoid day-flying, predatory birds. But flying at night exposes them to attacks by insectivorous bats.

Insectivorous bats hunting at night use echolocation to detect and track flying prey (see Chapter 34). The echolocation calls of bats hunting flying insects are usually intense, measuring about 130 decibels sound pressure level at 10 cm, making the calls stronger than the sound of a smoke detector alarm. The bats' calls can cover frequencies from ~10 kHz to >200 kHz, beyond the 20 kHz upper limit of human hearing. By comparing its calls with the echoes from its calls, the bat uses echolocation to detect, assess, and track its flying prey. However, a bat's echolocation calls give crickets (and other prey; see Chapter 34) warning of their approach (see *Echolocation: Communication*).

With ears on their front legs, black field crickets hear bat echolocation calls (see Figure 34.14, and the anatomical structure of the cricket's nervous system produces a behavioural response that takes the cricket out of harm's way. Sensory neurons connected to the ears fire in response to the bat's calls, and the information is immediately translated into evasive action. When a bat attacks from the cricket's right side, the right ear receives a stronger stimulation than the left ear. The cricket's nervous system relays incoming messages from the *right* ear to the motor neurons controlling the *left* hindleg. Sufficient stimulation on the right side induces firing by motor neurons for the left hindleg, causing the leg to jerk up. This, in turn, blocks the movement of the left hindwing and reduces the flight power generated on the left side of the cricket's body. These changes cause the flying cricket to swerve sharply to the left and lose altitude, effectively diving down and away from the approaching bat **(Figure 40.12)**.

The structure and neural connections of sensory systems allow some animals to distinguish potentially life-threatening situations from more mundane stimuli. Fiddler crabs live and feed on mud flats, where they dig burrows that provide safe refuge from predators such as crab-hunting shorebirds. To use its burrow to advantage, a crab must distinguish between predatory gulls and other fiddler crabs. Otherwise, it would dash for cover whenever anything moved in its field of vision.

Fiddler crabs have long-stalked eyes held above their carapaces and perpendicular to the ground **(Figure 40.13)**. John Layne wondered whether a crab might use a divided field of view to distinguish dangerous predators from fellow crabs. An approaching large gull would stimulate receptors on the upper part of the eye, whereas another crab's movements would be slightly below the midpoint of the eyes. A split field of view would allow the crab to distinguish between the two kinds of stimuli. To achieve this, receptors above and below the retinal equator must relay signals to different groups of neurons, effectively wiring the crab's nervous system to distinguish for a split field of view. If this were the case, stimulation of receptors

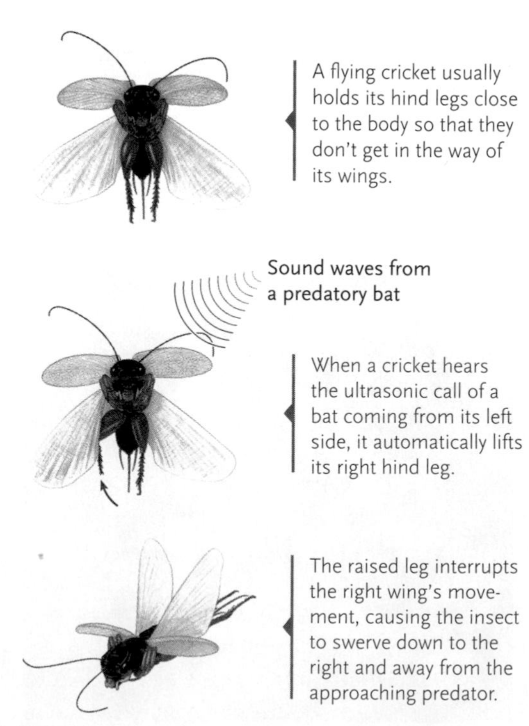

A flying cricket usually holds its hind legs close to the body so that they don't get in the way of its wings.
Sound waves from a predatory bat
When a cricket hears the ultrasonic call of a bat coming from its left side, it automatically lifts its right hind leg.
The raised leg interrupts the right wing's movement, causing the insect to swerve down to the right and away from the approaching predator.

Figure 40.12
A neural mechanism for escape behaviour in the black field cricket (*Teleogryllus oceanicus*).

Echolocation: Communication

In echolocation, the echolocator stores the outgoing signal in its brain for comparison with returning echoes. The difference between what the animal says and what it hears is the data used in echolocation. However, when an echolocating bat (see Figure 40.1) or dolphin produces echolocation signals, the signals can also be heard by other animals.

When the bat or dolphin is foraging, potential prey (some insects for the bat, some fish for the dolphin) hear the signals and flee from the sound source (= negative phonotaxis) in an effort to evade the approaching predator. When the bat is close (strong echolocation signals), moths with ears dive to the ground or go into erratic flight to evade the bats. Moths with ears sensitive to bat echolocation calls avoid bat attacks 40% of the time. Insects lacking bat detectors are caught at much higher rates, sometimes >90% of the time. Acoustic warfare between bats and insects entertains biologists, involving measures and countermeasures by both predator and prey.

The same echolocation calls that alert potential prey are also available to any other animals within earshot, provided that their ears are sensitive to the frequencies in the signals. Little brown bats may use feeding buzzes (signals associated with attacks on prey; see Figure 34.3) to locate concentrations of prey. Spotted bats (*Euderma maculatum*) either approach a calling conspecific, apparently to chase it away, or turn and leave the area. Resident killer whales (*Orcinus orca*) in the Pacific Ocean off the west coast of Canada typically use echolocation to detect, track, and locate the salmon they eat. Transient killer whales in the same area feed mainly on marine mammals. These killer whales rarely echolocate. Local marine mammals, such as seals, quickly leave the water when they hear killer whales approaching.

The study of echolocation is a rich source of information about signals, signal design, hearing systems, and behaviour.

© Jeff Foott/Dcom/DRK Photo

Figure 40.13
A fiddler crab, *Uca pugilator.*

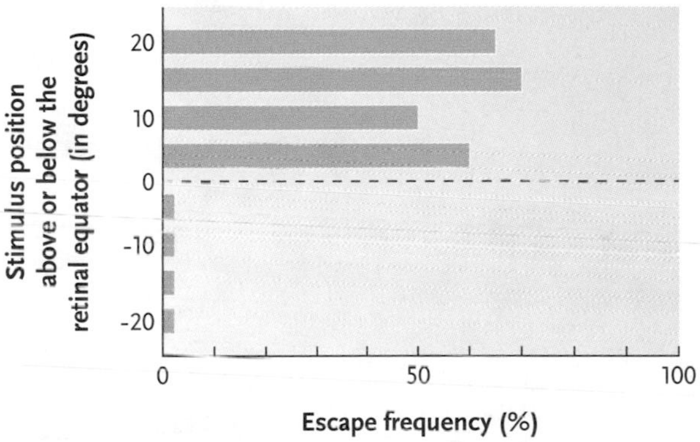

Stimulus position above or below the retinal equator (in degrees)

Escape frequency (%)

Figure 40.14
Stimuli that activated the upper part of the retinas of *Uca pugilator* elicited escape behaviour much more often than those activating the lower retinas.

above the midline of the eye would activate neurons controlling an escape response, triggering a dash for the burrow. A moving stimulus at or below eye level would stimulate a different response. Responses to other crabs are likely to be gender-dependent.

To explore this, Layne placed crabs one at a time in a glass jar on an elevated platform. He presented a black square to each crab from two different heights. Sometimes the stimulus circled the jar above the crab's eyes; sometimes it circled below them. Stimuli activating the upper part of the retina induced escape behaviour, whereas those below the retinal equator were usually ignored **(Figure 40.14).** Specific nervous system connections between a fiddler crab's eyes and brain provide appropriate responses to different specific stimuli.

The match between the structure of an animal's nervous system and the real-world challenges it faces extends beyond the ability to avoid predators. Star-nosed moles live in wet tunnels in North American marshlands and spend almost all of their lives in complete darkness. Like nocturnal insect-eating bats, star-nosed moles must find food without the benefit of visual cues. Like the bats, its receptor–perceptual system enables it to feed effectively. A star-nosed mole eats mainly earthworms it locates with its nose, but not by smell. As the mole proceeds down its tunnel, 22 fingerlike tentacles on its nose sweep the area directly ahead of it. Each tentacle is covered with thousands of Eimer's organs (touch receptors; **Figure 40.15, p. 978**). Sensory nerve terminals in Eimer's organs generate complex and detailed patterns of signals about the objects they contact. These messages are relayed by neurons to the cortex of the mole's brain,

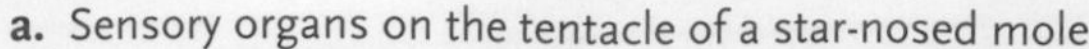

a. Sensory organs on the tentacle of a star-nosed mole

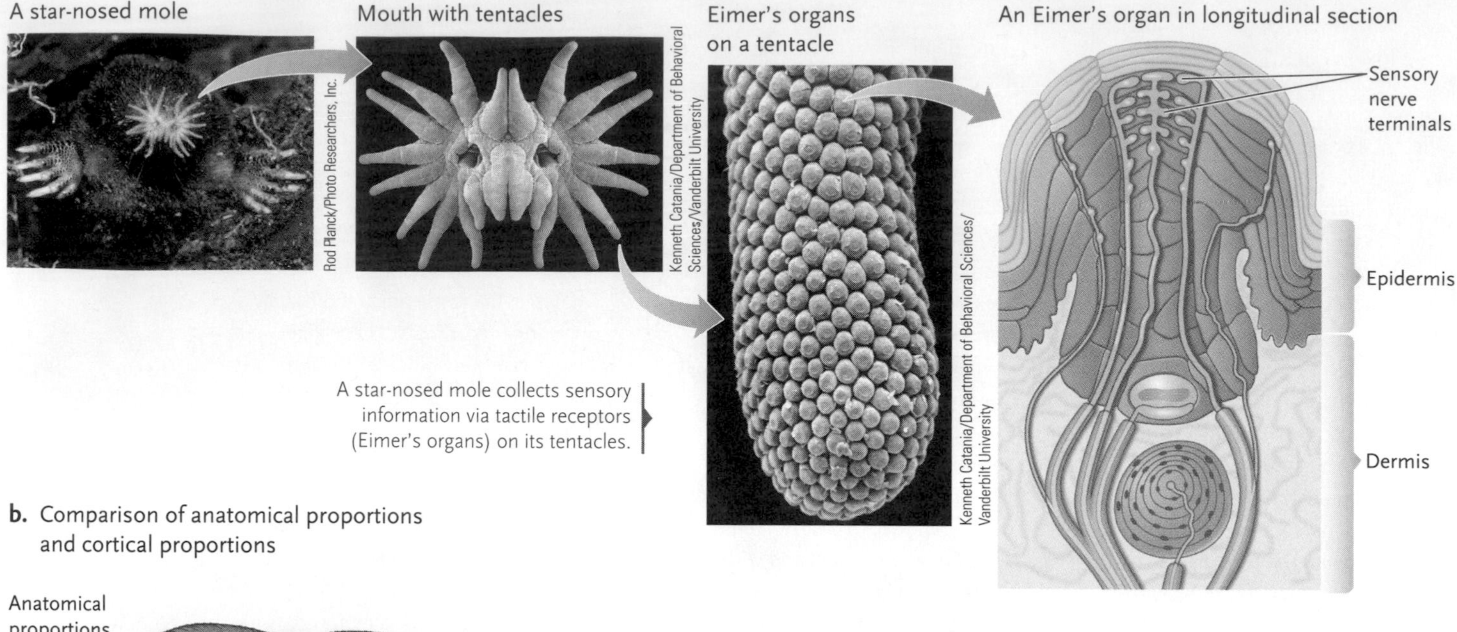

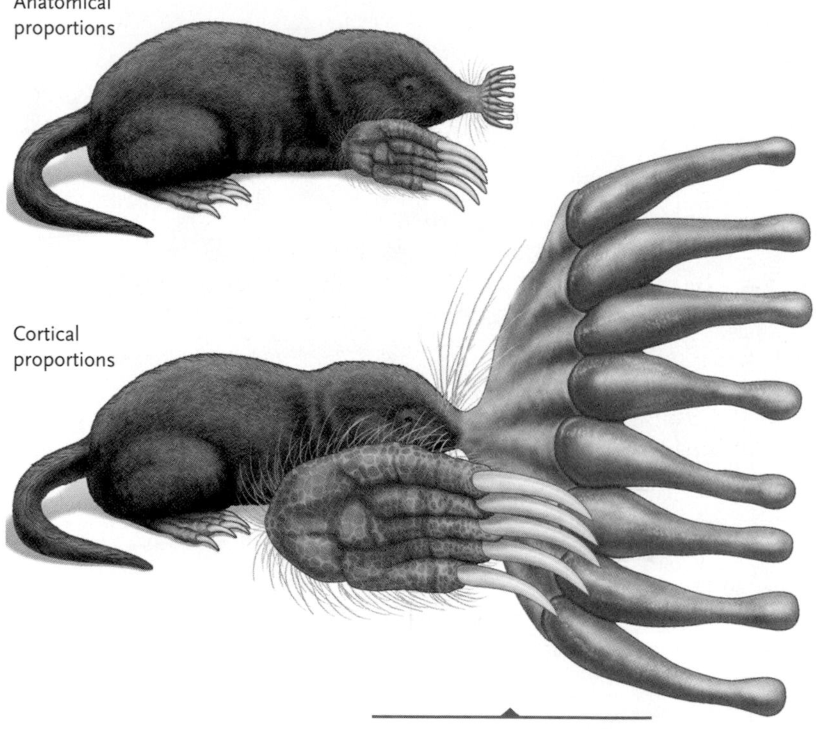

Figure 40.15
The collection and analysis of sensory information by the star-nosed mole (*Condylura cristata*). (a) The mole's nose has 22 fleshy tentacles covered with cylindrical tactile receptors called Eimer's organs. Each Eimer's organ contains sensory nerve terminals. **(b)** The mole's cerebral cortex devotes far more space and neurons to analysis of input from the tentacles than from elsewhere on the body. These drawings compare the relative amounts of sensory information coming from different parts of a mole's body.

much of which is devoted to the analysis of information received from the nose's touch receptors.

The structural basis of the mole's sensory analysis is reflected by the amount of brain tissue responding to signals from its nose. The mole's brain contains many more cells decoding input from Eimer's glands than the combined input received from all other parts of the animal's body (see Figure 40.15b). Moreover, the brain does not treat inputs from all 22 of the mole's "nose fingers" equally. Instead, the brain devotes more cells to input from tentacles closest to the mouth. Fewer cells analyze messages from those farther away. Processing tactile information by star-nosed moles is related to the importance of finding food in dark, underground tunnels. Moreover, the extra attention given to signals from certain tentacles helps the star-nosed mole locate prey that are close to its mouth, in turn allowing it to feed more efficiently (see Figure 34.31).

Animals' nervous systems do not offer neutral and complete pictures of the environment. Instead, the pictures are distorted, but the unbalanced perceptions of the world are advantageous because certain types of information are far more important than others for the animals' survival and reproductive success.

Study Break

1. How do crickets hear the echolocation calls of bats?
2. How does what they see influence the behaviour of fiddler crabs?

40.7 Communication

In animal communication, one individual produces a signal that is received by another, changing the behaviour of one or both individuals in a way that benefits signaller and/or signal receiver. The signaller is the individual transmitting information (the signal) and the signal *receiver* **(Figure 40.16)**, the one receiving the signal. Some animals have broken the signal codes of others and exploited them to their advantage. Some people who study animal communication consider that only signals intended to communicate should be called communication (think back to problems with the definition of species or genes).

Animals use a variety of sensory modalities when producing signals, including acoustical, chemical, electrical, vibrational, and visual. Some signals combine modalities. Sometimes the animal itself is a signal; in other situations, the animal's excretory or eliminated products are signals.

Bird songs are acoustical signals, heard by the signal receivers. The song of a male Whippoorwill (*Caprimulgis vociferous*) advertises his presence to females and may help him secure a mate. The same song is heard by other males, who recognize it as a territorial display. After the eggs have been laid, the same song is heard by the young developing in the eggs. Other birds, male Club-winged Manakins (e.g., *Machaeropterus deliciosus*), use sounds produced by feather stridulations as their acoustic courting signal. Sounds are used as signals by many other animals, such as insects and rattlesnakes. Pacific herring (*Clupea pallasi*) communicate with conspecifics through the noise generated with little bursts of gas (known as fast repetitive transient signals [f*rts]) passed from the anus.

A striped skunk's (*Mephitis mephitis*) black and white stripes constitute a visual signal. Other examples are humans' facial expressions and body language. These visual signals are available to anyone viewing them. Visual signals can be enhanced by morphological features, such as the erectile crest of a Royal Kingbird (*Tyrannus melancholicus*), or semaphore flags used by people. In darkness, some animals use bioluminescent signals (e.g., Figure 41.29). In many animals, visual signals are *ritualized*—they have become exaggerated and stereotyped, enhancing their function as signals **(Figure 40.17)**.

Many species produce chemical signals, well known to anyone who has walked a dog. Pheromones are distinctive volatile chemicals released in minute amounts to influence the behaviour of conspecifics. The body of a worker ant contains a battery of glands, each releasing a different pheromone **(Figure 40.18, p. 980)**. One set of pheromones recruits fellow workers to battle colony invaders, whereas another stimulates workers to collect food that has been discovered outside the colony. Pheromones are used by some animals to attract mates. Female silkworm moths (*Bombyx mori*) produce the pheromone bombykol (see *Molecule Behind Biology*).

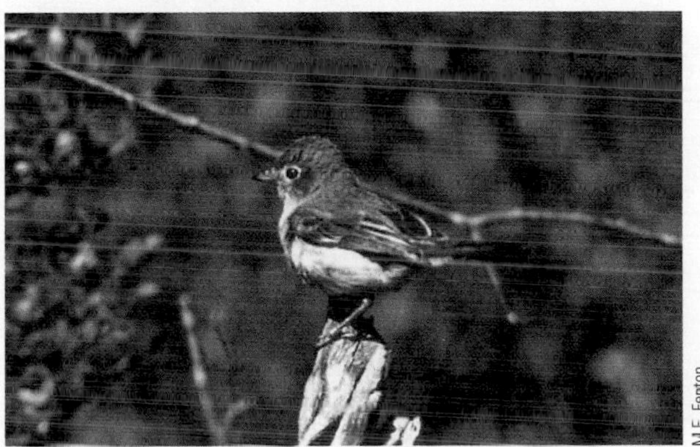
M.E. Fenton

Figure 40.16
Song birds, such as this Grey Vireo (*Vireo vincinior*), use songs to advertise their presence to unmated females and to other males.

© E. Mickleburgh/Ardea, London

Figure 40.17
Visual display. The courtship display of a male Albatross (*Diomedea exulans*) includes ritualized postures and movements of the wings and body.

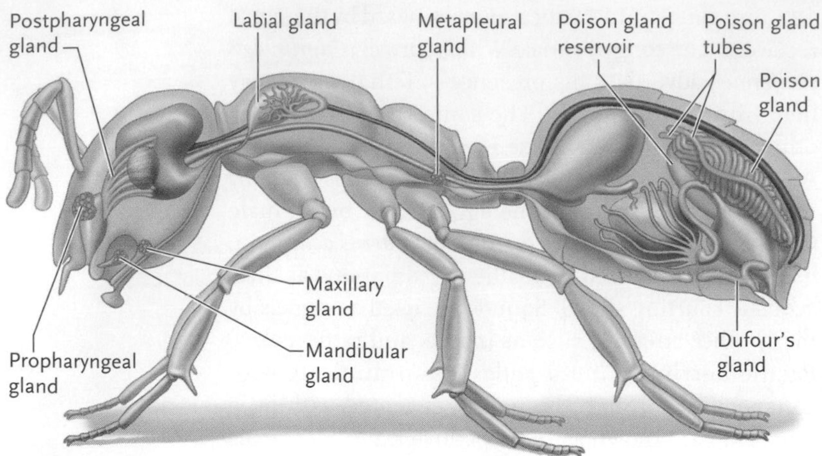

Figure 40.18
Chemical signals. An ant's body contains a host of pheromone-producing glands, each of which manufactures and releases its own volatile chemical or chemicals.

A single molecule of bombykol can generate a message in specialized receptors on the antennae of any male silkworm moth that is downwind (see *Knockouts: Genes and Behaviour*). Chemicals used as signals are often exploited by predators.

In many species, touch conveys important messages from a signaller to a receiver. **Tactile signals** can operate only over very short distances, but for social animals living in close company, they play a significant role in the development of friendly bonds between individuals **(Figure 40.19).**

Figure 40.19
Tactile signals. Grooming by Hyacinth Macaws (*Ano dorhynchus hyacinthinus*) removes ectoparasites and dirt from feathers. The close physical contact promotes friendly relationships between groomer and groomee.

a. Round dance

b. Waggle dance

c. Coding direction in the waggle dance

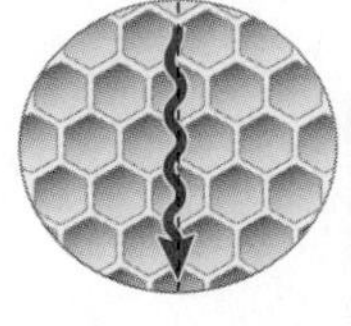

When the bee moves straight down the comb, other bees fly to the source directly away from the sun.

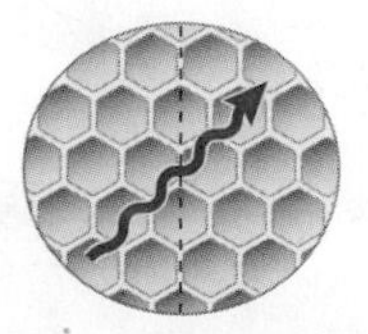

When the bee moves 45° to the right of vertical, other bees fly at a 45° angle to the right of the sun.

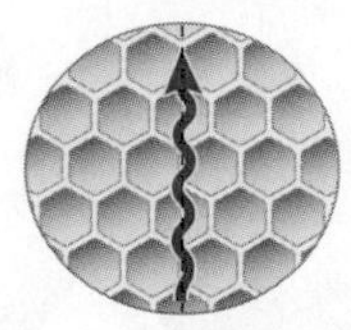

When the bee moves straight up the comb, other bees fly straight toward the sun.

Figure 40.20
Dance communication by honeybees (*Apis mellifera*). Foraging honeybees transmit information about the location and quality of a food source by dancing on vertical honeycomb. **(a)** If the food source is close to the hive, the forager performs a "round dance." **(b)** When food is farther from the hive, the honeybee performs a "waggle dance." **(c)** The dancing bee indicates the direction to the distant food source by the angle of the waggle run.

Some freshwater fish species, especially those that occupy murky tropical rivers where visual signals cannot be seen, use weak **electrical signalling** to communicate (see Figure 34.34). These fish have electric organs that can release charges of variable intensity, duration, and frequency, allowing substantial modulation of the message that a signaller sends. Among the New World knifefish (order Gymnotiformes), including the electric eel (Figure 34.34b), electrical discharges can signal threats, submission, or a readiness to breed.

Animals often use several channels of communication simultaneously. Karl von Frisch demonstrated that the famous dance of the honeybee involves tactile, acoustical, and chemical modes **(Figure 40.20).** When a foraging honeybee discovers a source of pollen or nectar, it returns to its colony. There, in the darkness of the hive, it performs a dance on the vertical surface of the honeycomb. The dancer moves in a circle, attracting a crowd of workers. Some workers follow and maintain physical contact with the dancer. The dance delivers information about food source, its quality, and the distance and direction observers will need to fly to locate it.

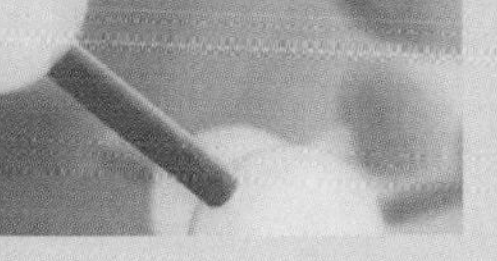

Molecule Behind Biology

Bombykol

Male silkworm moths (*Bombyx mori*) respond to the pheromone bombykol (Figure 1) produced and released by females. Bombykol is a pheromone designed to function in communication. Animals use pheromones to bring males and females together. Male *B. mori* detect bombykol using specialized receptors on their antennae (see Chapter 34).

Not surprisingly, predators exploit the powerful attractiveness of pheromones to lure prey. Female bolas spiders (*Mastophora cornigera* and other species in the genus) use a sticky ball of web impregnated with a chemical that mimics the odour of sex pheromones secreted by female moths. Male moths respond to the lure of these odours, approach the pheromone-soaked web, and are captured by the spiders.

Bolas spiders do not prey on just one species of moth. Adult female *M. cornigera* produce three sex pheromone compounds, (Z)-9-tetradecenyl acetate, (Z)-9-tetradecenal, and (Z)-11-hexadecenal. These pheromones attract several different species of moths. Moth attractants produced by *Mastiphora hutchinsoni* are effective on several moths that use quite different pheromones. *M. hutchinsoni* adjust the production of pheromone mimic to match the times of maximum activity by *Tetanolita mynesalis* (smoky tetanolita) and *Lacinipolia renigera* (bristly cutworm). The pheromone blend for the early-flying *L. renigera* interferes with attraction of the late-flying *T. mynesalis,* so the spider adjusts the blend of pheromone it uses in its lure. This spider lures the early-flying moth with one blend and the late-flying one with another.

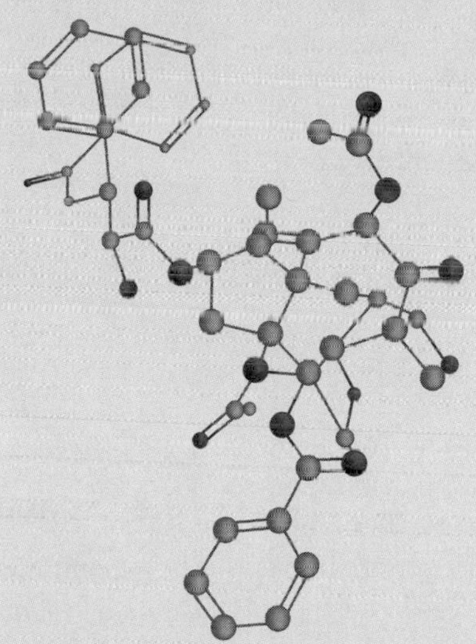

Figure 1
Bombykol.

When the food source is less than 75 m from the hive, the bee performs a "round dance" (see Figure 40.20a). Here the bee moves in tight circles, swinging its abdomen back and forth. Bees surrounding the dancer produce a brief acoustical signal that stimulates the dancer to regurgitate a sample of the food it discovered. The regurgitated sample serves as a chemical cue for other workers that search for the food.

When the food source is farther away, the forager performs the "waggle dance": a half-circle in one direction, then a straight line while waggling its abdomen, and then a half-circle in the other direction (see Figure 40.20b). With each waggle, the dancer produces a brief buzzing sound. The angle of the waggle run relative to the vertical honeycomb indicates the direction of the food source relative to the position of the Sun (see Figure 40.20c). The duration of the waggles and buzzes carries information about distance to the food. The more time spent waggling and buzzing, the farther the food is from the hive.

Signal receivers often respond to communication from signallers in predictable ways. A male White-crowned Sparrow generally avoids entering a neighbouring territory simply because it hears the song of the resident male. Similarly, young male baboons and mandrills often retreat without a fight when they see an older male's visual threat display **(Figure 40.21)**, even with the loss of a chance to mate with a female. Why do these receivers behave in ways that appear to be beneficial to their rivals but not to themselves?

Explaining behavioural interactions often means considering how an animal's actions affect its reproductive output. The retreating White-crowned Sparrow avoids wasting time and energy on a battle he is likely to lose. By retreating, the would-be intruder minimizes the chances of being injured or killed by a resident male. Moreover, ousting the current resident might be more tiring and risky than finding a suitable unoccupied breeding site. Resident males usually win physical contests, and intruders typically succeed in gaining a territory from a resident only after a prolonged series of exhausting clashes. Observations of territorial species, such as birds, lizards, frogs, fish, or insects, generally support these predictions.

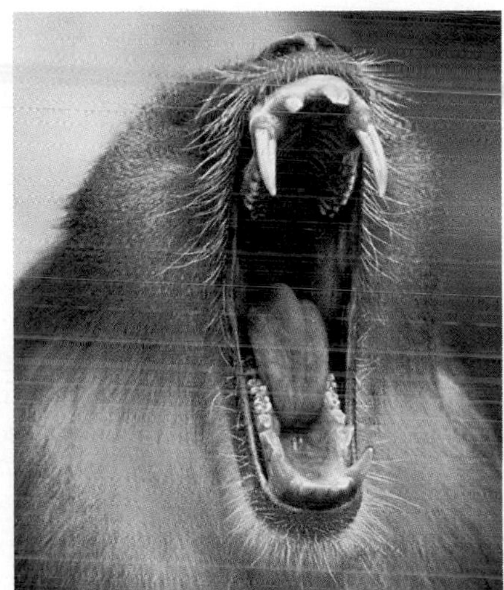

Tom and Pat Leeson

Figure 40.21
Threat display. Exposed canines epitomize the threat display of a dominant male mandrill (*Mandrillus sphinx*) that is used to drive away rival males.

Applying a similar argument to competition among male mandrills, we can predict that smaller or younger males will concede females to threatening older rivals without fighting. The signal receiver retreats after receiving the threat because he judges that he would not win, and a male mandrill's canine teeth are not just for show. Evolutionary analyses suggest that the signaller and signal receiver benefit from the exchange of signals.

In winter, some Ravens (*Corvus corax*) may emit a strange "yell" call when they find a carcass of a deer. The loud yell attracts a crowd of hungry Ravens. The calling behaviour puzzled Bernd Heinrich, who noted that when paired, territory-holding adult Ravens found a carcass, they fed quietly and did not yell. Yells are produced by young, wandering Ravens that happen on a carcass in another bird's territory. The yells attracted other Ravens that collectively overwhelmed the residents' efforts to defend the carcass and their territory. Wanderers used yells to exploit the food supply, whereas residents just ate. Bernd Heinrich concluded that the reproductive benefit of resident Ravens was enhanced by uninterrupted feeding. Wandering Ravens succeeded in their trespassing only when they attracted others.

40.7a Language: Syntax and Symbols

Although language is communication, not all communication is language. Many people believe that language is the exclusive domain of humans, but the distinction is not clear and crisp. The round and waggle dances of honeybees contain both syntax (the order in which information is presented) and symbols (a display that represents something else) and are considered by many to meet the criteria for language. Furthermore, by blackening the dancer's ocelli (see Chapter 34), James L. Gould was able to get a dancing bee to lie to other bees. When there is a light in the hive, the dancer orients the waggle dance to the light as if it were the Sun. Dancers with blackened ocelli do not see the light as do other bees—thus, the lie.

Vervet monkeys (see Figure 18.2) have a repertoire of signals to alert conspecifics to different predators. Vervet monkeys use one signal for snakes, another for leopards, and still another for raptors and show different predator-specific defensive behaviours. Chickadees (*Parus atricapillus*) also use different alarm calls to alert others to approaching danger. Captive, trained chimpanzees and gorillas (*Gorilla gorilla*) have been reported to use AMSLAN, American Sign Language.

In the area of communication, humans are not as distinct from other animals as some people would like to believe. To appreciate redundancy in animal communication, observe the body language and facial expressions of someone talking on a telephone. The eloquence of these signals is not conveyed to the signal receiver at the other end of the phone!

Study Break

1. What sensory modalities do animals use in communication?
2. How do "yells" influence the behaviour of Ravens? Explain.
3. What is the meaning and importance of syntax and symbols in signalling?

40.8 Space

The geographic range of many animal species includes a mosaic of habitat types. The breeding ranges of White-crowned Sparrows can encompass forests, meadows, housing developments, and city dumps. Other animals have a limited range, for example, a Kirtland's Warbler (*Dendroica kirtlandii*) is found only in young jackpine forests. An animal's choice of habitat is critically important because the habitat provides food, shelter, nesting sites, and the other organisms with which it interacts. If an animal chooses a habitat that does not provide appropriate resources, it will not survive and reproduce.

On a large spatial scale, animals almost certainly use multiple criteria to select the habitats they occupy, but no research has yet established any general principles about how animals make these choices. When a migrating bird arrives at its breeding range, it probably cues on large-scale geographic features, such as a pond or a patch of large trees. If the bird does not find the food or nesting resources it needs, or if other individuals have already occupied the space and perhaps depleted those resources, it may move to another habitat patch.

On a very fine spatial scale, basic responses to physical factors enable some animals to find suitable habitats. Kinesis (kine = movement; es = inward) is a change in the rate of movement or the frequency of turning movements in response to environmental stimuli. Wood lice (terrestrial crustaceans in the order Isopoda) typically live under rocks and logs or in other damp places. Although these arthropods are not attracted to moisture per se, when a wood louse encounters dry soil, it scrambles around, turning frequently. When it reaches a patch of moist soil, it moves much less. This kinesis results in wood lice accumulating in moist habitats. Wood lice exposed to dry soil quickly dehydrate and die, so those that move to moister habitats are more likely to survive.

A **taxis** (taxis = ordered movement) is a response directed either toward or away from a specific stimulus. Cockroaches (order Blattodea) exhibit negative phototaxis, meaning that they actively avoid light and seek darkness. Negative phototaxis makes cockroaches less vulnerable to predators that use vision to find their food.

Biologists generally assume that habitat selection is adaptive and has been shaped by natural selection. Some animals instinctively select habitats where they are well camouflaged and less detectable by predators. Predators would discover and eliminate individuals that do not select a matching background, along with any alleles responsible for the mismatch. Many insects have genetically determined preferences for the plants they eat as larvae (e.g., caterpillars). Adults often lay their eggs only on appropriate food plants, effectively selecting the habitats where their offspring will live and feed.

Vertebrates sometimes exhibit innate preferences, as demonstrated by two closely related species of European birds, Blue Tits (*Cyanistes cueruleus*) and Coal Tits (*Parus ater*). Adult Blue Tits forage mainly in oak trees and Coal Tits in pines. When researchers reared the young of both species in cages without any vegetation and then offered them a choice between oak branches and pine branches, Coal Tits immediately gravitated toward pines and Blue Tits toward oaks, suggesting an innate preference **(Figure 40.22).** Each species feeds most efficiently in the tree species it prefers.

Habitat preferences can also be moulded by experiences early in life. Tadpoles of red-legged frogs (*Rana aurora*) usually live in aquatic habitats cluttered with sticks, strands of algae, and plant stems. In the laboratory, these tadpoles prefer striped backgrounds to plain ones. In contrast, tadpoles of the closely related cascade frog (*Rana cascadae*) live over gravel bottoms and prefer plain substrates over striped ones. These habitat preferences do not appear when red-legged frogs are reared over plain substrates and cascade frogs over striped substrates and are later given a choice of substrate.

40.8a Home Range and Territory: Occupied and Defended Areas

Space is an important resource for animals. Although many animals are motile, moving about in space, others are sessile. Sessile species such as barnacles (see Figure 3.3g and Chapter 26) anchor themselves to the substrate but are motile as larvae. Barnacles that live on whales or the hulls of ships are sessile but mobile because of the substrate they selected. Motile animals have a home range, the space they regularly traverse during their lives. Home ranges or parts of home ranges become territories when they are defended. In species such as pronghorned antelopes **(Figure 40.23),** some males hold territories, but others do not. Females are not usually territorial. There is a direct connection between territory quality and male reproductive success. Male pronghorn antelopes defending the "best" territories (those with the best food resources) attract the most females, offering the male the most opportunities to mate with the most females.

Male Jarrow's spiny lizards **(Figure 40.24, p. 984)** are normally territorial during the autumnal mating season, when they have elevated levels of testosterone in their blood. Catherine Marler and Michael Moore implanted small doses of testosterone or a placebo under the skins of experimental animals during the nonmating season (June and July). Testosterone-enhanced males were more active and displayed more

Blue Tit | Coal Tit

Alan Williams/Alamy

Mark Hamblin/Oxford Scientific/Index Stock

Percent of time

100

50

0

Wild | Hand-reared

KEY

Pine | Oak

Figure 40.22
Habitat selection by birds. Wild Blue Tits (*Cyanistes caeruleus*) show a strong preference for oak trees; Coal Tits (*Parus ater*) show a strong preference for pines. Hand-reared birds raised in a vegetation-free environment showed identical but slightly weaker responses.

www.amazilia.net

Figure 40.23
Pronghorn antelopes, *Antilocapra americana.*

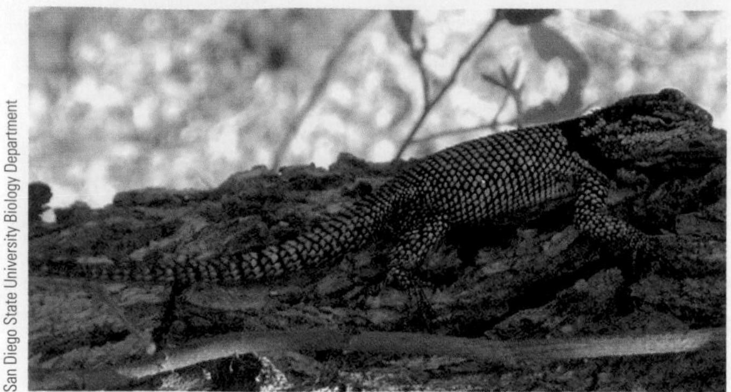

Figure 40.24
Jarrow's spiny lizard, *Sceloporus jarrovi.*

often than control males. Experimental males spent less time feeding, even though they used about 30% more energy per day than control males. In one seven-week period, testosterone-enhanced males suffered significantly higher mortality than placebo males. It can be expensive to be territorial.

Territorial defence is always a costly activity. Patrolling territory borders, performing displays hundreds of times per day, and chasing intruders take time and energy. Moreover, territorial displays increase an animal's likelihood of being injured or detected and captured by a predator.

But territorial behaviour has its benefits, such as access to females. Territorial surgeonfish (*Acanthurus lineatus*) living in coral reefs around American Samoa may engage in as many as 1900 chases per day, defending their small territories from incursions by other algae-eating fish. Territorial surgeonfish eat five times as much food as nonterritory holders because they have more exclusive access to the food in their territories. It also costs the territory holders more to patrol and defend their realm.

Figure 40.25
Long-distance migration. Arctic Terns (*Sterna paradisaea*) migrate from the high Arctic to Antarctica each year, a round-trip journey of 40 000 km. This species' summer breeding range is shaded on the map.

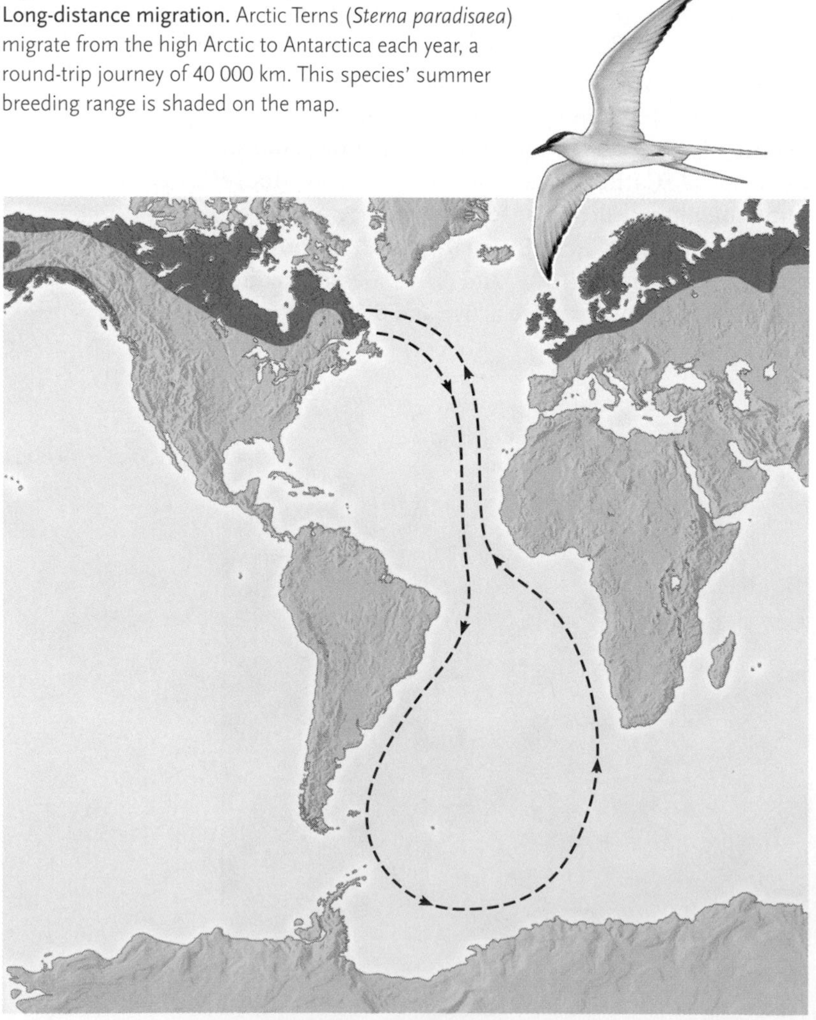

Study Break

1. Define kinesis and taxis.
2. What is the difference between a home range and a territory?
3. How are home ranges and territories different from a species' range?

40.9 Migration

Many animal species make a seasonal **migration**, travelling from the area where they were born or hatched to a distant and initially unfamiliar destination. The migration is complete when they later return to their natal site. The Arctic Tern, a seabird, makes an annual round-trip migration of 40 000 km **(Figure 40.25).** Other vertebrate species, such as grey whales (*Eschrichtius robustus*) and salmon (*Salmo* species), undertake long and predictable journeys. The same is true of arthropods such as spiny lobsters that form long conga lines and move seasonally between coral reefs and the open ocean floor **(Figure 40.26).**

Moving animals use various mechanisms to find their way during migration. There are three categories of way-finding mechanisms: **piloting, compass orientation**, and **navigation**. Many species probably use some combination of these mechanisms to guide their movements.

40.9a Piloting: Finding the Way

Piloting is the simplest way-finding mechanism, involving the use of familiar landmarks to guide a journey. Grey whales migrate from Alaska to Baja California and back using visual cues provided by the Pacific coastline of North America. When it is time to breed and lay eggs, Pacific salmon use olfactory cues to pilot their way from the ocean back to the stream in which they hatched.

Animals that do not migrate also use specific landmarks to identify their nest site or places where they have stored food. Female digger wasps (*Philanthus*

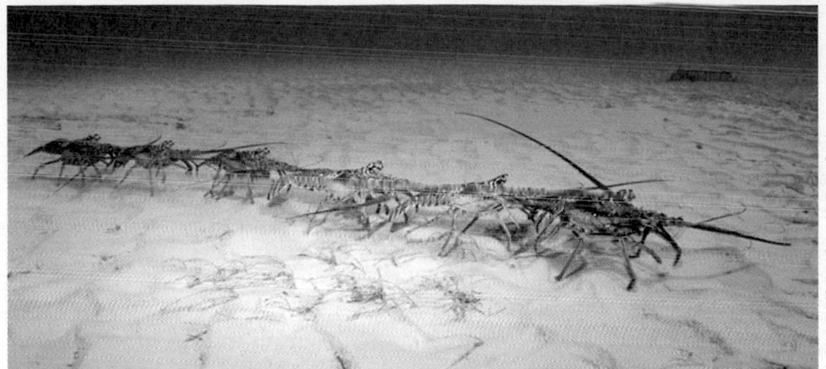

Figure 40.26
Migrating arthropods. Spiny lobsters (*Panulirus argus*) make seasonal migrations between coral reefs and the open ocean floor. As many as 50 individuals march in single file for several days.

triangulum) nest in soil. In 1938, Niko Tinbergen showed that after foraging flights, these wasps used visual landmarks to find their nests **(Figure 40.27)**. While the female wasp was in the nest, Tinbergen arranged pinecones in a circle around it. As she left, the wasp flew around the area, apparently noting nearby landmarks. Tinbergen then moved the circle of pinecones a short distance away. Each time the female returned, she searched for her nest within the pinecone circle. She never once found her nest unless the pinecones were returned to their original position. Later Tinbergen rearranged the pinecones into a triangle after females left their nests and added a ring of stones nearby. The returning females looked for their nest in the stone circle. Tinbergen concluded that digger wasps respond to the general outline or geometry of landmarks around their nests and not to the specific objects comprising the landmarks.

40.9b Compass: Which Way Is North?

Animals using compass orientation move in a particular direction, often over a specific distance or for a prescribed length of time. Some day-flying migratory birds orient themselves using the Sun's position in the sky in conjunction with an internal biological clock (see Chapter 1). The internal clock allows the bird to use the Sun as a compass, compensating for changes in its position through the day. The clock also may allow some birds to estimate how far they have travelled since beginning their journey. Other animals, including birds, mammals, reptiles, amphibians, fish, crustaceans, and insects, use Earth's magnetic field as a compass. This requires detection of weak magnetic fields (~50 μT – micro-Teslas). In 2008, some biologists suggested that magnetically sensitive free radical reactions could be the basis of a magnetic sense, but the search for the transducer(s) (see Chapter 34) is ongoing.

40.9c Stars: Celestial Navigation

Some birds that migrate at night determine their direction by using the positions of stars. The Indigo Bunting flies about 3500 km from the northeastern United States to the Caribbean or Central America each fall and makes the return journey each spring. Stephen Emlen demonstrated that Indigo Buntings direct their migration

Figure 40.27
Female digger wasps find their nets. A ring of pinecones serves as a landmark for a female digger wasp (*Philanthus triangulum*). By manipulating the location of landmarks, Nikko Tinbergen demonstrated the role they serve in the wasp's orientation behaviour.

using celestial cues (**Figure 40.28**). Emlen confined individual buntings in cone-shaped test cages whose sides were lined with blotting paper. He placed inkpads on the cage bottoms and kept the cages in an outdoor enclosure so that the birds had a full view of the night sky. Whenever a bird made a directed movement, its inky footprints indicated the direction in which it was trying to move. On clear nights in fall, the footprints pointed to the south, but in spring, they pointed north. On cloudy nights, when the buntings could not see the stars, Emlen recorded that their footprints were evenly distributed in all directions. The data indicated that the compass of indigo buntings required a view of the stars.

40.9d Navigation: A Complex Challenge

Navigation is the most complex way-finding mechanism. It occurs when an animal moves toward a specific destination, using both a compass and a "mental map" of where it is in relation to the destination. Hikers in unfamiliar surroundings routinely use navigation to find their way home. They use a map to determine their current position and the necessary direction of movement and a compass to orient themselves in that direction. Scientists have documented true navigation in a few animal species, notably the Homing Pigeon (*Columba livia*). These birds can navigate to their home coops from any direction, probably using the Sun's position as their compass and olfactory cues as their map.

40.9e Reasons for Migratory Behaviour

Migrations by White-crowned Sparrows and many other species are triggered by changes in day length. Shortening day length indicates approaching fall and winter; lengthening day length indicates spring. Day length changes the anterior pituitary of the bird's brain to generate a series of hormonal changes. In response, birds feed heavily and accumulate the fat reserves necessary to fuel their long journey. Sparrows also become increasingly restless at night, until one evening, they begin their nocturnal migration. Their ability to adopt and maintain a southerly orientation in autumn (and a northerly one in spring) rests in part on their capacity to use the positions of stars to provide directional information.

Migratory behaviour entails obvious costs, such as the time and energy devoted to the journey and the risk of death from exhaustion or predator attack. Migratory behaviour is not universal—many animals never migrate, spending their lives in one location. Why do some species migrate? What ecological pressures give migrating individuals higher fitness than individuals that do not migrate? Remember that many species of terrestrial animals migrate, such as wildebeest and caribou.

For migratory birds, seasonal changes in food supply are the most widely accepted hypothesis to explain migratory behaviour. Insects can be abundant in higher latitude (>50° N or S) habitats during the warm spring and summer, providing excellent resources for birds to raise offspring. As summer wanes and fall and winter approach, insects all but disappear. Bird species that remain in temperate habitats over winter eat mainly seeds and dormant insects. When it is winter at higher latitudes, energy supplies are more predictably available in the tropical grounds used by overwintering migratory birds.

Two-way migratory journeys may provide other benefits. Avoiding the northern winter is probably adaptive because endotherms must increase their metabolic rates just to stay warm in cold climates (see Chapter 43). Moreover, summer days are longer at high latitudes than they are in the tropics (see Chapter 3), giving adult birds more time to feed and rear a brood.

Seasonal changes in food supply also underlie the migration of monarch butterflies

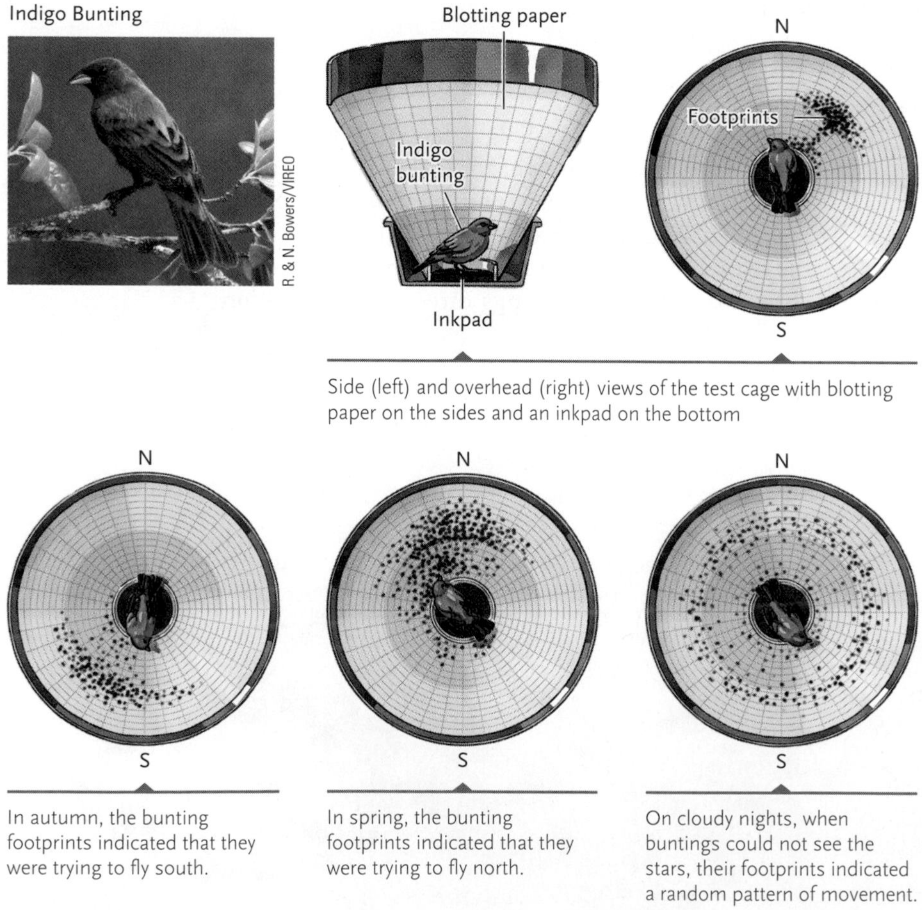

Indigo Bunting

R. & N. Bowers/VIREO

Blotting paper

Indigo bunting

Inkpad

Footprints

Side (left) and overhead (right) views of the test cage with blotting paper on the sides and an inkpad on the bottom

In autumn, the bunting footprints indicated that they were trying to fly south.

In spring, the bunting footprints indicated that they were trying to fly north.

On cloudy nights, when buntings could not see the stars, their footprints indicated a random pattern of movement.

Figure 40.28
Orientation by Indigo Buntings. The footprints of inked Indigo Buntings (*Passerina cyanea*) demonstrated migrating birds' responses to celestial cues.

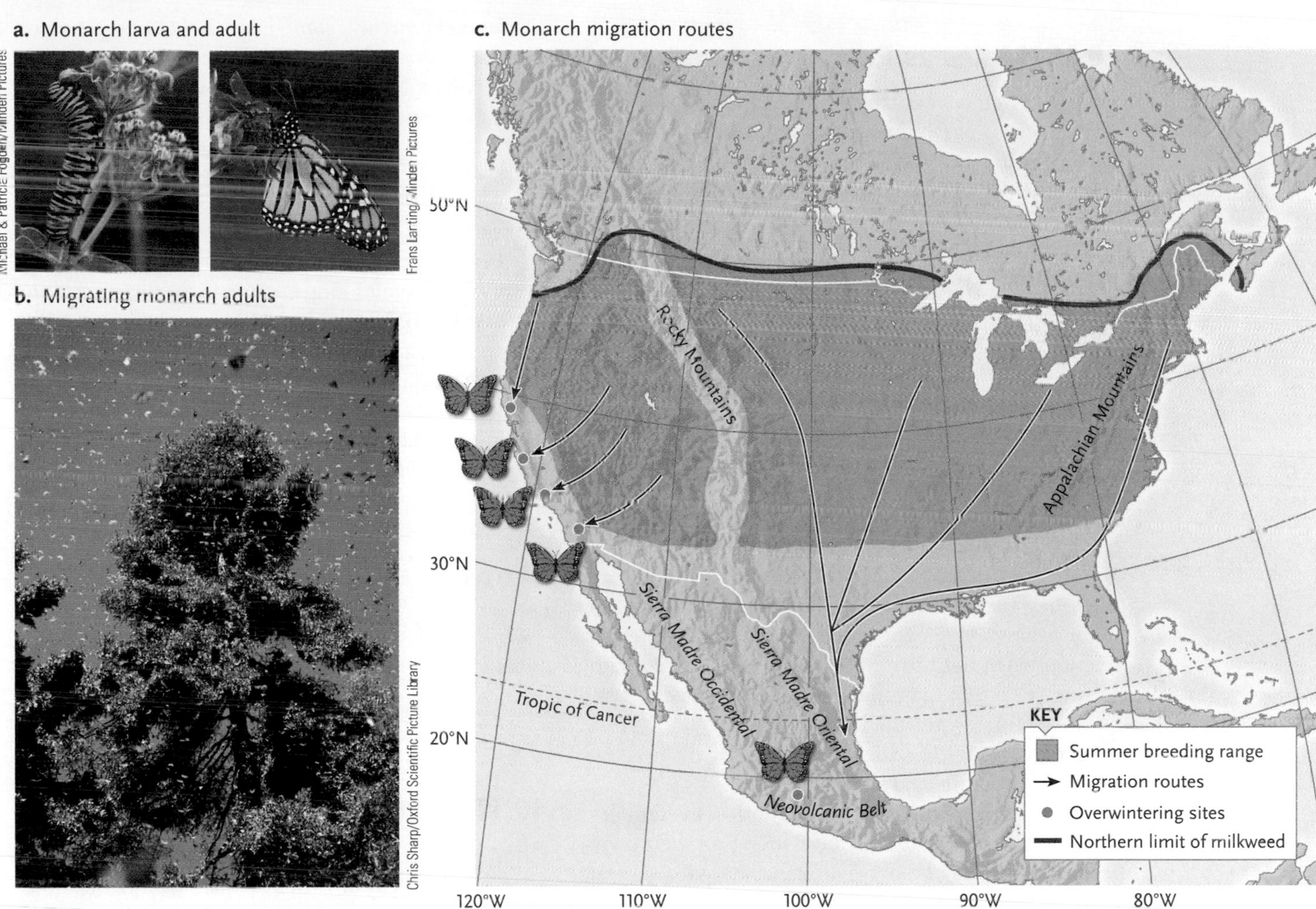

Figure 40.29
Migrating monarch butterflies. **(a)** Monarch butterflies (*Danaus plexippus*) eat milkweed plants as caterpillars. **(b)** When milkweed plants in their breeding range die back at the end of summer, monarchs migrate south. The following spring, after passing the winter in a semi-dormant state, they migrate north. **(c)** Monarchs that live and breed east of the Rocky Mountains migrate to Mexico. Those living west of the Rocky Mountains overwinter in coastal California.

that eat milkweed leaves as caterpillars and milkweed nectar as adults. In eastern North America, milkweed plants grow only during spring and summer. Many adult monarchs head south in late summer, when the plants begin to die. Some migrate as much as 4000 km from eastern and central North America to central Mexico, where they cluster in spectacular numbers **(Figure 40.29b)**, apparently using olfactory cues to find preferred resting places. Unlike migrant birds, these insects do not feed while at their overwintering grounds. Instead, their metabolic rate decreases in the cool mountain air, and the butterflies become inactive for months, conserving precious energy reserves. When spring arrives, the butterflies become active again and begin the return migration to northern breeding habitats. The northward migration is slow, however, and many individuals stop along the way to feed and lay eggs. These offspring, and their offspring, continue the northward migration through the summer. Some descendants of these migrants eventually reach Canada for a final round of breeding. The summer's last generation then returns south to the spot where their ancestors, two to five generations removed, spent the previous winter.

For other animals, migration to breeding grounds may provide the special conditions necessary for reproduction. Grey whales migrate south, where females give birth to their young in quiet, shallow lagoons where predators are rare and warm water temperatures are more conducive to the growth of their calves.

Study Break

1. Define migration. Give examples of migratory animals, including some not mentioned in the text. Do any humans migrate?
2. How do migrating animals find their way? Distinguish between navigation and compass orientation.

40.10 Mates as Resources

Mating systems have evolved to maximize reproductive success, partly in response to the amount of parental care that offspring require and partly in response to other aspects of a species' ecology. **Monogamy** describes the situation in which a male and a female form a pair bond for a mating season or, in some cases, for the individuals' reproductive lives. **Polygamy** occurs when one male has active pair bonds with more than one female (**polygyny**) or one female has active pair bonds with more than one male (**polyandry**). **Promiscuity** occurs when males and females have no pair bonds beyond the time it takes to mate.

When young require a great deal of care that both parents can provide, monogamy often prevails. Songbirds, such as the White-crowned Sparrow **(Figure 40.30)**, are altricial (naked and helpless) when they hatch. They beg for food, and both parents can bring it to them. Males and females achieve higher rates of reproduction when both parents are actively involved with raising young. In mammals, the situation is different because females provide the food (milk). Monogamy occurs in species in which males indirectly feed the young by bringing food to the mother.

If males have high-quality territories, the females living there may be able to raise young on their own. These males may be polygynous (mate with several females). The male's role is that of sperm donor and protector of the space rather than that of an active parent to all of his young. In birds such as Red-winged Blackbirds (*Agelaius phoenecius*), some males hold large, resource-filled territories that support several females. These males will be attractive to females even if a female (or females) already lives on the territory. Polygyny is prevalent among mammals because, compared with males, females make a much larger investment in raising young (through egg development and care of the young).

Promiscuous mating systems occur when females are only with males long enough to receive sperm and there is no pair bond. These males make no contribution to raising young. Sage Grouse **(Figure 40.31)** and hammer-headed bats (*Hysignathus monstrosus*) are examples of this approach. Both species form leks, congregations of displaying males, where females come only to mate. There are more details about Sage Grouse below.

© Edgar T. Jones/VIREO

Figure 40.30
Reproductive success. Parental care is just one of the many behaviours required for successful reproduction in White-crowned Sparrows and in many other animal species. The number of surviving nestlings will determine the reproductive success of their parents and the representation of their genes in the next generation.

Study Break

What do the terms monogamy, polygamy, and promiscuity mean?

40.11 Sexual Selection

Given the drive to reproduce (see Chapter 38), competition for access to mates coupled with mate choice sets the stage for sexual selection. Sexual dimorphism, in which one gender is larger or more colourful than the other, can be an outcome of sexual selection. When males compete for females, males are often larger than females and may have ornaments and weapons, such as horns and antlers, useful for attracting females and for butting, stabbing, or intimidating rival males. Displays of adornments or weapons can simultaneously warn off other males and attract the attention of females. Peacocks strut in front of female peahens while spreading a gigantic fan of tail feathers, which they shake, rattle, and roll.

Why should females choose males with exaggerated structures conspicuously displayed? A male's large size, bright feathers, or large horns might indicate that he is particularly healthy. His appearance could indicate that he can harvest resources efficiently or simply that he has managed to survive to an advanced age. The features are, in effect, signals of male quality, and if they reflect a male's genetic makeup, he is likely to fertilize a female's eggs with sperm containing successful alleles. Large showy males may hold large, rich territories. Females that choose these males can gain access to the resources their territories contain.

The degree to which females *actively* choose genetically superior mates varies among species. In northern elephant seals, female choice is more or less passive.

Ray Richardson/Animals Animals–Earth Scenes

Figure 40.31
Lekking behaviour. Male Sage Grouse (*Centrocercus urophasianus*) use their ornamental feathers in visual courtship displays performed at a lek. There each male has his own small territory. The smaller brown females observe the performing males before picking a mate.

Large numbers of females gather on beaches to give birth to their pups before becoming sexually receptive again (see Chapter 38, *Delaying Reproduction*). Males locate clusters of females and fight to keep other males away (see Figure 17.8). Males that win have exceptional reproductive success because they mate with many females, but only after engaging in violent and relentless combat with rival males. In this mating system, the females struggle during a male's attempts to mate with them. A female's struggles attract other males, who try to interrupt the attempted mating. Only the largest and most powerful males are not interrupted in their copulations, and they inseminate the most females. These attributes may be associated with alleles that will increase their offspring's chances of living long enough to reproduce.

In other species, females exercise more active mate choice, mating only after inspecting several potential partners. Among birds, active female mate choice is most apparent at **leks**, display grounds where each male holds a small territory from which it courts attentive females. The male is the only resource on the territory. Male Sage Grouse in western North America gather in open areas among stands of sagebrush. Each male defends a few square metres, where it struts in circles while emitting booming calls and showing off its elegant tail feathers and big neck pouches (see Figure 40.31). Females wander among displaying males, presumably observing the males' visual and acoustical displays. Eventually, each female selects one mate from among the dozens of males that are present. Females repeatedly favour males that come to the lek daily, defend their small area vigorously, and display more frequently than the average lek participant. Males preferred by females sustain their territorial defence and high display rate over long periods, abilities that may correlate with other useful genetic traits. Ultimately, the male holding the "best" position in the lek mates with the most females.

The results of experiments with peafowl suggest that the top Peacocks (*Pavo cristatus*) supply advantageous alleles to their offspring. In nature, peahens prefer males whose tails have many ornamental eyespots **(Figure 40.32).** In an experiment on captive birds, some peahens were mated to peacocks with highly attractive tails, but others were paired with males whose tails were less impressive. The offspring of both groups were reared under uniform conditions for several months and then released into an English woodland. After three months on their own, the offspring of fathers with impressive tails survived better and weighed significantly more than did those whose fathers had less attractive tails. The evidence demonstrates that a peahen's mate choice influences her offsprings' chances of survival.

According to the handicap hypothesis, females select males that are successful—the ones with ornate structures. These structures may impede their locomotion, and their elaborate displays may attract the attention of predators. Females select ornate males because they have survived *despite* carrying such a handicap. Successful alleles responsible for the ornamental handicap are passed to the female's offspring.

© Ashley Cooper/Corbis

Figure 40.32
Sexual selection for ornamentation. The attractiveness of a peacock to peahens depends in part on the number of eyespots in his extraordinary tail. The offspring of males with elaborate tails are more successful than the offspring of males with plainer tails.

Study Break

What are the distinguishing features of a lek?

40.12 Social Behaviour

Social behaviour, the interactions that animals have with other members of their species, has profound effects on an individual's reproductive success. Some animals are solitary, getting together only briefly to mate (house flies and leopards). Others spend most of their lives in small family groups (gorillas). Still others live in groups with thousands of relatives (termites and honeybees). Some species, such as caribou and humans, live in large social units composed primarily of nonrelatives. In many species, the level of social interactions varies seasonally, usually reflecting the timing of reproduction, which, in turn, is influenced by changes in day length.

40.12a African Lions: Infanticide

African lions (*Panthera leo*) usually live in prides, one adult male with several females and their young. Males typically sire the young born to the females in their pride, achieving a high reproductive output. Females benefit from the support of the others in the group, which includes caring for young and cooperating in foraging. Female lions living in prides wean more young per litter than those living alone. The females in a pride are often genetically related, and their estrus cycles are usually synchronized. Male lions are bigger (~200 kg) than females (~150 kg), and males fight vigourously for the position of pride male. Males protect their females from incursions by other males.

When a new male takes over a pride, he kills all nursing young, bringing the females into estrus. At first, this infanticide seems counterproductive. However, it benefits the male because it increases the chances of his succeeding at reproducing. Were he to wait until the females had raised their dependent young, his reproductive contributions could be delayed for some time, perhaps as much as a year or more.

Females are not large enough to protect their young from the male. If a female takes her nursing young and leaves the pride, her efficiency as hunter declines, and she is less able to protect her young. Her reproductive success plummets. Females can be more productive (measured by output of young) when they are part of a pride.

But why live in a group in the first place? By hunting together, lions are more efficient foragers than when they hunt alone; therefore, they raise more young. Perhaps more important is the threat posed by spotted hyenas, which live in large groups (clans). Although individually smaller (~60 kg), when spotted hyenas outnumber lions, they can chase lions from their kills. Furthermore, many of the lion's main prey also live in groups, and group defences affect lions' hunting success.

The situation in lions exemplifies some biological realities. Males and females do not have the same strategies when it comes to reproduction. Understanding behaviour means considering genetic relatedness and production of offspring, as well as the setting in which the animals live.

40.12b Group Living: Costs and Benefits

Social Behaviours. Ecological factors have a large impact on the reproductive benefits and costs of social living. Groups of cooperating predators frequently capture prey more effectively than they would on their own. White Pelicans (*Pelecanus erythrorhynchos*) often encircle a school of fish before attacking, so being part of a group provides a better yield to individuals than working alone. On the other hand, prey subject to intense predation may benefit from group defence. This can mean more pairs of watchful eyes or ears to detect an approaching danger. It may also translate into multiple lures so that when a predator attacks, it is more difficult to focus on an individual. When you are part of a group that is attacked, it may be someone other than you that is captured, diluting the risk to any one group member.

When attacked by wolves, adult muskoxen form a circle around the young, so attackers are always confronted by horns and hooves **(Figure 40.33).** Insects such as Australian sawfly caterpillars also show cooperative defensive behaviour **(Figure 40.34).** When predators disturb the caterpillars, all group members rear up, writhe about, and regurgitate sticky, pungent oils. The caterpillars collect the oils from the eucalyptus leaves they eat. The oils do not harm the caterpillars but are toxic and repellent to birds.

Living in groups can also be expensive. One cost can be increased competition for food. When thousands of royal penguins crowd together in huge colonies **(Figure 40.35),** the pressure on local food supplies is great, increasing the risk of starvation. Communal living may facilitate the spread of contagious diseases and parasites. Nestlings in large colonies of Cliff Swallows (*Petrochelidon pyrrhonota*) are often stunted in growth because the nests swarm with blood-feeding, bedbuglike parasites, *Oeciacus vicarious*, **(Figure 40.36, p. 992).** The parasites move readily from nest to nest in crowded conditions. Some social animals learn to recognize and avoid diseased group members. Caribbean spiny lobsters live in groups but avoid conspecifics infected by a lethal virus (PaV1). It is no surprise that most animals live alone.

Group living brings both costs and benefits. Not all animals that live in groups are "social," a term implying some organization of the group. The 10 million

Figure 40.33
Muskoxen.

Figure 40.34
Social defensive behaviour. Australian sawfly (*Perga dosalis*) caterpillars clump together on tree branches. They regurgitate yellow blobs of sticky aromatic fluid that repels birds. The accumulation of regurgitate from a group of caterpillars is an effective defence.

Brazilian free-tailed bats emerging from a cave roost near San Antonio, Texas, are no more a social group than the dozens of people leaving a high-rise apartment or university residence. Within the aggregation, there may be social units, but the aggregation itself is not necessarily a social unit.

Social animals usually live in groups characterized by some form of structure. Some individuals may dominate others (a dominance hierarchy), manifested in access to resources. Dominant (alpha or α) individuals get priority access to food (or mates or sleeping sites). In some situations, only dominant individuals (a male and a female) reproduce. Dominance hierarchies may be absolute, such as when the same individual always has priority access to any resource. In relative dominance hierarchies, an individual's status depends on the circumstance.

Dominance brings its costs. In animals such as wild dogs (*Lycaeon pictus*) or grey wolves, dominant animals must constantly defend their status. Dominants often have high levels of cortisol and other stress-related hormones in their blood (see Chapter 35) compared with subordinates. Elevated cortisol levels may induce high blood pressure, the disruption of sugar metabolism, and other pathological conditions.

Subordinance brings its benefits. Subordinate group members, like all members of the group, gain protection from predators. They may also gain experience by

Figure 40.35
Colonial living. Royal Penguins (*Eudyptes schlegeli*) on Macquarie Island between New Zealand and Antarctica experience benefits and costs from living together in huge groups.

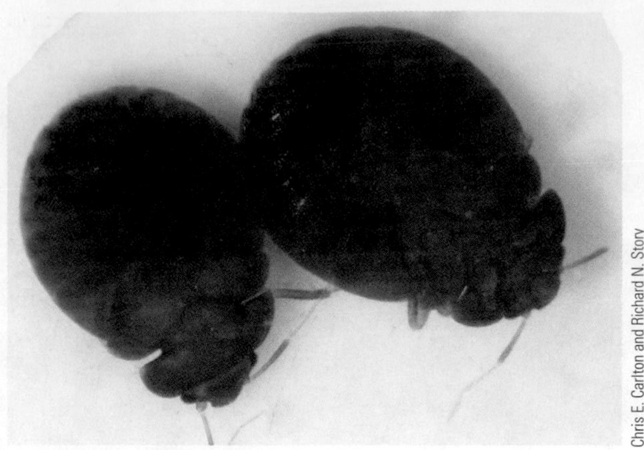

Figure 40.36 Dorsal and ventral views of a bedbug that specializes on birds (*Ornithocoris pallidus*).

Chris E. Carlton and Richard N. Story

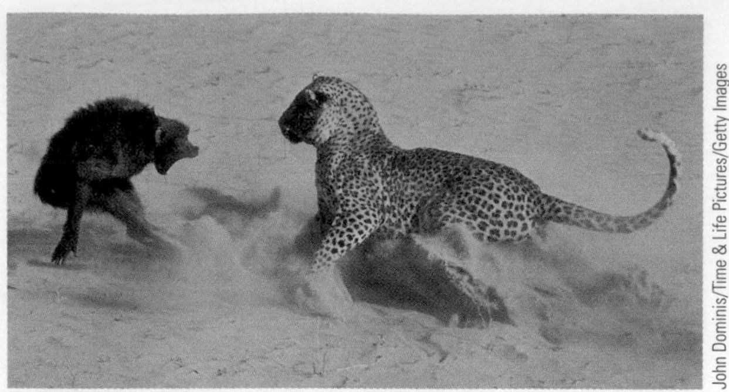

John Dominis/Time & Life Pictures/Getty Images

Figure 40.37 When attacked by a leopard (*Panthera pardus*), a solitary baboon (*Papio anubis*) is defiant but unlikely to survive.

helping dominant individuals raise young. Over time, subordinate individuals can rise in a dominance hierarchy and avoid some of the side effects of dominance. Many social animals cannot survive on their own **(Figure 40.37).**

Study Break

1. What is infanticide? Why does it occur?
2. Gives some examples of advantages and disadvantages of group living.

40.13 Kin Selection and Altruism

Behavioural ecologist William D. Hamilton recognized that helping genetic relatives effectively propagates the helper's genes because family members share alleles inherited from their ancestors. By calculating the degree of relatedness, we can quantify the average percentage of alleles shared by relatives **(Figure 40.38).** Half-siblings, by definition, share one genetic parent, so they share, on average, 0.25 of their alleles by inheritance from their shared parent. Their degree of relatedness is 0.25. Full siblings share both parents' share, 0.25 of their alleles through the mother and 0.25 through the father, for a total, on average, of $0.25 + 0.25 = 0.5$ of their alleles. The degree of relatedness between a nephew or niece and an aunt or uncle is 0.25 and between first cousins is 0.125. Individuals should be more likely to help close relatives because increasing a close relative's fitness means that the individual is helping to propagate some of its own alleles. This is **kin selection.**

A male grey wolf helps his parents rear four pups to adulthood, pups that would have died without the extra assistance he provided. The pups are his younger full siblings, sharing 0.5 of his genes, so, on average, the helper has created "by proxy" two ($0.50 \times 4 = 2$) copies of any allele they shared. However, the costs of his helping must be measured against this indirect reproductive success. If he had found a mate, sired offspring, and raised two of them, each would have carried half of his alleles, preserving only one ($0.50 \times 2 = 1$) copy of a given allele. In this situation, reproducing on his own would have produced fewer copies of his alleles in the next generation than helping to raise his siblings. This example is hypothetical, but sibling helpers have been documented in many species of birds and mammals. The phenomenon is especially common among animals in which inexperienced parents are not very successful at reproducing on their own offspring. By helping, they gain experience and realize some genetic benefit.

Altruism involves doing something that enhances the situation of another individual, but Hamilton's kin selection theory demonstrates why parental behaviour (or helping parents raise siblings) is genetically selfish, not altruistic. Therefore, the behaviour of the young wolf (above) is not altruistic. Robert Trivers proposed that individuals will help nonrelatives if they are likely to return the favour in the future. Trivers called this **reciprocal altruism** because each member of the partnership can potentially benefit from the relationship. Trivers hypothesized that reciprocal altruism would be favoured by natural selection as long as individuals that do *not* reciprocate (cheaters) are denied future aid.

Among the many features of social animals, the evolution of cooperative behaviour can be one of the most challenging to

Half Siblings

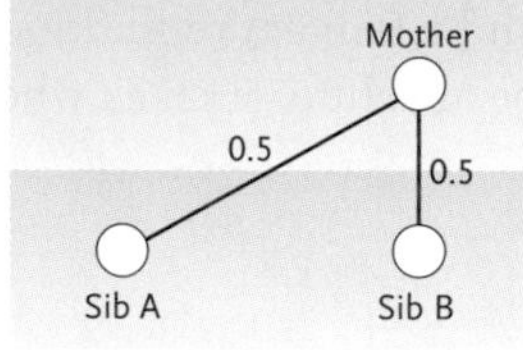

Full Siblings

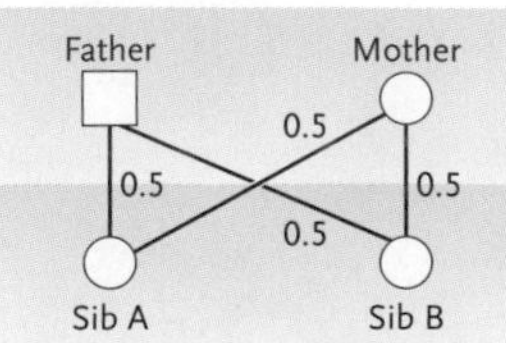

First Cousins

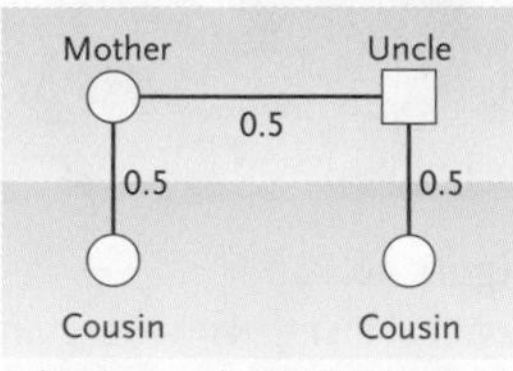

Figure 40.38 Calculating degrees of relatedness.

understand. Why has cooperative behaviour arisen in populations of animals? How does it arise? And how is it maintained in populations?

John M. McNamara and three colleagues wrote about the coevolution of choosiness and cooperation in a paper published in *Nature* in 2007. Using modelling and simulation experiments, these authors examined the consequences arising in situations in which one individual's cooperativeness influences the decisions about actions by other individuals toward group members. They postulated a situation of "competitive altruism" in which individuals actually compete with one another to be more cooperative.

The results of their analysis suggest that longer-lived species are more likely to develop cooperative behaviour than short-lived ones. This is important because the model does not require intermediate situations involving negotiation behaviour. The model helps us understand the appearance of cooperative behaviour in all animals, including in *Homo sapiens*.

Reciprocal altruism is one element of cooperative behaviour, and dolphins may be reciprocal altruists. Many species of dolphins are long-lived and social, living in groups. Dolphins and other cetaceans show many forms of aid-giving behaviour, from attending injured group members ("standing by" in naval parlance) to assisting with difficult births. They also use group behaviour to protect themselves from the attacks of sharks. Richard Connor and Kenneth Norris proposed that the persistent threat of attacks by sharks and the perils of living in the ocean combined to provide dolphins with many opportunities to help one another, even members of other species. Connor and Norris did not have specific details of genetic relationships among group members, but they proposed that dolphins are reciprocal altruists.

Study Break

1. What is the main argument in Hamilton's kin selection theory?
2. Imagine that four of your first cousins, two siblings, and two half-siblings are about to fall from a cliff and die. You have the option of taking their place. In terms of kin selection, which is more beneficial to you, your life or the life of your genetic relatives?
3. Which of the following behaviours is altruistic: parental care, mate selection, courtship feeding, self-defence, and/or helping nonrelatives? Why? Why not?

40.14 Eusocial Animals

Hamilton's insights led to the prediction that self-sacrificing behaviour should be directed to kin. Evidence from many species of animals, particularly bees, ants, termites, and wasps, overwhelmingly supports this prediction. In a colony of **eusocial** insects, thousands of genetically related individuals, most of them sterile workers, live and work together for the reproductive benefit of one individual, a single queen and her mate(s). The workers may even die in defence of their colonies.

a. Queen with sterile workers

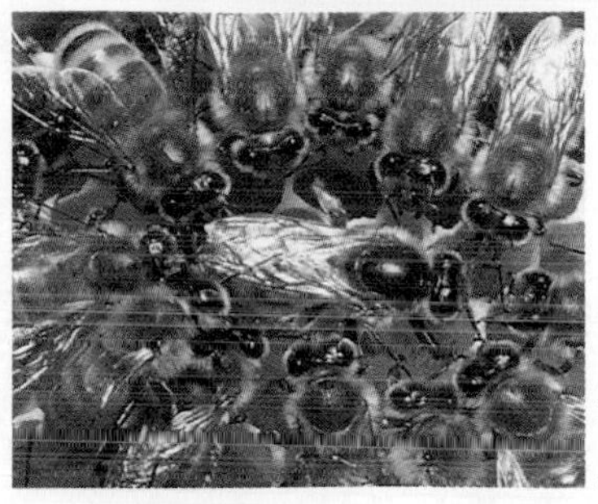

Kenneth Lorenzen

b. Workers sharing food and passing pheromones

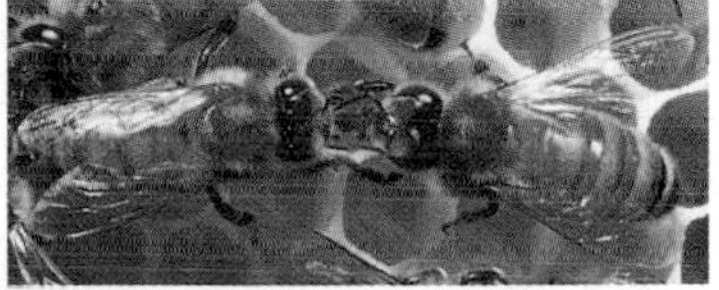

Kenneth Lorenzen

Figure 40.39
(a) In a hive of honeybees, a court of sterile workers (daughters) surround their mother (the queen). **(b)** Worker bees routinely share food and transfer pheromones to one another.

How did this social behaviour evolve, and why does it persist over time? A colony of honeybees may contain 30 000 to 50 000 related individuals, but only the queen bee is fertile. All of the workers are her daughters **(Figure 40.39)**. The queen's role in the colony is to reproduce. The workers perform all of the other tasks in maintaining the hive, from feeding the queen and her larvae to constructing new honeycomb and foraging for nectar and pollen. They also transfer food to one another and sometimes guard the entrance to the hive. Some pay the ultimate sacrifice when they sting intruders because stinging tears open the bee's abdomen, leaving the stinger and the poison sac behind in the intruder's skin but killing the bee.

In bees and other eusocial insects, sex is determined genetically through haplodiploidy **(Figure 40.40, p. 994)**. Female bees are diploid because they receive a set of chromosomes from each parent. Male bees are haploid because they hatch from unfertilized eggs. When a queen bee mates with a drone (a male), all of the sperm he delivers are genetically identical because males have only one set of chromosomes. When a queen bee mates with just one male, all of her worker offspring will inherit exactly the same set of alleles from their male parent, ensuring at least a 50% degree of relatedness among them. Like other diploid organisms, workers are related to each other by an average of 25% through their female parent. Adding these two components of relatedness, workers are related to each other by an average of 75%, a higher degree of relatedness than they would have to any offspring they would have produced had they been fertile.

The high degree of relatedness among workers in some colonies of eusocial insects may explain their exceptional level of cooperation. When Hamilton first worked out this explanation of eusocial behaviour, he suggested that workers devote their lives to caring for their siblings (the queen's other offspring) because a few of those siblings, those carrying 75% of the workers' alleles, may become future queens and produce enormous numbers of offspring themselves.

Naked mole rats are eusocial mammals with nonbreeding workers. In East Africa, these small, almost hairless animals live in underground colonies of 70 to

Life on the Edge
Advantage Social Behaviour

The McNamara et al. model of competitive altruism helps explain the evolution of blood-sharing behaviour in vampire bats (see Figure 3.19). Vampire bats are the only euthermic blood-feeders, and like many other bats, they are long-lived in the wild (recorded to at least 19 years of age). The three living species of vampire bats, common vampire bat (*Desmodus rotundus*), white-winged vampire bat (*Diaemus youngi*), and hairy-legged vampire bat (*Diphylla ecaudata*), all practise food sharing. An individual unsuccessful in foraging can return to its roost and beg blood from a successful forager among its roost mates. The donor bat regurgitates some of its blood meal to the recipient. G.S. Wilkinson's work with common vampire bats demonstrated that individuals roost together with both genetic relatives and nonrelatives. Familiarity, not relatedness, was the key to food sharing by these bats.

The selection process for the behaviour can be placed in context by evidence about a bat's success. Adult common vampire bats typically are unsuccessful in obtaining blood one night per month. An adult can survive two days (daytime periods) without feeding but not three. This means that on any night in any month in a colony of 30 adult vampire bats, one individual will benefit from the cooperativeness of a roost mate.

Even more importantly, young bats may be unsuccessful three or four times a week. Blood-feeding bats thus live on the edge of survival and likely depend on a network of cooperation by roost mates. The social network demonstrated for common vampire bats probably applies to white-winged and hairy-legged species as well. The network is based on cooperation and may be the key to being a successful euthermic blood-feeder.

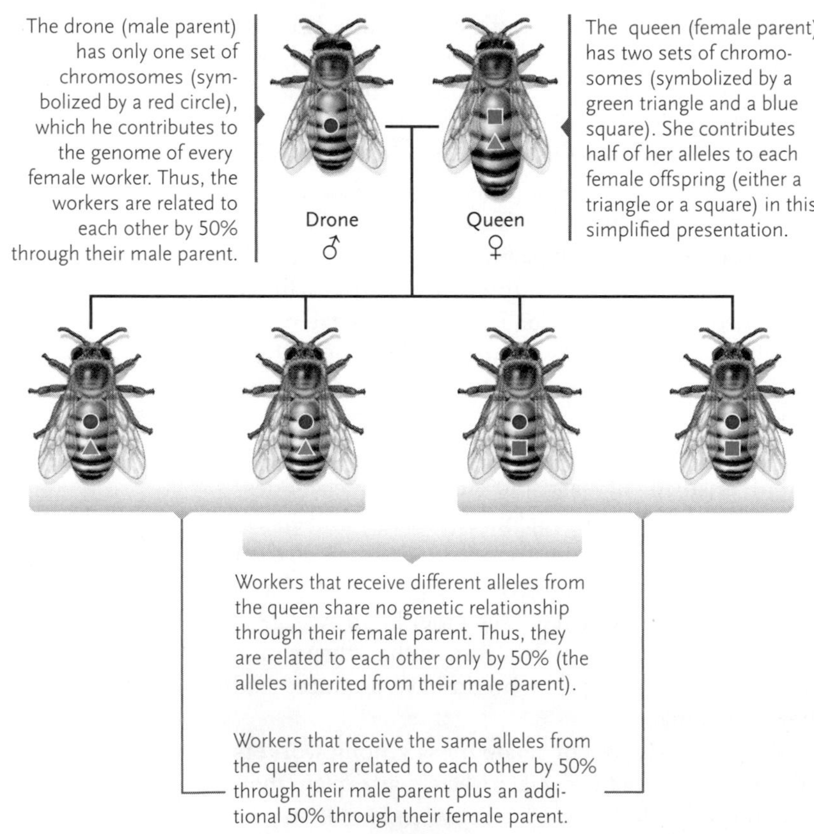

The drone (male parent) has only one set of chromosomes (symbolized by a red circle), which he contributes to the genome of every female worker. Thus, the workers are related to each other by 50% through their male parent.
Drone
♂
Queen
♀
The queen (female parent) has two sets of chromosomes (symbolized by a green triangle and a blue square). She contributes half of her alleles to each female offspring (either a triangle or a square) in this simplified presentation.
Workers that receive different alleles from the queen share no genetic relationship through their female parent. Thus, they are related to each other only by 50% (the alleles inherited from their male parent).
Workers that receive the same alleles from the queen are related to each other by 50% through their male parent plus an additional 50% through their female parent.

Figure 40.40
Haplodiploidy. The genetic system of eusocial insects produces full siblings with exceptionally high degrees of relatedness. Although this simplified model ignores recombination between the queen's two sets of chromosomes, it demonstrates how half of the workers are related to each other by 50% and half are related to each other by 100%. On average, the relatedness between workers is 75%.

80 individuals. Like eusocial insects, naked mole rats share an exceptionally high proportion of alleles (see Box: *Naked Mole Rats*).

Animals living in groups, whether they are aggregations or social units, may be at greater risk of inbreeding than those living alone. Dispersal is a mechanism that can reduce the chances of incestuous matings and inbreeding. Although spotted hyenas live in clans, the males tend to disperse from their natal units, minimizing the risk of inbreeding. Using microsatellite profiling, O.P. Höner and colleagues showed that a female preferred mates that had been born into or immigrated into the clan after she was born.

Study Break

1. What is haplodiploidy? How does it relate to Hamilton's prediction (above)?

40.15 Human Social Behaviour

Humans and chimpanzees share 95% of their genomes. In Chapter 27, we considered the relative importance of the 5% difference. Compared with humans, both chimpanzees and bonobos (*Pan paniscus*) live in relatively unstructured social groups. The brains of *Homo sapiens* are approximately three times larger than those of great apes such as the chimps and bonobos. Brain tissue has a very high metabolic rate, so growing and operating a large brain imposes significant costs.

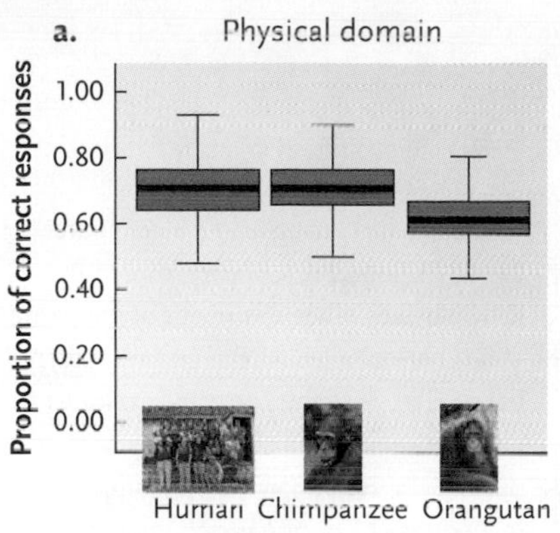

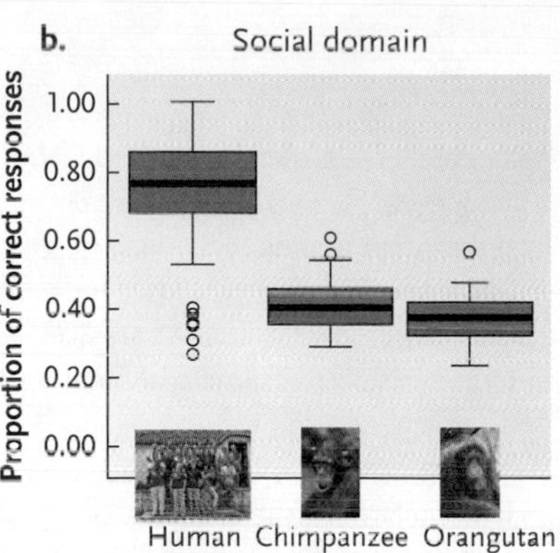

Figure 40.41
Humans, chimpanzees, orangutans. Box plots showing the proportion of correct responses to survey questions in the physical and the social domains. In the social domain, outlying data points (circles) were at least 1.5 times the interquartile distances (shown by the error bars).

The cultural intelligence hypothesis proposes that large brain size in humans reflects cognitive skill sets absent from great apes. Large brains allow humans to perform many cognitive tasks more rapidly and efficiently than other species with smaller brains. The tasks include those associated with memory, learning time, long-range planning, and complexity of interindividual interactions.

To test this, Esther Herrmann and her colleagues administered a large battery of cognitive tests to chimpanzees, orangutans (*Pongo pygmaeus*), and 2½-year-old human children. The children in the experiment were preschool and preliteracy. Although the children, chimpanzees, and orangutans had similar cognitive skills for dealing with the physical world, the children had more sophisticated cognitive skills for dealing with the social world **(Figure 40.41).** The data support the hypothesis that cultural intelligence is an important way to distinguish humans from their closest living relatives.

The ultimatum game is an economic decision-making tool for assessing the responses of individuals to opportunities and the behaviour of others. Responses allow researchers to distinguish between players on the basis of sensitivity and sense of fairness. Keith Jensen and his colleagues used the ultimatum game to compare humans and chimpanzees. Two anonymous individuals can play a round of this game. One, the proposer, is offered a sum of money (or a food reward) and can decide whether to share it with the other, the responder. The responder can accept or reject the proposer's offer. If the responder accepts the offer, then both receive their share of the reward. If the responder rejects the offer, then neither gets any reward. The economic model predicts that the proposer will offer the responder the minimum award.

When humans play the ultimatum game, proposers typically offer 40 to 50% of the reward, and responders typically reject offers of <20%, making them "rational maximizers." When chimpanzees play the game, they are rational maximizers **(Figure 40.42).** They follow the economic model and show little sensitivity to fairness or the interests of others.

Together, the cultural intelligence hypothesis and the results of the ultimatum game suggest social differences between humans and their closest relatives. These findings support the views of people who believe that humans are "not animals."

In other ways, humans behave like other animals. In the area of reproduction and genetic selfishness, some humans show little difference from their mammalian cousins. Kin selection predicts that humans (and other animals) that are genetic relatives will benefit from assisting the members of their family. What happens when there is no close genetic tie between parents and children?

Margo Wilson and Martin Daly wondered if child abuse might be more common in families with stepparents who are not genetically related to all of the children in their care. They examined data on criminal child abuse within families, made available by the police department of a Canadian city. They found that the chance that a young child would be subject to criminal abuse was 40 times higher when children lived with one stepparent and one genetic parent

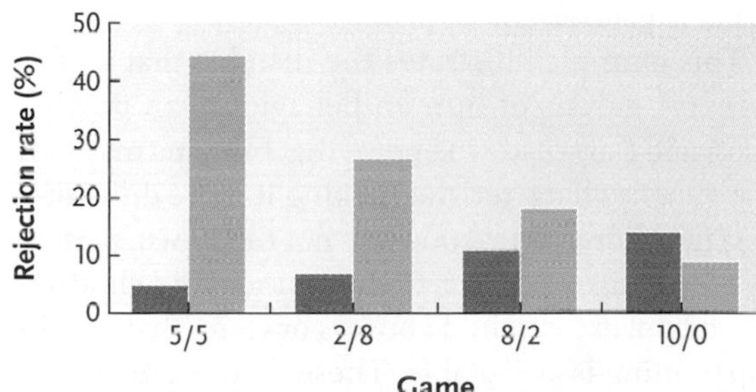

Figure 40.42
The ultimatum game. Data from chimpanzees (orange bars) and humans (green bars) show rejection rates (percentage of offers) indicating fundamental differences in the way that humans and chimps approach issues of fairness. The chimps are rational maximizers, whereas the humans are not.

Naked Mole Rats

Naked mole rats are sightless and essentially hairless burrowing mammals **(Figure 1)** that live in mazes of subterranean tunnels in parts of Ethiopia, Somalia, and Kenya. Colonies of naked mole rats may number from 25 to several hundred individuals. In each colony, a single "queen" and one to three males are the breeders. All of the others, males and females, are nonbreeding workers that, like worker bees, ants, and termites in insect colonies, do all of the labour, including digging and defending the tunnels and caring for the queen and her mates. H. Kern Reeve and his colleagues set out to determine if close kinship could explain the behaviour of worker naked mole rats. They used molecular techniques resembling DNA fingerprinting analysis (see Chapter 16) to obtain data about relatedness. The technique depends on a group of repeated DNA sequences that vary to a greater or lesser extent among individuals (e.g., they are polymorphic). No two individuals (except identical twins) are likely to have exactly the same combination of sequences. Brothers and sisters with the same parents have the most closely related sequences, and differences increase as genetic relationships become more distant.

Figure 1
Naked mole rats (*Heterocepahlus glaber*) live in colonies containing many workers that are effectively sterile.

Reeve and his colleagues captured mole rats living in four colonies in Kenya. Individuals from the same colony were placed together in a system of artificial tunnels. Samples of the entire DNA complement were extracted from individuals that died naturally in the artificial colonies. The extracted DNA was then "probed" with radioactively labelled DNA sequences that paired with and marked the three distinct groups of polymorphic sequences in the mole rat DNA.

Naked mole rat sequences were then fragmented by treatment with a restriction endonuclease. This procedure produced a group of fragments that, reflecting the variations in polymorphic sequences, is unique for each individual. As a final experimental step, the fragments for each individual were separated into a pattern of bands by gel electrophoresis. The pattern of bands, different for each individual, is the DNA fingerprint.

Reeve and his colleagues compared the DNA fingerprint of each mole rat with those of other members of the same and other colonies. In the comparisons, bands that were the same in two individuals were scored as "hits." The number of hits was then analyzed to assign relatedness by noting which individuals shared the greatest number of bands.

Individuals in the same mole rat colony were found to be closely related. They shared an unusually high number of bands, higher than human siblings, and approaching the kin similarity of identical twins. The number of bands shared between individuals of different colonies was significantly lower but still higher than that noted between unrelated individuals of other vertebrate species. Close relatedness of even separate colonies may be due to similar selection pressures or to recent common ancestry among colonies in the same geographic region.

In naked mole rats, close genetic relatedness among individuals in a colony could explain the altruistic behaviour of workers. The persistence of the social organization reflects its importance to the survival of individual naked mole rats, rather like the situation in lion prides.

compared with children living with both genetic parents **(Figure 40.43)**.

This example illustrates the insights that an evolutionary analysis of human behaviour can provide. Wilson and Daly made the point that humans may have some genetic characteristic making it more difficult to invest in children they know are not their own, particularly if they also care for their own genetic children. They did not excuse child abusers or claim that abusive stepparenting is acceptable. These results are not just academic. Most stepparents cope well with the difficulties of their role, but a few do not. Knowing the familial circumstances under which child abuse is more likely to occur may allow us to provide social assistance that could prevent some children from being abused in the future.

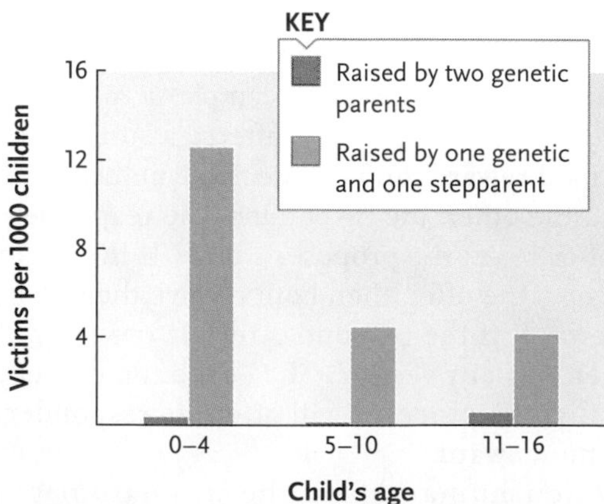

Figure 40.43
Children raised by one genetic parent and one stepparent were 40 times more likely to suffer criminal abuse at home than children living with two genetic parents.

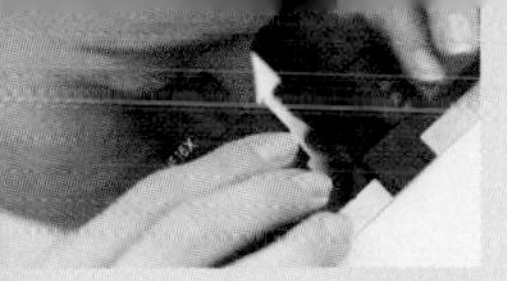

People Behind Biology

R.F. (Griff) Ewer

Born Rosalie Griffith, Griff Ewer was an outstanding leader in the study of animal behaviour. She married Denis William (Jakes) Ewer, and with their two children, they moved to the University of Natal in 1946 and from there to Rhodes University. In 1963, the family moved to the University of Ghana. To the unsuspecting person meeting her, the fact that she wore her hair short, dressed in slacks and a suit jacket, and smoked a pipe meant that some visitors were at first confused. On one paleontological expedition, she used the newspaper in which meat had been wrapped as a tablecloth. Her young daughter started to read the paper, drawing Dr. Ewer's attention to the fact that she was "in the tablecloth"—a story about the findings of a "woman paleontologist." Later, when she met the reporter who had written the story, she proceeded to express her annoyance about being identified as a "woman paleontologist." As she and her daughter walked away and were out of earshot, her daughter observed that she must have been annoyed with the man. Dr. Ewer said that she was not annoyed and was then told that her foot must have been. Dr. Ewer observed that from a child's perspective, her foot stamping was more obvious than it had been to the reporter (see Chapter 34, *Good Vibrations*)!

Dr. Griff Ewer had an insatiable curiosity about animal behaviour. In her classic book *Ethology of Mammals*, published in 1968, she encouraged would be students of animal behaviour to take animals into their homes and live with them. Animals had free run of her house. She observed that if there was something about their behaviour that you did not understand, the animal would patiently demonstrate the behaviour time and time again. A visitor to her house was usually quickly scent-marked by the resident mongooses. The book was dedicated to her pet meerkats. *Ethology of Mammals* stands as a classic book, a tribute to Dr. Ewer and her contributions.

In recent years, the application of evolutionary thinking to human behaviour has produced research on many kinds of questions. Some questions are interesting or even profound. Why do some tightly knit ethnic groups discourage intermarriage with members of other groups? At other times, the issues may seem frivolous. Why do men often find women with certain physical characteristics attractive? Although evolutionary hypotheses about the adaptive value of behaviour can be tested, helping us understand why we behave as we do, the hypotheses should never be used to justify behaviour that is harmful to other individuals. Understanding why we get along or fail to get along with each other and the ability to make moral judgments about our behaviour are uniquely human characteristics that set us apart from other animals.

Study Break

1. What is the ultimatum game? How does it help us understand behaviour?
2. What genetic reason helps explain the domestic risks to foster children and stepchildren?

Unanswered Question

How did echolocation behaviour evolve? Compare echolocation with electrolocation, radar, and sonar.

Review

Go to CENGAGENOW™ at http://hed.nelson.com/ to access quizzing, animations, exercises, articles, and personalized homework help.

40.1 Genes, Environment, and Behaviour

- Instinctive behaviours are genetically or developmentally "programmed." They appear in complete and functional form the first time they are used. Examples include eating, defence, mating, and parental care. Learned behaviours depend on having a particular kind of experience during development. Examples include language, mobility, and foraging. Marler's work with White-crowned Sparrows demonstrated some aspects of learned and instinctive behaviours.

40.2 Instinct

- Fixed action patterns are triggered by specific cues (sign stimuli). Fixed action patterns are repeated over and over in almost exactly the same way. The begging behaviour of Herring Gull chicks is a good example.
- Garter snakes from some areas of California often eat slugs, whereas those from other areas do not. Snakes that regularly eat slugs flick their tongues in response to the odour of slugs. Cross-breeding snakes from populations that eat slugs with those that do not demonstrate that the response to slugs was partly under genetic control.
- The feeding situations described in *Why It Matters* demonstrate how animals learn to adjust their foraging behaviour according to the availability of prey. The examples also demonstrate how some animals plan their meals ahead. The examples demonstrate the flexibility of animal behaviour.

40.3 Learning

- Research with White-crowned Sparrows and Zebra Finches demonstrated how the brains of these birds are involved in learning and in matching song outputs. The work also has revealed the neurophysiological networks involved in selective learning, including how individual birds learn to ignore (habituate to) familiar signals.

40.4 Neurophysiology and Behaviour

- Studies of bird brains have demonstrated how specific enzymes are turned on to activate different patterns of behaviour.
- Changes in the level of factors controlling synapses can clearly influence animal behaviour.

40.5 Hormones and Behaviour

- In honeybees, juvenile hormone stimulates genes in certain brain cells to produce proteins that affect functions of the nervous system. Octopamine is a product that stimulates neural transmissions and reinforces memories—it occurs in higher concentrations in older bees. This example shows how hormones and genes interact to affect behaviour.
- Gonadotropin-releasing hormone (GnRH) causes differences in the behaviour of fish such as *Haplochromis buroni*. Levels of GnRH are useful predictors of territorial behaviour.

40.6 Neural Anatomy and Behaviour

- Some crickets use ears (tympanic membranes) on their front legs to detect the echolocation calls of bats. Differential stimulation of left and right ears allows crickets to rapidly change their flight behaviour in response to approaching bats.
- Fiddler crabs (*Uca pugilator*) have compound eyes that give them a split field of view, which allows them to distinguish between the movements of other crabs and the approach of potential predators.

40.7 Communication

- Animals use at least five classes of signals in communication: acoustic signals such as songs used to attract a mate or warn intruders; visual signals such as the bioluminescent display of fireflies; chemical signals such as pheromones like bombykol, produced by female silkworm moths (and predatory spiders); tactile signals such as grooming in group-living primates; and electrical signals such as the pulses produced by knifefish or elephant fish.
- The "yells" of Ravens that have found a patch of food attract others. This behaviour allows nonresidents to gang up on resident ravens and obtain food that would otherwise not be available to them.
- Syntax (or grammar) and symbols are characteristic of language. Humans use words to represent objects (chair, table, dog), and the order of words (syntax) affects meaning (she was bitten by a dog versus she bit a dog). Dancing honeybees use symbols and syntax, and animals such as vervet monkeys use different calls to represent different predators.

40.8 Space

- Kinesis is a change in the rate of movement or the frequency of turning movements in response to environmental stimuli. A taxis is a response directed either toward or away from a specific stimulus.
- An animal's home range is the area it regularly uses, typically to move from where it sleeps to where it feeds. A territory is space that is defended to allow exclusive use by an individual or group of individuals. Home ranges and territories are features of individuals, whereas a range is a feature of a species (a population of individuals).

40.9 Migration

- Migration is a seasonal movement to and from an area. Migrations can be lengthy or short. Some birds, bats, insects, whales, and caribou migrate between different areas according to the season. Some nomadic populations of humans (and some retired people) move to and from habitats, also according to the season. Migrations are usually triggered by some combination of changes in day length and weather.
- Animals may find their way by piloting, landmarks, compass, or celestial (stars and the Sun) cues in navigation. Compass orientation involves movement in a specific direction as indicated by an external source such as the Sun, stars, or Earth's magnetic field. Animals continue to move in the same direction until they have completed their journey. Navigation is more complicated. Although still using compass orientation, navigation also requires the use of a "mental map," some independent indication of the animal's location. The "mental map" enables the animal to determine its relative position to the target location, and the compass provides the direction back to the target location.

40.10 Mates as Resources

- In many species, the behaviour of individuals of one sex is determined by the distribution of the other sex. In polygynous species, the distribution of males is influenced by the distribution of females, which are defended by the males. In other cases, albeit less common, males are defended by females. Be careful to distinguish situations in which the individuals are the resource that is defended as opposed to access to food or roosts (for example).

40.11 Sexual Selection

- Monogamy describes the situation when a male and a female form a pair bond and do not mate with others.
- Polygamy occurs when a male (polygyny) or a female (polyandry) mates with multiple partners. Polygamy usually involves pair bonds between the mating individuals. In promiscuity, there are no pair bonds, and males and females may mate with multiple partners.
- Lek mating systems are promiscuous. Males congregate in a display area (an arena), where they are visited by females. Females mate with the most attractive male (the one with the best display area). Males are the only resource at the display site. In leks, females typically mate with one male and males with multiple females.

40.12 Social Behaviour

- Infanticide is the killing of conspecific young. Male African lions practise infanticide when they take over a pride (group of females) because stopping nursing brings females back into heat, allowing the male to increase his direct fitness.
- Group living can provide significant advantages to animals such as easier-to-locate food resources either through cooperative hunting or simply an increased searching capacity (many eyes), ease in finding a mate, more efficient raising of young, more effective defence against predators, and increased vigilance. Group living also can present disadvantages, including increased competition for food, increased spread of parasites and disease, and increased conspicuousness to predators.

40.13 Kin Selection and Altruism

- Hamilton's kin selection theory states that helping genetic relatives effectively propagates the helper's genes because family members share alleles inherited from their ancestors. Individuals should be more likely to help close relatives because increasing a close relative's fitness means that the individual is helping to propagate some of its own alleles.
- Degree of relatedness between individuals

$$
\begin{aligned}
&= (4 \times \text{first cousin relatedness}) \\
&\quad + (2 \times \text{sibling relatedness}) \\
&\quad + (2 \times \text{half-sibling relatedness}) \\
&= (4 \times 0.125) + (2 \times 0.5) + (2 \times 0.25) \\
&= 0.5 + 1 + 0.5 \\
&= 2
\end{aligned}
$$

- Helping only nonrelatives is altruistic because each of the other examples involves genetically selfish behaviour (= getting the actor's genes into the next generation).

40.14 Eusocial Animals

- Haplodiploidy occurs when the females in a colony are diploid and the male are haploid. Females receive a set of chromosomes from each parent, but males hatch from unfertilized eggs (one set of chromosomes). This affects the level of genetic relationship among females. Worker bees hatching from eggs laid by one queen bee could all have the same father if the queen mated with only one male. We can use Hamilton's kinship theory to understand the behaviour of eusocial animals.

40.15 Human Behaviour

- In the ultimatum game, players have the opportunity to demonstrate their sense of fairness and their sensitivity to others. When people and chimps play the ultimatum game, the results demonstrate a fundamental difference in their levels of social behaviour.

Questions

Self-Test Questions

1. Peter Marler concluded that White-crowned Sparrows can learn their species' song only
   a. after receiving hormone treatments.
   b. during a critical period of their development.
   c. under natural conditions.
   d. from their genetic father.
   e. if they are reared in isolation cages.
2. In cichlid fish, high levels of the hormone GnRH
   a. make females more receptive to male attention.
   b. cause males to be sexually aggressive but not territorial.
   c. stimulate a male to defend its territory.
   d. cause males to abandon their territories.
   e. cause males to lose their bright colours.
3. Sensory bias in the nervous system of a cricket ensures that ultrasound perceived on one side of the body causes
   a. a movement in a leg on the same side of the body.
   b. a movement in a leg on the opposite side of the body.
   c. the cricket to respond with a vocalization.
   d. the cricket to stop vocalizing.
   e. the cricket to fly toward the sound.
4. In the brain of a star-nosed mole, more cells decode
   a. tactile information from its feet than from all other parts of its body.
   b. tactile information from the tentacles on its nose than from all other parts of its body.
   c. tactile information from its mouth than from all other parts of its body.
   d. visual information from the top part of its visual field than the bottom part.
   e. visual information from the bottom part of its visual field than the top part.
5. Which of the following statements about animal migration is true?
   a. Piloting animals use the position of the Sun to acquire information about their direction of travel.
   b. Animals migrating by compass orientation use mental maps of their position in space.
   c. Navigating animals use familiar landmarks to guide their journey.
   d. Navigating animals use a compass and a mental map of their position to reach a destination.
   e. Most migrating birds use olfactory cues to return to the place where they hatched from eggs.

6. Squashing an ant on a picnic blanket often attracts many other ants to its "funeral." What kind of signal did squashing the ant likely produce?
   a. an electrical signal
   b. a visual signal
   c. an acoustical signal
   d. a chemical signal
   e. a tactile signal
7. Compared with males, the females of many animal species
   a. compete for mates.
   b. choose mates that are well camouflaged in their habitats.
   c. choose to mate with many partners.
   d. are always monogamous.
   e. choose their mates carefully.
8. Social behaviour
   a. is exhibited *only* by animals that live in groups with close relatives.
   b. cannot evolve in animals that maintain territories.
   c. evolved because group living provides benefits to individuals in the group.
   d. is never observed in insects and other invertebrate animals.
   e. can only be explained by the hypothesis of kin selection.
9. Altruism is a behaviour that
   a. cannot evolve.
   b. advances the welfare of the entire species.
   c. increases the number of offspring an individual produces.
   d. can indirectly spread the altruist's alleles.
   e. can only evolve in animals with a haplodiploid genetic system.

Questions for Discussion

1. When can communication behaviour be called "language"? What is language?
2. Using an example from your own experience, explain why habituation to a frequent stimulus might be beneficial. Describe an example in which habituation might be harmful or even dangerous.
3. Is learning always superior to instinctive behaviour? If you think so, why do so many animals react instinctively to certain stimuli? Are there environmental circumstances in which being able to respond "correctly" the first time would have a big payoff?
4. What effects might global warming have on animal species that undertake seasonal migrations?
5. Develop three evolutionary hypotheses to explain why male birds are likely to involve themselves in caring for their young.

Foods that are high in starch include potatoes (*Solanum tuberosum*), corn (*Zea mays*), wild rice (*Zizania* species), and domestic rice (*Oryza* species).

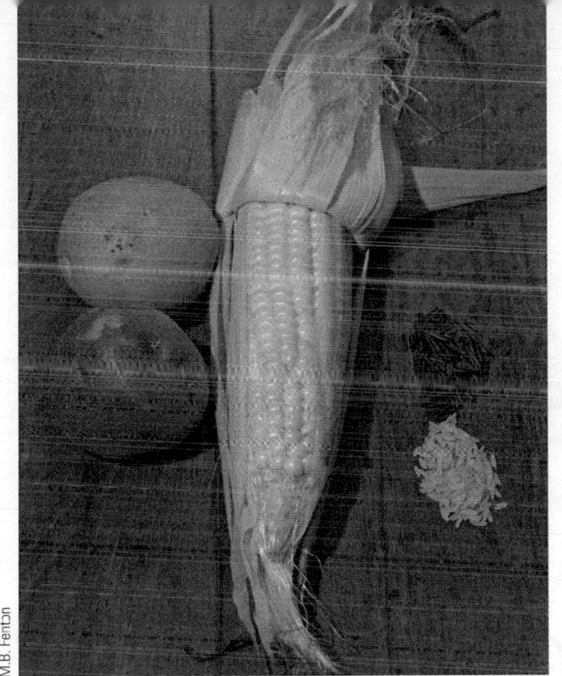

M.B. Fenton

Study Plan

41 Plant and Animal Nutrition

Why It Matters

Salivary amylase **(Figure 41.1, p. 1002)**, an enzyme produced by the saliva glands, initiates digestion of starch during chewing and can break down significant amounts of starch even before the food is swallowed. The action of salivary amylase explains why this happens. Blood glucose has been found to be significantly higher when high-starch foods (e.g., corn, rice, and potatoes) are first chewed and then swallowed rather than swallowed without chewing. The same is not true of low-starch foods such as apples. Immediate oral access to energy is especially important during episodes of diarrhea. Furthermore, in the stomach and intestines, salivary amylase augments the activity of pancreatic amylase and may further buffer the body against the impact of digestive disorders.

In humans, the salivary amylase gene (*AMY1*) varies in the numbers of copies according to the amount of starch in the diet of different populations. More copies of *AMY1* coincides with higher levels of salivary amylase in saliva **(Figure 41.2, p. 1002)** among seven populations of people, three with high-starch diets and four with low-starch diets. Humans living in agricultural societies and those in hunter–gatherer societies in arid environments have high-starch diets. Hunter–gatherers

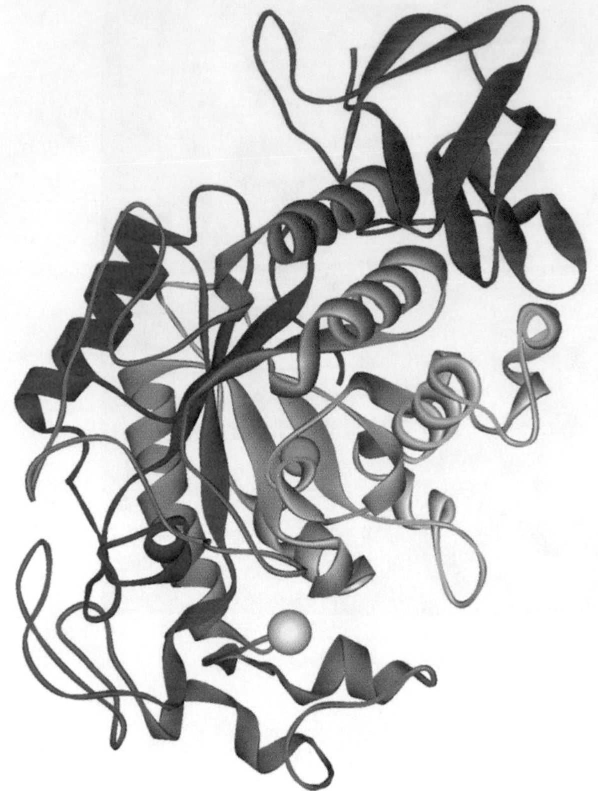

Figure 41.1 Salivary amylase molecule.

in rainforest and circumarctic habitats, as well as some pastoralists, have low-starch diets.

Although most digestion in mammals occurs beyond the esophagus, particularly in omnivores, salivary amylase presents an interesting exception. By hydrolyzing starch into the disaccharide maltose, salivary amylase can have an immediate impact on levels of blood sugar. The same impact on blood sugar is not achieved when people eat (and carefully chew) low-starch foods such as apples.

Figure 41.2 Salivary amylase. **(a)** In humans, more copies of the gene *AMY1* correlates with higher levels of salivary amylase **(b)** and more starch in the diet.

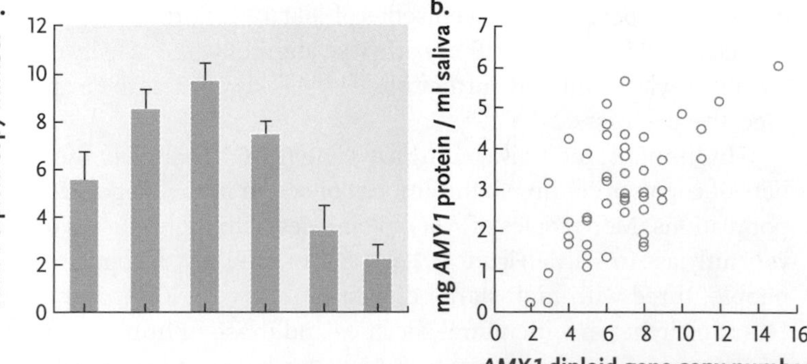

41.1 Nutrition: Essential Materials

All organisms require sources of matter and energy for metabolism and homeostasis (see Chapter 43), as well as growth and reproduction. No organism grows normally when deprived of a chemical element essential for its metabolism. In the latter half of the nineteenth century, plant physiologists exploited rapid advances in chemistry to explore the chemical composition of plants and the essential nutrients they needed to survive. Because living organisms require some nutrients in only trace amounts, biologists developed more sophisticated methods to understand the roles that trace elements play in organisms' nutrition and well-being.

41.1a Macronutrients and Micronutrients in Plant Metabolism

Most of a plant's nutrition is derived through photosynthesis, the combining of water and carbon dioxide to produce sugars and starches. Plants also require much smaller amounts of other nutrients, which they obtain from soil or water.

By weight, the tissues of most plants are >90% water. Burning a plant (or other organism) and analyzing the resulting ash was one way to obtain a rough estimate of the composition of a plant's dry weight. Although this method yielded a long list of elements, the results were flawed because chemical reactions during burning often dissipated quantities of some important elements (e.g., hydrogen, oxygen, and nitrogen). Furthermore, plants take up a variety of ions they do not use, and the exact combination of these ions depends on the minerals present in the soil where a plant grows. The tissues of organisms may contain non-nutritive elements such as gold, lead, arsenic, and uranium.

41.1b Hydroponics: A New Way to Study Plant Nutrition

In 1860, German plant physiologist Julius von Sachs pioneered hydroponics (*hydro* = water; *ponos* = work), an experimental method for identifying minerals absorbed into plant tissues that were essential for growth. Sachs carefully measured amounts of compounds containing specific minerals and mixed them in different combinations with pure water. He then grew plants in the solutions and studied their growth after eliminating one element at a time. In this way, Sachs deduced a list of six essential plant nutrients, in descending order of the amount required: nitrogen, potassium, calcium, magnesium, phosphorus, and sulphur.

Sachs's innovative research paved the way for decades of increasingly sophisticated studies of plant nutrition. One variation on his approach involved growing a plant in a solution containing a complete spectrum of known and possible essential nutrients **(Figure 41.3).** The healthy plant is then transferred to a solution that is identical except that it lacks one element with an unknown nutritional role. Abnormal growth of the plant in this solution is evidence that the missing element is essential. Normal growth indicates that the missing element may not be essential, but only further experimentation can confirm this hypothesis.

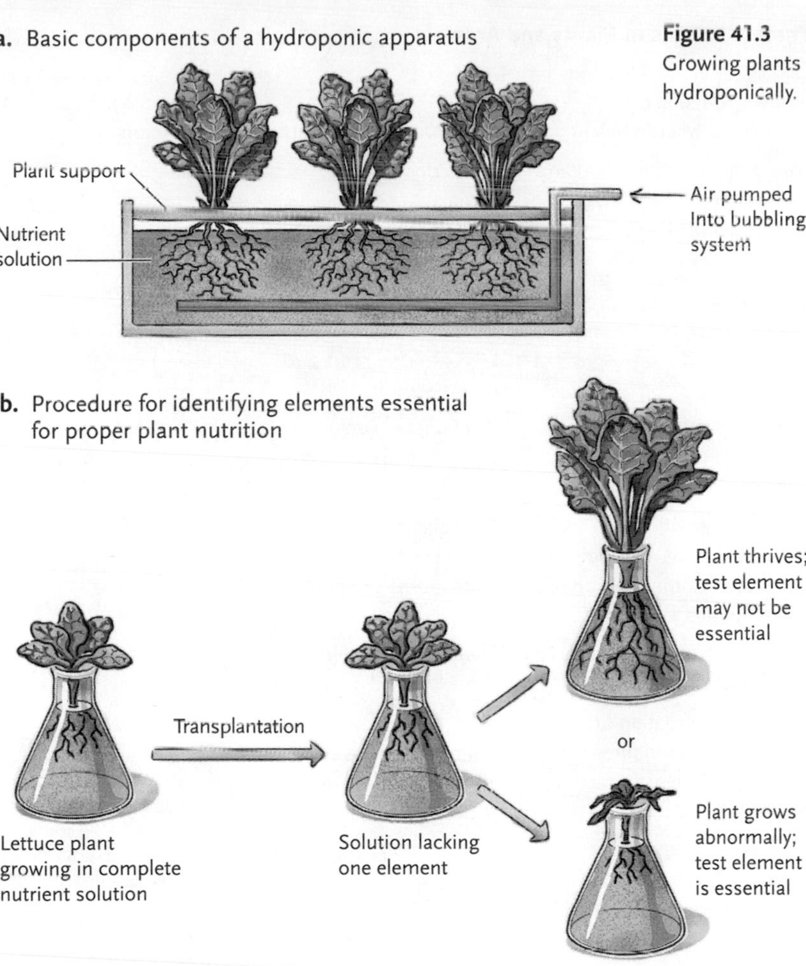

Figure 41.3 Growing plants hydroponically.

In a typical modern hydroponic apparatus (see Figure 41.3b), the nutrient solution is refreshed regularly and air is bubbled into it to supply oxygen to the roots. In the absence of sufficient oxygen for respiration, plants' roots do not absorb nutrients efficiently. The same thing occurs in poorly aerated soil. Hydroponics are used on a commercial scale to grow vegetables such as lettuce and tomatoes.

41.1c Essential Macro- and Micronutrients for Plants

Hydroponics research has revealed that plants generally require 17 essential elements **(Table 41.1, p. 1004–1005)**. An **essential element** is defined as one that is necessary for normal growth and reproduction and cannot be functionally replaced by a different element. Essential elements can have one or more roles in plant metabolism. With the combination of enough sunlight and the 17 essential elements, plants can synthesize all of the compounds they need.

Nine of the essential elements are **macronutrients** because plants incorporate relatively large amounts of them into their tissues. Together, carbon (C), hydrogen (H), and oxygen (O) account for about 96% of a plant's dry mass and are the key components of lipids and of carbohydrates such as cellulose. With the addition of nitrogen, C, H, and O are the basic building blocks of proteins and nucleic acids. Plants also add phosphorus to C, H, and O to construct nucleic acids, ATP, and phospholipids and potassium for functions ranging from enzyme activation to mechanisms that control the opening and closing of stomata. Rounding out the list of macronutrients are calcium, sulphur, and magnesium.

Carbon, hydrogen, and oxygen are the only plant nutrients not considered to be minerals. Plants obtain C, H, and O from the air and water. The other six macronutrients are mineral nutrients, inorganic substances available to plants through the soil as ions dissolved in water.

Micronutrients are mineral elements required in trace amounts, but they are as vital as macronutrients to a plant's health and survival. Although 2.5 tonnes of potatoes contain roughly the amount of copper in a single, copper-plated, Canadian penny, without it, potato plants are sickly and do not produce normal tubers.

Chlorine was identified as a micronutrient nearly a century after Sachs's experiments. Using hydroponic culture in a California laboratory near the Pacific Ocean, researchers discovered the vital role of Cl^- because the coastal air contains sodium chloride. The test plants obtained tiny but sufficient quantities of chlorine from the air or from sweat (which also contains NaCl) on the researchers' hands. Denying the plants access to Cl^- required careful control of the test environments in which they grew.

In some cases, plant seeds contain enough of certain trace minerals to sustain the adult plant. Nickel (Ni^{2+}) is a component of urease, the enzyme required to hydrolyze urea. Urea is a toxic by-product of the breakdown of nitrogenous compounds, and it will kill the cells in which it accumulates. In the late 1980s, investigators found that barley seeds contain enough Ni^{2+} to sustain two complete generations of barley plants. Plants grown in the absence of Ni^{2+} did not begin to show signs of Ni^{2+} deficiency until the third generation.Besides the 17 essential elements, some plant species may require additional micronutrients. Many, perhaps most, plants adapted to hot, dry conditions require sodium ions, including many plants using the C_4 pathway (see Chapter 7). A few plant species require selenium, also an essential micronutrient for animals (see Table 41.1). Horsetails (*Equisetum*) require silicon, as may some grasses (such as wheat). Scientists continue to discover additional micronutrients for specific plant groups.

Table 41.1	Essential Elements and Their Functions in Plants and Animals			
Element	**Commonly Absorbed Forms**	**Some Known Functions, Macronutrient or Micronutrient**	**Some Deficiency Symptoms**	**Sources for Humans**
Carbon*	CO_2	Essential elements for life, including raw materials for photosynthesis	Rarely deficient	
Hydrogen*	H_2O			
Oxygen*	O_2, H_2O, CO_2			
Boron	H_3BO_3	**Plants, micro:** roles in germination, flowering, fruiting, cell division, nitrogen metabolism	**Plants only:** terminal buds and lateral branches die; leaves thicken, curl, and become brittle	
Calcium	Ca^{2+}	**Plants, macro:** formation and maintenance of cell walls and membrane permeability, enzyme cofactor **Animals, macro:** bone and tooth formation, blood clotting, action of nerves and muscles	**Plants:** leaves deformed, terminal buds die, poor root growth **Animals:** stunted growth, diminished bone mass (osteoporosis in humans)	Dairy products, leafy green vegetables, legumes, whole grains, and nuts
Chlorine	Cl^-	**Plants, micro:** role in root and shoot growth and photosynthesis **Animals, macro:** formation of HCl (in stomach), contributes to acid–base balance, neural function, water balance	**Plants:** wilting, chlorosis, some leaves die (deficiency not seen in nature) **Animals:** muscle cramps, impaired growth, poor appetite	Table salt, meat, eggs, dairy products
Chromium	Cr	**Animals, macro:** roles in carbohydrate metabolism	**Animals only:** impaired responses to insulin (increased risk of type 2 diabetes mellitus in humans)	Meat, liver, cheese, whole grains, brewer's yeast, peanuts
Cobalt	Co	**Animals, macro:** constituent of vitamin B_{12} (required for normal red blood cell maturation)	**Animals only:** same as for vitamin B_{12} (see Table 41.2)	Meat, liver, fish, milk
Copper	Cu^+, Cu^{2+}	**Plants and animals, micro:** component of several enzymes **Animals:** used in synthesis of melanin, hemoglobin, and in some electron transport chain components in mitchondria	**Plants:** chlorosis, dead spots in leaves, stunted growth **Animals:** anemia, changes in bone and blood vessels	Nuts, legumes, seafood, drinking water, whole grains
Fluorine	F	**Animals, macro:** bone and tooth maintenance	**Animals only:** tooth decay	Fluoridated water, seafood, tea
Iodine	I	**Animals, macro:** thyroid hormone formation	**Animals only:** goitre (enlarged thyroid) and metabolic disorders	Marine fish, shellfish, iodized salt
Iron	Fe^{2+}, Fe^{3+}	**Plants and animals:** roles in electron transport, component of cytochrome **Plants micro:** role in chlorophyll synthesis **Animals, macro:** component of hemoglobin and myoglobin	**Plants:** chlorosis, yellow and green striping in grasses **Animals:** iron-deficiency anemia	Liver, whole grains, green leafy vegetables, legumes, nuts, eggs, lean meat, molasses, dried fruit, shellfish
Magnesium	Mg^{2+}	**Plants, macro:** component of chlorophyll, activation of enzymes **Animals, macro:** activation of enzymes, roles in functioning of nerves and muscles	**Plants:** chlorosis, drooping leaves **Animals:** weak and sore muscles, impaired neural function	Whole grains, green vegetables, legumes, nuts, dairy products

Table 41.1 *(continued)*

Element	Commonly Absorbed Forms	Some Known Functions, Macronutrient or Micronutrient	Some Deficiency Symptoms	Sources for Humans
Manganese	Mn^{2+}	**Plants and animals, macro:** role is activation of enzymes, coenzyme action **Plants:** involved in chlorophyll synthesis **Animals:** plays a role in synthesis of urea and fatty acids	**Plants:** dark veins, but leaves whiten and fall off **Animals:** abnormal bone and cartilage	Whole grains, nuts, legumes, many fruits
Molybdenum	MoO_4^{2-}	**Plants and animals, macro:** component of enzyme used in nitrogen metabolism **Animals:** components of some enzymes	**Plants:** pale green, rolled or cupped leaves **Animals:** impaired nitrogen excretion	Dairy products, whole grains, green vegetables, legumes
Nickel	Ni^{2+}	**Plants, micro:** component of enzyme required to break down urea generated during nitrogen metabolism	**Plants only:** dead spots on leaf tips (deficiency not seen in nature)	
Nitrogen	NO_3^-, NH_4^+	**Plants and animals, macro:** component of proteins, nucleic acids, coenzymes **Plants:** component of chlorophylls	**Plants:** stunted growth, light-green older leaves, older leaves yellow and die (chlorosis)	
Phosphorus	$H_2PO_4^-$, HPO_4^{2+}	**Plants and animals, macro:** component of nucleic acids, phospholipids, ATP, several coenzymes **Animals:** component of bones	**Plants:** purplish veins, stunted growth, fewer seeds, fruits **Animals:** muscular weakness, loss of minerals from bone	Whole grains, legumes, poultry, red meat, dairy products
Potassium	K^+	**Plants and animals, macro:** activation of enzymes, key role in maintaining water–solute balance and so influences osmosis **Animals:** involved in actions of nerves and muscles	**Plants:** reduced growth; curled, mottled, or spotted older leaves; burned leaf edges; weakened plant **Animals:** muscular weakness	Meat, many fruits and vegetables
Selenium	Se	**Animals, macro:** constituent of several enzymes, antioxidant	**Animals only:** muscle pain	Meat, seafood, cereal grains, poultry, garlic
Sodium	Na^+	**Animals, macro:** acid–base balance, roles in functioning of nerves and muscles	**Animals only:** muscle cramps	Table salt, dairy products, meats, eggs
Sulphur	SO_4^{2-}	**Plants and animals, macro:** component of most proteins, coenzyme A	**Plants:** light-green or yellowed leaves, reduced growth **Animals:** same symptoms as those associated with protein deficiencies	Meat, eggs, dairy products
Zinc	Zn^{2+}	**Plants, micro:** plays a role in formation of auxin, chloroplasts, and starch; enzyme component **Animals, micro:** component of digestive enzymes and transcription factors; role in normal growth, wound healing, sperm formation, as well as taste and smell	**Plants:** chlorosis, mottled or bronzed leaves, abnormal roots **Animals:** impaired growth, scaly skin, impaired immune function	Whole grains, legumes, nuts, meats, seafood

Micronutrients and macronutrients play vital roles in plant metabolism. Many function as cofactors or coenzymes in protein synthesis, starch synthesis, photosynthesis, and aerobic respiration. Some also have a role in creating solute concentration gradients across plasma membranes, which are responsible for the osmotic movement of water.

41.1d Consequences of Nutrient Deficiencies for Plants

Plant species differ in the quantity of each nutrient they require, so the amount of an essential element adequate for one plant species may be insufficient for another. Lettuce and other leafy plants require more N and magnesium than many other plants. Alfalfa requires significantly more K^+ than lawn grasses. The amount of an essential element adequate for one species may be toxic for another. The amount of boron required for normal growth of sugar beets is toxic for soybeans. Thus, the nutrient content of soils is an important factor determining which plants grow well in a given location.

Plants deficient in one or more of the essential elements develop characteristic abnormalities **(Figure 41.4**; see also Table 41.1), and the symptoms give an indication of the metabolic roles the missing elements play in plant growth and development (see Chapter 31). Deficiency symptoms typically include stunted growth, abnormal leaf colour, dead spots on leaves, or abnormally formed stems (see Figure 41.4). Iron is a component of cytochromes essential to the cellular electron transfer system and plays a role in reactions that synthesize chlorophyll. Chlorosis, a symptom of Fe deficiency, is a yellowing of plant tissues resulting from lack of chlorophyll (see Figure 41.4b). Because ionic iron (Fe^{3+}) is relatively insoluble in water, gardeners often fertilize plants with chelated Fe, a soluble Fe compound that staves off or cures chlorosis. Chelating agents are also used in *phytoremediation,* the use of plants to clean up contaminated soils (see Phytoremediation). Mg^{+2} is also a necessary component of chlorophyll, so plants deficient in it have fewer chloroplasts than normal. Plants that are Mg^{+2} deficient appear paler green than normal, and their growth is stunted because of reduced photosynthesis (see Figure 41.4c).

Plants that lack adequate nitrogen may also become chlorotic (see Figure 41.4d), with older leaves yellowing first because the N is preferentially shunted to younger, actively growing plant parts. This adaptation is not surprising, given N's central role in the synthesis of amino acids, chlorophylls, and other compounds vital to plant metabolism. However, young leaves are the first to show symptoms of some other mineral deficiencies. These observations underscore the point that plants use different nutrients in specific, often metabolically complex ways.

Soils often have too little rather than too much N, P, K, or some other essential mineral, so farmers and gardeners typically add nutrients to suit the types of plants they wish to cultivate. Farmers and gardeners can assess deficiency symptoms of plants grown in their

Figure 41.4 Leaves and stems of tomato plants showing visual symptoms of seven different mineral deficiencies. The plants were grown in the laboratory, where the experimenter could control which nutrients were available. (Photos by E. Epstein, University of California, Davis.)

a. Plant grown using a complete growth solution

Control

b. Iron deficiency

c. Magnesium deficiency

d. Nitrogen deficiency

e. Phosphorus deficiency

f. Potassium deficiency

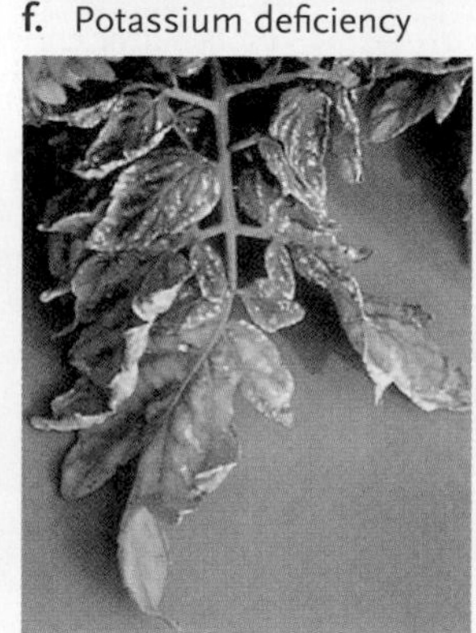

g. Sulphur deficiency

h. Calcium deficiency

Phytoremediation

The pollution of soils contaminated by industrial waste is a global environmental problem. The contamination includes a range of heavy metals as well as numerous toxic organic compounds. One high-profile target for cleanup is the highly toxic organic compound methylmercury (MeHg) because industrial and agricultural activities have released several hundred thousand tonnes of mercury into the biosphere during the past century. MeHg is present in coastal soils and wetlands that are contaminated by industrial wastes containing an ionic form of the element mercury called Hg(II). This builds up when bacteria in contaminated sediments metabolize Hg(II) and generate MeHg as a metabolic by product. Once MeHg forms, it enters the food web and eventually becomes concentrated in the tissues of fishes and other animals. MeHg is particularly toxic in humans as it can lead to degeneration of the nervous system and is the cause of most cases of mercury poisoning due to consuming contaminated fish (see Chapter 47).

To date, the remediation of mercury-polluted sites has been slow because chemical engineering methods currently employed to remove mercury-containing compounds are expensive and highly disruptive to the environment. Solutions such as "concrete capping" are designed to stabilize the mercury but render sites uninhabitable for plants, insects, and other organisms.

Phytoremediation, the use of plants as a natural means of removing contaminants from contaminated soils, wetlands, and aquatic habitats, may be a viable alternative for remediating contaminated sites. The procedure relies on the ability of a range of plant species to take up and sequester toxic compounds. In the 1990s, a team of scientists including Scott Bizily and Richard Meagher used genetic engineering to try to develop plants capable of detoxifying mercury-contaminated soil and wetlands. It was already known that bacteria in contaminated sediments possess two genes, *merA* and *merB*, that encode enzymes that convert MeHg into elemental mercury (Hg), a relatively inert substance that is much less dangerous to organisms. Using standard molecular biology techniques (see Chapter 16), the research team expressed both *merA* and *merB* in *Arabidopsis thaliana*, a model plant system for plant biology research **(Figure 1).**

The group produced three transgenic lines: one in which plants contained only the *merA* gene, some that contained only the *merB* gene, and some that contained both *merA* and *merB*. Seeds from each group were grown (along with wild-type controls) in five different growth media, one containing no mercury and the other four containing increasing concentrations of methylmercury. Wild-type and *merA* seeds germinated and grew only in the mercury-free growth medium. The *merB* seedlings fared somewhat better. They germinated and grew briefly even at the highest concentrations of MeHg but soon became chlorotic and died. Not only did the seeds with the *merA/merB* genotype germinate, but the resulting seedlings also grew into robust plants with healthy root and shoot systems. In later tests, *merA/merB* plants were grown in chambers in which the chemical composition of the air could be monitored. This study revealed that the doubly transgenic plants were transpiring large amounts of Hg. The results showed that *A. thaliana* with *merA* and *merB* genes could take up toxic methylmercury with no ill effects and convert it to a harmless form. Meagher and his colleagues are now experimenting with ways of increasing the efficiency of phytoremediating enzymes when plant cells express *merA* and *merB*. They are also studying the mechanisms by which ionic mercury taken up by roots may be transported via the xylem to leaves and other shoot parts. The goal is to engineer plants that accumulate large quantities of mercury in aboveground tissues that can be harvested, leaving the living plant to continue its "work" of detoxifying a contaminated landscape.

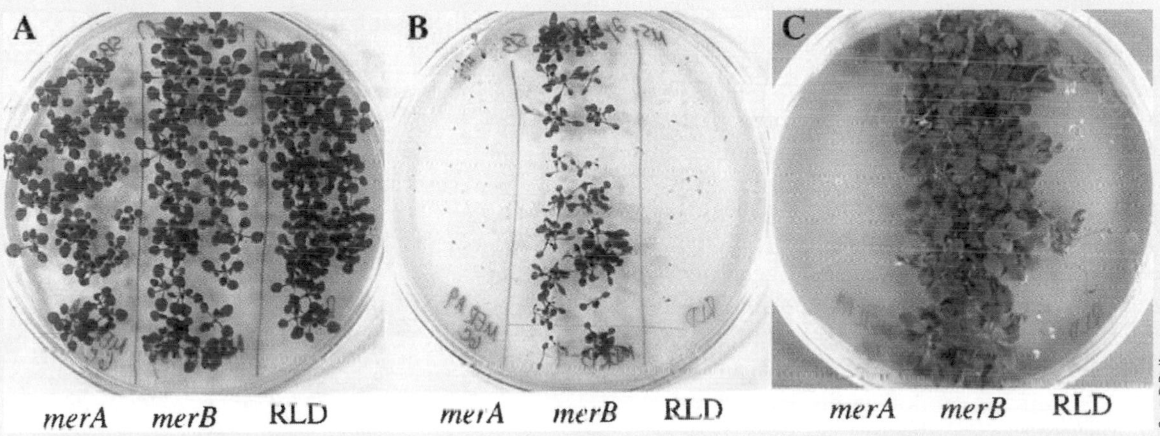

Figure 1
Plates of parental (RLD, a wild-type ecotype of *Arabidopsis*) and transgenic *Arabidopsis thaliana* (*merA* and *merB*) grown on media with no mercury **(a)** or 2 μM phenylmercuric acetate **(b** and **c)**; a and b were photographed after 4 weeks and c after 6 weeks. RLD and *merA* seeds did not germinate in the presence of mercury, whereas *merB* seeds did.

locale or have soil tested in a laboratory and then select a fertilizer with the appropriate balance of nutrients to compensate for deficiencies. Packages of commercial fertilizers use a numerical shorthand (e.g., 15-30-15) to indicate the percentages of N, P, and K they contain.

41.1e Essential Elements for Animals

Plants and other photosynthesizers use sunlight as an energy source and a supply of simple inorganic precursors such as water, carbon dioxide, and minerals to make all of the organic molecules they require. Animals require a diet of organic molecules as a source of energy and nutrients that they cannot make for themselves. Animals can be classified according to the sources of organic molecules they use (see Chapters 3 and 48). Primary consumers eat plants, whereas secondary consumers primarily eat other animals. "Primarily" is an appropriate modifier because many herbivores eat animal matter sometimes (e.g., insects on the plants), and secondary consumers often eat plant material (e.g., a cat eating grass). Animals that regularly take food from different trophic levels (see Chapter 48) are omnivores.

Organic molecules are the basis of two of the most fundamental processes of life, namely fuels for oxidative reactions supplying energy and as building blocks for making complex biological molecules.

Fuel. Animals must acquire enough fuel in their diets to cover their basic costs of operation. Carbohydrates and fats are primary organic fuel molecules used in cellular respiration (see Chapter 6). Undernourished animals suffer from inadequate intake of organic fuels or abnormal assimilation of these fuels. Undernutrition is commonly referred to as malnutrition, a condition resulting from an improper diet. Overnutrition is caused by excessive intake of specific nutrients and is another form of malnutrition.

An undernourished animal can be starving for one or more nutrients or just be eating fewer calories than needed for daily activities. Animals with chronic undernutrition lose weight because they use molecules of their own bodies as fuels. In times when food is abundant, some animals accumulate stores of fat for use in lean times. Birds on long migratory flights metabolize fat, as well as other tissues, to meet their energy needs. Relatively short-term use of an animal's own proteins as fuels leads to the wasting of muscles and other tissues and cannot be sustained over long periods of time.

Building Blocks. As in plants, organic molecules serve as building blocks for carbohydrates, lipids, proteins, and nucleic acids. Animals can synthesize many of the organic molecules that they do not obtain directly in their diet by converting one type of building block into another. But there are some amino acids and fatty acids that most animals cannot synthesize and must obtain from organic molecules in their food. Lack of these essential amino acids and essential fatty acids can have serious consequences. Protein synthesis cannot continue unless all 20 amino acids are present. In the absence of essential amino acids in the diet, an animal would have to break down its own proteins to obtain the necessary building blocks for new protein synthesis.

Vitamins and Coenzymes. Animals also must ingest **vitamins**, organic molecules that are required in small quantities. Many animals cannot synthesize these for themselves. Many vitamins are coenzymes, nonprotein organic subunits associated with enzymes that assist in enzymatic catalysis (see Chapter 4). Individual species differ in the vitamins and essential amino acids and fatty acids they require in their diets. Various species also have different dietary requirements for inorganic elements such as calcium, iron, and magnesium. Required inorganic elements are known collectively as essential minerals. Essential nutrients include amino acids, fatty acids, vitamins, and minerals, but the precise list varies from species to species, even from individual to individual.

As in plants, elemental macronutrients and micronutrients are essential in the animal diet (see Table 41.1). Humans require macronutrients in amounts ranging from 50 mg to more than 1 g per day and micronutrients (trace elements) such as zinc in small amounts, some <1 mg per day. All of the minerals, although listed as elements, are ingested by animals as compounds or as ions in solution.

41.1f Essential Elements for Humans

Adult humans require eight essential amino acids: lysine, tryptophan, phenylalanine, threonine, valine, methionine, leucine, and isoleucine. Infants and young children also require histidine. Proteins in fish, meat, egg whites, milk, and cheese supply all of the essential amino acids as long as they are eaten in adequate quantities. In contrast, the proteins of many plants are deficient in one or more of the amino acids essential to humans. Corn contains inadequate amounts of lysine, and beans contain little methionine. Vegetarians, especially vegans, whose diet includes no animal-derived nutrients, must choose their foods carefully to obtain all of the essential amino acids **(Figure 41.5)**.

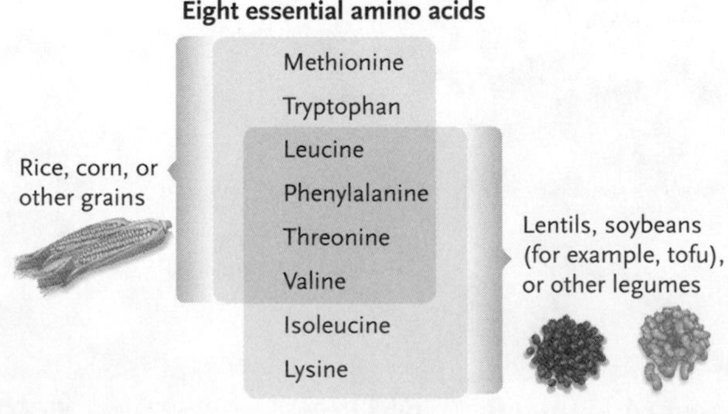

Figure 41.5
Obtaining essential amino acids in a human vegetarian diet.

Protein deficiency occurs when essential amino acids are not part of the diet. Consequently, many enzymes and other proteins cannot be synthesized in sufficient quantities. Protein deficiency is most damaging to the young because of their need for proteins for normal development and growth. Even mild protein starvation during pregnancy or for some months after birth can retard a child's growth and have negative effects on mental and physical development.

Two fatty acids, linoleic acid and linolenic acid, are essential because they are used in the synthesis of phospholipids that form parts of biological membranes and certain hormones. Because almost all foods contain these fatty acids, most people have no problem obtaining them. However, people on a low-fat diet deficient in linoleic acid and linolenic acid are at serious risk for developing coronary heart disease. There is an inverse correlation between the concentration of these essential fatty acids in the diet and the incidence of coronary heart disease. Hindu vegetarians from India eat mainly low-fat grains and legumes, a low-fat diet. Yet their rate of coronary heart disease is higher than rates in the United States and Europe, where dietary fat content is higher.

Humans require 13 known vitamins in their diet **(Table 41.2)**. Many metabolic reactions depend on vitamins, and the absence of one vitamin can affect the functions of the others. Vitamins fall into two classes: **water-soluble** (hydrophilic) **vitamins** and **fat-soluble** (hydrophobic) **vitamins**. The body stores excess fat-soluble vitamins in adipose tissues (fat), but any

Table 41.2 Vitamins: Sources, Functions, and Effects of Deficiencies in Humans

Vitamin	Common Sources	Main Functions	Effects of Chronic Deficiency
Fat-Soluble Vitamins			
A (retinol)	Yellow fruits, yellow or green leafy vegetables; also in fortified milk, egg yolk, fish liver	Used in synthesis of visual pigments, bone, teeth; maintains epithelial tissues	Dry, scaly skin; lowered resistance to infections; night blindness
D (calciferol)	Fish liver oils, egg yolk, fortified milk; manufactured when body exposed to sunshine	Promotes bone growth and mineralization; enhances calcium absorption from gut	Bone deformities (rickets) in children; bone softening in adults
E (tocopherol)	Whole grains, leafy green vegetables, vegetable oils	Antioxidant; helps maintain cell membrane and red blood cells	Lysis of red blood cells; nerve damage
K (napthoquinone)	Intestinal bacteria; also in green leafy vegetables, cabbage	Promotes synthesis of blood clotting protein by liver	Abnormal blood clotting, severe bleeding (hemorrhaging)
Water-Soluble Vitamins			
B_1 (thiamine)	Whole grains, green leafy vegetables, legumes, lean meats, eggs, nuts	Connective tissue formation; folate utilization; coenzyme forming part of enzyme in oxidative reactions	Beriberi; water retention in tissues; tingling sensations; heart changes; poor coordination
B_2 (riboflavin)	Whole grains, poultry, fish, egg white, milk, lean meat	Coenzyme	Skin lesions
Niacin	Green leafy vegetables, potatoes, peanuts, poultry, fish, pork, beef	Coenzyme of oxidative phosphorylation	Sensitivity to light; contributes to pellagra (damage to skin, gut, nervous system, etc.)
B_6 (pyridoxine)	Spinach, whole grains, tomatoes, potatoes, meats	Coenzyme in amino acid and fatty acid metabolism	Skin, muscle, and nerve damage
Pantothenic acid	In many foods (meats, yeast, egg yolk especially)	Coenzyme in carbohydrate and fat oxidation; fatty acid and steroid synthesis	Fatigue, tingling in hands, headaches, nausea
Folic acid	Dark green vegetables, whole grains, yeast, lean meats; intestinal bacteria produce some folate	Coenzyme in nucleic acid and amino acid metabolism; promotes red blood cell formation	Anemia; inflamed tongue; diarrhea; impaired growth; mental disorders; neural tube defects and low birth weight in newborns
B_{12} (cobalamin)	Poultry, fish, eggs, red meat, dairy foods (not butter)	Coenzyme in nucleic acid metabolism; necessary for red blood cell formation	Pernicious anemia; impaired nerve function
Biotin	Legumes, egg yolk; colon bacteria produce some	Coenzyme in fat and glycogen formation and amino acid metabolism	Scaly skin (dermatitis), sore tongue, brittle hair, depression, weakness
C (ascorbic acid)	Fruits and vegetables, especially citrus, berries, cantaloupe, cabbage, broccoli, green pepper	Vital for collagen synthesis; antioxidant	Scurvy, delayed wound healing, impaired immunity

amount of water-soluble vitamins above daily nutritional requirements is passed in urine. Thus, meeting the daily minimum requirements of water-soluble vitamins is critical. The body can tap its stores of fat-soluble vitamins to meet daily requirements; however, these stores can be quickly depleted, and prolonged deficiencies of the fat-soluble vitamins may also become critical to health.

Humans can synthesize vitamin D (calciferol) through the action of ultraviolet light on lipids in the skin. People who are not exposed to enough sunlight to make sufficient quantities of the vitamin must rely on dietary sources. Although we cannot make vitamin K, much of what we require is supplied through the metabolic activity of bacteria living in our large intestine. Vitamin K deficiency is rare in healthy people. Vitamin K plays a role in blood clotting, so individuals with vitamin K deficiency will bruise easily and show increased blood clotting times. Vitamin K deficiency can be caused in people on long-term antibiotic therapy because the antibiotics kill intestinal bacteria.

Other mammals have basically the same vitamin requirements as humans, with some differences. Most mammals can synthesize vitamin C, but not primates, guinea pigs, and fruit bats. To date, no mammals are known to synthesize B vitamins, but ruminants such as cattle and deer are supplied with these vitamins by microorganisms living in the digestive tract.

STUDY BREAK

1. What elements are essential to plants and to humans?
2. Why is iron essential for plants? For animals? What are the symptoms of iron deficiency in plants? In animals?
3. What do vitamins do for animals?

41.2 Soil

What is soil? Although we tend to think of soil as inert matter, just "dirt," it is really the living skin of the Earth: a complex mixture of mineral particles, organic matter, air, and water, combined with a great diversity of living organisms (e.g., Figure 19.3), many as yet unnamed. If you went outside and scooped up a handful of soil, you would be holding millions of prokaryotic and unicellular organisms, several kilometres of fungal hyphal filaments, and numerous invertebrates. If you took a larger volume of soil, you would also find a wide diversity of larger animals, some of which may never have been seen before. These organisms, along with plant roots, live in the soil and have a major influence on its composition and characteristics. Bacteria and fungi decompose organic matter; burrowing creatures such as earthworms aerate the soil; and when plant roots die, they contribute their organic matter to the soil.

Soil is also the source of water for most plants and of O_2 for cellular respiration in root cells. The physical texture of soil determines whether root systems have access to sufficient water and dissolved oxygen. The physical and chemical properties of soils in different habitats have a major impact on the ability of plant species to grow, survive, and reproduce there.

41.2a Soil Components and Particle Sizes Determine Properties of Soil

Most soils initially develop from the physical or chemical weathering of rock, which also liberates mineral ions. Different kinds of soil particles range in size from sand (2.0–0.02 mm in diameter) to silt (0.02–0.002 mm) and clay (<0.002 mm). The relative proportions of different sizes of mineral particles help determine the number and volume of pores—air spaces—soil contains. A soil that is sticky when wet with few air spaces is mostly clay, whereas one that dries quickly and may wash or blow away is mostly sand. The mineral particles alone do not make a soil; it also depends on the presence of living organisms and the accumulation of their products and decomposing bodies. In most soils, mineral particles are intermixed with various organic components, including **humus**, the decomposing parts of plants and animals, animal droppings, and other organic matter. Humus can absorb a great deal of water, contributing to the soil's capacity to hold water. Humus is a reservoir of nutrients vital to living plants, including N, P, and S. Organic material in humus feeds decomposers, whose metabolic activities, in turn, release minerals that plant roots can take up.

As soils develop naturally, they tend to take on a characteristic vertical profile, with a series of layers or **horizons** (**Figure 41.6**). Each horizon has a distinct texture and composition that varies with soil type. The *A horizon*, or topsoil, is the region with the most biological activity and usually is the most fertile layer. Most plant roots are concentrated in this layer, although some roots can extend much deeper in the soil (see Figure 46.14). Below the topsoil is the *B horizon*, or subsoil, characterized by the accumulation of mineral ions, including those needed by plants, washed down from above. Mature tree roots generally extend into this layer. The *C horizon*, the lowest layer, is the parent material. Regions where the topsoil is deep and rich in humus are ideal for agriculture, such as the vast grasslands of the Canadian prairies and Ukraine. Without soil management and intensive irrigation, crops usually cannot be grown in deserts because of the lack of rainfall and low humus in the soil—nor can agriculture flourish for long on land cleared of a tropical rainforest because rainforest soil is surprisingly poor and has very little humus.

41.2b Soil Characteristics Affect Nutrient Uptake by Plants

Some nutrients that plants require are present as mineral ions dissolved in the soil water. Soil composition influences the ability of plant roots to obtain nutrients, as outlined below.

Water Availability. As water flows through soil, gravity pulls much of it down through the spaces between soil particles into deeper soil layers. This available water is part of the **soil solution (Figure 41.7),** a combination of water and dissolved substances that coats soil particles and partially fills pore spaces. The solution develops through ionic interactions between water molecules and soil particles. The surfaces of clay particles and humus particles are often negatively charged and so attract polar water molecules, which form hydrogen bonds with the soil particles.

The proportion of the water entering a soil that is actually available to plants depends on the soil's composition—the size of the air spaces that allow water to flow and the proportions of water-attracting particles of clay and organic matter. By volume, soil is about one-half solid particles and one-half air space.

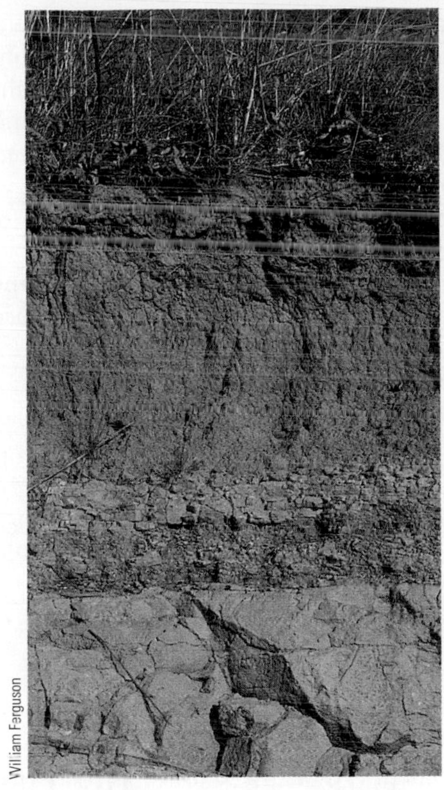
William Ferguson
Fallen leaves and other organic material littering the surface of mineral soil
A horizon
Topsoil, which contains some percentage of decomposed organic material and which is of variable depth; here it extends about 30 cm below the soil surface
B horizon
Subsoil; larger soil particles than the A horizon, not much organic material, but greater accumulation of minerals; here it extends about 60 cm below the A horizon
C horizon
No organic material, but partially weathered fragments and grains of rock from which soil forms; extends to underlying bedrock
Bedrock

Figure 41.6
A representative profile of soil horizons.

The size of the particles in a soil has a major effect on how well plants will grow there. Sandy soil has relatively large air spaces, so water drains rapidly down from the top two soil horizons, where most plant roots are located. Soils rich in clay or humus are often high in water content, but in the case of clay, ample water is not necessarily an advantage for plants. Whereas a humus-rich soil contains lots of air spaces, the closely spaced particles in clay allow few air spaces, and existing spaces tend to hold on to the water that enters them. "Air" spaces in clay soils filled with water also severely limit the supplies of oxygen to roots for cellular respiration, and the plant's metabolic activity suffers. Thus, few plants can grow well in clay soils, even when water content is high. Overwatered houseplants die because their roots are similarly "smothered" by water.

Mineral Availability. Most mineral ions enter plant roots passively along with the water in which they are dissolved. Plant cell membranes have ion-specific transport proteins by which they selectively absorb ions from soil (see Chapter 29). Some mineral nutrients enter plant roots as cations and others as anions. Although both cations and anions may be present in soil solutions, they are not equally available to plants.

Cations such as Mg^{2+}, Ca^{2+}, and K^+ cannot easily enter roots because they are attracted by the net negative charges on the surfaces of soil particles. To varying degrees, they become reversibly bound to negative ions on the surfaces. Attraction in this form is called *adsorption*. Cations are made available to plant roots through **cation exchange**, a mechanism in which one cation, usually H^+, replaces a soil cation **(Figure 41.8, p. 1012).** There are two main sources of H^+ ions. Respiring root cells release carbon dioxide, which dissolves in the soil solution, yielding carbonic acid (H_2CO_3). Subsequent reactions ionize H_2CO_3 to produce bicarbonate (HCO_3^-) and hydrogen ions (H^+). Reactions involving organic acids inside roots also

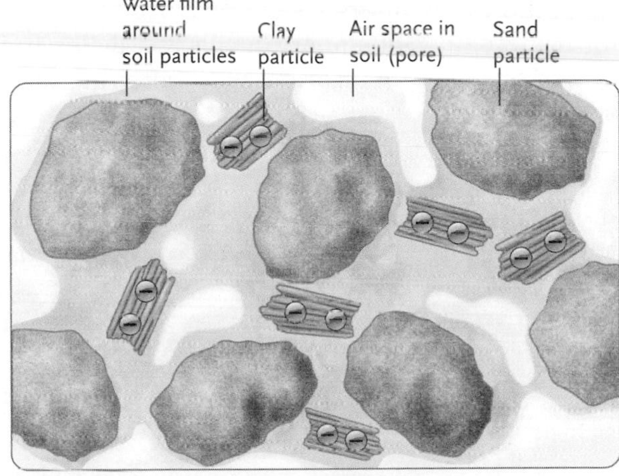
Water film around soil particles
Clay particle
Air space in soil (pore)
Sand particle

Figure 41.7
Location of the soil solution. Negatively charged ions on the surfaces of soil particles attract water molecules, which coat the particles and fill spaces between them (blue). Hydrogen bonds between water and soil components counteract the pull of gravity and help hold some water in soil spaces.

produce H^+, which is excreted. As H^+ enters the soil solution, it displaces adsorbed mineral cations attached to clay and humus, freeing them to move into roots. Other types of cations may also participate in this type of exchange (see Figure 41.8).

Meanwhile, anions in the soil solution, such as nitrate (NO_3^-), sulphate (SO_4^{2-}), and phosphate (PO_4^-), are only weakly bound to soil particles, so they generally move fairly freely into root hairs. However, because they are so weakly bound compared with cations, anions are more subject to loss from soil by leaching (draining from the soil, carried by excess water).

Soil pH also affects the availability of some mineral ions. Soil pH is a function of the balance between cation exchange and other processes that raise or lower the concentration of H^+ in soil. Areas receiving heavy rainfall tend to have acidic soils because moisture promotes the rapid decay of organic material in humus. As the material decomposes, the organic acids it contains are released. Acid precipitation, which results from the release of S and N oxides into the air, also contributes to soil acidification. Soils in arid regions are often alkaline.

Although most plants are not directly sensitive to soil pH, chemical reactions in very acid (pH <5.5) or very alkaline (pH >9.5) soils can have a major impact on whether plant roots can take up certain mineral cations. In the presence of OH^- ions in alkaline soil, Ca^{2+} and P^{3+} ions react to form insoluble calcium phosphates. Phosphate captured in these compounds is as unavailable to roots as if it were completely absent from the soil.

For a soil to sustain plant life over long periods, mineral ions that the plants take up must be replenished naturally or artificially. In the long run, some mineral nutrients enter the soil from ongoing weathering of rocks and smaller bits of minerals. Over the shorter term, nutrients are returned to the soil by the decomposition of organisms and their parts or wastes. Other inputs occur when airborne compounds, such as S in volcanic and industrial emissions, become dissolved in rain and fall to Earth. Still others, including compounds of N and P, enter soil in fertilizers.

Although using commercial fertilizers maintains high crop yields (see Chapter 49), it does not add humus to the soil. Fertilizers can also cause serious problems, as when N-rich runoff from agricultural fields promotes the serious overgrowth of algae in lakes and ocean shorelines.

Study Break

1. Why is humus an important component of fertile soil?
2. How does the composition of a soil affect a plant's ability to take up water?
3. What factors affect a plant's ability to absorb minerals from the soil?

41.3 Obtaining and Absorbing Nutrients

Natural habitats show a wide range of soil conditions (minerals, humus, pH, biota, and other factors) that influence the growth and health of plants. Soil managed for agriculture can be plowed, precisely irrigated, and chemically adjusted to provide air, water, and nutrients in optimal quantities for a particular crop. Natural habitats, on the other hand, show wide variations in soil minerals, humus, pH, the presence of other organisms, and other factors that influence the availability of essential elements. Some nutrients, particularly N, P, and K, are often relatively scarce in soil. The evolutionary solutions to these challenges include an array of adaptations in the structure and functioning of plant roots.

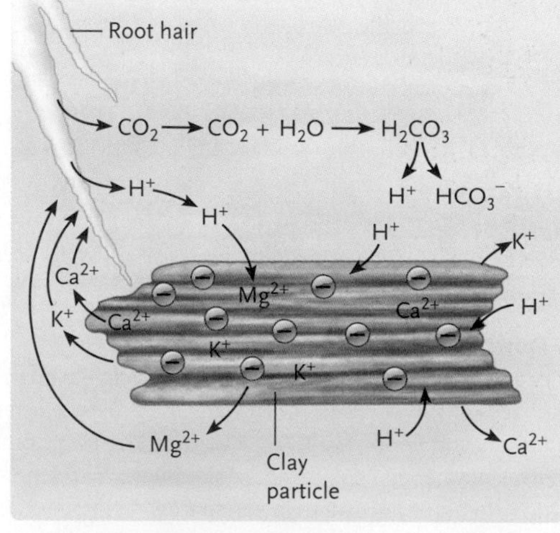

Figure 41.8
Cation exchange on the surface of a clay particle. When cations come into contact with the negatively charged surface of a clay particle, they become adsorbed. As one type of cation (e.g., H^+) is adsorbed, other ions are liberated and can be taken up by the roots of plants.

41.3a Acquisition of Nutrients by Plants

Immobile organisms such as plants must locate nutrients in their immediate environment. For plants, root systems are the adaptive solution to this problem. Roots make up 20 to 50% of the dry weight of many plants and even more in species that grow where water or nutrients are especially scarce, such as the Arctic tundra. As long as a plant lives, its root system continues to grow, branching out through the surrounding soil. Roots do not necessarily grow *deeper* as a root system branches out, however. In arid regions, a shallow but broad root system may be better positioned than a deep one to take up water from occasional rains that may never penetrate below the first few centimetres of soil.

A root system grows most extensively in soil where water and mineral ions are abundant (see Chapter 29). Roots take up ions in regions just above the root tips. Over successive growing seasons, long-lived plants such as trees can develop millions, even billions, of root tips, each one a potential absorption site. Root hairs are diminutive absorptive structures (see Figure 28.20a) that are also associated with the uptake of mineral ions and water. In a plant such as a mature red oak (*Quercus rubrum*) with a vast root system, the total number of root hairs is astonishing. Even in young plants, root hairs greatly increase the root surface area available for absorbing water and ions.

Plant cell membranes (see Chapter 29) have ion-specific transport proteins by which they selectively absorb ions from soil. Studies of *Arabidopsis thaliana*, a plant that has become a model organism for plant research, showed that transport channels for K^+ are embedded in the cell membranes of root cortical cells. These ion transporters absorb more or less of a particular ion depending on chemical conditions in the surrounding soil.

Plants can only take up inorganic or mineral forms of nutrients. A plant growing in a soil rich in organic forms of N such as proteins cannot access the N until decomposers have converted the protein into mineral forms such as ammonium (NH_4^+) or nitrate (NO_3^-). Associations with fungi and bacteria allow many plants to shortcut the decomposition process and gain access to organic and other forms of nutrients. **Mycorrhizas**, symbiotic associations between a fungus and the roots of a plant (see Chapter 24), increase the uptake of nutrients, especially P and N, by most species of vascular plants. The fungal partner in the association grows inside the plant's roots and in the soil beyond the roots, forming an extensive network of hyphal filaments. This network provides a very large surface area for absorbing ions from a large volume of soil. Furthermore, many mycorrhizal fungi can access forms of nutrients not available to plants. For instance, many fungi obtain nutrients from organic forms of nutrients (e.g., proteins) and even obtain other nutrients directly from rocks!

41.3b Movements of Nutrients in Plants

Most mineral ions enter plant roots passively along with the water in which they are dissolved. Some mineral ions enter root cells immediately, whereas others travel in solution *between* cells until they meet the endodermis sheathing the root's stele (see Figure 29.6). Here the ions are actively transported into the endodermal cells and then into the xylem for transport throughout the plant.

Inside cells, most mineral ions enter vacuoles or cell cytoplasm, where they become available for metabolic reactions. Nutrients, such as N-containing ions, move in phloem from site to site in the plant, as dictated by growth and seasonal needs. In plants that shed their leaves in autumn (= deciduous), significant amounts of N, P, K, and Mn move out of them and into twigs and branches before the leaves age and fall. This adaptation conserves the nutrients, which will be used in new growth the next season. Likewise, in late summer, mineral ions move to the roots and lower stem tissues of perennial range grasses that typically die back during the winter. These activities are regulated by hormonal signals (see Chapter 31).

41.3c Plants Can Be Limited by the Availability of Nitrogen

A lack of N is the single most common limit to plant growth. Although air contains plenty of gaseous N (~80% by volume), plants lack the enzyme necessary to break the three covalent bonds in each N_2 molecule ($N \equiv N$). Some N from the atmosphere reaches the soil in the form of nitrate, NO_3^-, and ammonium ions, NH_4^+. Plants can absorb both of these inorganic nitrogen compounds, but usually there is not nearly enough of them to meet plants' ongoing needs for N.

Organic N also enters the soil through decomposition of dead organisms and animal wastes. Dried blood is about 12% N by weight and chicken manure about 5%. But this N is bound up in complex organic molecules such as proteins that are not available to plants. The actions of bacteria are the main natural processes that replenish soil N and convert it to the absorbable form (see Figure 47.7). They are part of the *nitrogen cycle* (see Figure 47.15), the global movement of N in its various chemical forms from the environment to organisms and back to the environment.

N fixation is the incorporation of atmospheric N into compounds accessible to plants. Metabolic pathways of *nitrogen-fixing bacteria*, which live in the soil or in mutualistic association with plant roots, add H to atmospheric N_2, producing two molecules of NH_3 and one H_2 for each N_2 molecule **(Figure 41.9, p. 1014)**. The process requires a substantial input of ATP and is catalyzed by the enzyme nitrogenase. In a final step, H_2O and NH_3 react, forming NH_4^+ and OH^-. Ammonification is another bacterial process producing NH_4^+ when ammonifying soil bacteria break down decaying organic matter. This process recycles nitrogen previously incorporated in plants and other organisms. N fixation and ammonification form NH_4^+ that plant cells can use to synthesize organic compounds.

Most plants absorb N as nitrate, NO_3^-, which is produced in the soil by **nitrification** when NH_4^+ is oxidized to NO_3^-. Soils generally teem with *nitrifying bacteria* that carry out this process. Because of ongoing nitrification, nitrate is far more abundant than ammonium in most soils. Usually, plants take

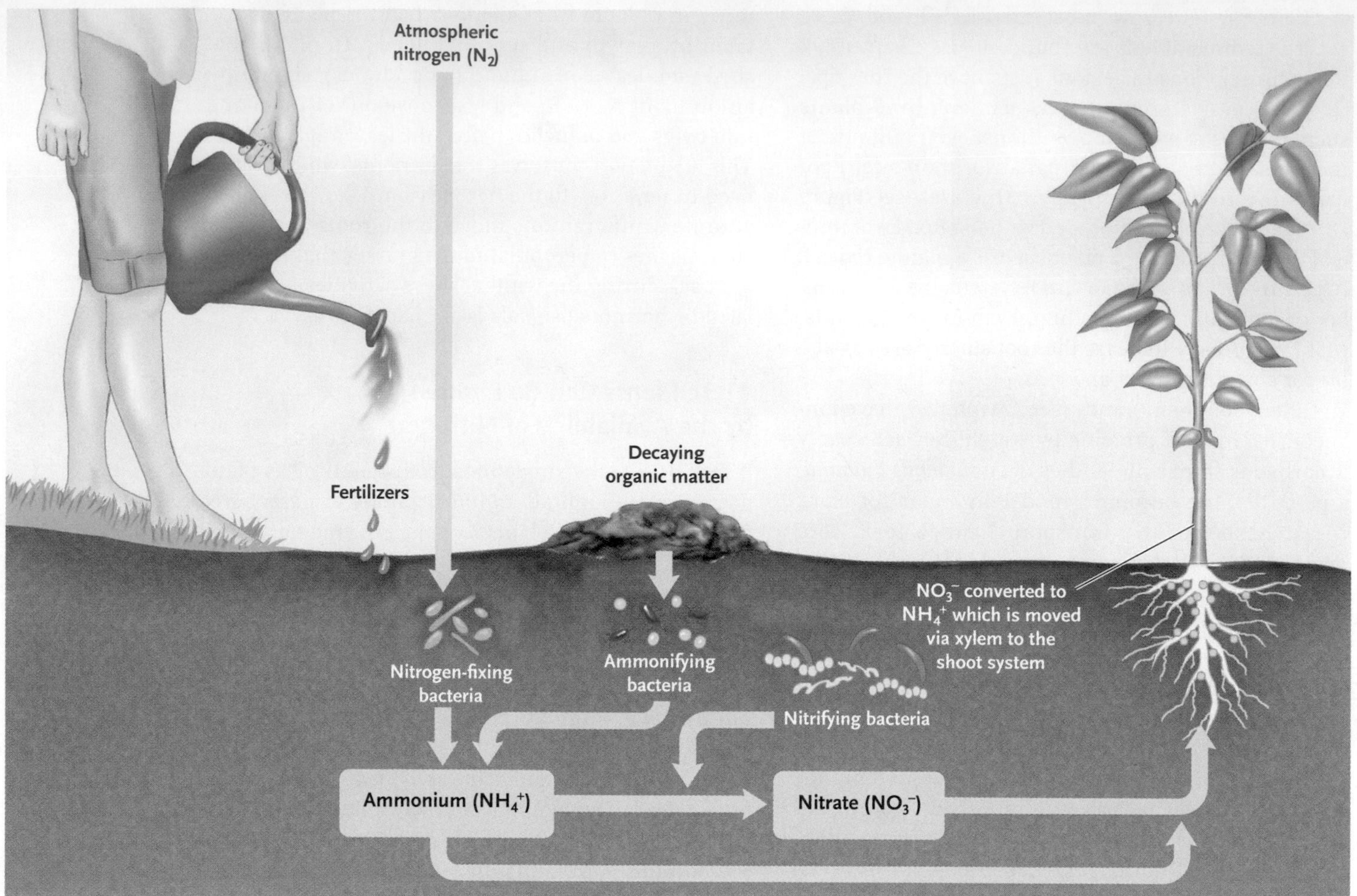

Figure 41.9
How plants obtain nitrogen from soil. Many commercial N fertilizers are nitrates that plant roots readily take up. Others are ammonium (NH_4), which nitrifying bacteria convert to nitrate.

up ammonium directly only in highly acidic soils, such as in bogs, where the low pH is toxic to nitrifying bacteria.

Within root cells, absorbed NO_3^- is converted by a multistep process back to NH_4^+, which is rapidly used to synthesize organic molecules, mainly amino acids. Amino acids pass into the xylem, which transports them throughout the plant. In some plants, nitrogen-rich precursors travel in xylem to leaves, where different organic molecules are synthesized, and, in turn, travel to other plant cells in the phloem.

Although some N-fixing bacteria live free in the soil (see Figure 41.9), by far the largest percentage of nitrogen is fixed by species of *Rhizobium* and *Bradyrhizobium* that form mutualistic associations with the roots of plants in the legume family (e.g., peas, beans, clover, alfalfa). The host plant supplies organic molecules used by the bacteria for cellular respiration, and the bacteria supply NH_4^+, which the plant uses to produce proteins and other nitrogenous molecules. The N-fixing bacteria reside in **root nodules**, localized swellings on legume roots **(Figure 41.10).** Rotating legumes with other crops (e.g., corn) allows farmers to increase soil N. When the legume crop is harvested, root nodules and other tissues remaining in the soil enrich its N content.

Decades of research have revealed the details of how the remarkable relationship between plant and bacteria unfolds. Usually, a single species of N-fixing bacteria colonizes a single legume species, drawn to the plant's roots by flavenoids, chemical attractants secreted by the roots. Through a sequence of exchanged molecular signals, bacteria penetrate a root hair and form a colony inside the root cortex **(Figure 41.11).**

The soybean (*Glycine max*) and its bacterial partner (*Bradyrhizobium japonicum*) illustrate the process. In response to a specific flavenoid released by the soybean's roots, *nod* (for nodule) genes in the bacteria begin to be expressed (see Figure 41.11a). Products of the *nod* gene cause the tip of the root hair to curl toward the bacteria and trigger the bacteria to release enzymes that break down the cell wall of the root hair (see Figure 41.11b). As bacteria enter the cell and multiply, the plasma membrane forms an *infection thread,* a tube that extends into the root cortex, allowing the bacteria to invade cells of the cortex (see Figure 41.11c). The enclosed bacteria, now called **bacteroids**, enlarge and become immobile. Stimulated by still other *nod* gene products, cells of the root cortex begin to divide, and this region of proliferating cortex cells forms the root nodule (see Figure 41.11d). Typically, each cell in a root nodule contains several thousand bacteroids. The plant takes up some of

Figure 41.10
(a) Root nodules. **(b)** When soybeans (*Glycine max*) are grown in nitrogen-poor soil (left), they do not thrive compared with their growth in soils innoculated with *Rhizobium* cells (right). Also, the plants on the right developed root nodules. **(c)** A false colour transmission electron micrograph shows membrane-bound bacteroids as red in a root nodule cell. Membranes that enclose the bacteroids appear blue. The large yellow-green structure is the nucleus.

the N fixed by the bacteroids, whereas the bacteroids use some compounds produced by the plant.

Inside bacteroids, nitrogenase catalyzes the reduction of N_2 to NH_4^+ using ATP produced by cellular respiration. NH_4^+ can be highly toxic to cells if it accumulates, so it is immediately moved out of the bacteroids and into the surrounding nodule cells and converted, for example, to the amino acids glutamine and asparagine.

The protein *leghemoglobin* ("legume hemoglobin") also results from stimulation of plant nodule cells by a product of the bacterial *nod* genes. Like the hemoglobin of animal red blood cells, leghemoglobin contains a reddish, iron-containing heme group that binds oxygen. Its colour gives root nodules a pinkish cast (see Figure 41.11). Leghemoglobin picks up oxygen at the cell surface and shuttles it inward to bacteroids. This method of oxygen delivery is vital because nitrogenase, the enzyme responsible for nitrogen fixation, is irreversibly inhibited by excess O_2. Leghemoglobin delivers just enough oxygen to maintain bacteroid respiration without shutting down the action of nitrogenase.

41.3d How Animals Eat to Acquire Nutrients

Animals are adapted to obtain the food they need (see Chapters 3 and 40). There are four basic groups of overall feeding methods and the physical states of the organic molecules they eat: fluid feeders, suspension feeders, deposit feeders, and bulk feeders **(Figure 41.12, p. 1016).**

Fluid feeders ingest liquids containing organic molecules in solution. Among invertebrates, aphids, mosquitoes, leeches, butterflies, and spiders are fluid feeders. Among vertebrates, lamprey eels, hummingbirds, nectar-feeding bats, and vampire bats are examples of fluid feeders (see Figure 41.12a). Many fluid

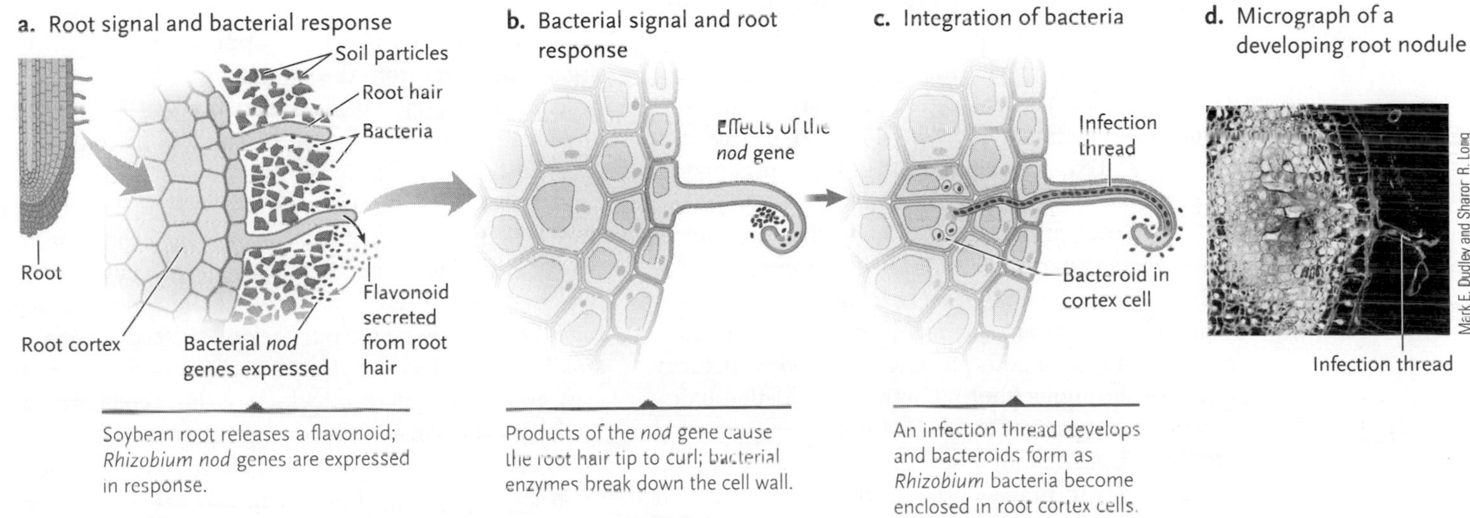

a. Root signal and bacterial response
Soil particles
Root hair
Bacteria
Root
Root cortex
Bacterial *nod* genes expressed
Flavonoid secreted from root hair
Soybean root releases a flavonoid; *Rhizobium nod* genes are expressed in response.
b. Bacterial signal and root response
Effects of the *nod* gene
Products of the *nod* gene cause the root hair tip to curl; bacterial enzymes break down the cell wall.
c. Integration of bacteria
Infection thread
Bacteroid in cortex cell
An infection thread develops and bacteroids form as *Rhizobium* bacteria become enclosed in root cortex cells.
d. Micrograph of a developing root nodule
Infection thread
Mark E. Dudley and Sharon R. Long

Figure 41.11
Root nodule formation in legumes, which interact mutualistically with the nitrogen-fixing bacteria *Rhizobium* and *Bradyrhizobium*.

a. Fluid feeder

b. Suspension feeder

c. Deposit feeder

d. Bulk feeder

Sanford/Angliolo/Corbis; James Watt/Animals, Animals—Earth Scenes; Joe McDonald/Corbis; Gunter Ziesler/Bruce Coleman, Inc.

Figure 41.12
General feeding methods in animals. **(a)** Fluid feeders, for example, the hummingbird that eats nectar. **(b)** Suspension feeders, for example, the northern right whale (*Balaena glacialis*) that gulps tonnes of water and filters out plankton. **(c)** Deposit feeders, for example, the fiddler crab (*Uca* species) that sifts edible material from detritus. **(d)** Bulk feeders, for example, this python that can open its mouth very wide and take in large objects such as a gazelle.

feeders have mouthparts specialized for reaching the source of their nourishment. Mosquitoes, bedbugs, and aphids have needlelike mouthparts that pierce body surfaces. Nectar-feeding butterflies, birds, and bats have long tongues that can extend deep within flowers. Some fluid feeders use enzymes or other chemicals to liquefy their food or to keep it liquid during feeding. Spiders inject digestive enzymes that liquefy tissues inside their victim, providing a nutrient soup they can ingest. The saliva of mosquitoes, leeches, and vampire bats includes chemicals that keep blood from clotting.

Suspension feeders ingest small organisms suspended in water, such as bacteria, protozoa, algae, and small crustaceans, or fragments of these organisms. Suspension feeders include aquatic invertebrates, such as clams, mussels, and barnacles, and vertebrates, such as many species of fishes, as well as some birds, pterosaurs, and whales (see Figure 41.12b). Suspension feeders strain (filter) food particles suspended in water through a body structure covered with sticky mucus or through a filtering network of bristles, hairs, or other body parts. Trapped particles are funnelled into the animal's mouth, and the water is pushed out. Bits of organic matter are trapped by the gills of bivalves such as clams and oysters, and plankton is filtered from water by the sievelike fringes of horny fibre, called baleen, hanging in the mouths of baleen whales (see Figure 41.12b).

Deposit feeders pick up or scrape particles of organic matter from solid material they live in or on. Earthworms are deposit feeders that eat their way through soil, taking the soil into their mouth and digesting and absorbing any organic material it contains. Some burrowing molluscs and tube-dwelling polychaete worms use body appendages to gather organic deposits from the sand or mud around them. Mucus on the appendages traps the organic material, and cilia move it to the mouth. The fiddler crab (*Uca* species) is a deposit feeder (see Figure 41.12c) with front claws differing dramatically in size. The small claw picks up sediment and moves it to the mouth, where the contents are sifted (the large claw is used in signalling). The edible parts of the sediment are ingested, and the rest is put back on the sediment as a small ball. The feeding-related movement of the small claw over the larger claw looks as if the crab is playing the large claw like a fiddle, giving the crab its name.

Bulk feeders consume sizable food items whole or in large chunks. Most mammals eat this way, as do reptiles, most birds and fishes, and adult amphibians. Depending on the animal, adaptations for bulk feeding include teeth for tearing or chewing, as well as claws and beaks for holding large food items. Some bulk feeders have flexible jaws allowing them to ingest objects that are larger in diameter than their head (see Figure 41.12d).

STUDY BREAK

1. What role do roots and root hairs play in the lives of plants?
2. What do mycorrhizae do for plants?
3. Describe the four basic feeding types in animals.

41.4 Digestive Processes in Animals

Most invertebrates and all vertebrates have a tubelike digestive system with two openings, a mouth for ingesting food and an anus for eliminating unused material. In these animals, contents move in one direction along the tube. The lumen of a digestive tube (also known as a gut, alimentary canal, digestive tract, or gastrointestinal tract) is external to all body tissues.

Mechanical and chemical digestive processes break food into its component parts, eventually breaking molecules into molecular subunits that can be absorbed into body fluids and transported to and moved into cells. Mechanical breakdown often involves grinding, sometimes with teeth or sometimes in a muscular gizzard. Chemical breakdown occurs by enzymatic hydrolysis, in which chemical bonds are broken by the addition of H^+ and OH^-, the components of water (see Chapter 3). Specific enzymes speed these reactions: *amylases* catalyze the hydrolysis of starches, *lipases* break down fats and other lipids, *proteases* hydrolyze proteins, and *nucleases* digest nucleic acids. Enzymatic hydrolysis of food molecules may take place inside or outside the body cells, depending on the animal.

41.4a Intracellular Digestion

In intracellular digestion, primarily in sponges and some cnidarians, cells take in food particles by endocytosis. Inside the cell, endocytic vesicles containing food particles fuse with a lysosome, a vesicle containing hydrolytic enzymes. The molecular subunits produced by the hydrolysis pass from the vesicle to the cytosol. Any undigested material remaining in the vesicle is released to the outside of the cell by exocytosis.

In sponges, water-containing particles of organic matter and microorganisms enter the body through pores in the body wall (see Figure 26.8). In the body cavity, individual *choanocytes* (collar cells) lining the body wall trap food particles, take them in by endocytosis, and transport them to amoeboid cells, where intracellular digestion takes place.

41.4b Extracellular Digestion

Extracellular digestion takes place in a pouch or tube enclosed within the body but outside the body cells—the digestive tract. Epithelial cells lining the pouch or tube secrete enzymes that digest the food. Processing food in this specialized compartment prevents self-digestion of the body tissues of the animal itself. Extracellular digestion, which occurs in most invertebrates and all vertebrates, greatly expands the range of available food sources by allowing animals to deal with much larger food items than those that can be engulfed by single cells. Extracellular digestion also allows animals to eat large batches of food that can be stored and digested while the animal continues other activities.

Some animals, including flatworms and cnidarians such as hydras, corals, and sea anemones, have a saclike digestive system with a single opening that serves as both the entrance for food and the exit for undigested material. In some of these animals, such as the flatworm *Dugesia* **(Figure 41.13)**, the digestive cavity is called a gastrovascular cavity because it circulates and digests food. Food is brought to the mouth by a protrusible pharynx (a throat that can be everted) and then enters the gastrovascular cavity (see Figure 41.13), where glands in the cavity wall secrete enzymes that begin the digestive process. Cells lining the cavity then take up the partially digested material by endocytosis and complete digestion intracellularly. Undigested matter is released to the outside through the pharynx and mouth.

41.4c Gastrointestinal Tracts

In most animals with a digestive tube, digestion occurs in five successive steps, each taking place in a specialized region of the tube. The tube is a biological disassembly line, with food entering at one end and leftovers leaving from the other. Five main processes occur from ingestion of food to expulsion of wastes:

1. *Mechanical processing.* Chewing, grinding, and tearing food chunks into smaller pieces, making them easier to move through the tract and increasing the surface area exposed to digestive enzymes.

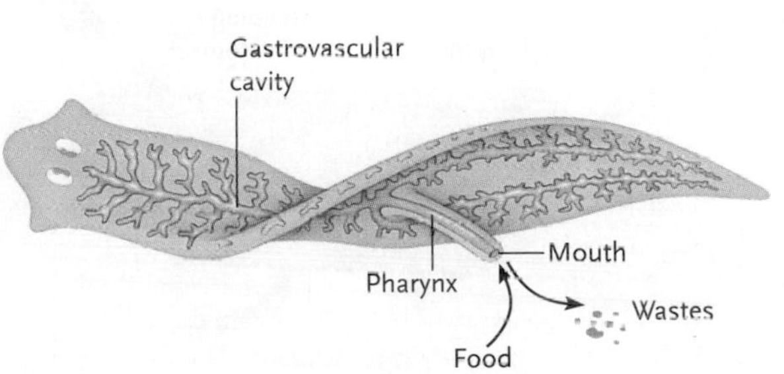

Figure 41.13
The digestive system of a flatworm (*Dugesia* species). The gastrovascular cavity (in blue) is a blind sac with one opening to the exterior through which food is ingested and wastes are expelled.

2. *Secretion of enzymes and other digestive aids.* Enzymes and other substances that aid the process of digestion, such as acids, emulsifiers, and lubricating mucus, are released into the tube.
3. *Enzymatic hydrolysis.* Food molecules are broken down through enzyme-catalyzed reactions into absorbable molecular subunits.
4. *Absorption.* The molecular subunits are absorbed from the digestive contents into body fluids and cells.
5. *Elimination.* Undigested materials are expelled through the anus.

Material being digested is pushed through the digestive tube by peristalsis, muscular contractions of its walls. During its progress through the tube, the digestive contents may be stored temporarily at one or more locations. Storage allows animals to take in larger quantities of food than they can process immediately, so feedings can be spaced in time rather than continuous.

Digestion in an Annelid. The earthworm (*Lumbricus* species, **Figure 41.14a**) is a deposit feeder that ingests a great deal of material, only some of which is edible. As it burrows, it pushes soil particles into its mouth. The particles pass from the mouth, through the esophagus, and into the crop (an enlargement of the digestive tube), where contents are stored and mixed with lubricating mucus. This mixture enters the muscular gizzard, where muscular contractions and abrasion by sand grains grind the food mixture into fine particles. The pulverized mixture then enters a long intestine, where organic matter is hydrolyzed by enzymes secreted into the digestive tube. As muscular contractions of the intestinal wall move the mixture along, cells lining the intestine absorb the molecular subunits produced by digestion. The absorptive surface of the intestine is increased by folds of the wall called *typhlosoles*. At the end of the intestine, the undigested residue is expelled through the anus.

Digestion in an Insect. Herbivorous insects such as grasshoppers **(Figure 41.14b)** are more selective in what they ingest. When eating, grasshoppers tear leaves and other plant parts into small particles with their mandibles, the hard external mouthparts. From the mouth, food particles pass through the pharynx, where salivary secretions moisten the mixture before it enters the esophagus and passes into the crop and begins the process of chemical digestion. From the crop, the food mass enters the muscular gizzard, where it is ground into smaller pieces. Food particles then enter the stomach, where food is stored and digestion continues. In gastric cecae (saclike outgrowths of the stomach; *cecum* = blind), enzymes hydrolyze food, and the products of digestion are absorbed through the walls of the ceca. Undigested food moves into the intestine for further digestion and absorption. At the end of the intestine, water is absorbed from undigested matter and the remnants (frass) are expelled through the anus. The digestive systems of other arthropods are similar to the insect system.

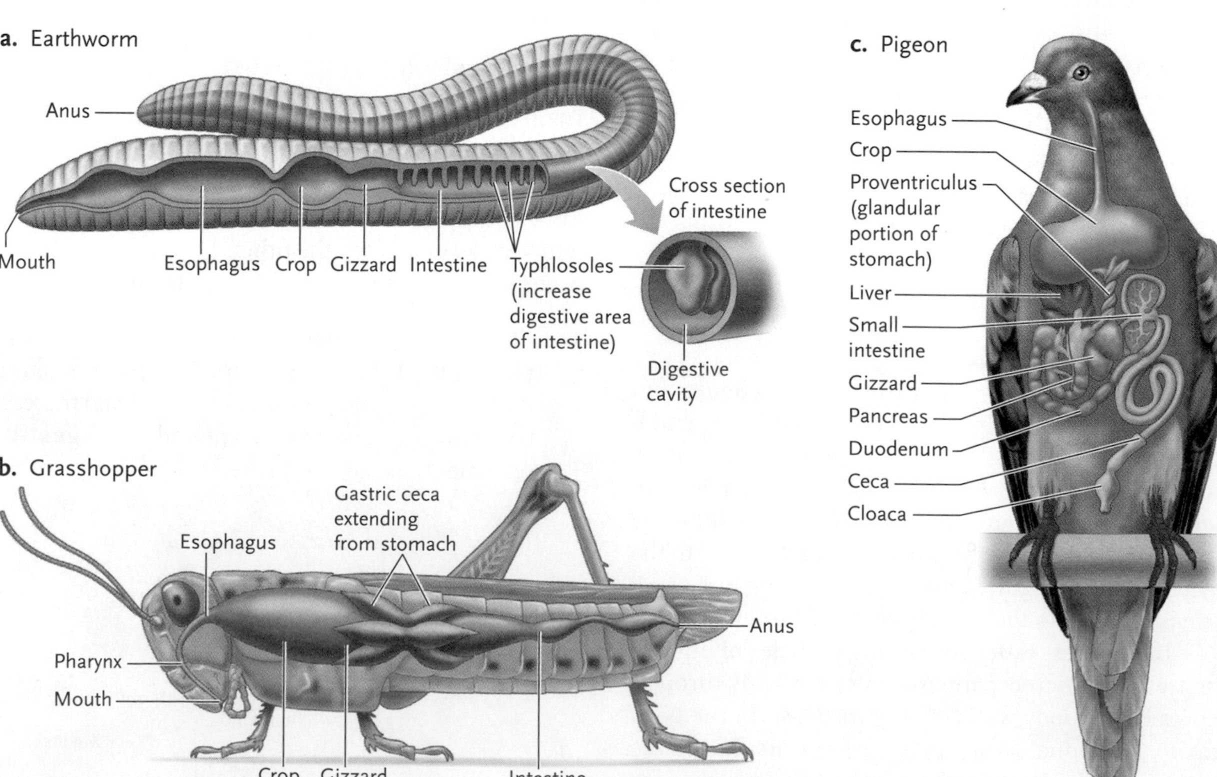

Figure 41.14
The digestive systems of **(a)** an annelid (earthworm), **(b)** an insect (grasshopper), and **(c)** a bird (pigeon).

Digestion in a Bird. A pigeon **(Figure 41.14c)** is also selective in what it ingests. A pigeon picks up seeds with its bill and uses its tongue to move them into its mouth, where they are moistened by mucus-filled saliva and swallowed whole. Seeds pass through the pharynx and into the esophagus. Birds such as parrots or cardinals use their bills to crack open seeds, but ingestion occurs as it does in pigeons. The anterior end of the esophagus is tubelike, but it opens into a crop, where food can be stored. The food moves to the proventriculus, the anterior glandular portion of the stomach that secretes digestive enzymes and acids. The food then passes to the gizzard, where muscular action grinds the seeds into fine particles, aided by ingested bits of sand and rock. Food particles then enter the intestine, where secretions from the liver (bile) and pancreas (digestive enzymes) are added. Molecular subunits produced by enzymatic digestion are absorbed as the mixture passes along the intestine, and the undigested residues are expelled through the anus, which opens to the cloaca. Structures such as the mouth, pharynx, esophagus, stomach, intestine, liver, and pancreas occur in almost all vertebrates.

Study Break

1. What is a gizzard? What does it do? Which animals have one?
2. What are choanocytes? What do they do?
3. Is the diet of *Dugesia* typical for flatworms? Why?

41.5 Digestion in Mammals

The mammalian digestive system is a series of specialized regions including the mouth, pharynx, esophagus, stomach, small and large intestines, rectum, and anus, that perform the five steps listed above **(Figure 41.15)**. These regions are under the control of the nervous and endocrine systems, allowing mammals to meet basic needs for fuel molecules and for a wide range of nutrients, including the molecular building blocks of carbohydrates, lipids, proteins, and nucleic acids. If the diet is adequate, the digestive system also absorbs the essential nutrients (the amino acids, fatty acids, vitamins, and minerals that cannot

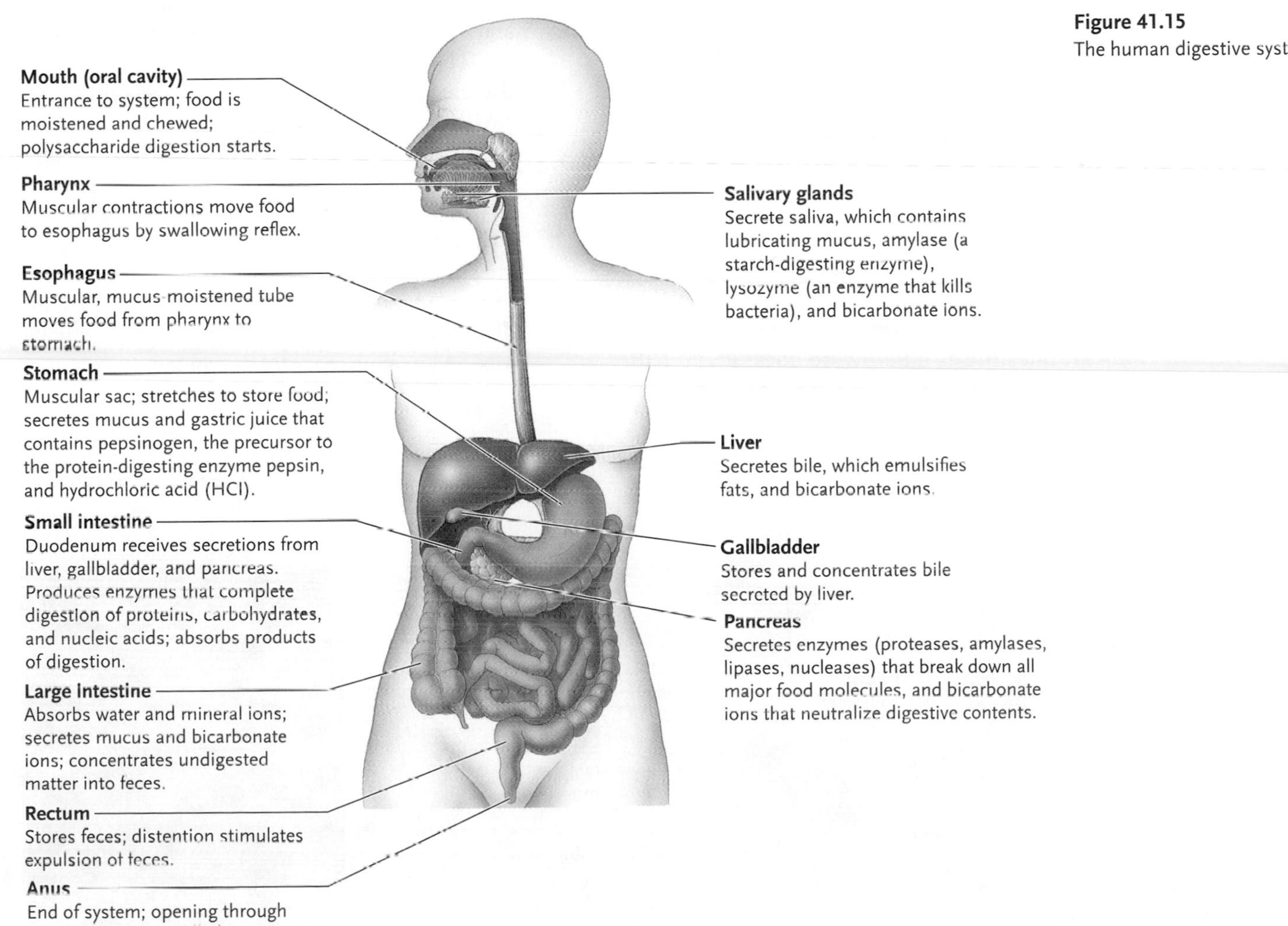

Mouth (oral cavity)
Entrance to system; food is moistened and chewed; polysaccharide digestion starts.
Pharynx
Muscular contractions move food to esophagus by swallowing reflex.
Esophagus
Muscular, mucus-moistened tube moves food from pharynx to stomach.
Stomach
Muscular sac; stretches to store food; secretes mucus and gastric juice that contains pepsinogen, the precursor to the protein-digesting enzyme pepsin, and hydrochloric acid (HCl).
Small intestine
Duodenum receives secretions from liver, gallbladder, and pancreas. Produces enzymes that complete digestion of proteins, carbohydrates, and nucleic acids; absorbs products of digestion.
Large intestine
Absorbs water and mineral ions; secretes mucus and bicarbonate ions; concentrates undigested matter into feces.
Rectum
Stores feces; distention stimulates expulsion of feces.
Anus
End of system; opening through which feces are expelled.
Salivary glands
Secrete saliva, which contains lubricating mucus, amylase (a starch-digesting enzyme), lysozyme (an enzyme that kills bacteria), and bicarbonate ions.
Liver
Secretes bile, which emulsifies fats, and bicarbonate ions.
Gallbladder
Stores and concentrates bile secreted by liver.
Pancreas
Secretes enzymes (proteases, amylases, lipases, nucleases) that break down all major food molecules, and bicarbonate ions that neutralize digestive contents.

Figure 41.15
The human digestive system.

Carnivore (a dog)

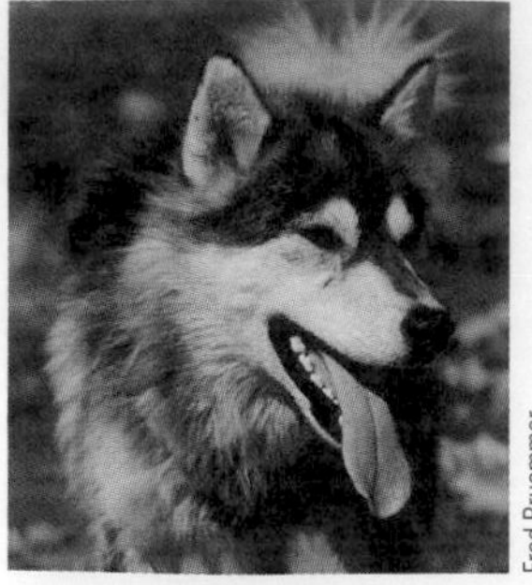

Herbivore (a rabbit)

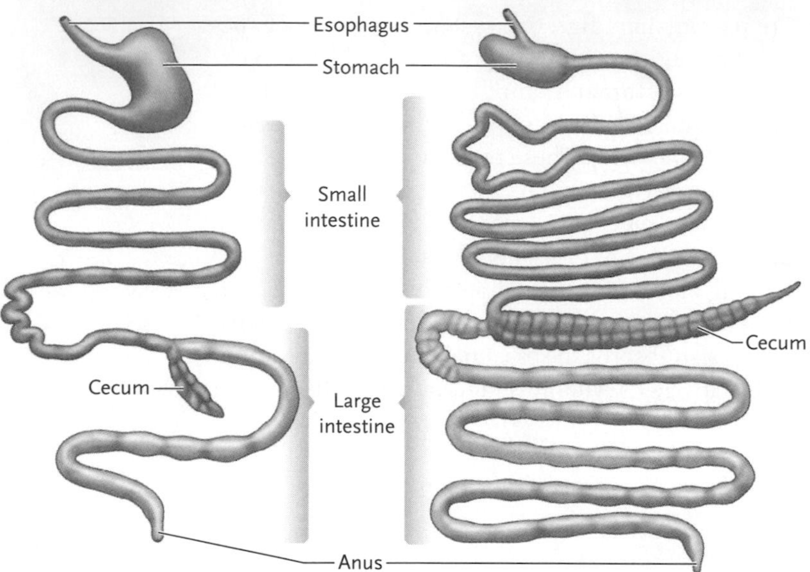

Figure 41.16
Comparison of the lengths of the digestive system of a carnivore (*Canis familiaris*) and a herbivore (*Oryctolagus cuniculus*). Note differences in length and the development of the cecae.

be synthesized within our bodies). In other mammals, differences in diet are reflected by the structure of the digestive tract **(Figure 41.16).** A carnivore's diet is relatively easy to digest; therefore, it does not require as long an intestine as a herbivore does. Plant matter, especially the cell walls, is particularly difficult to digest—hence the longer intestine. The rabbit cecum houses symbiotic, plant-digesting microorganisms that help extract nutrients from plants (see *Digesting Cellulose: Fermentation*).

41.5a Gut Layers

The wall of the gut in mammals and other vertebrates contains four major layers, each with specialized functions **(Figure 41.17),** from the inner surface outward:

1. The **mucosa** contains epithelial and glandular cells and lines the inside of the gut. Epithelial cells absorb digested nutrients and seal off the digestive contents from body fluids. The glandular cells secrete enzymes, aids to digestion such as lubricating mucus, and substances that adjust the pH of the digestive contents.
2. The **submucosa** is a thick layer of elastic connective tissue containing neuron networks and blood and lymph vessels. Neuron networks provide local control of digestive activity and carry signals between the gut and the central nervous system. Lymph vessels carry absorbed lipids to other parts of the body.
3. In most regions of the gut, the **muscularis** is formed by two smooth muscle layers, a *circular layer* that constricts the diameter of the gut when it contracts and a *longitudinal layer* that shortens and widens the gut. The stomach also has an *oblique layer* running diagonally around its wall. Peristalsis occurs when circular and longitudinal muscle layers of the muscularis coordinate their activities to push the digestive contents through the gut **(Figure 41.18, p. 1022).** In **peristalsis**, the circular muscle layer contracts in a wave that passes along the gut, constricting the gut and pushing the digestive contents onward. Just in front of the advancing constriction, the longitudinal layer contracts, shortening and expanding the tube and making space for the contents to advance.

Figure 41.17
Layers of the gut wall in vertebrates as seen in the stomach wall.

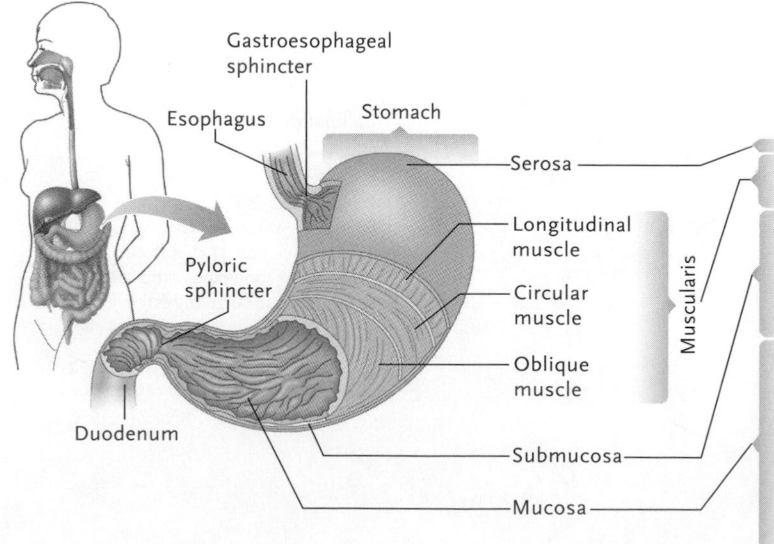

Digesting Cellulose: Fermentation

The digestive tracts of mammals vary in length (see Figure 41.16). Most animals cannot digest cellulose because they lack cellulase, which hydrolyzes cellulose into glucose subunits. Many herbivorous animals (primary consumers) use the hydrolytic capabilities of microorganisms that do produce cellulase. In this way, bacteria, protists, and fungi aid other animals to digest plant material.

Herbivores using microorganisms house these symbionts in specialized structures along the alimentary canal. These structures occur in the esophagus, stomach, or cecae, depending on the species. Ruminant mammals (Bovidae, Cervidae) and termites are well-known examples of animals that use symbionts to digest cellulose.

Ruminants use their teeth to crop and chew plant material. They swallow the masticated material, moving it to a complex, four-chambered rumen **(Figure 1).** The first three chambers of the rumen are derived from the esophagus, whereas the fourth, the abomasum, is the stomach. Swallowed food material arrives in the reticulum and then moves to the rumen. Then ruminants "chew their cuds," regurgitating material from the reticulum and rumen, rechewing it, and macerating it into smaller fragments before swallowing it again. This exposes more surface area to microbial enzymes, giving them more time to act.

Fermentation by the microorganisms occurs in the reticulum and in the rumen. Oxygen levels in the chambers are too low to support mitochondrial reactions (see Chapter 7). Matter digested and liquefied by microorganisms moves to the *omasum*, where water is absorbed from the mass. In the *abomasum* (the ruminant's true stomach), acids and pepsin are added to the food mass, killing the microorganisms and starting the process of "typical" vertebrate digestion. As the food mass moves to the small intestine, dead microorganisms, themselves a rich source of proteins, vitamins, and other nutrients, are digested and absorbed along with other hydrolyzable molecules.

Fermentation generates products such as alcohols and amino acids that are used as nutrients. It also produces volatile fatty acids that move from the rumen to the blood and are used as sources of carbon and energy. Microorganisms use 40 to 60% of the food protein produced by fermentation, and, in turn, their bodies are protein for the host. Methane, another product, collects in the fermentation chambers, so ruminants belch the gas in huge quantities. One cow can release more than 400 L of methane per day. Cattle are estimated to contribute 20% of the methane polluting our atmosphere. A 500-kg cow with a 70-L rumen produces about 60 L of saliva a day and ingests 40 L of water. Fermentation takes time: the leaves eaten by a cow take about 55 hours to move through its digestive system.

Many other mammals have esophageal or gastric chambers that house plant-digesting symbiotic microorganisms. Biologists had long thought that the weight of the fermentation chamber made digestion by fermentation inaccessible to birds. But at least one species of bird, the South American hoatzin, uses fermentation **(Figure 2).** Freshly caught hoatzins smell like cattle dung, perhaps giving a clue to their use of fermentation. Hoatzins eat young leaves that are fermented in the enlarged forestomach. This fermentation centre takes up some space occupied by flight muscles in "normal" birds. Hoatzins are weak fliers, probably because of reduction in the mass of their flight muscles to accommodate the enlarged forestomach.

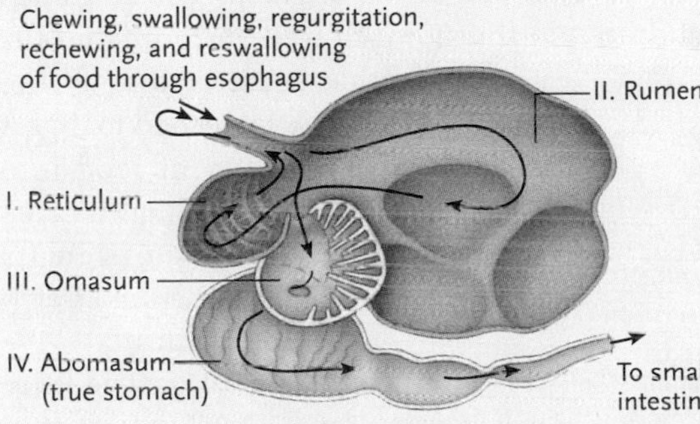

Figure 1
Ruminants, such as the pronghorn (*Antilocapra americanus*), have a four-chambered stomach system for digesting plant material (cellulose) by fermentation. Some other mammalian herbivores use the same approach, but others, such as the rabbit *O. cuniculus*, achieve fermentation in other parts of the digestive tract (see Figure 41.16).

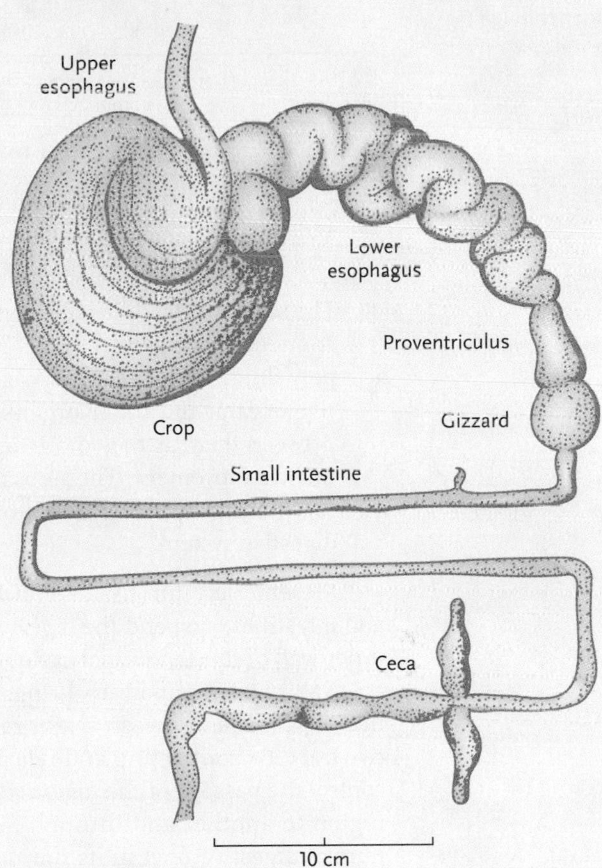

Figure 2
The hoatzin (*Opisthocomus hoatzin*) uses foregut fermentation to digest cellulose to meet a high percentage of its energy requirements. The contents of the crop and lower esophagus account for over 15% of adult mass. Deep ridges in the lining of the crop increase its surface area.

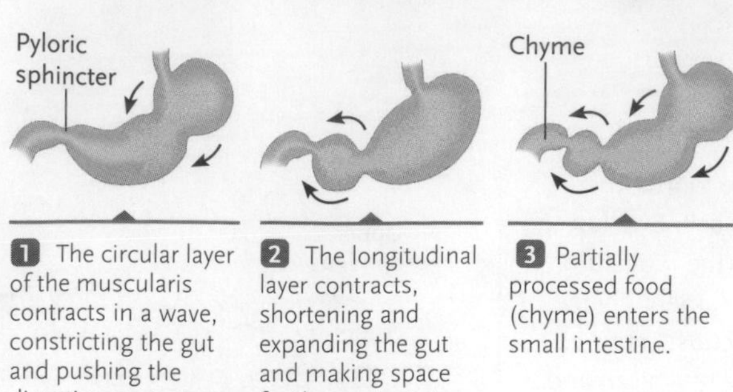

Pyloric
sphincter
Chyme
1 The circular layer of the muscularis contracts in a wave, constricting the gut and pushing the digestive contents onward.
2 The longitudinal layer contracts, shortening and expanding the gut and making space for the contents to advance.
3 Partially processed food (chyme) enters the small intestine.

Figure 41.18 The waves of peristaltic contractions moving food through the stomach.

4. The **serosa** is the outermost gut layer. It consists of connective tissue that secretes an aqueous, slippery fluid that lubricates areas between the digestive organs and other organs, reducing friction between them as they move together as a result of muscle movement. The serosa is continuous with the mesentery along much of the length of the digestive system.

Mesenteries, thin tissues attached to the stomach and intestines, suspend the digestive system from the inner wall of the abdominal cavity.

Sphincters are powerful rings of smooth muscle that form valves between major regions of the digestive tract. By contracting and relaxing, the sphincters control the passage of the digestive contents from one region to another and through the anus. The adult human digestive tract in its normal living contracted state is about 4.5 m long. It is about twice as long when fully extended, as in a cadaver (all muscles relaxed).

41.5b Down the Tube

Food begins its travel through the gastrointestinal tract in the mouth, where the teeth cut, tear, and crush food items. During chewing, three pairs of **salivary glands** secrete saliva through ducts that open on the inside of the cheeks and under the tongue. Saliva, which is more than 99% water, moistens the food and, as we have seen, begins digestion (salivary amylase; see *Why It Matters*). Saliva also contains mucus to lubricate the food mass and bicarbonate ions (HCO_3^-) to neutralize acids in the food and keep the pH of the mouth between 6.5 and 7.5, the optimal range for salivary amylase to function. Saliva also contains a *lysozyme*, an enzyme that kills bacteria by breaking open their cell walls.

After a suitable period of chewing, the food mass, called a bolus, is pushed by the tongue to the back of the mouth, where touch receptors detect the pressure and trigger the *swallowing reflex* **(Figure 41.19).** This reflex is an involuntary action produced by contractions of muscles in the walls of the pharynx that direct food into the esophagus. Peristaltic contractions of the esophagus, aided by mucus secreted by the esophagus, propel the bolus toward the stomach. The passage down the esophagus stimulates the gastroesophageal sphincter at the junction between the esophagus and the stomach to open and admit the bolus to the stomach. After the bolus enters the stomach, the sphincter closes tightly. If the closure is imperfect, the acidic stomach contents can enter the esophagus, in humans causing *acid reflux* or heartburn.

Mammals consciously initiate the swallowing reflex, but once it has begun, they cannot stop it because whereas the muscles of the pharynx and upper esophagus are skeletal muscles under voluntary control, the muscles below are smooth muscles under involuntary control.

Involuntary movements of the tongue and soft palate at the back of the mouth prevent food from backing into the mouth or nasal cavities. The glottis (space between vocal cords) and the epiglottis, a flap-like valve, prevent entry of food into the tracheae.

41.5c Stomach

The stomach is a muscular, elastic sac that stores food and adds secretions, furthering digestion. The stomach lining, the mucosa, is covered with tiny *gastric pits*, entrances to millions of *gastric glands*. These glands extend deep into the stomach wall and contain cells that secrete some of the products needed to digest food. Entry of food into the stomach activates stretch receptors in its wall. Signals from stretch receptors stimulate the secretion of gastric juice **(Figure 41.20),** which contains the digestive enzyme pepsin, hydrochloric acid (HCl), and lubricating mucus. The stomach secretes about 2 L of gastric juice each day.

Pepsin begins the digestion of proteins by

Figure 41.19 The swallowing reflex.

Structures of the mouth, pharynx, and esophagus involved in the swallowing reflex

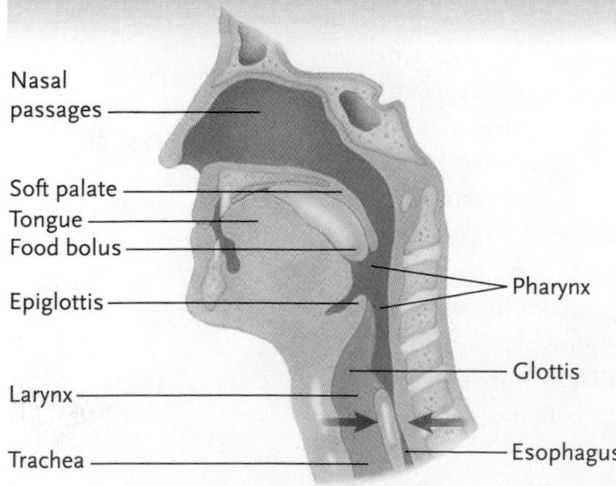

Motions that seal the nasal passages, mouth, and trachea during the swallowing reflex

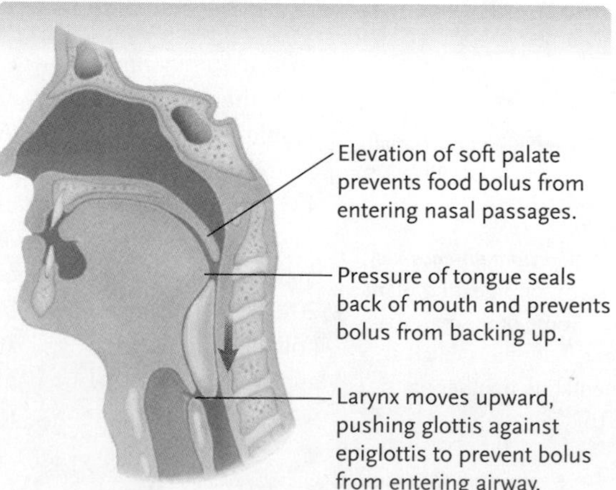

Elevation of soft palate prevents food bolus from entering nasal passages.
Pressure of tongue seals back of mouth and prevents bolus from backing up.
Larynx moves upward, pushing glottis against epiglottis to prevent bolus from entering airway.

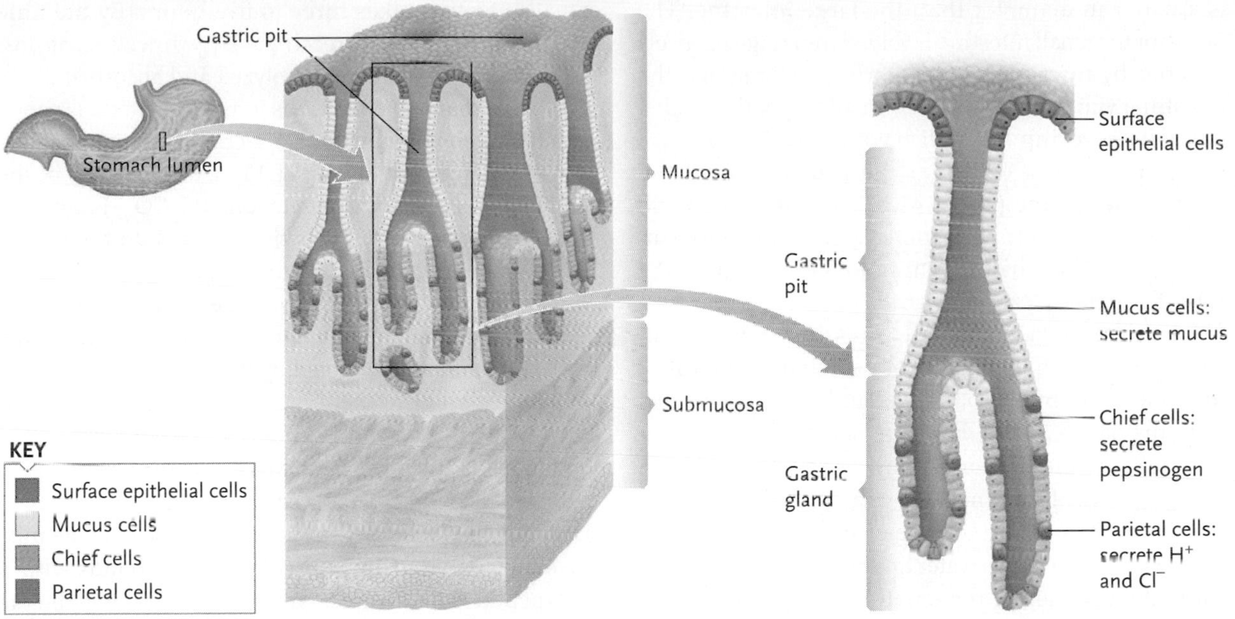

Figure 41.20 Cells that secrete mucus, pepsin, and HCl in the stomach lining.

introducing breaks in polypeptide chains. Pepsin is secreted in the form of an inactive precursor molecule, pepsinogen, by cells called *chief cells*. Pepsinogen is converted to pepsin by the highly acid conditions of the stomach. Once produced, pepsin itself can catalyze the reaction, converting more pepsinogen to pepsin. The activation of pepsin illustrates a common theme in digestion. Powerful hydrolytic enzymes such as pepsin would be dangerous to the cells that secrete them. However, enzymes are synthesized as inactive precursors and not converted into active form until exposed to digestive contents.

Parietal cells secrete H^+ and Cl^- that combine to form HCl in the lumen of the stomach. The HCl lowers the pH of the digestive contents to pH ≤ 2, the level at which pepsin reaches optimal activity. To put this pH in perspective, lemon juice is pH 2.4, and sulphuric acid or battery acid is about pH 1. The acidity of the stomach helps break up food particles and causes proteins in the stomach contents to unfold, exposing their peptide linkages to hydrolysis by pepsin. The acid also kills most bacteria that reach the stomach and stops the action of salivary amylase. Some nectar-feeding bats that digest pollen drink their own urine to make their stomach more acid.

A thick coating of alkaline mucus is secreted by *mucus cells* and protects the stomach lining from attack by pepsin and HCl. Behind the mucus barrier, tight junctions between cells prevent gastric juice from seeping into the stomach wall. Even so, there is some breakdown of the stomach lining. The damage is normally repaired by rapid division of mucosal cells, which replaces the entire stomach lining about every three days. Most bacteria cannot survive the highly acid environment of the stomach, but one, *Helicobacter pylori*, thrives there. Ulcers result when *H. pylori* breaks down the mucus barrier and exposes the stomach wall to attack by HCl and pepsin (see Chapter 21, *People Behind Biology*).

Contractions of the stomach walls continually mix and churn the contents. Peristaltic contractions move the digestive contents toward the *pyloric sphincter* (*pylorus* = gatekeeper) at the junction between the stomach and the small intestine. The arrival of a strong stomach contraction relaxes and opens the valve briefly, releasing a pulse of the stomach contents, **chyme**, into the small intestine.

Feedback controls regulate the rate of gastric emptying, matching it to the rate of digestion, so that food is not moved along more quickly than it can be chemically processed. In particular, chyme with high fat content and high acidity stimulates the secretion of hormones by cells in the mucosal layer of the duodenum. These hormones slow the process of stomach emptying. Fat is digested in the lumen of the small intestine and more slowly than other nutrients, so further emptying of the stomach is prevented until fat processing has been completed in the small intestine. This is why a fatty meal, such as a greasy pizza, feels so heavy in the stomach. Highly acidic chyme must be neutralized by bicarbonate in the small intestine. Unneutralized stomach acid inactivates digestive enzymes secreted in the small intestine and inhibits further emptying of the stomach until it is neutralized.

41.5d Small Intestine

The small intestine completes digestion and begins the absorption of nutrients. Nutrients are not absorbed in the mouth, pharynx, or esophagus. Substances such as alcohol, aspirin, caffeine, and water are absorbed in the stomach, but most absorption occurs in the small intestine, where digestion is completed. The small intestine is smaller in diameter than the large intestine. The lining of the small intestine is folded into ridges densely covered by microscopic, fingerlike extensions, the intestinal villi (singular, *villus*). In addition, the epithelial cells covering the villi have microvilli, a *brush border* consisting of fingerlike projections of the plasma membrane **(Figure 41.21).** The intestinal villi and microvilli in humans increase the absorptive surface area of the small intestine to 300 m^2, about the size of a doubles tennis court.

Digestion in the small intestine depends on enzymes and other substances secreted by the intestine itself and by the pancreas and liver. Secretions from the pancreas and liver enter a common duct that empties into the lumen of the dudodenum, a 20-cm long segment of the small intestine **(Figure 41.22).**

About 95% of the volume of material leaving the stomach is absorbed as water and nutrients as digestive contents travel along the small intestine. Movement of the contents from the duodenum to the end of the small intestine takes three to five hours. By the time the digestive contents reach the large intestine, almost all nutrients have been hydrolyzed and absorbed.

In humans, the pancreas is an elongated, flattened gland located between the stomach and duodenum (Figure 41.22; see also Figure 41.15). Exocrine cells in the pancreas secrete bicarbonate ions ($H_2CO_3^-$) and pancreatic enzymes into ducts that empty into the lumen of the duodenum. The bicarbonate ions neutralize the acid in chyme, bringing the digestive contents to a slightly alkaline pH. Alkaline pH allows optimal activity of the enzymes secreted by the pancreas, including proteases, an amylase, nucleases, and lipases. All of these enzymes act in the lumen of the small intestine. Like pepsin, the proteases released by the pancreas are secreted in an inactive precursor form and are activated by contact with the digestive contents. The enzyme mixture includes trypsin, which hydrolyzes bonds within polypeptide chains, and carboxypeptidase, which cuts amino acids from polypeptide chains one at a time.

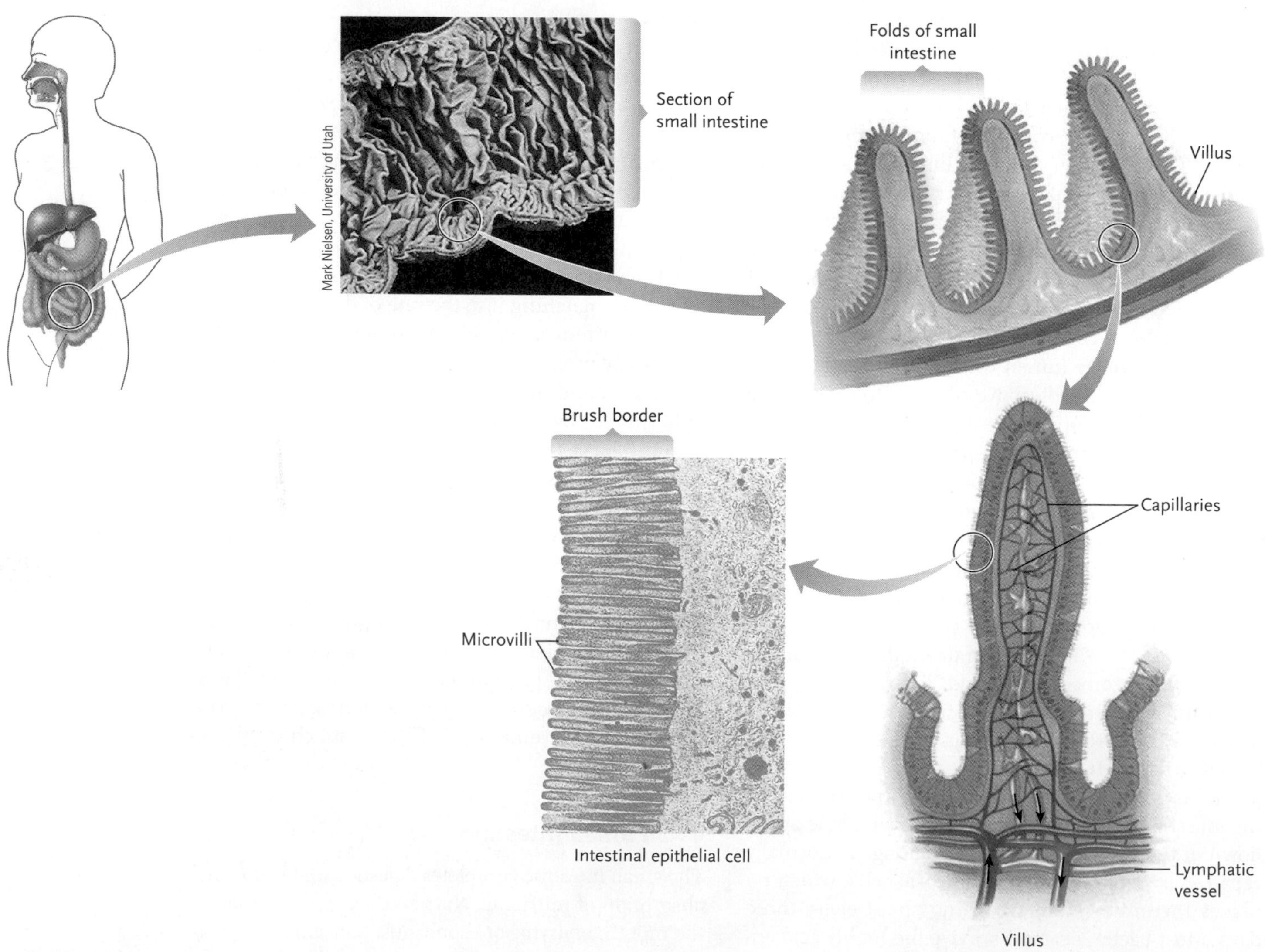

Figure 41.21
The structure of villi in the small intestine. The plasma membrane of individual epithelial cells of the villi extends into fingerlike projections, the microvilli, which greatly expand the absorptive surface of the small intestine. Collectively, the microvilli form the brush border of an epithelial cell of the intestinal mucosa.

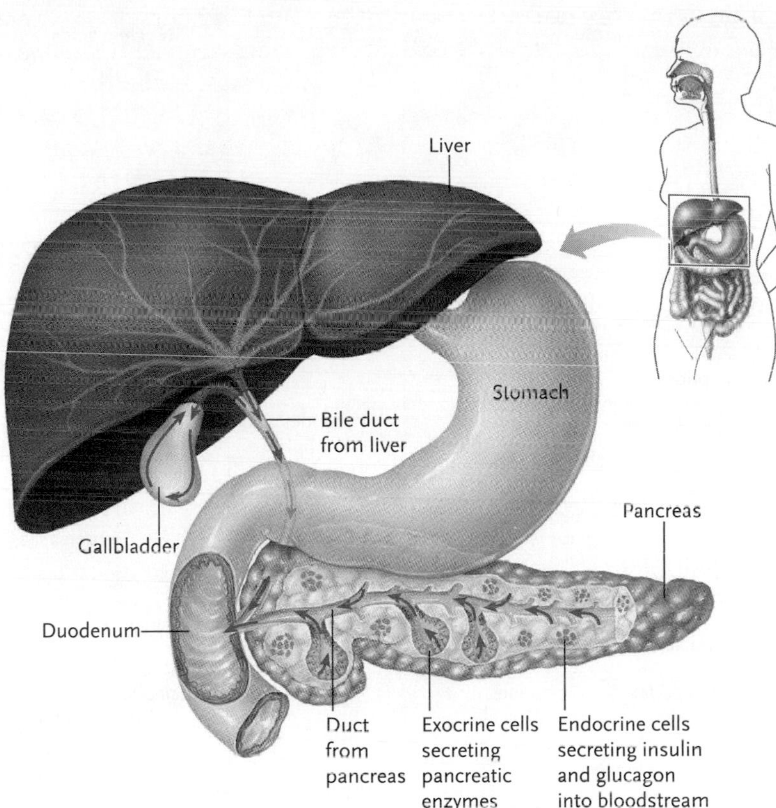

Figure 41.22
The ducts delivering bile and pancreatic juice to the duodenum of the small intestine.

The liver secretes bicarbonate ions and bile, a mixture of substances including bile salts, cholesterol, and bilirubin. Bile salts are derivatives of cholesterol and amino acids that aid fat digestion through their detergent action. They form a hydrophilic coating around fats and other lipids, allowing the churning motions of the small intestine to emulsify fats. During emulsification, fats are broken into tiny droplets called micelles, much the same effect as mixing oil and vinegar in a salad dressing. Lipase, a pancreatic enzyme, can then hydrolyze fats in the micelles to produce monoglycerides and free fatty acids. Bilirubin, a waste product derived from worn-out red blood cells, is yellow and gives the bile its colour. Bacterial enzymes in the intestines modify the pigment, resulting in the characteristic brown colour of feces.

The liver secretes bile continuously. Between meals, when no digestion is occurring, bile is stored in the gallbladder, where it is concentrated by the removal of water. After a meal, entry of chyme into the small intestine stimulates the gallbladder to release the stored bile into the small intestine.

Microvilli on the villi of the small intestine secrete water and mucus into the intestinal contents. They also carry out intracellular digestion by transporting products of earlier digestion, including disaccharides, peptides, and nucleotides, across their plasma membranes and producing enzymes to complete hydrolysis of these nutrients. Different disaccharidases break maltose, lactose, and sucrose into individual monosaccharides. Two proteases complete protein digestion: an aminopeptidase cuts amino acids from the end of a polypeptide, and a dipeptidase splits dipeptides into individual amino acids. Nucleases and other enzymes complete digestion of nucleic acids into five-carbon sugars and nitrogenous bases (**Figure 41.23, p. 1026**).

Water-soluble products of digestion enter the intestinal mucosa cells by active transport or facilitated diffusion (**Figure 41.24a, p. 1027**), and water follows by osmosis. The nutrients are then transported from the mucosal cells into the extracellular fluids, from where they enter the bloodstream in the capillary networks of the submucosa. The absorption of fatty acids, monoglycerides, fat-soluble vitamins, and cholesterol and other products of lipid breakdown by lipase occurs with the assistance of the micelles formed by bile salts (Figure 41.24b). When a micelle contacts the plasma membrane of a mucosal cell, the hydrophobic molecules within the droplet penetrate through the membrane and enter the cytoplasm.

In mucosal cells, fatty acids and monoglycerides are combined into fats (triglycerides) and packaged into chylomicrons, small droplets covered by a protein coat. Cholesterol absorbed in the small intestine is also packed into the chylomicrons. The protein coat of the chylomicrons provides a hydrophilic surface that keeps the droplets suspended in the cytosol. After travelling across the mucosal cells, the chylomicrons are secreted into the interstitial fluid of the submucosa, where they are taken up by lymph vessels. Eventually, they are transferred by lymph into the blood circulation.

Many nutrients absorbed by the small intestine are processed by the liver. Capillaries absorbing nutrient molecules in the small intestine collect into veins that join to form the hepatic portal vein, a larger blood vessel that leads to capillary networks in the liver. In the liver, some nutrients leave the bloodstream and enter liver cells for chemical processing. Among the reactions taking place in the liver is the combination of excess glucose units into glycogen that is stored in liver cells. This reaction reduces the glucose concentration in the blood exiting the liver to about 0.1%. If the glucose concentration in the blood entering the liver falls below 0.1% between meals, the reaction reverses. The reversal adds glucose to return the blood concentration to the 0.1% level before it exits the liver.

Figure 41.23
Enzymatic digestion of carbohydrates, proteins, fats, and nucleic acids in the human digestive system.

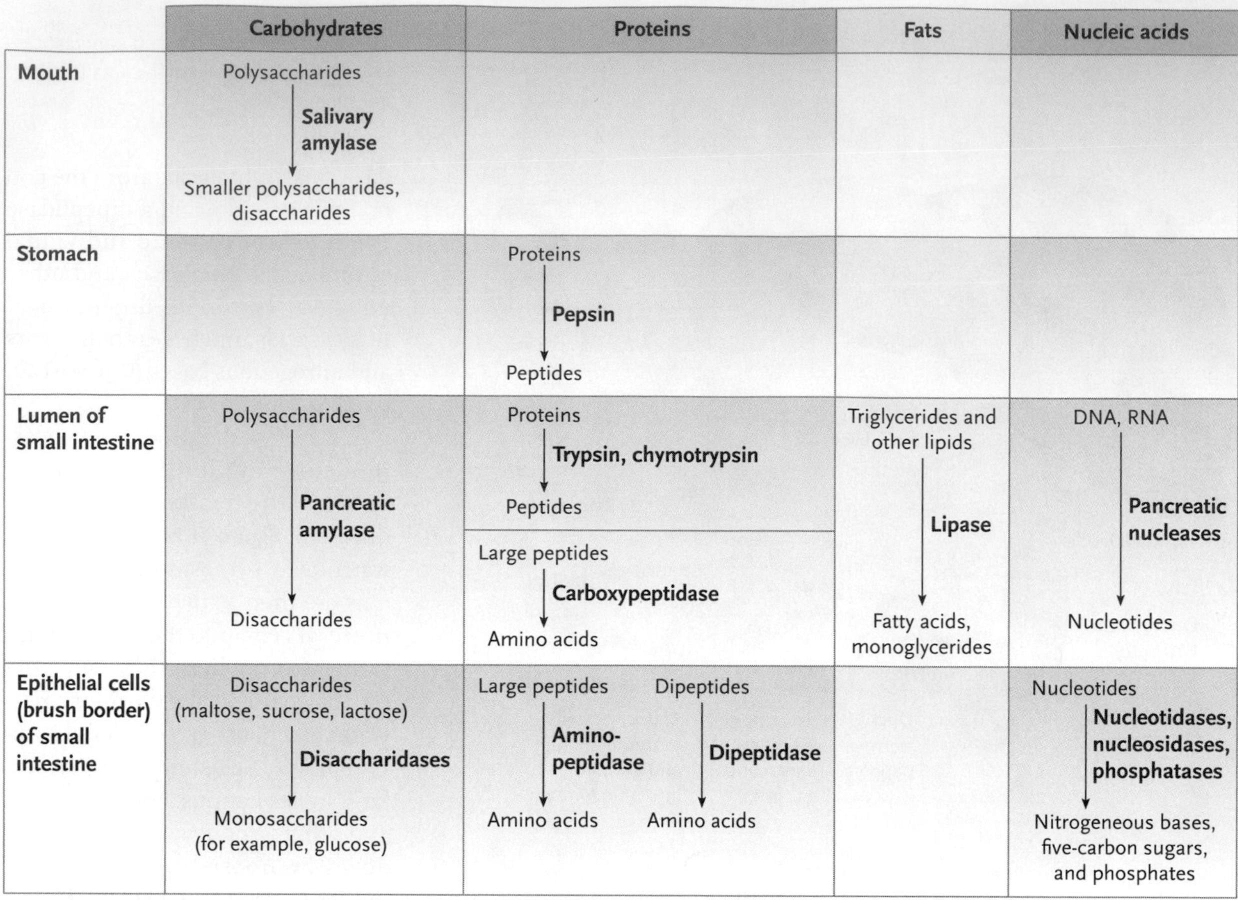

	Carbohydrates	Proteins	Fats	Nucleic acids
Mouth	Polysaccharides ↓ **Salivary amylase** ↓ Smaller polysaccharides, disaccharides			
Stomach		Proteins ↓ **Pepsin** ↓ Peptides		
Lumen of small intestine	Polysaccharides ↓ **Pancreatic amylase** ↓ Disaccharides	Proteins ↓ **Trypsin, chymotrypsin** ↓ Peptides; Large peptides ↓ **Carboxypeptidase** ↓ Amino acids	Triglycerides and other lipids ↓ **Lipase** ↓ Fatty acids, monoglycerides	DNA, RNA ↓ **Pancreatic nucleases** ↓ Nucleotides
Epithelial cells (brush border) of small intestine	Disaccharides (maltose, sucrose, lactose) ↓ **Disaccharidases** ↓ Monosaccharides (for example, glucose)	Large peptides ↓ **Amino-peptidase** ↓ Amino acids; Dipeptides ↓ **Dipeptidase** ↓ Amino acids		Nucleotides ↓ **Nucleotidases, nucleosidases, phosphatases** ↓ Nitrogeneous bases, five-carbon sugars, and phosphates

The liver also synthesizes lipoproteins that transport cholesterol and fats in the bloodstream, detoxifies ethyl alcohol and other toxic molecules, and inactivates steroid hormones and many types of drugs. As a result of the liver's activities, the blood leaving it has a markedly different concentration of nutrients than the blood carried into the liver by the hepatic portal vein. From the liver, blood goes to the heart and is then pumped to deliver nutrients to all parts of the body.

41.5e Large Intestine

From the small intestine, the contents move on to the large intestine, or colon. A sphincter at the junction between the small and large intestines controls the passage of material and prevents backward movement of contents. The inner surface of the large intestine is relatively smooth and contains no villi.

The large intestine has several distinct regions. At the junction with the small intestine, a part of the large intestine forms the **cecum**, a blind pouch. A fingerlike sac, the **appendix**, extends from the cecum. The cecum merges with the colon, which forms an inverted U, finally connecting with the **rectum**, the terminal part of the large intestine.

The large intestine secretes mucus and bicarbonate ions and absorbs water and other ions, primarily Na^+ and Cl^-. The absorption of water condenses and compacts the digestive contents into solid masses, the feces. Normally, fecal matter reaching the rectum contains less than 200 mL of the fluid that entered the digestive tract each day. Animals suffering from diarrhea produce liquid fecal matter. Diarrhea is a higher-than-normal rate of movement of materials through the small intestine, which does not leave adequate time for absorption of water. Diarrhea can be caused by irritation of the small intestine wall, caused by infection, emotional stress, or irritation of the small intestine wall.

As many as 500 species of bacteria comprise 30 to 50% of the dry matter of feces in humans and other vertebrates. Most of these bacteria live as essentially permanent residents in the large intestine. *Escherichia coli* is the most common in humans and other mammals. Intestinal bacteria metabolize sugars and other nutrients remaining in the digestive residue. They produce useful fatty acids and vitamins (such as vitamin K, the B vitamins, folic acid, and biotin), some of which are absorbed in the large intestine. Bacterial activity in the large intestines produces large quantities of gas (*flatus*), primarily CO_2, methane, and hydrogen sulphide. Most of the gas is absorbed through the intestinal mucosa, and the rest is expelled through the anus in the process of *flatulence*. The amount and composition of flatus depend on the type of food ingested and the particular population of bacteria present in the large intestine.

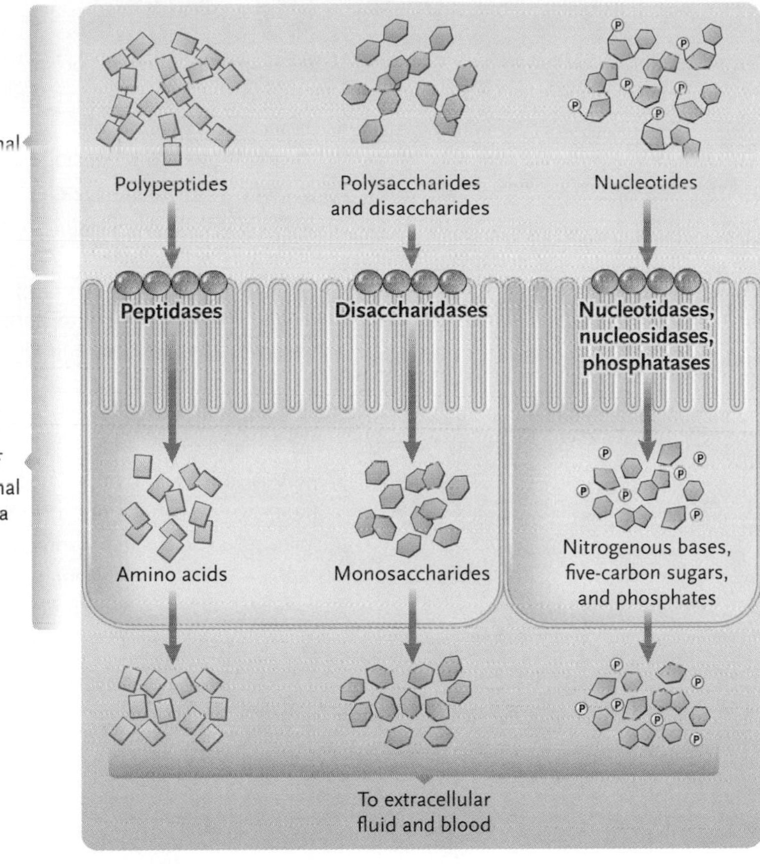

Water-soluble molecules are broken into absorbable subunits at brush borders of mucosal cells and transported inside; the subunits are transported on the other side to extracellular fluid and blood.

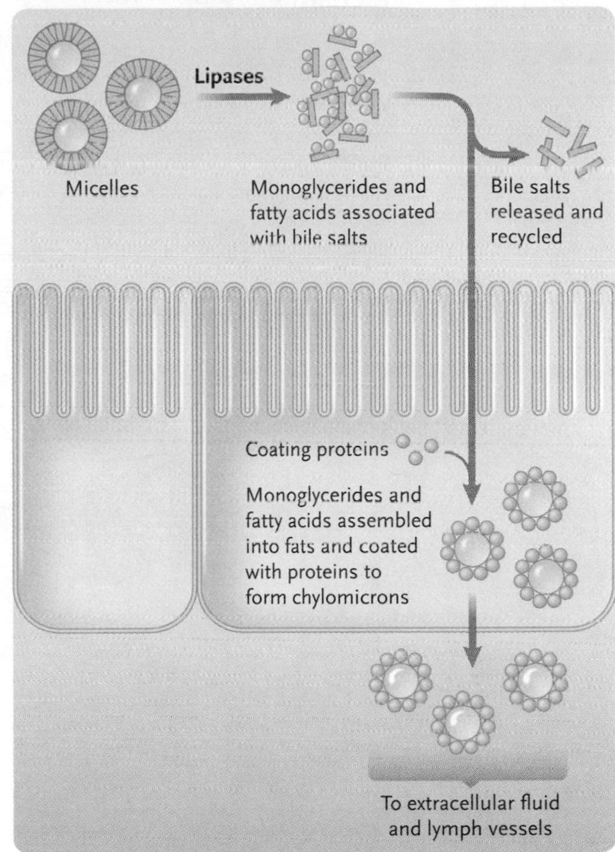

Micelles (fats coated with bile salts) are digested to monoglycerides and fatty acids, which penetrate into cells and are assembled into fats. The fats are coated with proteins to form chylomicrons, which are released by exocytosis to extracellular fluids, where they are picked up by lymph vessels.

Figure 41.24
Absorption of digestive products by the epithelial cells of the intestinal mucosa.

Foods such as beans contain carbohydrates that humans cannot digest. These carbohydrates can be metabolized by gas-producing intestinal bacteria, explaining the folkloric connection between beans and flatulence.

Feces entering the rectum stretch its walls, at some point triggering a *defecation reflex* that opens the *anal sphincter* and expels the feces through the anus. Because the anal sphincter contains rings of voluntary skeletal muscle as well as involuntary smooth muscle, animals can resist the defecation reflex by voluntarily tightening the striated muscle ring—to a point.

Study Break

1. Where and why is methane produced along the gastrointestinal tract?
2. What is peristalsis? What does it do? Is it unique to mammals?
3. How many species of bacteria can occur in a mammalian gastrointestinal tract?

41.6 Regulation of the Digestive Processes

Most of the digestive process is regulated and coordinated by largely automated controls, most of which originate in the neuron networks of the submucosa. Other controls, particularly those regulating appetite and oxidative metabolism, originate in the brain, in control centres that form part of the hypothalamus (see *People Behind Biology*).

Movement of food through the digestive system is controlled by receptors in and hormones secreted by various parts of the system **(Figure 41.25, p. 1029)**. Control starts with the mouth, where the presence of food activates receptors that increase the rate of salivary secretion by as much as 10-fold over the resting state.

Swallowed food expands the stomach and sets off signals from stretch receptors in the stomach walls. Chemoreceptors in the stomach respond to the presence of food molecules, particularly proteins. Signals from

People Behind Biology

Richard E. Peter

Our knowledge about the neuroendocrine regulation of reproduction and growth in fish was strongly influenced by the work of Dick Peter (1943–2007). Dr. Peter studied the physiological role of nuclei in the hypothalamus. He and his colleagues were among the first to measure the secretion of fish pituitary hormones, contributing to both our knowledge of fish and the broader field of comparative endocrinology.

In vertebrates, a complex set of interactions governs regulation of appetite and body mass. By combining techniques from animal behaviour, molecular biology, and immunohistochemistry, Dr. Peter explored neuroendocrine regulation of feeding behaviour and food intake in fish. Key factors from the hypothalamus stimulate food intake (orexigenic factors), whereas other factors inhibit it (anorexigenic factors). Pathways of interactions of various factors are shown in **Figure 1.**

Dr. Peter also contributed to the advancement of comparative endocrinology by initiating regional, national, and international meetings and organizations. At these meetings, colleagues and their students could interact and share ideas and data. His leadership extended into other areas, serving as chair of the Department of Zoology at the University of Alberta and later as the dean of science there.

Dr. Peter is particularly remembered for the excellence of his mentorship. During his career, he supervised the work of 17 Ph.D. students.

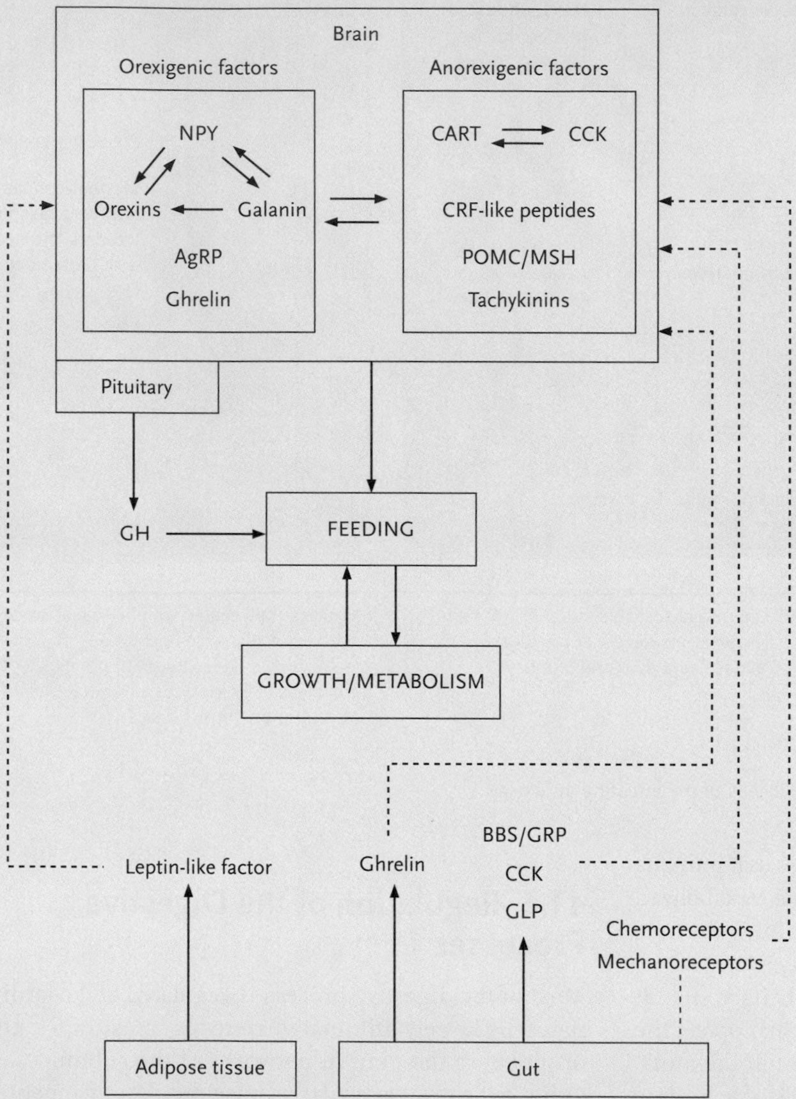

Figure 1
General schematic diagram showing how central and peripheral peptides regulate food intake in fish. AgRP – agouti-related protein; BBS/GRP – bombesin/gastrin releasing protein; CART – cocaine and amphetamine regulated transcript; CCK – cholecystokinin; CRF – corticotropin-releasing factor; GH – growth hormone; GLP – glucagonlike peptide: MSH – melanocyte-stimulating hormone; NPY – neuropeptide Y; POMCD – proopiomelanocortin.

these receptors are integrated in neuron networks in the stomach and autonomic nervous system to produce several reflex responses. One response is an increase in the rate and strength of stomach contractions. Another is secretion of a hormone, *gastrin,* into the blood leaving the stomach. After travelling through the circulatory system, gastrin returns to the stomach, where it stimulates the secretion of HCl and pepsinogen. These molecules are used in the digestion of the protein in the food that was responsible for their secretion. Gastrin also stimulates stomach and intestinal contractions, activities serving to keep the digestive contents moving through the digestive system when a new meal arrives.

Three hormones secreted into the lumen of the duodenum participate in regulating digestive processes. When chyme is emptied into the duodenum, its acidic nature stimulates the release of the hormone *secretin.* Secretin inhibits further gastric emptying to prevent more acid from entering the duodenum until the newly arrived chyme is neutralized. Secretin also

LIFE ON THE EDGE
Fuelling Hovering Flight

Hovering flight is extremely expensive in terms of fuel consumption whether the hoverer is a Harrier Jump Jet, a helicopter, or a hummingbird. In a hovering hummingbird, >90% of the animal's metabolic rate (overall energy consumption) is accounted for by the flight muscles. Hovering allows hummingbirds and some nectar-feeding bats to feed at flowers and tank up with nectar, which is essentially sugar-water. How do these animals pay the costs of hovering?

Some humans eat a lot of sugar before exercising, but only 25 to 30% of the energy they burn while running comes from the sugar ingested just before or during exercise. It is a mistake to think that eating a bar of chocolate as you run will immediately increase the energy available to you.

In contrast, hummingbirds fuel ~95% of the cost of hovering from the sugar they are ingesting as they hover. High levels of sucrase activity in the birds' intestines translate into rapid hydrolysis of sucrose, explaining the rapid mobilization of this fuel. Nectar produced by the flowers visited by hummingbirds is high in sucrose.

What happens with flower visiting bats? The Pallas' long-tongued bat (*Glossophaga soricina*, family Phyllostomidae) appears to be a nocturnal version of a hummingbird. These bats hover in front of flowers and use long, extensible tongues to extract nectar. Kenneth Welch and two colleagues used measures of oxygen consumption to indicate metabolism and the ratios of $^{13}\Delta/^{12}\Delta$ carbon to identify sources of energy for hovering Pallas' long-tongued bats. Their measurements indicated that these bats mobilized ~78% of the energy needed for hovering from sucrose ingested during hovering. Sucrase levels in the intestines of the bats are about half of those recorded for hummingbirds, probably accounting for the difference in immediate access to fuel. These results suggest convergent evolution between flower-visiting bats and birds. It remains to be determined if the flower-visiting bats of the Old World tropics (family Pteropodidae) have evolved the same adaptations.

The nectar content of flowers pollinated by hummingbirds is about 60% sucrose, whereas that of flowers pollinated by bats is 20% sucrose. These differences may make the bats less efficient at immediately covering the costs of hovering than the hummingbirds. Hovering to extract high-energy food (nectar) amounts to living on the edge, and animals that do so are highly adapted to pay the costs of this specialized flight behaviour (see *The Puzzling Biology of Weight Control*).

inhibits gastric secretion to reduce acid production in the stomach and stimulates HCO_3^- secretion into the lumen of the duodenum to neutralize the acid. If the acid is not neutralized, the duodenal wall can be damaged.

Fat and, to a lesser extent, protein in the chyme entering the duodenum stimulate the release of the hormone *cholecystokinin* (*CCK*). CCK inhibits gastric activity, allowing time for nutrients in the duodenum to be digested and absorbed. CCK also stimulates the secretion of pancreatic enzymes to digest macromolecules in chyme.

The hormone glucose-dependent insulinotrophic peptide (*GIP*) acts primarily to stimulate insulin release into the blood by the pancreas. Insulin changes the metabolic state of the body after a meal is ingested so that new nutrients, particularly glucose, are used and stored. Glucose in the duodenum increases GIP secretion, triggering the release of insulin.

Two interneuron centres in the hypothalamus work in opposition to control appetite and oxidative metabolism. One centre stimulates appetite and reduces oxidative metabolism; the other stimulates

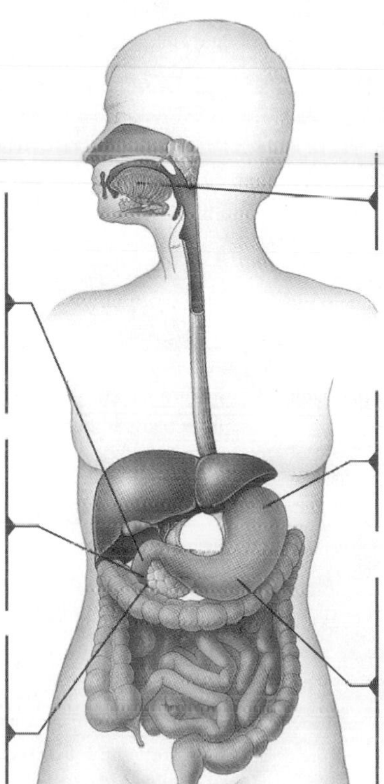

Hormone controls
Acidic chyme stimulates release of the hormone secretin in the small intestine. Secretin inhibits gastric emptying and gastric secretion and stimulates HCO_3^- secretion into the duodenum.
Fat (mostly) in chyme stimulates release of the hormone cholecystokinin (CCK). CCK inhibits gastric activity and stimulates secretion of pancreatic enzymes.
A meal entering the small intestine stimulates GIP secretion, which triggers insulin release. Insulin stimulates the uptake and storage of glucose from the digested food.
Receptor controls
Receptors in the mouth respond to food by increasing salivary secretion.
Stretch receptors in the stomach respond to food, signalling neuron networks to increase stomach contractions.
Chemoreceptors in the stomach respond to food, signalling neuron networks to stimulate the stomach to secrete the hormone gastrin, which, in turn, stimulate the stomach to secrete HCl and pepsinogen.

Figure 41.25
Control of digestion by receptors and hormones in the digestive system.

the release of α-melanocyte-stimulating hormone (α-MSH), a peptide hormone inihibiting appetite. Leptin (*leptos* = thin), a peptide hormone, is a major link between these two pathways. Leptin was discovered in mice by Jeffrey Friedman and his coworkers. Fat-storing cells secrete leptin when deposition of fat increases in the body. Leptin travels in the bloodstream and binds to receptors in both centres in the hypothalamus. Binding stimulates the centre that reduces appetite and inhibits the centre that stimulates appetite. Leptin also binds to receptors on body cells, triggering reactions that oxidize fatty acids rather than converting them to fats. When fat storage is reduced, leptin secretion drops off, and signals from other pathways activate the appetite-stimulating centre in the hypothalamus and turn off the appetite-inhibiting centre. These controls closely match the activity of the digestive system to the amount and types of foods ingested and coordinate appetite and oxidative metabolism with the body's needs for stored fats (see *The Puzzling Biology of Weight Control* and *Molecule Behind Biology*).

Study Break

What is leptin? What role does it play?

41.7 Variations in Obtaining Nutrients

The leaves of plants may be specialized to catch insect prey (see Figure 3.22f and Box 47.5), whereas the teeth of vertebrates, particularly those of mammals and fish, indicate the range of diets these animals can exploit (see Chapter 27). This is also reflected in the general lengths of the gastrointestinal tracts and the size and shape of cecae (see Figure 41.16). Some species of fungi lasso nematodes (see Chapter 24), whereas some sponges (see Chapter 26) use specialized spicules to impale prey. Many interesting adaptations and specializations are involved with feeding and digestion.

41.7a Bladderworts: Vacuum Feeding

Worldwide, about 200 species of aquatic bladderworts (*Utricularia* species) use underwater bladders to capture aquatic animals **(Figure 41.26a).** Bladderworts lack roots and get their name from the small bladderlike organs (utricles), thin-walled suction traps that draw in small animals. Bladderworts use active water transport to generate negative pressure inside the bladder, achieved by a two-step ATP-driven pump. Bladderworts have modified cytochrome *c* oxidase, a rate-limiting

a. Bladderwort

Perennou Nuridsany / Photo Researchers, Inc.

b. Dodder *(Cuscuta)*

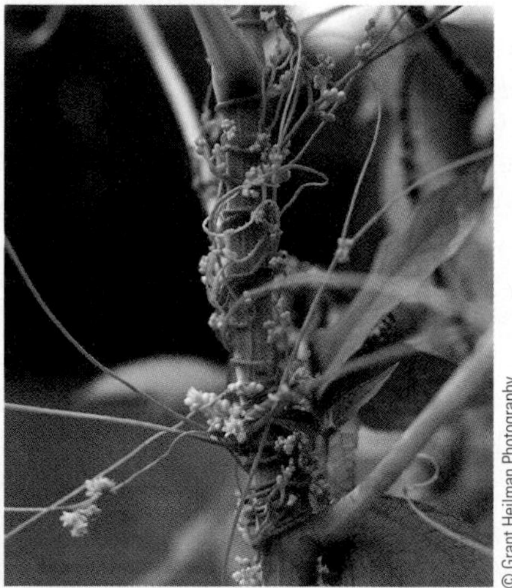

© Grant Heilman Photography

c. Snow plant *(Sarcodes sanguinea)*

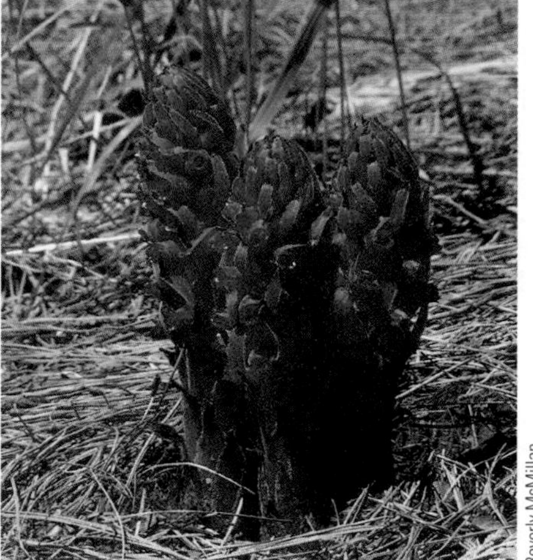

Beverly McMillan

d. Lady-of-the-night orchid *(Brassavola nodosa)*

© Prem Subrahmanyam/www.premdesign.com

Figure 41.26
(a) A bladderwort (*Utricularia* sp.) has bladders that serve as insect traps. **(b)** About 150 species of dodder (*Cuscuta* species) have slender yellow to orange stems that twine around host plants before producing haustorial roots that absorb nutrients and water from the host's xylem and phloem. **(c)** A snow plant (*Sarcodes sanguinea*) pops up in the deep humus of shady coniferous forests after snow melt in spring. Snow plants lack chlorophyll and do not photosynthesize, but their roots intertwine with the hyphae of soil fungi that are also associated with the roots of conifers. **(d)** The lady-of-the-night orchid (*Brassavola nodosa*) is a tropical epiphyte.

enzyme in cellular respiration (see Chapter 6), to set their traps. Opening the portal to the bladder is triggered by release of elastic instability.

41.7b Dodders: Parasitic Plants

Dodders **(Figure 41.26b)** and several thousand other species of flowering plants are parasites that obtain some or all of their nutrients from the tissues of other plants. Parasitic species develop haustorial roots (similar to the haustoria of fungi) that penetrate deep into the host plant and tap into its vascular tissues. Although some parasitic plants, such as mistletoe, contain chlorophyll and thus can photosynthesize, dodders and other nonphotosynthesizers rob the host of sugars as well as water and minerals (see also Figure 3.17).

41.7c Mycoheterotrophic Plants

Coralroot (*Coralloriza* species) is another variation on this theme. As its deep red colour suggests **(Figure 41.26c)**, coralroot lacks chlorophyll and does not have haustorial roots. Rather, these plants are mycoheterotrophs, which obtain carbon from other plants via shared mycorrhizal fungi (see Chapter 24).

41.7d Epiphytes: Plant Hangers-On

Epiphytes, such as some tropical orchids **(Figure 41.26d)** or Spanish moss **(Figure 41.27)**, are not parasitic even though they grow on other plants. Spanish moss is not a moss but a vascular plant, despite its common name. Some epiphytes trap falling debris and rainwater among their leaves, whereas their roots (including mycorrhizas, in the case of the orchid) invade the moist leaf litter and absorb nutrients from it as the litter decomposes. In temperate forests, many mosses and lichens are epiphytes.

41.7c Gutless Animals

Most molluscs have a prominent alimentary tract, from mouth to stomach to intestine to anus, whether the animal is a bivalve, a gastropod, or a cephalopod. But several species in the bivalve genus *Solemya* have smaller guts. At least one benthic species (*Solemya borealis*) from the northeastern Pacific is gutless, lacking any evidence of a digestive tract. This burrow-dwelling species lives in areas rich in nutrients and appears to use secretions from the pedal gland to effect extraorganism digestion. Ctenidial lamellae on the gills are probably used to absorb dissolved organic molecules. The lamellae are well serviced by circulating blood, and cilia clean the sediment from them. Gutlessness is also known from species in the phylum Pogonophora (beardworms), as well as in tapeworms (Playthelminthes, Cestoda).

41.7f A Termite-Eating Flatworm: Unusual Lifestyles

At night in a garden in Harare, Zimbabwe, flatworms, *Microplana termitophaga*, gather around the vents of termite mounds where they harvest termites, *Odontotermes transvaalensis* **(Figure 41.28, p. 1033)**. *M. termitophaga* are most numerous at termite mounds one to two hours after dawn, with peaks of activity after a rain. When hunting termites, *M. termitophaga* attach the posterior third of their bodies to the ground at the entrance to the termite mound, leaving the anterior end of the body mobile. The planarians appear to visually detect termites at ranges of 5 mm. Their eyes consist of groups of photoreceptors (see Figure 1.15), and although not image-forming, their eyes allow them to detect movement.

The flatworm uses its head, apparently with mucus and perhaps suction, to capture a termite, which is

a.

© Ellen McKnight/Alamy

b.

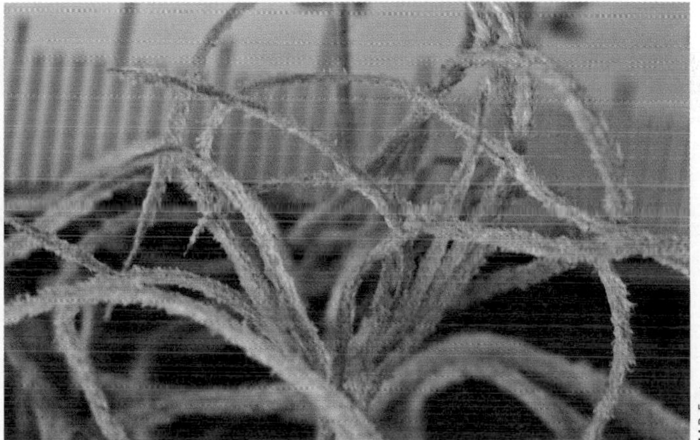

M.B. Fenton

Figure 41.27
(a) A forest in the southeastern United States has lush azaleas (*Rhododendron* species) as well as a southern oak (*Quercus virginiana*) draped with "Spanish moss" (*Tillandsia usnoides*), an unusual flowering plant. The roots of trees and shrubs and most other plants take up water and minerals from the soil. **(b)** Spanish moss is an epiphyte because it lives independently on other plants and obtains nutrients via absorptive hairs on its leaves and stems (background scale is in millimetres).

The Puzzling Biology of Weight Control

Obesity can lead to elevated blood pressure, heart disease, stroke, diabetes, and other ailments. Obese humans are ≥20% heavier than an optimal body weight. The body mass index (BMI), a measure of an individual's body fat, is a standard way to estimate obesity: BMI = weight in kilograms ÷ (height in metres)^2.

People with a BMI between 18.5 and 24.9 have a normal weight, whereas those with a BMI of 25 to 29.9 are considered overweight. People with a BMI of ≥30.0 are considered obese. People with a BMI >27 have a moderately increased risk for developing type 2 diabetes, high blood pressure, and heart disease. Those with a BMI >30 have a greatly increased risk for these conditions.

Conventional wisdom asserts that eating less is the way to lose weight. The relationship between eating and excessive body weight, however, is much more complex. One complicating factor is the probable existence of a genetically determined, homeostatic set point for body weight. If our body weight varies from the set point, compensating mechanisms adjust metabolism and eating behaviour to return body weight to the set point. Thus, if we diet and eat fewer calories, compensating mechanisms reduce the number of calories we use and make the diet less effective. Research shows that the metabolic activity of most body cells in a person on a crash diet decreases by about 15. Each person has a different set point: people of the same height who eat the same number of daily calories vary widely in body weight. Some remain thin, whereas others grow fatter every day on the same amount of food.

If a genetically determined set point governs human body weight, then why is the incidence of obesity increasing in the population? Some researchers speculate that our set points are changing toward greater deposition of fat because, on average, we are less active physically and have greater access to food, especially fatty foods and sugars. The average male Mennonite farmer takes >20 000 steps a day. Wear a pedometer and see how your activity compares. Our evolutionary history may also be a factor. Humans evolved under conditions in which food was occasionally scarce, so our built-in physiological mechanisms may actually favour raising the set point and thus storing extra nutrients when food is available. This would provide some protection against starvation if food becomes unavailable.

The search for factors governing the set point and general concern over growing obesity have sparked intensive research into the genetic mechanisms that might control fat deposition and maintain body weight. In this area, Jeffrey Friedman discovered leptin, and Louis Tartaglia and coworkers found leptin receptors. Leptin is a circulating hormone derived from adipocytes (fat cells). It informs the brain about energy stores. Mice with mutant forms of the genes encoding leptin or leptin receptors become morbidly fat.

The discovery of leptin seemed to offer a "magic bullet" to control human obesity: administer leptin to people and they will lose weight. Further studies revealed, however, that the genetics of weight control are considerably more complex in humans than they are in mice. In addition to genes controlling the production of leptin and the formation of receptors for it, in humans, at least four other genes are involved in appetite control and weight gain, complicating the effects of leptin compared with the situation in mice. In trials with humans, obese patients with mutant leptin genes benefitted from leptin injections, but some with normal leptin genes unexpectedly gained weight. Furthermore, none of the obese patients with normal leptin genes had any deficiency in leptin production. Obese individuals produced more leptin than people of normal weight.

Inconclusive results of leptin trials have turned attention to the development of other drugs to control obesity. PYY (pancreatic polypeptide YY), a recently discovered hormone, stimulates the appetite-suppressive centre in the hypothalamus and inhibits the appetite-stimulating centre. Trial injections of PYY in mice, rats, and humans have led to a significant decrease in appetite and eating.

Rimonabant is an experimental drug that shows promise in producing weight loss in obese patients. This drug works by blocking one of the receptors for the active ingredient in cannabis (marijuana). This receptor is widely distributed in the brain and other organs and helps regulate fat and sugar metabolism, energy balance, and appetite. The receptor is stimulated by cannabislike neurotransmitters produced in the body. When an individual smokes cannabis, the receptor is stimulated, increasing the appetite of the smoker. Blocking the receptor inhibits the stimulation of appetite by natural cannabislike neurotransmitters. In clinical trials, 363 obese Europeans who took rimonabant daily for a year lost an average of 8.6 kg and showed healthy changes in cholesterol triglycerides in the blood. Interestingly, rimonabant appears to be effective in controlling diabetes and helping people stop smoking tobacco.

The search for a magic pill for weight loss, which has gone on for decades, continues.

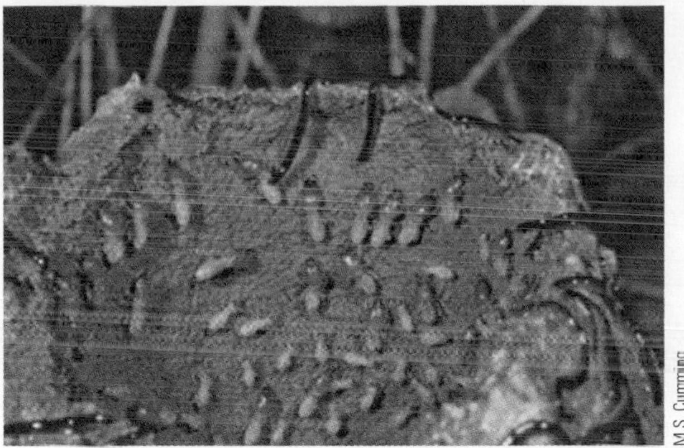

Figure 41.28
Microplana termitophaga hunting termites at a termite mound in Harare, Zimbabwe. One planarian (centre) has caught a termite. The termites include both soldiers (large head and jaws) and workers.

Figure 41.29
An anglerfish with a bioluminescent lure.

subdued and held against the pharyngeal region. In this position, *M. termitophaga* digests its prey, ingests the juices produced by digestion, and then expels the undigestable remains. In 135 captures, *M. termitophaga* took mainly worker termites rather than soldiers. On average, a flatworm ate a termite in 5 minutes 58 seconds. In 3 hours 14 minutes, one *M. termitophaga* ate 13 termites.

This pattern of feeding appears to be typical of predatory planarians. They may release poisonous secretions (to immobilize prey), adhesive mucus (to hold it), and copious amounts of digestive fluid from their extensible pharynges. Other species of flatworms eat earthworms (see Chapter 49), and some make group attacks on giant African land snails (*Achatina* species).

41.7g Fish Predation: More than You Imagined

Invisible in the inky darkness, a deep-sea anglerfish (*Chaenophryne longiceps*; order Lophiiformes) lies in wait for prey, its gaping mouth lined with sharp teeth. Just above the mouth dangles a glowing lure suspended from a fishing rod–like structure that is a spine of the fish's dorsal fin **(Figure 41.29)**. The lure resembles a tiny fish, wiggling back and forth. The lure's glow is produced by bioluminescent bacteria that live symbiotically in the fish's lure.

Attracted to the lure, a hapless fish comes within range. The oral cavity of the anglerfish expands suddenly, and powerful suction draws the prey into the gaping mouth. The angler's backward-angling teeth keep the prey from escaping, and it is swallowed. The strike takes 6 milliseconds, among the fastest of any known fish. Contractions of throat muscles send the prey to the anglerfish's stomach, which can expand to accommodate a meal as large as the fish itself. The anglerfish now digests, sits, and waits. Some cephalopods, some other fish, and the siphonophore *Erenna* species are examples of other animals using bioluminescent lures.

Other predatory fish hunt from ambush. Moray eels, such as *Muraena retifera*, hide and lie in wait in holes. Their eel-like shape makes it easy for them to fit into small openings. Like the anglerfish, moray eels can swallow items (fish and cephalopods) larger than their heads. But although moray eels lack the effective suction mechanisms of anglerfish, they have two sets of jaws **(Figure 41.30, p. 1034)**. Like other gnathostomes, the moray eel's mouth is bordered by upper (maxilla and premaxilla) and lower (mandibular) jaws bearing teeth. Unlike other gnathostomes, moray eels also have pharyngeal jaws. In the two upper pharyngeal jaws, pharyngobranchial bones bear teeth and connect to the lower pharyngeal jaws, which also bear teeth. Upper and lower pharyngeal jaws are connected by the epibranchial bones. The jaw arrangement of moray eels allows them to grab and transport (swallow) prey in a system similar to the mechanisms in snakes. The combination of hunting from ambush and quick swallowing of prey makes moray eels efficient predators.

Vandellia cirrhosa, the dreaded candiru **(Figure 40.31, p. 1035)**, is a specialized catfish that takes a completely different approach to feeding. Normally living as a gill parasite on larger fish, this small and slender predator lodges itself in the gills of a fish. There, like a leech or mosquito, tick, or lamprey eel, candirus drink the host's blood. To understand why the candiru is "dreaded," consider other aspects of its behaviour. Candirus locate hosts by swimming into currents, especially those bearing metabolic end products. Freshwater fish often pass metabolic end products out across their gills. The behaviour can also lead it into the urethra of an animal urinating while submerged in the water. In South American waters inhabited by candirus, local humans hold their water when swimming or bathing and may wear protective covers cut from coconuts to foil invasive candirus.

Molecule Behind Biology

Sorbitol

Based on the number of OH groups, sorbitol contains more energy than glucose **(Figure 1).** Yet a glance at the label of many "sugar-free" products reveals sorbitol as the major sweetener. How can the sugar-free product contain more calories than the "real" thing? The answer lies in taste. Sorbitol, like other sugar-free sweeteners, is much sweeter in flavour than glucose. This means that people who use sorbitol-based products to avoid the calories of sugar (glucose) are taking advantage of its sweetness. A little sorbitol makes that cup of coffee or tea or that sugar-free drink sweet with fewer calories (molecules of sorbitol). If the consumer used as much sorbitol as glucose, the sweetness would be overwhelming, rather like the calorie count.

Figure 1
Sorbitol.

The safety of food substitutes is often a concern for people who watch what they eat. In 2008, Juergen Bauditz and four colleagues reported two cases of severe weight loss and digestive upset associated with excessive consumption of chewing gum flavoured with sorbitol. One patient, a 21-year-old woman, had lost 11 kg and weighed 40.8 kg (body mass index 16.6) and suffered from severe diarrhea. At first, she was diagnosed as having infectious colitis, but further investigation revealed that her daily consumption of 18 to 20 g of sorbitol by chewing gum (1.25 g of sorbitol per stick of gum) was responsible for the condition. One year after going on a sorbitol-free diet, this patient had gained 7 kg, and her body mass index was 19.5. Another patient, a 46-year-old man, weighed 79.9 kg (body mass index 25.8) and had lost 22 kg before being examined by the physicians. He reported having eaten about 30 g of sorbitol every day. Six months after going on a sorbitol-free diet, he had gained 5 kg (body mass index 27.4). Both patients had normal bowel movements after going on sorbitol-free diets.

Two main ingredients of sorbitol are mannitol and xylitol, polyalcohol sugars that are common ingredients in laxatives. People often eat sugar substitutes such as sorbitol to minimize their caloric intake and to reduce the incidence of cavities in their teeth. Sorbitol is poorly absorbed by the small intestine and acts as an osmotic agent. Ingestion of 5 to 20 g of sorbitol daily can cause bloating and gas, as well as abdominal pain. Higher doses, such as those reported for the two patients in the case studies, cause osmotic diarrhea. It is likely that reducing caloric intake by eating less is a healthier alternative than eating large amounts of artificial sweeteners such as sorbitol.

41.7h Egg-Eating Snakes: Caviar of a Different Sort

Eggs well provisioned with yolk may be the ultimate food, rich in proteins and carbohydrates—everything a predator could want. Mammals such as mongooses break ostrich eggs by throwing rocks against them. Egyptian vultures (*Neophron percnopterus*) break these large eggs by dropping sticks or stones on them. But egg-eating snakes cannot throw stones or sticks.

Dasypeltus scabra is one of the best studied species of egg-eating snakes. Widespread in Africa, these snakes find birds' nests and help themselves to eggs. Like many other snakes, the jaws of *D. scabra* are loosely connected with elastic tendons and ligaments, allowing them to

a.

M.B. Fenton

b.

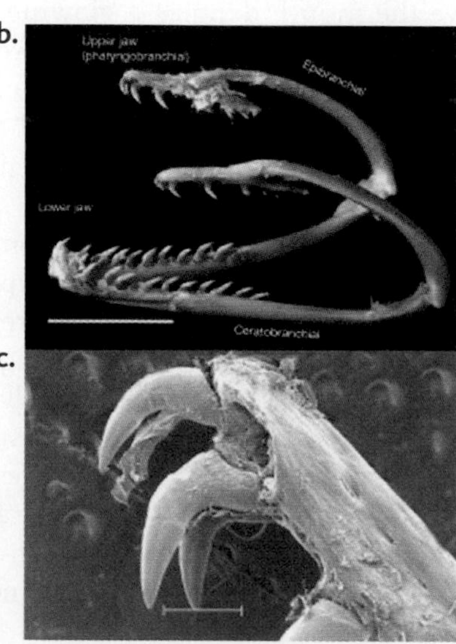

c.

Reprinted by permission from Macmillan Publishers Ltd: Nature, Vol. 449; pp. 79-82, Raptorial jaws in the throat help moray eels swallow large prey by Rita S. Mehta and Peter C. Wainwright, copyright (2007). 1035: bottom, Based on illustration from Gans 1974 Biomechanics Fig. 2-22

Figure 41.30
(a) A moray eel with its mouth open does not reveal its pharyngeal jaws, the second part of of its bite. **(b)** The skeleton and teeth of the pharyngeal jaws. **(c)** A scanning electron micrograph view of the upper pharyngeal recurved teeth. Scale bars 1 cm (b) and 500 μm (c).

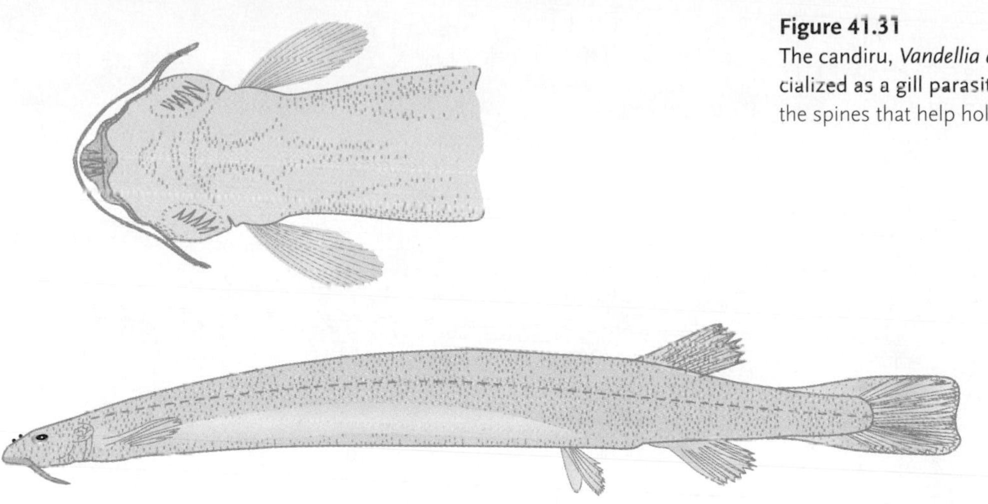

Figure 41.31
The candiru, *Vandellia cirrhosa*, is a catfish specialized as a gill parasite. The upper view shows the spines that help hold the fish in place.

open their mouths extremely wide **(Figure 41.32)**. In a bird's nest, the snake can push an egg against the rim of the nest and swallow it whole. A wide gape is important, but so are an extensible epiglottis and ribbed tracheae, which together allow the snake to breathe while it swallows an egg.

After the egg has passed out of the mouth and into the esophagus, the snake makes a coil in front of the swallowed egg. By moving the coil backward along its body, the snake moves the egg down its digestive tract. You can watch the egg move down the snake, but then, with a cracking noise, the outline of the egg disappears. The snake has pushed the egg against ventral hypophyses, anteriorly pointed extensions of specialized vertebrae **(Figure 41.33, p. 1036)** that protrude into the lumen of the gastrointestinal tract. *D. scabra* has a built-in egg-cracker.

Study Break

1. What do anglerfish and bladderworts have in common?
2. How do you define "carnivorous"?

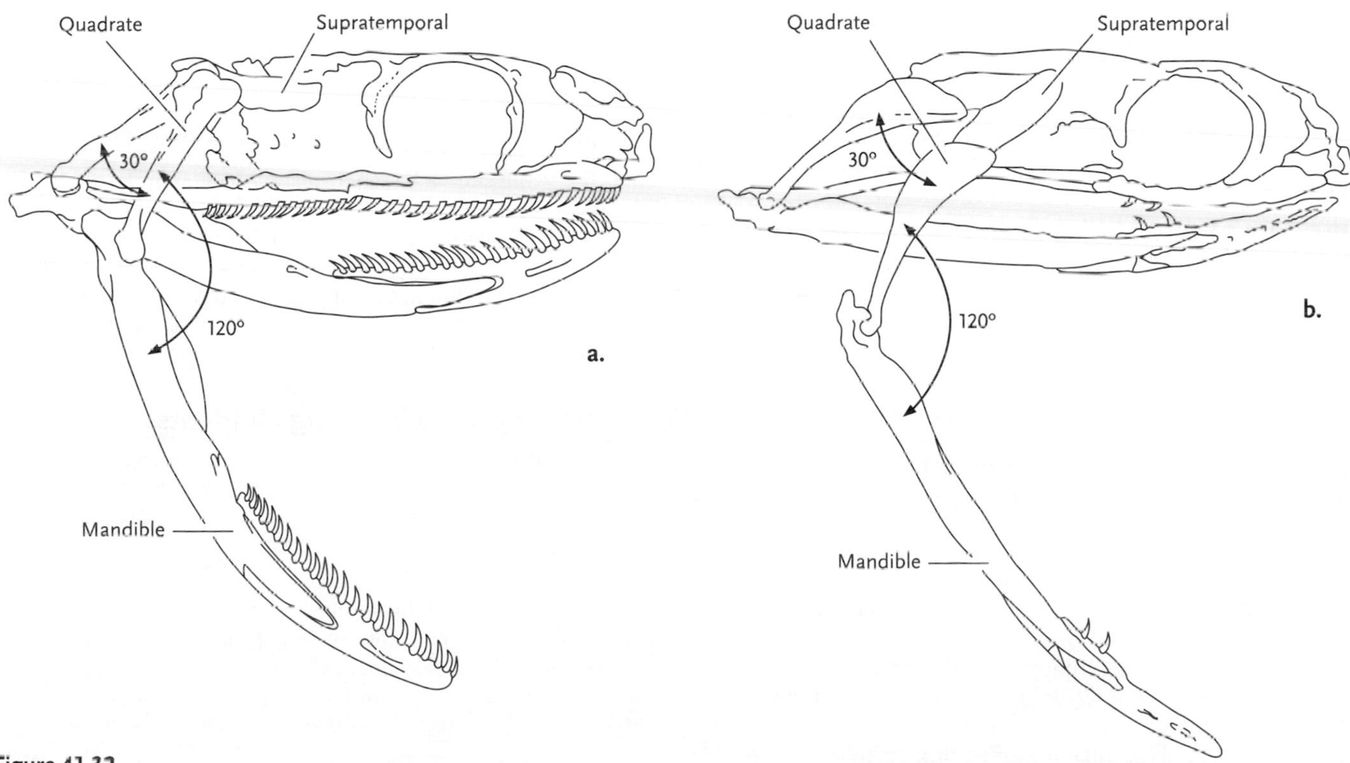

Figure 41.32
The articulation between the supratemporal bone and the braincase (more than between the quadrate and the supratemporal bones) is responsible for a great increase in the gape of a snake. Combined with the position of the quadrate, these features allow one snake **(b)** a 20% larger gape than the other **(a)**.

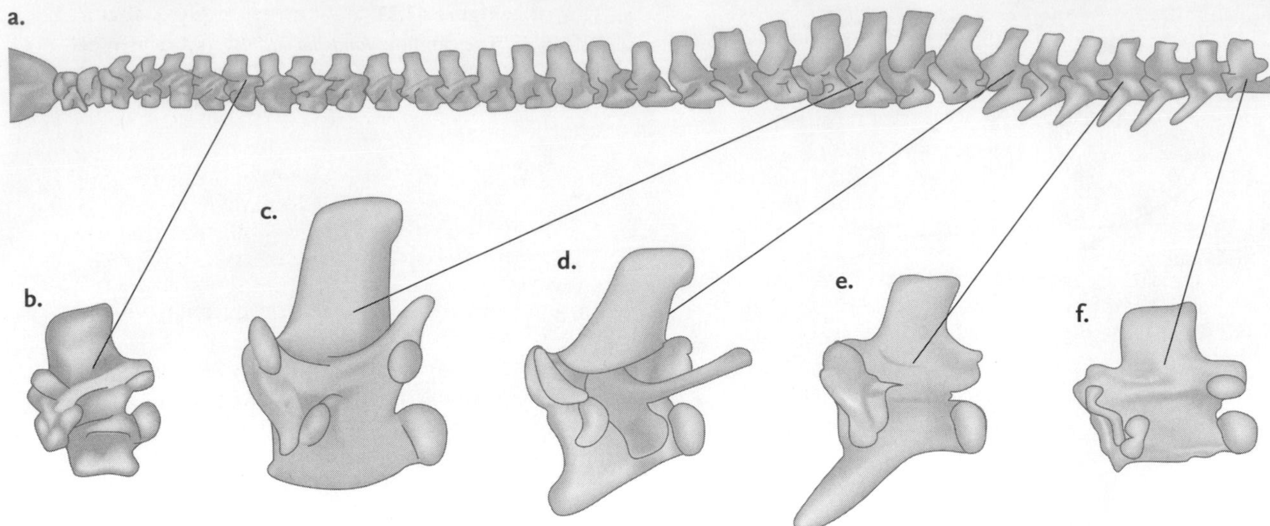

Figure 41.33
Dasypeltus scabrus has **(a)** a specialized vertebral column. **(b)** The anterior vertebrae are not especially modified, **(c)** whereas high neural arches make more posterior vertebrae highly modified. **(d)** Other vertebrae are transitional to **(e)** the highly modified, egg-breaking vertebrae. **(f)** Posterior, the vertebrae are more typical of snakes. The spines on the egg-breaking vertebrae are ventral hypophyses.

Unanswered Questions

Under what circumstances have achlorophyllous plants evolved? What opportunity are they exploiting?

Review

Go to CENGAGENOW™ at http://hed.nelson.com/ to access quizzing, animations, exercises, articles, and personalized homework help.

41.1 Nutrition: Essential Materials

- Living organisms require a variety of materials to survive. Use Table 41.1 to review and compare nutrients essential to plants and animals.
- Malnutrition can manifest itself as undernutrition or overnutrition, involving inadequate intake of organic fuels or abnormal ingestion of fuels, respectively. Undernutrition is commonly referred to as malnutrition and may involve ingestion of too little energy to fuel daily activities or failure to ingest essential nutrients. Malnutrition kills thousands of people annually (see Chapter 49). Overnutrition can result in excessive gain in body mass and other health problems.
- Hydroponics allowed biologists to explore the details of nutrients essential to plants and recognize symptoms of deficiencies of different nutrients in plants.
- Animals such as birds on long migratory flights may mobilize energy from their own bodies during prolonged periods of not feeding.
- In animals, vitamins are essential for different metabolic operations.

41.2 Soil

- Soil is the living skin of much terrestrial habitat on Earth. It provides essential materials for plants and a habitat for animals. Soil consists of particles of different sizes (<0.002–2 mm in diameter). Three main horizons (A, B, and C) develop in many soils.
- Soil composition influences plants' access to water and nutrients in soil. Roots anchor plants and also serve as connections between plants and soil.

41.3 Obtaining and Absorbing Nutrients

- Nutrients such as N, P, and K are often scarce in soil, so they are supplied in fertilizers used in agricultural operations.
- Mycorrhizas are symbiotic associations between fungi and the roots of plants.
- Specialized structures in plant roots, stems, and leaves conduct materials up and down the plant.
- Nitrogen can be an important limiting factor for many plants because atmospheric N is not available to them. Some carnivorous plants obtain N from animals they catch and digest. Other plants use associations with nitrogen-fixing bacteria to obtain N.

- Deposit feeders such as some burrowing molluscs and tube-dwelling polychaete worms (see Chapter 26) pick up or scrape particles of organic matter from their surroundings. Arthropods such as fiddler crabs sift food (organic matter) from sediments.

41.4 Digestive Processes in Animals

- The gizzard is a muscular structure that grinds food into small particles. In annelids such as earthworms, the gizzard uses sand to increase abrasive action. Birds and reptiles often pick up stones for the gizzard to achieve the same effect. Insects often have gizzards.
- Sponge chanocytes (collar cells) trap food particles and take them in by endocytosis. Amoeboid cells transfer food throughout the sponge.
- The diet of *Dugesia* is not typical of free-living flatworms (see Chapter 26). Whereas *Dugesia* mainly feed on detritis, other flatworms are predatory, taking earthworms, snails, or termites.
- Along the gastrointestinal tract, food is first mechanically processed, breaking it into smaller pieces. Then enzymes and other digestive aids, such as acids and mucus, are secreted and commence chemical breakdown of food. Enzymatic hydrolysis breaks food molecules into absorbable molecular subunits. This involves reactions catalyzed by enzymes. Then the food molecules are absorbed from the gastrointestinal tract. Finally, undigested materials are expelled through the anus.
- The hoatzin is a flying bird known to use fermentation to digest cellulose. Just-caught hoatzins often smell like cow dung. Their digestive systems include a fermentation centre that uses space normally occupied by flight muscles. Hoatzins are not strong fliers. Other animals from termites to some mammals use fermentation to digest cellulose.

41.5 Digestion in Mammals

- Living birds lack teeth and use the gizzard to break food into finer particles. Many (but not all) mammals use teeth to mechanically break up food.
- Mammals such as humans require eight essential amino acids: lysine, tryptophan, phenylalanine, threonine, valine, methionine, leucine, and isoleucine.
- The layers in the gut of a mammal are the mucosa, submucosa, muscularis, and serosa. Each plays a different role in the operation of the gastrointestinal tract. Sphincter muscles control the movement of material through the gastrointestinal tract.
- Peristalsis is rhythmic contractions of circular bands of smooth muscle. Peristalsis constricts the gut and moves food along the gastrointestinal tract. Peristalsis usually occurs in waves.
- Gastric juices are produced in gastric glands that line the stomach. Production and release of gastric juices are stimulated by output of stretch receptors. The 2 L of gastic juices secreted daily by the average human includes pepsin, hydrochloric acid, and lubricating mucus.
- The liver secretes bile salts, cholesterol, and bilirubin. Bile salts are derivates of cholesterol and amino acids and aid the digestion of fat. They operate by forming a hydrophilic coating around fats and other lipids, allowing the churning of the intestine to emulsify fats. Bilirubin is a waste product derived from worn-out erythrocytes.
- As many as 500 species of bacteria may be living in the gastrointestinal tract of mammals. Bacterial activity is partly responsible for flatus in the gastrointestinal tract, the production of CO_2, methane, and hydrogen sulphide. Bacteria may comprise 20 to 50% of the dry matter in feces.

41.6 Regulation of the Digestive Processes

- Leptin is a peptide hormone that links two interneuron centres in the hypothalamus. One centre stimulates appetite, whereas the other reduces oxidative metabolism. Fat-storing cells secrete leptin when deposition of fat increases in the body. Leptin moves through the bloodstream and binds to receptors in both centres in the hypothalamus. Binding stimulates the centre reducing appetite and inhibits the centre increasing appetite.

41.7 Variations in Obtaining Nutrients

- Bladderworts are vacuum-feeding carnivorous plants.
- Dodders are parasitic plants.
- Some plants are mycoheterotrophs.
- Epiphytes grow on other plants.
- Tapeworms and some species of molluscs lack digestive tracts.
- Some moray eels have two functional sets of jaws, each armed with teeth. In addition to their "normal" jaws, moray eels have pharyngeal jaws that make it easier for them to seize and then swallow prey. The mechanism works like a rachet and is reminiscent of similar systems in some snakes.
- Some egg-eating snakes swallow birds' eggs whole. They use hypophyses, ventral, anterior-pointing processes from some vertebrae, as egg-crackers.

Questions

Self-Test Questions

1. Vitamins are
   a. coenzymes.
   b. fatty acids.
   c. organic molecules.
   d. amino acids.
   e. carbohydrates.
2. Some plants can gain access to nitrogen (N) through
   a. direct absorption of atmospheric N.
   b. carnivory.
   c. nitrogen-fixing bacteria.
   d. fertilizers.
   e. b, c, and d.
3. Mycorrhizas are associations between
   a. fungi and mammals.
   b. roots of terrestrial plants and fungi.
   c. solar slugs and fungi.
   d. fungi and algae.
   e. all of the above.
4. The crop is part of the digestive tract in
   a. birds.
   b. mammals.
   c. reptiles.
   d. earthworms.
   e. a and d.
5. Humans require __ essential amino acids.
   a. 0
   b. 2
   c. 5
   d. 8
   e. 10
6. In humans, pepsin reaches optimal levels of activity at
   a. pH 1.
   b. pH 2.
   c. pH 4.
   d. pH 6.
   e. pH 8.
7. Epiphytes grow on other plants, usually trees. They include
   a. lichens.
   b. Spanish moss.
   c. some orchids.
   d. dodders.
   e. a, b, and c.
8. Cellulose is digested by fermentation in
   a. humans.
   b. ruminants.
   c. the hoatzin.
   d. carnivores.
   e. b and c.
9. Animals that eat blood and body fluids include
   a. leeches, vampire bats, and candirus.
   b. tapeworms, flukes, and mosquitoes.
   c. blackflies, lamprey eels, and bedbugs.
   d. wolves, cats, and vampire bats.
   e. a and c.
10. Sorbitol is an effective substitute for glucose because
    a. it has less energy.
    b. digesting it burns more energy than it produces.
    c. it is much sweeter than glucose.
    d. it is not toxic.
    e. All of the above are correct.

Questions for Discussion

1. How does secondment of chloroplasts benefit animals (see Chapter 3)? In what animals does it occur? Do these animals have genetic control over the chloroplasts? If so, how do they acquire this control?
2. Although humans evolved as omnivores, some eat only meat, others are vegetarian, and many (perhaps most) eat a combination of plant and animal material. What should a balanced diet include?
3. If you are planting a vegetable garden, what fertilizers would you plan to apply? For the vegetables to qualify as "organic" produce, what kinds of fertilizers would you be allowed to use? What constitutes "organic" meat?
4. Do animals that are usually vegetarian readily eat animal protein? Find an example of a disease associated with this behaviour.

Lining of the trachea (windpipe) shown in a colourized scanning electron micrograph, with mucus-secreting cells (white) and epithelial cells with cilia (pink). The trachea is positioned between the larynx and the lungs, providing a conduit for air entering and leaving the body.

Study Plan

42 Gas Exchange: The Respiratory System

Why It Matters

In Africa, a huge swarm of the desert locust, *Schistocerca gregaria* **(Figure 42.1, p. 1040)**, composed of millions of individuals, takes off, escaping the lack of food caused by their voracious feeding (a swarm may consume the equivalent of food for 2500 people in a single day). Driven by the wind, the swarm normally descends in the evening to take off again in the morning but may remain airborne for more than 24 hours. A swarm may continue to fly during the day for several days until the wind delivers it to food. The wings of each locust, which weighs about 2.5 grams, will beat about 20 times per second. Their relatively large flight muscles require very large amounts of oxygen to provide the energy derived from fat stores. Insects in flight have the highest O_2 consumption per gram ever recorded for animals.

Like these locusts, all organisms with active metabolism need to exchange gases with their surroundings. The chloroplasts of plant cells need CO_2 for the Calvin cycle, and in the light, these chloroplasts release O_2 by the action of photosystem II. Likewise, the mitochondria of eukaryotic cells need a constant supply of O_2 as it is required as the terminal electron acceptor of respiratory electron transport. In addition, respiration also produces CO_2, which needs to be rapidly

a.

b.

Emmanuel Boitier

© FAO

Figure 42.1
(a) Migratory locust. **(b)** A small portion of a locust swarm in Mauritania in 2004.

removed from cells because in animals, high cellular CO_2 is a narcotic poison, damaging nerve function. In this chapter, we introduce the physical basis for gas exchange and how evolution has produced a range of adaptations that maximizes the rate of gas exchange both into and out of animal tissues.

42.1 General Principles of Gas Exchange

Air normally contains about 78% diatomic nitrogen (N_2), 21% diatomic oxygen (O_2), and less than 1% carbon dioxide (CO_2) and other gases.

The percentage composition of air does not change with the total amount of air. Thus, as you climb a mountain, the total amount of air falls, and there are fewer molecules of O_2 (and any other gas) in the environment. The density of the air in the atmosphere is measured as the atmospheric pressure, which is greater the closer you are to sea level and falls with increasing altitude. The unit of measurement is often millimetres of mercury (mm Hg). At sea level, the atmospheric pressure is 760 mm Hg: the pressure is sufficient to support a vertical column of mercury 760 mm high. This pressure is the sum of the pressures of all of the gases in a mixture. The individual pressure exerted by each gas within a mixture of gases such as air is defined as its **partial pressure.** For any one gas, the partial pressure is calculated by multiplying the fractional composition of that gas by the atmospheric pressure. Given that O_2 is 0.21 of air, the partial pressure of O_2, abbreviated P_{O_2}, at sea level is 0.21×760 mm Hg or 160 mm Hg.

42.1a Fick's Equation of Diffusion

The partial pressure of a gas is the key factor in determining the direction in which a gas will move. You can think of the partial pressure of a gas as being similar to the concentration of a solute in solution. Just as a solute will move by simple diffusion from an area of high concentration to an area of low concentration, a gas will move down a partial pressure gradient, from a region of high partial pressure to an area of low partial pressure.

But the rate (amount per unit time) at which a gas will diffuse is dependent on a set of factors, only one of which is the difference in partial pressure between two regions. Fick's equation, which is important to understanding the diffusion of gases, recognizes the importance of these other factors. Fick's equation can be stated in a number of ways, but for the diffusion of gas across a membrane or other surface, it can be stated as follows:

$$Q = \frac{DA \times (P1 - P2)}{L}$$

where

- Q is the rate of diffusion between the two sides of the membrane.
- D is the diffusion coefficient for the gas involved. This is simply a factor specific to the gas molecule that recognizes its size and vibrational activity, the medium (gas, solid, liquid) in which the diffusion occurs, and the temperature.
- A is the area across which diffusion takes place.
- P1 and P2 are the partial pressures of the gases at the two locations.
- L is the path length or distance between the two locations (the thickness of the membrane).

42.1b Gas Exchange by Simple Diffusion

The additional variables introduced by Fick's equation are the area across which diffusion takes place and the distance over which diffusion occurs. Relying on diffusion alone for gas exchange limits both the size and to some degree the shape of the organism. The importance of these factors is made obvious by a consideration of the surface to volume ratio. Bacteria, with a volume of about 10^{-18} m^3 and a surface area of about 6×10^{-12} m^2, have a surface to volume ratio of 6 000 000:1. They can clearly rely on diffusion alone for gas exchange because the surface is large with respect to the volume, and the distance that the gases must diffuse is relatively small. The same is true of protists, with a surface to volume ratio of about 60 000:1. Among multicellular organisms, however, an increase in size can be accommodated only if the distance over which diffusion must occur is minimized. Gas exchange by diffusion can occur only if the organisms are thin and flat.

Flatworms **(Figure 42.2a)** represent an example of a multicellular organism that relies on simple diffusion for gas exchange. Most free-living flatworms are small but may range up to 10 cm or more in length, and parasitic forms such as tapeworms may be as long as 3 m or more (see Chapter 26). But all are thin, so L in Fick's equation is minimized and A is maximized.

a. Extended body surface: flatworm

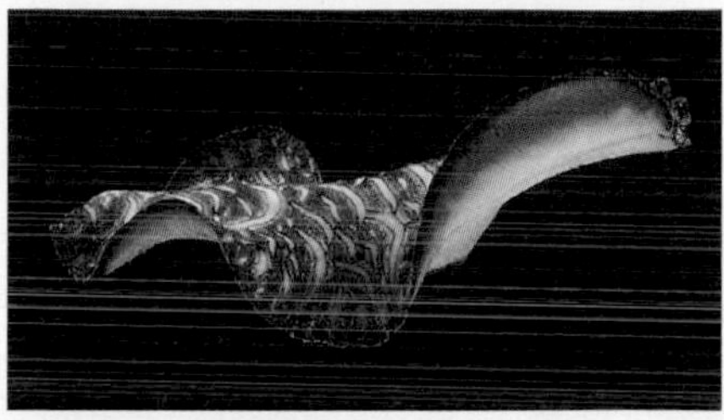

Peter Parks/Oxford Scientific Films/ Photolibrary.com

b. External gills: mudpuppy

Jack Dermid/Visuals Unlimited

c. Lungs: human

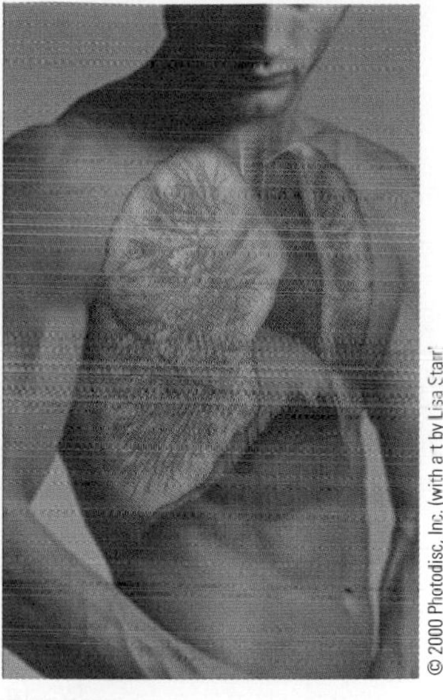

© 2000 Photodisc, Inc. (with art by Lisa Starr)

Figure 42.2
Adaptations increasing the area of the respiratory surface. (a) The flattened and elongated body surface of a flatworm. **(b)** The highly branched, feathery structure of the external gills in an amphibian, the mudpuppy (*Necturus*). **(c)** The many branches and pockets expanding the respiratory surface in the human lung.

42.1c The Plant Leaf Is a Special Case

Like flatworms, a plant leaf has a large surface area over which gas exchange can take place. However, unlike the flatworm, the external surface of a leaf is not available for gas exchange: leaves are covered by a waxy cuticle that is impermeable to gases. We learned in Chapter 28 that gases gain access to the interior of the leaf through pores called stomata. Inside the leaf, there is gas-filled space where gases can move such that the diffusion distance (L in Fick's equation) between the external environment (the air within the leaf) and the individual cells is very short **(Figure 42.3)**. Moreover, the total area (A in Fick's equation) of the cell walls inside the leaf is large. These two factors maximize the rate of diffusion of gases between the cells and the environment.

42.1d Adaptations That Increase the Surface Available for Gas Exchange in Animals

In animals, gas exchange occurs across a **respiratory surface,** which may consist of the external surface of the organism. We have seen, however, that Fick's equation limits the size and shape of such organisms. The evolution of larger specialized respiratory surfaces and/or some means of transporting gases to and from the surfaces of cells within the organism has permitted the development of larger and more complex organisms. The specialized respiratory surfaces are often very large, increasing A in Fick's equation. The total area of the lungs in humans is about 100 m^2. In addition, the cells that make up the specialized respiratory layer are squamous epithelium, decreasing L. If a circulatory system is bathing the inside of the respiratory surface, it will maintain a large difference between P1 and P2, increasing the value of Q. Both of these adaptations, the development of specialized respiratory surfaces and the development of circulatory systems that transport the gases, have reduced the limitation on size and shape imposed by reliance on simple diffusion

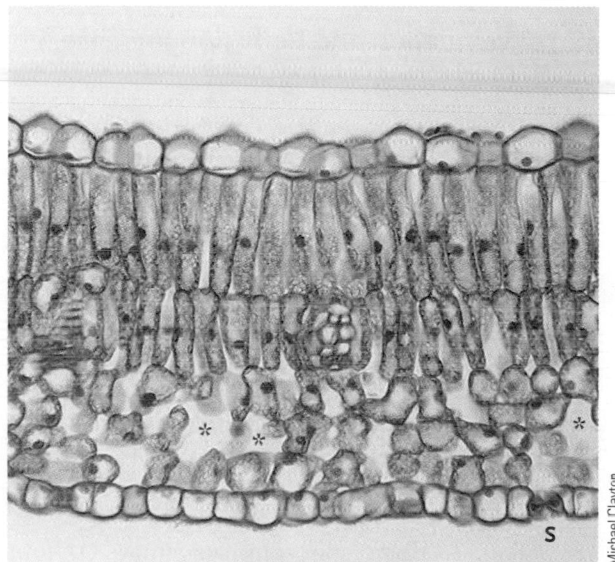

Michael Clayton

Figure 42.3
A cross section of a leaf of a lilac bush. The network of interconnecting spaces, marked by an asterisk, brings most cells in direct contact with gases. S marks a stomata through which gases gain access to the spaces inside the leaf.

through the animal's surface. These are among the adaptations that have permitted animals to penetrate a wider range of environments. We will see that insects, like the plant leaf, represent a special case. In insects, tubes called tracheae penetrate from the surface of the insect to every cell and carry respiratory gases to and from the surfaces of the cells.

For the gases to pass across the epithelium, they must be in solution. For aquatic and marine animals, for which the **respiratory medium** is water, that is already the case, and gills, outward extensions of the body surface (see Figure 42.2 b), are the site of gas exchange. For terrestrial animals, the respiratory medium is air and the respiratory epithelium is covered by a thin film of fluid. Loss of water is minimized by the location of the expanded respiratory epithelium, called lungs, deep within the body of an animal (see Figure 42.2c).

Some of the CO_2 produced by the cells remains in solution as a gas, but in many organisms, significant amounts may combine with water to produce carbonic acid (H_2CO_3), which dissociates into bicarbonate (HCO_3^-) and H^+ ions. This reaction maintains a maximal concentration gradient of CO_2 between the cells and the blood. Of course, the capacity of the blood or body fluids for CO_2 is limited. It is a means of storing the gas in a harmless form temporarily until it can be transported to the respiratory surface of the animal for release once more as a gas.

Most of the H^+ ions produced by the dissociation of carbonic acid combine with haemoglobin or with proteins in the blood. The combination, by removing excess H^+ from the blood solution, *buffers* the pH of the blood, helping to maintain it at the set point appropriate for the species, usually about 7.4.

42.1e Ventilation and Perfusion Increase the Rate of Gas Exchange

Although all gas exchange occurs by diffusion, two adaptations help most animals maintain the difference in concentration between gases outside and inside the respiratory surface. In Fick's equation, they maximize the value of P1-P2, maintaining a steep gradient of the partial pressure of the gas across the respiratory surface and enhancing the rate of diffusion. One is **ventilation**, the flow of the respiratory medium (air or water, depending on the animal) over the respiratory surface. The second is **perfusion**, the flow of blood or other body fluids on the internal side of the respiratory surface.

Ventilation. As they respire, animals remove O_2 from the respiratory medium and replace it with CO_2. Without ventilation, the concentration of O_2 would fall in the respiratory medium close to the respiratory surface, and the concentration of CO_2 would rise, gradually reducing the value of P1-P2 in the Fick equation for both gases and reducing the rate of diffusion below that necessary to sustain life. Examples of ventilation include the one-way flow of water over the gills in fishes and many other aquatic animals and the in-and-out flow of air in the lungs of most vertebrates and in the tracheal system of insects at rest.

Perfusion. The rate at which blood or other fluids are replaced on the internal side of the respiratory surface similarly helps keep P1-P2 at an acceptable level. In animals with a circulatory system, the circulatory system brings blood to the internal side of the respiratory surface, transporting CO_2 (often in the form of bicarbonate) from all cells of the body. At the surface, CO_2 is released into the medium, and a fresh supply of O_2 is picked up. Insects, as we will see, do not use blood to transport these gases.

42.1f Water and Air Have Advantages and Disadvantages as Respiratory Media

Because their respiratory surfaces are exposed directly to the environment, aquatic and marine animals have no problem keeping the respiratory surface wet. However, aquatic animals face challenges in obtaining O_2 from water compared with terrestrial animals. An important variable in Fick's equation is the diffusion coefficient, D. This factor varies with the gas, the medium, and the temperature. The difference between D in gas and water is large: for O_2 at 20°C, the value in water is 1.97×10^{-5}, whereas in air, it is 0.219—approximately 10 000 times greater. The rate of diffusion in air is thus 10 000 times faster than in water. In addition, for the same volume, there is approximately 30 times less O_2 in water than in air at 15°C, reducing the value of P1-P2. These two factors require animals that rely on water for their gas exchange to pass a vastly greater volume of water over the respiratory surface in order to be exposed to the same volume of O_2 as an animal relying on air. Moreover, the density of water is about 1000 times that of air, and its viscosity is about 50 times that of air. Therefore, it takes significantly more energy to move water than air over a respiratory surface. Ventilation in most aquatic animals takes place in a one-way direction, compensating to some degree for these two effects. In bony fishes, for instance, water enters the mouth, flows over the gills, and exits through the gill covers, all in one direction.

In addition, temperature and solutes affect the O_2 content of water. That is, as either the temperature or the amount of solutes increases, the amount of gas that can dissolve in water decreases. Therefore, with respect to obtaining O_2, aquatic animals that live in warm water are at a disadvantage compared with those that live in cold water. And because solutes (such as sodium chloride) are higher in seawater compared with freshwater, animals living in a marine environment are at a disadvantage compared with those living in an aquatic environment.

The relatively high O_2 content, low density, and low viscosity of air greatly reduce the energy required to ventilate the respiratory surface. These advantages allow animals with lungs to breathe in and out, reversing the direction of flow of the respiratory medium, without a large energy penalty.

A major disadvantage of air is that it constantly evaporates water from the respiratory surface unless it is saturated with water vapour. Therefore, except in an environment with 100% humidity, animals lose water by evaporation during breathing and must replace the water to keep the respiratory surface from drying.

We next turn to the adaptations that allow water-breathing and air-breathing animals to obtain O_2 and release CO_2 in aquatic and terrestrial environments. These adaptations allow animals to exploit the advantages and circumvent the disadvantages of water and air as respiratory media.

Study Break

1. What variables in Fick's equation affect the rate of diffusion across a membrane?
2. What are the disadvantages of water as a respiratory medium?

42.2 Adaptations for Gas Exchange

Although most animals that live in marine or aquatic environments exchange gases through the skin or gills, a few use lungs and breathe air. Whales, seals, and dolphins are mammals that have returned to the sea and have special adaptations that permit them to remain submerged for long periods, surfacing to breathe (see Chapter 37, *Life on the Edge*). Many amphibians respire through the skin as well as the lungs, and their larvae have gills. Some terrestrial arthropods, such as land crabs and some spiders, have internalized gills into lunglike structures.

42.2a External and Internal Gills

Gills are respiratory surfaces that are branched and folded evaginations (outward extensions) of the body. They increase the area over which diffusion can take place. **External gills (Figure 42.4a)** extend out from the body and do not have protective coverings. They occur in some molluscs, some annelids, the larvae of some aquatic insects, the larvae of some fishes, and the larvae of amphibians. **Internal gills (Figure 42.4c, d)** are located within chambers of the body. This not only provides protection for delicate structures but also allows currents of water to be directed over the gills.

a. External gills: nudibranch

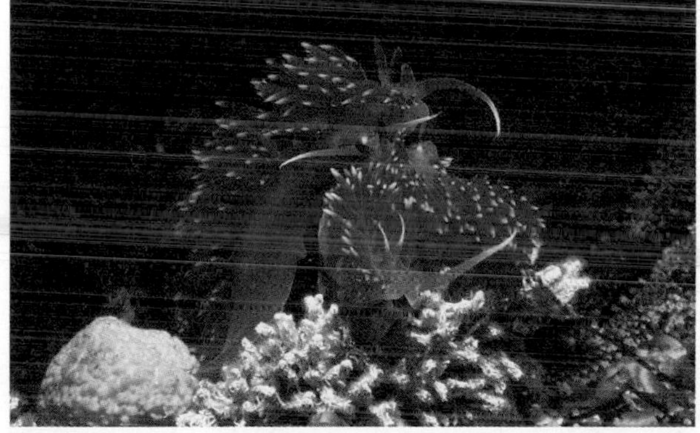
Alex Kirsitch

b. Internal gills: clam

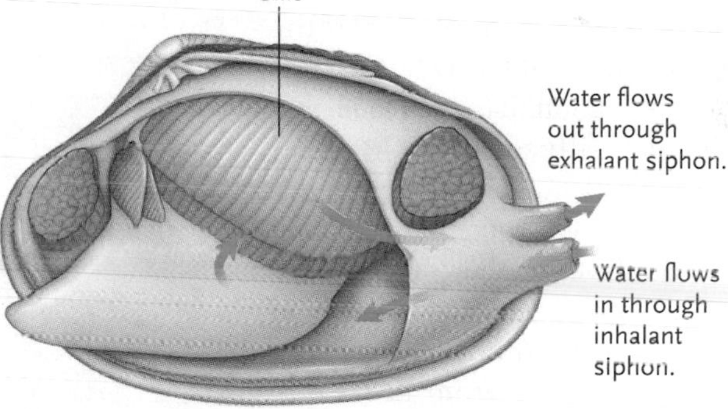
Gills
Water flows out through exhalant siphon.
Water flows in through inhalant siphon.

c. Internal gills: cuttlefish

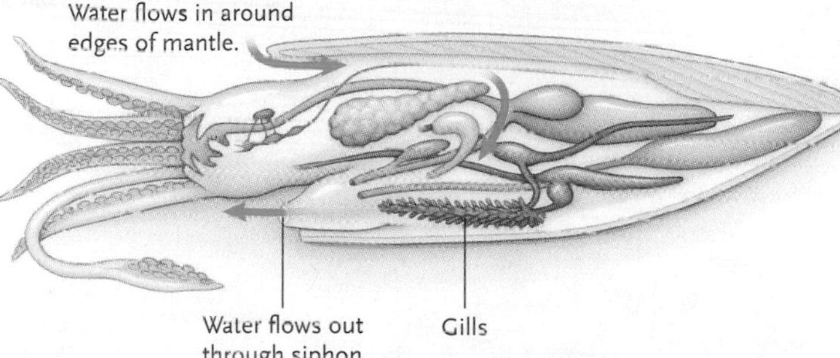
Water flows in around edges of mantle.
Water flows out through siphon.
Gills

d. Internal gills: fish

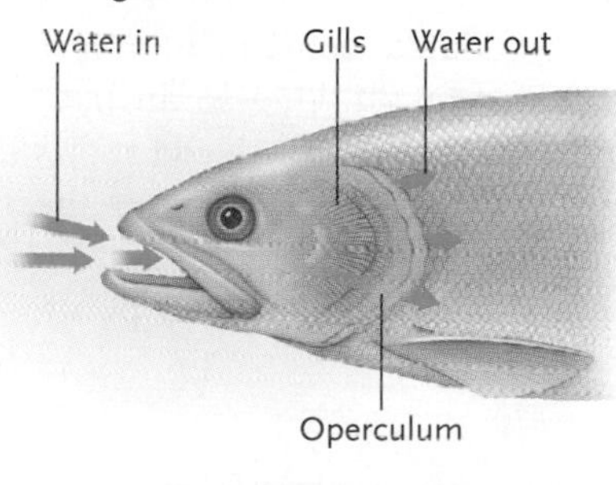
Water in
Gills
Water out
Operculum

Figure 42.4
External and internal gills. **(a)** The external gills of a nudibranch (*Flabellina iodinea*). **(b)** The internal gills in a clam. **(c)** The internal gills of a cuttlefish. **(d)** The internal gills of a bony fish. Water enters through the mouth and passes over the filaments of the gills before exiting through an opening at the edges of the flaplike protective covering, the operculum.

Most crustaceans, molluscs, sharks, and bony fishes have internal gills. Some invertebrates, such as clams and oysters, use beating cilia to circulate water over their internal gills **(Figure 42.4b)**. Others, such as the cuttlefish, use contractions of the muscular mantle to pump water over their gills **(see Figure 42.4c)**. In adult bony fishes, the gills extend into a chamber covered by gill flaps or *opercula* (singular, *operculum* = little lid) on either side of the head. The operculum serves as part of a one-way pumping system that ventilates the gills **(Figure 42.4d)**.

42.2b Many Animals with Internal Gills Use Countercurrent Flow to Maximize Gas Exchange

Sharks, fishes, and some Crustacea take advantage of one-way flow of water over the gills to maximize the amounts of O_2 and CO_2 exchanged with water. In this mechanism, called **countercurrent exchange**, the water flowing over the gills moves in a direction opposite to the flow of blood under the respiratory surface.

Figure 42.5 illustrates countercurrent exchange in the uptake of O_2. At the point where fully oxygenated water first passes over a gill filament in countercurrent flow, the blood flowing beneath it in the opposite direction is also almost fully oxygenated. However, the water still contains O_2 at a higher concentration than the blood, and the gas diffuses from the water into the blood, raising the concentration of O_2 in the blood almost to the level of the fully oxygenated water. At the opposite end of the filament, much of the O_2 has been removed from the water, but the blood flowing under the filament, which has just arrived from body tissues and is fully deoxygenated, contains even less O_2. As a result, O_2 also diffuses from the water to the blood at this end of the filament. All along the gill filament, the same relationship exists, so that at any point, the water is more highly oxygenated than the blood. P1-P2 is maximized, and O_2 diffuses at a high rate from the water and into the blood across the respiratory surface.

The overall effect of countercurrent exchange is the removal of 80 to 90% of the O_2 content of water as it flows over the gills. In comparison, by breathing in and out and constantly reversing the direction of air flow, mammals manage to remove only about 25% of the O_2 content of air. Efficient removal of O_2 from water is important because of the much lower O_2 content of water compared with air.

42.2c Insects Use a Tracheal System for Gas Exchange

Insects breathe air by a unique respiratory system consisting of air-conducting tubes called tracheae (*trachea* = windpipe) **(Figure 42.6)**. The tracheae are invaginations of the outer epidermis of the animal

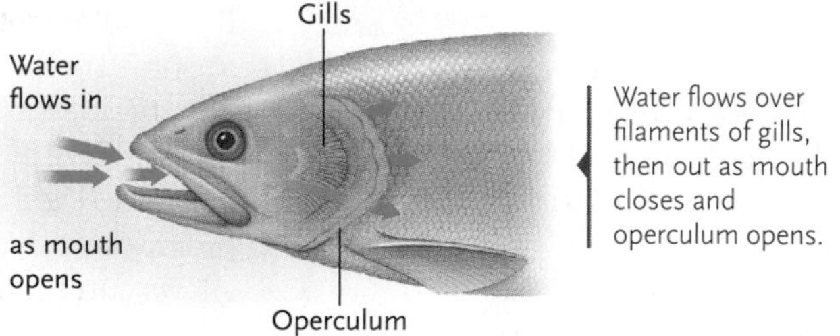

a. The flow of water around the gill filaments

b. Countercurrent flow in fish gills, in which the blood and water move in opposite directions

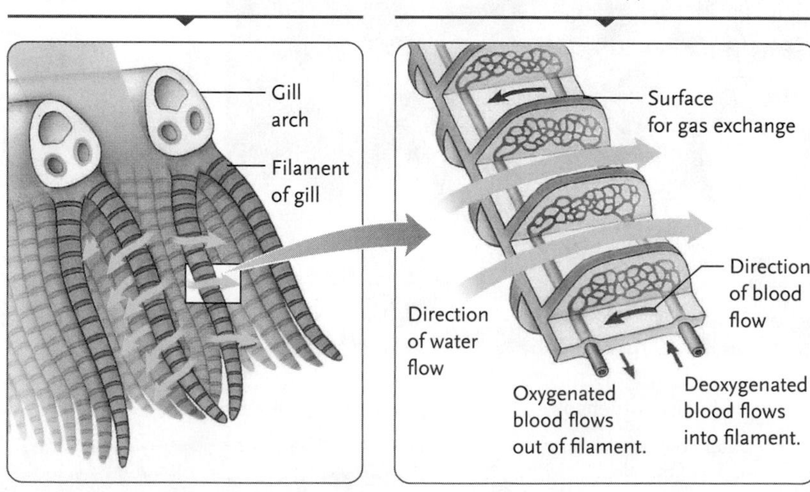

c. In countercurrent exchange, blood leaving the capillaries has the same O_2 content as fully oxygenated water entering the gills

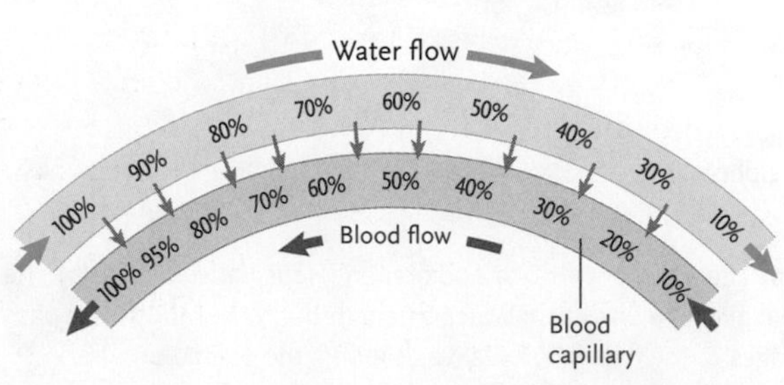

Figure 42.5
Ventilation and countercurrent exchange in bony fishes. **(a)** Water flows around the gill filaments. **(b)** Water and blood flow in opposite directions through the gill filaments. **(c)** Countercurrent exchange: oxygen from the water diffuses into the blood, raising its oxygen content. The percentages indicate the degree of oxygenation of water (blue) and blood (red).

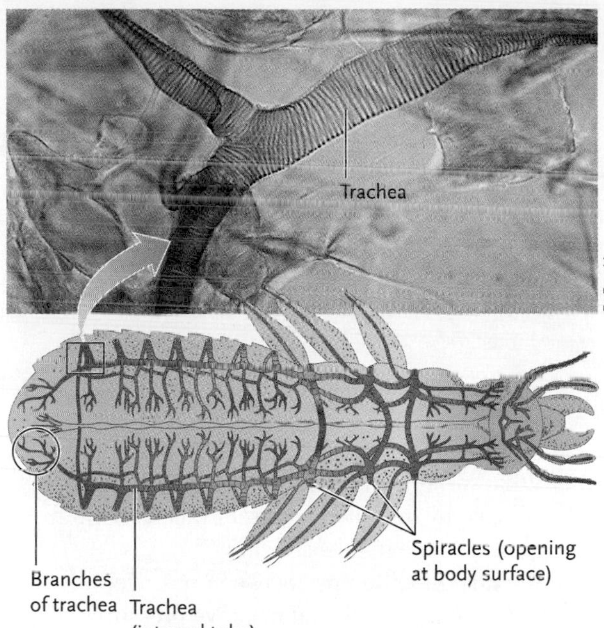

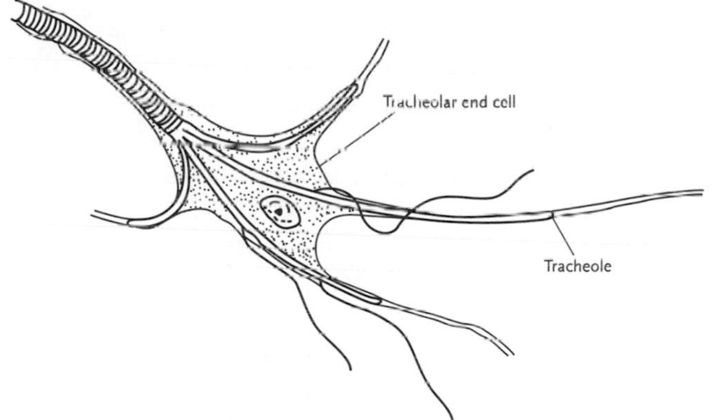

Figure 42.6
The tracheal system of insects. The photograph shows the chitinous rings that reinforce the tracheae, keeping them from collapsing. The tracheal system terminates in many tracheolar end cells that have branches with a diameter of less than 1 μM.

and as such consist of the epithelial cells and the cuticle secreted by those cells. They are lined with a thin layer of the same cuticle as the exoskeleton and are reinforced by rings of cuticle. They lead from the body surface and branch repeatedly. With each branching, the diameter of the tracheae is reduced, and the tracheae ultimately end as tracheoles less than 1 μM in diameter. Every cell except the hemocytes in an insect's body makes contact with at least one tracheole. In the case of large, metabolically active cells, such as the flight muscles, tracheoles may penetrate inside the cell via invaginations of the cell membrane. Tracheoles are dead-end tubes with very small tips filled with fluid that are in contact with cells of the body. Air is transported by the tracheal system to those tips, and gas exchange occurs directly across the very thin cuticle and epithelium of the tracheoles and the plasma membranes of the body cells. At places within the body, the tracheae may expand into internal air sacs that act as reservoirs to increase the volume of air in the system.

Air enters and leaves the tracheal system at openings in the insect's chitinous exoskeleton called **spiracles** (spiraculum = airhole). The spiracles are located in a row on either side of the thorax and abdomen, typically one pair per body segment. Each spiracle incorporates a muscle that allows the spiracles to open and close. For many insects at rest, the spiracles are minimally open, allowing a very small current of air to enter. O_2 is consumed by the tissues, and CO_2 is taken up by the bicarbonate buffering system, resulting in a small negative pressure inside the tracheal system. The small inward current of air flowing through the reduced opening of the spiracle prevents water vapour from escaping. As the bicarbonate buffering system becomes saturated, free CO_2 builds up inside the insect, causing the spiracles to open briefly, allowing CO_2 (and water vapour) to escape. In periods of greater activity, as in flight, this mechanism is replaced by one in which alternating compression and expansion of the thorax by the flight muscles also pumps air through the tracheal system. The spiracles open and close in synchrony with this rhythm.

42.2d Lungs Allow Animals to Live in Completely Terrestrial Environments

Lungs are one of the primary adaptations that allowed vertebrates to fully invade terrestrial environments. Many authorities believe that the bony fish evolved from a freshwater ancestor that had both fins and lungs, which arose as invaginations of the upper digestive tract. Two lines evolved from this ancestor. In one line, the lung lost its connection to the digestive system and became the swim bladder that controls buoyancy in the modern teleosts. The other line (Sarcopterygii), represented by only a few living species, retained the lung, enabling them to survive in O_2-poor water or periods when pools dried up. This line gave rise to the tetrapod vertebrates. In these fish, air is obtained by **positive pressure breathing**, a gulping or swallowing motion that forces air into the lungs (see Chapter 27).

The lungs of mature amphibians such as frogs and salamanders are also thin-walled sacs with relatively little folding or pocketing. Amphibians fill their lungs by positive pressure breathing **(Figure 42.7, p. 1046)**. A breathing cycle begins by opening the nostrils and lowering the floor of the mouth cavity

Figure 42.7
Positive pressure breathing in an amphibian (frog).

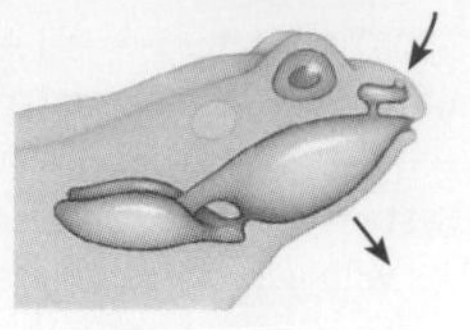
1 The frog lowers the floor of its mouth and inhales through its nostrils.

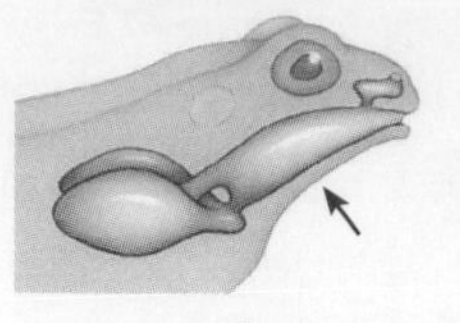
2 It closes its nostrils, opens the glottis, and elevates the floor of the mouth, forcing air into the lungs.

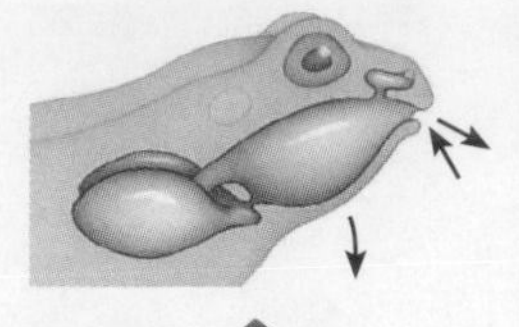
3 Rhythmic ventilation assists in gas exchange.

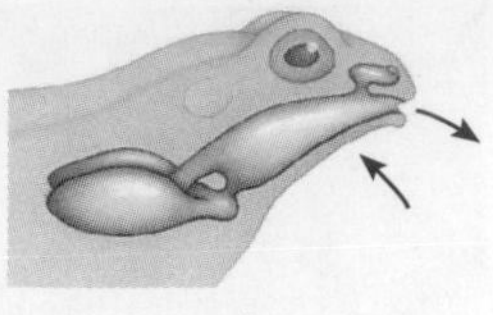
4 Air is forced out when muscles in the body wall above the lungs contract and the lungs recoil elastically.

with the entrance into the lungs constricted by the glottis. The nostrils are closed, the glottis is opened, and the floor of the mouth is raised, forcing air into the lungs. During this period, the floor of the mouth moves up and down, ensuring mixing of the gases. The nostrils open, and the gases in the lungs are expelled by contraction of muscles on the sides of the frog and the rebound elasticity of the lungs. Rhythmic motions of the floor of the mouth with the nostrils open ensure that the buccal cavity contains fresh air for the beginning of the next cycle. The efficiency of the system is increased because much of the CO_2 is lost through the skin. (Remember from Chapter 37 that frogs have a pulmonary-cutaneous circulation.)

In reptiles, birds, and mammals, the lungs become more folded, with many pockets, increasing the surface for gas exchange. Mammalian lungs consist of millions of tiny air pockets, the **alveoli** (singular, alveolus), each surrounded by dense capillary networks. Reptiles and mammals fill their lungs by **negative pressure breathing**, in which muscular contractions expand the lungs, lowering the pressure of the air in the lungs and causing air to be pulled inward. In crocodilians, for example, the contraction of a muscle connecting the liver to the pelvis pulls the liver back, causing the lungs to expand, and another muscle pulls the liver forward, forcing gases out of the lungs. The mechanism in mammals is described in detail in the next section.

In birds, a countercurrent exchange system provides the most complex and efficient vertebrate lungs **(Figure 42.8)**. In addition to paired lungs, birds have nine pairs of air sacs that branch off the respiratory tract. The air sacs, which collectively contain several times as much air as the lungs, are not respiratory surfaces. They set up a pathway that allows air to flow in one direction through the lungs rather than in and out, as in other vertebrates. Within the lungs, air flows through an array of fine, parallel tubes that are surrounded by a capillary network. The blood flows in the direction opposite to the air flow, setting up a countercurrent exchange. The countercurrent exchange allows bird lungs to extract about one-third of the O_2 from the air compared with about one-fourth in the lungs of mammals.

Study Break

1. What variable in Fick's equation is most affected by the countercurrent mechanism in gas exchange in teleost fish?
2. What is the difference between positive pressure breathing and negative pressure breathing?

42.3 The Mammalian Respiratory System

All mammals have a pair of lungs and a diaphragm in the chest cavity that plays an important role in negative pressure breathing. Rapid ventilation of the respiratory surface and perfusion by blood flow through dense capillary networks maximizes gas exchange.

42.3a The Airways Leading from the Exterior to the Lungs Filter, Moisten, and Warm the Entering Air

The human respiratory system is typical for a terrestrial mammal **(Figure 42.9, p. 1048)**. Air enters and leaves the respiratory system through the nostrils and mouth. Hairs in the nostrils and mucus covering the surface of the airways filter out and trap dust and other large particles. Inhaled air is moistened and warmed as it moves through the mouth and nasal passages.

Next, air moves into the throat or **pharynx**, which forms a common pathway for air entering the **larynx** or "voice box" and food entering the esophagus, which leads to the stomach. The airway through the larynx is open except during swallowing.

From the larynx, air moves into the **trachea**, which branches into two airways, the **bronchi** (singular, *bronchus*). The bronchi lead to the two elastic, cone-shaped lungs, one on each side of the chest cavity. Inside the lungs, the bronchi narrow and branch repeatedly, becoming progressively narrower and more numerous. The terminal airways, the **bronchioles**, lead into cup-shaped pockets, the alveoli; shown in Figure 42.9 insets).

a. Lungs and air sacs of a bird

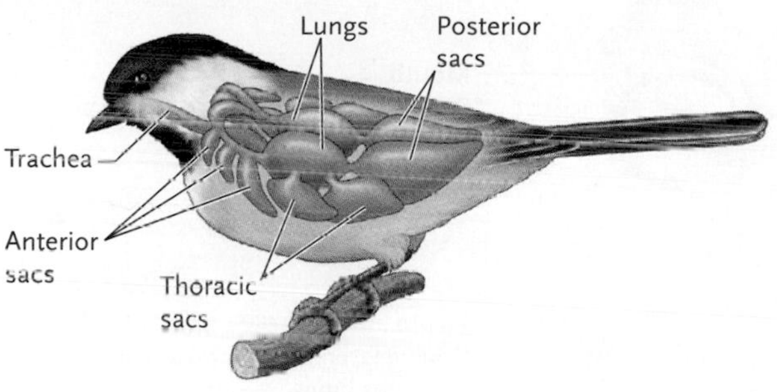

b. Countercurrent exchange

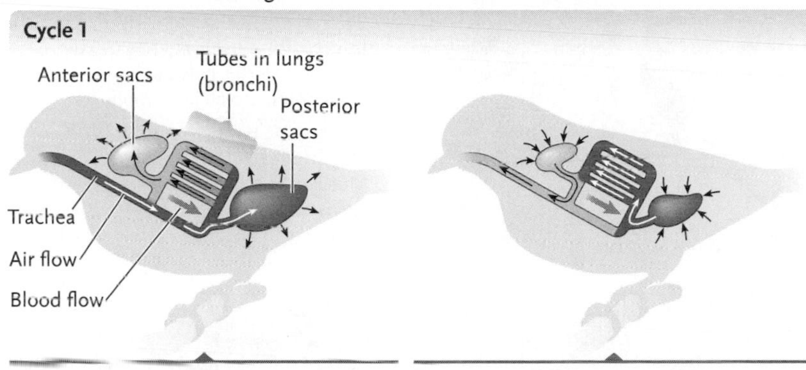

1 During the first inhalation, most of the oxygen flows directly to the posterior air sacs. The anterior air sacs also expand but do not receive any of the newly inhaled oxygen.

2 During the following exhalation, both anterior and posterior air sacs contract. Oxygen from the posterior sacs flows into the gas-exchanging tubes (bronchi) of the lungs.

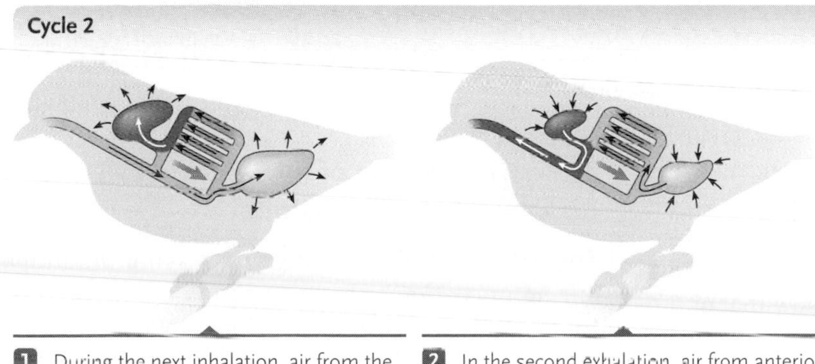

1 During the next inhalation, air from the lung (now deoxygenated) moves into the anterior air sacs.

2 In the second exhalation, air from anterior sacs is expelled to the outside through the trachea.

Figure 42.8

Countercurrent exchange in bird lungs. (a) Unlike mammalian lungs, bird lungs do not expand and contract. Changes in pressure in the expandable air sacs move air in and out. **(b)** Air flows in one direction through the tubes of the lungs; blood flows in the opposite direction in the surrounding capillary network. Two cycles of inhalation and exhalation are needed to move a specific volume of air through the bird respiratory system.

Each of the 150 million alveoli in each lung is surrounded by a dense network of capillaries. By the time inhaled air reaches the alveoli, it has been moistened to the saturation point and brought to body temperature. The many alveoli provide an enormous area for gas exchange. If the alveoli of an adult human were flattened out in a single layer, they would cover an area approaching 100 square metres, about the size of a tennis court! The epithelium of the alveoli is composed of very thin squamous cells. In terms of Fick's law, A is very large and D is minimized.

The tracheae and larger bronchi are nonmuscular tubes encircled by rings of cartilage that prevent the tubes from compressing (recall the analogous but not homologous arrangement in the tracheae of insects). The largest of the rings, which reinforces the larynx, stands out at the front of the throat as the Adam's apple, more prominent in males. The walls of the smaller bronchi and the bronchioles contain smooth muscle cells that contract or relax to control the diameter of these passages and with it the amount of air flowing to and from the alveoli.

The epithelium lining each bronchus contains cilia and mucus-secreting cells. Bacteria and airborne particles such as dust and pollen are trapped in the mucus (see *Molecule Behind Biology*) and then moved upward and into the throat by the beating of the cilia lining the airways. Infection-fighting macrophages (see Chapter 44) also patrol the respiratory epithelium.

42.3b Contractions of the Diaphragm and Muscles between the Ribs Ventilate the Lungs

The lungs are located in the rib cage above the *diaphragm*, a dome-shaped sheet of skeletal muscle separating the chest cavity from the abdominal cavity. The lungs are covered by a double layer of epithelial tissue called the **pleura.** The inner pleural layer is attached to the surface of the lungs, and the outer layer is attached to the surface of the chest cavity. A narrow space between the inner and outer layers is filled with slippery fluid, which allows the lungs to move within the chest cavity without rubbing or abrasion as they expand and contract.

Contraction of the diaphragm and the intercostal muscles between the ribs brings air into the lungs by a negative pressure mechanism. As an inhalation begins, the diaphragm contracts and

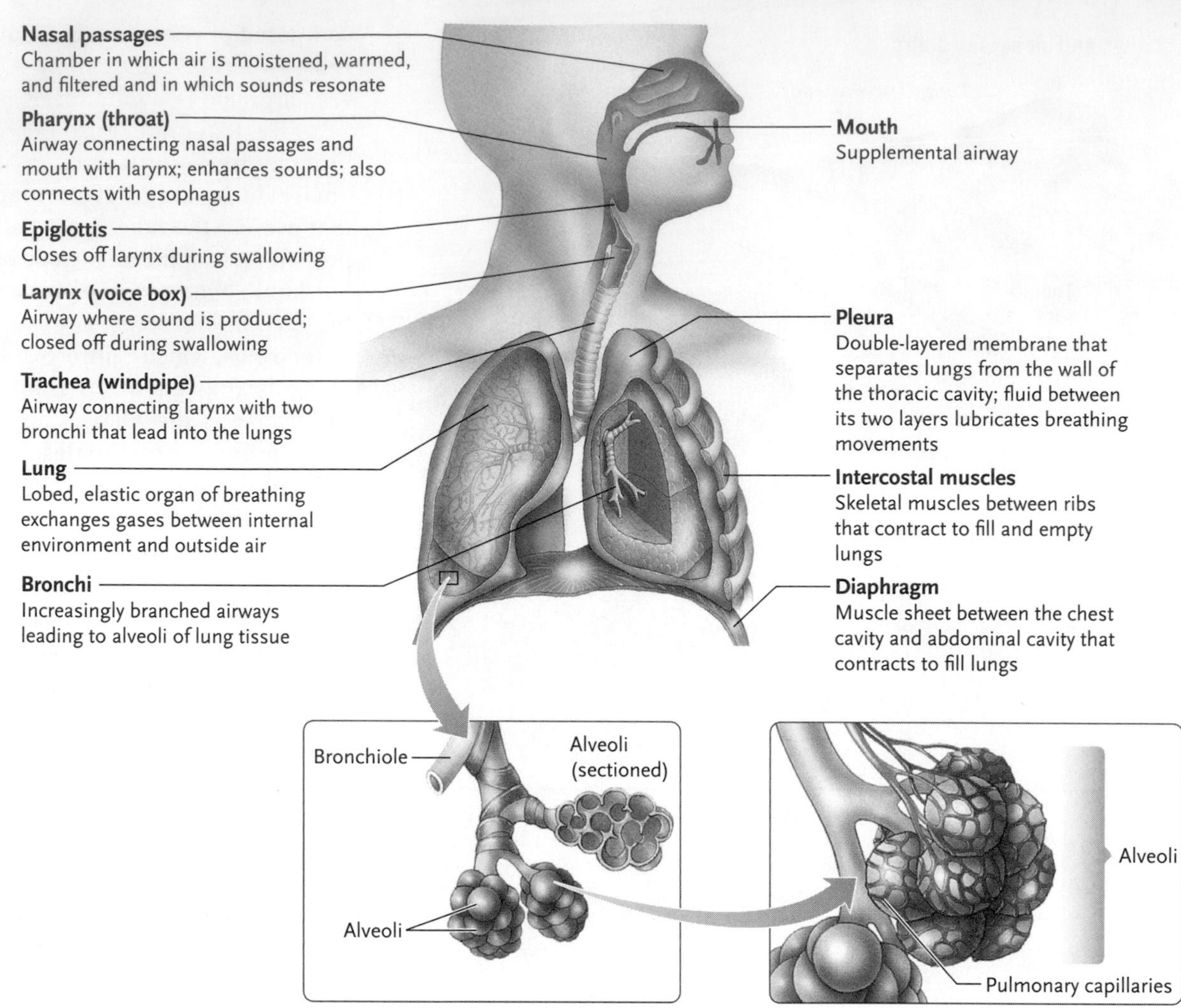
Nasal passages
Chamber in which air is moistened, warmed, and filtered and in which sounds resonate
Pharynx (throat)
Airway connecting nasal passages and mouth with larynx; enhances sounds; also connects with esophagus
Epiglottis
Closes off larynx during swallowing
Larynx (voice box)
Airway where sound is produced; closed off during swallowing
Trachea (windpipe)
Airway connecting larynx with two bronchi that lead into the lungs
Lung
Lobed, elastic organ of breathing exchanges gases between internal environment and outside air
Bronchi
Increasingly branched airways leading to alveoli of lung tissue
Mouth
Supplemental airway
Pleura
Double-layered membrane that separates lungs from the wall of the thoracic cavity; fluid between its two layers lubricates breathing movements
Intercostal muscles
Skeletal muscles between ribs that contract to fill and empty lungs
Diaphragm
Muscle sheet between the chest cavity and abdominal cavity that contracts to fill lungs
Bronchiole
Alveoli (sectioned)
Alveoli
Alveoli
Pulmonary capillaries

Figure 42.9
The human respiratory system, which is typical for a terrestrial mammal.

flattens, and one set of muscles between the ribs, the external intercostal muscles, contracts, pulling the ribs upward and outward **(Figure 42.10).** These movements expand the chest cavity and lungs, lowering the air pressure in the lungs below that of the atmosphere. As a result, air is drawn into the lungs, expanding and filling them.

The expansion of the lungs is much like filling two rubber balloons. Like balloons, the lungs are elastic and resist stretching as they are filled. And also like balloons, the stretching stores energy that can be released to expel air from the lungs. During an exhalation by a person at rest, the diaphragm and muscles between the ribs relax, and the elastic recoil of the lungs expels the air.

When physical activity increases the body's demand for O_2, contractions of other muscles help expel the air by forcefully reducing the volume of the chest cavity. That is, abdominal wall muscles contract, which increases abdominal pressure. That pressure exerts an upward-directed force on the diaphragm, which is pushed upward. In addition, internal intercostal muscles contract, pulling the chest wall inward and downward, causing it to flatten. As a result, the dimensions of the chest cavity decrease.

42.3c The Volume of Inhaled and Exhaled Air Varies over Wide Limits

The volume of air entering and leaving the lungs during inhalation and exhalation is called the **tidal volume.** In a person at rest, the tidal volume amounts to about 500 mL. As physical activity increases, the tidal volume increases to match the body's demands for O_2; at maximal levels, the tidal volume reaches about 3400 mL in females and 4800 mL in males. This maximum tidal volume is called the **vital capacity** of an individual.

Even after the most forceful exhalation, about 1200 mL of air remains in the lungs in males and about 1000 mL in females; this is the **residual volume** of the lungs. In fact, the lungs cannot be deflated completely because small airways collapse during forced exhalation, blocking further outflow of air. Because air cannot be removed from the lungs completely, some gas exchange can always occur between blood flowing through the lungs and the air in the alveoli.

The respiratory movements are controlled by centres in the medulla and pons, part of the brain stem (see Chapter 33). Nerve signals from these centres to the muscles involved in breathing can vary the intake of air from as little as 5 to 6 L per minute to as much as

Molecule Behind Biology

Mucin: Sticky Lubricant

The airways leading to the lungs have a surface coating of mucus secreted by specialized epithelial cells. The mucus traps dust particles, bacteria, and other foreign bodies and is swept upward by the action of cilia to be swallowed into the digestive tract or expelled by the act of blowing your nose or spitting. Mucus is composed of a rodlike protein, mucin, that is very heavily glycosylated (the addition of sugars) after translation and that forms giant polymers up to 10 million Da. The very dense coating of sugar provides a lot of water-holding capacity. This gives mucin its slippery character, which makes it useful as a lubricant. Mucins constitute a family of proteins, and at least 19 genes are known for humans. Three of these are expressed in airway epithelium. Mucins are also important in the mucus that coats the intestinal epithelium, where mucus serves as a lubricant and protects the epithelium from gastric acids and enzymes. Mucus also lines the reproductive tract. Mucins are important constituents of saliva, keeping the membranes of the oral cavity moist and lubricating the food as it is chewed. Tears contain mucins, continuously washing the eye free of dust. All of these mucins are produced continuously, often in large quantities.

Other mucins, the "tethered" or membrane-associated mucins, are attached to cell membranes, where they serve a variety of functions. In addition to the mucins in tears, there are also mucins attached to the membranes of the surface of the eye, a slippery surface over which tears can move more easily. The function of the several membrane-associated mucins is far from clear. They may have a role in preventing infection or in cell-to-cell attachment, or in some cases, they may be part of a cell-signalling mechanism.

Mucins are ancient molecules and occur in most metazoan phyla as well as in protists. In insects, a mucin gene is expressed in the intestine, and mucins are known from nematodes. In molluscs, mucins are found in the matrix that contains calcite to form the shell.

150 L per minute (for very brief periods). These centres integrate information about O_2 and CO_2 in the blood from O_2 and CO_2 receptors located in special sense organs (the carotid bodies) in the carotid arteries that supply the brain and in the aorta (the aortic body) that supplies blood to the rest of the body. These receptors are more sensitive to changes in CO_2: the P_{O_2} must drop below about 100 mm Hg before they are activated. The medulla integrates this information with information coming from its own receptors that monitor the pH of the cerebrospinal fluid. The pH of this fluid is determined mostly by the CO_2 concentration in the

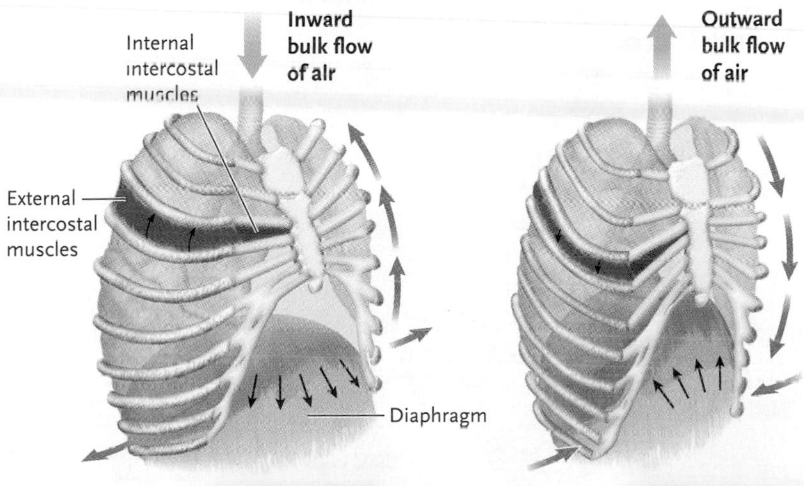

Inhalation. Diaphragm contracts and moves down. The external intercostal muscles contract and lift rib cage upward and outward. The lung volume expands.

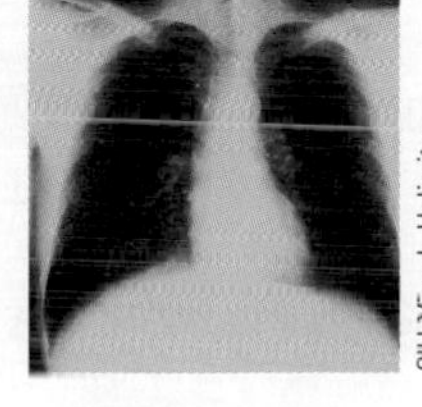

Exhalation during breathing or rest. Diaphragm and external intercostal muscles return to the resting positions. Rib cage moves down. Lungs recoil passively.

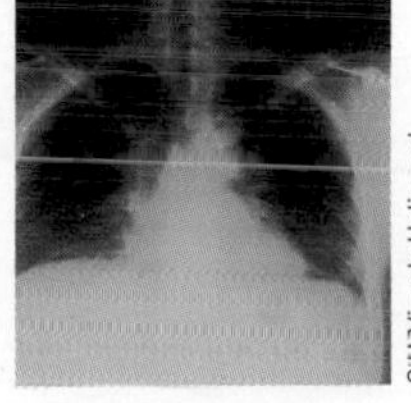

Figure 42.10
The respiratory movements of humans during breathing at rest. The movements of the rib cage and diaphragm fill and empty the lungs. Inhalation is powered by contractions of the external intercostal muscles and diaphragm, and exhalation is passive. During exercise or other activities characterized by deeper and more rapid breathing, contractions of the internal intercostal muscles and the abdominal muscles add force to exhalation. The X-ray images show how the volume of the lungs increases during inhalation and exhalation.

blood. (Remember that the pH decreases as CO_2 levels increase.) In general, the CO_2 level is most closely monitored. The O_2 receptors act as a backup system that comes into play only when blood O_2 concentration falls to critically low levels. The level of CO_2 in the blood and body fluids is much more closely monitored and has a much greater effect on breathing than the O_2 level. This reflects the fact that small fluctuations in blood pH have much greater effects on the ability of haemoglobin to carry oxygen and on enzyme activity in the blood and interstitial fluid than fluctuations in the O_2 level.

Study Break

1. What is the site of gas exchange in human lungs?
2. What is tidal volume?

42.4 Mechanisms of Gas Exchange and Transport

In both the lungs and body tissues, gas exchange occurs when the gas diffuses from an area of higher concentration to an area of lower concentration. In this section, we consider the mechanics of gas exchange between air and the blood in mammals and the means by which gases are transported between the lungs and other body tissues. A major part of this story involves haemoglobin, the vertebrate respiratory pigment.

In the lungs, even though the P_{O_2} is reduced by mixing with the air in the residual volume, it is still much higher than the P_{O_2} in deoxygenated blood entering the network of capillaries in the lungs **(Figure 42.11)**. As a result, O_2 readily diffuses from the alveolar air into the plasma solution in the capillaries.

42.4 a Haemoglobin Greatly Increases the O_2-Carrying Capacity of the Blood

After entering the plasma, O_2 diffuses into erythrocytes, where it combines with haemoglobin. The combination with haemoglobin removes O_2 from the plasma, lowering the P_{O_2} of the plasma and increasing P1-P2 between alveolar air and the blood. This increases the rate of diffusion of O_2 across the alveoli and into the plasma.

Recall from Chapter 37 that a mammalian haemoglobin molecule has four haem groups, each containing an iron atom that can combine reversibly with an O_2 molecule. A haemoglobin molecule can therefore bind a total of four molecules of O_2. The combination of O_2 with haemoglobin allows blood to carry about 60 times more O_2 (about 200 mL per litre) than it could if the O_2 simply dissolved in the plasma (about 3 mL per litre). About 98.5% of the O_2 in blood is carried by haemoglobin, and about 1.5% is carried in solution in the blood plasma.

The reversible combination of haemoglobin with O_2 is related to the P_{O_2} in a pattern shown by the *haemoglobin–O_2 dissociation curve* in **Figure 42.12.** (The curve is generated by measuring the amount of haemoglobin saturated at a given P_{O_2}.) The curve is S-shaped, with a plateau region, rather than linear. The top, plateau, part of the curve above 60 mm Hg is in the blood P_{O_2} range found in the pulmonary capillaries, where O_2 is binding to haemoglobin. For this part of the curve, the blood remains highly saturated with O_2 over a relatively large range of P_{O_2}. Even at P_{O_2} levels much higher than shown on the graph, only a

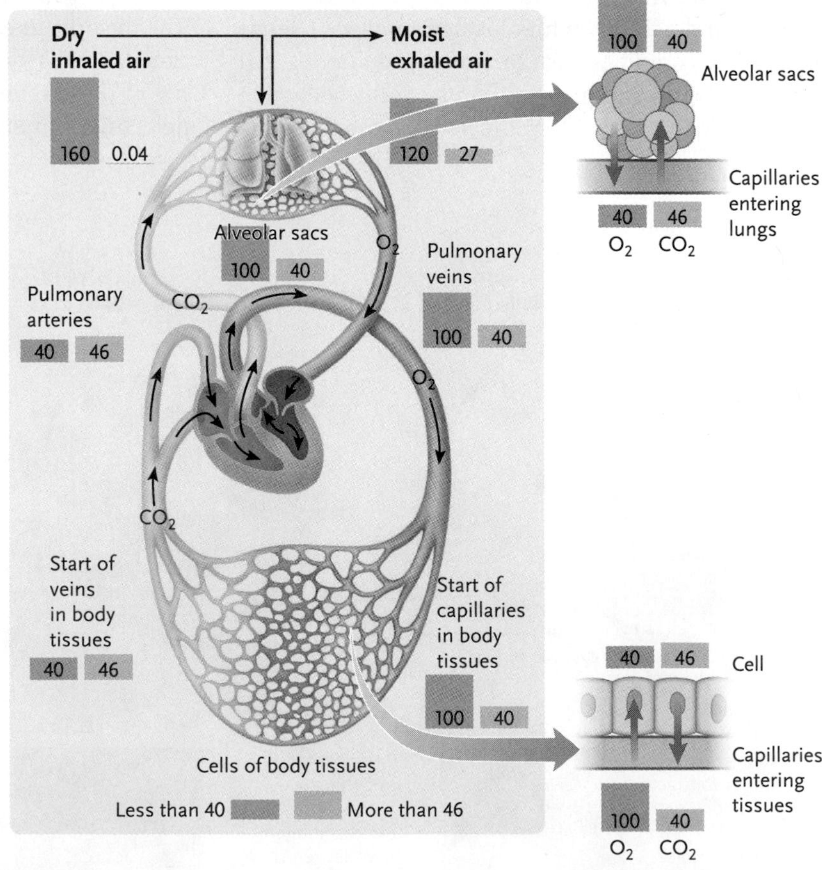

Figure 42.11
The partial pressures of O_2 (pink) and CO_2 (blue) in various locations in the body.

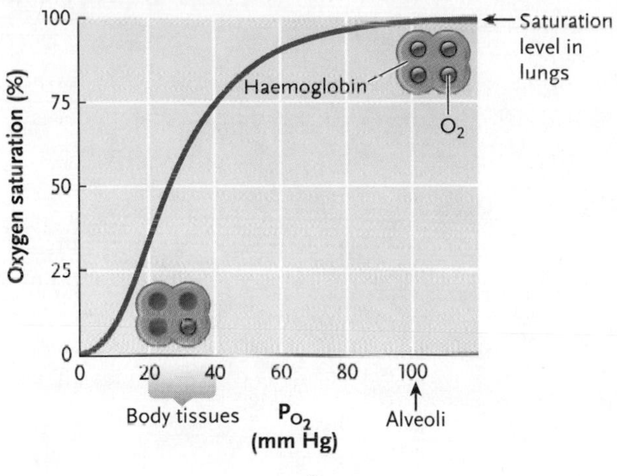

In the alveoli, in which the P_{O_2} is about 100 mm Hg and the pH is 7.4, most haemoglobin molecules are 100% saturated, meaning that almost all have bound four O_2 molecules.

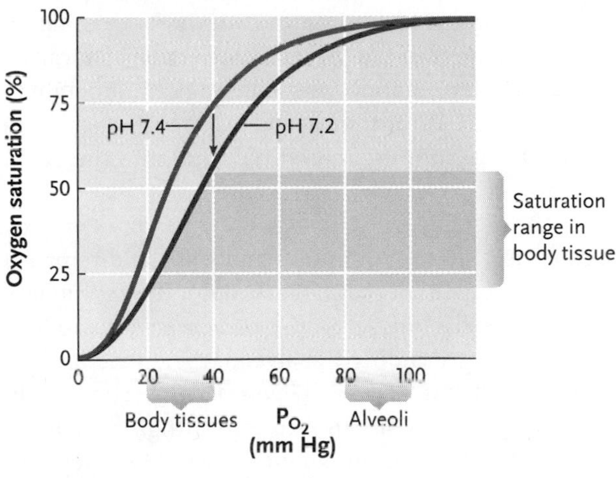

In the capillaries of body tissues, where the P_{O_2} varies between about 20 and 40 mm Hg depending on the level of metabolic activity and the pH is about 7.2, haemoglobin can hold less O_2. As a result, most haemoglobin molecules release two or three of their O_2 molecules to become between 25% and 50% saturated. Note that the drop in pH to 7.2 (red line) in active body tissues reduces the amount of O_2 haemoglobin can hold as a compared with pH 7.4. The reduction in binding affinity at lower pH increases the amount of O_2 released in active tissues.

Figure 42.12
Haemoglobin–O_2 dissociation curves, which show the degree to which haemoglobin is saturated with O_2 at increasing P_{O_2}.

small extra amount of O_2 will bind to haemoglobin. The steep part of the curve between 0 and 60 mm Hg is in the range found in the capillaries in the rest of the body. For this part of the curve, small changes in P_{O_2} result in large changes in the amount of O_2 bound to haemoglobin.

Because the P_{O_2} in alveolar air is about 100 mm Hg, most of the haemoglobin molecules in the blood leaving the alveolar networks are fully saturated, meaning that most of the haemoglobin molecules have bound four O_2 molecules (see Figure 42.12a). The P_{O_2} of the O_2 in solution in the blood plasma has risen to approximately the same level as in the alveolar air, about 100 mm Hg. The blood has also changed colour, reflecting the bright red colour of oxygenated haemoglobin compared with the darker red colour of deoxygenated haemoglobin.

The oxygenated blood exiting from the alveoli collects in venules, which merge to form the pulmonary veins leaving the lungs. These veins carry the blood to the heart, which pumps the blood through the systemic circulation to all parts of the body.

As the oxygenated blood enters the capillary networks of body tissues, it encounters regions in which the P_{O_2} in the interstitial fluid and body cells is lower than that in the blood, ranging from about 40 mm Hg downward to 20 mm Hg or less (see Figure 42.11b). As a result, O_2 diffuses from the blood plasma into the interstitial fluid and from the fluid into body cells. As O_2 diffuses from the blood plasma into body tissues, it is replaced by O_2 released from haemoglobin.

Several factors contribute to the release of O_2 from haemoglobin, including increased acidity (lower pH) in active tissues. The acidity increases because oxidative reactions release CO_2, which combines with water to form carbonic acid (H_2CO_3). The lowered pH reduces the affinity of haemoglobin for O_2, which is released and used in cellular respiration.

The net diffusion of O_2 from blood to body cells continues until by the time the blood leaves the capillary networks in the body tissues, much of the O_2 has been removed from haemoglobin. The blood, now with a P_{O_2} of 40 mm Hg or less, returns in veins to the heart, which pumps it through the pulmonary arteries to the lungs for oxygenation.

42.4b Carbon Dioxide Diffuses Down Concentration Gradients from Body Tissues and into the Blood and Alveolar Air

The CO_2 produced by cellular oxidations diffuses from active cells into the interstitial fluid, where it reaches a partial pressure of about 46 mm Hg. Because this P_{CO_2} is higher than the 40 mm Hg P_{CO_2} in the blood entering the capillary networks of body tissues, CO_2 diffuses from the interstitial fluid into the blood plasma **(Figure 42.13a, p. 1052)**.

Some of the CO_2 remains in solution as a gas in the plasma. Remember, however, that most of the free CO_2, about 70%, combines with water to produce carbonic acid (H_2CO_3), which dissociates into bicarbonate (HCO_3^-) and H^+ ions. In the erythrocyte, the enzyme carbonic anhydrase accelerates the reaction.

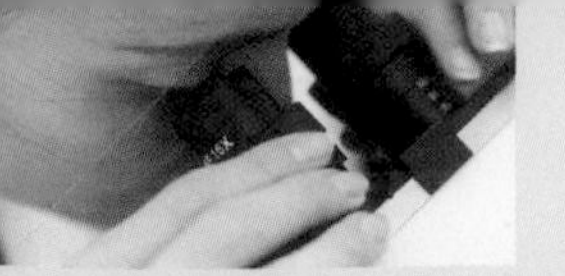

People Behind Biology

Peter Hochachka: Exploring Life at the Edge

Dr. Peter Hochachka (1937–2002), of the University of British Columbia, spent his career exploring the various biochemical mechanisms that allow animals to exploit extreme environments. Among his interests were the metabolic characteristics of animals in environments low in O_2. He brought Sherpas from the Himalaya and Quechuas from the high Andes as volunteer research subjects to his lab and used positron emission tomography (PET) and magnetic resonance spectroscopy, two techniques that permit the noninvasive characterisation of metabolic activity, as well as magnetic resonance imaging (MRI) to understand their metabolism. He and his collaborators showed that the brains of the volunteers living at high altitudes metabolized O_2 at lower rates. Their hearts relied more on glucose as a fuel, an arrangement that produces more work per O_2 molecule than the greater reliance on fatty acids characteristic of the hearts of people living nearer sea level. Thus, although the increased O_2 binding capacity of haemoglobin is important in animals that live at high altitudes, it is only one of a suite of genetic adaptations to living at high altitudes.

Figure 42.13
The reactions occurring during the transfer of CO_2 from body tissues to alveolar air.

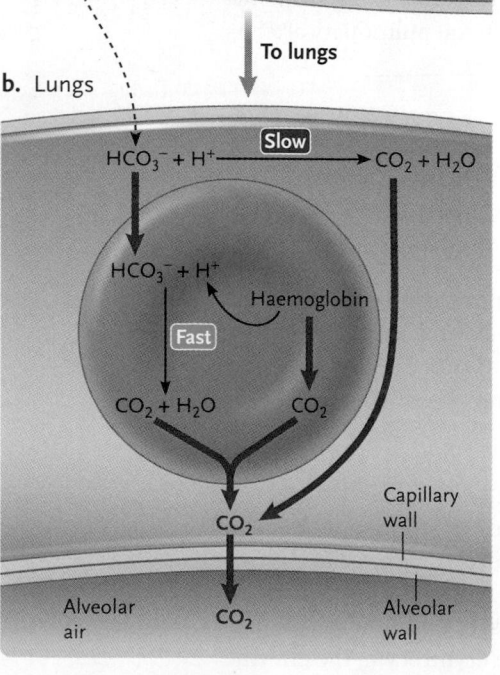

In body tissues, some of the CO_2 released into the blood combines with water in the blood plasma to form HCO_3^- and H^+. However, most of the CO_2 diffuses into erythrocytes, where some combines directly with haemoglobin and some combines with water to form HCO_3^- and H^+. The H^+ formed by this reaction combines with haemoglobin; the HCO_3^- is transported out of erythrocytes to add to the HCO_3^- in the blood plasma.

In the lungs, the reactions are reversed. Some of the HCO_3^- in the blood plasma combines with H^+ to form CO_2 and water. However, most of the HCO_3^- is transported into erythrocytes, where it combines with H^+ released from haemoglobin to form CO_2 and water. CO_2 is released from haemoglobin. The CO_2 diffuses from the erythrocytes and, with the CO_2 in the blood plasma, diffuses from the blood into the alveolar air.

Most of the H^+ ions produced by the dissociation of carbonic acid combine with haemoglobin or with proteins in the plasma, so that the pH is maintained. Note, however, that if CO_2 levels are high, pH will fall, resulting in changes in breathing. The combination of solution in the plasma, conversion to bicarbonate, and combination with haemoglobin operate to maximize P1-P2 of the gaseous CO_2 so that the rate of diffusion from the interstitial fluid into the blood is optimal.

The blood leaving the capillary networks of body tissues is collected in venules and veins and returned to the heart, which pumps it through the pulmonary arteries into the lungs. As the blood enters the capillary networks surrounding the alveoli, the entire process of CO_2 uptake is reversed **(Figure 42.13b)**. The P_{CO_2} in the blood, now about 46 mm Hg, is higher than the P_{CO_2} in the alveolar air, about 40 mm Hg (shown in Figure 42.11). As a result, CO_2 diffuses from the blood and into the air. The diminishing CO_2 concentrations in the plasma, along with the lower pH encountered in the lungs, promote the release of CO_2 from haemoglobin. As CO_2 diffuses away, bicarbonate ions in the blood combine with H^+ ions, forming carbonic acid molecules that break down into water and additional CO_2. This CO_2 adds to the quantities diffusing from the blood into the alveolar air. By the time the blood leaves the capillary networks in the lungs, its P_{CO_2} has been reduced to the same level as that of the alveolar air, about 40 mm Hg.

Study Break

1. In mammals, which lung tissue serves as a major site of gas exchange?
2. What is the role of pH in gas exchange?

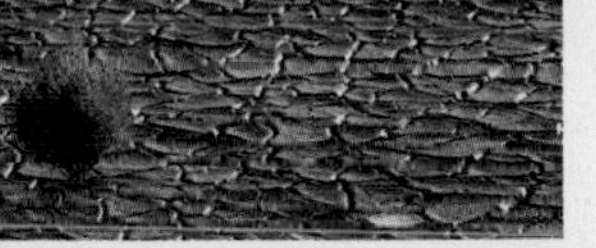

LIFE ON THE EDGE

Prospering in Thin Air

With increasing altitude, atmospheric pressure decreases, and with it, the P_{O_2} also decreases. At an elevation of 5000 M, the atmospheric pressure is about half that at sea level, and the P_{O_2} is thus 380 × 21/100 or 80 mm Hg, about half that at sea level. This reduces P1-P2 between the alveolar air and the blood, and, in turn, the supply of O_2 to the tissues is reduced. Humans who normally live at or near sea level and move to higher elevations above about 2000 M experience fatigue, dizziness, and nausea until their systems produce additional erythrocytes, a physiological response to the stress of reduced O_2.

However, there are animals that live at high altitudes, such as the llama (*Lama glama*), from the Andes at about 4000 M, or the bar-headed goose (*Anser indicus*), which migrates over the Himalaya mountains at elevations in excess of 8000 M. The major factor that permits these animals to exploit what is a marginal environment for other animals is a genetic difference in the haemoglobin molecule that produces a higher affinity for O_2. The haemoglobin in these animals shifts the haemoglobin–oxygen dissociation curve in Figure 42.10 to the left so that the haemoglobin is closer to saturation at lower P_{O_2} levels.

Haemoglobin is particularly polymorphic: the gene has a number of alleles, and the alleles present in the animals that can live at very high altitudes produce the appropriate forms of haemoglobin. This is well illustrated by the deer mouse, *Peromyscus maniculatus,* which occupies an extreme range of altitudes from below sea level in Death Valley to above 4300 M in the Sierra Nevada mountains. The populations of deer mice at higher altitudes have alleles of the haemoglobin genes with higher affinities for O_2 than the alleles of mice at low altitudes.

UNANSWERED QUESTIONS

We have become accustomed to thinking exclusively of physiological adaptation as the principal means for humans functioning at high altitudes. The discovery by Hochachka and others that there is a strong genetic component in humans and other animals and that this genetic component is not limited to the haemoglobin gene raises interesting questions. Which genes govern the improved performance at high altitudes? Did these genetic adaptations permit the astonishing feat of Rheinhold Messner, who, together with Peter Habelen in 1978, was the first human to climb to the pinnacle of Mount Everest without the use of supplementary O_2? A few others have matched this heroic achievement, and, indeed, Messner repeated his feat alone in 1980. Messner was born and raised in the mountainous Tyrol region of northern Italy. Although in no way diminishing this extraordinary accomplishment, he may have had some genetic predisposition that permitted his survival, however agonizing, at an altitude where the atmospheric pressure is reduced from 760 mm Hg at sea level to 250 mm and the P_{O_2} is only 53 mm **(Figure 1).**

The questions surrounding the genetic adaptations that permit survival in extreme environments involve more than scientific curiosity.

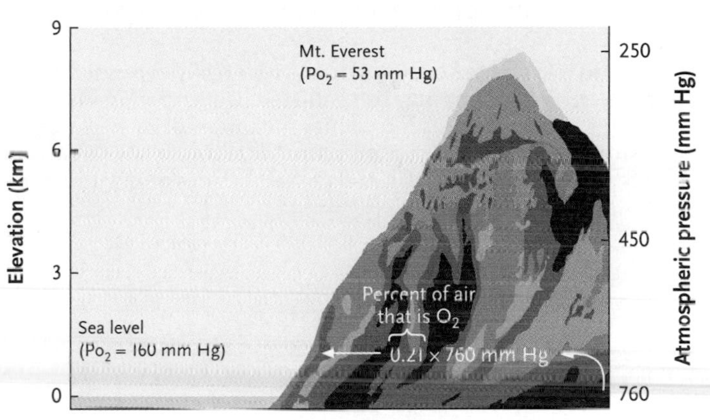

Figure 1
Changes in partial pressure of oxygen with height above sea level.

Humans have begun the exploration of space, and knowledge of the genetic control of those processes that are involved in our ability to tolerate extreme environments will be important.

Review

Go to CENGAGENOW™ at http://hed.nelson.com/ to access quizzing, animations, exercises, articles, and personalized homework help.

42.1 General Principles of Gas Exchange

- The percentage of a gas in a mixture of gases times the atmospheric pressure yields the partial pressure.
- Fick's equation describes the rate of diffusion across a biological membrane. The rate of diffusion is proportional to the product of the area over which diffusion occurs times the difference in partial pressures of the gas on either side of a membrane and is inversely proportional to the distance over which diffusion must occur.
- Gas exchange by simple diffusion is limited to small or flattened organisms.
- In larger animals, respiratory surfaces are increased, and the difference in partial pressures across a membrane is optimized by ventilation and perfusion.
- Water and air, as respiratory media, have different advantages and challenges. Water contains less oxygen, the rate of diffusion is greatly reduced, and its density requires greater energy for ventilation.

42.2 Adaptations for Gas Exchange

- Gills are evaginations of the body surface. Water moves over gills by the beating of cilia or by muscular pumping.
- Water moves over the gills of sharks, bony fishes, and some arthropods, allowing countercurrent exchange to maximize the difference in partial pressure across the respiratory surface.
- Insects have a tracheal system that brings air directly to every cell.
- Lungs are invaginated body surfaces with greatly expanded respiratory surfaces. They may be ventilated by positive pressure breathing, in which air is forced into the lungs, or by negative pressure breathing. Negative pressure breathing relies on muscles that alternately increase or decrease the pressure within the body cavity.

42.3 The Mammalian Respiratory System

- Air enters and leaves the lungs via the nostrils and mouth leading to the trachea, which branch into two bronchi. The bronchi branch many times into broncioles leading to alveoli, which are surrounded by blood capillaries.
- Mammals rely on a negative pressure mechanism. The tidal volume is the volume of air moved in and out of the lungs during normal breathing. The vital capacity is the volume that can be moved in and out by breathing as deeply as possible. The residual volume is the volume remaining in the lungs after exhaling as much as possible.
- Breathing is controlled by centres in the brain reacting to sensors for CO_2 and O_2 in the carotid arteries. The concentration of CO_2 has the greatest influence.

42.4 Mechanisms of Gas Exchange and Transport

- The site of gas exchange in mammals is at the alveolar surface. The P_{O_2} in the alveolar air is greater than that in the blood, causing O_2 to diffuse into the blood and enter the erythrocytes, where it is bound by haemoglobin, thus maximizing the difference in partial pressure of that gas between the air and the blood.
- In the tissues, the reverse is true, and O_2 leaves the blood for the tissues
- The P_{CO_2} is higher in the tissues than in the blood; P_{CO_2} leaves the tissues and dissolves in the plasma and enters the erythrocytes, where most of it is converted into H^+ and HCO_3^- and released back into the plasma. This causes a slight drop in pH, promoting the release of O_2 from haemoglobin. The remaining CO_2 combines with haemoglobin. At the alveolar surface, the P_{CO_2} in the alveolar cells and the air in the lungs is lower than that in the blood, the HCO_3^- releases its CO_2, and CO_2 flows down the gradient.

Questions

Self-Test Questions

1. Which statement is not true?
   a. The partial pressure of O_2 increases with altitude.
   b. The rate of diffusion of a gas increases with an increase in the difference of partial pressures on either side of a membrane.
   c. Countercurrent flow optimizes the difference in partial pressures of a gas across a respiratory surface.
   d. Gases are in aqueous solution at respiratory surfaces.
   e. The solubility of O_2 decreases with an increase in temperature.
2. Tracheal systems are characterized by
   a. closed tubes that circulate gases.
   b. uncontrolled diffusion of gases between the atmosphere and the tissues.
   c. the transport of respiratory gases directly to every cell.
   d. positive pressure breathing.
   e. CO_2 sensors in the segmental ganglia.
3. Which of the following statements is correct? (More than one may be correct.)
   a. The concentration of O_2 in water rises with increasing temperature.
   b An advantage of breathing in air is the reduced energy required to move the gases over the respiratory surface.
   c Birds use a one-way countercurrent flow through their lungs for gas exchange.
   d. O_2 receptors in the medulla have the greatest influence on mammalian breathing.
   e. CO_2 receptors in the carotid body influence mammalian breathing.
4. The Olympic speed skating champion Catriona LeMay Doan is finishing her last lap. At this time,
   a. the diaphragm and rib muscles contract when she exhales.
   b. positive pressure brings air into her lungs.

c. her lungs undergo an elastic recoil when she inhales.
d. her tidal volume is at vital capacity.
e. her residual volume momentarily reaches zero.

5. The haemoglobin–O_2 dissociation curve
   a. reflects about 50% dissociation in the alveoli.
   b. shifts to the left when pH rises.
   c. shows that haemoglobin holds less O_2 when the pH rises.
   d. shows a lack of dependence on CO_2 levels.
   e. explains how haemoglobin can bind more pH in the lungs and release it at the tissues where the pH is lower.

Questions for Discussion

1. The ability to live at high elevations appears to have genetic components beyond the properties of the blood in many animals. What experiments can you devise to explore this possibility? (Hint: some animals have high and low elevation populations.)
2. Hospital patients frequently have a small ring on the end of a finger that shines a red light from the pad of tissue to a detector on the fingernail. What do you think this apparatus measures, and why is it important to measure it continuously? What factors could change the value of this measurement?
3. The control of the spiracular opening in insects is assumed to be important in avoiding water loss during gas exchange. Suggest an experiment to test this hypothesis. How does this mechanism differ from that controlling the opening of the stomata in plants?

A nephron in a human kidney (colourized scanning electron micrograph). Nephrons are the specialized tubules in kidneys that filter the blood to conserve nutrients and water, balance salts in the body, and concentrate wastes for excretion from the body.

© Dennis Kunkel/Phototake

Study Plan

Continued on next page

43 Regulating the Internal Environment

Why It Matters

In the Miramichi River of New Brunswick, an Atlantic salmon (*Salmo salar*) has spent two or three years growing from an egg to a fish about 10 to 25 cm in length. In the spring, as day length increases and the water temperature begins to rise, it undergoes a number of physiological, morphological, and behavioural changes. It loses some of its mottled coloration, becoming silvery in appearance, and joins other similar fish in migrating downstream. It may pause at the estuary of the river for a day or two, but then it abandons its freshwater environment and enters the sea, where it will remain for two or more years, feeding and growing to maturity. Eventually, it will return to the Miramichi to spawn **(Figure 43.1, p. 1058).**

When the salmon leaves the freshwater of the river and enters the salt water of the North Atlantic Ocean, it moves from an environment in which the total concentration of solutes is about 0.1% to one with a concentration of about 3.5%. Its own body fluids contain about 1% of solutes. The salmon moves, over the course of a few days, to an

Continued from previous page

Herve Berthoule / Jacana / Photo Researchers, Inc.

Figure 43.1
An adult Atlantic salmon, ready to return to its river of birth.

environment in which the solute concentration is more than three times greater than the concentration of its body fluids. It thus faces a continuous loss of water. However, the physiological changes that accompany its morphological changes allow it to prosper in an environment that is potentially hostile.

Organisms, particularly those on land, are subject to seasonal and shorter-term fluctuations in their external environment that present challenges for them to maintain not only the integrity of their internal fluids but also the functioning of all the systems that sustain life. The maintenance of a steady internal environment, called **homeostasis** (introduced in Chapter 32), is the subject of this chapter. During evolution, a variety of physiological and behavioural mechanisms have appeared that have permitted organisms to exploit environments that may be highly variable.

In the background are those mechanisms that accompanied the emergence from aqueous to terrestrial environments. There are some important differences between aqueous and terrestrial environments. Water, essential to life, is obviously more abundant in aqueous environments. But aqueous environments may contain greater or lesser amounts of solutes than the body fluids do, posing different problems for homeostasis of the body fluids. Terrestrial environments require mechanisms to conserve water, but they are also subject to much greater variation in temperature. The temperature of aqueous environments is seldom greater than about 25°C, and the lower limit is a little above −2°C (salt water freezes at about this temperature). By contrast, organisms in the northern temperate zone of Canada, for example, encounter temperatures that may range between approximately 40°C and −40°C.

43.1 Introduction to Osmoregulation and Excretion

Living cells contain water, are surrounded by water, and constantly exchange water with their environment. The water of the external environment directly surrounds the cells of the simplest animals. For more complex animals, an aqueous extracellular fluid surrounds the cells and is separated from the external environment by a body covering. In animals with a circulatory system, the extracellular fluid includes both the blood and the interstitial fluid immediately surrounding the cells.

In this section, we review the mechanisms cells use to exchange water and solutes with the surrounding fluid through *osmosis*. We also look at how animals harness osmosis to regulate their internal *water balance*, the equilibrium between the inward and the outward flow of water.

43.1a Osmosis: Passive Diffusion

In osmosis (see Chapter 5), water molecules move across a selectively permeable membrane (one that lets water through but excludes most solutes) from a region where they are more highly concentrated to a region where their concentration is lower. The difference in water concentration is produced by different numbers of solute molecules or ions on each side of the membrane. The side of the membrane with a *lower* solute concentration has a *higher* concentration of water molecules, so water moves osmotically to the other side, where water concentration is *lower*. Selective permeability is a key factor in osmosis because it helps maintain differences in solute concentration on either side of biological membranes. Proteins are among the most important solutes in establishing the conditions producing osmosis.

The osmotic concentration of a solution, measured in *osmoles*, is determined by the total molal concentration of solute particles, both molecules and ions. A nonionic solute such as glucose contributes one osmole of osmotic concentration per mole. A fully dissociated ionic solute, such as NaCl, however, contributes two osmoles per mole of the salt. The osmotic concentration (osmotic pressure) of a solution, called its **osmolality**, is the number of osmoles per kilogram of solute. The molal standard is used rather than the molar (moles per litre of solution) partly because the volume of water changes with temperature.

Because of the complexity of biological fluids, their osmotic concentration is normally measured rather than calculated. The principles that determine osmotic concentration also determine the depression of the freezing point (or elevation of the boiling point) and lowering of the vapour pressure of a solution. Freezing point and vapour pressure of biological fluids are easily measured and calibrated to standard solutions of known osmotic concentration. Because the total solute concentration in the body fluids of most animals is less than 1 osmole, osmolality is usually expressed in thousandths of an osmole, or *milliosmoles* (mOsm) per kilogram. As shown in **Figure 43.2**, the osmolality of body fluids in mammals (including humans) is about 300 mOsm/kg; osmolality in a flounder, a marine teleost (bony fish), is about 330 mOsm/kg, and in a goldfish, a freshwater teleost, it is about 290 mOsm/kg. The relatively low osmotic concentration in marine teleosts reflects their evolutionary history. Early marine teleosts invaded freshwater and prospered there. During the extensive radiation of the group in freshwater, many have reinvaded the marine habitat. By contrast, sharks and many marine invertebrates such as lobsters have osmolalities close to that of seawater, about 1000 mOsm/kg, whereas freshwater invertebrates have an osmolality of about 225 mOsm/kg.

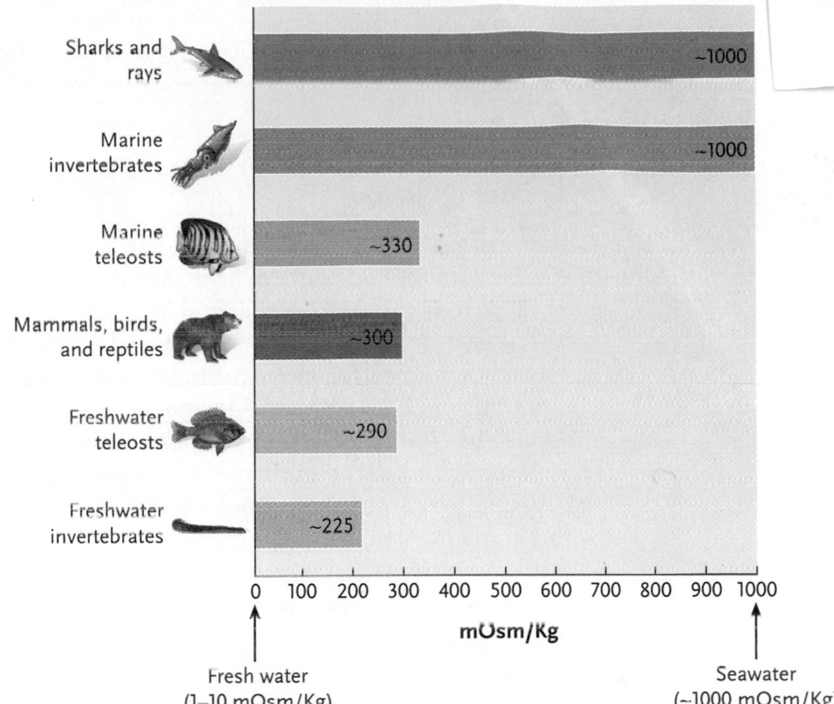

Figure 43.2 Osmolality of body fluids in some animal groups.

A solution of higher osmolality on one side of a selectively permeable membrane is said to be *hyperosmotic* to a solution of lower osmolality on the other side, and a solution of lower osmolality is said to be *hypoosmotic* to a solution of higher osmolality. If the solutions on either side of a membrane have the same osmotic concentrations, they are *isoosmotic*. Water moves across the membrane between solutions that differ in osmolality, whereas when two solutions are isoosmotic, no *net* water movement occurs, although water exchanges from one side to the other.

43.1b Animals Use Different Approaches to Regulate Osmosis

Because even small differences in osmotic concentration can cause cells to swell or shrink, animals must keep their cellular and extracellular fluids isoosmotic. In some animals, called **osmoconformers**, the osmotic concentrations of the cellular and extracellular solutions simply match that of the environment.

Many marine invertebrates are osmoconformers: when placed in dilute seawater, the osmotic concentration of their body fluids decreases, and their weight increases as a result of the osmotic influx of water. Other animals, called **osmoregulators**, use control mechanisms to keep the osmolality of cellular and extracellular fluids constant but at levels that may differ from the osmolality of the surroundings. Most freshwater and terrestrial invertebrates, and almost all vertebrates, are osmoregulators. It is important to recognize that the various solutes contributing to the osmotic concentration may be at different concentrations inside the cell, in the extracellular fluids, and in the environment.

43.1c Excretion Is Closely Tied to Osmoregulation

Cells must control their ionic and pH balance as well as their osmotic concentration. This may require the removal of certain ions from cells and body fluids and their release into the environment. The end products of metabolism of nitrogenous (nitrogen-containing) compounds such as amino acids and nucleic acids must also be eliminated. Water serves as a solvent for these waste products, and their elimination is thus closely tied to maintaining osmolality. For terrestrial animals, maintenance of osmotic concentration while eliminating nitrogenous wastes is a challenge, particularly since many animals may confront wet and dry seasonal conditions.

43.1d Animals Excrete Nitrogen Compounds as Metabolic Wastes

The metabolism of ingested food is a source of both energy and molecules for the biosynthetic activities of an animal. Importantly, metabolism of ingested food produces water, *metabolic water,* that is used in chemical reactions as well as being involved in physiological processes such as the excretion of wastes.

The proteins, amino acids, and nucleic acids in food are continually broken down as part of digestion (see Chapter 41) and from the constant turnover and replacement of these molecules in body cells. The nitrogenous products of this breakdown are excreted by most animals as *ammonia, urea,* or *uric acid* or a combination of these substances **(Figure 43.3).** The particular molecule or combination of molecules depends on a balance among toxicity, water conservation, and energy requirements.

Ammonia. Ammonia (NH_3) results from the metabolism of amino acids and proteins and is highly toxic: it can be safely transported and excreted from the body only in dilute solutions. Those animals with a plentiful supply of water, such as aquatic or marine invertebrates, teleost fish, and larval amphibians, excrete ammonia as their primary nitrogenous waste. Other animals detoxify ammonia by converting it to urea or uric acid.

Urea. All mammals, most amphibians, some reptiles, some marine fishes, and some terrestrial invertebrates combine ammonia with HCO_3^- and convert the product in a series of steps to *urea,* a soluble substance that is less toxic than ammonia. Although producing urea requires more energy than forming ammonia, excreting urea instead of ammonia requires much less water.

Uric Acid. Water is conserved further in some animals, including many terrestrial invertebrates, reptiles, and birds, by the formation of uric acid instead of ammonia or urea. Uric acid is nontoxic, but its great advantage is its low solubility. During the concentration of the urine in the final stages of its formation, the uric acid precipitates as crystals that can be expelled with minimal water. (The white substance in bird droppings is uric acid.) The embryos of reptiles and birds, which develop within leathery or hard-shelled eggs that are impermeable to liquids, also conserve water by forming uric acid, which is stored as a waste product inside the shell. Similarly, the pupae of insects store uric acid in the rectum.

Many animals have the capacity to form all three products of nitrogen metabolism. Mammalian urine, for example, contains small amounts of uric acid, although urea predominates. Some tree frogs, such as *Phyllomedusa sauvagei,* have uric acid as their principal excretory product. This has enabled them to exploit the woodlands of South America, where the dry season is extremely arid. Conversely, the American cockroach, *Periplaneta americana,* an insect that normally lives

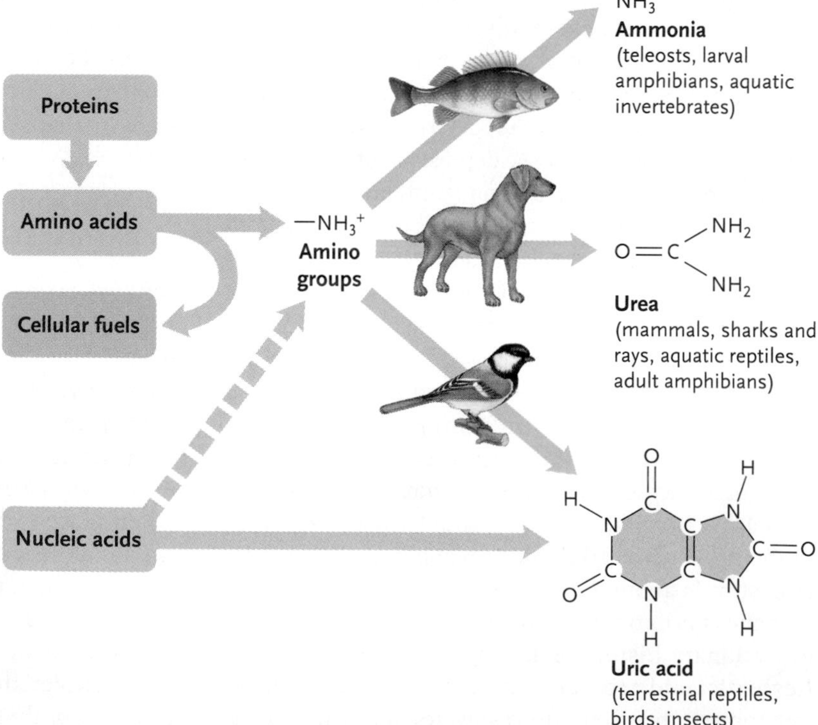

Figure 43.3
Nitrogenous wastes excreted by different animal groups. Although humans and other mammals primarily excrete urea, they also excrete small amounts of ammonia and uric acid.

in damp environments, uses ammonia as its primary excretory product and stores uric acid in special cells during periods when water is less available.

Sharks and rays maintain their osmotic concentration near that of their marine environment by retaining urea in their tissues and blood.

In the following sections, we look at the specifics of osmoregulation and excretion in different animal groups, beginning with the invertebrates.

STUDY BREAK

1. Define osmolality.
2. What are the sources of ammonia, urea, and uric acid in excretory products?

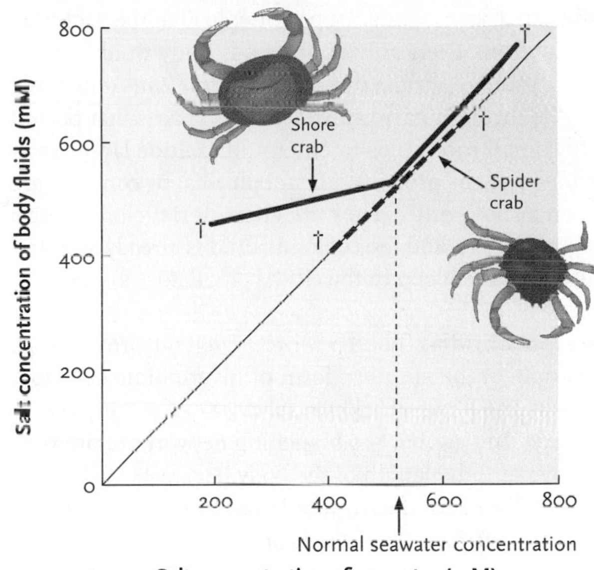

Figure 43.4 The concentration of the body fluids of two crabs when immersed in seawater of different concentrations. The spider crab lives in the sea, where it is not exposed to variation in the concentration of the water. The concentration of its fluids follows the 45° line that marks equivalency between the seawater and the body fluid concentration. By contrast, the shore crab, which lives in the intertidal zone and in estuaries, can regulate its body fluids to some degree. The crosses at the end of each line indicate the concentration at which each crab dies. Note that osmotic concentrations were not measured in this experiment.

43.2 Osmoregulation and Excretion in Invertebrates

Both osmoconformers and osmoregulators occur among the invertebrates, and most carry out excretion by specialized excretory structures.

43.2a Osmoconformers and Osmoregulators

Many marine invertebrates (sponges, cnidarians, some molluscs, and echinoderms) are osmoconformers. If placed in dilute solutions of seawater, they increase in weight because of the entry of water. They release nitrogenous wastes, usually in the form of ammonia, directly from body cells to the surrounding seawater. The cells of these animals do not normally swell or shrink because the osmotic concentrations of their intracellular and extracellular fluids and the surrounding seawater are the same, about 1000 mOsm/kg. Although they do not expend energy to maintain their osmolality, osmoconformers do expend energy to keep some ions, such as Na^+, at concentrations different from the concentration in seawater.

In general, the invertebrates that spend their entire lives in the open sea, where the environment is osmotically stable, have very little capacity for osmoregulation. Thus, many marine molluscs, such as squid and octopus, are osmoconformers, as are most marine arthropods, such as lobsters.

Other marine invertebrates are more diverse in their responses to variations in the osmotic concentration of the environment. Invertebrates living in the intertidal zone or at the mouths of tidal rivers experience regular changes in the osmotic concentration of their environment. Some marine annelids and arthropods that live in such environments are capable of short-term osmoregulation, slowing or delaying the changes in osmotic concentration of their body fluids that result from dilution of seawater by the outflow from rivers **(Figure 43.4)**. Some animals that live in the intertidal zone use behavioural responses, such as closing their shells (mussels and clams) or retreating into burrows (some annelids) to avoid desiccation when the tide is out.

By contrast, all freshwater and terrestrial invertebrates are osmoregulators. Those that live in aquatic environments are faced with a potential influx of water, diluting their body fluids. Although osmoregulation is energetically expensive, these invertebrates can live in more varied habitats than osmoconformers can.

The internal hyperosmocity of freshwater osmoregulators such as flatworms and mussels causes water to move constantly from the surroundings into their bodies. This excess water must be excreted, at a considerable cost in energy, to maintain this hyperosmocity. These animals obtain the salts they need from foods and by actively transporting salt ions from the water into their bodies (even freshwater contains some dissolved salts). This active ion transport occurs through the body surface or gills.

Terrestrial osmoregulators include annelids (earthworms), arthropods (insects, spiders and mites, millipedes, and centipedes), and molluscs (land snails and slugs). Although they do not have to excrete water entering by osmosis, they must constantly replace water lost from their bodies by evaporation and by excretion. Most obtain water from their food, and some drink water. Like their freshwater relatives, these invertebrates must obtain salts from their surroundings, usually in their foods.

43.2b Specialized Excretory Tubules Participate in Osmoregulation

Most invertebrates (except marine osmoconformers) use specialized tubular structures for carrying out excretion. These include *protonephridia* in flatworms and larval molluscs, *metanephridia* in annelids and most adult molluscs, and *Malpighian tubules* in insects and other arthropods. In protonephridia, the excretory tubules are open only at one end. Body fluids do not enter protonephridia directly. An *ultrafiltrate* enters the tubule through narrow extracellular spaces that permit only small molecules to enter and exclude larger molecules such as proteins. Metanephridia, by contrast, are open at both ends. They are characteristic of animals with coeloms, and the coelomic fluid is already an ultrafiltrate of the blood in the closed circulatory system.

Protonephridia. The flatworm *Dugesia* provides an example of the simplest form of invertebrate excretory tubule, the *protonephridium* (*proto* = before; *nephros* = kidney). In *Dugesia*, two branching networks of protonephridia run the length of the body **(Figure 43.5).** The cell at the blind end of each tubule has a bundle of cilia on its inner surface. The synchronous beating of the cilia resembles the flickering of a flame, and these cells are called *flame cells.* The cilia help draw a filtrate of body fluids through very small spaces between the cell membranes of the flame cell and those of the adjacent tubule cell and propel the filtrate along the tubule. As the fluids pass along the tubule, some molecules and ions are reabsorbed, whereas others are secreted into the tubules. The urine resulting from this filtration system is released through pores that connect the network of protonephridia to the body surface. The principal nitrogenous excretory product is ammonia. Although some ammonia passes out in the urine, most of it passes through the body wall.

Metanephridia. Animals with metanephridia have coelomic cavities (see Chapter 26) that are separate from the circulatory system. The fluid in the coelom is a filtrate of the haemolymph or blood. Coelomic fluid enters the proximal end of the excretory tubule, and ions and other solutes are reabsorbed or secreted as the fluid moves

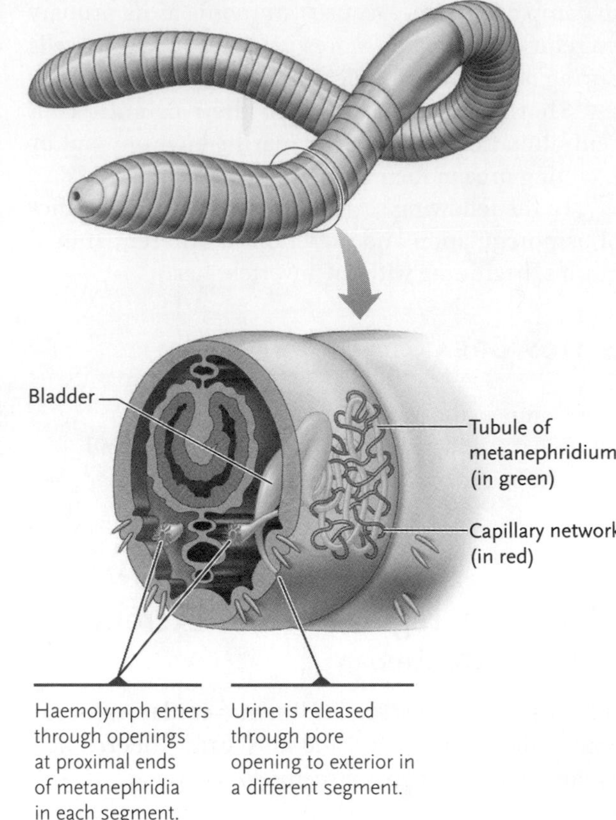

Figure 43.6
A metanephridium of an earthworm.

along the tubule. In annelids, the **metanephridium** **(Figure 43.6)** is a segmental structure. The proximal ends of a pair of metanephridia are located in each body segment, one on each side of the animal. A funnel-like opening surrounded by cilia admits coelomic fluid. Each tubule of the pair extends into the following segment, where it bends and folds into a convoluted arrangement surrounded by a network of blood vessels. Reabsorption and secretion of specific molecules and ions take place in the convoluted section. Urine from the distal end of the tubule collects in a saclike storage organ, the *bladder,* from where it is released through a pore in the surface of the segment.

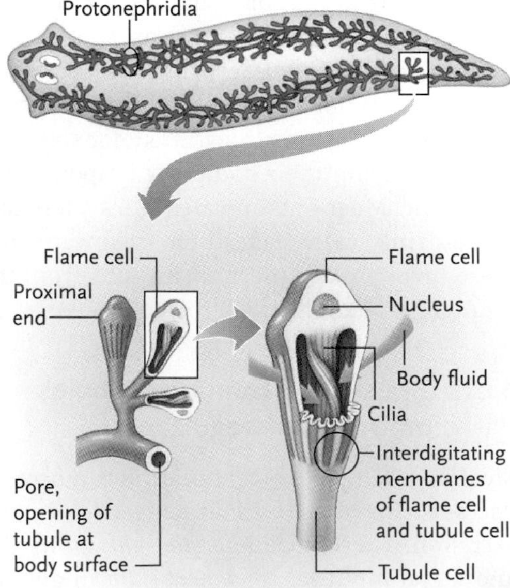

Figure 43.5
The protonephridia of the planarian *Dugesia*, showing the flame cells.

Malpighian Tubules. The excretory tubules of insects, the *Malpighian tubules,* have a closed proximal end that is immersed in the haemolymph **(Figure 43.7).** The distal ends of the tubules empty into the gut. The fluid in the tubules results primarily from secretion, although in some insects, an ultrafiltrate of the haemolymph may enter the upper part of the tubule through extracellular spaces. In particular, uric acid and several ions, including Na^+ and K^+, are actively secreted into the tubules. As the concentration of these substances rises, water moves osmotically from the haemolymph into the tubule. The fluid then passes into the hindgut (intestine and rectum) of the insect as dilute urine. Cells in the hindgut wall actively reabsorb most of the Na^+ and K^+ back into the haemolymph, and water

Life on the Edge
Surviving Drought

Some organisms live in temporary aquatic environments, consisting of ponds that dry up completely during periods of prolonged drought. One survival strategy involves complete desiccation of the animal, leading to anhydrobiosis (life without water). For example, the aquatic larvae of a midge (a small dipteran), *Polypedilum vanderplanki* **(Figure 1),** inhabit pools in Africa that can dry up completely for long periods. The larvae construct nests of mud, but within these nests, their water content is almost completely eliminated, and signs of life are absent. These desiccated larvae can withstand exposure to temperatures as low as −270°C and as high as +106°C. Immersed in water, the larvae recover within less than an hour, even after as long as 17 years of life without water. The precise mechanisms are not fully understood, but the animals accumulate high concentrations of the disaccharide trehalose as they enter the anhydrobiotic state. This sugar is thought to form a glasslike structure that prevents the formation of crystals that would damage the cells. Similar mechanisms are known in yeasts and other microorganisms.

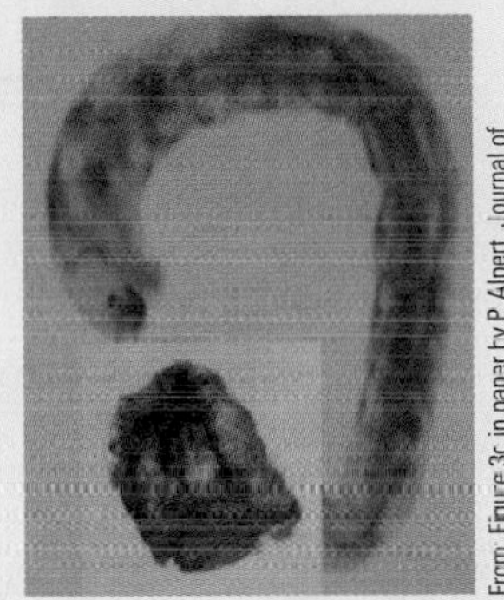

From: Figure 3c in paper by P. Alpert, Journal of Experimental Biology vol 209 p 1579, 2006.

Figure 1
The larva of *Polypedilum vanderplanki* in its active state and (inset) fully desiccated.

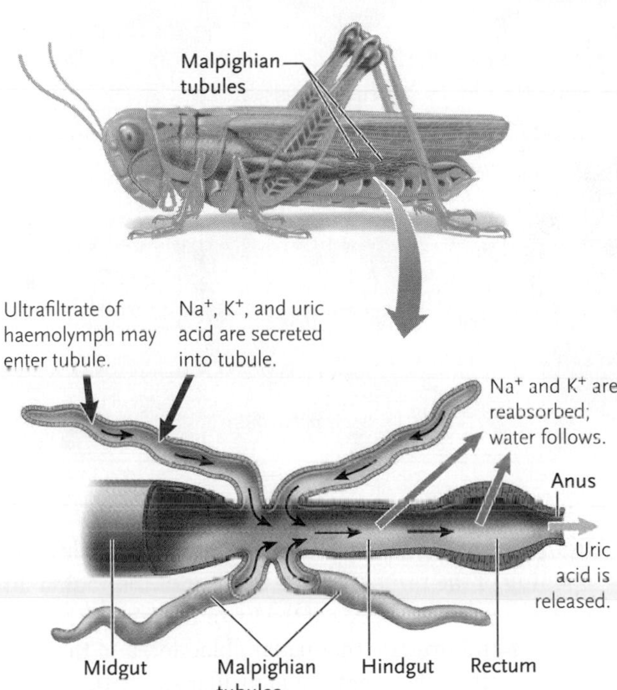

Figure 43.7
Excretion through Malpighian tubules in a grasshopper.

follows by osmosis. The uric acid left in the gut precipitates into crystals, which mix with the undigested matter in the rectum and are released with the faeces. This arrangement is important in conserving water.

Hydrostatic Skeleton. Nematodes have a hydrostatic skeleton that requires the maintenance of hydrostatic pressure in the body fluids against which the muscles can contract (see Chapter 26). Nematodes live in a wide range of environments, including marine, freshwater, terrestrial, and parasitic. They must maintain the osmotic concentration of their body fluids: a net entry of water would increase hydrostatic pressure, and a net loss of water would reduce the pressure. Either of these would make it difficult for the animal to move. Most nematodes have a system of two or three cells with ducts that run the length of the animal and open to the outside. These function in osmoregulation in some nematodes but not in others.

The body wall is important in osmoregulation. Researchers have cut parasitic cod worms and made sausagelike sacs by removing the intestine and closing the cut ends with ligatures. The sacs are capable of maintaining the internal osmotic concentration in environments of different osmotic concentrations.

Study Break

1. How does a protonephridium differ from a metanephridium?
2. What is the excretory product of most insects? How does it get into the urine?

43.3 Osmoregulation and Excretion in Mammals

In all vertebrates, specialized excretory tubules contribute to osmoregulation and excretion. The excretory tubules, called **nephrons**, are located in a specialized organ, the kidney. We begin our survey of vertebrate osmoregulation and excretion with a description of the structure and function of the mammalian kidney.

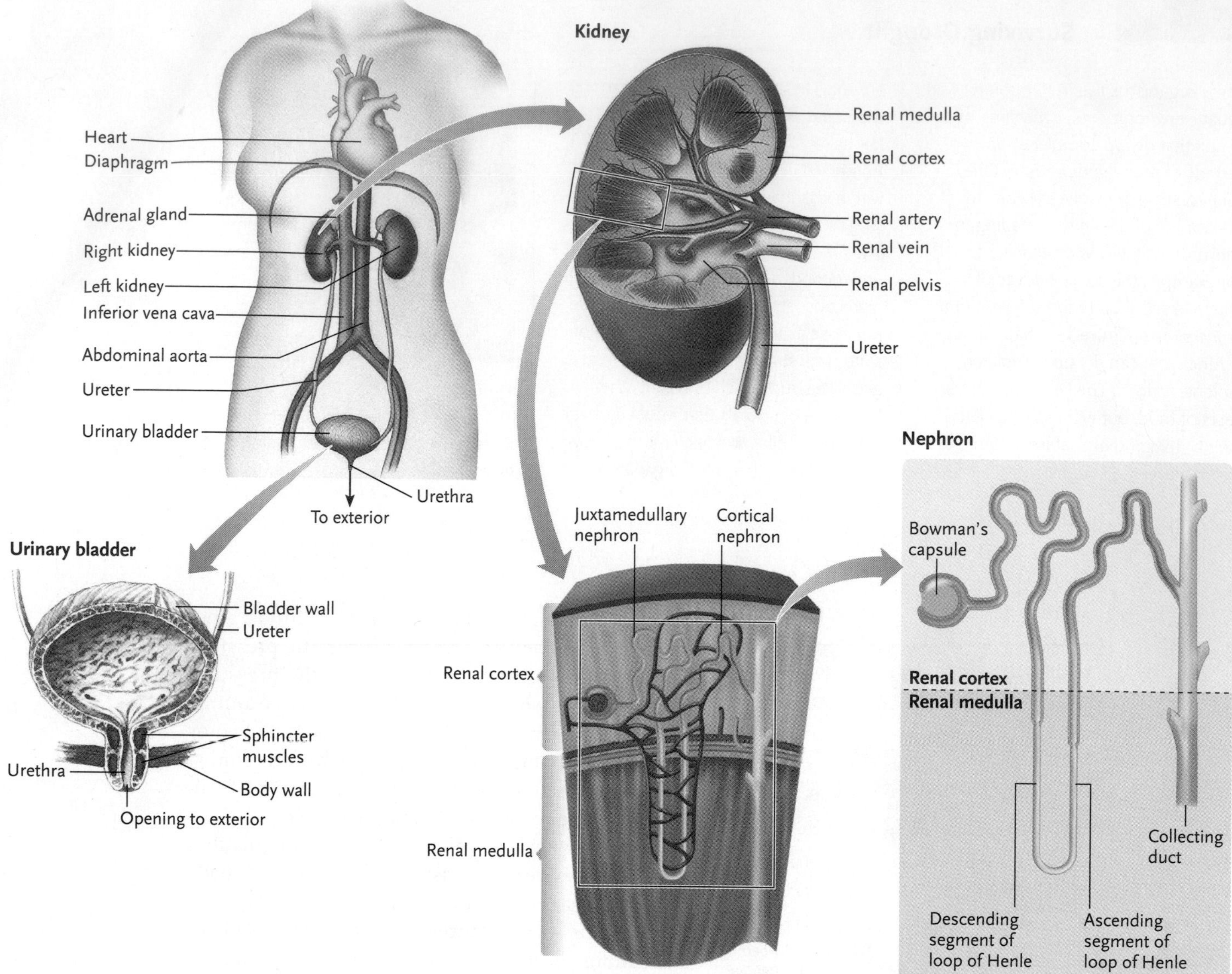

Figure 43.8
Human kidneys and urinary system in a female.

43.3a The Kidneys, Ureters, Bladder, and Urethra Constitute the Urinary System

Mammals have a pair of kidneys, located on each side of the vertebral column at the dorsal side of the abdominal cavity **(Figure 43.8)**. Internally, the mammalian kidney is divided into an outer **renal cortex** surrounding a central region, the **renal medulla**.

A **renal artery** carries blood to each kidney, where metabolic wastes and excess ions are moved into the urine by the action of the nephrons. The blood is routed away from the kidney by the **renal vein**. The urine leaving individual nephrons is processed further in **collecting ducts** and then drains into a central cavity in the kidney called the **renal pelvis**.

From the renal pelvis, the urine flows through a tube called the **ureter** to the **urinary bladder**, a storage sac located outside the kidneys. Urine leaves the bladder through another tube, the **urethra**, which opens to the outside. Two sphincter muscles control the flow of urine from the bladder to the urethra. In human females, the opening of the urethra is just in front of the vagina; in males, the urethra opens at the tip of the penis. The two kidneys and ureters, the urinary bladder, and the urethra constitute the mammalian urinary system.

43.3b Regions of Nephrons Have Specialized Functions

Mammalian nephrons are differentiated into regions that perform successive steps in excretion. At its proximal end, a nephron forms **Bowman's capsule**, an infolded region that cups around a ball of blood capillaries called the **glomerulus (Figure 43.9)**. The capsule and glomerulus are located in the renal cortex. Filtration takes place as fluids are forced into Bowman's capsule from the capillaries of the glomerulus.

Following Bowman's capsule, the nephron forms a **proximal convoluted tubule** in the renal cortex, which descends into the medulla in a U-shaped bend called

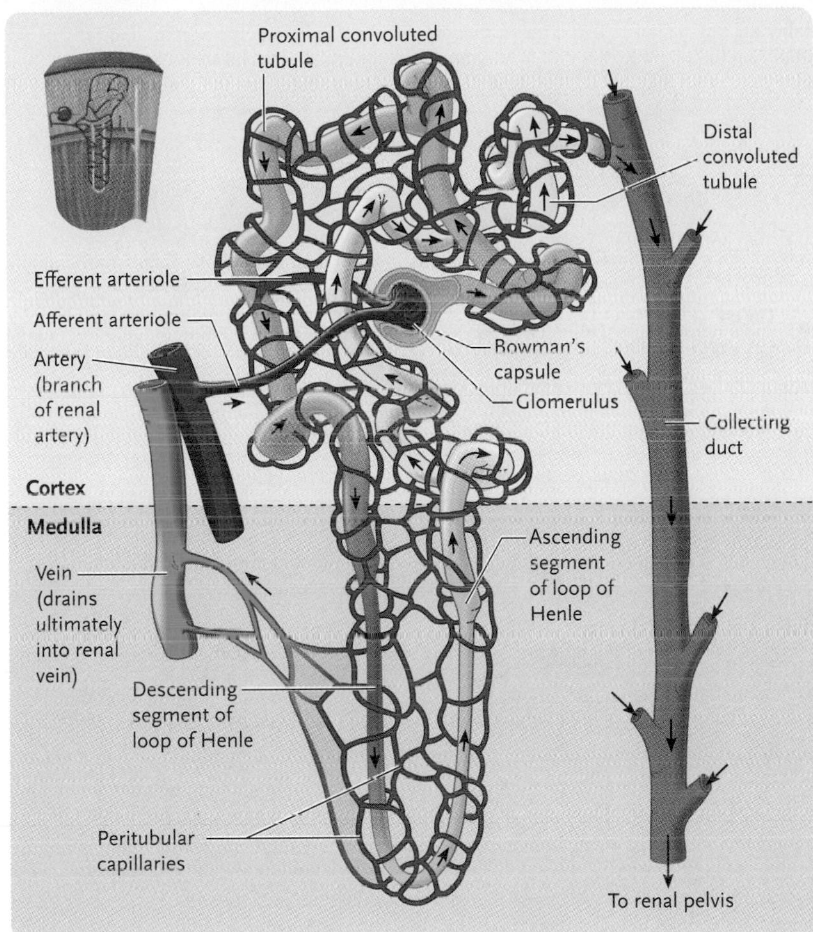

Figure 43.9
A nephron and its blood circulation.

the **loop of Henle** and then ascends again to form a **distal convoluted tubule.** The distal tubule drains the urine into a branching system of collecting ducts that lead to the renal pelvis. As many as eight nephrons may drain into a single branch. The combined activities of the proximal convoluted tubule, the loop of Henle, the distal convoluted tubule, and the collecting duct convert the filtrate that entered the nephron at the Bowman's capsule into urine.

Unlike most capillaries in the body, the capillaries in the glomerulus do not lead directly to venules. Instead, they form another arteriole that branches into a second capillary network called the **peritubular capillaries.** These capillaries thread around the proximal and distal convoluted tubules and the loop of Henle. Some molecules and ions are reabsorbed into the peritubular capillaries, whereas others are secreted from the blood into the nephron. However, because the capillaries and the tubules are not in physical contact due to the interstitial fluid between them, this transfer is not direct. Instead, the molecules or ions leave the tubule by passing through the one-cell-thick wall, diffuse through the interstitial fluid, and then pass into the capillary through its wall.

Each human kidney has more than a million nephrons. Of these, about 20% (the *juxtamedullary nephrons*) have long loops that descend deeply into the medulla of the kidney. The remaining 80% (the *cortical nephrons*) have shorter loops, most of which are located entirely in the cortex, and the remainder of which extend only partway into the medulla.

43.3c Nephrons and Other Kidney Structures Produce Hyperosmotic Urine

In mammals, urine is hyperosmotic to body fluids. Except for a few aquatic bird species, all other vertebrates produce urine that is hypoosmotic to body fluids or is at best isoosmotic. Production of hyperosmotic urine, a water-conserving adaptation, involves the activities of the mammalian nephron and an interaction between nephrons and the highly ordered structure of the mammalian kidney. Three features interact to conserve nutrients and water, balance salts, and concentrate wastes for excretion from the body:

- the arrangement of the loop of Henle, which descends into the medulla and returns to the cortex again;
- differences in the permeability of successive regions of the nephron, established by a specific group of membrane transport proteins in each region; and
- a gradient in the concentration of molecules and ions in the interstitial fluid of the kidney, which increases gradually from the renal cortex to the deepest levels of the renal medulla.

Researchers determined the transport activities of specific regions of nephrons by dissecting them out of an animal and experimentally manipulating them in vitro. They placed segments in different buffered solutions and passed solutions containing various components of filtrates through the segment. By labelling specific molecules or ions radioactively, the scientists followed the movements of molecules in the solution surrounding the nephron segment or in the filtrate.

43.3d Filtration in Bowman's Capsule Begins the Process of Excretion

The mechanisms of excretion (**Figure 43.10, p. 1066,** and summarized in **Table 43.1, p. 1066,**) begin in Bowman's capsule. The cells forming the walls of the capillaries surrounding Bowman's capsule, and the cells of the

Figure 43.10
The movement of ions, water, and other molecules to and from nephrons and collecting tubules in the human kidney. Nephrons in other mammals and in birds work in similar fashion. The numbers are osmolality values in mOsm/kg.

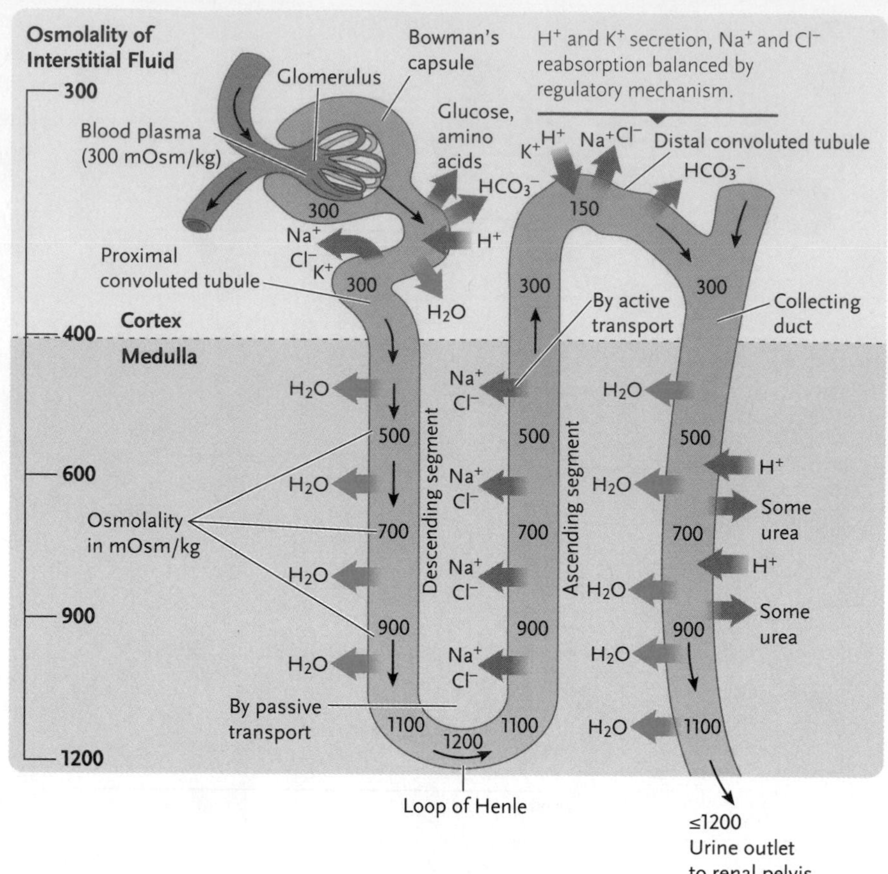

Table 43.1 **Filtration, Reabsorption, and Secretion in Nephrons and Collecting Ducts**

Segment	Location	Permeability and Movement	Osmolality of Filtrate and Urine	Result of Passage
Bowman's capsule	Cortex	Water, ions, small nutrients, and nitrogenous wastes move through spaces between epithelia	300 mOsm/kg, same as surrounding interstitial fluid	Water and small substances, but not proteins, pass into nephron
Proximal convoluted tubule	Cortex	Na^+ and K^+ actively reabsorbed, Cl^- follows; water leaves through aquaporins; H^+ actively secreted; HCO_3^- reabsorbed into plasma of peritubular capillaries; glucose, amino acids, and other nutrients actively reabsorbed	300 mOsm/kg	67% of ions, 65% of water, 50% of urea, and all nutrients return to interstitial fluid; pH maintained
Descending segment of loop of Henle	Cortex into medulla	Water leaves through aquaporins; no movement of ions or urea	From 300 mOsm/kg at top to 1200 mOsm/kg at bottom of loop	Additional water returned to interstitial fluid
Ascending segment of loop of Henle	Medulla into cortex	Na^+ and Cl^- actively transported out; no entry of water; no movement of urea	From 1200 mOsm/kg at bottom to 150 mOsm/kg at top of loop	Additional ions returned to interstitial fluid
Distal convoluted tubule	Cortex	K^+ and Na^+ secreted via active transport into urine; Na^+ and Cl^- reabsorbed; water moves into urine through aquaporins; HCO_3^- reabsorbed into plasma of peritubular capillaries	From 150 mOsm/kg at beginning to 300 mOsm/kg at junction with collecting duct	Ion balance, pH balance
Collecting ducts	Cortex through medulla, empties into renal pelvis	Water moves out via aquaporins; no movement of ions; some urea leaves at bottom of duct	From 300 mOsm/kg to 1200 mOsm/kg at junction with renal pelvis	More water and some urea returned to interstitial fluid; some H^+ added to urine

Molecule Behind Biology

Aquaporins: Facilitating Osmotic Water Transport

Aquaporins are membrane proteins that form channels through which water can diffuse more rapidly than it would otherwise do. They are widely distributed, occurring in organisms from bacteria and yeast to mammals. In humans, at least 10 different aquaporins are known. The very narrow pores **(Figure 1)** permit water molecules to pass in single file, but because the molecules forming the channel are charged, other molecules of similar dimensions, such as H_3O^+, are excluded. The water moves in either direction in response to osmotic gradients: a single channel can permit as many as 3 billion molecules to cross the membrane per second.

Aquaporins are important in the functioning of mammalian kidneys. For example, one aquaporin, aquaporin-2, resides on the membranes of vesicles within the cells of the collecting ducts. If the osmotic concentration of the body fluids increases, antidiuretic hormone from the pituitary gland causes the aquaporins from the vesicles to be inserted into the membrane of the cells of the collecting ducts. The presence of more aquaporins in the membrane greatly increases the rate of osmotic reabsorption of water. The urine becomes more concentrated, and the osmotic concentration of body fluids is reduced.

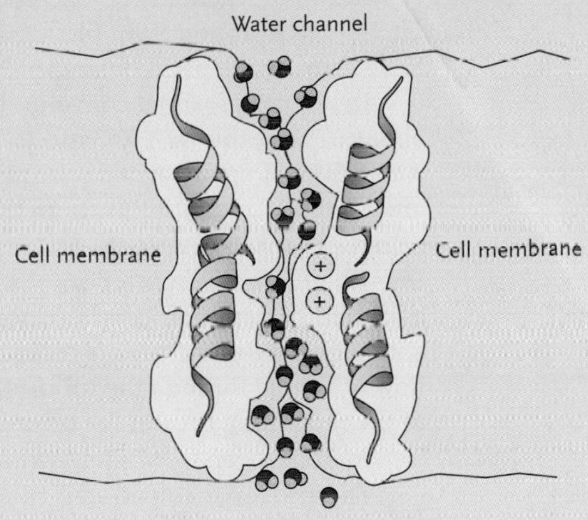

Figure 1
An aquaporin channel.

capsule itself, are separated by spaces just wide enough to admit water, ions, small nutrient molecules such as glucose and amino acids, and nitrogenous waste molecules, primarily urea. The higher pressure of the blood drives fluid containing these molecules and ions from the capillaries of the glomerulus into the capsule. A thin net of connective tissue between the capillary and Bowman's capsule epithelia contributes to the filtering process. Blood cells and plasma proteins are too large to pass and are retained inside the capillaries. The fluid entering the capsule is an ultrafiltrate of the blood.

Two factors help maintain the pressure driving fluid into Bowman's capsule. First, the diameters of the arteriole delivering blood to the glomerulus (called the **afferent arteriole**) and of the capillaries of the glomerulus itself are larger than that of arterioles and capillaries elsewhere in the body. The larger diameter maintains blood pressure by presenting less resistance to blood flow. Second, the diameter of the arteriole that receives blood from the glomerulus (called the **efferent arteriole**) is smaller than the diameter of the afferent arteriole, producing a damming effect that backs up the blood in the glomerulus and helps keep the pressure high.

In humans, Bowman's capsules collectively filter about 180 L of fluid each day, from a daily total of 1400 L of blood that pass through the kidneys. The human body contains only about 2.75 L of blood plasma, meaning that the kidneys filter a fluid volume equivalent to 65 times the volume of the blood plasma each day. On average, more than 99% of the filtrate, mostly water, is reabsorbed in the nephrons, leaving about 1.5 L to be excreted daily as urine.

43.3e Reabsorption and Secretion in the Nephron

The fluid filtered into Bowman's capsule contains water, other small molecules, and ions at the same concentrations as the blood plasma. By the time the fluid reaches the distal end of the collecting duct, reabsorption out of and secretion into the tubules and collecting duct have markedly altered the concentrations of all components of the filtrate.

The Proximal Convoluted Tubule. Reabsorption of water, ions, and nutrients back into the interstitial fluid is the main function of the proximal convoluted tubule. Na^+/K^+ pumps in the epithelium of the proximal convoluted tubule move Na^+ and K^+ from the filtrate into the interstitial fluid surrounding the tubule (see Figure 43.10). The movement of positive charges sets up a voltage gradient that causes Cl^- ions to be reabsorbed out of the tubule with the positive ions. Specific active transport proteins reabsorb essentially all the glucose, amino acids, and other nutrient molecules out of the filtrate into the interstitial fluid, making the filtrate hypoosmotic to the interstitial fluid surrounding the tubule. As a result, water moves from the tubule into the interstitial fluid by osmosis. The osmotic movement is aided by *aquaporins,* proteins that form passages for water molecules in the transport epithelium of the tubule cells (see *Molecule Behind Biology*). The nutrients and water that entered the interstitial fluid move into the capillaries of the peritubular network.

Some substances are secreted from the interstitial fluid into the tubule, primarily H^+ ions by active transport and the products of detoxified poisons by passive secretion (detoxification takes place in the liver).

Small amounts of ammonia are also secreted into the tubule. The secretion of H^+ ions into the filtrate helps balance the acidity constantly generated in the body by metabolic reactions. H^+ secretion is coupled with HCO_3^- reabsorption from the filtrate in the tubule to the plasma in the peritubular capillaries.

In all, the proximal convoluted tubule reabsorbs about 67% of the Na^+, K^+, and Cl^- ions; 65% of the water; 50% of the urea; and essentially all the glucose, amino acids, and other nutrient molecules from the filtrate. The ions, nutrients, and water reabsorbed by the tubule are transported into the interstitial fluid and then into capillaries of the peritubular network. Although 50% of the urea is reabsorbed, the constant flow of filtrate through the tubules, and the excretion of the remaining urea in the urine, keeps the concentration of nitrogenous wastes low in body fluids.

The proximal convoluted tubule has structural specializations that fit its function. The epithelial cells that make up its walls are carpeted on their inner surface by a brush border of microvilli. These microvilli greatly increase the surface area available for reabsorption and secretion.

The Descending Segment of the Loop of Henle. The filtrate flows from the proximal convoluted tubule into the descending segment of the loop of Henle, where water is reabsorbed. As this tubule segment descends, it passes through regions of increasingly higher solute concentrations in the interstitial fluid of the medulla (shown in Figure 43.10). (The generation of this concentration gradient is described later.) As a result, more water moves out of the tubule by osmosis as the fluid travels through the descending segment.

The descending segment has aquaporins, which allow the rapid transport of water but it has no other transport proteins. The outward movement of water concentrates the molecules and ions inside the tubule, gradually increasing the osmolality of the fluid to a peak of about 1200 mOsm/kg at the bottom of the loop. This is the same as the osmolality of the interstitial fluid at the bottom of the medulla.

The Ascending Segment of the Loop of Henle. The fluid then moves into the ascending segment of the loop of Henle, where Na^+ and Cl^- are reabsorbed into the interstitial fluid. As this segment ascends, it passes through regions of gradually lessening osmolality in the interstitial fluid of the medulla. The ascending segment has membrane proteins that transport salt ions but lacks aquaporins. Because water is trapped in the ascending segment, the osmolality of the urine is reduced as salt ions, primarily Na^+ and Cl^-, move out of the tubule.

In the part of the ascending segment immediately following the bottom of the loop, the ion concentrations in the tubule filtrate are still high enough to move Na^+ and Cl^- out of the tubule by passive diffusion. Toward the top of the segment, they are moved out by active transport. Besides reducing the osmolality of the filtrate in the ascending segment, the reabsorption of salt ions from the tubule into the interstitial fluid helps establish the concentration gradient of the medulla, high near the renal pelvis and low near the renal cortex. The energy required to transport NaCl from higher levels of the ascending segment makes the kidneys one of the major ATP-consuming organs of the body.

By the time the fluid reaches the cortex at the top of the ascending loop, its osmolality has dropped to about 150 mOsm/kg. During the travel of fluid around the entire loop of Henle, water, nutrients, and ions have been conserved and returned to body fluids, and the total volume of the filtrate in the nephron has been greatly reduced. Urea and other nitrogenous wastes have been concentrated in the filtrate. Little secretion into the tubule occurs in either the descending or ascending segments of the loop of Henle.

The Distal Convoluted Tubule. The transport epithelium of the distal convoluted tubule removes additional water from the filtrate in the tubule and works to balance the salt and bicarbonate concentrations of the filtrate against body fluids. In response to hormones triggered by changes in the body's salt concentrations, varying amounts of K^+ and H^+ ions are secreted into the filtrate, and varying amounts of Na^+ and Cl^- ions are reabsorbed. Bicarbonate ions are reabsorbed from the filtrate as in the proximal tubule.

In total, more ions move outward than inward in the distal tubule, and as a consequence, water moves out of the tubule by osmosis through aquaporins. The amounts of urea and other nitrogenous wastes remain the same. By the time the filtrate, now urine, enters the collecting ducts at the end of the nephron, its osmolality is about 300 mOsm/kg.

The Collecting Ducts. The collecting ducts concentrate the urine. These ducts, which are permeable to water but not to salt ions, descend downward from the cortex through the medulla of the kidney. As the ducts descend, they travel through the gradient of increasing solute concentration in the medulla. This increase makes water move osmotically out of the ducts and greatly increases the concentration of the urine, which can become as high as 1200 mOsm/kg at the bottom of the medulla. Near the bottom of the medulla, the walls of the collecting ducts contain passive urea transporters that allow a portion of this nitrogenous waste to pass from the duct into the interstitial fluid. This urea adds significantly to the concentration gradient of solutes in the medulla.

In addition to these mechanisms, H^+ ions are actively secreted into the fluid by the same mechanism as in the proximal and distal convoluted tubules. The balance of the H^+ and bicarbonate ions established in the urine, interstitial fluid, and blood, achieved by secretion of H^+ into the urine by the nephrons and collecting ducts, is important for regulating the pH of blood and body fluids. The kidneys thus provide a safety valve if the acidity of body fluids rises beyond levels that can be controlled by the blood's buffer system (see Chapter 42).

At its maximum value of 1200 mOsm/kg, reached when water conservation is at its maximum, the urine reaching the bottom of the collecting ducts is about four times more concentrated than body fluids. But it can also be as low as 50 to 70 mOsm/kg, when very dilute urine is produced in response to conditions such as excessive water intake.

The high osmolality of the interstitial fluid toward the bottom of the medulla would damage the medulla cells if they were not protected against osmotic water loss. The protection comes from high concentrations of otherwise inert organic molecules called *osmolytes* in these cells. The osmolytes, of which the most important is a sugar-alcohol called *sorbitol* (see Chapter 41, *Molecule Behind Biology*), raise the osmolality of the cells to match that of the surrounding interstitial fluid. Urine flows from the end of the collecting ducts into the renal pelvis and then through the ureters into the urinary bladder, where it is stored. From the bladder, urine exits through the urethra to the outside.

43.3f Terrestrial Mammals Have Water-Conserving Adaptations

Terrestrial mammals have other adaptations that complement the water-conserving activities of the kidneys. One is the location of the lungs deep inside the body, which reduces water loss by evaporation during breathing (see Chapter 42). Another is a body covering of keratinized skin. Skin is so impermeable that it almost eliminates water loss by evaporation, except for the controlled loss through evaporation of sweat in mammals with sweat glands.

Among mammals, water-conserving adaptations reach their greatest efficiency in desert rodents such as the kangaroo rat (**Figure 43.11**). The proportion of nephrons with long loops extending deep into the kidney medulla of kangaroo rats is very high, allowing them to excrete urine that is 20 times more concentrated than body fluids. Further, most of the water in the feces is absorbed in the large intestine and rectum. Lacking sweat glands, they lose little water by evaporation from the body surface. Much of the moisture in their breath is condensed and recycled by specialized passages in the nasal cavities. They stay in burrows during daytime and come out to feed only at night.

About 90% of the kangaroo rat's daily water supply is generated from oxidative reactions in its cells. (Humans, in contrast, can make up only about 12% of their daily water needs from this source.) The remaining 10% of the kangaroo rat's water comes from its food. These structural and behavioural adaptations are so effective that a kangaroo rat can survive in the desert without ever drinking water.

	Kangaroo Rat	Human
Water gain (millilitres)		
From ingesting food	6.0	850
From drinking liquids	0.0	1400
By metabolism	54.0	350
	60.0	2600
Water loss (millilitres)		
In urine	13.5	1500
In feces	2.6	200
By evaporation	43.9	900
	60.0	2600

David Noble

Claude Steelman/Tom Stack & Associates

Figure 43.11
A comparison of the sources of water for a human and a kangaroo rat (*Dipodymus* species). Water conservation in the kangaroo rat is so efficient that the animal never has to drink water.

Marine mammals, including whales, seals, and manatees, eat foods that are high in salt content. They are able to survive the high salt intake because they produce urine that is more concentrated than seawater. As a result, they are easily able to excrete all the excess salt they ingest in their diet.

Study Break

1. Where does active transport of ions occur in the nephron?
2. What is the major event in the descending segment of the loop of Henle?
3. What is the major event in the collecting duct?

43.4 Kidney Function in Nonmammalian Vertebrates

Among nonmammalian vertebrates, only a few species of aquatic birds produce urine that is hyperosmotic to body fluids. The particular adaptations that maintain osmolality and water balance among these animals vary depending on whether retention of water or of salts is the major issue.

43.4a Marine Fishes Conserve Water and Excrete Salts

Marine teleosts live in seawater, which is strongly hyperosmotic to their body fluids. As a result, they continually lose water to their environment by osmosis and must replace it by continual drinking. The kidneys of marine teleosts play little role in regulating salt in their body fluids because they cannot produce hyperosmotic urine that would both remove salt and conserve water. Instead, excess Na^+, K^+, and Cl^- ions are eliminated from the body by specialized cells in the gills, called *chloride cells,* which actively transport Cl^- into the surrounding seawater; the Na^+ and K^+ ions are also actively transported to maintain electrical neutrality **(Figure 43.12a)**. Divalent ions in the ingested seawater, such as Ca^{2+} and Mg^{2+}, are removed by the kidneys in an isosmotic urine. On balance, a marine teleost is able to retain most of the water it drinks and eliminate most of the salt, allowing its tissue fluids to remain hypoosmotic to the surrounding water without producing hyperosmotic urine. The kidneys play little role in the removal of nitrogenous wastes; these are released from the gills, primarily as ammonia, by simple diffusion.

Sharks and rays have a different adaptation to seawater—the osmolality of their body fluids is maintained close to that of seawater by retaining high levels of urea in body fluids, along with another nitrogenous waste, *trimethylamine oxide*. Elasmobranchs (see Chapter 27) may have concentrations of urea as high as 1300 mg per 100 mL of blood. The match in osmolality keeps sharks and rays from losing water to the surrounding sea by osmosis, and they do not have to drink seawater continually to maintain their water balance. Excess salts ingested with food are excreted in the kidney and by specialized secretory cells in a *rectal salt gland* located near the anal opening. The importance of urea as an osmolyte is illustrated by those species of stingrays that inhabit freshwater. In such species, the concentration of urea is reduced to about 2 to 3 mg per 100 mL of blood.

Figure 43.12
The mechanisms balancing the water and salt content of **(a)** marine teleosts and **(b)** freshwater teleosts.

a. Marine teleosts

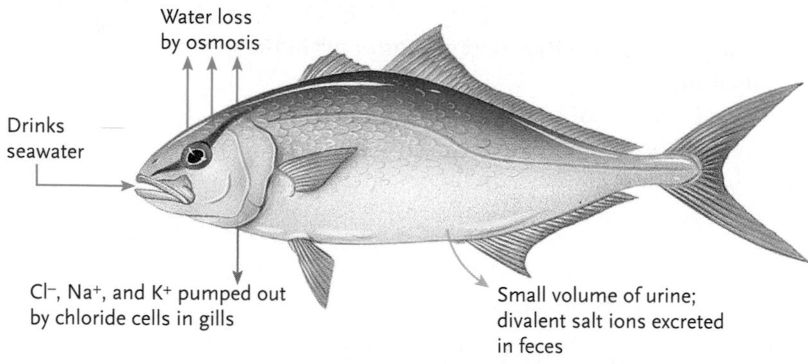

b. Freshwater teleosts

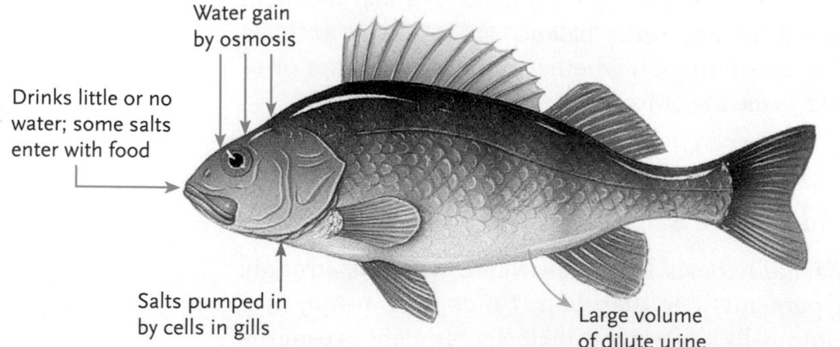

43.4b Freshwater Fishes and Amphibians Excrete Water and Conserve Salts

The body fluids of freshwater fishes and aquatic amphibians (no amphibians live in seawater) are hyperosmotic to the surrounding water, which usually ranges from about 1 to 10 mOsm/kg. Water therefore moves osmotically into their tissues. Such animals rarely drink, and they excrete large volumes of dilute urine to get rid of excess water **(Figure 43.12b).** In freshwater fishes, salt ions lost with the urine are replaced by salt in foods and by active transport of Na^+ and K^+ into the body by the gills; Cl^- follows to maintain electrical neutrality. Aquatic amphibians obtain salt in the diet and by active transport across the skin from the surrounding water. Nitrogenous wastes are excreted from the gills as ammonia in both freshwater fishes and aquatic amphibians.

Terrestrial amphibians must conserve both water and salt, which is obtained primarily in foods. In these animals, the kidneys secrete salt into the urine, causing water to enter the urine by osmosis. In the bladder, the salt is reclaimed by active transport and returned to body fluids. The water remains in the bladder, making the urine very dilute; during times of drought, the water can be resorbed. Terrestrial amphibians also have behavioural adaptations that help minimize water loss, such as seeking shaded, moist environments and remaining inactive during the day. Larval amphibians, which are completely aquatic, excrete nitrogenous wastes from their gills as ammonia.

Most adult amphibians excrete nitrogenous wastes through their kidneys as urea. The leaf frog, *Phyllomedusa sauvagii* **(Figure 43.13)**, however, produces uric acid as the principal nitrogenous waste. In addition, it secretes a waxy substance from glands in its skin and uses its legs to smear this over the entire surface, thereby minimizing water loss.

43.4c Reptiles and Birds Excrete Uric Acid to Conserve Water

Terrestrial reptiles and most birds conserve water by excreting nitrogenous wastes in the form of an almost water-free paste of uric acid crystals. Further water conservation occurs as the epithelial cells of the cloaca, the common exit for the digestive and excretory systems, absorb water from feces and urine before those wastes are eliminated. This arrangement is similar to the strategy used by insects, described

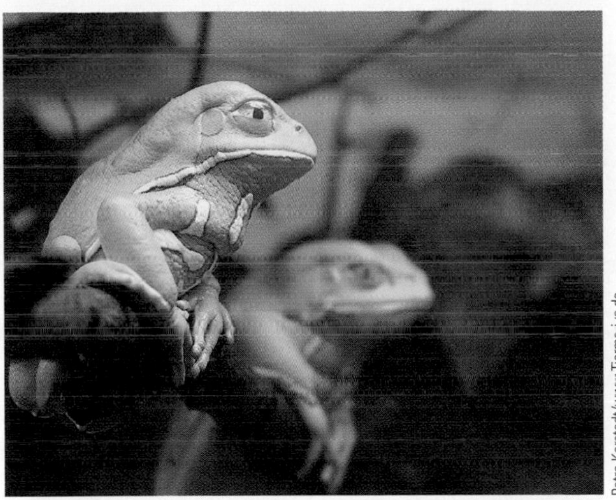

Figure 43.13
Phyllomedusa sauvagii is a tree frog that prospers in the dry woodlands of South America. Among its many adaptations to a dry environment are the production of uric acid and the secretion from skin glands of a waterproofing waxy material.

earlier. In reptiles, the scales covering the skin allow almost no water to escape through the body surface.

Reptiles and birds that live in or around seawater, including reptiles such as crocodilians, sea snakes, and sea turtles, and birds such as seagulls, penguins, and pelicans, take in large quantities of salt with their food and rarely or never drink freshwater. These animals typically excrete excess salt through specialized *salt glands* located in the head **(Figure 43.14)** that remove salts from the blood by active transport. The salts are secreted to the environment as a water solution in which salts are two to three times more concentrated than in body fluids. The secretion exits through the nostrils of birds and lizards, through the mouth of marine snakes, and as salty tears from the eye sockets of sea turtles and crocodilians.

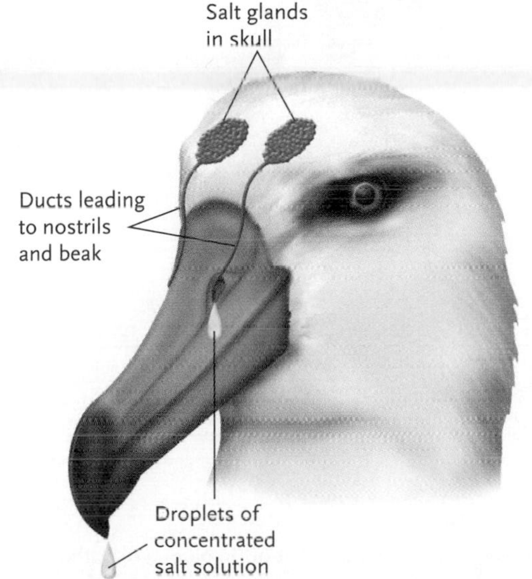

Figure 43.14
Salt glands in a bird living on a seacoast.

The adaptations described in this section allow animals to maintain the concentration of body fluids at levels that keep cells from swelling or shrinking and permit excretion of toxic wastes. An equally important challenge is maintaining an internal temperature that allows the organ systems to function with maximum efficiency. We look at these processes in the next section.

Study Break

1. What is the organ of osmoregulation in teleosts?
2. What excretory strategy is used by birds and reptiles to conserve water?
3. How do marine birds and reptiles excrete excess salts?

43.5 Introduction to Thermoregulation

Environmental temperatures vary enormously across Earth's surface. Temperatures in deserts in Australia, Africa, and the United States may reach 50°C, whereas some locations in the Antarctic experience −80°C. There are also seasonal variations. A single location in the boreal forest of Canada might experience temperatures as low as −40°C in the winter and as high as 35°C in the summer. However, animal cells can function only within a temperature range from about 0°C to 45°C. Not far below 0°C, the lipid bilayer of a biological membrane changes from a fluid to a frozen gel, which disrupts vital cell functions. Without protective measures, ice crystals will destroy the cell's organelles. At the other extreme, as temperatures approach 45°C, the kinetic motions of molecules become so great that most proteins and nucleic acids unfold from their functional form. Either condition leads quickly to cell death. Animals therefore usually maintain internal body temperatures somewhere within the 0°C to 45°C limits.

Temperature regulation (thermoregulation) is based on negative feedback pathways in which temperature receptors called *thermoreceptors* (see Chapter 34) detect changes from a temperature *set point*. Signals from the receptors trigger physiological and behavioural responses that return the temperature to the set point. The responses triggered by negative feedback mechanisms (see Chapter 32) involve adjustments in the rate of heat-generating oxidative reactions within the body, coupled with adjustments in the rate of heat gain or loss at the body surface. The particular adaptations that accomplish these responses vary widely among species, however. And although body temperature is closely regulated around a set point in all endotherms, the set point itself may vary over the course of a day and between seasons.

In this section, we describe the structures, mechanisms, and behavioural adaptations that enable animals to regulate their temperature.

43.5a Thermoregulation Allows Animals to Reach Optimal Physiological Performance

Within the 0°C to 45°C range of tolerable internal temperatures, an animal's *organismal performance* varies greatly. Organismal performance is a term that describes the rate and efficiency of an animal's biochemical, physiological, and whole-body processes. The speed at which the Middle Eastern lizard *Agama stellio* can sprint (one measure of organismal performance) is low when the animal's body temperature is cold, rises smoothly with body temperature until it levels to a fairly broad plateau, and then drops off dramatically with further increases in body temperature **(Figure 43.15a)**. Similar patterns of temperature dependence are observed for numerous other body functions **(Figure 43.15b)**. The range of temperatures that provides optimal organismal performance varies from one species to another.

Animals that maintain their body temperature within a fairly narrow optimal range can move quickly, digest food efficiently, and carry out necessary activities and processes rapidly and effectively (as shown in Figure 43.15b). In addition to keeping body temperatures within tolerable limits, thermoregulation allows animals to maintain an optimal level of organismal performance.

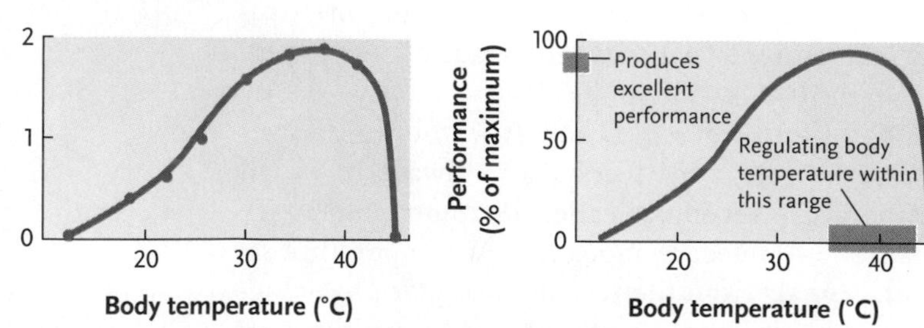

Figure 43.15
Body temperature and organismal performance. (a) The maximum sprint speed of a lizard (*Agama stellio*) changes dramatically with body temperature. **(b)** An animal's other behavioural and physiological processes respond to temperature changes in similar ways. The advantage of regulating body temperature within the range indicated by the bar on the horizontal axis is a high level of organismal performance, indicated by the bar on the vertical axis.

43.5b Animals Exchange Heat with Their Environments

As part of thermoregulation, animals exchange heat with their environment. Virtually all heat exchange occurs at surfaces where the body meets the external environment. As with all physical bodies, heat flows into animals if they are cooler than their surroundings and flows outward if they are warmer. This heat exchange occurs by four mechanisms: *conduction, convection, radiation,* and *evaporation* **(Figure 43.16)**.

Conduction is the flow of heat between atoms or molecules in direct contact. An animal loses heat by

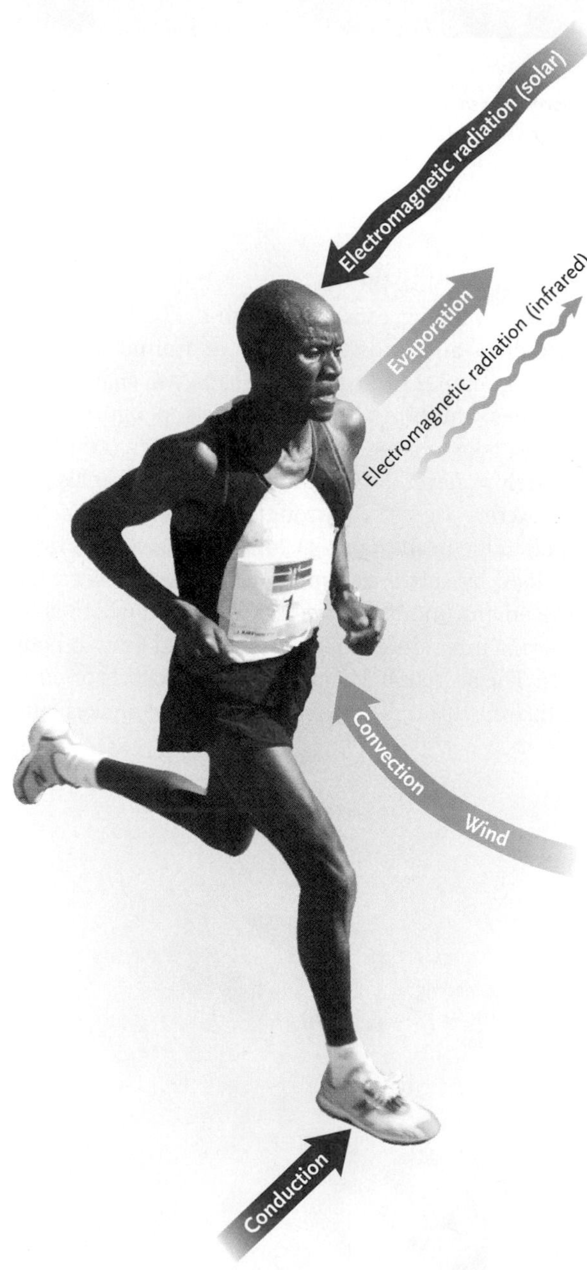

Figure 43.16
Heat flow into (in red) and out of (in blue) a marathon runner on a hot, sunny day. Unlike conduction, convection, and evaporation, which take place through the kinetic movement of molecules, electromagnetic radiation (infrared) is transmitted through space as waves of energy. (Photo: Rafael Winer/Corbis.)

conduction when it contacts a cooler object and gains heat when it contacts an object that is warmer. **Convection** is the transfer of heat from a body to a fluid (air or water) that passes over its surface. The movement maximizes heat transfer by replacing fluid that has absorbed or released heat with fluid at the original temperature. **Radiation** is the transfer of heat energy as electromagnetic radiation. Any object warmer than absolute zero (−273°C) radiates heat; as the object's temperature rises, the amount of heat it loses as radiation increases as well. Animals also gain heat through radiation, particularly by absorbing radiation from the Sun. **Evaporation** is heat transfer through the energy required to change a liquid to a gas. Evaporation of water from a surface is an efficient way to transfer heat; when the water in sweat evaporates from the body surface, the body cools down because heat is being transferred to the evaporated water in the surrounding air.

All animals gain or lose heat by a combination of these four mechanisms. A marathon runner or a bicycle racer struggling with the heat on a sunny summer day loses heat by the evaporation of sweat from the skin and from the surface of the lungs, by convection as air flows over the skin and passes out of the lungs, and by outward infrared radiation. The athlete gains heat from internal biochemical reactions (especially oxidations), by absorbing infrared and solar radiation, and by conduction as the feet contact the hot ground. To maintain a constant body temperature, the heat gained and lost through these pathways must balance.

43.5c Exothermic and Endothermic Animals

Different animals use one of two major strategies to balance heat gain and loss. Animals that obtain heat primarily from the external environment are known as **ectotherms** (*ecto* = outside); those obtaining most of their heat from internal physiological sources are called **endotherms** (*endo* = inside). All ectotherms generate at least some heat from internal reactions, however, and endotherms can obtain heat from the environment under some circumstances.

Most invertebrates, fishes, amphibians, and reptiles are ectotherms. Although these animals are popularly described as "cold-blooded," the body temperature of some, such as an active lizard, may be as high as or higher than ours on a sunny day. Ectotherms regulate body temperature by controlling the rate of heat exchange with the environment. Through behavioural and physiological mechanisms, they adjust body temperature toward a level that allows optimal physiological performance. However, most ectotherms are unable to maintain optimal body temperature when the temperature of their surroundings departs too far from that optimum, particularly when environmental temperatures fall. As a result, the body temperatures of ectotherms fluctuate with environmental temperatures, and ectotherms are typically less active when it is cold. Nevertheless, ectotherms are highly successful, particularly in warm environments.

The endotherms—birds, mammals, some fishes, sea turtles, and some invertebrates—keep their bodies at an optimal temperature by regulating two processes: (1) the amount of heat generated by internal oxidative reactions and (2) the amount of heat exchanged with the environment. Because endotherms use internal heat sources to maintain body temperature at optimal levels, they can remain active over a broader range of environmental temperatures than ectotherms. However, endotherms require a nearly constant supply of energy to maintain their body temperatures. And because that energy is provided by food, endotherms typically consume much more food than ectotherms of equivalent size.

The difference between ectotherms and endotherms is reflected in their metabolic responses to environmental temperature **(Figure 43.17)**. The metabolic rate of a resting mouse *increases* steadily as the environmental temperature falls from 25°C to 10°C. This increase reflects the fact that to maintain a constant body temperature in a colder environment, endotherms must process progressively more food and generate more heat to compensate for their increased rate of heat loss. In this respect, an endotherm can be likened to a house in winter. To maintain a constant internal temperature, the homeowner must burn more oil or gas on a cold day than on a warm day.

By contrast, the metabolic rate of a resting lizard typically *decreases* steadily over the same temperature range.

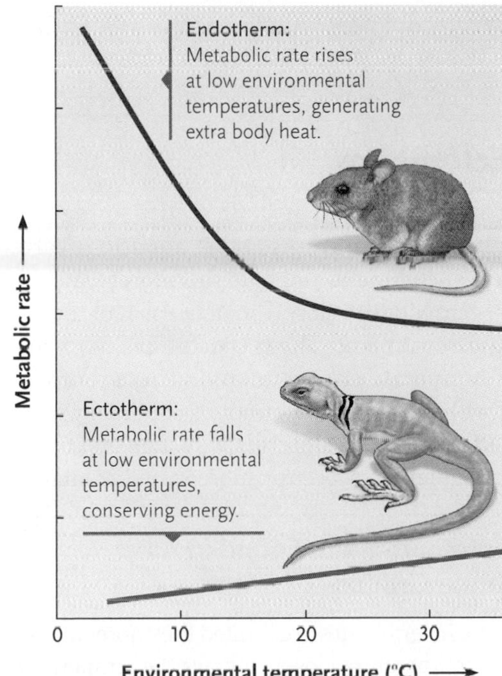

Figure 43.17
Metabolic responses of ectotherms and endotherms to cooling environmental temperatures. At any temperature, the metabolic rates of endotherms are always higher than those of endotherms of comparable size.

Because ectotherms do not maintain a constant body temperature, their biochemical and physiological functions, including oxidative reactions, slow down as environmental and body temperatures decrease. Thus, an ectotherm consumes less food and produces less energy when it is cold than when it is warm.

Ectothermy and endothermy represent different strategies for coping with the variations in environmental temperature that all animals encounter; neither strategy is inherently superior to the other. Endotherms can remain fully active over a wide temperature range. Cold weather does not prevent them from foraging, mating, or escaping from predators, but it does increase their energy and food needs—and to satisfy their need for food, they may not have the option of staying curled up safely in a warm burrow. Ectotherms do not have the capacity to be active when environmental temperatures drop too low; they move sluggishly and are unable to capture food or escape from predators. However, because their metabolic rates are lower under such circumstances, so are their food needs, and they do not have to actively look for food and expose themselves to danger to the extent that endotherms do.

Having laid the ground rules of heat transfer and weighed the relative advantages and disadvantages of ectothermy and endothermy, we now begin a more detailed examination of how individual animals actually regulate their body temperatures within these overall strategies.

Study Break

Distinguish between ectothermy and endothermy.

43.6 Ectothermy

Ectotherms vary widely in their ability to regulate internal body temperatures. Most aquatic invertebrates have such limited ability to thermoregulate that their body temperature closely matches that of the surrounding environment. These species live in or seek warm or temperate environments, where temperatures fall within a range that produces optimal physiological performance. Ectotherms with a greater ability to thermoregulate may occupy more varied habitats.

43.6a Ectotherms Are Found in All Invertebrate Groups

Most aquatic invertebrates are limited thermoregulators. Their body temperature closely follows the temperature of their surroundings. However, even among these animals, some use behavioural responses to regulate body temperature. For example, a South American intertidal mollusc, *Echinolittorina peruviana*, is longer than it is wide. Researchers in Chile have shown that this animal orients itself as a means of thermoregulation. On sunny summer days, it faces the Sun, offering a smaller surface area for the Sun's rays. On overcast summer days, or during the winter, it orients itself with its side, which has the larger surface area, toward the Sun's rays.

Invertebrates living in terrestrial habitats regulate body temperatures more closely. Many also use behavioural responses, such as moving between shaded and sunny regions, to regulate body temperature. Some winged arthropods, including bees, moths, butterflies, and dragonflies, use a combination of behavioural and heat-generating physiological mechanisms for thermoregulation. In cool weather, these animals warm up before taking flight by rapidly vibrating the large flight muscles in the thorax, in a mechanism similar to shivering in humans. The tobacco hawkmoth (*Manduca sexta*) vibrates its flight muscles until its thoracic temperature reaches about 36°C before flying. During flight, metabolic heat generated by the flight muscles sustains the elevated thoracic temperature, so much so that a flying sphinx moth produces more heat per gram of body weight than many mammals. Honeybees (*Apis mellifera*) form masses in the hive in winter and use the heat generated by vibrating their flight muscles to maintain temperature inside the hive. Even in a Manitoba winter, with external temperatures below –20°C, the temperature in the mass of bees is normally about 30°C, and the bees may continue to raise offspring, using food stored in the hive.

43.6b Most Fishes, Amphibians, and Reptiles Are Ectotherms

Vertebrate ectotherms (most fishes, amphibians, and reptiles) also vary widely in their ability to thermoregulate. Most aquatic species have a more limited thermoregulatory capacity than that found among terrestrial species, particularly the reptiles. Some fishes, however, are highly capable thermoregulators.

Fishes. The body temperatures of most fishes remain within one or two degrees of their aquatic environment. However, many fishes use behavioural mechanisms to keep body temperatures at levels that allow good physiological performance. Freshwater species may use opportunities provided by the thermal stratification of lakes and ponds. They remain in deep, cool water during hot summer days, moving to the shallows to feed only during early-morning and late-evening when air and water temperatures are lower. Some fishes and sharks use endothermy: they are discussed in the next section.

Amphibians and Reptiles. The body temperature of most amphibians also closely matches the environmental temperature. The tadpoles of foothill yellow-legged frogs (*Rana boylii*) regulate their body temperature to some degree by changing their

People Behind Biology

Ken Storey: Frozen Frogs

Ken Storey, who leads a busy laboratory at Carleton University in Ottawa, explores the biochemical changes associated with hibernation and estivation in a wide range of animals, including both invertebrates and vertebrates. The wood frog, *Rana sylvatica*, is of particular interest because it spends the winter in a frozen state under the leaves on the forest floor. These frozen frogs have no heartbeat, breathing, or brain activity. Storey's research has shown that the wood frog's tolerance of freezing involves the liberation of glucose from glycogen stores in the liver and its accumulation at extremely high concentrations within the cells, resulting in a slurry of small ice crystals and glucose. This suggests a suspension of the function of insulin, which normally controls glucose concentrations. Although it may be obvious that the frogs freeze from the outside in and that heart and brain function will be the last to be suspended, it is also true that the frogs thaw from the inside out. The coordination of the events governing freezing and thawing involves a number of signal cascades, which his lab has characterized. Storey is currently exploring gene expression during the process of freezing and thawing.

location in ponds and lakes to take advantage of temperature differences between deep and shallow water or between sunny and shaded regions. Some terrestrial amphibians bask in the Sun to raise their body temperature and seek shade to lower body temperature. However, basking can be dangerous to amphibians because they lose water rapidly through their permeable skin. We have already noted that the leaf frog *Phyllomedusa sauvagii*, which often basks in sunlight, avoids this problem by coating itself with waterproofing lipids secreted by glands in its skin.

Thermoregulation is more pronounced among terrestrial reptiles. Some lizard species can maintain temperatures that are nearly as constant as those of endotherms **(Figure 43.18)**. For small lizards, the most common behavioural thermoregulatory mechanism is moving between sunny (warmer) and shady (cooler) regions. In the desert, lizards and other reptiles retreat into burrows during the hottest part of summer days. Some, such as the desert iguana (*Dipsosaurus dorsalis*), lose excess heat by *panting*—rapidly moving air in and out of the airways. The air movement increases heat loss by convection and by evaporation of water from the respiratory tract.

Figure 43.18
An example of excellent thermoregulation in ectotherms. The body temperature of the Australian lizard *Varanus varius* rises quickly after the animal emerges from its burrow and remains relatively stable throughout the day.

Lizards also frequently adjust their posture to foster heat exchange with the environment and control the angle of their body relative to the rays of the Sun. Horned lizards (genus *Phrynosoma*) often warm up by flattening themselves against warm, sunlit rocks to maximize their rate of heat gain by conduction from the rock and radiation from the Sun. Snakes and lizards can often be found on large rocks and on roads on chilly nights, taking advantage of the heat retained by the stone or concrete. *Agama savignyi*, a lizard that lives in the Negev Desert in Israel, cools off at midday by climbing into shady bushes, moving away from the hot sand, and catching a cooling breeze.

Researchers have demonstrated experimentally that several lizard species couple physiological responses to behavioural mechanisms of thermoregulation. When a Galápagos marine iguana (*Amblyrhynchus cristatus*) is exposed to heat from infrared radiation, blood flow increases in the heated regions of the skin. The blood absorbs heat rapidly and carries it to critical organs in the core of the body. Conversely, when an area of skin is experimentally cooled, blood flow to it is restricted, thereby preventing the loss of heat to the external environment.

43.6c Ectotherms Can Compensate for Seasonal Variations in Environmental Temperature

Many ectotherms undergo seasonal physiological changes, called **thermal acclimatization**. These changes allow the animals to attain good physiological performance at both winter and summer temperatures.

For example, in the summer, bullhead catfish (*Ameiurus* species) can survive water temperatures as high as 36°C but cannot tolerate temperatures below 8°C.

In the winter, however, the bullhead cannot survive water temperatures above 28°C but can tolerate temperatures near 0°C. Scientists have hypothesized that the production of different versions of some enzymes (perhaps encoded by different genes or produced as a result of alternative splicing) with optimal activity at cooler or warmer temperatures underlies such acclimatization.

Another acclimatizing change involves the phospholipids of biological membranes. Membrane phospholipids have higher proportions of double bonds in carp living in colder environments than in carp living in warmer environments. The higher proportion of double bonds makes it harder for the membrane to freeze. A higher proportion of cholesterol also protects membranes from freezing.

Study Break

1. Describe two mechanisms an ectothermic animal can use to regulate its temperature.
2. What is thermal acclimatization?

43.7 Endothermy

Endotherms (mostly birds and mammals) have the most elaborate and extensive thermoregulatory adaptations of all animals. Set points vary with species and lie between about 39°C and 42°C in birds and 36°C and 39°C in mammals. We have already noted that the range of environmental temperatures that different organisms encounter is very great. A single species may encounter seasonal variations in environmental temperatures ranging over 70°C or more.

Some cold-water marine teleosts (such as tunas and mackerels) and some sharks (such as the great white) use endothermy in their aerobic swimming muscles to maintain a body core temperature as much as 10°C to 12°C warmer than their surroundings. These animals have in common the fact that they move over long distances, swimming continuously. The action of the muscles generates heat that permits the muscles and other organs to operate more efficiently.

Much of this heat would be lost at the gill–water interface. However, a *countercurrent heat exchanger* system between the swimming muscles and the gills minimizes this loss (see Chapter 42). The anatomical details of the heat exchanger vary. In principle, however, the venules containing warm blood from the muscles form a network with arterioles containing cold blood coming from the gills. The heat from the venules is transferred to the arterioles and is carried to the body tissues. Because this transfer occurs before the blood from the muscles enters the heart on its way to the gills, heat loss is minimized.

We begin by describing the basic feedback mechanisms that maintain body temperature, with primary emphasis on the human system. Later sections discuss variations in the responses of other mammals and of birds and daily and seasonal variations in the temperature set point.

43.7a The Hypothalamus Integrates Information from Thermoreceptors

Thermoreceptors are found in various locations in the human body, including the **integument** (skin), spinal cord, and hypothalamus. Two types of thermoreceptors occur in human skin (see Chapter 34). One, called a *warm receptor,* sends signals to the hypothalamus as the skin temperature rises above 30°C and reaches maximum activity when the temperature rises to 40°C. The other type, the *cold receptor,* sends signals when skin temperature falls below about 35°C and reaches maximum activity at 25°C. By contrast, the highly sensitive thermoreceptors in the hypothalamus itself produce signals when the blood temperature shifts from the set point by as little as 0.01°C.

Signals from the thermoreceptors are integrated in the hypothalamus and other regions of the brain to bring about compensating physiological and behavioural responses **(Figure 43.19)**. The responses keep body temperature close to the set point, which varies normally in humans between 35.5°C and 37.7°C for the head and trunk. The appendages may vary more widely in temperature. In very cold weather, for example, our arms, hands, legs, and feet are typically lower in temperature than the body core and the ears and nose especially so.

The hypothalamus was identified as a major thermoreceptor and response integrator in mammals by experiments on animals in which various regions of the brain were heated or cooled with a temperature probe. Within the brain, only the hypothalamus produced thermoregulatory responses such as shivering or panting. Later experiments revealed a similar response if regions of the spinal cord are cooled, indicating that thermoreceptors also occur in this location. The hypothalamus is also a major thermoreceptor and response integrator in fishes and reptiles. In birds, thermoreceptors in the spinal cord appear to be more significant in thermoregulation.

Responses When Core Temperature Falls Below the Set Point. When thermoreceptors signal a fall in core temperature below the set point, the hypothalamus triggers compensating responses by sending signals through the autonomic nervous system (see Chapter 33). Among the immediate responses is constriction of the arterioles in the skin (vasoconstriction), which reduces the flow of blood to the skin's capillary networks. The reduced flow cuts down the amount of heat delivered to the skin and therefore lost from the body surface. The reduction

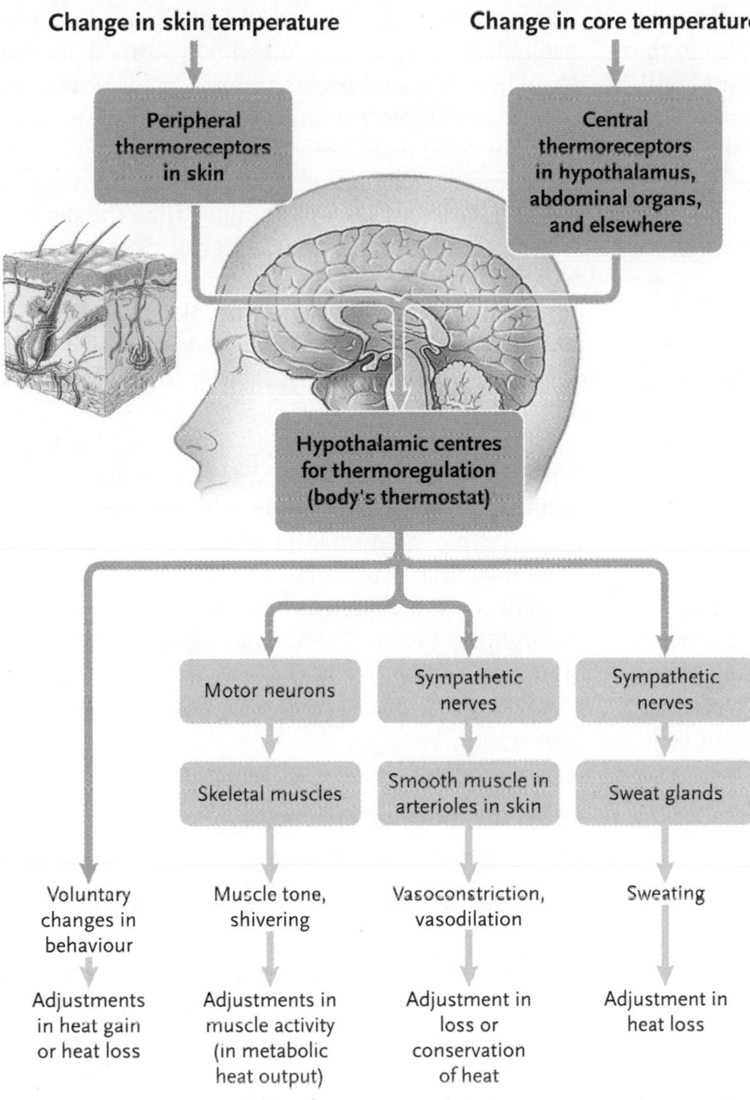

Figure 43.19
The physiological and behavioural responses of humans and other mammals to changes in skin and core temperature.

in flow is most pronounced in the skin covering the extremities, where blood flow may be reduced by as much as 99% when core temperature falls.

Another immediate response is contraction of the smooth muscles that erect the hair shafts in mammals and feather shafts in birds. This traps air in pockets over the skin, reducing convective heat loss. The response is minimally effective in humans because hair is sparse on most parts of the body, but it produces the goose bumps we experience when the weather gets chilly. However, in mammals with fur coats or in birds, erection of the hair or feather shafts significantly increases the thickness of the insulating layer that covers the skin.

Immediate behavioural responses triggered by a reduction in skin temperature also help reduce heat loss from the body. Mammals may reduce heat loss by moving to a warmer locale, curling into a ball, or huddling together. We have all seen puppies huddled together to keep warm; birds such as penguins also keep warm by huddling. We humans may also put on more clothes or slip into a tub of hot water.

If these immediate responses do not return body temperature to the set point, the hypothalamus triggers further responses, most notably the rhythmic tremors of skeletal muscle we know as shivering. The heat released by the muscle contractions and the oxidative reactions powering them can raise the total heat production of the body substantially. At the same time, the hypothalamus triggers secretion of *epinephrine* (from the adrenal medulla) and *thyroid hormone* (see Chapter 35), both of which increase heat production by stimulating the oxidation of fats and other fuels. The generation of heat by oxidative mechanisms in nonmuscle tissue throughout the body is termed **nonshivering thermogenesis.**

In human newborn babies and the young of many other mammals, the most intense heat generation by nonshivering thermogenesis takes place in a specialized **brown adipose tissue** (also called brown fat) that can produce heat rapidly. Heat is generated by a mechanism that uncouples electron transport from ATP production in mitochondria (see Chapter 6); the heat is transferred throughout the body by the blood. Animals that hibernate or are active in cold regions also contain brown adipose tissue. In most mammals, brown adipose tissue is concentrated between the shoulders in the back and around the neck. In human newborns, this tissue accounts for about 5% of body weight. The tissue normally shrinks during late childhood and is absent or nearly so in most adults. However, if exposure to cold is ongoing, the tissue remains. Some Japanese and Korean divers who harvest shellfish in frigid waters and male Finlanders who work outside during the year have significant amounts of brown adipose tissue.

If none of these responses succeed in raising body temperature to the set point, the result is **hypothermia,** a condition in which the core temperature falls below normal for a prolonged period. In humans, a drop in core temperature of only a few degrees affects brain function and leads to confusion; continued hypothermia can lead to coma and death.

Responses When Core Temperature Rises Above the Set Point. When the core temperature rises above the set point, the hypothalamus sends signals through the autonomic system that trigger responses that lower body temperature. As an immediate response, the signals relax smooth muscles of arterioles in the skin (vasodilation), increasing blood flow and with it the heat lost from the body surface. In addition, in humans and other mammals with sweat glands, such as antelopes, cows, and horses, signals from the hypothalamus trigger the secretion of sweat, which absorbs heat as it evaporates from the surface of the skin.

Some endotherms, including dogs (which have sweat glands only on their feet) and many birds (which have no sweat glands), use panting as a major way to release heat. These physiological changes are reinforced by behavioural responses such as seeking shade or a cool burrow, plunging into cold water, wallowing in mud, or taking a cold drink. Elephants take up water in their trunks and spray it over their bodies to cool off in hot weather.

When the heat gain of the body is too great to be counteracted by these responses, **hyperthermia** results. An increase of only a few degrees above normal for a prolonged period is enough to disrupt vital biochemical reactions and damage brain cells. Most adult humans become unconscious if their body temperature reaches 41°C and die if it goes above 43°C for more than a few minutes.

43.7b The Skin Controls Heat Transfer with the Environment

Besides its defensive role against infection, the skin of birds and mammals is an organ of heat transfer. The arterioles delivering blood to the capillary networks of the skin constrict or dilate to control blood flow and with it the amount of heat transferred from the body core to the surface.

The outermost living tissue of human skin, the **epidermis**, consists of cells that divide and grow rapidly **(Figure 43.20)**, becoming packed with fibres of a highly insoluble protein, *keratin*. When fully formed, the epidermal cells die and become compacted into a tough, impermeable layer that limits water loss to evaporation of the fluids secreted by the sweat glands.

The sweat glands and hair follicles are embedded in the layer below the epidermis. Called the **dermis**, it is packed with connective tissue fibres such as collagen, which resist the compression, tearing, or puncture of the skin. The dermis also contains thermoreceptors and the dense networks of arterioles, capillaries, and venules that transfer heat between the skin and the environment.

The innermost layer of the skin, the **hypodermis**, contains larger blood vessels and additional reinforcing connective tissue. The hypodermis also contains an insulating layer of fatty tissue below the dermal capillary network, which ensures that heat flows between the body core and the surface primarily through the blood. The insulating layer is thickest in mammals that live in cold environments, such as whales, seals, walruses, and polar bears, in which it is known as *blubber*.

43.7c Additional Thermoregulatory Structures and Responses

The thermoregulatory mechanisms we have described to this point are common to many birds and mammals. Many species also have specialized responses that enhance thermoregulation. In hot weather, many birds fly with their legs extended so that heat flows from their legs into the passing air. Similarly, penguins expose featherless patches of skin under their wings to cool off on days when the weather is too warm. Jackrabbits **(Figure 43.21a)** and elephants dissipate heat from their large ears, which are richly supplied with blood vessels. In times of significant heat

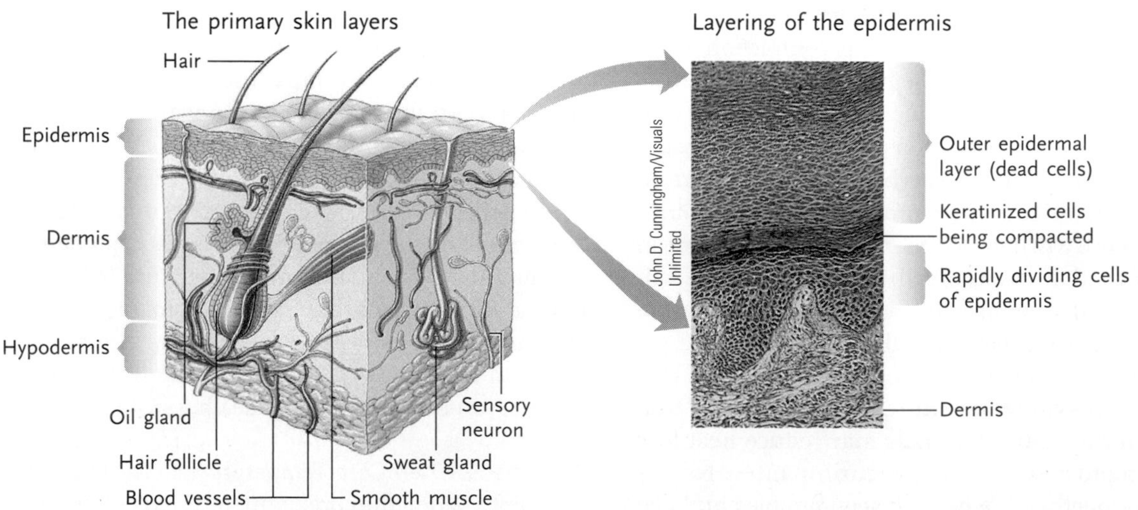

Figure 43.20
The structure of human skin.

a. Dissipating heat

b. Conserving heat

Figure 43.21
Structural and behavioural adaptations controlling heat transfer at the body surface. **(a)** A jackrabbit (*Lepus californicus*) dissipating heat from its ears on a hot summer day. Notice the dilated blood vessels in its large ears. Both the large surface area of the ears and the extensive network of blood vessels promote the dissipation of heat by convection and radiation. **(b)** A husky (*Canis lupus familiaris*) conserving heat by curling up with the limbs under the body and the tail around the nose.

stress, kangaroos and rats spread saliva on their fur to increase heat loss by evaporation; some bats coat their fur with both saliva and urine.

Many mammals have an uneven distribution of fur that aids thermoregulation. In a dog, for example, the fur is thickest over the back and sides of the body and the tail and thinnest under the legs and over the belly. In cold weather, dogs curl up, pull in their limbs, wrap their tail around the body, and bury their nose in the tail so that only body surfaces insulated by thick fur are exposed to the air **(Figure 43.21b)**. When the weather is hot, dogs spread their limbs, turn on their side or back, and expose the relatively bare skin of the belly, which acts as a heat radiator. These responses are combined with seeking Sun or shade or a warm or cool surface to lie on.

The veins and arteries to the legs of mammals and birds may form a simple countercurrent heat exchange system in which cold blood returning from the foot takes heat from the arterial blood entering the foot **(Figure 43.22)**. This minimizes heat loss from the foot while maintaining a nutritive flow of blood to the extremity. This is particularly important for animals in polar regions.

In marine mammals such as whales and seals, heat loss is regulated by adjustments in the blood flow through the thick blubber layer to the skin. In cold water, blood flow is minimized by constriction of the vessels, making the skin temperature close to that of the surrounding water while the body temperature remains constant under the insulating blubber. In warmer water, blood flow to the skin above the blubber increases, allowing excess heat to be lost from the body surface.

In addition, heat loss in whales and seals is controlled by adjustments of the flow of blood to the flippers, which are not insulated by blubber and act as heat radiators. When a whale generates excessive internal heat through the muscular activity of swimming, the flow of blood from the body core to the

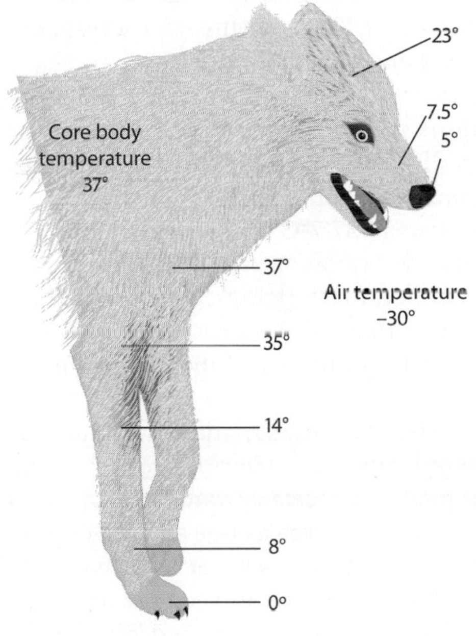

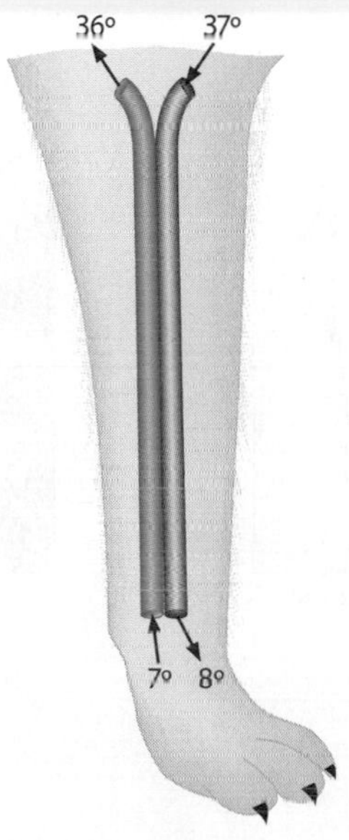

Figure 43.22
Countercurrent circulation in the leg of an Arctic wolf. The vein and artery are parallel and close together so that heat from the warm blood in the artery is transferred to the cold blood returning from the foot, minimizing heat loss through the foot.

flippers increases. In contrast, when heat must be conserved to maintain core temperature at the set point, blood flow to the flippers is reduced.

As with ectotherms, many mammals also undergo thermal acclimatization with seasonal temperature changes. Although, in many cases, a change in day length appears to be the actual trigger, the development of a thick fur coat in winter, which is shed in summer, enables them to adapt to seasonal temperatures. Some arctic and subarctic mammals develop a thicker layer of insulating fat in winter.

43.7d Daily and Seasonal Rhythms in Birds and Mammals

The temperature set point in many birds and mammals varies in a regular cycle during the day. In some, the daily variations are relatively small. In others, larger variations are correlated with daily or seasonal temperature changes. These rhythms are a response to day length rather than temperature change.

Humans are among the endotherms for which daily variations in the temperature set point are small. Normally, human core temperature varies from a minimum of about 35.5°C in the morning to a maximum of about 37.7°C in the evening. Women also show a monthly variation keyed to the menstrual cycle, with temperatures rising about 0.5°C from the time of ovulation until menstruation begins. The physiological significance of these variations is unknown.

Camels undergo a daily variation of as much as 7°C in set point temperature. During the day, a camel's set point gradually resets upward, an adaptation that allows its body to absorb a large amount of heat. The heat absorption conserves water that would otherwise be lost by evaporation to keep the body at a lower set point. At night, when the desert is cooler, the thermostat resets again, allowing the body temperature to cool several degrees, releasing the excess heat absorbed during the day.

When the environmental temperature is cool, having a lowered temperature set point greatly reduces the energy required to maintain body temperature. In many animals, the lowered set point is accompanied by reductions in metabolic, nervous, and physical activity (including slower respiration and heartbeat), producing a sleeplike state known as **torpor.**

Entry into **daily torpor,** a period of inactivity keyed to variations in daily temperature, is typical of many small mammals and birds. These animals typically expend more energy per unit of body weight to keep warm than larger animals because the ratio of body surface area to volume increases as body size decreases. Hummingbirds feed actively during the daytime, when their set point is close to 40°C. During the cool of night, however, the set point drops to as low as 13°C. This allows the birds to conserve enough energy to survive overnight without feeding. Otherwise, they would literally starve to death. Some nocturnal animals, including bats and small rodents, such as the deer mouse, become torpid in cool locations during daylight hours when they do not actively feed. At night, their temperature set point rises and they become fully active **(Figure 43.23).**

Many animals enter a prolonged state of torpor tied to the seasons, triggered in most cases by a change in day length that signals the transition between summer and winter. The importance of day length has been demonstrated by laboratory experiments in which animals have been induced to enter seasonal torpor by changing the period of artificial light to match the winter or summer day length.

Extended torpor of small mammals during winter, called **hibernation** (*hiberna* = winter), greatly reduces metabolic expenditures when food is unobtainable. Hibernators must store large quantities of fats to serve as energy reserves. The drop in body temperature during hibernation varies with the mammal. In some, such as hedgehogs, groundhogs, and squirrels, body temperature may fall by 20°C or more. In some species of hedgehogs, body temperature falls from about 38°C in the summer to as low as 5°C to 6°C during

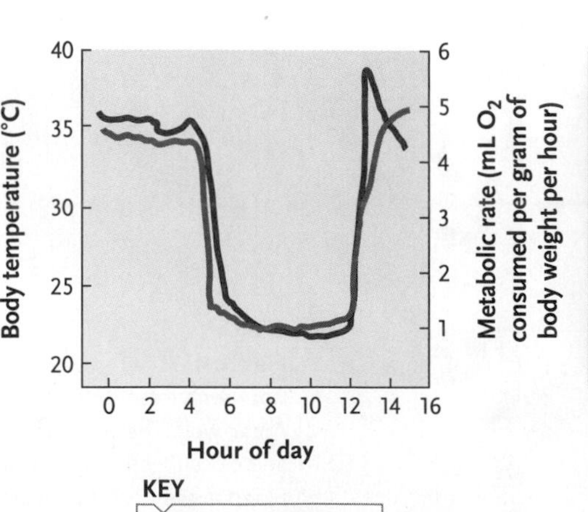

Figure 43.23
Cycle of daily torpor in a deer mouse (*Peromyscus maniculatus*).

Life on the Edge

Surviving Freezing

Many ectotherms encounter temperatures in winter that are well below the freezing point of their body fluids. The tiny second-stage caterpillar of the spruce budworm (*Choristoneura fumiferana*) spends the winter at the tips of spruce trees in Canada, where temperatures may reach –40°C. Their ability to survive depends on the production of an antifreeze protein. Antifreeze proteins also occur in marine fishes that occupy habitats where the water temperature may be below the freezing point of their body fluids. Research led by Peter Davies at Queen's University has shown that these proteins bond with forming ice crystals, limiting their growth, so although the water freezes, the crystals are small enough that cell structure is not disrupted.

The molecular structure of the antifreeze proteins is diverse, and at least four types are known. This diversity appears even within a single species: work in Garth Fletcher's laboratory at Memorial University in St. John's, Newfoundland, has shown that the protein found in plasma of several species of marine teleosts is different from that in the skin cells or gill cells. This diversity suggests that genes for the various types of antifreeze proteins in fish arose independently during the relatively recent cooling of the polar oceans.

winter hibernation. The Arctic ground squirrel's body supercools (goes to a below-freezing, unfrozen state) during hibernation, with its body temperature dropping to about –3°C. Hibernating mammals may experience brief periods of arousal during the course of the winter (see *Unanswered Questions*).

In larger mammals, such as bears and raccoons, the depth of torpor is less pronounced and is not considered by many scientists to be true hibernation. The core temperature of bears drops only a few degrees. Although sluggish, hibernating bears will waken readily if disturbed. They also waken normally from time to time, as when females wake to give birth during the winter season.

Some ectotherms, including amphibians and reptiles living in northern latitudes, also become torpid during winter. The Antarctic codfish, *Notothenia cordiceps,* spends the summer feeding on phytoplankton. In the winter, however, phytoplankton are reduced as a result of the low levels of light. The fish enter a state similar to hibernation. They remain relatively immobile in refuges, and their metabolic rate drops by about one-third. Because the temperature of the water remains constant over the seasons, the fish clearly have the capacity to control their metabolic rate independent of temperature.

Some mammals enter seasonal torpor during summer, called a **estivation** (*aestivalis* = of summer), when environmental temperatures are high and water is scarce. Some ground squirrels remain inactive in the cooler temperatures of their burrows during extreme summer heat. Many ectotherms, among them land snails, lungfishes, many toads and frogs, and some desert-living lizards, weather such climates by digging into the soil and entering a state of a estivation that lasts throughout the hot dry season.

Study Break

1. Where are thermoreceptors located in mammals?
2. What part of the brain integrates information from thermoreceptors, and what systems are activated by this region?

Unanswered Questions

Although active life normally occurs between relatively narrow limits of temperature and water content, there are exceptions, often involving a dormant stage. Animals can be totally frozen or almost completely desiccated, but we do not fully understand the mechanisms involved or the ultimate consequences. These phenomena of "suspended animation" have potential implications for humans. Preservation of human tissues, particularly in terms of prolonging the time that organs for transplant remain viable, is one example.

Hibernation may be of particular interest. In 1996, research by a team of Japanese scientists led by Noriaki Kondo identified a "hibernation protein complex" that appears in the blood of Asiatic chipmunks and acts on the brain as a hormone to control the onset and termination of hibernation. This raises the possibility that hibernation can be induced in nonhibernators. Can humans be induced to enter such states? Is this a potential treatment for trauma? The induction of a comalike state is already used in cases of severe brain injury. More distant, perhaps, is a potential role in exploration of space by humans. Some voyages may require months or years, and a state of suspended animation could be useful. Such questions make it important for scientists to explore more fully the states of torpor and hibernation.

Review

Go to CENGAGENOW™ at http://hed.nelson.com/ to access quizzing, animations, exercises, articles, and personalized homework help.

43.1 Introduction to Osmoregulation and Excretion

- Osmotic concentration of a solution is measured as osmolality in milliosmoles per kilogram (mOsm/kg) of solute. Both molecules and ions contribute to osmolality. Water moves osmotically from a solution of lower osmolality to one of higher osmolality. When comparing two solutions of different osmolality, the solution of higher osmolality is hyperosmotic and the solution of lower osmolality is hypoosmotic. Solutions of the same osmolality are isoosmotic.
- Osmoregulation describes the mechanisms that keep the osmolality of intracellular and extracellular fluids isotonic. Osmoregulators keep the osmolality of body fluids different from that of the environment. Osmoconformers allow the osmolality of their body fluids to match that of the environment.
- Osmoregulation is closely related to excretion because molecules and ions must be removed from the body to maintain the isotonicity of cells and extracellular fluids. Excretion also removes excess water, nitrogenous wastes, excess acid, and toxic molecules from the body.
- In most animals, tubules formed from a transport epithelium carry out the combined processes of osmoregulation and excretion. Extracellular fluids are filtered into the proximal end of the tubules; as the fluid moves through the tubules, some ions and molecules are reabsorbed from the fluid, and others are secreted into the fluid. Water is added or removed from the fluid to maintain the animal's water balance. The processed fluid is released to the exterior of the animal as urine.
- Nitrogenous wastes from the metabolism of amino acids and nucleic acids are excreted as ammonia, urea, or uric acid or as a combination of these substances.

43.2 Osmoregulation and Excretion in Invertebrates

- Most marine invertebrates are osmoconformers, whereas the invertebrates living in freshwater or terrestrial environments are osmoregulators.
- Because the body fluids of the marine osmoconformers are isoosmotic to seawater, they expend little or no energy on maintaining water balance. Body fluids in the osmoregulators living in freshwater and terrestrial environments are hyperosmotic to their surroundings. They must therefore expend energy to excrete water moving into their cells by osmosis and to obtain the salts required to maintain osmolality.
- Most invertebrates have specialized excretory tubules such as protonephridia, metanephridia, or Malpighian tubules that eliminate nitrogenous wastes and may assist in osmoregulation. A few groups eliminate wastes by diffusion.
- Protonephridia are blind tubes that produce an ultrafiltrate of the body fluids and adjust its ionic composition by secretion and reabsorption. Metanephridia are open tubes that take in coelomic fluid and adjust the ionic concentration.
- Malpighian tubules are blind tubes, and ions, uric acid, and other compounds enter by secretion.

43.3 Osmoregulation and Excretion in Mammals

- In mammals and other vertebrates, excretory tubules are concentrated in a specialized excretory organ, the kidney. Each of the pair of mammalian kidneys is divided into an outer renal cortex surrounding a central renal medulla. The mammalian excretory tubule, the nephron, has a proximal end at which filtration takes place, a middle region in which reabsorption and secretion occur, and a distal end that releases urine.
- The interstitial fluid reabsorbs ions, water, and other molecules from the nephron. A network of capillaries surrounding the nephron absorbs those materials. The urine leaving individual nephrons is processed further in collecting ducts and then pools in the renal pelvis. From there it flows through the ureter to the urinary bladder and through the urethra from the bladder to the exterior of the animal.
- At its proximal end, the mammalian nephron forms a cuplike Bowman's capsule around a cluster of capillaries, the glomerulus. A filtrate consisting of water, other small molecules, and ions is forced from the glomerulus into Bowman's capsule, from which it travels through the nephron and drains into the collecting ducts and renal pelvis.
- The proximal convoluted tubule of the nephron secretes H^+ into the filtrate and actively reabsorbs Na^+, K^+, HCO_3^-, and nutrients such as glucose and amino acids.
- In the descending segment of the loop of Henle, water is reabsorbed by osmosis.
- In the ascending segment of the loop, Na^+ and Cl^- move from the tubule by active transport.
- In the distal convoluted tubule, regulatory mechanisms operate to balance the concentrations of H^+ and salts between the urine and the interstitial fluid surrounding the nephron. K^+ and Na^+ move by active transport.
- In the collecting ducts, additional H^+ is secreted into the urine and water is reabsorbed; some urea is also reabsorbed at the bottom of the ducts.

43.4 Kidney Function in Nonmammalian Vertebrates

- Marine teleosts must continually drink seawater to replace body water lost by osmosis to their hyperosmotic environment. The Na^+, K^+, and Cl^- in the ingested seawater are excreted from the gills. Nitrogenous wastes are excreted by the gills as ammonia.
- Sharks use urea and trimethylamine oxide as osmolytes to maintain their body fluids isoosmotic with seawater. As a result, sharks and rays do not lose water by osmosis and do not drink seawater. Excess salts ingested in foods are excreted in the kidney and by a rectal salt gland.
- Body fluids of freshwater fishes and amphibians are hyperosmotic to their environment, and these animals must excrete the excess water that enters by osmosis. Body salts are obtained from food and, in fishes, by active transport through the gills. Nitrogenous wastes are excreted from the gills of fish and larval amphibians as ammonia and through the kidneys of adult amphibians as urea.
- Most reptiles and birds conserve water by secreting nitrogenous wastes as uric acid. Water is also absorbed from the urine and the feces in the cloaca.
- Marine birds and reptiles secrete excess salts through a gland in the head.

43.5 Introduction to Thermoregulation

- Animals maintain body temperature at a level that provides optimal physiological performance. Heat flows between animals and their environment by conduction, convection, radiation, and evaporation.

- Ectothermic animals obtain heat energy primarily from the environment, and endothermic animals obtain heat energy primarily from internal reactions.

43.6 Ectothermy

- Ectotherms, including all invertebrates and amphibians, reptiles, and most fishes among the vertebrates, control body temperature by regulating heat exchange with the environment. Their thermoregulatory responses may be physiological or behavioural. For most ectotherms, the ability to thermoregulate is limited, and body temperature does not differ widely from environmental temperature.
- Many animals undergo thermal acclimatization, a change in the limits of tolerable temperatures as the environment alternates between warm and cool seasons or between day and night. The acclimatization may involve structural changes and/or metabolic alterations.

43.7 Endothermy

- Endotherms, mostly birds and mammals, maintain body temperature over a narrow range by balancing internal heat production against heat loss from the body surface.
- Internal heat production is controlled by negative feedback pathways triggered by thermoreceptors in the skin, hypothalamus, and spinal cord.
- Signals from the receptors are integrated in the hypothalamus to bring about compensating responses by activating the autonomic nervous system, the endocrine system, and the motor nerves. These responses return the core temperature to a set point when deviations occur.
- When body temperature falls below a set point, responses include an increase in heat-generating metabolic reactions and a reduction of blood flow to the body surface. Behavioural responses also reduce heat loss.
- When body temperature rises above the set point, blood flow to the skin increases and sweating is induced in mammals with sweat glands. Mammals with no or few sweat glands and birds, which have no sweat glands, release heat by panting. Behavioural responses also contribute to heat loss.
- The skin of endotherms is water impermeable, reducing heat loss by direct evaporation of body fluids. Mammals with sweat glands regulate evaporative heat loss by releasing moisture to the skin surface when body temperature rises. The blood vessels of the skin regulate heat loss by constricting or dilating. A layer of insulating fatty tissue under the vessels limits losses to the heat carried by the blood. The hair of mammals and feathers of birds also insulate the skin. Erection of the hair or feathers reduces heat loss by thickening the insulating layer.
- The temperature set point in many birds and mammals varies in daily and seasonal patterns. During cooler conditions, a lowered set point is accompanied by torpor: a reduction in metabolic, nervous, and physical activity. Seasonal torpor includes winter hibernation and summer estivation.
- Some animals, such as certain cold-water marine fishes, exhibit a form of endothermy in which part, but not all, of their core is maintained at a temperature significantly higher than the surrounding environment.

Questions

Self-Test Questions

1. Which of the following statements about osmoregulation is true?
   a. In freshwater invertebrates, salts move out of the body because the body fluids are hypoosmotic to the environment.
   b. A marine teleost tends to gain water because it is isosmotic with respect to the sea.
   c. Most land animals are osmoconformers.
   d. Vertebrates are usually osmoregulators.
   e. Terrestrial animals do not expend energy to regulate their osmotic concentration.
2. Filtration and/or excretion can be carried out by
   a. ciliated metanephridia in insects.
   b. protonephridia containing flame cells in flatworms.
   c. a nephron and a bladder in insects.
   d. Malpighian tubules in the segments of earthworms.
   e. the hindgut of earthworms, which reabsorbs ions.
3. Which of the following statements are true? (Any number of the statements, from none to all five, may be correct.)
   a. The fluid that enters Bowman's capsule is an ultrafiltrate of the blood.
   b. In the ascending loop of Henle, Na^+ and K^+ enter the tubule by simple diffusion.
   c. In the descending loop of Henle, water leaves the tubule.
   d. In the proximal convoluted tubule, Na^+ and K^+ leave the tubule by active transport.
   e. In the collecting duct, water enters the tubule via aquaporins.
4. Unique to endotherms is
   a. a body temperature that does not change.
   b. torpor.
   c. thermal acclimatization.
   d. a response to seasonal temperature changes.
   e. thermoregulation by the hypothalamus.
5. Which best exemplifies ectotherms?
   a. The metabolic rate increases as the environmental temperature decreases.
   b. Body temperature remains constant when environmental temperatures change.
   c. All invertebrates are ectotherms.
   d. Food demand decreases when environmental temperatures decrease.
   e. No vertebrates are ectotherms.

Questions for Discussion

1. What is the evolutionary significance of the fact that most birds and reptiles produce uric acid as an excretory product, whereas most mammals produce urea?
2. Some insects feed on plants, such as tobacco, that contain poisons. Can you devise an experiment to test whether such poisons are eliminated by Malpighian tubules?
3. Hockey players are often advised to consume sports drinks containing salt before, during, and after a game. Why do you think this is?
4. Mammals that live in the desert are often nocturnal. What advantages are there in terms of thermoregulation?
5. The internal temperature of a reptile, such as a crocodile, varies with its developmental stage. Adult crocodiles tend to have a higher internal temperature less subject to change due to environmental variation in temperature. Why do you think this is?

Death of a cancer cell. A cytotoxic T cell (orange) induces a cancer cell (mauve) to undergo apoptosis (programmed cell death). Cytotoxic T cells are part of the body's immune response system, programmed to seek out, attach themselves, and kill cancer cells and pathogen-infected host cells.

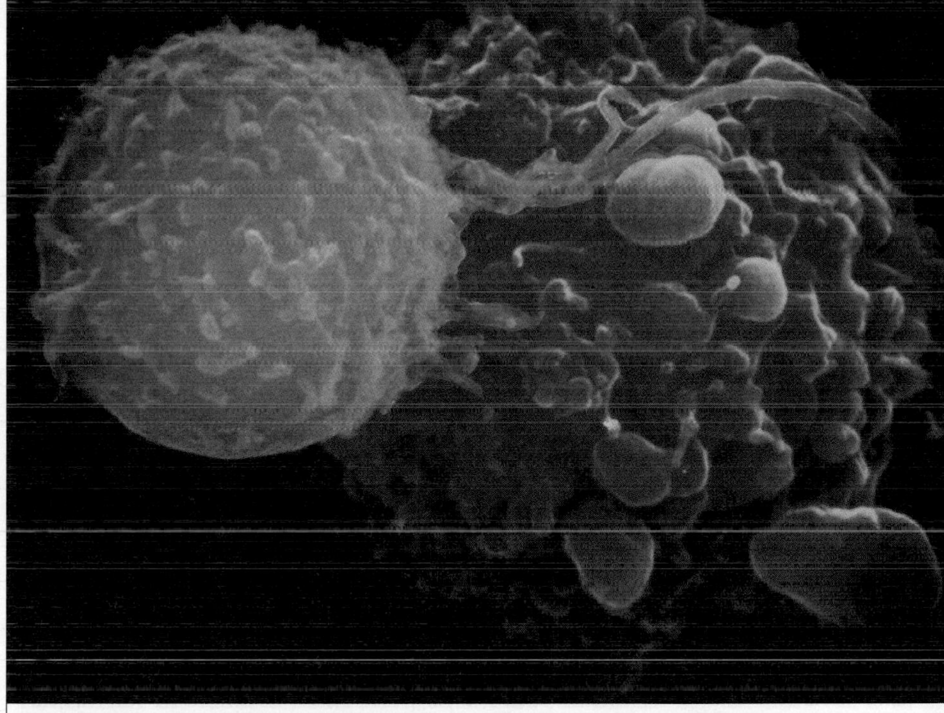

44 Defences against Disease

Study Plan

Why It Matters

Diseases have plagued all organisms including humans for billions of years. All animals, even insects, starfish, worms, and organisms too small to see with the naked eye, suffer from some sort of disease. In humans, acquired immune deficiency syndrome (AIDS), first identified in the early 1980s, now affects about 40 million people worldwide and continues to spread. Malaria affects around 500 million people. Similar diseases in other organisms, such as avian influenza or avian malaria, may significantly reduce bird populations, and insect populations may be killed by outbreaks of specific viruses. Overall, bacteria, viruses, and parasites all can cause disease in their hosts. However, our immune systems are able to regulate or eliminate the majority of pathogens that cause disease. We combat the other pathogens by developing effective drug treatments that eliminate the disease-causing organism or developing vaccines that provide protection from infection.

The development of vaccines began with efforts to control smallpox, a dangerous and disfiguring viral disease that once infected millions of people worldwide, killing more than one-third of its victims. As early as the twelfth century, healthy individuals in

China sought out people who were recovering from mild smallpox infections, ground up scabs from their lesions, and inhaled the powder or pushed it into their skin. Variations on this treatment were effective in protecting many people against smallpox infection.

In 1796, an English country doctor, Edward Jenner, used a more scientific approach. He knew that milkmaids never got smallpox if they had contracted cowpox, a similar but mild disease of cows that can be transmitted to humans. Jenner decided to see if a deliberate infection with cowpox would protect humans from smallpox. He scratched material from a cowpox sore into a boy's arm. Six weeks later, after the cowpox infection had subsided, he scratched fluid from human smallpox sores into the boy's skin. (Jenner's use of the boy as an experimental subject would now be considered unethical.) Remarkably, the boy remained free from smallpox. Jenner carried out additional, carefully documented case studies with other patients with the same results. His technique became the basis for worldwide **vaccination** (*vacca* = cow) against smallpox. With improved vaccines, smallpox has now been eradicated from the human population.

Vaccination takes advantage of the **immune system** (*immunis* = exempt), the natural protection that is our main defence against infectious disease. This chapter focuses on the roles of different components of the immune system that deal with infection. We describe aspects of immune systems in different organisms, from insects to humans, to examine their similarities and differences.

44.1 Three Lines of Defence against Invasion

Every organism is constantly exposed to *pathogens*, potentially disease-causing organisms such as viruses, bacteria, protists, fungi, and parasites. Humans and other animals have three lines of defence against these threats. The first line of defence involves physical barriers that prevent the entry of pathogens. The second is the *innate immune system;* inherited mechanisms that protect the body from pathogens in a nonspecific way. The third is the *adaptive immune system,* found only in vertebrates, and involves inherited mechanisms that lead to the synthesis of molecules such as antibodies that target pathogens in a specific way. Reaction to an infection takes minutes in the case of the innate immunity system versus several days for the adaptive immune system.

44.1a Epithelium as a Barrier to Infection

An organism's first line of defence is the body surface—the skin covering the body exterior, the cuticle of an arthropod, the outer layer of a plant, and the epithelial surfaces covering internal body cavities and ducts, such as the lungs and intestinal tract. The body surface forms a barrier of tight junctions between the epithelial cells that keeps most pathogens (as well as toxic substances) from entering the body.

In the respiratory tract, ciliated cells constantly sweep the mucus with its trapped bacteria and other foreign matter into the throat, where it is coughed out or swallowed. Many of the body cavities lined by mucus membranes have environments that are hostile to pathogens. For example, the strongly acidic environment inside the stomach kills most ingested bacteria and destroys many viruses, including those trapped in swallowed mucus from the respiratory tract. Most of the pathogens that survive the stomach acid are destroyed by the digestive enzymes and bile secreted into the small intestine. Reproductive tracts may be acidic or basic, which prevents many pathogens from surviving there, and many epithelial tissues secrete enzymes such as defensins or lysozymes that are lethal to many bacteria.

44.1b Immune Systems within the Body

The body's second line of defence is a series of generalized internal chemical, physical, and cellular reactions that attack pathogens that have breached the first line. These defences include inflammation, which creates internal conditions that inhibit or kill many pathogens, and specialized cells that engulf or kill pathogens or infected body cells. These initial responses to pathogens are called **innate immunity.**

The innate immune response relies on germline-encoded receptors that recognize a set of highly conserved molecular patterns that are present on the surface of pathogens but not found on host cells. Innate immunity provides an immediate, *nonspecific* response; that is, it targets any invading pathogen and has no memory of prior exposure to that specific pathogen.

Invertebrates and plants rely solely on innate immune responses, whereas vertebrates use the innate immune system in conjunction with the adaptive response for a more powerful overall response. This most complex line of defence, found only in vertebrates, is called **adaptive** (or **acquired**) **immunity.** Adaptive immunity is *specific:* it recognizes individual pathogens and mounts an attack that directly neutralizes or eliminates them. It is stimulated and shaped by the presence of a specific pathogen or foreign molecule in the body. This mechanism, which takes several days to become protective, is triggered by specific molecules on pathogens that are recognized as being foreign to the body. The body retains a memory of the first exposure to a foreign molecule, enabling it to respond more quickly if the pathogen is encountered again in the future.

Innate immunity and adaptive immunity together constitute the immune system, and the defensive reactions of the system are termed the **immune response**. Functionally, the two components of the immune system interconnect and communicate at the chemical and molecular levels. The immune system is the product of long-term coevolutionary interactions between pathogens and their hosts. Over millions of years, the mechanisms by which pathogens attack and invade have become more efficient, but the defences of organisms against the invaders have kept pace.

44.1c How Organisms Recognize Pathogens

The basic tenet of immunity is that an organism can recognize a pathogen as being different from the host. This is often termed recognition of "nonself" and is the essential first step before any immune response can be initiated. Different organisms do this in different ways. Most organisms recognize unique *pathogen-associated molecular patterns* (PAMPs) found on many microbial organisms, using host molecules called *pattern recognition receptors* (PRRs). Common PAMPs include carbohydrates, glycoproteins, lipids, and nucleic acids. Two classic examples of PAMPs are the bacterial cell wall components lipoteichoic acid found on Gram-positive bacteria and lipopolysaccharide on Gram-negative bacteria. Major invertebrate PRRs include the Gram-negative bacteria binding protein and β1,3-glucan recognition proteins that recognize and bind to common molecules found on many groups of pathogenic organisms rather than recognizing each pathogen species individually. For example, lipopolysaccharide is found on the outer surface of all Gram-negative bacteria and serves as a general PAMP to which a PRR can bind. Once specific PRRs are activated by the presence of the PAMP, signalling cascades are initiated that activate various components of the innate or acquired immune responses.

Plants respond to pathogens in a similar manner. They have two branches of immune responses: a system that uses transmembrane PRRs that respond to the PAMPs described for invertebrates and an intracellular response that uses protein products encoded by *R* genes that respond to infection and systemic signals from nearby infected cells. Damage to the plant cells by pathogen effector molecules is believed to be the signal that activates the expression of plant R proteins.

Different PAMPs may activate the same or different signalling pathways and elicit different responses. This has been studied best in the fruitfly, *Drosophila melanogaster*. Infection of *Drosophila* with fungi and bacteria activates the Toll and immune deficiency signalling pathways, which result in nuclear factor (NF)-κB-like transcription factors being translocated to the nucleus, activating many components of the innate immune response.

Study Break

1. What features of epithelial surfaces protect against pathogens?
2. What are the key differences between innate immunity and adaptive immunity?
3. How are pathogens recognized as nonself?

44.2 Nonspecific Defences: Innate Immunity

Invertebrates only have an innate response, and the PAMP–PRR interactions activate the signalling pathways described above. These activate processes such as **phagocytosis** (the internalization and destruction of particulate matter) of small pathogens by hemocytes (blood cells) or the coagulation of the hemolymph (invertebrate blood). Larger pathogens may be encapsulated by hemocytes and covered in a melanin-like material that kills them (**melanotic encapsulation**). This may be helped by the release of reactive intermediates of nitrogen and oxygen. The third component of the innate response involves the production of small **antimicrobial peptides** that kill pathogens not eliminated by the other responses. This coordinated, multifaceted, and integrated approach eliminates potential pathogens, preventing them from harming or killing the host.

The study of invertebrate immunology began when a Russian scientist poked a rose thorn into the body of a starfish and watched how the hemocytes surrounded the thorn **(Figure 44.1)**. The innate immune responses of invertebrates, now a rapidly developing

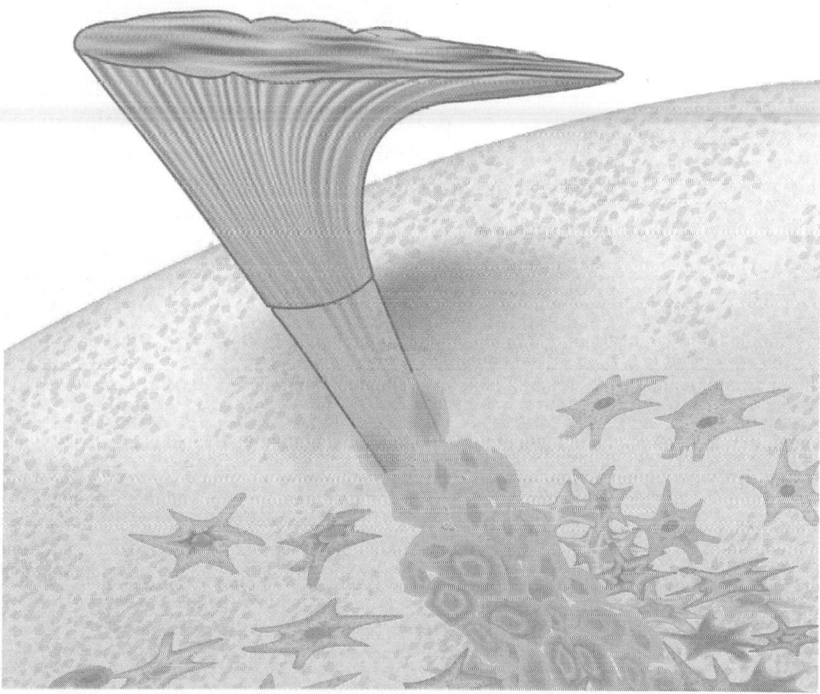

Figure 44.1 Innate immune responses demonstrated by the role of starfish blood cells responding to a thorn that has penetrated the cuticle.

MOLECULE BEHIND BIOLOGY

Defensins

Defensins are ubiquitous cationic molecules used in the defences of essentially all organisms. Defensins have been isolated from several orders of the higher insects, such as the Diptera (flies) and Coleoptera (beetles), and from ancient insects, such as the Odonata (dragonflies). Functional analogues have been isolated and characterized from amoebae, nematodes, scorpions, molluscs, mammals (including humans), and plants. In some organisms, these molecules are secreted into the body cavity, whereas in others, they are intracellular and are released only at a wound site.

This strong conservation suggests that this molecule is of ancient origin and has been maintained throughout evolution due to its importance in limiting the growth of microbial pathogens. Defensins are composed of a series of structures: an N-terminal loop, an α-helix, and twisted, antiparallel β-sheets **(Figure 1).** This three-dimensional shape of the molecule is stabilized by the presence of three disulphide bridges. Defensins are active against many Gram-positive bacteria, some Gram negative bacteria, and some fungi. The lethality occurs as the one region of the peptide binds to the outer surface of the bacteria, allowing other regions to form pores in the microbial membranes, causing a permeabilization that causes a loss of cytoplasmic potassium, a depolarization of the inner membrane, reduced amounts of cytoplasmic ATP, and a reduction in respiration. This can occur in single-celled organisms, in the body cavity of an insect, in plant tissues, or in the white blood cells of a vertebrate. Defensins represent one family of molecules conserved throughout all taxa for the same function and are truly universal immune molecules.

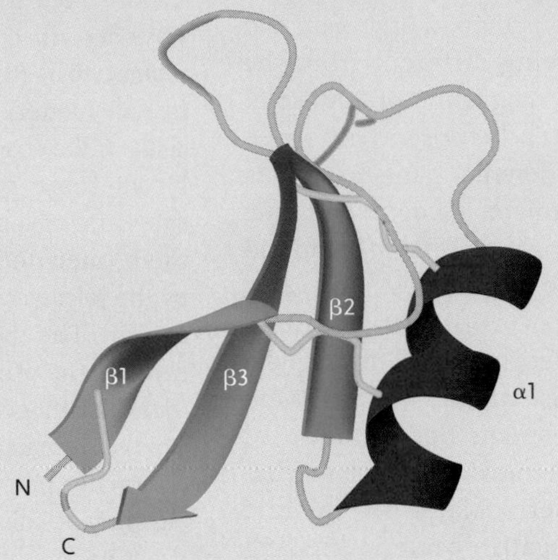

Figure 1
Computer-generated model of a defensin molecule showing the arrangement of the coiled α-helix (red) and the β-sheets (blue) that are held together by disulphide bridges (yellow).

field of research, have allowed us to understand how the innate system works in both invertebrates and vertebrates and what molecules are activated in response to different stimuli. Plants respond in a similar manner. They can wall off cells that are infected, undergo cell death to prevent pathogen development, and produce several small antimicrobial peptides that kill microbial pathogens.

Vertebrates use similar types of specific host cell-surface receptors that recognize the various PAMPs found on microbial pathogens. Some receptors activate signalling pathways that bring about the secretion of lethal antimicrobial peptides that kill the pathogen. Other receptors trigger the host cell to engulf the pathogen, as was described for phagocytosis in invertebrates, but in vertebrates, this also may initiate an inflammation response and may activate the soluble receptors of the *complement system*, described below. The innate responses that recognize and initiate immune pathways in plants, invertebrates, and vertebrates are strikingly similar.

Antimicrobial Peptides. All epithelial surfaces, namely skin; the lining of the gastrointestinal tract; the lining of the nasal passages, gills, and lungs; and the lining of the genitourinary tracts, are protected by antimicrobial peptides, some of which are called *defensins*. These epithelial cells secrete defensins upon attack by a microbial pathogen. The defensins attack the plasma membranes of the pathogens, eventually disrupting them and thereby killing the cells. In particular, defensins play a significant role in innate immunity of the intestinal tracts of vertebrates and invertebrates. Antimicrobial peptides such as the defensins are highly conserved in plants, invertebrates, vertebrates, and even single-celled organisms, indicating their important role in immunity throughout evolution. Other antimicrobial peptides are found only in specific groups, suggesting a more specialized role that has maintained their existence.

Inflammation. A tissue's rapid response to injury, including infection by most pathogens, involves **inflammation** (*inflammare* = to set on fire) the heat, pain, redness, and swelling that occur at the site of an infection.

Several interconnecting mechanisms initiate inflammation **(Figure 44.2)**. Let us consider bacteria entering a tissue as a result of a wound. **Monocytes** (a type of leukocyte) enter the damaged tissue from the bloodstream through the endothelial wall of the capillary. Once in the damaged tissue, the monocytes differentiate into **macrophages** ("big eaters"), which are phagocytes that are usually the first to recognize pathogens at the cellular level. (**Table 44.1, p. 1090** lists the major types of leukocytes such as macrophages; see also **Figure 44.3, p. 1090.**) Cell-surface receptors on the macrophages recognize and bind to surface molecules on the pathogen, activating the macrophage to phagocytize (engulf) the pathogen (see Figure 44.2, step 1). There may not be enough macrophages present at the site of infection to eliminate all the pathogens. Activated macrophages also secrete **cytokines**, molecules that activate and recruit more immune cells to increase the system's response to the pathogen.

The death of cells caused by the pathogen at the infection site activates cells that are dispersed throughout the connective tissue, called **mast cells**, which then release histamine (see Figure 44.2, step 2). This histamine, along with the cytokines from activated macrophages, dilates local blood vessels around the infection site and increases their permeability. This increases blood flow and leakage of fluid from the vessels into body tissues (step 3). The response

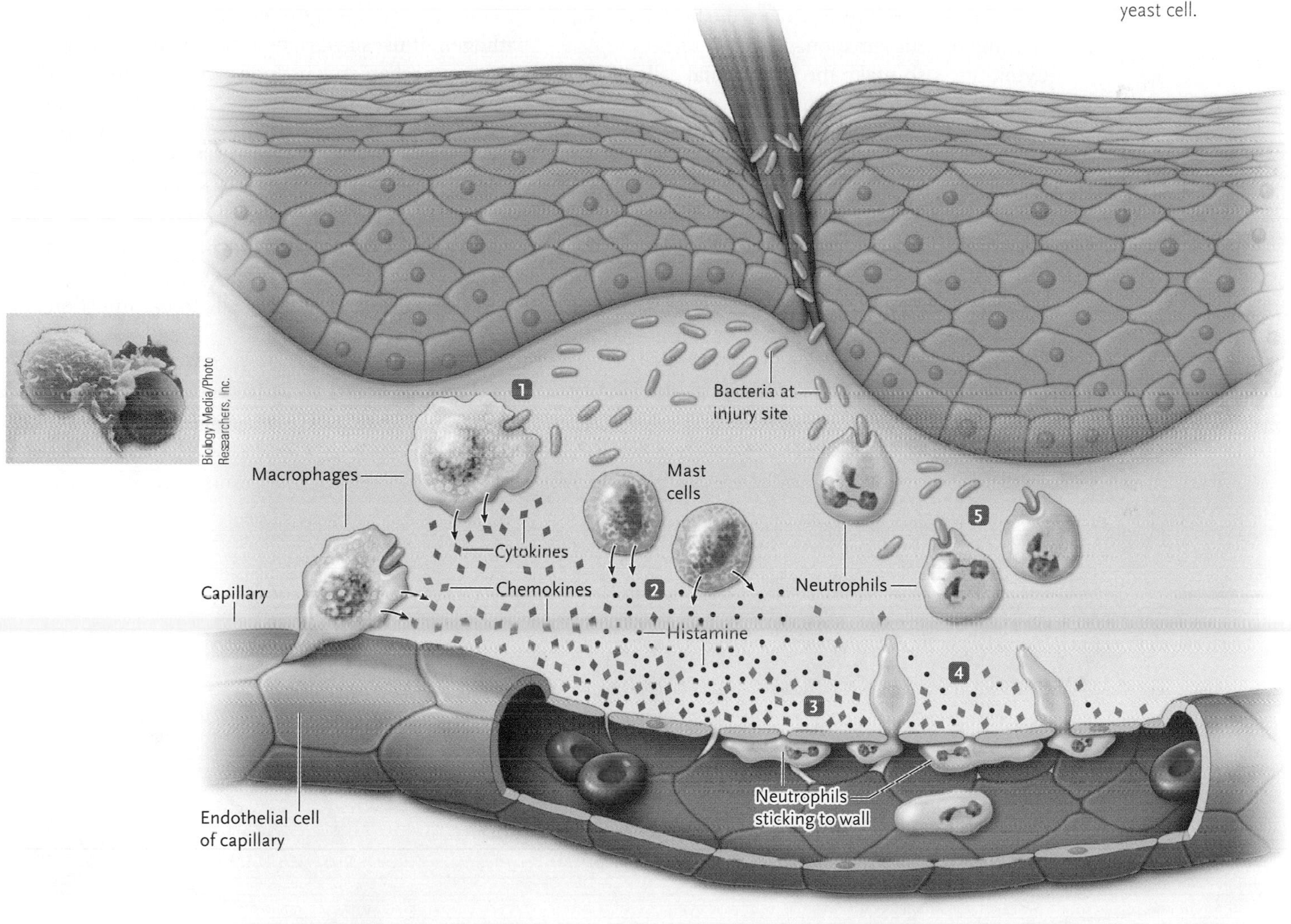

Figure 44.2 The steps producing inflammation. The colourized micrograph on the left shows a macrophage engulfing a yeast cell.

1 A break in the skin introduces bacteria, which reproduce at the wound site. Activated macrophages engulf the pathogens and secrete cytokines and chemokines.

2 Activated mast cells release histamine.

3 Histamine and cytokines dilate local blood vessels and increase their permeability. The cytokines also make the blood vessel wall sticky, causing neutrophils to attach.

4 Chemokines attract neutrophils, which pass between cells of the blood vessel wall and migrate to the infection site.

5 Neutrophils engulf the pathogens and destroy them.

Table 44.1 Major Types of Leukocytes and Their Functions

Type of Leukocyte	Function
Monocyte	Differentiates into a macrophage when released from blood into damaged tissue
Macrophage	Phagocyte that engulfs infected cells, pathogens, and cellular debris in damaged tissues; helps activate lymphocytes in carrying out immune response
Neutrophil	Phagocyte that engulfs pathogens and tissue debris in damaged tissues
Eosinophil	Secretes substances that kill eukaryotic parasites such as worms
Lymphocyte	Main subtypes involved in innate and adaptive immunity are natural killer (NK) cells, B cells, plasma cells, helper T cells, and cytotoxic T cells. NK cells function as part of innate immunity to kill virus-infected cells and some cancerous cells of the host. The other cell types function as part of adaptive immunity: they produce antibodies, destroy infected and cancerous body cells, and stimulate macrophages and other leukocyte types to engulf infected cells, pathogens, and cellular debris.
Basophil	Respond to IgE antibodies in an allergy response by secreting histamine, which stimulates inflammation

initiated by cytokines directly causes the heat, redness, and swelling of inflammation.

Cytokines also make the endothelial cells of the blood vessel wall stickier, causing circulating **neutrophils** (another type of phagocytic leukocyte) to attach to them in massive numbers. From there, the neutrophils are attracted to the infection site by **chemokines**, proteins also secreted by activated macrophages (see Figure 44.2, step 4). To get to the infection site, the neutrophils pass between endothelial cells of the blood vessel wall. Neutrophils also may be attracted directly to the pathogen by molecules released from the pathogens themselves. Like macrophages, neutrophils have cell-surface receptors that enable them to recognize and engulf pathogens (step 5).

Once a macrophage or neutrophil has engulfed the pathogen, it uses a variety of mechanisms to destroy it. These mechanisms include attacks by enzymes and defensins located in lysosomes and the production of toxic compounds. The harshness of these attacks usually kills the neutrophils as well, whereas macrophages usually survive to continue their pathogen-scavenging activities. Dead and dying neutrophils, in fact, are a major component of the pus formed at infection sites. The pain of inflammation is caused by the migration of macrophages and neutrophils to the infection site and their activities there.

Some pathogens, such as parasitic worms, are too large to be engulfed by macrophages or neutrophils. In that case, macrophages, neutrophils,

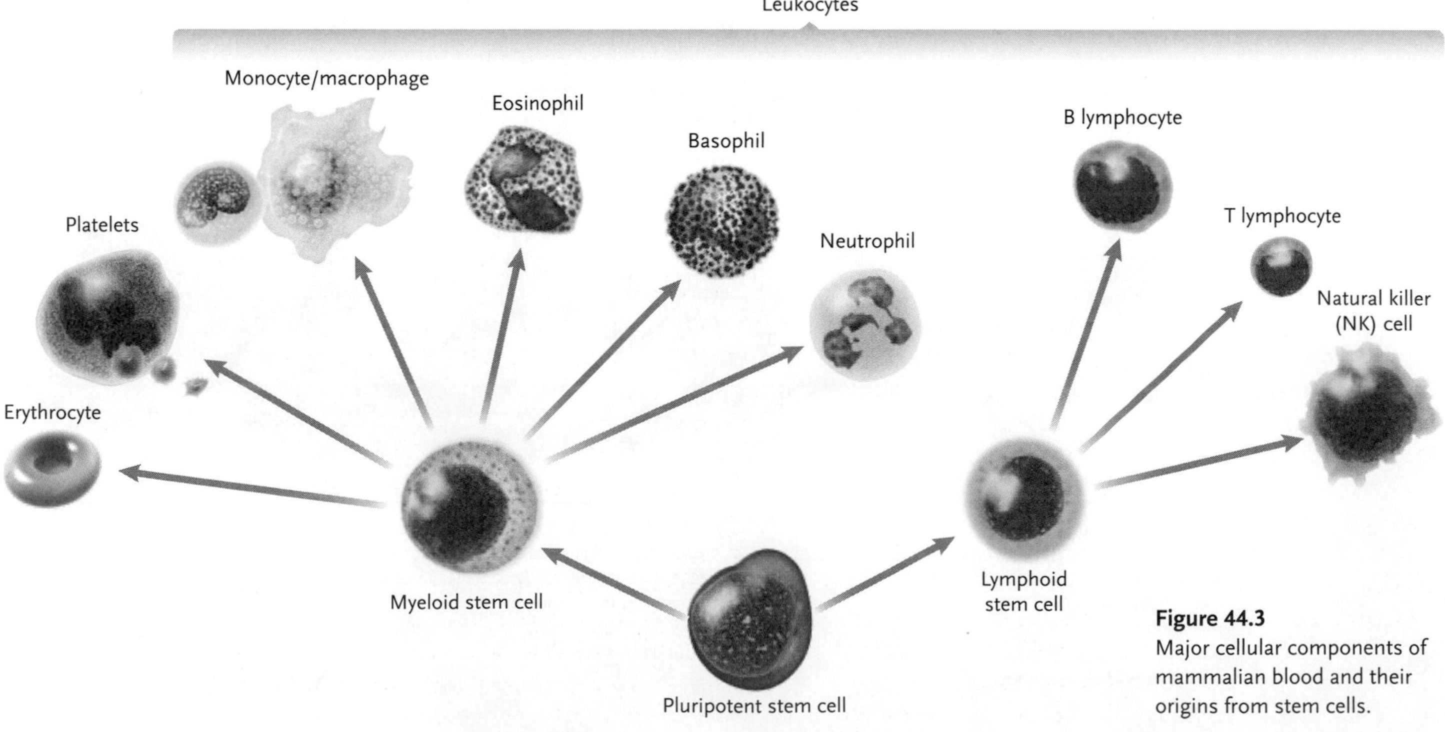

Figure 44.3
Major cellular components of mammalian blood and their origins from stem cells.

and **eosinophils** (another type of leukocyte) cluster around the pathogen and secrete lysosomal enzymes in amounts usually sufficient to kill the pathogen.

The Complement System. Another nonspecific defence mechanism activated by invading pathogens is the **complement system,** a group of more than 30 interacting soluble plasma proteins that circulate in the blood and interstitial fluid. Normally inactive, the proteins are activated when they recognize molecules on the surfaces of pathogens. Activated complement proteins participate in a cascade of reactions on pathogen surfaces, producing large numbers of different complement proteins, some of which assemble into *membrane attack complexes.* These complexes insert into the plasma membrane of many types of bacterial cells and create pores that allow ions and small molecules to pass readily through the membrane. As a result, the bacteria can no longer maintain osmotic balance, and they swell and lyse. For other types of bacterial cells, the cascade of reactions coats the pathogen with fragments of the complement proteins. Cell-surface receptors on phagocytes then recognize these fragments and engulf and destroy the pathogen.

Several activated proteins in the complement cascade also act individually to enhance the inflammatory response. For example, some of the proteins stimulate mast cells to enhance histamine release, whereas others increase the blood vessel permeability.

44.2a Combating Pathogenic Viruses

Specific molecules on pathogens such as bacteria are key to initiating innate immune responses. In contrast, the innate immunity system is often unable to distinguish between surface molecules of viral pathogens and host cells or to have access to small pathogens that live inside host cells. The host must, therefore, use other strategies to provide some immediate protection against these infections until the adaptive immunity system, which can discriminate between pathogen and host proteins, is effective. Three main strategies involve RNA interference, interferon, and natural killer cells.

RNA Interference. *RNA interference* (*RNAi*) is a cellular mechanism that is triggered by double-stranded (ds) RNA molecules (see Chapter 15). The dsRNA interferes with the ability of a cell to transcribe specific genes. Because dsRNA is a natural part of the life cycle of many viruses, the use of RNAi can inhibit the dsRNA found in many viruses and eliminate the infection.

Similarly, the virus can interfere with the host immune machinery, including RNAi pathways. Thus, the activities within a cell, and the success of a pathogen such as a virus, depend on the interplay between pro- and anti-infection responses. The only well-established antiviral mechanisms reported in insects such as the fruitfly, *D. melanogaster,* are RNAi and apoptosis. To combat this host response, many viruses contain genes that encode RNAi suppressors or inhibitors of apoptosis that help them survive.

Interferon. Viral dsRNA also may cause the infected host cell to produce two cytokines, interferon-α and interferon-β. **Interferons** can be produced by most cells of the body. These proteins act on both the infected cell that produces them, an autocrine effect, and neighbouring uninfected cells, a paracrine effect (see Chapter 35). They work by binding to cell-surface receptors, triggering a signal transduction pathway that changes the gene expression pattern of the cells. The key changes include the activation of a ribonuclease enzyme that degrades most cellular RNA and the inactivation of a key protein required for protein synthesis, thereby inhibiting most protein synthesis in the cell. These effects on RNA and protein synthesis inhibit replication of the viral genome while putting the cell in a weakened state from which it often can recover.

Apoptosis. Apoptosis, or programmed cell death, is a process inherent to all eukaryotic cells that has been highly conserved through evolution. It represents an intrinsic form of cell death that is tightly regulated by a variety of internal and external cellular signals to avoid killing healthy, productive cells. During development, apoptosis is required to sculpt tissues, remove old and dying cells, and eliminate embryonic cells with damaged DNA. Throughout life, apoptosis is also used as an immune response against intracellular pathogens and parasites. These organisms often trigger abnormal cellular activity that activates intrinsic apoptotic pathways, especially initiator and effector caspases, which dismantle the cell's structure. Once effector caspases have been activated, the cell is destined to die. Apoptotic cells fragment into membrane-bound apoptotic bodies that are readily phagocytosed and digested by macrophages or by neighbouring cells without generating an inflammatory response. If the pathogen is recognized as nonself and the apoptotic response is initiated in time, both the infected cell and the pathogen are eliminated, and no disease is seen. However, as discussed in Section 44.6, some pathogens have developed mechanisms to inactivate this response.

Natural Killer Cells. Cells that have been infected with a virus must be destroyed. That is the role of *natural killer (NK) cells.* NK cells are a type of *lymphocyte,* a leukocyte that carries out most of its activities in the tissues and organs of the lymphatic system (see Figure 37.17). NK cells circulate in the blood and kill target host cells—not only cells that are infected with virus but also some cells that have become cancerous.

NK cells can be activated by cell-surface receptors or by interferons secreted by virus-infected cells. NK cells are not phagocytes; instead, they secrete granules containing *perforin*, a protein that creates pores in the target cell's membrane. Unregulated diffusion of ions and molecules through the pores causes osmotic imbalance, swelling, and rupture of the infected cell. NK cells also kill target cells indirectly through the secretion of *proteases* (protein-degrading enzymes) that pass through the pores. The proteases trigger apoptosis (see Section 9.4f). That is, the proteases activate other enzymes that cause the degradation of DNA, which, in turn, induces pathways leading to the cell's death.

How does an NK cell distinguish a target cell from a normal cell? The surfaces of most vertebrate cells contain particular *major histocompatibility complex (MHC) proteins*. You will learn about the role of these proteins in adaptive immunity in the next section. NK cells monitor the level of MHC proteins and respond differently depending on their level. An appropriately high level, as occurs in normal cells, inhibits the killing activity of NK cells. Because intracellular pathogens often inhibit the synthesis of MHC proteins in the cells they infect, these cells are recognized by NK cells. Cancer cells also have low or, in some cases, no MHC proteins on their surfaces, which makes them a target for destruction by NK cells.

Study Break

1. What are the usual characteristics of the inflammatory response?
2. What processes specifically cause each characteristic of the inflammatory response?
3. What is the complement system?
4. Why does combating viral pathogens require a different response by the innate immunity system than combating bacterial pathogens? What are the four main strategies a host uses to protect against viral infections?

44.3 Specific Defences: Adaptive Immunity

Adaptive immunity is a defence mechanism that recognizes specific molecules as being foreign and clears those molecules from the body. The foreign or abnormal molecules that are recognized may be free, as in the case of toxins, or found on the surface of a virus or cell including pathogenic bacteria, cancer cells, pollen, and cells of transplanted organs. Adaptive immunity develops specifically in response to the presence of foreign molecules and therefore takes several days to become effective. This time delay to mount an adaptive response would be a significant problem in the case of invading pathogens were it not for the innate immune system, which combats the invading pathogens in its nonspecific way within minutes after they enter the body.

There are two key distinctions between innate and adaptive immunity:

- innate immunity is nonspecific, whereas adaptive immunity is specific, and
- innate immunity retains no memory of exposure to the pathogen, whereas adaptive immunity retains a memory of the foreign molecule that triggered the response, enabling a rapid, more powerful response if that pathogen is encountered again.

44.3a Antigens Cleared by B Cells or T Cells

A foreign molecule that triggers an adaptive immunity response is called an **antigen** (meaning "*anti*body *gen*erator"). Antigens are macromolecules; most are large proteins (including glycoproteins and lipoproteins) or polysaccharides (including lipopolysaccharides). Some types of nucleic acids can also act as antigens, as can various large, artificially synthesized molecules.

Antigens may be *exogenous*, meaning that they enter the body from the environment, or *endogenous*, meaning that they are generated within the body. Exogenous antigens include antigens on pathogens introduced beneath the skin, antigens in vaccinations, and inhaled and ingested macromolecules, such as toxins. Endogenous antigens include proteins encoded by viruses that have infected cells and altered proteins produced by mutated genes, such as those in cancer cells.

Antigens are recognized in the body by two types of lymphocytes, B cells and T cells. **B cells** differentiate from stem cells in the bone marrow (see Chapter 37). It is easy to remember this as "B for bone." However, the "B" actually refers to the *bursa of Fabricius*, a lymphatic organ found only in birds, where B cells were first discovered. After their differentiation, B cells are released into the blood and carried to capillary beds serving the tissues and organs of the lymphatic system. **T cells** are produced by the division of stem cells in the bone marrow. They are released into the blood and carried to the **thymus**, an organ of the lymphatic system (the "T" in "T cell" refers to the thymus).

The role of lymphocytes in adaptive immunity was demonstrated by experiments in which all of the leukocytes in mice were killed by irradiation. These mice were unable to develop adaptive immunity. Injecting lymphocytes from normal mice into the irradiated mice restored the response; other body cells extracted from normal mice and injected could not restore the response. (For more on the use of mice as an experimental organism in biology, see *Research Organisms: The Mighty Mouse and the Lowly Fruitfly*.)

Research Organisms: The Mighty Mouse and the Lowly Fruitfly

The house mouse (*Mus musculus*) **(Figure 1)** and its cells have been used as models for research on mammalian developmental genetics, immunology, and cancer and have enabled scientists to carry out experiments that would not be practical or ethical with humans. Mice are small, are easy to maintain in the laboratory, and have been used extensively as experimental animals. Gregor Mendel, the founder of genetics, kept mice as part of his studies. More recently, mouse genetic experiments have revealed more than 500 mutants that cause hereditary diseases, immunological defects, and cancer in mammals, including humans. The mouse also has been the model used to introduce and modify genes through genetic engineering, producing giant mice by introducing a human growth hormone gene or producing "knockout" mice, in which a gene of interest is rendered nonfunctional (see Chapter 16) to determine its normal function. By knocking out mouse genes that are homologous to human genes involved in diseases such as cystic fibrosis, researchers can study human diseases in these model organisms, opening pathways to cure human genetic diseases. In 2002, the sequence of the mouse genome was published, enabling researchers to refine and expand their use of the mouse as a model organism for studies of mammalian biology and mammalian diseases.

Similarly, the fruitfly (*Drosophila melanogaster*) (Figure 1) has become a major organism to study basic genetics, aspects of gene regulation, developmental biology, and especially the role of innate immunity against pathogens. This insect can be raised quickly, cheaply, and in massive numbers. *Drosophila* has been instrumental to our understanding of dorsal–ventral patterning during development and has been one of the major organisms used to identify pathways of immune signalling. Because insects do not have an adaptive immune system, the innate immune system can be studied by itself without the interaction with components of the adaptive system. Toll receptors, important in immune signalling, were found first in *Drosophila* and subsequently were used to identify similar molecules in vertebrates. Mutant lines lacking specific functional genes have been generated in *Drosophila* to study the roles of these genes in all organisms. Because the signalling pathways of the innate immune pathways are highly conserved, information learned on how fruitflies recognize and eliminate pathogens can be transferred to similar studies in other organisms. The genome of *Drosophila* was completed in 2000, allowing for comparisons among and between the genomes of vertebrates and invertebrates. The mighty mouse and the common fruitfly have provided researchers with amazing amounts of information to understand how our bodies work, how similar genes function in different groups of animals, and how we can apply what we learn about one animal to another.

a.

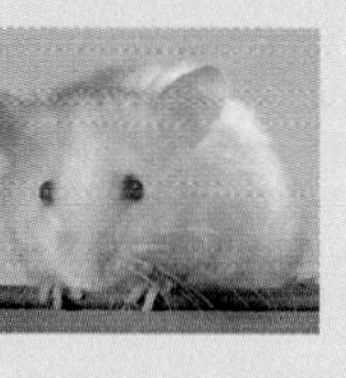

Courtesy of Kevin Wickenheiser, University of Michigan

b.

Edith M. Wallace

Figure 1
Two common research organisms: a mouse and a fruitfly.

There are two types of adaptive immune responses: **antibody-mediated immunity** (also called *humoral immunity*) and **cell-mediated immunity**. The steps involved in the adaptive immune response are similar for antibody-mediated immunity and cell-mediated immunity:

1. Lymphocyte encounter: The lymphocytes encounter, recognize, and bind to an antigen.
2. Lymphocyte activation: The lymphocytes are activated by binding to the antigen and proliferate by cell division to produce large numbers of clones.
3. Antigen clearance: The activated lymphocytes are responsible for clearing the antigen from the body.
4. Development of immunological memory: Some of the activated lymphocytes differentiate into **memory cells** that circulate in the blood and lymph, ready to initiate a rapid immune response on subsequent exposure to the same antigen.

These steps are explained in more detail in the following discussions of antibody-mediated immunity and cell-mediated immunity.

44.3b Antibody-Mediated Immunity

An adaptive immune response begins as soon as an antigen is encountered in the body and is recognized as foreign.

Antigen Encounter and Recognition by Lymphocytes. Exogenous antigens are encountered by lymphocytes in the lymphatic system. As already mentioned, the two key lymphocytes that recognize antigens are B cells and T cells. Each B cell and each T cell is specific for a particular antigen, meaning that the cell can bind to only one particular molecular structure. The binding is so specific because the plasma membrane of each B cell and T cell is studded with thousands of identical receptors for the antigen; in B cells, they are called

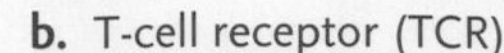

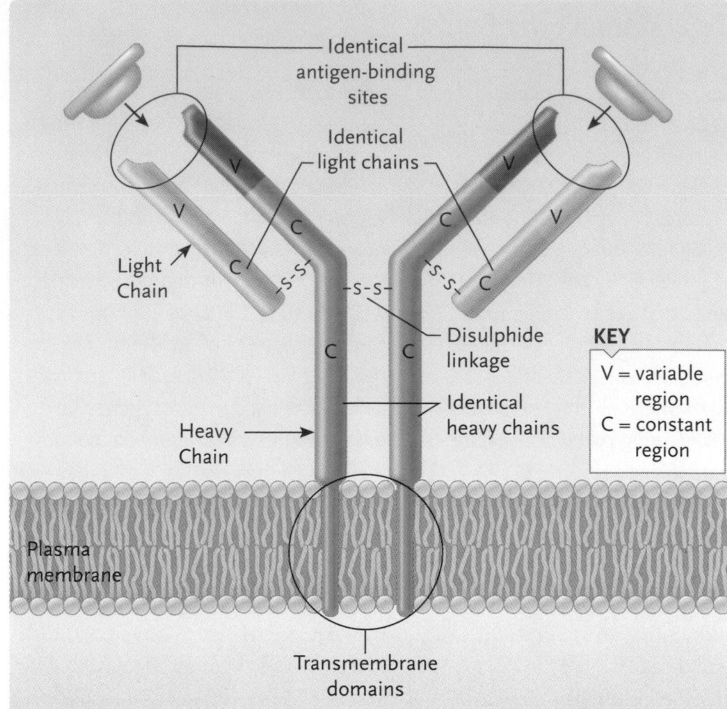

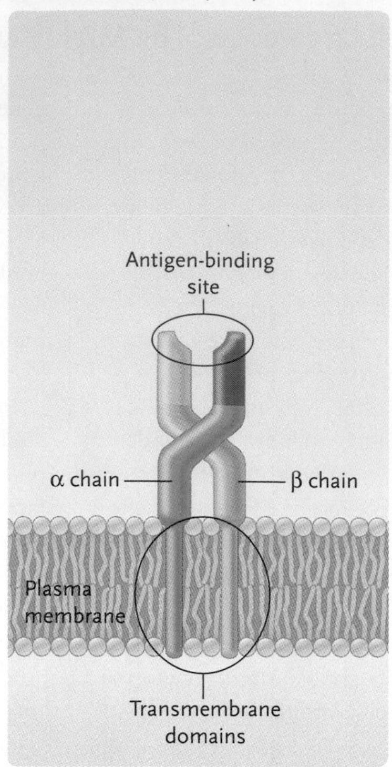

Figure 44.4
(a) Antigen-binding receptor on a B cell and the arrangement of light and heavy polypeptide chains in the antibody molecule. As shown, two sites, one at the tip of each arm of the Y, bind the same antigen. **(b)** Antigen-binding receptor on a T cell.

B-cell receptors (BCRs), and in T cells, they are called **T-cell receptors (TCRs) (Figure 44.4).** The populations of B cells and T cells contain cells capable of recognizing any antigen, and each antigen can be recognized by multiple cells. For example, each of us has about 10 trillion B cells that collectively have about 100 million different kinds of BCRs. And all of these cells are present *before* the body has encountered the antigens.

The binding between antigen and receptor is an interaction between two molecules that fit together like an enzyme and its substrate. A given BCR or TCR typically does not bind to the whole antigen molecule but to small regions of it called **epitopes** or *antigenic determinants*. Therefore, several different B cells and T cells may bind to the population of a particular antigen encountered in the lymphatic system.

BCRs and TCRs are encoded by different genes and thus have different structures (see *The Generation of Antibody Diversity*). When the BCR on a naive B cell matches a detected antigen, it is activated and may differentiate into a plasma cell that proliferates and secretes antibodies that recognize the same antigen (see Figure 44.4a).

As you will learn in more detail, an antibody molecule is a protein consisting of four polypeptide chains. At one end is a region that embeds in a plasma membrane, whereas at the other end are two identical *antigen-binding sites*, regions that bind to a specific antigen. TCRs are simpler than BCRs, consisting of a protein made up of two different polypeptides (see Figure 44.4b). Like BCRs, TCRs have an antigen-binding site at one end and a membrane-embedded region at the other end.

Antibodies. Antibodies are the core molecules of antibody-mediated immunity. Antibodies are large, complex proteins that belong to a class of proteins known as *immunoglobulins* (Ig). Each antibody molecule consists of four polypeptide chains: two identical *light chains* and two identical *heavy chains* about twice or more the size of the light chain (see Figure 44.4a). The chains are held together in the complete protein by disulphide (–S–S–) linkages and fold into a Y-shaped structure. The bonds between the two arms of the Y form a hinge that allows the arms to flex independently of one another.

Each polypeptide chain of an antibody molecule has a *constant region* and a *variable region*. Each antibody type has the same amino acid sequence in the constant region of the heavy chain and likewise for the constant region of the light chain. The variable

The Generation of Antibody Diversity

The human genome has approximately 20 000 to 25 000 genes, far fewer than necessary to encode 100 million different antibodies if two genes encoded one antibody, one gene for the heavy chain and one for the light chain. The great diversity in antigen-binding capability of those receptors is generated in a different way from one gene per chain. During B-cell differentiation, the DNA segments that encode parts of the light and heavy chains undergo three rearrangements. The genes for the two different subunits of the T-cell receptor undergo similar rearrangements.

The light chain expressed by an undifferentiated B cell is encoded by three types of DNA segments, and one of each type is needed to make a complete, functional light-chain gene. In humans, about 40 different V segments encode most of the variable regions of the chain, 5 different J (joining) segments encode the rest of the variable region, only one copy of the segment makes up the constant (C) part of the chain. Thus, a complete light chain comprises one V segment, adjacent to one J segment, adjacent to the C region, which is the same for all light chains regardless of V or J segment usage (see Figure 44.4).

During B-cell differentiation, a DNA rearrangement occurs in which one random V segment and one random J segment join with the C segment to form a functional light-chain gene. During this assembly, there is a deletion of DNA between the V and J segments, and the positions at which the DNA breaks and rejoins in the V- and J-joining reaction occur randomly over a distance of several nucleotides, which adds greatly to the variability of the final gene assembly. The DNA between the J segment and the C segment becomes an intron in the final assembled gene. Transcription of this newly assembled gene produces a typical pre-mRNA molecule (see Chapter 14). The introns are removed during the production of the mRNA by RNA processing. Translation of the mRNA produces the light chain with both the variable and the constant regions.

The assembly of functional heavy-chain genes occurs similarly. However, whereas light-chain genes have one C segment, heavy-chain genes have five types of C segments, each of which encodes one of the constant regions of IgM, IgD, IgG, IgE, and IgA. The inclusion of one of the five C-segment types in the functional heavy-chain gene therefore specifies the class of antibody that will be made by the B cell.

regions of both the heavy and the light chains, by contrast, have different amino acid sequences for each antibody molecule in a population. Structurally, the variable regions are the top halves of the polypeptides in the arms of the Y-shaped molecule. The three-dimensional folding of the heavy chain and light chain variable regions of each arm creates the antigen-binding site. The antigen-binding site is identical on both arms of the same antibody molecule because both ends of the Y have the same amino acid sequences in their variable regions. However, the antigen-binding sites are different from antibody molecule to antibody molecule (produced by different B-cell clones) because of the amino acid differences in the variable regions of the two chain types.

The constant regions of the heavy chains in the tail part of the Y-shaped structure determine the *class* of the antibody, that is, its location and function. Humans have five different classes of antibodies: IgM, IgG, IgA, IgE, and IgD **(Table 44.2, p. 1096)**.

IgM antibodies are the first antibodies produced in the early stages of an antibody-mediated response after BCRs are activated and B cells differentiate into plasma cells. When they bind an antigen, IgM antibodies activate the complement system and stimulate the phagocytic activity of macrophages.

IgG antibodies circulate in the highest concentration in the blood and lymphatic system, where they also stimulate phagocytosis and activate the complement system when it binds an antigen. IgG is produced in large amounts when the body is exposed a second time to the same antigen.

IgA is found mainly in body secretions such as saliva, tears, breast milk, and the mucus coating of body cavities such as the lungs, digestive tract, and vagina. In these locations, the antibodies bind to surface groups on pathogens and block their attachment to body surfaces. Breast milk transfers IgA antibodies, and thus immunity, to a nursing infant.

IgE is secreted by plasma cells of the skin and the tissues lining the gastrointestinal tract and respiratory tract. IgE binds to basophils and mast cells, where it mediates many allergic responses, such as hay fever, asthma, and hives. When its specific antigen binds to IgE, the basophils or mast cells release histamine, which triggers an inflammatory response. IgE also contributes to mechanisms that combat infection by parasitic worms.

Table 44.2 Five Classess of Antibodies

Class	Structure	Location	Functions
IgM		Surfaces of unstimulated B cells; free in circulation	First antibodies to be secreted by B cells in primary response. When bound to antigen, promotes agglutination reaction, activates complement system, and stimulates phagocytic activity of macrophages.
IgG		Blood and lymphatic circulation	Most abundant antibody in primary and secondary responses. Crosses placenta, conferring passive immunity to fetus; stimulates phagocytosis and activates complement system.
IgA		Body secretions such as tears, breast milk, saliva, and mucus	Blocks attachment of pathogens to mucus membranes; confers passive immunity for breast-fed infants
IgE		Skin and tissues lining gastrointestinal and respiratory tracts (secreted by plasma cells)	Stimulates mast cells and basophils to release histamine; triggers allergic responses
IgD		Surface of unstimulated B cells	Membrane receptor for mature B cells; probably important in B-cell activation (clonal selection)

IgD occurs with IgM as a receptor on the surfaces of B cells; its function is not well understood but may be involved in B-cell activation.

T-Cell Activation. Let us now follow the development of an antibody-mediated immune response by linking the recognition of an antigen by lymphocytes, the activation of lymphocytes by antigen binding, and the production of antibodies. Typically, the pathway begins when a type of T cell becomes activated and follows the steps outlined in **Figure 44.5** that determine the fate of pathogenic bacteria that have been introduced under the skin. Circulating viruses in the blood follow the same pathway.

First, a type of phagocyte called a **dendritic cell** engulfs a bacterium in the infected tissue by phagocytosis (**Figure 44.6**, step 1). Dendritic cells are so named because they have many surface projections resembling the dendrites of neurons. They have the same origin as leukocytes and recognize a bacterium as foreign by the same recognition mechanism used by macrophages in the innate immune system. In essence, the dendritic cell is part of the innate immunity system, but its primary role is to stimulate the development of an adaptive immune response.

Engulfing a bacterium activates the dendritic cell; the cell now migrates to a nearby lymph node. Within the dendritic cell, the endocytic vesicle containing the bacterium fuses with a lysosome. In the

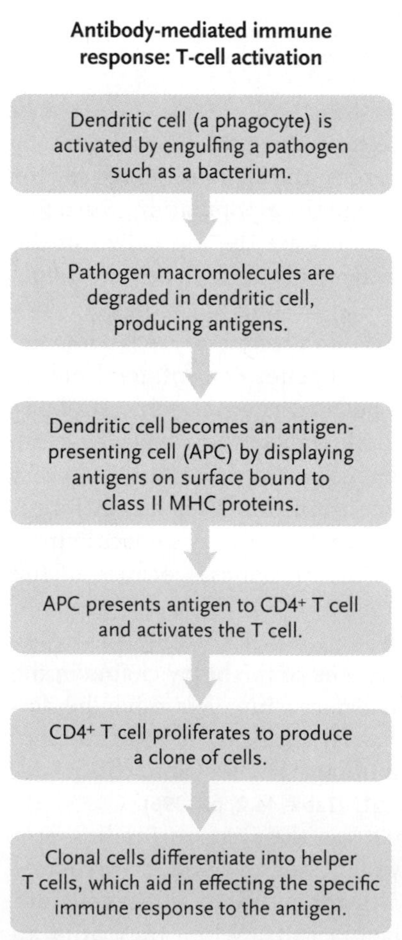

Antibody-mediated immune response: T-cell activation
Dendritic cell (a phagocyte) is activated by engulfing a pathogen such as a bacterium.
Pathogen macromolecules are degraded in dendritic cell, producing antigens.
Dendritic cell becomes an antigen-presenting cell (APC) by displaying antigens on surface bound to class II MHC proteins.
APC presents antigen to CD4+ T cell and activates the T cell.
CD4+ T cell proliferates to produce a clone of cells.
Clonal cells differentiate into helper T cells, which aid in effecting the specific immune response to the antigen.

Figure 44.5
An outline of T-cell activation in antibody-mediated immunity.

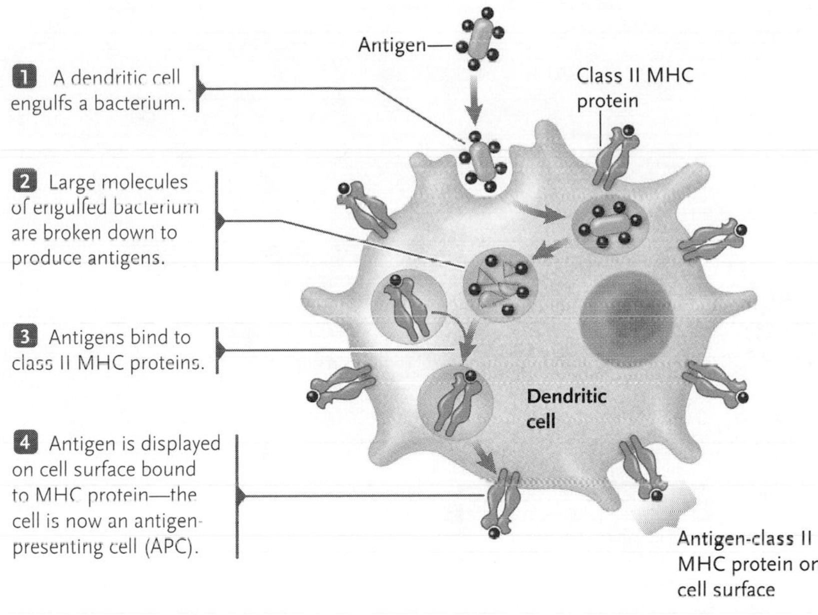
Antigen
1 A dendritic cell engulfs a bacterium.
Class II MHC protein
2 Large molecules of engulfed bacterium are broken down to produce antigens.
3 Antigens bind to class II MHC proteins.
Dendritic cell
4 Antigen is displayed on cell surface bound to MHC protein—the cell is now an antigen-presenting cell (APC).
Antigen-class II MHC protein on cell surface

Figure 44.6
Generation of an antigen-presenting cell after a dendritic cell engulfs a bacterium.

receptor on the T cell helps link the two cells together.

When the APC binds to the CD4$^+$ T cell, the APC secretes an *interleukin* (meaning "between leukocytes"), a type of cytokine, which activates the T cell (see Figure 44.7, step 3). The activated T cell then secretes cytokines (step 4), which act in an autocrine manner (see Chapter 35) to stimulate **clonal expansion**, the proliferation of the activated CD4$^+$ T cell by cell division to produce a clone of cells. These clonal cells differentiate into **helper T cells** (step 5), so named because they assist with the activation of B cells. A helper T cell is an example of an **effector T cell**, meaning that it is involved in effecting—bringing about—the specific immune response to the antigen.

lysosome, the bacterium's proteins are degraded into short peptides, which are antigens (see Figure 44.6, step 2). The antigens bind to **class II major histocompatibility complex (MHC)** proteins (step 3), and the interacting molecules then migrate to the cell surface where the antigen is displayed (step 4). These steps in the lymph node, which are recapped in **Figure 44.7, p. 1098**, step 1, have converted the cell into an **antigen-presenting cell (APC)**, ready to present the antigen to T cells in the next step of antibody-mediated immunity.

MHC proteins are named for a large cluster of genes encoding them, called the **major histocompatibility complex**. The complex spans 4 million base pairs and contains 128 genes. Many of these genes play important roles in the immune system. Each individual of each vertebrate species has a unique combination of MHC proteins on almost all body cells, meaning that no two individuals of a species except identical siblings are likely to have exactly the same MHC proteins on their cells. There are two classes of MHC proteins, class I and class II, which have different functions in adaptive immunity, as we will see.

The key function of an APC is to present the antigen to a lymphocyte. In the antibody-mediated immune response, the APC presents the antigen, bound to a class II MHC protein, to a type of T cell in the lymphatic system called a **CD4$^+$ T cell** because it has receptors named CD4 on its surface. A specific CD4$^+$ T cell, which has a TCR with an antigen-binding site that recognizes the antigen, binds to the antigen on the APC (see Figure 44.7, step 2). The CD4

B-Cell Activation. Antibodies are produced and secreted by B cells. The activation of a B cell that makes the specific antibody against an antigen requires the B cell to present the antigen on its surface and then to link with a helper T cell that has differentiated as a result of encountering and recognizing the same antigen. The process is outlined in **Figures 44.7** and **44.8, p. 1098**.

The process of antigen presentation on a B-cell surface begins when BCRs on the B cell interact directly with soluble bacterial (in our example) antigens in the blood or lymph. Once the antigen binds to a BCR, the complex is taken into the cell and the antigen is processed in the same way as in dendritic cells, being broken down into smaller fragments, culminating with a presentation of each antigen-derived peptide fragment on the B-cell surface in a complex with class II MHC proteins (see Figure 44.7, step 6).

When one of the helper T cells produced above encounters a B cell displaying the same antigen, usually in a lymph node or in the spleen, the T and B cells become tightly linked together (see Figure 44.7, step 7). The linkage depends on the TCRs, which recognize and bind the antigen displayed by the class II MHC molecules on the surface of the B cell, and on CD4, which stabilizes the binding as it did for T-cell binding to the dendritic cell. The linkage between the cells first stimulates the helper T cell to secrete interleukins that activate the B cell and then stimulates the B cell to proliferate, producing a clone of those B cells with identical B-cell receptors (step 8). Some of the cloned cells differentiate into relatively short-lived **plasma cells**, which now secrete the same antibody that was

a. Antibody-mediated immune response

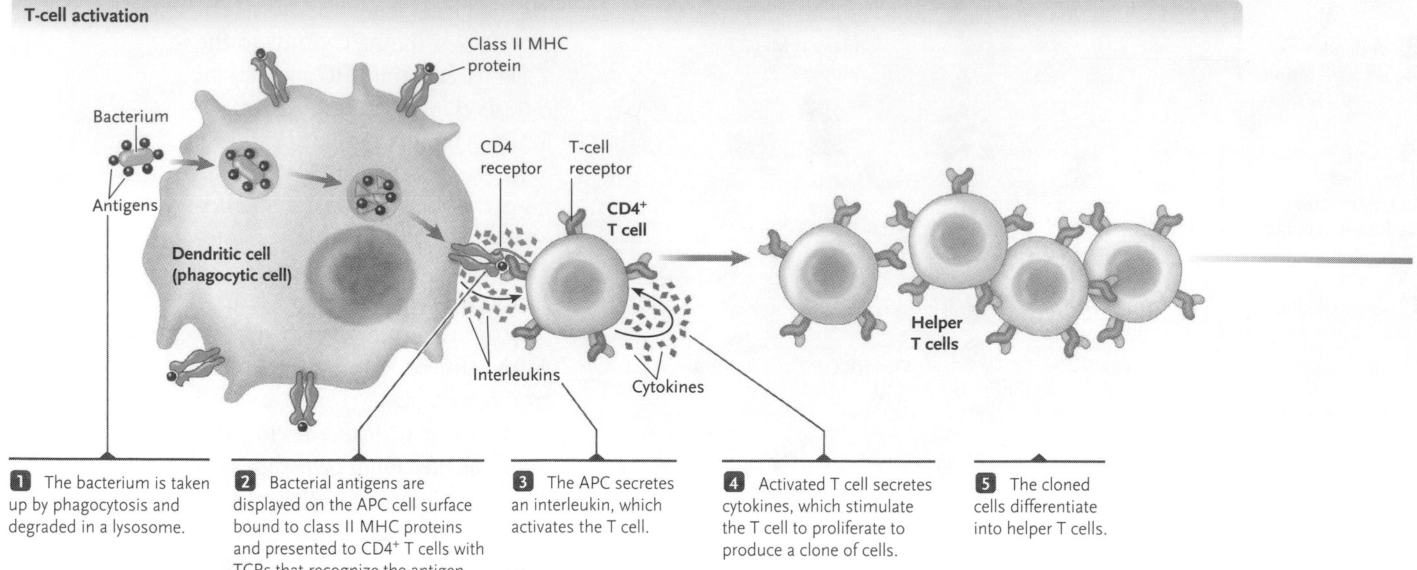

T-cell activation
Class II MHC protein
Bacterium
Antigens
Dendritic cell (phagocytic cell)
CD4 receptor
T-cell receptor
CD4⁺ T cell
Helper T cells
Interleukins
Cytokines
1 The bacterium is taken up by phagocytosis and degraded in a lysosome.
2 Bacterial antigens are displayed on the APC cell surface bound to class II MHC proteins and presented to CD4⁺ T cells with TCRs that recognize the antigen.
3 The APC secretes an interleukin, which activates the T cell.
4 Activated T cell secretes cytokines, which stimulate the T cell to proliferate to produce a clone of cells.
5 The cloned cells differentiate into helper T cells.

Figure 44.7
The antibody-mediated immune response.

Antibody-mediated immune response: B-cell activation

A BCR on a B cell recognizes an antigen on the surface of a bacterium and the bacterium is engulfed.

↓

Pathogen macromolecules are degraded in the B cell, producing antigens.

↓

B cell displays antigens on its surface bound to class II MHC proteins.

↓

Helper T cell with TCR that recognizes the same antigen links to the B cell.

↓

Helper T cell secretes interleukins that activate the B cell.

↓

B cell proliferates to produce a clone of cells.

↓

Some B-cell clones differentiate into plasma cells, which secrete antibodies specific to the antigen, and others differentiate into memory B cells.

Figure 44.8
An outline of B-cell activation in antibody-mediated immunity.

displayed on the parental B cell's surface to circulate in lymph and blood. Others differentiate into **memory B cells**, which are long-lived cells that set the stage for a much more rapid response should the same antigen be encountered later in life (step 9).

Clonal selection is the process by which a lymphocyte is specifically selected for cloning when it encounters a foreign antigen from among a randomly generated, enormous diversity of lymphocytes with receptors that specifically recognize the antigen **(Figure 44.9)**. The process of clonal selection was proposed in the 1950s by several scientists, most notably F. Macfarlane Burnet, Niels Jerne, and David Talmage. Their proposals, made long before the mechanism was understood, described clonal selection as a form of natural selection operating in miniature: antigens select the cells recognizing them, which reproduce and become dominant in the B-cell population. Burnet received the Nobel Prize in 1960 for his research in immunology.

Clearing the Body of Foreign Antigens. How do the antibodies produced in an antibody-mediated immune response clear different types of foreign antigens from the body? Toxins produced by invading bacteria, such as tetanus toxin, can be *neutralized* by antibodies **(Figure 44.10a, p. 1100)**. The antibodies bind to the toxin molecules, inactivating them.

Antibodies bind to antigens on the surfaces of intact bacteria at an infection site or in the circulatory system. Because the two arms of an antibody molecule bind to different copies of the antigen molecule, an antibody molecule may bind to two bacteria with the same antigen. A population of antibodies can link many bacteria together into a lattice, causing *agglutination*, or clumping of the bacteria **(Figure 44.10b, p. 1100)**. Agglutination immobilizes the bacteria, preventing them from infecting cells. Antibodies can also agglutinate viruses, also preventing them from infecting cells.

More importantly, antibodies bound to antigens aid the innate immune response that was initially set off by the pathogens by stimulating the complement

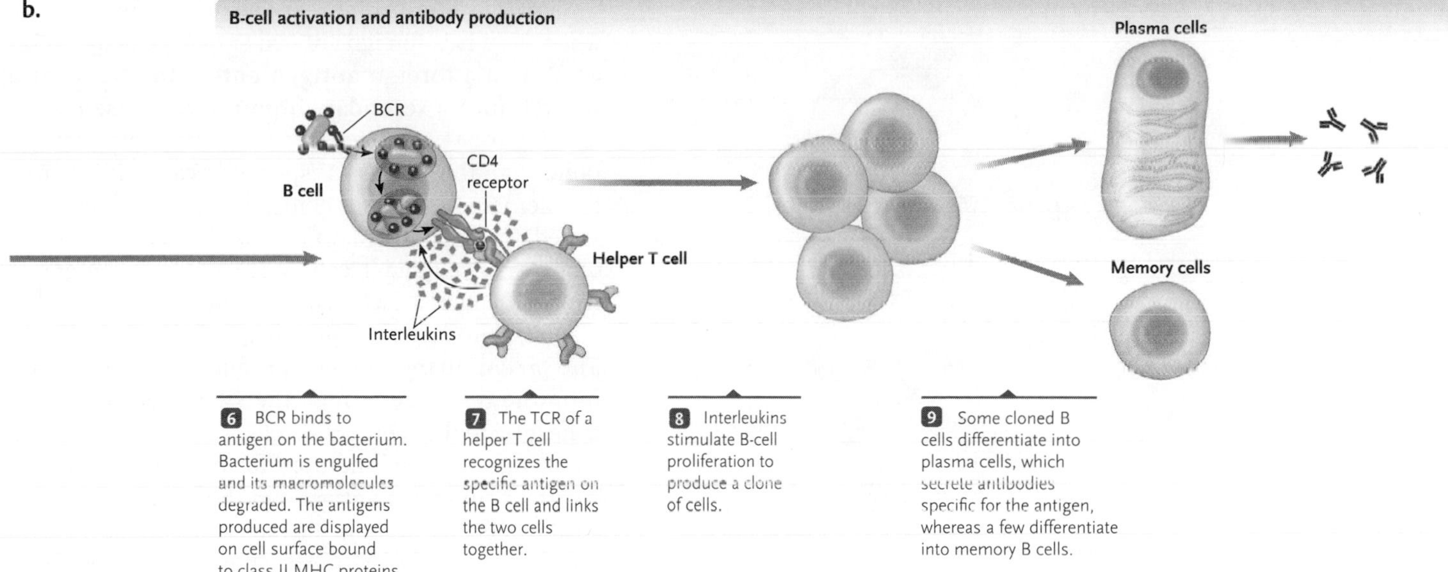

b.
B-cell activation and antibody production
BCR
B cell
CD4
receptor
Helper T cell
Interleukins
Plasma cells
Memory cells
6 BCR binds to antigen on the bacterium. Bacterium is engulfed and its macromolecules degraded. The antigens produced are displayed on cell surface bound to class II MHC proteins.
7 The TCR of a helper T cell recognizes the specific antigen on the B cell and links the two cells together.
8 Interleukins stimulate B-cell proliferation to produce a clone of cells.
9 Some cloned B cells differentiate into plasma cells, which secrete antibodies specific for the antigen, whereas a few differentiate into memory B cells.

system. Membrane attack complexes are formed and insert themselves into the plasma membranes of the bacteria, leading to their lysis and death. In the case of virus infections, membrane attack complexes can insert themselves into the membranes surrounding enveloped viruses, which disrupts the membrane and prevents the viruses from infecting cells.

Antibodies also enhance phagocytosis of bacteria and viruses. Phagocytic cells have receptors on their surfaces that recognize the heavy-chain end of antibodies (the end of the molecule opposite the antigen-binding sites). Antibodies bound to bacteria or viruses therefore bind to phagocytic cells, which then engulf the pathogens and destroy them.

For simplicity, the adaptive immune response has been described here in terms of a single antigen. Pathogens have many different types of antigens on their surfaces, which means that many different B cells are stimulated to proliferate and many different antibodies are produced. Pathogens are therefore attacked by many different antibodies, each targeted to one antigen on the pathogen's surface.

Immunological Memory. Once an immune reaction has run its course and the invading pathogen or toxic molecule has been eliminated from the body, division of the plasma cells and T-cell clones stops. Most or all of the clones die and are eliminated from the bloodstream and other body fluids. However, long-lived memory B cells and **memory helper T cells** (which differentiated from helper T cells) remain in an inactive state in the lymphatic system. Their persistence provides an **immunological memory** of the foreign antigen.

Immunological memory is illustrated in **Figure 44.11, p. 1100.** When the body is exposed to a foreign antigen for the first time, a **primary immune response** results,

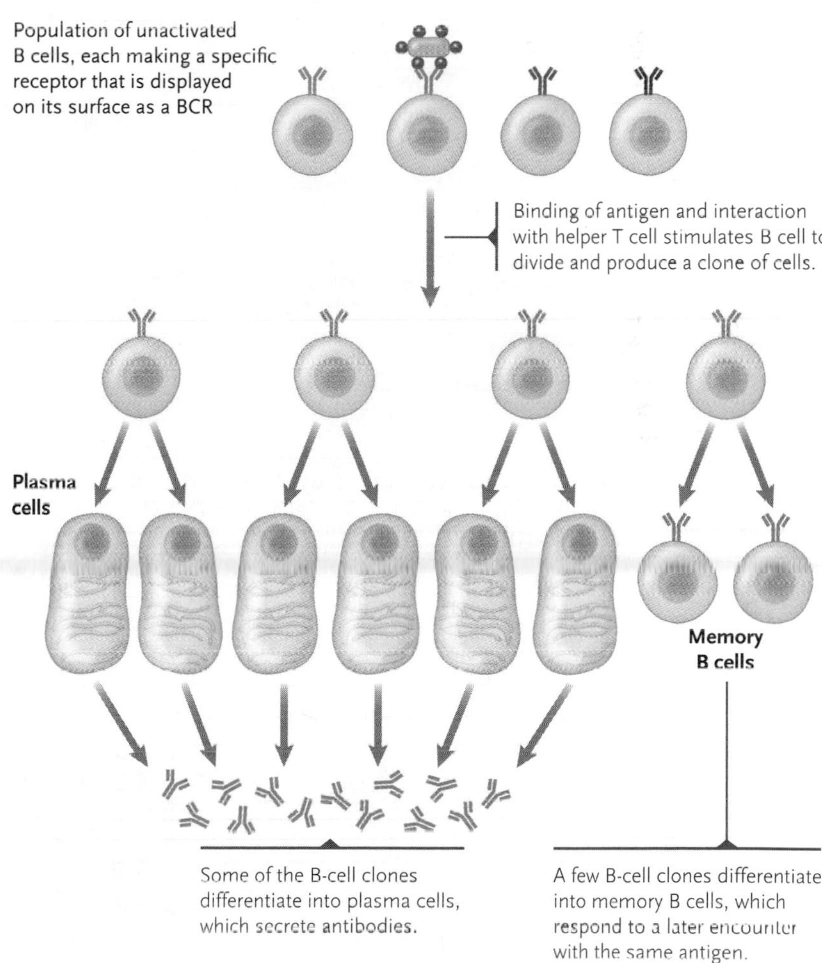

Figure 44.9
Clonal selection. The binding of an antigen to a B cell that already displays a specific antibody to that antigen stimulates the B cell to divide and differentiate into plasma cells, which secrete the antibody, and memory cells, which remain in the circulation ready to mount a response against the antigen at a later time.

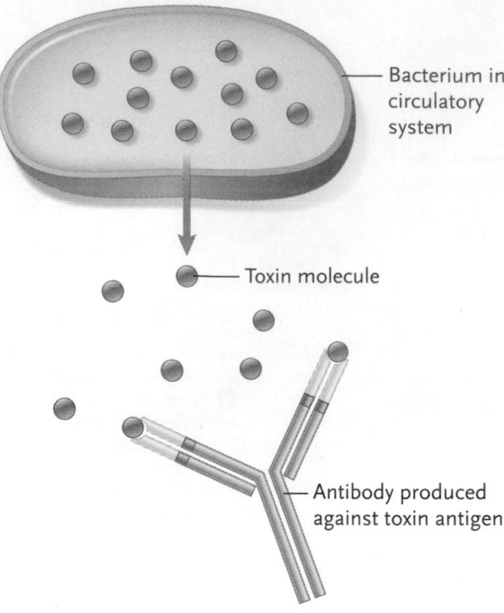

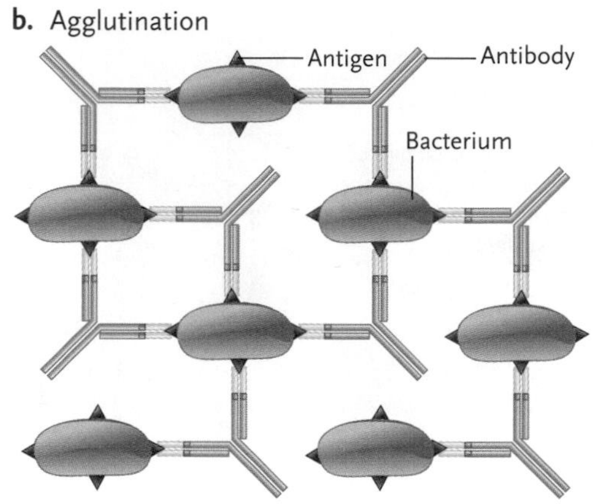

Figure 44.10
Examples of clearing antigens from the body.

following the steps already described. The first antibodies appear in the blood in 3 to 14 days, and by week 4, the primary response has essentially gone away. IgM is the first antibody type produced and secreted into the bloodstream in a primary immune response. This primary immune response curve is followed whenever a new foreign antigen enters the body.

When a foreign antigen enters the body for a second time, a **secondary immune response** results (see Figure 44.11). The secondary response is more rapid than the primary response because it involves the memory B cells and memory T cells that have been stored. It does not have to initiate the clonal selection of a new B cell and T cell. Moreover, less antigen is needed to elicit a secondary response than a primary response, and many more antibodies are produced. The predominant antibody produced in a secondary immune response is IgG; the switch occurs at the gene level in the memory B cells.

Immunological memory forms the basis of vaccinations, in which antigens in the form of living or dead pathogens or antigenic molecules themselves are introduced into the body. After the immune response, memory B cells and memory T cells remaining in the body can mount an immediate and intense immune reaction against similar antigens. As mentioned in *Why It Matters,* Edward Jenner introduced the cowpox virus—a virus closely related to, but less virulent than, the smallpox virus—into healthy individuals who initiated a primary immune response. After the response ran its course, a bank of memory B cells and memory T cells remained in the body, able to recognize quickly the similar antigens of the smallpox virus and initiate a secondary immune response. Similarly, the polio vaccine developed by Jonas Salk uses polioviruses that have been inactivated by exposing them to formaldehyde. Although the viruses are inactive, their surface groups can still act as antigens. The antigens trigger an immune response, leaving memory B and T cells able to mount an intense immune response against active polioviruses.

Active and Passive Immunity. **Active immunity** is the production of antibodies in response to exposure to a foreign antigen, as has just been described. **Passive immunity** is the acquisition of antibodies as a result of direct transfer from another person. This form of immunity provides immediate protection against the

Figure 44.11
Immunological memory: primary and secondary responses to the same antigen.

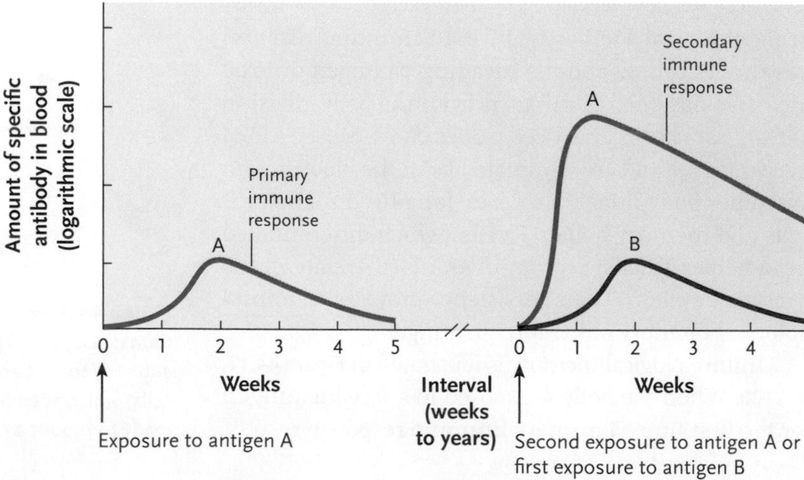

antigens that the antibodies recognize without the person receiving the antibodies having developed a primary immune response. Examples of passive immunity include the transfer of IgG antibodies from the mother to the fetus through the placenta and the transfer of IgA antibodies in the first breast milk fed from the mother to the baby. Compared with active immunity, passive immunity is a short-lived phenomenon with no memory, in that the antibodies typically break down within a month. However, in that time, the protection plays an important role. For example, a breast-fed baby is protected until it is able to mount an immune response itself, an ability that is not present until about a month after birth.

Drug Effects on Antibody-Mediated Immunity. Several drugs used to reduce the rejection of transplanted organs target helper T cells. Cyclosporin A, used routinely after organ transplants, blocks the activation of helper T cells and, in turn, the activation of B cells. Although very successful, cyclosporin and other immunosuppressive drugs also leave the treated individual more susceptible to infection by pathogens.

44.3c Cell-Mediated Immunity

In cell-mediated immunity, cytotoxic T cells directly destroy host cells infected by intracellular pathogens **(Figure 44.12).** The killing process begins when some of the pathogens are broken down by cytoplasmic enzymes inside infected host cells, and the smaller protein fragments (or antigen-derived peptide fragments) themselves act as antigens. These antigens bind to class I MHC proteins, which are delivered to the cell surface by essentially the same mechanisms as in B cells (step 1). At the surface, the antigens are displayed by the class I MHC protein and the cell then functions as an APC.

The APC presents the antigen to a type of T cell in the lymphatic system called a **CD8$^+$ T cell** because it has receptors named CD8 on its surface in addition to the TCRs. The presence of a CD8 receptor distinguishes this type of T cell from that involved in antibody-mediated immunity. A specific CD8$^+$ T cell that has a TCR that recognizes the antigen binds to that antigen on the APC (see Figure 44.12, step 2). The CD8 receptor on the T cell helps the two cells link together.

The link between the APC and the CD8$^+$ T cell activates the T cell, which then proliferates to form a clone. Some of the cells differentiate to become **cytotoxic T cells** (see Figure 44.12, step 3), whereas a few differentiate into *memory cytotoxic T cells.* Cytotoxic T cells are another type of effector T cell. TCRs on the cytotoxic T cells again recognize the antigen bound to class I MHC proteins on the infected cells (the APCs) (step 4). The cytotoxic T cell then destroys the infected cell using mechanisms similar to those used by NK cells. That is, an activated cytotoxic T cell releases perforin, which creates pores in the membrane of the target cell. The leakage of ions and other molecules

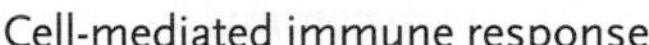

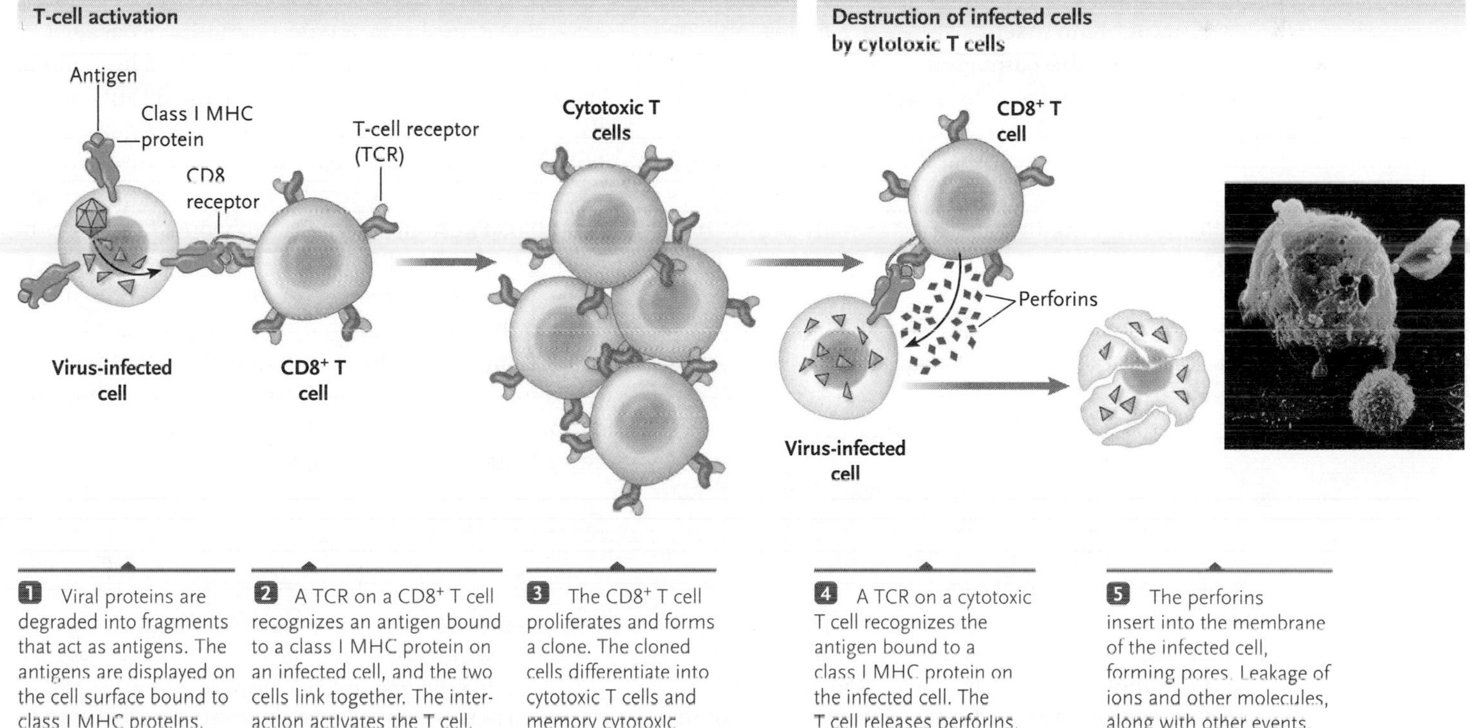

T-cell activation
Antigen
Class I MHC protein
CD8 receptor
T-cell receptor (TCR)
Virus-infected cell
CD8+ T cell
Cytotoxic T cells
Destruction of infected cells by cytotoxic T cells
CD8+ T cell
Perforins
Virus-infected cell
Lennart Nilsson/Bonnier Fakta AB
1 Viral proteins are degraded into fragments that act as antigens. The antigens are displayed on the cell surface bound to class I MHC proteins.
2 A TCR on a CD8+ T cell recognizes an antigen bound to a class I MHC protein on an infected cell, and the two cells link together. The interaction activates the T cell.
3 The CD8+ T cell proliferates and forms a clone. The cloned cells differentiate into cytotoxic T cells and memory cytotoxic T cells.
4 A TCR on a cytotoxic T cell recognizes the antigen bound to a class I MHC protein on the infected cell. The T cell releases perforins.
5 The perforins insert into the membrane of the infected cell, forming pores. Leakage of ions and other molecules, along with other events, causes the cell to lyse.

Figure 44.12
The cell-mediated immune response.

Some Cancer Cells Kill Cytotoxic T Cells to Defeat the Immune System

Among the arsenal of weapons employed by cytotoxic T cells to eliminate abnormal, infected, or cancerous body cells is apoptosis mediated by the *Fas–FasL* system. Fas is a receptor that occurs on the surfaces of many cells; FasL is a ligand displayed on the surfaces of some cell types, including cytotoxic T cells. If a cell carrying the Fas receptor contacts a cytotoxic T cell with the FasL signal displayed on its surface, a cascade of internal reactions initiates apoptosis and kills the cell with the Fas receptor.

Surprisingly, cytotoxic T cells also carry the Fas receptor, so they can kill each other by displaying the FasL signal. This mutual killing plays an important role in reducing the level of an immune reaction after a pathogen has been eliminated. In the case of **immune privilege,** cells in specific regions such as the cornea, nervous tissue, and testes express FasL to induce the apoptosis of infiltrating cytotoxic T cells and reduce inflammation.

Some cancer cells survive elimination by the immune system by making and displaying FasL and killing any cytotoxic T cells that attack the tumour. This was found first in patients suffering from malignant melanoma, a dangerous skin cancer, who had a breakdown product associated with FasL in their bloodstream.

Proteins extracted from melanoma cells, or sections made from melanoma tissue, tested positive (using antibodies) for the presence of FasL, indicating that FasL was present in the tumour cells. Similarly, the expression of FasL mRNA was also detected in the tumour cells. However, no Fas receptor was found in these samples, suggesting that Fas synthesis was turned off in the tumour cells.

FasL in melanoma cells kills cytotoxic T cells that invade the tumour, whereas the absence of Fas receptors ensures that the tumour cells do not kill each other. The presence of FasL and absence of the Fas receptor may explain why melanomas, and many other types of cancer, are rarely destroyed by the immune system.

Melanoma cells originate from pigment cells in the skin called *melanocytes.* Normal melanocytes do not contain FasL, indicating that synthesis of the protein is turned on as part of the transformation from normal melanocytes into cancer cells.

This research could lead to an effective treatment for cancer using the Fas–FasL system. If melanoma cells could be induced to make Fas as well as FasL, for example, they might eliminate a tumour by killing each other!

through the pores causes the infected cell to rupture. The cytotoxic T cell also secretes proteases that enter infected cells through the newly created pores and cause it to self-destruct by apoptosis (see Figure 44.12, step 5 and photo inset). The rupture of dead infected cells releases the pathogens to the interstitial fluid, where they are open to attack by antibodies and phagocytes.

Cytotoxic T cells can also kill cancer cells if their class I MHC molecules display fragments of altered cellular proteins that do not normally occur in the body. Another mechanism used by cytotoxic T cells to kill cells, and a process used by some cancer cells to defeat the mechanism, is described in *Some Cancer Cells Kill Cytotoxic T Cells to Defeat the Immune System.*

44.3d The Use of Antibodies in Research

The ability to generate antibodies against essentially any antigen provides an invaluable research tool for scientists. Most antibodies are obtained by injecting a molecule into a test animal such as a mouse, rabbit, or goat and collecting and purifying the antibodies from the blood. Scientists can then attach a visible marker such as a dye molecule or heavy metal atom to the antibody and determine when and where specific biological molecules are found in cells or tissues. Antibodies also can be used to "grab" a molecule of interest from a mixture of molecules by attaching antibodies to that molecule to plastic beads that are packed into a glass column. When the mixture is poured through the column, the molecule remains bound to the antibody in the column. It is then released from the column in purified form by adding a reagent that breaks the antigen–antibody bonds.

Injecting a molecule of interest into a test animal typically produces a wide spectrum of antibodies that react with different parts of the antigen. Some antibodies may cross-react with other similar antigens, producing false results that can complicate the research. These problems have been solved by producing **monoclonal antibodies,** each of which reacts only against the same segment (epitope) of a single antigen. In addition to their use in scientific research, monoclonal antibodies are also widely used in medical applications such as pregnancy tests, screening for prostate cancer, and testing for AIDS and other sexually transmitted diseases.

Study Break

1. How, in general, do the antibody-mediated and cell-mediated immune responses help clear the body of antigens?
2. Describe the general structure of an antibody molecule.
3. What is clonal selection?
4. How does immunological memory work?

44.4 Malfunctions and Failures of the Immune System

The immune system is highly effective, but it is not foolproof. Some malfunctions of the immune system cause the body to react against its own proteins or cells, producing *autoimmune diseases*. In addition, some viruses and other pathogens have evolved means to avoid destruction by the immune system. A number of these pathogens, including the AIDS virus, even use parts of the immune response to promote infection. Another malfunction causes the *allergic reactions* that many of us experience from time to time.

44.4a The Immune System Normally Protects against Attack

B cells and T cells are involved in the development of **immunological tolerance**, which protects the body's own molecules from attack by the immune system. Although the process is not understood, molecules present in an individual from birth are not recognized as foreign by circulating B and T cells and do not elicit an immune response. During their initial differentiation in the bone marrow and thymus, any B and T cells that react with "self" molecules carried by MHC proteins become suppressed or are induced to kill themselves by apoptosis. The process of excluding self-reactive B and T cells goes on throughout the life of an individual.

Evidence that immunological tolerance is established early in life comes from experiments with mice. For example, if a foreign protein is injected into a mouse at birth, during the period in which tolerance is established, the mouse will not develop antibodies against the protein if it is injected later in life. Similarly, if mutant mice are produced that lack a given complement protein, so that the protein is absent during embryonic development, they will produce antibodies against that protein if it is injected during adult life. Normal mice do not produce antibodies if the protein is injected.

44.4b When Immunological Tolerance Fails

The mechanisms setting up immunological tolerance sometimes fail, leading to an **autoimmune reaction**—the production of antibodies against molecules of the body. In most cases, the effects of such antiself antibodies are not serious enough to produce recognizable disease. However, in some individuals—about 5 to 10% of the human population—antiself antibodies cause serious problems.

For example, *type 1 diabetes* (see Chapter 35) is an autoimmune reaction against the pancreatic beta cells that produce insulin. The antiself antibodies gradually eliminate the beta cells until the individual is incapable of producing insulin. *Systemic lupus erythematosus* (*lupus*) is caused by production of a wide variety of antiself antibodies against blood cells, blood platelets, and internal cell structures and molecules such as mitochondria and proteins associated with DNA in the cell nucleus. People with lupus often become anemic and have problems with blood circulation and kidney function because the antibodies, combined with body molecules, accumulate and clog capillaries and the microscopic filtering tubules of the kidneys. Lupus patients also may develop antiself antibodies against the heart and kidneys. *Rheumatoid arthritis* is caused by a self-attack on connective tissues, particularly in the joints, causing pain and inflammation. *Multiple sclerosis* results from an autoimmune attack against a protein of the myelin sheaths that insulate the surfaces of neurons. Multiple sclerosis can seriously disrupt nervous function, producing such symptoms as muscle weakness and paralysis, impaired coordination, and pain.

The causes of most autoimmune diseases are unknown. In some cases, an autoimmune reaction can be traced to injuries that expose body cells or proteins that are normally inaccessible to the immune system, such as the lens protein of the eye, to B and T cells. In other cases, as in type 1 diabetes, an invading virus stimulates the production of antibodies that can also react with self proteins. Antibodies against the Epstein-Barr and hepatitis B viruses can react against myelin basic protein, the protein attacked in multiple sclerosis. Sometimes, environmental chemicals, drugs, or mutations alter body proteins so that they appear foreign to the immune system and come under attack.

Some viruses use parts of the immune system to get a free ride to the cell interior. For example, the AIDS virus has a surface molecule that is recognized and bound by the CD4 receptor on the surface of helper T cells. Binding to CD4 locks the virus to the cell surface and stimulates the membrane covering the virus to fuse with the plasma membrane of the helper T cell. (The protein coat of the virus is wrapped in a membrane derived from the plasma membrane of the host cell in which it was produced.) The fusion introduces the virus into the cell, initiating the infection and leading to the destruction and death of the T cell. (Further details on human immunodeficiency virus [HIV] infection and AIDS are presented in *Applied Research: HIV and AIDS*.)

44.4c Allergies: Overactivity of the Immune System

The substances responsible for allergic reactions form a distinct class of antigens called **allergens**, which induce B cells to secrete an overabundance of IgE antibodies **(Figure 44.13, p. 1104)**. IgE antibodies, in turn, bind to receptors on mast cells in connective tissue and on **basophils**, a type of leukocyte in the blood (see Table 44.1), inducing them to secrete histamine, which produces a severe inflammation. Most of the inflammation occurs in tissues directly exposed to the allergen, such as the surfaces of the eyes, the lining of the nasal passages, and the air passages of the lungs. Signal molecules

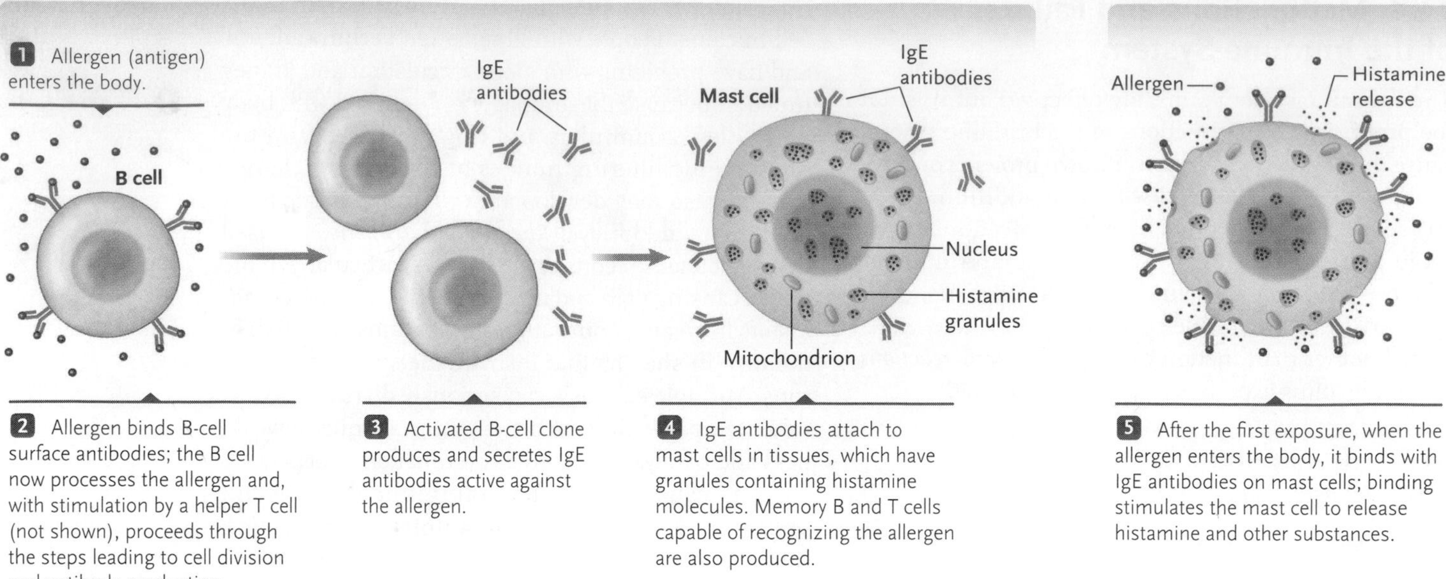

a. Initial exposure to allergen
b. Further exposures to allergen
1 Allergen (antigen) enters the body.
B cell
IgE antibodies
Mast cell
IgE antibodies
Nucleus
Histamine granules
Mitochondrion
Allergen
Histamine release
2 Allergen binds B-cell surface antibodies; the B cell now processes the allergen and, with stimulation by a helper T cell (not shown), proceeds through the steps leading to cell division and antibody production.
3 Activated B-cell clone produces and secretes IgE antibodies active against the allergen.
4 IgE antibodies attach to mast cells in tissues, which have granules containing histamine molecules. Memory B and T cells capable of recognizing the allergen are also produced.
5 After the first exposure, when the allergen enters the body, it binds with IgE antibodies on mast cells; binding stimulates the mast cell to release histamine and other substances.

Figure 44.13
The response of the body to allergens. (a) The steps in sensitization after initial exposure to an allergen. **(b)** Production of an allergic response by further exposures to the allergen.

released by activated mast cells also stimulate mucosal cells to secrete floods of mucus and cause smooth muscle in airways to constrict (histamine also causes airway constriction). The resulting allergic reaction can vary in severity from a mild irritation to serious and even life-threatening debilitation. *Asthma* is a severe response to allergens involving constriction of airways in the lungs. Antihistamines, medications that block histamine receptors, are usually effective in countering the effects of the histamine released by mast cells.

An individual is *sensitized* by a first exposure to an allergen, which may produce only mild allergic symptoms or no reaction at all (see Figure 44.13a). However, the sensitization produces memory B and T cells. At subsequent exposures, the system is poised to produce a greatly intensified allergic response (see Figure 44.13b).

In some persons, inflammation stimulated by an allergen is so severe that the reaction brings on a life-threatening condition called **anaphylactic shock**. Extreme swelling of air passages in the lungs interferes with breathing, and massive leakage of fluid from capillaries causes the blood pressure to drop precipitously. Death may result in minutes if the condition is not treated promptly. In persons who have become sensitized to the venom of wasps and bees, for example, a single sting may bring on anaphylactic shock within minutes. Allergies developed against drugs such as penicillin and certain foods can have the same drastic effects. Anaphylactic shock can be controlled by immediate injection of epinephrine (adrenaline), which reverses the condition by constricting blood vessels and dilating air passages in the lungs.

Study Break

1. What is immunological tolerance?
2. Explain how a failure in the immune system can result in an allergy.

44.5 Defences in Other Organisms

All organisms must be able to defend themselves, and we can compare what we know in mammals with what we know about the immune systems of other organisms. Molecular studies in sharks and rays have revealed DNA sequences that are clearly related to the sequences coding for antibodies in mammals, and sharks produce antibodies capable of recognizing and binding specific antigens. Antibody diversity is produced by the same kinds of genetic rearrangements in both sharks and mammals, although the embryonic gene segments for the two polypeptides are arranged differently in these organisms. Sharks also mount nonspecific defences, including the production of a steroid that appears to kill bacteria and neutralizes viruses nonspecifically and with high efficiency.

We have demonstrated that invertebrates lack the adaptive immune system and instead rely on innate responses that allow them to eliminate pathogens via phagocytosis, encapsulation, or the expression of antimicrobial peptides. Similarly, plants rely on innate responses only and recognize and eliminate the pathogens or infected cells, often using plant antimicrobial peptides.

Applied Research: HIV and AIDS

Acquired immune deficiency syndrome (AIDS) is a constellation of disorders that follows infection by the **human immunodeficiency virus, HIV (Figure 1).** First reported in the late 1970s, HIV now infects more than 40 million people worldwide, 64% of them in Africa. AIDS is a potentially lethal disease, although drug therapy has reduced the death rate for HIV-infected individuals.

HIV is transmitted when an infected person's body fluids, especially blood or semen, enter the blood or tissue fluids of another person. The entry may occur during vaginal, anal, or oral intercourse, or the virus may be transmitted via contaminated needles shared by intravenous drug users or from infected mothers to their infants during pregnancy, birth, and nursing. HIV is rarely transmitted through casual contact, food, or body products such as saliva, tears, urine, or feces.

The primary cellular hosts for HIV are macrophages and helper T cells, which are ultimately destroyed by the virus. Infection makes helper T cells unavailable for the stimulation and proliferation of B cells and cytotoxic T cells. The assault on lymphocytes and macrophages cripples the immune system and makes the body highly vulnerable to otherwise non–life-threatening infections.

In 1996, researchers confirmed the process by which HIV initially infects its primary target, the helper T cells. First, a glycoprotein of the viral coat, called *gp120*, attaches the virus to a helper T cell by binding to its CD4 receptor. Another viral protein triggers fusion of the viral surface membrane with the T-cell plasma membrane, releasing the virus into the cell. Once inside, a viral enzyme, *reverse transcriptase,* uses the viral RNA as a template for making a DNA copy. (When it is outside a host cell, the genetic material of HIV is RNA rather than DNA.) Another viral enzyme, *integrase,* then splices the viral DNA into the host cell's DNA **(Figure 2).** Once it is part of the host cell DNA, the viral DNA is replicated and passed on as the cell divides. As part of the host cell DNA, the virus is effectively hidden in the helper T cell and protected from attack by the immune system.

When the infected helper T cell is stimulated by an antigen, the viral

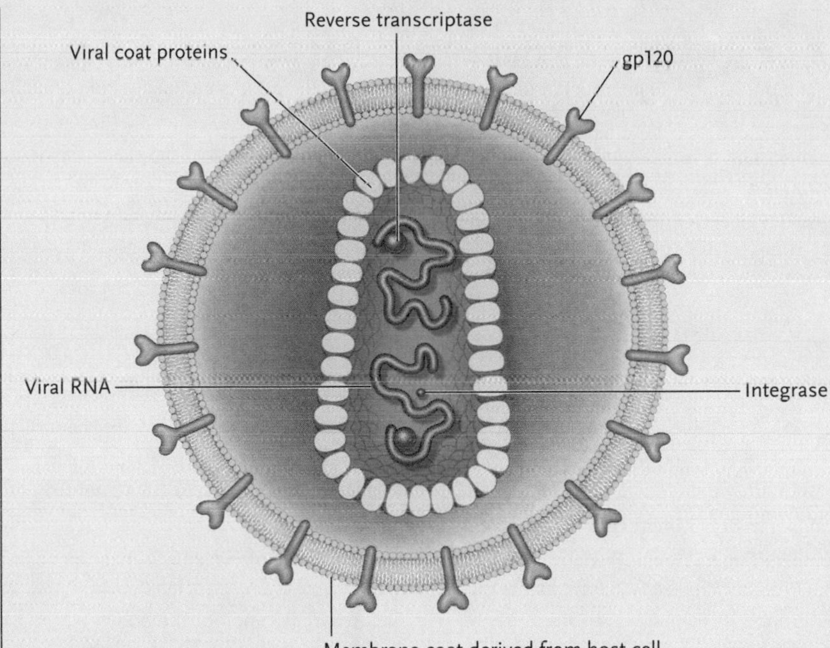

Figure 1
Structure of a free HIV viral particle.

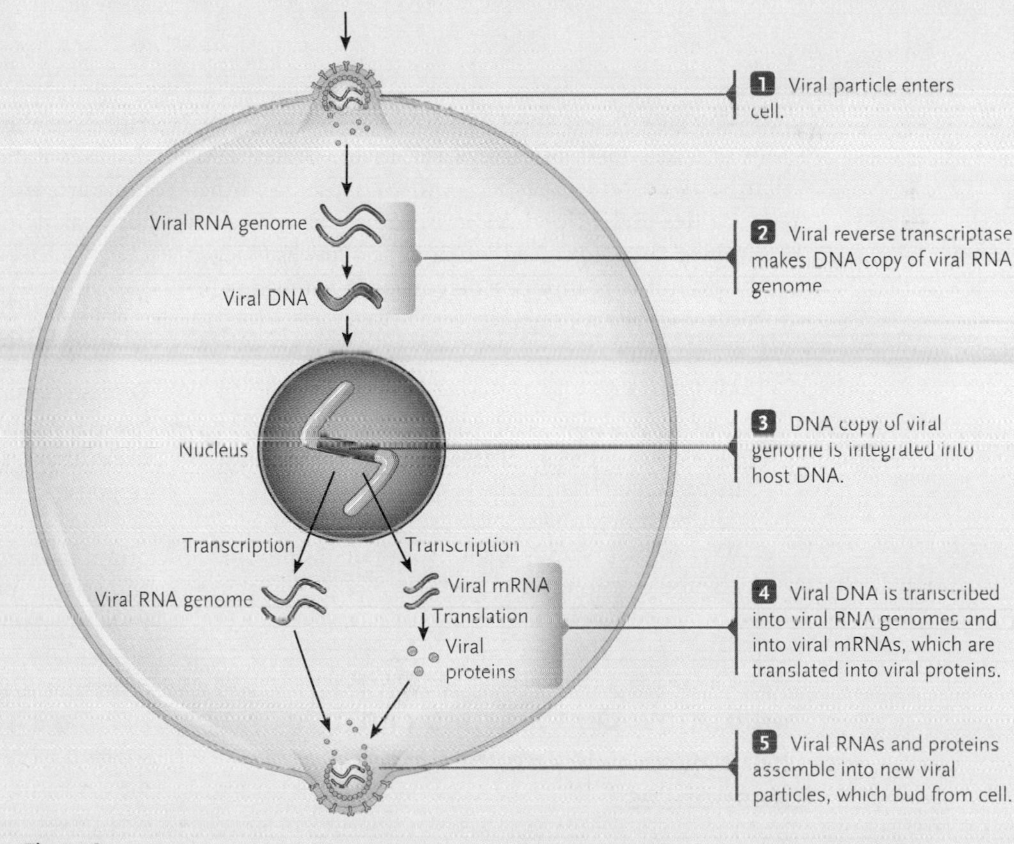

Viral RNA genome
Viral DNA
Nucleus
Transcription
Transcription
Viral RNA genome
Viral mRNA
Translation
Viral proteins
1 Viral particle enters cell.
2 Viral reverse transcriptase makes DNA copy of viral RNA genome.
3 DNA copy of viral genome is integrated into host DNA.
4 Viral DNA is transcribed into viral RNA genomes and into viral mRNAs, which are translated into viral proteins.
5 Viral RNAs and proteins assemble into new viral particles, which bud from cell.

Figure 2
The steps in HIV infection of a host cell.

(continued on page 1106)

(continued from page 1105)

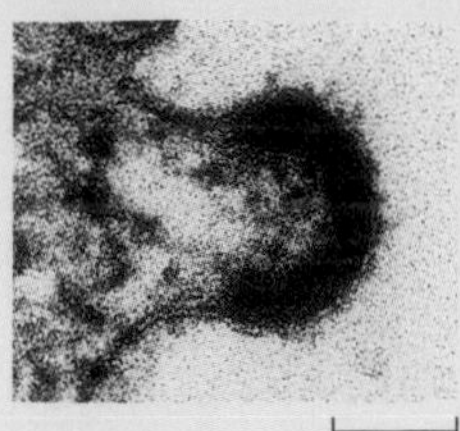

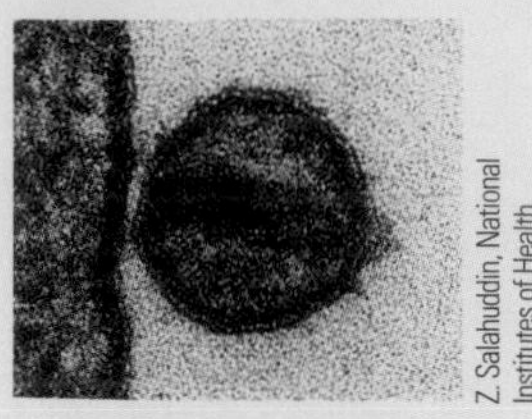

Figure 3
An HIV particle budding from a host cell. As it passes from the host cell, it acquires a membrane coat derived from the host cell plasma membrane.

DNA is copied into new viral RNA molecules and into mRNAs that direct host cell ribosomes to make viral proteins. The viral RNAs are added to the viral proteins to make infective HIV particles, which are released from the host cell by budding **(Figure 3).** The infection also leads uninfected helper T cells to destroy themselves in large numbers by apoptosis, through mechanisms that are still unknown.

Initially, infected people suffer a mild fever and other symptoms that may be mistaken for the flu or the common cold. The symptoms disappear as antibodies against viral proteins appear in the body, and the number of viral particles drops in the bloodstream. An infected person may remain apparently healthy for years yet can infect others. Both the transmitter and the recipient of the virus may be unaware that the virus is present, making it difficult to control the spread of HIV.

Eventually, more and more helper T cells and macrophages are destroyed, wiping out the body's immune response. The infected person becomes susceptible to secondary, opportunistic infections, such as a pneumonia caused by a fungus (*Pneumocystis carinii*); tuberculosis; persistent yeast (*Candida albicans*) infections of the mouth, throat, rectum, or vagina; and infection by many common bacteria and viruses that rarely infect healthy humans. These infections signal the appearance of "full-blown" AIDS. If untreated, this results in a steady debilitation and death, typically within 5 years.

Currently, there is no cure for HIV and no vaccine that can prevent infection. The coat proteins of HIV mutate constantly, making a vaccine developed against one form of the virus useless when the next form appears. Most mutations occur during replication of the virus during reverse transcription of viral RNA.

The development of AIDS can be greatly slowed by drugs that interfere with reverse transcription of the viral RNA. Treatment with a "cocktail" of drugs called *reverse transcriptase inhibitors* inhibits viral reproduction and destruction of helper T cells, extending the lives of people with HIV. The inhibiting cocktails are not a cure, however, because the virus is still present. If the therapy is stopped, the virus again replicates and the T-cell population drops.

The significant similarities between the innate immune responses of vertebrates, invertebrates, and plants, as described earlier in this chapter, and the similarities and differences in immune responses in "primitive" and "advanced" organisms allow us to look at the evolution of immune responses to pathogens in very diverse types of organisms.

Study Break

1. How can studies on "primitive organisms" help us understand immune responses in more advanced organisms such as humans?
2. Why is understanding the evolution of immune responses important?

44.6 How Do Parasites and Pathogens Circumvent Host Responses?

The immune systems of all organisms arose to recognize and eliminate pathogens. Some of the complexities of these systems have been detailed in this chapter. However, the fact that all organisms still suffer from diseases indicates that as strong as our immune systems are, pathogens and parasites are always looking for weak points to exploit.

44.6a Hiding, Confusing, and Manipulating the Host

Disease-causing organisms can develop in regions of the host's body that do not have a strong immune response, hide in host defence cells, confuse the immune response, or directly manipulate host responses.

Many bacteria, nematodes, trematodes, and other parasites enter via the mouth, establish in some region of the alimentary tract, and allow their eggs or offspring to exit with the feces. Although the alimentary tract of most organisms has some level of immune activity, the immune response is not as strong as it is in other regions. Thus, these organisms develop where the immune response is limited. We do not recognize broccoli as "foreign" and generate antibodies against broccoli in our guts. Organisms do not normally produce immune responses to gut contents; in fact, this might be counterproductive. Many organisms rely on symbiotic microbial organisms to

People Behind Biology
Élie Metchnikoff

In 1882, a Russian zoologist named Élie Metchnikoff, working in Italy, pierced a larva of a common starfish with a rose thorn. Later he observed cells collecting around the thorn. He recognized that these cells were trying to isolate and eliminate the thorn through what we now term phagocytosis. Although phagocytosis was known to occur in human bacterial infections, Metchnikoff's initial studies with the starfish, and later with animal models injected with human pathogens, demonstrated that this response was used universally by animals to eliminate pathogens. These initial experiments have led to scientific disciplines such as cellular immunology, innate immunity, and comparative immunology and have contributed to our understanding of the evolution of immune responses. For this pioneering work and keen observation, Metchnikoff shared the Nobel Prize in medicine in 1908 with Paul Ehrlich.

help digest food and produce vitamins. Killing these organisms could kill the host.

Some pathogens enter the cerebrospinal fluid, which often shows a reduced immune response. Although relatively protected here, the pathogens have a problem in dispersing their offspring to subsequent hosts.

Many pathogens make themselves look like the host. They invade the body cavities of vertebrates or invertebrates or the circulatory system of vertebrates and coat themselves with host factors to confuse the immune response. Trematodes, such as *Shistosoma* species, that live in our blood/lymphatic system cover themselves in host proteins so that they are hidden from the antibody response of the host and then use host factors to stimulate their development: tumour necrosis factor (TNF) stimulates egg production, and growth is stimulated by interleukin-7. Much of the pathology caused by this parasite is due to the immune response of the host rather than to any direct damage by the parasite.

Intracellular pathogens such as *Leishmania* species live and reproduce in the macrophages that normally eliminate pathogens, developing in the last place the host would look. They survive by producing antioxidant enzymes to detoxify superoxide molecules, they downregulate the signal transduction pathways that produce lethal molecules, and they produce surface glycoproteins that are refractory to host lysosomal enzymes. Therefore, the very cells the host relies on to eliminate parasites serve as incubators for these organisms. Because infected cells are considered "self," they are not eliminated by other host immune responses.

Some pathogens regularly change their surface coats to avoid recognition and destruction by the immune system. When the host develops antibodies against one version of the surface proteins, the pathogens produce different surface proteins, and the host produces new antibodies. These changes continue indefinitely, allowing the pathogens to keep one step ahead of the immune system. This strategy, called **antigenic variation**, is used by organisms such as the protozoan parasite that causes African sleeping sickness, the bacterium that causes gonorrhea, and the viruses that cause influenza, the common cold, and AIDS.

In insect vectors of viruses such as dengue, the virus manipulates the insect's immune response. Normally, intracellular pathogens are eliminated via apoptosis (see Section 44.2). The dengue virus, however, induces the expression of *inhibitors of apoptosis* (IAPs) to prevent cell degradation until it has established and replicated, after which, it allows the cells to rupture, releasing virus particles that then enter new cells.

Many viruses also produce RNAi suppressors that prevent the host cells from preventing the viruses' multiplication using RNAi strategies, as described in Section 44.2.

44.6b Mechanisms to Evade Host Immune Responses

Several very different groups of organisms work together symbiotically to overcome the response of a host. Whereas individually they would be eliminated by the host, the combination overwhelms the ability of the host to eliminate either organism.

Nematodes + Bacteria. Soil-living nematodes that enter the body cavity of insects are killed by a combination of encapsulation and melanization described previously, and many soil bacteria cannot enter the insects. Some nematodes have teamed up with specific bacteria in a symbiotic relationship to overcome host defences. Nematodes penetrate the insect and release bacteria that are phagocytosed but are not killed. These bacteria multiply within hours and produce compounds that inactivate the insect's immune response. The nematodes feed and reproduce using the bacteria and host tissues as food. When resources for growth and reproduction become limited, millions of infective nematodes store some of these specific bacteria and leave the dead insect en masse in search of new hosts.

Wasps and Viruses. Some insect *parasitoids* such as wasps, lay their eggs in other insects. Normally, these would be eliminated via encapsulation. However, some parasitoid wasps have formed an allegiance with a polyDNA virus. The virus is injected into the host insect along with the wasp egg. This virus inactivates the host's immune response, allowing the wasp larva to develop, mature, and emerge from the host, carrying some of the virus within its reproductive tract.

In the continuing battle between host and parasite/pathogen, there are constant interactions and feedback mechanisms. Each development by the host to eliminate the pathogen is countered by pathogen factors to ensure the pathogen's survival. And some of the mechanisms used are very ingenious!

Study Break

1. Compare invertebrate and mammalian immune defences.
2. How do pathogens avoid the immune responses of their hosts?
3. What mechanisms can pathogens use to avoid detection by the host?
4. How can different organisms work together to overcome host defences?
5. How can we compare immune responses between animals, and what benefit would such comparisons provide?

Review

Go to CENGAGENOW™ at http://hed.nelson.com/ to access quizzing, animations, exercises, articles, and personalized homework help.

44.1 Three Lines of Defence against Invasion

- Humans and other vertebrates have three lines of defence against pathogens. The first, which is nonspecific, is the barrier set up by the skin and mucus membranes.
- The second line of defence, also nonspecific, is innate immunity, an innate system that defends the body against pathogens and toxins penetrating the first line. This is the only kind of immune system found in invertebrates.
- The third line of defence, adaptive immunity, is specific: it recognizes and eliminates particular pathogens and retains a memory of that exposure so as to respond rapidly if the pathogen is encountered again. The response is carried out by lymphocytes, a specialized group of leukocytes.

44.2 Nonspecific Defences: Innate Immunity

- In the innate immunity system, molecules on the surfaces of pathogens are recognized as foreign by receptors on host cells. This is common to all animals and plants. In invertebrates, this activates systems to remove the pathogen via phagocytosis, encapsulation, or the production of antimicrobial peptides. In vertebrates, the pathogen is combated by the inflammation and complement systems.
- In both vertebrates and invertebrates, epithelial surfaces and specific tissues secrete antimicrobial peptides in response to attack by microbial pathogens. These disrupt the plasma membranes of pathogens, killing them.
- Inflammation is characterized by heat, pain, redness, and swelling at the infection site. Several interconnecting mechanisms initiate inflammation, including pathogen engulfment, histamine secretion, and cytokine release, which dilates the local blood vessels, increases their permeability, and allows for leakage into body tissues.
- Large arrays of complement proteins are activated when they recognize molecules on the surfaces of pathogens. Some complement proteins form membrane attack complexes, which insert into the plasma membrane of many types of bacteria and cause their lysis. Fragments of other complement proteins coat pathogens, stimulating phagocytes to engulf them.
- Four nonspecific defences are used to combat viral pathogens: RNA interference, interferons, natural killer cells, and apoptosis.

44.3 Specific Defences: Adaptive Immunity

- Adaptive immunity, which is carried out by B and T cells, targets particular pathogens or toxin molecules.
- Antibodies consist of two light and two heavy polypeptide chains, each with variable and constant regions. The variable regions of the chains combine to form the specific antigen-binding site.
- Antibodies occur in five different classes: IgM, IgD, IgG, IgA, and IgE. Each class is determined by its constant region.
- Antibody diversity is produced by genetic rearrangements in developing B cells that combine gene segments into intact genes encoding the light and heavy chains. The rearrangements producing heavy-chain genes and T-cell receptor genes are similar. The light and heavy chain genes are transcribed into precursor mRNAs, which are processed into finished mRNAs, which are translated on ribosomes into the antibody polypeptides.
- The antibody-mediated immune response has two general phases: (1) T-cell activation and (2) B-cell activation and antibody production. T-cell activation begins when a dendritic cell engulfs a pathogen and produces antigens, making the cell an antigen-presenting cell (APC). The APC secretes interleukins, which activate the T cell. The T cell then secretes cytokines, which stimulate the T cell to proliferate, producing a clone of cells. The clonal cells differentiate into helper T cells.
- B-cell receptors (BCRs) on B cells recognize antigens on a pathogen and engulf it. The B cells then display the antigens. The TCR on a helper T cell activated by the same antigen binds to the antigen on the B cell. Interleukins from the T cell stimulate the B cell to produce a clone of cells with identical BCRs. The clonal cells differentiate into plasma cells, which secrete antibodies specific for the antigen, and memory B cells, which provide immunological memory of the antigen encounter.
- Clonal expansion is the process of selecting a lymphocyte specifically for cloning when it encounters an antigen from among a

randomly generated, large population of lymphocytes with receptors that specifically recognize the antigen.

- Antibodies clear the body of antigens by neutralizing or agglutinating them or by aiding the innate immune response.
- In immunological memory, the first encounter of an antigen elicits a primary immune response. Later exposure to the same antigen elicits a more rapid secondary response with a greater production of antibodies.
- Active immunity is the production of antibodies in response to an antigen. Passive immunity is the acquisition of antibodies by direct transfer from another person.
- In cell-mediated immunity, cytotoxic T cells recognize and bind to antigens displayed on the surfaces of infected body cells or to cancer cells. They then kill the infected body cell.
- Antibodies are widely used in research to identify, locate, and determine the functions of molecules in biological systems.

44.4 Malfunctions and Failures of the Immune System

- In immunological tolerance, molecules present in an individual at birth normally do not elicit an immune response.
- In some people, the immune system malfunctions and reacts against the body's own proteins or cells, producing autoimmune disease.
- The first exposure to an allergen sensitizes an individual by leading to the production of memory B and T cells, which cause a greatly intensified response to subsequent exposures.
- Most allergies result when antigens act as allergens by stimulating B cells to produce IgE antibodies, which lead to the release of histamine. Histamine produces the symptoms characteristic of allergies (see Figure 44.13).

44.5 Defences in Other Organisms

- Antibodies, complement proteins, and other molecules with defensive functions have been identified in all vertebrates.
- Invertebrates and plants rely on nonspecific defences, including surface barriers, phagocytes, encapsulation, melanization, and antimicrobial molecules.

44.6 How Do Parasites and Pathogens Circumvent Host Responses?

- Pathogens develop in regions of the host where the immune response is limited.
- Parasites and pathogens cover themselves with host material so that they are not recognized as "nonself."
- Parasites and pathogens develop in host immune cells by inactivating the immune response.
- Some pathogens use antigenic variation to keep one step ahead of the host response.
- Some pathogens manipulate the gene expression of host molecules.
- Pathogens may work together to overcome host responses that would kill either of the participants.

Questions

Self-Test Questions

1. Viruses are controlled by
   a. $CD8^+$ T cells that bind class I MHC proteins holding viral antigens.
   b. $CD4^+$ T cells that bind free viruses in the blood.
   c. B cells secreting perforin.
   d. antibodies that bind the viruses with their constant ends.
   e. natural killer cells secreting antiviral antibodies.
2. Components of the inflammatory response include all *except*
   a. macrophages.
   b. neutrophils.
   c. B cells.
   d. mast cells.
   e. eosinophils.
3. When a person resists infection by a pathogen after being vaccinated against it, this is the result of
   a. innate immunity.
   b. immunological memory.
   c. a response with defensins.
   d. an autoimmune reaction.
   e. an allergy.
4. One characteristic of a B cell is that it
   a. has the same structure in both invertebrates and vertebrates.
   b. recognizes antigens held on class I MHC proteins.
   c. binds viral infected cells and directly kills them.
   d. makes many different BCRs on its surface.
   e. has a BCR on its surface, which is the IgM molecule.
5. Antibodies
   a. are each composed of four heavy and four light chains.
   b. display a variable end, which determines the antibody's location in the body.
   c. that belong to the IgE group are the major antibody class in the blood.
   d. that are found in large numbers in the mucous membranes belong to class IgG.
   e. function primarily to identify and bind antigens free in body fluids.
6. The generation of antibody diversity includes the
   a. joining of V to C to J segments to make a functional light-chain gene.
   b. choice from several different types of C segments to make a functional light-chain gene.
   c. deletion of the J segment to make a functional light-chain gene.
   d. joining of V to J to C segments to make a functional light-chain gene.
   e. initial generation of IgG followed later by IgM on a given cell.
7. An APC:
   a. can be a $CD8^+$ T cell.
   b. derives from a phagocytic cell and is lymphocyte stimulating.
   c. secretes antibodies.
   d. cannot be a B cell.
   e. cannot stimulate helper T cells.

8. One function of antibodies is to
   a. deactivate the complement system.
   b. neutralize natural killer cells.
   c. clump bacteria and viruses for easy phagocytosis by macrophages.
   d. eliminate the chance for a secondary response.
   e. kill viruses inside of cells.
9. Jen punctured her hand with a muddy nail. In the emergency room, she received both a vaccine and someone else's antibodies against tetanus toxin. The immunity conferred here is
   a. both active and passive.
   b. active only.
   c. passive only.
   d. first active and later passive.
   e. innate.
10. Medicine attempts to enhance the immune response when treating
   a. organ transplant recipients.
   b. anaphylactic shock.
   c. rheumatoid arthritis.
   d. HIV infection.
   e. type 1 diabetes.

Questions for Discussion

1. HIV wreaks havoc with the immune system by attacking helper T cells and macrophages. Would the impact be altered if the virus attacked only macrophages? Explain.
2. Given what you know about how foreign invaders trigger immune responses, explain why mutated forms of viruses, which have altered surface proteins, pose a monitoring problem for memory cells.
3. Cats, dogs, and humans may develop myasthenia gravis, an autoimmune disease in which antibodies develop against acetylcholine receptors in the synapses between neurons and skeletal muscle fibres. Based on what you know of the biochemistry of muscle contraction (see Chapter 36), explain why people with this disease typically experience severe fatigue with even small levels of exertion, drooping of facial muscles, and trouble keeping their eyelids open.

The large number of gulls (*Larus* species) is obvious at a landfill site near Thunder Bay, Ontario. The population of gulls reflects the local population of humans.

M.B. Fenton

Study Plan

45 Population Ecology

Why It Matters

Controlling rabies in wildlife involves understanding many aspects of biology, from populations to epidemiology and behaviour. Rabies, from the Latin *rabere* (to rage or rave), affects the nervous system of terrestrial mammals. Caused by a *Lyssavirus*, rabies is usually spread by bites because the virus accumulates in the saliva of infected animals. Before 1885, when Louis Pasteur in France developed a vaccine for it, rabies was common in Europe, and many people died from it every year. In 2007, the World Health Organization estimated that worldwide, more than 50 000 people die annually from rabies, usually people in the "developing world." Between 1980 and the end of 2000, 43 people in the United States and Canada died of rabies.

Animals with "furious" rabies become berserk, attacking anything and everything in their path, a behaviour that spreads the virus and helps ensure its survival. Animals with paralytic rabies ("dumb rabies") suffer from increasing paralysis that progresses forward from the hindlimbs. Animals with either manifestation of rabies can spread the disease by biting when there is virus in their saliva. Paralysis of the throat muscles means that rabid animals cannot swallow the saliva they produce, so they appear to foam at the mouth.

Rabies is almost invariably fatal once an animal or a human shows clinical symptoms of the disease, so immunization of

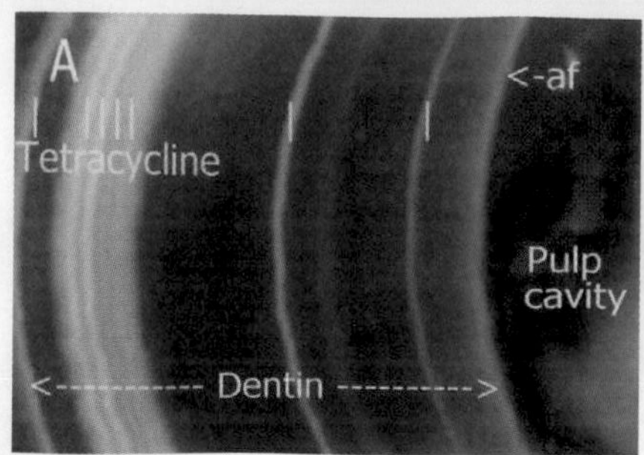

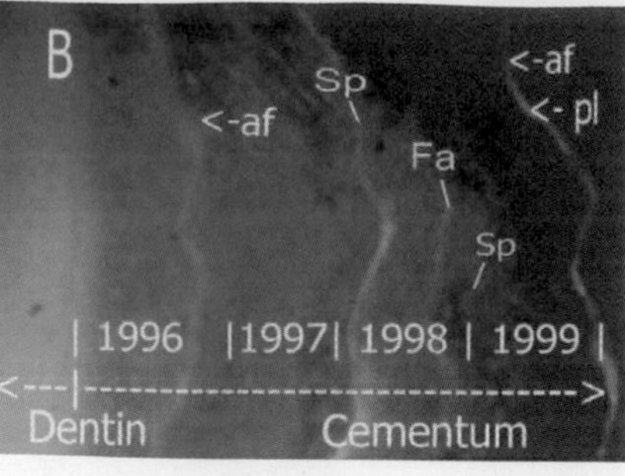

Figure 45.1
Tetracycline rings in carnivore teeth. Yellow fluorescent lines from ingestion of rabies baits with tetracycline as a biomarker. The sections are undecalcified, ultraviolet fluorescent × 100. **(a)** Coyote (*Canis latrans*) tooth with seven daily tetracycline lines from vaccine baits. **(b)** Canine tooth of a four-year-old raccoon (*Procyon lotor*) with yearly tetracycline lines in cementum. af = autofluorescent collagen; Fa = fall baits, 1998; pl = periodontal ligament; Sp = spring baits, 1998 and 1999.

someone exposed to the disease should start as soon as possible after exposure. Since 1980, human diploid vaccines have been commonly available, raising the level of protection against rabies.

From the 1960s to the 1990s, a visit to almost any rural hospital in southern Ontario (Canada) would have revealed at least one farmer receiving postexposure rabies shots. Then red foxes (*Vulpes vulpes*) were the main vector for rabies in Ontario, and cows (*Bos taurus*) exposed to rabies through fox bites in turn exposed farmers to the virus. Many farmers are accustomed to treating choking cows by reaching into the cow's gullet to clear an obstruction. A farmer dealing with a rabid cow could have been scratched and exposed to the virus, and then, after the cow died of rabies, the farmer would have received postexposure rabies shots. Rabies transmitted to cows from foxes posed a threat to human lives and was a significant drain on the economy through compensation paid to farmers whose cattle succumbed to the disease.

In 1967, 4-year-old Donna Featherstone of Richmond Hill, Ontario, died of rabies after being bitten by a stray cat. The resulting public outcry set the stage for a rabies eradication program in Ontario. Controlling fox rabies in southern Ontario was achieved by a combination of innovation and knowledge of basic biology. There were three phases: (a) developing an oral vaccine; (b) developing a means of vaccinating foxes; and (c) monitoring the impact of the program on the fox population.

First, two main baits for the oral vaccine were developed, and one, Evelyn, Rocketniki, Abelseth (ERA), was a modified live virus replicated in tissues of the mouth and throat. ERA successfully stimulated seroconversion in red foxes and vaccinated them against rabies. Second, foxes ate baits scented with chicken, and when the baits contained ERA, foxes that took the baits were vaccinated. The baits were small, the size of packets of jam one receives in restaurants, and easy to distribute widely from low-flying aircraft, allowing vaccination of foxes across large areas of southern Ontario. Third, each bait contained tetracycline, a biomarker absorbed into the system of any mammal that ate the bait. Once in the body, some tetracycline penetrated the dentine of the animals' teeth, especially in younger individuals. Biologists sectioned and stained teeth from foxes taken by trappers. In the sections, bands of tetracyline in tooth rings (**Figure 45.1**) identified foxes that had taken baits, and biologists established that over 70% of red foxes had been vaccinated by this method.

Before the bait vaccination program, on average, 211 cattle annually died of rabies in southern Ontario. The baiting program started in 1989, and by 1996, rabies in cattle dropped to an average of 11 cases a year and the levels of rabies in foxes in Ontario were dramatically reduced. The example demonstrates how problems in biology are solved by combined approaches, from population biology, behaviour, immunology, and epidemiology.

The purpose of this chapter is to introduce you to ecology in general, particularly population ecology.

45.1 The Science of Ecology

Ecology encompasses two related disciplines. In *basic ecology*, major research questions relate to the distribution and abundance of species and how they interact with each other and the physical environment. Using these data as a baseline, workers in *applied ecology* develop conservation plans and amelioration programs to limit, repair, and mitigate ecological damage caused by human activities (see also Chapter 48). Ecology has its roots in descriptive natural history dating back to the ancient Greeks. Modern ecology was born in 1870 when the German biologist Ernst Haeckel coined the term (from *oikos* = house). Contemporary researchers still gather descriptive information about ecological relationships, often as the starting points for other studies. Although ecological research is dominated by hypotheticodeductive approaches, initial inductive approaches allow biologists to generate appropriate hypotheses about how systems function. Research in ecology is often linked to work in genetics, physiology, anatomy, behaviour, paleontology, and evolution, as well as geology, geography, and environmental science. Many ecological phenomena, such as climate change, occur over huge areas and long time spans, so ecologists must devise ways to determine how environments influence organisms and how organisms change the environments in which they live.

Ecology can be divided into four increasingly complex and inclusive levels of organization. First, in **organismal ecology**, researchers study organisms to determine the genetic, biochemical, physiological, morphological, and behavioural adaptations to the abiotic environment (see Chapter 3). Second, in **population ecology**, researchers focus on groups of individuals of the same species that live together. Population ecologists study how the size and other characteristics of populations change in space and time. Third, in **community ecology**, biologists examine populations of different species that occur together in one area (are sympatric). Community ecologists study interactions between species, analyzing how predation, competition, and environmental disturbances influence a community's development, organization, and structure (see Chapter 47). Fourth, those studying **ecosystem ecology** explore how nutrients cycle and energy flows between the biotic components of an ecological community and the abiotic environment (see Chapter 47).

Ecologists can create hypotheses about ecological relationships and how they change through time or differ from place to place. Some formalize these ideas in mathematical models that express clearly defined, but hypothetical, relationships among important variables in a system. Manipulation of a model, usually with the help of a computer, can allow researchers to ask what would happen if some of the variables or their relationships change. Thus, researchers can simulate natural events and large-scale experiments before investing time, energy, and money in fieldwork and laboratory work. Bear in mind that mathematical models are no better than the ideas and assumptions they embody, and useful models are constructed only after basic observations define the relevant variables.

Ecologists use field or laboratory studies to test predictions of their hypotheses about relationships among variables in systems. In controlled experiments, researchers compare data from an experimental treatment (involving manipulation of one or more variables) with data from a control (in which nothing is changed). In some cases, "natural experiments" can be conducted because of the patterns of distribution and/or behaviour of species. This has the advantage of allowing ecologists to test predictions about how systems are operating without manipulating variables. Two species of fish, cutthroat trout (*Oncorhynchus clarki*) and Dolly Varden char (*Salvelinus malma*), live in coastal lakes of British Columbia. Some lakes have either trout or char, but others contain both species. The natural distributions of these fishes allowed researchers to measure the effect of each species on the other. In lakes in which both species live, each restricts its activities to fewer areas and eats a smaller variety of prey than it does in lakes in which it occurs alone.

Study Break

1. What are four levels of organization in ecology? Give a brief description of each.
2. What is a mathematical model? Why are such models important in ecology?
3. What two treatments are important when doing experiments? Why?

45.2 Population Characteristics

Seven characteristics can be described for any population.

45.2a Geographic Range: Boundaries of Distribution

Populations have characteristics that transcend those of the individuals comprising them. Every population has a **geographic range**, the overall spatial boundaries within which it lives. Geographic ranges vary enormously. A population of snails might inhabit a small tidepool, whereas a population of marine phytoplankton might occupy an area orders of magnitude larger. Every population also occupies a **habitat**, the specific environment in which it lives, as characterized by its biotic and abiotic features. Ecologists also measure other population characteristics, such as size, distribution in space, and age structure.

45.2b Population Size and Density: Numbers of Individuals per Unit Area

Population size is the number of individuals comprising the population at a specified time (N_t). **Population density** is the number of individuals per unit area or per unit volume of habitat. Species with a large body size generally have lower population densities than those with a small body size (**Figure 45.2, p. 1114**). Although population size and density are related measures, knowing a population's density provides more information about its relationship to the resources it uses. If a population of 200 oak trees occupies 1 hectare (10 000 m^2), the population density is 200 × 10 000 m^{-2} or 1 tree per 50 m^2. But if 200 oaks are spread over 5 hectares, the density is 1 tree per 250 m^2. Clearly, the second population is less dense than the first, and its members will have greater access to sunlight, water, and other resources.

Ecologists measure population size and density to monitor and manage populations of endangered species, economically important species, and agricultural pests. For large-bodied species, a simple head count could provide accurate information. For example, ecologists survey the size and

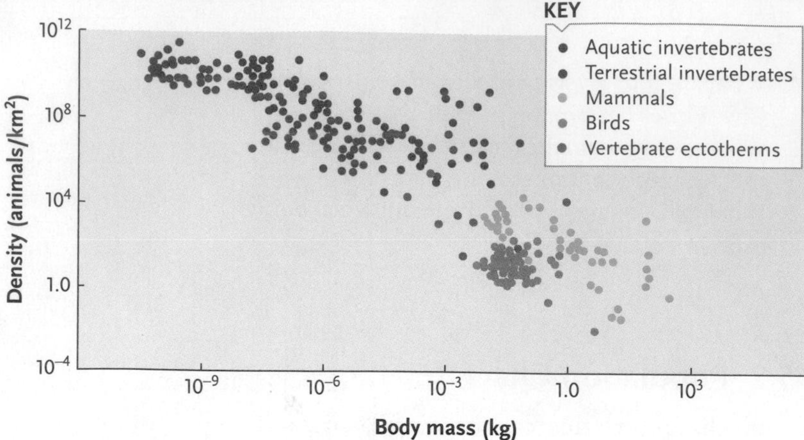

Figure 45.2
Population density and body size. Population density generally declines with increasing body size among animal species. There are similar trends for other organisms.

density of African elephant populations by flying over herds and counting individuals **(Figure 45.3).** Researchers use a variation on that technique to *estimate* population size in tiny organisms that live at high population densities. To estimate the density of aquatic phytoplankton, for example, you might collect water samples of known volume from representative areas in a lake and count them by looking through a microscope. These data allow you to estimate population size and density based on the estimated volume of the entire lake. In other cases, researchers use the mark–release–recapture sampling technique (see *Capture–Recapture*). One ongoing challenge is measuring population size in organisms that are clones, for example, stands of poplar trees (*Populus* spp.).

45.2c Population Dispersion: The Distribution of Individuals in Space

Populations can vary in their **dispersion**, the spatial distribution of individuals within the geographic range. Ecologists define three theoretical patterns of dispersion: *clumped, uniform,* and *random* **(Figure 45.4).**

Clumped dispersion (see Figure 45.4a) is common and occurs in three situations. First, suitable conditions are often patchily distributed. Certain pasture plants, for instance, may be clumped in small, scattered areas where cowpats had fallen for months, locally enriching the soil. Second, populations of some social animals (see Chapter 40) are clumped because mates are easy to locate within groups, and individuals may cooperate in rearing offspring, feeding, or defending themselves from predators. Third, populations can be clumped when species reproduce by asexual clones that remain attached to the parents. Aspen trees and sea anemones reproduce this way and often occur in large aggregations (see Chapter 18). Clumping may also occur in species in which seeds, eggs, or larvae lack dispersal mechanisms and offspring grow and settle near their parents.

Uniform distributions can occur when individuals repel one another because resources are in short supply. Creosote bushes are uniformly distributed in the dry scrub deserts of the American Southwest (see **Figure 45.4b).** Mature bushes deplete the surrounding soil of water and secrete toxic chemicals, making it impossible for seedlings to grow. This chemical warfare is called "allelopathy." Moreover, seed-eating ants and rodents living at the bases of mature bushes eat any seeds that fall nearby. In these situations, the distributions of species of plants and animals can

a.

b.

Figure 45.3
Counting elephants. It is easy to think that large animals such as African elephants (*Loxodonta africana*) would be easy to count from the air **(a).** This may or may not be true, depending on vegetation. But it can be easy to overlook animals, particularly young ones **(b)** in the shade.

Capture–Recapture

Ecologists use the mark–release–recapture technique to estimate the population size of mobile animals that live within a restricted geographic range. To do this, a sample of organisms (n_1) is captured, marked, and released. Ideally, the marks (or tags) are permanent and do not harm the tagged animal. Insects and reptiles often are marked with ink or paint, birds with rings (bands) on their legs, and mammals with ear tags or collars.

Later, a second sample (n_2) of the population is captured. In the second sample, the proportion of marked (n_{2m}) to unmarked individuals is used to estimate the total population (x) of the study area by solving the equation for x.

$$n_1/x = n_{2m}/n_2.$$

Assume that you capture a sample of 120 butterflies **(Figure 1)**, mark each one, and release them. A week later, you capture a sample of 150 butterflies, 30 that you marked. Thus, you had marked 30 of 150, or 1 of every 5 butterflies, on your first field trip. Because you captured 120 individuals on that first excursion, you would estimate that the total population size is 120 × (150/30) = 600 butterflies.

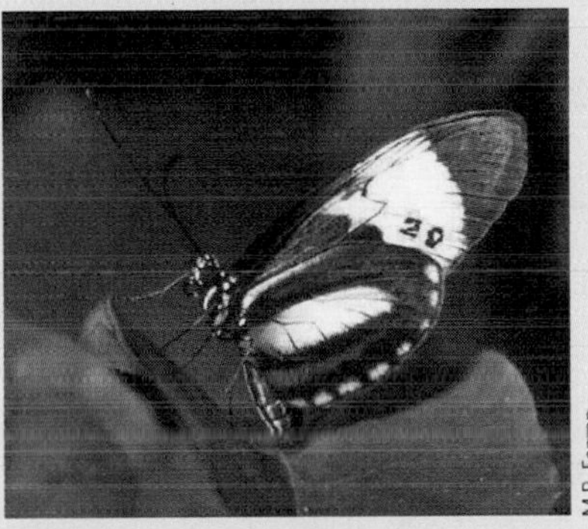

Figure 1
This butterfly has been captured and marked before release in a capture–recapture experiment.

The capture–recapture technique is based on several assumptions that are critical to its accuracy: (1) that being marked has no effect on survival; (2) that marked and unmarked animals mix randomly in the population; (3) that no migration into or out of the population takes place during the estimating period; and (4) that marked individuals are just as likely to be captured as unmarked individuals. (Sometimes animals become "trap shy" or "trap happy," a violation of the fourth assumption.)

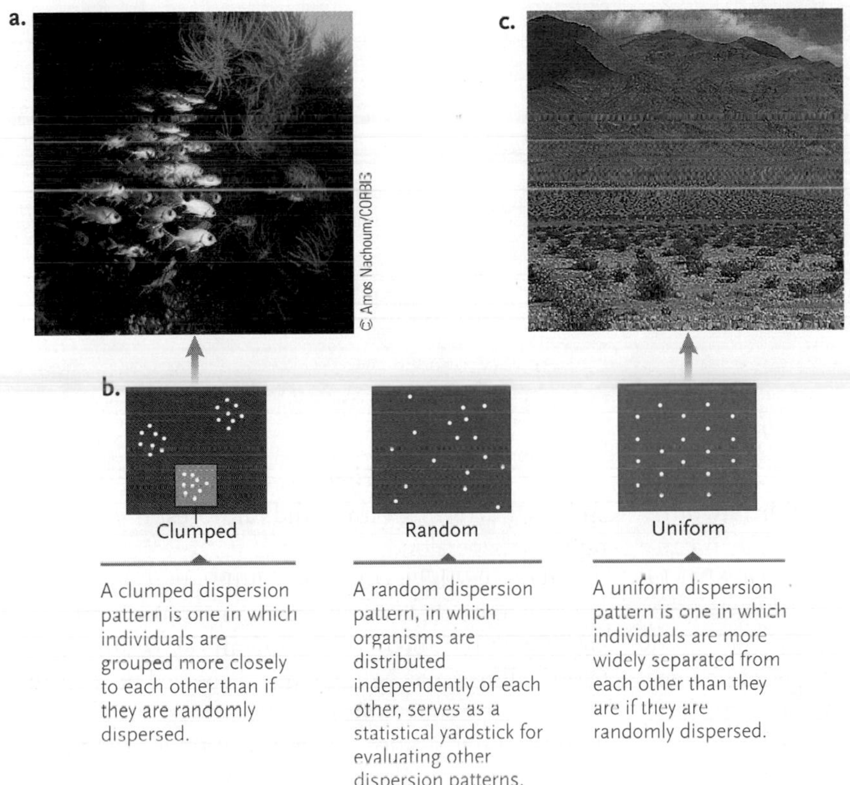

a.
© Amos Nachoum/CORBIS
c.
E. K. Degginger
b.
Clumped
Random
Uniform
A clumped dispersion pattern is one in which individuals are grouped more closely to each other than if they are randomly dispersed.
A random dispersion pattern, in which organisms are distributed independently of each other, serves as a statistical yardstick for evaluating other dispersion patterns.
A uniform dispersion pattern is one in which individuals are more widely separated from each other than they are if they are randomly dispersed.

Figure 45.4
Dispersion patterns. A clumped pattern **(a)** is evident in fish that live in social groups. A random pattern **(b)** of dispersion appears to be rare in nature, where it occurs in organisms that are neither attracted to nor repelled by conspecifics. Nearly uniform patterns **(c)** are demonstrated by creosote bushes (*Larrea tridentata*) near Death Valley, California.

Black-Footed Ferret, *Mustela Nigripes*

Black-footed ferrets **(Figure 1)** are crepuscular and nocturnal hunters of the prairie. Weighing 0.6 to 1.1 kg, these weasel relatives (family Mustelidae, order Carnivora) were once abundant in western North America, from Texas in the United States to Saskatchewan and Alberta in Canada. Like other mustelids, males are larger than females. In the wild, these predators probably fed mainly on prairie dogs (*Cynomys* species) and lived around prairie dog towns. Litters range in size from one to five. Females bear a single litter a year, and males and females are sexually mature at age one year.

By 1987, *M. nigripes* was probably extinct in the wild. The last known wild population was discovered near Meeteetse, Wyoming, in 1981. Seven animals from this population were captured and brought into captivity and served as the genetic founders for a captive breeding program. Over 4800 juvenile black-footed ferrets were produced by this program, and wildlife officials began to release captive-bred animals into suitable habitat.

At Shirley Basin, Wyoming, 228 captive-born black-footed ferrets were received between 1991 and 1994. By 1996, only 25 were observed in the wild and 5 by 1997. This decline reflected the impact of diseases, specifically canine distemper and plague. In 1996, it seemed that the reintroductions would fail, and *M. nigripes* would again be extinct in the wild.

In 2003, however, 52 black-footed ferrets were observed in the field at Shirley Basin, and since then, the population has increased significantly **(Figure 2).** The increase reflects an $r = 0.47$ and can be attributed to success in the first year of life, a combination of survival and fertility.

There appears to be hope for the future of *M. nigripes*. It remains to be determined if the genetic bottleneck (see Chapter 18) that the species has endured will prove to be an important handicap to long-term survival.

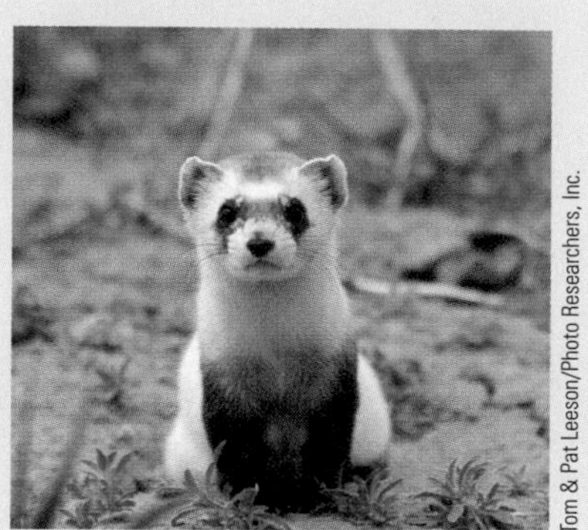

Figure 1
Mustela nigripes, the black-footed ferret. This critically endangered carnivore from the North American prairie shows evidence of a comeback.

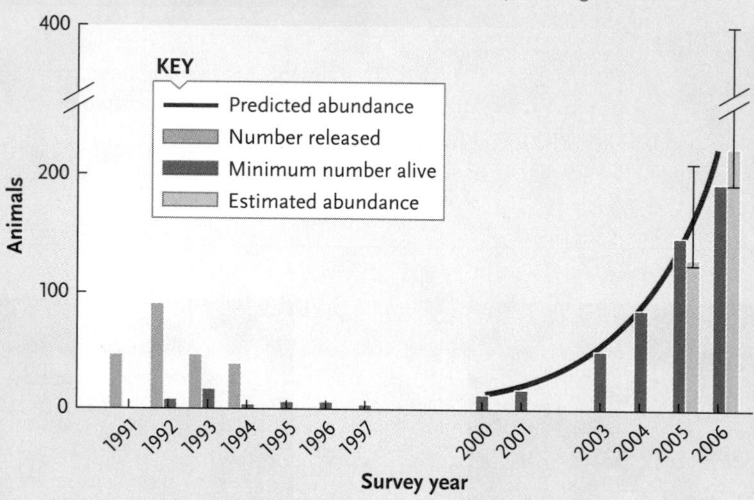

Figure 2
Population growth. Black-footed ferrets in Shirley Basin, Wyoming, have shown rapid popuation growth. The 95% confidence limits suggest a population of 192 to 401 in 2006.

be uniform and interrelated. Territorial behaviour, the defence of an area and its resources, also can produce uniform dispersion in some species of animals, such as nests in colonies of colonial birds (see Chapter 40).

Random dispersion (see Figure 45.4c) occurs when environmental conditions do not vary much within a habitat, and individuals are neither attracted to nor repelled by others of their species (conspecifics). Ecologists use formal statistical definitions of "random" to establish a theoretical baseline for assessing the pattern of distribution. In cases of random dispersion, individuals are distributed unpredictably. Some spiders, burrowing clams, and rainforest trees exhibit random dispersion.

Whether the spatial distribution of a population appears to be clumped, uniform, or random depends partly on the size of the organisms and of the study area. Oak seedlings may be randomly dispersed on a spatial scale of a few square metres, but over an entire mixed hardwood forest, they are clumped under the parent trees. Therefore, dispersion of a population depends partly on the researcher's scale of observation.

In addition, the dispersion of animal populations often varies through time in response to natural environmental rhythms. Few habitats provide a constant supply of resources throughout the year, and many animals move from one habitat to another on a seasonal cycle, reflecting the distribution of resources such as food. Tropical birds and mammals are often widely dispersed in deciduous forests during the wet season, when food is widely available. During the dry season, these species crowd into narrow "gallery forests" along watercourses, where evergreen trees provide food and shelter.

45.2d Age Structure: Numbers of Individuals of Different Ages

All populations have an **age structure**, a statistical description of the relative numbers of individuals in each age class (discussed further in Chapter 46). Individuals can be categorized roughly as prereproductive (younger than the age of sexual maturity), reproductive, or postreproductive (older than the maximum age of reproduction). A population's age structure reflects its recent growth history and predicts its future growth potential. Populations composed of many prereproductive individuals obviously grew rapidly in the recent past. These populations will continue to grow as young individuals mature and reproduce.

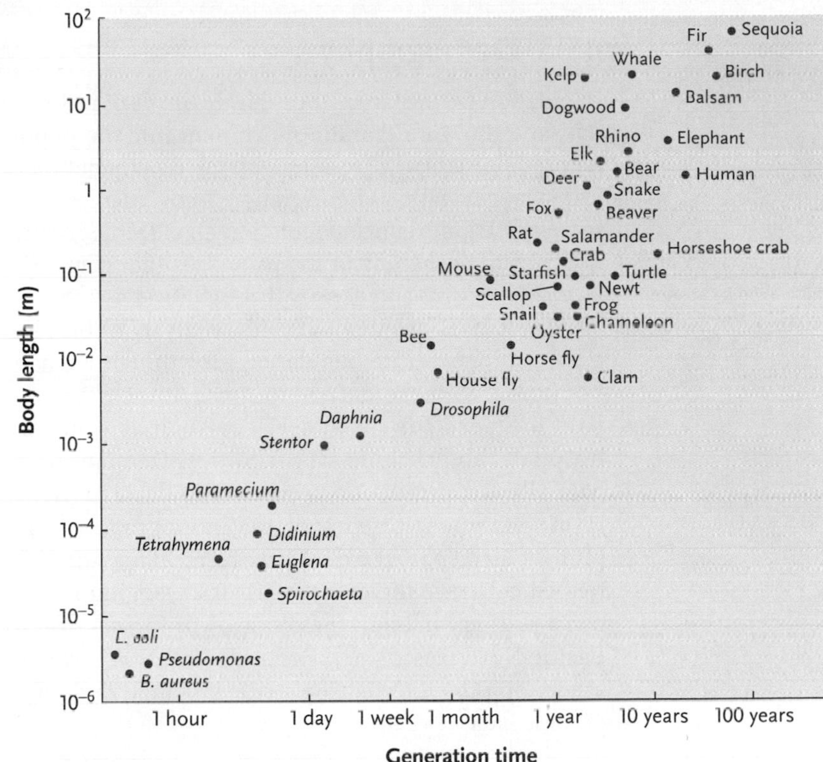

Figure 45.5
Generation time and body size. Generation time increases with body size among bacteria, protists, plants, and animals. The logarithmic scale on both axes compresses the data into a straight line.

45.2e Generation Time: Average Time between Birth and Death

Another characteristic that influences a population's growth is its **generation time**, the average time between the birth of an organism and the birth of its offspring. Generation time is usually short in species that reach sexual maturity at a small body size **(Figure 45.5)**. Their populations often grow rapidly because of the speedy accumulation of reproductive individuals.

45.2f Sex Ratio: Females:Males

Populations of sexually reproducing organisms also vary in their **sex ratio**, the relative proportions of males and females. In general, the number of females in a population has a bigger impact on population growth than the number of males because only females actually produce offspring. Moreover, in many species, one male can mate with several females, and the number of males may have little effect on the population's reproductive output. In northern elephant seals (see Chapter 17), mature bulls fight for dominance on the beaches where the seals mate. Only a few males may ultimately inseminate a hundred or more females. Thus, the presence of other males in the group may have little effect on the size of future generations. In animals that form lifelong pair bonds, such as geese and swans, the numbers of males and females influence reproduction in the population.

45.2g Proportion Reproducing: Incidence of Reproducing Individuals in a Population

Population ecologists try to determine the proportion of individuals in a population that are reproducing. This issue is particularly relevant to the conservation of any species in which individuals are rare or widely dispersed in the habitat (see Chapter 48).

Study Break

1. What is the difference between geographic range and habitat?
2. What are the three types of dispersion? What is the most common pattern found in nature? Why?
3. What is the common pattern of generation time among bacteria, protists, plants, and animals?

45.3 Demography

Populations grow larger through the birth of individuals and the **immigration** (movement into the population) of organisms from neighbouring populations. Conversely, death and **emigration** (movement out of the population) reduce population size. **Demography** is the statistical study of the processes that change a population's size and density through time.

Ecologists use demographic analysis to predict a population's future population growth. For human populations, these data help governments anticipate the need for social services such as schools, hospitals, and chronic care facilities. Demographic data allow conservation ecologists to develop plans to protect endangered species. Demographic data on northern spotted owls (*Strix occidentalis caurina*) helped convince the courts to restrict logging in the owl's primary habitat, the old growth forests of the Pacific Northwest. *Life tables* and *survivorship curves* are among the tools ecologists use to analyze demographic data.

45.3a Life Tables: Numbers of Individuals in Each Age Group

Although every species has a characteristic life span, few individuals survive to the maximum age possible. Mortality results from starvation, disease, accidents, predation, or inability to find a suitable habitat. Life insurance companies first developed techniques for measuring mortality rates (known as actuarial science), and ecologists adapted these approaches to the study of nonhuman populations.

A **life table** summarizes the demographic characteristics of a population **(Table 45.1)**. To collect life table data for short-lived organisms, demographers typically mark a **cohort**, a group of individuals of similar age, at birth and monitor their survival until all members of the cohort die. For organisms that live more than a few years, a researcher might sample the population for one or two years, recording the ages at which individuals die and then extrapolating those results over the species' life span. The approach to the timing of collection of data about reproduction and longevity will depend on the details of the species under study.

In any life table, life spans of organisms are divided into age intervals of appropriate length. For short-lived species, days, weeks, or months are useful, whereas for longer-lived species, years or groups of years will be better. Mortality can be expressed in two complementary ways. **Age-specific mortality** is the proportion of individuals alive at the start of an age interval that died during that age interval. Its more cheerful reflection, **age-specific survivorship**, is the proportion of individuals alive at the start of an age interval that survived until the start of the next age interval. Thus, for the data shown in Table 45.1, the age-specific mortality rate during the 3- to 6-month age interval is 195/722 = 0.270, and the age-specific survivorship rate is 527/722 = 0.730. For any age interval, the sum of age-specific mortality and age-specific survivorship must equal 1. Life tables also summarize the proportion of the cohort that survived to a particular age, a statistic identifying the probability that any randomly selected newborn will still be alive at that age. For the 3- to 6-month age interval in Table 45.1, this probability is 722/843 = 0.856.

Table 45.1 Life Table for a Cohort of 843 Individuals of the Grass *Poa annua* (Annual Bluegrass)

Age Interval (in months)	Number Alive at Start of Age Interval	Number Dying during Age Interval	Age-Specific Mortality Rate	Age-Specific Survivorship Rate	Proportion of Original Cohort Alive at Start of Age Interval	Age-Specific Fecundity (Seed Production)
0–3	843	121	0.144	0.856	1.000	0
3–6	722	195	0.270	0.730	0.856	300
6–9	527	211	0.400	0.600	0.625	620
9–12	316	172	0.544	0.456	0.375	430
12–15	144	90	0.625	0.375	0.171	210
15–18	54	39	0.722	0.278	0.064	60
18–21	15	12	0.800	0.200	0.018	30
21–24	3	3	1.000	0.000	0.004	10
24–	0	—	—	—	—	—

Source: Begon, M., and M. Mortimer. *Population Ecology*. Sunderland, MA: Sinauer Associates, 1981. Adapted from R. Law, 1975.

Life tables also include data on **age-specific fecundity**, the average number of offspring produced by surviving females during each age interval. Table 45.1 shows that plants in the 3- to 6-month age interval produced an average of 300 seeds each. In some species, including humans, fecundity is highest in individuals of intermediate age. Younger individuals have not yet reached sexual maturity, and older individuals are past their reproductive prime. However, fecundity increases steadily with age in some plants and animals.

45.3b Survivorship Curves: Timing of Deaths of Individuals in a Population

Survivorship data are depicted graphically in a **survivorship curve** that displays the rate of survival for individuals over the species' average life span. Ecologists have identified three generalized survivorship curves (blue lines in **Figure 45.6**), although most organisms exhibit survivorship patterns falling between these idealized patterns.

Type I curves reflect high survivorship until late in life (see Figure 45.6a). They are typical of large animals that produce few young and provide them with extended care, which reduces juvenile mortality. Large mammals, such as Dall mountain sheep, produce only one or two offspring at a time and nurture them through their vulnerable first year. At that time, the young are better able to fend for themselves and are at lower risk for mortality (compared with younger animals). The picture of survivorship in mammals could change if one starts with the time of conception, as opposed to birth. The change would reflect problems of pregnancy (see Chapter 18) and health of mothers.

Type II curves reflect a relatively constant rate of mortality in all age classes, a pattern that produces steadily declining survivorship (see Figure 45.6b). Many lizards, such as the five-lined skink, as well as songbirds and small mammals, face a constant probability of mortality from predation, disease, and starvation and show a type II pattern.

Type III curves reflect high juvenile mortality, followed by a period of low mortality once offspring reach a critical age and size (see Figure 45.6c). *Cleome droserifolia*, a desert shrub from the Middle East, experiences extraordinarily high mortality in its seed and seedling stages. Researchers estimate that for every 1 million seeds produced, fewer than 1000 germinate, and only about 40 individuals survive their first year. Once a plant becomes established, however, its likelihood of future survival is higher, and the survivorship curve flattens out. Many plants, insects, marine invertebrates, and fishes exhibit type III survivorship.

Study Break

1. What is the relationship between age-specific mortality and age-specific survivorship? If age-specific mortality is 0.384, what is the age-specific survivorship?
2. What is age-specific fecundity?
3. Describe three survivorship curves. In which curve do humans fall? Songbirds? Insects?

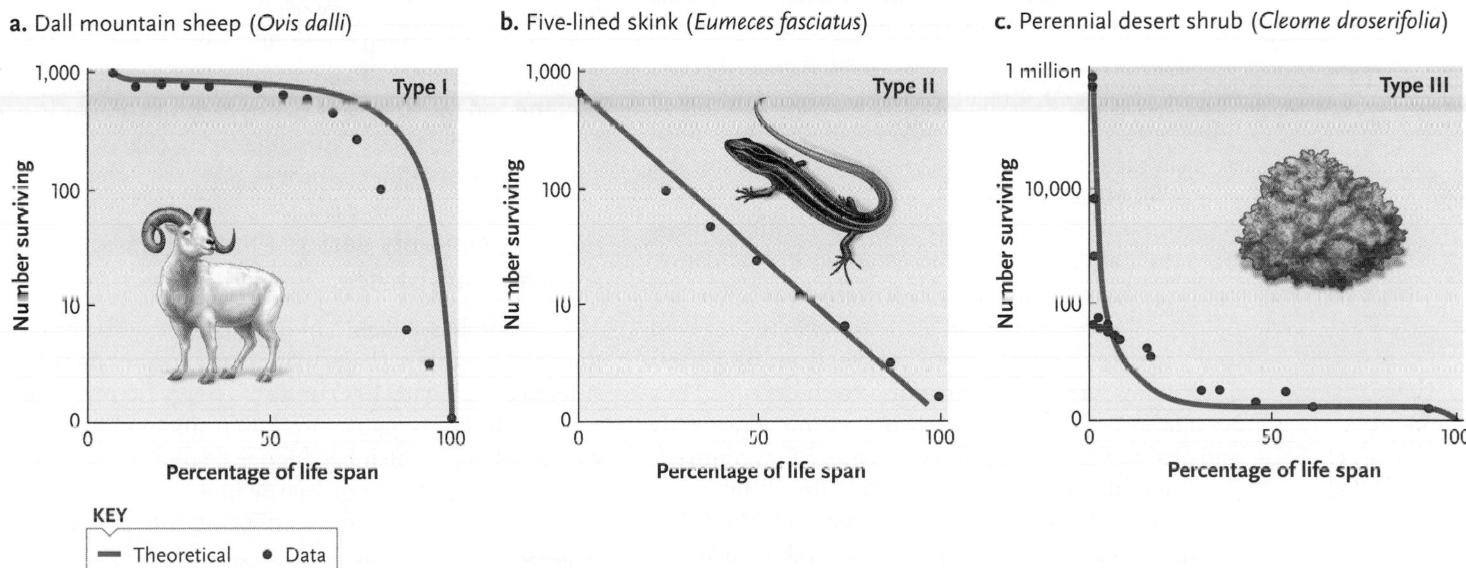

Figure 45.6
Survivorship curves. The survivorship curves of many organisms (pink) roughly match one of three idealized patterns (blue).

45.4 The Evolution of Life Histories

Analysis of life tables reveals how natural selection affects an organism's **life history**, which includes the lifetime patterns of growth, maturation, and reproduction. Ecologists study life histories to understand tradeoffs in the allocation of resources to these three activities. The results of their research suggest that natural selection adjusts the allocation of resources to maximize an individual's number of surviving offspring.

Every organism is constrained by a finite **energy budget**, the total amount of energy it can accumulate and use to fuel its activities. An organism's energy budget is like a savings account. When the individual accumulates more energy than it needs, it makes deposits to this account, storing energy as starch, glycogen, or fat. When the individual expends more energy than it harvests, it makes withdrawals from its energy stores. But unlike a bank account, an organism's energy budget cannot be overdrawn, and no loans against future "earnings" are possible.

Just as humans find clever ways to finance their schemes, many organisms use different ways to mortgage their operations. Organisms that enter states of inactivity or dormancy can maximize the time over which they use stored energy. An extreme example would be animals and plants that can survive freezing, an obvious strategy for conserving energy. Hibernation and estivation in animals are other examples. Hibernating animals use periods of reduced body temperatures to survive prolonged periods of cold weather. Estivation is inactivity during prolonged periods of high temperatures. In some cases, specialized spores are resistant to heat and desiccation. Migrating birds on long flights get energy by metabolizing fat as well as other body structures, such as muscle or digestive tissue. Organisms use the energy they harvest for three broadly defined functions: maintenance (the preservation of good physiological condition), growth, and reproduction. When an organism devotes energy to any one of these functions, the balance in its energy budget is reduced, leaving less energy for other functions.

A fish, a deciduous tree, and a mammal illustrate the dramatic variations existing in life history patterns. Larval coho salmon (*Oncorhynchus kisutch*) hatch in the headwaters of a stream, where they feed and grow for about a year before assuming their adult body form and swimming to the ocean. They remain at sea for a year or two, feeding voraciously and growing rapidly. Eventually, using a Sun compass, geomagnetic, and chemical cues, salmon return to the rivers and streams where they hatched. The fishes swim upstream. Males prepare nests and try to attract females. Each female lays hundreds or thousands of relatively small eggs. After breeding, the body condition of males and females deteriorates, and they die.

Most deciduous trees in the temperate zone, such as oaks (genus *Quercus*), begin their lives as seeds (acorns) in late summer. The seeds remain metabolically inactive until the following spring or a later year. After germinating, seedling trees collect nutrients and energy and continue to grow throughout their lives. Once they achieve a critical size, they may produce thousands of acorns annually for many years. Thus, growth and reproduction occur simultaneously through much of the trees' life.

European red deer (*Cervus elaphus*) are born in spring, and the young remain with their mothers for an extended period, nursing and growing rapidly. After weaning, the young feed on their own. Female red deer begin to breed after reaching adult size in their third year, producing one or two offspring annually until they are about 16 years old, when they reach their maximum life span and die.

How can we summarize the similarities and differences in the life histories of these organisms? All three species harvest energy throughout their lives. Salmon and deciduous trees continue to grow until old age, whereas deer reach adult size fairly early in life. Salmon produce many offspring in a single reproductive episode, whereas deciduous trees and deer reproduce repeatedly. However, most trees produce thousands of seeds annually, whereas deer produce only one or two young each spring.

What factors have produced these variations in life history patterns? Life history traits, like all population characteristics, are modified by natural selection. Thus, organisms exhibit evolutionary adaptations that increase the fitness of individuals. Each species' life history is, in fact, a highly integrated "strategy" or suite of selection-driven adaptations.

In analyzing life histories, ecologists compare the number of offspring with the amount of care provided to each by the parents. They also determine the number of reproductive episodes in the organism's lifetime and the timing of first reproduction. Because these characteristics evolve together, a change in one trait is likely to influence others.

45.4a Fecundity versus Parental Care: Cutting Your Losses

If a female has a fixed amount of energy for reproduction, she can package that energy in various ways. A female duck with 1000 units of energy for reproduction might lay 10 eggs with 100 units of energy per egg. A salmon, which has higher fecundity, might lay 1000 eggs with 1 unit of energy in each. The amount of energy invested in each offspring *before* it is born is **passive parental care** provided by the female. Passive parental care is provided through yolk in an egg, endosperm in a seed, or, in mammals, nutrients that cross the placenta.

Many animals also provide **active parental care** to offspring *after* their birth. In general, species producing many offspring in a reproductive episode (e.g., the coho salmon) provide relatively little active parental care *to each offspring*. In fact, female coho salmon, each producing 2400 to 4500 eggs, die before their eggs even hatch. Conversely, species producing few offspring at a time (e.g., European red deer) provide much more care to each one. A red deer doe nurses its single fawn for up to eight months before weaning it.

45.4b How Often to Breed: Once or Repeatedly?

The number of reproductive episodes in an organism's life span is a second life history characteristic adjusted by natural selection. Some organisms, such as coho salmon, devote all of their stored energy to a single reproductive event. Any adult that survives the upstream migration is likely to leave some surviving offspring. Other species, such as deciduous trees and red deer, reproduce more than once. In contrast to salmon, individuals of these species devote only some of their energy budget to reproduction at any time, with the balance allocated to maintenance and growth. Moreover, in some plants, invertebrates, fishes, and reptiles, larger individuals produce more offspring than smaller ones. Thus, one advantage of using only part of the energy budget for reproduction is that continued growth may result in greater fecundity at a later age. However, if an organism does not survive until the next breeding season, the potential advantage of putting energy into maintenance and growth would be lost.

45.4c Age at First Reproduction: When to Start Reproducing

Individuals that first reproduce at the earliest possible age may stand a good chance of leaving some surviving offspring. But the energy they use in reproduction is not available for maintenance and growth. Thus, early reproducers may be smaller and less healthy than individuals that delay reproduction in favour of other functions. Conversely, an individual that delays reproduction may increase its chance of survival and its future fecundity by becoming larger or more experienced. But there is always some chance that it will die before the next breeding season, leaving no offspring at all. Therefore, a finite energy budget and the risk of mortality establish a tradeoff in the timing of first reproduction. Mathematical models suggest that delayed reproduction will be favoured by natural selection if a sexually mature individual has a good chance of surviving to an older age, if organisms grow larger as they age, and if larger organisms have higher fecundity. Early reproduction will be favoured if adult survival rates are low, if animals do not grow larger as they age, or if larger size does not increase fecundity. These characteristics apply more readily to some animals and plants than they do to others. Among animals, the features discussed above apply more readily to vertebrate than to invertebrate animals. Parasitic organisms may have quite different patterns of life history.

Life history characteristics vary from one species to another, and they can vary among populations of a single species. Predation differentially influences life history characteristics in natural populations of guppies (*Poecilia reticulata*) in Trinidad (see *Life Histories of Guppies*).

STUDY BREAK

1. Organisms use energy for what three main operations?
2. Explain passive and active parental care in humans.
3. When would early reproduction be favoured?

45.5 Models of Population Growth

We now examine two mathematical models of population growth, exponential and logistic. *Exponential* models apply when populations experience unlimited growth. *Logistic* models apply when population growth is limited, often because available resources are finite. These simple models are tools that help ecologists refine their hypotheses, but neither provides entirely accurate predictions of population growth in nature. In the simplest versions of these models, ecologists define births as the production of offspring by any form of reproduction and ignore the effects of immigration and emigration.

45.5a Exponential Models: Populations Taking Off

Sometimes populations increase in size for a period of time with no apparent limits on their growth. In models of exponential growth, population size increases steadily by a constant ratio. Populations of bacteria and prokaryotes provide the most obvious examples, but multicellular organisms also sometimes exhibit exponential population growth.

Bacteria reproduce by binary fission. A parent cell divides in half, producing two daughter cells, and each can divide to produce two granddaughter cells. Generation time in a bacterial population is simply the time between successive cell divisions. If no bacteria in the population die, the population doubles in size each generation.

Bacterial populations grow quickly under ideal temperatures and with unlimited space and food. Consider a population of the human intestinal bacterium *Escherichia coli*, for which the generation time can be as short as 20 minutes. If we start with a population

Life Histories of Guppies

Figure 1
David Reznick surveys a shallow stream in the mountains of Trinidad.

Male guppy (right) that shared a stream with pike-cichlids (below)
Male guppy (right) that shared a stream with killifish (below)

Figure 2
Male guppies from streams where pike–cichlids live (top) are smaller and more streamlined and have duller colours than those from streams where killifish live (bottom). The pike–cichlid prefers to eat large guppies, and the killifish feeds on small guppies. Guppies are shown approximately life-sized; adult pike–cichlids grow to 16 cm in length, and adult killifish grow to 10 cm. (Guppy photos: David Reznick/University of California, Riverside: computer enhanced by Lisa Starr; predator photos: Hippocampus Bildarchiv.)

Some years ago, drenched with sweat and with fishnets in hand, two ecologists were engaged in fieldwork on the Caribbean island of Trinidad. They were after guppies (*Poecilia reticulata*), small fish most of us see in pet shops. In their native habitats, guppies bear live young in shallow mountain streams **(Figure 1),** and John Endler and David Reznick were studying the environmental variables influencing the evolution of their life history patterns.

Male guppies are easy to distinguish from females. Males stop growing at sexual maturity. They are smaller, and their scales have bright colours that serve as visual signals in intricate courtship displays. Females are drably coloured and continue to grow larger throughout their lives. In the mountains of Trinidad, guppies live in different streams, even in different parts of the same stream. Two other species of fish eat guppies **(Figure 2).** In some streams, a small killifish (*Rivulus hartii*) preys on immature guppies but does not have much success with the larger adults. In other streams, a large pike–cichlid (*Crenicichla alta*) prefers mature guppies and rarely hunts small, immature ones.

Reznick and Endler found that the life history patterns of guppies vary among streams with different predators. In streams with pike–cichlids, male and female guppies mature faster and begin to reproduce at a smaller size and younger age than their counterparts in streams where killifish live. Female guppies from pike–cichlid streams reproduce more often, producing smaller and more numerous young. These differences allow guppies to avoid some predation. Those in pike–cichlid streams begin to reproduce when they are smaller than the size preferred by that predator. Those from killifish streams grow quickly to a size that is too large to be consumed by killifish **(Figure 3).**

Although these life history differences were correlated with the distributions of the two predatory fishes, they might result from some other, unknown differences between the streams. Endler and Reznick investigated this possibility with controlled laboratory experiments. They carefully shipped groups of guppies to California, where they bred guppies from each kind of stream for two generations. Both types of experimental populations were raised under identical conditions in the absence of predators. Even in the absence of predators, the two types of experimental populations retained their life history differences. These results provided evidence of a genetic (heritable) basis for the observed life history differences.

Endler and Reznick also examined the role of predators in the *evolution* of the size differences **(Figure 4).** They raised guppies for many generations in the laboratory under three experimental conditions: some alone, some with killifish, and some with pike-cichlids. As predicted, the guppy lineage subjected to predation by killifish became larger at

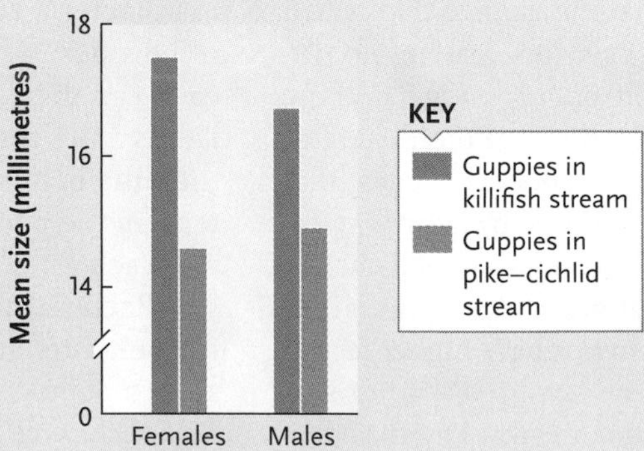

Figure 3
Guppies in streams occupied by pike–cichlids are smaller than those in streams occupied by killifish.

maturity. Individuals that were small at maturity were frequently eaten, and their reproduction was limited. The lineage raised with pike–cichlids showed a trend toward earlier maturity. Individuals that matured at a larger size faced a greater likelihood of being eaten before they had reproduced.

When they first visited Trinidad, Endler and Reznick had introduced guppies from a pike–cichlid stream to another stream that contained killifish but no pike–cichlids or guppies. There, 11 years later, guppy populations had changed. As the researchers predicted, the guppies became larger and reproduced more slowly, characteristics typical of natural guppy populations that live and die with killifish.

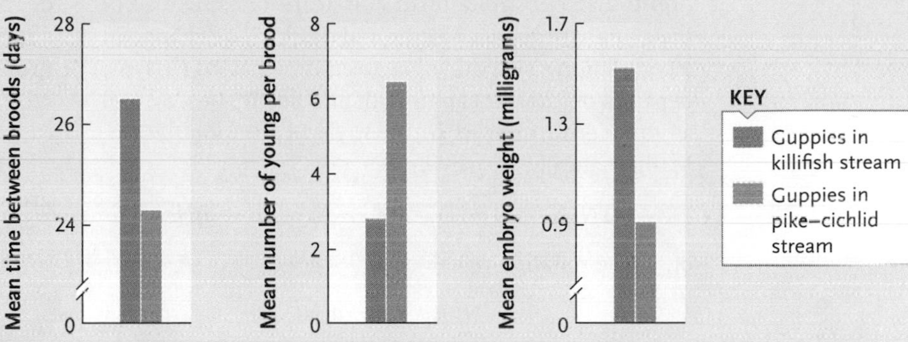

Figure 4
Female guppies from streams occupied by pike–cichlids reproduce more often (shorter time between broods) and produce more young per brood and smaller young (lower embryo weight) than females living in streams occupied by killifish.

of one bacterium, the population doubles to two cells after one generation, to four cells after two generations, and to eight cells after three generations **(Figure 45.7)**. After only 8 hours (24 generations), the population will number more than 16 million. And after a single day (72 generations), the population will number nearly 5×10^{21} cells. Although other bacteria grow more slowly than *E. coli*, it is no wonder that pathogenic bacteria, such as those causing cholera or plague, can quickly overtake the defences of an infected animal.

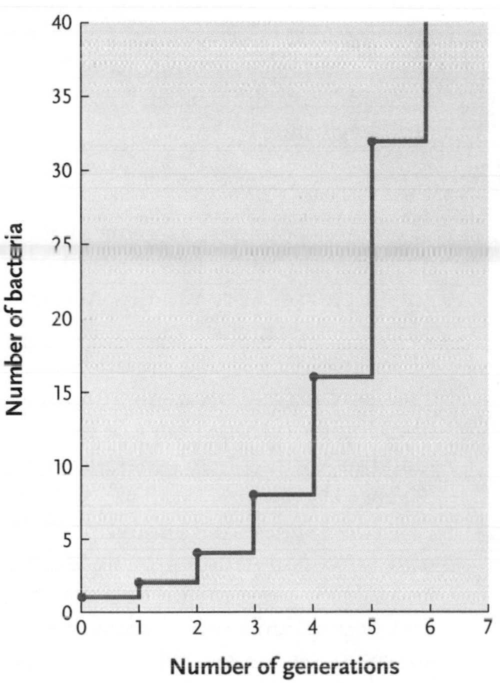

Figure 45.7
Bacterial population growth. If all members of a bacterial population divide simultaneously, a plot of population size over time forms a stair-stepped curve in which the steps get larger as the number of dividing cells increases.

When populations of multicellular organisms are large, they have the potential for exponential growth, as we shall see below for our own species. In any event, over a given time period,

$$\text{change in population size} = \text{number of births} - \text{number of deaths}.$$

We express this relationship mathematically by defining N as the population size; ΔN (pronounced "delta N") as the change in population size; Δt as the time period during which the change occurs; and B and D as the numbers of births and deaths, respectively, *during that time period*. Thus, $\Delta N/\Delta t$ symbolizes the change in population size over time, and

$$\Delta N/\Delta t = B - D.$$

The above equation applies to any population for which we know the exact numbers of births and deaths. Ecologists usually express births and deaths as *per capita* (per individual) rates, allowing them to apply the model to a population of any size. The per capita birth rate (b) is the number of births in the population during the specified time period divided by the population size: $b = (B/N)$. Similarly, the per capita death rate, d, is the number of deaths divided by the population size: $d = (D/N)$.

If in a population of 2000 field mice, 1000 mice are born and 200 mice die during 1 month, $b = 1000/2000 = 0.5$ births per individual per month, and $d = 200/2000 = 0.1$ deaths per individual per month. Of course, no mouse can give birth to half an offspring, and no individual can die one-tenth of a death. But these rates tell us the per capita birth and death rates *averaged over all mice in the population*. Per capita birth and death rates are always expressed over a specified time period. For long-lived organisms, such as humans, time is measured in years. For short-lived organisms, such as fruit flies, time is measured in days. We can calculate per capita birth and death rates from data in a life table.

Now we can revise the population growth equation to use per capita birth and death rates instead of the actual numbers of births and deaths. The change in a population's size during a given time period ($\Delta N/\Delta t$) depends on the per capita birth and death rates, as well as on the number of individuals in the population. Mathematically, we can write

$$\Delta N/\Delta t = B - D = bN - dN = (b - d)N$$

or, in the notation of calculus,

$$dN/dt = (b - d)N.$$

This equation describes the **exponential model of population growth.** (Note that in calculus, dN/dt is the notation for the population growth rate. The "d" in dN/dt is *not* the same "d" we use to symbolize the per capita death rate.)

The difference between the per capita birth rate and the per capita death rate, $b - d$, is the **per capita growth rate** of the population, symbolized by r. Like b and d, r is always expressed per individual per unit time. Using the per capita growth rate, r, in place of $(b - d)$, the exponential growth equation is written

$$dN/dt = rN.$$

If the birth rate exceeds the death rate, r has a positive value ($r > 0$), and the population is growing. In our example with field mice, r is $0.5 - 0.1 = 0.4$ mice per mouse per month. If, on the other hand, the birth rate is lower than the death rate, r has a negative value ($r < 0$), and the population is shrinking. In populations in which the birth rate equals the death rate, r is zero, and the population's size is not changing—a situation known as **zero population growth**, or ZPG. Even under ZPG, births and deaths still occur, but the numbers of births and deaths cancel each other out.

Populations will grow as long as the per capita growth rate is positive ($r > 0$). In our hypothetical population of field mice, we started with $N = 2000$ mice and calculated a per capita growth rate of 0.4 mice per individual per month. In the first month, the population grows by $0.4 \times 2000 = 800$ mice **(Figure 45.8)**. At the start of the second month, $N = 2800$ and r still $= 0.4$. Thus, in the second month, the population grows by $0.4 \times 2800 = 1120$ mice. Notice that even though r remains constant, the *increase* in population size grows each month because more individuals are reproducing. In less than two years, the mouse population will increase to more than one million! A graph of exponential population growth has a characteristic J shape, getting steeper through time. The population grows at an ever-increasing pace because the change in a population's size depends on the number of individuals in the population and its per capita growth rate.

Imagine a hypothetical population living in an ideal environment with unlimited food and shelter; no predators, parasites, or disease; and a comfortable abiotic environment. Under such circumstances (admittedly unrealistic), the per capita birth rate is very high, the per capita death rate is very low, and the per capita growth rate, r, is as high as it can be. This maximum per capita growth rate, symbolized r_{max}, is the population's **intrinsic rate of increase.** Under these ideal conditions, our exponential growth equation is

$$dN/dt = r_{max}N.$$

When populations grow at their intrinsic rate of increase, population size increases very rapidly. Across a wide variety of protists and animals, r_{max} varies inversely with generation time: species with a short generation time have higher intrinsic rates of increase than those with a long generation time **(Figure 45.9)**.

The exponential model predicts unlimited population growth. But we know from even casual observations that population sizes of most species are somehow limited. We are not knee-deep in bacteria, rosebushes, or garter snakes. What factors limit the growth of populations? As a population gets larger, it uses more vital resources,

Month	Old Population Size		Net Monthly Increase		New Population Size
1	2 000	+	800	=	2 800
2	2 800	+	1 120	=	3 920
3	3 920	+	1 568	=	5 488
4	5 488	+	2 195	=	7 683
5	7 683	+	3 073	=	10 756
6	10 756	+	4 302	=	15 058
7	15 058	+	6 023	=	21 081
8	21 081	+	8 432	=	29 513
9	29 513	+	11 805	=	41 318
10	41 318	+	16 527	=	57 845
11	57 845	+	23 138	=	80 983
12	80 983	+	32 393	=	113 376
13	113 376	+	45 350	=	158 726
14	158 726	+	63 490	=	222 216
15	222 216	+	88 887	=	311 103
16	311 103	+	124 441	=	435 544
17	435 544	+	174 218	=	609 762
18	609 762	+	243 905	=	853 667
19	853 677	+	341 467	=	1 195 134

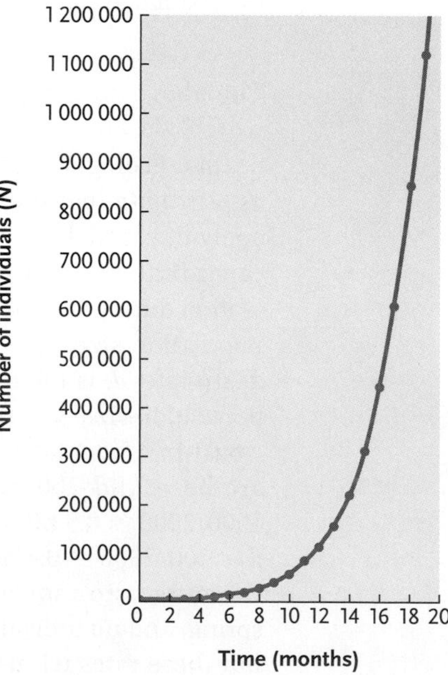

Figure 45.8
Exponential population growth. Exponential population growth produces a J-shaped curve when population size is plotted against time. Although the per capita growth rate (r) remains constant, the increase in population size gets larger every month because more individuals are reproducing.

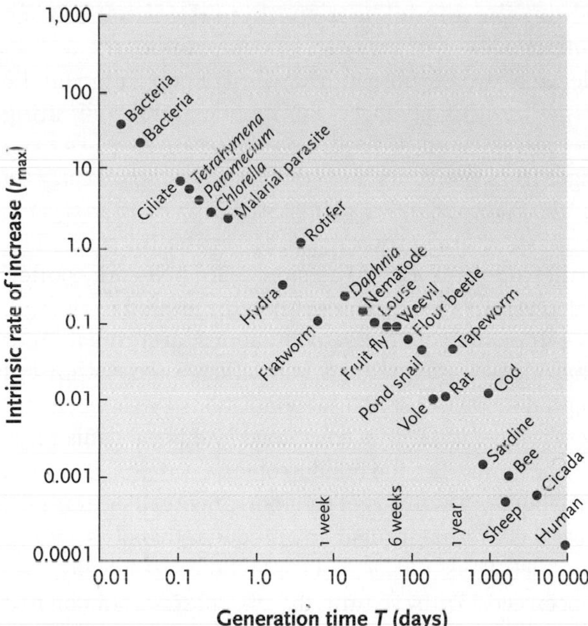

Figure 45.9
Generation time and r_{max}. The intrinsic rate of increase (r_{max}) is high for protists and animals with short generation times and low for those with long generation times.

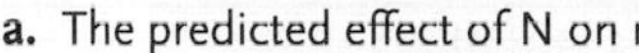

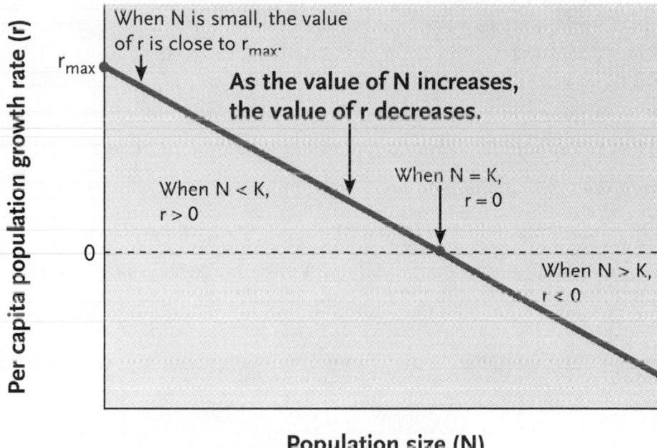

b. Population size through time

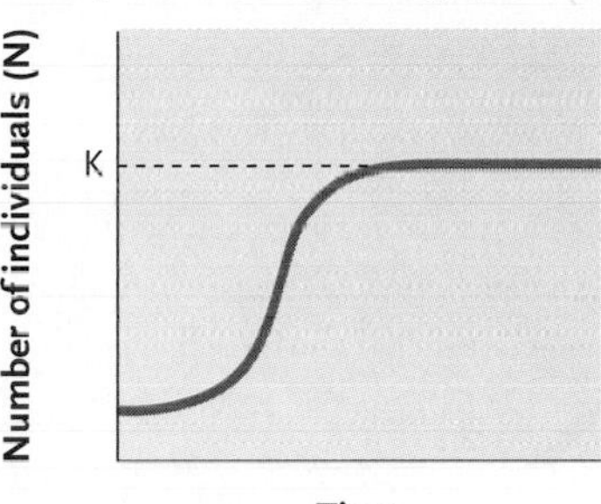

Figure 45.10
The logistic model of population growth. The logistic model **(a)** assumes that the per capita population growth rate (r) decreases linearly as population size (N) increases. The logistic model also predicts that population size **(b)** increases quickly at first but then slowly approaches carrying capacity (K).

perhaps leading to a shortage of resources. In this situation, individuals may have less energy available for maintenance and reproduction, causing decreases in per capita birth rates and increases in per capita death rates. Energy in food is not always equally available, and when an animal spends time handling food to eat it, the ratio of cost (handling) to benefit (energy in the food) diminishes, affecting return on investment. Such rate changes can affect a population's per capita growth rate, causing population growth to slow or stop.

45.5b Logistic Models: Populations and Carrying Capacity (K)

Environments provide enough resources to sustain only a finite population of any species. The maximum number of individuals that an environment can support indefinitely is termed its **carrying capacity**, symbolized as K. K is defined for each population. It is a property of the environment that can vary from one habitat to another and in a single habitat over time. The spring and summer flush of insects in temperate habitats supports large populations of insectivorous birds. But fewer insects are available in autumn and winter, causing a seasonal decline in K for birds, and autumnal migrations occur in birds seeking more food and less inclement weather. Other cycles are annual, such as variation in water levels in wetlands from year to year.

The **logistic model of population growth** assumes that a population's per capita growth rate, r, decreases as the population gets larger **(Figure 45.10)**. In other words, population growth slows as the population size approaches K. The mathematical expression $(K - N)$ tells us how many individuals can be added to a population before it reaches K. The expression $(K - N)/K$ indicates what percentage of the carrying capacity is still available.

To create the logistic model, we factor the impact of K into the exponential model by multiplying r_{max} by $(K - N)/K$ to reduce the per capita growth rate (r) from its maximum value (r_{max}) as N increases:

$$dN/dt = r_{max}N(K - N)/K.$$

The calculation of how r varies with population size is straightforward **(Table 45.2, p. 1126)**. In a very small population (N much smaller than K), plenty of resources are available; the value of $(K - N)/K$ is close to 1. Here the per capita growth rate (r) approaches the maximum possible (r_{max}). Under these conditions, population growth is close to exponential. If a population is large (N close to K), few additional resources are available. Now the value of $(K - N)/K$ is small, and the per capita growth rate (r) is very low. When the size of the population exactly equals K, $(K - N)/K$ becomes 0, as does the population growth rate, the situation defined as ZPG.

The logistic model of population growth predicts an S-shaped graph of population size over time, with

Table 45.2 **The Effect of N on r and ΔN^* in a Hypothetical Population Exhibiting Logistic Growth in which K equals 2000 and r_{max} is 0.04 per capita per year**

N (population size)	(K − N)/K (% of K available)	$r = r_{max}(K - N/K)$ (per capita growth rate)	$\Delta N = rN$ (change in N)
50	0.990	0.0396	2
100	0.950	0.0380	4
250	0.875	0.0350	9
500	0.750	0.0300	15
750	0.625	0.0250	19
1000	0.500	0.0200	20
1250	0.375	0.0150	19
1500	0.250	0.0100	15
1750	0.125	0.0050	9
1900	0.050	0.0020	4
1950	0.025	0.0010	2
2000	0.000	0.0000	0

*ΔN rounded to the nearest whole number.

the population slowly approaching K and remaining at that level **(Figure 45.11b)**. According to this model, the population grows slowly when the population size is small because few individuals are reproducing. It also grows slowly when the population size is large because the per capita population growth rate is low. The population grows quickly (dN/dt is highest) at intermediate population sizes, when a sizable number of individuals are breeding and the per capita population growth rate (r) is still fairly high (see Table 45.2).

The logistic model assumes that vital resources become increasingly limited as a population grows. Thus, the model is a mathematical portrait of **intraspecific** (within species) **competition**, the dependence of two or more individuals in a population on the same limiting resource. For mobile animals, limiting resources could be food, water, nesting sites, and refuges from predators. For sessile species, space can be a limiting resource. For plants, sunlight, water, inorganic nutrients, and growing space can be limiting. The pattern of uniform dispersion described earlier often reflects intraspecific competition for limited resources.

In some very dense populations, accumulation of poisonous waste products may reduce survivorship and reproduction. Most natural populations live in open systems where wastes are consumed by other organisms or flushed away. But the buildup of toxic wastes is common in laboratory cultures of microorganisms. For example, yeast cells ferment sugar and produce ethanol as a waste product. Thus, the alcohol content of wine usually does not exceed 13% by volume, the ethanol concentration that poisons yeasts that are vital to the wine-making process.

How well do species conform to the predictions of the logistic model? In simple laboratory cultures, relatively small organisms, such as *Paramecium*, some crustaceans, and flour beetles, often show an S-shaped pattern of population growth **(Figure 45.11a, b)**. Moreover, large animals introduced into new environments sometimes exhibit a pattern of population growth that matches the predictions of the logistic model **(Figure 45.11c)**.

Nevertheless, some assumptions of the logistic model are unrealistic. For example, the model predicts that survivorship and fecundity respond immediately to changes in a population's density. Many organisms exhibit a delayed response (a **time lag**) because fecundity has been determined by resource availability at some time in the past. This may reflect conditions that prevailed when individuals were adding yolk to eggs or

Figure 45.11 Examples of logistic population growth.

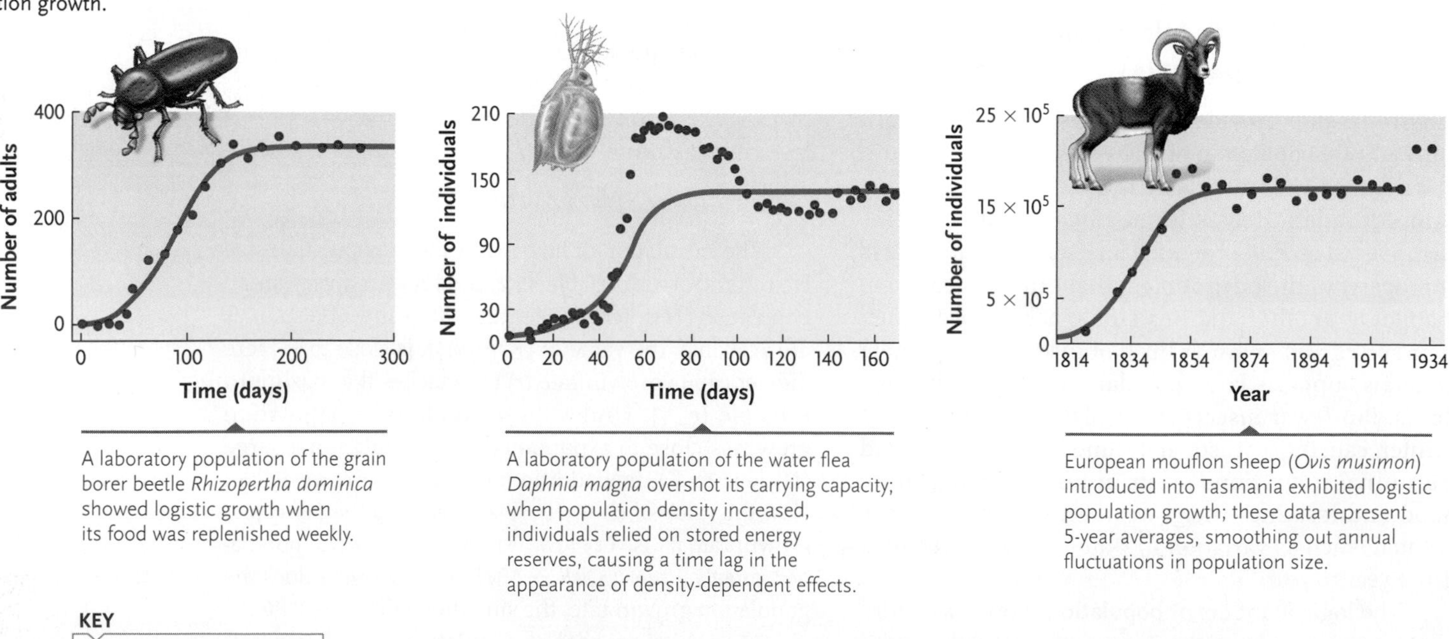

A laboratory population of the grain borer beetle *Rhizopertha dominica* showed logistic growth when its food was replenished weekly.

A laboratory population of the water flea *Daphnia magna* overshot its carrying capacity; when population density increased, individuals relied on stored energy reserves, causing a time lag in the appearance of density-dependent effects.

European mouflon sheep (*Ovis musimon*) introduced into Tasmania exhibited logistic population growth; these data represent 5-year averages, smoothing out annual fluctuations in population size.

endosperm to seeds. Moreover, when food resources become scarce, individuals may use stored energy reserves to survive and reproduce. This delays the impact of crowding until stored reserves are depleted and means that population size may overshoot K (see Figure 45.11b). Deaths may then outnumber births, causing the population size to drop below K, at least temporarily. Time lags often cause a population to oscillate around K.

The assumption that the addition of new individuals to a population always decreases survivorship and fecundity is unrealistic. In small populations, modest population growth may not have much impact on survivorship and fecundity. In fact, most organisms probably require a minimum population density to survive and reproduce. Some plants flourish in small clumps that buffer them from physical stresses, whereas a single individual living in the open would suffer adverse effects. In some animal populations, a minimum population density is necessary for individuals to find mates. Determining the minimum viable population for a species is an important issue in conservation biology (see Chapter 48).

Study Break

1. When do you use an exponential model rather than a logistic one?
2. Define the terms in the equation $dN/dt = (b - d)N$.
3. What does it mean when $r < 0$, $r > 0$, or $r = 0$? What is r_{max}, and how does it vary with generation time?

45.6 Population Regulation

What environmental factors influence population growth rates and control fluctuations in population size? Some factors affecting population size are **density dependent** because their influence increases or decreases with the density of the population. Intraspecific competition and predation are examples of density-dependent environmental factors. The logistic model includes the effects of density dependence in its assumption that per capita birth and death rates change with population density.

Numerous laboratory and field studies have shown that crowding (high population densities) decreases individual growth rate, adult size, and survival of plants and animals **(Figure 45.12).** Organisms living in extremely dense populations are unable to harvest enough resources. They grow slowly and tend to be small, weak, and less likely to survive. Gardeners understand this relationship and thin their plants to achieve a density that maximizes the number of vigorous individuals that survive to be harvested.

Crowding has a negative effect on reproduction **(Figure 45.13, p. 1128).** When resources are in short supply, each individual has less energy for reproduction after meeting its basic maintenance needs. Hence, females in crowded populations produce either fewer offspring or smaller offspring that are less likely to survive.

In some species, crowding stimulates developmental and behavioural changes that may influence the density of a population. Migratory locusts can

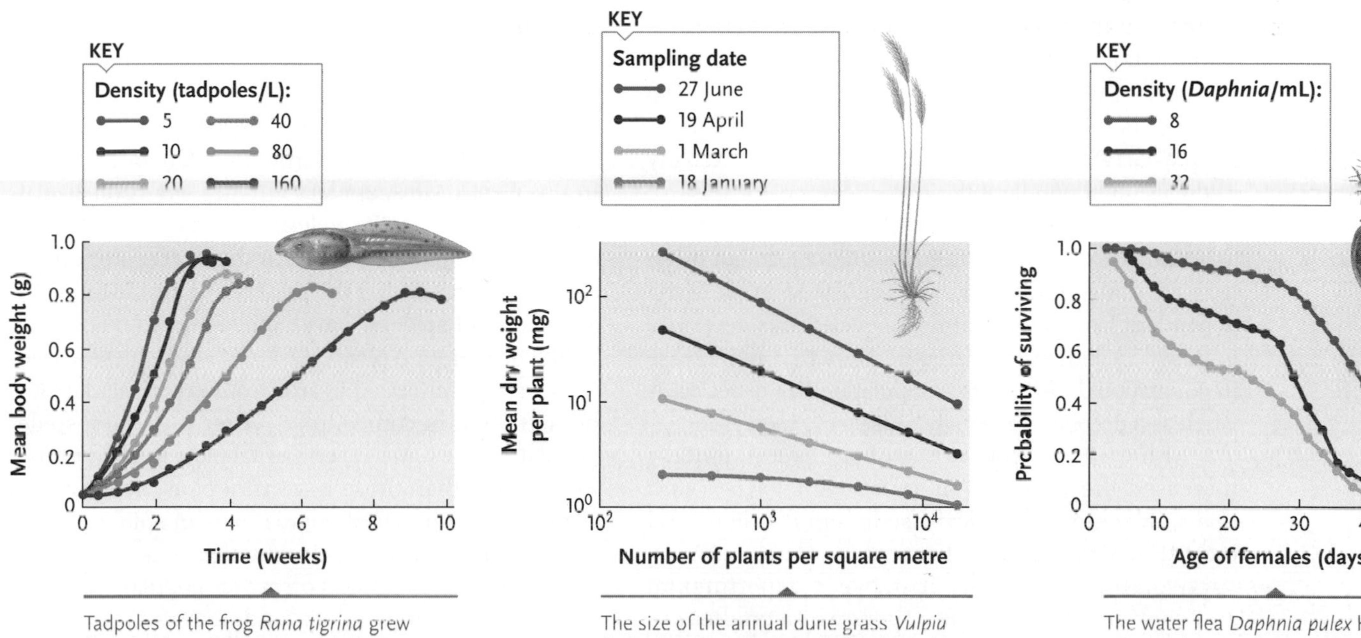

Tadpoles of the frog *Rana tigrina* grew faster and reached larger adult body size at low densities than at high densities.

The size of the annual dune grass *Vulpia fasciculata* decreased markedly when plants were grown at high density. Density effects became more accentuated through time as the plants grew larger (indicated by the progressively steeper slopes of the lines).

The water flea *Daphnia pulex* had higher survivorship at a density of 8/mL than at densities of 16/mL or 32/mL.

Figure 45.12 Effects of crowding on individual growth, size, and survival.

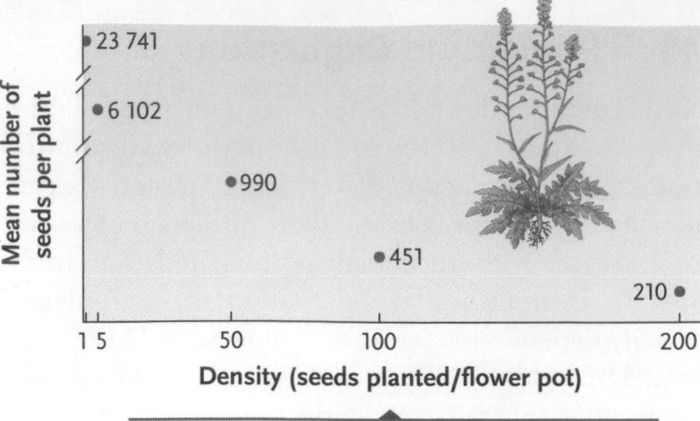

The number of seeds produced by shepherd's purse (*Capsella bursa-pastoris*) decreased dramatically with increasing density in experimental plots.

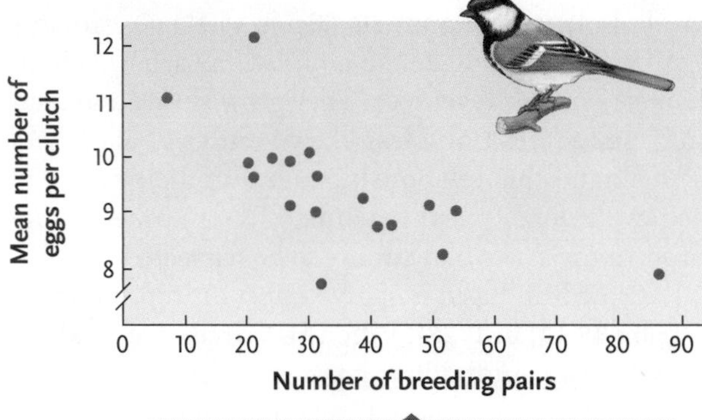

The mean number of eggs produced by the Great Tit (*Parus major*), a woodland bird, declined as the number of breeding pairs in Marley Wood increased.

Figure 45.13
Effects of crowding on fecundity.

Figure 45.14
A swarm of locusts. Migratory locusts (*Locusta migratoria*) moving across an African landscape can devour their own weight in plant material every day.

develop into either solitary or migratory forms in the same population. Migratory individuals have longer wings and more body fat, characteristics that allow long-distance dispersal. High population density increases the frequency of the migratory form. So many locusts move away from the area of high density **(Figure 45.14),** reducing the size and thus the density of the original population.

Although these data about locusts confirm the assumptions of the logistic equation, they do not prove that natural populations are regulated by density-dependent factors. Experimental evidence is necessary to provide a convincing demonstration that an increase in population density causes population size to decrease, whereas a decrease in density causes it to increase.

In the 1960s, Robert Eisenberg experimentally increased the numbers of aquatic snails (*Lymnaea elodes*) in some ponds, decreased them in others, and maintained natural densities in control ponds. Adult survivorship did not differ between experimental and control treatments. But there was a gradient in egg production from few eggs (snails in high-density ponds), to more (control density), to most (control density). Furthermore, survival rates of young snails declined as density increased. After four months, densities in the two experimental groups converged on those in the control, providing strong evidence of density-dependent population regulation.

At this stage, intraspecific competition appears to be the primary density-dependent factor regulating population size. Competition between populations of different species also can exert density-dependent effects on population growth (see Chapter 46).

But predation also can cause density-dependent population regulation. As a particular prey species becomes more numerous, predators may consume more of it because it is easier to find and catch. Once a prey species exceeds some threshold density, predators may consume a larger percentage of its population, a density-dependent effect. On rocky shores in California, sea stars feed mainly on the most abundant invertebrate there. When one prey species becomes common, predators feed on it disproportionately, drastically reducing its numbers. Then they switch to now more abundant alternate prey.

Sometimes several density-dependent factors influence a population at the same time. On small islands in the West Indies, spiders are rare wherever lizards (*Ameiva festiva, Anolis carolinensis,* and *Anolis sagrei*) are abundant but common where the lizards are rare or absent. To test whether the presence of lizards limits the abundance of spiders, David Spiller and Tom Schoener built fences around plots on islands where these species occur. They eliminated lizards from experimental plots but left them in control plots. After two years, spider populations in some experimental plots were five times more dense than those in control plots, suggesting a strong impact of lizard populations on spider populations **(Figure 45.15).** In this situation, lizards had two density-dependent effects on spider populations. First, lizards ate spiders, and, second, they competed with them for food. Experimental evidence made it possible for biologists to better understand the situation.

Predation, parasitism, and disease can cause density-dependent regulation of plant and animal pop-

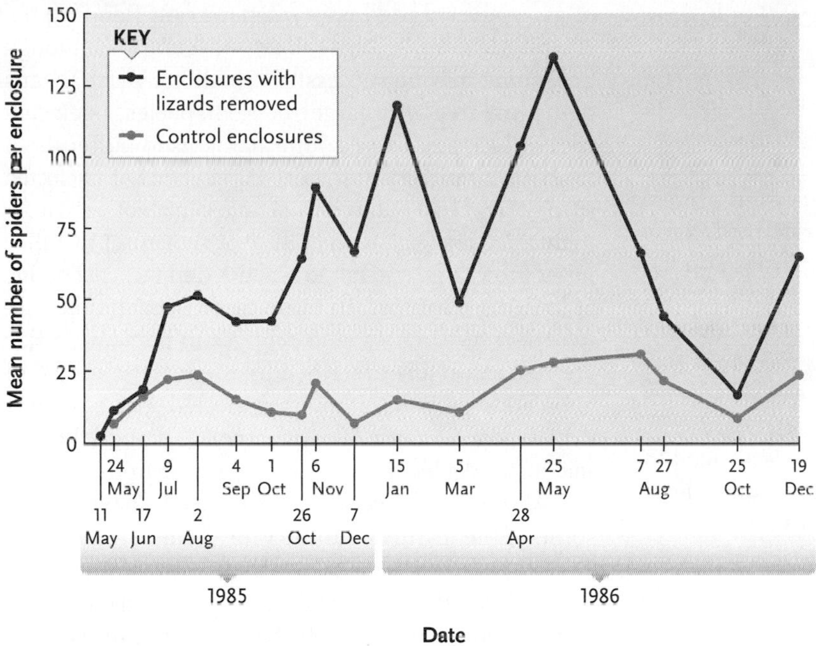

Figure 45.15
Populations of spiders (*Metepeira dantona*) on a small island in the Bahamas (Caribbean) are influenced by the presence of lizards. Note how much higher the population densities of spiders are in the absence versus the presence of lizards.

ulations. Infectious microorganisms spread quickly in a crowded population (e.g., rabies). In addition, if crowded individuals are weak or malnourished, they are more susceptible to infection and may die from diseases that healthy organisms would survive. Effects on survival can be direct or indirect.

45.6a Density-Independent Factors: Reducing Population in Spite of Density

Some populations are affected by **density-independent** factors that reduce population size regardless of its density. If an insect population is not physiologically adapted to high temperature, a sudden hot spell may kill 80% of them whether they number 100 or 100 000. Fires, earthquakes, storms, and other natural disturbances can contribute directly or indirectly to density-independent mortality. Because such factors do not cause a population to fluctuate around its K, these density-independent factors can reduce but do not *regulate* population size.

Density-independent factors have a particularly strong effect on populations of small-bodied species that cannot buffer themselves against environmental change. Their populations grow exponentially for a time, but shifts in climate or random events cause high mortality before populations reach a size at which density-dependent factors would regulate their numbers. When conditions improve, populations grow exponentially, at least until another density-independent factor causes them to crash again. A small Australian insect, a thrip, eats the pollen and flowers of plants in the rose family. These thrips can be abundant enough to damage blooms. Populations of thrips grow exponentially in spring, when many flowers are available, and the weather is warm and moist **(Figure 45.16).** But their populations crash predictably during summer because Thrips imaginis do not tolerate hot and dry conditions. After the crash, a few individuals survive in remaining flowers, and they are the stock from which the population grows exponentially the following spring.

45.6b Interactions between Density-Dependent and Density-Independent Factors: Sometimes Population Density Affects Mortality

Density-dependent factors can interact with density-independent factors and limit population growth. Food shortage caused by high population density (a density-dependent factor) may lead to malnourishment. Malnourished individuals may be more likely to succumb to the stress of extreme weather (a density-independent factor).

Populations can be affected by density-independent factors in a density-dependent manner. Some animals retreat into shelters to escape environmental stresses, such as floods or severe heat. If a population is small, most individuals can be accommodated in available refuges. But if a population is large (exceeds the capacity of shelters), only a proportion will find suitable shelter. The larger the population, the greater the percentage of individuals exposed to the stress(es). Thus, although the density-independent effects of weather limit populations of thrips, the availability of flowers in summer (a density-dependent factor) regulates the size of the starting populations of thrips the following spring. Hence, both density-dependent and density-independent factors influence the size of populations of thrips.

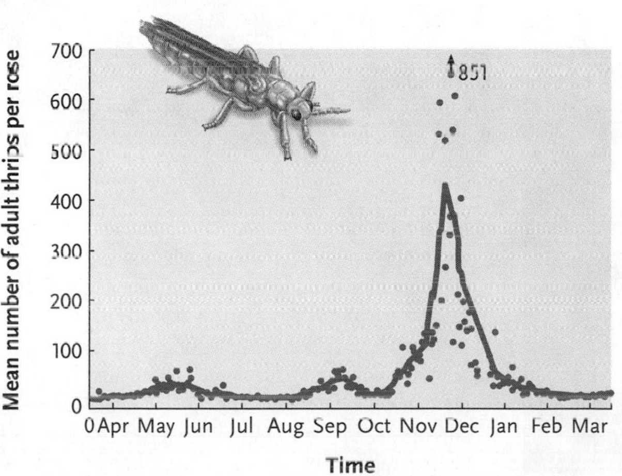

Figure 45.16
Booms and busts in a *Thrips* population. Populations of the Australian insect *thrips imaginis* grow exponentially when conditions are favourable during spring (which begins in September in the Southern Hemisphere). The populations crash in summer, however, when hot and dry conditions cause high mortality.

45.6c Life History Characteristics: Evolution of Strategies for Population Growth

Even casual observation reveals tremendous variation in how rapidly population sizes change in different species. New weeds often appear in a vegetable garden overnight, whereas the number of oak trees in a forest may remain relatively stable for years. Why do only some species have the potential for explosive population growth? The answer lies in how natural selection has moulded life history strategies adapted to different ecological conditions. Some ecologists recognize two quite different life history patterns, ***r*-selected** species and ***K*-selected** species (**Table 45.3; Figure 45.17**).

On the face of it, *r*-selected species are adapted to rapidly changing environments, and many have at least some of the features outlined in Table 45.3. The success of an *r*-selected life history depends on flooding the environment with a *large quantity* of young even though only some may be successful. Small body size means that compared with larger bodied species, *r*-selected species lack physiological mechanisms to buffer them from environmental variation. Populations of *r*-selected species can be so reduced by changes in abiotic environmental factors (e.g., temperature or moisture) that they never grow large enough to reach *K* and face a shortage of limiting resources. In these cases, *K* cannot be estimated by researchers, and changes in population size are not accurately described by the logistic model of population growth. Although *r*-selected species appear to have poor tolerance of environmental change, they are said to be adapted to rapidly changing environments.

At the same time, *K*-selected species have at least some of the features outlined for them in Table 49.3. These organisms survive the early stages of life (type I or type II survivorship), and a low r_{max} means that their populations grow slowly. The success of a *K*-selected life history is linked to the production of a relatively small number of *high-quality* offspring that join an already well-established population. Generalizations about *r*-selected and *K*-selected species are misleading. We can recognize this by comparing two species of mammals.

Peromyscus maniculatus, deer mice, occur widely in North America. In southern Ontario, adults weigh 12 to 31 g, females produce average litters of 4 (range 2 to 8), and each can have 4 or 5 litters a year. Females become sexually mature at age 2 months and breed in their first year. Occasionally, deer mice mice live to age 3 years in the wild. Throughout their extensive range in North America, *Myotis lucifugus,* little brown bats, weigh 7 to 12 g; females bear a single young per litter and have one litter per year. Females may breed a year after they are born, but many may wait until they are two years old. In the wild, little brown bats can live over 30 years. Using these data, one small mammal (deer mouse) is an *r*-strategist, whereas another (little brown bat) is a *K*-strategist. To complicate matters, deer mice living in Kananaskis in the mountains near Calgary, Alberta, mature at one year and may have two litters per year, typically five young per litter. Compared to little brown bats, Kananaskis deer mice are *r*-strategists. Compared with Ontario deer mice, they are more like *K*-strategists.

Biologists may find the idea of *r*-strategists and *K*-strategists useful, but too often the idea means imposing some human view of the world on a natural system. *K*-strategists and *r*-strategists may be more like "beauty," defined by the eye of the beholder. Elephants (*Loxodonta africana, Loxodonata cyclotis, Elephas maximus*) are big and meet all *K*-strategist criteria. Many insects are small but in all other respects meet the criteria considered typical of *K*-strategists because of their patterns of reproduction. Codfish (*Gadus morhua*) are big (compared to insects or bats) but meet most of the criteria used to identify *r*-strategists, such as their patterns of reproduction.

Table 45.3 Characteristics of *r*-Selected and *K*-Selected Species

Characteristic	r-Selected Species	K-Selected Species
Maturation time	Short	Long
Life span	Short	Long
Mortality rate	Usually high	Usually low
Reproductive episodes	Usually one	Usually several
Time of first reproduction	Early	Late
Clutch or brood size	Usually large	Usually small
Size of offspring	Small	Large
Active parental care	Little or none	Often extensive
Population size	Fluctuating	Relatively stable
Tolerance of environmental change	Generally poor	Generally good

a. An *r*-selected species

Nigel Cattlin/Holt/Holt Studios International, Ltd.

b. A *K*-selected species

© Goodshoot/CORBIS

Figure 45.17
Life history differences. An r-selected species, **(a)** *Chenopodium quinoa*, matures in one growing season and produces many tiny seeds. Quinoa was a traditional food staple for indigenous people of North and South America. A *K*-selected species, **(b)** *Cocos nucifera*, a coconut palm, grows slowly and produces a few large seeds repeatedly during its long life.

45.6d Population Cycles: Ups and Downs in Numbers of Individuals

Population densities of many insects, birds, and mammals in the northern hemisphere fluctuate between species-specific lows and highs in a multiyear cycle. Arctic populations of small rodents (*Lemmus lemmus*) vary in size over a 4-year cycle, whereas snowshoe hares (*Lepus americanus*), ruffed grouse (*Bonasa umbellis*), and lynx have 10-year cycles. Ecologists documented these cyclic fluctuations more than a century ago, but none of the general hypotheses proposed to date explain cycles in all species. Availability and quality of food, abundance of predators, prevalence of disease-causing microorganisms, and variations in weather can influence population growth and declines. Furthermore, food supply for a cycling population and its predators are themselves influenced by a population's size.

Theories of *intrinsic control* suggest that as an animal population grows, individuals undergo hormonal changes that increase aggressiveness, reduce reproduction, and foster dispersal. The dispersal phase of the cycle may be dramatic. When populations of Norway lemming (*Lemmus lemmus*), a rodent that lives in the Scandinavian arctic, reach their peak density, aggressive interactions drive younger and weaker individuals to disperse. The dispersal of many thousands of lemmings during periods of population growth has sometimes been incorrectly portrayed in nature films as a suicidal mass migration.

Other explanations focus on extrinsic control, such as the relationship between a cycling species and its food or predators. A dense population may exhaust its food supply, increasing mortality and decreasing reproduction. The die-off of large numbers of African elephants in Tsavo National Park in Kenya is an example of the impact of overpopulation. There elephants overgrazed vegetation in most of the park habitat. In 1970, the combination of overgrazing and a drought caused high mortality of elephants. The picture is not always clear because experimental food supplementation does not always prevent decline in mammal populations. This suggests some level of intrinsic control.

Cycles in populations of predators could be induced by time lags between populations of predators and prey and vice versa **(Figure 45.18)**. The 10-year cycles of snowshoe hares and their feline predators, Canada lynx, were often cited as a classic example of

© Ed Cesar/Photo Researchers, nc.

Figure 45.18

The predator–prey model. Predator–prey interactions may contribute to density-dependent regulation of both populations. A mathematical model **(a)** predicts cycles in the numbers of predators and prey because of time lags in each species' responses to changes in the density of the other. (Predator population size is exaggerated in this graph.) **(b)** Canada lynx (*Lynx canadensis*) and snowshoe hare (*Lepus americanus*) were often described as a typical cyclic predator–prey interaction. The abundances of lynx (red line) and snowshoe hare (blue line) are based on counts of pelts trappers sold to the Hudson's Bay Company over a 90-year period. Recent research shows that population cycles in snowshoe hares are caused by complex interactions between the snowshoe hares, its food plants, and its predators.

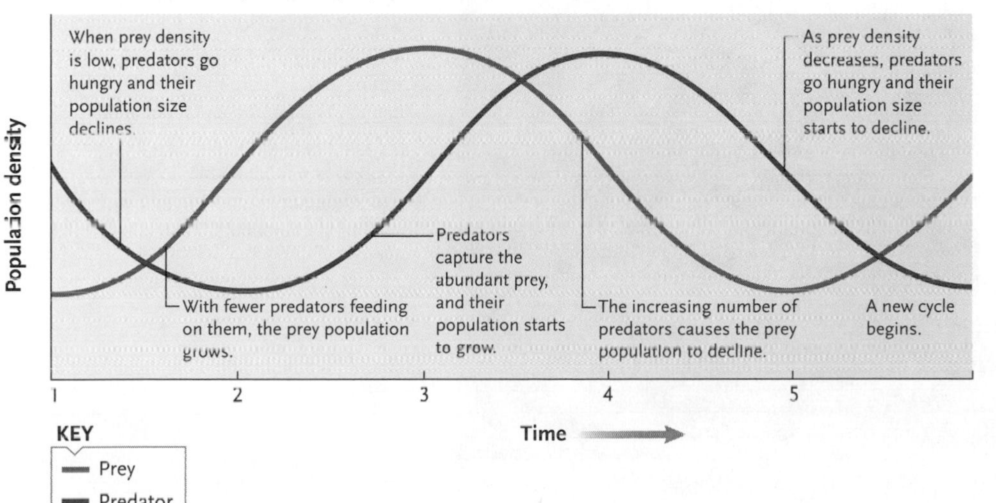
a. Predictions of a predator–prey model
When prey density is low, predators go hungry and their population size declines.
As prey density decreases, predators go hungry and their population size starts to decline.
Predators capture the abundant prey, and their population starts to grow.
With fewer predators feeding on them, the prey population grows.
The increasing number of predators causes the prey population to decline.
A new cycle begins.
Population density
1
2
3
4
5
Time
KEY
Prey
Predator

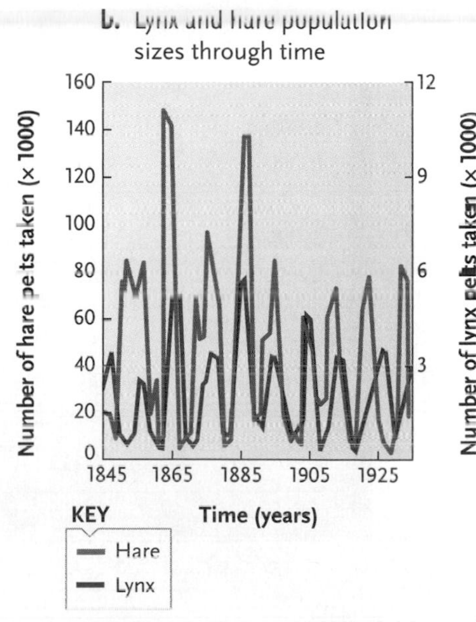
b. Lynx and hare population sizes through time
Number of hare pelts taken (× 1000)
160
140
120
100
80
60
40
20
0
1845
1865
1885
1905
1925
Time (years)
12
9
6
3
Number of lynx pelts taken (× 1000)
KEY
Hare
Lynx

such an interaction. But snowshoe hare populations can exhibit a 10-year fluctuation even on islands where lynx are absent. Thus, lynx is not solely responsible for population cycles in snowshoe hares. To further complicate matters, the database demonstrating fluctuations was often the numbers of pelts purchased by the Hudson's Bay Company. Here, fur price influenced the trapping effort and the numbers of animals harvested. This economic reality brought into question the relationship between the numbers of pelts and actual population densities of lynx and snowshoe hares.

Charles Krebs and his colleagues studied hare and lynx interactions with a large-scale, multiyear experiment in Kluane in the southern Yukon. Using fenced experimental areas, they could add food for snowshoe hares, exclude mammalian predators, or apply both experimental treatments while monitoring unmanipulated control plots. When mammalian predators were excluded, densities of snowshoe hares approximately doubled relative to controls. Where food was added, densities of snowshoe hares tripled relative to controls. In plots where food was added *and* predators were excluded, densities of snowshoe hares increased 11-fold compared with controls. Krebs and his colleagues concluded that neither food availability nor predation is solely responsible for population cycles in snowshoe hares. They postulated that complex interactions between snowshoe hares, their food plants, and their predators generate cyclic fluctuations in populations of snowshoe hares.

Study Break

1. What are density-dependent factors? Why do dense populations tend to decrease in size?
2. Define density-independent factors and give some examples.
3. Describe two key differences between *r*-selected species and *K*-selected species.

45.7 Human Population Growth

How do human populations compare with those of other species? The worldwide human population surpassed 6 billion on October 12, 1999. Like many other species, humans live in somewhat isolated populations that vary in their demographic traits and access to resources. Although many of us live comfortably, at least a billion people are malnourished or starving, lack access to clean drinking water, and live without adequate shelter or health care.

For most of human history, our population grew slowly, reflecting the impact of a range of restraints. Over the past two centuries, the worldwide human population has grown exponentially **(Figure 45.19).** Demographers identified three ways in which we have avoided the effects of density-dependent regulating factors.

First, humans have expanded their geographic range into virtually every terrestrial habitat, alleviating competition for space. Our early ancestors lived in tropical and subtropical grasslands, but by 40 000 years ago, they had dispersed through much of the world (see Chapter 27). Their success resulted from their ability to solve ecological problems by building fires, assembling shelters, making clothing and tools, planning community hunts, and sharing information. Vital survival skills spread from generation to generation and from one population to another because language allowed communication of complex ideas and knowledge.

Second, we have increased *K* in habitats we occupy, isolating us, as a species, from restrictions associated with access to resources. This change began to occur about 11 000 years ago, when populations in different parts of the world began to shift from hunting and gathering to agriculture (see Chapter 49). At that time, our ancestors cultivated wild grasses and other plants, diverted water to irrigate crops, and used domesticated

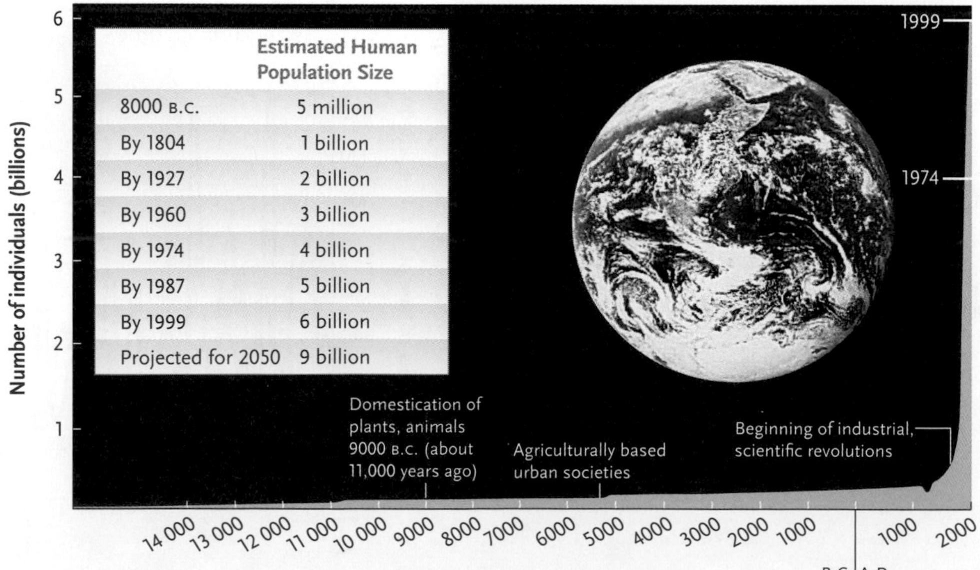

Estimated Human Population Size	
8000 B.C.	5 million
By 1804	1 billion
By 1927	2 billion
By 1960	3 billion
By 1974	4 billion
By 1987	5 billion
By 1999	6 billion
Projected for 2050	9 billion

Figure 45.19
Human population growth. The worldwide human population grew slowly until 200 years ago, when it began to increase explosively. The dip in the mid-fourteenth century represents the death of 60 million Asians and Europeans from the bubonic plague. The table shows how long it took for the human population to add each billion people. (Photo: NASA.)

animals for food and labour. Innovations such as these increased the availability of food, raising both K and rates of population growth. In the mid-eighteenth century, people harnessed the energy in fossil fuels, and industrialization began in Western Europe and North America. Food supplies and K increased again, at least in industrialized countries, largely through the use of synthetic fertilizers, pesticides, and efficient methods of transportation and food distribution.

Third, advances in public health reduced the effects of critical population-limiting factors such as malnutrition, contagious diseases, and poor hygiene. Over the past 300 years, modern plumbing and sewage treatment, removal of garbage, and improvements in food handling and processing, as well as medical discoveries, have reduced death rates sharply. Births now greatly exceed deaths, especially in less industrialized countries, resulting in rapid population growth. Note, however, that problems of hygiene and access to fresh water and food had been solved in some societies at least hundreds of years ago. Rome, for example, had a population of about 1 million people by A.D. 2, and this was supported by an excellent infrastructure for importing and distributing food, providing fresh water, and dealing with human wastes.

45.7a Age Structure and Economic Growth: Phases of Development

Where have our migrations and technological developments taken us? It took about 2.5 million years for the human population to reach 1 billion, 80 years to reach the second billion, and only 12 years to jump from 5 billion to 6 billion (see the inset table in Figure 45.19). Rapid population growth now appears to be an inevitable consequence of our demographic structure and economic development.

45.7b Population Growth and Age Structure: Not All Populations Are the Same

In A.D. 2000, the worldwide annual growth rate for the human population averaged nearly 1.26% ($r = 0.0126$ new individuals per individual per year). Population experts expect that rate to decline, but even so, the human population will probably exceed 9 billion by 2050.

In 2000, population growth rates of individual nations varied widely, ranging from much less than 1% to more than 3% **(Figure 45.20a)**. Industrialized countries of Western Europe have achieved nearly ZPG, but other countries, particularly those in Africa, Latin America, and Asia, will experience huge increases over the next 20 or 25 years **(Figure 45.20b)**.

For all long-lived species, differences in age structure are a major determinant of differences in population growth rates **(Figure 45.21, p. 1134)**. There are three basic patterns in the graphs in Figure 45.21. In the first, in countries with ZPG, there are approximately equal numbers of people of reproductive and prereproductive ages. Second, in countries with negative growth (without immigration), postreproductives outnumber reproductives, and these populations will not experience a growth spurt when today's children reach reproductive age. Third are countries where reproductives vastly outnumber postreproductives. The ZPG

a. Mean annual population growth rates

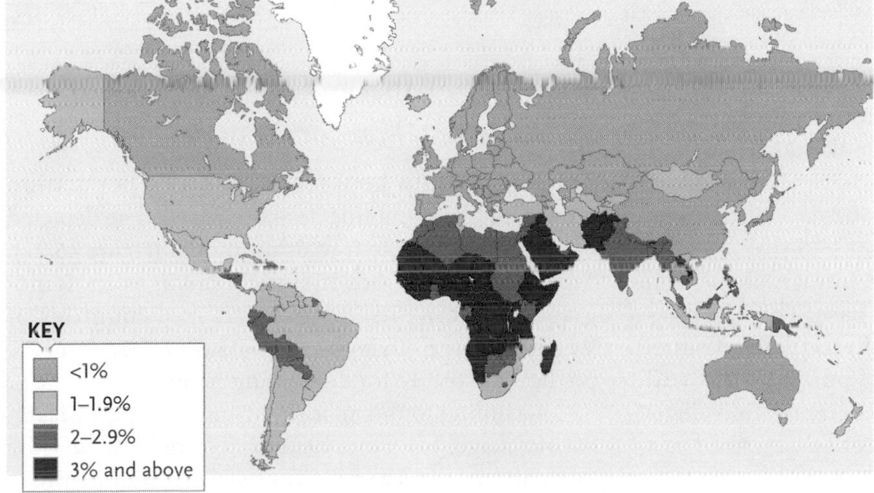

b. Projected population sizes for 2025

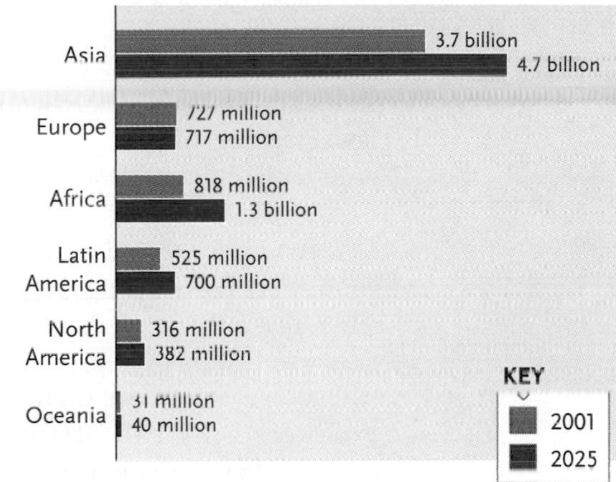

Figure 45.20
Local variation in human population growth rates. In 2001, **(a)** average annual population growth rates vary among countries and continents. In some regions **(b)**, the population is projected to increase greatly by 2025 (red) compared with the population size in 2001 (orange). The population of Europe will likely decline.

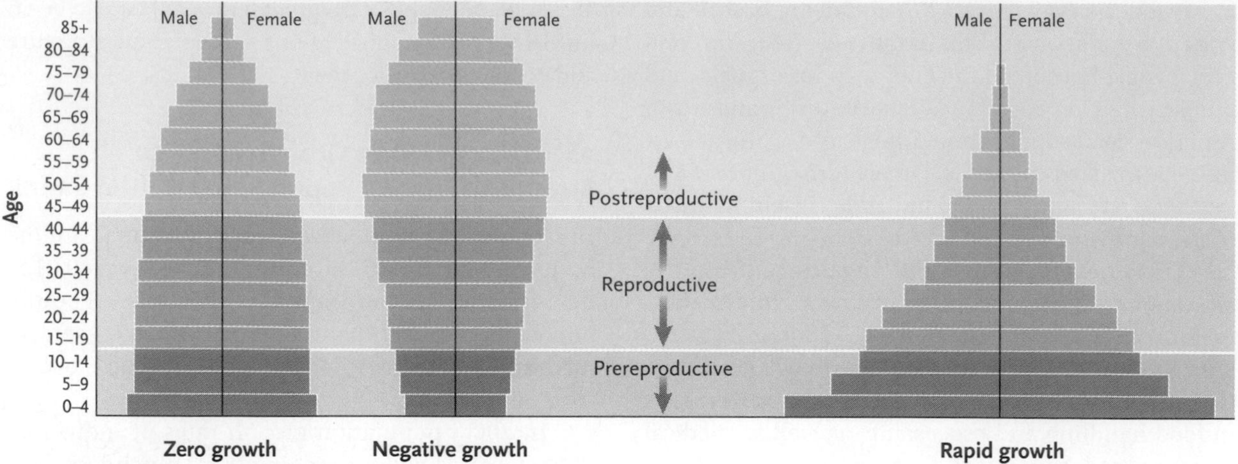

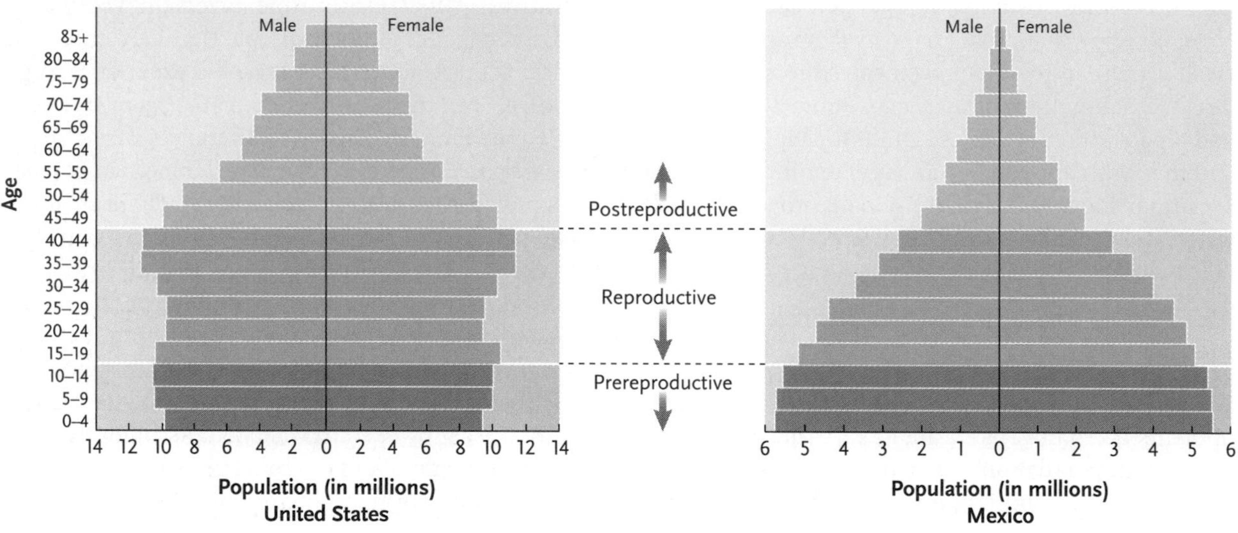

Figure 45.21

Age structure diagrams. Age structure diagrams **(a)** differ for countries with zero, negative, and rapid population growth rates. The width of each bar represents the proportion of the population in each age class. Age structure diagrams for the United States and Mexico **(b)** in 2000 (measured in millions of people) suggest that these countries will experience different growth rates.

situation is exacerbated when reproductives have very few offspring, meaning that prereproductives may not even replace themselves in the population.

Countries with rapid growth have a broad-based age structure (pattern three, above), with many youngsters born during the previous 15 years. Worldwide, more than one-third of the human population falls within this prereproductive base. This age class will soon reach sexual maturity. Even if each woman produces only two offspring, populations will continue to grow rapidly because so many individuals are reproducing. This situation can be described as a "population bomb."

The age structures of the United States and Mexico differ, which has consequences for population growth in the two jurisdictions. Remember the potential importance of immigration and emigration when considering the longer term impact of the population bomb.

45.7c Population Growth and Economic Development: Interconnections

The relationship between a country's population growth and its economic development can be depicted by the **demographic transition model (Figure 45.22).** This model describes historical changes in demographic patterns in the industrialized countries of Western Europe. Today, we do not know if it accurately predicts the future for developing nations.

According to this model, during a country's *preindustrial* stage, birth and death rates are high, and the population grows slowly. Industrialization begins a *transitional* stage, when food production rises, and health care and sanitation improve. Death rates decline, resulting in increased rates of population growth. Later, as living conditions improve, birth rates decline, causing a drop in rates of population growth. When

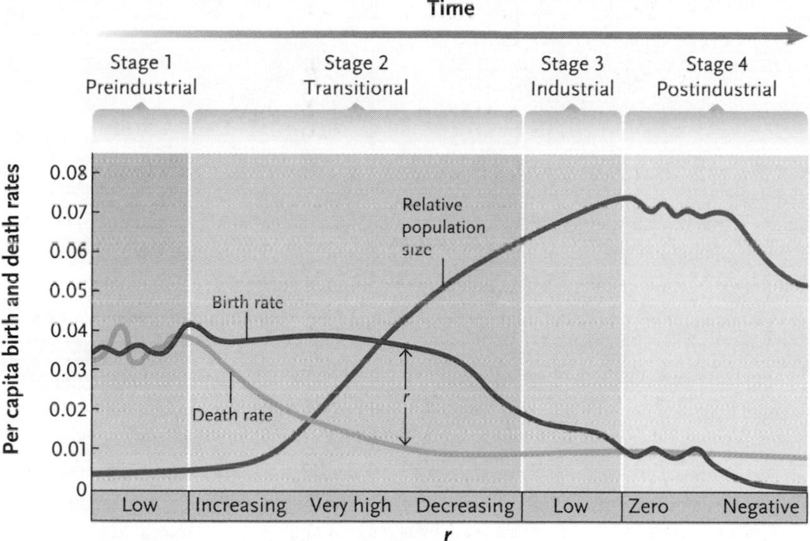

Figure 45.22
The demographic transition. The demographic transition model describes changes in the birth and death rates and relative population size as a country passes through four stages of economic development. The bottom bar describes the net population growth rate, *r*.

the *industrial* stage is in full swing, population growth slows dramatically. Now people move from countryside to cities, and urban couples often choose to accumulate material goods instead of having large families. ZPG is reached in the *postindustrial* stage. Eventually, the birth rate falls below the death rate, *r* falls below zero, and population size begins to decrease.

Today, United States, Canada, Australia, Japan, Russia, and most of Western Europe are in the industrial stage. Their growth rates are slowly decreasing. In Germany, Bulgaria, and Hungary (and other European countries), birth rates are lower than death rates, and populations are shrinking, indicating entry into the postindustrial stage. Kenya and other less industrialized countries are in the transitional stage, but they may not have enough skilled workers or enough capital to make the transition to an industrialized economy. For these reasons, many poorer nations may be stuck in the transitional stage. Third world countries experience rapid population increase because they experience declines in death rates associated with the transitional stage without decreases in birth rates typical of industrial and postindustrial stages.

45.7d Controlling Reproductive Output: Planned Reproduction

Most governments realize that increased population size is now the major factor causing resource depletion, excessive pollution, and an overall decline in quality of life. The principles of population ecology demonstrate that slowing the rate of population growth and effecting an actual decline in population size can be achieved only by decreasing the birth rate or increasing the death rate. Increasing mortality is neither a rational nor humane means of population control. Some governments use family planning programs in an attempt to lower birth rates. In other countries, any form of family planning is unlawful. This topic is discussed further in Chapter 38, where we will see that education of women is a vital undertaking.

To achieve ZPG, the average *replacement rate* should be just slightly higher than two children per couple. This is necessary because some female children die before reaching reproductive age. Today's replacement rate averages about 2.5 children in less industrialized countries with higher mortality rates in prereproductive cohorts and 2.1 in more industrialized countries. However, even if each couple on Earth produced only 2 children, the human population would continue to grow for at least another 60 years (the impact of the population bomb). Continued population growth is inevitable because today's children, who outnumber adults, will soon mature and reproduce. The worldwide population will stabilize only when the age distributions of all countries resemble that for countries with ZPG.

Family planning efforts encourage women to delay their first reproduction. Doing so reduces the average family size and slows population growth by increasing generation time (see Figure 45.9). Imagine two populations in which each woman produces two offspring. In the first population, women begin reproducing at age 32 years, and in the second, they begin reproducing at age 16 years. We can begin with a cohort of newborn baby girls in each population. After 32 years, women in the first population will be giving birth to their first offspring, but women in the second population will be new grandmothers. After 64 years, women in the first population will be new grandmothers, but women in the second population will witness the birth of their first great-great grandchildren (if their daughters also bear their first children at age 16 years). Obviously, the first population will grow much more slowly than the second.

45.7e The Future: Where Are We Going?

Homo sapiens has arrived at a turning point in our cultural evolution and in our ecological relationship with Earth. Hard decisions await us, and we must make them soon. All species face limits to their population growth, and it is naive to assume that our unique abilities exempt us from the laws of population growth. We have postponed the action of most factors that limit population growth, but no amount of invention and intervention

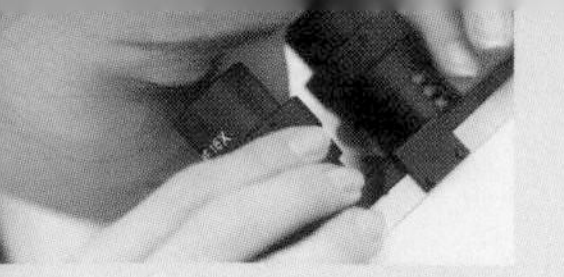

People Behind Biology

John (Jack) S. Millar

Jack Millar, a professor of biology at the University of Western Ontario in London, and his students study the life histories of small mammals such as mice, voles, and wood rats. They do most of this work in the field, mainly at sites in the Kananaskis Valley in southwestern Alberta. The work involves trapping the small mammals and marking them so that they can recognize them later. Recaptures of known individuals allow the researchers to track the performances of individuals. Millar and his students have been following populations of deer mice for over 20 years, and their records have allowed them to ask basic questions about life history.

Most deer mice born in any year in the Kananaskis Valley are dead by the end of September of that year. Although a few females are able to bear two litters in a year, most do not. Compared with deer mice living in southwestern Ontario (see Section 45.6c), the mice in Kananaskis are barely hanging on. But Millar and his students were interested to learn what factors limit age at first reproduction and the ability of a female to breed more than once a year. Female mice given protein-rich diets (cat food) sometimes were able to breed in their first summer, suggesting a strong influence of food quality on life history traits.

With data on deer mice covering a span of more than 20 years, Millar was able to explore the possible effects of climate change on deer mice living in the Kananaskis Valley. Specifically, between 1985 and 2003, female deer mice typically conceived their first litters on May 2 and the first births occurred on May 26. There were no statistically significant changes in the timing of first births, although the average temperatures in early May had declined by about 2°C during this period. Spring breeding of the deer mice was not related to temperatures or snowfall. The decline in temperature had no effect on the mice's reproductive success. Changes in photoperiod appear to be responsible for initiating reproductive activity in the mice. Their access to protein did affect their reproductive output.

Discoveries about diseases associated with wildlife are a side benefit of his endeavours. The work that Millar and his students have done provided a different view of the role of beavers in the spread of giardiasis, also known as "beaver fever." Giardiasis is caused by infections of a protozoan species in the genus *Giardia*. Humans can be infected if they drink water containing spores or trophozoites of *Giardia* species. Humans with giardiasis suffer from intestinal distress. As the name beaver fever implies, these aquatic rodents have been presumed to be the source of human infections. Using specimens, some provided by Millar and his students, P.M. Wallis and colleagues determined that 20 of 21 red-backed voles (*Clethrionomys gapperi*) were infected by *Giardia* at a much higher rate of infection than any other small mammals and also higher than beavers (2 of 50 infected).

Jack Millar's work has demonstrated how long-term experimental research involving both observations and experiments can shed light on life history strategies.

can expand the ultimate limits set by resource depletion and a damaged environment. We now face two options for limiting human population growth: we can make a global effort to limit our population growth, or we can wait until the environment does it for us.

Return to Figure 45.19 and observe that only the Plague (also known as the Black Death) caused any deflection from the trajectory of the curve tracking growth in the human population. The Plague appears to have been spread into Europe by the Mongols. The Plague, long established in China, arrived in the Mongol summer capital of Shangdu in 1332. By 1351, the population of China had been reduced by 50 to 66%. By 1345, the Plague had reached Feodosija in the Ukraine (then Kaffa). Between 1340 and 1400, it is estimated that the population of Africa declined from 80 million to 68 million and the world population from 450 million to between 350 million and 375 million. These data do not include the Americas because the Plague did not reach there until about 1600.

To put these percentages in context, consider human deaths associated with World War II. In this conflict, Great Britain lost less than 1% of its population, France about 1.5%, and Germany 9.1%. In Poland and the Ukraine, where there was a postwar famine, 19% of the human populations there are said to have died.

These sobering figures remind us that we are animals, vulnerable to many of the factors that affect other species on Earth. Now, look back at the chapter opening image and note the large numbers of gulls at a landfill site. The gulls and the landfill (a polite word for "dump") illustrate a fundamental point in population biology, namely, the ability of populations to reach large numbers and have large environmental impacts whether the species are gulls or people.

Study Break

1. In what three ways have humans avoided the effects of density-dependent regulation factors?
2. What is a population bomb?
3. What does family planning encourage women to do?

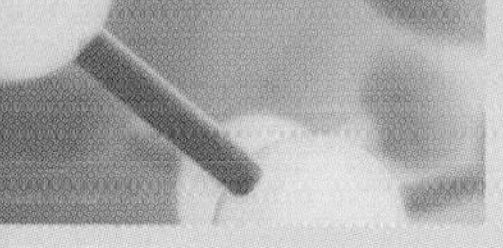

Progesterone

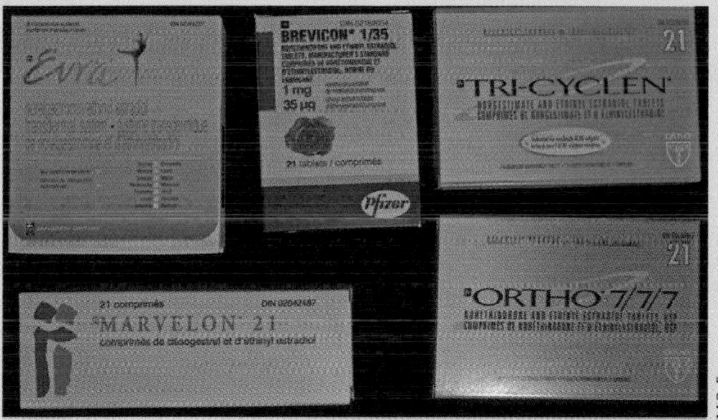

M.B. Fenton

Figure 1
Birth control pills, a selection of products.

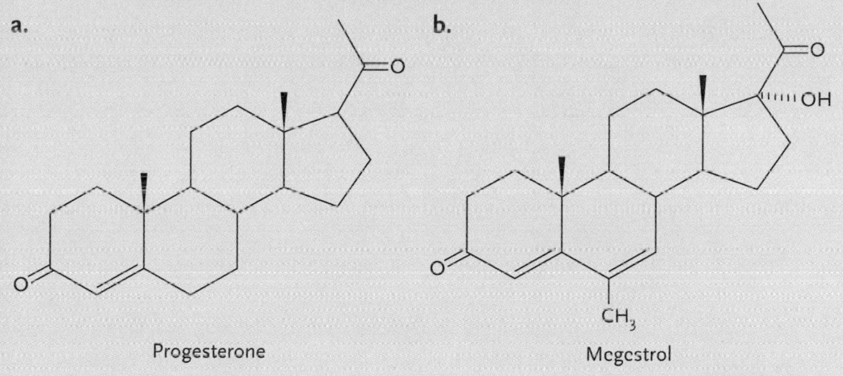

a. Progesterone

b. Megestrol

Figure 2
Progesterone and the synthetic megestrol.

The advent of birth control pills **(Figure 1)** had a great impact on the behaviour of people. Women using birth control pills had more control over their fertility. Central to the development of an effective oral contraceptive was a change in the molecular structure of progesterone **(Figure 2a).** Specifically, the addition of a CH_3 group **(Figure 2b)** meant that the new molecule, megestrol, had the same effect on a woman's reproductive system, but it was not quickly metabolized and remained in the system long enough to have the desired effect (suppressing ovulation). Similarly, slight modifications to the estradiol molecule turned it into ethinylestradiol **(Figure 3).** Megestrol is an analogue of progesterone, and ethinylestradiol is an analogue of estradiol.

Today, biologists working in zoos use a variety of birth control methods to control the fertility of animals in their collections. For critically endangered species such as black-footed ferrets (see *Black-Footed Ferret, Mustela nigripes*) this means using information about cycles of fertility to maximize reproductive output.

For animals whose populations are growing at a rapid pace, birth control gives keepers the chance to control growth of the populations. The same principles apply to working with organisms in the wild, but getting African elephants to take their birth control pills has not proved to be easy.

Hormones and their analogues are common in untreated municipal wastewaters. In some cases, male fish exposed to these wastewaters are becoming feminized **(Figure 4).** Specifically, some male fish produce vitellogenin mRNA and protein, substances normally associated with the maturation of oocytes in females. Males thus exposed produce early-stage eggs in their testes. This feminization occurs in the presence of estrogenic substances, including natural estrogen (17b-estradiol) and the synthetic estrogen 17a-ethinylestradiol.

Do a few feminized male fish in the population matter? Karen A. Kidd and six colleagues conducted a seven-year whole-lake experiment in northwestern Ontario (the Experimental Lakes Area). Male fathead minnows (*Pimephales promeles*) chronically exposed to low levels (5–6 $ng{\cdot}L^{-1}$) showed feminizing effects and the development of intersex males, whereas females had altered oogenesis. The situation led to the near-extinction of fathead minnows in the experimental lake.

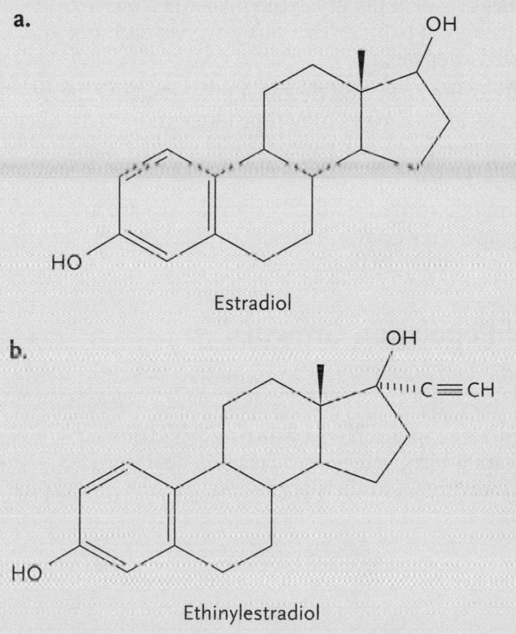

a. Estradiol

b. Ethinylestradiol

Figure 3
Estradiol and the synthetic ethinylestradiol.

Konrad P. Schmidt

Figure 4
Pimpheles promeles, the fathead minnow.

Unanswered Questions

1. What factors establish *K* (carrying capacity) for humans living in a large (population > 1 million) city? What factors would establish *K* in a mining town? How could you define the worldwide carrying capacity for humans?

2. Choose an animal or plant species living in your neighbourhood and identify density-dependent and density-independent factors that might influence its population size. How could you demonstrate conclusively that the factors work in either a density-dependent or a density-independent fashion?

Review

Go to CENGAGENOW™ at http://hed.nelson.com/ to access quizzing, animations, exercises, articles, and personalized homework help.

45.1 The Science of Ecology

- Organismal ecology is the study of organisms to determine adaptations to the abiotic environment, including morphological, physiological, biochemical, behavioural, and genetic adaptations. Population ecologists document changes in size and other characteristics of populations of species over space and time. Community ecologists study sympatric populations, interactions among them, and how interactions affect the community's growth. Interactions may include predation and competition. Ecosystem ecologists study nutrient cycling and energy flow through the biotic and the abiotic environment.
- Mathematical models express hypotheses about ecological relationships and different variables, allowing researchers to manipulate the model and document resulting changes. In this way, researchers can simulate natural events before investing in lab work.
- Experimental and control treatments are necessary because they allow ecologists to separate cause and effect.

45.2 Population Characteristics

- Geographic range is the overall spatial boundary around a population. Individuals in the population often live in a specific habitat within the range.
- A lower population density means that individuals have a greater access to resources such as sunlight and water. The capture–mark–recapture technique assumes that (1) a mark has no effect on an individual's survival; (2) marked and unmarked individuals mix randomly; (3) there is no migration throughout the estimation period; and (4) marked and unmarked individuals are equally likely to be caught.
- Three types of dispersion are clumped, uniform, and random. Clumped is most commonly in nature because suitable conditions usually are patchily distributed and animals often live in social groups. Asexual reproduction patterns also can lead to clumped aggregations.
- Generation time increases with body size.
- The number of males in a population of mammals has little impact on population growth because females bear the costs of reproduction (pregnancy and lactation), thus limiting population growth. Sea horses are different because males get pregnant.

45.3 Demography

- Age-specific mortality and age-specific survivorship deal with age intervals. In any one interval, age-specific mortality is the proportion of individuals that died during that time. Age-specific survival is the number surviving during the interval. The two values must sum to 1. In the example, age-specific survivorship = 0.616 or 1 − 0.384.
- Age-specific fecundity is the average number of offspring produced by surviving females during each age interval.
- In a type I curve, high survivorship at a young age decreases rapidly later in life. Type I curves are common for large animals, including humans. In a type II curve, the relationship is linear because there is a constant rate of mortality across the life span. Songbirds fit in this category. A type III curve shows high mortality at a young age that stabilizes as individuals grow older and larger. Insects fall into this category.

45.4 The Evolution of Life Histories

- Maintenance, growth, and reproduction are the three main energy-consuming processes.
- Passive care occurs as nutrients cross the placenta from the mother to the developing baby. Active care involves nursing and other care provided after birth.
- Salmon have a short life span and devote a great deal of energy to reproduction. Deciduous trees may reproduce more than once and use only some energy in any reproductive event, balancing reproduction and growth.
- Early reproduction is favoured if adult survival rates are low or if, when animals age, they do not increase in size. In this case, fecundity does not increase with size.

45.5 Models of Population Growth

- An exponential model is used when a population has unlimited growth.
- dN/dt = change in a population's size during a given time period; b = per capita birth rate; d = per capita death rate; N = number of individuals in the population; $b - d$ = per capita growth rate, equals r.

- When $r > 0$, the birth rate exceeds the death rate, and the population is growing. When $r < 0$, the birth rate is less than the death rate, and the population is shrinking. When $r = 0$, the birth and death rates are equal, and the population is neither growing nor shrinking. The intrinsic rate of increase (r_{max}) is the maximum per capita growth rate. This value usually varies inversely with generation time, so a shorter generation time means a higher r_{max}.
- Intraspecific competition occurs when two or more individuals of the same species depend on the same limiting resource. For deer, this could include food, water, or refuge from predators.
- A logistic model has this pattern because when the population growth is low, the population is small. At intermediate population sizes, growth is more rapid because more individuals breed and *r* is high. When population growth approaches *K* (carrying capacity), competition increases, *r* decreases, and the growth of the population is reduced.

45.6 Population Regulation

- Density-dependent factors include intraspecific competition and predation. At high density, fewer resources are available for individuals, which, in turn, use more energy in maintenance needs and less in reproduction. Offspring produced at higher population densities are often smaller in number or size and less likely to survive. At high population levels, adults may be smaller and weaker.
- Density-independent factors reduce a population size regardless of density, for example, fire, earthquakes, storms, floods, and other natural disturbances.
- The *r*-selected species often have large numbers of small young, whereas the *K*-selected species usually have small numbers of larger young. Other answers may include characteristics from Table 45.3.
- Extrinsic control includes interactions between individuals in a population and their food and predators. Once a food supply is exhausted, reproduction will decrease and mortality will increase. Intrinsic control can be hormonal changes within a population that cause increased aggressiveness and faster dispersal and reduce reproduction. Aggressiveness can cause weaker individuals to be forced to disperse to reduce the population density.

45.7 Human Population Growth

- Humans have avoided the effects of density-dependent regulation factors by expanding their geographic range into virtually every habitat, increasing *K* through agriculture, and reducing population-limiting factors resulting from poor hygiene, malnutrition, and contagious diseases.
- A population bomb is when many offspring are born in one time period, first forming the prereproductive base. At sexual maturity, populations can grow rapidly because of the large number of individuals in this cohort.
- The preindustrial stage is characterized by slow population growth as birth and death rates are high. The transitional stage has better health care and sanitation, as well as increased food production. In the transitional stage, there is a decline in death rates, allowing population growth, but birth rates eventually decline as living conditions improve. In the industrial stage, there is slow population growth as family size decreases because couples choose to have fewer children and accumulate more material goods. In the postindustrial stage, the population size decreases as the birth rate falls below the death rate.
- Family planning encourages women to delay first reproduction, decreasing the size of the average family and, in turn, reducing the population size as generation time has increased. Decisions about reproduction should involve couples.

Questions

Self-Test Questions

1. Ecologists sometimes use mathematical models to
   a. avoid conducting laboratory studies or fieldwork altogether.
   b. simulate natural events before conducting detailed field studies.
   c. make basic observations about ecological relationships in nature.
   d. collect survivorship and fecundity data to construct life tables.
   e. determine the geographic ranges of populations.
2. The numbers of individuals per unit area or volume of habitat is called the population's
   a. geographic range.
   b. dispersion pattern.
   c. density.
   d. size.
   e. age structure.
3. One day you caught and marked 90 butterflies in a population. A week later, you returned to the population and caught 80 butterflies, including 16 that had been marked previously. What is the size of the butterfly population?
   a. 170
   b. 450
   c. 154
   d. 186
   e. 106
4. A uniform dispersion pattern implies that members of a population
   a. cooperate in rearing their offspring.
   b. work together to escape from predators.
   c. use resources that are patchily distributed.
   d. may experience intraspecific competition for vital resources.
   e. have no ecological interactions with each other.
5. The model of exponential population growth predicts that the per capita population growth rate (*r*)
   a. does not change as a population gets larger.
   b. gets larger as a population gets larger.
   c. gets smaller as a population gets larger.
   d. is always at its maximum level (r_{max}).
   e. fluctuates on a regular cycle.
6. A population of 1000 individuals experiences 452 births and 380 deaths in 1 year. What is the value of *r* for this population?
   a. 0.842/individual/year
   b. 0.452/individual/year
   c. 0.380/individual/year
   d. 0.820/individual/year
   e. 0.082/individual/year
7. According to the logistic model of population growth, the absolute number of individuals by which a population grows during a given time period
   a. gets steadily larger as the population size increases.
   b. gets steadily smaller as the population size increases.

c. remains constant as the population size increases.
d. is highest when the population is at an intermediate size.
e. fluctuates on a regular cycle.

8. Which example might reflect density-dependent regulation of population size?
    a. An exterminator uses a pesticide to eliminate carpenter ants from a home.
    b. Mosquitoes disappear from an area after the first frost.
    c. The lawn dies after a month-long drought.
    d. Northeast storms blow over and kill all willow trees along a lake.
    e. A clam population declines in numbers in a bay as the number of predatory herring gulls increases.
9. A *K*-selected species is likely to exhibit
    a. a type I survivorship curve and a short generation time.
    b. a type II survivorship curve and a short generation time.
    c. a type III survivorship curve and a short generation time.
    d. a type I survivorship curve and a long generation time.
    e. a type II survivorship curve and a long generation time.
10. One reason that human populations have sidestepped factors that usually control population growth is that
    a. the carrying capacity for humans has remained constant since humans first evolved.
    b. agriculture and industrialization have increased the carrying capacity for our species.
    c. the population growth rate (r) for the human population has always been small.
    d. the age structure of human populations has no impact on its population growth.
    e. plagues have killed off large numbers of humans at certain times in the past.

Questions for Discussion

1. Do you expect to see a genetic bottleneck effect in *Mustela nigripes* populations in the wild in the future? How long will they take to appear?
2. Design an income tax policy and social services plan that would encourage people to have either larger or smaller families.
3. Many city-dwellers have noted that the density of cockroaches in apartment kitchens appears to vary with the habits of the occupants. People who wrap food carefully and clean their kitchen frequently tend to have fewer arthropod roommates than those who leave food on kitchen counters and clean less often. Interpret these observations from the viewpoint of a population ecologist.

Sphingid (hornworm) caterpillar feeding on leaves.

Study Plan

M.B Fenton

46 Population Interactions and Community Ecology

Why It Matters

It is easy to believe that there are many more species (= much more species richness) in the tropics than there are in temperate zones. On a visit to tropical locations, it is easy to be impressed by the diversity of life, whether you go snorkelling at a coral reef, for a boat ride along a tropical river, or on a hike through a rain forest. Is there really such a difference between the two zones? Does it matter what organisms you look for? Consider herbivorous insects (those eating leaves), of which there are more species in the tropics than in temperate zones. Why is this the case?

Ecological theory suggests that in the tropics, greater uniformity in climate is associated with increased ecological specialization of species. For plant-eating insects in the tropics, this means that each species tends to eat a narrower range of plant species compared with their temperate counterparts. This means that each species occupies a narrower niche in the tropics, so there are more niches and hence more species.

In animals such as insects with different life stages (see Chapter 26), each life cycle stage (in some insects, egg, larva [caterpillar], pupa, and adult) fills a different niche and plays a different role in the species' life history. The eggs are development machines, the larvae are eating machines, the pupae are metamorphosis machines, and the adults are mating machines.

Biologists can obtain a picture of the feeding niche of a species of butterfly or moth by documenting the food habits of caterpillars. In this way, L.A. Dyer and 12 colleagues studied the diets of moth and butterfly (Lepidoptera) caterpillars at 8 forest sites in the New World (North, South, and Central America) between latitudes 15° S and 55° N. On average, tropical species are more specialized in their diets than temperate ones **(Figure 46.1)**. Each species of caterpillar in the tropics ate fewer species of plants than its temperate counterpart. The prediction that tropical herbivorous insects occupy narrower feeding niches than temperate ones is supported by these data for Lepidoptera. One consequence of specialization is that, there are more species of Lepidoptera in the tropics than in temperate zones.

Other tropical locations may have many species but perhaps less local variation. On the island of Papua New Guinea, many species of butterflies and moths (with herbivorous caterpillars) live in extensive geographic ranges across 75 000 km^2 tracts of rain forest **(Figure 46.2)**. Vojtjch Novotny and 15 colleagues reported that consistency of diversity is typical of herbivorous insects, including Lepidoptera, beetles eating wood, and fruit flies and other flies eating fruit.

Making sense of the patterns of life's diversity means exploring the details of communities of organisms. Diversity is the watchword, and it can support almost as many theories as there are ecologists. The purpose of this chapter is to explore interactions between species of organisms and place the interactions in an ecological context.

46.1 Interspecific Interactions

Interactions between species typically benefit or harm the organisms involved, although they may be neutral **(Table 46.1)**. Furthermore, where interactions with other species affect individuals' survival and reproduction, many of the relationships we witness today are the products of long-term evolutionary modification. Good examples range from predator–prey interactions to those associated with pollination or dispersal of seeds.

Interactions between species can change constantly, but remember that the interactions occur at the individual level. Some individuals of a species may be better adapted when another species exerts selection pressure on that species. This adaptation can, in turn, help those individuals exert selection pressure on the other species. This pressure can, in turn, exert selection pressure on the first species in the chain. The situation, known as **coevolution,** is defined as genetically based, reciprocal adaptation in two or more interacting species.

Some coevolutionary relationships are straightforward. Ecologists describe the coevolutionary interactions between some predators and their prey as a race in which each species evolves adaptations that temporarily allow it to outpace the other. When antelope populations suffer predation by cheetahs, natural selection fosters the evolution of faster antelopes. Faster cheetahs may be the result of this situation, and if their offspring are also fast, then antelopes will also become more fleet of foot. Other coevolved interactions provide benefits to both partners. Flower structures of different monkey-flower species have evolved characteristics that allow them to be visited by either bees or hummingbirds (see Chapter 18).

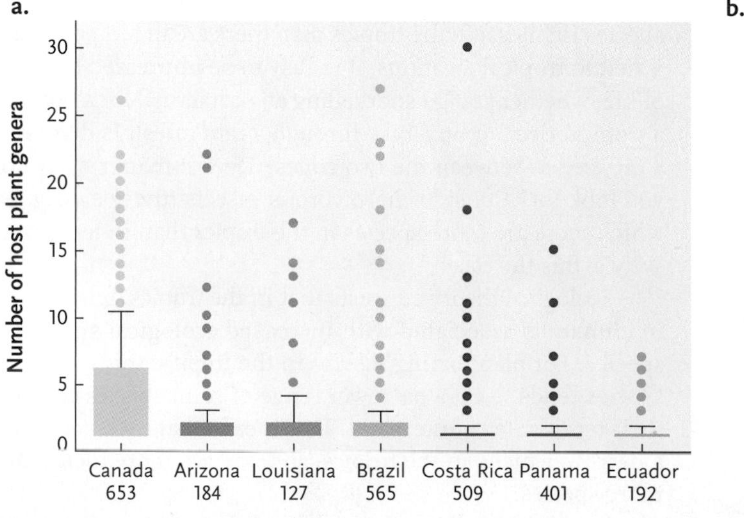

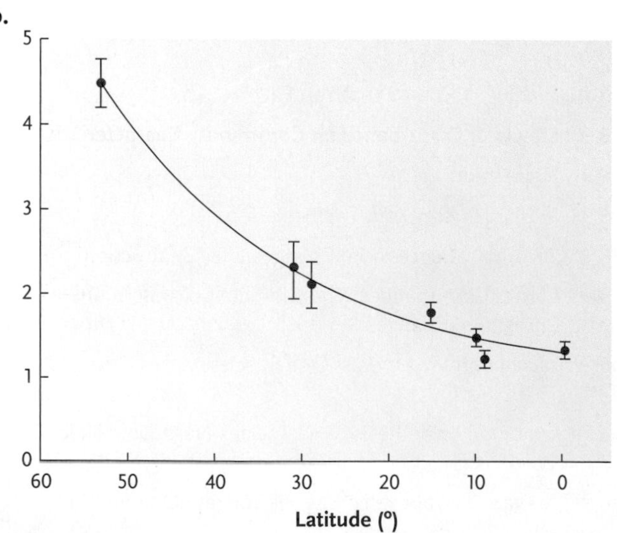

Figure 46.1
Caterpillar diet breadth. Numbers of host plant genera per caterpillar species at seven sites along a latitudinal gradient.

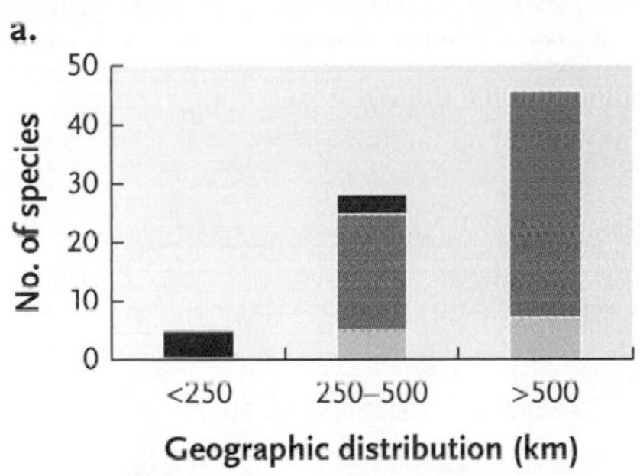

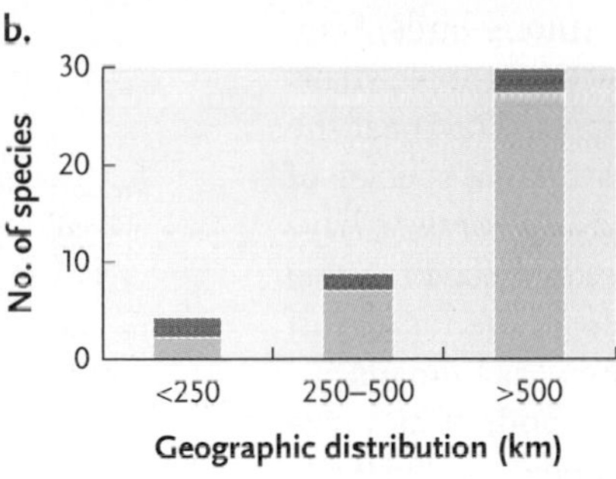

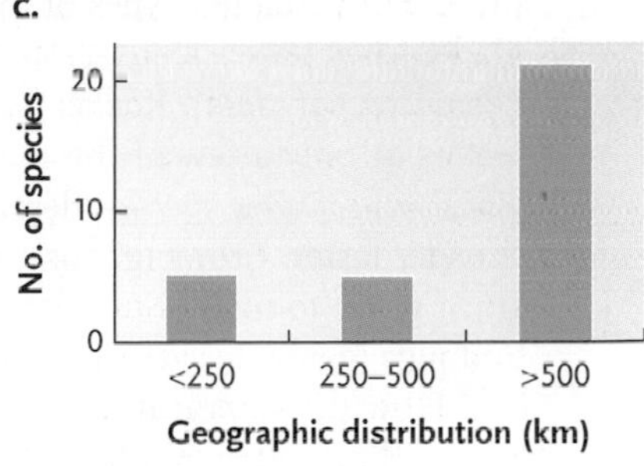

Figure 46.2
Papua New Guinea. Geographic distribution of **(a)** a caterpillar, **(b)** an ambrosia beetle, and **(c)** fruit fly species in the lowlands. Caterpillar and beetle species are classified as generalists (orange; feeding on more than one genus), clade specialists (blue; feeding on more than one species from a single genus), or monophagous (green; feeding on a single plant species). Note the differences between the caterpillars, beetles, and fruitflies.

Table 46.1 Population Interactions and Their Effects

Interaction	Effects on Interacting Populations	
Predation	+/−	Predators gain nutrients and energy; prey are killed or injured.
Herbivory	+/−	Herbivores gain nutrients and energy; plants are killed or injured.
Competition	−/−	Both competing populations lose access to some resources.
Commensalism	+/0	One population benefits; the other population is unaffected.
Mutualism	+/+	Both populations benefit.
Parasitism	+/−	Parasites gain nutrients and energy; hosts are injured or killed.

One can hypothesize a coevolutionary relationship between any two interacting species, but documenting the evolution of reciprocal adaptations is difficult. Coevolutionary interactions often involve more than two species, and most organisms experience complex interactions with numerous other species in their communities. Cheetahs take several prey species. Antelopes are prey for many species of predators, from cheetahs to lions, leopards, and hyenas, as well as some larger birds of prey. Not all predators use the same hunting strategy. Therefore, the simple portrayal of coevolution as taking place between two species rarely does justice to the complexity of these relationships.

Study Break

What is coevolution? Is it usually restricted to two species?

46.2 Getting Food

Because animals typically acquire nutrients and energy by consuming other organisms, **predation** (the interaction between predatory animals and the animal prey they consume) and **herbivory** (the interaction between herbivorous animals and the plants they eat) can be the most conspicuous relationships in ecological communities.

Both predators and herbivores have evolved characteristics allowing them to feed effectively. Carnivores use sensory systems to locate animal prey and specialized behaviours and anatomical structures to capture and consume it. Herbivores use sensory systems to identify preferred food or to avoid food that is toxic.

Rattlesnakes, such as species in the genus *Crotalus*, use heat sensors on pits in their faces (see Figure 34.32) to detect warm-blooded prey. The snakes deliver venom through fangs (hollow teeth) by open-mouthed strikes on prey. After striking, the snakes wait for the venom to take effect and then use chemical sensors also on the roofs of their mouths to follow the scent trail left by its dying prey. The venom is produced in the snakes' salivary glands. It contains neurotoxins that paralyze prey and protease enzymes that begin to digest it. Elastic ligaments connecting the bones of the snakes' jaws (mandibles) to one another and the mandibles to the skull allow snakes to open their mouths very wide to swallow prey larger than their heads (see Chapter 41).

Herbivores have comparable adaptations for locating and processing their food plants. Insects use chemical sensors on their legs and mouthparts to identify edible plants and sharp mandibles or sucking mouthparts to consume plant tissues or sap. Herbivorous mammals have specialized teeth to harvest and grind tough vegetation (see Figure 27.56). Herbivores, such as farmer ants (see Chapter 49), ruminants, or termites (see Chapter 41), may also coopt other species to gain access to nutrients locked up in plant materials.

All animals select food from a variety of potential items. Some species, described as *specialists*, feed on one or just a few types of food. Among birds, Everglades kites (*Rostrhamus sociabilis*) eat only apple snails (*Pomacea paludosa*). Koalas (see Figure 27.51) eat the leaves of only a few of the many available species of *Eucalyptus*. Other species, described as *generalists*, have broader tastes. Crows (genus *Corvus*) take food ranging from grain to insects to carrion. Bears (genus *Ursus*) and pigs (genus *Sus*) are as omnivorous as humans.

How does an animal select its food? Why pizza rather than salad? Mathematical models, collectively described as **optimal foraging theory**, predict that an animal's diet is a compromise between the costs and benefits associated with different types of food. Assuming that animals try to maximize their energy intake at any meal, their diets should be determined by the ratio of costs to benefits: the costs of obtaining the food versus the benefits of consuming it. Costs are the time and energy it takes to pursue, capture, and consume a particular kind of food. Benefits are the energy provided by that food. A cougar (*Felis concolor*) will invest more time and energy hunting a mountain goat (*Oreamnos americanus*) than a jackrabbit (*Lepus townsendii*), but the payoff for the cat is a bigger meal. One important element in food choice is the relative abundance of prey. "Encounter rate" (denoted as λ in optimal foraging theory) is usually influenced by population density and can influence a predator's diet. For the cougar, λ determines the time between jackrabbits, and when they are abundant, they can be a more economical target than larger, scarcer prey.

Food abundance affects food choice. When prey are scarce, animals often take what they can get, settling for food that has a higher cost-to-benefit ratio. When food is abundant, they may specialize, selecting types that provide the largest energetic return. Bluegill sunfishes eat *Daphnia* and other small crustaceans. When crustacean density is high, these fishes hunt mostly large *Daphnia*, which provide more energy for their effort. When prey density is low, bluegills eat *Daphnia* of all sizes **(Figure 46.3).**

Think of yourself at a buffet. The array of food can be impressive, if not overwhelming. But your state of hunger, the foods you like, the ones you do not like, and any to which you are allergic all influence your selection. You may also be influenced by choices made by others. In your feeding behaviour, you betray your animal heritage.

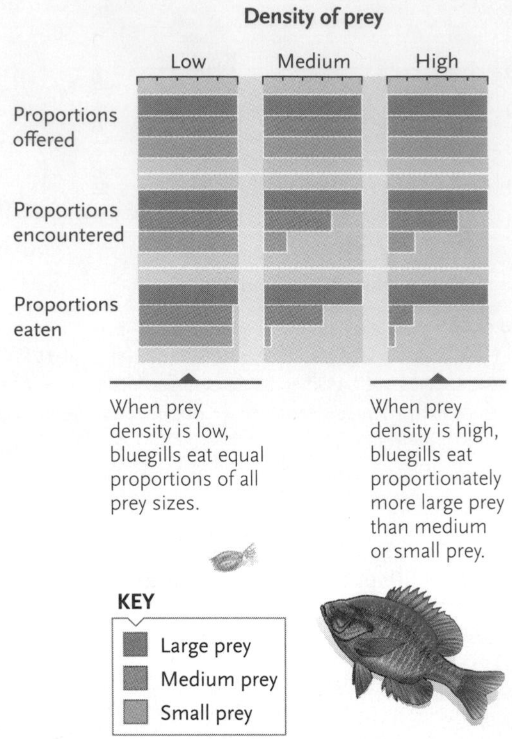

Figure 46.3
An experiment demonstrating that prey density affects predator food choice. Bluegill sunfishes (*Lepomis macrochirus*) were offered equal numbers of small, medium, and large prey (*Daphnia magna*) at three different total densities of prey. Because large prey are easy to find, the fishes encountered them more often, especially at the highest prey densities than either medium-sized or small prey. The fishes' choice of prey varied with prey density, but they always chose the largest prey available.

Study Break

1. How do predators differ from herbivores? How are they similar?
2. Is a koala a generalist or a specialist? What is the difference?
3. What does optimal foraging theory predict? Describe the costs and benefits central to this theory.

46.3 Defence

Predation and herbivory have a negative impact on the species being eaten, so animals and plants have evolved mechanisms to avoid being caught and eaten. Some plants use spines, thorns, and irritating hairs to protect themselves from herbivores. Plant tissues often contain poisonous chemicals that deter herbivores from feeding. When damaged, milkweed plants (family Asclepiadaceae) exude a milky, irritating sap **(Figure 46.4)** that contains poisons that affect the heart (cardiac glycosides). Even small amounts of cardiac glycosides are toxic to the heart muscles of some vertebrates. Other plants have compounds that mimic the structure of insect hormones, disrupting the development of insects that eat them. Most of these poisonous compounds are volatile, giving plants their typical aromas. Some herbivores have developed the ability to recognize these odours and avoid toxic plants. Some plants increase their production of toxic compounds in response to herbivore feeding. Potato and tomato plants damaged by herbivores have higher levels of protease-inhibiting chemicals. These compounds

Figure 46.4
Protective latex sap. Milky sap laced with cardiac glycosides oozes from a cut milkweed (*Asclepius* species) leaf. Milky sap does not always mean dangerous chemicals, for example, the sap of dandelions.

prevent herbivores from digesting the proteins they have eaten, reducing the food value of these plants.

46.3a Size: Too Big to Tackle

Size can be a defence. At one end of the spectrum, this means being too small to be considered food. At the other end, it means being so big that few, if any, predators can succeed in attacking and killing the prey. Today, elephants and some other large herbivores (megaherbivores) are species with few predators (other than humans). But 50 000 years ago, there were larger predators (see Figure 20.1), including one species of "lion" that was one-third larger than an African lion.

46.3b Eternal Vigilance: Always Be Alert

A first line of defence of many animals is avoiding detection. This often means not moving, but it also means keeping a sharp lookout for approaching predators and the danger they represent **(Figure 46.5).**

46.3c Avoiding Detection: Freeze—Movement Invites Detection

Many animals are cryptic, camouflaged so that a predator does not distinguish them from the background. Patterns, such as the stripes of a zebra (*Equus burchellii*), make the animal conspicuous at close range, but at a distance, patterns break up the outline, rendering the animals almost invisible. Many other animals look like something that is not edible. Some caterpillars look like bird droppings, whereas other insects look like thorns or sticks. Neither bird droppings nor thorns are usually eaten by insectivores.

46.3d Thwarting Attacks: Take Evasive Action

Animals resort to other defensive tactics once they have been discovered and recognized. Running away is a typical next line of defence. Taking refuge in a shelter and getting out of a predator's reach is an alternative. African pancake tortoises (*Malacochersus tornieri*) are flat, as the name implies. When threatened, they retreat into rocky crevices and puff themselves up with air, becoming so tightly wedged that predators cannot extract them.

If cornered by a predator, offence becomes the next line of defence. This can involve displays intended to startle or intimidate by making the prey appear large and/or ferocious. Such a display might dissuade a predator or confuse it long enough to allow the potential victim to escape. Many animals use direct attack in these situations, engaging whatever weapons they have (biting, scratching, stinging, etc.).

46.3e Spines and Armour: Be Dangerous or Impossible to Attack

Other organisms use active defence in the form of spines or thorns **(Figure 46.6, p. 1146).** North American porcupines (genus *Erethizon*) release hairs modified

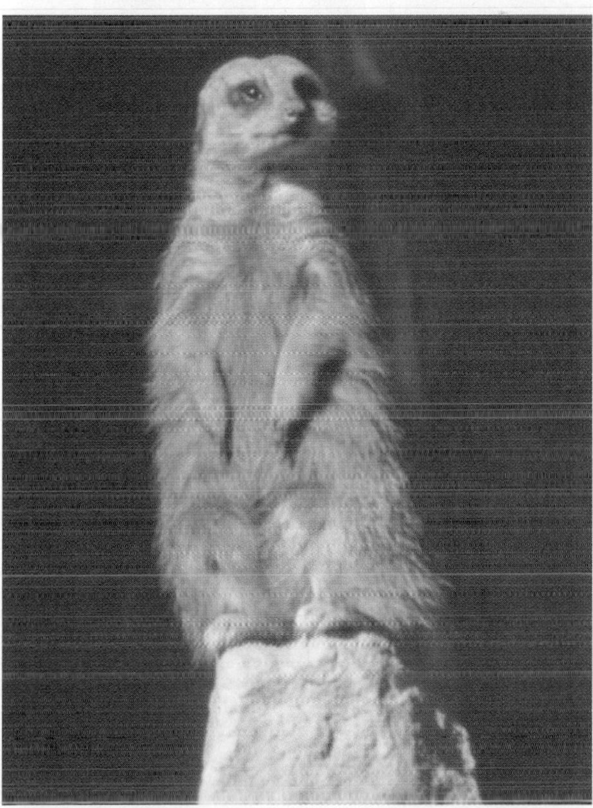

Figure 46.5
Eternally vigilant. The sentry of a group of meerkats (*Suricatta suricatta*).

a.

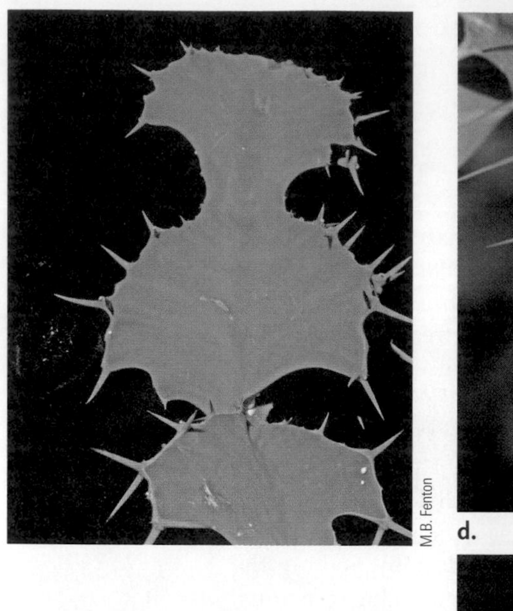

b.

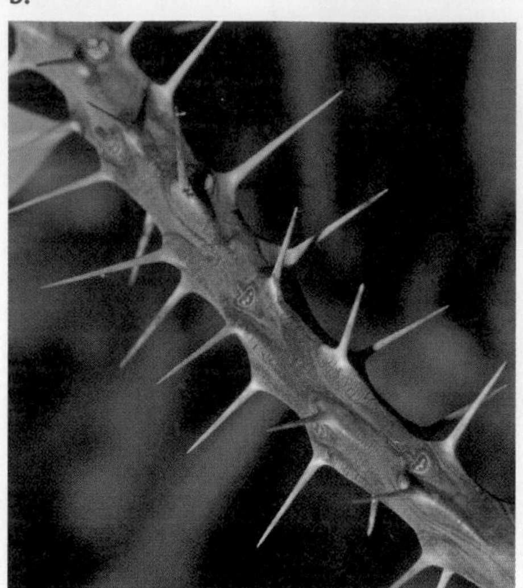

c.

d.

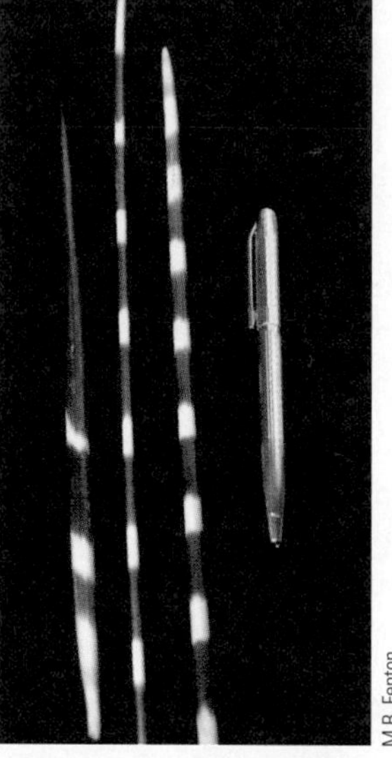

Figure 46.6
Defensive spines. Plants such as **(a)** the cowhorn euphorb (*Euphorbia gandicornis*) and **(b)** crown of thorns (*Euphorbia milli*) and animals such as **(c)** spiny anteaters (*Tachyglossus* species) and **(d)** porcupines (*Hystrix* species) both use thorns or spines in defence. Pen shown for scale with quills in **(d)**.

into sharp, barbed quills that, when stuck into a predator, cause severe pain and swelling. The spines detach easily from the porcupine, and the nose, lips, and tongue of an attacker are particularly vulnerable. There are records of leopards (*Panthera pardus*) being killed by porcupine spines. In these instances, the damage to the leopards' mouths, combined with infection, was probably the immediate cause of death. Many other mammals, from monotremes (spiny anteaters) to tenrecs (insectivores from Madagascar, *Tenrec* species and *Hemicentetes* species), hedgehogs (*Erinaceus* species), and porcupines in the Old World use the same defence. So do some fishes and many plants.

Other organisms are armoured **(Figure 46.7)**. Examples include bivalve and gastropod molluscs, chambered nautiluses, arthropods such as horseshoe crabs (*Limulus* species), trilobites (see Chapter 26), fishes such as catfish (*Siluriformes*), reptiles (turtles; see Figure 27.38), and mammals (armadillos, scaly anteaters; see Figure 3.3b). We know a great deal about extinct species that were armoured (see Chapter 20) because they often made good fossils.

46.3f Chemical Defence: From Bad Taste to Deadly

Like plants that produce chemicals to repel herbivores, many animals make themselves chemically unattractive. At one level, this can be as simple as smelling or tasting bad. Remember the last time your dog or cat was sprayed by a skunk (*Mephitis mephitis*)? Many animals vomit and defecate on their attackers. Skunks and bombardier beetles escalate this strategy by producing and spraying a noxious chemical. Other animals go beyond spraying. Many species of cnidarians, annelids, arthropods, and chordates produce dangerous toxins and deliver them directly into their victims. These toxins may be synthesized by the user (e.g., snake venom; see *Molecule Behind Biology*) or sequestered from other sources, often plants or other animals (see *Nematocysts*). Caterpillars of monarch butterflies (see Figure 1.29) are immune to the cardiac glycosides in the milkweed leaves they eat. They extract, concentrate, and store these chemicals, making them poisonous to potential predators. The concentrations of defensive chemicals may be higher in the animal than they were in its food. Cardiac glycosides persist through metamorphosis, making adult monarchs poisonous to vertebrate predators.

46.3g Warnings: Danger Signals

Many animals that are noxious or dangerous are **aposematic**: they advertise their unpalatability with an appropriate display (**Figure 46.8;** see Chapter 17).

Figure 46.7
Armour. Turtles and their allies (see Chapter 27) live inside shells. This leopard tortoise (*Geochelone pardalis*) is inspecting the remains of a conspecific. Armour does not guarantee survival.

M.B. Fenton

Figure 46.8
Warning colours. This arrowhead frog gets its name from toxins in its skin that were used to poison arrowheads.

Aposematic displays are designed to "teach" predators to avoid the signaller, reducing the chances of harm to would-be predators and prey. Predators that attack a brightly coloured bee or wasp and are stung learn to associate the aposematic pattern with the sting. Many predators quickly learn to avoid black-and-white skunks, yellow-banded wasps, or orange monarch butterflies because they associate the warning display with pain, illness, or severe indigestion.

But for every ploy there is a counterploy, and some predators eat mainly dangerous prey. Bee-eaters (family Meropidae) are birds that eat hymenopterans (bees and wasps). Some individual African lions specialize on porcupines, and animals such as hedgehogs (genus *Erinaceus*) seem able to eat almost anything and show no ill effects. Indeed, some hedgehogs first lick toads and then their own spines, anointing them with toad venom. Hedgehog spines treated with toad venom are more irritating (at least to people) than untreated ones, enhancing their defensive impact.

46.3h Mimicry: Advertising, True and False

If predators learn to recognize warning signals, it is no surprise that many harmless animals' defences are based on imitating (mimicking) species that are dangerous or distasteful. **Mimicry** occurs when one species evolves to resemble another **(Figure 46.9)**. **Batesian mimicry,** named for English naturalist Henry W. Bates, occurs when a palatable or harmless species (the **mimic**) resembles an unpalatable or poisonous one (the **model**). Any predator that eats the poisonous model and suffers accordingly will subsequently avoid other organisms that resemble it. However, the predator must survive the encounter. **Müllerian mimicry,** named for German zoologist Fritz Müller, involves two or more unpalatable species looking the same, presumably to reinforce lessons learned by a predator that attacks any species in the mimicry complex.

For mimicry to work, the predator must learn (see Chapter 40) to recognize and then avoid the prey. The more deadly the toxin, the less likely an individual predator is to learn by its experience. In many cases, predators learn by watching the discomfort of a conspecific that has eaten or attacked an aposematic prey.

Plants often use toxins to protect themselves against herbivores. Is this also true of toxins in mushrooms (see Chapter 18)?

46.3i No Perfect Defence: The Helmet Reality

Helmets protect soldiers, motorcyclists, and cyclists, but not completely because no defence provides perfect protection. Some predators learn to circumvent defences. Many predators learn to deal with a diversity of prey species and a variety of defensive tactics. Orb web spiders confronting a captive in a web adjust their behaviour according to the prey. They treat moths differently from beetles and bees in yet another way. When threatened by a predator, headstand beetles raise their rear ends and spray a noxious chemical from a gland at the tip of the abdomen. This behaviour deters many would-be predators. But experienced grasshopper mice from western North America circumvent this defence. An experienced mouse grabs the beetle, averts its face

a. Batesian mimicry

Nigel Cattlin/Frank Lane Picture Agency

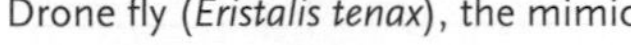

Drone fly (*Eristalis tenax*), the mimic

© Simon Colmer and Abby Rex/Alamy

Honeybee (*Apis mellifera*), the model

b. Müllerian mimicry

Robert Lubeck/Animals Animals—Earth Scenes

Heliconius erato

© Patti Murray/Animals Animals—Earth Scenes

Heliconius melpone

Figure 46.9
Mimicry. **(a)** Batesian mimics are harmless animals that mimic a dangerous one. The harmless drone fly (*Eristalis tenax*) is a Batesian mimic of the stinging honeybee (*Apis mellifera*). **(b)** Müllerian mimics are poisonous species that share a similar appearance. Two distantly related species of butterfly, *Heliconius erata* and *Heliconius melpone*, have nearly indistinguishable patterns on their wings.

Molecule Behind Biology

Taipoxin: Snake Presynaptic Phospholipase A_2 Neurotoxins

Snake venoms typically are a concoction of ingredients designed to immobilize and digest prey. Like the venom of nematocysts, the effects of snake venom can include symptoms associated with neurotoxins, cardiotoxins, hemolytic actions, and digestion (necrosis) of tissues. Not all snakes (or other venomous animals) have the same venom.

Snake presynaptic phospholipase A_2 neurotoxins, or SPANS, have neurotoxic effects and work by blocking neuromuscular junctions. Phospholipase A_2 activity varies greatly among SPANS. Using mouse neuromuscular junction hemidiaphragm preparations and neurons in culture, M. Rigoni and seven colleagues explored the way in which SPANS work. They used SPANS from single-chain notexin (from *Notecis scutatis*, the eastern tiger snake), a two-subunit B-bungarotoxin (from *Bungarus multicinctus*, the many-banded krait), the three-subunit taipoxin (from *Oxyuranus scutellatus*, the taipan; **Figure 1**). and the five-unit textilotoxin (from *Pseudonaja textilis*, the eastern brown snake).

The results showed that administration of SPANS to neuromuscular junctions causes enlargement of the junctions and reduction in the contents of synaptic vessicles. SPANS also induce exocytosis of neurotransmitters. In other words, SPANS bind nerve terminals via receptors **(Figure 2),** the results indicate

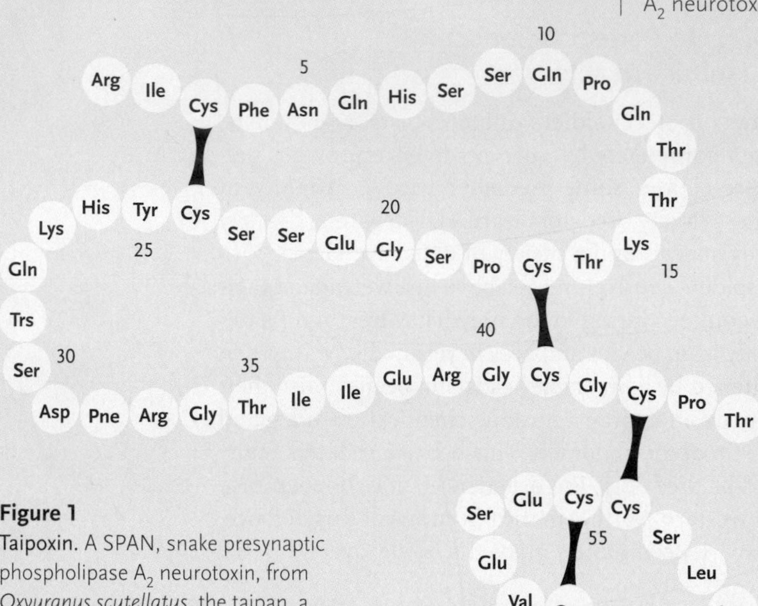

Figure 1
Taipoxin. A SPAN, snake presynaptic phospholipase A_2 neurotoxin, from *Oxyuranus scutellatus*, the taipan, a venomous elapid snake from Australia.

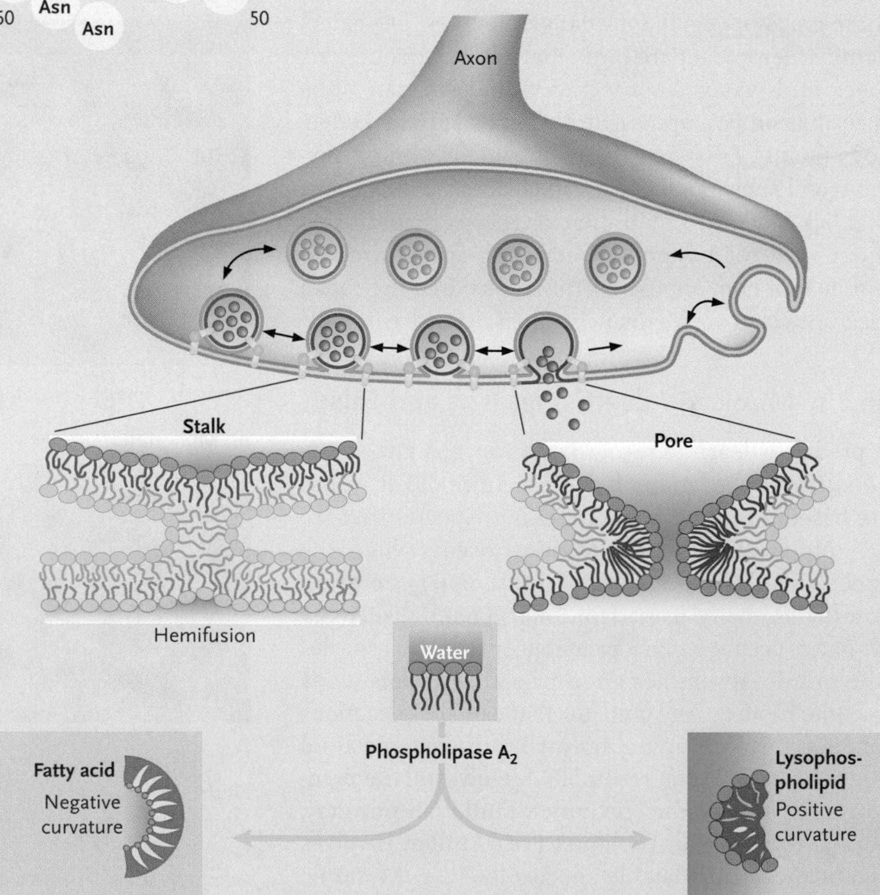

Figure 2
Under normal conditions, lipids alter membrane bending at the synapse, and this controls vesicle fusion and synaptic activity. Membrane fusion between the plasma membrane of a presynaptic neuron and a synaptic vesicle with molecules of neurotransmitter (red) leads to the formation of a pore. Mixing of lipids from inner (purple) and outer (green) leaflets is probably restricted by proteins (yellow ribbons) around the site of fusion. Phospholipase A_2 cleaves lipids, forming flat monolayers into fatty acids (negative curvature) and lysophospholipids (positive curvature). This change explains the effect of SPANS at neuromuscular junctions.

that venoms can be used to further our understanding of what happens at neuromuscular junctions.

Among extant lepidosauran reptiles, two lineages have venom delivery systems, advanced snakes and helodermatid (gila monster) lizards. The traditional view is that the evolution of venom systems is fundamental to the radiation of snakes, although they occur in just two species of lizards. Using tools of molecular genetics, B.G. Fry and 13 colleagues explored the early evolution of venom systems in lizards and snakes. The ancestral condition (represented by venomous lizards) has lobed, noncompound, venom-secreting glands on upper and lower jaws. Advanced snakes and two lizards have more derived venom systems involving the loss of upper (maxillary) or lower (mandibular) venom glands. Analysis of venoms indicates that snakes, iguanians (monitor lizards), and anguimorphs form a single clade **(Figure 3),** suggesting that venom is an ancestral trait in this evolutionary line of reptiles.

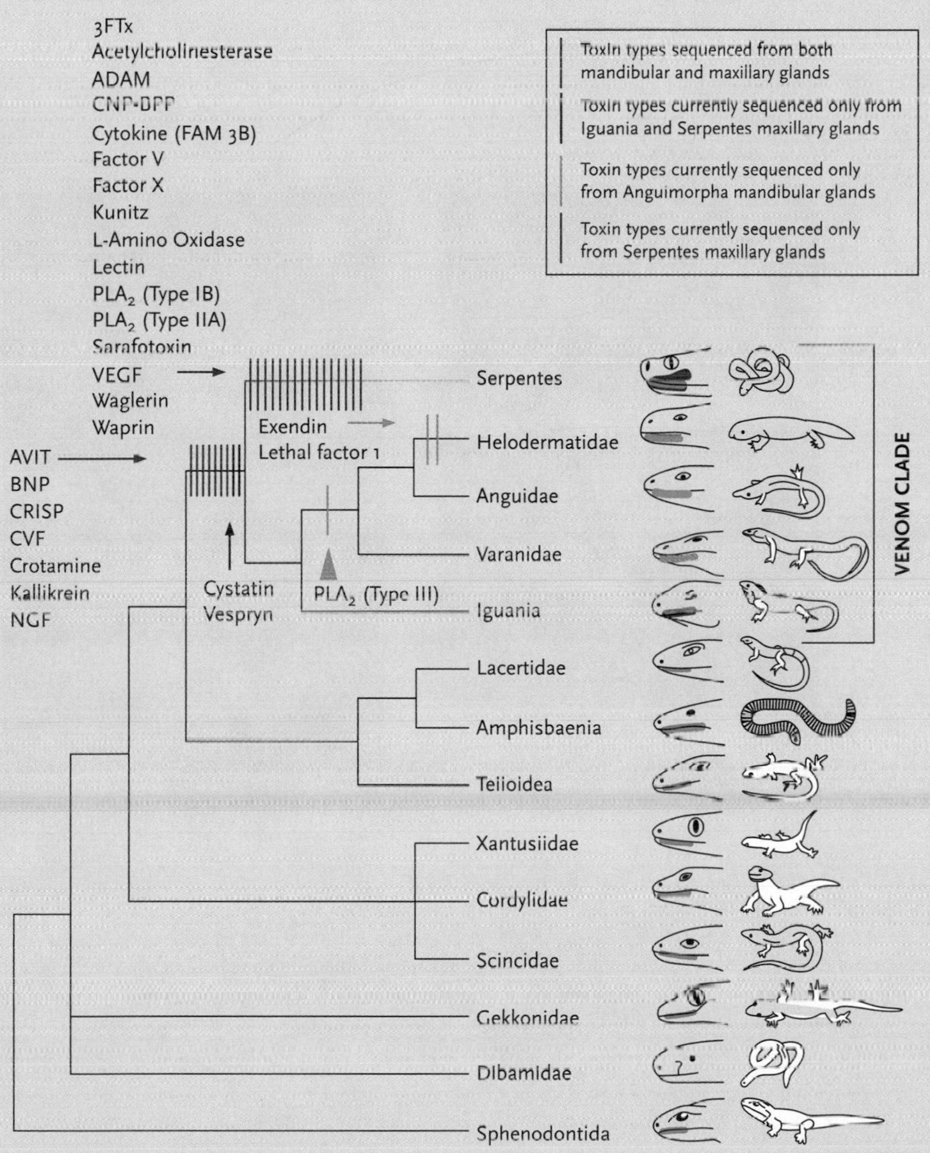

Figure 3
Snake and lizard phylogeny based on the appearance of venom. Shown here are the relative glandular development and appearance of toxin recruitment in squamate reptile phylogeny. Glands secreting mucus are blue, ancestral venom glands are red, and derived venom is orange. Elements in venom include the following: three-finger toxins (3FTx); a disintegrin and metalloproteinase (ADAM); C-type natriuretic peptide–bradykinin–potentiating peptide (CNP-BPP); cobra venom factor (CVF); nerve growth factor (NGF); and vascular endothelial growth factor (VEGF).

Nematocysts

Swimmers at ocean beaches in warmer parts of the world can be exposed to stings from the Portuguese man-of-war. In the United States, at least three human deaths have been caused by exposure to the venom of its nematocysts. First aid for someone who has been stung includes (a) using seawater to flush away any tentacles still clinging to the victim (or pick them off if necessary); (b) applying ice or cold packs to the area of the sting(s) and leaving them in place for 5 to 15 minutes; (3) using an inhaled analgesic to reduce pain; and (4) seeking additional medical aid.

Beaches where Portuguese man-of-war and other jellyfish may occur must be supervised by lifeguards who understand the danger. The inflatable bladders (sails; see **Figure 2**) make Portuguese man-of-war easy to see in the water, and swimming is not permitted when they are near.

In 1968, lifeguards and others at a beach at Port Stephens, New South Wales, in Australia were surprised and concerned when they realized that some people had been stung by Portuguese man-of-war when none of these animals had been spotted near the beach. The stinging animals turned out to be sea slugs, *Glaucus* species (see also the solar-powered sea slug, Chapter 3). Since 1903, it had been known that sea slugs use nematocysts as a defence.

Glaucus atlanticus **(Figure 3)** feed on the cnidosacs that contain the nematocysts, preferentially selecting and storing those of Portuguese man-of-war, which have two sizes of nematocysts. The sea slugs take the larger nematocysts that, when discharged, have the longest penetrants. It is likely that the same digestive processes other sea slugs use to extract chloroplasts (see Chapter 3) can be used to extract nematocysts.

This situation demonstrates the versatility of defensive systems in animals.

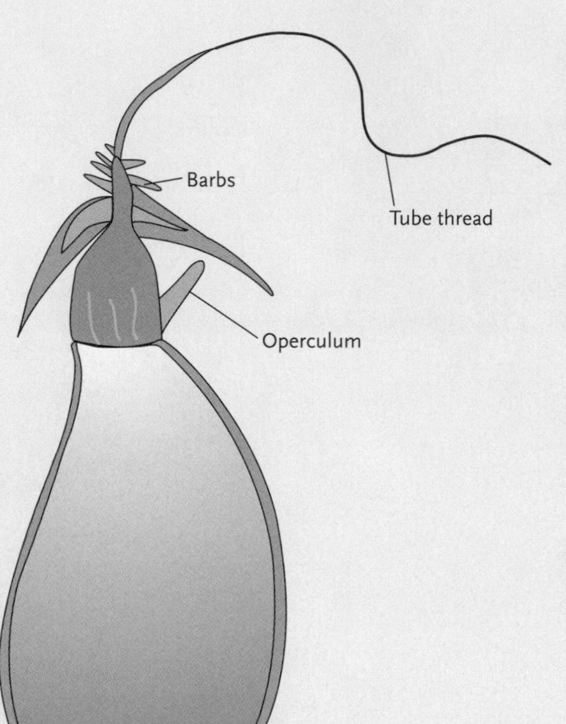

Figure 1
Nematocyst. Nematocysts (Figure 1) are stinging cells occurring in animals in the phylum Cnidaria (see Chapter 26). Nematocysts of *Physalia physalia* (Portuguese man-of-war; Figure 2) contain toxic proteins and at least six or seven enzymes that can be injurious. Unpurified nematocyst venoms have several effects, some of which can be lethal. The venoms can be neurotoxic, cardiotoxic, or myotoxic or cause lysis of red blood cells or mitochondria. Like other venoms, nematocyst venom from the Portuguese man-of-war can interfere with the transport of Na^+ and Ca^{2+} ions.

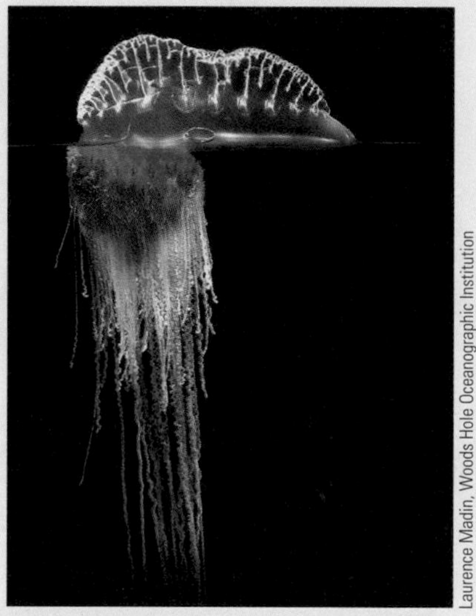

Laurence Madin, Woods Hole Oceanographic Institution

Figure 2
Physalia physalia, Portuguese man-of-war.

© Muséum de Genève; photo Philippe Wagneur

Figure 3
Glaucus atlanticus, a sea slug that ingests nematocysts from *Physalia physalia.*

a. *Eleodes* bettle

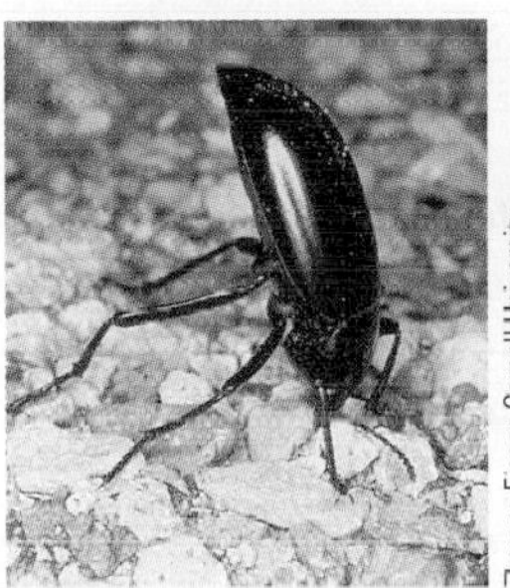

b. Grasshopper mouse

Figure 46.10
Defence and learning. When confronted by a predator, **(a)** the headstand beetle (*Eleodes longicollis*) raises its abdomen and sprays a noxious chemical from its hind end. Experienced **(b)** grasshopper mice (*Onychomys leucogaster*) thwart the beetle's defence by grabbing it, turning it upside down, and eating it headfirst.

(to avoid the spray), turns the beetle upside down so that the gland discharges into the ground, and eats the beetle from the head down **(Figure 46.10).**

Study Break

1. List the eight defence techniques used by animals and/or plants. Provide an example of each.
2. How do animals using chemical defences obtain the chemicals they use in this way?
3. What is the purpose of aposematic displays?

46.4 Competition

Different species using the same limiting resources experience **interspecific competition** (competition between species). Competing individuals may experience increased mortality and decreased reproduction, responses similar to the effects of intraspecific competition. Interspecific competition can reduce the size and population growth rate of one or more of the competing populations.

Community ecologists identify two main forms of interspecific competition. In **interference competition**, individuals of one species harm individuals of another species directly. Here animals may fight for access to resources, as when lions chase smaller predators such as hyenas, jackals, and vultures from their kills. Many plant species, including creosote bushes (see Figure 45.4), release toxic chemicals into the soil, which prevent other plants from growing nearby.

In **exploitative competition**, two or more populations use ("exploit") the same limiting resource, and the presence of one species reduces resource availability for others. Exploitative competition need not involve snout-to-snout or root-to-root confrontations. In the deserts of the American Southwest, many bird and ant species eat mainly seeds, and each seed-eating species may deplete the food supply available to others without necessarily encountering each other.

46.4a Competition and Niches: When Resources Are Limited

In the 1920s, the Russian mathematician Alfred J. Lotka and the Italian biologist Vito Volterra independently proposed a model of interspecific competition, modifying the logistic equation (see Chapter 45) to describe the effects of competition between two species. In their model, an increase in the size of one population reduces the population growth rate of the other.

In the 1930s, a Russian biologist, G.F. Gause, tested the model experimentally. He grew cultures of two *Paramecium* species (ciliate protozoans) under constant laboratory conditions, regularly renewing food and removing wastes. Both species feed on bacteria suspended in the culture medium. When grown alone, each species exhibited logistic growth. When grown together in the same dish, *Paramecium aurelia* persisted at high density, but *Paramecium caudatum* was almost eliminated **(Figure 46.11).** These results

Figure 46.11
Gause's experiments on interspecific competition in *Paramecium*.

P. caudatum alone

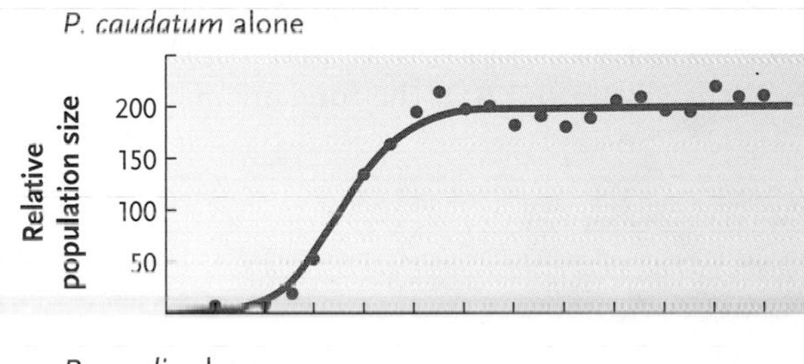

P. aurelia alone

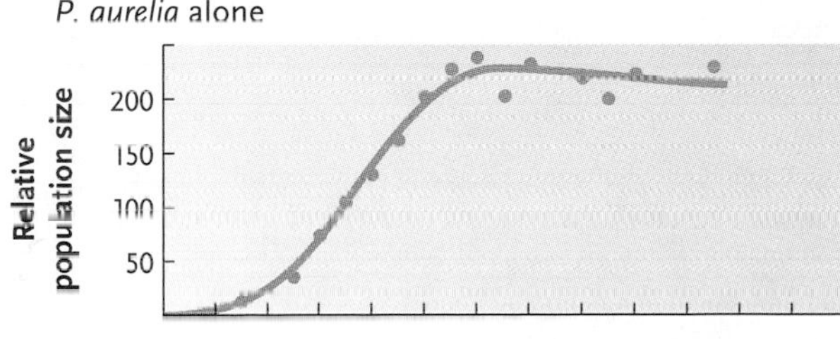

Mixed culture

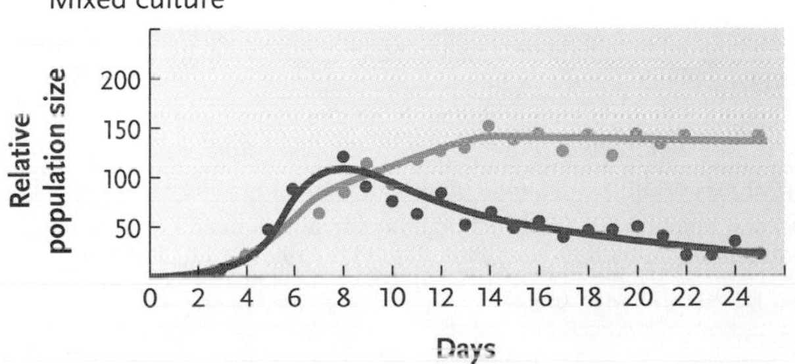

Paramecium caudatum

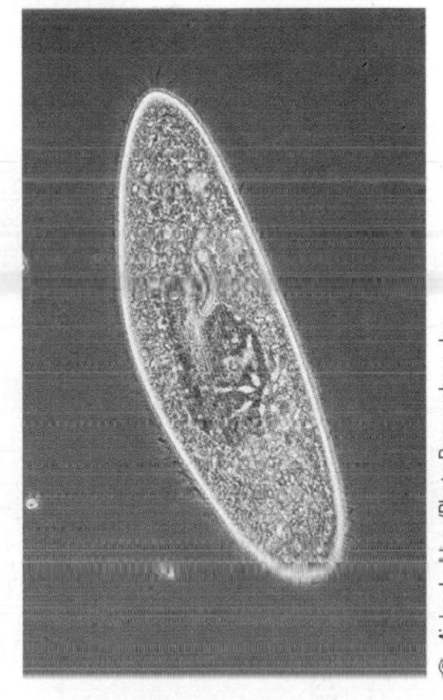

Paramecium aurelia

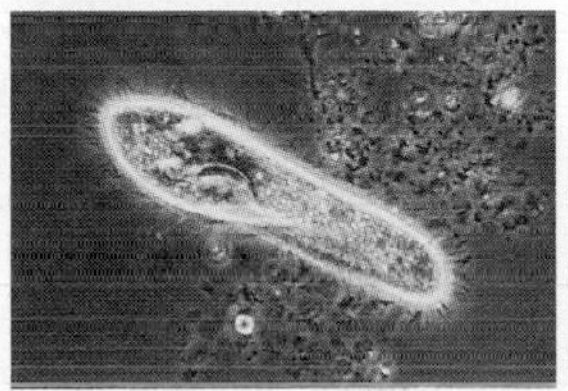

inspired Gause to define the competitive exclusion principle. Populations of two or more species cannot coexist indefinitely if they rely on the same limiting resources and exploit them in the same way. One species inevitably harvests resources more efficiently, produces more offspring than the other, and, by its actions, negatively affects the other species.

Ecologists developed the concept of the **ecological niche** to visualize resource use and the potential for interspecific competition in nature. They define a population's niche by the resources it uses and the environmental conditions it requires over its lifetime. In this context, niche includes food, shelter, and nutrients, as well as nondepletable abiotic conditions such as light intensity and temperature. In theory, an almost infinite variety of conditions and resources could contribute to a population's niche. In practice, ecologists usually identify the critical resources for which populations might compete. Sunlight, soil moisture, and inorganic nutrients are important resources for plants, so differences in leaf height and root depth, for example, can affect plants' access to these resources. Food type, food size, and nesting sites are important for animals. Often, when several species coexist, they use food and nest resources in different ways.

Ecologists distinguish the **fundamental niche** of a species, the range of conditions and resources it could tolerate and use, from its **realized niche,** the range of conditions and resources it actually uses in nature. Realized niches are smaller than fundamental niches, partly because all tolerable conditions are not always present in a habitat and partly because some resources are used by other species. We can visualize competition between two populations by plotting their fundamental and realized niches with respect to one or more resources **(Figure 46.12).** If the fundamental niches of two populations overlap, they *might* compete in nature.

Observing that several species use the same resource does not demonstrate that competition occurs (or does not occur). All terrestrial animals consume oxygen but do not compete for oxygen because it is usually plentiful. Nevertheless, two general observations provide *indirect* evidence that interspecific competition may have important effects.

Resource partitioning occurs when several species living in the same place (sympatric) use different resources or the same resources in different ways. Although plants might compete for water and dissolved nutrients, they may avoid competition by partitioning these resources, collecting them from different depths in the soil **(Figure 46.13).** This allows coexistence of different species.

Character displacement can be evident when comparing species that are sometimes sympatric and sometimes allopatric (live in different places). Allopatric populations of some animal species are morphologically similar and use similar resources, whereas sympatric populations are morphologically different and use different resources. Differences between sympatric species allow them to coexist without competing. Allen Keast studied honey-eaters (family Meliphagidae), a group of birds from Australia, to illustrate this situation. In mainland Australia, up to six species in the genus *Melithreptus* occur in some habitats. Just off the coast of Kangaroo Island, there are two species. When two species are sympatric, each feeds in a wider range of situations than when six species live in the same area, reflecting the use of broader niches. Behavioural and

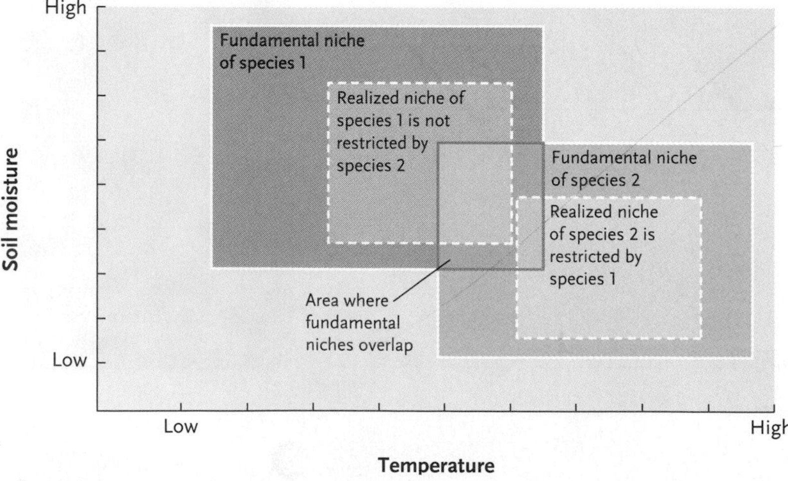

Figure 46.12
Fundamental versus realized niches. In this hypothetical example, both species 1 and species 2 can survive intermediate temperature conditions, as indicated by the shading where their fundamental niches overlap. Because species 1 actually occupies most of this overlap zone, its realized niche is not much affected by the presence of species 2. In contrast, the realized niche of species 2 is restricted by the presence of species 1, and species 2 occupies warmer and drier parts of the habitat.

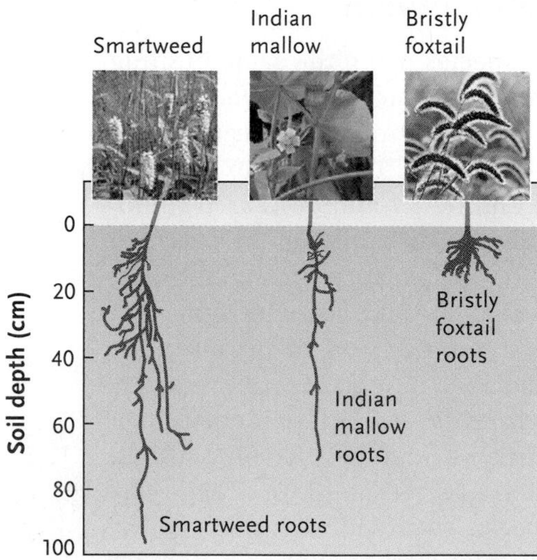

Figure 46.13
Resource partitioning. The root systems of three plant species that grow in abandoned fields partition water and nutrient resources in soil. Bristly foxtail grass (*Setaria faberii*) has a shallow root system, Indian mallow (*Abutilon theophraste*) has a moderately deep taproot, and smartweed (*Polygonum pennsylvanicum*) has a deep taproot that branches at many depths.
Photos: left, © Tony Wharton, Frank Lane Picture Agency/Corbis; middle, © Hal Horwitz/Corbis; right, © Joe McDonald/Corbis.

Realized niches before experimental treatments

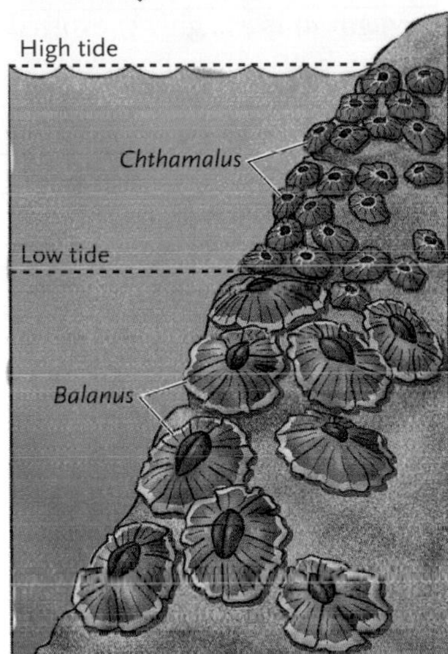

Treatment 1: Remove *Balanus*
In the absence of *Balanus*, *Chthamalus* occupies both shallow water and deep water.

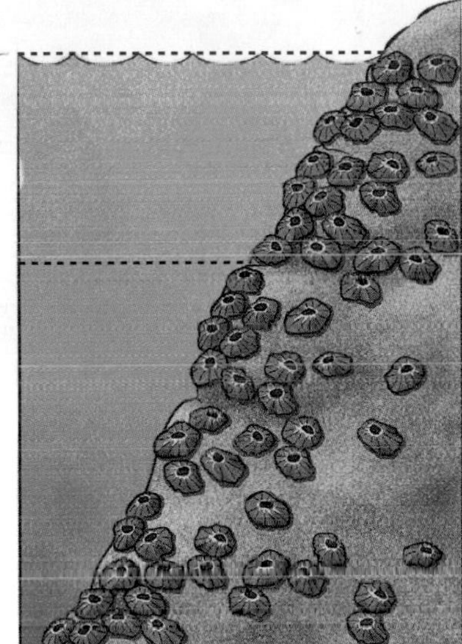

Treatment 2: Remove *Chthamalus*
In the absence of *Chthamalus*, *Balanus* still occupies only deep water.

Figure 46.14
Demonstration of competition between two species of barnacles.

morphological differences are evident when species are compared between the different situations.

Data on resource partitioning and character displacement suggest, but do not prove, that interspecific competition is an important selective force in nature. To demonstrate *conclusively* that interspecific competition limits natural populations, one must show that the presence of one population reduces the population size or density of its presumed competitor. In a classic field experiment, Joseph Connell examined competition between two barnacle species **(Figure 46.14).** Connell first observed the distributions of both species of barnacles in undisturbed habitats to establish a reference baseline. *Chthamalus stellatus* is generally found in shallow water on rocky coasts, where it is periodically exposed to air. *Balanus balanoides* typically lives in deeper water, where it is usually submerged.

In the absence of *Balanus* on rocks in deep water, larval *Chthamalus* colonized the area and produced a flourishing population of adults. *Balanus* physically displaced *Chthamalus* from these rocks. Thus, interference competition from *Balanus* prevents *Chthamalus* from occupying areas where it would otherwise live. Removal of *Chthamalus* from rocks in shallow water did not result in colonization by *Balanus*. *Balanus* apparently cannot live in habitats that are frequently exposed to air. Connell concluded that there was competition between the two species. But competition was asymmetrical because *Chthamalus* did not affect the distribution of *Balanus*, whereas *Balanus* had a substantial effect on *Chthamalus*.

46.4b Symbiosis: Close Associations

Symbiosis occurs when one species has a physically close ecological association with another (*sym* = together; *bio* = life; *sis* = process). Biologists define three types of symbiotic interactions: *commensalism*, *mutualism*, and *parasitism* (see Table 46.1).

In **commensalism**, one species benefits and the other is unaffected by the interactions. Commensalism appears to be rare in nature because few species are unaffected by interactions with another. One possible example is the relationship between Cattle Egrets (*Bubulcus ibis*, birds in the heron family) and the large grazing mammals with which they associate **(Figure 46.15).** Cattle Egrets eat insects and other small animals that their commensal partners flush from grass. Feeding rates of Cattle Egrets are higher when they associate with large grazers than when they do not. The birds clearly benefit from this interaction, but the presence of birds has no apparent positive or negative impact on the mammals.

In **mutualism**, both partners benefit. Mutualism appears to be common and includes coevolved relationships between flowering plants and animal pollinators. Animals that feed on a plant's nectar or

Figure 46.15
Commensalism. Cattle Egrets (*Bubulcus ibis*) feed on insects and other small animals flushed by the movements of large grazing animals such as African elephants (*Loxodonta africana*).

Life on the Edge

Some Perils of Mutualism

Living organisms offer many examples of mutalistic interactions in which one species (or group of species) shows varying levels of dependence on another or others. Mutualistic situations can place species on the edge of survival. Where one species depends entirely on another, the extinction of one must lead to change or the extinction of both (e.g., Dodos, see Chapter 48, and yucca plants and their moths). There are many other examples of close relationships, including a desert melon (*Cucumis humifructus*) that depends perhaps entirely on aardvarks (*Orycteropus afer*) for dispersal of its seeds. Aardvarks can sniff out the underground melons, dig them up, and eat them to obtain water. When aardvarks bury their dung, they plant the melon's seeds and fertilize them. The survival of the melon depends on the aardvark but not vice versa.

Mutualistic interactions between species can be even more complex. In the African savannah, ants often live in mutualistic relationships with trees. In east Africa, whistling thorn acacia trees (*Acacia drepanolobium*) are host to four species of ants. One species of ant (*Crematogaster mimosae*) in particular depends on room (hollows in swollen thorns, called domatia) provided by the trees along with board (carbohydrates secreted from extrafloral glands and the bases of leaves). Another species of ant (*Crematogaster sjostedti*) also lives on the trees but usually nests in holes made by cerambycid beetles that burrow into and harm the trees.

The ants, particularly *C. mimosae*, attack animals that attempt to browse on the foliage or branches of *A. drepanolobium*. They deter many herbivores, from large mammals to wood-boring beetles (such as cerambycids). If large, browsing mammals are excluded from the area, *A. drepanolobium* produce fewer domatia and fewer carbohydrates for *C. mimosae*. The decline in this species of ant leads to higher damage by cerambycid beetles and increases in populations of *C. sjostedti*.

Many other plants also use ants as mercenaries (see Figure 46.18), and it is becoming clear that survival of these systems depends on the continued presence of participating species.

but constantly change in response to disturbance and environmental variation.

In the 1960s, Robert Whittaker suggested that ecologists could determine which hypothesis was correct by analyzing communities along environmental gradients, such as temperature or moisture **(Figure 46.19).** Clements' interactive hypothesis predicted that species typically occupying the same communities should always occur together. Thus, their distributions along the gradient would be clustered in discrete groups with sharp boundaries between groups (see Figure 46.19a). According to Gleason's individualistic hypothesis, each species is distributed over the section of an environmental gradient to which it is adapted. Different species would have unique distributions, and species composition would change continuously along the gradient. Communities would not be separated by sharp boundaries (see Figure 46.19b).

Most gradient analyses support Gleason's individualistic view of ecological communities. Environmental conditions vary continuously in space, and most plant distributions match these patterns (see Figure 46.19c, d). But the individualistic view does not fully explain all patterns observed in nature. Ecologists recognize certain assemblages of species as distinctive communities and name them accordingly, for example, redwood forests and coral reefs.

Ecotones, the borders between communities, are sometimes wide transition zones. Ecotones are generally species rich because they include plants and animals from both neighbouring communities, as well as some species that thrive only under transitional conditions. Although ecotones are usually relatively broad, places where there is a discontinuity in a critical resource or important abiotic factor may have a sharp community boundary. Chemical differences between soils derived from serpentine rock and sandstone establish sharp boundaries between communities of native California wildflowers and introduced European grasses **(Figure 46.20).**

Study Break

1. What two hypotheses were developed by ecologists about the nature of ecological communities? How does each relate to the equilibrium state of the existing community?
2. Are ecotones generally species rich or species poor?

46.6 Community Characteristics

Growth forms (sizes and shapes) of plants vary markedly in different environments, so the appearances of plants can often be used to characterize communities. Warm, moist environments support complex vegetation

a. Interactive hypothesis

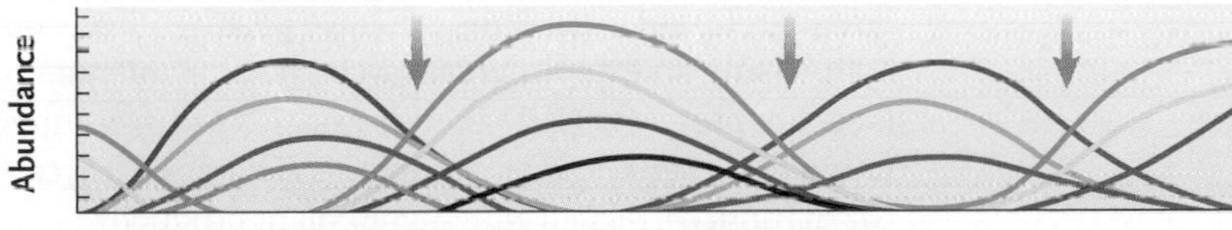

The interactive hypothesis predicts that species within communities exhibit similar distributions along environmental gradients (indicated by the close alignment of several curves over each section of the gradient) and that boundaries between communities (indicated by arrows) are sharp.

b. Individualistic hypothesis

The individualistic hypothesis predicts that species distributions along the gradient are independent (indicated by the lack of alignment of the curves) and that sharp boundaries do not separate communities.

c. Siskiyou Mountains

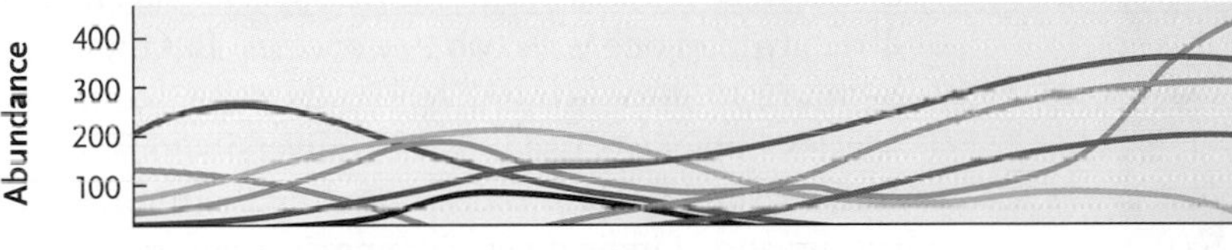

d. Santa Catalina Mountains

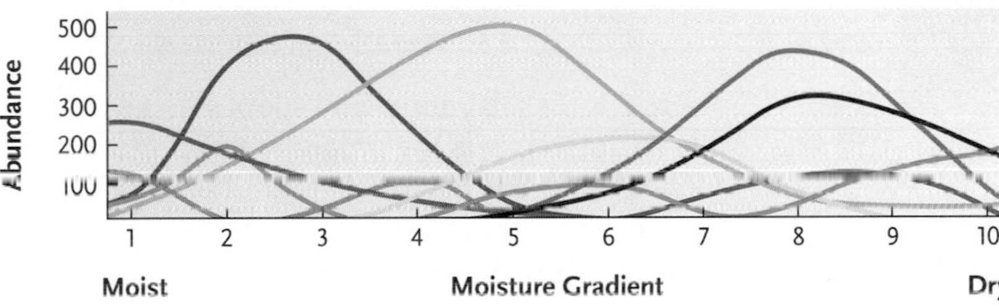

Most gradient analyses support the individualistic hypothesis, as illustrated by distributions of tree species along moisture gradients in Oregon's Siskiyou Mountains and Arizona's Santa Catalina Mountains.

Figure 46.19
Two views of ecological communities. Each graph line indicates a different species.

with multiple vertical layers. Tropical forests include a canopy formed by the tallest trees, an understorey of shorter trees and shrubs, and a herb layer under openings in the canopy. Vinelike lianas and epiphytes grow on the trunks and branches of trees **(Figure 46.21, p. 1158)**. In contrast, physically harsh environments are occupied by low vegetation with simple structure. Trees on mountainsides buffeted by cold winds are short, and the plants below them cling to rocks and soil. Other environments support growth forms between these extremes.

Communities differ greatly in species richness, the number of species that live within them. The harsh environment on a low desert island may support just a few species of microorganisms, fungi, algae, plants, and arthropods. In contrast, tropical forests that grow under milder physical conditions include many thousands of species. Ecologists have studied global patterns of species richness (see Chapter 48) for decades. Today, as human disturbance of natural communities has reached a crisis point, conservation biologists try to understand global patterns of species richness to determine which regions of Earth are most in need of preservation.

Jasper Ridge Biological Preserve

Figure 46.20
Sharp community boundaries. Soils derived from serpentine rock have high magnesium and heavy metal content, which many plants cannot tolerate. Although native California wildflowers (bright yellow in this photograph) thrive on serpentine soil at the Jasper Ridge Preserve of Stanford University, introduced European grasses (green in this photograph) competitively exclude them from adjacent soils derived from sandstones.

Figure 46.21
Layered forests. Tropical forests, such as one near the Mazaruni River in Guyana (South America), include a canopy of tall trees and an understorey of short trees and shrubs. Huge vines (lianas) climb through the trees, eventually reaching sunlight in the canopy. Epiphytic plants grow on trunks and branches, increasing the structural complexity of the habitat.

The relative abundances of species varies across communities. Some communities have one or two abundant species and a number of rare species. In others, the species are represented by more equal numbers of individuals. In a temperate deciduous forest in southern Quebec, red oak trees (*Quercus rubra*) and sugar maples (*Acer saccharum*) might together account for nearly 85% of the trees. A tropical forest in Costa Rica may have more than 200 tree species, each making up a small percentage of the total.

The factors underlying diversity and community structure can be expected to vary among groups of organisms, and the interactions between very different groups of organisms can have positive effects on both. Using an experimental mycorrhizal plant system (see Chapter 24), H. Maherali and J.N. Klironomos found that after one year, the species richness of mycorrhizal fungi correlated with higher plant productivity. In turn, the diversity and species richness of mycorrhizal fungi were highest when their starting community had more distinct evolutionary lineages. This example illustrates the importance of diversity and interactions.

46.6a Measuring Species Diversity and Evenness: Calculating Indices

The number of species is the simplest measure of diversity, so a forest with four tree species has higher diversity than one with two tree species. But there can be more to measuring diversity than just counting species. Biologists use indices of diversity to facilitate comparison of data sets documenting the numbers of species and of individuals. Shannon's index of diversity (H'), one commonly used measure, is calculated using the formula

$$H' = -\Sigma_{i=1}^{S} pi \ln p_i$$

where S is the total number of species in the community (richness), p_i is the proportion of S made up by species I, and ln is the natural logarithm.

Another index, Shannon's evenness index (E_H), is calculated using the forumula

$$E_H = H'/\ln S$$

where $\ln S$ is the natural log of the number of species. Evenness is an indication of the mixture of species. Indices of diversity and evenness allow population biologists to objectively portray and compare the diversity of communities.

Use the two indices to compare the 3 forests of 50 trees each **(Figure 46.22)**. The number of species and number of individuals of each species in each forest are shown in **Table 46.2.** In Table 46.2, the values of H' and E_H provide an indication of the diversity of the three hypothetical forests and the evenness of species representations. Lower values of H' and E_H suggest com-

Figure 46.22
Species diversity. In this hypothetical example, each of three samples of forest communities (A, B, and C) contains 50 trees. Indices allow biologists to express the diversity of species and evenness of numbers (see Table 46.2).

munities with few species (low H' values) or uneven distribution (low E_H values). Higher values of H' and E_H suggest a richer array of species with evenly distributed individuals.

Measures of diversity can be used to advantage. Ecologists refer to "α" diversity to represent the numbers of species sympatric in one community and "β" diversity to depict the numbers in a collection of communities. The number of herbivorous Lepidoptera species in one national park is α diversity, whereas β diversity is the number of species in the country in which the park is located. The trend to establish parks that cross international boundaries is a step toward recognizing the reality that political and biological boundaries can be quite different. Measures of diversity can be used directly in some conservation plans (see Chapter 48).

46.6b Trophic Interactions: Between Nourishment Levels

Every ecological community has trophic structure (*troph* = nourishment; see Chapter 3), comprising all plant–herbivore, predator–prey, host–parasite, and potential competitive interactions **(Figure 46.23, p. 1160)**. We can visualize the trophic structure of a community as a hierarchy of trophic levels, defined by the feeding relationships among its species (see Figure 46.23a). Photosynthetic organisms are primary producers, the first trophic level. Primary producers are photoautotrophs (*auto* = self) because they capture sunlight and convert it into chemical energy that is used to make larger organic molecules that plants can use directly.

Table 46.2 Shannon's Indices for Measuring Diversity and Evenness

Numbers of Individuals Per Species			
	Forest A*	Forest B*	Forest C*
Species 1	39	5	25
Species 2	2	5	25
Species 3	2	5	0
Species 4	1	5	0
Species 5	1	5	0
Species 6	1	5	0
Species 7	1	5	0
Species 8	1	5	0
Species 9	1	5	0
Species 10	1	5	0
Shannon Indices			
H' diversity	0.6	2.3	0.7
E_h evenness	0.26	1.0	1.0

*Forests from Figure 46.22.

Plants are the main primary producers in terrestrial communities. Multicellular algae and plants are the major primary producers in shallow freshwater and marine environments, whereas photosynthetic protists and cyanobacteria play that role in deep, open water.

All consumers in a community (animals, fungi, and diverse microorganisms) are heterotrophs (*hetero* = other) because they acquire energy and nutrients by eating other organisms or their remains. Animals are consumers. Herbivores (primary consumers) feed directly on plants and form the second trophic level. Secondary consumers (mesopredators) eat herbivores and form the third trophic level. Animals that eat secondary consumers comprise the fourth trophic level, the tertiary consumers. At one meal, animals that are omnivores (e.g., humans, pigs, and bears) can act as primary, secondary, and tertiary consumers.

Detritivores (scavengers) form a separate and distinct trophic level. These organisms extract energy from organic detritus produced at other trophic levels. Detritivores include fungi, bacteria, and animals such as earthworms and vultures that ingest dead organisms, digestive wastes, and cast-off body parts, such as leaves and exoskeletons. Decomposers, a type of detritivore, are small organisms, such as bacteria and fungi, that feed on dead or dying organic material. Detritivores and decomposers serve a critical ecological function because their activity reduces organic material to small inorganic molecules that producers can assimilate (see Chapters 3 and 21).

Although omnivores obviously do not fit exclusively into one trophic level, this also can be true of other organisms. Sea slugs that use chloroplasts or carnivorous plants are examples of species that do not fit readily into trophic categories.

46.6c Food Chains and Webs: Connections in Ecosystems

Ecologists use food chains and webs to illustrate the trophic structure of a community. Each link in a food chain is represented by an arrow pointing from food to consumer (see Figure 46.23). Simple, straight-line food chains are rare in nature because most consumers feed on more than one type of food and because most organisms are eaten by more than one type of consumer. Complex relationships are portrayed as food webs, sets of interconnected food chains with multiple links.

In the food web for the waters off the coast of Antarctica (see Figure 46.23), primary producers and primary consumers are small organisms occurring in vast numbers. Microscopic diatoms (phytoplankton) are responsible for most photosynthesis, and small shrimplike krill (zooplankton) are the major primary consumers. These tiny organisms, in turn, are eaten by larger species such as fish and seabirds, as well as

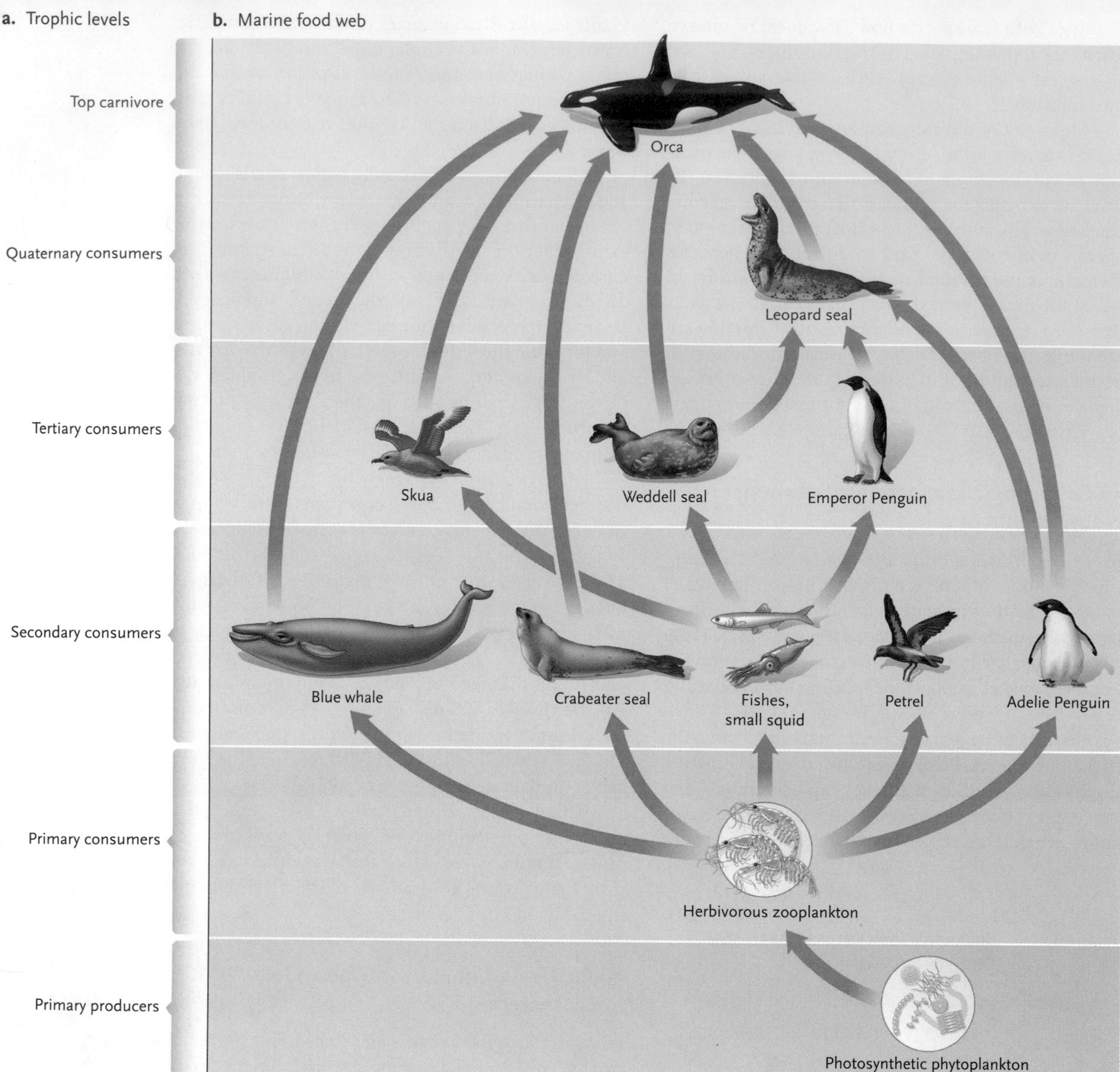

Figure 46.23
The marine food web off the coast of Antarctica.

by suspension-feeding baleen whales. Some secondary consumers are eaten by birds and mammals at higher trophic levels. The top carnivore in this ecosystem, the orca, feeds on carnivorous birds and mammals.

Ideally, depictions of food webs would include all species in a community, from microorganisms to top consumer. But most ecologists simply cannot collect data on every species, particularly those that are rare or very small. Instead, they study links between the most important species and simplify analysis by grouping together trophically similar species. Figure 46.23 categorizes the many different species of primary producers and primary consumers as phytoplankton and zooplankton, respectively.

Many biological "hot spots" exist, from thermal vents on the floor of some oceans to deposits of bat guano in some caves. A more recently described example is icebergs drifting north from Antarctica. The icebergs can be hot spots of enrichment because of the nutrients and other materials they shed into surrounding waters. The water around two free-drifting icebergs (0.1 km^2 and 30.8 km^2 in area) was sampled in the Weddell Sea. High concentrations of chlorophyll, krill, and seabirds extended about 3.7 km around each iceberg. These data, reported by K.L. Smith Jr. and seven colleagues, demonstrate that icebergs can have substantial effects on pelagic ecosystems.

In the late 1950s, Robert MacArthur analyzed food webs to determine how the many links between trophic levels may contribute to a community's stability. The stability of a community is defined as its ability to maintain species composition and relative abundances when environmental disturbances eliminate some species from the community. MacArthur hypothesized that in species-rich communities, where animals feed on many food sources, the absence of one or two species would have only minor effects on the structure and stability of the community as a whole. He proposed a connection between species diversity, food web complexity, and community stability.

Subsequent research has confirmed MacArthur's reasoning. The average number of links per species generally increases with increasing species richness. Comparative food web analysis reveals that the relative proportions of species at the highest, middle, and lowest trophic levels are reasonably constant across communities. In 92 communities, MacArthur found two or three prey species per predator species, regardless of species richness.

Interactions among species in most food webs can be complex, indirect, and hard to unravel. In contrast, rodents and ants living in desert communities of the American Southwest potentially compete for seeds, their main food source. Plants that produce the seeds compete for water, nutrients, and space. Rodents generally prefer to eat large seeds, whereas ants prefer small seeds. Thus, feeding by rodents reduces the potential population sizes of plants that produce large seeds. As a result, the population sizes of plants that produce small seeds may increase, ultimately providing more food for ants (see Chapter 41). Compared with the Antarctic system described above (see Figure 46.23), this community is not particularly complex.

Study Break

1. Why are indices important for population biologists? What do Shannon's indices measure?
2. Differentiate between α and β diversity.
3. Are herbivores primary or secondary consumers? Which trophic level do they form? Where do omnivores belong?

46.7 Effects of Population Interactions on Community Structure

Observations of resource partitioning and character displacement suggested that some process had fostered differences in resource use among coexisting species, and competition provided the most straightforward explanation of these patterns.

Interspecific competition can cause local extinction of species or prevent new species from becoming established in a community, reducing its species richness. During the 1960s and early 1970s, ecologists emphasized competition as the primary factor structuring communities.

46.7a Competition: More than One Species Competing for a Resource

To further explore the role of competition, ecologists undertook field experiments on competition in natural populations. The experiment on barnacles (see Figure 46.14) is typical of this approach—the impact on one species' potential competitors of adding or removing another species changed patterns of distribution or population size. The picture that emerges from the results of these experiments is not clear, even to ecologists. In the early 1980s, Joseph Connell surveyed 527 published experiments on 215 species. He found that competition was demonstrated in roughly 40% of the experiments and more than 50% of species. At the same time, Thomas W. Schoener used different criteria to evaluate 164 experiments on approximately 400 species. He found that competition affected more than 75% of species.

It is not surprising that there is no single answer to the question about how competition works in communities and influences them. Plant ecologists and vertebrate ecologists working with *K*-selected species generally believe that competition has a profound effect on species distributions and resource use. Insect ecologists and marine ecologists working with *r*-selected species argue that competition is not the major force governing community structure, pointing instead to predation or parasitism and physical disturbance. We know that even categorizing a species as "*r*-" or "*K*-" is open to discussion (see Chapter 45).

46.7b Feeding: You Are What You Eat

Predators can influence the species richness and structure of communities by reducing the sizes of prey populations. On the rocky coast of British Columbia, different species that fill different trophic roles compete for attachment sites on rocks, a requirement for life on a wave-swept shore. Mussels are the strongest competitors for space, eliminating other species from the community (see *Effect of a Predator on the Species Richness of Its Prey*). At some sites, predatory sea stars preferentially eat mussels, reducing their numbers and creating space for other species to grow. Because the interaction between

Effect of a Predator on the Species Richness of Its Prey

Biologists used a predatory sea star (*Pisaster ochraceus*) to assess the influence a predator can have on species richness and relative abundance of prey **(Figure 1).** *P. ochraceus* preferentially eats mussels (*Mytilus californicus*), one of the strongest competitors for space in rocky intertidal pools. Robert Paine removed *Pisaster* from caged experimental study plots, leaving control study plots undisturbed, and then monitored the species richness of *Pisaster*'s invertebrate prey over many years.

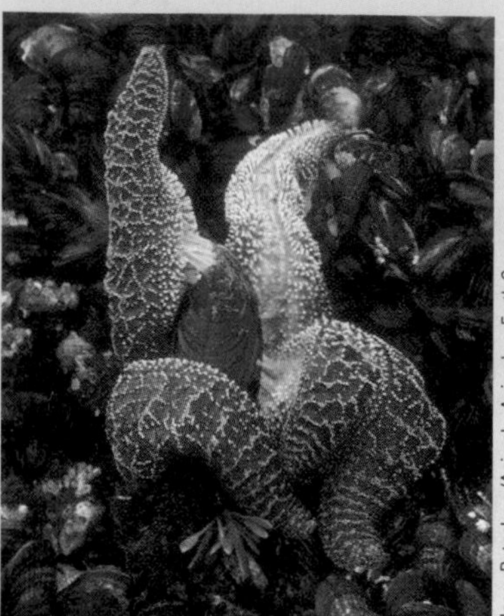

Figure 1
A predatory sea star (*Pisaster ochraceus*) feeding on a mussel (*Mytilus californicus*).

Paine documented an increase in mussel populations in the experimental plots as well as complex changes in the feeding relationships among species in the intertidal food web **(Figure 2).** When he removed *P. ochraceus*, the top predator in this food web, he observed a rapid decrease in the species richness of invertebrates and algae. Species richness on control plots did not change over the course of the experiment.

Predation by *P. ochraceus* prevents mussels from outcompeting other invertebrates on rocky shores.

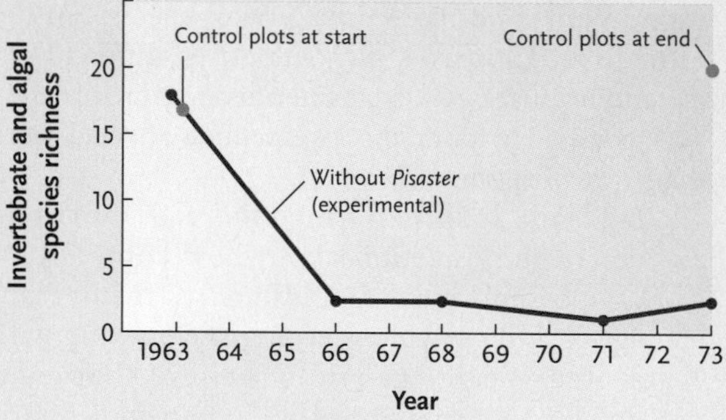

Figure 2
Changes in the species richness of invertebrates and algal species according to changes in populations of sea stars.

Pisaster and *Mytilus* affects other species as well, it qualifies as a strong interaction.

In the 1960s, Robert Paine used removal experiments to evaluate the effects of predation by *Pisaster* (see *Effect of a Predator on the Species Richness of Its Prey*). In predator-free experimental plots, mussels outcompeted barnacles, chitons, limpets, and other invertebrate herbivores, reducing species richness from 15 species to 8. In control plots containing predators, all 15 species persisted. Ecologists describe predators such as *Pisaster* as keystone species, defined as species with a greater effect on community structure than their numbers might suggest.

Herbivores also exert complex effects on communities. In the 1970s, Jane Lubchenco studied herbivory in a periwinkle snail, believed to be a keystone species on rocky shores in Massachusetts (see *The Complex Effects of an Herbivorous Snail on Algal Species Richness*). The features of plants and algae and the food preferences of animals that eat them together can influence community structure.

Study Break

1. How does the importance of competition vary between *K*-selected and *r*-selected species?
2. Does predation or herbivory increase or decrease species richness? Explain.
3. What is a keystone species?

The Complex Effects of an Herbivorous Snail on Algal Species Richness

Jane Lubchenco made enclosures that prevented periwinkle snails (*Littorina littorea*) from entering or leaving study plots in tidepools and on exposed rocks in rocky intertidal habitat **(Figure 1).** She then monitored the algal species composition in the plots, comparing them to the density of the periwinkles. In this way, she examined the influence of the periwinkles on the species richness of algae in intertidal communities.

The results varied dramatically between the study plots in tidepools and on exposed rocks. In tidepools, periwinkle snails preferentially ate *Enteromorpha*, the competitively dominant alga. At intermediate densities of *Enteromorpha*, the periwinkles remove some of these algae, allowing weakly competitive species to grow. The snails' grazing increases species richness. But grazing by periwinkles when *Enteromorpha* is at low or high densities reduces the species richness of algae in tide pools. On exposed rocks, where periwinkle snails rarely eat the competitively dominant alga *Chondrus*, feeding by snails reduces algal species richness **(Figure 2).**

Periwinkle snails (*Littorina littorea*)

Enteromorpha growing in tidepools

Chondrus growing on exposed rocks

Figure 1
The distribution of periwinkle snails and two kinds of algae.

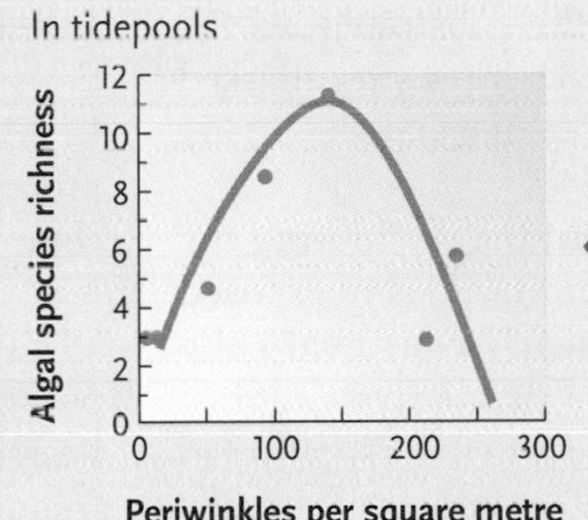

In tidepools, snails at low densities eat little algae and *Enteromorpha* competitively excludes other algal species, reducing species richness. At high snail densities, heavy feeding on all species reduces algal species richness. At intermediate snail densities, grazing eliminates some *Enteromorpha*, allowing other species to grow.

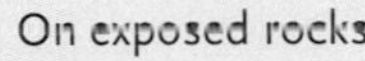

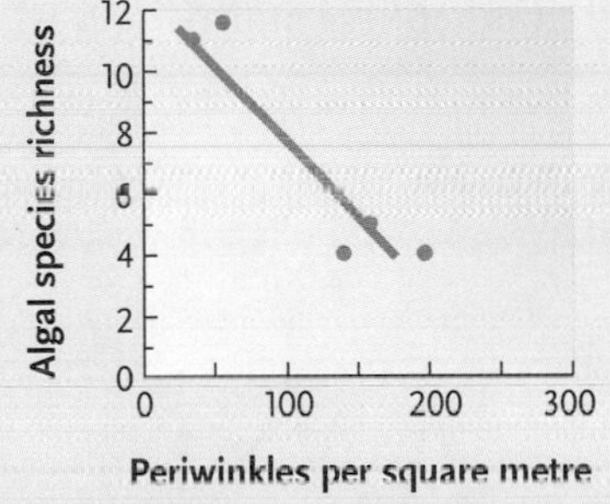

On exposed rocks, periwinkles never eat much *Chondrus*, but they consume the tender, less successful competitors. Thus, feeding by periwinkles reinforces the competitive superiority of *Chondrus:* as periwinkle density increases, algal species richness declines.

Figure 2
Density of periwinkles versus algal species richness in tidepools and on exposed rocks.

46.8 Effects of Disturbance on Community Characteristics

Recent research tends to support the individualistic view that many communities are not in equilibrium and that species composition changes frequently. Environmental disturbances such as storms, landslides, fires, floods, avalanches, and cold spells often eliminate some species and provide opportunities for others to become established. Frequent disturbances keep some ecological communities in a constant state of flux.

Physical disturbances are common in some environments. Lightning-induced fires commonly sweep through grasslands, powerful hurricanes often demolish patches of forest and coastal habitats, and waves wash over communities at the edge of the sea and sweep away organisms as well as landforms and other structures.

Joseph Connell and his colleagues conducted an ambitious long-term study of the effects of disturbance on coral reefs, shallow tropical marine habitats that are among the most species-rich communities on Earth. In some parts of the world, reefs are routinely battered by violent storms that wash corals off the substrate, creating bare patches in the reef. The scouring action of storms creates opportunities for coral larvae to settle on bare substrates and start new colonies.

From 1963 to 1992, Connell and his colleagues tracked the fate of the Heron Island Reef at the south end of Australia's Great Barrier Reef **(Figure 46.24).** The inner flat and protected crests of the reef are sheltered from severe wave action during storms, whereas some pools and crests are routinely exposed to physical disturbance. Because corals live in colonies of variable size, the researchers monitored coral abundance by measuring the percentage of the substrate (i.e., the seafloor) that colonies covered. They revisited marked study plots at intervals, photographing and identifying individual coral colonies.

Five major cyclones crossed the reef during the 30-year study period. Coral communities in exposed areas of the reef were in a nearly continual state of flux. In exposed pools, four of the five cyclones reduced the percentage of cover, often drastically. On exposed crests, the cyclone of 1972 eliminated virtually all corals, and subsequent storms slowed the recovery of these areas for more than 20 years. In contrast, corals in sheltered areas suffered much less storm damage. Nevertheless, their coverage also declined steadily during the study as a natural consequence of the corals' growth. As colonies grew taller and closer to the ocean's surface, their increased exposure to air resulted in substantial mortality.

Connell and his colleagues also documented *recruitment*, the growth of new colonies from settling larvae, in their study plots. They discovered that the rate at which new colonies developed was almost always higher in sheltered than in exposed areas. Recruitment rates were extremely variable, depending in part on the amount of space that storms or coral growth had made available.

This long-term study of coral reefs illustrates that frequent disturbances prevent some communities from reaching an equilibrium determined by interspecific interactions. Changes in the coral reef community at Heron Island result from the effects of external disturbances that remove coral colonies from the reef as well as internal processes (growth and recruitment) that either eliminate colonies or establish new ones. In this community, growth and recruitment are slow processes, and disturbances are frequent. Thus, the community never attains equilibrium, and moderate levels of disturbance can foster high species richness.

The intermediate disturbance hypothesis, proposed by Connell in 1978, suggests that species richness is greatest in communities experiencing fairly frequent disturbances of moderate intensity. Moderate disturbances create openings for *r*-selected species to arrive and join the community while allowing *K*-selected species to survive. Thus, communities that

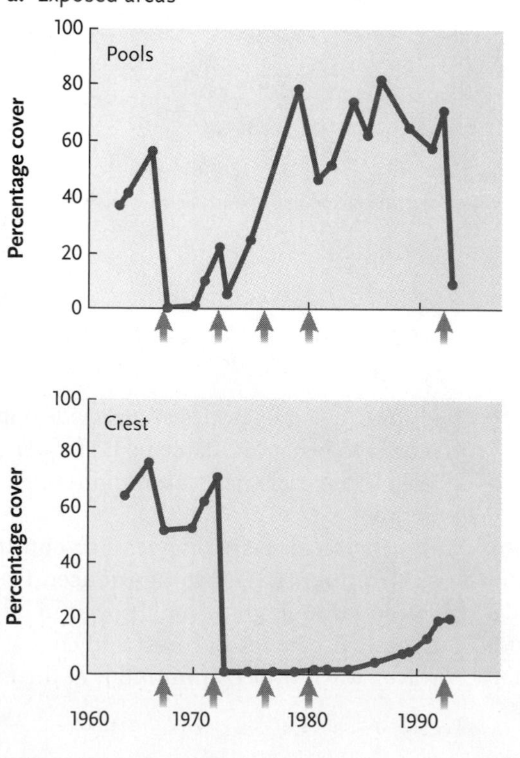

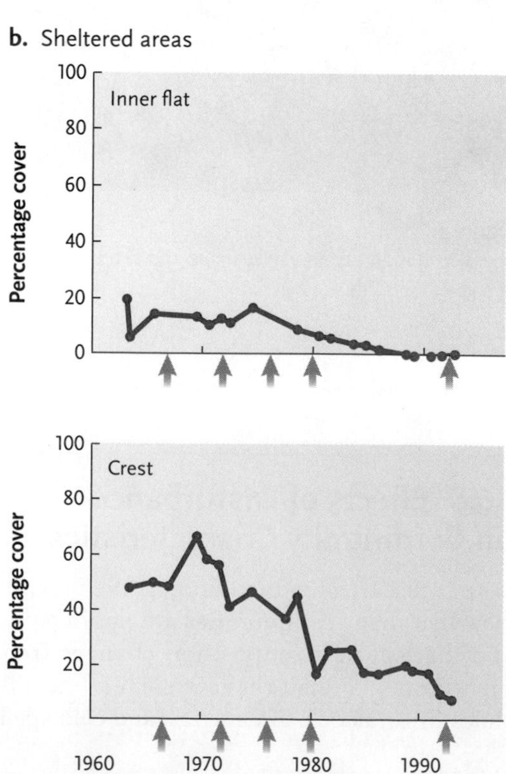

Figure 46.24
The effects of storms on corals. Five tropical cyclones (marked by grey arrows) damaged corals on the Heron Island Reef during a 30-year period. Storms reduced the percentage cover of corals in **(a)** exposed parts of the reef much more than in **(b)** sheltered parts of it.

experience intermediate levels of disturbance contain a rich mixture of species. Where disturbances are severe and frequent, communities include only *r*-selected species that complete their life cycles between catastrophes. Where disturbances are mild and rare, communities are dominated by long-lived *K*-selected species that competitively exclude other species from the community.

Major hydrodynamic disturbances to coral reefs, such as tsunamis and severe storms, have important impacts on coral reefs. Using oceanographic and engineering models, it is possible to predict the degree of dislodgement of benthic reef corals and, in this way, predict how coral shape and size indicate vulnerability to major disturbances. The use of these models is particularly important during times of climate change.

Several studies in diverse habitats have confirmed the predictions of the intermediate disturbance hypothesis. Colin R. Townsend and his colleagues studied the effects of disturbance at 54 stream sites in the Taieri River system in New Zealand. Disturbance occurs in these communities when water flow from heavy rains moves rocks, soil, and sand in the streambed, disrupting animal habitats. Townsend and his colleagues measured how much the substrate moved in different streambeds to develop an index of the intensity of disturbance. Their results indicate that species richness is highest in areas that experience intermediate levels of disturbance **(Figure 46.25)**.

Some ecologists have suggested that species-rich communities recover from disturbances more readily than less diverse communities. In the United States, David Tilman and his colleagues conducted large-scale experiments in midwestern grasslands. They examined relationships between species number and the ability of communities to recover from disturbance. Grassland plots with high species richness recover from drought faster than plots with fewer species.

Study Break

1. What did Connell's 30-year study of coral reefs illustrate about the ability of communities to reach a state of equilibrium?
2. What is the intermediate disturbance hypothesis? Describe one study that supports this hypothesis.
3. How does species richness affect the rate of recovery following a disturbance?

46.9 Succession

Ecosystems change over time, a process called **succession,** the change from one community type to another.

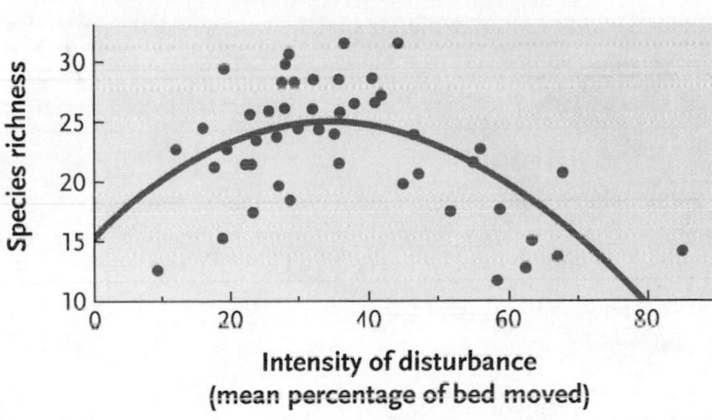

Figure 46.25
An observational study that supports the intermediate disturbance hypothesis. In the Taieri River system in New Zealand, species richness was highest in stream communities that experienced an intermediate level of disturbance.

46.9a Primary Succession: The First Steps

Primary succession begins when organisms first colonize habitats without soil, such as those created by erupting volcanoes and retreating glaciers **(Figure 46.26, p. 1166)**. Lichens are often among the very first colonists (see Chapter 24), deriving nutrients from rain and bare rock. They secrete mild acids that erode rock surfaces, initiating the slow development of soil, which is enriched by the organic material lichens produce. After lichens modify a site, mosses (see Chapter 25) colonize patches of soil and grow quickly.

As soil accumulates, hardy, opportunistic plants (grasses, ferns, and broad-leaved herbs) colonize the site from surrounding areas. Their roots break up rock, and when they die, their decaying remains enrich the soil. Detritivores and decomposers facilitate these processes. As the soil becomes deeper and richer, increased moisture and nutrients support bushes and, eventually, trees. Late successional stages are often dominated by *K*-selected species with woody trunks and branches that position leaves in sunlight and large root systems that acquire water and nutrients from soil.

In the classical view of ecological succession, long-lived species, which replace themselves over time, eventually dominate a community, and new species join it only rarely. This relatively stable, late successional stage is called a **climax community** because the dominant vegetation replaces itself and persists until an environmental disturbance eliminates it and allows other species to invade. Local climate and soil conditions, the surrounding communities where colonizing species originate, and chance events determine the species composition of climax communities. We now know that even climax communities change slowly in response to environmental fluctuations.

46.9b Secondary Succession: Changes after Destruction

Secondary succession occurs after existing vegetation is destroyed or disrupted by an environmental disturbance, such as a fire, a storm, or human activity. The presence of soil makes disturbed sites ripe for colonization and may contain numerous seeds that

Roger K. Burnard

1 The glacier has retreated about 8 m per year since 1794.

Roger K. Burnard

2 This site was covered with ice less than 10 years before this photo was taken. When a glacier retreats, a constant flow of melt water leaches minerals, especially nitrogen, from the newly exposed substrate.

Roger K. Burnard

3 Once lichens and mosses have established themselves, mountain avens (genus *Dryas*) grows on the nutrient-poor soil. This pioneer species benefits from the activity of mutualistic nitrogen-fixing bacteria, spreading rapidly over glacial till.

Roger K. Burnard

4 Within 20 years, shrubby willows (genus *Salix*), cottonwoods (genus *Populus*), and alders (genus *Alnus*) take hold in drainage channels. These species are also symbiotic with nitrogen-fixing microorganisms.

Roger K. Burnard

5 In time, young conifers, mostly hemlocks (genus *Tsuga*) and spruce (genus *Picea*), join the community.

Ed Degginger

6 After 80 to 100 years, dense forests of Sitka spruce (*Picea sichensis*) and western hemlock (*Tsuga heterophylla*) have crowded out the other species.

Figure 46.26
Primary succession following glacial retreat. The retreat of glaciers at Glacier Bay, Alaska, has allowed ecologists to document primary succession on newly exposed rocks and soil.

germinate after disturbance. Early stages of secondary succession proceed rapidly, but later stages parallel those of primary succession.

46.9c Climax Communities: The Ultimate Ecosystems until Something Changes

Similar climax communities can arise from several different successional sequences. Hardwood forests can also develop in sites that were once ponds. During **aquatic succession,** debris from rivers and runoff accumulates in a pond, filling it to its margins. Ponds are first transformed into swamps, inhabited by plants adapted to a semisolid substrate. As larger plants get established, their high transpiration rates dry the soil, allowing other plant species to colonize. Given enough time, the site may become a meadow or forest in which an area of moist, low-lying ground is the only remnant of the original pond.

Because several characteristics of communities can change during succession, ecologists try to document how patterns change. First, because *r*-selected species are short-lived and *K*-selected species are long-lived, species composition changes rapidly in the early stages and more slowly in later stages of succession. Second, species richness increases rapidly during early stages because new species join the community faster than resident species become extinct. In later stages, species richness stabilizes or may even decline. Third, in terrestrial communities receiving sufficient rainfall, the maximum height and total mass of the vegetation increase steadily as large species replace small ones, creating the complex structure of the climax community.

Because plants influence the physical environment below them, the community itself increasingly moderates its microclimate. The shade cast by a forest canopy helps retain soil moisture and reduce temperature fluctuations. The trunks and canopy also reduce wind speed. In contrast, the short vegetation in an early successional stage does not effectively shelter the space below it.

Although ecologists usually describe succession in terms of vegetation, animals can show similar patterns. As the vegetation shifts, new resources become available, and animal species replace each other over time. Herbivorous insects, often with strict food preferences, undergo succession along with their food plants. And as herbivores change, so do their predators, parasites, and parasitoids. In old-field succession in eastern North America, different vegetation stages harbour a changing assortment of bird species **(Figure 46.27).**

Differences in dispersal abilities (see *Dispersal*), maturation rates, and life spans among species are partly responsible for ecological succession. Early successional stages harbour many *r*-selected species because they produce numerous small seeds that colonize open habitats and grow quickly. Mature successional stages are dominated by *K*-selected species because they are long-lived. Nevertheless, coexisting populations inevitably affect one another. Although the role of population interactions in succession is generally acknowledged, ecologists debate the relative importance of processes that either facilitate or inhibit the turnover of species in a community.

46.9d Facilitation Hypothesis: One Species Makes Changes That Help Others

The facilitation hypothesis suggests that species modify local environment in ways that make it less suitable for themselves but more suitable for colonization by species typical of the next successional stage. When lichens first colonize bare rock, they produce a small quantity of soil that is required by mosses and grasses that grow there later. According to this hypothesis, changes in species composition are both orderly and predictable because the presence of each stage facilitates the success of the next one. Facilitation is important in primary succession, but it may not be the best model of interactions that influence secondary succession.

46.9e Inhibition Hypothesis: One Species Negatively Affects Others

The inhibition hypothesis suggests that new species are prevented from occupying a community by species that are already present. According to this hypothesis, succession is neither orderly nor predictable because each stage is dominated by the species that happened to have colonized the site first. Species replacements occur only when individuals of dominant species die of old age or when an environmental disturbance reduces their numbers. Eventually, long-lived species replace

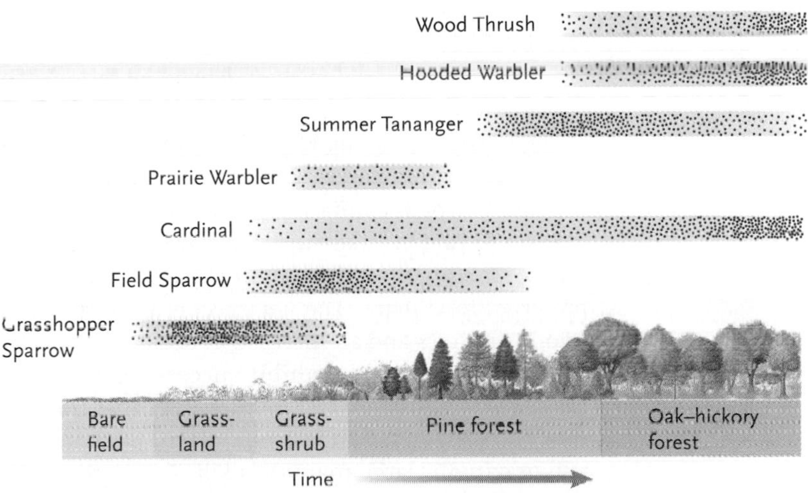

Figure 46.27
Succession in animals. Successional changes in bird species composition in an abandoned agricultural field in eastern North America parallel the changes in plant species composition. The residence times of several representative species are illustrated. The density of stippling inside each bar illustrates the density of each species through time.

short-lived species, but the precise species composition of a mature community is open to question. Inhibition appears to play a role in some secondary successions. The interactions among early successional species in an old field are highly competitive. Horseweed inhibits the growth of asters that follow them in succession by shading aster seedlings and releasing toxic substances from their roots. Experimental removal of horseweed enhances the growth of asters, confirming the inhibitory effect.

46.9f Tolerance Hypothesis: Species Tolerate One Another

The tolerance hypothesis asserts that succession proceeds because competitively superior species replace competitively inferior ones. According to this model, early-stage species neither facilitate nor inhibit the growth of later-stage species. Instead, as more species arrive at a site and resources become limiting, competition eliminates species that cannot harvest scarce resources successfully. In the Piedmont region of North America, young hardwood trees are more tolerant of shade than are young pine trees, and hardwoods gradually replace pines during succession. Thus, the climax community includes only strong competitors. Tolerance may explain the species composition of many transitional and mature communities.

At most sites, succession probably results from some combination of facilitation, inhibition, and tolerance, coupled with interspecific differences in dispersal, growth, and maturation rates. Moreover, within a community, the patchiness of abiotic factors strongly influences plant distributions and species composition. In deciduous forests of eastern North America, maples (*Acer* species) predominate on wet, low-lying ground, but oaks (*Quercus* species) are more abundant at higher and drier sites. Thus, a mature deciduous forest is often a mosaic of species and not a uniform stand of trees.

Disturbance and density-independent factors play important roles, in some cases speeding successional change. Moose (*Alces alces*) prefer to feed on deciduous shrubs in northern forests. This disturbance accelerates the rate at which conifers replace deciduous shrubs. On Isle Royale in Lake Superior, however, grazing by moose strongly affects balsam fir (*Abies balsamea*), their preferred food there. The net effect is a severe reduction in conifers and an increase in deciduous shrubs. Disturbance can also inhibit successional change, establishing a *disturbance climax* or **disclimax community.** In many grassland communities, periodic fires and grazing by large mammals kill seedlings of trees that would otherwise become established. Thus, disturbance prevents the succession from grassland to forest, and grassland persists as a disclimax community.

Animals such as moose can alter patterns of succession and vegetation in some communities, but the effect also extends to small mammals. Removal experiments involving kangaroo rats and plots of shrubland in the Chihuahuan Desert (southeastern Arizona) allowed J.H. Brown and E.J. Heske to demonstrate that these rodents were a "keystone guild." Kangaroo rats affect the plants in several ways. They are seed predators, and their burrowing activities disturb soils. Excluding kangaroo rats from experimental plots led to a threefold increase in the density of tall perennials and annual grasses **(Figure 46.28),** suggesting that by predation on seeds and burrowing, these rodents affected the vegetation in the experimental areas.

On a local scale, disturbances often destroy small patches of vegetation, returning them to an earlier successional stage. A hurricane, tornado, or ava-

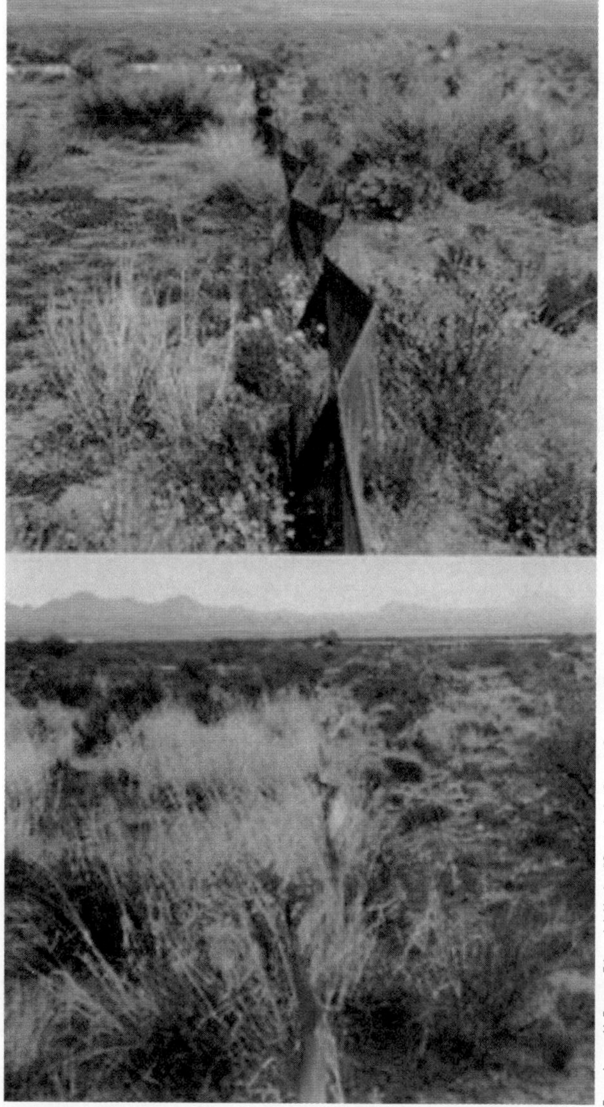

Figure 46.28
Predation and succession. Kangaroo rats (*Dipodomys*) were removed from the left sides of the fence, which excluded them from the plot on the left. The top photograph was taken 5 years after the removals and the bottom one 13 years after. A large-seeded annual (after 5 years) and tall grasses are present in the *Dipodomys*-free plots.

lanche may topple trees in a forest, creating small, sunny patches of open ground. Locally occurring *r*-selected species take advantage of newly available resources and quickly colonize the openings. These local patches then undergo succession that is out of step with the immediately surrounding forest. Thus, moderate disturbance, accompanied by succession in local patches, can increase species richness in many communities.

Study Break

1. What are the two types of succession? How do they differ?
2. What is a climax community? What determines the species composition of a climax community?
3. Identify and briefly describe the three hypotheses used to explain how succession proceeds.

46.10 Variations in Species Richness among Communities

Species richness often varies among communities according to a recognizable pattern. Two large-scale patterns of species richness—latitudinal trends and island patterns—have captured the attention of ecologists for more than a century.

46.10a Latitudinal Effects: From South to North

Ever since Darwin and Wallace travelled the globe (see Chapter 20), ecologists have recognized broad latitudinal trends in species richness. For many but not all plant and animal groups, species richness follows a latitudinal gradient, with the most species in the tropics and a steady decline in numbers toward the poles (**Figure 46.29**). Several general hypotheses may explain these striking patterns.

Some hypotheses propose historical explanations for the *origin* of high species richness in the tropics. The benign climate in tropical regions allows some tropical organisms to have more generations per year than their temperate counterparts. Small seasonal changes in temperature mean that tropical species may be less likely than temperate species to migrate from one habitat to another, reducing gene flow between geographically isolated populations (see Chapter 18). These factors may have fostered higher speciation rates in the tropics, accelerating the accumulation of species. Tropical communities may also have experienced severe disturbance less often than communities at higher latitudes, where periodic glaciations have caused repeated extinctions. Thus, new species may have accumulated in the tropics over longer periods of time.

Other hypotheses focus on ecological explanations for the *maintenance* of high species richness in the tropics. Some resources are more abundant, predictable, and diverse in tropical communities. Tropical regions experience more intense sunlight, warmer temperatures in most months, and higher annual rainfall than temperate and polar regions (see Chapter 3). These factors provide a long and predictable growing season for the lush tropical vegetation, which supports a rich assemblage of herbivores, and through them many carnivores and parasites. Furthermore, the abundance, predictability, and year-round availability of resources allow some tropical animals to have specialized diets. Tropical forests support many species of fruit-eating bats and birds, which could not survive in temperate forests where fruits are not available year-round.

Species richness may be a self-reinforcing phenomenon in tropical communities. Complex webs of population interactions and interdependency have coevolved in relatively stable and predictable tropical climates. Predator–prey, competitive, and symbiotic interactions may prevent individual species from dominating communities and reducing species richness.

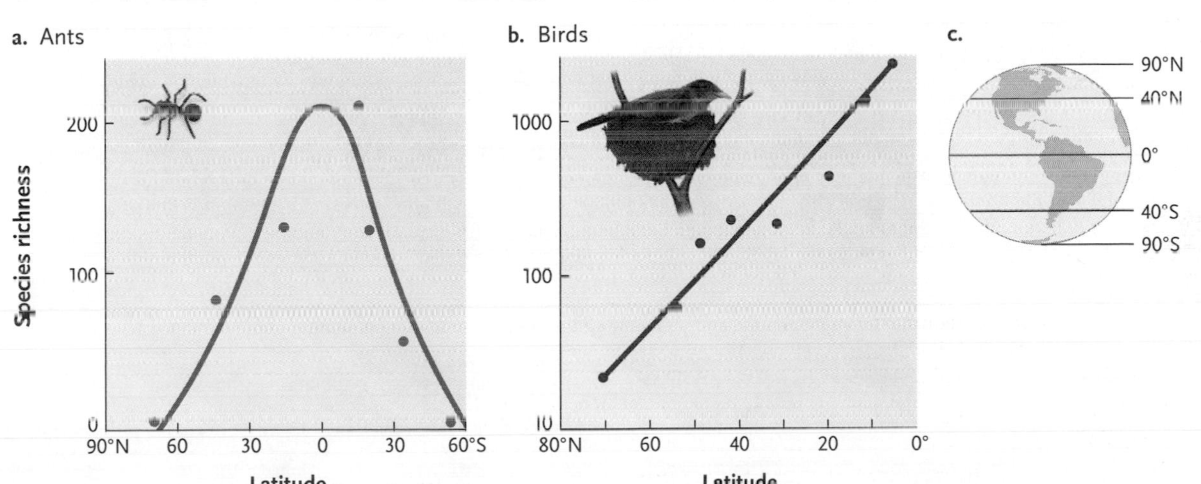

Figure 46.29
Latitudinal trends in species richness.
The species richness of many animals and plants varies with latitude as illustrated here for **(a)** ants in North, Central, and South America and **(b)** birds in North and Central America. The species richness data used in **(c)** are based on records of where these birds breed.

Dispersal

Organisms often show astonishing dispersal abilities. In some cases, long-distance dispersal by plants in the Arctic is effected by the combination of strong winds and extensive expanses of ice and snow. The Svalbard Archipelago **(Figure 1)** is an interesting location for the study of plant dispersal. The islands were glaciated 20 000 years ago, and it is likely that plants did not survive this condition. The fossil record indicates that plants have been present on Svalbard for fewer than 10 000 years, although between 9500 and 4000 years ago, the climate was warmer there (by 1° to 2°C) than it is now.

Using DNA fingerprinting, I.G. Alsos and eight colleagues demonstrated that plant colonization of the Svalbard Archipelago has involved the arrival of plants from all possible adjacent regions **(Figure 2).** In eight of nine species, genetic evidence indicates

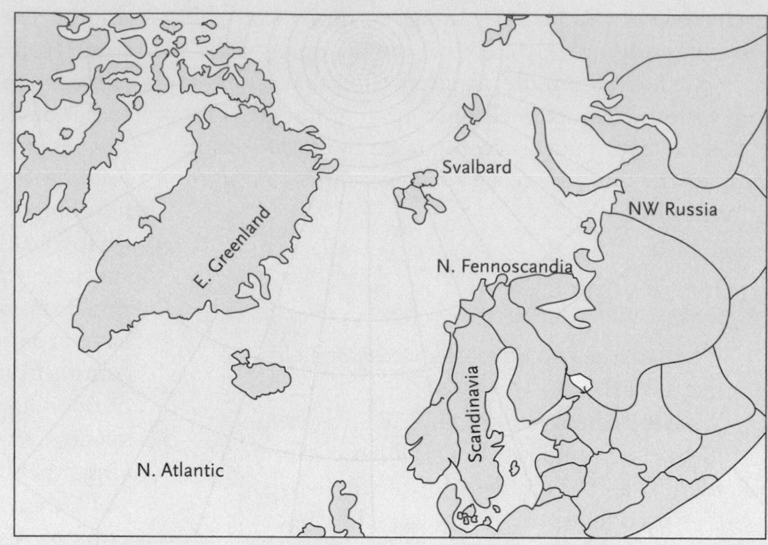

Figure 1
The location of the Svalbard Archipelago.

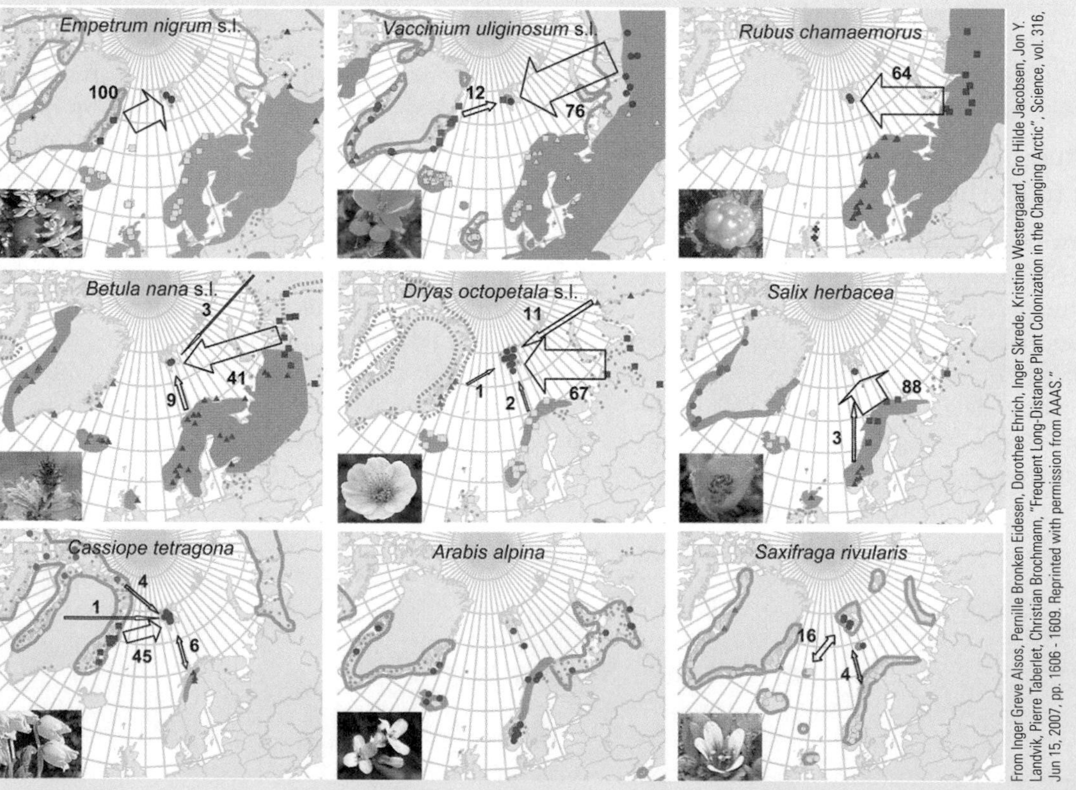

Figure 2
Source regions for Svalbard plants. Shading shows the geographic distribution of nine species of plants, and dotted lines show the distributions of related species. The main genetic groups are represented by colours, although some populations (*) could not be assigned to a genetic group. Arrows identify source populations, and the numbers indicate the percentage allocation by source region.

multiple colonization events. Plants can obviously disperse without assistance from animals.

In other situations, plants disperse with the assistance of animals through pollination and seeds. Using *Prunus maheleb*, the mahaleb cherry **(Figure 3),** and genetic techniques, P. Jordano and two colleagues examined the role of birds and mammals in pollination and dispersing seeds. Small passerine birds dispersed seeds short distances (most < 50 m) from the parent tree, whereas medium-sized birds (*Corvus corone* and *Turdus viscivorus*) usually dispersed seeds over longer distances (>110 m). Mammals (usually *Martes foina* and *Vulpes vulpes* but sometimes *Meles meles*) dispersed seeds ~500 m. The genetic work also provided an indication of the extent of gene flow during pollination.

It is obvious that plants capable of self-fertilization or vegetative reproduction can be more effective colonists than those depending on outcrossing, especially with the help of animal pollinators.

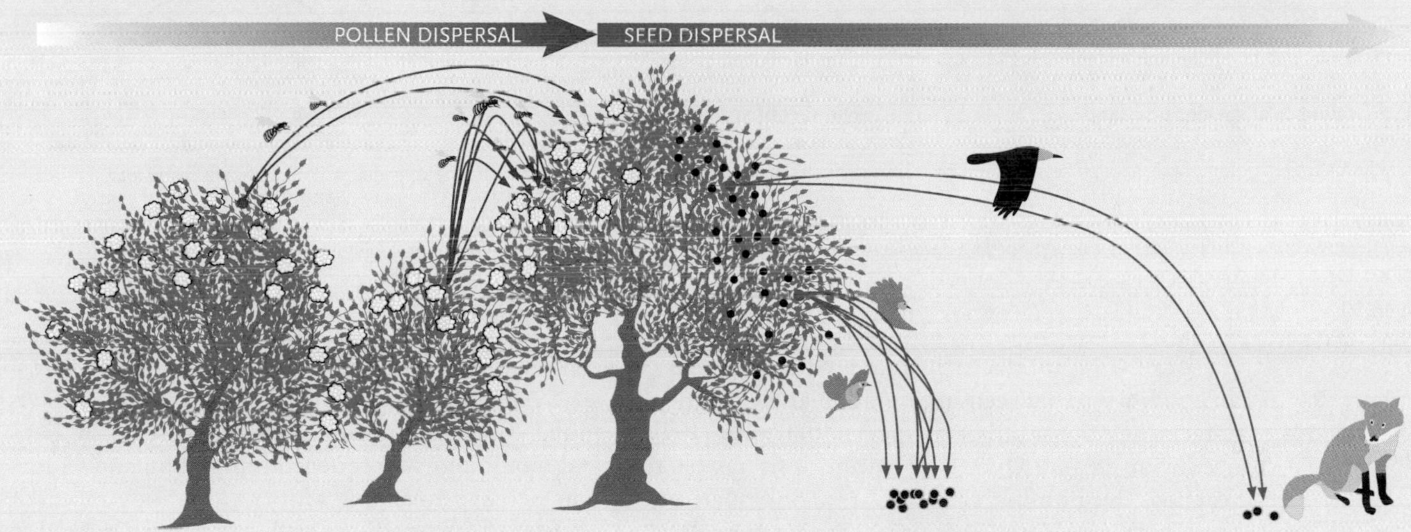

Figure 3
The movement of pollen and seeds from mahaleb cherry trees. Gene flow occurs through pollination and seed dispersal (see Chapter 18).

46.10b Equilibrium Theory of Island Biogeography

In 1883, a volcanic eruption virtually obliterated the island of Krakatoa. Within 50 years, what was left of Krakatoa had been recolonized by plants and animals, providing biologists with a clear demonstration of the dispersal powers of many living species. The colonization of islands and the establishment of biological communities there have provided many natural experiments that have advanced our knowledge of ecology and populations. Islands are attractive sites for experiments because although the species richness of communities may be stable over time, the species composition is often in flux as new species join a community and others drop out. In the 1960s, Robert MacArthur and Edward O. Wilson used islands as model systems to address the question of why communities vary in species richness. Islands provide natural laboratories for studying ecological phenomena, just as they do for evolution (see Chapter 3). Island communities can be small, with well-defined boundaries, and are isolated from surrounding communities.

MacArthur and Wilson developed the equilibrium theory of island biogeography to explain variations in species richness on islands of different size and different levels of isolation from other landmasses. They hypothesized that the number of species on any island was governed by give and take between two processes: the immigration of new species to an island and the extinction of species already there **(Figure 46.30, p. 1172).**

According to their model, the mainland harbours a *species pool* from which species immigrate to offshore islands. Seeds and small arthropods are carried by wind or floating debris. Animals such as birds arrive under their own power. When only a few species are on an island, the rate at which new species immigrate to the island is high. But as more species inhabit the island over time, the immigration rate declines because fewer species in the mainland pool can still arrive on the island as *new* colonizers (see Chapter 3). Once some species arrive on an island, their populations grow and persist for variable lengths of time. Other immigrants die without reproducing. As the number of species on an island increases, the rate of species extinction also rises. Extinction rates increase over time partly because more species can go extinct there. In addition, as the number of species on the island increases, competition and predator–prey interactions can reduce the population sizes of some species and drive them to extinction.

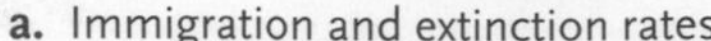

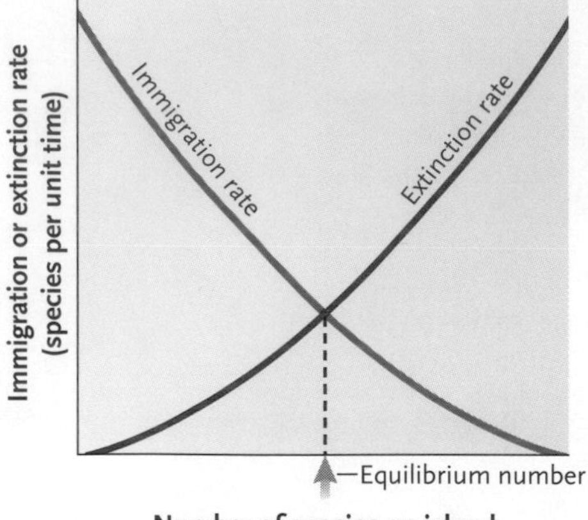

The number of species on an island at equilibrium (indicated by the arrow) is determined by the rate at which new species immigrate and the rate at which species already on the island go extinct.

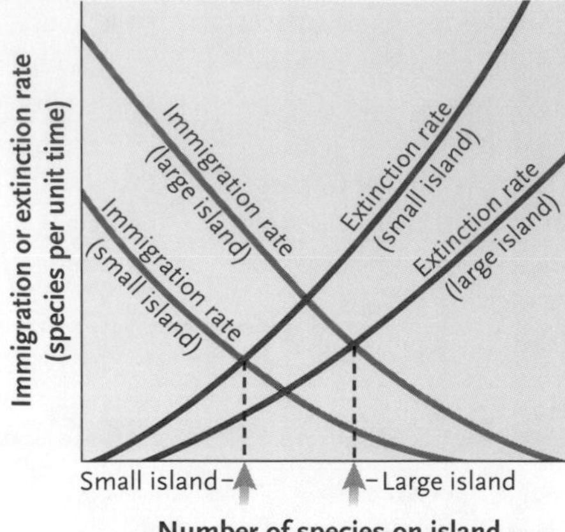

Immigration rates are higher and extinction rates lower on large islands than on small islands. Thus, at equilibrium, large islands have more species.

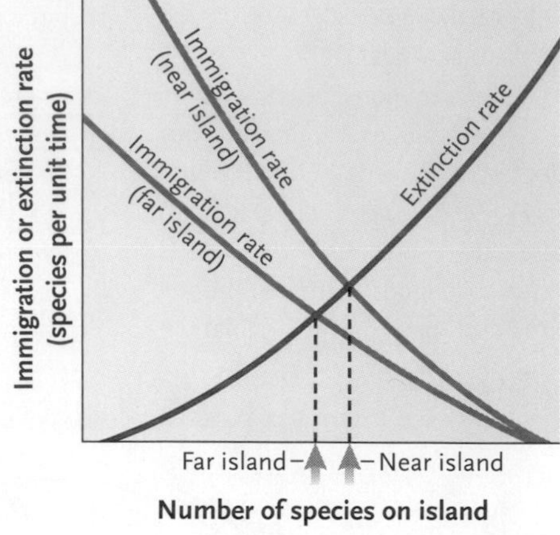

Organisms leaving the mainland locate nearby islands more easily than distant islands, causing higher immigration rates on near islands. Thus, near islands support more species than far ones.

Figure 46.30
Predictions of the theory of island biogeography. The x axes of the graphs are time.

According to MacArthur and Wilson's theory, an equilibrium between immigration and extinction determines the number of species that ultimately occupy an island. Once that equilibrium has been reached, the number of species remains relatively constant because one species already on the island becomes extinct in about the same time it takes a new one to arrive. The model does not specify which species immigrate or which ones already on the island become extinct. It simply predicts that the number of species on the island is in equilibrium, although species composition is not. The ongoing processes of immigration and extinction establish a constant turnover in the roster of species that live on any island.

The MacArthur–Wilson model also explains why some islands harbour more species than others. Large islands have higher immigration rates than small islands because they are larger targets for dispersing organisms. Moreover, large islands have lower extinction rates because they can support larger populations and provide a greater range of habitats and resources. At equilibrium, large islands have more species than small islands do (see Figure 46.30b). Islands near the mainland have higher immigration rates than distant islands because dispersing organisms are more likely to arrive at islands close to their point of departure. Distance does not affect extinction rates, so, at equilibrium, nearby islands have more species than distant islands (see Figure 46.30c).

The equilibrium theory's predictions about the effects of area and distance are generally supported by data on plants and animals **(Figure 46.31).** Experimental work has verified some of its basic assumptions. Amy Schoener found that more than 200 species of marine organisms colonized tiny artificial "islands" (plastic kitchen scrubbers) within 30 days after she placed them in a Bahaman lagoon. Her research also confirmed that immigration rate increases with island size. Daniel Simberloff and Edward O. Wilson exterminated insects on tiny islands in the Florida Keys and monitored subsequent immigration and extinction (see *Experimenting with Islands*). Their research confirmed the equilibrium theory's predictions that an island's size and distance from the mainland influence how many species will occupy it.

The equilibrial view of species richness can also apply to mainland communities that exist as islands in a metaphorical sea of dissimilar habitat. Lakes are "islands" in a "sea" of dry land, and mountaintops are habitat "islands" in a "sea" of low terrain. Species richness in these communities is partly governed by the immigration of new species from distant sources and the extinction of species already present. As human activities disrupt environments across the globe, undisturbed sites function as islandlike refuges for threatened and endangered species. Conservation biologists apply the general lessons of MacArthur and Wilson's theory to the design of nature preserves (see Chapter 48).

The study of community ecology promises to keep biologists busy for some time to come.

Study Break

1. How does species richness change with increasing latitude?
2. In the island biogeography model proposed by MacArthur and Wilson, what processes govern the number of species on an island? What happens to the number of species once equilibrium is reached?
3. What effect do island size and distance from the mainland have on immigration and extinction of colonizing species?

People Behind Biology

Bridget J. Stutchbury

Bridget Stutchbury studies the behaviour and ecology of songbirds, working at sites in eastern North America (United States and Canada), as well as sites in the Neotropics. One aspect of her research is documenting the reproductive behaviour of birds. Although songbirds were thought to be monogamous over at least a breeding season, using genetic techniques, Dr. Stutchbury and others are discovering that both males and females often mate with a bird that is not their mate. This behaviour is called extrapair copulation if it is just mating or extrapair fertilization when young result from the matings.

Using radio tracking to follow individual birds combined with DNA fingerprinting, Dr. Stutchbury and her colleagues were able to look at the movement patterns of Acadian Flycatchers (*Empidonax virescens*) and determine how far males and females travelled to meet their extrapair partners. Males travelled 50 to 1500 m from their nests to meet partners.

Work with other species such as Hooded Warblers (*Wilsonia citrina*) demonstrated that when these birds lived in small forest fragments, their mating behaviours were disturbed compared with the behaviours of those nesting in larger tracts of forest.

Overall, her research has demonstrated that whereas some songbirds in eastern United States and Canada depend on corridors connecting habitat fragments, other species cross open habitats to use different patches of forest.

In 2007, her book *Silence of the Songbirds* reported declines in numbers of migrating songbirds and raised concerns about their future.

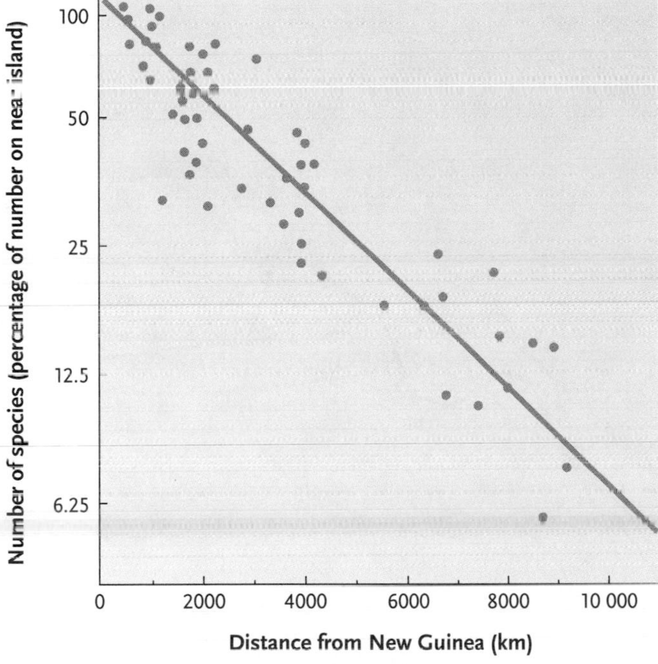

The number of lowland bird species on islands of the South Pacific declines with the islands' distance from the species source, the large island of New Guinea. Data in this graph were corrected for differences in the sizes of the islands. The number of bird species on each island is expressed as a percentage of the number of bird species on an island of equivalent size close to New Guinea.

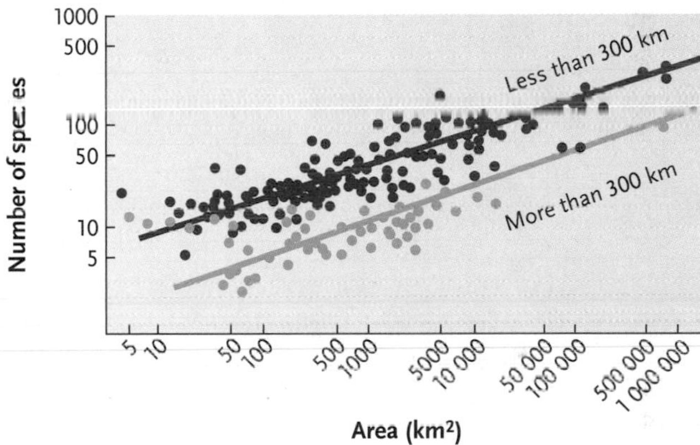

The number of bird species on tropical and subtropical islands throughout the world increases dramatically with island area. The data for islands near to a source and islands far from a mainland source are presented separately to minimize the effect of distance. Notice that the "distance effect" reduces the number of bird species on islands that are more than 300 km from a mainland source.

Figure 46.31

Factors that influence bird species richness on islands. **(a)** Evidence that fewer bird species colonize islands that are distant from the mainland source. **(b)** Evidence that more bird species colonize large islands than small ones.

Experimenting with Islands

Shortly after Robert MacArthur and Edward O. Wilson published the equilibrium theory of island biogeography in the 1960s, Wilson and Daniel Simberloff, one of Wilson's graduate students at Harvard University, undertook an ambitious experiment in community ecology. Simberloff reasoned that the best way to test the theory's predictions was to monitor immigration and extinction on barren islands.

Simberloff and Wilson devised a system for removing all the animals from individual red mangrove trees in the Florida Keys. The trees, with canopies that spread from 11 to 18 m in diameter, grow in shallow water and are isolated from their neighbours. Thus, each tree is an island that harbours an arthropod community. The species pool on the Florida mainland includes about 1000 species of arthropods, but each mangrove island contains no more than 40 species at one time.

After cataloguing the species on each island, Simberloff and Wilson hired an extermination company to erect large tents over each mangrove island and fumigate them to eliminate all arthropods on them **(Figure 1).** The exterminators used methylbromide, a pesticide that does not harm trees or leave any residue. The tents were then removed.

Simberloff then monitored both the immigration of arthropods to the islands and the extinction of species that became established on them. He surveyed four islands regularly for two years and at intervals thereafter.

The results of this experiment confirm several predictions of MacArthur and Wilson's theory **(Figure 2).** Arthropods rapidly recolonized the islands, and within eight or nine months, the number of species living on each island had reached an equilibrium that was close to the original species number. The island nearest the mainland had more species than the most distant island. However, immigration and extinction were rapid, and Simberloff and Wilson suspected that some species went extinct even before they had noted their presence. The researchers also discovered that three years after the experimental treatments, the species composition of the islands was still changing constantly and did not remotely resemble the species composition on the islands before they were defaunated.

Simberloff and Wilson's research was a landmark study in ecology because it tested the predictions of an important theory using a field experiment. Although such efforts are now almost routine in ecological studies, this project was one of the first to demonstrate that large-scale experimental manipulations of natural systems are feasible and that they often produce clear results.

Daniel Simberloff, University of Tennessee

Daniel Simberloff, University of Tennessee

Figure 1
After cataloguing the arthropods, Simberloff and Wilson hired an extermination company to eliminate all living arthropods.

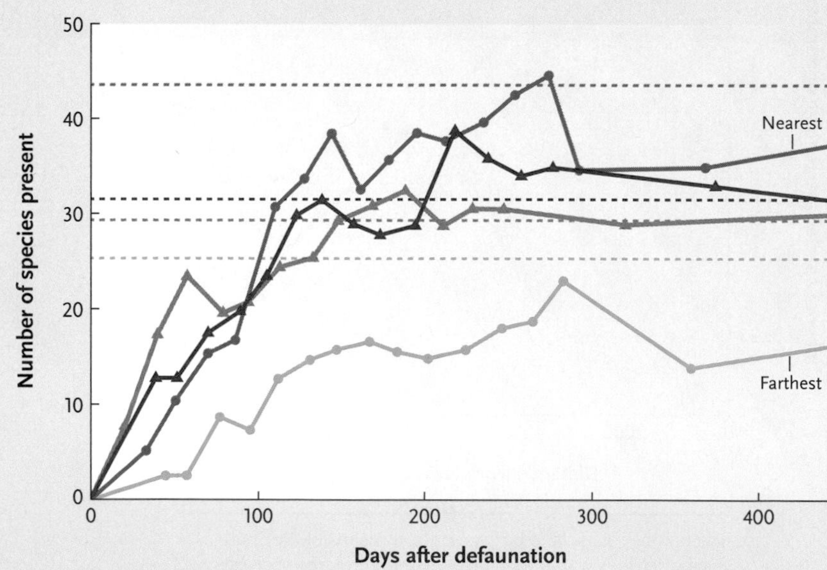

Figure 2
On three of four islands, species richness slowly returned to the predefaunation level (indicated by colour-coded dotted lines). The most distant island had not reached its predefaunation species richness after two years.

Unanswered Questions

If solar slugs can take up chloroplasts and/or nematocysts and control them, could this be possible in chordates? What are the essential conditions? What are the limiting ones?

Review

Go to CENGAGENOW™ at http://hed.nelson.com/to access quizzing, animations, exercises, articles, and personalized homework help.

46.1 Interspecific Interactions

- Coevolution involves genetically based, reciprocal adaptations in two or more interacting species. Coevolution is not restricted to two species but often involves complex interactions among several species in a community.

46.2 Getting Food

- Predators eat animal prey, whereas herbivores eat plants. Predators and herbivores are animals with characteristics allowing them to feed efficiently. Predation and herbivory are the most conspicuous relationships in ecological communities.
- A koala is a specialist because it eats the leaves of only a few of the available species of *Eucalyptus*. Specialists tend to eat only a few types of food, whereas generalists take a broader diet.
- Optimal foraging theory predicts that an animal's diet is a compromise between the costs and the benefits associated with different types of food. Costs include the time and energy it takes to pursue, capture, and consume a particular kind of food. Benefits are the energy that the food provides.

46.3 Defence

- Size: the large size of elephants means that they have few natural predators.
- Eternal vigilance: meerkats are constantly on the lookout for potential predators.
- Avoiding detection: caterpillars that look like bird droppings are not recognized as edible.
- Counterattack: the sting of a bee or a scorpion, as well as the spines of porcupines and other mammals.
- Chemical defence: skunks spray a noxious chemical at potential predators.
- Warnings: black and white coloration of skunks and orange and black coloration of monarch butterflies.
- Mimicry: the harmless drone fly mimics the coloration and behaviour of the stinging bee or wasp.
- Animals using chemical defences either synthesize the chemicals themselves or sequester them from other sources. This can include plants that the organism eats.
- Aposematic displays teach would-be predators to avoid the signaller.
- Batesian mimicry occurs when an edible or harmless species mimics an inedible or a poisonous one. In Müllerian mimicry, two or more unpalatable or poisonous species have a similar appearance.

46.4 Competition

- Intraspecific competition can occur between two different species. Two types of competition are interference and exploitative. The competitive exclusion principle states that two or more species cannot coexist indefinitely if both rely on the same limiting resources and exploit them in the same way. One species will be able to harvest the available resources better and eventually outcompete the other species.
- A population's ecological niche is defined as the resources it uses and the environmental conditions it requires over its lifetime. A fundamental niche, larger than a realized niche, includes all conditions and resources a population can tolerate. A realized niche is the range of conditions and resources that a population actually encounters in nature.
- Resource partitioning occurs when sympatric species use different resources or the same resources in different ways. Plants may position their root systems at different levels, which avoids competition for water and nutrients.
- Character displacement results in sympatric species that differ in morphology and use different resources even though they would not do so in allopatric situations. An example of character displacement is the honey-eaters of Australia.

46.5 The Nature of Ecological Communities

Type of Interaction	Effect on Species Involved	Example
Commensalism	One species benefits; the other is unaffected (+/0)	Egrets and the large grazers that flush insects out of grasses during feeding
Mutualism	Both species benefit (+/+)	Bull's horn acacia tree and a species of small ants
Parasitism	One species benefits (parasite); the other is harmed (host) (+/−)	Ectoparasites such as mosquitoes and leeches and their mammalian hosts

- Two hypotheses about ecological communities have been developed by ecologists. The interactive hypothesis predicts that mature communities are at equilibrium and, if disturbed, will return to the predisturbed state. The individualistic hypothesis predicts that communities do not achieve equilibrium but rather are in a steady state of flux in response to disturbance and environmental change.
- Ecotones are generally species rich because they contain species from both communities, as well as species that occur only in transition zones.

46.6 Community Characteristics

- Indices allow population biologists to objectively compare the diversity of communities. Shannon's indices provide a measure of diversity (H') and evenness (E_H).
- Alpha (α) diversity is the number of species living in a single community. Beta (β) diversity is the number of species living in a collection of communities.
- Herbivores are primary consumers and form the second trophic level. Omnivores can be primary, secondary, and tertiary consumers (second, third, and fourth trophic levels, respectively) in a single meal.
- Generally, communities that support complex food webs are more stable. The disappearance of one or even two species does not have a major impact on the food web and thus community structure.

46.7 Effects of Population Interactions on Community Structure

- Species distribution and resource use in *K*-selected species are profoundly affected by competition. However, competition seems to have little effect on the community structure of *r*-selected species.
- Predation and herbivory can increase and/or decrease species richness, depending on the circumstances. Species richness can increase if a predator eliminates a strong competitor, allowing other organisms to exploit the available resources, for example, predatory sea stars reducing populations of mussels. Species richness can decrease when a predator eats less abundant species, further reducing their numbers.
- A keystone species has a much greater effect on the community than its numbers might suggest. Only a few individuals can have a profound impact on community structure.

46.8 Effects of Disturbance on Community Characteristics

- A community may never attain equilibrium because of disturbances such as cyclones, mortality caused by internal processes, and the recruitment of new colonies.
- The intermediate disturbance hypothesis states that species richness is greatest in communities experiencing fairly frequent disturbances of moderate intensity. Data gathered about a river system in New Zealand revealed that areas with moderate disturbance (e.g., moved rocks, soil, and sand in the streambed) had the highest species diversity.
- Generally, communities with a higher species richness recover from disturbance much more quickly than those with a low species richness.

46.9 Succession

- Primary succession begins when organisms first colonize habitats without soil, whereas secondary succession occurs after existing vegetation is destroyed or disrupted by an environmental disturbance.
- A climax community is a late successional stage that can be found in both primary and secondary succession. Climax communities are dominated by a few species that replace themselves and persist until a disturbance eliminates them. Species composition of a climax community is determined by local climate and soil conditions, surrounding vegetation, and chance events.
- The facilitation hypothesis holds that species modify the environment in a way that makes it less suitable for themselves but more suitable for those species that follow them in succession. The inhibition hypothesis contends that species currently occupying a successional stage prevent new species from occupying the same community. The tolerance hypothesis holds that early-stage species neither facilitate nor inhibit the growth of new species. Instead, succession proceeds because new species are able to outcompete and replace early-stage species.

46.10 Variance in Species Richness among Communities

- Species richness generally decreases with increasing latitude.
- The numbers of species on an island is governed by immigration of new species and extinction of species already there. Once equilibrium between immigration and extinction is reached, the number of species on an island remains relatively constant. As one species goes extinct, it is replaced by a newly arrived immigrant species.
- Large islands have higher immigration rates and lower extinction rates than small islands. Islands near the mainland have higher immigration rates than distant islands. Distance does not affect extinction rates. As a result, at equilibrium, near islands have more species than far islands.

Questions

Self-Test Questions

1. According to optimal foraging theory, predators
   a. always eat the largest prey possible.
   b. always eat the prey that are easiest to catch.
   c. choose prey based on the costs of consuming it compared to the energy it provides.
   d. eat plants when animal prey are scarce.
   e. have coevolved mechanisms to overcome prey defences.
2. Use of the same limiting resource by two species is called
   a. brood parasitism.
   b. interference competition.
   c. exploitative competition.
   d. mutualism.
   e. optimal foraging.
3. The range of resources that a population of one species can possibly use is called
   a. its fundamental niche.
   b. its realized niche.
   c. character displacement.
   d. resource partitioning.
   e. its relative abundance.
4. Differences in molar (tooth) structure of sympatric mammals may reflect
   a. predation.
   b. character displacement.
   c. mimicry.
   d. interference competition.
   e. cryptic coloration.
5. Bacteria that live in the human intestine assist human digestion and eat nutrients the human consumed. This relationship might best be described as
   a. commensalism.
   b. mutualism.
   c. endoparasitism.
   d. ectoparasitism.
   e. predation.

6. In the table below, the letters refer to five communities, and the numbers indicate how many individuals were recorded for each of five species. Which community has the highest species diversity?

	Species 1	Species 2	Species 3	Species 4	Species 5
a	90	10	0	0	0
b	80	10	10	0	0
c	25	25	25	25	0
d	2	4	6	8	80
e	20	20	20	20	20

7. A keystone species
   a. is usually a primary producer.
   b. has a critically important role in determining the species composition of its community.
   c. is always a predator.
   d. usually reduces the species diversity in a community.
   e. usually exhibits aposematic coloration.
8. Species richness can be highest in communities where disturbances are
   a. very frequent and severe.
   b. very frequent and of moderate intensity.
   c. very rare and severe.
   d. of intermediate frequency and moderate intensity.
   e. very rare frequency and mild.
9. The change in the species composition of a community from bare and lifeless rock to climax vegetation is called
   a. disturbance.
   b. competition.
   c. secondary succession.
   d. primary succession.
   e. facilitation.
10. The equilibrium theory of island biogeography predicts that the number of species found on an island
    a. increases steadily until it equals the number in the mainland species pool.
    b. is greater on large islands than on small ones.
    c. is smaller on islands near the mainland than on distant islands.
    d. can never reach an equilibrium number.
    e. is greater for islands near the equator than for islands near the poles.

Questions for Discussion

1. Many landscapes dominated by agricultural activities also have patches of forest of various sizes. What is the minimum amount of habitat required by different species? Focus on 10 species—5 animals and 5 plants. For each species, can you estimate minimum viable population?
2. Using the terms and concepts introduced in this chapter, describe the interactions that humans have with 10 other species. Try to choose at least eight species we do not eat.
3. After reading about the two potential biases in the scientific literature on competition, describe how future studies of competition might avoid such biases.

Among the fastest growing ecosystem in the world—shopping malls and residential areas sprawl in the north part of London, Ontario.

M.B. Fenton

47 Ecosystems

Study Plan

Why It Matters

As shown in the chapter opening photograph, the most rapidly growing habitat on the planet is urban ecosystems. They are replacing existing habitats at an astonishing rate partly because of growth in populations and in economies. The system portrayed in the photograph is low-density housing with services (water and electricity), but in many parts of the world, housing expansions are high density, with few, if any, services. Apart from humans and our domesticated plant and animal species, what components of the original flora and fauna persist? Walk around your neighbourhood and check it out.

How does the urban ecosystem differ from what was there before? In what ways does it differ? Think of runoff from rain and snow, of the heat-absorbing and reflecting properties of buildings, concrete, and asphalt. What are the effects of gardeners and landscapers, however well meaning? The urban ecosystem offers people in general, and biologists in particular, many opportunities for research and study. We must determine what changes we can effect in the construction and design of neighbourhoods to maximize their compatibility with native organisms. How can we make urban neighbourhoods more useful to migrating songbirds?

Archaeological evidence indicates that urban sprawl occurred around 6000 years before present around the site of Tell Brak in what is now northern Syria. Then the "city" that stood at Tell Brak occupied about 55 ha when other contemporary settlements rarely exceeded 3 ha and the largest of its neighbours was just 15 ha. There is evidence of spatial separation between subcommunities at Tell Brak, where neighbourhoods were divided by walls and limited points of access.

Urban sprawl may not be new, but the current scale makes it a frontier for action to achieve conservation of biodiversity. The purpose of this chapter is to explore some aspects of ecosystems and introduce them as objects of biological study.

47.1 Energy Flow and Ecosystem Energetics

Ecosystems receive a steady input of energy from an external source, usually the Sun. Energy flows through an ecosystem, but, as dictated by the laws of thermodynamics, much of that energy is lost without being used by organisms. In contrast, materials cycle between living and nonliving reservoirs, both locally and on a global scale. The flow of energy through and the cycling of materials around an ecosystem make resident organisms highly dependent on one another and on their physical surroundings.

Food webs define the pathways by which energy and nutrients move through an ecosystem's biotic components (see Chapter 3). In most ecosystems, nutrients and energy move simultaneously through a grazing food web and a detrital *food web* **(Figure 47.1).** The grazing food web includes the producer, herbivore, and secondary consumer trophic levels. The detrital food web includes detritivores and decomposers. Because detritivores and decomposers subsist on the remains and waste products of organisms at every trophic level, the two food webs are closely interconnected. Detritivores also contribute to the grazing food web when carnivores eat them.

All organisms in a particular trophic level are the same number of energy transfers from the ecosystem's ultimate energy source. Photosynthetic plants

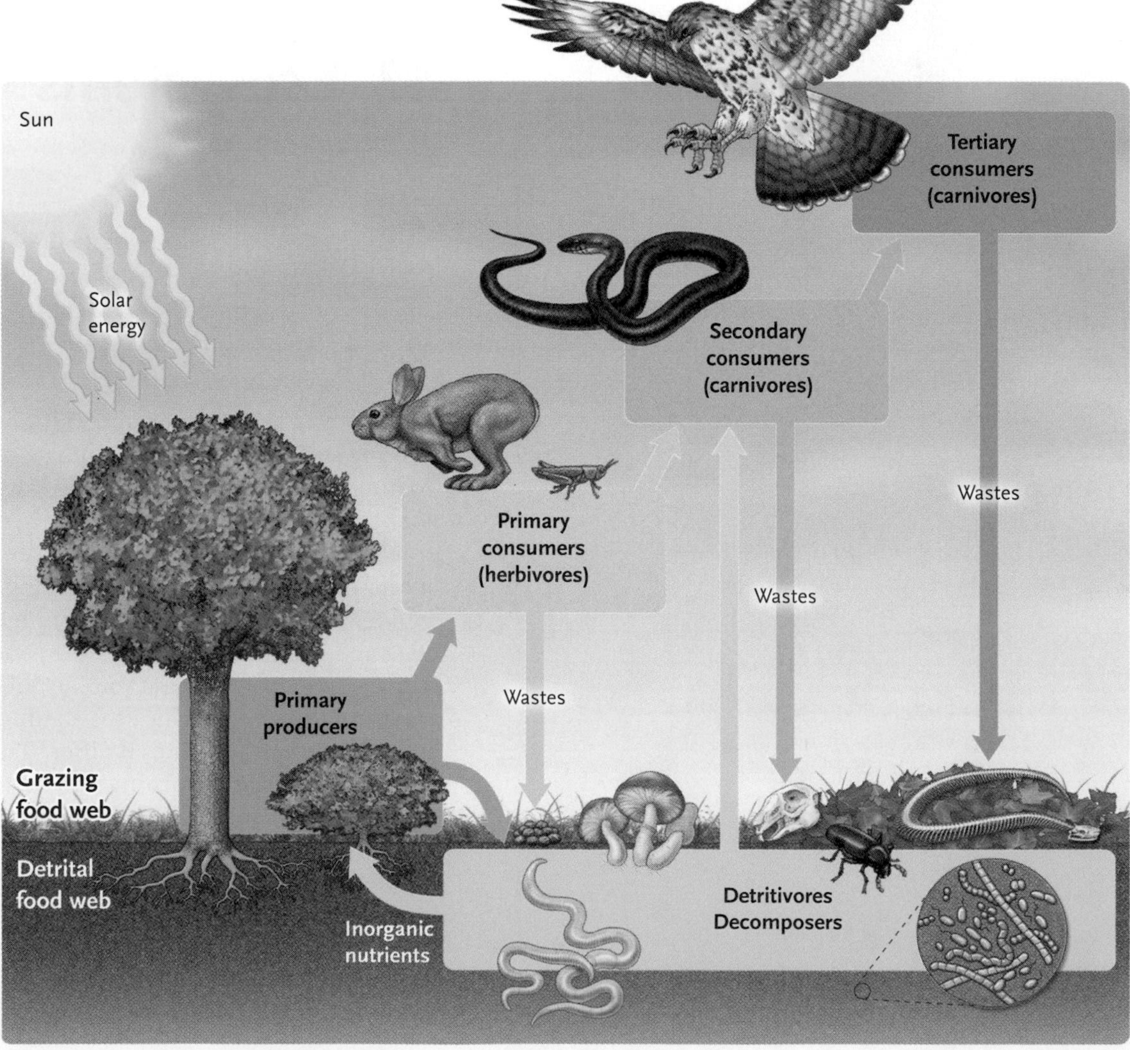

Figure 47.1
Grazing and detrital food webs. Energy and nutrients move through two parallel food webs in most ecosystems. The grazing food web includes producers, herbivores, and carnivores. The detrital food web includes detritivores and decomposers. Each box in this diagram represents many species, and each arrow represents many arrows.

are one energy transfer removed from sunlight, herbivores (primary consumers) are two, secondary consumers are three, and tertiary consumers are four.

47.1a Primary Productivity: Fixing Carbon

Virtually all life on Earth depends on the input of solar energy. Every minute of every day, Earth's atmosphere intercepts roughly 80 kJ (kilojoules) of energy per square metre (see Chapter 1). About half of that energy is absorbed, scattered, or reflected by gases, dust, water vapour, and clouds before it reaches the planet's surface (see Chapter 3). Most energy reaching the surface falls on bodies of water or bare ground, where it is absorbed as heat or reflected back into the atmosphere. Reflected energy warms the atmosphere. Only a small percentage contacts primary producers, and most of that energy evaporates water, driving transpiration in plants (see Chapter 7).

Ultimately, photosynthesis converts less than 1% of the solar energy arriving at Earth's surface into chemical energy. But primary producers still capture enough energy to produce an average of several kilograms of dry plant material per square metre per year. On a global scale, they produce more than 150 billion tonnes of new biological material annually. Some of the solar energy that producers convert into chemical energy is transferred to consumers at higher trophic levels.

The rate at which producers convert solar energy into chemical energy is an ecosystem's **gross primary productivity.** But like other organisms, producers use energy for their own maintenance functions. After deducting energy used for these functions (see Chapter 6), whatever chemical energy remains is the ecosystem's **net primary productivity.** In most ecosystems, net primary productivity is 50 to 90% of gross primary productivity. In other words, producers use between 10 and 50% of the energy they capture for their own respiration.

Ecologists usually measure primary productivity in units of energy captured ($kJ \cdot m^{-2} \cdot yr^{-1}$) or in units of biomass created ($kg \cdot m^{-2} \cdot yr^{-1}$). **Biomass** is the dry weight of biological material per unit area or volume of habitat. (We measure biomass as the *dry* weight of organisms because their water content, which fluctuates with water uptake or loss, has no energetic or nutritional value.) Do not confuse an ecosystem's productivity with its **standing crop biomass,** the total dry weight of plants present at a given time. Net primary productivity is the *rate* at which the standing crop produces *new* biomass (see Chapter 7).

Energy captured by plants is stored in biological molecules, mostly carbohydrates, lipids, and proteins. Ecologists can convert units of biomass into units of energy or vice versa as long as they know how much carbohydrate, protein, and lipid a sample of biological material contains. For reference, 1 g of carbohydrate and 1 g of protein each contains about 17.5 kJ of energy. Thus, net primary productivity indexes the rate at which producers accumulate energy as well as the rate at which new biomass is added to an ecosystem. Ecologists measure changes in biomass to estimate productivity because it is far easier to measure biomass than energy content. New biomass takes several forms, including

- growth of existing producers,
- creation of new producers by reproduction, and
- storage of energy as carbohydrates.

Because herbivores eat all three forms of new biomass, net primary productivity also measures how much new energy is available for primary consumers.

The potential rate of photosynthesis in any ecosystem is proportional to the intensity and duration of sunlight, which varies geographically and seasonally (see Chapters 3, 6, and 7). Sunlight is most intense and day length is least variable near the equator. In contrast, the intensity of sunlight is weakest and day length is most variable near the poles. This means that producers at the equator can photosynthesize nearly 12 hours a day, every day of the year, whereas near the poles, photosynthesis is virtually impossible during the long, dark winter. In summer, however, photosynthesis occurs virtually around the clock.

Sunlight is not the only factor influencing the rate of primary productivity. Temperature and availability of water and nutrients also affect this rate. Many of the world's deserts receive plenty of sunshine but have low rates of productivity because water is in short supply and the soil is poor in nutrients. Mean annual primary productivity varies greatly on a global scale **(Figure 47.2),** reflecting variations in these environmental factors (see Chapter 3).

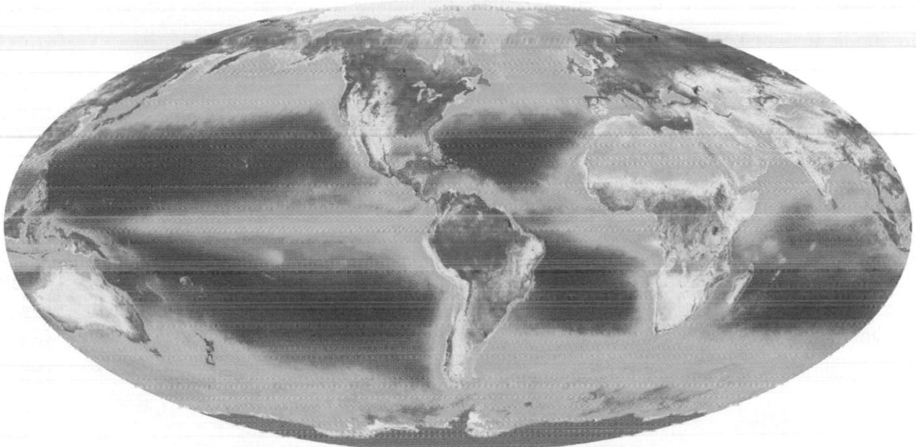

SeaWiFS Project, NASA/Goddard Space Flight Centre and ORBIMAGE

Figure 47.2
Global variation in primary productivity. Satellite data from 2002 provide a visual portrait of net primary productivity across Earth's surface. High-productivity regions on land are dark green; low-productivity regions are yellow. For aquatic environments, the highest productivity is red, down through orange, yellow, green, blue, and purple (lowest).

On a finer geographic scale, within a particular terrestrial ecosystem, mean annual net productivity often increases with the availability of water **(Figure 47.3)**. In systems with sufficient water, a shortage of mineral nutrients may be limiting. All plants need specific ratios of macronutrients and micronutrients for maintenance and photosynthesis (see Chapter 7). But plants withdraw nutrients from soil, and if nutrient concentration drops below a critical level, photosynthesis may decrease or stop altogether. In every ecosystem, one nutrient inevitably runs out before the supplies of other nutrients are exhausted. The element in shortest supply is called a **limiting nutrient** because its absence curtails productivity. Productivity in agricultural fields is subject to the same constraints as productivity in natural ecosystems. Farmers increase productivity by irrigating (adding water to) and fertilizing (adding nutrients to) their crops.

In freshwater and marine ecosystems, where water is always readily available, the depth of water and combined availability of sunlight and nutrients govern the rate of primary productivity. Productivity is high in near-shore ecosystems, where sunlight penetrates shallow, nutrient-rich waters. Kelp beds and coral reefs along temperate and tropical marine coastlines, respectively, are among the most productive ecosystems on Earth (**Table 47.1**; see also Figure 47.2). In contrast, productivity is low in the open waters of a large lake or ocean. There sunlight penetrates only the upper layers, and nutrients sink to the bottom; thus, the two requirements for photosynthesis—sunlight and nutrients—are available in different places.

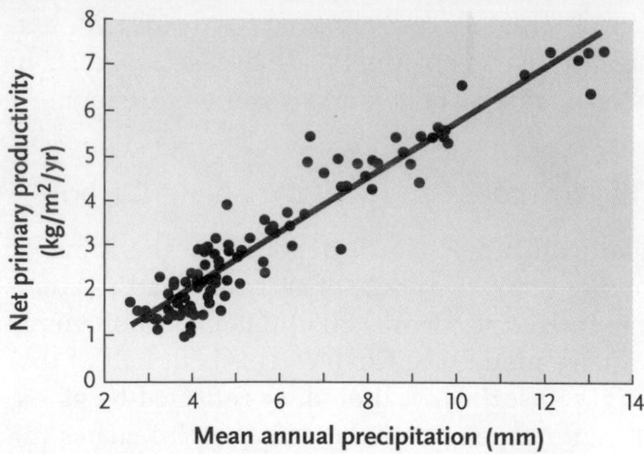

Figure 47.3
Water and net primary productivity. Mean annual precipitation among 100 sites in the Great Plains of North America. These data include only above-ground productivity.

Table 47.1 **Standing Crop Biomass and Net Primary Productivity of Different Ecosystems**

Ecosystem	Mean Standing Crop Biomass (kg/m^2)	Mean Net Primary Productivity (kg/m^2/y^1)
Terrestrial Ecosystems		
Tropical rain forest	450	22.0
Tropical deciduous forest	350	16.0
Temperate rain forest	350	13.0
Temperate deciduous forest	300	12.0
Savanna	40	9.0
Boreal forest (taiga)	200	8.0
Woodland and shrubland	60	7.0
Agricultural land	10	6.5
Temperate grassland	16	6.0
Tundra and alpine tundra	6.0	1.4
Desert and thornwoods	7.0	0.9
Extreme desert, rock, sand, ice	0.2	0.03
Freshwater Ecosystems		
Swamp and marsh	150	20
Lake and stream	0.2	2.5
Marine Ecosystems		
Open ocean	0.03	1.3
Upwelling zones	0.2	5.0
Continental shelf	0.1	3.6
Kelp beds and reefs	20	25
Estuaries	10	15
World Total	**36**	**3.3**

From Whittaker, R.H. 1975. *Communities and Ecosystems*. 2nd ed. Macmillan.

Although ecosystems vary in their rates of primary productivity, these differences are not always proportional to variations in their standing crop biomass (see Table 47.1). For example, biomass amounts in temperate deciduous forests and temperate grasslands differ by a factor of 20, but the difference in their rates of net primary productivity is much smaller. Most biomass in trees is present in nonphotosynthetic tissues such as wood, so their ratio of productivity to biomass is low ($12\ kg \cdot m^{-2}/300\ kg \cdot m^{-2} = 0.04$). By contrast, grasslands do not accumulate much biomass because annual mortality, herbivores, and fires remove plant material as it is produced, so their productivity to biomass ratio is much higher ($6.0\ kg \cdot m^{-2}/16\ kg \cdot m^{-2} = 0.375$).

Some ecosystems contribute more than others to overall net primary productivity **(Figure 47.4)**. Ecosystems covering large areas make substantial total contributions, even if their productivity per unit area is low. Conversely, geographically restricted ecosystems make large contributions if their productivity is high. Open ocean and tropical rain forests contribute about equally to total global productivity, but for different reasons. Open oceans have low productivity, but they cover nearly two-thirds of Earth's surface. Tropical rain forests are highly productive but cover only a relatively small area.

Net primary productivity ultimately supports all consumers in grazing and detrital food webs. Consumers

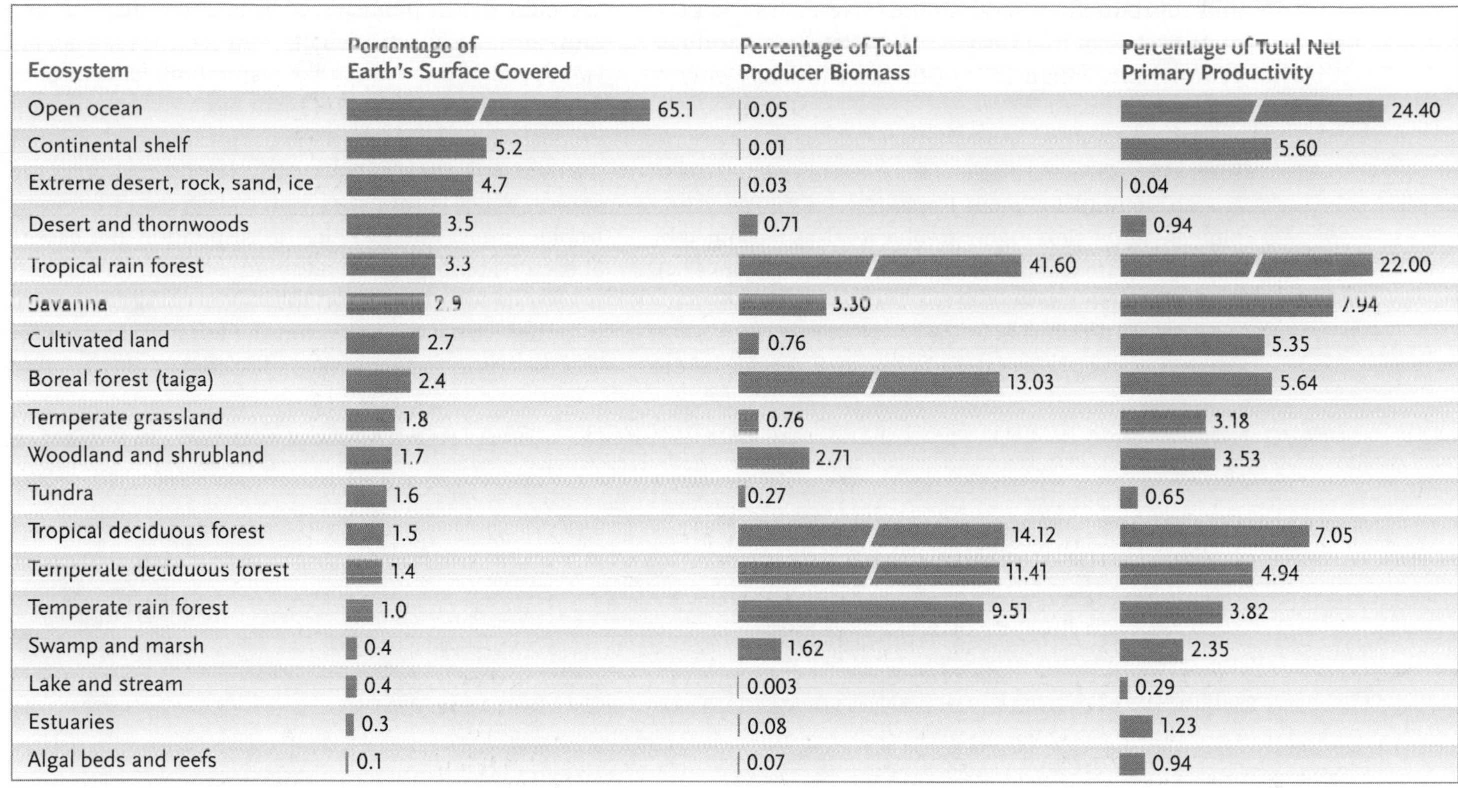

Ecosystem
Percentage of Earth's Surface Covered
Percentage of Total Producer Biomass
Percentage of Total Net Primary Productivity
Open ocean 65.1 0.05 24.40
Continental shelf 5.2 0.01 5.60
Extreme desert, rock, sand, ice 4.7 0.03 0.04
Desert and thornwoods 3.5 0.71 0.94
Tropical rain forest 3.3 41.60 22.00
Savanna 2.9 3.30 7.94
Cultivated land 2.7 0.76 5.35
Boreal forest (taiga) 2.4 13.03 5.64
Temperate grassland 1.8 0.76 3.18
Woodland and shrubland 1.7 2.71 3.53
Tundra 1.6 0.27 0.65
Tropical deciduous forest 1.5 14.12 7.05
Temperate deciduous forest 1.4 11.41 4.94
Temperate rain forest 1.0 9.51 3.82
Swamp and marsh 0.4 1.62 2.35
Lake and stream 0.4 0.003 0.29
Estuaries 0.3 0.08 1.23
Algal beds and reefs 0.1 0.07 0.94

Figure 47.4

Biomass and net primary productivity. An ecosystem's percentage coverage of Earth's surface is not proportional to its contribution to total biomass of producers or its contribution to the total net primary productivity.

in the grazing food web eat some biomass at every trophic level except the highest. Uneaten biomass eventually dies and passes into detrital food webs. Moreover, consumers assimilate only a portion of the material they ingest, and unassimilated material is passed as feces that also supports detritivores and decomposers.

47.1b Secondary Productivity: Moving Up the Trophic Scale

As energy is transferred from producers to consumers, some is stored in new consumer biomass, called **secondary productivity.** Nevertheless, two factors cause energy to be lost from the ecosystem every time it flows from one trophic level to another. First, animals use much of the energy they assimilate for maintenance and locomotion rather than for production of new biomass. Second, as dictated by the second law of thermodynamics, no biochemical reaction is 100% efficient, so some of the chemical energy liberated by cellular respiration is converted to heat, which most organisms do not use.

47.1c Ecological Efficiency: Use of Energy

Ecological efficiency is the ratio of net productivity at one trophic level to net productivity at the trophic level below. If plants in an ecosystem have a net primary productivity of 1.0 $kg \cdot m^{-2} \cdot y^{-1}$ of new tissue, and the herbivores that eat those plants produce 0.1 kg of new tissue $m^{-2} \cdot y^{-1}$, the ecological efficiency of the herbivores is 10%. The efficiencies of three processes (harvesting food, assimilating ingested energy, and producing new biomass) determine the ecological efficiencies of consumers.

Harvesting efficiency is the ratio of the energy content of food consumed compared with the energy content of food available. Predators harvest food efficiently when prey are abundant and easy to capture (see Chapter 46).

Assimilation efficiency is the ratio of the energy absorbed from consumed food to the total energy content of the food. Because animal prey is relatively easy to digest, carnivores absorb between 60 and 90% of the energy in their food. Assimilation efficiency is lower for prey with indigestible parts such as bones or exoskeletons. Herbivores assimilate only 15 to 80% of the energy they consume because cellulose is not very digestible. Herbivores lacking cellulose-digesting systems are on the low end of the scale, whereas those that can digest cellulose are at the higher end.

Production efficiency is the ratio of the energy content of new tissue produced to the energy assimilated from food. Production efficiency varies with maintenance costs. Endothermic animals often use less than 10% of their assimilated energy for growth and reproduction because they use energy to generate body heat (see Chapter 43). Ectothermic animals channel more than 50% of their assimilated energy into new biomass.

The overall ecological efficiency of most organisms is 5 to 20%. As a rule of thumb, only about 10% of energy accumulated at one trophic level is converted into biomass at the next higher trophic level, as illustrated by energy transfers at Silver Springs, Florida **(Figure 47.5).** Silver Springs is an ecosystem that has been studied for many years. Producers in the Silver Springs ecosystem convert 1.2% of the solar energy they intercept into chemical energy (represented by 86 986 $\mathrm{kJ \cdot m^{-2} \cdot yr^{-1}}$ of gross primary productivity). However, they use about two-thirds of this energy for respiration, leaving one-third to be included in new plant biomass, net primary productivity. All consumers in the grazing food web (on the right in Figure 47.5) ultimately depend on this energy source, which diminishes with each transfer between trophic levels. Energy is lost to respiration and export at each trophic level. In addition, organic wastes and uneaten biomass represent substantial energy that flows into the detrital food web (on the left in Figure 47.5). To determine the ecological efficiency of any trophic

Figure 47.5
Energy flow through the Silver Springs ecosystem.

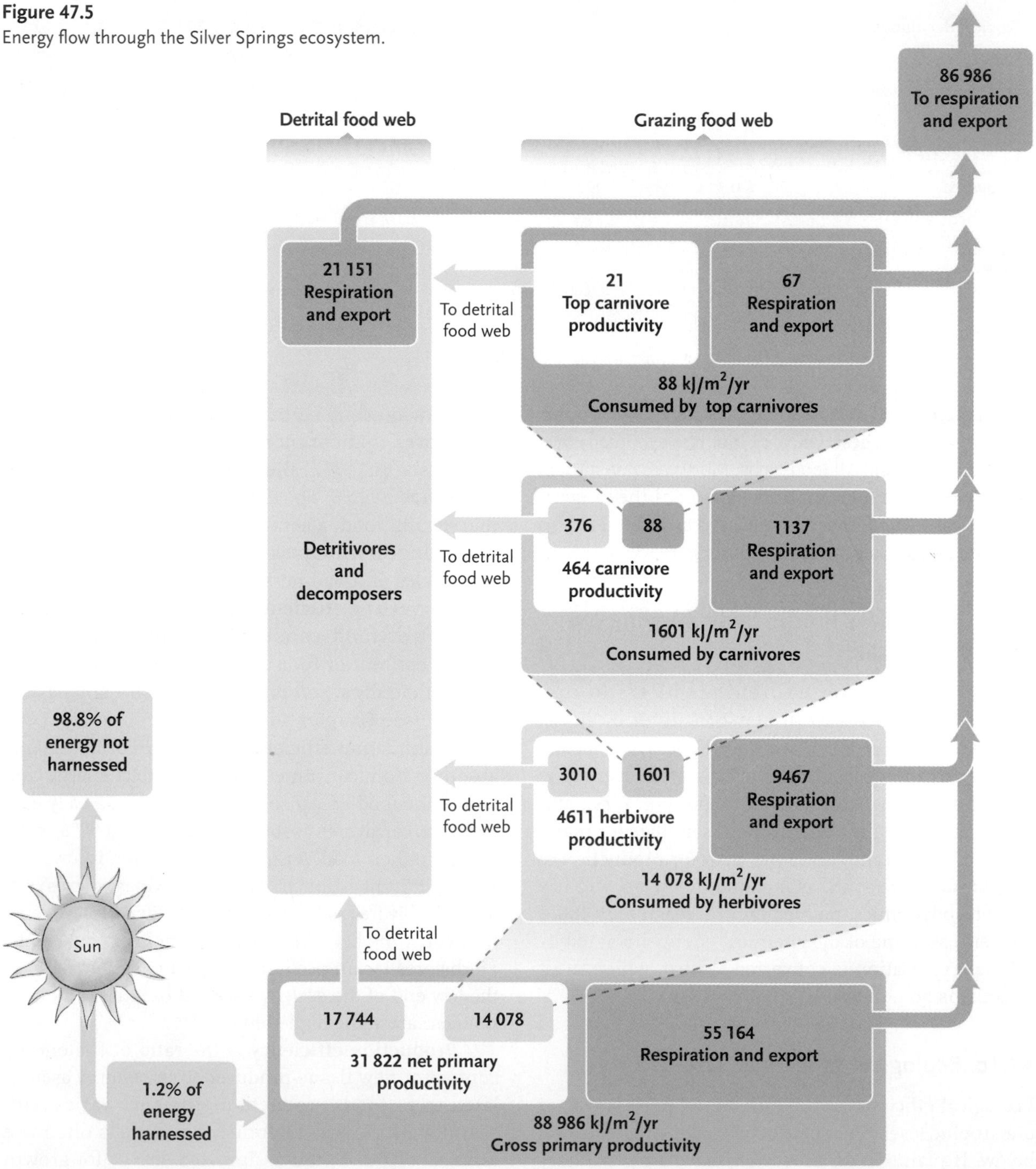

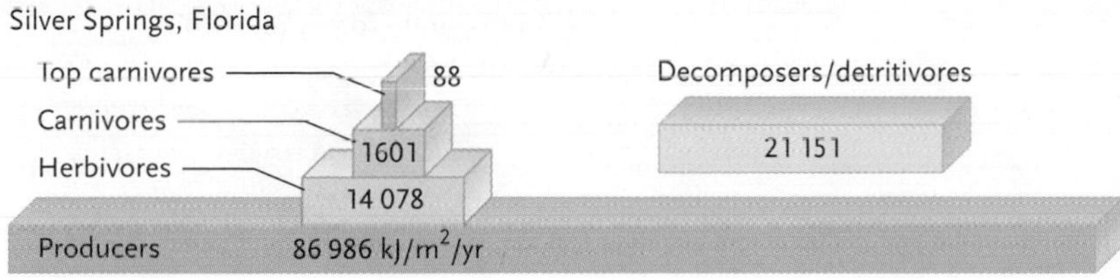

Figure 47.6
Pyramids of energy. The pyramid of energy for Silver Springs, Florida, shows that the amount of energy ($kJ \cdot m^{-2} \cdot yr^{-1}$) passing through each trophic level decreases as it moves up the food web.

level, we divide its productivity by the productivity of the level below it. The ecological efficiency of midlevel carnivores at Silver Springs is 10.06%, $464\ kJ \cdot m^{-2} \cdot yr^{-1}/4611\ kJ \cdot m^{-2} \cdot yr^{-1}$.

47.1d Pyramids: Energy, Biomass, and Numbers

As energy works its way up a food web, energy losses are multiplied in successive energy transfers, greatly reducing the energy available to support the highest trophic levels (see Figure 47.5). Consider a hypothetical example in which ecological efficiency is 10% for all consumers. Assume that the plants in a small field annually produce new tissues containing 100 kJ of energy. Because only 10% of that energy is transferred to new herbivore biomass, the 100 kJ in plants produces 10 kJ of new herbivorous insects, 1 kJ of new songbirds that eat insects, and only 0.1 kJ of new falcons that eat songbirds. About 0.1% of the energy from primary productivity remains after three trophic levels of transfer. If the energy available to each trophic level is depicted graphically, the result is a **pyramid of energy**, with primary producers on the bottom and higher level consumers on the top **(Figure 47.6)**.

The low ecological efficiencies that characterize most energy transfers illustrate one advantage of eating "lower on the food chain." Even though humans digest and assimilate meat more efficiently than we do vegetables, we might be able to feed more people if we all ate more primary producers directly instead of first passing them through another trophic level, such as cattle or chickens, to produce meat. Production of animal protein is costly because much of the energy fed to livestock is used for their own maintenance rather than production of new biomass. But despite the economic and health-related logic of a more vegetarian diet, change in our eating habits alone will not eliminate food shortages or the frequency of malnutrition. Many regions of Africa, Australia, North America, and South America support vegetation that is suitable only for grazing by large herbivores. These areas could not produce significant quantities of edible grains and vegetables without significant additions of water and fertilizer (see Chapter 49).

Inefficiency of energy transfer from one trophic level to the next has profound effects on ecosystem structure. Ecologists illustrate these effects in diagrams called **ecological pyramids.** Trophic levels are drawn as stacked blocks, with the size of each block proportional to the energy, biomass, or numbers of organisms present. Pyramids of energy typically have wide bases and narrow tops (see Figure 47.6) because each trophic level contains only about 10% as much energy as the trophic level below it.

Progressive reduction in productivity at higher trophic levels usually establishes a **pyramid of biomass (Figure 47.7).** The biomass at each trophic level is proportional to the amount of chemical energy temporarily stored there. Thus, in terrestrial ecosystems, the total mass of producers is generally greater than the total mass of herbivores, which is, in turn, greater than the total mass of predators (see **Figure 47.7a**). Populations of top predators, from killer whales to lions and crocodiles, contain too little biomass and energy to support another trophic level; thus, they have no nonhuman predators.

Freshwater and marine ecosystems sometimes exhibit inverted pyramids of biomass (see **Figure 47.7b**). In the open waters of a lake or ocean, primary consumers (zooplankton) eat primary producers (phytoplankton) almost as soon as they are produced. As a result, the standing crop of primary consumers at any moment in time is actually larger than the standing crop of primary producers. Food webs

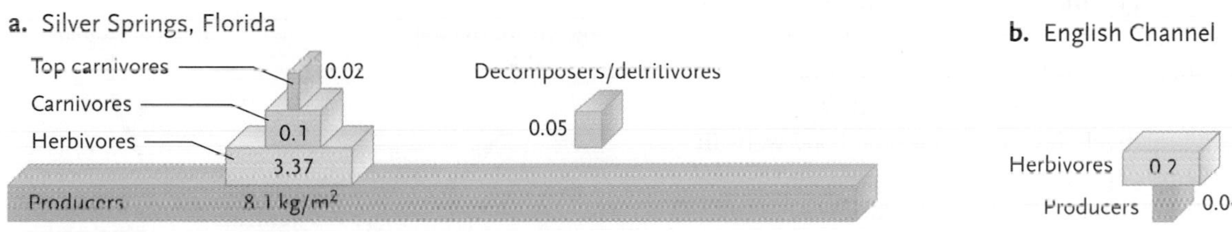

Figure 47.7
Pyramids of biomass. **(a)** The pyramid of standing crop biomass for Silver Springs is bottom heavy, as it is for most ecosystems. **(b)** Some marine ecosystems, such as that in the English Channel, have an inverted pyramid of biomass because producers are quickly eaten by primary consumers. Only the producer and herbivore trophic levels are illustrated here. The data for both pyramids are given in $kg \cdot m^{-2}$ of dry biomass.

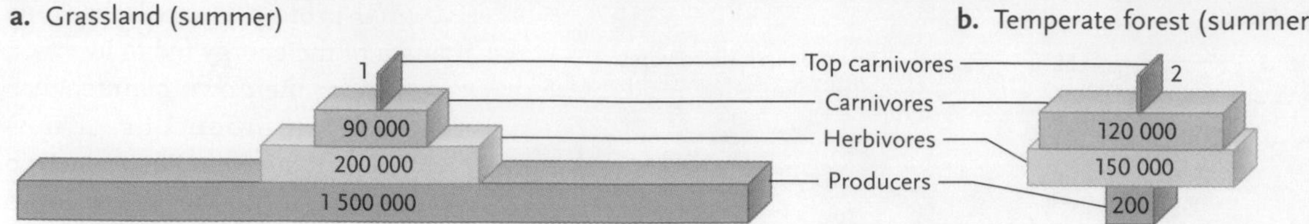

Figure 47.8
Pyramids of numbers. (a) The pyramid of numbers (numbers of individuals per 1000 m^2) for temperate grasslands is bottom heavy because individual producers are small and very numerous. **(b)** The pyramid of numbers for forests may have a narrow base because herbivorous insects usually outnumber the producers, many of which are large trees. Data for both pyramids were collected in summer. Detritivores and decomposers (soil animals and microorganisms) are not included because they are difficult to count.

in these ecosystems are stable because producers have exceptionally high **turnover rates.** In other words, producers divide and their populations grow so quickly that feeding by zooplankton does not endanger their populations or reduce their productivity. However, on an annual basis, the *cumulative total* biomass of primary producers far outweighs that of primary consumers.

The reduction of energy and biomass affects population sizes of organisms at the top of a food web. Top predators can be relatively large animals, so the limited biomass present in the highest trophic levels is concentrated in relatively few animals **(Figure 47.8).** The extremely narrow top of this **pyramid of numbers** has grave implications for conservation biology (see Chapter 48). Top predators tend to be large animals with small population sizes. And because each individual must patrol a large area to find sufficient food, members of a population are often widely dispersed within their habitats. As a result, they are subject to genetic drift (see Chapter 18) and are highly sensitive to hunting, habitat destruction, and random events that can lead to extinction. Top predators may also suffer from the accumulation of poisonous materials that move through food webs (see the next section). Even predators that feed below the top trophic level often suffer the ill effects of human activities. Consumers sometimes regulate ecosystem processes.

Numerous abiotic factors, such as the intensity and duration of sunlight, rainfall, temperature, and the availability of nutrients, have significant effects on primary productivity. Primary productivity, in turn, profoundly affects the populations of herbivores and predators that feed on them. But what effect does feeding by these consumers have on primary productivity?

Consumers sometimes influence rates of primary productivity, especially in ecosystems with low species diversity and relatively few trophic levels. Food webs in lake ecosystems depend primarily on the productivity of phytoplankton **(Figure 47.9).** Phytoplankton are, in turn, eaten by herbivorous zooplankton, themselves consumed by predatory invertebrates and fishes. The top nonhuman carnivore in these food webs is usually a predatory fish.

Herbivorous zooplankton play a central role in regulation of lake ecosystems. Small zooplankton species

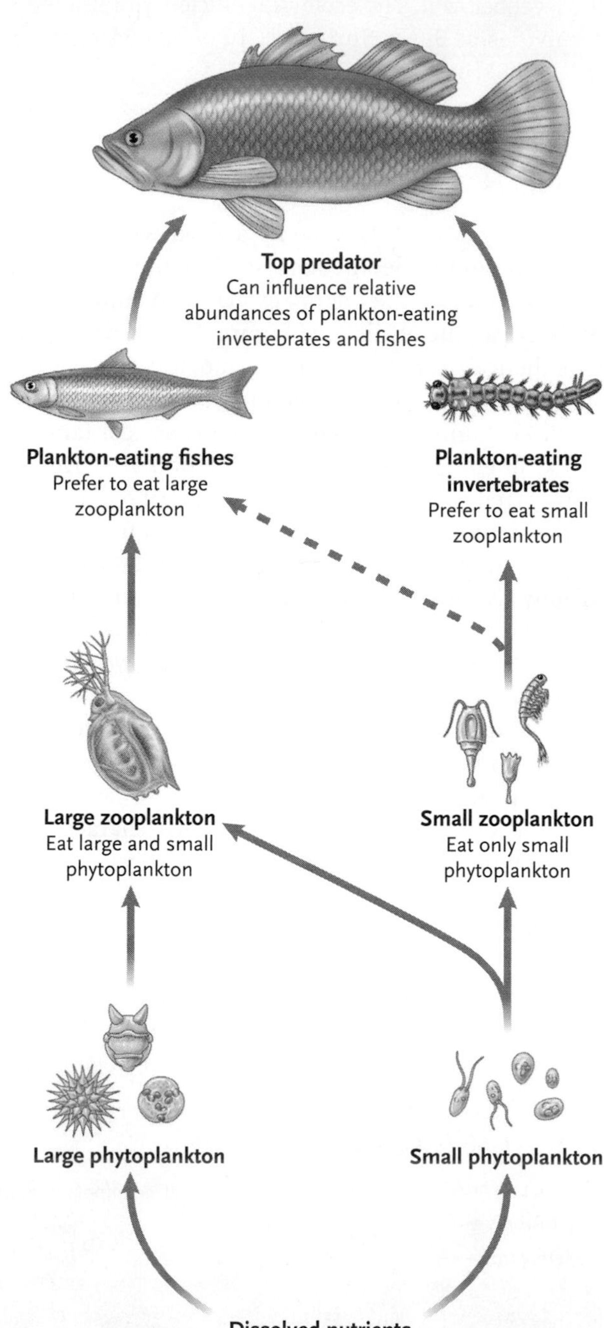

Figure 47.9
Consumer regulation of primary productivity. A simplified food web illustrates that lake ecosystems have relatively few trophic levels. The effects of feeding by top carnivores can cascade downward, exerting an indirect effect on the phytoplankton and thus on primary productivity.

Fishing Fleets at Loggerheads with Sea Turtles

Populations of loggerhead sea turtles (*Caretta caretta*) that nest on Western Pacific beaches in Australia and Japan have been in decline. Like other sea turtles, *C. caretta* hatch from eggs that females bury on sandy beaches. Immediately after hatching, the young turtles rush to the surf and the open ocean. Turtles mature at sea and return to their hatching beaches to lay eggs. Using mitochondrial DNA (mtDNA), Bruce Bowen and colleagues explored the situation sea turtles face.

The researchers took mtDNA samples from nesting populations in Australia and Japan, from populations of turtles feeding in Baja California, and from turtles drowned in fishing nets in the north Pacific. One 350-base-pair segment of mtDNA included sequence variations that are characteristic of different loggerhead populations. After samples were amplified by the polymerase chain reaction, sequencing revealed three major variants of mtDNA, which the researchers designated sequences A, B, and C. The sequences were distributed among loggerhead turtles, as shown in **Table 1.**

The mtDNA of most *C. caretta* found in Baja California and in fishing nets in the north Pacific matched that of turtles from the Japanese nesting areas. These data support the idea that loggerhead turtles hatched in Japan make the 10 000-km long migration across the North Pacific to Baja California. The data also indicate that a few turtles that hatched in Australia may follow the same migratory route.

This migration could be aided by the North Pacific Current, which moves from west to east, whereas the return trip from Baja to Japan could be made via the North Equatorial Current that runs from east to west just north of the equator. Loggerhead turtles have been found in these currents, and further tests will reveal whether they have the mtDNA sequence characteristic of the individuals nesting in Japan and feeding in Baja California.

The nesting population of *C. caretta* in Japan is 2000 to 3000 females. It is uncertain if this population can survive the loss of thousands of offspring to fishing in the North Pacific. The number of female loggerhead turtles nesting in Australia has declined by 50 to 80% in the last decade, so the loss of only a few individuals in fishing nets could also have a drastic impact on this population. To save the loggerhead turtles, wildlife managers and international agencies must establish and enforce limits on the number of migrating individuals trapped and killed in the ocean fisheries.

Like other sea turtles, the loggerheads are severely impacted by fishing. As many as 4000 loggerheads drown in nets every year, and others are caught in longline fisheries. Adoption of a new fish hook **(Figure 1)** could reduce the turtle catch in longline fishing operations.

Table 1 Sources of Turtles by Nesting Grounds

Number of Turtles			
Location	**Sequence A**	**Sequence B**	**Sequence C**
Australian nesting areas	26	0	0
Japanese nesting areas	0	23	3
Baja California feeding grounds	2	19	5
North Pacific	1	28	5

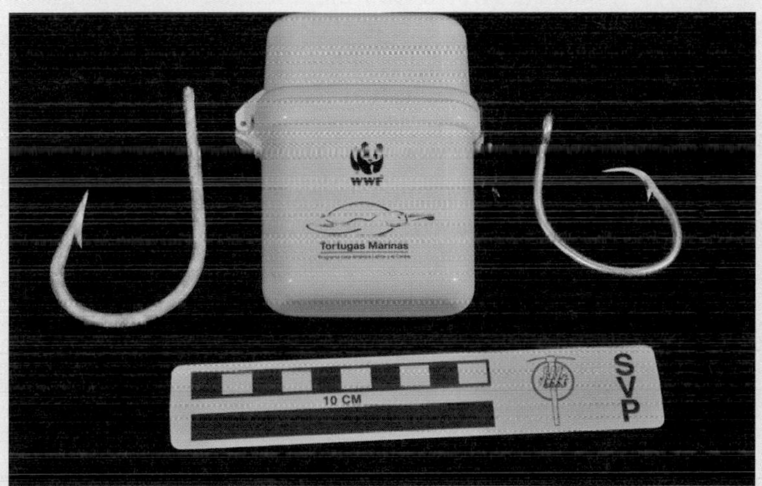

Figure 1
Sea turtles and longlining. Conventional longline hooks (left) readily catch sea turtles, whereas the hook on the right does not. The World Wildlife Fund is promoting the use of hooks that are friendly to sea turtles in an effort to reduce their losses to longline fishing.

consume only small phytoplankton. Thus, when *small* zooplankton are especially abundant, large phytoplankton escape predation and survive, and the lake's primary productivity is high. By contrast, large zooplankton are voracious, eating both small and large phytoplankton. When large zooplankton are especially abundant, they reduce the overall biomass of phytoplankton, lowering the ecosystem's primary productivity.

In this trophic cascade, predator–prey effects reverberate through population interactions at two or more trophic levels in an ecosystem. Feeding by plankton-eating invertebrates and fishes has a *direct* impact on herbivorous zooplankton populations and an *indirect* impact on phytoplankton populations (the ecosystem's primary producers). Invertebrate predators prefer small zooplankton. And when the invertebrates that eat small zooplankton are the dominant predators in the ecosystem, large zooplankton become more abundant; they consume many phytoplankton, causing a decrease in productivity. But plankton-eating fishes prefer to eat large zooplankton (see Figure 47.9), so when they are abundant, small zooplankton become the dominant herbivores, leading large phytoplankton to become more numerous, which raises the lake's productivity.

Large predatory fishes may add an additional level of control to the system because they feed on and regulate the population sizes of plankton-eating invertebrates and fishes. Thus, the effects of feeding by the top predator can cascade downward through the food web, affecting the densities of plankton-eating invertebrates and fishes, herbivorous zooplankton, and phytoplankton. Research in Norway with brown trout (*Salmo trutta*), a top predator, and Arctic char (*Salvelinus alpinus*), the prey, demonstrated how culling prey can promote the recovery of top predators. In this case, Lake Takvatn was the scene of a large-scale experiment. Older, stunted prey species (*S. alpinus*) were removed. These fish had eaten small prey, so in an increase in the availability of prey and recovery of the predator resulted. In this case, *S. trutta* was the top predator, and *S. alpinus*, an introduced species, was culled to rejuvenate the system. Another process of bioremediation, the addition of piscivorous fish to a lake, also has been successful in restoring ecosystem balance in other parts of the world.

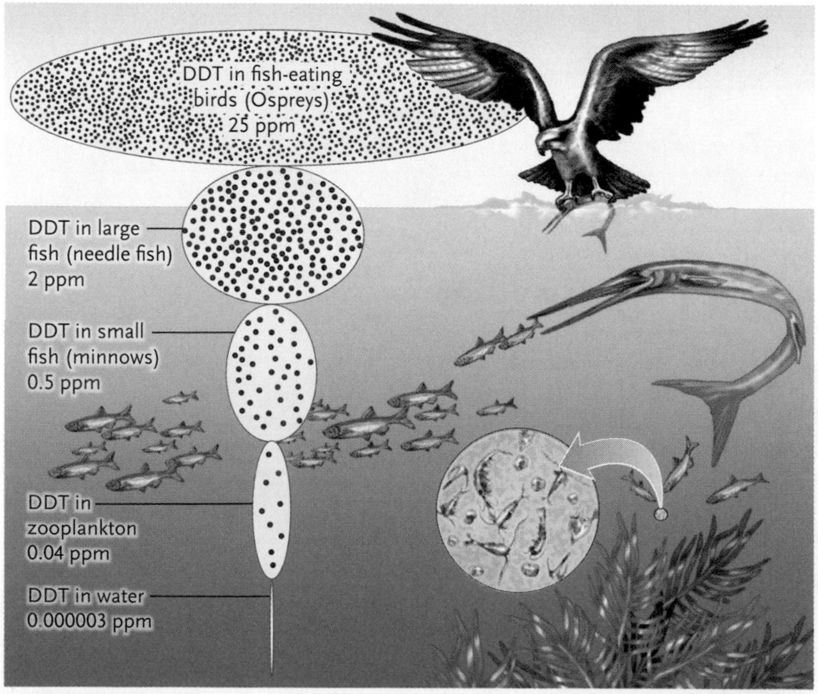

47.1e Biological Magnification: Movement of Contaminants Up the Food Chain

Ironically, DDT (a formerly popular insecticide; see *Molecule Behind Biology*) provided a clear demonstration of the interconnectedness of organisms. Consumers accumulate DDT from all the organisms they eat in their lifetimes. Primary consumers, such as herbivorous insects, may ingest relatively small amounts of DDT, but a songbird that eats many of these insects accumulates all the collected DDT consumed by its prey. A predator such as a raptor, perhaps a Sharp-shinned Hawk (*Accipiter striatus*) that eats songbirds, accumulates even more. Whether the food chain (web) is aquatic or terrestrial, the net effect on higher level consumers is the same **(Figure 47.10).**

Natural systems have provided many examples of biological magnification. In cities where DDT was used in an effort to control the spread of Dutch elm disease, songbirds died from DDT poisoning after eating insects that had been sprayed (whether or not they were involved in spreading the disease). In forests, DDT was used in an effort to control spruce budworm moths (*Choristoneura occidentalis*), and salmon died because runoff carried DDT into their streams and rivers, where their herbivorous prey consumed it.

Despite the ban on the use of DDT in the United States in 1973, in 1990, the California State Department of Health recommended closing a fishery off the coast of California because of DDT accumulating there. DDT discharged in industrial waste 20 years earlier was still moving through the ecosystem. The half-life of DDT in an organism's body fat is eight years.

Other contaminants emulate DDT. Mercury contamination is common in many parts of the world, often as a by-product of the pulp and paper industry. Minamata, the disease humans get from mercury poisoning, is usually linked to the consumption of fish taken from contaminated watersheds. Eating fish contaminated with mercury can result in mercury concentrations in people's hair (0.9 to 94 mg $\times$ kg^{-1}) and otters (*Lontra canadensis*; 0.49 to 54.37 mg $\times$ kg^{-1}). In southern Ontario, the hair of bats that eat insects that emerge from mercury-contaminated sediments contains

Figure 47.10
Biological magnification. In this marine food web in northeastern North America, DDT concentration (measured in parts per million, ppm) was magnified nearly 10 million times between zooplankton and the Osprey (*Pandion haliaetus*).

Molecule Behind Biology

DDT: Dichloro-Diphenyl-Trichloroethane

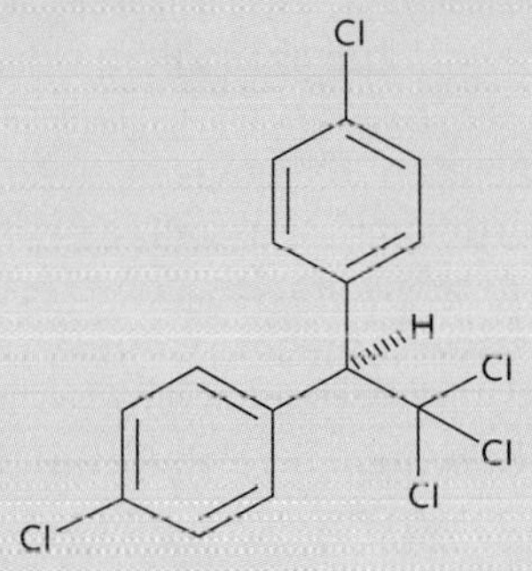

Figure 1
A molecule of DDT.

Originally formulated in 1873, DDT's potential as an insecticide was only recognized in 1939 by Paul Muller of Geigy Pharmaceutical in Switzerland. DDT, the first of the chlorinated insecticides, was used extensively in some theatres of World War II, notably in Burma (now Myanmar) in 1944, when the Japanese forces were on the brink of moving into India. There Allied forces suffered from "three m's": mud, morale, and malaria. Meanwhile, in 1943 in southern Italy, DDT was instrumental in controlling populations of lice that plagued Canadian troops there. Widespread application of DDT in Burma reduced the incidence of malaria by killing mosquitoes, the vectors for the disease (see Chapter 26). After World War II, the use of DDT spread rapidly, and the World Health Organization (WHO) credited this molecule with saving 25 million human lives (mainly through control of mosquitoes that carry malaria).

At first, DDT appeared to be an ideal insecticide. In addition to being inexpensive to produce, it had low toxicity to mammals (300 to 500 $mg \cdot kg^{-1}$ is the LD_{50}, the amount required to kill half of the target population). But many insects subsequently developed immunity to DDT, reducing its effectiveness.

DDT is chemically stable and soluble in fat, so instead of being metabolized by mammals, it is stored in their fat. The biological half-life of DDT is approximately eight years (it takes about eight years for a mammal to metabolize half of the amount of DDT it has assimilated). DDT is released when fat is metabolized, so when mammals metabolize fat (for example, when humans go on a diet), they are exposed to higher concentrations of DDT in their blood. DDT also had dramatic effects on some birds, notably those higher up the food chain. Eggshell thinning was a consequence of exposure to DDT. Populations of birds such as peregrine falcons (*Falco peregrinus*) plummeted.

Since 1985, the use of DDT has been totally banned in Canada, and it is now banned in many other countries. But DDT is still produced in counties such as the United States and still used in countries where malaria is a prominent problem because the ecological costs of DDT are considered secondary to the importance of controlling the mosquitoes. WHO estimates that every 30 seconds, a child dies of malaria. Approximately 40% of the world's population of humans is at risk of contracting malaria where they live, mainly in Africa. Malaria also remains a problem in tropical and subtropical Asia and Central and South America. People in southern Europe and the Middle East may also be at risk.

By the early 1970s, cetaceans in the waters around Antarctica had DDT in their body fat even though DDT had never been used there. The movement of DDT up the food chain and through food webs demonstrated the interconnections in biological systems. The movement of DDT also provides a graphic demonstration of the transfer of materials from one trophic level to another.

concentrations up to 13 $mg \times kg^{-1}$. Fish obviously are not essential to this chain of biomagnification.

Study Break

1. What is net primary productivity? How does it differ from standing crop biomass? Are the pyramids useful?
2. Many deserts have low levels of productivity, yet they receive a lot of sunlight. Why?
3. What are assimilation efficiency and production efficiency?

47.2 Nutrient Cycling in Ecosystems

The availability of nutrients is as important to ecosystem function as the input of energy. Photosynthesis requires carbon, hydrogen, and oxygen, which producers acquire from water and air. Primary producers also need nitrogen, phosphorus, and other minerals (see Chapter 41). A deficiency in any of these minerals can reduce primary productivity.

Earth is essentially a closed system with respect to matter, even though cosmic dust enters the atmosphere. Thus, unlike energy, for which there is a constant cosmic input, virtually all the nutrients that will ever be available for biological systems are already present. Nutrient ions or molecules constantly circulate between the abiotic environment and living organisms in **biogeochemical cycles**. And unlike energy, which flows through ecosystems and is gradually lost as heat, matter is conserved in biogeochemical cycles. Although there may be local shortages of specific nutrients, Earth's overall supplies of these chemical elements are never depleted or increased.

Nutrients take various forms as they pass through biogeochemical cycles. Materials such as carbon, nitrogen, and oxygen form gases that move through global *atmospheric cycles*. Geologic processes move other materials, such as phosphorus, through local *sedimentary cycles,* carrying them between dry land and the seafloor. Rocks, soil, water, and air are the reservoirs where mineral nutrients accumulate, sometimes for many years.

Ecologists use a **generalized compartment model** to describe nutrient cycling **(Figure 47.11).** Two criteria divide ecosystems into four compartments in which nutrients accumulate. First, nutrient molecules and ions are either *available* or *unavailable,* depending on whether they can be assimilated by organisms. Second, nutrients are present either in *organic* material, living or dead tissues of organisms, or *inorganic* material, such as rocks and soil. Minerals in dead leaves on the forest floor are in the available-organic compartment because they are in the remains of organisms that can be eaten by detritivores. Calcium ions in limestone rocks are in the unavailable-inorganic compartment because they are in a nonbiological form that producers cannot assimilate.

Nutrients move rapidly within and between the available compartments. Living organisms are in the available-organic compartment, and whenever heterotrophs consume food, they recycle nutrients within that reservoir (indicated by the circular arrow in the upper left of Figure 47.11). Producers acquire nutrients from the air, soil, and water of the available-inorganic compartment. Consumers acquire nutrients from the available-inorganic compartment when they drink water or absorb mineral ions through their integument. Several processes routinely transfer nutrients from organisms to the available-inorganic compartment. Respiration releases carbon dioxide, moving both carbon and oxygen from the available-organic compartment to the available-inorganic compartment.

By contrast, the exchange of materials into and out of the unavailable compartments is generally slow. Sedimentation, a long-term geologic process, converts ions and particles of the available-inorganic compartment into rocks of the unavailable-inorganic compartment. Materials are gradually returned to the available-inorganic compartment when rocks are uplifted and eroded or weathered. Similarly, over millions of years, the remains of organisms in the available-organic compartment were converted into the coal, oil, and peat of the unavailable-organic compartment.

Except for the input of solar energy, we have described energy flow and nutrient cycling as though ecosystems were closed systems. In reality, most ecosystems exchange energy and nutrients with neighbouring ecosystems. Rainfall carries nutrients into a forest ecosystem, and runoff carries nutrients from a forest into a lake or river. Ecologists have mapped biogeochemical cycles of important elements, often by using radioactively labelled molecules that they can follow in the environment.

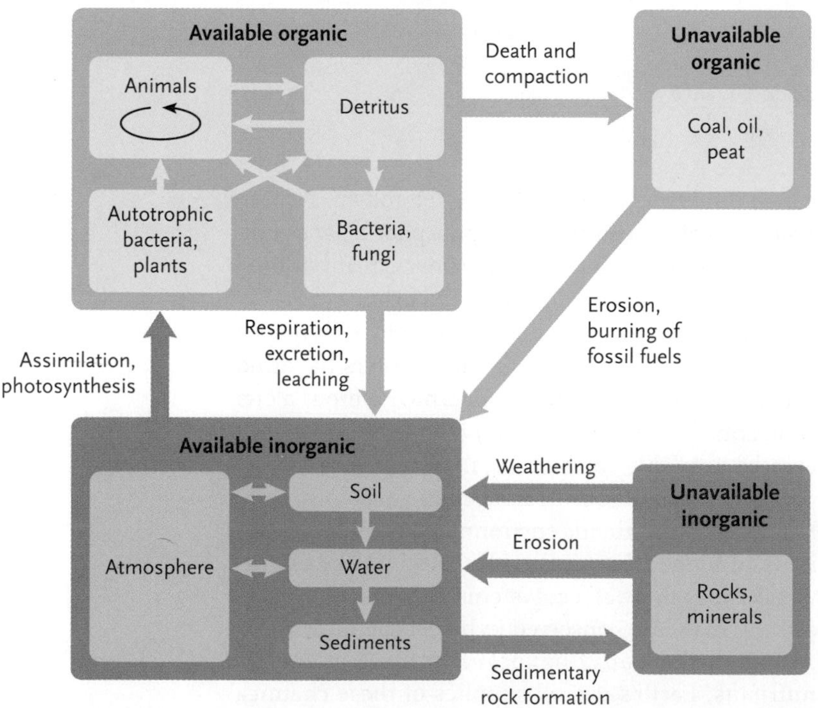

Figure 47.11
A generalized compartment model of nutrient cycling. Nutrients cycle through four major compartments within ecosystems. Processes that move nutrients from one compartment to another are indicated on the arrows. The circular arrow under "Animals" represents animal predation on other animals.

47.2a Water: Staff of Life

Although it is not a mineral nutrient, water is the universal intracellular solvent for biochemical reactions. Nevertheless, only a fraction of 1% of Earth's total water is present in biological systems at any time.

The cycling of water, the **hydrogeologic cycle,** is global, with water molecules moving from oceans into the atmosphere, to land, through freshwater ecosystems, and back to the oceans **(Figure 47.12).** Solar energy causes water to evaporate from oceans, lakes, rivers, soil, and living organisms, entering the atmosphere as a vapour and remaining aloft as a gas, as droplets in clouds, or as ice crystals. Water falls as precipitation, mostly in the form of rain and snow. When precipitation falls on land, water flows across the surface or percolates to great depths in soil, eventually reentering the ocean reservoir through the flow of streams and rivers.

The hydrogeologic cycle maintains its global balance because the total amount of water entering the atmosphere is equal to the amount that falls as precipitation. Most water that enters the atmosphere evaporates from the oceans, which are the largest reservoir of water on the planet. A much smaller fraction evaporates from terrestrial ecosystems, and most of that is through transpiration by green plants.

Constant recirculation provides fresh water to terrestrial organisms and maintains freshwater ecosystems such as lakes and rivers. Water also serves as a

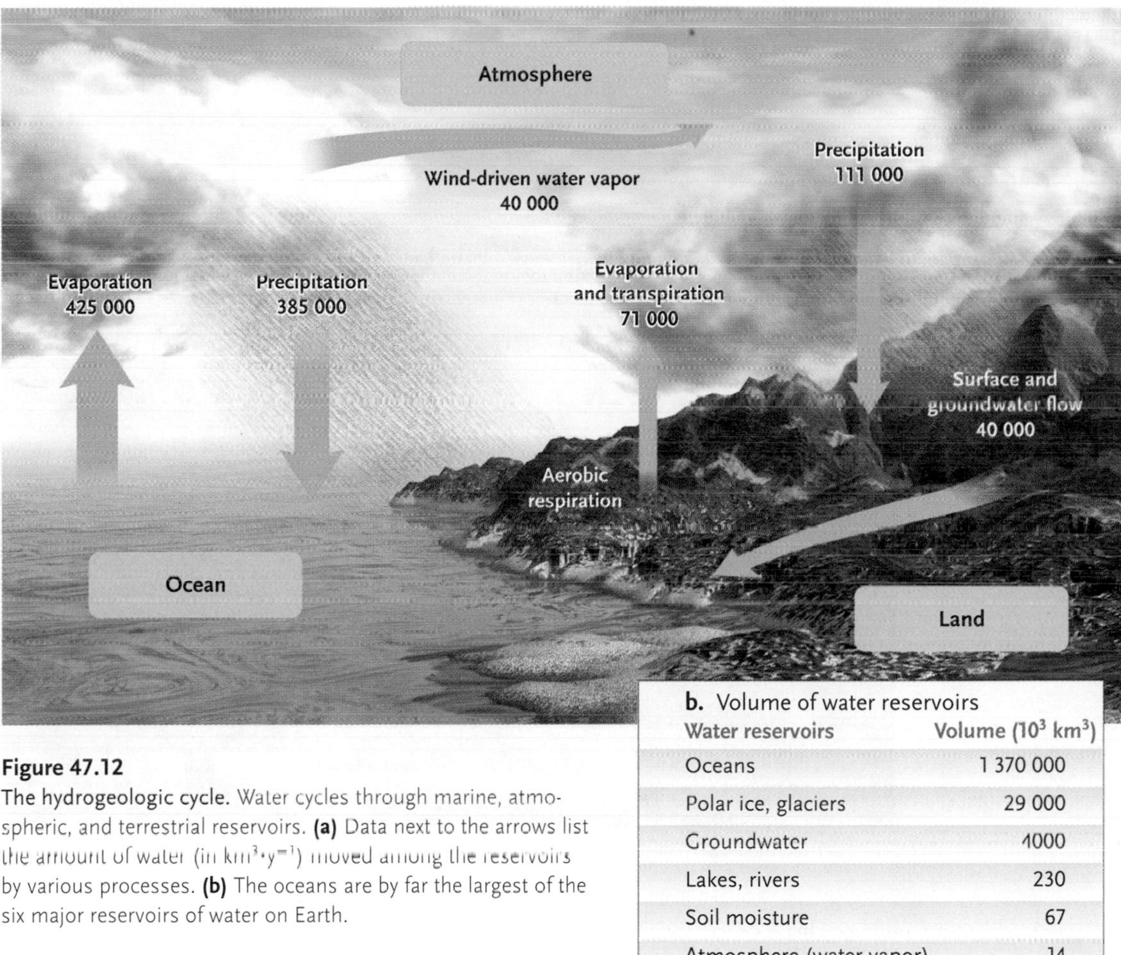

b. Volume of water reservoirs

Water reservoirs	Volume (10^3 km^3)
Oceans	1 370 000
Polar ice, glaciers	29 000
Groundwater	4000
Lakes, rivers	230
Soil moisture	67
Atmosphere (water vapor)	14

Figure 47.12
The hydrogeologic cycle. Water cycles through marine, atmospheric, and terrestrial reservoirs. **(a)** Data next to the arrows list the amount of water (in $km^3 \cdot y^{-1}$) moved among the reservoirs by various processes. **(b)** The oceans are by far the largest of the six major reservoirs of water on Earth.

transport medium that moves nutrients within and between ecosystems, as demonstrated in a series of classic experiments in the Hubbard Brook Experimental Forest (see *Studies of the Hubbard Brook Watershed*).

47.2b Carbon: Backbone of Life

Carbon atoms provide the backbone of most biological molecules, and carbon compounds store the energy captured by photosynthesis (see Chapter 7). Carbon enters food webs when producers convert atmospheric carbon dioxide (CO_2) into carbohydrates. Heterotrophs acquire carbon by eating other organisms or detritus. Although carbon moves somewhat independently in sea and on land, a common atmospheric pool of CO_2 creates a global **carbon cycle (Figure 47.13, p. 1192).**

The largest reservoir of carbon is sedimentary rock, such as limestone. Rocks are in the unavailable-inorganic compartment, and they exchange carbon with living organisms at an exceedingly slow pace. Most *available* carbon is present as dissolved bicarbonate ions (HCO_3^-) in the ocean. Soil, atmosphere, and plant biomass are significant, but much smaller, reservoirs of available carbon. Atmospheric carbon is mostly in the form of molecular CO_2, a product of aerobic respiration. Volcanic eruptions also release small quantities of CO_2 into the atmosphere.

Sometimes carbon atoms leave organic compartments for long periods of time. Some organisms in marine food webs build shells and other hard parts by incorporating dissolved carbon into calcium carbonate ($CaCO_3$) and other insoluble salts. When shelled organisms die, they sink to the bottom and are buried in sediments. Other animals, notably vertebrates, store calcium in bone. Insoluble carbon that accumulates as rock in deep sediments may remain buried for millions of years before tectonic uplifting brings it to the surface, where erosion and weathering dissolve sedimentary rocks and return carbon to an available form.

Carbon atoms are also transferred to the unavailable-organic compartment when soft-bodied organisms die and are buried in habitats where low oxygen concentration prevents decomposition. In the past, under suitable geologic conditions, these carbon-rich tissues were slowly converted to gas, petroleum, or coal, which we now use as fossil fuels. Human activities, especially burning fossil fuels, are transferring carbon into the atmosphere at an unnaturally high rate. The resulting change in the worldwide distribution of carbon is having profound consequences for Earth's atmosphere and

a. Amount of carbon in major reservoirs

Carbon reservoirs	Mass (10^{12} g)
Sediments and rocks	770 000 000
Ocean (dissolved forms)	397 000
Soil	15 000
Atmosphere	7500
Biomass on land	7150

b. Annual global carbon movement between reservoirs

Direction of movement	Mass (10^{12} kg)
From atmosphere to plants (carbon fixation)	1200
From atmosphere to ocean	1070
To atmosphere from ocean	1050
To atmosphere from plants	600
To atmosphere from soil	600
To atmosphere from burning fossil fuel	50
To atmosphere from burning plants	20
To ocean from runoff	4
Burial in ocean sediments	1

c. The global carbon cycle

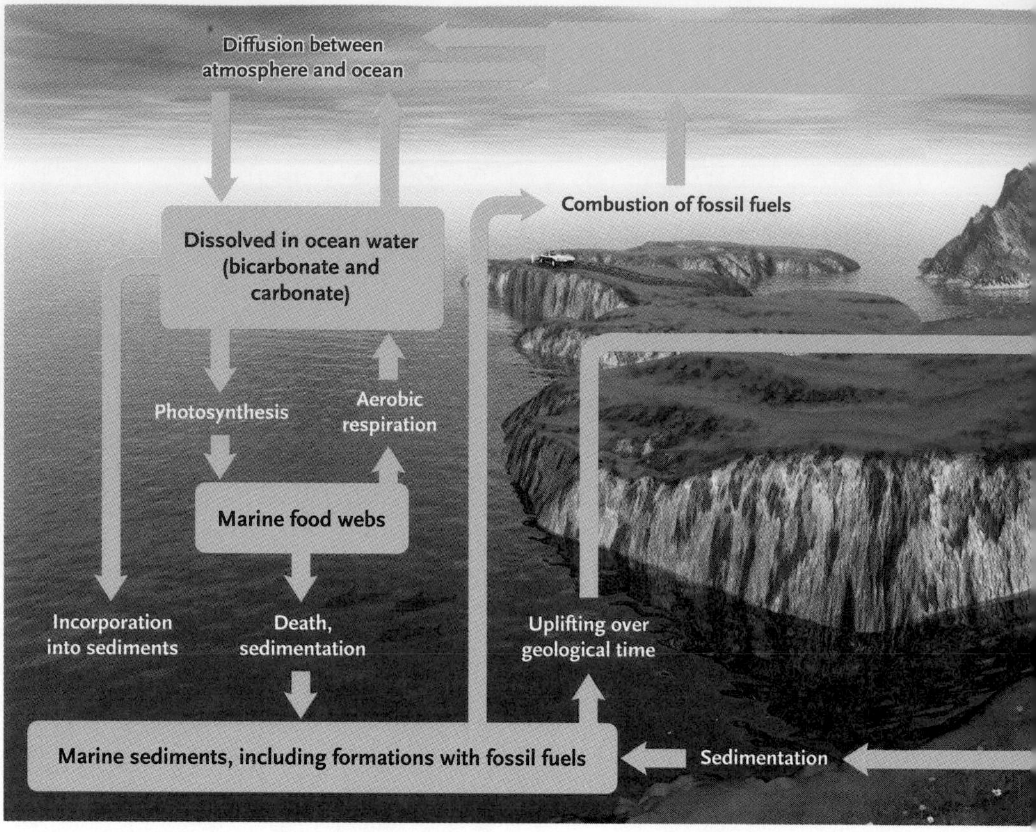

Figure 47.13
The carbon cycle. Marine and terrestrial components of the global carbon cycle are linked through an atmospheric reservoir of carbon dioxide. **(a)** By far the largest amount of Earth's carbon is found in sediments and rocks. **(b)** Earth's atmopshere mediates most of the movement of carbon. **(c)** In this illustration of the carbon cycle, boxes identify major reservoirs and labels on arrows identify the processes that cause carbon to move between reservoirs.

climate, including a general warming of the climate and a rise in sea level (see *Disruption of the Carbon Cycle*).

47.2c Nitrogen: A Limiting Element

All organisms require nitrogen to construct nucleic acids, proteins, and other biological molecules (see Chapter 41). Earth's atmosphere had a high nitrogen concentration long before life began. Today, a global **nitrogen cycle** moves this element between the huge atmospheric pool of gaseous molecular nitrogen (N_2) and several much smaller pools of nitrogen-containing compounds in soils, marine and freshwater ecosystems, and living organisms **(Figure 47.14)**.

Molecular nitrogen is abundant in the atmosphere, but triple covalent bonds bind its two atoms so tightly that most organisms cannot use it. Only certain microorganisms, volcanic action, and lightning can convert N_2 into ammonium (NH_4^+) and nitrate (NO_3^-) ions. This conversion is called **nitrogen fixation** (see Chapter 21). Once nitrogen is fixed, primary producers can incorporate it into biological molecules such as proteins and nucleic acids. Secondary consumers obtain nitrogen by consuming these molecules.

Several biochemical processes produce different nitrogen-containing compounds and thus move nitrogen through ecosystems. These processes are nitrogen fixation, ammonification, nitrification, and denitrification **(Table 47.2, p. 1195)**.

In nitrogen fixation, several kinds of microorganisms convert molecular nitrogen (N_2) to ammonium ions (NH_4^+). Certain bacteria, which collect molecular nitrogen from the air between soil particles, are the major nitrogen fixers in terrestrial ecosystems (see Table 47.2). The cyanobacteria partners in some lichens (see Chapter 24) also fix molecular nitrogen. Other cyanobacteria are important nitrogen fixers in aquatic ecosystems, whereas the water fern (genus *Azolla*) plays that role in rice paddies. Collectively, these organisms fix an astounding 200 million tonnes of nitrogen each year. Plants and other primary producers assimilate and use this nitrogen in the biosynthesis of amino acids, proteins, and nucleic acids, which then circulate through food webs.

Some plants, including legumes (such as beans and clover), alders (*Alnus* species), and some members of the rose family (Rosaceae), are mutualists with nitrogen-fixing bacteria. These plants acquire nitrogen from soils much more readily than plants

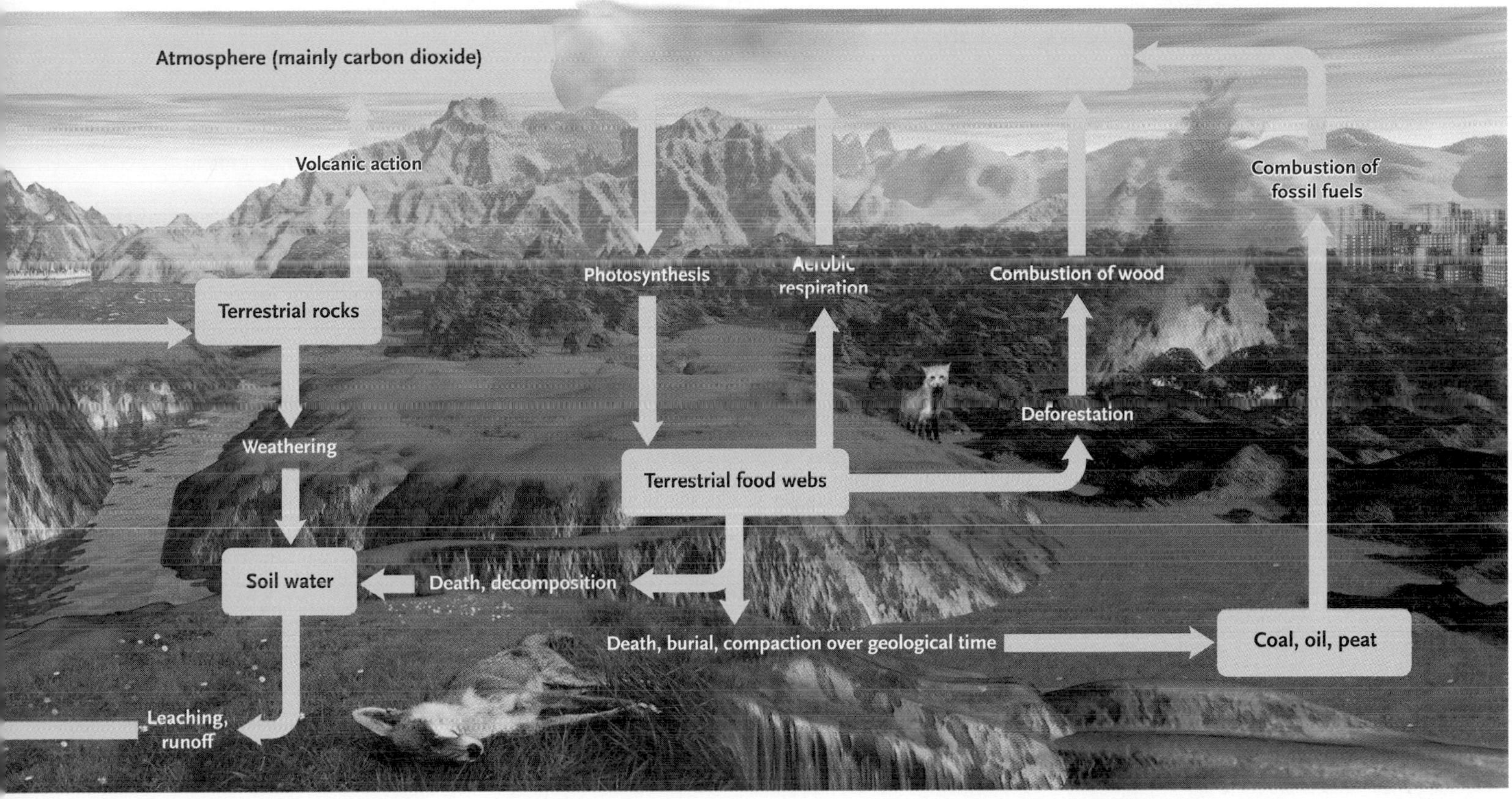

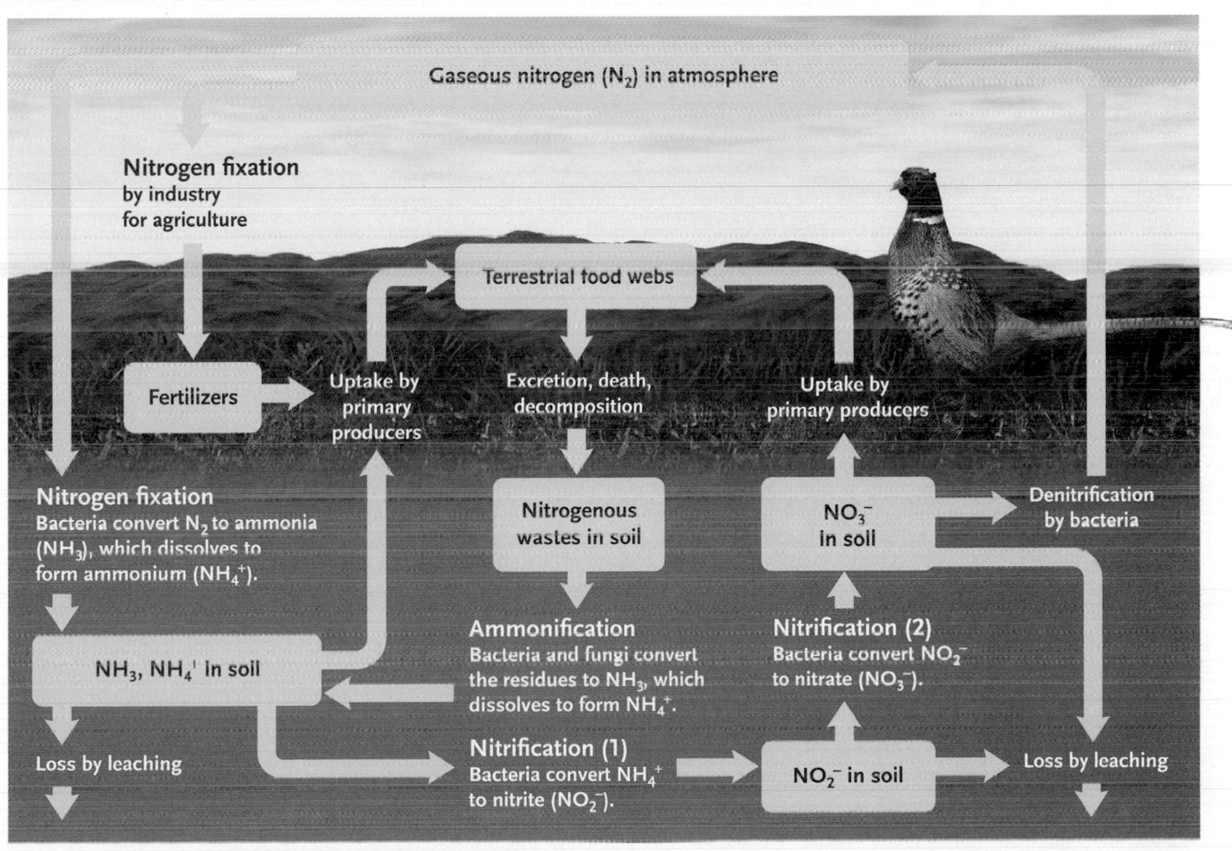

Figure 47.14
The nitrogen cycle in a terrestrial ecosystem. Nitrogen cycles through terrestrial ecosystems when unavailable molecular nitrogen is made available through the action of nitrogen-fixing bacteria. Other bacteria recycle nitrogen within the available-organic compartment through ammonification and two types of nitrification, converting organic wastes into ammonium ions and nitrates. Denitrification converts nitrate to molecular nitrogen, which returns to the atmosphere. Runoff carries nitrogen from terrestrial ecosystems into aquatic ecosystems, where it is recycled in freshwater and marine food webs.

Studies of the Hubbard Brook Watershed

Water flows downhill, so local topography affects the movement of dissolved nutrients in terrestrial ecosystems. A **watershed** is an area of land from which precipitation drains into a single stream or river. Each watershed represents a part of an ecosystem from which nutrients exit through a single outlet. When several streams join to form a river, the watershed drained by the river encompasses the smaller watersheds drained by the streams. The Mackenzie River watershed covers roughly 20% of Canada and includes the watersheds of the Peace and Athabasca rivers, as well as many other watersheds drained by smaller streams and rivers.

Watersheds are ideal for large-scale field experiments about nutrient flow in ecosystems because they are relatively self-contained units. Herbert Bormann and Gene Likens conducted a classic experiment on nutrients in watersheds in the 1960s. Bormann and Likens manipulated small watersheds of temperate deciduous forest in the Hubbard Brook Experimental Forest in the White Mountain National Forest of New Hampshire. They measured precipitation and nutrient input into the watersheds, the uptake of nutrients by vegetation, and the amount of nutrients leaving the watershed via streamflow. They monitored nutrients exported in streamflow by collecting water samples from V-shaped concrete weirs built into bedrock below the streams that drained the watersheds **(Figure 1).** Impermeable bedrock underlies the soil, preventing water from leaving the system by deep seepage.

Gene E. Likens from Gene E. Likens et al., Ecology Micrograph, 40(1): 23–47, 1970

Figure 1
Weir used to measure the volume and nutrient content of water leaving a watershed by streamflow.

Bormann and Likens collected several years of baseline data on six undisturbed watersheds. Then, in 1965 and 1966, they felled all of the trees in one small watershed and used herbicides to prevent regrowth. After these manipulations, they monitored the output of nutrients in streams that drained experimental and control watersheds. They attributed differences in nutrient export between undisturbed watersheds (controls) and the clear-cut watershed (experimental treatment) to the effects of deforestation.

Bormann and Likens determined that vegetation absorbed substantial water and conserved nutrients in undisturbed watersheds. Plants used about 40% of the precipitation for transpiration. The rest contributed to runoff and groundwater. Control watersheds lost only about 8 to 10 kg of calcium per hectare each year, an amount replaced by erosion of bedrock and input from rain. Moreover, control watersheds actually accumulated about 2 kg of nitrogen per hectare per year and slightly smaller amounts of potassium.

The experimentally deforested watershed experienced a 40% annual increase in runoff, a 300% increase during a 4-month period in summer. Some mineral losses were similarly large. The net loss of calcium was 10 times higher **(Figure 2)** than in the control watersheds and of potassium was 21 times higher. Phosphorus losses did not increase because this mineral was apparently retained by the soil. The loss of nitrogen, however, was very large—120 $kg \cdot ha^{-1} \cdot y^{-1}$. The washing out of nitrogen meant that the stream draining the experimental watershed became choked with algae and cyanobacteria. The Hubbard Brook experiment demonstrated that deforestation increases flooding and decreases the fertility of ecosystems.

Figure 2
Calcium losses from the deforested watershed were much greater than those from controls. The arrow indicates the time of deforestation in early winter. Mineral losses did not increase until after the ground thawed the following spring. Increased runoff also caused large water losses from the watershed.

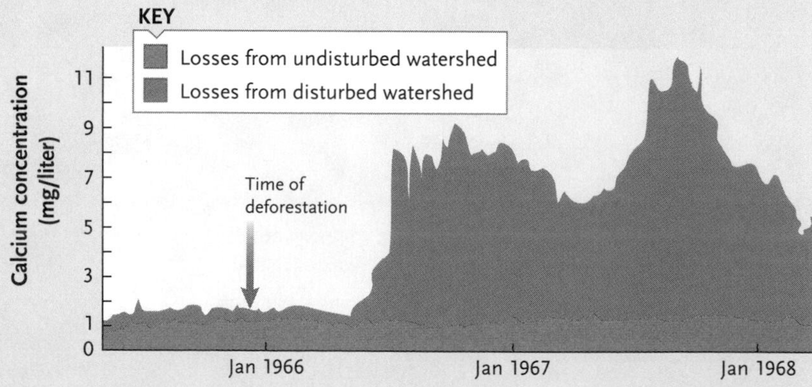

Table 47.2 Biochemical Processes That Influence Nitrogen Cycling in Ecosystems

Process	Organisms Responsible	Products	Outcome
Nitrogen fixation	Bacteria: *Rhizobium, Azotobacter, Frankia* Cyanobacteria: *Anabaena, Nostoc*	Ammonia (NH_3), ammonium ions (NH_4^+)	Assimilated by primary producers
Ammonification of organic detritus	Soil bacteria and fungi	Ammonia (NH_3), ammonium ions (NH_4^+)	Assimilated by primary producers
Nitrification			
(1) Oxidation of NH_3	Bacteria: *Nitrosomonas, Nitrococcus*	Nitrite (NO_2^-)	Used by nitrifying bacteria
(2) Oxidation of NO_2^-	Bacteria: *Nitrobacter*	Nitrate (NO_3^-)	Assimilated by primary producers
Denitrification of NO_3^-	Soil bacteria	Nitrous oxide (N_2O), molecular nitrogen (N_2)	Released to atmosphere

that lack such mutualists. Although these plants have the competitive edge in nitrogen-poor soil, nonmutualistic species often displace them in nitrogen-rich soil. In an interesting twist on the usual predator–prey relationships, several species of flowering plants living in nitrogen-poor soils capture and digest insects (see *Pitcher Plant Ecosystems*).

In addition to nitrogen fixation, other biochemical processes make large quantities of nitrogen available to producers. **Ammonification** of detritus by bacteria and fungi converts organic nitrogen into ammonia (NH_3), which dissolves in water to produce ammonium ions (NH_4^+) that plants can assimilate. Some ammonia escapes into the atmosphere as a gas. **Nitrification** by certain bacteria produces nitrites (NO_2^-), which are then converted by other bacteria to usable nitrates (NO_3^-). All of these compounds are water soluble, and water rapidly leaches them from soil into streams, lakes, and oceans.

Under conditions of low oxygen availability, **denitrification** by still other bacteria converts nitrites or nitrates into nitrous oxide (N_2O) and then into molecular nitrogen (N_2), which enters the atmosphere (see Table 47.2). This action can deplete supplies of soil nitrogen in waterlogged or otherwise poorly aerated environments, such as bogs and swamps.

In 1909, Fritz Haber developed a process for fixing nitrogen, and with the help of Carl Bosch, the process was commercialized for fertilizer production. The Haber–Bosch process has altered Earth's nitrogen cycles and is said to be responsible for the existence of 40% of the people on Earth. Before the implementation of the Haber–Bosch process, the amount of nitrogen available for life was limited by the rates at which N_2 was fixed by bacteria or generated by lightning strikes. Today, spreading fertilizers rich in nitrogen is the basis for most of the agriculture's productivity. This practice has quadrupled some yields over the past 50 years (see Chapter 49). Of all nutrients required for primary production, nitrogen is often the least abundant. Agriculture routinely depletes soil nitrogen, which is removed from fields through the harvesting of plants that have accumulated nitrogen in their tissues. Soil erosion and leaching remove more. Traditionally, farmers rotated their crops, alternately planting legumes and other crops in the same fields. In combination with other soil conservation practices, crop rotation stabilized soils and kept them productive, sometimes for hundreds of years. Some of the most arable land in New York State was farmed by members of the Mohawk Iroquois First Nations. The evidence of this comes from the locations of palisaded villages. The people moved their villages and farming operations every 10 to 20 years, changing fields repeatedly over hundreds of years.

The production of synthetic fertilizers is expensive, using fossil fuels as both raw material and an energy source. Fertilizer becomes increasingly costly as supplies of fossil fuels dwindle. Furthermore, rain and runoff leach excess fertilizer from agricultural fields and carry it into aquatic ecosystems. Nitrogen has become a major pollutant of freshwater ecosystems, artificially enriching the waters and allowing producers to expand their populations.

47.2d Phosphorus: Another Essential Element

Phosphorus compounds lack a gaseous phase, and this element moves between terrestrial and marine ecosystems in a sedimentary cycle **(Figure 47.15, p. 1199)**. Earth's crust is the main reservoir of phosphorus, as it is for other minerals, such as calcium and potassium, that also undergo sedimentary cycles.

Phosphorus is present in terrestrial rocks in the form of phosphates (PO_4^{3-}). In the **phosphorus cycle,** weathering and erosion add phosphate ions to soil and carry them into streams and rivers, which eventually transport them to the ocean. Once there, some phosphorus enters marine food webs, but most of it precipitates out of solution and accumulates for millions of years as insoluble deposits, mainly on continental

Disruption of the Carbon Cycle

The concentrations of gases in the lower atmosphere have a profound effect on global temperature, in turn affecting global climate. Molecules of CO_2, water vapour, ozone, methane, nitrous oxide, and other compounds collectively act like a pane of glass in a greenhouse (hence the term *greenhouse gases*). They allow short wavelengths of visible light to reach Earth's surface while impeding the escape of longer, infrared wavelengths into space, trapping much of their energy as heat **(Figure 1).** Greenhouse gases foster the accumulation of heat in the lower atmosphere, a warming action known as the **greenhouse effect**. This natural process prevents Earth from being a cold and lifeless planet.

Data from air bubbles trapped in glacial ice indicate that atmospheric CO_2 concentrations have fluctuated widely over Earth's history **(Figure 2).** Since the late 1950s, scientists have measured atmospheric concentrations of CO_2 and other greenhouse gases at remote sampling sites such as the top of Mauna Loa in the Hawaiian Islands. These sites are free of local contamination and reflect average global conditions. Concentrations of greenhouse gases have increased steadily for as long as they have been monitored **(Figure 3).**

The graph for atmospheric CO_2 concentration has a regular zigzag pattern that follows the annual cycle of plant growth (see Figure 3). The concentration of CO_2 decreases during the summer because photosynthesis withdraws so much from the atmospheric available-inorganic pool. The concentration of CO_2 is higher during the winter when photosynthesis slows while aerobic respiration continues, returning carbon to the atmospheric available-inorganic pool. Whereas the zigs and zags in the data for CO_2 represent seasonal highs and lows, the midpoint of the annual peaks and troughs has increased steadily for 40 years. These data are evidence of a rapid buildup of atmospheric CO_2, representing a shift in the distribution of carbon in the major reservoirs on Earth. The best estimates suggest that CO_2 concentration has increased by 35% in the last 150 years and by more than 10% in the last 30 years.

The increase in the atmospheric concentration of CO_2 appears to result from combustion, whether we burn fossil fuels or wood. Today, humans burn more wood and fossil fuels than ever before. Vast tracts of tropical forests are being cleared and burned (see Chapter 48). To make matters worse, deforestation reduces the world's biomass of plants that assimilate CO_2 and help maintain the carbon cycle as it existed before human activities disrupted it.

The increase in the concentration of atmospheric CO_2 is alarming because plants with C_3 metabolism respond to increased CO_2 concentrations with increased growth rates. This is not true of C_4 plants (see Chapter 7). Thus, rising atmospheric levels of CO_2 will probably alter the relative abundances of many plant species, changing the composition and dynamics of their communities.

Simulation models suggest that increasing concentrations of any greenhouse gas may intensify the greenhouse effect, contributing to a trend of global warming. Should we be alarmed about the prospect of a warmer planet? Some models predict that the mean temperature of the lower atmosphere will rise by 4°C, enough to increase ocean surface temperatures. In some areas, such as the Canadian Arctic and the Antarctic, warming has occurred much more rapidly than predicted or expected. Water expands when heated, and global sea level could rise as much as 0.6 m just from this expansion. In addition, atmospheric temperature is rising fastest near the poles.

Figure 1
The greenhouse effect.

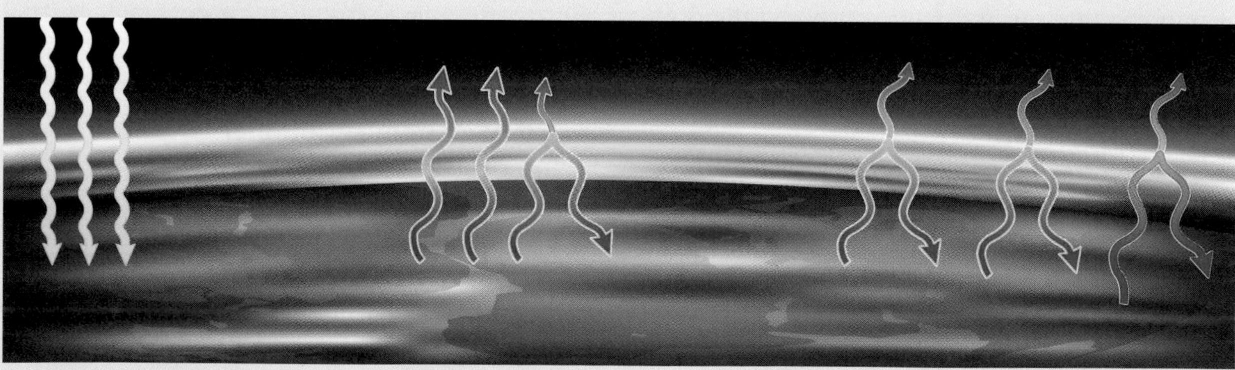

Sunlight penetrates the atmosphere and warms the Earth's surface.

The Earth's surface radiates heat (infrared wavelengths) to the atmosphere. Some heat escapes into space. Greenhouse gases and water vapor absorb some infrared energy and reradiate the rest of it back toward Earth.

When atmospheric concentrations of greenhouse gases increase, the atmosphere near the Earth's surface traps more heat. The warming causes a positive feedback cycle in which rising ocean temperatures cause increased evaporation of water, which further enhances the greenhouse effect.

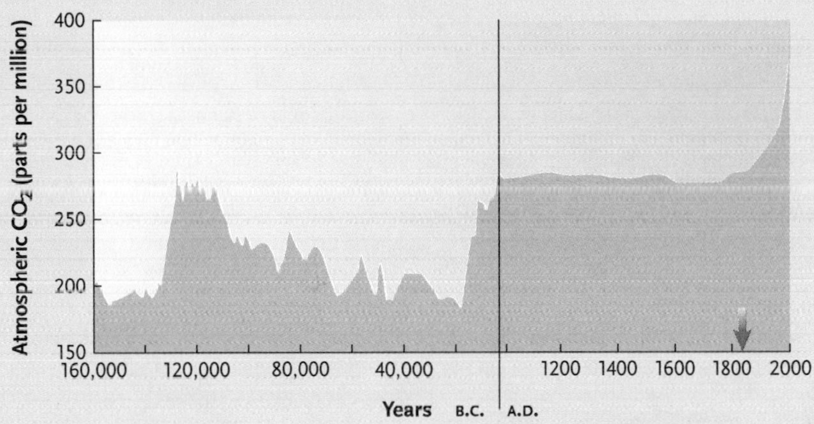

Figure 2
Carbon dioxide levels over time. The amount of atmospheric CO_2 has risen dramatically since about 1850 (arrow).

that global temperature may rise by several degrees. At the Earth Summit in 1992, leaders of the industrialized countries agreed to try to stabilize CO_2 emissions by the end of the twentieth century. We have already missed that target, and some countries, including the United States (then the largest producer of greenhouse gases), have now forsaken that goal as too costly. In 2008, it is likely that China and perhaps India will have surpassed the United States in production of greenhouse gases as these countries become more industrialized. Stabilizing emissions at current levels will not reverse the damage already done, nor will it stop the trend toward global warming. We should begin preparing for the consequences of global warming now. We might increase reforestation efforts because a large tract of forest can withdraw significant amounts of CO_2 from the atmosphere. We might also step up genetic engineering studies to develop heat-resistant and drought-resistant crop plants, which may provide crucial food reserves in regions of climate change.

Thus, global warming may also foster melting of glaciers and the Antarctic ice sheet, which might raise sea level as much as 50 to 100 m, inundating low coastal regions. Waterfronts in Vancouver, Los Angeles, Hong Kong, Durban, Rio de Janeiro, Sydney, New York, and London would be submerged. So would agricultural lands in India, China, and Bangladesh, where much of the world's rice is grown.

Moreover, global warming could disturb regional patterns of precipitation and temperature. Areas that now produce much of the world's grains would become arid scrub or deserts, and the now-forested areas to their north would become dry grasslands.

Many scientists believe that atmospheric levels of greenhouse gases will continue to increase at least until the middle of the twenty-first century and

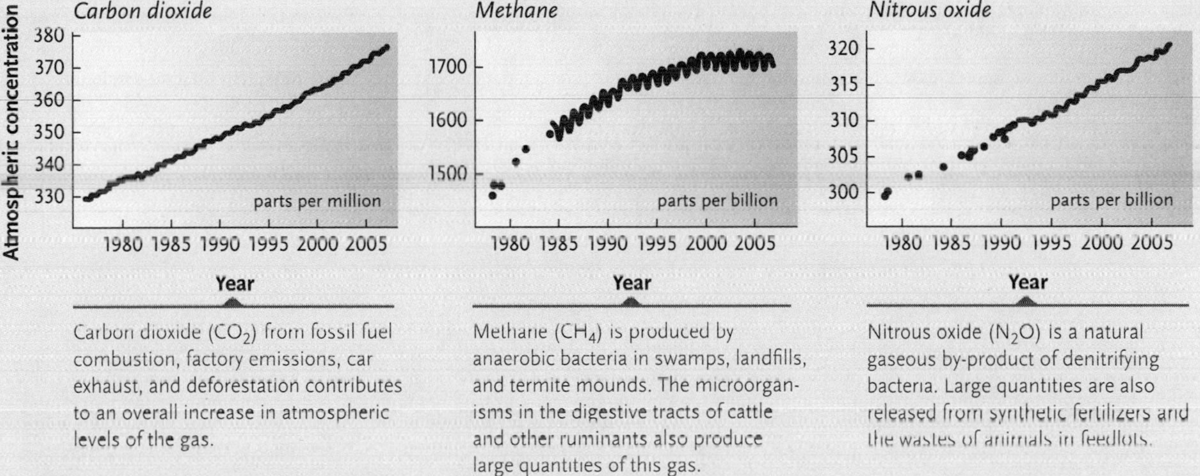

Carbon dioxide
Methane
Nitrous oxide
Atmospheric concentration
380
370
360
350
340
330
parts per million
1700
1600
1500
parts per billion
320
315
310
305
300
parts per billion
1980 1985 1990 1995 2000 2005
Year
Carbon dioxide (CO_2) from fossil fuel combustion, factory emissions, car exhaust, and deforestation contributes to an overall increase in atmospheric levels of the gas.
Methane (CH_4) is produced by anaerobic bacteria in swamps, landfills, and termite mounds. The microorganisms in the digestive tracts of cattle and other ruminants also produce large quantities of this gas.
Nitrous oxide (N_2O) is a natural gaseous by-product of denitrifying bacteria. Large quantities are also released from synthetic fertilizers and the wastes of animals in feedlots.

Figure 3
Increases in atmospheric concentrations of three greenhouse gases, mid-1970s through 2004. The data were collected at a remote monitoring station in Australia (Cape Grim, Tasmania) and compiled by scientists at the Commonwealth Scientific and Industrial Research Organization, an agency of the Australian government.

Pitcher Plant Ecosystems

Pitcher plants have modified leaves (pitchers) that act as pitfall traps for drowning and digesting insect prey. Pitchers have developed in at least five different evolutionary lines of vascular plants (see Chapter 29). Throughout much of North America, pitcher plants (the provincial flower of Newfoundland and Labrador; **Figure 1**) are common in bogs. *Sarracenia purpurea*, like other carnivorous plants, obtain much of their nitrogen from the insects they capture.

The captured arthropod prey, mainly ants and flies, is the base of a food web inside the pitchers. These are shredded and partly consumed by larvae of midges (*Metriocnemus knabi*) and sarcophagid flies (*Fletcherimyia fletcheri*; **Figure 2**). A subweb of bacteria and protozoa processes shredded prey, which are themselves prey for filter-feeding rotifers (*Habrotrocha rosa*; **Figure 3**) and mites (*Sarraceniopus gibsonii*). Mosquito larvae (*Wyeomyia smithii*) eat the bacteria, protozoa, and rotifers, whereas the larger sarcophagid fly larvae eat the rotifers and smaller mosquito larvae. Populations of bacteria, protozoa, and rotifers grow much more rapidly than populations of mosquito or midge larvae, making the system sustainable.

Pitchers are essential to the life cycles of two species of insects whose larvae live in them. A mosquito and a midge coexist in the same pitchers, and their populations are limited by the availability of insect carcasses. In any pitcher, growth in populations of the midge larvae is not affected by increases in the numbers of mosquito larvae. But populations of mosquito larvae increase as populations of midge larvae increase (see Figure 2).

The situation is an example of processing-chain commensalism because the action of one species creates opportunities for another. In this case, midge larvae feed on the hard parts of insect carcasses and break them up in the process. Mosquito larvae are filter-feeders, consuming particles derived from the decaying matter. The feeding of the midges generates additional food for the mosquito larvae. Although the populations of midge and mosquito larvae can be large in any pitcher, only a single sarcophagid fly larva occurs in any pitcher. *F. fletcheri* is a *K*-strategist (see Chapter 45) and gives birth to larvae. If you place more than one *F. fletcheri* larvae in a pitcher, a fight ensues. The larger larva either wins or leaves the pitcher to pupate in the sphagnum around it.

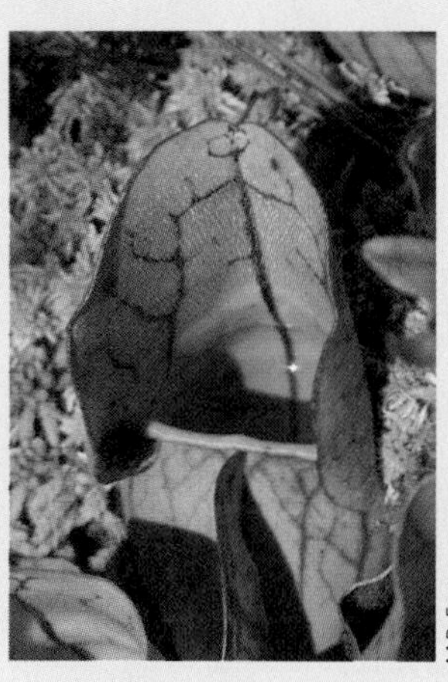

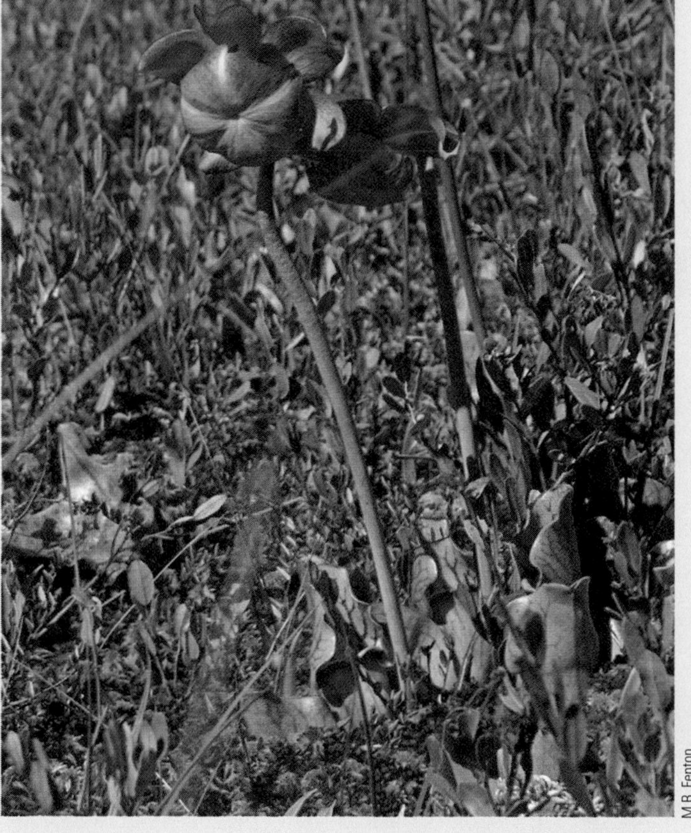

Figure 1
***Sarracenia purpurea*, a pitcher plant.** The flower on a long stalk extends above the pitchers. One pitcher is shown in the photo on the left.

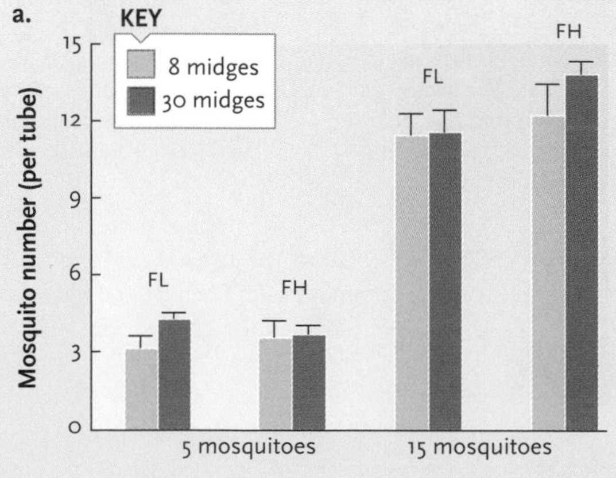

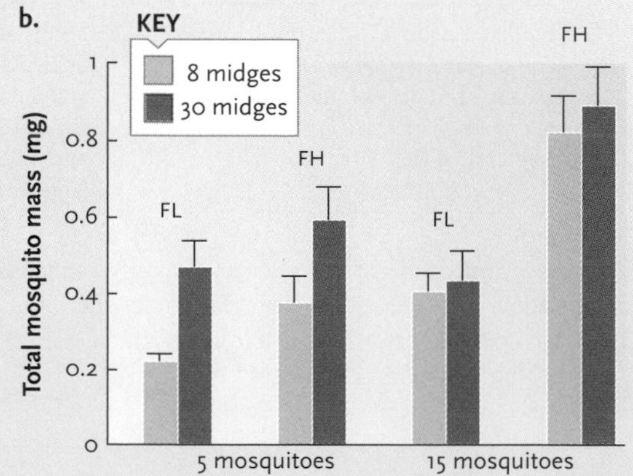

Figure 2
Midge and mosquito larvae in pitchers. (a) The density and **(b)** total dry mass of mosquito larvae are the same whether the population of midges is low (8 midges) or high (30 midges). FH = high food availability; FL = low food availability. Error bars show standard errors of the mean.

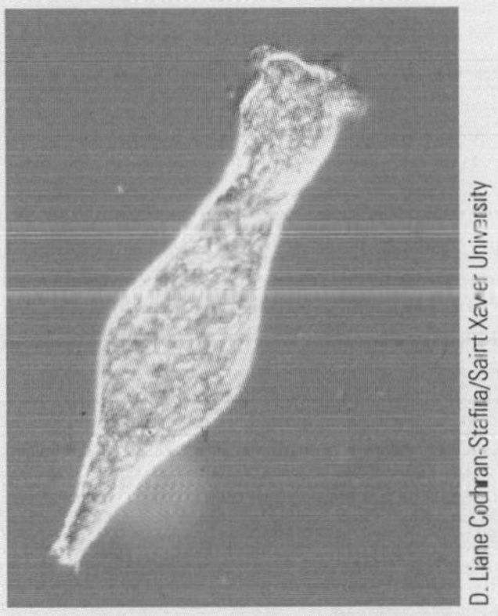

Figure 3
A bdelloid rotifer, *Habrotrocha rosa*, from a *Sarracenia purpurea* pitcher.

Figure 4
Moths whose caterpillars eat *Sarracenia purpurea*. The caterpillars of **(a)** *Exyra fax* and **(b)** *Papaipema appassionata* feed on pitcher plants, either **(a)** the lining of pitchers or **(b)** the rhizomes.

These insects do not appear to compete with their hosts, the pitcher plants. The abundance of rotifers living in the pitchers of *S. purpurea* is negatively associated with the presence of midge and mosquito larvae (which eat the rotifers). Rotifers are detritivores, and their excretory products (NO_3-N, NH_4OH, P) account for a major portion of the N acquired by the plants from their insect prey.

Two species of moths also exploit *Sarracenia purpurea* **(Figure 4)**. *Exyra fax* and *Papaipema appassionata* do not live in the pitchers. *E. fax* caterpillars eat the interior surface of the pitcher chambers, whereas *P. appassionata* caterpillars consume the rhizomes. Although predation by *E. fax* caterpillars does not kill the plants, predation by *P. appassionata* does. To what trophic level does one assign moths whose caterpillars are herbivores feeding on primary producers that eat insects?

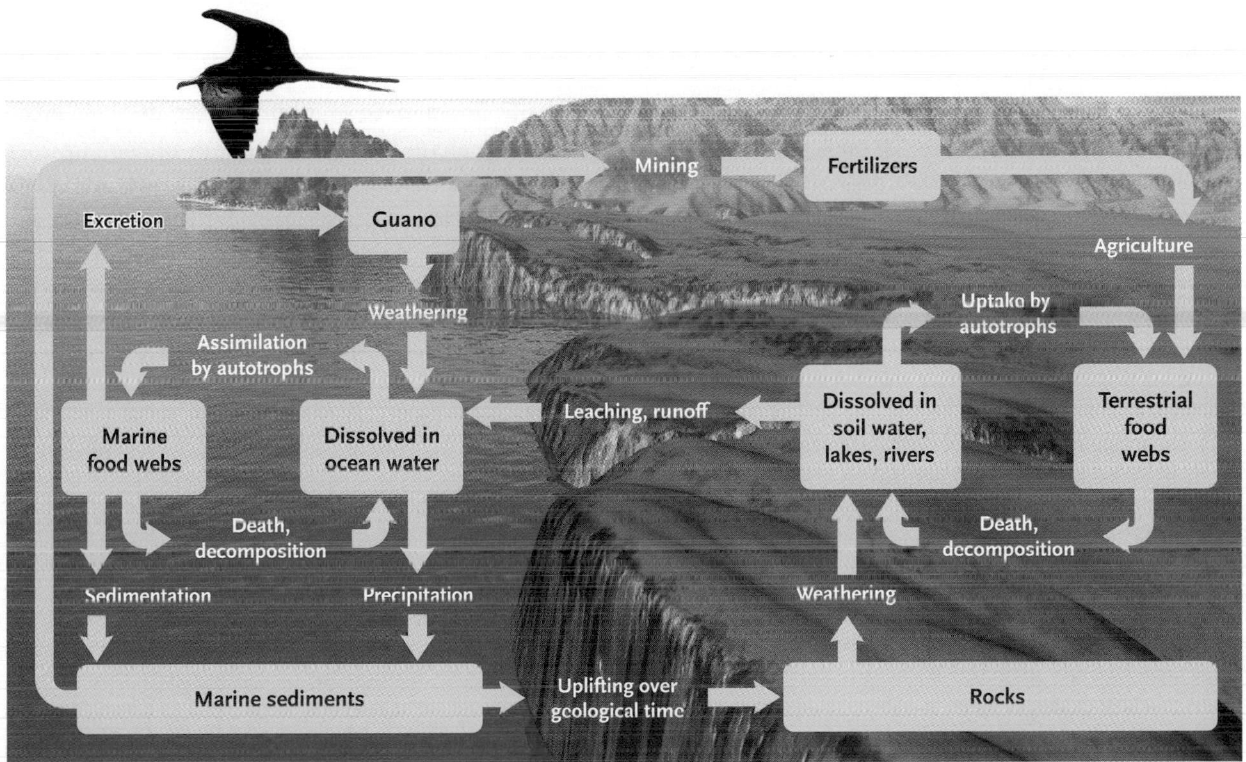

Figure 47.15
The phosphorus cycle. Phosphorus becomes available to biological systems when wind and rainfall dissolve phosphates in rocks and carry them into adjacent soil and freshwater ecosystems. Runoff carries dissolved phosphorus into marine ecosystems, where it precipitates out of solution and is incorporated into marine sediments.

People Behind Biology
Lenore Fahrig

The fragmentation of habitats is a ubiquitous effect of human activity on landscapes. In many parts of the world, land areas that used to be continuous forest are now large expanses of agricultural or urban landscapes dotted with small fragments of forest **(Figure 1)**. Lenore Fahrig examines the impact of landscape structure on the abundance, distribution, and persistence of organisms.

In her research, Dr. Fahrig uses a variety of organisms, from beetles to plants and birds. She considers habitats and the impacts of roads and fence lines. She and her students try to identify the habitat features associated with the persistence of species after fragmentation and the role of connectivity between fragments in the persistence of populations in the fragments.

Using a combination of theoretical and fieldwork, she has assessed the responses of species in different trophic roles to the fragmentation of habitat. Her work demonstrates that not all species respond in the same way and that some benefit from fragmentation.

The connections between theoretical work and reality emerge clearly from her research, and the implications for conservation of biodiversity (see Chapter 48) are clear.

Figure 1
An aerial view of farmland in southwestern Ontario illustrates isolated patches of forest (woodlots) and bands of woodland (riparian) along the edges of a creek. The woodlots are varied in their size and shape and in the degree of their isolation or connection to other woodlots.

shelves. When parts of the seafloor are uplifted and exposed, weathering releases the phosphates.

Plants absorb and assimilate dissolved phosphates directly, and phosphorus moves easily to higher trophic levels. All heterotrophs excrete some phosphorus as a waste product in urine and feces that become available after decomposition. Primary producers readily absorb the phosphate ions, so phosphorus cycles rapidly *within* terrestrial communities.

Supplies of available phosphate are generally limited, however, and plants acquire it so efficiently that they reduce soil phosphate concentration to extremely low levels. Thus, like nitrogen, phosphorus is a common ingredient in agricultural fertilizers, and excess phosphates are pollutants of freshwater ecosystems. A particularly good example is Lake Erie, one of the Great Lakes that was heavily affected by accumulations of phosphorus. The example here is more convincing because the problem has largely been resolved over the years.

For many years, phosphate for fertilizers was obtained from *guano* (the droppings of seabirds that consume phosphorus-rich food), which was mined on small islands that hosted seabird colonies, for example, in Polynesia and Micronesia. We now obtain most phosphate for fertilizer from phosphate rock mined in places such as Saskatchewan, with abundant marine deposits.

Study Break

1. How is balance maintained in the hydrogeologic cycle?
2. How do consumers obtain carbon?
3. What is the role of cyanobacteria in the nitrogen cycle? Why is their role important?

47.3 Ecosystem Modelling

Ecologists use modelling to make predictions about how an ecosystem will respond to specific changes in physical factors, energy flow, or nutrient availability. Analyses of energy flow and nutrient cycling allow us to create a *conceptual model* of how ecosystems function **(Figure 47.16)**. Energy that enters ecosystems is gradually dissipated as it flows through a food web. By contrast, nutrients are conserved and recycled among the system's living and nonliving components. This general model does not include processes that carry nutrients and energy out of one ecosystem and into another.

More importantly, the model ignores the nuts-and-bolts details of exactly how specific ecosystems function. Although it is a useful tool, a conceptual model does not really help us predict what would happen, say, if we harvested 10 million tonnes of introduced salmon from Lake Erie every year. We could simply harvest the fishes and see what happens. But ecologists prefer less intrusive approaches to study the potential effects of disturbances.

One approach to predicting "what would happen if ... " is **simulation modelling.** Using this approach, researchers gather detailed information about a specific ecosystem. They then derive a series of mathematical equations that define its most important relationships. One set of equations might describe how nutrient availability limits productivity at various trophic levels. Another might relate the population growth of zooplankton to the productivity of phytoplankton. Other equations would relate the population dynamics of primary carnivores to the availability of their food, and still others would describe how the densities of primary carnivores influence reproduction in populations at both lower and higher trophic levels. Thus, a complete simulation model is a set of interlocking equations that collectively predict how changes in one feature of an ecosystem might influence others.

Creating a simulation model is a challenge because the relationships within every ecosystem are complex. First, you must identify the important species, estimate their population sizes, and measure the average energy and nutrient content of each. Next, you would describe the food webs in which they participate, measure the quantity of food each species consumes, and estimate the productivity of each population. And, for the sake of completeness, you would determine the ecosystem's energy and nutrient gains and losses caused by erosion, weathering, precipitation, and runoff. You would repeat these measurements seasonally to identify annual variation in these factors. Finally, you might repeat the measurements over several years to determine the effects of year-to-year variation in climate and chance events.

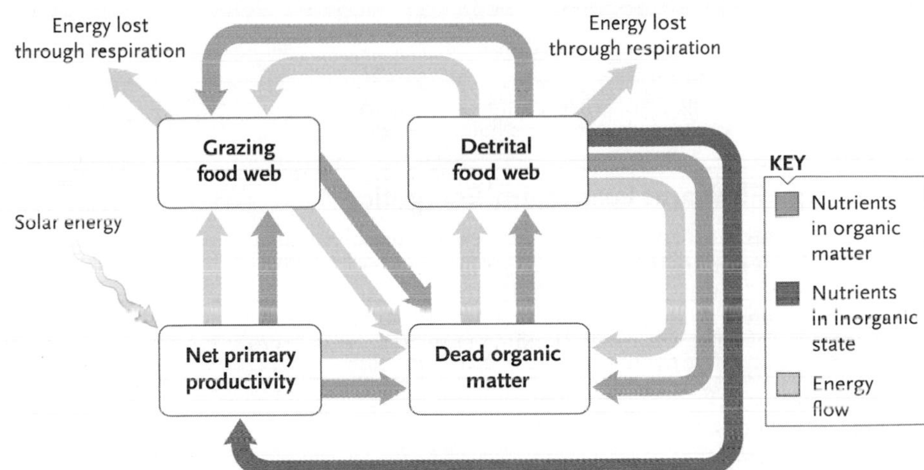

Figure 47.16
A conceptual ecosystem model. A simple conceptual model of an ecosystem illustrates how energy flows through the system and is lost from both detrital and grazing food webs. Nutrients are recycled and conserved.

After collecting these data, you would write equations that quantify the relationships in the ecosystem, including information about how temperature and other abiotic factors influence the ecology of each species. Having completed that job, you could begin to predict, possibly in great detail, the effects of adding 1000 new housing units to an area of native prairie or boreal forest. Of course, you would have to refine the model whenever new data became available.

Some ecologists devote their professional lives to studying ecosystem processes and creating simulation models. The long-term initiative at the Hubbard Brook Forest provides a good example (see *Studies of the Hubbard Brook Watershed*). As we attempt to understand larger and more complex ecosystems (and as we create larger and more complex environmental problems), modelling becomes an increasingly important tool. If a model is based on well-defined ecological relationships and good empirical data, it can allow us to make accurate predictions about ecosystem changes without the need for costly and environmentally damaging experiments. But, like all ideas in science, a model is only as good as its assumptions, and models must constantly be adjusted to incorporate new ideas and recently discovered facts.

Study Break

1. Briefly describe the process of simulation modelling.
2. Why is simulation modelling necessary?

Unanswered Questions

The impact of a large meteorite on Earth is said to have caused worldwide changes in climate. What biosphere and ecosystem changes would you expect to occur?

Review

Go to CENGAGENOW™ at http://hed.nelson.com/ to access quizzing, animations, exercises, articles, and personalized homework help.

47.1 Energy Flow and Ecosystem Energetics

- Net primary productivity is the chemical energy remaining in a system after energy has been used by producers to complete life processes and cellular respiration. Net primary productivity differs from standing crop biomass in that net primary productivity is a measure of energy, whereas standing crop biomass is a measure of dry weight.
- Other factors affect primary productivity, such as water and access to nutrients.
- Assimilation efficiency refers to energy absorbed from eating compared with the total energy in the food. Production efficiency is the energy content of new tissue material compared with the energy absorbed from food intake.
- Some energy is lost during transfer by consumption. The process becomes less efficient as the number of transfers increases, meaning that less energy is transferred to the final consumer.
- Biological magnification occurs when material (e.g., DDT) present in small amounts in a producer or "low-level" organism is consumed by another organism, transferring the material to the predator. DDT accumulates with each successive transfer. Top predators exhibit the highest concentrations of contaminants such as DDT.

47.2 Nutrient Cycling in Ecosystems

- The amount of water that leaves the Earth and enters the atmosphere through evaporation is equal to the amount of water reaching Earth by precipitation.
- Producers transfer atmospheric carbon (CO_2) into carbohydrates. Consumers then eat the producers and take in the carbohydrates.
- Cyanobacteria can fix nitrogen, which is crucial because although atmospheric nitrogen levels are high, this nitrogen is not accessible to plants or animals. Atmospheric nitrogen must be converted or "fixed" into a usable form such as ammonium and nitrate.
- Phosphate ions are carried to bodies of water through weathering and erosion, where most of it precipitates. Eventually, weathering releases phosphates, which are then directly absorbed by plants.

46.3 Ecosystem Modelling

- Modelling involves collecting data about an ecosystem and deriving mathematical equations about the relationships in the ecosystem. Data collected over different seasons and annual changes can be used to simulate the effects of a disruption on various levels of the ecosystem in question.
- Simulation modelling helps us understand and predict the impact of influences on certain ecosystems without actually conducting an experiment. Altering anything in an ecosystem without knowledge of its possible effects can be devastating on many or all levels.

Questions

Self-Test Questions

1. Which of the following events moves energy and material from a detrital food web into a grazing food web?
   a. A beetle eating the leaves of a living plant
   b. An earthworm eating dead leaves on the forest floor
   c. A robin catching and eating an earthworm
   d. A crow eating a dead robin
   e. A bacterium decomposing the feces of an earthworm
2. The total dry weight of plant material in a forest is a measure of the forest's
   a. gross primary productivity.
   b. net primary productivity.
   c. cellular respiration.
   d. standing crop biomass.
   e. ecological efficiency.
3. Which of the following ecosystems has the highest rate of net primary productivity?
   a. open ocean
   b. temperate deciduous forest
   c. tropical rain forest
   d. desert shrubs and thornwoods
   e. agricultural land
4. Endothermic animals exhibit a lower ecological efficiency than ectothermic animals because
   a. endotherms are less successful hunters than ectotherms.
   b. endotherms eat more plant material than ectotherms.
   c. endotherms are larger than ectotherms.
   d. endotherms produce fewer offspring than ectotherms.
   e. endotherms use more of their energy to maintain body temperature than ectotherms.
5. The amount of energy available at the highest trophic level in an ecosystem is determined by
   a. only the gross primary productivity of the ecosystem.
   b. only the net primary productivity of the ecosystem.
   c. the gross primary productivity and the standing crop biomass.
   d. the net primary productivity and the ecological efficiencies of herbivores.
   e. the net primary productivity and the ecological efficiencies at all lower trophic levels.
6. Some freshwater and marine ecosystems exhibit an inverted pyramid of
   a. biomass.
   b. energy.
   c. numbers.
   d. turnover.
   e. ecological efficiency.
7. Which process moves nutrients from the available-organic compartment to the available-inorganic compartment?
   a. respiration
   b. erosion
   c. assimilation
   d. sedimentation
   e. photosynthesis
8. Identify which of the following materials has a sedimentary cycle.
   a. water
   b. oxygen
   c. nitrogen
   d. phosphorus
   e. carbon

9. Which of the following statements is supported by the results of studies at the Hubbard Brook Experimental Forest?
   a. Most energy captured by primary producers is lost before reaching the highest trophic level in an ecosystem.
   b. Deforested watersheds experience a more significant decrease in runoff than undisturbed watersheds.
   c. Deforested watersheds lose more calcium and nitrogen in runoff than undisturbed watersheds.
   d. Nutrients generally move through biogeochemical cycles very quickly.
   e. Deforested watersheds generally receive more rainfall than undisturbed watersheds.
10. Biological magnification describes a phenomenon in which certain materials
   a. become increasingly concentrated in the tissues of animals at higher trophic levels.
   b. become most concentrated in the tissues of animals at the lowest trophic levels.
   c. accumulate only in the tissues of primary producers.
   d. accumulate only in the tissues of tertiary consumers.
   e. accumulate only in the tissues of detritivores.

Questions for Discussion

1. Identify 12 ecosystem changes associated with hydroelectric power projects. Consider upstream and downstream changes as well as those associated with transmission of generated power. How does preparing your answers draw on information presented in this chapter?
2. A lake near your home became overgrown with algae and pondweeds a few months after a new housing development was built nearby. What data would you collect to determine whether the housing development might be responsible for the changes in the lake?
3. Some politicians question whether recent increases in atmospheric temperature result from our release of greenhouse gases into the atmosphere. They argue that atmospheric temperature has fluctuated widely over Earth's history, and the changing temperature is just part of an historical trend. What information would allow you to refute or confirm their hypothesis? From another perspective, describe the pros and cons of reducing greenhouse gases as soon as possible versus taking a "wait and see" approach to this question.

A leopard photographed in the wild in South Africa.

Laura Erin Barclay

48 Conservation of Biodiversity

Study Plan

Why It Matters

Achieving preservation of the Earth's biodiversity is one of the most pressing challenges facing our species today. Numbers of species are a simple indicator of biodiversity, perhaps the most apparent and easy to grasp. But as we have seen, many species of organisms remain undescribed and unnamed. Without names and descriptions, how can we recognize or count them? As we shall see shortly, being unnamed means being unprotected. The Barcode of Life project (see Chapter 3) is one promising effort to better catalogue biodiversity by identifying and allowing us to name its components.

Research on ecosystems shows repeatedly how the numbers of species are associated with stability and productivity. The natural order (association between productivity and biodiversity), however, does not coincide with the productivity that our own species must achieve to feed our ever-expanding populations. Creating and maintaining agricultural monocultures is a way for us to maximize food production and efficiency of harvest. In many areas, this approach leads to the disappearance of family-operated farms. Is this progress that is justified by efforts to increase efficiency and yield? Humans also use genetically modified organisms to increase productivity and marketability, as well as other features, such as shelf life and portability. All too often, increased agricultural productivity is achieved by the use of more fertilizer, water, and energy. Does agriculture have to be the enemy of biodiversity?

Some people have connected humans' attitude to Earth and its riches with religious teachings. In 1967, Lynn White Jr., a professor of medieval history, explored the historical roots of our ecological crisis. He focused on the Christian view of creation, the importance of science, and the separation of humans from their environmental roots. A dualism between humans and nature had emerged in some Christian societies more than in others. Inherent in these societies was the prevailing idea that it is God's will that humans exploit nature for their own ends. White nominated St. Francis of Assisi **(Figure 48.1)** as the patron saint of ecologists. He said that appreciating the virtue of humility was key to understanding the teachings of St. Francis. His point was that as soon as an animal or a plant (or a meadow, lake, or grove of trees) has its own place in nature (in God's eyes), then it can become as important as we believe we are.

The onus is on us as citizens of the planet to conserve biodiversity. One of the main problems we must overcome is the attitude of many humans, as reviewed by White. Today a common reflection of this attitude is that being able to do something (afford to, have the means to) is justification enough for doing it—whether the project involves making space for a shopping mall by draining a wetland or cutting down the trees in a woodlot.

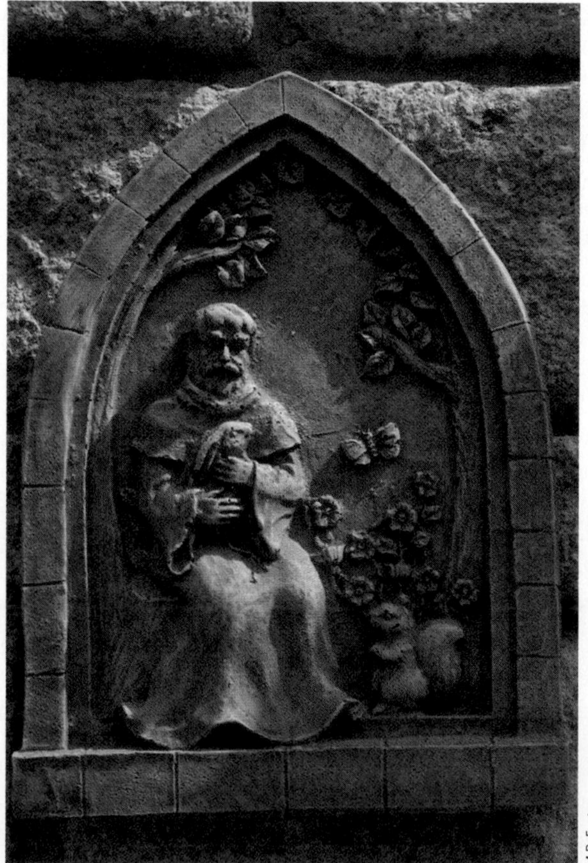
M.B. Fenton

Figure 48.1
St. Francis of Assisi.

If we as a species can recognize the importance of biodiversity and accept that the world is not ours to do with as we please, what, then, is the best route to protecting and conserving biodiversity? Should we focus on species? On genetic diversity? On ecosystems? How should we blend these approaches to achieve the best support for the endeavour? How can we engage people in this important activity and perhaps move them away from a human-centric view of the world?

As we shall see, at almost every turn are examples of human activities driving other species to extinction. The motivations for human actions range from little more than greed to the daily effort to survive. The purpose of this chapter is to introduce you to a range of situations and examples associated with the reduction of biodiversity by causing extinctions and the threat of extinction. We also consider steps that can be taken to protect biodiversity, including some successes and some failures.

48.1 Extinction

Extinction is part of the process of evolution. Given that life has been on Earth for about 3 billion years, today there are more extinct than living species. Occasionally, the fossil record demonstrates a continuum in time from one species to another, sometimes blurring the boundaries between taxa (see Chapter 18). In this case, one could argue that the original species in a series lives on in its descendants. For example, the discovery that the genome of *Homo sapiens sapiens* contains some genes from *Homo sapiens neanderthalensis* leaves open the question about the distinctness of the two taxa. Although data for fossil species usually do not permit us to assess the levels of gene flow between populations, the Neanderthals provide an interesting exception. The difficulties inherent in applying the species concept to fossil material is familiar to paleontologists but less so to biologists.

Species and lineages have been going extinct since life first appeared. We should expect species to disappear at some low rate, the **background extinction rate**; as environments change, poorly adapted organisms do not survive and reproduce. In all likelihood, more than 99.9% of the species that have ever lived are now extinct. David Raup has suggested that, on average, as many as 10% of species go extinct every million years and more than 50% go extinct every 100 million years. Thus, the history of life has been characterized by an ongoing turnover of species.

The fossil record indicates that extinction rates rose well above the background rate at least five times in Earth's history. These events are referred to as mass extinctions. One extinction occurred at the end of the

Ordovician and the beginning of the Devonian, the next at the end of the Devonian, then the end of the Permian, the end of the Triassic, and the end of the Cretaceous. The Permian extinction was the most severe, and more than 85% of the species alive at that time disappeared forever. This extinction was the end of the trilobites, many amphibians, and the trees of the coal swamp forests. During the last mass extinction, at the end of the Cretaceous, half of the species on Earth, including most dinosaurs, disappeared. A sixth mass extinction, potentially the largest of all, is occurring now as a result of human degradation of the environment.

Different factors were responsible for the five mass extinctions. Some were probably caused by tectonic activity and associated changes in climate. For example, the Ordovician extinction occurred after Gondwana moved toward the South Pole, triggering a glaciation that cooled the world's climate and lowered sea levels. The Permian extinction coincided with a major glaciation and a decline in sea level induced by the formation of Pangea (see Chapter 20).

Many researchers believe that an asteroid impact caused the Cretaceous mass extinction. The resulting dust cloud may have blocked the sunlight necessary for photosynthesis, setting up a chain reaction of extinctions that began with microscopic marine organisms. Geologic evidence supports this hypothesis. Rocks dating to the end of the Cretaceous period (65 million years ago) contain a highly concentrated layer of iridium, a metal that is rare on Earth but common in asteroids. The impact from an iridium-laden asteroid only 10 km in diameter could have caused an explosion equivalent to a billion tonnes of TNT that scattered iridium dust around the world. Geologists have identified the submarine Chicxulub crater, 180 km in diameter, off Mexico's Yucatán peninsula as the likely site of the impact.

Although scientists agree that an asteroid struck Earth at that time, many question its precise relationship to the mass extinction. Dinosaurs had begun their decline at least 8 million years earlier, but many persisted for at least 40 000 years after the impact. Moreover, other groups of organisms did not suddenly disappear, as one would expect after a global calamity. The Cretaceous extinction took place over tens of thousands of years. Furthermore, some organisms survived periods of extinction, such as ginkgo trees (*Ginkgo biloba*), horseshoe crabs (*Limulus polyphemus*), and coelocanths (*Latimeria chalumnae*).

Even today we cannot blame the extinctions of most species on the activities of humans. But our increasing technological capability and prowess coincide with a burgeoning population of people. This situation is exacerbated by the philosophical view that humans are disconnected from nature. Thus, we are becoming better and better at destroying the biota of the planet. Taking action requires identifying root causes and then trying to make changes that will alleviate the problems.

First, we consider extinctions not linked to humans and then review examples of situations in which our actions have either directly or indirectly led to the extinction of species. The fact that extinction is integral to the process of evolution is hardly justification or rationalization for our driving so many species there. Put another way, invoking "survival of the fittest" may not be adequate justification for eradicating other species.

48.1a Dinosaurs: The Most Notable Extinction

Why do species go extinct? There could be as many theories as there are extinct species! The disappearance of the dinosaurs is one of the best-known extinction events in the Earth's history. At the end of the Cretaceous about 65.5 million years ago, the dinosaurs disappeared. The ancestors of dinosaurs had appeared in the Triassic, and the group underwent extensive adaptive radiation reflected in body size, lifestyle, and distribution. Although people think of large and spectacular carnivorous dinosaurs such as *Tyrannosaurus rex* or the huge herbivore *Apatosaurus* (previously known as *Brontosaurus*), in reality, many species of dinosaurs were small and delicate.

Evidence from deposits in Alberta suggests that the carnivorous dinosaurs *Albertosaurus* **(Figure 48.2)** showed age-specific mortality and high juvenile survival **(Figure 48.3a, p. 1208)**. Indeed, the survivorship curves (see Chapter 45) for *Albertosaurus* resemble those for humans **(Figure 48.3b)**. The data do not

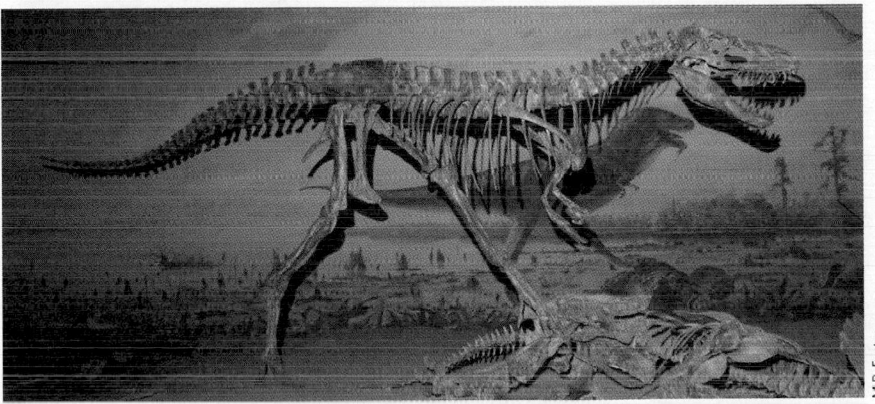

Figure 48.2
Mounted skeleton of *Albertosaurus* on display in the Royal Tyrrell Museum, Drumheller, Alberta.
This late Cretaceous carnivore is abundant in fossil beds in Alberta and elsewhere.

Life on the Edge

Sex Determination and Global Warming

Failure to reproduce puts the survival of a species on the edge, so anything that interferes with reproduction can be threatening. Genetic recombination is a fundamental benefit of sexual reproduction, enabling it to increase genetic diversity and eliminate deleterious mutants. Effective sexual reproduction means having male and female systems, sometimes in one individual (hermaphrodites) and perhaps more often in different individuals. Males and females differ in many fundamental ways—genetically, hormonally, physiologically, and anatomically.

In humans and many other animals, gender is determined by genotype, with males having an X and a Y chromosome and females having two X chromosomes. In many reptiles, however, gender is determined environmentally. Eggs incubated at some temperatures develop into males; when incubated at other temperatures, they produce females.

In 2008, D.A. Warner and R. Shine reported the results of experiments done with jacky dragons (*Amphibolurus muricatus*), an Australian lizard in which gender is determined by temperature. Eggs incubated at 23° to 26°C or 30° to 33°C produce females; those incubated from 27° to 29°C produce males. Warner and Shine tested the hypothesis that temperature-dependent sex determination ensured production of females when they had an advantage and males when the advantage was to them. Using a combination of temperature and hormonal manipulations, Warner and Shine could produce males or females at any temperature. They used analysis of paternity to assess the reproductive output of these males and observation of eggs laid and hatching to document these females' reproductive output.

In female jacky dragons, larger body sizes occur at higher temperatures, and larger females have higher fecundity than smaller ones. Higher temperatures also correlate with larger body size in males. However, males hatched from eggs incubated between 27° and 29°C sired more offspring than those hatched from eggs incubated at lower or higher temperatures.

Change in climate, such as global warming, could put species with temperature-dependent sex determination at risk by effectively eliminating males or females from the population. Eggs incubated at the "wrong" temperatures will fail to hatch. The importance of variation in temperature during development in ectothermic organisms could explain the prevalence of genotypic-dependent sex determination in euthermic (homeothermic) viviparous animals. Viviparous or ovoviviparous ectotherms (fish, amphibians, reptiles, other animals) could also rely on temperature-dependent gender determination, provided that their developing young experience an appropriate range of temperatures.

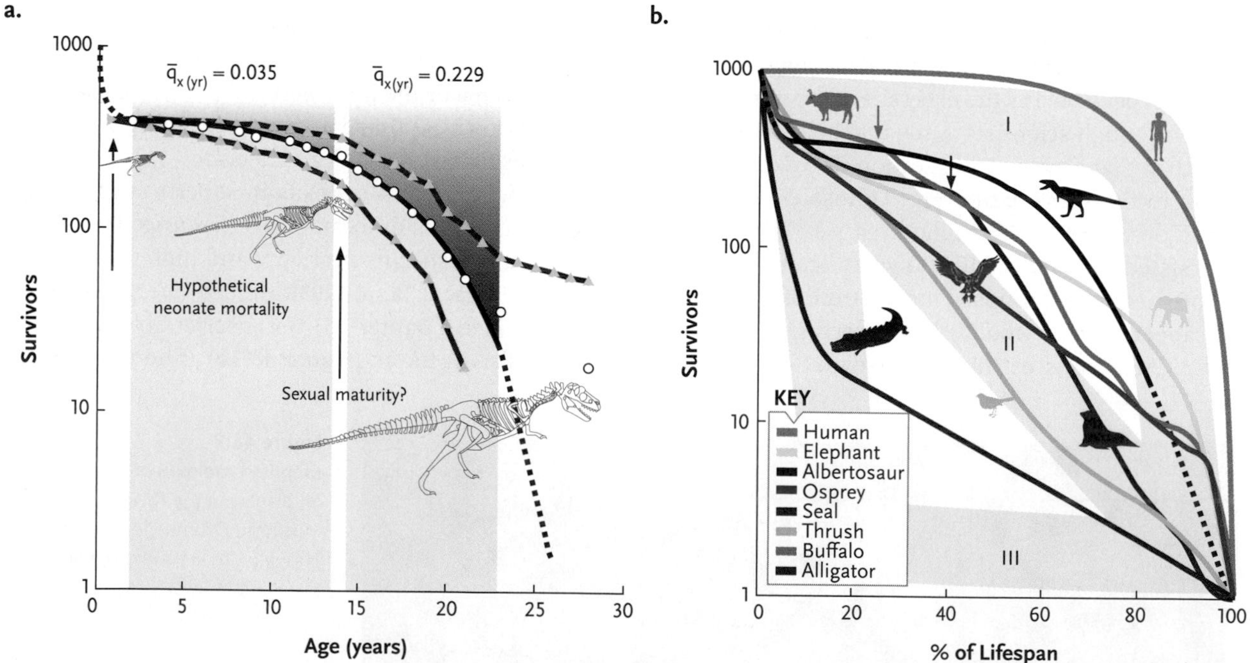

Figure 48.3
(a) Survivorship curve for a hypothetical cohort of 1000 *Albertosaurus* presumed neonatal mortality of 60%. **(b)** Survivorship of *Albertosaurus* compared with that of other animals, including humans from developed countries, short-lived birds, mammals, and lizards, as well as crocodilians and some captive mammals.

People Behind Biology
Amanda Vincent

Sea horses (see Figure 39.1) are a central focus for Professor Amanda Vincent's research. She holds a Canada Research Chair in marine conservation and is the director of Project Seahorse. Sea horses are notable for the details of their biology (see Chapter 41) and because they are big business.

Dr. Vincent has studied the behaviour of sea horses. During mating, the male's sperm fertilizes the female's eggs, but the female then transfers the fertilized eggs to the male's brood pouch; thus, the male gets "pregnant." Males and females are in regular contact during the period of pregnancy. These contact behaviours may be key to the monogamy that appears to be typical of male–female relationships in sea horses.

The world trade in sea horses involves an estimated 20 million of them each year. In Asia, millions of dried sea horses are traded each year, mainly for use in traditional Chinese medicines. Remedies that include sea horses are said to be useful in treating symptoms from asthma and skin problems to incontinence and disorders of the thyroid. Dried sea horses may also be ingredients in aphrodisiacs.

Amanda Vincent has been very active in efforts to conserve sea horses, including working with local fishing communities to conserve them and maintain a sustainable harvest. This means establishing local protected areas and growing some sea horses in controlled conditions so that they, rather than wild stock, are harvested.

Professor Vincent is an example of a biologist who combines an academic interest with its practical applications. Her work in conservation connects the realities of harvesting animals with the demands for their conservation.

provide any indication of a flaw that predisposed dinosaurs to extinction. This is sobering, given the similarity between some aspects of dinosaur population biology and our own. The prevailing view today is that the disappearance of the dinosaurs is linked to the impact of an asteroid. Many other theories have been proposed to explain extinction, but the fact that birds and mammals and many other groups of organisms showed widespread extinctions at the end of the Cretaceous implies a pervasive catastrophic event.

48.1b Multituberculates: A Mammalian Example

There is more to extinction than dinosaurs. Competition (see Chapter 46) has been proposed as a mechanism that can lead to extinction. Among mammals, the adaptive radiation of rodents (order Rodentia; **Figure 48.4a**) in the early Oligocene coincides with the disappearance of multituberculates (order Multituberculata; **Figure 48.4b**). As a group, multituberculates were prominent and persisted for 100 million years (compared with 150 million years for dinosaurs), making them the most successful mammals to date.

Multituberculates ranged from small (~20 g) to medium (5 to 10 kg) in size and exhibited both terrestrial and arboreal lifestyles. We can only speculate what happened to them, and why they became extinct. The widespread success of rodents almost worldwide could lend credibility to competition as the reason for the multituberculates' demise. However, the fossil record does not tell us what rodents and multituberculates competed for: food? nest sites?

Study Break

1. What is extinction?
2. What were multituberculates?

a.

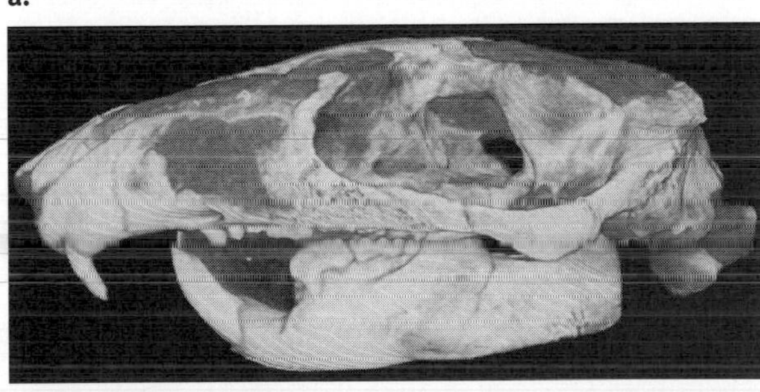

Dr. Ted Macrini, 2001, "Kryptobaatar dashzevegi" (On-line), Digital Morphology. Accessed from: http://digimorph.org/specimens/Kryptobaatar_dashzevegi/

b.

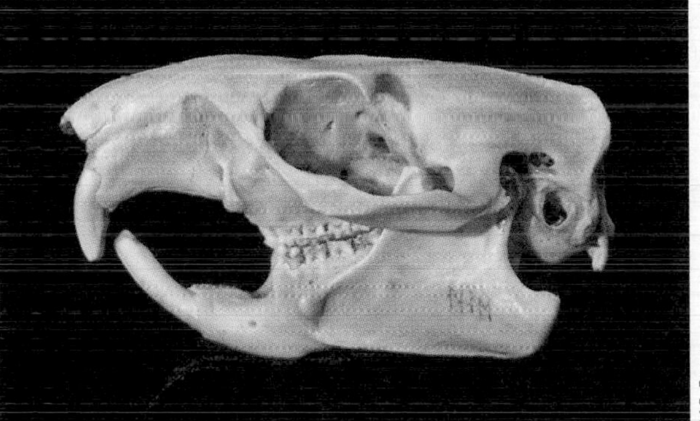

M.B. Fenton

Figure 48.4
(a) A skull of a groundhog (*Marmota monax*), a North American rodent, compared with **(b)** a skull of a multituberculate (*Kryptobaatar dashzevegi*) from the Mongolian late Cretaceous.

48.2 The Impact of Humans

When it comes to extinctions, we know most about those resulting from our activities, usually because these records are relatively recent and accessible. If you recently visited Mauritius, you might have noticed that the few remaining Mauritian calvaria trees were slowly dying of old age. Their passing will mark the extinction of this species, which has occurred even though the trees continued to bloom and produce seeds. The key to the pending extinction of *Sideroxylon majus* is the earlier extinction of Dodos. To germinate, seeds of Mauritian calvaria trees had to pass through the Dodo's digestive tract. The Dodo **(Figure 48.5)** was a medium-sized flightless bird that lived on the island of Mauritius. When European sailors first visited the island, they used Dodos as a source of fresh meat. Then, as the island was settled, the birds were exposed to introduced predators (cats, dogs, rats) and an expanding human population. Dodos vanished by 1690.

Species confined to islands often have small populations and are unaccustomed to terrestrial predators, making them vulnerable to extinction. The fossil and subfossil records show that many species of birds disappeared from islands in the South Pacific as Polynesians arrived there from the west. This occurred from Tonga to Easter Island and beyond **(Figure 48.6)**. The Galápagos, only discovered by people in 1535, was sheltered from the wave of human-induced extinctions. On Easter Island, endemic species of sea birds and other species disappeared soon after people settled there. These examples demonstrate that humans do not have to be industrial or "high tech" to effect extinctions.

Meanwhile, in the North Atlantic, people hunted *Pinguinus impennis*, the great auk, to extinction. However, land birds with large distributions and huge populations have also disappeared, such as *Ectopistes migratorius*, the passenger pigeon in eastern North America. Large-scale harvesting of these birds, combined with their low reproductive rate (clutch size: one egg), made the birds vulnerable in spite of their enormous populations. Animals that produce one young per year and suffer "normal" mortality must live at least 10 years to replace themselves in the population (see Chapter 45).

b.

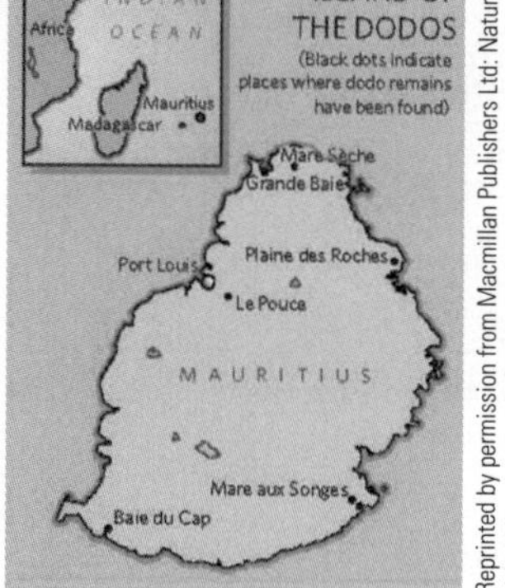

Figure 48.5
(a) A reconstruction of a *Raphus cucullatus*, the Dodo, an extinct flightless bird from **(b)** Mauritius.

Study Break

1. When did the five mass extinctions occur? Which was the most severe? Which extinction affected the dinosaurs?
2. What caused these extinctions?
3. Why are island animals and plants particularly susceptible to extinction due to human impacts?

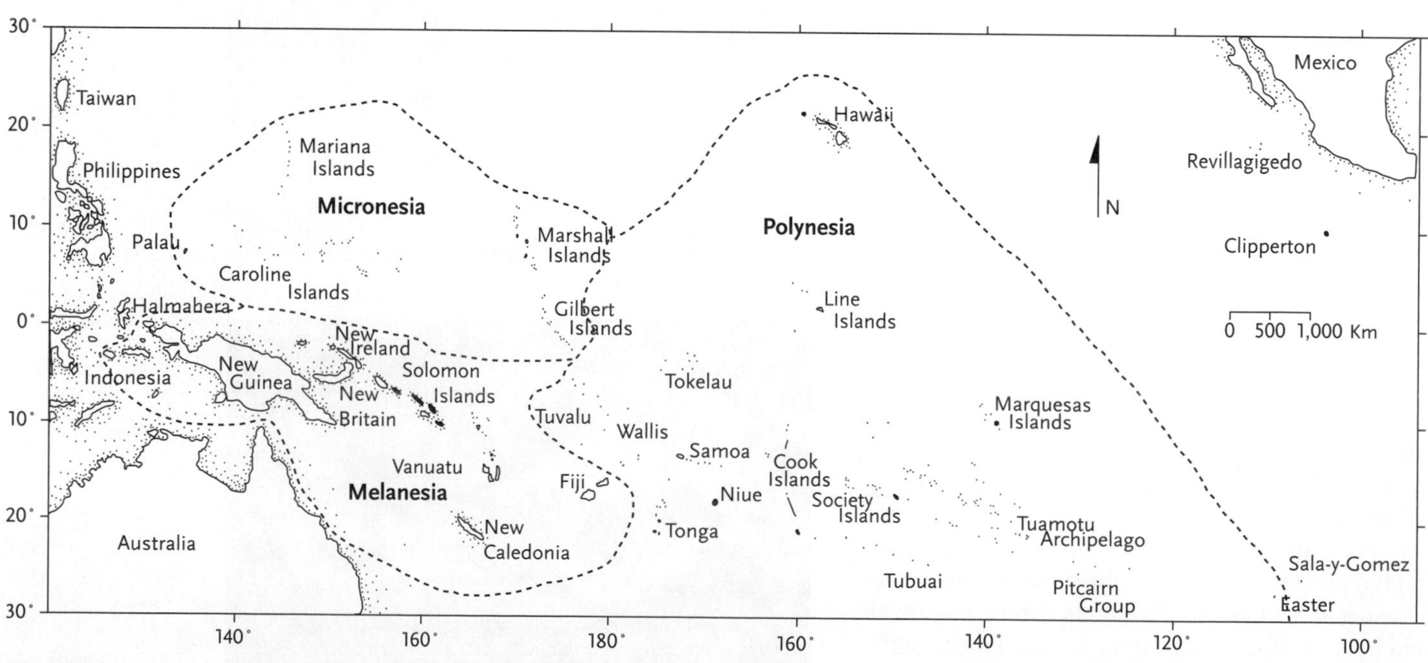

Figure 48.6
Islands in the South Pacific where the arrival of Polynesians coincided with the extinction of many island species of birds.

Molecule Behind Biology

The 2,4-D Molecule and Resiliency

Resiliency is one of the most impressive features of life at the species and/or ecosystem levels. In one respect, this feature complicates the challenges of conserving biodiversity because introduced species can be so invasive, reflecting their adaptability.

Humans first identified 2,4-D (2,4-dichlorophenoxyacetic acid; **Figure 1**) in 1942, and from 1944, it was marketed as a herbicide more effective against broad-leaved plants than against grasses. Technically, 2,4-D is a hormone absorbed by the plant and translocated to the growing points of roots and shoots. 2,4-D kills weeds by inhibiting growth. The global market for 2,4-D is probably more than U.S.$300 million, and it is mainly used to control broad-leaved weeds in cereal crops. According to the World Health Organization (WHO), 2,4-D is a "moderately hazardous pesticide" known to affect a variety of animals (e.g., dogs but not rats). Curiously, it turns out that other animals may use 2,4-D for their own ends.

In 1971, Thomas Eisner and colleagues reported that a grasshopper (*Romalea microptera*; **Figure 2**) produced a froth of chemicals **(Figure 3)** for protection against ants. One of the main ingredients in the froth was 2,5-dichlorophenol, apparently derived from 2,4-D. This is an astonishing demonstration of adaptability that can underlie resiliency.

Resiliency and the recuperative powers of ecosystems are demonstrated by stories of "lost cities," for example, structures built by Maya in Central America, being found in a jungle. Archaeological evidence reveals that in some habitats, these buildings and pyramids were overgrown by the rain forest in ~100 years. The Great Zimbabwe Ruins in southern Africa were overgrown by savannah woodland in a period of 100 to 200 years and only latterly "discovered" by European explorers.

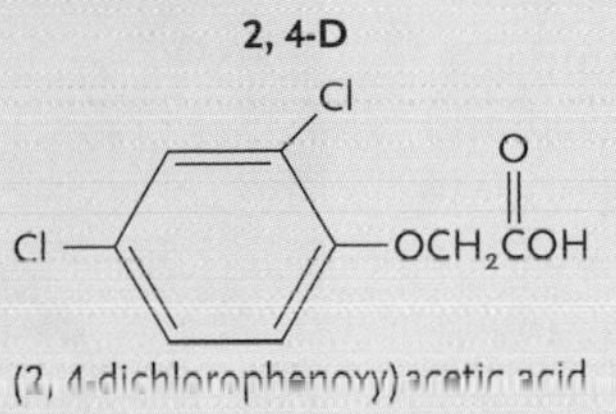

2, 4-D

Cl — Cl — OCH_2COH (O)

(2, 4-dichlorophenoxy)acetic acid

Figure 1
2,4-Dichlorophenoxyacetic acid, 2,4-D.

Figure 2
Romalea microptera, a grasshopper that uses an ant repellent with a 2,4-D derivative.

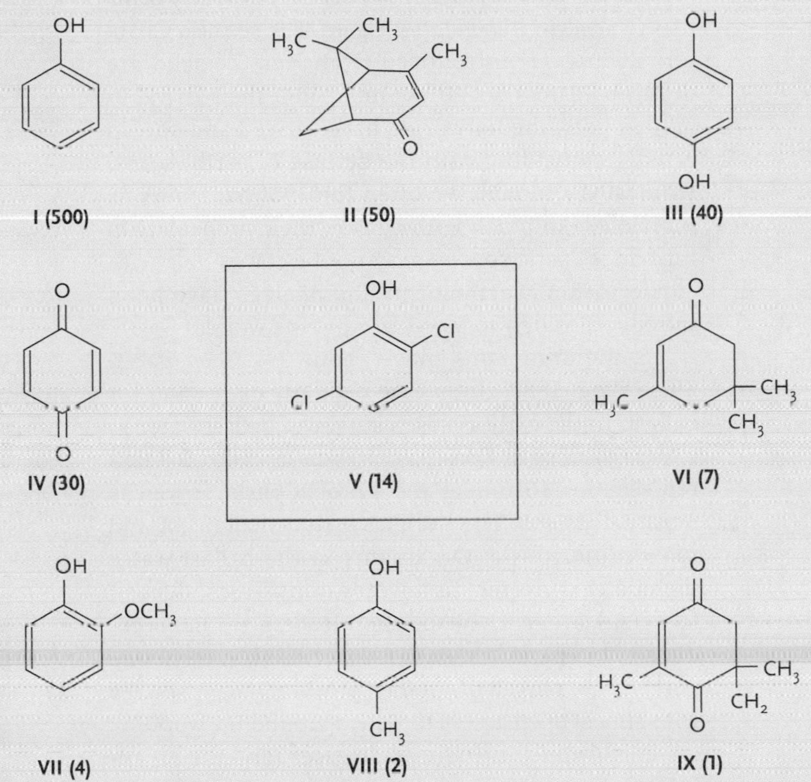

Figure 3
Active ingredients in the defensive froth of the grasshopper, *Romalea microptera*. 2,5-Dichlorophenol (boxed) is apparently derived from 2,4-D.

48.3 Introduced and Invasive Species

Humans cause extinction through hunting and by the introduction of other species. House cats, *Felis domesticus*, are among the worst introductions people have made. Anecdotal records suggest that in 1894, one house cat (named "Tibbles") exterminated an entire population of flightless wrens **(Figure 48.7, p. 1212)** on Stephen's Island, a 2.6 km^2 island off the north shore of New Zealand. Fossils indicate that the wrens had occurred widely in New Zealand. This record stands for one individual, Tibbles, taking out the remaining ~10 pairs and exterminating the species.

Figure 48.7
Stephen's Island Wren, *Xenicus lyalli.* This species was exterminated by one cat.

It should be obvious that moving species from one part of the world to another, whether done willfully or by accident, can have calamitous impacts. The invaders, once arrived and established, may outcompete resident species, laying waste to species and ecosystems. The list of introduced organisms is very long and includes many domesticated or commensal species of animals and plants. The arrival of zebra mussels **(Figure 48.8a)** in the Great Lakes is the main reason for the decline of the now endangered eastern pond mussels **(Figure 48.8b).** The immigrant mussels outcompeted and overgrew the native ones, reducing their range and populations to levels that resulted in eastern pond mussels being recommended for listing as endangered in Canada in 2007.

Meanwhile, in parts of the British Isles, flatworms (*Arthurdendyus triangulatus*; **Figure 48.9;** see also Chapters 26 and 41) introduced from New Zealand are deadly predators of earthworms. Since their arrival in garden pots, the flatworms have thrived and spread rapidly, coinciding with the demise of earthworms. Ironically, although we often think of gardeners as individuals in touch with nature, their propensity to introduce exotic species may not be compatible with conservation. Earthworms themselves have been introduced widely to places around the world.

Some organisms move about in ballast water. Since about 1880, ships have regularly used water for ballast. In the early 1990s, a survey of ballast water in 159 cargo ships in Coos Bay, Oregon, revealed 367 taxa representing 16 animal and 3 protist phyla, as well as 3 plant divisions. The samples included all major and most minor phyla. Organisms in the ballast water included carnivores, herbivores, omnivores, deposit feeders, scavengers, suspension feeders, primary producers, and parasites. Ballast water is taken on in one port and discharged in another, providing many species with almost open access to waters around the world.

Meanwhile, introduced diseases (and the organisms that cause them) have decimated, if not obliterated, resident species. When Europeans arrived in the New World, *Castanea dentata*, the American chestnut tree, was widespread in forests from southern Ontario to Alabama. This large tree of the forest canopy grew to heights of 30 m. Often most abundant on prime agricultural soils, the distribution and density of the species were reduced as settlers from Europe cleared more and more land for agriculture. *Endothia parasitica*, the chestnut blight, was introduced perhaps around 1904 from Asian nursery stock. This introduced blight killed the American chestnut trees by the 1930s. By 2000, only scattered American chestnut trees remained, most of them stump sprouts.

a.

b.

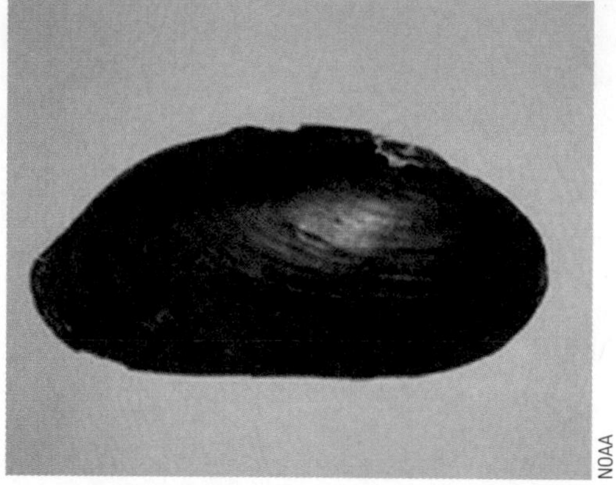

Figure 48.8
(a) Zebra mussels, *Dressina polymorpha*, were introduced to the Great Lakes in North America, where they have spread rapidly. **(b)** They are directly responsible for the declines in eastern pond mussels (*Lampsilis radiata*), a local mussel species.

Why are invading species so successful? Does the spread of Starlings (*Sturnus vulgaris*) or dandelions (*Taraxacum officinale*) after introduction to new continents suggest that they moved into vacant niches? Does it mean that they are better competitors? In the

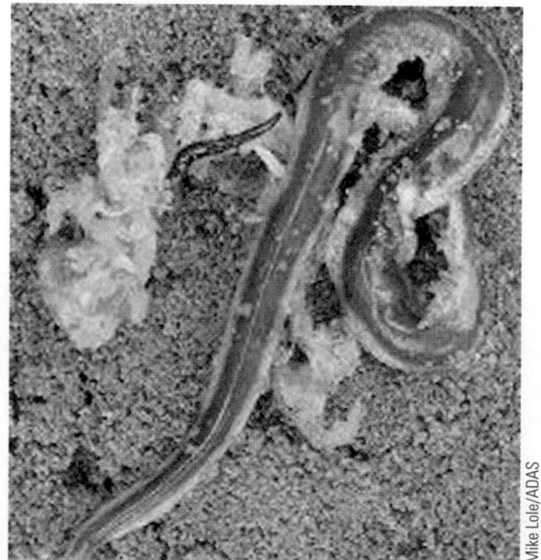

Figure 48.9
This earthworm-eating planarian (*Arthurdendyus triangulatus*) was introduced to the British Isles from New Zealand. It has had a devastating effect on local populations of earthworms.

case of starlings, 13 birds were introduced to Central Park in New York City in 1890, and they have spread far and wide. Once they are established, invading or introduced species can pose huge conservation problems because of their effects on ecosystems and diversity.

Although many invaders arrive, only a few are widely successful and become large-scale problems in their new settings. Invading plants are most often successful in nutrient-rich habitats, where they can achieve high growth rates, early reproduction, and maximal production of offspring. What happens in resource-poor settings? In the past, conventional wisdom has suggested that low-resource settings could be reservoirs for native species that could outcompete invaders.

However, an experimental examination of the responses of native and introduced species to challenging conditions revealed that invasive plant species almost always fared better **(Figure 48.10)**. *Resource use efficiency* (RUE), calculated by measuring carbon assimilation per unit of resource, provides an indicator of success. Many invasive species, such as ferns, C_3 and C_4 grasses, herbs, shrubs, and trees, were more successful in low-resource systems than native species were.

This research was conducted in Hawaii, an excellent place for studying invasive species because so many are there. Among the invaders were *Bromus tectorum* (cheatgrass), *Heracleum mantegazzianum* (cartwheel flower or giant hogweed), and *Pinus radiata* (Monterey pine). Humans have introduced these plants for gardening (cheatgrass and cartwheel flower) or commercial timber production (Monterey pine). The data demonstrate that attempting to restore ecosystems and exclude invading species by reducing resource availability does not succeed because of the efficiency with which some species use resources.

Study Break

1. Give two examples of invasive species, one animal and one plant. Describe the history of the invasion.
2. Are invasive species more apt to be successful than native species? Why? Why not?
3. What is ballast water? Why does it figure in transporting species from one place to another?

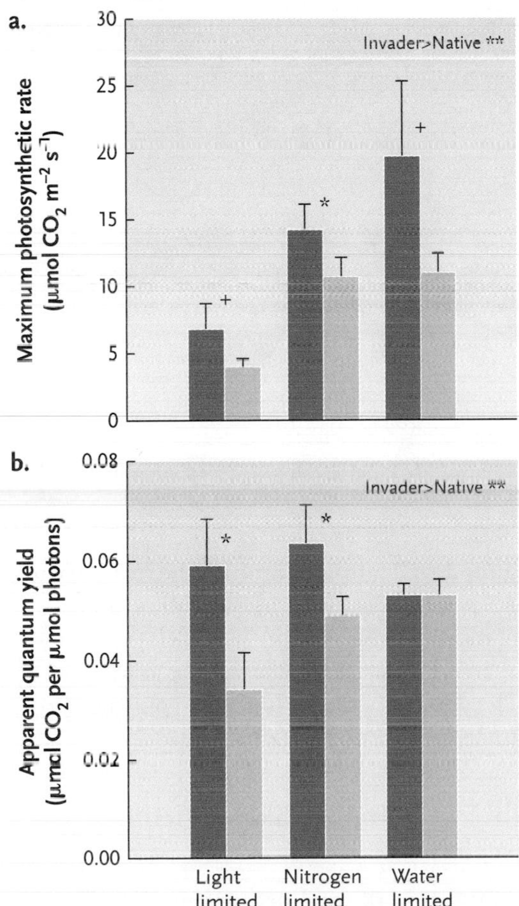

Figure 48.10
(a) Photosynthetic rates (resource use efficiency [RUE]) and **(b)** light-use efficiency of invasive plant species (blue bars) make them more competitive than native ones (yellow bars). The plants were from three different habitats in Hawaii.

48.4 How We Got/Get There

Lamentably, we know that humans can exterminate species that are populous and widespread as well as ones that have small populations and occur in a small area.

48.4a The Black Rhinoceros: Its Demise

It is estimated that 60 000 black rhinos (*Diceros bicornis*) lived in the wild in Africa in 1960 **(Figure 48.11a, p. 1214)**. This large (1.5 m at the shoulder, 1400 kg) browsing mammal was widespread in sub-Saharan Africa **(Figure 48.11b)**. Adult males and females have two distinctive "horns" **(Figure 48.12a, p. 1214;** see also Figure 48.11a), actually formed from hair. Rhinos use the horns to protect themselves and their young from predators and other rhinos. By 1981, the populations in the wild had been reduced to 10 000 to 15 000, and again reduced to about 3500 by 1987. Today only a few individuals survive in some protected areas in Africa. In less than 30 years, the species was almost exterminated in the wild.

In 1960, black rhinos were one of the "big five" on the list of big game for which hunters made safaris to Africa to shoot as trophies. Others on the list included the African lion, African elephant, Cape buffalo (*Syncerus caffer*), and leopard. Safari hunters then paid large sums of money to go to Africa and obtain licences to kill trophy specimens of each of the big five. But this hunting pressure, which has since stopped, did not lead to the extermination of black rhinos.

Figure 48.11
(a) Black rhinos (*Diceros bicornis*) were widespread and common in Africa in 1960 (orange area on the map). **(b)** Today their range (dark spots in orange areas) is much reduced, reflecting diminished poulations. Note the oxpecker (*Buphagus africana*) sitting on the rhino.

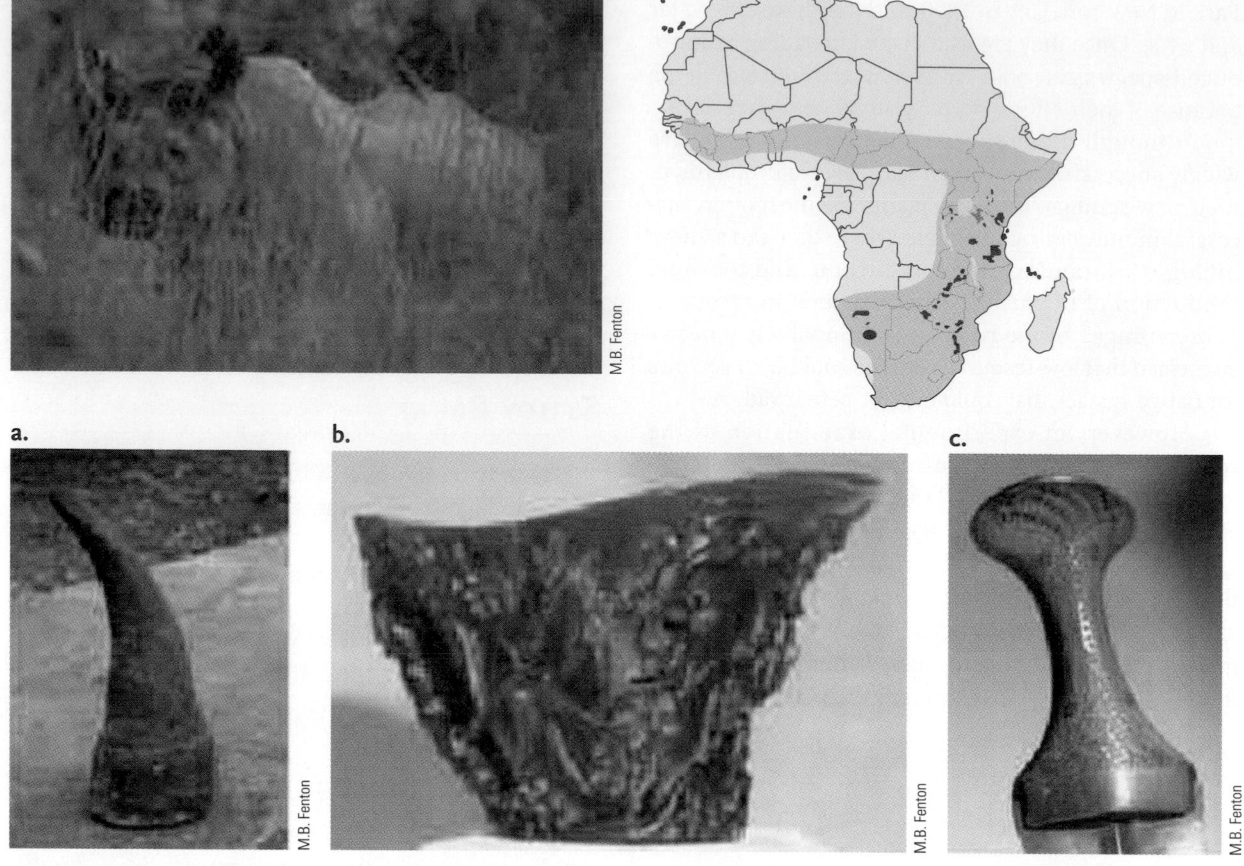

Figure 48.12
(a) A horn from a black rhino in Zimbabwe is shown with **(b)** a rhino horn bowl from China and **(c)** a jambiya with a rhino horn handle.

People have long used the horns of all species of rhino in different ways. In China, bowls made from rhino horn **(Figure 48.12b)** were believed to have magical properties in that they could remove or neutralize poisons. Travelling nobles were served wine in their own rhino horn bowls to minimize the chances of their being poisoned. In India and some other areas from India to Korea, powdered rhino horn was used as a fever suppressant. Contrary to popular belief, rhino horn does not appear to have been used as an aphrodisiac, an early version of Viagra®.

An Arabian Peninsula tradition is the carrying of a jambiya or ceremonial dagger. Jambiyas with rhino horn handles **(Figure 48.12c)** were highly prized. In 1973, when the price of oil jumped from U.S.$4 to U.S.$12 a barrel, the ensuing "energy crisis" meant a larger market for jambiyas. Increased cash flow and easy access to military weapons such as Kalashnikov assault rifles **(Figure 48.13)** provided an incentive and a means to kill rhinos. The epidemic of poaching started in northern Kenya and spread southward throughout the continent. Thus, poaching for their horns led to the catastrophic reduction in the populations of black rhinos. The large population of rhinos that had long survived in the presence of predators, including *Homo sapiens*, was not protected from extermination. In 1984, going for a walk at night around the headquarters of Mana Pools National Park in Zimbabwe almost always meant meeting a black rhino. By 1987, the rhinos were very scarce, and by 1990 they did not exist in the area.

Figure 48.13
A Kalashnikov assault rifle (an AK), a weapon widely used in the poaching of animals in many parts of the world.

The demise of black rhinos can only be attributed to human greed.

48.4b The Barndoor Skate: Victim of Bycatch

Our harvesting of food organisms can affect more than just the target species on land and at sea. Barndoor skates (*Dipturus laevis*; **Figure 48.14**) are elasmobranchs that used to occur widely in the northwest Atlantic. With a maximum body width of ~1 m, this is one of the largest skates. Dramatic reductions

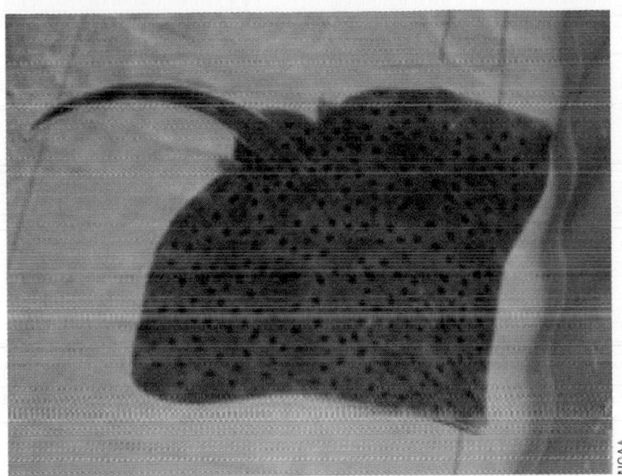

Figure 48.14
The barndoor skate (*Dipturus laevis*) was once widespread in the northwestern Atlantic Ocean. Mortality associated with bycatch has severely reduced its populations.

in the biomass of barndoor skates are obvious from locations ranging from the southern Grand Bank to southern New England **(Figure 48.15).**

Recent captures of barndoor skates have been at depths greater than 1000 m, which may be one of the last refuges for this distinctive species. A combination of directed fishing for skates off the coasts of Newfoundland and Nova Scotia and bycatch of barndoor skates may spell the end for this species. In fishing terms, "bycatch" occurs when nontarget species are taken by fishers. Victims of bycatch include other species of fish, as well as sea turtles and marine mammals.

Removing species from ecosystems or depleting their numbers can also affect many other species in the ecosystem.

48.4c The Bay Scallop: Overfishing of Sharks

Populations of organisms we harvest for food often show marked declines. The annual harvest of bivalve molluscs has been a local fishery in Chesapeake Bay in the United States and elsewhere along the eastern seaboard for hundreds of years. In 1999, populations of bay scallops (*Agropecten irradians*; **Figures 48.16 and 48.17, p. 1216**), a main target of the fishery, were very low. The immediate reason for the low populations was the impact of predation by skates and rays that feed heavily on bivalve molluscs. Skates and rays are tertiary consumers and in turn are eaten by larger elasmobranchs, specifically various species of sharks.

Among tertiary consumers, the cownose ray **(Figure 48.18, p. 1216)** showed a marked increase in population. Evidence from surveys on the U.S. Atlantic coast estimates an order-of-magnitude increase in populations of cownose rays, and the total population of 14 species of rays and skates exceeds 40 million. So the decline in scallop (and other bivalve) populations can be explained by the increase in predation by tertiary consumers, especially skates and rays.

The picture becomes clearer when the population data for the local great sharks are added to the

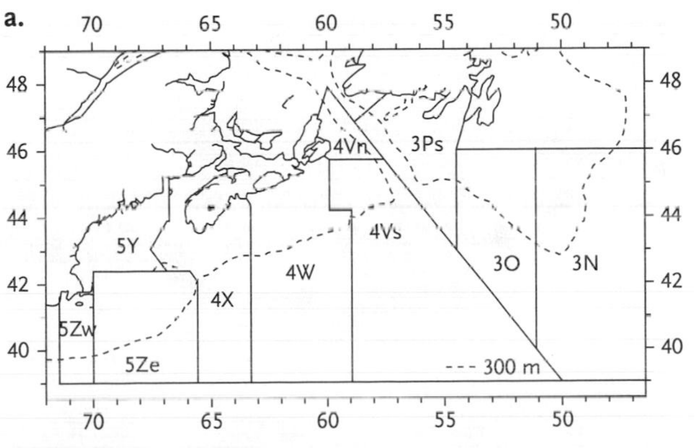

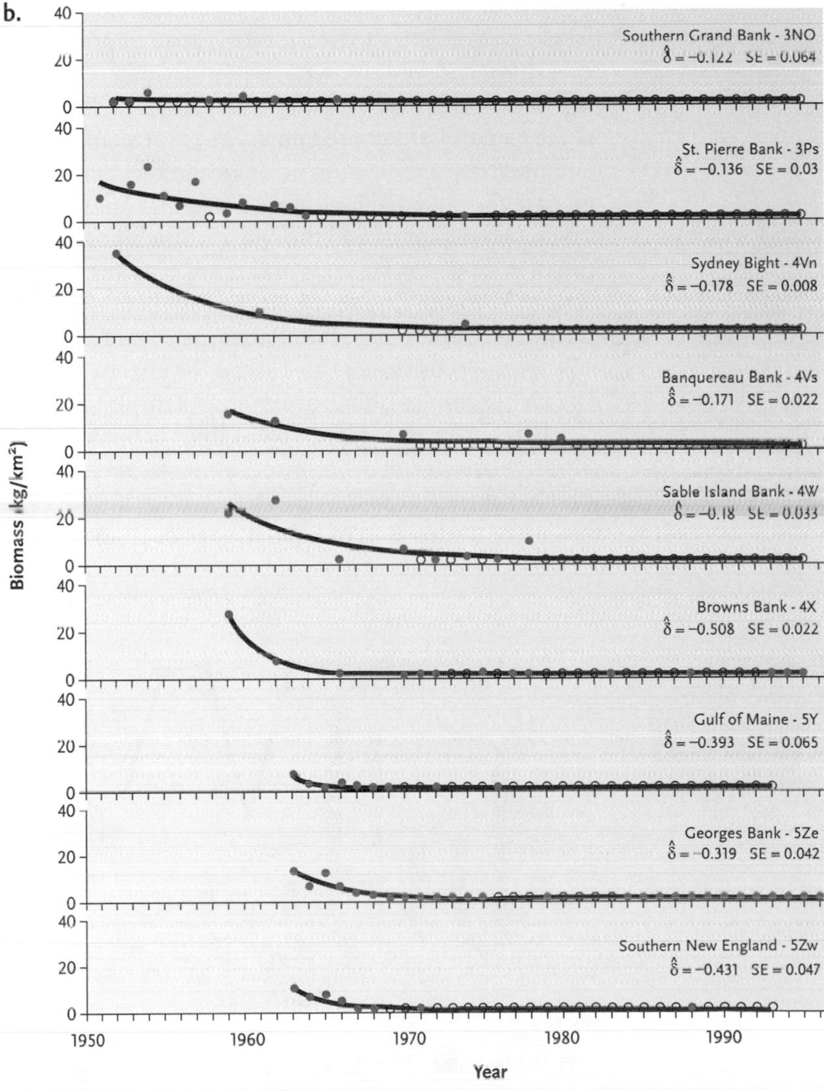

Figure 48.15
(a) Fishery subdivisions off the east coast of Canada and the U.S. providing data about the abundances of barndoor skates. **(b)** Catch records of barndoor skates from those fishing subdivisions.

Figure 48.16
A handful of bay scallops (*Agropecten irradians*).

mix **(Figure 48.19)**. Prolonged and intensive fishing of 12 species of sharks accounts for a 35-year decline in their populations (see Figure 48.19, top row). The sharks have been taken primarily for their fins and meat. In some parts of the world, shark fins sell for ~U.S.$700 per kilogram and are used to make shark fin soup.

The data demonstrate how a century-old scallop fishery was effectively destroyed because of predation by tertiary consumers, whose populations, in turn, had been enhanced (see Figure 48.19, middle row) by the removal of top predators, the great sharks. The data illustrate a cascading ecological effect and demonstrate the potential long-term harm that our species can do to ecosystems and the species inhabiting them. The demise of bay scallops and other bivalves can be attributed to the impact of large-scale harvesting of marine resources. The late Ransome Myers and his colleagues documented this cascade of effects.

The examples above are merely samples from a long list of species. Evidence of declines of populations of native species can be found almost everywhere. Whether the root cause is overharvesting, introduced species, or destruction of habitat, species from whales to songbirds are threatened by human activity. What can we do about it?

Study Break

1. Why was Tibbles so successful at exterminating the remaining Stephen's Island Wrens?
2. What risk does ballast water pose to native ecosystems?
3. What is the significance of RUE?

48.5 Protecting Species

The widespread recognition of trademarks such as the World Wildlife Fund (WWF) panda demonstrates how associating a cause with an icon can be very successful. It is not surprising that many conservation efforts began with a focus on one species—such as giant pandas (*Ailuropoda melanoleuca*), polar bears (*Ursus maritimus*), or redwood trees (*Sequoia sempervirens*). The lure of conservation movements that focus on charismatic species is very strong. But charismatic organisms may not need protection, whereas some species that are unattractive, dangerous, or mundane are in desperate need of our assistance. Unfortunately, mundane, ugly, and dangerous (to us) species are unlikely to serve as a call to arms (or to attract financial support). Worldwide, the WWF panda is one of the most recognized logos, whether or not pandas are in the neighbourhood.

A critical first step toward conservation is the development and adoption of objective, data-based criteria for assessing the risk posed to different species. This process has been developed on several fronts around the world. The criteria and assessment procedures perfected by the International Union for the Conservation of Nature (IUCN) are used widely. There are many records of success, but there also are many examples of species and situations in which we

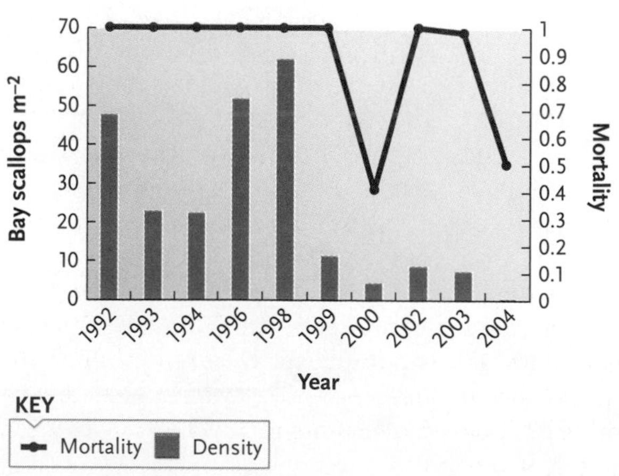

Figure 48.17
Numbers of bay scallops off the east coast of the United States.

Figure 48.18
A cownose ray (*Rhinoptera bonasus*).

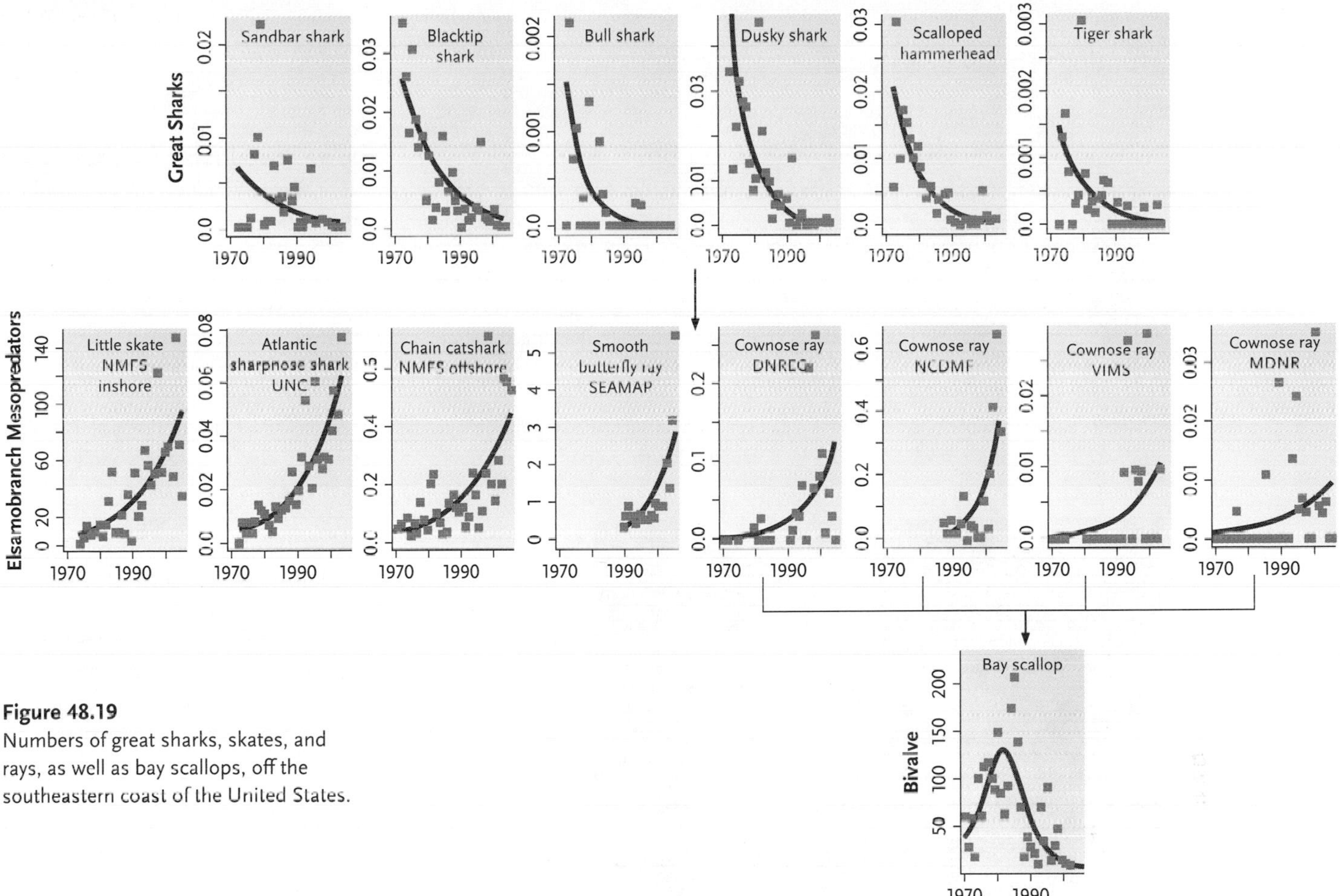

Figure 48.19
Numbers of great sharks, skates, and rays, as well as bay scallops, off the southeastern coast of the United States.

have failed. Making arguments based on data does not guarantee success. Using a data-based approach, some species emerge as being in need of protection, but others do not. Being rare or unusual, by itself, will not warrant protection. The species concept and the Linnaean system of nomenclature (see Chapter 19) are fundamental to conservation.

In Canada, recommendations about the conservation status of species involve the Committee on the Status of Endangered Wildlife in Canada (COSEWIC). The definition of wildlife includes plants and animals. Like IUCN, COSEWIC recognizes six categories for assessing species at risk:

- *Extinct:* a wildlife species that no longer exists
- *Extirpated:* a species no longer existing in one location in the wild but occurring elsewhere
- *Endangered:* a species facing imminent extirpation or extinction
- *Threatened:* a species likely to become endangered if limiting factors are not reversed
- *Special concern:* a species that may become threatened or endangered because of a combination of biological characteristics and identified threats
- *Data deficient:* a category used when available information is insufficient either to resolve a wildlife species' eligibility of assessment or to permit an assessment of its risk of extinction.

A seventh category—*not at risk*—is used to identify species not at risk of extinction under current circumstances.

COSEWIC members vote on the appropriate conservation category for each species whose status they review. The members consider the area of occupancy, an indication of the range of a species and the availability of suitable habitat. They take into consideration population information, including trends in the numbers of organisms, correcting for species that show extreme fluctuations in numbers from year to year. They consider the demographics of the species and the variability in the habitat where the species occurs. Generation time also is considered, along with specific habitat features that may be essential for the species' survival. Data on population size, particularly the numbers of reproducing adults, are important, as well as risks to the species' survival.

In a biological context, the criteria used by COSEWIC (and similar agencies elsewhere) are familiar to population biologists (see Chapter 45). The data describe the numbers of individuals in the population, fecundity, mortality, and the intrinsic rate of increase. Carrying capacity also is important, as is the area (range) over which the species occurs. These criteria are designed to promote data-based decisions about the conservation status of species.

Hunting: Threat or Salvation?

We saw earlier (see Chapter 19) how the Linnaean system of nomenclature is used to name species. Once a species has a name, however acquired, it may benefit from protection under CITES, the Convention for International Trade in Endangered Species. But will data-based decisions about what counts as endangered be consistent and predictable? The answer is "yes" and "no." The example of black rhinos showed one situation in which protection under CITES did not work. There are others.

Also in Africa, the leopard (see the chapter opening photograph) was accorded protection under CITES. The passing of the Endangered Species Act (ESA) in the United States (1972) precipitated an interesting situation: it obliged Americans to "obey" the listing of leopards on CITES Appendix 1, which banned the importation of leopard skins, including those shot on safari hunts. The rationale for the listing was the belief that leopards were endangered and their survival was threatened by hunting.

There were quick, negative responses to the ban on importing leopard skins into the United States from two different groups. First was the hunting and related associations and lobbies whose members were anxious to be able to bring home trophies. Second, leaders and governments in many African countries that benefitted from the hunts objected to the ban because safaris were (and still are) an important source of foreign exchange. In many of these countries, "safari hunting areas" were set aside to accommodate visitors, and these large tracts of land also protected populations of nongame species and appropriate habitat.

What do the data show? Leopards are 40 to 80 kg, solitary cats that hunt by stealth. They are widespread in Africa but have been little studied. The estimate is that there are more than 700 000 leopards in the wild in Africa, with resident populations in all but very small countries with high human population densities. In 2000, Zimbabwe alone had a population of more than 16 000 leopards in the wild. The 1969 safari harvest of 6100 leopards throughout Africa and the export of their skins were not a threat to the population in Zimbabwe, let alone to leopards in the whole continent.

Ecologists studied the population of leopards in the Matetsi Safari Area in Zimbabwe. Before 1974, the 4300 km^2 area was a cattle ranch whose operators made strong efforts to eradicate leopards to protect their livestock. After conversion to a hunting area, people on the first safaris rarely succeeded in shooting leopards. By 1984, the leopard population in the Matetsi Safari Area was 800 to 1000, and in 1988, the annual safari quota there was 3.6% (12 to 28 leopards). When leopards shot in the mid-1980s were compared with those taken in the 1970s, no change in leopard size was found. But by 1986, the average

Figure 1
Polar bear, *Ursus maritimus.*

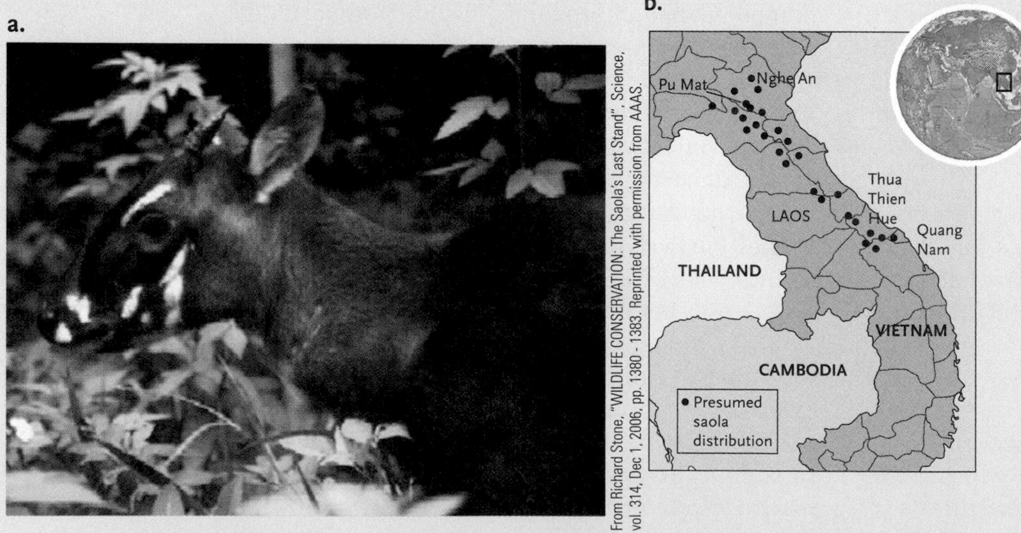

Figure 2
(a) Saola (*Pseudoryx nghetinhensis*) and **(b)** its distribution.

age of leopards taken as trophies was 5.4 years, compared with 3.2 years from the earlier period. These data show that leopards can persist even when subjected to heavy hunting pressure. On average, leopards live longer in a safari hunting regime than when they are being hunted in the context of predator control operations. Other evidence suggests that populations of leopards persist even in urban areas—trapping evidence suggests that resident leopards live in Nairobi, the capital of Kenya.

Leopards are an interesting example of human responses to conservation. Hunting or some other form of harvesting is not necessarily a threat to the survival of some species. Indeed, some harvesting may be critical to the livelihood of some people and can advance efforts to protect some species. But decisions about harvesting made in one part of the world can influence what happens elsewhere. Today there are quotas for the numbers of leopards that can be harvested in different countries in Africa. Safari hunters must obtain licences to take trophies, and skins exported must be accompanied by paperwork showing that the harvest was legal. The documentation allows a citizen, for example of Canada or of a European Union country, to import a leopard skin. This was not possible in the United States in the 1970s, but it is in 2009. In Africa, local farmers are permitted to kill "problem" animals that threaten their livestock or themselves and their families and may be supported in this by government officials.

Key elements in the success of harvesting include having data about the population of organisms, the rates of reproduction, and the rates of harvest. Enforcement of quotas is essential if this approach is to succeed. Legal harvest quotas do not require people who object to hunting to be hunters. Trophy hunting is not the exclusive preserve of countries in Africa. On April 3, 2007, *The Globe and Mail* (a national newspaper published in Toronto) reported that the economy of the Canadian territory of Nunavut received Can$2.9 million from polar bear **(Figure 1)** hunting. Hunters can pay U.S.$20 000 for a polar bear hunt.

In 1992, saola **(Figure 2)** made the news as one of the first "new" species of large mammals to be discovered in recent times. These goatlike animals live in a restricted area of Vietnam, where they have been and are hunted by local people. Saolas are rare, and little is known about them. There are no quotas for the local hunters, and it is not practical to enforce a ban on their harvest. In reality, we probably lack critical information about the biology of many species of wildlife today. However, once they have names, they have a chance of being protected.

Study Break

1. What is IUCN? What role does it play in conservation?
2. What criteria would identify a species as endangered? Give an example.

48.6 Protecting What?

Before data are used to address questions of species-at-risk status, conservation biologists must decide about eligibility. The conservation jargon for this is "designatable unit." Are the organisms "real" species? Are they subspecies? Are they distinct populations? Are they really Canadian? Do they regularly occur in Canada or perhaps turn up here by accident? If the species does not breed here, is the habitat they use in Canada essential to their survival? Most species of wildlife in Canada occur close to the border with the United States, and many species widespread in the United States just make it into Canada. In some cases, a distinct population is treated as a designatable unit. Distinct populations may be recognized by their geographic distribution and/or their genetic structure.

Questions about what units are designatable harken back to the definition of species (see Chapter 18). Off the west coast of Canada, striking differences in behaviour can be used to distinguish between two "kinds" of killer whales. The "resident" killer whales eat mainly fish and often echolocate. The "transient" killer whales eat mainly marine mammals and rarely produce echolocation signals. Furthermore, repeated sightings of recognizable individual whales indicate that different groups of these animals live in different areas along the coast **(Figure 48.20, p. 1220)**.

In reviewing the conservation status of killer whales, COSEWIC recognized different designatable units based on behaviour and geography **(Figure 48.21, p. 1221)**. The different units faced different threats to their survival.

Questions about what to protect often reflect different realities of biology. Migrating birds may be blown off course and end up in southern Ontario instead of their usual habitat much farther south. Marine birds or mammals may feed in Canadian waters but breed elsewhere. Many organisms commonly hitchhike, using ocean vessels, aircraft, or automobiles as vehicles of dispersal. But some hitchhikers,

An Endangered Species

Banff Springs snails, *Physella johnsoni* **(Figure 1),** live and eat algae in five hot springs on Sulphur Mountain in Banff National Park, Alberta. Not very long ago, Banff Springs snails were found in nine springs. In 1996, the total population of snails was ~5000. Water temperatures in the springs occupied by the snails range from 26° to 48°C, but temperatures less than 44°C seem best for them. Their very limited occurrence makes them vulnerable to extinction (COSEWIC, 2000).

Humans appear to be the main threat to the survival of Banff Springs snails. By discarding unsightly (to humans) accumulations of algae from pools, people have killed some snails that were in the algal mats. Changes in the patterns of water circulation may subject some snails to high temperatures that could be lethal. Well-wishers that throw copper coins into the pools may have harmed snails because of contamination arising from the interaction of copper with sulphurous water in the springs.

Other impacts of people are not clear, but one threat is entertaining to contemplate—people "skinny-dipping" in the pools are thought to threaten the snails. Some skinny-dippers have been caught and charged. Bathers in the pools, clad or unclad, may have crushed snails while getting into or out of the water. Bathers doused in sunscreen or insect repellants may have introduced chemicals into the snails' habitat and further reduced their populations.

Banff Springs snails are neither charismatic nor prominent, but the data-based approach to decision making has provided the basis for identifying them as endangered.

C.M. & L. Degner/Parks Canada

Figure 1
Banff Springs snail, *Physella johnsoni*.

a.

M.B. Fenton

b.

M.B. Fenton

c.

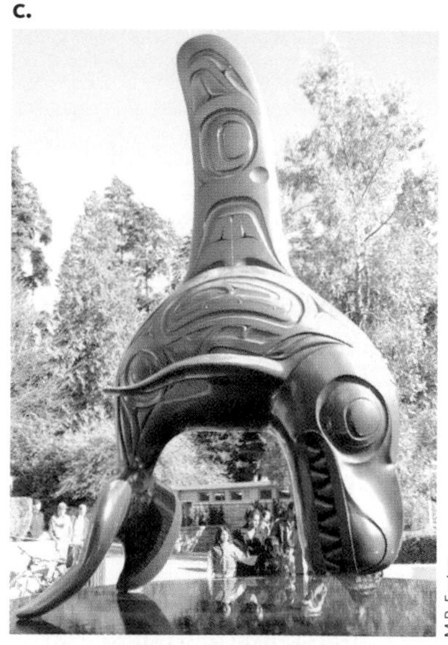

M.B. Fenton

Figure 48.20
Three views of a killer whale (*Orcinus orca*). **(a)** A captive animal in Vancouver, **(b)** a wild orca swimming off the Queen Charlotte Islands, and **(c)** a Haida representation.

for example, some snails, travel with birds, making the association and the dispersal more "natural."

People can be quick to try to protect species they consider to be important or distinctive. In 2003, the Ontario Ministry of Natural Resources reported four to six white-coloured moose (*Alces alces*) among the approximately 1900 moose in two wildlife management areas near Foleyet in northeastern Ontario. Should white-coloured moose be protected? There was local support for protecting the moose, animals that have cultural and spiritual significance for First Nations communities. White moose have been reported from other places in northern Ontario, Newfoundland and Labrador, and elsewhere. Although the population of white moose is small and widespread, there is no evidence that they are a designatable unit. In Canada, they have not been accorded special protection.

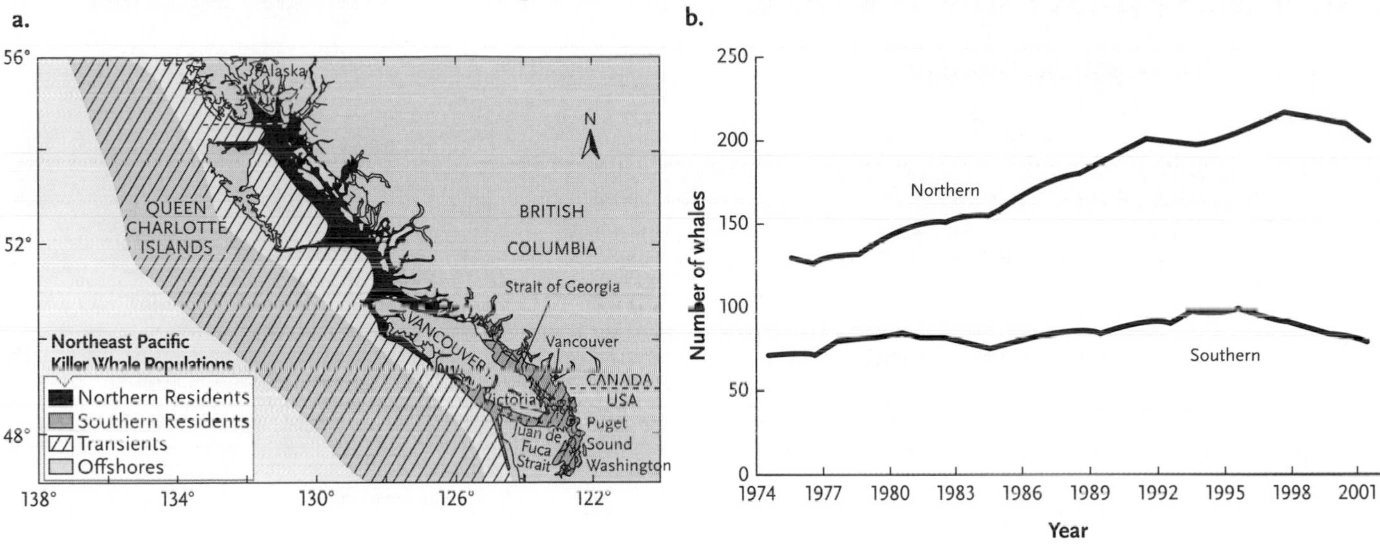

Figure 48.21
(a) The population distribution (designatable units) of killer whales off the coast of British Columbia and **(b)** estimates of population sizes of northern and southern resident killer whales (British Columbia).

Study Break

1. Give an example of a designatable unit that is a species.
2. Give an example of a designatable unit that is a population.
3. Is "designatable unit" synonymous with "species"?

48.7 The Downside of Being Rare

Whether the commodity is coins, stamps, antiques, or endangered species, as soon as something is rare enough, there is a market for it. This "get them while they last" attitude is exemplified by trade in *Leucopsar rothschildi*, Bali Starlings **(Figure 48.22a)**. This bird, another island species, faces immediate extinction, but it is in high demand as an exotic pet. In 1982, when there were fewer than 150 individuals in the wild, 35 were for sale as pets, 19 in Singapore and 16 in Bali.

Rare species also may be in demand for use of their body parts in traditional medicine. One stark example is the swim bladders of *Bahaba taipingensis*, the Chinese bahaba **(Figure 48.22b)**. At a time when fewer than 6 individuals are caught each year, more than 100 boats are trying to catch them. The swim bladders are used in traditional medicine. They are worth at least seven times their weight in gold. Shark fins are even more valuable. These are extreme examples of the earlier story about rhino horns and jambiyas.

Before criticizing and condemning the users or consumers of jambiyas or Chinese bahaba swim bladders, think about the overall impact of our lifestyle on other species of animals and plants. Of particular note is an insatiable demand for energy. Are sport utility vehicles necessary? Jet skis? Snowmobiles? All-terrain vehicles? The list goes on. Is a Canadian as justified in buying a large SUV as a North Yemenese a jambiya with a rhino horn handle? Once again, might (the ability or capacity to do something) may not be right.

a.

b.

Figure 48.22
(a) A Bali Starling (*Leucopsar rothschildi*) and **(b)** Chinese bahaba (*Bahaba taipingensis*).

Who Gets Protection?

Being recognized as rare and considered to be endangered does not necessarily translate into protection.

Because the Endangered Species Act (ESA) in the United States does not protect hybrids, this can affect the conservation of, for example, the "Florida panther" **(Figure 1),** a subspecies of cougar. Cougars, also known as panthers, used to occur widely in North, South, and Central America. Although still widespread in some areas, the current range of cougars in most of the United States and Canada is much less than it was when Columbus arrived in the New World in 1482. Florida panthers, a small population recognized as a subspecies, occur mainly in the Florida keys. Florida panthers were protected under the ESA.

Using techniques of molecular genetics, biologists determined that Florida panthers carried the genes of cougars from South America. This situation probably arose when panthers originally caught in South America were brought to the United States as zoo animals or for display in circuses or animal shows. Some of these animals escaped and interbred with local Florida panthers. Florida panthers with genes from South American cougars are technically hybrids and therefore are not protected by the ESA.

There are many other examples of situations in which genetic tools allow clearer delineation of boundaries between populations (designatable units) and species. In some cases, however, removal of protection from other "species" because of their genetic status can lead to their extinction. *Ammodramus maritimus nigrescens* or the Dusky Seaside Sparrow was previously considered to be a distinct form living in Florida. When genetic evidence showed that these darker animals were not genetically distinct, they lost their protected status and have virtually disappeared.

Other species, such as round-nosed grenadier, have suffered calamitous declines in population. These cod-like fish **(Figure 2)** were taken in large numbers after cod populations had declined **(Figure 3).** The species was on the verge of extinction even before much was known about it. We do know that round-nosed grenadiers are late to mature, and their populations are slow to recover.

Although round-nosed grenadiers and at least four other species meet the IUCN criteria for listing as "endangered," these fish have not been or are not protected. Fisheries and Oceans Canada has not supported a move to protect round-nosed grenadiers. Changing fishing practices to avoid catching the few remaining round-nosed grenadiers is not economically feasible when other species are still being caught in sufficient numbers to justify a continued fishery. The situation differs only from that facing the barndoor skate in that the round-nosed grenadiers have been the targets of an active fishery.

We have seen that the hunt for polar bears can bring significant income to the economy of Nunavut, and the same is true of other

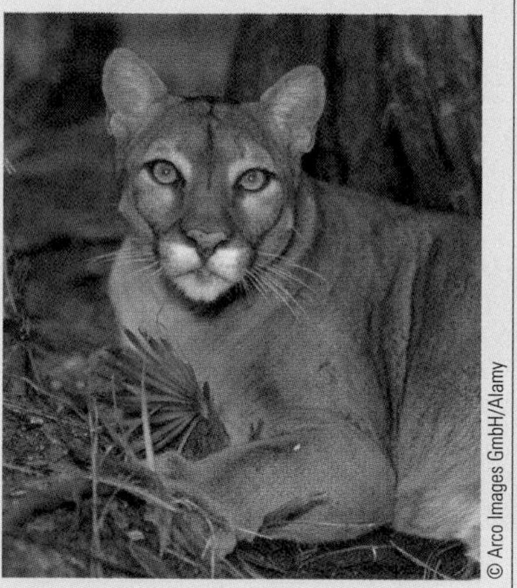

Figure 1
A Florida panther (*Felis concolor coryi*).

Figure 2
Coryphaenoides rupestris, a round-nosed grenadier.

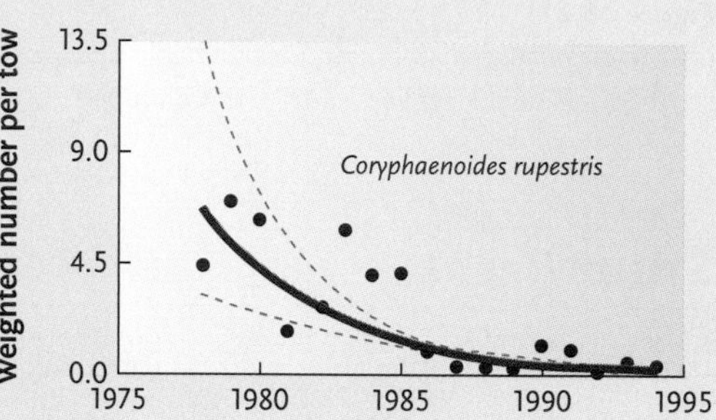

Figure 3
Captures of round-nosed grenadiers.

jurisdictions within the bear's range. There are distinct populations of polar bears **(Table 1),** even within Canada's jurisdiction. The occurrence of bears in political jurisdictions including Canada, the United States, Russia, Iceland, Denmark (Greenland), Norway, Finland, and Sweden makes achieving their protection more difficult. The apparent vulnerability of the bears to global warming and their value as trophies may combine to hasten their demise.

Table 1 **Status of Canadian Polar Bear Populations (January 1997).**

Population	% Females in harvest	Number	Sustainable Annual Kill	Mean Annual Kill	Environ. Concern	Status[1]	Quality of Estimate	Degree of Bias	Age of Estimate	Harvest/ Capture Data
Western Hudson Bay	31	1200	54	44	None	S[a]	Good	None	Current	Good (>15 yr)
Southern Hudson Bay	35	1000	43	45	None	S[a]	Fair	Moderate	Old	Fair (5–10 yr)
Foxe Basin	38	2300	91	118	None	S[a]	Good	None	Current	Good (>15 yr)
Lancaster Sound	25	1700	77	81	None	S[a]	Fair	None	Current	Good (>15 yr)
Baffin Bay	35	2200	94	122	None	D?[b]	Fair	None	Current	Fair (>15 yr)
Norwegian Bay	30	100	4	4	None	S[a]	Fair	None	Current	Good (>15 yr)
Kane Basin	37	200	8	6	None	S	Fair	None	Current	Fair (>15 yr)
Queen Elizabeth	–	(200?)	9?	0	Possible	S?[b]	None	–	–	–
Davis Strait	36	1400	58	57	None	S?[b]	Fair	Moderate	Outdated	Good (>15 yr)
Gulf of Boothia	42	900	32	37	None	S[a]	Poor	Moderate	Outdated	Good (>15 yr)
M'Clintock Channel	33	700	32	25	None	S[a]	Poor	Moderate	Outdated	Good (>15 yr)
Viscount Melville sound	0	230	4	0	None	I	Good	None	Current	Good (>15 yr)
Northern Beaufort Sea	43	1200	42	29	None	S	Good	None	Recent	Good (>15 yr)
Southern Beaufort Sea	36	1800	75	56	None	S	Good	Moderate	Recent	Good (>15 yr)

- [1]D = decreasing; I = increasing; S = stationary; ? = indicated trend uncertain
- [a]Population is managed with a flexible quota system in which overharvesting in a given year results in a fully compensatory reduction to the following year's quota
- [b]See text, "Population Size and Trend," for discussion.

Study Break

1. What is the value of the International Union for the Conservation of Nature (IUCN)?
2. Why do species description and formal naming affect the Convention for International Trade in Endangered Species (CITES)?
3. What is the difference between an extinct species and an extirpated species? Give an example of each.

48.8 Protecting Habitat

It is obvious from many of the examples above that protecting species has not been entirely successful as a conservation strategy. As a species, we are much better at killing than we are at conserving. Whether the persecution is direct or indirect, the end result can be the same. It is also clear that destruction of habitat is an effective way to remove a species. For example, populations of mosquitoes can be limited by denying them places to lay their eggs. This is a common theme in public education programs designed to reduce the incidence of West Nile virus (or other mosquito-borne diseases).

Is protection of habitat an effective strategy? The answer can be "yes," particularly for species that are not motile. Many species of plants have specific habitat requirements. From trees to shrubs, forbs, ferns, and mosses, we know that we can protect species by protecting habitat. Furthermore, protecting large tracts of habitat can also protect large, mobile species. Rain forests, whether tropical or temperate, are examples of habitats that can be flagships for protection and conservation. They also are considered by many to be storehouses of wealth associated with biodiversity, from building materials to compounds of pharmacological value.

The case of the black rhino demonstrated how a species targeted for harvesting can be driven to the brink of extinction even when it is protected (or lives in national parks or game reserves). *Panax quinquifolius,* American ginseng, is another target species, now endangered in Canada because of harvesting. The species used to grow wild from southwestern Quebec and southern Ontario and south to Louisiana and Georgia. This 20- to 70-cm tall perennial is long-lived in rich, moist, mature, sugar maple–dominated woods. Although the species has been listed on Appendix II of COSEWIC since 1973, populations have continued to decline. In 2000, there were 22 viable populations in Ontario and Quebec, but none were secure. Black rhinos and ginseng were common ~50 years ago, but by 2008, both demonstrated the risks of being rare and expensive. They also are examples of the need for immediate on-the-ground enforcement of regulations and laws protecting species and habitats.

Protecting habitats can be most challenging in areas with larger human populations. None of the viable poplulations of American ginseng in Ontario and Quebec were far from a road, making the plants vulnerable to anyone who knew about them and wished to take advantage of the economic opportunity they presented. *Sorex bendiri,* the Pacific water shrew, is another example of a species whose future in Canada is threatened by expanding human populations and the associated value of real estate **(Figure 48.23).**

Also in British Columbia, expanding human population and the wine industry in the southern Okanagan Valley have combined to dramatically reduce a local ecosystem dominated by antelope bush **(Figure 48.24, p. 1226).** The antelope bush system, one of the most endangered ecosystems in Canada, is home to a number of species of plants and animals whose future is now threatened by the demise of the habitat they require. The boom in real estate for people looking for retirement properties, more than just the density of human populations, is a key factor in this situation. Meanwhile, in southern Ontario, the demand for real estate to accommodate the expanding housing and business market is reducing both the available natural habitats and farmland.

Study Break

1. Give examples of how protecting a habitat can work.
2. How do market forces influence the abundance of species?

48.9 Effecting Conservation

Today we face many challenges when trying to protect biodiversity. Too many of the immediate threats are the direct or indirect consequences of human activities. Walt Kelly, the creator of *Pogo* (a cartoon of yesteryear), identified the problem **(Figure 48.25, p. 1226)**—us. We must protect species by acting at levels ranging from species to populations and habitats.

48.9a Human Population: A Root Problem in Conservation

One fundamental root cause of declining biodiversity is the human population and the energy and habitat consumed in trying to feed, house, and protect our flourishing species. Visit the Web site http://www.popexpo.ined.fr/english.html and use it to determine the estimated human population in the year you were born and then for the years in which your parents and grandparents were born. Even when many people are killed, the momentum of our population

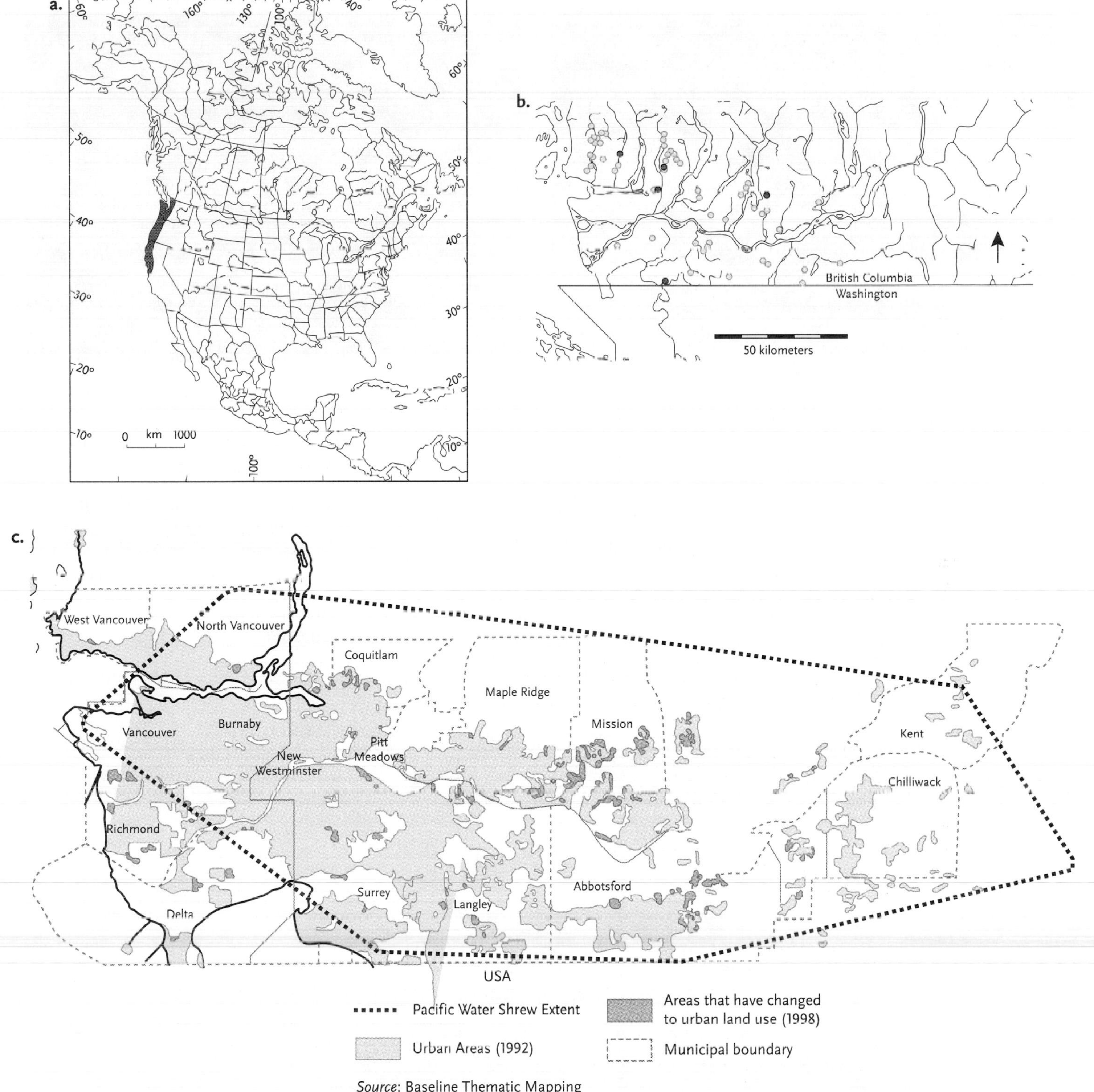

Figure 48.23
(a) The distribution of *Sorex bendiri*. **(b)** Lower Fraser Valley locations where it was found (solid circles) or not found (open circles) in recent surveys. **(c)** For comparison, the same area is shown with changes in the availability of urban lands in 1992 and 1998.

increase does not slow down. The December 2004 tsunami killed approximately 250 000 people, at a time when the world population was estimated at 6 billion. By comparison, the 1883 explosion of the island Krakatoa (and resulting tsunamis) is thought to have killed 35 000 people when the global human population was about 1.5 billion. If these estimates are correct, $4.1 \times 10^{-3}\%$ of the human population at the time was killed by the 2004 tsunami and $2.3 \times 10^{-3}\%$ by the explosion of Krakatoa. Neither calamity caused

a.

b.

Figure 48.24
Antelope bush, *Purshia tridentata*, showing **(a.)** the bush and **(b.)** a cross section of the stem. These woody shrubs have long life spans, and the ecosystem they typify is home to a variety of species.

the human population growth curve (see Chapter 45) to waiver.

If human population growth continues at the same rate as it grows now, it would double in 40 years. However, studies show that our population is not growing as quickly as it did during much of the twentieth century **(Figure 48.26).** The United Nations Development Program (UNDP) has released data on human fertility (the total number of births per woman) for 162 countries **(Table 48.1).** Compared with 1970–75, 152 countries had lower human fertility in 2000–05, 3 countries showed increases in fertility, and 7 showed no change.

Concerned about the global population and its effect on Earth, world leaders adopted the United Nations Millennium Development Goals in 2000, committing their nations to achieving the following goals by 2015:

- Ending poverty and hunger
- Universal education
- Gender equality
- Child health
- Maternal health
- Combatting HIV/AIDS
- Environmental sustainability
- Global partnerships

Figure 48.25
Walt Kelly's famous cartoon character, Pogo the Possum, in conversation with Porky (the porcupine), summed up the problem.

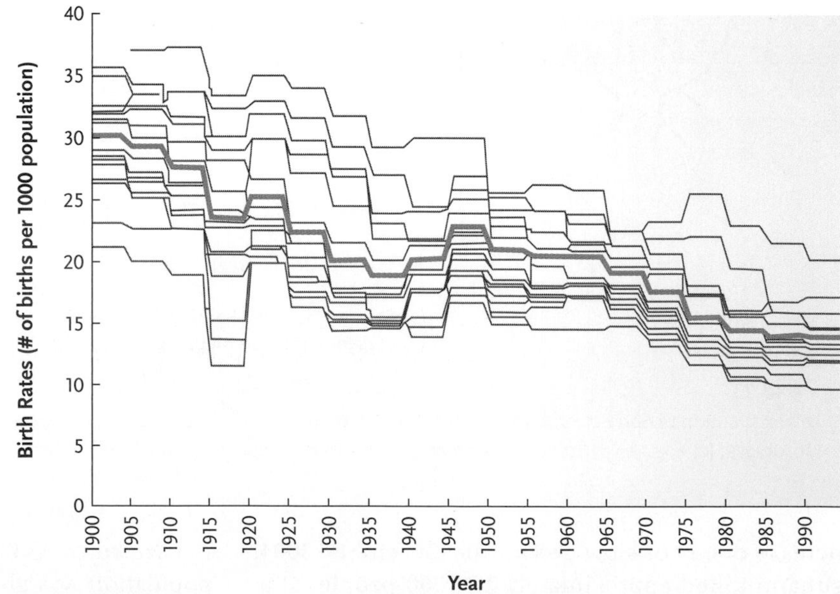

Figure 48.26
Changes in human birth rates (fertility = births per 1000 population per year) in 19 industrialized countries, plotted against increasing temperatures.

Table 48.1 Variations in Fertility Rate (Total Births per Woman): A Sample of UNDP Data for 162 Countries

Country	Human Development Index (HDI) rank	1970–75	2000–05
Norway	2	2.2	1.8
Canada	4	2.0	1.5
U.S.A.	12	2.0	2.0
Portugal	29	2.7	1.5
Brazil	70	4.7	2.3
China	81	4.9	1.7
Indonesia	107	5.2	2.4
India	128	5.4	3.1

These goals can be achieved only if reproduction is controlled (see Chapter 38). In 1994, the United Nations held an International Conference on Population and Development (ICPD), which set a target for global investment in family planning. By 2004, the amount spent had fallen to 13% of this target. Consequently, family planning information and devices (usually for fertility control) are not readily available in many of the lowest income countries. In 1950, Sri Lanka and Afghanistan had the same population. Sri Lanka began strong efforts to make family planning available in culturally acceptable ways. This did not happen in Afghanistan. By 2050, Afghanistan will have four times as many people as Sri Lanka. The solution centres around controlling the fertility of women, but more particularly on giving them the power to control their own fertility in culturally acceptable ways. As seen in Chapter 45, the growth potential of a population is determined by the numbers of females of reproductive age. Why females? Because females are the limiting step in reproduction, they are the ones who produce the eggs or young.

48.9b Signs of Stress: On Systems and on Species

People's demand for food, water, and energy puts thousands of other species at risk. We do not have to look far to see examples of species and ecosystems under stress (see Chapter 47). For example, we are losing birds. We know this because for years, birdwatchers and ornithologists have counted them and monitored their behaviour and activity. Locally, birds are affected by changes in habitat availability as cities and towns and their suburbs expand into adjoining land. Birds also lose habitat when agricultural operations expand to increase productivity. Birds that make annual migrations from temperate areas of the world to tropical and subtropical ones must survive the changes that accumulate across their entire circuit of habitats, each one essential to their survival.

"Bird flu" is a looming crisis for humans, one that appears to involve birds as central players. The issue here is another one involving basic biology, namely the outcome when a disease-causing organism jumps from one species (host) to another. Bird flu could have as much to do with our insatiable demand for poultry as food as it does with birds. In 2006, 12 billion chickens were farmed in China. Worldwide, poultry farms housed over 100 billion broiler chickens. Raising organisms at very high densities (see Chapter 45) provides an ideal setting for the spread of disease. Humans have responded to the threat of bird flu by wholesale slaughter of fowl, raising concerns about the roles played by migrating birds, and efforts to develop a vaccine that will protect humans from bird flu. All involve basic biology.

Drylands are arid, semiarid, and subhumid areas where precipitation is scarce and more or less unpredictable. In drylands, the combination of high temperatures, low relative humidities, and abundant solar radiation means high potential evapotranspiration. Drylands cover approximately 41% of Earth's land surface and are home to about 38% of the human population. Drylands are not just a problem of "deserts" but cover large expanses, for example, of Canada's prairie provinces. However, between 10 and 20% of the drylands are subject to some form of severe land degradation, directly affecting the lives of at least 250 million people. The complexity of the situation is clear in **Table 48.2, p. 1228.** Climate change, combined with increasing pressure on water resources for these people, their crops, and animals, compound the problems that confront them. Competition for limited resources, such as water, can generate local and international strife.

We have seen that complexity is an important and pervasive feature of ecosystems. Biodiversity is intimately associated with complexity, and disruption of this complexity often translates into reduced biodiversity and decay of ecosystems. Ironically, many social and economic systems that humans have developed are also subject to disruption by stress. This places the onus on our species to develop sustainable operations, whether in the area of agriculture, resource use and exploitation, or conservation.

Study Break

1. How is reproductive effort different between males and females in birds and in mammals?
2. List the United Nations Millennium Development Goals.
3. How are drylands at risk?

Table 48.2 Principles of the Drylands Development Paradigm, with a brief overview of their importance vis-à-vis the five main components of the dryland syndrome (ds-1 to ds-5, see text) and their implications for research, management, and policy, [Based on Stafford Smith and Reynolds (77)] H-E, human-environmental systems; LEK, local environmental knowledge.

Principles	Why important in drylands	Links to dryland syndrome (ds-1 to ds-5)	Key implications (ki) for research management, and policy
P1: H-E systems are coupled, dynamic, and coadapting, so that their structure, function, and interrelationships change over time	The close dependency of most drylands' livelihoods on the environment imposes a greater cost if the coupling becomes dysfunctional; variability caused by biophysical factors as well as markets and policy processes, which are generally beyond local control, means that tracking the evolving changes and their functionality is relatively harder and more important in drylands.	ds-1: variability ds-4: remoteness	ki-1: Understanding dryland desertification and development issues always requires the simultaneous consideration of both human and ecological drivers and the recognition that there is no static equilibrium "to aim for."
P2: A limited suite of "slow" variables are critical determinants of H-E system dynamics	Identifying and monitoring the key slow H and E variables is particularly important in drylands because high variability in "fast" variables masks fundamental change indicated by slow variables.	ds-1: variability	ki-2: A limited suite of critical processes and variables at any scale makes a complex problem tractable.
P3: Thresholds in key slow variables define different states of H-E systems, often with different controlling processes; thresholds may change over time	Thresholds particularly matter in drylands because the capacity to invest in recovering from the impacts of crossing undesirable thresholds is usually lower per unit (area of land, person, etc.); and where outside agencies must be called upon, the transaction costs of doing so to distant policy centres are usually higher.	ds-1: variability ds-2: low productivity ds-4: remoteness ds-5: distant voice	ki-3: The costs of intervention rise nonlinearly with increasing land degradation or the degree of socioeconomic dysfunction; yet high variability means great uncertainty in detecting thresholds, implying that managers should invoke the precautionary principles.
P4: Coupled H-E systems are hierarchical, nested, and networked across multiple scales.	Drylands are often more distant from economic and policy centres, with weak linkages; additionally, regions with sparse populations may have qualitatively different hierarchical relationships between levels	ds-3: sparse population ds-4: remoteness ds-5: distant voice	ki-4: H-E systems must be managed at the appropriate scale; cross-scale linkages are important in this but are often remote and weak in drylands, requiring special institutional attention.
P5: The maintenance of a body of up-to-date LEK is key to functional coadaptation of H-E system	Support for LEK is critical in drylands because experiential learning is slower where monitoring feedback is harder to obtain (owing to more variable system, larger management units, in sparsely populated area) and, secondarily, where there is relatively less research	ds-1: variability ds-3: sparse population	ki-5: The development of appropriate hybrid scientific and LEK must be accelerated for both local management and regional policy.

48.10 Taking Action

It is easy to believe that nothing can change, that as individuals we have no power. Yet we also can think of things that have changed dramatically in a relatively short time. Two good examples are the abolition of slavery and the emancipation of women, proving humans' capacity for effecting change. On a more local level, the acceptance of the use of tobacco in public has declined remarkably in the last 20 years—in Canada and elsewhere. We also have seen the abolition of capital punishment and much more ready access to abortion in Canada.

But none of these changes are universal. Daily in the news we find stories about people living in virtual slavery, of people executed in public, of women with few or no rights in their home countries. We only need to travel short distances to learn that not everyone in Canada can eat in a smoke-free restaurant. To complicate the matter, not everyone agrees that the changes listed above are for the better.

Effecting changes in our approach to conservation means identifying the root causes for the erosion of biodiversity and the things that are impediments to conservation. This means starting by changing our own lifestyles, the food we eat, our use of energy, and our lifestyles. We must be wary of simple solutions that are often misleading and avoid blaming someone else because it is just a way of self-exoneration. Respect the rights of others. Use education and training to become informed. Learn to be objective, to examine and evaluate data or evidence. The outpouring of support for victims of the 2004 tsunami demonstrated

Figure 48.27
Eat yourself out of house and home—like this African elephant (*Loxodonta africana*) trekking across the shore to Lake Kariba.

that humans have great empathy for their fellows, and we need to extend this concern to the other species with whom we share the planet.

We have seen that action is needed at the species and the habitat level, and there is a propensity to focus more on species. But in the human view, all species are not equal. The 2006 IUCN list of threatened species shows that whereas 20% of the described species of mammals were listed as threatened, only 0.07% of the insect species received this level of attention. Other interesting numbers from this table are 12% of described species of birds listed as threatened, 4% of fish species, 3.5% of dicotyledonous plants, and 0.006% of species of mushrooms. In Canada, the same situation prevails, with mammals and birds dominating the list of threatened species, with other taxa receiving less attention. Do these data about threatened species mean that mammals are more vulnerable than insects? That we care more about mammals than about insects? Or does it mean that there are more "experts" to offer opinions and data about mammals than about insects? Are the possibilities mutually exclusive?

Biology can be at the centre of the movement to achieve conservation of biodiversity while being part of our efforts to achieve sustainable use of the resources we need as a species **(Figure 48.27)**. Conservation begins at home when we modify our lifestyles and become active on any front, from protecting local habitat and species to protecting charismatic species elsewhere. To better appreciate the situation, try to answer the questions posed in **Figure 48.28.** Elephants are an excellent example of how the objectivity that can be inherent in data is vulnerable to emotional responses.

Study Break

1. Is hunting compatible with conservation?
2. Give examples of resiliency in natural systems.
3. Are hybrids protected by the Endangered Species Act (ESA) in the United States? What are the conservation implications of this stance?

a.

b.

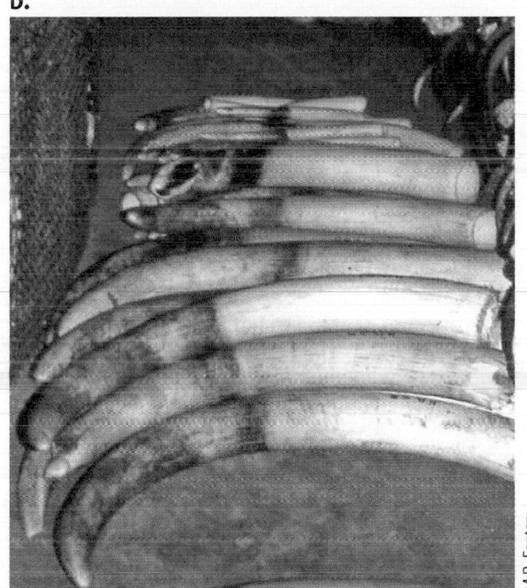

c.

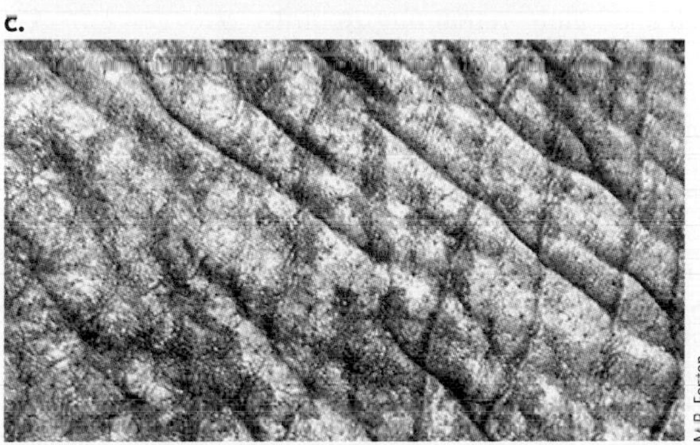

Figure 48.28
To understand some of the dilemmas facing conservationists, use the Internet to explore the situation of African elephants. **(a)** How many species are there? What are the populations in the wild? What products from elephants do we use? **(b)** and **(c)** Are elephants endangered? How can they be protected? What are the main threats to their survival?

Unanswered Questions

Should harvesting of species be permitted in protected areas such as conservation areas and provincial or national parks? Why is sport fishing permitted in some parks and protected areas, whereas hunting of birds and mammals is not?

Review

Go to CENGAGENOW™ at http://hed.nelson.com/ to access quizzing, animations, exercises, articles, and personalized homework help.

48.1 Extinction

- A species is said to be extinct when there are no living representatives known on Earth. Conservation organizations usually say that a species is extinct when it has not been seen or recorded for 50 years.
- Mass extinctions occurred at the end of the Ordovician and the beginning of the Devonian, at the end of the Devonian, at the end of the Permian, at the end of the Triassic, and at the end of the Cretaceous. The Permian extinction was the most severe, and more than 85% of the species alive at that time disappeared forever, including the trilobites, many amphibians, and the trees of the coal swamp forests. Dinosaurs did not survive the extinction that occurred at the end of the Cretaceous.
- The extinction at the end of the Cretaceous is believed to have been caused by an asteroid impact. Dust clouds resulting from the impact blocked the sunlight necessary for photosynthesis, setting up a chain reaction of extinctions that began with microscopic marine organisms and finished with dinosaurs (as well as many birds and mammals).
- Measured by time on earth, multituberculates were the most successful mammals.

48.2 The Impact of Humans

- Species (particularly flightless birds) that are confined to islands often have small populations and are unaccustomed to introduced terrestrial predators (such as cats, dogs, rats, etc.), making them vulnerable to extinction when human populations settle and expand.
- The demise of the calvaria trees (*Sideroxylum majus*) on the island of Mauritius will occur even though the trees continue to bloom and produce seeds. The extinction of the tree is linked to the earlier extinction of Dodos since *S. majus* seeds had to pass through the Dodo's digestive tract to germinate.

48.3 Introduced and Invasive Species

- Stephen's Island wrens were flightless and unaccustomed to predators. The population on the island was small, and it was easy for Tibbles to catch and kill the remaining 20 birds.
- Since about 1880, ships have regularly used ballast water. A survey of ballast water in 159 ships in Coos Bay, Oregon, revealed 367 species of organisms representing 19 animal phyla and 3 plant divisions. When ships empty their ballast, the organisms in it are introduced to the system where the ship is anchored.
- RUE, resource use efficiency, is measured as carbon assimilation per unit resource. Many invasive plant species in Hawaii are more efficient than native species. This means that conserving native biodiversity in the face of invasive and introduced organisms is a pervasive problem.

48.4 How We Got/Get There

- Horns of rhinos, particularly black rhinos (*Diceros bicornis*), have been used to make handles for ornamental daggers (jambiyas) in some parts of the Arabian peninsula. Increasing oil prices in the early 1970s increased the demand for jambiyas. The main source of rhino horn was from poaching rhinos in Africa.
- During fishing operations, nontarget species are often caught in nets. They are "bycatch." Barndoor skates once occurred across the North Atlantic. Today these skates are almost gone, although they never were the targets of a fishery.
- The demise of the bay scallops occurred because of an increase in the populations of skates and rays that are predators of bay scallops. The increase in skates and rays was attributed to the decline of populations of their predators, sharks. The sharks were extensively fished for their fins. Large-scale harvesting of the scallops for human consumption also compounded the impacts and attributed to their demise.

48.5 Protecting Species

- The International Union for the Conservation of Nature (IUCN) has established objective criteria identifying species that are at risk. Extinct means the species no longer exists; extirpated means the species is locally extinct; endangered means the species is facing imminent extirpation or extinction; threatened means the species is likely to become endangered if limiting factors are not reversed; and special concern means the species may become threatened or endangered because of biological characteristics and identified threats. The criteria take into account data on populations, their patterns of distribution, and their population status.
- The Convention for International Trade on Endangered Species (CITES) attempts to prohibit international trade in endangered species. Newly described and as yet undescribed (and therefore unnamed) species are not protected because they have no legal identity.
- Species such as passenger pigeons or Dodos that have been exterminated are extinct. Extirpated species are locally extinct. Black-footed ferrets (see Chapter 45, *Black-Footed Ferret, Mustela nigripes*) have been extirpated in Canada but still occur in the United States.
- In Canada, recommendations about the conservation status of species involve the Committee on the Status of Endangered Wildlife in Canada (COSEWIC). COSEWIC members vote on the appropriate conservation category for each species whose status they review and use IUCN criteria to assess the status of species.

48.7 The Downside of Being Rare

- An animal on the list of endangered species is more likely to become a commodity in high demand because it has become rare. The Bali starling is an example.

48.9 Effecting Conservation

- In 1994, the International Conference on Population and Development (ICPD) outlined a plan for investing in family planning.
- United Nations Millennium Development Goals of 2000 are ending poverty and hunger, universal education, gender equality, child and maternal health, combatting HIV/AIDS, environmental sustainability, and global partnerships.
- Drylands cover 41% of Earth's land surface, and 10 to 20% of drylands are subject to severe land degradation, affecting, in 2008, the lives of at least 250 million people.
- Climate change and increasing pressure on water supplies negatively affect drylands.
- The case of leopards (*Panthera pardus*) demonstrates how some species persist even in the face of considerable hunting pressure.
- Targeted hunting—selection of "trophy" or spectacular specimens—can be less threatening to a species' survival than bycatch or eradication programs (bounties on predators such as wolves). Extensive killing, even of species with large populations, can drive them to the brink of extinction. Black rhinos are a telling example.
- The overgrowth of Mayan cities or ruins in Africa demonstrates the resiliency of ecosystems. A grasshopper's use of 2,4-D to synthesize an ant repellent demonstrates the resiliency of individuals.
- Hybrids are not protected by the U.S. Endangered Species Act, putting species such as Florida panthers at risk because their populations have been genetically contaminated.

Questions

Self-Test Questions

1. Extinction is a natural part of the process of speciation. Some estimates suggest that ____ of the species that have ever lived are now extinct.
   a. >20%
   b. >30%
   c. >50%
   d. >80%
   e. >99%
2. Some researchers use evidence from a variety of sources to support the suggestion that an asteroid striking Earth in the __________ largely explains the extinction of the dinosaurs.
   a. Cambrian
   b. Ordovician
   c. Triassic
   d. Cretaceous
   e. Pleistocene
3. If our species first appeared 200 000 years before present, the multituberculates survived ____ longer than we have to date.
   a. 10
   b. 50
   c. 100
   d. 500
   e. 1000
4. Hunting by people is largely responsible for the extinction of
   a. multituberculates, Dodos, and passenger pigeons.
   b. barndoor skates, black-footed ferrets, and giant auks.
   c. Dodos, passenger pigeons, and Stephen's Island wrens.
   d. passenger pigeons, giant auks, and Dodos.
   e. black rhinos, Bali starlings, and ginseng.
5. The ballast water of ships is responsible for the spread of
   a. *Arthurdendyus triangulatus.*
   b. *Dressina polymorpha.*
   c. *Rattus norvegicus.*
   d. *Salmo salar.*
   e. *Lampsilis radiata.*
6. In Hawaii, high resource use efficiency (RUE), measured as carbon use, partly explains the success of invading
   a. rats.
   b. ferns.
   c. C_3 and C_4 grasses.
   d. flatworms.
   e. Both b and c are correct.
7. Increases in populations of tertiary consumers such as __________ appear to explain the demise of scallops off the southeastern coast of the United States.
   a. rats
   b. skates and rays
   c. sharks
   d. killer whales
   e. pelagic seabirds
8. Species such as black-footed ferrets (*Mustela nigripes*) no longer occur in Canada but still live in the United States, so they are
   a. extinct.
   b. at risk.
   c. extirpated.
   d. highly endangered.
   e. not at risk.
9. CITES is designed to stop international trade in
   a. passenger pigeons.
   b. black rhinos.
   c. Canadian beavers.
   d. Canada geese.
   e. leopards.
10. Differences in government support for family planning explain the differences in the growth of human populations in
    a. Canada and Australia.
    b. Great Britain and France.
    c. Afghanistan and Sri Lanka.
    d. Mexico and Germany.
    e. India and South Africa.

Questions for Discussion

1. Should gardeners and farmers be exempt from rules concerning the introduction of foreign species? Why? Why not?
2. In situations in which the behaviour of one endangered species threatens the survival of another (or others), how should authorities proceed?
3. What species are "rare" on your campus? What is a good working definition of rare? What steps can you take to protect rare species?

Sunflowers. Originally from the New World, sunflowers (*Helianthus annuus*) are grown as a source of oil. In terms of harvest and area under cultivation, in 1998, sunflowers ranked twelfth in importance among domesticated plants in the world. Domesticated sunflowers often hybridize with local wild species, creating a challenge for those concerned about biodiversity.

M.B. Fenton

Study Plan

49 Domestication

Why It Matters

In 1960, an estimated 1.8 billion people in the world (60% of the population) did not receive enough food every day to sustain themselves fully over the longer period—they were hungry. This number was reduced to 1.1 billion (17%) in 2000. Even though the world population had grown by 3 billion in the intervening period, about 700 million fewer people were hungry in 2000.

Worldwide in 2000, subsistence farmers accounted for about 66% of the hungry people. The reduction in the numbers of hungry people can be tied to changes in agriculture that have increased yields. Specifically, the combination of new genetic strains, better fertilizers, and more efficient harvesting and processing means more productivity. One indication of this change is provided by data about corn yields. In Iowa in 1935, corn yields were ~1600 $kg \cdot ha^{-1}$ compared with ~10 700 $kg \cdot ha^{-1}$ in 2000. Changes in crop yield are part of the "green revolution." Agriculture in general and the green revolution in particular have allowed humans to continue to redefine one element of carrying capacity (see Chapter 45): the amount of food available to our populations.

But agricultural improvements are not enough. Climate (see Chapter 3) also influences crop yield. In 2006 in southwestern Ontario (~42° N in Canada), the corn yield was ~10 000 kg · ha^{-1}, whereas in Zimbabwe (~18° S), on commercial farms, it was ~5500 to 6600 kg · ha^{-1}, compared with ~500 to 1000 kg · ha^{-1} on communal lands where farming was low tech. Irrigation also influences yield: in Zimbabwe, irrigated cornfields produce 8500 to 10 000 kg · ha^{-1}, much more than nonirrigated commercial farms.

Although increases in crop yield and a reduced incidence of malnutrition and starvation sound like good news, in 2007, hunger still claimed the lives of about 20 000 children a day. Worldwide, one child in three is underweight and malnourished. Ironically, at the same time in some developed countries, obesity in children reached almost epidemic proportions.

49.1 Domesticate

The purpose of this chapter is to explore how humans have used selection to put biodiversity to work. Biologists and anthropologists believe that our ancestors originally gathered plants and hunted animals in the wild for use as food, building products, or fuel (see *Molecule Behind Biology*). From gathering, our ancestors progressed to cultivating plants, a process involving the systematic sowing of wild plant seeds. Over time, cultivation improved when people provided more care to their crops and eventually involved repetitive cycles of sowing, collecting, and sowing wild stock **(Figure 49.1)**. **Domestication** is more than just taming. It occurs when people selectively bred individuals of other species (plants and animals) to increase the desirable characteristics in the progeny (e.g., in plants: yield, taste, colour, shelf life). This marked the birth of agriculture. The progression from gathering to cultivation to domestication of plants occurred independently at several locations around the world. The beginning of the Neolithic Period is often defined by the domestication of other species, and this period started at different times in different parts of the world.

But agriculture is not the exclusive domain of humans. Recall that about 50 million years ago, ants of the tribe Attini were the first to manipulate other species (fungi) to increase food availability (see Chapter 24). Today at least 200 species of ants in this tribe are obligate farmers. These early farmers have lost their own digestive enzymes and rely on fungal enzymes to digest the food for them. The ant farmers propagate their fungal crops asexually, with each colony or village working with one species. Therefore, any single species of farmer ant may propagate several different species of fungi. These ants have been involved in at least five domestication events, and there are a number of interesting parallels between these ants and people.

The list of species that humans have domesticated is long. It includes many land plants (~250 species), some yeasts, and terrestrial animals from insects to birds and mammals (~44 species). Biogeographic and genetic evidence shows that domestication of some species by humans occurred at different places and at different times. Domestication was not a one-time (or one-location) event and appears to have arisen independently in 8 to 10 environmentally and biotically diverse areas in the world.

49.1a When and Where? Tracking the History of Domestication

Data provided by the tools of molecular genetics (see Chapter 16) have made it easier to determine where and when domestication events took place. In the past, archaeologists had to try to recognize the

M.B. Fenton

Figure 49.1
The way in which garlic (*Allium sativum*) is grown influences the size and development of the bulbs. From left to right, **(a)** one domesticated, **(b)** two cultivated, and **(c)** two wild garlic bulbs.

Molecule Behind Biology
Salicylic Acid

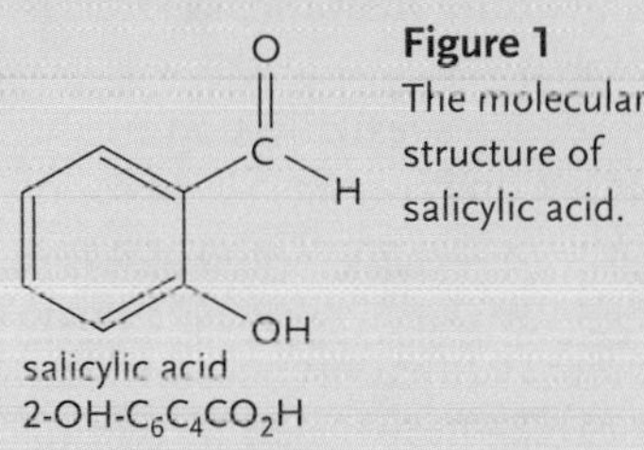

Figure 1
The molecular structure of salicylic acid.

The precursor of the main active ingredient in Aspirin™ is salicylic acid, which is obtained from the bark of willow trees (*Salix* species). Over 2500 years B.P., Chinese medical practitioners used an extract of willow bark to relieve pain and fever. The same kinds of extracts were used in medicine as practised in Greece and in Assyria. In Iceland 500 years ago, willow bark extracts were used to treat the symptoms of colds and headaches. Willow extract was widely used among First Nations people in North America, who commonly used it to staunch bleeding. They also used the supple willow twigs in other applications, from snares for catching mammals to nets for catching fish. This is not an example of domestication.

The spread of traditional knowledge about plants and their products among peoples is pervasive.

remains of domesticated species and distinguish them from wild species. This was often impossible because individual bones or pieces of plant did not always provide a clear indication of domestication. In 1973, radiocarbon dates (see the Preface and Chapter 20) suggested that the first dogs (*Canis familiaris*) were domesticated by 9500 years B.P. (Before Present), based on remains found in England and elsewhere in Europe. In 2002, mitochondrial DNA (mtDNA) evidence suggested an East Asian origin of domestication of dogs dating from 15 000 years B.P. But pictures based on genetic evidence also can change. In 2003, morphological and genetic evidence suggested a southeast Asian origin of domesticated pigs (*Sus scrofa*), whereas in 2005, new genetic data indicated multiple origins of domestication of pigs across Eurasia **(Figure 49.2)**.

Worldwide, domestication of aquatic species has lagged behind that of terrestrial ones. Although there are ~180 species of domesticated freshwater animals, ~250 species of marine animals, and ~19 species of marine plants, all were domesticated in the last 1000 years, most in the last 100 years **(Figure 49.3, p. 1236)**.

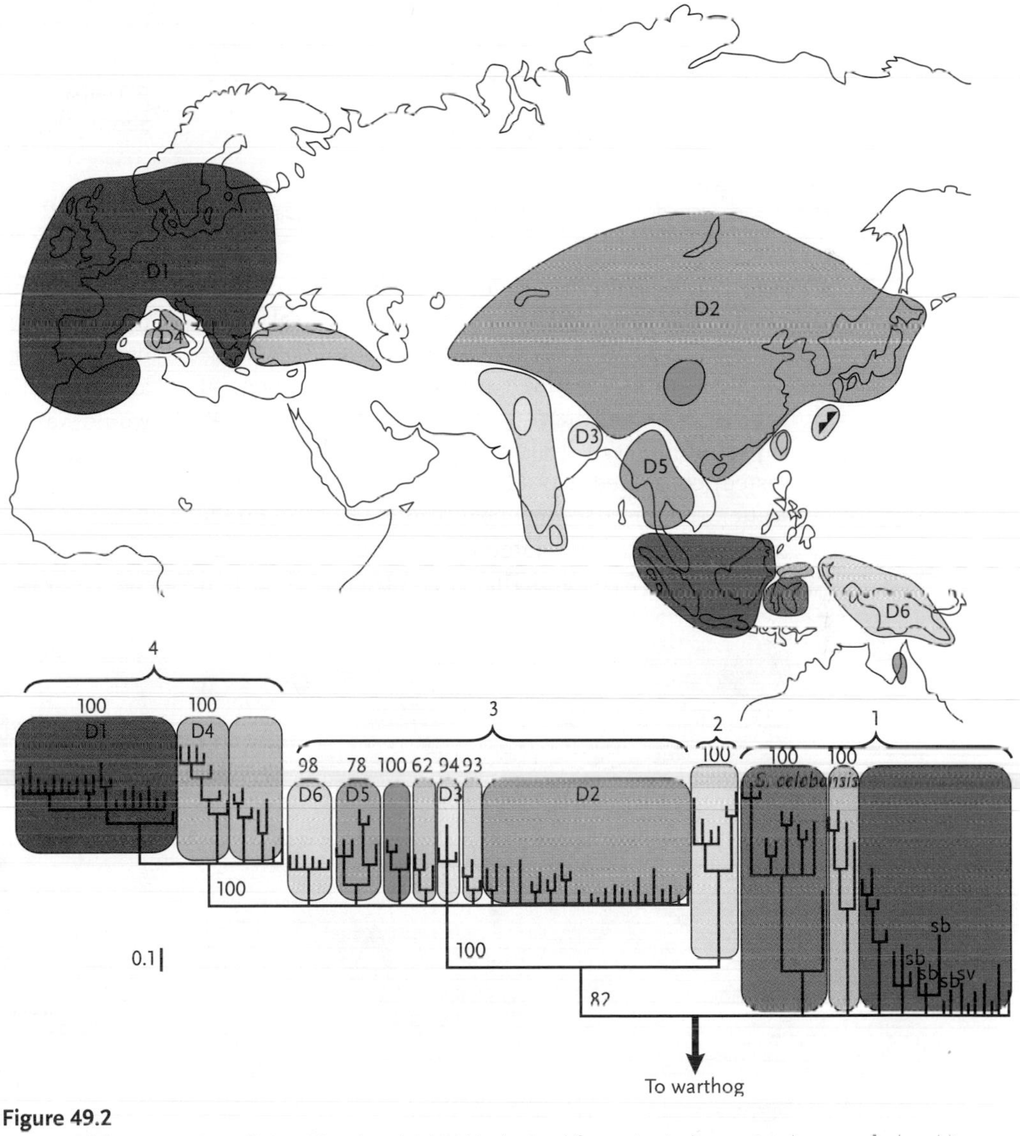

Figure 49.2
Origins of domestication of pigs. Mitochondrial DNA obtained from pigs indicates 14 clusters of related lineages, each identified by a different colour. The geographic relationships are shown with the phylogeny. Pigs were domesticated in numerous centres.

49.1b How Long Did Domestication Take? Archaeological Evidence

The time it takes to progress from harvesting tended wild crops to cultivating them and then to domesticating them varies with species and situation. When there are clear morphological or chemical differences between cultivated and domesticated stocks, determining the place and time of domestication is

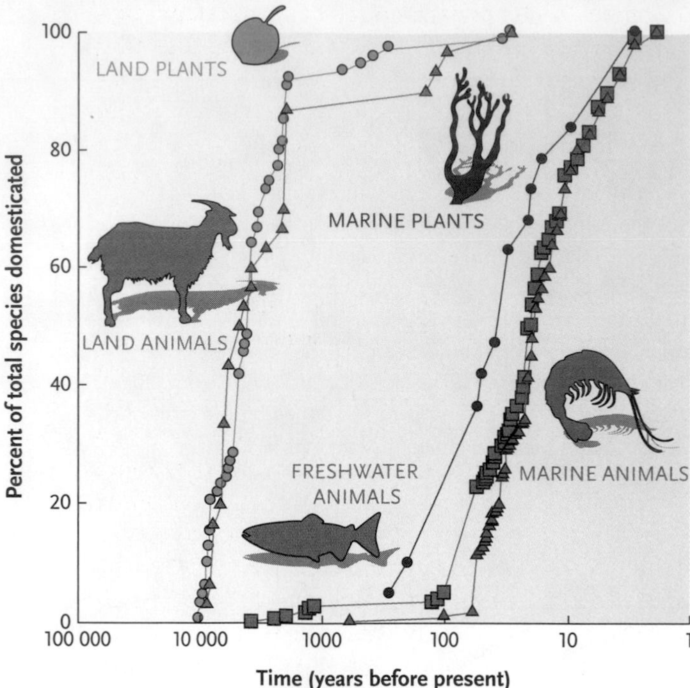

Figure 49.3
Most land species were domesticated much earlier than most aquatic ones.

possible. Wheat provides an example of such a morphological change. In wheat, as in other cereal crops, inflorescences of domesticated stocks hold on to the ripened grains (= indehiscence), whereas those of wild stocks shed them (= dehiscence) **(Figure 49.4).** Ripe indehiscent grains are easily gathered (harvested) compared with dehiscent ones that naturally scatter. Indehiscence in wheat results from a naturally occurring mutation. Material recovered from sites in northeastern Syria and Turkey has been radiocarbon dated and shows that wild varieties of wheat were cultivated for at least 1000 years before domestication **(Figure 49.5).** When sexual reproduction is involved in the breeding process, the time to domestication is partly determined by life cycle.

When organisms reproduce asexually, domestication may occur more rapidly. Common figs (*Ficus carica* var. *domestica*) are gynodioecious and provide an example of more rapid domestication. In parthenocarpic female figs, ovaries develop without pollination and fertilization. Parthenocarpic figs can be propagated by cutting branches, sticking them in the ground, and waiting for them to grow into trees. When figs reproduce sexually, symbiotic fig wasps (*Blastophaga psenes;* **Figure 49.6**) serve as pollinators. The absence of access holes for wasps in fossil figs allows biologists to recognize parthenocarpic figs and date early incidences of fig domestication. At one site in the lower Jordan Valley (Middle East), parthenocarpic figs date to between 11 400 and 10 500 years B.P., perhaps preceding the domestication of cereal crops by about 1000 years.

Figure 49.4
(a) Some plants readily shed ripe seeds from the inflorescence; these plants show dehiscence. **(b)** Indehiscence is the propensity to hold them. These two herbarium specimens, **(a)** bottle brush grass (*Elymus hysterix*) and **(b)** riverbank wild rye (*Elymus riparius*), illustrate dehiscence and indehiscence, respectively.

49.1c In What Setting? Habitats Where Domestication Occurred

The transition from nomadic hunters and gatherers to people living more localized lives in more permanent dwellings appears to have been a prelude to cultivation and domestication. These changes meant that people would have been available to care for their "crops,"

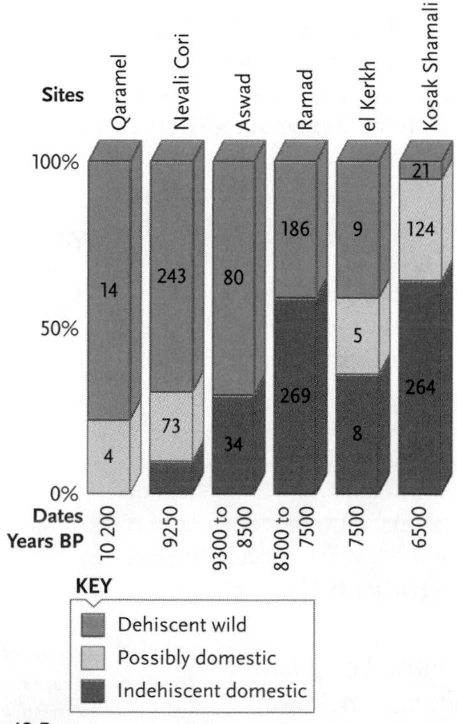

Figure 49.5
Timing of domestication of wheat. Data from archaeological digs at six locations in the Middle East demonstrate the transition from wild (dehiscent) to domesticated (indehiscent) wheat from 10 200 to 6500 years B.P.

CEFE - UMF 5175

Figure 49.6
Female flowers on some fig trees (*Ficus carica*) are fertilized by symbiotic wasps, *Blastophaga psenes*.

whether grown from seeds or from parthenocarpic plants, and whether cultivated or domesticated.

Were changes in habitat associated with domestication? Evidence from pollen shows that from 7500 years B.P. in the lower Yangtze region of China, people used fire to clear alders, small woody bushes (*Alnus* species). This element in the process of domestication is called "niche construction" or "ecosystem engineering," modifying the environment and setting the stage for domestication. At that lower Yangtze Neolithic site, people used fire to prepare and maintain sites in lowland swamps, where they cultivated rice **(Figure 49.7)**. This region in China was a major centre of rice domestication. The evidence suggests that rice cultivation began in coastal wetlands in an ecosystem vulnerable to coastal change. This system was very fertile and productive and used for at least 200 years before the land was inundated by seawater.

Although controlled burning has been documented at many sites in the last 10 000 years, there is evidence of it 50 000 to 55 000 years ago **(Figure 49.8, p. 1238)** at sites near Mossel Bay in South Africa. Archaeological evidence indicates that some humans were increasingly using some plant resources and used local burning to increase productivity. The increased use of plant resources and fire occurred during a period of harsh environmental conditions. These changes in human behaviour coincided with the appearance of more sophisticated tools, the use of marine organisms as food, and the first use of ochre for decoration. These modifications suggest differences in human behaviour that may have assisted the emergence of domestication.

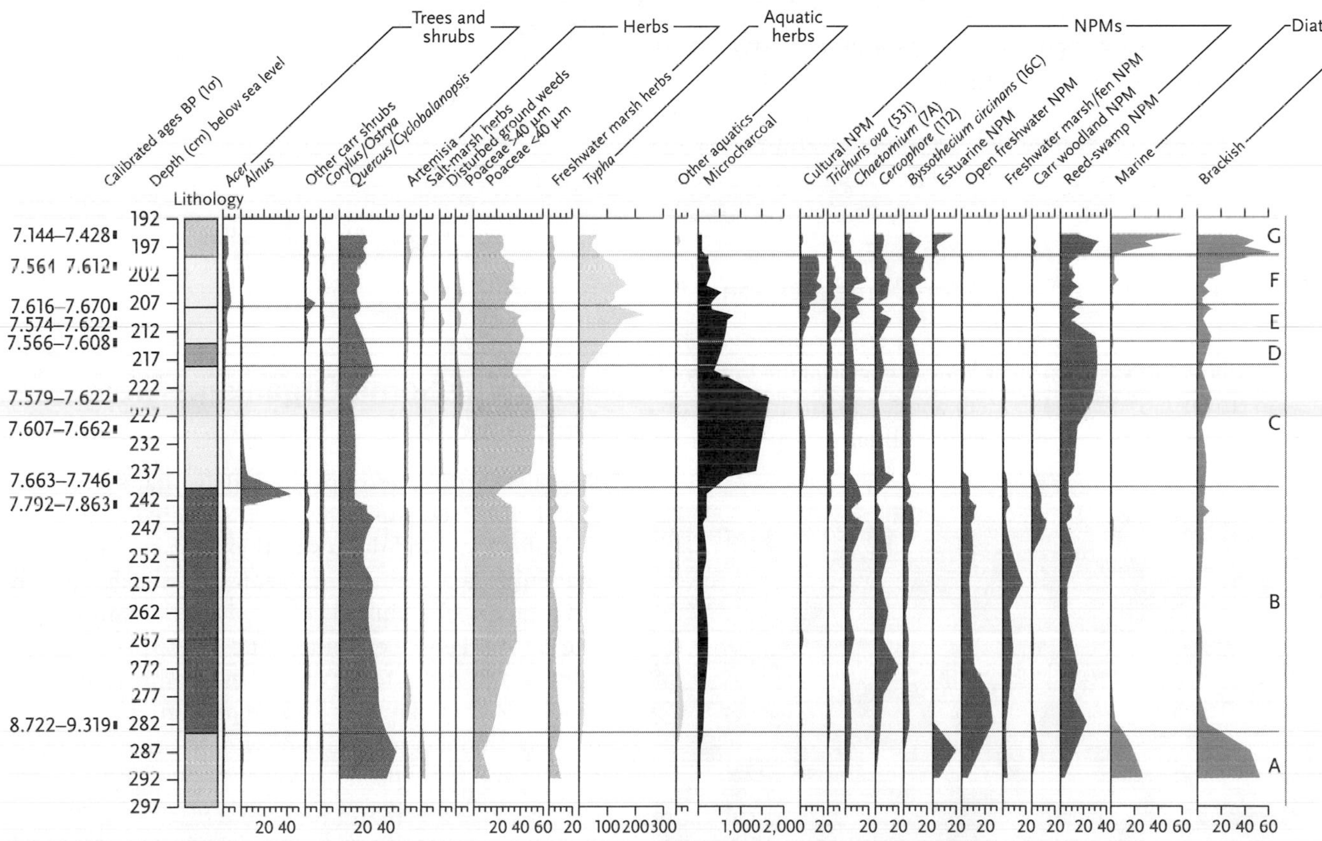

Figure 49.7
The climatic setting for rice domestication at Kuahugiao in China. Shown here are generalized stratigraphic units and their associated pollen (shown in colours) and microscopic charcoal (black) that indicate conditions of climate and habitat. The data support the use of fire to establish favourable conditions for growing rice. "NPMs" are nonpollen microfossils that provide paleoecological data. The increases in charcoal, grasses (Poaceae), and reed swamp microfossils in phases C, E, and F (right edge) indicate the use of fire to establish favourable conditions for growing rice.

M.B. Fenton

Figure 49.8
In Ghana (West Africa), fire is still used to clear the underbrush from an area where forest trees have been felled.

Meanwhile, at sites on the coast of Peru, occupied between 3800 and 3500 years B.P., people ate marine organisms as the main animal food, combined with cultivated plants (squashes, *Cucurbita* species; beans, *Phaseolus lunatus* and *P. vulgaris;* peppers, *Capsicum* species; jicama, *Pachyrrhizus tuberosus*); and wild plants (guava, *Psidium guajava;* lacuma, *Lucuma bifera;* and pacay, *Inga feuillei*). Cotton was an important crop used for making fishing tackle and clothing. The findings from these Peruvian sites and many other sites around the world suggest a progression toward domestication, including the range of foods consumed, the development of more sophisticated tools, and the use of materials from plants and animals as tools, as well as in food.

49.1d Abu Hureyra on the Euphrates: An Example of a Setting for Domestication

This prehistoric settlement (a recent photograph is shown in **Figure 49.9**), on the south side of the Euphrates River (35° 52 N, 38° 24 E) about 130 km from Aleppo (a modern Syrian city), also illustrates progression toward domestication. The first habitations that we know of in Abu Hureyra date from about 12 000 years B.P. Its population was estimated at 100 to 200 people who lived in semisubterranean pit dwellings clustered together on a low promontory overlooking the river. By 7000 to 9400 years ago, 4000 to 6000 people lived at the same site, now in multiroomed family dwellings made of mud and brick. This settlement was built over the remains of the earlier one.

Artwork from The Tell of Abu Hureyra From The West. Reprinted with permission of Oxford University Press.

Figure 49.9
Abu Hureyra in Syria, the site of an early village.

People living at Abu Hureyra about 12 000 years ago ate the fruits and seeds of over 100 species of local plants as well as local animals such as gazelles. Many of the plants and animals appear to have come from the adjoining oak-dominated park woodland. It appears to have been a time of plentiful food. The situation changed, however, and by 9400 years ago, the climate was cooler and drier, and the people relied more on cultivated plants and less on wild ones. By this time, there was little evidence of use of plants from the oak-dominated parkland, which by then was at least 14 km from the settlement. These changes were evident in pollen records and in plant and animal remains associated with the dwellings. The climate change likely triggered the start of cultivation of foods that could serve as caloric staples. Despite the changing climate and the focus on fewer food staples, the human population at the site dramatically increased.

Study Break

1. Explain the benefits of the "green revolution"? What is responsible for it?
2. How did domestication develop?
3. Why can domestication take place more rapidly in asexually reproducing organisms?

49.2 Why Some Organisms Were Domesticated

We can surmise, perhaps accurately, that securing a sustainable food supply provided an initial motivation for cultivation and domestication. It is certainly true that cultivated plants from beans to squash, corn to rice, and cereal grains all help feed many, many people worldwide. People eat different parts of plants, from flowers and fruits to seeds, leaves, stems, roots, and tubers. Plants may be a source of energy (calories), or their products may be used to enhance flavours, to control and repel pests, or as medicines. Still others, such as the bottle gourd (*Lagenaria siceraria*), are used as containers (see *People Behind Biology*). Domesticated animals provide food, but many are also used as a source of labour. The following are examples of four very different domesticated species and how people use them.

Figure 49.10
Today there are two varieties of domesticated cattle: **(a)** the humped *Bos indicus* and **(b)** the humpless Bos *taurus*.

49.2a Cattle

Cattle were among the first of the large herd mammals to be domesticated, at least 9000 years B.P. One theory proposes that the domesticators of cattle were sedentary farmers, not nomadic hunters. Some anthropologists maintain that a religious motivation was behind the domestication of cattle because the curve of their horns resembled the crescent of the moon and hence the mother-goddess. Imposing horns were particularly prominent in some male *Bos primigenius* (called "urus"), the apparent Pleistocene ancestor of domesticated cattle. Whatever the original impetus, today there are two basic stocks of cattle **(Figure 49.10)**, the humped *Bos indicus* and the humpless *Bos taurus*. Cattle provide us with labour, milk, meat, hides, and blood, and in some societies, they are symbols of wealth.

49.2b Honeybees

Domestic honeybees provide us with honey and pollination services. Steps to domestication of honeybees included changes in their behaviour compatible with large population size in hives. The changes could have involved hygiene, aggression, and foraging. Although everyone recognizes honey as a product of bees, the service provided by bees is often overlooked. In 2000 in the United States, it is estimated that bees contributed about U.S.$14.5 billion through their role as pollinators. Plants such as alfalfa, apples, almonds, onions, broccoli, and sunflowers are exclusively pollinated by insects, usually more than 90% by honeybees. Many beekeepers earn significant income by moving their bees from location to location, thus providing a mobile pollinator service for farmers. Declines in populations of honeybees have serious economic implications throughout the world, but many conservationists are also concerned about the impact of populations of honeybees on native bee species.

49.2c Cotton

At least four species of cotton **(Figure 49.11)** have been domesticated: two diploid species from the Old World (*Gossypium arboreum, G. herbaceum*) and two tetraploids from the New World (*G. hirsutum* and *G. barbadense*). The domestication events appear to have been independent, and one site on the Mexican gulf coast of Tabasco shows evidence of people growing cotton by 4400 years B.P. Cotton seeds were a source of oil, whereas fibre was and is still used in applications ranging from clothing to implements.

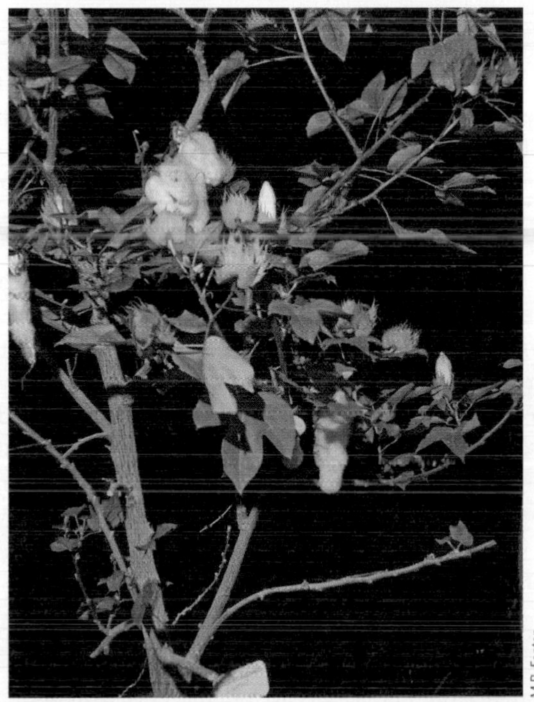

Figure 49.11
Cotton, *Gossypium herbaceum*, showing flowers and cotton bolls.

People Behind Biology
Richard Keith Downey

Richard Keith Downey was born in 1927 in Saskatchewan and attended the University of Saskatchewan and Cornell University. He is best known for his work on rapeseed. In 1928, rapeseed had been brought to Shellbrook, Saskatachewan, by Fred and Olga Solovonuk when they immigrated to Canada from their native Poland. They had brought seeds of *Brassica rapa*, although *Brassica napus* from Argentina was the main traditional source of rapeseed oil. During World War II, rapeseed was grown as a source of industrial lubricants because erucic acid and glucosinolates in the oil precluded its use as food for people and livestock.

Dr. Downey was the leader of a team of researchers at Agriculture and Agrifoods Canada who developed canola (the name comes from "Canada" and "oil"), an edible, high-value crop high in proteins. The team's work resulted in a crop that went from 2600 to 4.25 million ha under cultivation in Canada. Canola is now grown around the world, and the high-protein crop is used in cooking oils and feed for livestock.

Downey and his team developed the "half-seed" method, partitioning a seed so that half could be tested for composition using gas–liquid chromatography. The researchers could then select and germinate the half-seeds with the most promising features. Using this approach, Downey and his team developed 18 varieties of canola and several of table mustard. This work had a huge impact on the economy of Canada in general and the prairies in particular, as well as an influence on food availability throughout the world.

Dr. Downey is also known for a program that introduced children in elementary school to the scientific method. The approach involved using canola seeds that had travelled into space aboard the space shuttle *Columbia* in 1996. Children in over 2000 classrooms in Canada received space seeds along with control seeds and germinated them. Downey helped analyze the results of the experiments. Space seeds germinated faster and at higher rates than control seeds and grew more rapidly. In this way, Downey introduced elementary students to plant science and the space environment.

49.2d Yeast

Strains of the yeast *Saccharomyces cerevisiae* have been used by people in bread making beginning at least 6000 years B.P. Evidence of this is in archaeological finds in Egypt, indicating the presence of bakeries and breweries, two yeast-based operations. Analysis of 12 DNA microsatellites obtained from 651 strains of *S. cerevisiae* collected at 56 locations around the world revealed 575 distinct genotypes. Yeasts associated with bread were intermediate between wild types and those used in making beer and wine, whereas those used in the production of rice wine and saki were more similar to those used for beer. About 28% of the genetic variation in yeast genotypes was associated with geographic location. The basal group of these 12 DNA microsatellites was samples from Lebanon, suggesting a Mesopotamian origin and a spread of yeast types along the Danube River and around the Mediterranean. Different strains of yeast have different capacities for maltose fermentation. Commercial bakers' yeast strains are more effective at maltose fermentation than nonindustrial strains. Domesticated yeast makes important contributions to providing humans with food and drink and supports lucrative industries.

49.2e Rice

Rice (*Oryza sativa*) is one of the world's most important food crops, and its domestication depended on the change from dehiscence to indehiscence. Although the genetic changes involved were presumed to be minor, their exact nature has only recently become clear. Domesticated rice is derived from two wild species (*Oryza rufipogon* and *Oryza indica*). In 2006, Changbao Li and his colleagues reported that three quantitative trait loci (QTL) in F_1 hybrids between these two species were responsible for a reduction of grain shattering (dehiscence) in rice. Specifically, *sh3, sh4,* and *sh8* were involved, with *sh4* explaining 64% of the phenotypic variance. In the wild species, *sh4* was dominant and caused the shattering. The genetic changes in *sh3, sh4,* and *sh8* affected normal development of the abscission layer, explaining the change to indehiscence **(Figure 49.12).** We

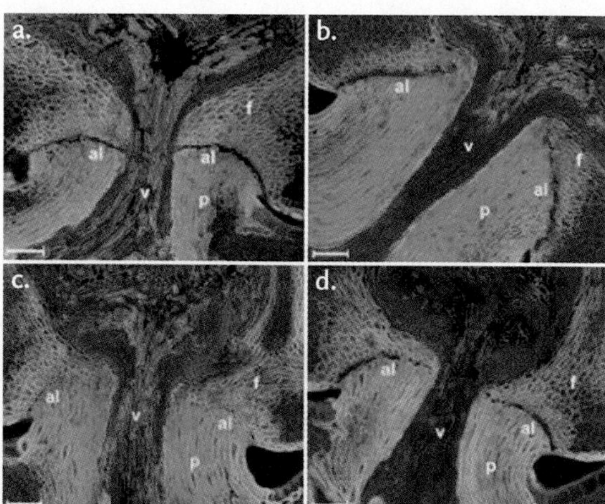

Figure 49.12
Rice dehiscence and indehiscence. Under a fluorescence microscope, a longitudinal section of the junction between the rice flower and its pedicel shows a complete abscission layer (al in a) and an incomplete one (al in b). In these figures, f = flower side; p = pedicel side; and v = vascular bundles. *Oryza nivara* is shown in **(a)**, *O. sativa* in **(b)**, *O. sativa japonica* in **(c)**, and transformed *O. sativa japonica* in **(d)**.

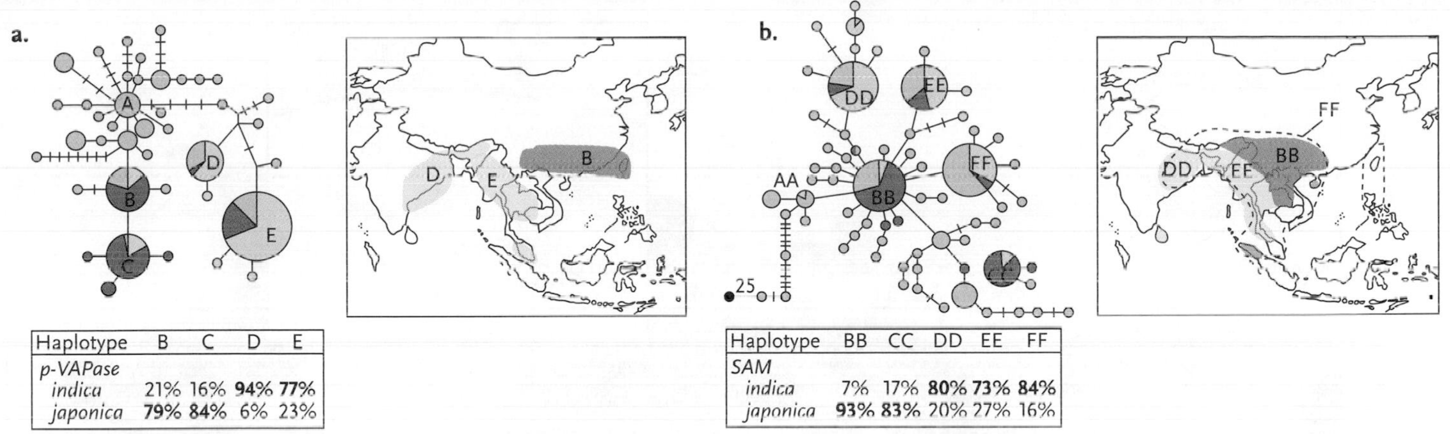

Figure 49.13
Geography of rice domestication. Genetic haplotype information allows identification of major domestication regions for rice. The haplotype network of the neutral nuclear p-VAPase region is shown in A, compared with B, the haplotype of the functional nuclear SAM region. In this diagram, purple represents *Oryza japonica;* green, *O. indica* (Aus cultivar); and pink, *O. indica*. Lines joining haplotypes represent mutational steps.

can now better understand the genetics of changes associated with domestication of rice.

These changes occur in the two major varieties of domesticated rice, *Oryza sativa japonica* and *Oryza sativa indica*. Jason Londo and his colleagues used DNA sequence variation to demonstrate multiple independent domestication events. Although *O. sativa indica* was probably domesticated in eastern India, Myanmar, and Thailand south of the Himalayan mountains, *O. sativa japonica* was domesticated in southern China **(Figure 49.13).**

49.2f Wheat

Other major domestications appear to stem from single domestication events, including wheat, barley **(Figure 49.14),** and corn. DNA fingerprinting was used by Manfred Heun and his colleagues to identify the Karacadağ mountains **(Figure 49.15, p. 1242)** in today's Turkey as *the* site of domestication of einkorn wheat. Einkorn wheat is derived from the wild *Triticum monococcum boeoticum*. Einkorn wheat is indehiscent and has a firm stalk, heavier seeds, and denser seed masses than its progenitor (see Figure 18.7), all contributing to the ease and efficiency of harvest. The genetic changes between einkorn wheat and the wild stock from which it was derived were relatively minor, and domestication probably occurred in a short period of time.

Archaeological evidence reveals that einkorn wheat spread rapidly throughout the immediate area and beyond. The same single domestication event and rapid spread of the new crop also appear to be true of barley (**Figure 49.16b, p. 1242;** *Hordeum vulgare* derived from *Hordeum spontaneum*). More recent wheat domestication is discussed in *Marquis Wheat.*

49.2g Lentils

Lentils (*Lens culinaris* from *Lens orientalis;* **Figure 49.16a, p. 1242**) were more difficult to domesticate than wheat or rice. Wild lentils are small plants, producing, on average, 10 seeds per plant. Furthermore, these seeds go through a period of programmed dormancy. The combination of low yield and dormancy means that relatively few seeds germinate. Lentils could have been cultivated only after a dormancy-free mutant had appeared. Archaeological evidence suggests that the first stages of lentil domestication (loss of dormancy) occurred in what is now southeastern Turkey and northern Syria, suggesting a single initial domestication event. The second phase was selection for strains that produced large numbers of seeds. This change may have occurred some distance (hundreds or even thousands of kilometres) from the original sites of domestication.

M.B. Fenton

M.B. Fenton

Figure 49.14
A barley field near London, Ontario, illustrates the consistency of a monoculture, one plant dominating an area, in this case for artificial reasons.

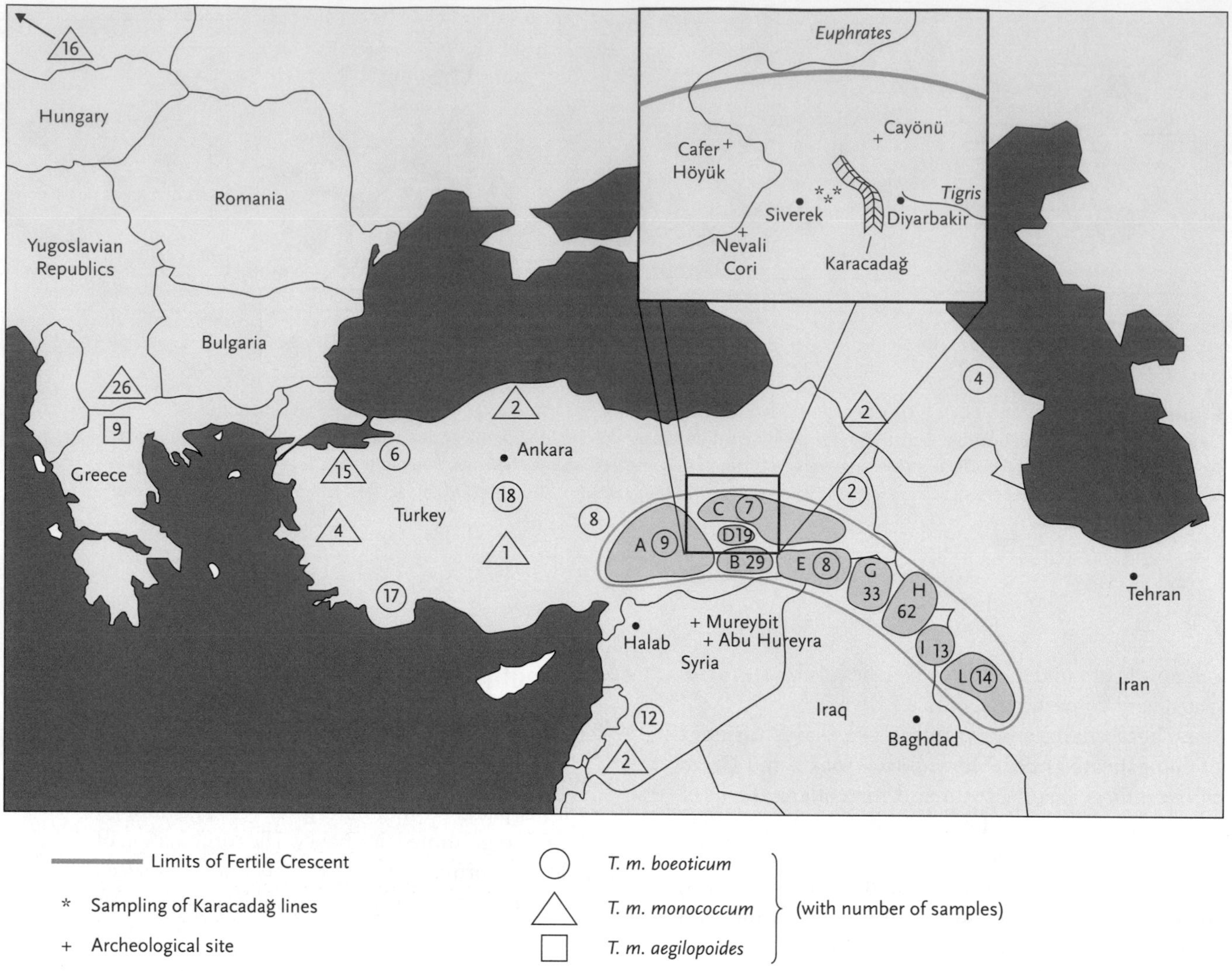

Limits of Fertile Crescent

* Sampling of Karacadağ lines

\+ Archeological site

A–L: areas of wild *T. m. boeoticum* sampling in the Fertile Crescent

○ *T. m. boeoticum*; △ *T. m. monococcum*; □ *T. m. aegilopoides* (with number of samples)

Figure 49.15
Site of wheat domestication. A phylogenetic analysis base on allelic frequency at 288 amplified fragment length polymorphism marker loci revealed the progenitor of *T. m. boeoticum* came from what is now southeastern Turkey.

49.2h Corn

Corn (*Zea mays*), like wheat and barley, appears to have been domesticated at one location. Unlike wheat or barley, domestication of corn required drastic changes from the ancestral teosinte (*Zea mays parviglumis;* **Figure 49.17**). Corn kernels do not disassociate from the cob, presumably reflecting changes associated with domestication (and analogous to indehiscence). Analysis of some of the most ancient inflorescences of teosinte indicates that by 6250 years B.P., the kernels did not disassociate, suggesting that domestication was under way at that time. Corn appears to have been domesticated in the Central Balsas Valley of south central Mexico or in the Mexican State of Puebla at altitudes of 1000 to 1500 m. The deposits that contained the undissociated teosinte kernels also had the remains of squash (*Cucurbita pepo*). Although squash appears to have been domesticated in the same area, remains from a cave in Puebla and Oxa States in Mexico suggest that the people there were cultivating it by about 4000 years before corn. These data again demonstrate that some people were responsible for multiple domestication events.

Figure 49.16
Two important domesticated crops are **(a)** lentils (*Lens culinaris*) and **(b)** barley (*Hordeum vulgare*). In each case, individual grains are about 6 mm long.

Figure 49.17
Teosinte and domesticated corn. Ears of domesticated corn (*Zea mays*, right) are larger than those of one species of its wild relative teosinte (*Zea diploperennis*, left). Crossing domesticated corn and teosinte produces intermediate forms (centre).

49.2i Grapes

The Eurasian grape (*Vitus vinifera sylvestris*), a dioecious plant, is widespread from the Atlantic coasts of Europe to the western Himalayas, and its fruits were often eaten by Paleolithic hunter–gatherers. Domestication of *V. vinifera* involved the selection of hermaphroditic genotypes that produced larger, more colourful fruit, along with the development of techniques for vegetative propagation. Domesticated grapes have a higher sugar content than wild ones, ensuring better fermentation, greater yield, and more regular production. Domestication of grapes is associated with the production of wine, which also required storage in containers made of pottery, which appeared only about 10 500 years B.P.

Genetic analyses suggest at least two important origins of grape domestication: one in the near East and the other in the region of the western Mediterranean. Many wine-grape cultivars from Europe can be traced to western Mediterranean stock, as can over 70% of the cultivars on the Iberian Peninsula. It is possible that the original wild stock of *V. vinifera* has vanished due to genetic contamination by various cultivars.

49.2j Plants in the Family Solonaceae

Solanaceous plants include species such as deadly nightshade (*Atropa belladonna*) that produce virulent poisons, as well as food species (tomatoes, *Solanum lycopersicum;* potatoes, *Solanum tuberosum;* and eggplant, *Solanum melongena*) that are staples of many meals worldwide **(Figure 49.18).**

Potatoes originated in western South America, specifically in areas of what is now Chile. Today, local varieties (also known as breeds, cultivars, or landraces) of potatoes are adapted to the local conditions where they grow. These landraces form the *Solanum brevicaule* complex. Genotypes from multilocus amplified fragment length polymorphisms were determined from 261 wild and 98 landrace samples. The resulting data suggest that potatoes (*S. tuberosum*) arose from one domestication event. Today, wild potatoes still occur in Chile, along with eight cultivar groups of potatoes—some diploid and some triploid, others tetraploid or pentaploid (see Chapter 18). They vary noticeably in leaf shape, floral patterns, and tuber colour. Domesticated potatoes have been selected for short stolons, large tubers, and various colours of tubers from white to yellow to black. After being introduced to Europe, potatoes became an important food staple, and millions of people were adversely affected when potato crops failed because of a blight caused by the fungus *Phytophthora infestans*. The resulting "potato famine" in Ireland had huge social repercussions: many people died, and others emigrated to Canada, the United States, and Australia.

Tomatoes (*Solanum lycopersicum*) were domesticated from plants that grew in South and Central America, but there is considerable debate about when they were domesticated. Two modern forms, wild cherry tomatoes and currant tomatoes, were recently domesticated from stock native to eastern Mexico. Eaten raw or cooked, tomatoes come in different sizes, shapes, and colours. Different strains grow well in a variety of situations, meaning that tomatoes

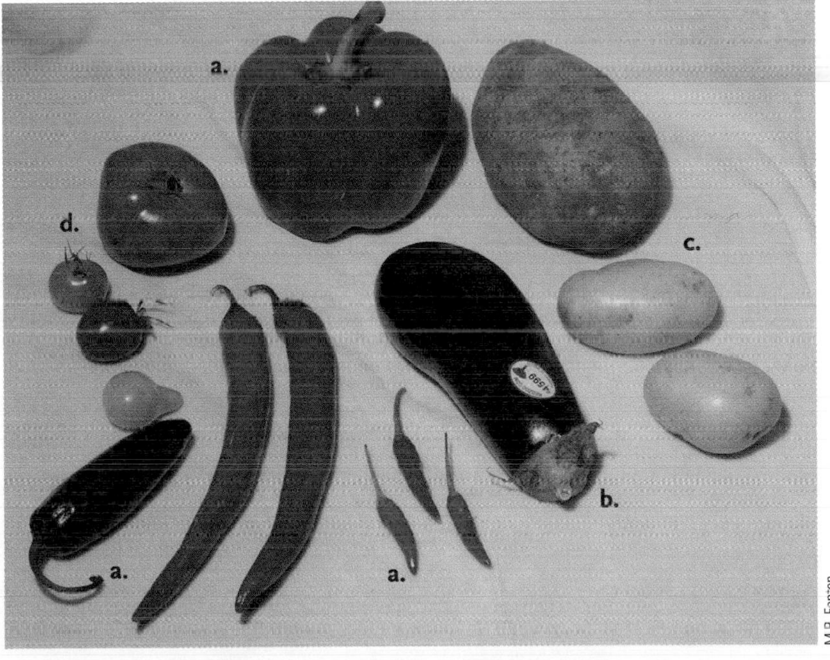

Figure 49.18
Solonaceae. Domesticated species include **(a)** capsicum peppers, **(b)** eggplant, **(c)** potato, and **(d)** tomato.

Marquis Wheat

Different strains of domesticated crops, such as wheat or corn, have different features that make them better suited to some areas (climates) than to others. Whereas Red Fife wheat matures in 130 days and produces 3270 $kg \cdot ha^{-1}$, Hard Red Calcutta wheat matures in 110 days but yields only 1240 $kg \cdot ha^{-1}$. In an effort to find a wheat variety that would grow well and produce a good yield in the Canadian Prairies, Sir Charles E. Saunders made extensive crosses and developed Marquis wheat by 1906. To do this involved selective breeding: a planned program of hybridization of different wheat varieties, rigid selection of the best available material, preliminary and final evaluations of the results from replicated trials, and extensive testing of the new varieties. In the 1880s, Dr. William Saunders (Sir Charles's father) had introduced and tested many strains of wheat, often from Russia and India.

Crosses that led to the emergence of Marquis wheat were mainly focused on Hard Red Calcutta and Red Fife. The products of the crosses were tested at stations near Agassiz, British Columbia; Indian Head, Saskatchewan; and Brandon, Manitoba. At the latter two locations, these two varieties differed by three weeks in reaching maturity.

Sir Charles is famous for the "chewing test" he used to test the products of the crosses. He observed that chewing allowed him to determine the elasticity of the gummy substance produced (gluten). Other tests included baking bread with flour ground from the different strains to ensure that the product was satisfactory.

In 1906, Marquis wheat emerged as the product of a cross between a Hard Red Calcutta female and a Red Fife male. The kernels were dark red and hard, medium in size, and short. Heads were medium in length and bearded. Marquis ripens a few days before Red Fife and produces flour that is strong and of good colour. Tested at Brandon in 1908, Marquis wheat was the earliest to ripen and yielded 4336 $kg \cdot ha^{-1}$—the best among the strains compared. Note that in Ottawa, Marquis wheat was not as productive, yielding only 2522 $kg \cdot ha^{-1}$, reflecting the effect of climate and conditions on yield.

can be grown in many different climate zones. When grown in greenhouses, tomatoes are often pollinated by resident bumblebees, although many cultivars are self-pollinating.

Eggplants include three closely related cultivated species: *Solanum melongena,* the brinjal eggplant or aubergine; *Solanum aethiopicum,* the scarlet eggplant; and *Solanum macrocarpum,* the gboma eggplant. All cultivated species are native to the Old World, with *S. macrocarpum* and *S. aethiopicum* having been domesticated in Africa. The origin of the brinjal eggplant is less certain, but it may have originated in Africa and been domesticated in India and southeast China. During the Arab conquests, it spread from there to the Mediterranean and today is cultivated around the world. Brinjal eggplants and tomatoes are autogamous diploids.

Chili peppers, *Capsicum* species, are another member of the Solonaceae that originated in the New World. Known as producers of capsaicin (see Chapter 34, *Molecule Behind Biology*), chili peppers are often used to spice food. Cultivation of *Capsicum* species was well advanced and widespread in the Americas by 6000 years B.P., and then, as now, they were used as condiments and components of complex diets.

People use other members of this family as the source of hallucinogenic compounds. Notable examples are tobacco and species in the genus *Datura.* Jimson weed or locoweed (*Datura stramonium*) contains strong poisons, including belladonna alkaloids, atropine, and scopalamine. It grows in many parts of the world and has often been used as a hallucinogenic drug because one active ingredient interferes with neurotransmitters (see Chapter 33) and can induce violent hallucinations. The name "locoweed" is a useful, important warning.

Another plant genus, *Brassica,* also includes many varieties seen on dinner tables worldwide (see *Domesticated Plants in the Genus* Brassica).

49.2k Squash

At least five species of squash (*Cucurbita;* **Figure 49.19**) were domesticated in the Americas before European settlers arrived, some of them at least 10 000 years B.P. Squash, beans, and corn were the "three sisters", staple foods farmed by many First Nations peoples in the New World. Genetic data obtained from an intron region of the mitochondrial *nad1* gene suggest that at least six independent domestication events occurred. *Cucurbita argyrosperma* appears to have been domesticated from *C. sororia,* a wild Mexican gourd that grew in the general area of Mexico as teosinte. *C. moschata* was probably domesticated somewhere in lowland South America and *C. maxima* in the humid lowlands of Bolivia from *C. andreana.* The *Cucurbita pepo* complex seems to be derived from at least two domestication events, one in eastern North America and one in northeastern Mexico.

Many people are familiar with *C. pepo* as the pumpkin or jack-o'-lantern, but the species also includes summer squashes and zucchinis. *Cucurbita maxima* is the Hubbard and other winter squashes,

Figure 49.19
Many cultivars of squash, *Cucurbita* species, are New World domesticates, some first domesticated in southwestern Mexico at least 10 000 years ago.

which also include some *C. pepo* and *C. moshata*. The diversity of these cultivars is astonishing. The intraspecific variations entailed provide another example of the difficulty of applying the species concept to the diversity of life (see Chapter 18).

49.2l Dogs

Behaviour provides clues to important aspects about domestication of dogs. Dogs are much better than chimps and wolves at understanding human communication signals. Specifically, researchers assessed the abilities of these three animals to read human signals indicating the location of food. Even young puppies with little human contact were more skillful at these social cognition skills than chimpanzees and wolves. Interspecific communication appears to have been strongly selected for during the domestication of dogs, building on the evolutionary history of social skills associated with cooperative hunting inherited from their wolf ancestors.

Dogs were among the first animals to have been domesticated, presumably to help people with hunting. Genetic, behavioural, and morphological evidence indicates that dogs were derived from wolves. The earliest morphological evidence suggests domestication of dogs by 14 500 years B.P., whereas mtDNA data suggest a date of 15 000 years B.P. Genetic data suggest an East Asian origin for dogs. Other mtDNA data from specimens in Latin American and Alaska indicate that dogs crossed into North America via the Bering Land Bridge, with people producing a group (clade) of dogs unique to the New World. The mtDNA data imply that European colonists actively prevented dogs that they brought with them from interbreeding with dogs already present in the New World.

49.2m *Salmo salar*, Atlantic Salmon

Naturally occurring widely around the North Atlantic (locations in North America, Greenland, and Europe), Atlantic salmon have been introduced to many sites around the world, from Jordan and Greece to Australia, New Zealand, Chile, Argentina, Brazil, and the Falkland Islands. There are both landlocked natural and introduced freshwater populations of Atlantic salmon. This species has been a traditional target of subsistence, sport, and commercial fishing and more recently the focus of aquaculture operations. The farmed fish have been selectively bred; thus, they are domesticated. Farmed fish are larger and more aggressive than those from wild stock, and they mature later.

Intensive fishing reduced natural stocks of Atlantic salmon, in some areas to the brink of extinction. Aquaculture operations have proven to be very lucrative, leading to a proliferation of these facilities in many areas. But there are negative impacts of some aquacultural operations. For example, escaped fish are thought to interbreed with local species (on the west coast of North America), threatening their genetic survival. This threat may be reduced by using sterile triploid Atlantic salmon for aquaculture. Sterile triploids can be mass produced, making it relatively feasible to use them in many areas. But concerns about the productivity and survival of triploid fish compared with diploid individuals have slowed the spread of their use.

Aquaculture can bring other problems. Sea lice, such as *Lepeophtheirus salmonis*, are parasitic copepod crustaceans that can cause serious problems for salmon aquacultural facilities. Recurrent sea lice infestations of aquacultured populations have spread to and decimated some wild salmon populations. Infestations by sea lice originating from cultured salmon have also caused a 99% collapse of some wild populations of pink salmon (*Oncorhynchus gorbuscha*) in coastal British Columbia.

The scale of aquaculture operations involving Atlantic salmon is astounding. In 2006, in the province of Nova Scotia (Canada) alone, 35 000 tonnes of Atlantic salmon were produced by aquaculture. Atlantic salmon also dominate farmed stock in British Columbia. The scale of production has wide social and economic implications for human nutrition, employment, and habitat.

49.2n Organisms Domesticated for More than One Use

Some animals and plants provide more than one crop. Cotton, as noted above, provides oilseed and fibre. Cattle are sources of meat, milk, blood, hides, and labour. Sheep provide wool, milk, meat, and hides. Sheep skins with the wool attached are used to make clothing, but the term "golden fleece" refers to their use to trap particles of placer gold.

Figure 49.20
Pearls for sale in the Pearl Market in Beijing, China.

49.2o Cultivated But Not Domesticated Organisms

People cultivate many species that have not been domesticated because there is no evidence of selective breeding. Mushrooms are examples because although they have been cultivated and used as a source of protein for several thousand years, there is less information about selective breeding of specific lines (= domestication). Some species of mushrooms are also used as the source of biologically (hallucinogenic) active compounds.

Ostriches (*Strutio camelus*) are ranched (= cultivated) for their meat, hides, feathers, and eggs, but they are not domesticated. Crocodiles (*Crocodylus* species) are also ranched for their hides and meat. Oysters (*Pinctata fucata*) and other species of molluscs have been cultivated for hundreds of years mainly for pearls **(Figure 49.20)**. Other animals, such as *Python regius* (ball pythons), are bred and sold to snake fanciers. Breeders may select individuals with specific traits in their breeding programs, technically making the animals domesticated because the definition does not speak to use.

Study Break

1. What are the differences between cultivation and domestication? Give examples.
2. How has domestication affected *K*, carrying capacity?
3. Use two of the examples to compare the timing, location, and path of domestication. Be sure to explain how the domesticated organisms are used.
4. How did the domestication of rice, wheat, barley, and lentils differ from that of squash and potatoes?
5. Use an example to show how domestication of animals depends on their behaviour.

49.3 Yields

In his book *The Upside of Down: Catastrophe, Creativity and the Renewal of Civilization*, Thomas Homer-Dixon calculated the amount of energy it would have taken to build the Coliseum in Rome. He estimated that it would have taken 44 billion kilocalories of energy: 34 billion for oxen and 10 billion for human workers (assuming that both worked 220 days a year for 5 years and that the humans received 12 500 $kJ \cdot day^{-1}$). The Roman workers would have eaten grain, mainly wheat, as well as legumes, vegetables, wine, and a little meat. The oxen would have been fed hay, mainly alfalfa, as well as legumes, millet, clover, tree foliage, and wheat chaff. Records from the time indicate a yield of wheat of about 1160 $kg \cdot ha^{-1}$ and alfalfa of about 2600 $kg \cdot ha^{-1}$. Wheat delivers 1.0×10^7 $kJ \cdot ha^{-1}$ and alfalfa 1.6×10^7 $kJ \cdot ha^{-1}$. Growing wheat would have required 58 days of slave labour per hectare per year. If farmers had had to pay labourers, the cost of production would have been higher.

Based on these data, Homer-Dixon calculated that building the Coliseum would have required the wheat grown on 19.8 km^2 of land and the alfalfa on 35.2 km^2. At its peak around 1 and 2 A.D., the population of the city of Rome was 1 million, and that number would have required the food produced on 8800 km^2 of land, equivalent to the area of Lebanon today. Much of the wheat that fed Rome came from North Africa, as well as Sicily, Etrusca, and Campania.

On average, one adult human needs 8300 $kJ \cdot day^{-1}$ to maintain a stable body mass, 3.0×10^6 $kJ \cdot yr^{-1}$. This assumes a much lower level of exercise and physical exertion than the Roman worker in Homer-Dixon's calculations. If people were to meet their caloric demands from wheat alone, and if wheat delivers about 8700 $kJ \cdot kg^{-1}$, at 8300 $kJ \cdot day^{-1}$, each person would need to consume about 350 kg of wheat a year. In 2007 in southwestern Ontario, a wheat yield of 6600 $kg \cdot ha^{-1}$ meant that 1 ha (2.5 acres) of land would support 18.8 people for a year. A city of 50 000, eating only wheat, would need the wheat produced on 2660 ha **(Figures 49.21 and 49.22)**.

Figure 49.21
The field marked with the "*" is 20 hectares (50 acres) and, if planted in wheat, should yield 13 200 kg in southwestern Ontario. Note that the area is also being used to harvest wind energy.

Table 49.1	Balancing Cost and Yield, a Farm in Southwestern Ontario (Costs as of Autumn, 2007)	
Crop/Material/Process	**Yield kg·ha^{-1}**	**Can\$·ha^{-1}**
Corn	10 000	1650
Soy beans	3 500	1300
Wheat	6 600	900
Costs		
Seed		150
Fertilizer		125–225
Spray		50–100
Planting		38
Labour		40–190
Combine		100
Trucking		25
Crop insurance		20
Field rental		325

When put into this perspective, the variations in crop yields noted at the beginning of this chapter have huge repercussions. The data can be considered from a farmer's perspective **(Table 49.1)**, and the difference in farm income would be substantial if the yield of corn were 1600 kg·ha^{-1} versus 10 000 kg·ha^{-1}. These data do not include costs of transportation (from farm to market), but they illustrate the impact of the cost of fuel. Spraying, planting, and trucking all require diesel fuel, so any change in the price of this commodity influences the costs of farm operations.

Terrain influences the level of technology that can be used in farming practices. Small terraced plots **(Figure 49.23, p. 1249)** must be worked by hand or with the help of animals. Large expanses of relatively flat land can be worked effectively and efficiently with machinery **(Figure 49.24, p. 1250)**, increasing the energy consumption associated with farming but also the yield.

Study Break

1. How must crop yield be balanced against the cost of achieving it? Does this apply to a kitchen garden (as opposed to a functioning farm)?
2. What factors were fundamental in allowing the city of Rome to have a population of over 1 million people in 2 A.D.?

a.

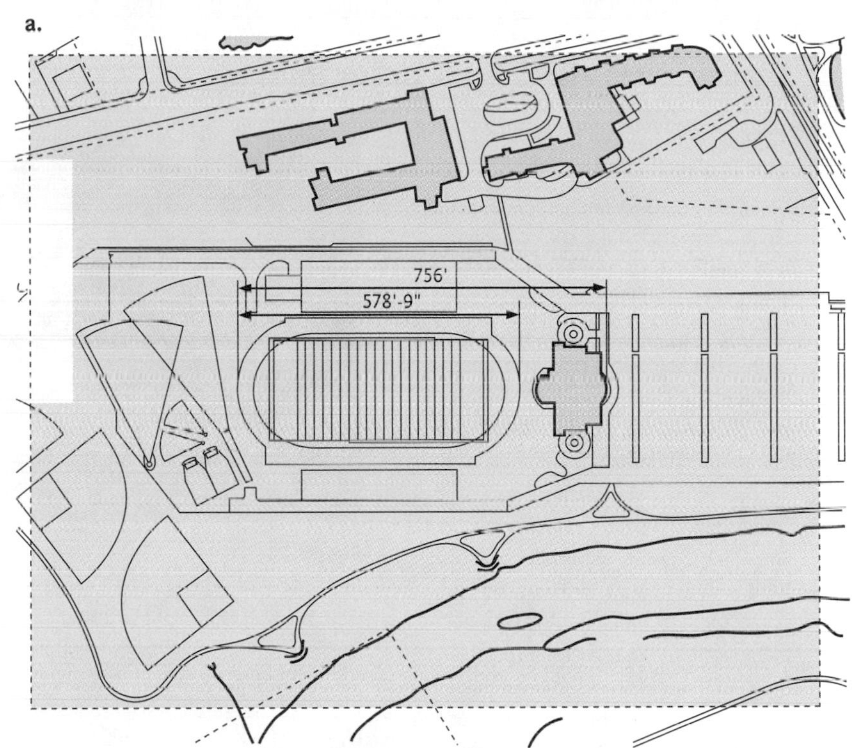

b.

Figure 49.22
Envisioning 20 hectares (50 acres). Two views of the same area: a drawing **(a)** in which the coloured area represents 20 hectares and an aerial photograph **(b)** showing the same football stadium on the campus of the University of Western Ontario, in London, Ontario.

49.4 Complications

As anyone who has ever gardened or worked a farm well knows, there is more to growing crops than putting seeds or small plants in the ground and then harvesting the crops.

49.4a Fertilizer, Water, Yield, and Pests: Care of Crops

In the course of operating an experimental farm in the Negev Desert in southern Israel **(Figure 49.25, p. 1250)**, researchers established several basic truths. By providing 20 m^3 of manure (sheep and goat) and

Domesticated Plants in the Genus *Brassica*

Some plants have provided humans with an embarrassment of riches. Imagine plants in one genus (*Brassica*) whose flowers, roots, stems, leaves, and seeds are all important food crops **(Figure 1).** Foods from these vegetables are high in vitamin C and soluble fibre. They contain a rich mixture of nutrients, including some (diindolylmethane, sulforaphane, and selenium) thought to have anticancer effects.

A sample of an all-*Brassica* meal could include broccoli, cauliflower, Brussels sprouts, kale, and cabbage, all variations of one species, *Brassica oleracea*. You could add rutabaga (*Brassica napus*) along with turnip and rapini (*Brassica rapa*) to the menu and use canola oil (see *People Behind Biology*) and mustard (*B. rapa, B. carinata, B. elongata, B. juncea, B. nigra, B. ruprestris*) to dress the parts of the meal presented as salad.

Nuclear restriction fragment length polymorphisms (RFLPs), obtained from 10 different *Brassica rapa*, 9 cultivated types of *B. oleracea*, and 6 other species in *Brassica* and related genera, suggest two basic evolutionary pathways **(Figure 2)** for diploid species: one that gave rise

Figure 1
Brassicas in our diets. Shown here are cultivars of brassicas that commonly appear in people's diets, including **(a)** radishes, **(b)** Brussels sprouts, **(c)** cauliflower, **(d)** broccoli, **(e)** turnip, **(f)** rutabaga, **(g)** mustard, **(h)** cabbage, and **(i)** canola oil.

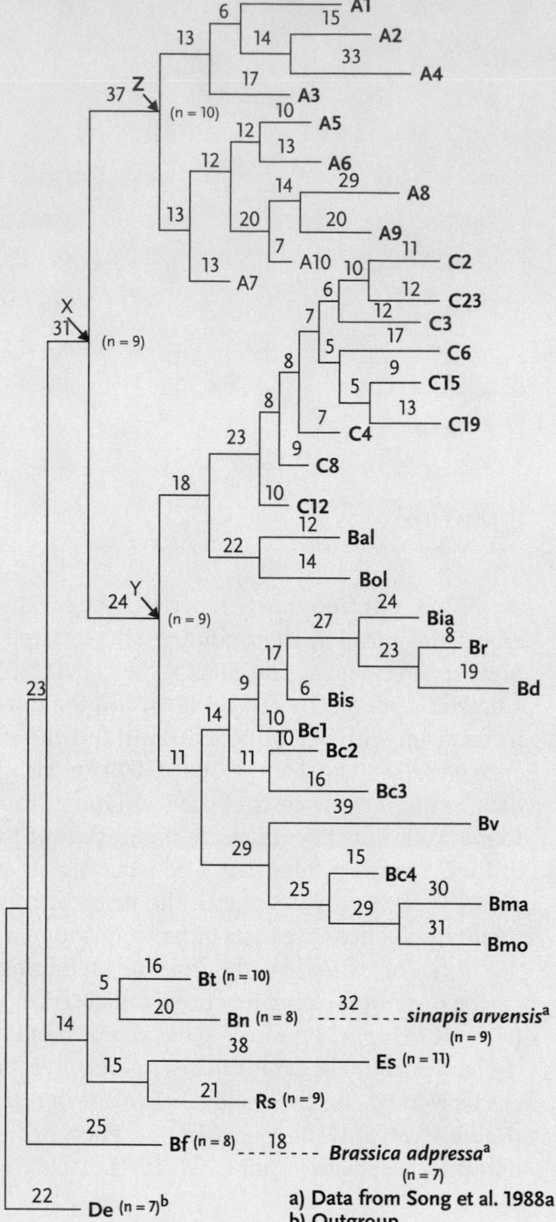

Figure 2
The shortest phylogenetic tree showing the relationships between different species of Brassica, including cultivars and wild species. A1–A5 *B. rapa* cultivars: 1 = flowering pak choi; 2 = pak choi; 3 = *B. narinosa;* 4 = Chinese cabbage; 5 = turnip; A6–A10 *B. rapa* wild: Bal = *B. alboglabra;* Bc 1–4 = *B. cretica;* Bd = *B. drepanensis;* Bia = *B. incana;* Bis = *B. isularis;* Bma = *B. macrocarpa;* Bmo = *B. montana;* Bol = *B. oleracea;* Br = *B. Rupestris;* BBv = *B. villosa;* C2–C23 *B. oleracea cultivars:* 2 = broccoli; 3 = broccoli (packman); 4 = cabbage; 8 = Portuguese tree kale; 12 = Chinese kale; 15 = kohlrabi; 19 = borecole; 23 = cauliflower; Bf = *B. fruticulosa;* Bn = *B. nigra;* Bt = *B. tournefortii;* De = *Diplotaxis erucoides;* Es = *Eruca sativa;* Rs = *Raphanus sativus.*

600 kg of ammonium sulphate per hectare, they could obtain good yields: 4800 $kg \cdot ha^{-1}$ of barley (where less tended crops yielded 400 to 600 $kg \cdot ha^{-1}$) and 4400 $kg \cdot ha^{-1}$ (nanasit strain) or 2700 $kg \cdot ha^{-1}$ (Florence strain) of wheat. They were able to produce 750 $kg \cdot ha^{-1}$ of carrots and 650 $kg \cdot ha^{-1}$ of onions. Achieving these yields required cultivation of the soil, irrigation, and dealing with a variety of pests. Their farm became an oasis of green that attracted hares, gazelles, porcupines, desert partridges, and a host of insects, meaning that control of pest species had to be routine.

Irrigation was a key to good crops, and the experiment had been designed to test the prediction that by collecting runoff water and storing it in cisterns, the people there then could farm in an area with little and highly seasonal rainfall. In 2006–07, the 60-mm total rainfall in the area occurred between November 20

to *B. fruticulosa*, *B. nigra*, and *Sinapis arvensis* (*Brassica adpressa* is a close relative), and the other to *B. oleracea* and *B. rapa* **(Figure 3).** *Raphanus sativus* and *Eruca sativa* appear to be intermediate between the two lineages (see Figure 2). Europe and East Asia appear to have been centres of domestication for *Brassica* species. The related *Arabidopsis* is an important experimental tool used in understanding the genetics and selection of desirable traits in *Brassica*.

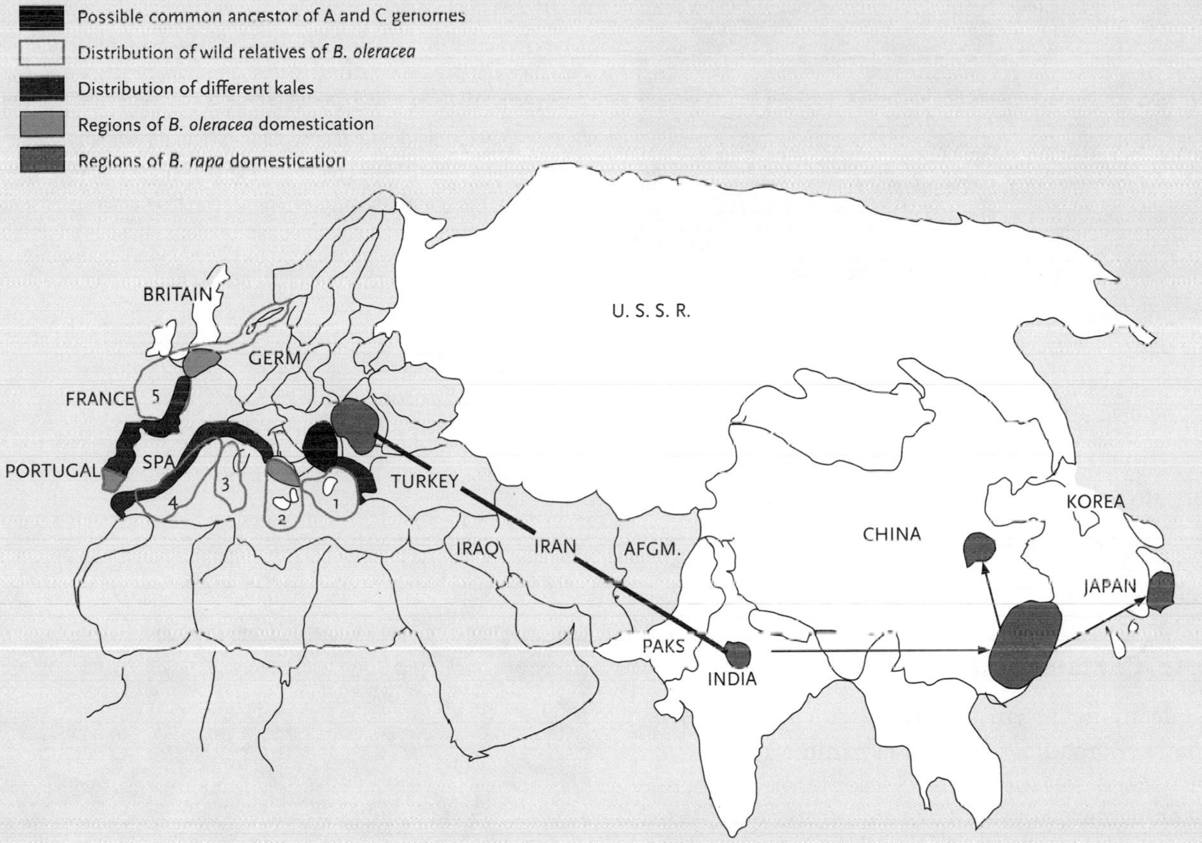

Possible common ancestor of A and C genomes
Distribution of wild relatives of *B. oleracea*
Distribution of different kales
Regions of *B. oleracea* domestication
Regions of *B. rapa* domestication

BRITAIN
GERM
FRANCE 5
PORTUGAL
SPA
3
4
2
1
TURKEY
IRAQ
IRAN
AFGM.
PAKS
INDIA
U. S. S. R.
CHINA
KOREA
JAPAN

Figure 3
Geographic distribution and hypothetical origins and evolutionary pathways of *Brassica oleracea* and *B. rapa*, which may have shared a common ancestor in Europe.

and April 16. Water collected as runoff and stored in a 1400- m^3 cistern could last the farm (people, animals, and crops) over 2 years.

49.4b Cats as Workers

The need to control rodent pests in areas where grain is stored **(Figure 49.26, p. 1250)** might be one factor explaining the domestication of cats, *Felis silvestris catus*. Carlos A. Driscoll and colleagues examined short tandem repeat (STR) and mtDNA data from 979 cats and wild progenitors to examine relationships among them. The evidence suggested at least five founder populations, including the European wildcat (*Felis silvestris silvestris*), near Eastern wildcat (*F. s. lybica*), central Asian wildcat (*F. s. ornata*), southern African wildcat (*F. s. cafra*), and Chinese desert cat (*F. s. bieti*). Each of these populations represents a distinct subspecies. Cats were thought to have been domesticated in the Near East, and their descendants were transported across the world with

Figure 49.23
A series of rock walls creates terraced areas for growing crops near Beijing in China. The terraces hold soil, but the setting precludes extensive use of mechanized farming equipment.

Figure 49.24
Large expanses of relatively flat land lend themselves to mechanized farming, allowing more uniform conditions and crops.

assistance from humans **(Figure 49.27).** Driscoll and his colleagues proposed that domestication of cats coincided with the development of agriculture in different locations.

49.4c Contaminants in Crops

People living in rural parts of Bosnia, Bulgaria, Croatia, Romania, and Serbia exhibit a high incidence of a devastating renal disease termed "endemic Balkan nephropathy" (known as EN). People afflicted with EN progress from chronic renal failure to a high incidence of cancer of the upper urinary tract. EN and its associated cancer can be related to chronic dietary poisoning by aristolochic acid. The source of the poisoning is contamination of grain crops with the plant *Aristolochia clematitis*. A clue to this situation came from horses that developed renal failure after being fed hay contaminated with *A. clematitis*. The presence of weeds or other contaminants in crops **(Figure 49.28, p. 1252)** poses an important challenge to farmers.

Ironically, the medicinal virtues of extracts of *A. clematitis* are extolled on some Web sites selling homeopathic remedies. A first step in solving the mystery of EN came from case studies of some Belgian women who had developed renal problems after taking extracts of *A. clematitis* as part of a weight loss program.

Study Break

1. What factors influence crop yield?
2. How does crop yield vary?
3. What are some of the problems associated with crops?

Figure 49.25
An experimental farm plot near Avdot in the Negev Desert in southern Israel. The green areas are irrigated with water stored in an underground cistern. The experimental farm was established on an ancient farm site. Other fields previously under cultivation are shown. By collecting runoff during and after rainfall, farmers have stored water for their families and crops for hundreds of years.

Figure 49.26
Harvested crops can be stored in different ways. Near Tien in China, farmers hang collections of corn cobs after harvest. This approach to crop storage suggests a dearth of local birds and rodents that might consume the corn.

Figure 49.27
The origins of domestic cats. Genetic assessment of 979 cats (*Felis silvestris catus*) based on short tandem repeats (STR) and mtDNA identifies different contributors to cat genotypes. The accompanying phenogram of 851 domesticated and wild cats illustrates the relationships between domestic cats and wild genetic contributors.

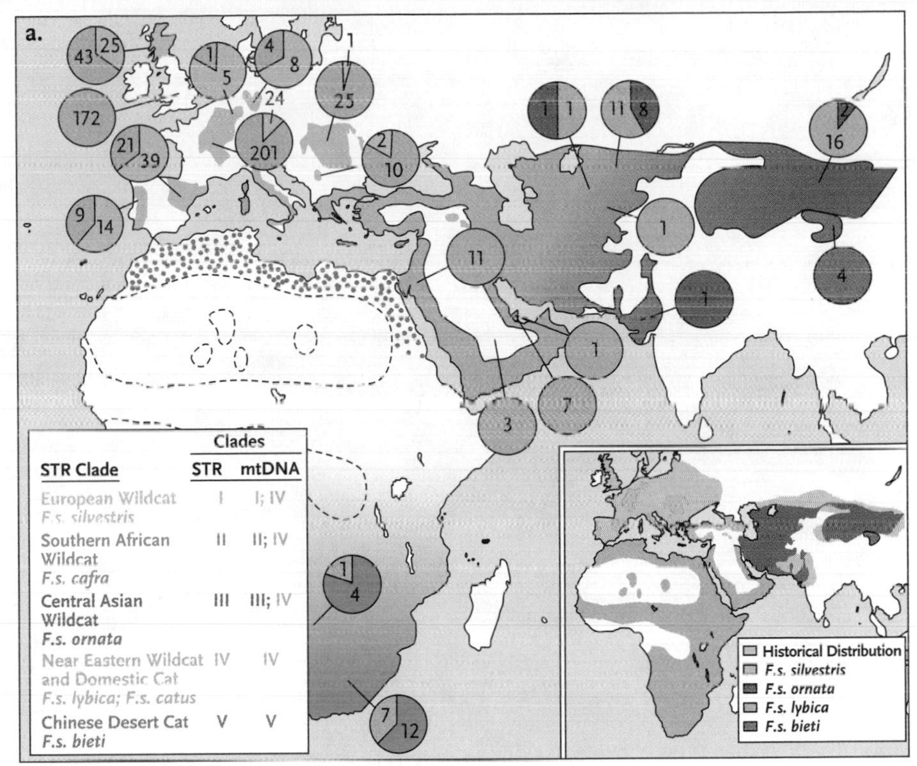

a.
Clades
STR Clade
STR
mtDNA
European Wildcat F.s. silvestris
I
I; IV
Southern African Wildcat F.s. cafra
II
II; IV
Central Asian Wildcat F.s. ornata
III
III; IV
Near Eastern Wildcat and Domestic Cat F.s. lybica; F.s. catus
IV
IV
Chinese Desert Cat F.s. bieti
V
V
Historical Distribution
F.s. silvestris
F.s. ornata
F.s. lybica
F.s. bieti

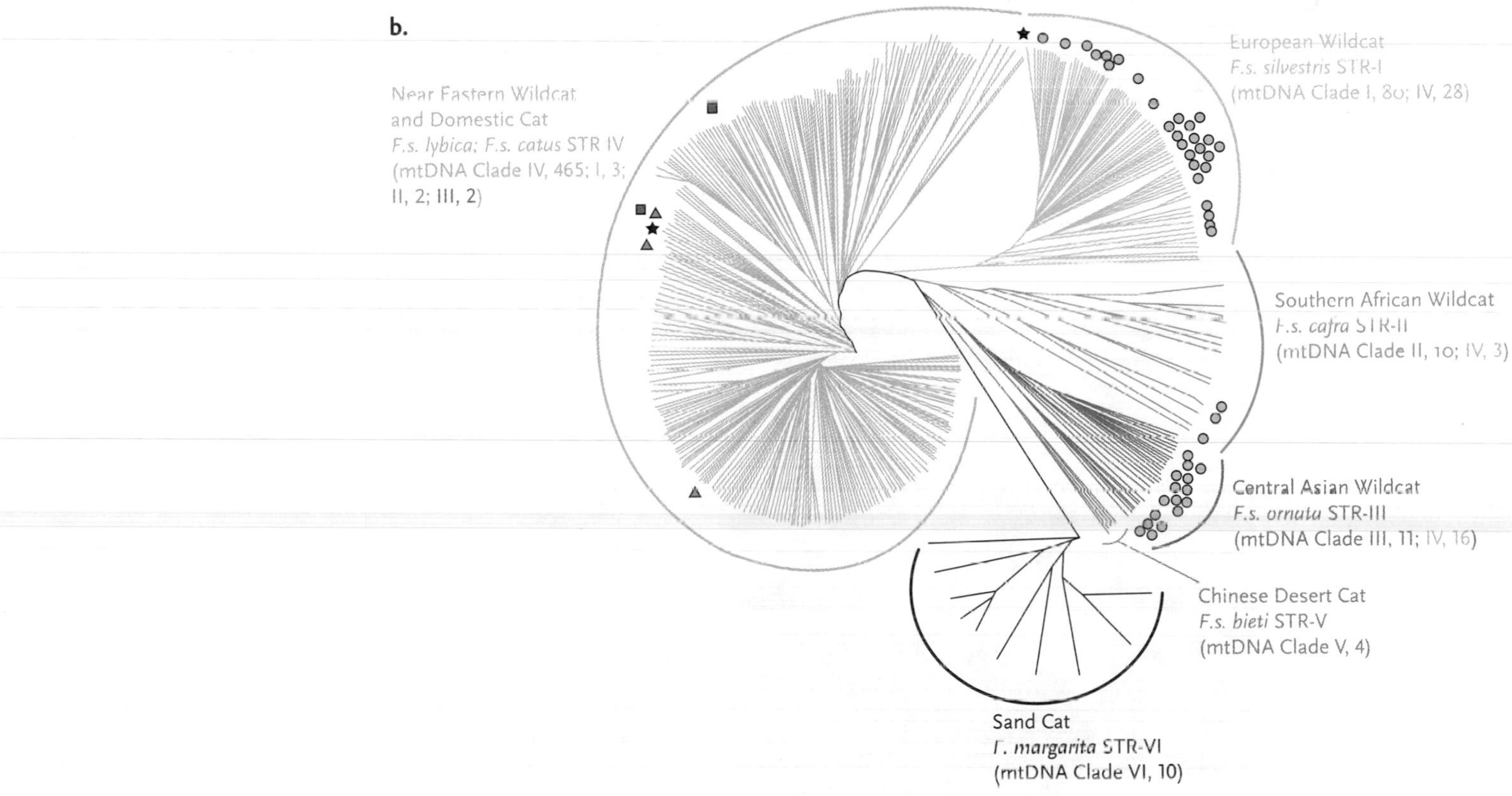

49.5 Chemicals, Good and Bad

Plants are often treasured as much for the chemicals they produce as for their use as food. The chef who adds rosemary (*Rosmarinus officinalis;* **Figure 49.29, p. 1252**) to a dish as it is cooking knows that the flavour will enhance the final product. Other plant products are used as medicines. Phenolic compounds are responsible for the distinctive flavours of coffee, cinnamon, cloves, and nutmeg, which add flavour and

M.B. Fenton

Figure 49.28
Weeds, such as the milkweeds (*Asclepias* species) growing in this barley field in southwestern Ontario, can pose a problem at harvesting. If the weeds are toxic, they must be extracted from the harvested crop to ensure the safety of animals and people that consume the barley.

aroma to food. Some of these compounds, such as caffeine, can be addictive.

Ginsenosides (obtained from ginseng, *Panax quinquefolius*) appear to be used by ginseng plants as fungicides, whereas humans take them to stimulate the immune system. Other plant products are

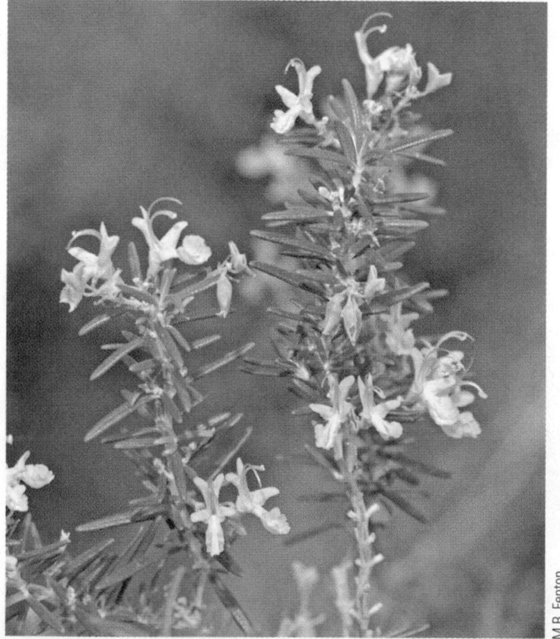

M.B. Fenton

Figure 49.29
Herbs such as rosemary (*Rosmarinus officinalis*) are used to add flavour during cooking.

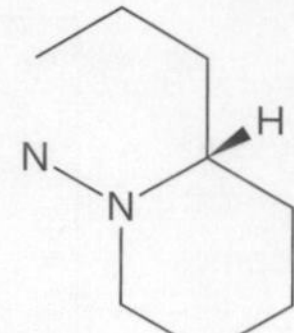

Figure 49.30
Conine, the poison from poison hemlock.

toxic. Conine, produced by poison hemlock (*Conium maculatum;* not to be confused with the hemlock tree), is an active ingredient used by the plant to defend against herbivores **(Figure 49.30).** It was the "hemlock" used to kill Socrates. Plants that look the same often produce quite different chemicals. Poison hemlock, for example, superficially resembles Queen Anne's lace (*Daucus carota*), a common weed. It also can be confused with fennel (*Foeniculum vulgare*) and parsley (*Petroselinum crispum*), two herbs often used in cooking.

The speed with which changes can occur in biological systems can be astonishing, exemplified by the assimilation of new foods into our own diets whether the product is natural or synthetic. This is not a feature unique to humans. Work on ant farmers revealed that one species (*Cyphomyrmex rimosus*) introduced to Florida quickly acquired a crop cultivated by another species of ant indigenous there (*Cyphomyrmex minutus*). Also in Florida, the grasshopper *Romalea microptera* uses a mix of chemicals to repel ants (see Chapter 48, *Molecule Behind Biology*). Soon after people began to use 2,4-D (2,4-dichlorophenoxyacetic acid) to kill weeds, the grasshopper added 2,5-dichlorophenol to its ant repellent mixture. This situation is analogous to humans cultivating and domesticating new crop species.

The pharmacological potential of plant products for treating and preventing human ailments has not been lost on three groups of people: those interested in conserving biodiversity, those concerned about alleviating human suffering, and those anxious to make money by selling biopharmaceuticals to others.

Study Break

1. Why do humans use 2,4-D? What other uses could it have?
2. Why are spices important?
3. What is poison hemlock?

49.6 Molecular Farming

Many native peoples in the New World used tobacco (*Nicotiana tabacum*) as a traditional medicine to ease the pain of childbirth, stave off hunger, and treat various ailments **(Figure 49.31).** Tobacco was dried and smoked in ceremonies, used in poultices, brewed as a

Figure 49.31
A tobacco field in southwestern Ontario.

tea, and used as an emetic, an expectorant, and a laxative. By 1540, tobacco reached Europe, where it was said to cure illnesses ranging from epilepsy to plague. People have also used nicotine, an alkaloid in tobacco, in the same way as tobacco plants do, as an insecticide. The recreational use of tobacco has given the plant a bad name, even though other *Nicotiana* species are commonly used in gardens for their aromatic white or pink flowers.

Tobacco, however, is undergoing a rebirth as a positive contributor. *Molecular farming* involves the use of plants as producers of specific proteins useful as human medications. Plants can be genetically modified to produce large amounts of these proteins at low cost. Concerns about using plants as molecular farms reflect the possibility of biologically active products entering ecosystems and dispersing through food webs, via pollen or seeds, all of which could negatively affect existing crops. Enter tobacco, a nonfood plant that is harvested before flowering. Tobacco is not cold hardy (in Canada), but it is easy to genetically modify and is highly productive (40-day production cycle). Using appropriate DNA technology (see Chapter 16), T-DNA containing the human *IL-10* gene was inserted into the tobacco genome by connecting it to a plant promoter and an *Agrobacterium* terminator. In this way, tobacco plants are modified to produce interleukin-10 (*IL-10*), which can be used to treat irritable bowel disease in humans. Interleukin is a cytokine involved in the regulation of inflammatory diseases, reducing the production of necrosis factor by tumours. The IL-10 was found not to enter the soil in which the tobacco was grown or the aphids or other insects that fed on the tobacco plants. The vast amounts of agricultural land that was used to grow tobacco for recreational use can now be used for molecular farming. This change to molecular farming of tobacco could produce many different useful compounds.

Study Break

1. How are plant products used in addition to their role as food?
2. What is "molecular farming"?
3. What conservation risks are associated with molecular farming? With agriculture in general?

49.7 The Future

It is tempting to believe that the diversity of life will continue to provide humans with solutions to many of their problems in the world: food for the hungry, poisons to selectively control pests, and biopharmaceuticals to cure diseases. Molecular farming potentially allows new approaches to solve old problems. Although we can continue to domesticate other species, effectively taking evolution in directions that suit us, we must remember that when new forms require higher investments in energy and fertilizer, costs can outweigh benefits.

In 2008, global increases in the price of food were partly due to our using traditional food crops (e.g., corn) to produce ethanol to fuel vehicles. In 2007, the energy return on investment (EROI) for biofuel (ethanol, or food for internal combustion engines) from corn was ~1. This means that every litre of ethanol produced from corn consumes about a litre of petroleum fuel. Other crops, for example, poplar trees, have much better EROIs. Although biofuels potentially are low-carbon-emitting energy sources, the means of production dramatically influences their "greenness." In many cases, production of biofuels generates a "biofuel carbon debt." In Brazil, Southeast Asia, and the United States, converting native habitat (rain forest, peatlands, savanna, and grasslands) to produce biofuels generates 17 to 420 times more CO_2 than the habitats normally produce. When these costs are taken into account, biofuels are not feasible environmentally friendly alternatives.

Calculating EROI and tracking it over time helps put energy use in perspective. In Rome in 1 A.D.,

Life on the Edge

Feeding People and Keeping Them Healthy

We have seen how humans' ability to harness nature has allowed us to reduce the numbers of hungry people in the world. Nevertheless, in 2008, converting food crops to biofuels in the interest of being "green" meant less food. This development coincided with climate change, which further reduced the availability of food worldwide. This impact was amplified by increases in the prices of food crops, in turn making food less accessible to many poor people.

We use plants for more than food. In 2008, over 1 million people died from malaria, caused by a blood parasite (see Chapter 26). Some 300 to 500 million people worldwide suffer from malaria. Most (over 75%) of the deaths were of children under 5 years of age and living in Africa. For years, alkaloids (quinine, quinidine, cichonidine, and cinchonine) extracted from the bark of four species of tree in the genus *Cinchona* have been used to treat agues and periodic fevers. Cinchona alkaloids have been particularly effective against malaria, but some strains of malaria are resistant to quinines and other treatments suggesting that they are not the solution to malaria.

Enter qinghao, also known as huang hua hao, an extract from a ubiquitous shrub, *Artemisia annua*. Extracts of qinghao (artemisinin) have long been used in traditional Chinese medicine. In 1971, Chinese scientists discovered its effectiveness in treating malaria and reported it to the world in 1979. In 2008, artemisinin combination treatments became first-line drugs for some forms of malaria (uncomplicated falciparum malaria), but they were not available worldwide. Using improved agriculture techniques—selection of high-yielding hybrids, microbial production, and synthetic peroxidases—could lower prices, increase the availability of artemisinin, and save many lives.

In 2007, about one-third of the annual U.S.$30 billion worldwide investment in agriculture research was aimed at solving the problems of agriculture in developing countries—home to about 80% of the global population. This investment is less than 3% of the amount that countries of the Organization for Economic Co-operation and Development (OECD) spend to subsidize their own agricultural production. Ensuring continued reduction of human hunger, OECD countries must invest more to solve the agriculture problems in the developing world.

We know that our agricultural prowess can be used to increase production of food and medicines such as artemisinin. Golden rice provides another example. In 1984, the World Health Organization estimated that 250 000 to 500 000 children a year had diets lacking in vitamin A. This deficiency damaged their retinas and corneas, so many of them went blind and half of them died.

By the early 2000s, Ingo Potrykus and Peter Byer had used genetic engineering to splice two daffodil genes and a bacterial gene into the rice genome. The genetically modified rice, "golden rice," was golden in colour and produced precursors to vitamin A in its endosperm. Golden rice offered a way to address the results of vitamin A deficiency. Growing golden rice was field tested in Louisiana in 2004 and 2005.

In 2008, it appears that even though golden rice offered the ability to prevent the suffering arising from vitamin A deficiency, it is unlikely that any will be planted before 2012. The delay reflects a combination of widespread public suspicion about genetically modified organisms (GMOs) and the high cost of obtaining approval to use GMOs. The costs associated with getting approval mean that only large companies with large budgets are likely to succeed in getting GMO products approved.

Moving more people away from "the edge" means investing more in finding solutions to agricultural operations in the developing world to ensure that discoveries such as artemisinin and golden rice are used to advantage. This requires policies and investments that support small-scale operations. Our ancestors who domesticated crops such as wheat and corn, lentils and squash, and potatoes and rice changed the world for us. We should ensure that their legacy lives on.

the EROI for wheat was 12:1, and for alfalfa, it was 27:1. In 2007, the EROI value for gasoline was ~17:1, whereas in the 1930s, it was ~100:1. The values of EROI speak to the sustainability of process, so Canadians must be concerned that the EROI on the tar sands is less than 4:1 without taking into consideration the water consumed by the process.

The development of resistance to toxins, whether of bacteria to antibiotics or of insect pests to insecticides, demonstrates that evolution works both ways. Perfecting genetic strains of crops protected by resistance to a pathogen or pest and using them exclusively can make the crops vulnerable to pathogens or pests that are resistant to the defence(s). The potato famine was exacerbated by the lack of genetic diversity of the potatoes used in Europe: they were vulnerable to blight.

Over evolutionary history, individuals able to exploit other species had an advantage over those that did not, whether within a society or between societies. The same principles apply to our own species. Our advantages of exploiting other species include increased access to food (quantity and quality), labour, materials for constructing things, and chemicals for treating disorders or controlling pests. These advantages were amplified through domestication, which meant increasing control over the other species, leading to several net effects. One effect was achieving larger populations of humans because of better access to food and/or protection from disease. Another was probably the increase in available time for the development and perfection of new tools and techniques and the emergence of groups of people in society who did not contribute directly by gathering or processing food. Such people could have contributed to society through their talents as artisans, soldiers, or even politicians.

The range of possibilities seems endless, particularly with the advent of the ability to directly modify genotypes and thus phenotypes. Perhaps we should be glad that the Attine ants have domesticated only fungi.

Study Break

What is artemisinin? What is golden rice? Why are they important?

Unanswered Questions

Are genetically modified organisms (GMOs) domesticated, or do they represent distinct species? What legal limits should our society impose on the use of GMOs?

Review

Go to CENGAGENOW™ at http://hed.nelson.com/ to access quizzing, animations, exercises, articles, and personalized homework help.

49.1 Domesticate

- The green revolution is credited with reducing the number of hungry people in the world by increasing agricultural productivity. Increased productivity reflects the use of improved strains of crops, increased applications of fertilizers, and more extensive irrigation. Higher productivity (crop yields) also reflects more dependence on mechanized (fossil fuel based) farming operations.
- There are three stages in the exploitation of biodiversity for human benefit. The initial stage involves "hunting and gathering," collecting organisms in the wild. The second stage is cultivation or caring for organisms under progressively controlled conditions. The third stage, domestication, involves selective breeding to enhance desired characteristics and features. The domestication process can apply to animals, plants, or other organisms, such as yeast and fungi.
- Domestication of asexually reproducing organisms does not involve selective breeding, providing more control, allowing shorter generation times, or speeding up the process of selection.
- Living in the same sites year-round allowed people to tend and protect their crops. Increased time in one place also would have facilitated the process of selective breeding.
- At least 200 species of ants in the tribe Attini are obligate farmers. Other ants also tend seed gardens.
- The first evidence of domestication appears to be figs by about 12 000 years B.P. Cultivation may have been practised for 1000 years before domestication. Many crops had been domesticated by 6000 years B.P.

49.2 Why Some Organisms Were Domesticated

- Yeast appears to have been domesticated in Egypt by 6000 years B.P., when it was used in making bread and beer. Cotton may have been domesticated in at least four sites, two in the Old World and two in the New World. Cotton is used as a source of oil seed and fibre, and some domestication had occurred by 4400 years B.P.
- The change from dehiscence to indehiscence was critical in the domestication of plants, such as grasses, whose seeds were the crop to be harvested.
- Squash and potatoes provide carbohydrates from fruits or tubers; the seeds are not the target of domestication.
- The domestication of dogs appears to have been based, in part, on their social behaviour, including their ability to communicate with people. Some experiments show that dogs are better at reading communication signals from people than other animals, such as chimps.
- Some animals are farmed for meat and hides (and for ostrich feathers and eggs), but there is no evidence of selective breeding.

49.3 Yields

- The level of farming intensity, the strains of crops, the application of fertilizers, and irrigation affect crop yields. Terrain can influence the level of mechanization.
- The data on corn and wheat yields clearly demonstrate variation over time and location.

49.4 Complications

- Rich patches of food reflect higher productivity but can attract pests.

49.5 Chemicals, Good and Bad

- Various plant chemicals are used as stimulants, medicines, hallucinogens, pesticides, and flavourings.

49.6 Molecular Farming

- Molecular farming is the use of plants to produce various useful proteins in large amounts at lower cost. Molecular farming may prove to be an inexpensive way to manufacture medicines and other substances.

49.7 The Future

- Escape of cultivated plants poses a significant risk to native species (e.g., grapes) and ecosystems. Monocultures can attract and support high levels of pests that may affect neighbouring natural systems.

Questions

Self-Test Questions

1. The first evidence of humans domesticating other organisms dates from
   a. 2000 years B.P.
   b. 6000 years B.P.
   c. 8000 years B.P.
   d. 12 000 years B.P.
   e. 20 000 years B.P.
2. The process of moving from cultivation to domestication involved dehiscence to indehiscence in
   a. rice.
   b. wheat.
   c. squash.
   d. potatoes.
   e. Both a and b are correct.
3. Parthenocarpy was important in the domestication of
   a. dogs.
   b. pigs.
   c. figs.
   d. lentils.
   e. cotton.
4. At Abu Hureyra, settlers domesticated
   a. olives.
   b. some grains.
   c. cattle.
   d. hot peppers.
   e. rice.
5. Domesticated organisms include (one or more answers may be correct)
   a. yeast, mushrooms, pigs, and oysters.
   b. yeast, pigs, rice, and corn.
   c. honeybees, yeast, rice, and ostriches.
   d. cattle, pigs, cats, and dogs.
   e. lentils, mushrooms, yeast, and crocodiles.
6. Plants in the family Solonaceae include
   a. tomatoes, potatoes, and eggplant.
   b. potatoes, hot peppers, and deadly nightshade.
   c. corn, tobacco, and hot peppers.
   d. rice, wheat, and barley.
   e. Both a and b are correct.
7. If a person needs 8300 $kJ \cdot day^{-1}$ and wheat yields 6,638 $kg \cdot ha^{-1}$, a city of 20 000 people who ate only wheat would need the wheat produced by ______ over 1 year.
   a. 155 ha.
   b. 555 ha.
   c. 1055 ha.
   d. 2055 ha.
   e. 5055 ha.
8. Endemic Balkan nephropathy is an example of a disorder arising when people eat crops
   a. irrigated with polluted water.
   b. of grain contaminated with *Aristolochia clematitis.*
   c. of grain contaminated with fungi.
   d. of grain contaminated with *Rosmarinus officinalis.*
   e. of grain contaminated with *Asclepias exultata.*
9. *Nicotiana tabacum* is being used to produce
   a. nicotine.
   b. interleukin.
   c. acetylcholine.
   d. conine.
   e. capsaicin.
10. EROI, energy return on investment, suggests that alfalfa in Roman times was ___ times more efficient at energy production than the tar sands in Alberta in 2008.
    a. 4×
    b. 6×
    c. 10×
    d. 20×
    e. 50×

Questions for Discussion

1. When is domestication complete? At what point is a domesticated stock a separate species? Is domestication ever complete?
2. Why have so few aquatic species been domesticated? Why has there been a recent increase in the numbers of domesticated aquatic organisms?
3. How do domesticated populations threaten native species? Should this be a concern for conservation biologists? What can be done to minimize this threat to native species?

Appendix A

Answers to Self-Test Questions

Chapter 1

1. e 2. d 3. b 4. a 5. e 6. d 7. e 8. d 9. d 10. e

Chapter 2

1. c 2. b 3. c 4. e 5. e 6. e 7. d 8. b 9. e 10. b

Chapter 3

1. c 2. c 3. b 4. a 5. b 6. b 7. b 8. e 9. e 10. c

Chapter 4

1. e 2. d 3. d 4. d 5. d 6. c 7. e 8. c 9. d 10. e

Chapter 5

1. d 2. a 3. e 4. d 5. d 6. e 7. c 8. b 9. a 10. c

Chapter 6

1. c 2. d 3. c 4. d 5. e 6. b 7. c 8. d 9. d 10. e

Chapter 7

1. e 2. c 3. a 4. b 5. e 6. b 7. c 8. e 9. c 10. b

Chapter 8

1. b 2. d 3. c 4. c 5. e

Chapter 9

1. c 2. b 3. d 4. b 5. b 6. d 7. a 8. b 9. b 10. c

Chapter 10

1. a 2. c 3. d 4. a 5. e 6. b 7. d 8. c 9. b 10. b 11. a 12. d 13. b

Chapter 11

1. (a) The *CC* parent produces all *C* gametes, and the *Cc* parent produces 1/2 *C* and 1/2 *c* gametes. All offspring would have coloured seeds—half homozygous *CC* and half heterozygous *Cc*. (b) Both parents produce 1/2 *C* and 1/2 *c* gametes. Of the offspring, three-fourths would have coloured seeds (1/4 *CC* + 1/2 *Cc*) and one-fourth would have colourless seeds (1/4 *cc*). (c) The *Cc* parent produces 1/2 *C* gametes and 1/2 *c* gametes, and the *cc* parent produces all *c* gametes. Half of the offspring are coloured (1/2 *Cc*) and half are colourless (1/2 *cc*).
2. The genotypes of the parents are *Tt* and *tt*.
3. The taster parents could have a nontaster child, but nontaster parents are not expected to have a child who can taste PTC. The chance that they might have a taster child is 3/4. The chance of a nontaster child being born to the taster couple would be 1/4. Because each combination of gametes is an independent event, the chance of the couple having a second child, or any child, who cannot taste PTC is expected to be 1/4.
4. (a) All *A B*. (b) 1/2 *A B* + 1/2 *a B*. (c) 1/2 *A b* + 1/2 *a b*. (d) 1/4 *A B* + 1/4 *A b* + 1/4 *a B* + 1/4 *a b*.
5. (a) All *Aa BB*. (b) 1/4 *AA BB* + 1/4 *AA Bb* + 1/4 *Aa BB* + 1/4 *Aa Bb*. (c) 1/4 *Aa Bb* _ 1/4 *Aa bb* + 1/4 *aa Bb* + 1/4 *aa bb*. (d) 1/4 *Aa Bb* + 1/8 *AA Bb* + 1/8 *Aa BB* + 1/8 *Aa bb* + 1/8 *aa Bb* + 1/16 *AA BB* + 1/16 *AA bb* + 1/16 *aa BB* + 1/16 *aa bb*.
6. (a) All *A B C*. (b) 1/2 *A B c* + 1/2 *a B c*. (c) 1/4 *A B C* + 1/4 *A B c* + 1/4 *a B C* + 1/4 *a B c*. (d) 1/8 *A B C* + 1/8 *A B c* + 1/8 *A b C* + 1/8 *A b c* + 1/8 *a B C* + 1/8 *a B c* + 1/8 *a b C* + 1/8 *a b c*.
7. Because the man can produce only 1 type of allele for each of the 10 genes, he can produce only 1 type of sperm cell with respect to these genes. The woman can produce 2 types of alleles for each of her 2 heterozygous genes, so she can produce 2 × 2 = 4 different types of eggs with respect to the 10 genes. In general, as the number of heterozygous genes increases, the number of possible types of gametes increases as 2^n, where n = the number of heterozygous genes.
8. Use a standard testcross; that is, cross the guinea pig with rough, black fur with a double recessive individual, *rr bb* (smooth, white fur). If your animal is homozygous *RR BB*, you would expect all the offspring to have rough, black fur.
9. One gene probably controls pod colour. One allele, for green pods, is dominant; the other allele, for yellow pods, is recessive.
10. The cross *RR* × *Rr* will produce 1/2 *RR* and 1/2 *Rr* offspring. The cross *Rr* × *Rr* will produce 1/4 *RR*, 1/2 *Rr*, and 1/4 *rr* as combinations of alleles. However, the 1/4 *rr* combination is lethal, so it does not appear among the offspring. Therefore, the offspring will be born with only two types, *RR* and *Rr*, with twice as many *Rr* as *rr* in a 1:2 ratio (or 1/3 *RR* + 2/3 *Rr*).
11. The parental cross is *GG TT RR* × *gg tt rr*. All offspring of this cross are expected to be tall plants with green pods and round seeds, or *Gg Tt Rr*. When crossed, this heterozygous F1 generation is expected to produce eight different

phenotypes among the offspring: green-tall-round, green-dwarf-round, yellow-tall-round, green-tall-wrinkled, yellow-dwarf-round, green-dwarf-wrinkled, yellow-tall-wrinkled, yellow-dwarf-wrinkled, in a 27:9:9:9:3:3:3:1 ratio.

12. The genotypes are: bird 1, *Ff Pp*; bird 2, *FF PP*; bird 3, *Ff PP*; bird 4, *Ff Pp*.
13. Yes, it can be determined that the child is not hers, because the father must be AB to have both an A and B child with a type O wife; none of the woman's children could have type O blood with an AB father.
14. The cross is expected to produce white, tabby, and black kittens in a 12:3:1 ratio.
15. The mother is homozygous recessive for both genes, and the father must be heterozygous for both genes. The child is homozygous recessive for both genes. The chance of having a child with normal hands is 1/2, and that of having a child with woolly hair is 1/2. Using the product rule of probability, the probability of having a child with normal hands and woolly hair is $1/2 \times 1/2 = 1/4$.

Chapter 12

1. All sons will be colour-blind, but none of the daughters will be. However, all daughters will be heterozygous carriers of the trait.
2. The chance that her son will be colour-blind is 1/2, regardless of whether she marries a normal or colour-blind male.
3. All these questions can be answered from the pedigree. Polydactyly is caused by a dominant allele, and the trait is not sex linked. The genotypes of each person are:

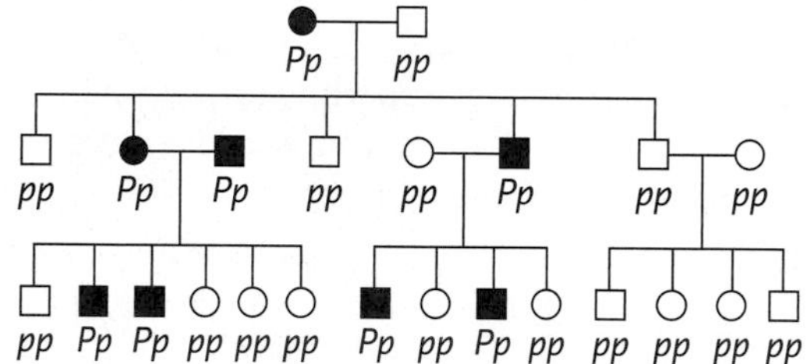

4. The sequence of the genes is ADBC.
5. Let the allele for wild-type gray body colour = b^+, and the allele for black body = b. Let the allele for wild-type red eye colour = p^+, and the allele for purple eyes = p. Then the parents are:

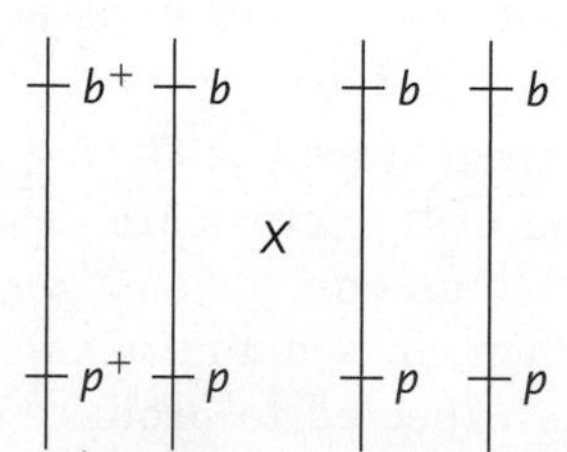

The F_1 flies with black bodies and red eyes are:

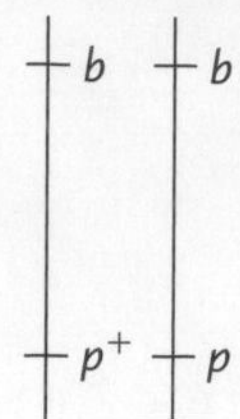

and the flies with gray bodies and purple eyes are:

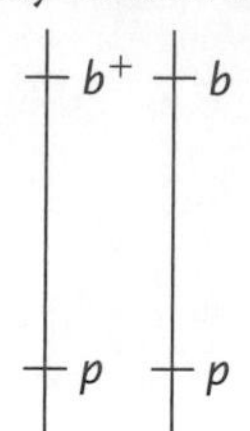

6. The genes are linked by their presence on the same chromosome (an autosome), but they are not sex linked. Because the F_1 females must have produced 600 gametes to give these 600 progeny, and because 42 + 30 of these were recombinant, the percentage of recombinant gametes is 72/600, or 12%, which implies that 12 map units separate the two genes.
7. Because this trait is probably carried on the Y chromosome, which a man transmits to all his sons, all will have hairy ears. None of the daughters will have hairy ears because they do not have a Y chromosome.
8. You might suspect that a recessive allele is sex linked and is carried on one of the two X chromosomes of the female parent in the cross. When present on the single X of the male (or if present on both Xs of a female) the gene is lethal.

Chapter 13

1. b 2. d 3. a 4. a 5. d 6. c 7. b 8. a 9. c 10. b

Chapter 14

1. b 2. a 3. e 4. d 5. b 6. c 7. d 8. b 9. a 10. e

Chapter 15

1. d 2. c 3. a 4. b 5. e 6. b 7. d 8. a 9. d 10. b

Chapter 16

1. e 2. c 3. d 4. a 5. b 6. b 7. e 8. a 9. e 10. d

Chapter 17

1. c 2. b 3. c 4. d 5. b 6. e 7. a 8. b 9. c 10. d

Chapter 18

1. e 2. e 3. c 4. b 5. b 6. e 7. c 8. a 9. a 10. b

Chapter 19

1. b 2. b 3. a 4. d 5. b 6. e 7. a 8. a 9. e 10. d

Chapter 20

1. b 2. b 3. d 4. b 5. c 6. b 7. a 8. b 9. d 10. d

Chapter 21

1. a 2. d 3. e 4. e 5. b 6. d

Chapter 22

1. c 2. a 3. d 4. a 5. e 6. b 7. a

Chapter 23

1. d 2. b 3. c 4. b 5. a 6. c

Chapter 24

1. a 2. d 3. d 4. e 5. c 6. c 7. e

Chapter 25

1. b 2. d 3. e 4. e 5. a 6. d 7. b 8. a

Chapter 26

1. c. 2. d. 3. e. 4. d. 5. b.

Chapter 27

1. a 2. c 3. d 4. b 5. a 6. c 7. c 8. d 9. c 10. a

Chapter 28

1. d 2. c 3. b 4. c 5. a 6. d 7. b

Chapter 29

1. b 2. d 3. a 4. e 5. a 6. b 7. e 8. d 9. c 10. b

Chapter 30

1. c 2. a 3. b 4. e 5. d

Chapter 31

1. e 2. a 3. b 4. b 5. b 6. a 7. d 8. c

Chapter 32

1. a 2. a 3. e 4. e 5. d

Chapter 33

1. d 2. a 3. c 4. b 5. c

Chapter 34

1. d 2. c 3. d 4. e 5. b 6. c 7. d 8. a 9. e 10. b

Chapter 35

1. a 2. e 3. d 4. d 5 b

Chapter 36

1. c 2. e 3. a 4. c 5. a

Chapter 37

1. e 2. b 3. a, d 4. e 5. a

Chapter 38

1. a 2. c 3. d 4. e 5. a 6. b 7. a 8. c 9. b

Chapter 39

1. a 2. e 3. c 4. c 5. e 6. e 7. d 8. e 9. b 10. c

Chapter 40

1. b 2. c 3. b 4. b 5. e 6. d 7. e 8. c 9. d

Chapter 41

1. a 2. e 3. b 4. e 5. d 6. b 7. e 8. e 9. e 10. c

Chapter 42

1. a 2. c 3. b and c 4. d 5. c

Chapter 43

1. d 2. b 3. a, c, d 4. e 5. d

Chapter 44

1. a 2. c 3. b 4. e 5. e 6. d 7. b 8. c 9. a 10. d

Chapter 45

1. b 2. c 3. b 4. d 5. a 6. e 7. d 8. e 9. d 10. b

Chapter 46

1. c 2. c 3. a 4. b 5. b 6. e 7. b 8. d 9. d 10. b

Chapter 47

1. b 2. d 3. c 4. e 5. e 6. c 7. a 8. d 9. c 10. a

Chapter 48

1. e 2. d 3. e 4. d 5. b 6. e 7. b 8. c 9. b (and e) 10. c

Chapter 49

1. d 2. e 3. c 4. b 5. d 6. e 7. c 8. b 9. b 10. b

Glossary

3′ end The end of a polynucleotide chain at which a hydroxyl group is bonded to the 3 carbon of a deoxyribose sugar.

5′ cap In eukaryotes, a guanine-containing nucleotide attached in a reverse orientation to the 5′ end of pre-mRNA and retained in the mRNA produced from it. The 5′ cap on an mRNA is the site where ribosomes attach to initiate translation.

5′ end The end of a polynucleotide chain at which a phosphate group is bound to the 5 carbon of a deoxyribose sugar.

10-nm chromatin fibre The most fundamental level of chromatin packing of a eukaryotic chromosome in which DNA winds for almost two turns around an eight-protein nucleosome core particle to form a nucleosome and linker DNA extends between adjacent nucleosomes. The result is a beads-on-a-string type of structure with a 10 nm diameter.

30-nm chromatin fibre Level of chromatin packing of a eukaryotic chromosome in which histone H1 binds to the 10-nm chromatin fibre, causing it to package into a coiled structure about 30 nm in diameter and with about six nucleosomes per turn. Also referred to as a *solenoid*.

A site The site where the incoming amino-acyl-tRNA carrying the next amino acid to be added to the polypeptide chain binds to the mRNA.

abdomen The region of the body that contains much of the digestive tract and sometimes part of the reproductive system; in insects, the region behind the thorax.

abiotic Nonbiological, often in reference to physical factors in the environment.

abscisic acid (ABA) A plant hormone involved in the abscission of leaves, flowers, and fruits; dormancy of buds and seeds; and closing of stomata.

abscission In plants, the dropping of flowers, fruits, and leaves in response to environmental signals.

absorption spectrum Curve representing the amount of light absorbed at each wavelength.

absorptive nutrition Mode of nutrition in which an organism secretes digestive enzymes into its environment and then absorbs the small molecules thus produced.

accommodation A process by which the lens changes to enable the eye to focus on objects at different distances.

acid Proton donor that releases H (and anions) when dissolved in water.

acid precipitation Rainfall with low pH, primarily created when gaseous sulphur dioxide (SO_2) dissolves in water vapour in the atmosphere, forming sulphuric acid.

acid-growth hypothesis A hypothesis to explain how the hormone auxin promotes the growth of plant cells; it suggests that auxin stimulates H pumps in the plasma membrane to move H from the cell interior into the cell wall, which increases wall acidity, making the wall expandable.

acidity The concentration of H in a water solution, compared with the concentration of OH^-.

acoelomate A body plan of bilaterally symmetrical animals that lack a body cavity (coelom) between the gut and the body wall.

acorn worms Sedentary marine animals living in U-shaped tubes or burrows in coastal sand or mud.

acquired immune deficiency syndrome (AIDS) A constellation of disorders that follows infection by the HIV virus.

acrosome A specialized secretory vesicle on the head of an animal sperm, which helps the sperm penetrate the egg.

acrosome reaction The process in which enzymes contained in the acrosome are released from an animal sperm and digest a path through the egg coats.

action potential The abrupt and transient change in membrane potential that occurs when a neuron conducts an electrical impulse.

action spectrum Graph produced by plotting the effectiveness of light at each wavelength in driving photosynthesis.

activation energy The initial input of energy required to start a reaction.

activator A regulatory protein that controls the expression of one or more genes.

active immunity The production of antibodies in the body in response to exposure to a foreign antigen.

active parental care Parents' investment of time and energy in caring for offspring after they are born or hatched.

active site The region of an enzyme that recognizes and combines with a substrate molecule.

active transport The mechanism by which ions and molecules move against the concentration gradient across a membrane, from the side with the lower concentration to the side with the higher concentration.

adaptation Characteristic or suite of characteristics that helps an organism survive longer or reproduce more under a particular set of environmental conditions.

adaptation, evolutionary The accumulation of adaptive traits over time.

adaptation, sensory *See* sensory adaptation.

adaptive (acquired) immunity A specific line of defence against invasion of the body in which individual pathogens are recognized and attacked to neutralize and eliminate them.

adaptive radiation A cluster of closely related species that are each adaptively specialized to a specific habitat or food source.

adaptive trait A genetically based characteristic, preserved by natural selection, that increases an organism's likelihood of survival or its reproductive output.

adaptive zone A part of a habitat that may be occupied by a group of species exploiting the same resources in a similar manner.

adductor muscle A muscle that pulls inward toward the median line of the body; in bivalve molluscs, it pulls the shell closed.

adenine A purine that base-pairs with either thymine in DNA or uracil in RNA.

adhesion The adherence of molecules to the walls of conducting tubes, as in plants.

adiabatic cooling A decrease in temperature without the actual loss of heat energy, occurring in air masses that expand as they rise in the atmosphere.

adipose tissue Connective tissue containing large, densely clustered cells called adipocytes that are specialized for fat storage.

adrenal cortex The outer region of the adrenal glands, which contains endocrine cells that secrete two major types of steroid hormones, the glucocorticoids and the mineralocorticoids.

adrenal medulla The central region of the adrenal glands, which contains neurosecretory neurons that secrete the catecholamine hormones epinephrine and norepinephrine.

adrenocorticotropic hormone (ACTH) A hormone that triggers hormone secretion by cells in the adrenal cortex.

adult stem cell Mammalian stem cells that can differentiate into a limited number of cell types associated with the tissue in which they occur.

adventitious root A root that develops from the stem or leaves of a plant.

aerobe An organism that requires oxygen for cellular respiration.

afferent arteriole The vessel that delivers blood to the glomerulus of the kidney.

afferent neuron A neuron that transmits stimuli collected by a sensory receptor to an interneuron.

African emergence hypothesis A hypothesis proposing that modern humans first evolved in Africa and then dispersed to other continents.

agar A gelatinous product extracted from certain red algae or seaweed used as a culture medium in the laboratory and as a gelling or stabilizing agent in foods.

agarose gel electrophoresis Technique by which DNA, RNA, or molecules are separated in a gel subjected to an electric field.

age structure A statistical description or graph of the relative numbers of individuals in each age class in a population.

age-specific fecundity The average number of offspring produced by surviving females of a particular age.

age-specific mortality The proportion of individuals alive at the start of an age interval that died during that age interval.

age-specific survivorship The proportion of individuals alive at the start of an age interval that survived until the start of the next age interval.

aggregate fruit A fruit that develops from multiple separate carpels of a single flower, such as a raspberry or strawberry.

agonist A muscle that causes movement in a joint when it contracts.

albumin The most abundant protein in blood plasma, important for osmotic balance and pH buffering; also, the portion of an egg that serves as the main source of nutrients and water for the embryo.

alcohol A molecule of the form R—OH in which R is a chain of one or more carbon atoms, each of which is linked to hydrogen atoms.

alcoholic fermentation Reaction in which pyruvate is converted into ethyl alcohol and CO_2 in a two-step series that also converts NADH into NAD^+.

aldehyde Molecule in which the carbonyl group is linked to a carbon atom at the end of a carbon chain, along with a hydrogen atom.

aldosterone A mineralocorticoid hormone released from the adrenal cortex that increases the amount of Na reabsorbed from the urine in the kidneys and absorbed from foods in the intestine, reduces the amount of Na secreted by salivary and sweat glands, and increases the rate of K excretion by the kidneys, keeping Na and K balanced at the levels required for normal cellular function.

algin Alginic acid, found in the cell walls of brown algae.

allantoic membrane Forms from mesoderm and endoderm that has bulged outward from the gut and encloses the allantois.

allantois In an amniote egg, an extraembryonic membrane sac that fills much of the space between the chorion and the yolk sac and stores the embryo's nitrogenous wastes.

allele One of two or more versions of a gene.

allele frequency The abundance of one allele relative to others at the same gene locus in individuals of a population.

allergen A type of antigen responsible for allergic reactions, which induces B cells to secrete an overabundance of IgE antibodies.

allometric growth A pattern of postembryonic development in which parts of the same organism grow at different rates.

allopatric speciation The evolution of reproductive isolating mechanisms between two populations that are geographically separated.

allopolyploidy The genetic condition of having two or more complete sets of chromosomes from different parent species.

all-or-nothing principle The principle that an action potential is produced only if the stimulus is strong enough to cause depolarization to reach the threshold.

allosteric activator Molecule that converts an enzyme with an allosteric site, a regulatory site outside the active site, from the inactive form to the active form.

allosteric inhibitor Molecule that converts an enzyme with an allosteric site, a regulatory site outside the active site, from the active form to the inactive form.

allosteric regulation Specialized control mechanism for enzymes with an allosteric site, a regulatory site outside the active site, that may either slow or accelerate activity depending on the enzyme.

allosteric site A regulatory site outside the active site.

alpine tundra A biome that occurs on high mountaintops throughout the world, in which dominant plants form cushions and mats.

alternation of generations The regular alternation of mode of reproduction in the life cycle of an organism, such as the alternation between diploid (sporophyte) and haploid (gametophyte) phases in plants.

alternative hypothesis An explanation of an observed phenomenon that is different from the explanation being tested.

alternative splicing Mechanism that joins exons in different combinations to produce different mRNAs from a single gene.

altricial Helpless at birth.

altruism A behavioural phenomenon in which individuals appear to sacrifice their own reproductive success to help other individuals.

alveolus (plural, alveoli) One of the millions of tiny air pockets in mammalian lungs, each surrounded by dense capillary networks.

amacrine cell A type of neuron that forms lateral connections in the retina of the eye, connecting bipolar cells and ganglion cells.

amino acid A molecule that contains both an amino and a carboxyl group.

amino group Group that acts as an organic base, consisting of a nitrogen atom bonded on one side to two hydrogen atoms and on the other side to a carbon chain.

aminoacylation The process of adding an amino acid to a tRNA. Also referred to as *charging*.

aminoacyl–tRNA A tRNA linked to its "correct" amino acid, which is the finished product of charging.

aminoacyl–tRNA synthetase An enzyme that catalyzes aminoacylation.

ammonification A metabolic process in which bacteria and fungi convert organic nitrogen compounds into ammonia and ammonium ions; part of the nitrogen cycle.

amniocentesis Technique of prenatal diagnosis in which cells are obtained from the amniotic fluid.

amnion In an amniote egg, an extraembryonic membrane that encloses the embryo, forming the amniotic cavity and secreting amniotic fluid, which provides an aquatic environment in which the embryo develops.

Amniota The monophyletic group of vertebrates that have an amnion during embryonic development.

amniote (amniotic) egg A shelled egg that can survive and develop on land.

amphipathic Contains a region that is hydrophobic and a region that is hydrophilic.

amplification An increase in the magnitude of each step as a signal transduction pathway proceeds.

amygdala A grey-matter centre of the brain that works as a switchboard, routing information about experiences that have an emotional component through the limbic system.

amyloplast Colourless plastid that stores starch in plants.

anabolic pathway Type of metabolic pathway in which energy is consumed to build complicated molecules from simpler ones; often called a biosynthetic pathway.

anabolic reaction Metabolic reaction that requires energy to assemble simple substances into more complex molecules.

anabolic steroid A steroid hormone that stimulates muscle development.

anaerobe An organism that does not require oxygen to live.

anaerobic respiration The process by which molecules are oxidized to produce ATP via an electron transport chain and ATP synthase, but unlike aerobic respiration, oxygen is not the final electron acceptor.

anagenesis The slow accumulation of evolutionary changes in a lineage over time.

anaphase The phase of mitosis during which the spindle separates sister chromatids and pulls them to opposite spindle poles.

anaphylactic shock A severe inflammation stimulated by an allergen, involving extreme swelling of air passages in the lungs that interferes with breathing and massive leakage of fluid from capillaries that causes blood pressure to drop precipitously.

anapsid (lineage Anapsida) A member of the group of amniote vertebrates with no temporal arches and no spaces on the sides of the skull (includes turtles).

anatomy The study of the structures of organisms.

ancestral character A trait that was present in a distant common ancestor.

anchoring junction Cell junction that forms belts that run entirely around cells, "welding" adjacent cells together.

androgen One of a family of hormones that promote the development and maintenance of sex characteristics.

aneuploid An individual with extra or missing chromosomes.

angiosperm A flowering plant. Its egg-containing ovules mature into seeds within protected chambers called ovaries.

angiotensin A peptide hormone that raises blood pressure quickly by constricting arterioles in most parts of the body; it also stimulates release of the steroid hormone aldosterone.

animal behaviour The responses of animals to specific internal and external stimuli.

animal pole The end of the egg where the egg nucleus is located, which typically gives rise to surface structures and the anterior end of the embryo.

Animalia The taxonomic kingdom that includes all living and extinct animals.

anion A negatively charged ion.

annual A herbaceous plant that completes its life cycle in one growing season and then dies.

annulus In ferns, a ring of thick-walled cells that nearly encircles the sporangium and functions in spore release.

antagonistic pair Two skeletal muscles, one of which flexes as the other extends to move joints.

antenna A chemosensory appendage attached to the head of some adult arthropods.

antenna complex (light-harvesting complex) In photosystems, the sites at which light is absorbed and converted into chemical energy during photosynthesis, an aggregate of many chlorophyll pigments and a number of carotenoid pigments that serves as the primary site of absorbing light energy in the form of photons.

antennal glands Excretory structures at the base of the antennae in some crustaceans.

anterior Indicating the head end of an animal.

anterior pituitary The glandular part of the pituitary, composed of endocrine cells that synthesize and secrete several tropic and nontropic hormones.

anther The pollen-bearing part of a stamen.

antheridium (plural, antheridia) In plants, a structure in which sperm are produced.

Anthocerophyta The phylum comprising hornworts.

Anthophyta The phylum comprising flowering plants.

antibiotic A natural or synthetic substance that kills or inhibits the growth of bacteria and other microorganisms.

antibody A highly specific soluble protein molecule that circulates in the blood and lymph, recognizing and binding to antigens and clearing them from the body.

antibody-mediated immunity Adaptive immune response in which plasma cells secrete antibodies.

anticodon The three-nucleotide segment in tRNAs that pairs with a codon in mRNAs.

antidiuretic hormone (ADH) A hormone secreted by the posterior pituitary that increases water absorption in the kidneys, thereby increasing the volume of the blood.

antigen A foreign molecule that triggers an adaptive immunity response.

antigen-presenting cell (APC) A cell that presents an antigen to T cells in antibody-mediated immunity and cell-mediated immunity.

antigenic variation The process by which an infectious organism alters its surface proteins to evade a host immune response. Parasites such as the trypanosomes that cause sleeping sickness in humans have 10% of their genes dedicated to generating new surface glycoproteins.

antimicrobial peptides Small, potent, broad-spectrum antibiotic peptides that are used by hosts collectively to eliminate bacterial and fungal pathogens. Some antimicrobial peptides also may act as immunomodulators.

antiparallel Strands of DNA that run in opposite directions.

antiport A secondary active transport mechanism in which a molecule moves through a membrane channel into a cell and powers the active transport of a second molecule out of the cell. Also referred to as *exchange diffusion*.

aorta A large artery from the heart that branches into arteries leading to all body regions except the lungs.

aortic body One of several small clusters of chemoreceptors, baroreceptors, and supporting cells located along the aortic arch that measures changes in blood pressure and the composition of arterial blood flowing past it.

apical dominance Inhibition of the growth of lateral buds in plants due to auxin diffusing down a shoot tip from the terminal bud.

apical growth Growth from the tip of a cell or tissue.

apical meristem A region of unspecialized dividing cells at the shoot tips and root tips of a plant.

apicomplexan A group or parasitic organisms with specific structures in their apical complex to penetrate and enter the cells they parasitize.

apomixis In plants, the production of offspring without meiosis or formation of gametes.

apoplastic pathway The route followed by water moving through plant cell walls and intercellular spaces (the apoplast). *Compare* symplastic pathway.

apoptosis Programmed cell death.

aposematic Refers to bright, contrasting patterns that advertise the unpalatability of poisonous or repellent species.

appendicular skeleton The bones comprising the pectoral (shoulder) and pelvic (hip) girdles and limbs of a vertebrate.

appendix A fingerlike sac that extends from the cecum of the large intestine.

applied research Research conducted with the goal of solving specific practical problems.

aquaporin A specialized protein channel that facilitates diffusion of water through cell membranes.

aquatic succession A process in which debris from rivers and runoff accumulates in a body of fresh water, causing it to fill in at the margins.

aqueous humour A clear fluid that fills the space between the cornea and the lens of the eye.

arbuscular mycorrhizas Symbiotic association between a glomeromycete fungus and the roots of a wide range of plants, including nonvascular, nonseed, and seed plants.

arbuscule Highly branched hypha produced inside root cells by arbuscular mycorrhizal fungi; nutrient-exchange site between plant and fungus.

Archaea One of two domains of prokaryotes; archaeans have some unique molecular and biochemical traits, but they also share some traits with Bacteria and other traits with Eukarya.

archegonium The flask-shaped structure in which bryophyte eggs form.

archenteron The central endoderm-lined cavity of an embryo at the gastrula stage, which forms the primitive gut.

Archosauromorpha A diverse group of diapsids that comprises crocodilians, pterosaurs, and dinosaurs (including birds).

arctic tundra A treeless biome that stretches from the boreal forests to the polar ice cap in Europe, Asia, and North America.

arteriole A branch from a small artery at the point where it reaches the organ it supplies.

artery A vessel that conducts blood away from the heart at relatively high pressure.

artificial selection Selective breeding of animals or plants to ensure that certain desirable traits appear at higher frequency in successive generations.

ascocarp A reproductive body that bears or contains asci.

ascospore Spore formed by meiosis in ascus, a saclike cell produced by ascomycete fungi.

ascus (plural, asci) A saclike cell in ascomycetes (sac fungi) in which meiosis gives rise to haploid sexual spores (meiospores).

asexual reproduction Any mode of reproduction in which a single individual gives rise to offspring without fusion of gametes, that is, without genetic input from another individual. See also *vegetative reproduction*.

assimilation efficiency The ratio of the energy absorbed from consumed food to the total energy content of the food.

association area One of several areas surrounding the sensory and motor areas of the cerebral cortex that integrate information from the sensory areas, formulate responses, and pass them on to the primary motor area.

assumption of parsimony Assumption that the simplest explanation should be the most accurate.

aster Radiating array produced as microtubules extending from the centrosomes of cells grow in length and extent.

astrocyte A star-shaped glial cell that provides support to neurons in the vertebrate central nervous system.

asymmetrical Characterized by a lack of proportion in the spatial arrangement or placement of parts.

atmosphere The component of the biosphere that includes the gases and airborne particles enveloping the planet.

atom The smallest unit that retains the chemical and physical properties of an element.

atomic nucleus The nucleus of an atom, containing protons and neutrons.

atomic number The number of protons in the nucleus of an atom.

atomic weight The weight of an element in grams, equal to the mass number.

ATP (adenosine triphosphate) The primary agent that couples exergonic and endergonic reactions.

ATP cycle Continued breakdown and resynthesis of ATP.

ATP synthase A membrane-spanning protein complex that couples the energetically favourable transport of protons across a membrane to the synthesis of ATP.

atrial siphon A tube through which invertebrate chordates expel digestive and metabolic wastes.

atriopore The hole in the body wall of a cephalochordate through which water is expelled from the body.

atrioventricular node (AV node) A region of the heart wall that receives signals from the sinoatrial node and conducts them to the ventricle.

atrioventricular valve (AV valve) A valve composed of endocardium and connective tissue between each atrium and ventricle that prevents backflow of blood from the ventricle to the atrium during emptying of the heart.

atrium (plural, atria) A body cavity or chamber surrounding the perforated pharynx of invertebrate chordates; also one of the chambers that receive blood returning to the heart.

autoimmune reaction The production of antibodies against molecules of the body.

autonomic nervous system A subdivision of the peripheral nervous system that controls largely involuntary processes, including digestion, secretion by sweat glands, circulation of the blood, many functions of the reproductive and excretory systems, and contraction of smooth muscles in all parts of the body.

autopolyploidy The genetic condition of having more than two sets of chromosomes from the same parent species.

autosomal dominant inheritance Pattern in which the allele that causes a trait is dominant, and only homozygous recessives are unaffected.

autosomal recessive inheritance Pattern in which individuals with a trait are homozygous for a recessive allele.

autosome Chromosome other than a sex chromosome.

autotroph An organism that produces its own food using CO_2 and other simple inorganic compounds from its environment and energy from the sun or from oxidation of inorganic substances.

auxin Any of a family of plant hormones that stimulate growth by promoting cell elongation in stems and coleoptiles; inhibit abscission; govern responses to light and gravity, and have other developmental effects.

auxotrophs Mutant strains that are unable to synthesize amino acids.

Avogadro's number The number 6.022×10^{23}, derived by dividing the atomic weight of any element by the weight of an atom of that element.

***Avr* gene** A gene in certain plant pathogens that encodes a product triggering a defensive response in the plant.

axial skeleton The bones comprising the head and trunk of a vertebrate: the cranium, vertebral column, ribs, and sternum (breastbone).

axil The upper angle between the stem and an attached leaf.

axon The single elongated extension of a neuron that conducts signals away from the cell body to another neuron or an effector.

axon hillock A junction with the cell body of a neuron from which the axon arises.

axon terminal A branch at the tip of an axon that ends as a small, buttonlike swelling.

axopods Slender, raylike strands of cytoplasm supported internally by long bundles of microtubules.

B cell A lymphocyte that recognizes antigens in the body.

bacillus (plural, bacilli) A cylindrical or rod-shaped prokaryote.

background extinction rate The average rate of extinction of taxa through time.

bacteria One of the two domains of prokaryotes; collectively, bacteria are the most metabolically diverse organisms.

bacterial chromosome DNA molecule in bacteria in which hereditary information is encoded.

bacteriophage A virus that infects bacteria. Also referred to as a *phage*.

bacteroid A rod-shaped or branched bacterium in the root nodules of nitrogen-fixing plants.

balanced polymorphism The maintenance of two or more phenotypes in fairly stable proportions over many generations.

bark The tough outer covering of woody stems and roots, composed of all of the living and nonliving tissues between the vascular cambium and the stem surface.

Barr body The inactive, condensed X chromosome seen in the nucleus of female mammals.

basal angiosperm Any of the earliest branches of the flowering plant lineage; includes the star anise group and water lilies.

basal lamina A membrane secreted at the inner surface of epithelial cells.

basal nucleus One of several grey-matter centres that surround the thalamus on both sides of the brain and moderate voluntary movements directed by motor centres in the cerebrum.

base Proton acceptor that reduces the H concentration of a solution.

base-pair mismatch An error in the assembly of a new nucleotide chain in which bases other than the correct ones pair together.

base-pair substitution mutation A particular mutation involving a change from one base pair to another in DNA.

basement membrane A membrane at the inner surface of epithelia in vertebrates. It consists of the basal lamina and a layer of connective tissue.

basic research Research conducted to search for explanations about natural phenomena to satisfy curiosity and advance collective knowledge of living systems.

basidiocarp A fruiting body of a basidiomycete; mushrooms are examples.

basidiospore A haploid sexual spore produced by basidiomycete fungi.

basidium (plural, basidia) A small, club-shaped structure in which sexual spores of basidiomycetes arise.

basilar membrane A stiff structural element within the cochlea.

basophil A type of leukocyte that is induced to secrete histamine by allergens.

Batesian mimicry The form of defence in which a palatable or harmless species resembles an unpalatable or poisonous one.

B-cell receptor (BCR) The receptor on B cells that is specific for a particular antigen.

behavioural isolation A prezygotic reproductive isolating mechanism in which two species do not mate because of differences in courtship behaviour; also known as ethological isolation.

beta (β) sheet A type of primary structure in a polypeptide in which the amino acid chain zigzags in a flat plane to form a beta strand, and beta strands then align side by side in the same or opposite direction.

biennial A plant that completes its life cycle in two growing seasons and then dies; limited secondary growth occurs in some biennials.

bilateral symmetry The body plan of animals in which the body can be divided into mirror image right and left halves by a plane passing through the midline of the body.

bilayer A membrane with two molecular layers.

bile A mixture of substances including bile salts, cholesterol, and bilirubin that is made in the liver, stored in the gallbladder, and used in the digestion of fats.

binary fission Prokaryotic cell division—splitting or dividing into two parts.

binomial Relating to or consisting of two names or terms.

biodiversity The richness of living systems as reflected in genetic variability within and among species, the number of species living on Earth, and the variety of communities and ecosystems.

biofilm A microbial community consisting of a complex aggregation of microorganisms attached to a surface.

biogeochemical cycle Any of several global processes in which a nutrient circulates between the abiotic environment and living organisms.

biogeographic region A major region of Earth that is occupied by distinct evolutionary lineages of plants and animals.

biogeography The study of the geographic distributions of plants and animals.

bioinformatics Field that fuses biology with mathematics and computer science that is used for the analysis of genome sequences.

biological clock An internal time-measuring mechanism that adapts an organism to recurring environmental changes.

biological evolution The process by which some individuals in a population experience changes in their DNA and pass those modified instructions to their offspring.

biological lineage An evolutionary sequence of ancestral organisms and their descendants.

biological magnification The increasing concentration of nondegradable poisons in the tissues of animals at higher trophic levels.

biological research The collective effort of individuals who have worked to understand how living systems function.

Biological Species Concept The definition of species based on the ability of populations to interbreed and produce fertile offspring.

bioluminescent An organism that glows or releases a flash of light, particularly when disturbed.

biomass The dry weight of biological material per unit area or volume of habitat.

biome A large-scale vegetation type and its associated microorganisms, fungi, and animals.

bioremediation Applications of chemical and biological knowledge to decontaminate polluted environments.

biosphere All regions of Earth's crust, waters, and atmosphere that sustain life.

biota The total collection of organisms in a geographic region.

biotechnology The manipulation of living organisms to produce useful products.

biotic Biological, often in reference to living components of the environment.

bipedalism The habit in animals of walking upright on two legs.

bipolar cell A type of neuron in the retina of the eye that connects the rods and cones with the ganglion cells.

blade The expanded part of a leaf that provides a large surface area for absorbing sunlight and carbon dioxide.

blastocoel A fluid-filled cavity in the blastula embryo.

blastocyst An embryonic stage in mammals; a single cell–layered hollow ball of about 120 cells with a fluid-filled blastocoel in which a dense mass of cells is localized to one side.

blastodisk A disklike layer of cells at the surface of the yolk produced by early cleavage divisions.

blastomere A small cell formed during cleavage of the embryo.

blastopore The opening at one end of the archenteron in the gastrula that gives rise to the mouth in protostomes and the anus in deuterostomes.

blastula The hollow ball of cells that is the result of cleavage divisions in an early embryo.

blending theory of inheritance Theory suggesting that hereditary traits blend evenly in offspring through mixing of the blood of the two parents.

blood A fluid connective tissue composed of blood cells suspended in a fluid extracellular matrix, plasma.

blood–brain barrier A specialized arrangement of capillaries in the brain that prevents most substances dissolved in the blood from entering the cerebrospinal fluid and thus protects the brain and spinal cord from viruses, bacteria, and toxic substances that may circulate in the blood.

bolting Rapid formation of a floral shoot in plant species that form rosettes, such as lettuce.

bolus The food mass after chewing.

bone The densest form of connective tissue, in which living cells secrete the mineralized matrix of collagen and calcium salts that surrounds them; forms the skeleton.

book lungs Pocketlike respiratory organs found in some arachnids consisting of several parallel membrane folds arranged like the pages of a book.

boreal forest A biome that is a circumpolar expanse of evergreen coniferous trees in Europe, Asia, and North America.

Bowman's capsule An infolded region at the proximal end of a nephron that cups around the glomerulus and collects the water and solutes filtered out of the blood.

brain A single, organized collection of nervous tissue in an organism's head that forms the control centre of the nervous system and major sensory structures.

brain hormone (BH) A peptide hormone secreted by neurosecretory neurons in the brain of insects.

brain stem A stalklike structure formed by the pons and medulla, along with the midbrain, which connects the forebrain with the spinal cord.

brassinosteroid Any of a family of plant hormones that stimulate cell division and elongation and differentiation of vascular tissue.

breathing The exchange of gases with the respiratory medium by animals.

bronchiole One of the small, branching airways in the lungs that lead into the alveoli.

bronchus (plural, bronchi) An airway that leads from the trachea to the lungs.

brown adipose tissue A specialized tissue in which the most intense heat generation by nonshivering thermogenesis takes place.

Bryophyta The phylum of nonvascular plants, including mosses and their relatives.

bryophyte A general term for plants (such as mosses) that lack internal transport vessels.

budding A mode of asexual reproduction in which a new individual grows and develops while attached to the parent.

buffer Substance that compensates for pH changes by absorbing or releasing H^+.

bulbourethral gland One of two pea-sized glands on either side of the prostate gland that secrete a mucous fluid that is added to semen.

bulk feeder An animal that consumes sizable food items whole or in large chunks.

bulk flow The group movement of molecules in response to a difference in pressure between two locations.

bulk-phase endocytosis Mechanism by which extracellular water is taken into a cell together with any molecules that happen to be in solution in the water. Also referred to as *pinocytosis*.

C4 cycle A reaction series that allows CO_2 to be fixed by a carboxylase that is unaffected by high oxygen concentrations.

Ca^{2+} pump (calcium pump) Pump that pushes Ca^{2+} from the cytoplasm to the cell exterior and from the cytosol into the vesicles of the endoplasmic reticulum.

cadherin A cell surface protein responsible for selective cell adhesions that require calcium ions to set up adhesions.

calcitonin A nontropic peptide hormone that lowers the level of Ca^{2+} in the blood by inhibiting the ongoing dissolution of calcium from bone.

callus An undifferentiated tissue that develops on or around a cut plant surface or in tissue culture.

calorie (cal) The amount of heat required to raise 1 g of water by 1°C, known as a "small" calorie; when capitalized, a unit equal to 1000 small calories.

Calvin cycle *See* light-independent reaction.

calyx The outermost whorl of a flower, made up of sepals, early in the development of a flower, it encloses all of the other parts, as in an unopened bud.

CAM plant A C_4 plant that runs the Calvin and C_4 cycles at different times to circumvent photorespiration. CAM stands for "crassulacean acid metabolism."

canines Pointed, conical teeth of a mammal, located between the incisors and the first premolars, that are specialized for biting and piercing.

capillary The smallest diameter blood vessel, with a wall that is one cell thick, which forms highly branched networks well adapted for diffusion of substances.

capsid *See* coat.

capsule An external layer of sticky or slimy polysaccharides coating the cell wall in many prokaryotes.

carapace A protective outer covering that extends backward behind the head on the dorsal side of an animal, such as the shell of a turtle or lobster.

carbon cycle The global circulation of carbon atoms, especially via the processes of photosynthesis and respiration.

carbonyl group The reactive part of aldehydes and ketones, consisting of an oxygen atom linked to a carbon atom by a double bond.

carboxyl group The characteristic functional group of organic acids, formed by the combination of carbonyl and hydroxyl groups.

cardiac cycle The systole–diastole sequence of the heart.

cardiac muscle The contractile tissue of the heart.

carnivore An animal that primarily eats other animals.

carotenoid Molecule of yellow-orange pigment by which light is absorbed in photosynthesis.

carotid body A small cluster of chemoreceptors and supporting cells located near the bifurcation of the carotid artery that measures changes in the composition of arterial blood flowing through it.

carpel The reproductive organ of a flower that houses an ovule and its associated structures.

carrageenan A chemical extracted from the red alga *Eucheuma* that is used to thicken and stabilize paints, dairy products such as pudding and ice cream, and many other creams and emulsions.

carrier An individual who carries a mutant allele and could pass it on to offspring but does not display its symptoms.

carrier protein Transport protein that binds a specific single solute and transports it across the lipid bilayer.

carrying capacity The maximum size of a population that an environment can support indefinitely.

Cartagena Protocol on Biosafety An international agreement that promotes biosafety as it relates to genetically modified organisms.

cartilage A tissue composed of sparsely distributed chondrocytes surrounded by networks of collagen fibres embedded in a tough but elastic matrix of the glycoprotein.

Casparian strip A thin, waxy impermeable band that seals abutting cell walls in roots; the strip helps control the type and amount of solutes that enter the stele by blocking the apoplastic pathway at the endodermis and forcing substances to pass through cells (the symplast).

caspase A protease involved in programmed cell death.

catabolic pathway Type of metabolic pathway in which energy is released by the breakdown of complex molecules to simpler compounds.

catabolic reaction Cellular reaction that breaks down complex molecules such as sugar to make their energy available for cellular work.

catalyst Substance with the ability to accelerate a spontaneous reaction without being changed by the reaction.

catastrophism The theory that Earth has been affected by sudden, violent events that were sometimes worldwide in scope.

catecholamine Any of a class of compounds derived from the amino acid tyrosine that circulates in the bloodstream, including epinephrine and norepinephrine.

cation A positively charged ion.

cation exchange Replacement of one cation with another, as on a soil particle.

CD4+ T cell A type of T cell in the lymphatic system that has CD4 receptors on its surface. This type of T cell binds to an antigen-presenting cell in antibody-mediated immunity.

CD8+ T cell A type of T cell in the lymphatic system that has CD8 receptors on its surface. This type of T cell binds to an antigen-presenting cell in cell-mediated immunity.

cDNA library The entire collection of cloned cDNAs made from the mRNAs isolated from a cell.

cecum A blind pouch formed at the junction of the large and small intestine.

cell Smallest unit with the capacity to live and reproduce.

cell adhesion molecule A cell surface protein responsible for selectively binding cells together.

cell adhesion protein Protein that binds cells together by recognizing and binding receptors or chemical groups on other cells or on the extracellular matrix.

cell body The portion of the neuron containing genetic material and cellular organelles.

cell culture A living cell grown in a laboratory vessel.

cell cycle The sequence of events during which a cell experiences a period of growth followed by nuclear division and cytokinesis.

cell differentiation A process in which changes in gene expression establish cells with specialized structure and function.

cell expansion A mechanism that enlarges the cells in specific directions in a developing organ.

cell junction Junction that seals the spaces between cells and provides direct communication between cells.

cell lineage Cell derivation from the undifferentiated tissues of the embryo.

cell plate In cytokinesis in plants, a new cell wall that forms between the daughter nuclei and grows laterally until it divides the cytoplasm.

cell theory Three generalizations yielded by microscopic observations: all organisms are composed of one or more cells; the cell is the smallest unit that has the properties of life; and cells arise only from the growth and division of preexisting cells.

cell wall A rigid external layer of material surrounding the plasma membrane of cells in plants, fungi, bacteria, and some protists, providing cell protection and support.

cell-mediated immunity An adaptive immune response in which a subclass of T cells—cytotoxic T cells—becomes activated and, with other cells of the immune system, attacks host cells infected by pathogens, particularly those infected by a virus.

cellular respiration The process by which energy-rich molecules are broken down to produce energy in the form of ATP.

cellular senescence Loss of proliferative ability over time.

cellular slime mould Any of a variety of primitive organisms of the phylum Acrasiomycota, especially of the genus *Dictyostelium*; the life cycle is characterized by a slimelike amoeboid stage and a multicellular reproductive stage.

cellulose One of the primary constituents of plant cell walls, formed by chains of carbohydrate subunits.

centimorgan *See* map unit.

central canal The central portion of the vertebral column in which the spinal cord is found.

central nervous system (CNS) One of the two major divisions of the nervous system containing the brain and spinal cord.

central vacuole A large, water-filled organelle in plant cells that maintains the turgor of the cell and controls movement of molecules between the cytosol and sap.

centriole A cylindrical structure consisting of nine triplets of microtubules in the centrosomes of most animal cells.

centromere A specialized chromosomal region that connects sister chromatids and attaches them to the mitotic spindle.

centrosome (cell centre) The main microtubule organizing centre of a cell, which organizes the microtubule cytoskeleton during interphase and positions many of the cytoplasmic organelles.

cephalization The development of an anterior head where sensory organs and nervous system tissue are concentrated.

cephalothorax The anterior section of an arachnid, consisting of a fused head and thorax.

cerebellum The portion of the brain that receives sensory input from receptors in muscles and joints, from balance receptors in the inner ear, and from the receptors of touch, vision, and hearing.

cerebral cortex A thin outer shell of grey matter covering a thick core of white matter within each hemisphere of the brain; the part of the forebrain responsible for information processing and learning.

cerebrospinal fluid Fluid that circulates through the central canal of the spinal cord and the ventricles of the brain, cushioning the brain and spinal cord from jarring movements and impacts, as well as nourishing the CNS and protecting it from toxic substances.

cervix The lower end of the uterus.

channel protein Transport protein that forms a hydrophilic channel in a cell membrane through which water, ions, or other molecules can pass, depending on the protein.

chaperone protein (chaperonin) "Guide" protein that binds temporarily with newly synthesized proteins, directing their conformation toward the correct tertiary structure and inhibiting incorrect arrangements as the new proteins fold.

character A heritable characteristic.

character displacement The phenomenon in which allopatric populations are morphologically similar and use similar resources, but sympatric populations are morphologically different and use different resources; may also apply to characters influencing mate choice.

charging *See* aminoacylation.

charophyte A member of the group of green algae most similar to the algal ancestors of land plants.

checkpoint Internal control of the cell cycle that prevents a critical phase from beginning until the previous phase is complete.

chelicerae The first pair of fanglike appendages near the mouth of an arachnid, used for biting prey and often modified for grasping and piercing.

chemical bond Link formed when atoms of reactive elements combine into molecules.

chemical equation A chemical reaction written in balanced form.

chemical reaction A reaction that occurs when atoms or molecules interact to form new chemical bonds or break old ones.

chemical signal Any secretion from one cell type that can alter the behaviour of a different cell that bears a receptor for it; a means of cell communication.

chemical synapse A type of communicating connection between two neurons or a neuron and an effector cell in which an electrical impulse arriving at an axon terminal of the presynaptic cell triggers release of a neurotransmitter that crosses the gap and binds to a receptor on the postsynaptic cell, triggering an electrical impulse in that cell.

chemiosmosis Ability of cells to use the proton-motive force to do work.

chemoautotroph An organism that obtains energy by oxidizing inorganic substances such as hydrogen, iron, sulphur, ammonia, nitrites, and nitrates and uses carbon dioxide as a carbon source.

chemoheterotroph An organism that oxidizes organic molecules as an energy source and obtains carbon in organic form.

chemokine A protein secreted by activated macrophages that attracts other cells, such as neutrophils.

chemoreceptor A sensory receptor that detects specific molecules or chemical conditions such as acidity.

chemotroph An organism that obtains energy by oxidizing inorganic or organic substances.

chiasmata *See* crossover.

chitin A polysaccharide that contains nitrogen and is present in the cell walls of fungi and the exoskeletons of arthropods.

chlorophyll Molecule of green pigment that absorbs photons of light in photosynthesis.

chloroplast The site of photosynthesis in plant cells.

chlorosis An abnormal yellowing of plant tissues due to a lack of chlorophyll; a sign of nutrient deficiency or infection by a pathogen.

choanocyte One of the inner layer of flagellated cells lining the body cavity of a sponge.

Choanoflagellata A group of minute, single-celled protists found in water; the flask-shaped body has a collar of closely packed microvilli that surrounds the single flagellum by which it moves and takes in food.

cholesterol The predominant sterol of animal cell membranes.

chondrocyte A cartilage-producing cell.

chorion In an amniote egg, an extraembryonic membrane that surrounds the embryo and yolk sac completely and exchanges oxygen and carbon dioxide with the environment; becomes part of the placenta in mammals.

chorionic villus (plural, villi) One of many treelike extensions from the chorion, which greatly increase the surface area of the chorion.

chorionic villus sampling Technique of prenatal diagnosis in which cells are obtained from portions of the placenta that develop from tissues of the embryo.

chromatin The structural building block of a chromosome, which includes the complex of DNA and its associated proteins.

chromatin remodelling Process in which the state of the chromatin is changed so that the proteins that initiate transcription can bind to their promoters.

chromosomal protein The histone and nonhistone protein associated with DNA structure and regulation in the nucleus.

chromosome The nuclear unit of genetic information, consisting of a DNA molecule and associated proteins.

chromosome segregation The equal distribution of daughter chromosomes to each of the two cells that result from cell division.

chromosome theory of inheritance The principle that genes and their alleles are carried on the chromosomes.

chylomicron A small triglyceride droplet covered by a protein coat.

chyme Digested content of the stomach released for further digestion in the small intestine.

ciliary body A fine ligament in the eye that anchors the lens to a surrounding layer of connective tissue and muscle.

cilium Motile structure, extending from a cell surface, that moves a cell through fluid or fluid over a cell.

circadian rhythm Any biological activity that is repeated in cycles, each about 24 hours long, independently of any shifts in environmental conditions.

circulatory system An organ system consisting of a fluid, a heart, and vessels for moving important molecules, and often cells, from one tissue to another.

circulatory vessel An element of the circulatory system through which fluid flows and carries nutrients and oxygen to tissues and removes wastes.

circumcision Removal of the prepuce for religious, cultural, or hygienic reasons.

cisternae (singular, cisterna) Membranous channels and vesicles that make up the endoplasmic reticulum.

citric acid cycle Series of reactions in which acetyl groups are oxidized completely to carbon dioxide and some ATP molecules are synthesized. Also referred to as *Krebs cycle* and *tricarboxylic acid cycle.*

clade A monophyletic group of organisms that share homologous features derived from a common ancestor.

cladistics An approach to systematics that uses shared derived characters to infer the phylogenetic relationships and evolutionary history of groups of organisms.

cladogenesis The evolution of two or more descendant species from a common ancestor.

cladogram A branching diagram in which the end points of the branches represent different species of organisms, used to illustrate phylogenetic relationships.

claspers A pair of organs on the pelvic fins of male crustaceans and sharks, which help transfer sperm into the reproductive tract of the female.

class A Linnaean taxonomic category that ranks below a phylum and above an order.

class II major histocompatibility complex (MHC) A collection of proteins that present antigens on the cell surface of an antigen-presenting cell in an antibody-mediated immune response.

classical conditioning A type of learning in which an animal develops a mental association between two phenomena that are usually unrelated.

classification An arrangement of organisms into hierarchical groups that reflect their relatedness.

clathrin The network of proteins that coat and reinforce the cytoplasmic surface of cell membranes.

cleavage Mitotic cell divisions of the zygote that produce a blastula from a fertilized ovum.

climate The weather conditions prevailing over an extended period of time.

climax community A relatively stable, late successional stage in which the dominant vegetation replaces itself and persists until an environmental disturbance eliminates it, allowing other species to invade.

cline A pattern of smooth variation in a characteristic along a geographic gradient.

clitoris The structure at the junction of the labia minora in front of the vulva, homologous to the penis in the male.

clonal expansion The proliferation of the activated CD4 T cell by cell division to produce a clone of cells.

clonal selection The process by which a lymphocyte is specifically selected for cloning when it encounters a foreign antigen from among a randomly generated, enormous diversity of lymphocytes with receptors that specifically recognize the antigen.

clone An individual genetically identical to an original cell from which it descended.

closed circulatory system A circulatory system in which the fluid, blood, is confined in blood vessels and is distinct from the interstitial fluid.

clumped dispersion A pattern of distribution in which individuals in a population are grouped together.

cnidocyte A prey-capturing and defensive cell in the epidermis of cnidarians.

CO_2 fixation Process in which electrons are used as a source of energy to convert inorganic CO_2 to an organic form.

coactivator (mediator) In eukaryotes, a large multiprotein complex that bridges between activators at an enhancer and proteins at the promoter and promoter proximal region to stimulate transcription.

coat The protective layer of protein that surrounds the nucleic acid core of a virus in free form; also known as a capsid.

coated pit A depression in the plasma membrane that contains receptors for macromolecules to be taken up by endocytosis.

coccoid Spherical prokaryotic cell.

coccus (plural, cocci) A spherical prokaryote.

cochlea A snail-shaped structure (in vertebrates) in the inner ear containing the organ of hearing.

codominance Condition in which alleles have approximately equal effects in individuals, making the alleles equally detectable in heterozygotes.

codon Each three-letter word (triplet) of the genetic code.

coelom A fluid-filled body cavity in bilaterally symmetrical animals that is completely lined with derivatives of mesoderm.

coelomate A body plan of bilaterally symmetrical animals that have a coelom.

coenzymes Organic cofactors that include complex chemical groups of various kinds.

coevolution The evolution of genetically based, reciprocal adaptations in two or more species that interact closely in the same ecological setting.

cofactor An inorganic or organic nonprotein group that is necessary for catalysis to take place.

cohesion The high resistance of water molecules to separation.

cohesion–tension mechanism of water transport A model of how water is transported from roots to leaves in vascular plants; the evaporation of water from leaves pulls water up in the xylem by creating a continuous negative pressure (tension) that extends to roots.

cohort A group of individuals of similar age.

coleoptile A protective sheath that covers the shoot apical meristem and plumule of the embryo in monocots, such as grasses, as it pushes up through soil.

coleorhiza A sheath that encloses the radicle of an embryo until it breaks out of the seed coat and enters the soil as the primary root.

collagen Fibrous glycoprotein—very rich in carbohydrates—embedded in a network of proteoglycans.

collecting duct A location where urine leaving individual nephrons is processed further.

collenchyma One of three simple plant tissues. Flexibly supports rapidly growing plant parts. Its elongated cells are alive at maturity and collectively often form strands or a sheathlike cylinder under the dermal tissue of growing shoot regions and leaf stalks.

colon The main part of the large intestine.

colony Multiple individual organisms of the same species living in a group.

combinatorial gene regulation The combining of a few regulatory proteins in particular ways so that the transcription of a wide array of genes can be controlled and a large number of cell types can be specified.

commaless The sequential nature of the words of the nucleic acid code, with no indicators such as commas or spaces to mark the end of one codon and the beginning of the next.

commensalism A symbiotic interaction in which one species benefits and the other is unaffected.

community Populations of all species that occupy the same area.

community ecology The ecological discipline that examines groups of populations occurring together in one area.

companion cell A specialized parenchyma cell that is connected to a mature sieve tube member by plasmodesmata and assists sieve tube members with both the uptake of sugars and the unloading of sugars in tissues.

comparative morphology Analysis of the structure of living and extinct organisms.

compass orientation A wayfinding mechanism that allows animals to move in a particular direction, often over a specific distance or for a prescribed length of time.

competitive exclusion principle The ecological principle stating that populations of two or more species cannot coexist indefinitely if they rely on the same limiting resources and exploit them in the same way.

competitive inhibition Inhibition of an enzyme reaction by an inhibitor molecule that resembles the normal substrate closely enough so that it fits into the active site of the enzyme.

complement system A nonspecific defence mechanism activated by invading pathogens, made up of more than 30 interacting soluble plasma proteins circulating in the blood and interstitial fluid.

complementary base pairing Feature of DNA in which the specific purine–pyrimidine base pairs A–T (adenine–thymine) and G–C (guanine–cytosine) occur to bridge the two sugar–phosphate backbones.

complementary DNA (cDNA) A DNA molecule that is complementary to an mRNA molecule, synthesized by reverse transcriptase.

complete digestive system A digestive system with a mouth at one end, through which food enters, and an anus at the other end, through which undigested waste is voided.

complete metamorphosis The form of metamorphosis in which an insect passes through four separate stages of growth: egg, larva, pupa, and adult.

compound A molecule whose component atoms are different.

compound eye The eye of most insects and some crustaceans, composed of many-faceted, light-sensitive units called ommatidia fitted closely together, each with its own refractive system and each forming a portion of an image.

concentration The number of molecules or ions of a substance in a unit volume of space.

concentration gradient The concentration difference that drives diffusion.

condensation reaction Reaction during which the components of a water molecule are removed, usually as part of the assembly of a larger molecule from smaller subunits. Also referred to as *dehydration synthesis reaction*.

conduction The flow of heat between atoms or molecules in direct contact.

cone In the vertebrate eye, a photoreceptor in the retina that is specialized for detection of different wavelengths (colours). In cone-bearing plants, a cluster of sporophylls.

conformation The overall three-dimensional shape of a protein.

conformational change Alteration in the three-dimensional shape of a protein.

conidiophore A fungal hypha that gives rise to conidia.

conidium (plural, conidia) An asexually produced fungal spore.

Coniferophyta The major phylum of cone-bearing gymnosperms, most of which are substantial trees; includes pines, firs, and other conifers.

conjugation In bacteria, the process by which a copy of part of the DNA of a donor cell moves through the cytoplasmic bridge into the recipient cell where genetic recombination can occur. In ciliate protozoans, a process of sexual reproduction in which individuals of the same species temporarily couple and exchange genetic material.

connective tissue Tissue with cells scattered through an extracellular matrix; forms layers in and around body structures that support other body tissues, transmit mechanical and other forces, and in some cases act as filters.

conodont An abundant, bonelike fossil dating from the early Paleozoic era through the early Mesozoic era, now described as a feeding structure of some of the earliest vertebrates.

consciousness Awareness of oneself, one's identity, and one's surroundings, with understanding of the significance and likely consequences of events.

conservation biology An interdisciplinary science that focuses on the maintenance and preservation of biodiversity.

consumer An organism that consumes other organisms in a community or ecosystem.

contact inhibition The inhibition of movement or proliferation of normal cells that results from cell–cell contact.

continental climate Climate not moderated by the distant ocean.

continental drift The long-term movement of continents as a result of plate tectonics.

continuous distribution A geographic distribution in which a species lives in suitable habitats throughout a geographic area.

contractile vacuole A specialized cytoplasmic organelle that pumps fluid in a cyclical manner from within the cell to the outside by alternately filling and then contracting to release its contents at various points on the surface of the cell.

control Treatment that tells what would be seen in the absence of the experimental manipulation.

convection The transfer of heat from a body to a fluid, such as air or water, that passes over its surface.

convergent evolution The evolution of similar adaptations in distantly related organisms that occupy similar environments.

coral reef A structure made from the hard skeletons of coral animals or polyps; found largely in tropical and subtropical marine environments.

core The nucleic acid centre of a virus in the free form.

corepressor In the regulation of gene expression in bacteria, a regulatory molecule that combines with a repressor to activate it and shut off an operon.

cork A nonliving, impermeable secondary tissue that is one element of bark.

cork cambium A lateral meristem in plants that forms periderm, which in turn produces cork.

cornea The transparent layer that forms the front wall of the eye, covering the iris.

corolla The structure formed collectively by the petals of a flower.

corona The ciliated crownlike organ at the anterior end of rotifers used for feeding or locomotion.

corpus callosum A structure formed of thick axon bundles that connect the two cerebral hemispheres and coordinate their functions.

corpus luteum Cells remaining at the surface of the ovary during the luteal phase; the structure acts as an endocrine gland, secreting several hormones: estrogens, large quantities of progesterone, and inhibin.

cortex Generally, an outer, rindlike layer. In mammals, the outer layer of the brain, the kidneys, or the adrenal glands. In plants, the outer region of tissue in a root or stem lying between the epidermis and the vascular tissue, composed mainly of parenchyma.

cortical granule A secretory vesicle just under the plasma membrane of an egg cell.

cortisol The major glucocorticoid steroid hormone secreted by the adrenal cortex, which increases blood glucose by promoting breakdown of proteins and fats.

cotransport *See* symport.

cotyledon A leaf of a seed plant embryo; also known as a seed leaf.

countercurrent exchange A mechanism in which the water flowing over the gills moves in a direction opposite to the flow of blood under the respiratory surface (can also apply to transfer of heat).

coupled reaction Reaction that occurs when an exergonic reaction is joined to an endergonic reaction, producing an overall reaction that is exergonic.

courtship display A behaviour performed by males to attract potential mates or to reinforce the bond between a male and a female.

covalent bond Bond formed by electron sharing between atoms.

cranial nerve A nerve that connects the brain directly to the head, neck, and body trunk.

cranium The part of the skull that encloses the brain.

crassulacean acid metabolism (CAM) A biochemical variation of photosynthesis that was discovered in a member of the plant family Crassulaceae. Carbon dioxide is taken up and stored during the night to allow the stomata to remain closed during the daytime, decreasing water loss.

Crenarchaeota A major group of the domain Archaea, separated from the other archaeans based mainly on rRNA sequences.

crista Fold that expands the surface area of the inner mitochondrial membrane.

critical period A restricted stage of development early in life during which an animal has the capacity to respond to specific environmental stimuli.

crop Of birds, an enlargement of the digestive tube where the digestive contents are stored and mixed with lubricating mucus.

crossing-over The recombination process in meiosis, in which chromatids exchange segments.

crossover Site of recombination during meiosis. Also referred to as a *chiasmata*.

cross-pollination Fertilization of one plant by a different plant.

cross-talk Interaction by which cell signalling pathways communicate with one another to integrate their responses to cellular signals.

cryptic coloration Coloration that allows an organism to match its background and hence become less vulnerable to predation or recognition by prey.

cryptochrome A light-absorbing protein that is sensitive to blue light and that may also be an important early step in various light-based growth responses.

C-terminal end The end of an amino acid chain with a —COO group.

cupula In certain mechanoceptors, a gelatinous structure with stereocilia extending into it that moves with pressure changes in the surrounding water; movement of the cupula bends the stereocilia, which triggers release of neurotransmitters.

cuticle The outer layer of plants and some animals, which helps prevent desiccation by slowing water loss.

Cycadophyta A phylum of palmlike gymnosperms known as cycads; the pollen-bearing and seed-bearing cones (strobili) occur on separate plants.

cyclic AMP (cAMP) In particular signal transduction pathways, a second messenger that activates protein kinases, which elicit the cellular response by adding phosphate groups to specific target proteins. cAMP functions in one of two major G protein–coupled receptor–response pathways.

cyclic electron transport An electron transport pathway associated with photosystem I in photosynthesis that produces ATP without the synthesis of NADPH.

cyclin In eukaryotes, protein that regulates the activity of CDK (cyclin-dependent kinase) and controls progression through the cell cycle.

cyclin-dependent kinase (CDK) A protein kinase that controls the cell cycle in eukaryotes.

cytochrome Protein with a heme prosthetic group that contains an iron atom.

cytokine A molecule secreted by one cell type that binds to receptors on other cells and, through signal transduction pathways, triggers a response. In innate immunity, cytokines are secreted by activated macrophages.

cytokinesis Division of the cytoplasm into two daughter cells following the nuclear division stage of mitosis.

cytokinin A hormone that promotes and controls growth responses of plants.

cytoplasm All parts of the cell that surround the central nuclear or nucleoid region.

cytoplasmic determinants The mRNA and proteins stored in the egg cytoplasm that direct the first stages of animal development in the period before genes of the zygote become active.

cytoplasmic inheritance Pattern in which inheritance follows that of genes in the cytoplasmic organelles, mitochondria, or chloroplasts.

cytoplasmic streaming Intracellular movement of cytoplasm.

cytosine A pyrimidine that base-pairs with guanine in nucleic acids.

cytoskeleton The interconnected system of protein fibres and tubes that extends throughout the cytoplasm of a eukaryotic cell.

cytosol Aqueous solution in the cytoplasm containing ions and various organic molecules.

cytotoxic T cell A T lymphocyte that functions in cell-mediated immunity to kill body cells infected by viruses or transformed by cancer.

daily torpor A period of inactivity and lowered metabolic rate that allows an endotherm to conserve energy when environmental temperatures are low.

dalton A standard unit of mass, about 1.66×10^{24} grams.

day-neutral plant A plant that flowers without regard to photoperiod.

decomposer A small organism, such as a bacterium or fungus, that feeds on the remains of dead organisms, breaking down complex biological molecules or structures into simpler raw materials.

degeneracy (redundancy) The feature of the genetic code in which, with two exceptions, more than one codon represents each amino acid.

dehydration synthesis reaction *See* condensation reaction.

deletion Chromosomal alteration that occurs if a broken segment is lost from a chromosome.

demographic transition model A graphic depiction of the historical relationship between a country's economic development and its birth and death rates.

demography The statistical study of the processes that change a population's size and density through time.

denaturation A loss of both the structure and function of a protein due to extreme conditions that unfold it from its conformation.

dendrite The branched extension of the nerve cell body that receives signals from other nerve cells.

dendritic cell A type of phagocyte, so called because it has many surface projections that resemble dendrites of neurons, that engulfs a bacterium in infected tissue by phagocytosis.

denitrification A metabolic process in which certain bacteria convert nitrites or nitrates into nitrous oxide and then into molecular nitrogen, which enters the atmosphere.

density-dependent Description of environmental factors for which the strength of their effect on a population varies with the population's density.

density-independent Description of environmental factors for which the strength of their effect on a population does not vary with the population's density.

deoxyribonucleic acid (DNA) The large, double-stranded, helical molecule that contains the genetic material of all living organisms.

deoxyribose A five-carbon sugar to which the nitrogenous bases in nucleotides of DNA link covalently.

depolarized State of the membrane (which was polarized at rest) as the membrane potential becomes less negative.

deposit feeder An animal that consumes particles of organic matter from the solid substrate on which it lives.

derivative One of the daughter cells produced when a plant cell divides; it typically divides once or twice and then enters on the path to differentiation.

derived character A new version of a trait found in the most recent common ancestor of a group.

dermal tissue system The plant tissue system that comprises the outer tissues of the plant body, including the epidermis and periderm; it serves as a protective covering for the plant body.

dermis The skin layer below the epidermis; it is packed with connective tissue fibres such as collagen, which resist compression, tearing, or puncture of the skin.

desaturases A group of enzymes that synthesize unsaturated fatty acids.

descent with modification Biological evolution.

desert A sparsely vegetated biome that forms where rainfall averages less than 25 cm per year.

determinate cleavage A type of cleavage in protosomes in which each cell's developmental path is determined as the cell is produced.

determinate growth The pattern of growth in most animals in which individuals grow to a certain size and then their growth slows dramatically or stops.

determination Mechanism in which the developmental fate of a cell is set.

detritivore An organism that extracts energy from the organic detritus (refuse) produced at other trophic levels.

deuterostome A division of the Bilateria in which blastopore forms the anus during development and the mouth appears later (includes Echinodermata and Chordata).

development A series of programmed changes encoded in DNA, through which a fertilized egg divides into many cells that ultimately are transformed into an adult, which is itself capable of reproduction.

diabetes mellitus A disease that results from problems with insulin production or action.

diacylglycerol (DAG) In particular, signal transduction pathways, a second messenger that activates protein kinases, which elicit the cellular response by adding phosphate groups to specific target proteins. DAG is involved in one of two major G protein–coupled receptor–response pathways.

diapsid (lineage Diapsida) A member of a group within the amniote vertebrates with a skull with two temporal arches. Their living descendants include lizards and snakes, crocodilians, and birds.

diastole The period of relaxation and filling of the heart between contractions.

diatom Photosynthetic single-celled organisms with a glassy silica shell; also called bacillariophytes.

differentiation Follows determination and involves the establishment of a cell-specific developmental program in the cells. Differentiation results in cell types with clearly defined structures and functions.

diffusion The net movement of ions or molecules from a region of higher concentration to a region of lower concentration.

digestion The splitting of carbohydrates, proteins, lipids, and nucleic acids in foods into chemical subunits small enough to be absorbed into the body fluids and cells of an animal.

digestive tube A tubelike digestive system with two openings that form a separate mouth and anus; the digestive contents move in one direction through specialized regions of the tube, from the mouth to the anus.

dihybrid A zygote produced from a cross that involves two characters.

dihybrid cross A cross between two individuals that are heterozygous for two pairs of alleles.

dikaryon The life stage in certain fungi in which a cell contains two genetically distinct haploid nuclei.

dikaryotic hyphae Hyphae containing two separate nuclei in one cell.

dioecious Having male flowers and female flowers on different plants of the same species.

diploblastic An animal body plan in which adult structures arise from only two cell layers, the ectoderm and the endoderm.

diploid An organism or cell with two copies of each type of chromosome in its nucleus.

direct neurotransmitter A neurotransmitter that binds directly to a ligand-gated ion channel in the postsynaptic membrane, opening or closing the channel gate and altering the flow of a specific ion or ions in the postsynaptic cell.

directional selection A type of selection in which individuals near one end of the phenotypic spectrum have the highest relative fitness.

Discicristates A protist group of single-celled, highly motile organisms that swim by means of flagella and that have characteristic disk-shaped mitochondrial cristae (inner mitochondrial membranes).

disclimax community An ecological community in which regular disturbance inhibits successional change.

discontinuous replication Replication in which a DNA strand is formed in short lengths that are synthesized in the direction opposite of DNA unwinding.

disjunct distribution A geographic distribution in which populations of the same species or closely related species live in widely separated locations.

dispersal The movement of organisms away from their place of origin.

dispersion The spatial distribution of individuals within a population's geographic range.

disruptive selection A type of natural selection in which extreme phenotypes have higher relative fitness than intermediate phenotypes.

dissociation The separation of water to produce hydrogen ions and hydroxide ions.

distal convoluted tubule The tubule in the human nephron that drains urine into a collecting duct that leads to the renal pelvis.

disulphide linkage Linkage that occurs when two sulfhydryl groups interact during a linking reaction.

DNA *See* deoxyribonucleic acid.

DNA chip *See* DNA microarray.

DNA fingerprinting Technique in which DNA samples are used to distinguish between individuals of the same species.

DNA helicase An enzyme that catalyzes the unwinding of DNA template strands.

DNA hybridization Technique in which a gene or sequence of interest is identified in a set of clones when it base-pairs with a single-stranded DNA or RNA molecule called a nucleic acid probe.

DNA ligase In DNA replication, an enzyme that seals the nicks left after RNA primers are replaced with DNA.

DNA methylation Process in which a methyl group is added enzymatically to cytosine bases in the DNA.

DNA microarray A solid surface divided into a microscopic grid of thousands of spaces each containing thousands of copies of a DNA probe. DNA chips are used commonly for analysis of gene activity and for detecting differences between cell types. Also referred to as a *DNA chip*.

DNA polymerase An enzyme that assembles complementary nucleotide chains during DNA replication.

DNA repair mechanism Mechanism to correct base-pair mismatches that escape proofreading.

DNA technologies Techniques to isolate, purify, analyze, and manipulate DNA sequences.

domain In protein structure, a distinct, large structural subdivision produced in many proteins by the folding of the amino acid chain. In systematics, the highest taxonomic category; a group of cellular organisms with characteristics that set it apart as a major branch of the evolutionary tree.

domestication Selective breeding of other species to increase desirable characteristics in progeny.

dominance The masking effect of one allele over another.

dominance hierarchy A social system in which the behaviour of each individual is constrained by that individual's status in a highly structured social ranking.

dominant The allele expressed when more than one allele is present.

dormancy A period in the life cycle in which biological activity is suspended.

dorsal Indicating the back side of an animal.

dorsal lip of the blastopore A crescent-shaped depression rotated clockwise 90° on the embryo surface that marks the region derived from the grey crescent, to which cells from the animal pole move as gastrulation begins.

double fertilization The characteristic feature of sexual reproduction in flowering plants. In the embryo sac, one sperm nucleus unites with the egg to form a diploid zygote from which the embryo develops, and another unites with two polar nuclei to form the primary endosperm nucleus.

double helix Two nucleotide chains wrapped around each other in a spiral.

double-helix model Model of DNA consisting of two complementary sugar–phosphate backbones.

duodenum A short region of the small intestine where secretions from the pancreas and liver enter a common duct.

duplication Chromosomal alteration that occurs if a segment is broken from one chromosome and inserted into its homologue.

E site The site where an exiting tRNA binds prior to its release from the ribosome.

ecdysis Shedding of the cuticle, exoskeleton, or skin; moulting.

ecdysone A steroid hormone that controls cuticle formation in insects and crustaceans and possibly nematodes.

echolocation A behaviour in which animal compares echoes of sounds it produced to the original signals. Differences between pulses and echoes allow location of obstacles and prey.

ecological community An assemblage of species living in the same place.

ecological efficiency The ratio of net productivity at one trophic level to net productivity at the trophic level below it.

ecological isolation A prezygotic reproductive isolating mechanism in which species that live in the same geographic region occupy different habitats.

ecological niche The resources a population uses and the environmental conditions it requires over its lifetime.

ecological pyramid A diagram illustrating the effects of energy transfer from one trophic level to the next.

ecological succession A somewhat predictable series of changes in the species composition of a community over time.

ecology The study of the interactions between organisms and their environments.

ecosystem A group of biological communities interacting with their shared physical environment.

ecosystem ecology An ecological discipline that explores the cycling of nutrients and the flow of energy between the biotic components of an ecological community and the abiotic environment.

ecotone A wide transition zone between adjacent communities.

ectoderm The outermost of the three primary germ layers of an embryo, which develops into epidermis and nervous tissue.

ectomycorrhiza A mycorrhiza that grows between and around the young roots of trees and shrubs but does not enter root cells.

ectoparasite A parasite that lives on the exterior of its host organism.

ectotherm An animal that obtains its body heat primarily from the external environment.

effector In signal transduction, a plasma membrane–associated enzyme, activated by a G protein, that generates one or more second messengers. In homeostatic feedback, the system that returns the condition to the set point if it has strayed away.

effector T cell A cell involved in effecting—bringing about—the specific immune response to an antigen.

efferent arteriole The arteriole that receives blood from the glomerulus.

efferent neuron A neuron that carries the signals indicating a response away from the interneuron networks to the effectors.

egg cell The female reproductive cell.

eggs Nonmotile gametes.

Elasmobranchii Cartilaginous fishes, including the skates and rays.

elastin A rubbery protein in some connective tissues that adds elasticity to the extracellular matrix. It is able to return to its original shape after being stretched, bent, or compressed.

electrical signalling A means of animal communication in which a signaller emits an electric discharge that can be received by another individual.

electrical synapse A mechanical and electrically conductive link between two abutting neurons that is formed at the gap junction.

electrocardiogram (ECG) Graphic representation of the electrical activity within the heart, detected by electrodes placed on the body.

electrochemical gradient A difference in chemical concentration and electric potential across a membrane.

electromagnetic spectrum The range of wavelengths or frequencies of electromagnetic radiation extending from gamma rays to the longest radio waves and including visible light.

electron Negatively charged particle outside the nucleus of an atom.

electron microscope Microscope that uses electrons to illuminate the specimen.

electron transfer system Stage of cellular respiration in which high-energy electrons produced from glycolysis, pyruvate oxidation, and the citric acid cycle are delivered to oxygen by a sequence of electron carriers.

electronegativity The measure of an atom's attraction for the electrons it shares in a chemical bond with another atom.

electroreceptor A specialized sensory receptor that detects electrical fields.

element A pure substance that cannot be broken down into simpler substances by ordinary chemical or physical techniques.

embryo An organism in its early stage of reproductive development, beginning in the first moments after fertilization.

embryo sac The female gametophyte of angiosperms, within which the embryo develops; it usually consists of seven cells: an egg cell, an endosperm mother cell, and five other cells with fleeting reproductive roles.

embryonic stem cell Stem cells in the mammalian embryo that can differentiate into any cell type.

emigration The movement of individuals out of a population.

enantiomers Isomers that are mirror images of each other. Also referred to as *optical isomers*.

endangered species A species in immediate danger of extinction throughout all or a significant portion of its range.

endemic species A species that occurs in only one place on Earth.

endergonic reaction Reaction that can proceed only if free energy is supplied.

endocrine gland Any of several ductless secretory organs that secrete hormones into the blood or extracellular fluid.

endocrine system The system of glands that release their secretions (hormones) directly into the circulatory system.

endocytic vesicle Vesicle that carries proteins and other molecules from the plasma membrane to destinations within the cell.

endocytosis In eukaryotes, the process by which molecules are brought into the cell from the exterior involving a bulging in of the plasma membrane that pinches off to form an endocytic vesicle.

endoderm The innermost of the three primary germ layers of an embryo, which develops into the gastrointestinal tract and, in some animals, the respiratory organs.

endodermis The innermost layer of the root cortex; a selectively permeable barrier that helps control the movement of water and dissolved minerals into the stele.

endomembrane system In eukaryotes, a collection of interrelated internal membranous sacs that divide a cell into functional and structural compartments.

endoparasite A parasite that lives in the internal organs of its host organism.

endoplasmic reticulum (ER) In eukaryotes, an extensive interconnected network of cisternae that is responsible for the synthesis, transport, and initial modification of proteins and lipids.

endorphin One of a group of small proteins occurring naturally in the brain and around nerve endings that bind to opiate receptors and thus can raise the pain threshold.

endoskeleton A supportive internal body structure, such as bones, that provides support.

endosperm Nutritive tissue inside the seeds of flowering plants.

endospore A small, metabolically inactive, asexual spore that develops within some bacterial cells when environmental conditions become unfavourable.

endosporous Pattern of development in some plants (e.g., seed plants) in which the gametophyte develops inside the spore wall.

endosymbiont hypothesis The proposal that the membranous organelles of eukaryotic cells (mitochondria and chloroplasts) may have originated from symbiotic relationships between two prokaryotic cells.

endotherm An animal that obtains most of its body heat from internal physiological sources.

endothermic Reactions that absorb energy.

endotoxin A lipopolysaccharide released from the outer membrane of the cell wall when a bacterium dies and lyses.

end-product inhibition *See* feedback inhibition.

energy The capacity to do work.

energy budget The total amount of energy that an organism can accumulate and use to fuel its activities.

energy coupling The process by which ATP is brought in close contact with a reactant molecule involved in an endergonic reaction, and when the ATP is hydrolyzed, the terminal phosphate group is transferred to the reactant molecule.

energy levels Regions of space within an atom where electrons are found. Also referred to as *energy shells*.

enhancer In eukaryotes, a region at a significant distance from the beginning of a gene containing regulatory sequences that determine whether the gene is transcribed at its maximum possible rate.

enterocoelom In deuterostomes, the body cavity pinched off by outpocketings of the archenteron.

enthalpy Potential energy in a system.

entropy Disorder, in thermodynamics.

envelope Outer glycoprotein layer surrounding the capsid of some viruses, derived in part from host cell plasma membrane.

enveloped virus A virus that has a surface membrane derived from its host cell.

enzymatic hydrolysis A process in which chemical bonds are broken by the addition of H^+ and OH^-, the components of a molecule of water.

enzyme Protein that accelerates the rate of a cellular reaction.

enzyme specificity The ability of an enzyme to catalyze the reaction of only a single type of molecule or group of closely related molecules.

eosinophil A type of leukocyte that targets extracellular parasites too large for phagocytosis in the inflammatory response.

epiblast The top layer of the blastodisk.

epicotyl The upper part of the axis of an early plant embryo, located between the cotyledons and the first true leaves.

epidermis A complex tissue that covers an organism's body in a single continuous layer or sometimes in multiple layers of tightly packed cells.

epididymis A coiled storage tubule attached to the surface of each testis.

epiglottis A flaplike valve at the top of the trachea.

epinephrine A nontropic amine hormone secreted by the adrenal medulla.

epiphyte A plant that grows independently on other plants and obtains nutrients and water from the air.

epistasis Interaction of genes, with one or more alleles of a gene at one locus inhibiting or masking the effects of one or more alleles of a gene at a different locus.

epithelial tissue Tissue formed of sheetlike layers of cells that are usually joined tightly together, with little extracellular matrix material between them. They protect body surfaces from invasion by bacteria and viruses and secrete or absorb substances.

epitope The small region of an antigen molecule to which BCRs or TCRs bind.

equilibrium point A state of balance between opposing factors that push a reaction in either direction.

equilibrium theory of island biogeography An hypothesis suggesting that the number of species on an island is governed by a give and take between the immigration of new species to the island and the extinction of species already there.

ER (endoplasmic reticulum) lumen The enclosed space surrounded by a cisterna.

erythrocyte A red blood cell that contains hemoglobin, a protein that transports O_2 in blood.

erythropoietin (EPO) A hormone that stimulates stem cells in bone marrow to increase erythrocyte production.

esophagus A connecting passage of the digestive tube.

essential amino acid Any amino acid that is not made by the human body but must be taken in as part of the diet.

essential element Any of a number of elements required by living organisms to ensure normal reproduction, growth, development, and maintenance.

essential fatty acid Any fatty acid that the body cannot synthesize but needs for normal metabolism.

essential mineral Any inorganic element such as calcium, iron, or magnesium that is required in the diet of an animal.

essential nutrient Any of the essential amino acids, fatty acids, vitamins, and minerals required in the diet of an animal.

estivation Seasonal torpor in an animal that occurs in summer.

estradiol A form of estrogen.

estrogen Any of the group of female sex hormones.

estuary A coastal habitat where tidal seawater mixes with fresh water from rivers, streams, and runoff.

ethology A discipline that focuses on how animals behave.

ethylene A plant hormone that helps regulate seedling growth, stem elongation, the ripening of fruit, and the abscission of fruits, leaves, and flowers.

euchromatin In eukaryotes, regions of loosely packed chromatin fibres in interphase nuclei.

eudicot A plant belonging to the Eudicotyledones, one of the two major classes of angiosperms; their embryos generally have two seed leaves (cotyledons), and their pollen grains have three grooves.

Eukarya The domain that includes all eukaryotes, organisms that contain a membrane-bound nucleus within each of their cells; all protists, plants, fungi, and animals.

eukaryote Organism in which the DNA is enclosed in a nucleus.

eukaryotic chromosome A DNA molecule, with its associated proteins, in the nucleus of a eukaryotic cell.

euploid An individual with a normal set of chromosomes.

Euryarchaeota A major group of the domain Archaea, members of which are found in different extreme environments. They include methanogens, extreme halophiles, and some extreme thermophiles.

eusocial A form of social organization, observed in some insect species, in which numerous related individuals—a large percentage of them sterile female workers—live and work together in a colony for the reproductive benefit of a single queen and her mate(s)

eustachian tube A duct leading from the air-filled middle ear to the throat that protects the eardrum from damage caused by changes in environmental atmospheric pressure.

evaporation Heat transfer through the energy required to change a liquid to a gas.

evolutionary developmental biology A field of biology that compares the genes controlling the developmental processes of different animals to determine the evolutionary origin of morphological novelties and developmental processes.

evolutionary divergence A process whereby natural selection or genetic drift causes populations to become more different over time.

exchange diffusion *See* antiport.

excitatory postsynaptic potential (EPSP) The change in membrane potential caused when a neurotransmitter opens a ligand-gated Na^+ channel and Na^+ enters the cell, making it more likely that the postsynaptic neuron will generate an action potential.

excretion The process that helps maintain the body's water and ion balance while ridding the body of metabolic wastes.

exergonic reaction Reaction that has a negative ΔG because it releases free energy.

exocrine gland A gland that is connected to the epithelium by a duct and that empties its secretion at the epithelial surface.

exocytosis In eukaryotes, the process by which a secretory vesicle fuses with the plasma membrane and releases the vesicle contents to the exterior.

exodermis In the roots of some plants, an outer layer of root cortex that may limit water losses from roots and help regulate the absorption of ions.

exon An amino acid–coding sequence present in pre-mRNA that is retained in a spliced mRNA that is translated to produce a polypeptide.

exon shuffling Process by which existing amino acid–coding regions or domains are mixed into novel combinations to create new proteins.

exoskeleton A hard external covering of an animal's body that blocks the passage of water and provides support and protection.

exothermic Processes that release energy.

exotic species A non-native organism.

exotoxin A toxic protein that leaks from or is secreted from a bacterium and interferes with the biochemical processes of body cells in various ways.

experimental data Information that describes the result of a careful manipulation of the system under study.

experimental variable The variable to which any difference in observations of experimental treatment subjects and control treatment subjects is attributed.

exploitative competition Form of competition in which two or more individuals or populations use the same limiting resources.

exponential model of population growth Model that describes unlimited population growth.

external fertilization The process in which sperm and eggs are shed into the surrounding water, occurring in most aquatic invertebrates, bony fishes, and amphibians.

external gill A gill that extends out from the body and lacks a protective covering.

extinction The death of the last individual in a species or the last species in a lineage.

extracellular digestion Digestion that takes place outside body cells, in a pouch or tube enclosed within the body.

extracellular fluid The fluid occupying the spaces between cells in multicellular animals.

extracellular matrix (ECM) A molecular system that supports and protects cells and provides mechanical linkages.

extraembryonic membrane A primary tissue layer extended outside the embryo that conducts nutrients from the yolk to the embryo, exchanges gases with the environment outside the egg, or stores metabolic wastes removed from the embryo.

eye The organ animals use to sense light.

F pilus Structure on the cell surface that allows an F^+ donor bacterial cell to attach to an F^- recipient bacterial cell. Also referred to as a *sex pilus*.

F^- cell Recipient cell in conjugation between bacteria.

F^+ cell Donor cell in conjugation between bacteria.

F1 generation The first generation of offspring from a genetic cross.

F2 generation The second generation of offspring from a genetic cross.

facilitated diffusion Mechanism by which polar and charged molecules diffuse across membranes with the help of transport proteins.

facilitation hypothesis A hypothesis that explains ecological succession, suggesting that species modify the local environment in ways that make it less suitable for themselves but more suitable for colonization by species typical of the next successional stage.

facultative anaerobe An organism that can live in the presence or absence of oxygen, using oxygen when it is present and living by fermentation under anaerobic conditions.

family A Linnaean taxonomic category that ranks below an order and above a genus.

family planning program A program that educates people about ways to produce an optimal family size on an economically feasible schedule.

fast block to polyspermy The barrier set up by the wave of depolarization triggered when sperm and egg fuse, making it impossible for other sperm to enter the egg.

fast muscle fibre A muscle fibre that contracts relatively quickly and powerfully.

fat Neutral lipid that is semisolid at biological temperatures.

fate map Mapping of adult or larval structures onto the region of the embryo from which each structure developed.

fat-soluble vitamin A vitamin that dissolves in liquid fat or fatty oils, in addition to water.

fatty acid One of two components of a neutral lipid, containing a single hydrocarbon chain with a carboxyl group linked at one end.

feather A sturdy, lightweight structure of birds, derived from scales in the skin of their ancestors.

feces Condensed and compacted digestive contents in the large intestine.

feedback inhibition In enzyme reactions, regulation in which the product of a reaction acts as a regulator of the reaction. Also referred to as *end-product inhibition*.

fermentation Process in which electrons carried by NADH are transferred to an organic acceptor molecule rather than to the electron transfer system.

fertilization The fusion of the nuclei of an egg and sperm cell, which initiates development of a new individual.

fetus A developing human from the eighth week of gestation onward, at which point, the major organs and organ systems have formed.

fibre In sclerenchyma, an elongated, tapered, thick-walled cell that gives plant tissue its flexible strength.

fibrin A protein necessary for blood clotting; fibrin forms a weblike mesh that traps platelets and red blood cells and holds a clot together.

fibrinogen A plasma protein that plays a central role in the blood-clotting mechanism.

fibroblast The type of cell that secretes most of the collagen and other proteins in the loose connective tissue.

fibronectin A class of glycoproteins that aids in the attachment of cells to the extracellular matrix and helps hold the cells in position.

fibrous connective tissue Tissue in which fibroblasts are sparsely distributed among dense masses of collagen and elastin fibres that are lined up in highly ordered, parallel bundles, producing maximum tensile strength and elasticity.

fibrous root system A root system that consists of branching roots rather than a main taproot; roots tend to spread laterally from the base of the stem.

filament In flowers, the stalk of a stamen, which supports the anther.

filtration The nonselective movement of some water and a number of solutes—ions and small molecules, but not large molecules such as proteins—into the proximal end of the renal tubules through spaces between cells.

first law of thermodynamics The principle that energy can be transferred and transformed but cannot be created or destroyed.

first messenger The extracellular signal molecule in signal transduction pathways controlled by G protein–coupled receptors.

fission The mode of asexual reproduction in which the parent separates into two or more offspring of approximately equal size.

fixed action pattern A highly stereotyped instinctive behaviour; when triggered by a specific cue, it is performed over and over in almost exactly the same way.

flagellum (plural, flagella) A long, threadlike, cellular appendage responsible for movement; found in both prokaryotes and eukaryotes, but with different structures and modes of locomotion.

flame cell The cell that forms the primary filtrate in the excretory system of many bilateria. The urine is propelled through ducts by the synchronous beating of cilia, resembling a flickering flame.

flower The reproductive structure of angiosperms, consisting of floral parts grouped on a stem; the structure in which seeds develop.

fluid feeder An animal that obtains nourishment by ingesting liquids that contain organic molecules in solution.

fluid mosaic model Model proposing that the membrane consists of a fluid phospholipid bilayer in which proteins are embedded and float freely.

follicle The ovum and follicle cells.

follicle cell A cell that grows from ovarian tissue and nourishes the developing egg.

follicle-stimulating hormone (FSH) The pituitary hormone that stimulates oocytes in the ovaries to continue meiosis and become follicles. During follicle enlargement, FSH interacts with luteinizing hormone to stimulate follicular cells to secrete estrogens.

food chain A depiction of the trophic structure of a community, a portrait of who eats whom.

food vacuole A membrane-bound sac used for digestion.

food web A set of interconnected food chains with multiple links.

forebrain The largest division of the brain, which includes the cerebral cortex and basal ganglia. It is credited with the highest intellectual functions.

foreskin A loose fold of skin that covers the glans of the penis.

formula The name of a molecule written in chemical shorthand.

fossil The remains or traces of an organism of a past geologic age embedded and preserved in Earth's crust.

founder effect An evolutionary phenomenon in which a population that was established by just a few colonizing individuals has only a fraction of the genetic diversity seen in the population from which it was derived.

fovea The small region of the retina around which cones are concentrated in mammals and birds with eyes specialized for daytime vision.

fragmentation A type of vegetative reproduction in plants in which cells or a piece of the parent break off and then develop into new individuals.

frameshift mutation Mutation in a protein-coding gene that causes the reading frame of an mRNA transcribed from the gene to be altered, resulting in the production of a different, and nonfunctional, amino acid sequence in the polypeptide.

free energy The energy in a system that is available to do work.

freeze-fracture technique Technique in which experimenters freeze a block of cells rapidly and then fracture the block to split the lipid bilayer and expose the hydrophobic membrane interior.

frequency-dependent selection A form of natural selection in which rare phenotypes have a selective advantage simply because they are rare.

fruit A mature ovary, often with accessory parts, from a flower.

fruiting body In some fungi, a stalked, spore-producing structure such as a mushroom.

functional genomics The study of the functions of genes and of other parts of the genome.

functional groups The atoms in reactive groups.

fundamental niche The range of conditions and resources that a population can possibly tolerate and use.

furrow In cytokinesis, a groove that girdles the cell and gradually deepens until it cuts the cytoplasm into two parts.

fusiform initial A cell derived from cambium inside a vascular bundle; gives rise to secondary xylem and phloem cells.

futile cycle Occurs when two metabolic pathways run simultaneously in opposite directions and have no overall effect other than wasting energy.

G0 phase The phase of the cell cycle in eukaryotes in which many cell types stop dividing.

G1 phase The initial growth stage of the cell cycle in eukaryotes, during which the cell makes proteins and other types of cellular molecules but not nuclear DNA.

G2 phase The phase of the cell cycle in eukaryotes during which the cell continues to synthesize proteins and grow, completing interphase.

gallbladder The organ that stores bile between meals, when no digestion is occurring.

gametangium A cell or organ in which gametes are produced.

gamete A haploid cell, and egg or sperm. Haploid cells fuse during sexual reproduction to form a diploid zygote.

gametic isolation A prezygotic reproductive isolating mechanism caused by incompatibility between the sperm of one species and the eggs of another; may prevent fertilization.

gametogenesis The formation of male and female gametes.

gametophyte An individual of the haploid generation produced when a spore germinates and grows directly by mitotic divisions in organisms that undergo alternation of generations.

ganglion A functional concentration of nervous system tissue composed principally of nerve cell bodies, usually lying outside the central nervous system.

ganglion cell A type of neuron in the retina of the eye that receives visual information from photoreceptors via various intermediate cells such as bipolar cells, amacrine cells, and horizontal cells.

gap gene In *Drosophila* embryonic development, the first activated set of segmentation genes that progressively subdivide the embryo into regions, determining the segments of the embryo and the adult.

gap junction Junction that opens direct channels allowing ions and small molecules to pass directly from one cell to another.

gastric juice A substance secreted by the stomach that contains the digestive enzyme pepsin.

gastrodermis The derivative of endoderm that lines the gastrovascular cavity of radially symmetrical animals and forms the epithelial lining of the midgut in bilaterally symmetrical anmals.

gastrovascular cavity A saclike body cavity with a single opening, a mouth, which serves both digestive and circulatory functions.

gastrula The developmental stage resulting when the cells of the blastula migrate and divide once cleavage is complete.

gastrulation The second major process of early development in most animals, which produces an embryo with three distinct primary tissue layers.

gated channel Ion transporter in a membrane that switches between open, closed, or intermediate states.

germ-line gene therapy Therapy in which a gene is introduced into germ-line cells of an animal to correct a genetic disorder.

gemma (plural, gemmae) Small cell mass that forms in cuplike growths on a thallus.

gemmules Clusters of cells with a resistant covering that allows them to survive unfavourable conditions.

gene A unit containing the code for a protein molecule or one of its parts, or for functioning RNA molecules such as tRNA and rRNA.

gene flow The transfer of genes from one population to another through the movement of individuals or their gametes.

gene pool The sum of all alleles at all gene loci in all individuals in a population.

gene therapy Correction of genetic disorders using genetic engineering techniques.

gene-for-gene recognition A mechanism in which plants can detect an attack by a specific pathogen; the product of a specific plant gene interacts with the product of a specific pathogen gene, triggering the plant's defensive response.

general transcription factor (basal transcription factor) In eukaryotes, a protein that binds to the promoter of a gene in the area of the TATA box and recruits and orients RNA polymerase II to initiate transcription at the correct place.

generalized compartment model A model used to describe nutrient cycling in which two criteria—organic versus inorganic nutrients and available versus unavailable nutrients—define four compartments where nutrients accumulate.

generalized transduction Transfer of bacterial genes between bacteria using virulent phages that have incorporated random DNA fragments of the bacterial genome.

generation time The average time between the birth of an organism and the birth of its offspring.

genetic code The nucleotide information that specifies the amino acid sequence of a polypeptide.

genetic counselling Counselling that allows prospective parents to assess the possibility that they might have a child affected by a genetic disorder.

genetic drift Random fluctuations in allele frequencies as a result of chance events; usually reduces genetic variation in a population.

genetic engineering The use of DNA technologies to alter genes for practical purposes.

genetic equilibrium The point at which neither the allele frequencies nor the genotype frequencies in a population change in succeeding generations.

genetic recombination The process by which the combinations of alleles for different genes in two parental individuals become shuffled into new combinations in offspring individuals.

genetic screening Biochemical or molecular tests for identifying inherited disorders after a child is born.

genetically modified organism (GMO) A transgenic organism.

genomic imprinting Pattern of inheritance in which the expression of a nuclear gene is based on whether an individual organism inherits the gene from the male or the female parent.

genomic library A collection of clones that contains a copy of every DNA sequence in a genome.

genotype The genetic constitution of an organism.

genotype frequency The percentage of individuals in a population possessing a particular genotype.

genus A Linnaean taxonomic category ranking below a family and above a species.

geographic range The overall spatial boundaries within which a population lives.

germ cell An animal cell that is set aside early in embryonic development and gives rise to the gametes.

germ layer The layers (up to three) of cells produced during the early development of the embryo of most animals.

germ-line gene therapy Experiment in which a gene is introduced into germ-line cells of an animal to correct a genetic disorder.

gestation The period of mammalian development in which the embryo develops in the uterus of the mother.

gibberellin Any of a large family of plant hormones that regulate aspects of growth, including cell elongation.

gill A respiratory organ formed as evagination of the body that extends outward into the respiratory medium.

gill arch One of the series of curved supporting structures between the slits in the pharynx of a chordate.

gill slit One of the openings in the pharynx of a chordate through which water passes out of the pharynx.

Ginkgophyta A plant phylum with a single living species, the ginkgo (or maidenhair) tree.

gizzard The part of the digestive tube that grinds ingested material into fine particles by muscular contractions of the wall.

gland A cell or group of cells that produces and releases substances nearby, in another part of the body, or to the outside.

glans A soft, caplike structure at the end of the penis, containing most of the nerve endings producing erotic sensations.

glial cell A nonneuronal cell contained in the nervous tissue that physically supports and provides nutrients to neurons, provides electrical insulation between them, and scavenges cellular debris and foreign matter.

globulin A plasma protein that transports lipids (including cholesterol) and fat-soluble vitamins; a specialized subgroup of globulins, the immunoglobulins, constitute antibodies and other molecules contributing to the immune response.

glomerulus A ball of blood capillaries surrounded by Bowman's capsule in the human nephron.

glucagon A pancreatic hormone with effects opposite to those of insulin: it stimulates glycogen, fat, and protein degradation.

glucocorticoid A steroid hormone secreted by the adrenal cortex that helps maintain the blood concentration of glucose and other fuel molecules.

glycocalyx A carbohydrate coat covering the cell surface.

glycogen Energy-providing carbohydrates stored in animal cells.

glycolysis Stage of cellular respiration in which sugars such as glucose are partially oxidized and broken down into smaller molecules.

glycosidic bond Bond formed by the linkage of two-glucose molecules with oxygen as a bridge between a carbon of the first glucose unit and a carbon of the second glucose unit.

Gnathostomata The group of vertebrates with movable jaws.

Golgi complex In eukaryotes, the organelle responsible for the final modification, sorting, and distribution of proteins and lipids.

Golgi tendon organ A proprioceptor of tendons.

gonad A specialized gamete-producing organ in which the germ cells collect. Gonads are the primary source of sex hormones in vertebrates: ovaries in the female and testes in the male.

gonadotropin A hormone that regulates the activity of the gonads (ovaries and testes).

gonadotropin-releasing hormone (GnRH) A tropic hormone secreted by the hypothalamus that causes the pituitary to make luteinizing hormone (LH) and follicle-stimulating hormone (FSH).

G protein–coupled receptor In signal transduction, a surface receptor that responds to a signal by activating a G protein.

graded potential A change in membrane potential that does not necessarily trigger an action potential.

gradualism The view that Earth and its living systems changed slowly over its history.

gradualist hypothesis The hypothesis that large changes in either geologic features or biological lineages result from the slow, continuous accumulation of small changes over time.

Gram stain procedure A procedure of staining bacteria to distinguish between types of bacteria with different cell wall compositions.

Gram-negative Describing bacteria that do not retain the stain used in the Gram stain procedure.

Gram-positive Describing bacteria that appear purple when stained using the Gram stain technique.

gravitropism A directional growth response to Earth's gravitational pull that is induced by mechanical and hormonal influences.

grey crescent A crescent-shaped region of the underlying cytoplasm at the side opposite the point of sperm entry exposed after fertilization when the pigmented layer of cytoplasm rotates toward the site of sperm entry.

grey matter Areas of densely packed nerve cell bodies and dendrites in the brain and spinal cord.

greater vestibular gland One of two glands located slightly below and to the left and right of the opening of the vagina in women. They secrete mucus to provide lubrication, especially when the woman is sexually aroused.

greenhouse effect A phenomenon in which certain gases foster the accumulation of heat in the lower atmosphere, maintaining warm temperatures on Earth.

gross primary productivity The rate at which producers convert solar energy into chemical energy.

ground meristem The primary meristematic tissue in plants that gives rise to ground tissues, mostly parenchyma.

ground tissue system One of the three basic tissue systems in plants; includes all tissues other than dermal and vascular tissues.

growth factor Any of a large group of peptide hormones that regulates the division and differentiation of many cell types in the body.

growth hormone (GH) A hormone that stimulates cell division, protein synthesis, and bone growth in children and adolescents, thereby causing body growth.

guanine A purine that base-pairs with cytosine in nucleic acids.

guard cell Either of a pair of specialized crescent-shaped cells that control the opening and closing of stomata in plant tissue.

guttation The exudation of water from leaves as a result of strong root pressure.

gymnosperm A seed plant that produces "naked" seeds not enclosed in an ovary.

H^+ pump *See* proton pump.

habitat The specific environment in which a population lives, as characterized by its biotic and abiotic features.

habitat fragmentation A process in which remaining areas of intact habitat are reduced to small, isolated patches.

habituation The learned loss of responsiveness to stimuli.

half-life The time it takes for half of a given amount of a radioisotope to decay.

haplodiploidy A pattern of sex determination in insects in which females are diploid and males are haploid.

haploid An organism or cell with only one copy of each type of chromosome in its nuclei.

Hardy–Weinberg principle An evolutionary rule of thumb that specifies the conditions under which a population of diploid organisms achieves genetic equilibrium.

harvesting efficiency The ratio of the energy content of food consumed compared with the energy content of food available.

haustorium (plural, haustoria) The hyphal tip of a parasitic fungus that penetrates a host plant and absorbs nutrients from it; likewise in parasitic flowering plants, a root that can penetrate a host's tissues and absorb nutrients.

head The anteriormost part of the body, containing the brain, sensory structures, and feeding apparatus.

head–foot In molluscs, the region of the body that provides the major means of locomotion and contains concentrations of nervous system tissues and sense organs.

heartwood The inner core of a woody stem; composed of dry tissue and nonliving cells that no longer transport water and solutes and may store resins, tannins, and other defensive compounds.

heat of vaporization The heat required to give water molecules enough energy of motion to break loose from liquid water and form a gas.

heat-shock protein (HSP) Any of a group of chaperone proteins that are present in all cells in all life forms. They are induced when a cell undergoes various types of environmental stresses such as heat, cold, and oxygen deprivation.

heavy chain The heavier of the two types of polypeptide chains that are found in immunoglobulin and antibody molecules.

helical virus A virus in which the protein subunits of the coat assemble in a rodlike spiral around the genome.

helper T cell A clonal cell that assists with the activation of B cells.

hemocoel A cavity in the body of some coelomic invertebrates (arthropods and some molluscs) filled with blood. The hemocoel displaces the coelom, which persists as a small chamber surrounding the gonads or heart.

hemolymph The circulatory fluid of invertebrates with open circulatory systems, including molluscs and arthropods.

hepatic portal vein The blood vessel that leads to capillary networks in the liver.

Hepatophyta The phylum that includes liverworts and their bryophyte relatives.

herbicide A compound that, at proper concentration, kills plants.

herbivore An animal that obtains energy and nutrients primarily by eating plants.

herbivory The interaction between herbivorous animals and the plants they eat.

hermaphroditism The mechanism in which both mature egg-producing and mature sperm-producing tissue are present in the same individual.

heterochromatin In eukaryotes, regions of densely packed chromatin fibres in interphase nuclei.

heterochrony Changes in the relative rate of development of morphological characters.

heterosporous Producing two types of spores, "male" microspores and "female" megaspores.

heterotroph An organism that acquires energy and nutrients by eating other organisms or their remains.

heterozygote An individual with two different alleles of a gene.

heterozygote advantage An evolutionary circumstance in which individuals that are heterozygous at a particular locus have higher relative fitness than either homozygote.

heterozygous The state of possessing two different alleles of a gene.

Hfr cell A special donor cell that can transfer genes on a bacterial chromosome to a recipient bacterium.

hibernation Extended torpor during winter.

hindbrain The lower area of the brain that includes the brain stem, medulla oblongata, and pons.

hippocampus A grey-matter centre that is involved in sending information.

histone A small, positively charged (basic) protein that is complexed with DNA in the chromosomes of eukaryotes.

historical biogeography The study of the geographic distributions of plants and animals in relation to their evolutionary history.

Holocephali The chimeras, another group of cartilaginous fishes.

homeobox A region of a homeotic gene that corresponds to an amino acid section of the homeodomain.

homeodomain An encoded transcription factor of each protein that binds to a region in the promoters of the genes whose transcription it regulates.

homeostasis A steady internal condition maintained by responses that compensate for changes in the external environment.

homeostatic mechanism Any process or activity responsible for homeostasis.

homeotic gene Any of the family of genes that determines the structure of body parts during embryonic development.

hominid A member of a monophyletic group of primates, characterized by an erect bipedal stance, that includes modern humans and their recent ancestors.

Hominoidea The monophyletic group of primates that includes apes and humans.

homologies Characteristics shared by a set of species because they inherited them from their common ancestor.

homologous Similar.

homologous traits Characteristics that are similar in two species because they inherited the genetic basis of the trait from their common ancestor.

homoplasies Characteristics shared by a set of species, often because they live in similar environments, but not present in their common ancestor; often the product of convergent evolution.

homosporous Producing only one type of spore.

homozygote An individual with two copies of the same allele.

homozygous State of possessing two copies of the same allele.

horizon A noticeable layer of soil, such as topsoil, with a distinct texture and composition that varies with soil type.

horizontal cell A type of neuron that forms lateral connections among photoreceptor cells in the retina of the eye.

hormone A signalling molecule secreted by a cell that can alter the activities of any cell with receptors for it; in animals, typically a molecule produced by one tissue and transported via the bloodstream to another specific tissue to alter its physiological activity.

host A species that is fed upon by a parasite.

host race A population of insects that may be reproductively isolated from other populations of the same species as a consequence of their adaptation to feed on a specific host plant species.

human chorionic gonadotropin (hCG) A hormone that keeps the corpus luteum in the ovary from breaking down.

human immunodeficiency virus (HIV) A retrovirus that causes acquired immune deficiency syndrome (AIDS).

humus The organic component of soil remaining after decomposition of plants and animals, animal droppings, and other organic matter.

hybrid breakdown A postzygotic reproductive isolating mechanism in which hybrids are capable of reproducing, but their offspring have either reduced fertility or reduced viability.

hybrid inviability A postzygotic reproductive isolating mechanism in which a hybrid individual has a low probability of survival to reproductive age.

hybrid sterility A postzygotic reproductive isolating mechanism in which hybrid offspring cannot form functional gametes.

hybrid zone A geographic area where the hybrid offspring of two divergent populations or species are common.

hybridization When two species interbreed and produce fertile offspring.

hybridoma A B cell that has been induced to fuse with a cancerous lymphocyte called a myeloma cell, forming a single, composite cell.

hydration layer A surface coat of water molecules that covers other polar and charged molecules and ions.

hydrocarbon Molecule consisting of carbon linked only to hydrogen atoms.

hydrogen bond Noncovalent bond formed by unequal electron sharing between hydrogen atoms and oxygen, nitrogen, or sulphur atoms.

hydrogeologic cycle The global cycling of water between the ocean, the atmosphere, land, freshwater ecosystems, and living organisms.

hydrolysis Reaction in which the components of a water molecule are added to functional groups as molecules are broken into smaller subunits.

hydrophilic Polar molecules that associate readily with water.

hydrophobic Nonpolar substances that are excluded by water and other polar molecules.

hydroponic culture A method of growing plants not in soil but with the roots bathed in a solution that contains water and mineral nutrients.

hydrosphere The component of the biosphere that encompasses all of the waters on Earth, including oceans, rivers, and polar ice caps.

hydrostatic skeleton A structure consisting of muscles and fluid that, by themselves, provide support for the animal or part of the animal; no rigid support, such as a bone, is involved.

hydroxyl group Group consisting of an oxygen atom linked to a hydrogen atom on one side and to a carbon chain on the other side.

hymen A thin flap of tissue that partially covers the opening of the vagina.

hyomandibular bones Bones that support the hyoid and throat.

hyperpolarized The condition of a neuron when its membrane potential is more negative than the resting value.

hypersensitive response A plant defence that physically cordons off an infection site by surrounding it with dead cells.

hypertension Commonly called high blood pressure, a medical condition in which blood pressure is chronically elevated above normal values.

hyperthermia The condition resulting when the heat gain of the body is too great to be counteracted.

hypertonic Solution containing dissolved substances at higher concentrations than the cells it surrounds.

hypha (plural, hyphae) Any of the threadlike filaments that form the mycelium of a fungus.

hypoblast The bottom layer of a blastodisk.

hypocotyl The region of a plant embryo's vertical axis between the cotyledons and the radicle.

hypodermis The innermost layer of the skin that contains larger blood vessels and additional reinforcing connective tissue.

hypothalamus The portion of the brain that contains centres regulating basic homeostatic functions of the body and contributing to the release of hormones.

hypothermia A condition in which the core temperature falls below normal for a prolonged period.

hypothesis A "working explanation" of observed facts.

hypotonic Solution containing dissolved substances at lower concentrations than the cells it surrounds.

imbibition The movement of water into a seed as the water molecules are attracted to hydrophilic groups of stored proteins; the first step in germination.

immigration Movement of organisms into a population.

immune privilege The situation in which certain sites in the body tolerate the presence of an antigen without mounting an inflammatory immune response. These sites include the brain, eyes, and testicles.

immune response The defensive reactions of the immune system.

immune system The combined defences, innate and acquired, a body uses to eliminate infections.

immunoglobulin A specific protein substance produced by plasma cells to aid in fighting infection.

immunological memory The capacity of the immune system to respond more rapidly and vigorously to the second contact with a specific antigen than to the primary contact.

immunological tolerance The process that protects the body's own molecules from attack by the immune system.

imperfect flower A type of incomplete flower that has stamens or carpels, but not both.

imprinting The process of learning the identity of a caretaker and potential future mate during a critical period.

inbreeding A special form of nonrandom mating in which genetically related individuals mate with each other.

incisors Flattened, chisel-shaped teeth of mammals, located at the front of the mouth, that are used to nip or cut food.

incomplete dominance Condition in which the effects of recessive alleles can be detected to some extent in heterozygotes.

incomplete metamorphosis In certain insects, a life cycle characterized by the absence of a pupal stage between the immature and adult stages.

incurrent siphon A muscular tube that brings water containing oxygen and food into the body of an invertebrate.

incus The second of the three sound-conducting middle ear bones in vertebrates, located between the malleus and the stapes.

independent assortment Mendel's principle that the alleles of the genes that govern two characters segregate independently during formation of gametes.

indeterminate cleavage A type of cleavage, observed in many deuterostomes, in which the developmental fates of the first few cells produced by mitosis are not determined as soon as cells are produced.

indeterminate growth Growth that is not limited by an organism's genetic program, so that the organism grows for as long as it lives; typical of many plants. *Compare* determinate growth.

indirect neurotransmitter A neurotransmitter that acts as a first messenger, binding to a G protein–coupled receptor in the postsynaptic membrane, which activates the receptor and triggers generation of a second messenger such as cyclic AMP or other processes.

inducer Concerning regulation of gene expression in bacteria, a molecule that turns on the transcription of the genes in an operon.

inducible operon Operon whose expression is increased by an inducer molecule.

induction A mechanism in which one group of cells (the inducer cells) causes or influences another nearby group of cells (the responder cells) to follow a particular developmental pathway.

infection thread In the formation of root nodules on nitrogen-fixing plants, the tube formed by the plasma membrane of root hair cells as bacteria enter the cell.

inflammation The heat, pain, redness, and swelling that occur at the site of an infection.

ingestion The feeding methods used to take food into the digestive cavity.

inheritance The transmission of DNA (that is, genetic information) from one generation to the next.

inhibin A peptide that, in females, is an inhibitor of FSH secretion from the pituitary, thereby diminishing the signal for follicular growth. In males, inhibin inhibits FSH secretion from the pituitary, thereby decreasing spermatogenesis.

inhibiting hormone (IH) A hormone released by the hypothalamus that inhibits the secretion of a particular anterior pituitary hormone.

inhibition hypothesis A hypothesis suggesting that new species are prevented from occupying a community by whatever species are already present.

inhibitory postsynaptic potential (IPSP) A change in membrane potential caused when hyperpolarization occurs, pushing the neuron farther from threshold.

initial A plant cell that remains permanently as part of a meristem and gives rise to daughter cells that differentiate into specialized cell types.

initiator codon *See* start codon.

initiator RNA The aminoacyl–tRNA used for initiation, with an anticodon to the methionine-specifying AUG start codon.

innate immunity A nonspecific line of defence against pathogens that includes inflammation, which creates internal conditions that inhibit or kill many pathogens, and specialized cells that engulf or kill pathogens or infected body cells.

inner boundary membrane Membrane lying just inside the outer boundary membrane of a chloroplast, enclosing the stroma.

inner cell mass The dense mass of cells within the blastocyst that will become the embryo.

inner ear That part of the ear, particularly the cochlea, that converts mechanical vibrations (sound) into neural messages that are sent to the brain.

inner mitochondrial membrane Membrane surrounding the mitochondrial matrix.

inorganic molecule Molecule without carbon atoms in its structure.

inositol triphosphate (IP3) In particular, signal transduction pathways, a second messenger that activates transport proteins in the endoplasmic reticulum to release Ca^{2+} into the cytoplasm. IP_3 is involved in one of two major G protein–coupled receptor–response pathways.

insertion sequence A transposable element that contains only genes for its transposition.

insight learning A phenomenon in which animals can solve problems without apparent trial-and-error attempts at the solution.

instar The stage between successive moults in insects and other arthropods.

instinctive behaviour A genetically "programmed" response that appears in complete and functional form the first time it is used.

insulin A hormone secreted by beta cells in the islets, acting mainly on cells of nonworking skeletal muscles, liver cells, and adipose tissue (fat) to lower blood glucose, fatty acid, and amino acid levels and promote the storage of those molecules.

insulinlike growth factor (IGF) A peptide that directly stimulates growth processes.

integral membrane protein Protein embedded in a phospholipid bilayer.

integration The sorting and interpretation of neural messages and the determination of the appropriate response(s).

integrator In homeostatic feedback, the control centre that compares a detected environmental change with a set point.

integument Skin.

interference competition Form of competition in which individuals fight over resources or otherwise harm each other directly.

interferon A cytokine produced by infected host cells affected by viral dsRNA, which acts on both the infected cell that produces it, an autocrine effect, and neighbouring uninfected cells, a paracrine effect.

interkinesis A brief interphase separating the two meiotic divisions.

intermediate disturbance hypothesis Hypothesis proposing that species richness is greatest in communities that experience fairly frequent disturbances of moderate intensity.

intermediate filament A cytoskeletal filament about 10 nm in diameter that provides mechanical strength to cells in tissues.

intermediate-day plant A plant that flowers only when day length falls between the values for long-day and short-day plants.

internal fertilization The process in which sperm are released by the male close to or inside the entrance of the reproductive tract of the female.

internal gill A gill located within the body that has a cover providing physical protection for the gills. Water must be brought to internal gills.

interneuron A neuron that integrates information to formulate an appropriate response.

internode The region between two nodes on a plant stem.

interphase The first stage of the mitotic cell cycle, during which the cell grows and replicates its DNA before undergoing mitosis and cytokinesis.

interspecific competition The competition for resources between species.

interstitial fluid The fluid occupying the spaces between cells in multicellular animals.

intertidal zone The shoreline that is alternately submerged and exposed by tides.

intestinal villus A microscopic, fingerlike extension in the lining of the small intestine.

intestine The portion of digestive system where organic matter is hydrolyzed by enzymes secreted into the digestive tube. As muscular contractions of the intestinal wall move the mixture along, cells lining the intestine absorb the molecular subunits produced by digestion.

intracellular digestion The process in which cells take in food particles by endocytosis.

intraspecific competition The dependence of two or more individuals in a population on the same limiting resource.

intrinsic rate of increase The maximum possible per capita population growth rate in a population living under ideal conditions.

intron A non–protein-coding sequence that interrupts the protein-coding sequence in a eukaryotic gene. Introns are removed by splicing in the processing of pre-mRNA to mRNA.

invagination The process in which cells changing shape and pushing inward from the surface produce an indentation, such as the dorsal lip of the blastopore.

inversion Chromosomal alteration that occurs if a broken segment reattaches to the same chromosome from which it was lost, but in reversed orientation, so that the order of genes in the segment is reversed with respect to the other genes of the chromosome.

invertebrate An animal without a vertebral column.

inverted repeat Enables the transposase enzyme to identify the ends of the transposable element when it catalyzes transposition.

involution The process by which cells migrate into the blastopore.

ion A positively or negatively charged atom.

ionic bond Bond that results from electrical attractions between atoms that have lost or gained electrons.

iris Of the eye, the coloured muscular membrane that lies behind the cornea and in front of the lens, which by opening or closing determines the size of the pupil and hence the amount of light entering the eye.

islets of Langerhans Endocrine cells that secrete the peptide hormones insulin and glucagon into the bloodstream.

isomers Two or more molecules with the same chemical formula but different molecular structures.

isotonic Equal concentration of water inside and outside cells.

isotope A distinct form of the atoms of an element, with the same number of protons but a different number of neutrons.

jasmonate Any of a group of plant hormones that help regulate aspects of growth and responses to stress, including attacks by predators and pathogens.

juvenile hormones A family of fatty acid hormones that govern metamorphosis and reproduction in insects and crustaceans.

juxtaglomerular apparatus A group of receptors that monitor the pressure and flow of fluid through the distal tubule of the kidney.

karyogamy In plants, the fusion of two sexually compatible haploid nuclei after cell fusion (plasmogamy).

karyotype A characteristic of a species consisting of the shapes and sizes of all of the chromosomes at metaphase.

keeled sternum The ventrally extended breastbone of a bird to which the flight muscles attach.

ketone Molecule in which the carbonyl group is linked to a carbon atom in the interior of a carbon chain.

keystone species A species that has a greater effect on community structure than its numbers might suggest.

kilocalorie (kcal) The scientific unit equivalent to a calorie and equal to 1000 small calories.

kin selection Altruistic behaviour to close relatives, allowing them to produce proportionately more surviving copies of the altruist's genes than the altruist might otherwise have produced on its own.

kinesis A change in the rate of movement or the frequency of turning movements in response to environmental stimuli.

kinetic energy The energy of motion.

kinetochore A specialized structure consisting of proteins attached to a centromere that mediates the attachment and movement of chromosomes along the mitotic spindle.

kingdom A Linnaean taxonomic category that ranks below a domain and above a phylum.

kingdom Animalia The taxonomic kingdom that includes all living and extinct animals.

kingdom Fungi The taxonomic kingdom that includes all living or extinct fungi.

kingdom Plantae The taxonomic kingdom encompassing all living or extinct plants.

kingdom Protoctista A diverse and polyphyletic group of single-celled and multicellular eukaryotic species.

Korarchaeota A group of Archaea recognized solely on the basis of rRNA coding sequences in DNA taken from environmental samples.

Krebs cycle *See* citric acid cycle.

K-selected species Long-lived, slow reproducing species that thrive in more stable environments.

labia majora A pair of fleshy, fat-padded folds that partially cover the labia minora.

labia minora Two folds of tissue that run from front to rear on either side of the opening to the vagina.

lactate fermentation Reaction in which pyruvate is converted into lactate.

lagging strand A DNA strand assembled discontinuously in the direction opposite to DNA unwinding.

landscape ecology The field that examines how large-scale ecological factors—such as the distribution of plants, topography, and human activity—influence local populations and communities.

larva (larval form) A sexually immature stage in the life cycle of many animals that is morphologically distinct from the adult.

larynx The voice box.

latent phase The time during which a virus remains in the cell in an inactive form.

lateral bud A bud on the side of a plant stem from which a branch may grow.

lateral geniculate nuclei Clusters of neurons located in the thalamus that receive visual information from the optic nerves and send it on to the visual cortex.

lateral inhibition Visual processing in which lateral movement of signals from a rod or cone proceeds to a horizontal cell and continues to bipolar cells with which the horizontal cell makes inhibitory connections, serving both to sharpen the edges of objects and enhance contrast in an image.

lateral line system The complex of mechanoreceptors along the sides of some fishes and aquatic amphibians that detect vibrations in the water.

lateral meristem A plant meristem that gives rise to secondary tissue growth. *Compare* primary meristem.

lateral root A root that extends away from the main root (or taproot).

lateralization A phenomenon in which some brain functions are more localized in one of the two hemispheres.

lateral-line system The complex of organs and sensory receptors along the sides of many fishes and amphibians that detects vibrations in water.

leaching The process by which soluble materials in soil are washed into a lower layer of soil or are dissolved and carried away by water.

leading strand A DNA strand assembled in the direction of DNA unwinding.

leaf primordium A lateral outgrowth from the apical meristem that develops into a young leaf.

learned behaviour A response of an animal that is dependent on having a particular kind of experience during development.

learning A process in which experiences stored in memory change the behavioural responses of an animal.

leghemoglobin An iron-containing, red-pigmented protein produced in root nodules during the symbiotic association between *Bradyrhizobium* or *Rhizobium* and legumes.

lek A display ground where males each possess a small territory from which they court attentive females.

lens The transparent, biconvex intraocular tissue that helps bring rays of light to a focus on the retina.

Lepidosauromorpha A monophyletic lineage of diapsids that includes both marine and terrestrial animals, represented today by sphenodontids, lizards, and snakes.

leukocyte A white blood cell, which eliminates dead and dying cells from the body, removes cellular debris, and participates in defending the body against invading organisms.

Leydig cell A cell that produces the male sex hormones.

lichen A single vegetative body that is the result of an association between a fungus and a photosynthetic partner, often an alga.

life cycle The sequential stages through which individuals develop, grow, maintain themselves, and reproduce.

life history The lifetime pattern of growth, maturation, and reproduction that is characteristic of a population or species.

life table A chart that summarizes the demographic characteristics of a population.

ligament A fibrous connective tissue that connects bones to each other at a joint.

ligand-gated ion channel A channel that opens or closes when a specific chemical, such as a neurotransmitter, binds to the channel.

light The portion of the electromagnetic spectrum that humans can detect with their eyes.

light chain The lighter of the two types of polypeptide chains found in immunoglobulin and antibody molecules.

light microscope Microscope that uses light to illuminate the specimen.

light-dependent reaction The first stage of photosynthesis, in which the energy of sunlight is absorbed and converted into chemical energy in the form of ATP and NADPH.

light-independent reaction The second stage of photosynthesis, in which electrons are used as a source of energy to convert inorganic CO_2 to an organic form. Also referred to as the *Calvin cycle*.

lignification The deposition of lignin in plant cell walls; it anchors the cellulose fibres in the walls, making them stronger and more rigid, and protects the other wall components from physical or chemical damage.

lignin A tough, rather inert polymer that strengthens the secondary walls of various plant cells and thus helps vascular plants grow taller and stay erect on land.

limbic system A functional network formed by parts of the thalamus, hypothalamus, and basal nuclei, along with other nearby grey-matter centres—the amygdala, hippocampus, and olfactory bulbs—sometimes called the "emotional brain."

limiting nutrient An element in short supply within an ecosystem, the shortage of which limits productivity.

limnetic zone The sunlit, open water in a lake, beyond the zone where plants rooted in the bottom can grow.

linkage The phenomenon of genes being located on the same chromosome.

linkage map Map of a chromosome showing the relative locations of genes based on recombination frequencies.

linked genes Genes on the same chromosome.

linker A short segment of DNA extending between one nucleosome and the next in a eukaryotic chromosome.

lipopolysaccharide A large molecule that consists of a lipid and a carbohydrate joined by a covalent bond.

lithosphere The component of the biosphere that includes the rocks, sediments, and soils of the crust.

liver A large organ whose many functions include aiding in digestion, removing toxins from the body, and regulating the chemicals in the blood.

loam Any well-aerated soil composed of a mixture of sand, clay, silt, and organic matter.

locus The particular site on a chromosome at which a gene is located.

logistic model of population growth Model of population growth that assumes that a population's per capita growth rate decreases as the population gets larger.

long-day plant A plant that flowers in spring when dark periods become shorter and day length becomes longer.

long-term memory Memory that stores information from days to years or even for life.

long-term potentiation A long-lasting increase in the strength of synaptic connections in activated neural pathways following brief periods of repeated stimulation.

loop of Henle In mammals, a U-shaped bend of the proximal convoluted tubule.

loose connective tissue A tissue formed of sparsely distributed cells surrounded by a more or less open network of collagen and other glycoprotein fibres.

lophophore The circular or U-shaped fold with one or two rows of hollow, ciliated tentacles that surrounds the mouth of brachiopods, bryozoans, and phoronids and is used to gather food.

loss of imprinting A phenomenon in which the imprinting mechanism for a gene does not work, resulting in both alleles of the gene being active.

lumen The inside of the digestive tube.

lung One of a pair of invaginated respiratory surfaces, buried in the body interior where they are less susceptible to drying out; the organs of respiration in mammals, birds, reptiles, and most amphibians.

luteinizing hormone (LH) A hormone secreted by the pituitary that stimulates the growth and maturation of eggs in females and the secretion of testosterone in males.

Lycophyta The plant phylum that includes club mosses and their close relatives.

lymph The interstitial fluid picked up by the lymphatic system.

lymph node One of many small, bean-shaped organs spaced along the lymph vessels that contain macrophages and other leukocytes that attack invading disease organisms.

lymphatic system An accessory system of vessels and organs that helps balance the fluid content of the blood and surrounding tissues and participates in the body's defences against invading disease organisms.

lymphocyte A leukocyte that carries out most of its activities in the tissues and organs of the lymphatic system. Lymphocytes play major roles in immune responses.

lysed Refers to a cell that has ruptured or undergone lysis.

lysogenic cycle Cycle in which the DNA of the bacteriophage is integrated into the DNA of the host bacterial cell and may remain for many generations.

lysosome Membrane-bound vesicle containing hydrolytic enzymes for the digestion of many complex molecules.

lytic cycle The series of events from infection of one bacterial cell by a phage through the release of progeny phages from lysed cells.

macroevolution Large-scale evolutionary patterns in the history of life, producing major changes in species and higher taxonomic groups.

macromolecule A very large molecule assembled by the covalent linkage of smaller subunit molecules.

macronucleus In ciliophorans, a single large nucleus that develops from a micronucleus but loses all genes except those required for basic "housekeeping" functions of the cell and for ribosomal RNAs.

macronutrient In humans, a mineral required in amounts ranging from 50 mg to more than 1 g per day. In plants, a nutrient needed in large amounts for the normal growth and development.

macrophage A phagocyte that takes part in nonspecific defences and adaptive immunity.

magnetoreceptor A receptor found in some animals that navigate long distances that allows them to detect and use Earth's magnetic field as a source of directional information.

magnification The ratio of an object as viewed to its real size.

magnoliids An angiosperm group that includes magnolias, laurels, and avocados; they are more closely related to monocots than to eudicots.

major histocompatibility complex A large cluster of genes encoding the MHC proteins.

malleus The outermost of the sound-conducting bones of the middle ear in vertebrates.

malnutrition A condition resulting from a diet that lacks one or more essential nutrients.

Malpighian tubule The main organ of excretion and osmoregulation in insects, helping them maintain water and electrolyte balance.

mammary glands Specialized organs of female mammals that produce energy-rich milk, a watery mixture of fats, sugars, proteins, vitamins, and minerals.

mandible In arthropods, one of the paired head appendages posterior to the mouth used for feeding. In vertebrates, the lower jaw.

mantle One or two folds of the body wall that lines the shell and secretes the substance that forms the shell in molluscs.

mantle cavity The protective chamber produced by the mantle in many molluscs.

map unit The unit of a linkage map, equivalent to a recombination frequency of 1%. Also referred to as a *centimorgan*.

maritime climate Climate tempered by ocean winds.

marsupium An external pouch on the abdomen of many female marsupials, containing the mammary glands, and within which the young continue to develop after birth.

mass extinctions The disappearance of a large number of species in a relatively short period of geologic time.

mass number The total number of protons and neutrons in the atomic nucleus.

mast cell A type of cell dispersed through connective tissue that releases histamine when activated by the death of cells, caused by a pathogen at an infection site.

mastax The toothed grinding organ at the anterior of the digestive tract in rotifers.

maternal chromosome The chromosome derived from the female parent of an organism.

maternal-effect gene One of a class of genes that regulate the expression of other genes expressed by the mother during oogenesis and that control the polarity of the egg and, therefore, of the embryo.

mating The pairing of a male and a female for the purpose of sexual reproduction.

mating systems The social systems describing how males and females pair up.

mating type A genetically defined strain of an organism (such as a fungus) that can only mate with an organism of the opposite mating type; mating types are often designated + and −.

matter Anything that occupies space and has mass.

maxilla (plural, maxillae) One of the paired head appendages posterior to the mouth used for feeding in arthropods.

mechanical isolation A prezygotic reproductive isolating mechanism caused by differences in the structure of reproductive organs or other body parts.

mechanoreceptor A sensory receptor that detects mechanical energy, such as changes in pressure, body position, or acceleration. The auditory receptors in the ears are examples of mechanoreceptors.

medusa (plural, medusae) The tentacled, usually bell-shaped, free-swimming sexual stage in the life cycle of a coelenterate.

megapascal A unit of pressure used to measure water potential.

megaspore A plant spore that develops into a female gametophyte; usually larger than a microspore.

meiocytes Cells that are destined to divide by meiosis.

meiosis The division of diploid cells to haploid progeny, consisting of two sequential rounds of nuclear and cellular division.

meiosis I The first division of the meiotic cell cycle in which homologous chromosomes pair and undergo an exchange of chromosome segments, and then the homologous chromosomes separate, resulting in two cells, each with the haploid number of chromosomes and with each chromosome still consisting of two chromatids.

meiosis II The second division of the meiotic cell cycle in which the sister chromatids in each of the two cells produced by meiosis I separate and segregate into different cells, resulting in four cells each with the haploid number of chromosomes.

melanocyte-stimulating hormone (MSH) A hormone secreted by the anterior pituitary that controls the degree of pigmentation in melanocytes.

melatonin A peptide hormone secreted by the pineal gland that helps maintain daily biorhythms.

melanotic encapsulation The mechanism by which hemocytes move toward and form a capsule around pathogens that are too big to phagocytose. The capsule may then be melanized by the deposition of phenolic compounds that further isolate the pathogen.

membrane attack complexes An abnormal activation of the complement (protein) portion of the blood, forming a cascade reaction that brings blood proteins together, binds them to the cell wall, and then inserts them through the cell membrane.

membrane potential An electrical voltage that measures the potential inside a cell membrane relative to the fluid just outside; it is negative under resting conditions and becomes positive during an action potential.

memory The storage and retrieval of a sensory or motor experience or a thought.

memory B cell In antibody-mediated immunity, a long-lived cell expressing an antibody on its surface that can bind to a specific antigen. A memory B cell is activated the next time the antigen is encountered, producing a rapid secondary immune response.

memory cell An activated lymphocyte that circulates in the blood and lymph, ready to initiate a rapid immune response on subsequent exposure to the same antigen.

memory helper T cell In cell-mediated immunity, a long-lived cell differentiated from a helper T cell, which remains in an inactive state in the lymphatic system after an immune reaction has run its course and ready to be activated on subsequent exposure to the same antigen.

meninges Three layers of connective tissue that surround and protect the spinal cord and brain.

menstrual cycle A cycle of approximately 1 month in the human female during which an egg is released from an ovary and the uterus is prepared to receive the fertilized egg; if fertilization does not occur, the endometrium breaks down, which releases blood and tissue breakdown products from the uterus to the outside through the vagina.

meristem An undifferentiated, permanently embryonic plant tissue that gives rise to new cells forming tissues and organs.

mesenteries Sheets of loose connective tissue, covered on both surfaces with epithelial cells, which suspend the abdominal organs in the coelom and provide lubricated, smooth surfaces that prevent chafing or abrasion between adjacent structures as the body moves.

mesoderm The middle layer of the three primary germ layers of an animal embryo, from which the muscular, skeletal, vascular, and connective tissues develop.

mesoglea A layer of gel-like connective tissue separating the gastrodermis and epidermis in radially symmetrical animals. It contains widely dispersed amoeboid cells.

mesohyl The gelatinous middle layer of cells lining the body cavity of a sponge.

mesophyll The ground tissue located between the two outer leaf tissues, composed of loosely packed parenchyma cells that contain chloroplasts.

messenger RNA (mRNA) An RNA molecule that serves as a template for protein synthesis.

metabolism The biochemical reactions that allow a cell or organism to extract energy from its surroundings and use that energy to maintain itself, grow, and reproduce.

metamorphosis A reorganization of the form of certain animals during postembryonic development.

metanephridium (plural, metanephridia) The excretory tubule of most annelids and molluscs.

metaphase The phase of mitosis during which the spindle reaches its final form and the spindle microtubules move the chromosomes into alignment at the spindle midpoint.

metapopulation A group of neighbouring populations that exchange individuals.

micelle A sphere composed of a single layer of lipid molecules.

microbody A small, membrane-bound organelle that carries out vital reactions linking metabolic pathways.

microclimate The abiotic conditions immediately surrounding an organism.

microevolution Small-scale genetic changes within populations, often in response to shifting environmental circumstances or chance events.

microfilament A cytoskeletal filament composed of actin.

micronucleus In ciliophorans, one or more diploid nuclei that contains a complete complement of genes, functioning primarily in cellular reproduction.

micronutrient Any mineral required by an organism only in trace amounts.

micropyle A small opening at one end of an ovule through which the pollen tube passes prior to fertilization.

microscope Instrument of microscopy with different magnifications and resolutions of specimens.

microscopy Technique for producing visible images of objects that are too small to be seen by the human eye.

microspore A plant spore from which a male gametophyte develops; usually smaller than a megaspore.

microsporidium (plural, microsporidia) A fungal parasite of animals; many mycologists believe that they make up a possible sixth phylum within the kingdom Fungi.

microtubule A cytoskeletal component formed by the polymerization of tubulin into rigid, hollow rods about 25 nm in diameter.

microtubule organizing centre (MTOC) An anchoring point near the centre of a eukaryotic cell from which most microtubules extend outward.

microvilli Fingerlike projections forming a brush border in epithelial cells that cover the villi.

midbrain The uppermost of the three segments of the brain stem, serving primarily as an intermediary between the rest of the brain and the spinal cord.

middle ear The air-filled cavity containing three small, interconnected bones: the malleus, incus, and stapes.

middle lamella Layer of gel-like polysaccharides that holds together walls of adjacent plant cells.

migration The predictable seasonal movement of animals from the area where they are born to a distant and initially unfamiliar destination, returning to their birth site later.

mimic The species in Batesian mimicry that resembles the model.

mimicry A form of defence in which one species evolves an appearance resembling that of another.

mineralocorticoid A steroid hormone secreted by the adrenal cortex that regulates the levels of Na and K in the blood and extracellular fluid.

minimal medium A growth medium containing the minimal ingredients that enable a nonmutant organism, such as *E. coli*, to grow.

minimum viable population size The smallest population size that is likely to survive both predictable and unpredictable environmental variation.

mismatch repair Repair system that removes mismatched bases from newly synthesized DNA strands.

missense mutation A base-pair substitution mutation in a protein-coding gene that results in a different amino acid in the encoded polypeptide than the normal one.

mitochondrial electron transfer system Series of electron carriers that alternately pick up and release electrons, ultimately transferring them to their final acceptor, oxygen.

mitochondrial matrix The innermost compartment of the mitochondrion.

mitochondrion Membrane-bound organelle responsible for synthesis of most of the ATP in eukaryotic cells.

mitosis Nuclear division that produces daughter nuclei that are exact genetic copies of the parental nucleus.

mobile elements Particular segments of DNA that can move from one place to another; they cut and paste DNA backbones using a type of recombination that does not require homology.

model The species in Batesian mimicry that is resembled by the mimic.

model organism An organism with characteristics that make it a particularly useful subject of research because it is likely to produce results widely applicable to other organisms.

modern synthesis A unified theory of evolution developed in the middle of the twentieth century.

molarity (M) The number of moles of a substance dissolved in 1 L of solution.

molars Posteriormost teeth of mammals, with a broad chewing surface for grinding food.

mould Asexual, spore-producing stage of many multicellular fungi.

mole (mol) The atomic weight of an element or the molecular weight of a compound.

molecular clock A technique for dating the time of divergence of two species or lineages, based on the number of molecular sequence differences between them.

molecular weight The weight of a molecule in grams, equal to the total mass number of its atoms.

molecule A unit composed of atoms combined chemically in fixed numbers and ratios.

moult-inhibiting hormone (MIH) A peptide neurohormone secreted by a gland in the eye stalks of crustaceans that inhibits ecdysone secretion.

monoclonal antibody An antibody that reacts only against the same segment (epitope) of a single antigen.

monocot A plant belonging to the Monocotyledones, one of the two major classes of angiosperms; monocot embryos have a single seed leaf (cotyledon) and pollen grains with a single groove.

monocyte A type of leukocyte that enters damaged tissue from the bloodstream through the endothelial wall of the blood vessel.

monoecious Having both "male" flowers (which possess only stamens) and "female" flowers (which possess only carpels).

monogamy A mating system in which one male and one female form a long-term association.

monohybrid An F1 heterozygote produced from a genetic cross that involves a single character.

monohybrid cross A genetic cross between two individuals that are each heterozygous for the same pair of alleles.

monomers Identical or nearly identical subunits that link together to form polymers during polymerization.

monophyletic taxon A group of organisms that includes a single ancestral species and all of its descendants.

monosaccharides The smallest carbohydrates, containing three to seven carbon atoms.

monotreme A lineage of mammals that lay eggs instead of bearing live young.

monounsaturated Fatty acids with one double bond.

monsoon cycle A wind pattern that brings seasonally heavy rain to a region by blowing moisture-laden air from the sea to the land.

morphogenesis Orderly, genetically programmed changes in the size, shape, and proportion of body parts of an organism; the process by which specialized tissues and organs form.

Morphological Species Concept The concept that all individuals of a species share measurable traits that distinguish them from individuals of other species.

morphology The form or shape of an organism or of part of an organism.

morula The first stage of animal development, a solid ball or layer of blastomeres.

mosaic evolution The tendency of characteristics to undergo different rates of evolutionary change within the same lineage.

motif A highly specialized region in a protein produced by the three-dimensional arrangement of amino acid chains within and between domains.

motile Capable of self-propelled movement.

motor neuron An efferent neuron that carries signals to skeletal muscle.

motor unit A block of muscle fibres that is controlled by branches of the axon of a single efferent neuron.

moult-inhibiting hormone (MIH) A peptide neurohormone secreted by cells in the eyestalks (extensions of the brain leading to the eyes).

mRNA splicing Process that removes introns from pre-mRNAs and joins exons together.

mucosa The lining of the gut that contains epithelial and glandular cells.

Müllerian duct The bipotential primitive duct associated with the gonads that leads to a cloaca.

Müllerian mimicry A form of defence in which two or more unpalatable species share a similar appearance.

multicellular organism Individual consisting of interdependent cells.

multiple alleles More than two different alleles of a gene.

multiple fruit A fruit that develops from several ovaries in multiple flowers; examples are pineapples and mulberries.

Multiregional Hypothesis A hypothesis proposing that after archaic humans migrated from Africa to many regions on Earth, their different populations evolved into modern humans simultaneously.

muscle fibre A bundle of elongated, cylindrical cells that make up skeletal muscle.

muscle spindle A stretch receptor in muscle; a bundle of small, specialized muscle cells wrapped with the dendrites of afferent neurons and enclosed in connective tissue.

muscle tissue Cells that have the ability to contract (shorten) forcibly.

muscle twitch A single, weak contraction of a muscle fibre.

muscularis The muscular coat of a hollow organ or tubular structure.

mutation A spontaneous and heritable change in DNA.

mutualism A symbiotic interaction between species in which both partners benefit.

mycelium A network of branching hyphae that constitutes the body of a multicellular fungus.

mycobiont The fungal component of a lichen.

mycorrhiza A mutualistic symbiosis in which fungal hyphae associate intimately with plant roots.

myoblast An undifferentiated muscle cell.

myofibril A cylindrical contractile element about 1 m in diameter that runs lengthwise inside the muscle fibre cell.

myogenic heart A heart that maintains its contraction rhythm with no requirement for signals from the nervous system.

myoglobin An oxygen-storing protein closely related to hemoglobin.

Na^+/K^+ pump Pump that pushes 3 Na^+ out of the cell and 2 K^+ into the cell in the same pumping cycle. Also referred to as the *sodium–potassium pump*.

Nanoarchaeota A group of Archaea that was proposed based on rRNA sequence analysis of a thermophilic archaean found in a symbiotic relationship with another thermophilic archaean; most probably a subgroup of the Euryarchaeota.

nastic movement In plants, a reversible response to nondirectional stimuli, such as mechanical pressure or humidity.

natural history The branch of biology that examines the form and variety of organisms in their natural environments.

natural killer (NK) cell A type of lymphocyte that destroys pathogen infected cells.

natural selection The evolutionary process by which alleles that increase the likelihood of survival and the reproductive output of the individuals that carry them become more common in subsequent generations.

natural theology A belief that knowledge of God may be acquired through the study of natural phenomena.

navigation A wayfinding mechanism in which an animal moves toward a specific destination, using both a compass and a "mental map" of where it is in relation to the destination.

negative feedback The primary mechanism of homeostasis, in which a stimulus—a change in the external or internal environment—triggers a response that compensates for the environmental change.

negative pressure breathing Muscular contractions that expand the lungs, lowering the pressure of the air in the lungs and causing air to be pulled inward.

nematocyst A coiled thread, encapsulated in a cnidocyte, that cnidarians fire at prey or predators, sometimes releasing a toxin through its tip.

nephron A specialized excretory tubule that contributes to osmoregulation and carries out excretion, found in all vertebrates.

nerve A bundle of axons enclosed in connective tissue and all following the same pathway.

nerve cord A bundle of nerves that extends from the central ganglia to the rest of the body, connected to smaller nerves.

nerve net A simple nervous system that coordinates responses to stimuli but has no central control organ or brain.

nervous tissue Tissue that contains neurons, which serve as lines of communication and control between body parts.

net primary productivity The chemical energy remaining in an ecosystem after a producer's cellular respiration is deducted.

neural crest A band of cells that arises early in the embryonic development of vertebrates near the region where the neural tube pinches off from the ectoderm; later, the cells migrate and develop into unique structures.

neural plate Ectoderm thickened and flattened into a longitudinal band, induced by notochord cells.

neural signalling The process by which an animal responds appropriately to a stimulus.

neural tube A hollow tube in vertebrate embryos that develops into the brain, spinal cord, spinal nerves, and spinal column.

neurogenic heart A heart that beats under the control of signals from the nervous system.

neuromuscular junction The junction between a nerve fibre and the muscle it supplies.

neuron An electrically active cell of the nervous system responsible for controlling behaviour and body functions.

neuronal circuit The connection between axon terminals of one neuron and the dendrites or cell body of a second neuron.

neuropile The region of a ganglion in which branching axons and dendrites make interconnections.

neuroscience The integrated study of the structure, function, and development of the nervous system.

neurosecretory neuron A neuron that releases a neurohormone into the circulatory system when appropriately stimulated.

neurotransmitter A chemical released by an axon terminal at a chemical synapse.

neurulation The process in vertebrates by which organogenesis begins with development of the nervous system from ectoderm.

neutral lipid Energy-storing molecule consisting of a glycerol backbone and three fatty acid chains.

neutral variation hypothesis An evolutionary hypothesis that some variation at gene loci coding for enzymes and other soluble proteins is neither favoured nor eliminated by natural selection.

neutron Uncharged particle in the nucleus of an atom.

neutrophil A type of phagocytic leukocyte that attaches to blood vessel walls in massive numbers when attracted to the infection site by chemokines.

nitrification A metabolic process in which certain soil bacteria convert ammonia or ammonium ions into nitrites that are then converted by other bacteria to nitrates, a form usable by plants.

nitrogen cycle A biogeochemical cycle that moves nitrogen between the huge atmospheric pool of gaseous molecular nitrogen and several much smaller pools of nitrogen-containing compounds in soils, marine and freshwater ecosystems, and living organisms.

nitrogen fixation A metabolic process in which certain bacteria and cyanobacteria convert molecular nitrogen into ammonia and ammonium ions, forms usable by plants.

nitrogenous base A nitrogen-containing molecule with the properties of a base.

nociceptor A sensory receptor that detects tissue damage or noxious chemicals; their activity registers as pain.

node The point on a stem where one or more leaves are attached.

node of Ranvier The gap between two Schwann cells, which exposes the axon membrane directly to extracellular fluids.

noncompetitive inhibition Inhibition of an enzyme reaction by an inhibitor molecule that binds to the enzyme at a site other than the active site and, therefore, does not compete directly with the substrate for binding to the active site.

noncyclic electron flow Pathway in photosynthesis in which electrons travel in a one-way direction from H_2O to $NADP^+$.

nondisjunction The failure of homologous pairs to separate during the first meiotic division or of chromatids to separate during the second meiotic division.

nonhistone protein All of the proteins associated with DNA in a eukaryotic chromosome that are not histones.

nonpolar association Association that occurs when nonpolar molecules clump together.

nonpolar covalent bond Bond in which electrons are shared equally.

nonsense codon *See* stop codon.

nonsense mutation A base-pair substitution mutation in a gene in which the base-pair change results in a change from a sense codon to a nonsense codon in the mRNA. The polypeptide translated from the mRNA is shorter than the normal polypeptide because of the mutation.

nonshivering thermogenesis The generation of heat by oxidative mechanisms in nonmuscle tissue throughout the body.

nonvascular plant *See* bryophyte.

norepinephrine A nontropic amine hormone secreted by the adrenal medulla.

notochord A flexible rodlike structure constructed of fluid-filled cells surrounded by tough connective tissue, which supports a chordate embryo from head to tail.

N-terminal end The end of a polypeptide chain with an $—NH_3$ group.

nuclear envelope In eukaryotes, membranes separating the nucleus from the cytoplasm.

nuclear pore Opening in the membrane of the nuclear envelope through which large molecules, such as RNA and proteins, move between the nucleus and the cytoplasm.

nucleoid The central region of a prokaryotic cell with no boundary membrane separating it from the cytoplasm, where DNA replication and RNA transcription occur.

nucleolus The nuclear site of rRNA transcription, processing, and ribosome assembly in eukaryotes.

nucleoplasm The liquid or semiliquid substance within the nucleus.

nucleosome The basic structural unit of chromatin in eukaryotes, consisting of DNA wrapped around a histone core.

nucleosome core particle An eight-protein particle formed by the combination of two molecules each of H2A, H2B, H3, and H4, around which DNA winds for almost two turns.

nucleotide The monomer of nucleic acids consisting of a five-carbon sugar, a nitrogenous base, and a phosphate.

nucleus The central region of eukaryotic cells, separated by membranes from the surrounding cytoplasm, where DNA replication and messenger RNA transcription occur.

null hypothesis A statement of what would be seen if the hypothesis being tested were wrong.

null model A conceptual model that predicts what one would see if a particular factor had no effect.

nutrition The processes by which an organism takes in, digests, absorbs, and converts food into organic compounds.

obligate aerobe A microorganism that uses oxygen for cellular respiration and requires oxygen in its surroundings to support growth.

obligate anaerobe A microorganism that cannot use oxygen and can grow only in the absence of oxygen.

observational data Basic information on biological structures or the details of biological processes.

ocellus (plural, ocelli) The simplest eye, which detects light but does not form an image.

oil Neutral lipid that is liquid at biological temperatures.

olfactory bulb A grey-matter centre that relays inputs from odour receptors to both the cerebral cortex and the limbic system.

oligodendrocyte A type of glial cell that populates the CNS and is responsible for producing myelin.

oligosaccharin A complex carbohydrate that in plants serves as a signalling molecule and as a defence against pathogens.

oligotrophic lake A lake that is poor in nutrients and organic matter but rich in oxygen.

ommatidium (plural, ommatidia) A faceted visual unit of a compound eye.

omnivore An animal that feeds at several trophic levels, consuming plants, animals, and other sources of organic matter.

oncogene A gene capable of inducing one or more characteristics of cancer cells.

one gene–one enzyme hypothesis Hypothesis showing the direct relationship between genes and enzymes.

one gene–one polypeptide hypothesis Restatement of the one gene–one enzyme hypothesis, taking into account that some proteins consist of more than one polypeptide and not all proteins are enzymes.

oocyte A developing gamete that becomes an ootid at the end of meiosis.

oogenesis The process of producing eggs.

oogonium A cell that enters meiosis and gives rise to gametes, produced by mitotic divisions of the germ cells in females.

open circulatory system An arrangement of internal transport in some invertebrates in which the vascular fluid, hemolymph, is released into sinuses, bathing organs directly, and is not always retained within vessels.

operant conditioning A form of associative learning in which animals learn to link a voluntary activity, an operant, with its favourable consequences, the reinforcement.

operator A DNA regulatory sequence that controls transcription of an operon.

operculum A lid or flap of the bone serving as the gill cover in some fishes.

operon A cluster of prokaryotic genes and the DNA sequences involved in their regulation.

opsin One of several different proteins that bond covalently with the light-absorbing pigment of rods and cones (retinal).

optic chiasm Location just behind the eyes where the optic nerves converge before entering the base of the brain, a portion of each optic nerve crossing over to the opposite side.

optical isomers *See* enantiomers.

optimal foraging theory A set of mathematical models that predict the diet choices of animals as they encounter a range of potential food items.

oral hood Soft fleshy structure at the anterior end of a cephalochordate that frames the opening of the mouth.

orbital The region of space where the electron "lives" most of the time.

order A Linnaean taxonomic category of organisms that ranks above a family and below a class.

organ Two or more different tissues integrated into a structure that carries out a specific function.

organ of Corti An organ within the cochlear duct that contains the sensory hair cells detecting sound vibrations transmitted to the inner ear.

organ system The coordinated activities of two or more organs to carry out a major body function such as movement, digestion, or reproduction.

organelles The nucleus and other specialized internal structures and compartments of eukaryotic cells.

organic acid (carboxylic acid) Acid for which the characteristic functional group is a carboxyl group (—COOH).

organic molecule Molecule based on carbon.

organismal ecology An ecological discipline in which researchers study the genetic, biochemical, physiological, morphological, and behavioural adaptations of organisms to their abiotic environments.

organogenesis The development of the major organ systems, giving rise to a free-living individual with the body organization characteristic of its species.

oriented cell division Cell division in different planes; establishes the overall shape of a plant organ.

origin of replication (ori) A specific region at which replication of a bacterial chromosome commences.

orthogenesis An obsolete theory that evolution is goal oriented, striving to perfect organisms.

oscula One or more openings in a sponge through which water is expelled.

osmoconformer An animal in which the osmolarity of the cellular and extracellular solutions matches the osmolarity of the environment.

osmolality A measure of the osmotic concentration of a solution. It is measured in osmoles (the number of solute molecules and ions) per kilogram of solvent.

osmoreceptor A chemoreceptor in the hypothalamus that responds to changes in the osmolarity of the fluid surrounding it, which reflects the osmolarity generally of the body fluids.

osmoregulation The regulation of water and ion balance.

osmoregulator An animal that uses control mechanisms to keep the osmolarity of cellular and extracellular fluids the same but at levels that may differ from the osmolarity of the surroundings.

osmosis The passive transport of water across a selectively permeable membrane in response to solute concentration gradients, a pressure gradient, or both.

osmotic pressure A state of dynamic equilibrium in which the pressure of the solution on one side of a selectively permeable membrane exactly balances the tendency of water molecules to diffuse passively from the other side of the membrane due to a concentration gradient.

osteoblast A cell that produces the collagen and mineral of bone.

osteoclast A cell that removes bone minerals and recycles them through the bloodstream.

osteocyte A mature bone cell.

osteon The structural unit of bone, consisting of a minute central canal surrounded by osteocytes embedded in concentric layers of mineral matter.

ostracoderm One of an assortment of extinct, jawless fishes that were covered with bony armour.

otolith One of many small crystals of calcium carbonate embedded in the otolithic membrane of the hair cells.

outer boundary membrane A smooth membrane that surrounds a chloroplast, enclosing the stroma.

outer ear The external structure of the ear, consisting of the pinna and meatus.

outer membrane In Gram-negative bacteria, an additional boundary membrane that covers the peptidoglycan layer of the cell wall.

outer mitochondrial membrane The smooth membrane covering the outside of a mitochondrion.

outgroup comparison A technique used to identify ancestral and derived characters by comparing the group under study with more distantly related species that are not otherwise included in the analysis.

oval window An opening in the bony wall that separates the middle ear from the inner ear.

ovarian cycle The cyclic events in the ovary leading to ovulation.

ovary In animals, the female gonad, which produces female gametes and reproductive hormones. In flowering plants, the enlarged base of a carpel in which one or more ovules develop into seeds.

overexploitation The excessive harvesting of an animal or plant species, potentially leading to its extinction.

overnutrition The condition caused by excessive intake of specific nutrients.

oviduct The tube through which the egg moves from the ovary to the outside of the body.

oviparous Referring to animals that lay eggs containing the nutrients needed for development of the embryo outside the mother's body.

ovoviviparous Referring to animals in which fertilized eggs are retained within the body and the embryo develops using nutrients provided by the egg; eggs hatch inside the mother.

ovulation The process in which oocytes are released into the oviducts as immature eggs.

ovule In plants, the structure in a carpel in which a female gametophyte develops and fertilization takes place.

ovum A female sex cell, or egg.

oxidation The removal of electrons from a substance.

oxidative phosphorylation Synthesis of ATP in which ATP synthase uses an H^+ gradient built by the electron transfer system as the energy source to make the ATP.

oxidized Substance from which the electrons are removed during oxidation.

oxytocin A hormone that stimulates the ejection of milk from the mammary glands of a nursing mother.

P generation The parental individuals used in an initial cross.

P site The site in the ribosome where the tRNA carrying the growing polypeptide chain is bound.

pacemaker cell A specialized cardiac muscle cell in the upper wall of the right atrium that sets the rate of contraction in the heart.

pairing Process in meiosis in which homologous chromosomes come together and pair. Also referred to as *synapsis*.

pair-rule genes In *Drosophila* embryonic development, the set of segmentation regulatory genes activated by gap genes that divide the embryo into units of two segments each.

paleobiology The study of ancient organisms.

pancreas A mixed gland composed of an exocrine portion that secretes digestive enzymes into the small intestine and an endocrine portion, the islets of Langerhans, that secretes insulin and glucagon.

parapatric speciation Speciation between populations with adjacent geographic distributions.

paraphyletic taxon A group of organisms that includes an ancestral species and some, but not all, of its descendants.

parapodia Fleshy lateral extensions of the body wall of aquatic annelids, used for locomotion and gas exchange.

parasite An organism that feeds on the tissues of or otherwise exploits its host.

parasitism A symbiotic interaction in which one species, the parasite, uses another, the host, in a way that is harmful to the host.

parasitoid An insect species in which a female lays eggs in the larva or pupa of another insect species, and her young consume the tissues of the living host.

parasympathetic division The division of the autonomic nervous system that predominates during quiet, low-stress situations, such as while relaxing.

parathyroid gland One of a pair of glands that produce parathyroid hormone (PTH) (found only in tetrapod vertebrates).

parathyroid hormone (PTH) The hormone secreted by the parathyroid glands in response to a fall in blood Ca^{2+} levels.

parental Phenotypes identical to the original parental individuals.

parental investment The time and energy devoted to the production and rearing of offspring.

parthenogenesis A mode of asexual reproduction in which animals produce offspring by the growth and development of an egg without fertilization.

partial diploid A condition in which part of the genome of a haploid organism is diploid. Recipients in bacterial conjugation between an Hfr and an F cell become partial diploids for part of the Hfr bacterial chromosome.

partial pressure The individual pressure exerted by each gas within a mixture of gases.

parturition The process of giving birth.

passive immunity The acquisition of antibodies as a result of direct transfer from another person.

passive parental care The amount of energy invested in offspring—in the form of the energy stored in eggs or seeds or energy transferred to developing young through a placenta—before they are born.

passive transport The transport of substances across cell membranes without expenditure of energy, as in diffusion.

paternal chromosome The chromosome derived from the male parent of an organism.

pathogenesis-related (PR) protein A hydrolytic enzyme that breaks down components of a pathogen's cell wall.

pattern formation The arrangement of organs and body structures in their proper three-dimensional relationships.

pectoral girdle A bony or cartilaginous structure in vertebrates that supports and is attached to the forelimbs.

pedicellariae Small pincers at the base of short spines in starfishes and sea urchins.

pedigree Chart that shows all parents and offspring for as many generations as possible, the sex of individuals in the different generations, and the presence or absence of a trait of interest.

pedipalp The second pair of appendages in the head of chelicerates.

pedomorphosis A common form of heterochrony in which juvenile characteristics are retained in a reproductive adult.

pelagic province The water in a marine biome.

pellicle A layer of supportive protein fibres located inside the cell, just under the plasma membrane, providing strength and flexibility instead of a cell wall.

pelvic girdle A bony or cartilaginous structure in vertebrates that supports and is attached to the hindlimbs.

pepsin An enzyme made in the stomach that breaks down proteins.

pepsinogen The inactive precursor molecule for pepsin.

peptide bond A link formed by a dehydration synthesis reaction between the —NH_2 group of one amino acid and the —COOH group of a second.

peptidoglycan A polymeric substance formed from a polysaccharide backbone tied together by short polypeptides, which is the primary structural molecule of bacterial cell walls.

peptidyl transferase An enzyme that catalyzes the reaction in which an amino acid is cleaved from the tRNA in the P site of the ribosome and forms a peptide bond with the amino acid on the tRNA in the A site of the ribosome.

peptidyl–tRNA A tRNA linked to a growing polypeptide chain containing two or more amino acids.

per capita growth rate The difference between the per capita birth rate and the per capita death rate of a population.

perennial A plant in which vegetative growth and reproduction continue year after year.

perfect flower A flower that has both male (stamen) and female (carpel) sexual organs.

perfusion The flow of blood or other body fluids on the internal side of the respiratory surface.

pericarp The fruit wall.

pericycle A tissue of plant roots, located between the endodermis and the phloem, which gives rise to lateral roots.

periderm The outermost portion of bark; consists of cork, cork cambium, and secondary cortex.

peripheral nervous system (PNS) All nerve roots and nerves (motor and sensory) that supply the muscles of the body and transmit information about sensation (including pain) to the central nervous system.

peripheral membrane protein Protein held to membrane surfaces by noncovalent bonds formed with the polar parts of integral membrane proteins or membrane lipids.

peristalsis The rippling motion of muscles in the intestine or other tubular organs characterized by the alternate contraction and relaxation of the muscles that propel the contents onward.

peritoneum The thin tissue derived from mesoderm that lines the abdominal wall and covers most of the organs in the abdomen.

peritubular capillary A capillary of the network surrounding the glomerulus.

permafrost Perpetually frozen ground below the topsoil.

peroxisome Microbody that produces hydrogen peroxide as a by-product.

petal Part of the corolla of a flower, often brightly coloured.

petiole The stalk by which a leaf is attached to a stem.

pH scale The numerical scale used by scientists to measure acidity.

phage *See* bacteriophage.

phagocytosis Process in which some types of cells engulf bacteria or other cellular debris to break them down.

pharynx The throat. In some invertebrates, a protrusible tube used to bring food into the mouth for passage to the gastrovascular cavity; in mammals, the common pathway for air entering the larynx and food entering the esophagus.

phenotype The outward appearance of an organism.

phenotypic variation Differences in appearance or function between individual organisms.

pheromone A distinctive volatile chemical released in minute amounts to influence the behaviour of members of the same species.

phloem The food-conducting tissue of a vascular plant.

phloem sap The solution of water and organic compounds that flows rapidly through the sieve tubes of flowering plants.

phosphate group Group consisting of a central phosphorus atom held in four linkages: two that bind —OH groups to the central phosphorus atom, a third that binds an oxygen atom to the central phosphorus atom, and a fourth that links the phosphate group to an oxygen atom.

phosphodiester bond The linkage of nucleotides in polynucleotide chains by a bridging phosphate group between the 5 carbon of one sugar and the 3 carbon of the next sugar in line.

phospholipid A phosphate-containing lipid.

phosphorus cycle A biogeochemcial cycle in which weathering and erosion carry phosphate ions from rocks to soil and into streams and rivers, which eventually transport them to the ocean, where they are slowly incorporated into rocks.

phosphorylation The addition of a phosphate group to a molecule.

photoautotroph A photosynthetic organism that uses light as its energy source and carbon dioxide as its carbon source.

photobiont The photosynthetic component of a lichen.

photoheterotroph An organism that uses light as the ultimate energy source but obtains carbon in organic form rather than as carbon dioxide.

photons Discrete particles or packets of energy.

photoperiodism The response of plants to changes in the relative lengths of light and dark periods in their environment during each 24-hour period.

photophosphorylation The synthesis of ATP coupled to the transfer of electrons energized by photons of light.

photopigment Light-absorbing pigment.

photopsin One of three photopigments in which retinal is combined with different opsins.

photoreceptor A sensory receptor that detects the energy of light.

photorespiration A process that metabolizes a by-product of photosynthesis.

photosynthesis The conversion of light energy to chemical energy in the form of sugar and other organic molecules.

photosystem A large complex into which the light-absorbing pigments for photosynthesis are organized with proteins and other molecules.

photosystem I In photosynthesis, a protein complex in the thylakoid membrane that uses energy absorbed from sunlight to synthesize NADPH.

photosystem II In photosynthesis, a protein complex in the thylakoid membrane that uses energy absorbed from sunlight to synthesize ATP.

phototroph An organism that obtains energy from light.

phototropism The tendency of a plant shoot to bend toward a source of light.

PhyloCode A formal set of rules governing phylogenetic nomenclature.

phylogenetic species concept A concept that seeks to delineate species as the smallest aggregate population that can be united by shared derived characters.

phylogenetic tree A branching diagram depicting the evolutionary relationships of groups of organisms.

phylogeny The evolutionary history of a group of organisms.

phylum (plural, phyla) A major Linnaean division of a kingdom, ranking above a class.

physiological respiration The process by which animals exchange gases with their surroundings—how they take in oxygen from the outside environment and deliver it to body cells and remove carbon dioxide from body cells and deliver it to the environment.

physiology The study of the functions of organisms—the physicochemical processes of organisms.

phytoalexin A biochemical that functions as an antibiotic in plants.

phytochrome A blue-green pigmented plant chromoprotein involved in the regulation of light-dependent growth processes.

phytoplankton Microscopic, free-flowing aquatic plants and protists.

phytosterol A sterol that occurs in plant cell membranes.

pigment A molecule that can absorb photons of light.

piloting A wayfinding mechanism in which animals use familiar landmarks to guide their journey.

pilus (plural, pili) A hair or hairlike appendage on the surface of a prokaryote.

pinacoderm In sponges, an unstratified outer layer of cells.

pineal gland A light-sensitive, melatonin-secreting gland that regulates some biological rhythms.

pinna The external structure of the outer ear, which concentrates and focuses sound waves.

pinocytosis *See* bulk-phase endocytosis.

pith The soft, spongelike, central cylinder of the stems of most flowering plants, composed mainly of parenchyma.

pituitary A gland consisting mostly of two fused lobes suspended just below the hypothalamus by a slender stalk of tissue that contains both neurons and blood vessels; it interacts with the hypothalamus to control many physiological functions, including the activity of some other glands.

placenta A specialized temporary organ that connects the embryo and fetus with the uterus in mammals, mediating the delivery of oxygen and nutrients. Analagous structures occur in other animals.

plasma The clear, yellowish fluid portion of the blood in which cells are suspended. Plasma consists of water, glucose and other sugars, amino acids, plasma proteins, dissolved gases, ions, lipids, vitamins, hormones and other signal molecules, and metabolic wastes.

plasma cell A large antibody-producing cell that develops from B cells.

plasma membrane The outer limit of the cytoplasm responsible for the regulation of substances moving into and out of cells.

plasmid A DNA molecule in the cytoplasm of certain prokaryotes, which often contains genes with functions that supplement those in the nucleoid and which can replicate independently of the nucleoid DNA and be passed along during cell division.

plasmodesma A minute channel that perforates a cell wall and contains extensions of the cytoplasm that directly connect adjacent plant cells.

plasmodial slime mould A slime mould of the class Myxomycetes.

plasmodium The composite mass of plasmodial slime moulds consisting of individual nuclei suspended in a common cytoplasm surrounded by a single plasma membrane.

plasmogamy The sexual stage of fungi during which the cytoplasms of two genetically different partners fuse.

plasmolysis Condition due to outward osmotic movement of water, in which plant cells shrink so much that they retract from their walls.

plastids A family of plant organelles.

plastron The ventral part of the shell of a turtle.

plate tectonics The geologic theory describing how Earth's crust is broken into irregularly shaped plates of rock that float on its semisolid mantle.

platelet An oval or rounded cell fragment enclosed in its own plasma membrane, which is found in the blood; they are produced in red bone marrow by the division of stem cells and contain enzymes and other factors that take part in blood clotting.

pleiotropy Condition in which single genes affect more than one character of an organism.

pleura The double layer of epithelial tissue covering the lungs.

ploidy The number of chromosome sets of a cell or species.

plumule The rudimentary terminal bud of a plant embryo located at the end of the hypocotyl, consisting of the epicotyl and a cluster of tiny foliage leaves.

poikilohydric Having little control over internal water content.

polar association Association that occurs when polar molecules attract and align themselves with other polar molecules and with charged ions and molecules.

polar body A nonfunctional cell produced in oogenesis.

polar covalent bond Bond in which electrons are shared unequally.

polar nucleus In the embryo sac of a flowering plant, one of two nuclei that migrate into the centre of the sac, become housed in a central cell, and eventually give rise to endosperm.

polar transport Unidirectional movement of a substance from one end of a cell (or other structure) to the other.

polarity The unequal distribution of yolk and other components in a mature egg.

pollen grain The male gametophyte of a seed plant.

pollen sac The microsporangium of a seed plant, in which pollen develops.

pollen tube A tube that grows from a germinating pollen grain through the tissues of a carpel and carries the sperm cells to the ovary.

pollination The transfer of pollen to a flower's reproductive parts by air currents or on the bodies of animal pollinators.

pollutant Materials or energy in a form or quantity that organisms do not usually encounter.

poly(A) tail The string of A nucleotides added posttranscriptionally to the 3′ end of a pre-mRNA molecule and retained in the mRNA produced from it that enables the mRNA to be translated efficiently and protects it from attack by RNA-digesting enzymes in the cytoplasm.

polyandry A polygamous mating system in which one female mates with multiple males.

polygamy A mating system in which either males or females may have many mating partners.

polygenic inheritance Inheritance in which several to many different genes contribute to the same character.

polygyny A polygamous mating system in which one male mates with many females.

polyhedral virus A virus in which the coat proteins form triangular units that fit together like the parts of a geodesic sphere.

polymerase chain reaction (PCR) Process that amplifies a specific DNA sequence from a DNA mixture to an extremely large number of copies.

polymerization Process in which monomers link together to form a polymer.

polymorphic development The production during development of one or more morphologically distinct forms.

polymorphism The existence of discrete variants of a character among individuals in a population.

polyp The tentacled, usually sessile stage in the life cycle of a coelenterate.

polypeptide The chain of amino acids formed by sequential peptide bonds.

polyphyletic taxa A group of organisms that belong to different evolutionary lineages and do not share a recent common ancestor.

polyploid An individual with one or more extra copies of the entire haploid complement of chromosomes.

polyploidy The condition of having one or more extra copies of the entire haploid complement of chromosomes.

polysaccharide Chain with more than 10 linked monosaccharide subunits.

polysome The entire structure of an mRNA molecule and the multiple associated ribosomes that are translating it simultaneously.

polyunsaturated Fatty acid with more than one double bond.

population All individuals of a single species that live together in the same place and time.

population bottleneck An evolutionary event that occurs when a stressful factor reduces population size greatly and eliminates some alleles from a population.

population density The number of individuals per unit area or per unit volume of habitat.

population ecology The ecological discipline that focuses on how a population's size and other characteristics change in space and time.

population genetics The branch of science that studies the prevalence and variation in genes among populations of individuals.

population size The number of individuals in a population at a specified time.

population viability analysis A mathematical analysis used by conservation biologists to determine the minimum viable population size for threatened or endangered species.

positive feedback A mechanism that intensifies or adds to a change in internal or external environmental condition.

positive pressure breathing A gulping or swallowing motion that forces air into the lungs.

posterior Indicating the tail end of an animal.

posterior pituitary The neural portion of the pituitary, which stores and releases two hormones made by the hypothalamus, antidiuretic hormone and oxytocin.

postsynaptic cell The neuron or the surface of an effector after a synapse that receives the signal from the presynaptic cell.

postsynaptic membrane The plasma membrane of the postsynaptic cell.

postzygotic isolating mechanism A reproductive isolating mechanism that acts after zygote formation.

potential energy Stored energy.

preadaptation A characteristic evolved by an ancestral species that serves an adaptive but different function in a descendant species or population.

precocial Born with fur and quickly mobile.

precursor mRNA (pre-mRNA) The primary transcript of a eukaryotic protein-coding gene, which is processed to form messenger RNA.

predation The interaction between predatory animals and the animal prey they consume.

prediction A statement about what the researcher expects to happen to one variable if another variable changes.

pregnancy The period of mammalian development in which the embryo develops in the uterus of the mother.

premolars Teeth located in pairs on each side of the upper and lower jaws of mammals, positioned behind the canines and in front of the molars.

prenatal diagnosis Techniques in which cells derived from a developing embryo or its surrounding tissues or fluids are tested for the presence of mutant alleles or chromosomal alterations.

prepuce Foreskin; a loose fold of skin that covers the glans of the penis.

pressure flow mechanism In vascular plants, pressure that builds up at the source end of a sieve tube system and pushes solutes by bulk flow toward a sink, where they are removed.

presynaptic cell The neuron with an axon terminal on one side of the synapse that transmits the signal across the synapse to the dendrite or cell body of the postsynaptic cell.

presynaptic membrane The plasma membrane of the axon terminal of a presynaptic cell, which releases neurotransmitter molecules into the synapse in response to the arrival of an action potential.

prezygotic isolating mechanism A reproductive isolating mechanism that acts prior to the production of a zygote, or fertilized egg.

primary active transport Transport in which the same protein that transports a substance also hydrolyzes ATP to power the transport directly.

primary cell layers The ectoderm, mesoderm, and endoderm layers that form the embryonic tissues.

primary cell wall The initial cell wall laid down by a plant cell.

primary consumer A herbivore, a member of the second trophic level.

primary endosymbiosis In the model for the origin of plastids in eukaryotes, the first event in which a eukaryotic cell engulfed a photosynthetic cyanobacterium.

primary growth The growth of plant tissues derived from apical meristems. *Compare* secondary growth.

primary immune response The response of the immune system to the first challenge by an antigen.

primary meristem Root and shoot apical meristems, from which a plant's primary tissues develop. *Compare* lateral meristem.

primary motor area The area of the cerebral cortex that runs in a band just in front of the primary somatosensory area and is responsible for voluntary movement.

primary plant body The portion of a plant that is made up of primary tissues.

primary producer An autotroph, usually a photosynthetic organism, a member of the first trophic level.

primary somatosensory area The area of the cerebral cortex that runs in a band across the parietal lobes of the brain and registers information on touch, pain, temperature, and pressure.

primary structure The sequence of amino acids in a protein.

primary succession Predictable change in species composition of an ecological community that develops on bare ground.

primary tissue A plant tissue that develops from an apical meristem.

primase An enzyme that assembles the primer for a new DNA strand during DNA replication.

primer A short nucleotide chain made of RNA that is laid down as the first series of nucleotides in a new DNA strand or made of DNA for use in the polymerase chain reaction (PCR).

primitive groove In the development of birds, the sunken midline of the primitive streak that acts as a conduit for migrating cells to move into the blastocoel.

primitive streak In the development of birds, the thickened region of the embryo produced by cells of the epiblast streaming toward the midline of the blastodisk.

Principle of Independent Assortment Mendel's principle that the alleles of the genes that govern two characters segregate independently during formation of gametes.

principle of monophyly A guiding principle of systematic biology that defines monophyletic taxa, each of which contains a single ancestral species and all of its descendants.

principle of parsimony A principle of systematic biology that states that a particular trait is unlikely to evolve independently in separate evolutionary lineages.

Principle of Segregation Mendel's principle that the pairs of alleles that control a character segregate as gametes are formed and that half the gametes carry one allele and the other half carry the other allele.

prion An infectious agent that contains only protein and does not include a nucleic acid molecule.

probability The possibility that an outcome will occur if it is a matter of chance.

procambium The primary meristem of a plant that develops into primary vascular tissue.

product An atom or molecule leaving a chemical reaction.

product rule Mathematical rule in which the final probability is found by multiplying individual probabilities.

production efficiency The ratio of the energy content of new tissue produced to the energy assimilated from food.

progesterone A female sex hormone that stimulates growth of the uterine lining and inhibits contractions of the uterus.

progestin A class of sex hormones synthesized by the gonads of vertebrates and active predominantly in females.

proglottid One of the segmentlike repeating units that constitute the body of a tapeworm.

prokaryote Organism in which the DNA is suspended in the cell interior without separation from other cellular components by a discrete membrane.

prokaryotic chromosome A single, typically circular DNA molecule.

prokaryotic flagellum A long, threadlike protein fibre that rotates in a socket in the plasma membrane and cell wall to push a prokaryotic cell through a liquid medium.

prolactin (PRL) A peptide hormone secreted by the anterior pituitary that stimulates breast development and milk secretion in mammals.

prometaphase A transition period between prophase and metaphase during which the microtubules of the mitotic spindle attach to the kinetochores and the chromosomes shuffle until they align in the centre of the cell.

promiscuity A mating system in which individuals do not form close pair bonds, and both males and females mate with multiple partners.

promoter The site to which RNA polymerase binds for initiating transcription of a gene.

promoter proximal region Upstream of a eukaryotic gene, a region containing regulatory sequences for transcription called promoter proximal elements.

proofreading mechanism Mechanism of DNA polymerase to back up and remove mispaired nucleotides from a newly synthesized DNA strand.

propagation In animal nervous systems, the concept that the action potential does not need further trigger events to keep going.

prophage A viral genome inserted in the host cell DNA.

prophase The beginning phase of mitosis during which the duplicated chromosomes within the nucleus condense from a greatly extended state into compact, rodlike structures.

proprioceptor A mechanoreceptor that detects stimuli used in the CNS to maintain body balance and equilibrium and to monitor the position of the head and limbs.

prostaglandin One of a group of local regulators derived from fatty acids that are involved in paracrine and autocrine regulation.

prostate gland An accessory sex gland in males that adds a thin, milky fluid to the semen and adjusts the pH of the semen to the level of acidity best tolerated by sperm.

protein Molecules that carry out most of the activities of life, including the synthesis of all other biological molecules. A protein consists of one or more polypeptides depending on the protein.

protein chip *See* protein microarray.

protein kinase Enzyme that transfers a phosphate group from ATP to one or more sites on particular proteins.

protein microarray Similar in concept to a DNA microarray, a solid surface with a microscopic grid with thousands of spaces containing probes for analyzing the proteome, the complete set of proteins encoded by the genome of an organism. Also referred to as a *protein chip*.

protein phosphatase Enzyme that removes phosphate groups from target proteins.

proteome The complete set of proteins that can be expressed by the genome of an organism.

proteomics The study of the proteome.

protist Organism currently classified in the kingdom Protista.

protobiont The term given to a group of abiotically produced organic molecules that are surrounded by a membrane or membranelike structure.

protocell A primitive cell-like structure that has some of the properties of life and that might have been the precursor of cells.

Protoctista The kingdom that includes all of the eukaryotes that are not fungi, plants, or animals.

protoderm The primary meristem that will produce stem epidermis.

proton Positively charged particle in the nucleus of an atom.

proton pump Pump that moves hydrogen ions across membranes and pushes hydrogen ions across the plasma membrane from the cytoplasm to the cell exterior. Also referred to as *H^+ pump*.

protonema The structure that arises when a liverwort or moss spore germinates and eventually gives rise to a mature gametophyte.

protonephridium The simplest form of invertebrate excretory tubule.

proton-motive force Stored energy that contributes to ATP synthesis and to the cotransport of substances to and from mitochondria.

proto-oncogene A gene that encodes various kinds of proteins that stimulate cell division. Mutated proto-oncogenes contribute to the development of cancer.

protoplast The cytoplasm, organelles, and plasma membrane of a plant cell.

protoplast fusion A plant-breeding process in which protoplasts are fused into a single cell.

protostome A division of the Bilateria in which the blastopore forms the mouth during development of the embryo and the anus appears later.

prototrophs Strains that are able to synthesize the necessary amino acids.

provirus The inserted viral DNA.

proximal convoluted tubule The tubule between the Bowman's capsule and the loop of Henle in the nephron of the kidney, which carries and processes the filtrate.

pseudocoelom A fluid- or organ-filled body cavity between the gut (a derivative of endoderm) and the muscles of the body wall (a derivative of mesoderm).

pseudocoelomate A body plan of bilaterally symmetrical animals with a body cavity that lacks a complete lining derived from mesoderm.

pseudopod (plural, pseudopodia) A temporary cytoplasmic extension of a cell.

psychrophile An archaean or bacterium that grows optimally at temperatures in the range of −10 to −20°C.

Pterophyta The plant phylum of ferns and their close relatives.

pulmocutaneous circuit In amphibians, the branch of a double blood circuit that receives deoxygenated blood and moves it to the skin and lungs or gills.

pulmonary circuit The circuit of the cardiovascular system that supplies the lungs.

pulvinus (plural, pulvini) A jointlike, thickened pad of tissue at the base of a leaf or petiole; flexes when the leaf makes nastic movements.

punctuated equilibrium hypothesis The evolutionary hypothesis that most morphological variation arises during speciation events in isolated populations at the edge of a species' geographic distribution.

Punnett square Method for determining the genotypes and phenotypes of offspring and their expected proportions.

pupa The nonfeeding stage between the larva and adult in the complete metamorphosis of some insects, during which the larval tissues are completely reorganized within a protective cocoon or hardened case.

pupil The dark centre in the middle of the iris through which light passes to the back of the eye.

purine A type of nitrogenous base with two carbon–nitrogen rings.

pyramid of biomass A diagram that illustrates differences in standing crop biomass in a series of trophic levels.

pyramid of energy A diagram that illustrates the amount of energy that flows through a series of trophic levels.

pyramid of numbers A diagram that illustrates the number of individual organisms present in a series of trophic levels.

pyrimidine A type of nitrogenous base with one carbon–nitrogen ring.

pyruvate oxidation (pyruvic acid oxidation) Stage of cellular respiration in which the three-carbon molecule pyruvate is converted into a two-carbon acetyl group that is completely oxidized to carbon dioxide.

qualitative variation Variation that exists in two or more discrete states, with intermediate forms often being absent.

quantitative variation Variation that is measured on a continuum (such as height in human beings) rather than in discrete units or categories.

quaternary structure The arrangement of polypeptide chains in a protein that contains more than one chain.

quiescent centre A region in a root apical meristem where there is no cell division.

quorum sensing The use of signalling molecules by prokaryotes to communicate and to coordinate their behaviour.

R gene A resistance gene in a plant; dominant R alleles confer enhanced resistance to plant pathogens.

R plasmid A bacterial plasmid containing genes that provide resistance to unfavourable conditions.

radial cleavage A cleavage pattern in deuterostomes in which newly formed cells lie directly above and below other cells of the embryo.

radial symmetry A body plan of organisms in which structures are arranged regularly around a central axis, like spokes radiating out from the centre of a wheel.

radiation The transfer of heat energy as electromagnetic radiation.

radicle The rudimentary root of a plant embryo.

radioactivity The giving off of particles of matter and energy by decaying nuclei.

radioisotope An unstable, radioactive isotope.

radiometric dating A dating method that uses measurements of certain radioactive isotopes to calculate the absolute ages in years of rocks and minerals.

radula The tooth-lined "tongue" of molluscs that scrapes food into small particles or drills through the shells of prey.

rain shadow An area of reduced precipitation on the leeward side of a mountain.

random coil An arrangement of the amino acid chain providing flexible regions that allow sections of the chain to bend.

random dispersion A pattern of distribution in which the individuals in a population are distributed unpredictably in their habitat.

rapid eye movement (REM) sleep The period during deep sleep when the delta wave pattern is replaced by rapid, irregular beta waves characteristic of the waking state. The person's heartbeat and breathing rate increase, the limbs twitch, and the eyes move rapidly behind the closed eyelids.

ray initial A cell in vascular cambium that gives rise to spokelike rays of parenchyma cells.

reabsorption The process in which some molecules (for example, glucose and amino acids) and ions are transported by the transport epithelium back into the body fluid (animals with open circulatory systems) or into the blood in capillaries surrounding the tubules (animals with closed circulatory systems) as the filtered solution moves through the excretory tubule.

reactants The atoms or molecules entering a chemical reaction.

reaction centre Part of photosystems I and II in chloroplasts of plants. In the light dependent reactions of photosynthesis, the reaction centre receives light energy absorbed by the antenna complex in the same photosystem.

reading frame A particular grouping of triplet bases read by transfer RNA during translation.

realized niche The range of conditions and resources that a population actually uses in nature.

receptacle The expanded tip of a flower stalk that bears floral organs.

reception In signal transduction, the binding of a signal molecule with a specific receptor in a target cell.

receptor protein Protein that recognizes and binds molecules from other cells that act as chemical signals.

receptor tyrosine kinase In signal transduction, a surface receptor with built-in protein kinase activity.

receptor-mediated endocytosis The selective uptake of macromolecules that bind to cell surface receptors concentrated in clathrin-coated pits.

recessive An allele that is masked by a dominant allele.

reciprocal altruism Form of altruistic behaviour in which individuals help nonrelatives if they are likely to return the favour in the future.

recognition protein Protein in the plasma membrane that identifies a cell as part of the same individual or as foreign.

recombinant Phenotype with a different combination of traits from those of the original parents.

recombinant DNA DNA from two or more different sources joined together.

recombination The physical exchange of segments between the chromatids of homologous chromosomes or between the chromosomes of prokaryotic cells or viruses.

recombination frequency In the construction of linkage maps of diploid eukaryotic organisms, the percentage of testcross progeny that are recombinants.

rectum The final segment of the large intestine.

red tide A growth in dinoflagellate populations that causes red, orange, or brown discoloration of coastal ocean waters.

redox reaction Coupled oxidation–reduction reaction in which electrons are removed from a donor molecule and simultaneously added to an acceptor molecule.

reduced Substance that receives electrons during reduction.

reduction The addition of electrons to a substance.

reflex A programmed movement that takes place without conscious effort, such as the sudden withdrawal of a hand from a hot surface.

refractory period A period that begins at the peak of an action potential and lasts a few milliseconds, during which the threshold required for generation of an action potential is much higher than normal.

reinforcement The enhancement of reproductive isolation that had begun to develop while populations were geographically separated.

relative abundance The relative commonness of populations within a community.

relative fitness The number of surviving offspring that an individual produces compared with the number left by others in the population.

release The process in which urine is released into the environment from the distal end of the excretory tubule.

release factor A protein that recognizes stop codons in the A site of a ribosome translating an mRNA and terminates translation. Also referred to as the *termination factor*.

releasing hormone (RH) A peptide neurohormone that controls the secretion of hormones from the anterior pituitary.

renal artery An artery that carries bodily fluids into the kidney.

renal cortex The outer region of the mammalian kidney that surrounds the renal medulla.

renal medulla The inner region of the mammalian kidney.

renal pelvis The central cavity in the kidney where urine drains from collecting ducts.

renal vein The vein that routes filtered blood away from the kidney.

renin An enzyme secreted by cells in the juxtaglomerular apparatus into the bloodstream that converts a blood protein into the peptide hormone angiotensin.

renin–angiotensin–aldosterone system (RAAS) The most important hormonal system involved in regulation of Na in mammals.

replica plating Technique for identifying and counting genetic recombinants in conjugation, transformation, or transduction experiments in which the colony pattern on a plate containing solid growth medium is pressed onto sterile velveteen and transferred to other plates containing different combinations of nutrients.

replicates Multiple subjects that receive either the same experimental treatment or the same control treatment.

replication fork The region of DNA synthesis where the parental strands separate and two new daughter strands elongate.

replication origin The site at which DNA replication begins.

repressible operon Operon whose expression is prevented by a repressor molecule.

repressor A regulatory protein that prevents the operon genes from being expressed.

reproduction The process in which parents produce offspring.

reproductive isolating mechanism A biological characteristic that prevents the gene pools of two species from mixing.

reproductive strategy A set of behaviours that lead to reproductive success.

residual volume The air that remains in lungs after exhalation.

resolution The minimum distance two points in a specimen can be separated and still be seen as two points.

resource partitioning The use of different resources or the use of resources in different ways by species living in the same place.

respiratory medium The environmental source of O_2 and the "sink" for released CO_2. For aquatic animals, the respiratory medium is water; for terrestrial animals, it is air.

respiratory surface A layer of epithelial cells that provides the interface between the body and the respiratory medium.

respiratory system All parts of the body involved in exchanging air between the external environment and the blood.

response In signal transduction, the last stage in which the transduced signal causes the cell to change according to the signal and to the receptors on the cell. In the nervous system, the output resulting from the integration of neural messages.

resting potential A steady negative membrane potential exhibited by the membrane of a neuron that is not stimulated—that is, not conducting an impulse.

restriction endonuclease (restriction enzyme) An enzyme that cuts DNA at a specific sequence.

restriction fragment A DNA fragment produced by cutting a long DNA molecule with a restriction enzyme.

restriction fragment length polymorphisms When comparing different individuals, restriction enzyme–generated DNA fragments of different lengths from the same region of the genome.

reticular formation A complex network of interconnected neurons that runs through the length of the brain stem, connecting to the thalamus at the anterior end and to the spinal cord at the posterior end.

retina A light-sensitive membrane lining the posterior part of the inside of the eye.

retrotransposon A transposable element that transposes via an intermediate RNA copy of the transposable element.

retrovirus A virus with an RNA genome that replicates via a DNA intermediate.

reverse transcriptase An enzyme that uses RNA as a template to make a DNA copy of the retrotransposon. Reverse transcriptase is used to make DNA copies of RNA in test tube reactions.

reversible The term indicating that a reaction may go from left to right or from right to left, depending on conditions.

rhizoid A modified hypha that anchors a fungus to its substrate and absorbs moisture.

rhizome A horizontal, modified stem that can penetrate a substrate and anchor the plant.

rhodopsin The retinal–opsin photopigment.

rhynchocoel A coelomic cavity that contains the proboscis of nemerteans.

ribonucleic acid (RNA) A polymer assembled from repeating nucleotide monomers in which the five-carbon sugar is ribose. Cellular RNAs are mRNA (which is translated to produce a polypeptide), tRNA (which brings an amino acid to the ribosome for assembly into a polypeptide during translation), and rRNA (which is a structural component of ribosomes). The genetic material of some viruses is RNA.

ribose A five-carbon sugar to which the nitrogenous bases in nucleotides link covalently.

ribosomal RNA (rRNA) The RNA component of ribosomes.

ribosome A ribonucleoprotein particle that carries out protein synthesis by translating mRNA into chains of amino acids.

ribosome binding site In translation initiation in prokaryotes, a sequence just upstream of the start codon that directs the small ribosomal subunit to bind and orient correctly for the complete ribosome to assemble and start translating in the correct spot.

ribozyme An RNA-based catalyst that is part of the biochemical machinery of all cells.

ring species A species with a geographic distribution that forms a ring around uninhabitable terrain.

RNA *See* ribonucleic acid.

RNA interference (RNAi) The phenomenon of silencing a gene posttranscriptionally by a small, single-stranded RNA that is complementary to part of an mRNA.

RNA polymerase An enzyme that catalyzes the assembly of nucleotides into an RNA strand.

rod In the vertebrate eye, a type of photoreceptor in the retina that is specialized for detection of light at low intensities.

root An anchoring structure in land plants that also absorbs water and nutrients and (in some plant species) stores food.

root cap A dome-shaped cell mass that forms a protective covering over the apical meristem in the tip of a plant root.

root hair A tubular outgrowth of the outer wall of a root epidermal cell; root hairs absorb much of a plant's water and minerals from the soil.

root nodule A localized swelling on a root in which symbiotic nitrogen-fixing bacteria reside.

root pressure The pressure that develops in plant roots as the result of osmosis, forcing xylem sap upward and out through leaves. *See also* guttation.

root primordium A rudimentary root.

root system An underground (or submerged) network of roots with a large surface area that favours the rapid uptake of soil water and dissolved mineral ions.

rough ER Endoplasmic reticulum with many ribosomes studding its outer surface.

round window A thin membrane that faces the middle ear.

r-selected species A short-lived species adapted to function well in a rapidly changing environment.

RuBP carboxylase/oxygenase (rubisco) An enzyme that catalyzes the key reaction of the Calvin cycle, carbon fixation, in which CO_2 combines with RuBP (ribulose 1,5-bisphosphate) to form 3-phosphoglycerate.

ruminant An animal that has a complex, four-chambered stomach.

S phase The phase of the cell cycle during which DNA replication occurs.

saccule A fluid-filled chamber in the vestibular apparatus that provides information about the position of the head with respect to gravity (up versus down), as well as changes in the rate of linear movement of the body.

salicylic acid (SA) In plants, a chemical synthesized following a wound that has multiple roles in plant defences, including interaction with jasmonates in signalling cascades.

salivary amylase A substance that hydrolyzes starches to the disaccharide maltose.

salivary gland A gland that secretes saliva through a duct on the inside of the cheek or under the tongue; the saliva lubricates food and begins digestion.

salt marsh A tidal wetland dominated by emergent grasses and reeds.

saltatory conduction A mechanism that allows small-diameter axons to conduct impulses rapidly.

saprotroph An organism nourished by dead or decaying organic matter.

sapwood The newly formed outer wood located between heartwood and the vascular cambium. Compared with heartwood, it is wet, lighter in colour, and not as strong.

sarcomere The basic unit of contraction in a myofibril.

sarcoplasmic reticulum In vertebrate muscle fibres, a complex system of vesicles modified from the smooth endoplasmic reticulum that encircles the sarcomeres. The sarcoplasmic reticulum is part of the pathway for the stimulation of muscle contraction by neural signals.

saturated enzymes Enzymes for which increases in substrate concentration have no effect on the reaction rate.

saturated fatty acid Fatty acid with only single bonds linking the carbon atoms.

savanna A biome comprising grasslands with few trees, which grows in areas adjacent to tropical deciduous forests.

schizocoelom In protostomes, the body cavity that develops as inner and outer layers of mesoderm separate.

Schwann cell A type of glial cell in the PNS that wraps nerve fibres with myelin and also secretes regulatory factors.

scientific method An investigative approach in which scientists make observations about the natural world, develop working explanations about what they observe, and then test those explanations by collecting more information.

scientific name A two-part name identifying the genus to which a species belongs and designating a particular species within that genus.

scientific theory A broadly applicable idea or hypothesis that has been confirmed by every conceivable test.

sclereid A type of sclerenchyma cell; sclereids typically are short and have thick, lignified walls.

sclerenchyma A ground tissue in which cells develop thick secondary walls, which commonly are lignified and perforated by pits through which water can pass.

sclerotium Tough mass of hyphae, often serving as a survival or overwintering structure.

scolex The anterior (head) of a tapeworm, adapted for fastening the worm to the intestinal epithelium of its host.

scrotum The baglike sac in which the testes are suspended in many mammals.

scutellum The shield-shaped cotyledon of a grass.

second law of thermodynamics Principle that for any process in which a system changes from an initial to a final state, the total disorder of the system and its surroundings always increases.

second messenger In particular, signal transduction pathways, an internal, nonprotein signal molecule that directly or indirectly activates protein kinases, which elicit the cellular response.

secondary active transport Transport indirectly driven by ATP hydrolysis.

secondary cell wall A layer added to the cell wall of plants that is more rigid and may become many times thicker than the primary cell wall.

secondary consumer A carnivore that feeds on herbivores, a member of the third trophic level.

secondary endosymbiosis In the model for the origin of plastids in eukaryotes, the second event, in which a nonphotosynthetic eukaryote engulfed a photosynthetic eukaryote.

secondary growth Plant growth that originates at lateral meristems and increases the diameter of older roots and stems. *Compare* primary growth.

secondary immune response The rapid immune response that occurs during the second (and subsequent) encounters of the immune system of a mammal with a specific antigen.

secondary metabolite Organic compound not required for the growth or survival of an organism; tends to be biologically active.

secondary plant body The part of a plant made up of tissues that develop from lateral meristems.

secondary productivity Energy stored in new consumer biomass as energy is transferred from producers to consumers.

secondary structure Regions of alpha helix, beta strand, or random coil in a polypeptide chain.

secondary succession Predictable changes in species composition in an ecological community that develops after existing vegetation is destroyed or disrupted by an environmental disturbance.

secondary tissue In plants, the tissue that develops from lateral meristems.

secretion A selective process in which specific small molecules and ions are transported from the body fluids (in animals with open circulatory systems) or blood (in animals with closed circulatory systems) into the excretory tubules.

secretory vesicle Vesicle that transports proteins to the plasma membrane.

seed The structure that forms when an ovule matures after a pollen grain reaches it and a sperm fertilizes the egg.

seed coat The outer protective covering of a seed.

segment polarity genes In *Drosophila* embryonic development, the set of segmentation regulatory genes activated by pair-rule genes that set the boundaries and anterior–posterior axis of each segment in the embryo.

segmentation The production of body parts and some organ systems in repeating units.

segmentation genes Genes that work sequentially, progressively subdividing the embryo into regions, determining the segments of the embryo and the adult.

segregation The separation of the pairs of alleles that control a character as gametes are formed.

selective cell adhesion A mechanism in which cells make and break specific connections to other cells or to the extracellular matrix.

selectively neutral *See* neutral variation hypothesis.

selectively permeable Membranes that selectively allow, impede, or block the passage of atoms and molecules.

self-fertilization (self-pollination) Fertilization in which sperm nuclei in pollen produced by anthers fertilize egg cells housed in the carpel of the same flower.

self-incompatibility In plants, the inability of a plant's pollen to fertilize ovules of the same plant.

semen The secretions of several accessory glands in which sperm are mixed prior to ejaculation.

semicircular canal A part of the vestibular apparatus that detects rotational (spinning) motions.

semiconservative replication The process of DNA replication in which the two parental strands separate and each serves as a template for the synthesis of new progeny double-stranded DNA molecules.

semilunar valve (SL valve) A flap of endocardium and connective tissue reinforced by fibres that prevent the valve from turning inside out.

seminal fluid Fluid secreted by the seminal vesicles that contains prostaglandins, which, when ejaculated into the female, trigger contractions of the female reproductive tract that help move the sperm into and through the uterus.

seminal vesicle A vesicle that secretes seminal fluid.

seminiferous tubule One of the tiny tubes in the testes where sperm cells are produced, grow, and mature.

senescence The biologically complex process of aging in mature organisms that leads to the death of cells and eventually the whole organism.

sense codon A codon that specifies an amino acid.

sensitization Increased responsiveness to mild stimuli after experiencing a strong stimulus; one of the simplest forms of memory.

sensor A tissue or organ that detects a change in an external or internal factor such as pH, temperature, or the concentration of a molecule such as glucose.

sensory adaptation A condition in which the effect of a stimulus is reduced if it continues at a constant level.

sensory hair cell A hair cell that sends impulses along the auditory nerve to the brain when alternating changes of pressure agitate the basilar membrane on which the organ of Corti rests, moving the hair cells.

sensory neuron A neuron that transmits stimuli collected by their sensory receptors to interneurons.

sensory receptor (transducer) A receptor formed by the dendrites of afferent neurons or by specialized receptor cells making synapses with afferent neurons that pick up information about the external and internal environments of the animal.

sensory transduction The conversion of a stimulus into a change in membrane potential.

sepal One of the separate, usually green parts forming the calyx of a flower.

septum (plural, septa) A thin partition or cross wall that separates body segments.

sequential hermaphroditism The form of hermaphroditism in which individuals change from one sex to the other.

serosa The serous membrane: a thin membrane lining the closed cavities of the body; has two layers with a space between that is filled with serous fluid.

Sertoli cell One of the supportive cells that completely surrounds developing spermatocytes in the seminiferous tubules. Follicle-stimulating hormone stimulates Sertoli cells to secrete a protein and other molecules that are required for spermatogenesis.

sessile Unable to move from one place to another.

set point The level at which the condition controlled by a homeostatic pathway is to be maintained.

seta (plural, setae) A chitin-reinforced bristle that protrudes outward from the body wall in some annelid worms.

sex chromosomes Chromosomes that are different in male and female individuals of the same species.

sex pilus *See* F pilus.

sex ratio The relative proportions of males and females in a population.

sex-linked gene Gene located on a sex chromosome.

sexual dimorphism Differences in the size or appearance of males and females.

sexual reproduction The mode of reproduction in which male and female parents produce offspring through the union of egg and sperm generated by meiosis.

sexual selection A form of natural selection established by male competition for access to females and by the females' choice of mates.

shells *See* energy levels.

shoot system The stems and leaves of a plant.

short-day plant A plant that flowers in late summer or early autumn when dark periods become longer and light periods become shorter.

short-term memory Memory that stores information for seconds.

sieve tube A series of phloem cells joined end to end, forming a long tube through which nutrients are transported; seen mainly in flowering plants.

sieve tube member Any of the main conducting cells of phloem that connect end to end, forming a sieve tube.

sign stimulus A simple cue that triggers a fixed action pattern.

signal peptide A short segment of amino acids to which the signal recognition particle binds, temporarily blocking further translation. A signal peptide is found on polypeptides that are sorted to the endoplasmic reticulum. Also referred to as *signal sequence*.

signal recognition particle (SRP) Protein–RNA complex that binds to signal sequences and targets polypeptide chains to the endoplasmic reticulum.

signal sequence *See* signal peptide.

signal transduction The series of events by which a signal molecule released from a controlling cell causes a response (affects the function) of target cells with receptors for the signal. Target cells process the signal in the three sequential steps of reception, transduction, and response.

silencing Phenomenon in which methylation of cytosines in eukaryotic promoters inhibits transcription and turns the genes off.

silent mutation A base-pair substitution mutation in a protein-coding gene that does not alter the amino acid specified by the gene.

simple diffusion Mechanism by which certain small substances diffuse through the lipid part of a biological membrane.

simple fruit A fruit that develops from a single ovary; in many of them, at least one layer of the pericarp is fleshy and juicy.

simulation modelling An analytical method in which researchers gather detailed information about a system and then create a series of mathematical equations that predict how the components of the system interact and respond to change.

simultaneous hermaphroditism A form of hermaphroditism in which individuals develop functional ovaries and testes at the same time.

single lens eye An eye type that works by changing the amount of light allowed to enter into the eye and by focusing this incoming light with a lens.

single-stranded binding protein Protein that coats single-stranded segments of DNA, stabilizing the DNA for the replication process.

sink Any region of a plant where organic substances are being unloaded from the sieve tube system and used or stored.

sink population In metapopulation analysis, a population that routinely declines in size after being replenished by immigrants from a source population.

sinoatrial node (SA node) The region of the heart that controls the rate and timing of cardiac muscle cell contraction.

sinus A body space that surrounds an organ.

sister chromatid One of two exact copies of a chromosome duplicated during replication.

skeletal muscle A muscle that connects to bones of the skeleton, typically made up of long and cylindrical cells that contain many nuclei.

slime layer A coat typically composed of polysaccharides that is loosely associated with bacterial cells.

SLOSS (Single Large Or Several Small) The debate among conservation biologists about the relative merits of establishing fewer large preserves or more numerous small ones.

slow block to polyspermy The process in which enzymes released from cortical granules alter the egg coats within minutes after fertilization so that no other sperm can attach and penetrate to the egg.

slow muscle fibre A muscle fibre that contracts relatively slowly and with low intensity.

small interfering RNA (siRNA) A class of single-stranded RNAs that cause RNA interference.

small ribonucleoprotein particle A complex of RNA and proteins.

smooth ER Endoplasmic reticulum with no ribosomes attached to its membrane surfaces. Smooth ER has various functions, including synthesis of lipids that become part of cell membranes.

smooth muscle A relatively small and spindle-shaped muscle cell in which actin and myosin molecules are arranged in a loose network rather than in bundles.

social behaviour The interactions that animals have with other members of their species.

sodium–potassium pump *See* Na^+/K^+ pump.

soil solution A combination of water and dissolved substances that coats soil particles and partially fills pore spaces.

solenoid *See* 30 nm chromatin fibre.

solute The molecules of a substance dissolved in water.

solution Substance formed when molecules and ions separate and are suspended individually, surrounded by water molecules.

solvent The water in a solution in which the hydration layer prevents polar molecules or ions from reassociating.

somaclonal selection A procedure in which somatic embryos derived from tissue culture are screened to identify those having desired characteristics, such as disease resistance.

somatic cell Any of the cells of an organism's body other than reproductive cells.

somatic embryo A plant embryo that is genetically identical to the parent because it arose through asexual means.

somatic gene therapy Gene therapy in which genes are introduced into somatic cells.

somatic nervous system A subdivision of the peripheral nervous system controlling body movements that are primarily conscious and voluntary.

somites Paired blocks of mesoderm cells along the vertebrate body axis that form during early vertebrate development and differentiate into dermal skin, bone, and muscle.

soredium (plural, soredia) A specialized cell cluster produced by lichens, consisting of a mass of algal cells surrounded by fungal hyphae; soredia function like reproductive spores and can give rise to a new lichen.

sorus (plural, sori) A cluster of sporangia on the underside of a fern frond; reproductive spores arise by meiosis inside each sporangium.

source In plants, any region (such as a leaf) where organic substances are being loaded into the sieve tube system of phloem.

source population In metapopulation analyses, a population that is either stable or increasing in size.

Southern blot analysis Technique in which labelled probes are used to detect specific DNA fragments that have been separated by gel electrophoresis.

spatial summation The summation of EPSPs produced by firing of different presynaptic neurons.

specialized transduction Transfer of bacterial genes between bacteria using temperate phages that have incorporated fragments of the bacterial genome as they make the transition from the lysogenic cycle to the lytic cycle.

speciation The process of species formation.

species A group of populations in which the individuals are so closely related in structure, biochemistry, and behaviour that they can successfully interbreed.

species cluster A group of closely related species recently descended from a common ancestor.

species composition The particular combination of species that occupy a site.

species diversity A community characteristic defined by species richness and the relative abundance of species.

species richness The number of species that live within an ecological community.

species selection A type of natural selection that acts on species rather than on populations.

specific epithet The species name in a binomial.

specific heat The amount of heat required to increase the temperature of a given quantity of water.

sperm Motile gamete.

spermatocyte A developing gamete that becomes a spermatid at the end of meiosis.

spermatogenesis The process of producing sperm.

spermatogonium (plural, spermatogonia) A cell that enters meiosis and gives rise to gametes, produced by mitotic divisions of the germ cells in males.

spermatozoon Also called sperm; a haploid cell that develops into a mature sperm cell when meiosis is complete.

sphincter A powerful ring of smooth muscle that forms a valve between major regions of the digestive tract.

spinal cord A column of nervous tissue located within the vertebral column and directly connected to the brain.

spinal nerve A nerve that carries signals between the spinal cord and the body trunk and limbs.

spindle The structure that separates sister chromatids and moves them to opposite spindle poles.

spindle pole One of the pair of centrosomes in a cell undergoing mitosis from which bundles of microtubules radiate to form the part of the spindle from that pole.

spinneret A modified abdominal appendage from which spiders secrete silk threads.

spiracle An opening in the chitinous exoskeleton of an insect through which air enters and leaves the tracheal system.

spiral cleavage The cleavage pattern in many protostomes in which newly produced cells lie in the space between the two cells immediately below them.

spiral valve A corkscrew-shaped fold of mucous membrane in the digestive system of elasmobranchs, which slows the passage of material and increases the surface area available for digestion and absorption.

spirillum (plural, spirilla) Any flagellated aerobic bacterium twisted helically like a corkscrew.

spliceosome A complex formed between the pre-mRNA and small ribonucleoprotein particles, in which mRNA splicing takes place.

spongocoel The central cavity in a sponge.

spontaneous reaction Chemical or physical reaction that occurs without outside help.

sporangium (plural, sporangia) A single-celled or multicellular structure in fungi and plants in which spores are produced.

spore A haploid reproductive structure, usually a single cell, that can develop into a new individual without fusing with another cell; found in plants, fungi, and certain protists.

sporophyll A specialized leaf that bears sporangia (spore-producing structures).

sporophyte An individual of the diploid generation produced through fertilization in organisms that undergo alternation of generations; it produces haploid spores.

sporopollenin A tough polymer in the walls of spores and pollen grains, the presence of which helps such structures resist decay.

spring overturn The mixing of surface water with deep water in a lake or pond, causing oxygen at the surface to move to the bottom and nutrients from the bottom to move to the surface.

squalene A liver oil found in sharks that is lighter than water, which increases their buoyancy.

SRP (signal recognition particle) receptor A protein on the membrane of the endoplasmic reticulum that binds the signal recognition particle.

stability The ability of a community to maintain its species composition and relative abundances when environmental disturbances eliminate some species from the community.

stabilizing selection A type of natural selection in which individuals expressing intermediate phenotypes have the highest relative fitness.

stamen A "male" reproductive organ in flowers, consisting of an anther (pollen producer) and a slender filament.

standing crop biomass The total dry weight of plants present in an ecosystem at a given time.

stapes The smallest of three sound-conducting bones in the middle ear of tetrapod vertebrates.

starch Energy-providing carbohydrates stored in plant cells.

start codon The first codon read in an mRNA in translation—AUG. Also referred to as the *initiator codon*.

statocyst A mechanoreceptor in invertebrates that senses gravity and motion using statoliths.

statolith A movable starch- or carbonate-containing stonelike body involved in sensing gravitational pull.

stele The central core of vascular tissue in roots and shoots of vascular plants; it consists of the xylem and phloem together with supporting tissues.

stem cell Undifferentiated cells in most multicellular organisms that can divide without differentiating and also can divide and differentiate into specialized cell types.

stereocilia Microvilli covering the surface of hair cells clustered in the base of neuromasts.

steroid A type of lipid derived from cholesterol.

steroid hormone receptor Internal receptor that turns on specific genes when it is activated by binding a signal molecule.

steroid hormone response element The DNA sequence to which the hormone receptor complex binds.

sterol Steroid with a single polar —OH group linked to one end of the ring framework and a complex, nonpolar hydrocarbon chain at the other end.

sticky end End of a DNA fragment, with a single-stranded structure that can form hydrogen bonds with a complementary sticky end on any other DNA molecule cut with the same enzyme.

stigma The receptive end of a carpel where deposited pollen germinates.

stoma (plural, stomata) The opening between a pair of guard cells in the epidermis of a plant leaf or stem, through which gases and water vapour pass.

stomach The portion of the digestive system in which food is stored and digestion begins.

stop codon A codon that does not specify amino acids. The three nonsense codons are UAG, UAA, and UGA. Also referred to as the *nonsense codon* and *termination codon.*

stratification Horizontal layering of sedimentary rocks beneath the soil surface.

stretch receptor A proprioceptor in the muscles and tendons of vertebrates that detects the position and movement of the limbs.

strict aerobe Cell with an absolute requirement for oxygen to survive, unable to live solely by fermentations.

strict anaerobe Organism in which fermentation is the only source of ATP.

strobilus *See* cone.

stroma An inner compartment of a chloroplast, enclosed by two boundary membranes and containing a third membrane system.

stromatolite Fossilized remains of ancient cyanobacterial mats that carried out photosynthesis by the water-splitting reaction.

structural genomics The sequencing of genomes and the analysis of the nucleotide sequences to locate genes and other functionally important sequences within the genome.

structural isomers Two molecules with the same chemical formula but atoms that are arranged in different ways.

style The slender stalk of a carpel situated between the ovary and the stigma in plants.

suberin A waxy, waterproof substance present in cork cells.

submucosa A thick layer of elastic connective tissue that contains neuron networks and blood and lymph vessels.

subsoil The region of soil beneath topsoil, which contains relatively little organic matter.

subspecies A taxonomic subdivision of a species.

substrate The particular reacting molecule or molecular group that an enzyme catalyzes.

substrate-level phosphorylation An enzyme-catalyzed reaction that transfers a phosphate group from a substrate to ADP.

succession The change from one community type to another.

sugar–phosphate backbone Structure in a polynucleotide chain that is formed when deoxyribose sugars are linked by phosphate groups in an alternating sugar–phosphate–sugar–phosphate pattern.

sulfhydryl group A group that works as a molecular fastener, consisting of a sulphur atom linked on one side to a hydrogen atom and on the other side to a carbon chain.

sum rule Mathematical rule in which final probability is found by summing individual probabilities.

surface tension The force that places surface water molecules under tension, making them more resistant to separation than the underlying water molecules.

survivorship curve Graphic display of the rate of survival of individuals over a species' life span.

suspension feeder An animal that ingests small food items suspended in water.

suspensor In seed plants, a stalklike row of cells that develops from a zygote and helps position the embryo close to the nourishing endosperm.

swim bladder A gas-filled internal organ that helps fish maintain buoyancy.

symbiont An organism living in symbiosis with another organism; the symbionts are not usually closely related.

symbiosis An interspecific interaction in which the ecological relations of two or more species are intimately tied together.

symmetry (adj., symmetrical) Exact correspondence of form and constituent configuration on opposite sides of a dividing line or plane.

sympathetic division Division of the autonomic nervous system that predominates in situations involving stress, danger, excitement, or strenuous physical activity.

sympatric Occupying the same spaces at the same time.

sympatric speciation Speciation that occurs without the geographic isolation of populations.

symplastic pathway The route taken by water that moves through the cytoplasm of plant cells (the symplast). *Compare* apoplastic pathway.

symport The transport of two molecules in the same direction across a membrane. Also referred to as *cotransport.*

synapse A site where a neuron makes a communicating connection with another neuron or an effector such as a muscle fibre or gland.

synapsid One of a group of amniotes with one temporal arch on each side of the head, which includes living mammals.

synapsis *See* pairing.

synaptic cleft A narrow gap that separates the plasma membranes of the presynaptic and postsynaptic cells.

synaptic vesicle A secretory vesicle in the cytoplasm of an axon terminal of a neuron, in which neurotransmitters are stored.

synaptonemal complex A protein framework that tightly holds together homologous chromosomes as they pair.

systematics The branch of biology that studies the diversity of life and its evolutionary relationships.

systemic acquired resistance A plant defence response to microbial invasion; defensive chemicals including salicylic acid may spread throughout a plant, rendering healthy tissues less vulnerable to infection.

systemic circuit In amphibians, the branch of a double blood circuit that receives oxygenated blood and provides the blood supply for most of the tissues and cells of a body.

systemin A plant peptide hormone that functions in defence responses to wounds.

systems biology An area of biology that studies the organism as a whole to unravel the integrated and interacting network of genes, proteins, and biochemical reactions responsible for life.

systole The period of contraction and emptying of the heart.

T cell A lymphocyte produced by the division of stem cells in the bone marrow and then released into the blood and carried to the thymus. T cells participate in adaptive immunity.

T (transverse) tubule The tubule that passes in a transverse manner from the sarcolemma across a myofibril of striated muscle.

tactile signal A means of animal communication in which the signaller uses touch to convey a message to the signal receiver.

taiga *See* boreal forest.

taproot system A root system consisting of a single main root from which lateral roots can extend; often stores starch.

TATA box A regulatory DNA sequence found in the promoters of many eukaryotic genes transcribed by RNA polymerase II.

taxis A behavioural response that is directed either toward or away from a specific stimulus.

taxon (plural, taxa) A name designating a group of organisms included within a category in the Linnaean taxonomic hierarchy.

taxonomic hierarchy A system of classification based on arranging organisms into ever more inclusive categories.

taxonomy The science of the classification of organisms into an ordered system that indicates natural relationships.

T-cell receptor (TCR) A receptor that covers the plasma membrane of a T cell, specific for a particular antigen.

telomerase An enzyme that adds telomere repeats to chromosome ends.

telomeres Repeats of simple-sequence DNA that maintain the ends of linear chromosomes.

telophase The final phase of mitosis, during which the spindle disassembles, the chromosomes decondense, and the nuclei re-form.

temperate bacteriophage Bacteriophage that may enter an inactive phase (lysogenic cycle) in which the host cell replicates and passes on the bacteriophage DNA for generations before the phage becomes active and kills the host (lytic cycle).

temperate deciduous forest A forested biome found at low to middle altitudes at temperate latitudes, with warm summers, cold winters, and annual precipitation between 75 and 250 cm.

temperate grassland A nonforested biome that stretches across the interiors of most continents, where winters are cold and snowy and summers are warm and fairly dry.

temperate rain forest A coniferous forest biome supported by heavy rain and fog, which grows where winters are mild and wet and the summers are cool.

template A nucleotide chain used in DNA replication for the assembly of a complementary chain.

template strand The DNA strand that is copied into an RNA molecule during gene transcription.

temporal isolation A prezygotic reproductive isolating mechanism in which species live in the same habitat but breed at different times of day or different times of year.

temporal summation The summation of several EPSPs produced by successive firing of a single presynaptic neuron over a short period of time.

tendon A type of fibrous connective tissue that attaches muscles to bones.

terminal bud A bud that develops at the apex of a shoot.

termination codon *See* stop codon.

termination factor *See* release factor.

terminator Specific DNA sequence for a gene that signals the end of transcription of a gene. Terminators are common for prokaryotic genes.

territory A plot of habitat, defended by an individual male or a breeding pair of animals, within which the territory holders have exclusive access to food and other necessary resources.

tertiary consumer A carnivore that feeds on other carnivores, a member of the fourth trophic level.

tertiary structure The overall three-dimensional folding of a polypeptide chain.

testcross A genetic cross between an individual with the dominant phenotype and a homozygous recessive individual.

testis (plural, testes) The male gonad. In male vertebrates, they secrete androgens and steroid hormones that stimulate and control the development and maintenance of male reproductive systems.

testosterone A hormone produced by the testes, responsible for the development of male secondary sex characteristics and the functioning of the male reproductive organs.

tetanus A situation in which a muscle fibre cannot relax between stimuli, and twitch summation produces a peak level of continuous contraction.

tetrad Homologous pair consisting of four chromatids.

Tetrapoda A monophyletic lineage of vertebrates that includes animals with four feet, legs, or leglike appendages.

T-even bacteriophage Virulent bacteriophages, T2, T4, and T6, that have been valuable for genetic studies of bacteriophage structure and function.

thalamus A major switchboard of the brain that receives sensory information and relays it to the regions of the cerebral cortex concerned with motor responses to sensory information of that type.

thallus A plant body not differentiated into stems, roots, or leaves.

thermal acclimatization A set of physiological changes in ectotherms in response to seasonal shifts in environmental temperature, allowing the animals to attain good physiological performance at both winter and summer temperatures.

thermodynamics The study of the energy flow during chemical and physical reactions.

thermoreceptor A sensory receptor that detects the flow of heat energy.

thermoregulation The control of body temperature.

thick filament A type of filament in striated muscle composed of myosin molecules; they interact with thin filaments to shorten muscle fibres during contraction.

thigmomorphogenesis A plant response to a mechanical disturbance, such as frequent strong winds; includes inhibition of cellular elongation and production of thick-walled supportive tissue.

thigmotropism Growth in response to contact with a solid object.

thin filament A type of filament in striated muscle composed of actin, tropomyosin, and troponin molecules; they interact with thick filaments to shorten muscle fibres during contraction.

thorax The central part of an animal's body, between the head and the abdomen.

thorn forest A forested biome that grows at the arid borders of true savanna, where large mammals are less abundant.

threshold potential In signal conduction by neurons, the membrane potential at which the action potential fires.

thylakoids Flattened, closed sacs that make up a membrane system within the stroma of a chloroplast.

thymine A pyrimidine that base-pairs with adenine.

thymus An organ of the lymphatic system that plays a role in filtering viruses, bacteria, damaged cells, and cellular debris from the lymph and bloodstream and in defending the body against infection and cancer.

thyroid gland A gland located beneath the voice box (larynx) that secretes hormones regulating growth and metabolism.

thyroid-stimulating hormone (TSH) A hormone that stimulates the thyroid gland to grow in size and secrete thyroid hormones.

thyroxine (T4) The main hormone of the thyroid gland, responsible for controlling the rate of metabolism in the body.

Ti (tumour-inducing) plasmid A plasmid used to make transgenic plants.

tidal volume The volume of air entering and leaving the lungs during inhalation and exhalation.

tight junction Region of tight connection between membranes of adjacent cells.

time lag The delayed response of organisms to changes in environmental conditions.

tissue A group of cells and intercellular substances with the same structure that function as a unit to carry out one or more specialized tasks.

tolerance hypothesis Hypothesis asserting that ecological succession proceeds because competitively superior species replace competitively inferior ones.

tonoplast The membrane that surrounds the central vacuole in a plant cell.

topoisomerase An enzyme that relieves the overtwisting and strain of DNA ahead of the replication fork.

topsoil The rich upper layer of soil where most plant roots are located; it generally consists of sand, clay particles, and humus.

torpor A sleeplike state produced when a lowered set point greatly reduces the energy required to maintain body temperature, accompanied by reductions in metabolic, nervous, and physical activity.

torsion The realignment of body parts in gastropod molluscs that is independent of shell coiling.

totipotent Having the capacity to produce cells that can develop into or generate a new organism or body part.

trace element An element that occurs in organisms in very small quantities (0.01%); in nutrition, a mineral required by organisms only in small amounts.

tracer Isotope used to label molecules so that they can be tracked as they pass through biochemical reactions.

trachea In insects, an extensively branched, air-conducting tube formed by invagination of the outer epidermis of the animal and reinforced by rings of chitin. In vertebrates, the windpipe, which branches into the bronchi.

tracheal system A branching network of tubes that carries air from small openings in the exoskeleton of an insect to tissues throughout its body.

tracheid A conducting cell of xylem, usually elongated and tapered.

tracheophyte A plant with xylem, phloem, and usually well-developed roots, stems, and leaves.

traditional evolutionary systematics An approach to systematics that uses phenotypic similarities and differences to infer evolutionary relationships, grouping together species that share both ancestral and derived characters.

trait A particular variation in a genetic or phenotypic character.

transcription The mechanism by which the information encoded in DNA is made into a complementary RNA copy.

transcription factor Proteins that recognize and bind to the TATA box and then recruit the polymerase.

transcription initiation complex Combination of general transcription factors with RNA polymerase II.

transcription unit A region of DNA that transcribes a single primary transcript.

transcriptional regulation The processes that directly control gene activity.

transduction In cell signalling, the process of changing a signal into the form necessary to cause the cellular response. In prokaryotes, the process in which DNA is transferred from donor to recipient bacterial cells by an infecting bacteriophage.

transfer cell Any of the specialized cells that form when large amounts of solutes must be loaded or unloaded into the phloem; they facilitate the short-distance transport of organic solutes from the apoplast into the symplast.

transfer RNA (tRNA) The RNA that brings amino acids to the ribosome for addition to the polypeptide chain.

transformation The conversion of the hereditary type of a cell by the uptake of DNA released by the breakdown of another cell.

transgenic An organism that has been modified to contain genetic information from an external source.

transition state An intermediate arrangement of atoms and bonds that both the reactants and the products of a reaction can assume.

translation The use of the information encoded in the RNA to assemble amino acids into a polypeptide.

translocation In genetics, a chromosomal alteration that occurs if a broken segment is attached to a different, nonhomologous chromosome. In vascular plants, the long-distance transport of substances by xylem and phloem.

transmembrane pathway The path followed by water when it enters root cells by crossing across the plasma membrane.

transmission In neural signalling, the sending of a message along a neuron and then to another neuron or to a muscle or gland.

transpiration The evaporation of water from a plant, principally from the leaves.

transport The controlled movement of ions and molecules from one side of a membrane to the other.

transport epithelium A layer of cells with specialized transport proteins in their plasma membranes.

transport protein A protein embedded in the cell membrane that forms a channel allowing selected polar molecules and ions to pass across the membrane.

transposable element (TE) A sequence of DNA that can move from one place to another within the genome of a cell.

transposase An enzyme that catalyzes some of the reactions inserting or removing the transposable element from the DNA.

transposition Mechanism of movement of transposable elements involving nonhomologous recombination.

transposon A bacterial transposable element with an inverted repeat sequence at each end enclosing a central region with one or more genes.

tricarboxylic acid cycle *See* citric acid cycle.

trichocyst A dartlike protein thread that can be discharged from a surface organelle for defence or to capture prey.

trichome A single-celled or multicellular outgrowth from the epidermis of a plant that provides protection and shade and often gives the stems or leaves a hairy appearance.

triglyceride A nonpolar compound produced when a fatty acid binds by a dehydration synthesis reaction at each of glycerol's three —OH-bearing sites.

triiodothyronine (T3) A hormone secreted by the thyroid gland that regulates metabolism.

trimester A division of human gestation, three months in length.

triploblastic An animal body plan in which adult structures arise from three primary germ layers: endoderm, mesoderm, and ectoderm.

trochophore The small, free-swimming, ciliated aquatic larva of various invertebrates, including certain molluscs and annelids.

trophic cascade The effects of predator–prey interactions that reverberate through other population interactions at two or more trophic levels in an ecosystem.

trophic level A position in a food chain or web that defines the feeding habits of organisms.

trophoblast The outer single layer of cells of the blastocyst.

trophozoite Motile, feeding stage of *Giardia* and other single-celled protists.

tropic hormone A hormone that regulates hormone secretion by another endocrine gland.

tropical deciduous forest A tropical forest biome that occurs where winter drought reduces photosynthesis and most trees drop their leaves seasonally.

tropical forest Any forest that grows between the Tropics of Capricorn and Cancer, a region characterized by high temperature and rainfall and thin, nutrient-poor topsoil.

tropical montane forest A tropical forest biome of short trees, which are frequently enveloped in mist; also known as a "cloud forest."

tropical rain forest A dense tropical forest biome that grows where some rain falls every month, mean annual rainfall exceeds 250 cm, mean annual temperature is at least 25°C, and humidity is above 80%.

tropics The latitudes between 23.5° N and 23.5° S, the Tropics of Cancer and Capricorn.

tropism The turning or bending of an organism or one of its parts toward or away from an external stimulus, such as light, heat, or gravity.

true-breeding Individual that passes traits without change from one generation to the next.

tumour-suppressor gene A gene that encodes proteins that inhibit cell division.

turgor pressure The internal hydrostatic pressure within plant cells.

turgor pressure The normal fullness or tension produced by the fluid content of plant and animal cells.

turnover rate The rate at which one generation of producers in an ecosystem is replaced by the next.

tympanum A thin membrane in the auditory canal that vibrates back and forth when struck by sound waves.

umbilical cord A long tissue with blood vessels linking the embryo and the placenta.

umbilicus Navel; the scar left when the short length of umbilical cord still attached to the infant after birth dries and shrivels within a few days.

undernutrition A condition in animals in which intake of organic fuels is inadequate or whose assimilation of such fuels is abnormal.

undulating membrane In parabasalid protists, a finlike structure formed by a flagellum buried in a fold of the cytoplasm that facilitates movement through thick and viscous fluids. An expansion of the plasma membrane in some flagellates that is usually associated with a flagellum.

unicellular organism Individual consisting of a single cell.

uniform dispersion A pattern of distribution in which the individuals in a population are evenly spaced in their habitat.

uniformitarianism The concept that the geologic processes that sculpted Earth's surface over long periods of time—such as volcanic eruptions, earthquakes, erosion, and the formation and movement of glaciers—are exactly the same as the processes observed today.

universal A feature of the nucleic acid code, with the same codons specifying the same amino acids in all living organisms.

unreduced gamete A gamete that contains the same number of chromosomes as a somatic cell.

unsaturated Fatty acid with one or more double bonds linking the carbons.

ureter The tube through which urine flows from the renal pelvis to the urinary bladder.

urethra The tube through which urine leaves the bladder. In most animals, the urethra opens to the outside.

urinary bladder A storage sac located outside the kidneys.

uterine cycle The menstrual cycle.

uterus A specialized saclike organ, in which the embryo develops in viviparous animals.

utricle A fluid-filled chamber of the vestibular apparatus that provides information about the position of the head with respect to gravity (up versus down), as well as changes in the rate of linear movement of the body.

vaccination The process of administering a weakened form of a pathogen to patients as a means of giving them immunity to subsequent infection, and disease, caused by that pathogen.

vagina The muscular canal that leads from the cervix to the exterior.

valence electron An electron in the outermost energy level of an atom.

van der Waals forces Weak molecular attractions over short distances.

variable An environmental factor that may differ among places or an organismal characteristic that may differ among individuals.

vas deferens The tube through which sperm travel from the epididymis to the urethra in the male reproductive system.

vascular bundle A cord of plant vascular tissue; often multistranded with both xylem and phloem.

vascular cambium A lateral meristem that produces secondary vascular tissues in plants.

vascular plant *See* tracheophyte.

vascular tissue system One of the three tissue systems in plants that provide the foundation for plant organs; it consists of transport tubes for water and nutrients.

vegetal pole The end of the egg opposite the animal pole, which typically gives rise to internal structures such as the gut and the posterior end of the embryo.

vegetative reproduction Asexual reproduction in plants by which new individuals arise (or are created) without seeds or spores; examples include fragmentation from the parent plant or the use of cuttings by gardeners.

vein In a plant, a vascular bundle that forms part of the branching network of conducting and supporting tissues in a leaf or other expanded plant organ. In an animal, a vessel that carries the blood back to the heart.

veliger A second larva that occurs after the trochophore in some molluscs.

ventilation The flow of the respiratory medium (air or water, depending on the animal) over the respiratory surface.

ventral Indicating the lower or "belly" side of an animal.

ventricle In the brain, an irregularly shaped cavity containing cerebrospinal fluid. In the heart, a chamber that pumps blood out of the heart.

venule A capillary that merges into the small veins leaving an organ.

vernalization The stimulation of flowering by a period of low temperature.

vertebrae The series of bones that form the vertebral column of vertebrate animals.

vertebral column The series of vertebrae that surrounds and protects the dorsal nerve cord and forms the supporting axis of the body.

vertebrate A member of the monophyletic group of tetrapod animals that possess a vertebral column.

vesicle A small, membrane-bound compartment that transfers substances between parts of the endomembrane system.

vessel In plants, one of the tubular conducting structures of xylem, typically several centimetres long; most angiosperms and some other vascular plants have xylem vessels.

vessel member Any of the short cells joined end to end in tubelike columns in xylem.

vestibular apparatus The specialized sensory structure of the inner ear of most terrestrial vertebrates that is responsible for perceiving the position and motion of the head and, therefore, for maintaining equilibrium and for coordinating head and body movements.

vestigial structure An anatomical feature of living organisms that no longer retains its function.

vibrio Any of various short, motile, S-shaped or comma-shaped bacteria of the genus *Vibrio*.

vicariance The fragmentation of a continuous geographic distribution by nonbiological factors.

virion A complete virus particle.

viroid A plant pathogen that consists of strands or circles of RNA, smaller than any viral DNA or RNA molecule, that have no protein coat.

virulent bacteriophage Bacteriophage that kills its host bacterial cells during each cycle of infection.

virus An infectious agent that contains either DNA or RNA surrounded by a protein coat.

visceral mass In molluscs, the region of the body containing the internal organs.

visual signal A means of communication in which animals use facial expressions or body language to send messages to other individuals.

vital capacity The maximum tidal volume of air that an individual can inhale and exhale.

vitamin An organic molecule required in small quantities that the animal cannot synthesize for itself.

vitamin D A steroidlike molecule that increases the absorption of Ca^{2+} and phosphates from ingested food by promoting the synthesis of a calcium-binding protein in the intestine; it also increases the release of Ca^{2+} from bone in response to PTH.

vitelline coat A gel-like matrix of proteins, glycoproteins, or polysaccharides immediately outside the plasma membrane of an egg cell.

vitreous humour The jellylike substance that fills the main chamber of the eye, between the lens and the retina.

viviparous Referring to animals that retain the embryo within the mother's body and nourish it during at least early embryo development.

voltage-gated ion channel A membrane-embedded protein that opens and closes as the membrane potential changes.

vulva The external female sex organs.

water lattice An arrangement formed when a water molecule in liquid water establishes an average of 3.4 hydrogen bonds with its neighbours.

water potential The potential energy of water, representing the difference in free energy between pure water and water in cells and solutions; it is the driving force for osmosis.

watershed An area of land from which precipitation drains into a single stream or river.

water-soluble vitamin A vitamin with a high proportion of oxygen and nitrogen able to form hydrogen bonds with water.

wavelength The distance between two successive peaks of electromagnetic radiation.

wax A substance insoluble in water that is formed when fatty acids combine with long-chain alcohols or hydrocarbon structures.

wetland A highly productive ecotone often at the border between a freshwater biome and a terrestrial biome.

white matter The myelinated axons that surround the grey matter of the central nervous system.

wilting The drooping of leaves and stems caused by a loss of turgor.

wobble hypothesis Hypothesis stating that the complete set of 61 sense codons can be read by fewer than 61 distinct tRNAs because of particular pairing properties of the bases in the anticodons.

Wolffian duct A bipotential primitive duct associated with the gonads that leads to a cloaca.

wood The secondary xylem of trees and shrubs, lying under the bark and consisting largely of cellulose and lignin.

X chromosome Sex chromosome that occurs paired in female cells and single in male cells.

X-linked recessive inheritance Pattern in which displayed traits are due to inheritance of recessive alleles carried on the X chromosome.

X-ray diffraction Method for deducing the position of atoms in a molecule.

xylem The plant vascular tissue that distributes water and nutrients.

xylem sap The dilute solution of water and solutes that flows in the xylem.

Y chromosome Sex chromosome that is paired with an X chromosome in male cells.

yeast A single-celled fungus that reproduces by budding or fission.

yolk The portion of an egg that serves as the main energy source for the embryo.

yolk sac In an amniote egg, an extraembryonic membrane that encloses the yolk.

zero population growth A circumstance in which the birth rate of a population equals the death rate.

zona pellucida A gel-like matrix of proteins, glycoproteins, or polysaccharides immediately outside the plasma membrane of the egg cell.

zone of cell division The region in a growing root that consists of the root apical meristem and the actively dividing cells behind it.

zone of elongation The region in a root where newly formed cells grow and elongate.

zone of maturation The region in a root above the zone of elongation where cells do not increase in length but may differentiate further and take on specialized roles.

zooplankton Small, usually microscopic, animals that float in aquatic habitats.

zygospore A multinucleate, thick-walled sexual spore in some fungi that is formed from the union of two gametes.

zygote A fertilized egg.

Credits

This page constitutes an extension of the copyright page. We have made every effort to trace the ownership of all copyrighted material and to secure permission from copyright holders. In the event of any question arising as to the use of any material, we will be pleased to make the necessary corrections in future printings. Thanks are due to the following authors, publishers, and agents for permission to use the material indicated.

CHAPTER 1 **1:** (top left) The Bridgeman Art Library/Getty Images **1:** (top right) © The London Art Archive / Alamy **2:** NASA **6:** (a) NASA **6:** (b) Photo in 2004 by L. Lodwick **7:** (bottom right) PLANT CELL. ONLINE by Melanie Schmidt, Gunther Geßner, Matthias Luff, Ines Heiland, Volker Wagner, Marc Kaminski, Stefan Geimer, Nicole Eitzinger, Tob. Copyright 2006 by American Society of Plant Biologists. Reproduced with permission of American Society of Plant Biologists in the format Textbook, CD-ROM and DVD via Copyright Clearance Center. **8:** (top left) Photo: M.B. Fenton **9:** (top) © E. R. Degginger **9:** (bottom) © Chris Newbert **13:** Photo: M.B. Fenton **15:** (a) Photo: M.B. Fenton **15:** (b) Photo: M.B. Fenton **15:** (c) Photo: M.B. Fenton **15:** (bottom left) Corel **16:** (all photos) M.B. Fenton **17:** (a–c) Corel **17:** (bottom right) Image collection of the University of Wisconsin-La Crosse. Image used with permission **18:** (top left) Photo: Thomas Hawk **18:** (top right) Reprinted by permission from Macmillan Publishers Ltd: Nature, vol. 427, Issue 6973, copyright 2004. **19:** (top left a, b) W. R. Jeffery, "Adaptive Evolution of Eye Degeneration in the Mexican Blind Cavefish", The Journal of Heredity, 2004, vol. 96, issue number 3, pp. 186, by permission of Oxford University Press. **19:** ((bottom left) a) Steve Miller/Naval Research Lab **19:** ((bottom left) b) Photo: Steven Haddock **19:** ((bottom left) c) Cas Liber **19:** ((bottom left) d) Photo: Mike Sauder

CHAPTER 2 **23:** Time & Life Pictures/Getty Images **24:** (top right) Art Wolfe/Stone/Getty Images **24:** (bottom right) Credit: US Government Public Domain **24:** (top left) Sascha Burkard/Shutterstock **24:** (top right) Steve Byland/Shutterstock **24:** (top right) harmeet/StockXchng **24:** (top right) © Karin Duthie / Alamy **24:** (top right) © PHOTOTAKE Inc. / Alamy **24:** (top right) © Tim Pannell/ CORBIS **24:** (top right) © Visuals Unlimited/ Corbis **25:** (top left) US Government Public Domain **25:** (a) Tony Brain /SPL/Photo Research ers **25:** (b) M. Abbey/Visuals Unlimited **25:** (c) Wim van Egmond/ Visuals Unlimited **25:** (d) Manfred Kage/Peter Arnold **25:** (e) C. E. Jeffree, et al, Planta, 172 (1):20–37, 1987. Reprinted. **26:** (left) From Freeman, S. Biological Science, 2/E. Published by Benjamin Cummings. Copyright © 2004 by Pearson Education. Adapted by permission of the publisher. **26:** (right) World Perspectives/Getty Images **27:** Photo by Chesley Bonestell **28:** (top left) Dr. Ken Macdonald/SPL/Photo Researchers, Inc. **28:** (bottom right) Dr. W. Hargreaves and D. Deamer **32:** (a) Bill Bachmann, Photo Researchers, Inc. **32:** (b) Stanley M. Awramik **33:** Dr. G. Cohen-Bazire **34:** (top left) Yuri Arcurs/ Shutterstock **34:** a) © Visuals Unlimited/Corbis **34:** b) © Visuals Unlimited/Corbis **34:** c) Ed Reschke / Peter Arnold Inc. **39:** (a) J. U. Shuler/ Photo Researchers **39:** (b) Courtesy of Mary Osborn, Max Planck Institute for Biophysical Chemistry, Goettingen FRG **39:** (c) Courtesy of Dr. Vincenzo Cirulli, Lab. of Developmental Biology, The Whittier Inst. for Diabetes, Univ. of Cal.-San Diego, La Jolla, CA **41:** (b) Don Fawcett/Photo Researchers **42:** (top) Lennart Nilsson **42:** (bottom) CNRI/SPL/Photo Researchers **43:** Gary Carlson / Photo Researchers, Inc.

CHAPTER 3 **47:** From Russell et al., SCIENCE 320, p. 340–346 (18 April 2008). Reprinted with permission from AAAS. **48:** Edward Snow/ Bruce Coleman USA **48:** Jamie and Judy Wild/ Danita Delimont. com **48:** Jamie and Judy Wild/ Danita Delimont. com **48:** Ron Sefton/ Bruce Coleman USA **48:** © Bryan Allen/ Corbis **49:** (a) Photo: UBC Botanical Garden and Centre for Plant Research. **49:** (b) Photo by M.B. Fenton **49:** (c) Stephen Sharnoff **49:** (d) Image: Natural History Museum **49:** (e) Photo by M.B. Fenton **49:** (f) Photo by M.B. Fenton **49:** (g) Photo by M.B. Fenton **49:** (h) Photo by M.B. Fenton **53:** From Miller, J.D., Scott, E.C., Okamoto, S., Public Acceptance of Evolution, Science, Vol. 313, 11 August 2006: pp. 765–766. Reprinted with permission from AAAS. **55:** Reprinted by permission from Macmillan Publishers Ltd: Nature, Vol. 389: pp. 33–39. The origin and early evolution of plants on land by Paul Kenrick, Peter R. Crane, copyright (1997). **56:** From Francesca D. Ciccarelli, Tobias Doerks, Christian von Mering, Christopher J. Creevey, Berend Snel, Peer Bork, "Public Toward Automatic Reconstruction of a Highly Resolved Tree of Life", Science, Vol. 311, 3 March 2006: pp. 1283–1287. Reprinted with permission from AAAS. **61:** Photo: Skip Pierce **62:** (a, b) Photo by M.B. Fenton **62:** (bottom right) Photo by Andy Didyk **63:** (top left) © DLILLC/Corbis **63:** (center left) Photo by M.B. Fenton **63:** (bottom left) Photo by M.B. Fenton **63:** (bottom right) Photo by M.B. Fenton **64:** (a) Photo by M.B. Fenton **64:** (b) Photo by M.B. Fenton **64:** (c) Photo by M.B. Fenton **64:** (d) Photo by M.B. Fenton **64:** (e) Photo by M.B. Fenton **64:** (f) Photo by M.B. Fenton **64:** (g) Photo by M.B. Fenton **64:** (h) Photo by M.B. Fenton **66:** (top left) Yuri Arcurs/Shutterstock **66:** Clare et al. 2007. Molecular Ecology notes, 7:184–190. Reprinted by permission of Blackwell Publishing **67:** Alex Borisenko, © 2006, Royal Ontario Museum **68:** Barcode of Life

CHAPTER 4 **73:** © Corel **74:** (a) © Lehtikuva [2005] all rights reserved **74:** (b) © Wally McNamee/ CORBIS **74:** (bottom right) © David Young-Wolff / PhotoEdit **75:** Monkey Business Images/Shutterstock **76:** Anna Lyubimtseva/iStockPhoto **82:** (top left) Yuri Arcurs/Shutterstock **82:** (a, b) Photo: Denis Maxwell **89:** Douglas Faulkner/ Sally Faulkner Collection

CHAPTER 5 **96:** Don W. Fawcett/ Photo Researchers, Inc. **105:** (all photos) M. Sheetz, R. Painter, and S. Singer. Journal of Cell Biology, 70:493 (1976). By permission of Rockefeller University Press **108:** (d) M. M. Perry and A. M. Gilbert **109:** Mike Abbey/Visuals Unlimited **111:** (top left) Yuri Arcurs/Shutterstock

CHAPTER 6 **115:** Professors P. Motta & T. Naguro/ SPL/ Photo Researchers, Inc. **123:** Micrographs, M. Sheetz, R. Painter, and S. Singer. Journal of Cell Biology, 70:493, 1976. By permission of Rockefeller University Press. **127:** (top left) Yuri Arcurs/Shutterstock **133:** David M. Phillips/ Visuals Unlimited

CHAPTER 7 **139:** NASA/Goddard Space Flight Centre **141:** Craig Tuttle/CORBIS **150:** (top left) Yuri Arcurs/Shutterstock **154:** © PHOTOTAKE Inc. / Alamy **156:** (top right) PhotoDisc/ Getty Images **156:** (bottom right) Chris Heller/Corbis

CHAPTER 8 **161:** © Russell Kightley Media **162:** Visuals Unlimited **164:** (top left) Yuri Arcurs/ Shutterstock

CHAPTER 9 **179:** Dr. Paul Andres, University of Dundee/Science Photo Library/Photo Researchers, Inc. **180:** (top left) Photo used with permission from Damn Funny Pictures **180:** (a) © John Cancalosi / Alamy **180:** (b) © M.Brodie / Alamy **181:** Conly Rieder **183:** Photo provided by Fengtang Yang and Malcolm Ferguson-Smith of Cambridge University. **184–185:** (all photos) Ed Reschke **186:** (left, all) Ed Reschke **186:** (right) Leonard Lessin / Peter Arnold Inc. **187:** (top) D.M. Phillips / Visuals Unlimited **187:** (bottom) R. Calentine / Visuals Unlimited **189:** Photograph by Dr. Conly L. Rieder, Wadsworh Center, Albany, New York 12201-0509 **192:** Courtesy of Professor Pierre Chambon, Institut Clinique de la Souris, University of Strasbourg. Reprinted by permission from Nature 348:699. Copyright 1990 Macmillan Magazines, Ltd. **193:** Courtesy of Dr. Sydney Brenner **196:** (top left) Yuri Arcurs/Shutterstock

CHAPTER 10. **199:** © VOLVOX Inc. Tsuneo Nakamura Marine Photo Office **203:** (left, a) © Dennis Kunkel **203:** (left, b) Courtesy of L. G. Caro and Academic Press, Inc. (London) Ltd. from Journal of Molecular Biology 16.269.1966 **203:** (right, a) Dr. Huntington Porter and Dr. David Dressler **203:** (right, b) Prof. Stanley Cohen/SPL/Photo Researchers, Inc. **214–215:** Micrographs with thanks to the John Innes Foundation Trustees **216:** (top row, left) Marc Henrie/Dorling Kindersley/Getty Images **216:** (top row, centre) Dave King/Dorling Kindersley/Getty Images **216:** (top row, right) Elena Butinova/Shutterstock **216:** (bottom row, left) Dave King/Dorling Kindersley/Getty Images **216:** (bottom row, centre) Lexx/Shutterstock **216:** (bottom row, right) Dave King/Dorling Kindersley/ Getty Images **217:** (top left) Yuri Arcurs/Shutterstock **217:** (top right) Photo by Oana Marcu **220:** Courtesy Oliver von Weinstein **223:** Nik Kleinberg

CHAPTER 11 **229:** Carolyn A. McKeone/Science Photo Library/Photo Researchers, Inc. **230:** (a, b) Stanley Flegler/Visuals Unlimited **230:** (bottom left) Moravian Museum, Brno **239:** (a) Dr. P. Marazzi/Photo Researchers, Inc. **239:** (b) St. Bartholomew's Hospital/Photo Researchers, Inc. **239:** (c) David Frazier/Photo Researchers, Inc. **240:** (top left) William Ferguson **240:** (top right) William Ferguson **240:** (bottom) Francese Muntada/CORBIS **243:** (a) Michael Stuckey/ Comstock, Inc. **243:** (b) Bosco Broyer, Photo by Gary Head **243:** (c) Michael Stuckey/Comstock, Inc. **244:** Dan Fairbanks/Brigham Young University **246:** (top left) Yuri Arcurs/Shutterstock

CHAPTER 12 **249:** Regents of University of California 2005/Dr. Uli Weier/Photo Researchers, Inc. **250:** Eddie Adams/AP Wide World Photos **255:** (right) Eyewire/ Getty Images **255:** (left) Photodisc/Getty Images **256:** (a) © Carolina Biological Supply/Visuals Unlimited **256:** (b) © Terry Gleason/Carolina Biological Supply **258:** © Bettman/CORBIS **259:** Ulrike Schanz/ Animals, Animals—Earth Scenes **262:** (top left) © 1997, Hironao Numabe, M.D., Tokyo Medical University **262:** (top right) Permission of Carol Lafrate **263:** (top left) Yuri Arcurs/Shutterstock **264:** © Abraham Menashe **270:** (bottom) Bonnie Kamin/ Stuart Kenter Associates **270:** (top) Carolina Biological Supply Company

CHAPTER 13 **271:** Kenneth Edward/ Photo Researchers, Inc. **272:** A. C. Barrington Brown © 1968 J.D. Watson **277:** SPL/Photo Researchers, Inc **289:** (top left) Yuri Arcurs/Shutterstock **290:** (left) O.L. Miller, Jr. Steve McKnight **290:** (right) B. Hamkalo

CHAPTER 14 **295:** © LookatSciences/Phototake **296:** (left) Dennis Hallinan **296:** (right) Bob Evans/ Peter Arnold, Inc. **307:** (left) Yuri Arcurs/ Shutterstock **307:** (right) From: Structure and in vitro activity of group II introns (G. Bassi, M. Costa, F. Michel), CNRS. **313:** © Arco Images GmbH / Alamy **314:** Courtesy Barbara A. Hamkalo

CHAPTER 15 **321:** Abby Dernburg and Terumi Kohwi-Shigematsu/ Lawrence Berkeley National Laboratory **322:** Lennart Nilsson/ Bonnier Fakta **334:** (top left) Yuri Arcurs/Shutterstock **338:** Lennart Nilsson ©Boehringer Ingelheim International GmbH

CHAPTER 16 **343:** Pasteka/ SPL/ Photo Researchers, Inc. **347:** Photo courtesy of Lucigen Corporation, Middleton, WI **351:** Damon Biotech, Inc. **358:** R. Brinster, R.E. Hammer, School of Veterinary Medicine, University of Pennsylvania **359:** PA News Photo Library/AP Wide World Photos **360:** Stephen Wolfe, Molecular and Cellular Biology **362:** (bottom) Dr. Jorge Mayer, Golden Rice Project **362:** (top) Kevin V. Wood **366:** (top left) Yuri Arcurs/Shutterstock **368:** Courtesy Ludwig Institute for Cancer Research

CHAPTER 17 **373:** © Mark Moffett/Foto Natura/ Minden Pictures **374:** (top) The Advertising Archives, London **374:** (a) George Vernard/Foto Natural/Photo Researchers, Inc. **374:** (b) Timothy A. Pearce, Ph.D./Section of Mollusks/Carnegie Museum of Natural History. Photograph by Mindy McNaugher **375:** Arthur Morris/VIREO **376:** (left) Eric Crichton/Bruce Coleman, Inc. **376:** (right) William E. Ferguson **381:** (top) David Neal Parks **381:** (bottom) W. Carter Johnson **382:** Frans Lanting/ Minden Pictures **386:** Forrest W. Buchanan/Visuals Unlimited **386:** (top left) Modified from Weis & Abrahamson. 1986. American Naturalist 127 p. 687 **386:** (top right) Gregory K. Scott/Photo Researchers, Inc. **386:** (bottom) Heather Angel/Natural Visions **387:** (left) © 2008 Josef Hlasek **387:** (right) Modified from Andersson. 1982. Nature 299: 818–820 (Figure 1b) **390:** Modified from Cain & Sheppard. 1954. Natural selection in Cepaea. Genetics 39: 89–116. **392:** (top left) Yuri Arcurs/Shutterstock

CHAPTER 18 **395:** © Waterscan **396:** Photo by M.B. Fenton **397:** (top) Ingo Schlupp photo **397:** (bottom) From Evolutionary Ecology: Sex and the Single Killifish by Elizabeth Pennisi, Science, Vol. 313, p. 1381. Reprinted with permission from AAAS. **398:** © David Hosking / Alamy **399:** Photo by B. Clare **400:** COSEWIC **401:** (top right) Reprinted by permission from Macmillan Publishers Ltd: Nature, "Biogeography: Molecular trails from hitch-hiking snails", by Edmund Gittenberger, Dick S. J. Groenenberg, Bas Kokshoorn and Richard C. Preece, vol. 439, p. 409, copyright (2006). **401:** (bottom left) © 4nature.at / Alamy **401:** (bottom right) From Hale et al., "Impact of Landscape Management on the Genetic Structure of Red Squirrel Populations.", Science, Vol. 293, pp. 2246–2248, Sep 21, 2001. Reprinted with permission from AAAS. **402:** (bottom left) Credit: K. Roy, UCSD **402:** (bottom right) From Hale et al., "Impact of Landscape Management on the Genetic Structure of Red Squirrel Populations.", Science, Vol. 293, pp. 2246–2248, Sep 21, 2001. Reprinted with permission from AAAS. **403:** From Michael E. Hellberg, Deborah P. Balch, Kaustuv Roy, "Climate-Driven Range Expansion and Morphological Evolution in a Marine Gastropod", Science, vol. 292, Jun 1, 2001, pp. 1707–1710. Reprinted with permission from AAAS. **403:** From Michael E. Hellberg, Deborah P. Balch, Kaustuv Roy, "Climate-Driven Range Expansion and Morphological Evolution in a Marine Gastropod", Science, vol. 292, Jun 1, 2001, pp. 1707–1710. Reprinted with permission from AAAS. **405:** Courtesy of James E. Lloyd. Miscellaneous Publications of the Museum of Zoology of the University of Michigan, 130:1–195, 1966. **406:** (all photos) Reny Parker **407:** (top left) © DLILLC/Corbis **408:** © DLILLC/Corbis **409:** (left) Patrice Geisel/Visuals Unlimited **409:** (centre) Tom Van Sant/The Geosphere Project, Santa Monica, CA **409:** (right) Fred McConnaughey/Photo Researchers, Inc. **410:** (top left) Yuri Arcurs/Shutterstock **410:** (bottom left) Photo by Jeremy McNeil **410:** (bottom right) Photo by Jeremy McNeil **412:** Dr. Jim Smith, Michigan State University **413:** (left) Andrew Parkinson/Frank Lane Photo Agency **413:** (right) Eric Soder/Foto Natura/Photo Researchers, Inc.

CHAPTER 19 **419:** Photo by M.B. Fenton **420:** (left, a) Edward S. Ross **420:** (left, b) Edward S. Ross **420:** (right, a) Juan M. Renjifo/Animals Animals—Earth Scenes **420:** (right, b) Photo: Gary Fewless **421:** (a) © Peter Arnold, Inc. / Alamy **421:** (b) © imagebroker / Alamy **421:** (c) © OVIA IMAGES / Alamy **421:** (d) Photo © D. Smirnov **421:** (e) Image is courtesy of Angie from St. Paul, Minnesota **422:** (a–c) Photo: Al and Betty Schneider **423:** From Qiang Ji, Zhe-Xi Luo, Chong-Xi Yuan, Alan R. Tabrum, "A Swimming Mammaliaform from the Middle Jurassic and Ecomorphological Diversification of Early Mammals", Science, vol. 311, Feb 24, 2006, pp. 1123–1127. Reprinted with permission from AAAS. **423:** From Qiang Ji, Zhe-Xi Luo, Chong-Xi Yuan, Alan R. Tabrum, "A Swimming Mammaliaform from the Middle Jurassic and Ecomorphological Diversification of Early Mammals", Science, vol. 311, Feb 24, 2006, pp. 1123–1127. Reprinted with permission from AAAS." **423:** Photo by M.B. Fenton **423:** Photo by M.B. Fenton **423:** Photo by M.B. Fenton **423:** Photo by M.B. Fenton **423:** Photo by M.B. Fenton **423:** Photo by M.B. Fenton **423:** Photo by M.B. Fenton **423:** Photo by M.B. Fenton **423:** Photo by M.B. Fenton **423:** Photo by M.B. Fenton **423:** Photo: Skulls Unlimited International, Inc. **423:** a) Photo: Professor Dr. Wilhelm Barthlott **424:** Photo by M.B. Fenton **426:** (left) Nature's Images/Photo Researchers, Inc. **426:** (centre) Neil Bowman/ Frank Lane Picture Agency **426:** (right) Millard Sharp/Photo Researchers, Inc. **433:** (top left) Yuri Arcurs/Shutterstock **434:** (a) Thomas J. Lemieux, University of Colorado **434:** (b) Sandra Floyd, University of Colorado **436:** (top) From VA Albert, SE Williams, MW Chase, "Carnivorous plants: phylogeny and structural evolution", Science, vol. 257, Sep 11, 1992, pp. 1491–1495. Reprinted with permission from AAAS.

CHAPTER 20 **439:** Photo by M.B. Fenton **440:** C.S. Churcher **442:** Photo by M.B. Fenton **443:** (b) D. Kaleth/Image Bank/Getty Images **443:** (c) William Paton/Foto Natural/Photo Researchers, Inc. **443:** (d) Heather Angel/Natural Visions **446:** (a) © George H. H. Huey/CORBIS **446:** (b) Neville Pledge/South Australian Museum **446:** (c) Jack Koivula/Photo Researchers, Inc. **446:** (d) Novosti/ Photo Researchers, Inc. **447:** (top) From White, "PALEOANTHROPOLOGY: Early Hominids—Diversity or Distortion?", Science, vol. 299, Mar 28, 2003, pp. 1994–1997. Reprinted with permission from AAAS. **447:** (bottom) David Noble/ FPG/Getty Images **448:** (top left) Yuri Arcurs/ Shutterstock **450:** (all photos) Photo by M.B. Fenton **454:** (all) Alan Cheetham et al, Department of Paleobiology, National Museum of Natural History, Smithsonian Institution, Washington, D.C. **455:** Photo by M.B. Fenton **457:** (top left) David Scott/SREL **457:** (a, b) Gary Head **459:** © Michael D. Shapiro and David Kingsley **461:** Photo by M.B. Fenton **462:** From Irmis et al, "A Late Triassic Dinosauromorph Assemblage from New Mexico and the Rise of Dinosaurs", Science, vol. 317, Jul 20, 2007, pp. 358–361. Reprinted with permission from AAAS.

CHAPTER 21 **465:** Copyright Dennis Kunkel Microscopy, Inc. **466:** (a–c) Tony Brian, David Parker/SPL/, Photo Researchers, Inc. **467:** (a–c) David M. Phillips/Visuals Unlimited **467:** (bottom left) icrobiologybytes.wordpress.com **468:** Copyright Dennis Kunkel Microscopy, Inc. **469:** (a, b) T. J. Beveridge/ Visuals Unlimited **470:** (top left) © Frank Dazzo, Michigan State University **470:** (a) CNRI/SPL/, Photo Researchers, Inc. **470:** (b) Copyright Dennis Kunkel Microscopy, Inc. **470:** (c) Photo: New Scientist **471:** Dr. Ken Macdonald/ SPL/Photo Researchers, Inc. **472:** Copyright Dennis Kunkel Microscopy, Inc. **473:** ©Phototake, Inc. **474:** Source: Emerg Infect Dis (c) 2002 Centers for Disease Control and Prevention (CDC) **476:** Hans Reichenbach, Gesellschaft for Biotechnologische Forschung, Braunsweig, Germany **477:** (top left) Yuri Arcurs/Shutterstock **477:** (center right) Courtesy of Luke Marshall **477:** (a) Dr. Jeremy Burgess/SPL/Photo Researchers, Inc. **477:** (b, top) Tony Brian/SPL/Photo Researchers, Inc. **477:** (b, bottom) P. W. Johnson and J. McN. Sieburth, University of Rhode Island/Biological Photo Service **478:** (bottom left) David M. Phillips/Visuals Unlimited **478:** (top right) Copyright Dennis Kunkel Microscopy, Inc. **479:** (a) Barry Rokeach **479:** (b) Alan L. Detrick/Science Source/ Photo Researchers, Inc. **480:** R. Robinson/Visuals Unlimited

CHAPTER 22 **483:** K. G. Murti/Visuals Unlimited **487:** Eye of Science/Photo Researchers, Inc. **491:** Credit: St. Edward's University **493:** APHIS photo by Dr. Al Jenny **494:** (top left) Yuri Arcurs/Shutterstock

CHAPTER 23 **497:** (a) Copyright Dennis Kunkel Microscopy, Inc. **497:** (b) Photo: Dennis Anderson **498:** (a) Edward S. Ross **498:** (b) Gary W. Grimes and Steven L'Hernault **498:** (c) Daniel Mosquin **498:** (d) Wim van Egmond/Visuals Unlimited **501:** (top left) Wim van Egmond **501:** (top right) MI Walker/Photo Researchers, Inc. **501:** (center right) Redrawn from V. & J. Pearse and M. & R. Buchsbaum, Living Invertebrates, The Boxwood Press, 1987. **501:** (bottom right) © Micropolitan, org **502:** M. Abbey/Visuals Unlimited **503:** (a) Dr. Dennis Kunkel/Visuals Unlimited **503:** (b) The Systematic Biology Biodiversity Collection **503:** (bottom right) Tom E. Adams / Peter Arnold Inc. **504:** Oliver Meckes/Photo Researchers, Inc. **505:** (a) Jacek Gaertig, University of Georgia, Athens **505:** (b) Louis De Vos, Free University of Brussels, BIODIC **506:** (a) Hong Kong Red Tide Information Network/The Agriculture, Fisheries and Conservation Department **506:** (b) Dr. David Phillips/Visuals Unlimited/Getty Images **507:** (left) Mike Sauder **507:** (right) © REEF RELIEF All Rights Reserved **508:** Ariena van Bruggen **509:** (a) Claude Taylor and the University of Wisconsin Dept. of Botany **509:** (b) Heather Angel **509:** (c) W. Merrill **509:** (bottom right) Jan Hinsch/SPL/Photo Researchers, Inc. **510:** (a) Ron Hoham, Dept. of Biology, Colgate University **510:** (b) © Phillip Colla **510:** (c) © Phillip Colla **511:** (centre right) Walter Meayers Edwards/National Geographic/Getty Images **512:** (a) Manfred Kage / Peter Arnold Inc. **512:** (b) Wim van Egmond/ Visuals Unlimited **512:** (c) Courtesy of Allen W. H. Be and David A. Caron **512:** (d) John Clegg/Ardea, London **512:** (e) Redrawn from V. & J. Pearse and M. & R. Buchsbaum, Living Invertebrates, The Boxwood Press, 1987. **513:** Wim van Egmond **514:** (a) Carolina Biological Supply **514:** (b) Carolina Biological Supply **514:** (c) Courtesy Robert R. Kay from R. R Kay, et al, Development, 1989 Supplement, pp. 81–90. ©The Company of Biologists Ltd., 1989 **515:** (top left) Yuri Arcurs/ Shutterstock **515:** (top centre) New Scientist **515:** (a) Photo: George Barron **515:** (b) Photo: Greg Thorn **516:** (a) Wim van Egmond/Visuals Unlimited **516:** (b) Douglas Faulkner/Sally Faulkner Collection **517:** (a) Wim van Egmond/Visuals Unlimited **517:** (b) Brian Parker/ Tom Stack and Associates **517:** (c) Manfrage Kage/Peter Arnold, Inc. **518:** Dr. John Clayton, National Institute of Water and Atmospheric Research, New Zealand

CHAPTER 24 **523:** Fritz Polking/ Peter Arnold, Inc. **524:** (a) Tim Flach/Stone/Getty Images **524:** (b) Photo: Alex Wild **524:** (bottom) Robert C. Simpson/Nature Stock **525:** (top left) Yuri Arcurs/ Shutterstock **525:** (a–c) From Cameron R. Currie, Michael Poulsen, John Mendenhall, Jacobus J. Boomsma, Johan Billen, "Coevolved crypts and exocrine glands support mutualistic bacteria in fungus-growing ants", Science, Vol. 311, 6 January 2006, pp. 81–83. Reprinted with permission from AAAS. **526:** (a) Garry T. Cole, University of Texas, Austin/BPS **526:** (c) Photo by Dr. George Knaphus **526:** (right) Copyright © by The American Phytopathological Society **527:** © Andrew Darrington / Alamy **529:** (a) John Taylor/Visuals Unlimited **529:** (b) Center for Disease Control **529:** (c) Courtesy Ken Nemuras **530:** (center left) Micrograph Ed Reschke **530:** (center right) Micrograph Ed Reschke **530:** (bottom) © A.J. Silverside **531:** ((top) a) J.D. Cunningham/Visuals Unlimited **531:** (top, b) John Hodgin **531:** (bottom, a) Science VU/R. Hussey/Visuals Unlimited **532:** (top, b) © North Carolina State University, Department of

Plant Pathology **532:** (top, c) © Michael Wood/mykob.com **532:** (top, d) © Fred Stevens/mykob.com **532:** (bottom, a) N. Allin and G.L Barron **532:** (bottom, b) Reproduced with the permission of the Minister of Public Works and Government Services Canada, 2009. **533:** Gary T. Cole, University of Texas, Austin/BPS **534:** (top) © Arco Images GmbH / Alamy **534:** (bottom left) Reproduced with the permission of the Minister of Public Works and Government Services Canada, 2009. **534:** (bottom right) © PHOTOTAKE Inc. / Alamy **535:** (a) Robert C. Simpson/Nature Stock **535:** (b) Robert C. Simpson/Nature Stock **535:** (c) Jeffrey Lepore/Photo Researchers, Inc. **535:** (d) Jane Burton/Bruce Coleman Ltd. **535:** (e) Robert C. Simpson/Nature Stock **537:** Biophoto Associates/Photo Researchers, Inc. **538:** © Dennis Kunkel Microscopy, Inc. **539:** (top, a) U.S. Environmental Protection Agency **539:** (top, b) Photo: DIY Doctor **539:** (bottom, b) V. Ahmadjian and J.B. Jacobs **539:** (bottom, c) Jane Burton/Bruce Coleman Ltd. **539:** (bottom, d) Eye of Science/Science Photo Library/Photo Researchers, Inc. **540:** (a) Prof. D.J. Read, University of Sheffield **540:** (b) © 1999 Gary Braasch **541:** (top left) © DLILLC/Corbis **541:** (a) © University of Canterbury–Christchurch, New Zealand **541:** (b) Photo courtesy of NASA **541:** (bottom right) F. B. Reeves **542:** (bottom left) photo by Nicholas Hill **542:** (bottom right) photo by Craig Roberts

CHAPTER 25 **547:** © Peter F. Zika/Visuals Unlimited **549:** © Courtesy Microbial Culture Collection, National Institute for Environmental Studies, Japan **550:** (top, a) Craig Wood/Visuals Unlimited **550:** (top, b) Michael P. Gadomski / Photo Researchers, Inc. **550:** (top, c) © Don Enright/iStockPhoto **550:** (bottom, a) George S. Ellmore **550:** (bottom, b) Jeremy Burgess/SPL/Photo Researchers, Inc. **550:** (bottom right) Prof. D.J. Read, University of Sheffield **551:** (top left) Yuri Arcurs/Shutterstock **552:** Reprinted with permission from Elsevier **554:** (top left) © DLILLC/Corbis **554:** (centre) With kind permission from Springer Science + Business Media: Planta, "Molecular cloning of abscisic acid-modulated genes which are induced during desiccation of the resurrection plant", volume 181, April 1, 1990, pp. 27–34, Dorothea Bartels, figure: An illustration of the remarkable ability for extreme vegetative desiccation tolerance in an angiosperm species. **554:** (bottom) Courtesy of UW-Madison Department of Botany **556:** (a) © blickwinkel / Alamy **556:** (b) Courtesy of Northwest Habitat Institute **557:** (a, left) Photo: The Hidden Forest **557:** (a, right) © Roger Butterfield **557:** (b) Martin Hutten/National Park Service **557:** (c) Paul Stehr-Green/National Park Service **557:** (d) Wayne P. Armstrong, Professor of Biology and Botany, Palomar College, San Francisco, CA **558:** © Clive/hiddenforest.co.nz **559:** Jane Burton/ Bruce Coleman USA **560:** Dr. Judith Jernstedt, University California, Davis **561:** (top) Field Museum of Natural History, Chicago **561:** (bottom) © Ed Reschke/Peter Arnold, Inc. **562:** (top) A. & E. Bomford/Ardea, London **562:** (bottom) © Hubert Klein/Peter Arnold, Inc. **563:** (bottom left) Kingsley R. Stern **563:** (top right) Scanning electron micrograph by Karen Renzaglia. Color enhancement by Steve Mueller, IMAGE Facility. **563:** (a) William Ferguson **563:** (b) W. H. Hodges **563:** (c) © Kratz/Zefa/CORBIS **565:** Photo: Thomas R. Holtz, Jr. **566:** (left) Robert Potts, California Academy of Science **566:** (top right) Robert and Linda Mitchell Photography **566:** (bottom right) © R. J. Erwin/Photo Researchers, Inc. **567:** (top) Carlton Ray/Science Photo Library/Photo Researchers, Inc. **567:** (a) © Joyce Photographics/Photo Researchers, Inc. **567:** (b) Runk/Schoenberger/Grant Heilman **567:** (c) William Ferguson **567:** (d) Kingsley R. Stern **568:** (a) Edward S. Ross **568:** (b) William Ferguson **568:** (c) Robert and Linda Mitchell Photography **568:** (d) © Fletcher and Baylis/Photo Researchers, Inc. **569:** (a) © Bob Rowan, Progressive Image/Corbis **569:** (b) Bill Coster/ Peter Arnold, Inc. **569:** (c) © John Mason/Ardea, London **569:** (d) Howard Miller / Photo Researchers, Inc. **570:** (top, a) Dorling Kindersley/Getty Images **570:** (top, b–c) Ed Reschke / Peter Arnold Inc. **570:** (top left) Jerome Wexler/Visuals Unlimited/Getty Images **570:** (centre) Joel Blit/Shutterstock **570:** (top left) John Gerlach/Visuals Unlimited/Getty Images **570:** (bottom right) John M. Roberts/Corbis **570:** (top left) Jubal Harshaw/Shutterstock **570:** (top left) Nigel Cattlin/Visuals Unlimited/Getty Images **570:** (centre left) Triff/Shutterstock **570:** (bottom centre) © Bob Gibbons / Alamy **570:** (top left) © Daniel L. Geiger/SNAP / Alamy **570:** (centre right) © Louise Heusinkveld / Alamy **570:** (bottom left) © Organica / Alamy **572:** (a) Merlin D. Tuttle, Bat Conservation International **572:** (b) Photo by Marcel Lecoufle **572:** (c) Robert A. Tyrrell **572:** (d) Thomas Eisner/Cornell University

CHAPTER 26 **577:** Mark Moffett/ Minden Pictures **578:** (all photos) Dr. Chip Clark, National Museum of Natural History, Smithsonian Institution **585:** (top) Marty Snyderman/Planet Earth Pictures **585:** (bottom) Don W. Fawcett/Visuals Unlimited **587:** (all photos) Kim Taylor/Bruce Coleman Inc. **589:** (a) © Michael Durham/Minden Pictures **589:** (b) Credit: Anders Garm **590:** (a) Christian DellaCorte **590:** (b, all) F.S. Westmorland **590:** (bottom left) © Norbert Wu/Minden Pictures **591:** (a) © blickwinkel/Hecker/Alamy **591:** (b) Andrew J. Martinez/Photo Researchers, Inc. **591:** (c) Lawrence Naylor/Photo Researchers, Inc. **592:** © Cory Gray **593:** (top) E.R. Degginger/Photo Researchers, Inc. **593:** (a) Robert and Linda Mitchell Photography **593:** (b) Cath Ellis, University of Hull/SPL/Photo Researchers, Inc. **594:** (top) Herve Chaumeton/Agence Nature **594:** (bottom) Kjell B. Sandved **595:** From RUPPERT. Invertebrate Zoology. © 1994 Nelson Education Ltd. Reproduced by permission. www.cengage.com/permissions **596:** (left) From RUPPERT. Invertebrate Zoology. © 1994 Nelson Education Ltd. Reproduced by permission. www.cengage.com/permissions **596:** (right) Entomological Society of America **598:** (top left) Jeff Foott/Tom Stack & Associates **598:** (b) J. Kottmann/Peter Arnold, Inc. **598:** (c) © Ralph A. Clevenger/CORBIS **599:** (top left) Simon Colmer/Nature Picture Library **599:** (b) Herve Chaumeton/Agence Nature **599:** (c) Tom McHugh/Photo Researchers, Inc. **600:** (a) Bob Cranston **600:** (b) Grossauer/ZEFA **600:** (c, top) A. Ketitch, © 1992 Sea World of California. All rights reserved **600:** (c, bottom) © E. Webber/Visuals Unlimited **602:** (top left) Kjell B. Sandved **602:** (top right) © Duncan Mcewan/npl/Minden Pictures **602:** (bottom right) J.A. L. Cooke/Oxford Scientific Films/Photolibrary.com **603:** (top left) © DLILLC/Corbis **603:** (centre) Canadian Scientific Submersible Facility **603:** (bottom) © 2006 Alistair Dove/Image Quest Marine **605:** (top) © Cliff B. Brith/Bruce Coleman USA **605:** (bottom) Mitsuhiko Imamori/Minden Pictures **606:** Dr. Chip Clark **607:** (d) Andrew Syred/Photo Researchers, Inc. **607:** (bottom left) Jane Burton/Bruce Coleman Inc. **607:** (a, c) P.J. Bryand, University of California-Irvine/BPS **608:** (b) Herve Chaumeton/Agence Nature **608:** (bottom) Herve Chaumeton/Agence Nature **608:** (a) Jane Burton/Bruce Coleman Inc. **609:** (top left) Runk/Schoenberger/Grant Heilman **609:** (a) Steve Martin/Tom Stack & Associates **609:** (b) Z. Leszczynski/Animals, Animals—Earth Scenes **610:** (a) Arthur Evans/Animals, Animals—Earth Scenes **610:** (b, d, e) Edward S. Ross **610:** (c) BIOS Borrell Bartomeu/Peter Arnold, Inc. **610:** (f) Michael Durham/Minden Pictures **610:** (g) C.P. Hichman, Jr. **610:** (h) S.J. Krasemann/Peter Arnold, Inc. **612:** (top left) Yuri Arcurs/Shutterstock **612:** (top right) From: Plate II a opposite p 45 of the "Physiology of Insect Metamorphosis" by VB Wigglesworth. Cambridge University Press 1954 **612:** (centre) Photo: Ken Davey **613:** Photo: Ken Davey

CHAPTER 27 **617:** Photo by M.B. Fenton **620:** (a) Jan Haaga, Kodiak Lab, AFSC/NMFS **620:** (c) Peter Parks/Oxford Scientific Films/Animals, Animals—Earth Scenes **620:** (d) Gary Bell/Taxi/Getty Images **620:** (e) Runk and Schoenberger/Grant Heilman Photography, Inc. **620:** (f) Reprinted by permission from Macmillan Publishers Ltd: Nature, "Xenoturbella is a deuterostome that eats molluscs", Sarah J. Bourlat, Claus Nielsen, Anne E. Lockyer, D. Timothy J. Littlewood and Maximilian J. Telford, vol. 424, pp. 925–928, copyright (2003). **621:** (a) Herve Chaumeton/Agence Nature **621:** (b) George Perina, www.seapix.com **621:** (c) Edward Snow/Bruce Coleman USA **621:** (d) Chris Huss/The Wildlife Collection **621:** (e) Herve Chaumeton/Agence Nature **622:** Photo by M.B. Fenton **623:** Photo by M.B. Fenton **627:** Reprinted by permission from Macmillan Publishers Ltd: Nature, "A role for the immunological synapse in lineage commitment of CD4 lymphocytes", Roberto A. Maldonado, Darrell J. Irvine, Robert Schreiber and Laurie H. Glimcher, vol. 431, pp. 527–532, copyright (2004). **628:** (top left) Heather Angel **628:** (top right) Reprinted by permission from Macmillan Publishers Ltd. Nature, "A lamprey from the Devonian period of South Africa", Robert W. Gess, Michael I. Coates and Bruce S. Rubidge, vol. 443, pp. 981–984, copyright (2006). **628:** (bottom) Reprinted by permission from Macmillan Publishers Ltd: Nature, "Evolutionary biology Born-again hagfishes", Philippe Janvier, vol. 446, pp. 622–623, copyright (2007). **630:** (bottom left) Bill Wood/Bruce Coleman **630:** (bottom right) Photo by M.B. Fenton **631:** (top left) © Gido Braase/Deep Blue Productions **631:** (bottom left) Jonathan Bird/Oceanic Research Group, Inc. **631:** (right) Alex Kerstitch/Visuals Unlimited **632:** (top left) Photo by M.B. Fenton **632:** (top right) Photo by M.B. Fenton **632:** (bottom left) Ken Lucas/Visuals Unlimited **632:** (bottom right) Patrice Ceisel/© 1986 John G. Shedd Aquarium **633:** (b) Digital Vision/Getty Images **633:** (c) Kit Kittle/CORBIS **633:** (d) F. Graner/Peter Arnold, Inc. **633:** (e) Brandon Cole/Visuals Unlimited **633:** (f) Arthur W. Ambler/Photo Researchers, Inc. **634:** (top left) Photo by M.B. Fenton **634:** (top right) Photo by M.B. Fenton **634:** (bottom left) Norbert Wu/Peter Arnold, Inc. **634:** (bottom right) Wernher Krutein/photovault.com **636:** (top) Photo by M.B. Fenton **636:** (bottom left) Photo by M.B. Fenton and D. Kocinski **636:** (bottom right) Photo by M.B. Fenton and D. Kocinski **637:** (left) Stephen Dalton/Photo Researchers, Inc **637:** (top right) Bill M. Campbell, MD **637:** (bottom right) Juan M. Renjifo/Animals, Animals—Earth Scenes. **640:** (all photos) M.B. Fenton **641:** (all photos) M.B. Fenton **642:** (all photos) M.B. Fenton **643:** Paul J. Fusco/Photo Researchers, Inc. **644:** (top left) Pete & Judy Morrin/Ardea London **644:** (top right) Stephen Dalton/Photo Researchers, Inc. **644:** (bottom left) Andrew Dennis/A.N.T. Photo Library **644:** (bottom right) Mary Ann McDonald/CORBIS **645:** (left) From Zulma Gasparini, Diego Pol, Luis A. Spalletti, "An Unusual Marine Crocodyliform from the Jurassic-Cretaceous Boundary of Patagonia", Science, Jan 6, 2006, vol. 311, pp. 70–73. Reprinted with permission from AAAS. **645:** (right) Photo by M.B. Fenton **646:** Gerard Lacz/ANT Photolibrary **647:** (top, a–d) Photo by M.B. Fenton **647:** (bottom, a) Kevin Schafer/CORBIS **647:** (bottom, b) Arthur Morris/Visuals Unlimited **647:** (bottom, c) Ron Sanford/CORBIS **647:** (bottom, d) WIM KLOMP/FOTO NATURA/Minden Pictures **647:** (bottom, e) Robert A. Tyrrell **647:** (bottom, f) Tim Zurowski/CORBIS **648:** (top left) Photo by M.B. Fenton **648:** (top right) Photo by M.B. Fenton **648:** (bottom) From Alan Feduccia, "Explosive Evolution in Tertiary Birds and Mammals", Science, 3 February 1995, vol. 267, pp. 637–638. Reprinted with permission from AAAS. **649:** (top, a–b) Photo by M.B. Fenton **650:** Reprinted from Trends in Ecology & Evolution, Vol 19, Mark S. Springer, Michael J. Stanhope, Ole Madsen and Wilfried W. de Jong, "Trends in Ecology & Evolution", Pages No. 430-438, Copyright (2004), with permission from Elsevier. **651:** (top, a–b) Photo by M.B. Fenton **651:** (centre) D. & V. Blagden/ANT Photo Library **651:** (bottom) Jean Phillipe Varin/Jacana/Photo Researchers, Inc. **652:** (left) Milse, T./Arco Images/Peter Arnold **652:** (centre) Photo by M.B. Fenton **652:** (right) Photo by M.B. Fenton **653:** (top, a) Theo Allofs/Photonica/Getty Images **653:** (top, b) J. Scott Altenbach, University of New Mexico **653:** (top, c) Leonard Lee Rue III/FPG/Getty Images **653:** (top, d) Martin Harvey/Peter Arnold **653:** (top, e) David Parker/SPL/Photo Researchers, Inc. **653:** (bottom) From Zhe-Xi Luo, John R. Wible, "A Late Jurassic Digging Mammal and Early Mammalian Diversification", Science, Apr 1, 2005, vol. 308, pp. 103–107. Reprinted with permission from AAAS. **654:** (top, a–b) From Zhe-Xi Luo, John R. Wible, "A Late Jurassic Digging Mammal and Early Mammalian Diversification", Science, Apr 1, 2005, vol. 308, pp. 103–107. Reprinted with permission from AAAS. **654:** (top, c) Photo by M.B. Fenton **654:** (bottom) From Zhe-Xi Luo, John R. Wible, "A Late Jurassic Digging Mammal and Early Mammalian Diversification", Science, Apr 1, 2005, vol. 308, pp. 103–107. Reprinted with permission from AAAS. **655:** (all photos) M.B. Fenton **656:** (all photos) M.B. Fenton **657:** (left) Photo by M.B. Fenton **657:** (right) Reprinted by permission from Macmillan Publishers Ltd: Nature, "A reversible wet/dry adhesive inspired by mussels and geckos", Haeshin Lee, Bruce P. Lee and Phillip B. Messersmith, vol. 448, pp. 338–341, copyright (2007). **659:** (left, a) Dr. Donald Johanson, Institute of Human Origins **659:** (left, b) Louise M. Robbins **659:** (right, a) Science VU/NM/Visuals Unlimited **659:** (right, b) AAAC/Tophan/The Image Works **660:** Yuri Arcurs/Shutterstock **661:** From Jun Z. Li, Devin M. Absher, Hua Tang, Audrey M. Southwick, Amanda M. Casto, Sohini Ramachandran, Howard M. Cann, Gregory S. Barsh, Marcus Feldman, Luigi L. Cavalli-Sforza, Richard M. Myers, "Worldwide Human Relationships Inferred from Genome-Wide Patterns of Variation", Science, Feb 22, 2008, vol. 319, pp. 1100–1104. Reprinted with permission from AAAS.

CHAPTER 28 **667:** (inset) Photo: Adrian Jones, IAN Image Library (www.ian.umces.edu/imagelibrary/) **667:** (main) Photo: Isabella M. Gioia **668:** Photo: Brian Ecott **671:** © Biophoto Associates/ Photo Researchers, Inc. **673:** (top left) © Bruce Iverson **673:** (top right) © Mike Clayton/University of Wisconsin Department of Botany **673:** (centre left) © Ernest Manewal/ Index Stock Imagery **673:** (centre right) © Darrell Gulin/ Corbis **673:** (bottom left) © Simon Fraser/ Photo Researchers, Inc. **673:** (bottom right) Gary Head **674:** (micrograph) Ed Reschke / Peter Arnold Inc. **675:** (top, a–c) © Biophoto Associates **675:** (bottom left) © Kingsley R. Stern **675:** (bottom right) © D.E. Akin and I.L. Rigsby, Richard B. Russel Agricultural Research Service, U.S. Department of Agriculture, Athens, Georgia **676:** (bottom left) Alison W. Roberts, University **676:** (bottom centre) H.A. Cote, W.A. Cote and A.C. Day, Wood Structure and Identification, second edition, Syracuse University Press **677:** (top left) James D. Mauseth, University of Texas **677:** (centre left) Courtesy of Professor John Main, Pacific Luthern University **677:** (bottom, a) George S. Ellmore **677:** (bottom, b) © Dr. Jeremy Burgess/SPL/ Photo Researchers, Inc **677:** (bottom, c) Courtesy Mark Holland, Salisbury University. **678:** Jakub Jasinski/Visuals Unlimited **679:** (top centre) Robert and Linda Mitchell Photography **679:** (top right) Richard Dute **680:** (top centre) Ray F. Evert **680:** (top right) James W. Perry **680:** (bottom centre) Carolina Biological Supply **680:** (centre right) James W. Perry **681:** (top, a) Mike Hill/Getty Images **681:** (top, b) Wally Eberhart/Visuals Unlimited **681:** (top, c) Joerg Boethling/Peter Arnold, Inc. **681:** (top, d) © Alan & Linda Detrick/ Photo Researchers, Inc. **681:** (top, e) Michael P. Gadomski/Photo Researchers, Inc. **681:** (bottom left) Joseph Devenney/Getty Images **681:** (bottom right) Maxine Adcock/Science Photo Library/ Photo Researchers, Inc. **682:** C.E. Jeffree, et al, Planta 172 (1):20–37, 1987. Reprinted by permission of C.E. Jeffree and Springer-Verlag **683:** Beth Davidow/Visuals Unlimited **684:** John Limbaugh/ Ripon Microslides, Inc. **685:** (top left) Chuck Brown **685:** (top right) Carolina Biological Supply **685:** (bottom) Omnikron/Photo Researchers, Inc. **687:** Photo: Daniel Mosquin **688:** © George Bernard/SPL/ Photo Researchers, Inc. **689:** (right) Photo: Cliff Ecology Research Group, Department of Integrative Biology, University of Guelph **689:** (top left) Yuri Arcurs/Shutterstock **690:** (top left) © DLILLC/Corbis **690:** bottom, Photo: Raymond G. Milewski

CHAPTER 29 **695:** ©Steve Gschmeissner/ SPL/ Photo Researchers, Inc. **696:** Owaki–Kulla/ CORBIS **697:** Micrograph Chuck Brown **700:** (micrographs) © Claude Nuridsany and Marie Perennou/ Science Photo Library/ Photo Researchers, Inc. **702:** Micrograph Chuck Brown **705:** Dr. John D. Cunningham/Visuals Unlimited **706:** (right, a) T. A. Masefield **706:** (right, b) T. A. Masefield **708:** (top left) BIOS Matt Alexander/ Peter Arnold, Inc. **708:** (top right) Thomas L. Rost **708:** (bottom left) Fritz Polking/Visuals Unlimited **708:** (bottom right) Fritz Polking/Visuals Unlimited **709:** (top left) Yuri Arcurs/Shutterstock

CHAPTER 30 **715:** © Ted Kinsman/ SPL/ Photo Researchers, Inc. **716:** (top left) Kashfia Rahman/ StockXchng **716:** (top right) Ian Britton/FreeFoto.com **716:** (centre left) Photographer: David/ www.3d-images.ws **716:** (bottom left) NASA Earth Observatory **717:** (top) Photo: Tom Horton **717:** (inset) Photographer: Allan Carson **719:** (left) Justin Voight/iStockPhoto **719:** (top right) Photo: Doug Waylett **719:** (bottom right) Photo: Doug Waylett **721:** (bottom left) David M. Phillips/ Visuals Unlimited **721:** (bottom centre) Dr. Jeremy Burgess/SPL/Photo Researchers, Inc. **721:** (bottom right) David Scharf/Peter Arnold, Inc. **722:** Photographer: Quimbaya **723:** (top left) Yuri Arcurs/Shutterstock **723:** (centre) William E. Friedman, University of Georgia **725:** (b) Siegel, R./ Arco Images/Peter Arnold **725:** (c, top) Richard H. Gross **725:** (c, bottom) Andrew Syred/SPL/Photo Researchers, Inc. **725:** (d) Mark Rieger **725:** (e) R. Carr **727:** Dr. John D. Cunningham/Visuals Unlimited **728:** Herve Chaumeton/ Agence Nature **729:** (top right) Barry L. Runk/Grant Heilman, Inc. **729:** (centre right) James Mauseth **729:** (bottom right) Ed Reschke/Peter Arnold **730:** (left) R-R/S/Grant Heilman Photography, Inc. **730:** (centre top) Professor Dr. Hans Hanks-Ulrich Koop **730:** (centre bottom) Professor Dr. Hans Hanks-Ulrich Koop **730:** (right) Professor Dr. Hans Hanks-Ulrich Koop

CHAPTER 31 **735:** © Garry Black/ Masterfile **736:** (top left) Source: Christian Krupke, John Obermeyer, and Larry Bledsoe/Purdue University **736:** (top right) Dr. L. T. Kok, Professor of Entomology, Virginia Tech, Blacksburg, VA **736:** (bottom) Marietta College **738:** (top left) Yuri Arcurs/Shutterstock **738:** (right) William Perlman/ Star Ledger/ Corbis **740:** Kingsley R. Stern **742:** Sylvan H. Wittwer/Visuals Unlimited **743:** Sylvan Wittwer/ Visuals Unlimited **744:** (top) Photo: Kurt Stepnitz, Instructional Media Center, Michigan State University, East Lansing, MI 48824 **744:** (bottom) N.R. Lersten **745:** Larry D. Nooden **746:** Amanda Darcy/Getty Images **749:** David Cavagnaro/Peter Arnold, Inc. **750:** Nigel Cattlin/ Photo Researchers Inc. **753:** (top left) Cathlyn Melloan/Stone/Getty Images **753:** (centre) Micrographs courtesy of Randy Moore, from "How Roots Respond to Gravity," M. L. Evans, R. Moore, and K. Hasenstein, Scientific American, December 1986. **753:** (bottom left) Michael Clayton, University of Wisconsin **753:** (bottom right) John Digby and Richard Firn **754:** (bottom) Cary Mitchell **755:** (top) Frank B. Salisbury **755:** (centre right) David Sieren/Visuals Unlimited **755:** (bottom right) David Sieren/Visuals Unlimited **757:** Dwight Kuhn **758:** (top left) Jan Zeevart **758:** (top right) Eric Crichton/CORBIS **759:** R. J. Downs **760:** Eric Welzel/Fox Hill Nursery, Freeport, Maine

CHAPTER 32 **765:** Simon Fraser/SPL/Photo Researchers, Inc. **766:** David Macdonald **769:** (top left) Yuri Arcurs/Shutterstock **769:** (left) Ray Simmons/Photo Researchers, Inc. **769:** (centre) Ed Rescheke/Peter Arnold, Inc. **769:** (right) Don Fawcett **770:** (left) Gregory Dimijian/Photo Researchers, Inc. **771:** Photo: Darren Wong, Dr David Merrit. **772:** (a) Ed Reschke **772:** (b) Ed Reschke **772:** (c) Fred Hossier/Visual Unlimited **772:** (d) Ed Reschke **772:** (e) Ed Reschke **772:** (f) Ed Reschke **774:** (left) Ed Reschke **774:** (centre) Ed Reschke **774:** (right) BioPhoto Associates/Photo Researchers, Inc. **775:** (bottom) Lennart Nilsson from Behold Man, ©1974 Albert Bonniers Forlag and Little, Brown and Company, Boston **778:** Fred Bruemmer

CHAPTER 33 **783:** © C. J. Guerin, Ph. D., MRC Toxicology Unit/SPL/Photo Researchers, Inc. **784:** Photo by Drees **786:** (top) Triarch/Visuals Unlimited **786:** (bottom) Society for Neuroscience **787:** C. Raines/Visuals Unlimited **795:** Dennis Kunkel/ Visuals Unlimited **798:** E.R. Lewis, T.E. Everhart, Y. Y. Zevi/Visuals Unlimited **800:** (top left) Reproduced with the permission of the Minister of Public Works and Government Services Canada, 2009. **800:** (bottom left) From RUPPERT. Invertebrate Zoology. © 1994 Nelson Education Ltd. Reproduced by permission. www.cengage.com/ permissions **801:** (top) Reproduced with the permission of the Minister of Public Works and Government Services Canada, 2009. **802:** Used with permission by Cornell University Press **803:** From Pough, Heiser, McFarland. Vertebrate Life, 4E. Published by Prentice-Hall. Reprinted by permission of Pearson Education, Ltd. **806:** Courtesy of Dr. Marcus Raichle, courtesy of Washington University School of Medicine, St. Louis **810:** (top left) Yuri Arcurs/Shutterstock

CHAPTER 34 **819:** Photo by M.B. Fenton **820:** (top left) Photo by Gord Temple **820:** (bottom left) Data by M.B. Fenton **823:** (centre right) BIOSCIENCE by Narins. Copyright 1990 by American Institute of Biological Sciences (AIBS). Reproduced with permission of American Institute of Biological Sciences (AIBS) in the format Textbook, CD-ROM and DVD via Copyright Clearance Center. **823:** (bottom) With kind permission from Springer Science+Business Media: Journal of Comparative Physiology A, "Detection of vibrations in sand by tarsal sense organs of the nocturnal scorpion, Paruroctonus mesaensis", volume 131, Mar 1, 1979, pp. 23–30, Philip Brownell. **824:** Reprinted by permission of Blackwell Publishing **825:** From Kurt Schwenk, "Why Snakes Have Forked Tongues", Science, Mar 18, 1994, vol. 263, pp. 1573–1577. Reprinted with permission from AAAS. **826:** Herve Chaumeton/Agence Nature **827:** bottom, From Sanjay P. Sane, Alexandre Dieudonne, Mark A. Willis, Thomas L. Daniel, "Antennal Mechanosensors Mediate Flight Control in Moths", Science, Feb 9, 2007, vol. 315, pp. 863–866. Reprinted with permission from AAAS. **827:** (top left and right) Photo by A Percival-Smith **828:** (left) Photo by M.B. Fenton **828:** (top right) Photo: William Pflieger **828:** (bottom right) © William R. Elliot **830:** Reprinted by permission from Macmillan Publishers Ltd: Nature, F. Spoor, S. Bajpai, S. T. Hussain,K. Kumar and J. G. M. Thewissen, "Vestibular evidence for the evolution of aquatic behaviour in early cetaceans", Vol. 417, pp. 163–166, copyright (2002). **831:** Andrew Syred/Photo Researchers, Inc. **833:** (all photos) M.B. Fenton **834:** (all photos) M.B. Fenton **835:** Reprinted by permission from Macmillan Publishers Ltd: Nature, Gebhard F. X. Schertler, "Signal transductionThe rhodopsin story continued", Vol. 453, pp. 292–293, copyright (2008). **839:** (top left) Yuri Arcurs/Shutterstock **840:** © A & J Visage / Alamy **841:** (top) Dr. M.V. Parthasarathy/Cornell Integrated Microscopy Center **841:** (bottom left) © A. Shay/OSF/Animals Animals—Earth Scenes **841:** (bottom right) Louisa Howard, Dartmouth College EM Facility **843:** Reprinted by permission from Macmillan Publishers Ltd: Nature, Gordon M. Shepherd, "Smell images and the flavour system in the human brain", Vol. 444, pp. 316–321, copyright (2006). **844:** (left) Reprinted by permission from Macmillan Publishers Ltd: Nature, Kenneth C. Catania, "OlfactionUnderwater 'sniffing' by semi-aquatic mammals", Vol. 444, pp. 1024–1025, copyright (2006). **844:** (top right) David Hosking/Frank Lane Picture Agency **844:** (bottom right) Photo by G.G. Carter **846:** Kenneth Lohmann/University of North Carolina **847:** (top and bottom) M.B. Fenton

CHAPTER 35 **851:** Dr. Richard B. Dominick **861:** Mirror Syndication International Ltd., 1986 **862:** © John Shaw/Tom Stack & Associates, Inc. **867:** (top left) Yuri Arcurs/Shutterstock **868:** (top left) © DLILLC/Corbis

CHAPTER 36 **873:** G. Delpho/Peter Arnold, Inc. **874:** Kiisa Nishikawa/Northern Arizona University **875:** (inset photos) Don Fawcett/Visuals Unlimited **880:** (bottom) From RUPPERT. Invertebrate Zoology. © 1994 Nelson Education Ltd. Reproduced by permission. www.cengage.com/permissions **881:** Linda Pitkin/Planet Earth Pictures **884:** (all photos) M.B. Fenton **886:** (top left) Yuri Arcurs/Shutterstock **887:** (left) Jupiter Images **887:** (right) Petr Kratochvil/Public Domain Pictures

CHAPTER 37 **891:** (top) © The Print Collector / Alamy **891:** (bottom) © The Print Collector / Alamy **892:** From A. D. Waller, Physiology, The Servant of Medicine, Hitchcock Lectures, University of London Press, 1910 **896:** Reprinted by permission of McGraw-Hill Companies **897:** National Cancer Institute/Photo Researchers, Inc. **899:** Professor P. Motta/Department of Anatomy/ University La Sapienca, Rome/SPL/Photo Researchers, Inc. **901:** (top left) Yuri Arcurs/Shutterstock **905:** Lennart Nilsson from Behold Man © 1974 published by Albert Bonniers Forlag and Loitt, Brown and Company **907:** (top left) © DLILLC/Corbis **907:** (bottom) © Rolf Hicker

CHAPTER 38 **911:** ZEOvit.com **912:** Photo: Robert Poulin **913:** Dr. Stanley Flegler/Visuals Unlimited **914:** Nature's Images, Inc. / Photo Researchers, Inc. **916:** (left) Dr. David M. Phillips / Visuals Unlimited **916:** (right) Ryuzo Yanagimachi **918:** (top) Hans Pfletschinger **918:** (bottom) David M. Phillips/Visuals Unlimited **919:** Copyright (2001) National Academy of Sciences, U.S.A. **920:** From David N. Reznick, Mariana Mateos, Mark S. Springer, "Independent Origins and Rapid Evolution of the Placenta in the Fish Genus Poeciliopsis", Science, Nov 1, 2002, vol. 298, pp. 1018–1020. Reprinted with permission from AAAS. **921:** From David N. Reznick, Mariana Mateos, Mark S. Springer, "Independent Origins and Rapid Evolution of the Placenta in the Fish Genus Poeciliopsis", Science, Nov 1, 2002, vol. 298, pp. 1018–1020. Reprinted with permission from AAAS. **922:** (left) John Cancalosi/Peter Arnold, Inc. **922:** (top right) Robin Chittenden; Frank Lane Picture Agency/Corbis **922:** (bottom right) Andrew J. Martinez / Photo Researchers, Inc. **924:** (left) Photo by M.B. Fenton **924:** (top right) Photo by M.B. Fenton **924:** (bottom right) Copyright © 1987 Society for Reproduction and Fertility **925:** Lennart Nilsson from A Child is Born, © 1966, 1977 Dell Publishing Company, Inc. **928:** (top) Michael C. Webb/Visuals Unlimited **928:** (bottom) Photo by M.B. Fenton **929:** (top left) Yuri Arcurs/ Shutterstock **931:** Lennart Nilsson From A Child Is Born, © 1966, 1977 Dell Publishing Company, Inc.

CHAPTER 39 **935:** Photo by M.B. Fenton **936:** © Rudie Kuiter/OceanwideImages.com **937:** (top left) Joseph G. Kunkel **937:** (bottom left) Photo by M.B. Fenton **937:** (top right) Reprinted by permission from Macmillan Publishers Ltd: Nature, Alexander Kupfer, Hendrik Muller, Marta M. Antoniazzi, Carlos Jared, Hartmut Greven et al., "Parental investment by skin feeding in a caecilian amphibian", Vol. 440, pp. 926–929, copyright (2006). **937:** (bottom right) Reprinted by permission from Macmillan Publishers Ltd: Nature, Alexander Kupfer, Hendrik Muller, Marta M. Antoniazzi, Carlos Jared, Hartmut Greven et al., "Parental investment by skin feeding in a caecilian amphibian", Vol. 440, pp. 926–929, copyright (2006). **938:** Reprinted by permission from Macmillan Publishers Ltd: Nature, Alexander Kupfer, Hendrik Muller, Marta M. Antoniazzi, Carlos Jared, Hartmut Greven et al., "Parental investment by skin feeding in a caecilian amphibian", Vol. 440, pp. 926–929, copyright (2006). **939:** (all bottom photos) Carolina Biological Supply Company **943:** (all top photos) Carolina Biological Supply Company **944:** Peter B. Armstrong, University of California, Davis. **945:** Carolina Biological Supply Company **946:** Carolina Biological Supply Company **947:** (top left) Yuri Arcurs/Shutterstock **950:** (all photos) Lennart Nilsson, A Child is Born, © 1966, 1977, Dell Publishing Company, Inc. **952:** (top left) Photo by M.B. Fenton **952:** (bottom left) Copyright (2001) National Academy of Sciences, U.S.A. **961:** (top) Oliver Meckes / Nicole Ottawa / Photo Researchers, Inc. **961:** (bottom) UCSF Computer Graphics Laboratory, National Institutes, NCRR Grant 01081 **962:** (top left) Carolina Biological Supply Company **962:** (top right) Lennart Nilsson from A Child is Born, © 1966, 1977 Dell Publishing Company, Inc.

CHAPTER 40 **967:** Photo by M.B. Fenton **968:** (left) A. & J. Binns/ Vireo **968:** (centre) © J. Schumacher/ VIREO **968:** (right) © G. Mc Elroy/ VIREO **968:** (bottom) Dr. Stephen Yezerinac, Bishop's University, Lennoxville, Quebec, Canada **969.** Marie Read Natural History Photography **970:** (top left) Evan Cerasoli **970:** (bottom left) © Stephen Dalton/Photo Researchers, Inc. **970:** (top right) Eugene Kozloff **970:** (centre right) Stevan Arnold **970:** (bottom right) Stevan Arnold **972:** © Nina Leen/Time and Life Pictures/Getty Images **973:** © imagebroker / Alamy **975:** (bottom left) Russell Fernald, Stanford University **975:** (all top photos) Russell Fernald, Stanford University **976:** (bottom right) American Scientist 79:316–329 article by M. May 1991 **977:** © Jeff Foott/Dcom/ DRK Photo **978:** (left) Rod Planck/ Photo Researchers, Inc. **978:** (centre) Kenneth Catania/ Department of Behavioral Sciences/Vanderbilt University **978:** (right) Kenneth Catania/Department of Behavioral Sciences/Vanderbilt University **979:** (left) Photo by M.B. Fenton **979:** (right) © E. Mickleburgh/Ardea, London **980:** © Kenneth W. Fink/ Photo Researchers, Inc. **981:** (bottom) Tom and Pat Leeson **983:** (bottom left) © Alan Williams / Alamy **983:** (centre left) Mark Hamblin/ Oxford Scientific/ Index Stock **983:** (bottom right) Picture courtesy of: www.amazilia.net **984:** (bottom right) San Diego State University Biology Department **985:** Howard Hall/ Oxford Scientific/ Index Stock **986:** R. & N. Bowers/ VIREO **987:** (top right) Michael & Patricia Fogden/ Minden Pictures **987:** (top left) Frans Lanting/ Minden Pictures **987:** (bottom left) Chris Sharp/ Oxford Scientific Picture Library/Photolibrary.com **988:** © Edgar T. Jones/VIREO **989:** (top left) Ray Richardson/ Animals, Animals—Earth Scenes **989:** (bottom right) © Ashley Cooper/Corbis **991:** (top left) © Paul Nicklen/National Geographic/Getty Images **991:** (bottom) A. E. Zuckerman/Tom Stack & Associates **991:** (top right) John Alcock/Arizona State University **992:** (left) Chris E. Carlton and Richard N. Story **992:** (right) John Dominis/Time & Life Pictures/Getty Images **993:** (top) Kenneth Lorenzen **993:** (bottom) Kenneth Lorenzen **994:** © DLILLC/Corbis **995:** From Esther Herrmann, Josep Call, Maria Victoria Hernandez-Lloreda, Brian Hare, Michael Tomasello, "Humans Have Evolved Specialized Skills of Social Cognition: The Cultural Intelligence Hypothesis", Science, vol. 317, Sep 7, 2007, pp. 1360–1366. Reprinted with permission from AAAS. **995:** From Keith Jensen, Josep Call, Michael Tomasello, "Chimpanzees Are Rational Maximizers in an Ultimatum Game", Science, vol. 318, Oct 5, 2007, pp. 107–109. Reprinted with permission from AAAS." **995:** (top, Chimpanzee) Holger Ehlers /Shutterstock **995:** (top, Human) Photo: Brock Fenton **995:** (top, Orangutan) Philip Date /Shutterstock **996:** © Gregory D. Dimijian/Photo Researchers, Inc. **997:** Yuri Arcurs/Shutterstock

CHAPTER 41 **1001:** Photo by M.B. Fenton **1002:** Reprinted by permission from Macmillan Publishers Ltd: Nature Genetics, Vol. 39: pp. 1256–1260, Diet and the evolution of human amylase gene copy number variation by Paul George H Perry, Nathaniel J Dominy, Katrina G Claw, Arthur S Lee, Heike Fiegler et al., copyright (2007). **1006:** Photos by E. Epstein, University of California, Davis **1007:** (top) © DLILLC/Corbis **1007:** (bottom) Photo: Scott P. Bizily **1011:** William Ferguson **1015:** (top left) Adrian P. Davies/ Bruce Coleman **1015:** (top centre) NifTAL Project, University of Hawaii, Maui **1015:** (top right) © Dr. Jeremy Burgess/ SPL/ Photo Researchers, Inc. **1015:** (bottom) Mark E. Dudley and Sharon R. Long **1016:** (top left) Sandford/Angliolo/Corbis **1016:** (top right) James Watt/Animals Animals—Earth Scenes **1016:** (bottom left) Joe McDonald/ Corbis **1016:** (bottom right) Gunter Ziesler/Bruce Coleman, Inc. **1020:** (top left) Fred Bruemmer **1020:** (top right) Jane Burton/Bruce Coleman, Inc. **1020:** (bottom) Dr. Richard Kessel & Dr. Randy Kardon/Tissues & Organs/Visuals Unlimited **1021:** (top left) © DLILLC/Corbis **1021:** (centre left) D. Robert Franz/Plant Earth Pictures **1021:** From ALEJANDRO GRAJAL, STUART D. STRAHL, RODRIGO PARRA, MARIA GLORIA DOMINGUEZ, ALFREDO NEHER, "Foregut Fermentation in the Hoatzin, a Neotropical Leaf-Eating Bird", Science, vol. 245, Sep 15, 1989, pp. 1236–1238. Reprinted with permission from AAAS." **1024:** D.W. Fawcett/Photo Researchers, Inc. **1024.** (photo) Mark Nielsen, University of Utah **1028:** Yuri Arcurs/Shutterstock **1029:** © DLILLC/Corbis **1030:** (left) Perennou Nuridsany / Photo Researchers, Inc. **1030:** (top centre) © Grant Heilman Photography **1030:** (bottom centre) © Prem Subrahmanyam/www.premdesign.com **1030:** (right) Beverly McMillan **1031:** (left) © Ellen McKnight/Alamy **1031:** (right) Photo by M.B. Fenton **1032:** © DLILLC/Corbis **1033:** (left) Photo by M.S. Cumming **1033:** (right) David Shale/mpl/Minden Pictures **1034:** (left) Photo by M.B. Fenton **1034:** (right) Reprinted by permission from Macmillan Publishers Ltd: Nature, Vol. 449: pp. 79–82, Raptorial jaws in the throat help moray eels swallow large prey by Rita S. Mehta and Peter C. Wainwright, copyright (2007). **1035:** (top) Based on illustration from Norman, J.R. 1963. A history of fishes; Fig. 96. **1035:** (bottom) Based on illustration from Gans 1974 Biomechanics Fig. 2–22. **1036:** Based on illustration from Gans 1974 Biomechanics Fig. 2–16.

CHAPTER 42 **1039:** © Steve Gschmeissner/ Science Photo Library/Photo Researchers, Inc. **1040:** (left) Photo: Emmanuel Boitier **1040:** (right) © FAO **1041:** (a) Peter Parks/Oxford Scientific Films/Photolibrary.com **1041:** (b) Jack Dermid/ Visuals Unlimited **1041:** (c) © 2000 Photodisc, Inc. (with art by Lisa Starr) **1041:** (bottom) Photographer: Michael Clayton **1043:** Alex Kirstitch **1045:** Ed Reschke **1049:** (left) SIU/Visuals Unlimited **1049:** (right) SIU/Visuals Unlimited **1052**: Yuri Arcurs/Shutterstock **1053:** © DLILLC/ Corbis

CHAPTER 43 **1057:** © Dennis Kunkel/ Phototake **1058:** Herve Berthoule / Jacana / Photo Researchers, Inc. **1063:** From: Figure 3c in paper by P. Alpert, Journal of Experimental Biology vol 209 p 1579, 2006. **1069:** (top) David Noble **1069:** (bottom) Claude Steelman/Tom Stack & Associates **1071:** Petra Karstedt/www.Tiermotive.de **1072** Photo: Rafael Winer/Corbis. **1075:** Yuri Arcurs/Shutterstock **1078:** John D. Cunningham/ Visuals Unlimited **1079:** (top left) Joe McDonald/ Corbis **1079:** (top right) Fredrik Broman/ Iconica/ Getty Images Inc. **1079:** (bottom) Reprinted by permission of The McGraw-Hill Companies. **1080:** Inga Spence /Visuals Unlimited **1081:** © DLILLC/Corbis

CHAPTER 44 **1085:** © Dr. Andrejs Liepins/Science Photo Library/Photo Researchers, Inc. **1088:** La Trobe University **1089:** Biology Media/Photo Researchers, Inc. **1093:** (left) Courtesy of Kevin Wickenheiser, University of Michigan **1093:** (right) Watercolor illustration of Drosophila by Edith M. Wallace, Thomas Hunt Morgan's illustrator. This image was published in C.B. Bridges and T.H. Morgan, Contributions to the Genetics of Drosophila melanogaster (Washington, DC: Carnegie Institution; 1919), CIW publication #278. **1101:** Lennart Nilsson/Bonnier Fakta AB **1106:** Peter Skinner/ Photo Researchers, Inc. **1106:** Z. Salahuddin, National Institutes of Health **1107:** Yuri Arcurs/Shutterstock

CHAPTER 45 **1111:** Photo by M.B. Fenton **1112:** Reprinted with the kind permission of Elsevier **1114:** (bottom left and right) Photo by M.B. Fenton **1115:** (top) Photo by M.B. Fenton **1115:** (bottom left) Amo Nachoum/CORBIS **1115:** (bottom right) E.R. Degginger **1116:** (photo) Tom & Pat Leeson / Photo Researchers, Inc. **1116:**

From M. B. Grenier, D. B. McDonald, S. W. Buskirk, "Rapid Population Growth of a Critically Endangered Carnivore", Science, vol. 317, Aug 10, 2007, pp. 779. Reprinted with permission from AAAS. **1122:** (left) David Reznick/University of California, Riverside **1122:** Guppy photos: David Reznick/University of California, Riverside: computer enhanced by Lisa Starr; predator photos: Hippocampus Bildarchiv. **1128:** Alain Beignet BIOS/Peter Arnold, Inc. **1130:** (left) © Nigel Cattlin / Alamy **1130:** (right) © Goodshoot/CORBIS **1131:** © Ed Cesar/Photo Researchers, Inc. **1132:** NASA **1136:** Yuri Arcurs/Shutterstock **1137:** (top left) Photo by M.B. Fenton **1137:** (bottom left) Professor John Wiebe **1137:** (top right) Professor John Wiebe **1137:** (bottom right) Photo: Konrad P. Schmidt

CHAPTER 46 **1141:** Photo by M.B. Fenton **1145:** (top) Photo by M.B. Fenton **1145:** (bottom) Photo by M.B. Fenton **1146:** (top a–d) Photo by M.B. Fenton **1146:** (bottom) Photo by M.B. Fenton **1147:** (top left) Photo by M.B. Fenton **1147:** (bottom a, left) Nigel Cattlin/Frank Lane Picture Agency **1147:** (bottom a, right) © Simon Colmer and Abby Rex / Alamy **1147:** (bottom b, left) Robert Lubeck/Animals, Animals—Earth Scenes **1147:** (bottom b, right) Patti Murray/Animals, Animals—Earth Scenes **1148:** From Joshua Zimmerberg, Leonid V. Chernomordik, "NEUROSCIENCE: Enhanced: Synaptic Membranes Bend to the Will of a Neurotoxin", Science, vol. 310, Dec 9, 2005, pp. 1626–1627. Reprinted with permission from AAAS. **1148:** © C. Busse **1149:** Reprinted by permission from Macmillan Publishers Ltd: Nature, Vol. 439: pp. 584–588, Early evolution of the venom system in lizards and snakes by Bryan G. Fry, Nicolas Vidal, Janette A. Norman, Freek J. Vonk, Holger Scheib et al., copyright (2006). **1150:** (centre) Photo by Laurence Madin, Woods Hole Oceanographic Institution **1150:** (right) © Muséum de Genève; photo Philippe Wagneur **1151:** (top left) Thomas Eisner, Cornell University **1151:** (top right) Thomas Eisner, Cornell University **1151:** (centre right) © Michael Abbey/Photo Researchers, Inc. **1151:** (bottom right) © Eric V. Grave/Photo Researchers, Inc. **1152:** (left) © Tony Wharton; Frank Lane Picture Agency/CORBIS **1152:** (centre) © Joe McDonald/CORBIS **1152:** (right) © Hal Horwitz/CORBIS **1153:** Photo by M.B. Fenton **1154:** (top left) Harlow H. Hadow **1154:** (top centre) Bob and Miriam Francis/ Tom Stack & Associates **1154:** (top right) Harlow H. Hadow **1154:** (bottom) © Erik Schlogl **1155:** (top left) Marie Read Natural History Photography **1155:** (top centre) Photo by M.B. Fenton **1155:** (top right) Photo by M.B. Fenton **1156:** © DLILLC/Corbis **1157:** Jasper Ridge Biological Preserve **1162:** Nancy Rotenberg/Animals, Animals—Earth Scenes **1163:** (top) © Jane Burton/Bruce Coleman, Ltd. **1163:** (centre) © Jane Burton/Bruce Coleman, Ltd. **1163:** (bottom) Heather Angel/Natural Visions **1166:** (top left) Roger K. Burnard **1166:** (centre left) Roger K. Burnard **1166:** (bottom left) Roger K. Burnard (top right) Roger K. Burnard **1166:** (centre right) Roger K. Burnard **1166:** (bottom right) Ed Degginger **1168:** From James H. Brown, Edward J. Heske, "Control of a Desert-Grassland Transition by a Keystone Rodent Guild", Science, vol. 250, Dec 21, 1990, pp. 1705–1707. Reprinted with permission from AAAS. **1170:** From Inger Greve Alsos, Pernille Bronken Eidesen, Dorothee Ehrich, Inger Skrede, Kristine Westergaard, Gro Hilde Jacobsen, Jon Y. Landvik, Pierre Taberlet, Christian Brochmann, "Frequent Long-Distance Plant Colonization in the Changing Arctic", Science, vol. 316, Jun 15, 2007, pp. 1606–1609. Reprinted with permission from AAAS. **1170:** From Inger Greve Alsos, Pernille Bronken Eidesen, Dorothee Ehrich, Inger Skrede, Kristine Westergaard, Gro Hilde Jacobsen, Jon Y. Landvik, Pierre Taberlet, Christian Brochmann, "Frequent Long-Distance Plant Colonization in the Changing Arctic", Science, vol. 316, Jun 15, 2007, pp. 1606–1609. Reprinted with permission from AAAS. **1171:** From Katriona Shea, "ECOLOGY: How the Wood Moves", Science, vol. 315, Mar 2, 2007, pp. 1231– 1232. Reprinted with permission from AAAS. **1173:** Yuri Arcurs/Shutterstock **1174:** (top) Daniel Simberloff, University of Tennessee **1174:** (bottom) Daniel Simberloff, University of Tennessee

CHAPTER 47 **1179:** Photo by M.B. Fenton **1181:** SeaWiFS Project, NASA/Goddard Space Flight Center and ORBIMAGE **1182:** From Whittaker, R.H., 1975. Communities and Ecosystems, 2nd ed. Macmillan. **1187:** Photo by M.B. Fenton **1194:** Gene E. Likens from Gene E. Likens et al., Ecology Micrograph, 40(1): 23–47, 1970. **1198:** Photos by M.B. Fenton **1199:** (top left) D. Liane Cochran-Stafira/Saint Xavier University **1199:** (top centre and right) Photo: Jim Vargo **1200:** (top left) Yuri Arcurs/Shutterstock **1200:** Photo by M.B. Fenton

CHAPTER 48 **1205:** Photo by Laura Erin Barclay **1206:** Photo by M.B. Fenton **1207:** Photo by M.B. Fenton **1208:** © DLILLC/Corbis **1208:** From Gregory M. Erickson, Philip J. Currie, Brian D. Inouye, Alice A. Winn, "Tyrannosaur Life Tables: An Example of Nonavian Dinosaur Population Biology", Science, vol. 313, Jul 14, 2006, pp. 213–217. Reprinted with permission from AAAS. **1209:** (top left) Yuri Arcurs/Shutterstock **1209:** Photo by M.B. Fenton **1210:** (c) The Natural History Museum, London **1210:** Reprinted by permission from Macmillan Publishers Ltd: Nature, Vol. 443: pp. 138–140, OrnithologyDigging for dodo by Henry Nicholls, copyright (2006). **1210:** (bottom) From David W. Steadman, "Prehistoric Extinctions of Pacific Island Birds: Biodiversity Meets Zooarchaeology", Science, vol. 267, Feb 24, 1995, pp.1123–1131. Reprinted with permission from AAAS. **1211:** © KHALED KASSEM/Alamy **1212:** (top left) Michigan Science Art **1212:** (top right, a and b) NOAA **1212:** (bottom right) Photo:Mike Lole/ADAS **1214:** (top left) Photo by M.B. Fenton **1214:** (centre a–c) Photo by M.B. Fenton **1214:** (bottom right) Cpl. D.A. Haynes **1215:** (top) Photo: NOAA **1215:** (bottom left) From Jill M. Casey, Ransom A. Myers, "Near Extinction of a Large, Widely Distributed Fish", Science, vol. 281, Jul 31, 1998, pp. 690–692. Reprinted with permission from AAAS. **1215:** (bottom right) From Jill M. Casey, Ransom A. Myers, "Near Extinction of a Large, Widely Distributed Fish", Science, vol. 281, Jul 31, 1998, pp. 690–692. Reprinted with permission from AAAS. **1216:** (top left) Photo: Warren Gaines **1216:** (bottom right) NOAA **1216:** (top right) Photographer : Degner, M. & L, used with permission of Parks Canada **1217:** (bottom right) From Ransom A. Myers, Julia K. Baum, Travis D. Shepherd, Sean P. Powers, Charles H. Peterson, "Cascading Effects of the Loss of Apex Predatory Sharks from a Coastal Ocean", Science, vol. 315, Mar 30, 2007, pp. 1846–1850. Reprinted with permission from AAAS. **1218:** (centre) Photo by M.B. Fenton **1218:** (bottom) From Richard Stone, "WILDLIFE CONSERVATION: The Saola's Last Stand", Science, vol. 314, Dec 1, 2006, pp. 1380–1383. Reprinted with permission from AAAS. **1220:** (bottom a–c) Photo by M.B. Fenton **1221:** (top) COSEWIC **1221:** (centre right) © Genevieve Vallee/Alamy **1221:** (bottom right) Photo: Chinese Academy of Fishery Sciences **1222:** (bottom left) © Arco Images GmbH/Alamy **1222:** (top right) PROMA/Marine Girard **1223:** COSEWIC **1225:** COSEWIC **1226:** (top) Photo by M.B. Fenton **1226:** (bottom left) 1971 Earth Day poster written and illustrated by Walt Kelly, featuring Pogo and Porkypine **1229:** (left) Photo by M.B. Fenton **1229:** (right a–c) Photo by M. B. Fenton

CHAPTER 49 **1233:** Photo by M.B. Fenton **1234:** Photo by M.B. Fenton **1235:** (bottom) From Greger Larson, Keith Dobney, Umberto Albarella, Meiying Fang, Elizabeth Matisoo-Smith, Judith Robins, Stewart Lowden, Heather Finlayson, Tina Brand, Eske Willerslev, Peter Rowley-Conwy, Leif Andersson, Alan Cooper, "Worldwide Phylogeography of Wild Boar Reveals Multiple Centers of Pig Domestication", Science, vol. 307, Mar 11, 2005, pp. 1618–1621. Reprinted with permission from AAAS. **1236:** (top left) From Carlos M. Duarte, Nuria Marba, Marianne Holmer, "ECOLOGY: Rapid Domestication of Marine Species", Science, vol. 316, Apr 20, 2007, pp. 382–383. Reprinted with permission from AAAS. **1236:** (bottom left) Photo by M.B. Fenton **1236:** (bottom right) From Ken-ichi Tanno, George Willcox, "How Fast Was Wild Wheat Domesticated?", Science, vol. 311, Mar 31, 2006, pp. 1886. Reprinted with permission from AAAS. **1237:** (top left) CEFE–UMR 5175 **1237:** (bottom) Reprinted by permission from Macmillan Publishers Ltd: Nature, Vol. 449: pp. 459–462, Fire and flood management of coastal swamp enabled first rice paddy cultivation in east China by Y. Zong, Z. Chen, J. B. Innes, C. Chen, Z. Wang et al., copyright (2007). **1238:** (top left) Photo by M.B. Fenton **1238:** (bottom left) Photo by M.B. Fenton **1239:** (top left) Tom McHugh / Photo Researchers, Inc. **1239:** (top right) Photo by M.B. Fenton **1239:** (bottom right) Photo by M.B. Fenton **1240:** (top) Yuri Arcurs/Shutterstock **1240:** (bottom) From Changbao Li, Ailing Zhou, Tao Sang, "Rice Domestication by Reducing Shattering", Science, vol. 311, Mar 31, 2006, pp. 1936–1939. Reprinted with permission from AAAS. **1241:** (top) Copyright (2001) National Academy of Sciences, U.S.A. **1241:** (bottom left) Photo by M.B. Fenton **1241:** (bottom right) Photo by M.B. Fenton **1242:** (top) From Manfred Heun, Ralf Schafer-Pregl, Dieter Klawan, Renato Castagna, Monica Accerbi, Basilio Borghi, Francesco Salamini, "Site of Einkorn Wheat Domestication Identified by DNA Fingerprinting", Science, vol. 278, Nov 14, 1997, pp. 1312–1314. Reprinted with permission from AAAS. **1242:** (bottom) Photo by M.B. Fenton **1243:** (top) John Doebley **1243:** (bottom) Photo by M.B. Fenton **1245:** Photo by M.B. Fenton **1246:** (top) Photo by M.B. Fenton **1246:** (bottom) Photo by M.B. Fenton **1247:** (top) Drawing courtesy of University of Western, Ontario **1247:** (bottom) Photo by M.B. Fenton **1248:** (top left) Photo by M.B. Fenton **1248:** (top right) With kind permission from Springer Science+Business Media: Theoretical and Applied Genetics, "Brassica: taxonomy based on nuclear restriction fragment length polymorphisms (RFLPs)", volume 79, Apr 1, 1990, pp. 497–506, K. Song. **1249:** (top) With kind permission from Springer Science+Business Media: Theoretical and Applied Genetics, "Brassica: taxonomy based on nuclear restriction fragment length polymorphisms (RFLPs)", volume 79, Apr 1, 1990, pp. 497–506, K. Song. **1249:** (bottom) Photo by M.B. Fenton **1250:** (top) Photo by M.B. Fenton **1250:** (bottom left) Photo by M.B. Fenton **1250:** (bottom right) Photo by M.B. Fenton **1251:** From Carlos A. Driscoll, Marilyn Menotti-Raymond, Alfred L. Roca, Karsten Hupe, Warren E. Johnson, Eli Geffen, Eric H. Harley, Miguel Delibes, Dominique Pontier, Andrew C. Kitchener, Nobuyuki Yamaguchi, Stephen J. O'Brien, David W. Macdonald, "The Near Eastern Origin of Cat Domestication", Science, vol. 317, Jul 27, 2007, pp. 519–523. Reprinted with permission from AAAS. **1252:** Mark Bernards **1252:** (top) Photo by M.B. Fenton **1252:** (bottom) Photo by M.B. Fenton **1253:** Photo by M. B. Fenton **1254:** © DLILLC/Corbis

THE CHEMICAL AND PHYSICAL FOUNDATIONS OF BIOLOGY **F-3:** (bottom left) Steve Lissau/Rainbow, (bottom right) Jack Carey **F-7:** Bruce Iverson **F-11:** Wolfgang Kaehler **F-12:** H. Eisenbeiss/Frank Lane Picture Agency **F-23:** (top, a.) Ed Reschke/Peter Arnold, Inc. (middle, b.) Dennis Kunkel/Phototake (middle, c.) © Biophoto Associates/Photo Researchers, Inc. (bottom, d.) David Scharf/Peter Arnold, Inc. **F-35:** Dennis Kunkel Microscopy, Inc. **F-36:** (top) Adrian Warren/Ardea/London (bottom) Herman Eisenbeiss/Photo Researchers, Inc. **F-37:** (top) J. Sulston, MRC Laboratory of Molecular Biology (bottom) Courtesy of the Arabidopsis Information Resource, 2005. **F-38:** David M. Parichy **F-39:** © Peter Skinner/Photo Researchers, Inc. **F-40:** Manuel Leal, Duke University

ICONS
People Behind Biology: Yuri Arcurs/Shutterstock
Life on the Edge: © DLILLC/Corbis

Index

The letter i *designates illustration;*
t *designates table;* **bold** *designates*
defined or introduced term.